# Lights, camera

**This eight page colour section is in tribute to our**
**who travel around the country in any weather to**

FC UNITED
WE ARE THE
FCUM
FCUM
THE RED
GLAZE
OOFING

FA VASE WINNERS

ecotricity

Gallagher
Maidstone

EVO-STIK

SUTTON

Who said being a sports photographer was glamorous!

I haven't captioned the photos within so I could get more in but I would like to thank,
Peter Barnes
Keith Clayton
Alan Coomes
Jonathan Holloway
Roger Turner and
Gordon Whittington
for helping bring the statistics to life in this book.

These last few photos were designed to do just as the advert suggests, smile - great save by the way!

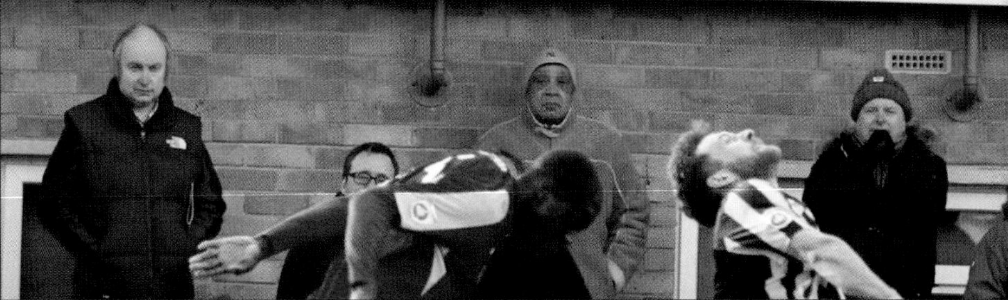

# NON-LEAGUE CLUB DIRECTORY 2017

(39th Edition)

EDITORS
MIKE WILLIAMS & TONY WILLIAMS

# NON-LEAGUE CLUB DIRECTORY 2017

ISBN 978-1-869833-69-5



Editors
Mike Williams
(Tel: 01548 531 339)
tw.publications@btinternet.com)
Tony Williams
(Tel: 01823 490 684)
Email: t.williams320@btinternet.com

Published by Tony Williams Publications Ltd
(Tel: 01548 531 339)
Email: tw.publications@btinternet.com

Printed by Wheatons Exeter Ltd

Sales & Distribution
T.W. Publications (01548 531 339)

Front Cover: Westfields keeper, Matt Gwynne, stretches to collect the ball from a Kidsgrove corner, during this FA Cup Preliminary match which ended in a 1-1 draw.
Photo: Jonathan Holloway.

KENSINGTON PALACE

Association football is enjoyed by all ages across the length and breadth of the country. The great thing about football in this country is that there are levels of the game available for all - whatever their standard.

There are leagues for inter-village rivalries, leagues for work teams and groups of friends - leagues for almost every type of group imaginable, not to mention semi-professional and full-time players. These competitions make up our country's impressive 'Non-League football', involving all clubs below the Premier League and The Football League.

Like you, I am a football fan. I have loved the game from a very young age - as a player, and as a supporter of club and country. As President of The Football Association, I am honoured to be involved with a sport that reaches every community and is part of the fabric of our society.

The team spirit that develops on the pitch and in the dressing room is something that should be encouraged and nurtured – a sporting tradition that forms part of our way of life.

This Non-League Club Directory provides an annual record for the massive world of football enthusiasts who play, administer and support their local clubs across England. Read it with pleasure, then head outside for a game!

# CONTENTS

**Tony** Williams has asked me to do a few important things over the 16 years since I first met him when I joined The Non-League Paper in May 2000.

The first was to stand on stage at the launch of the Non-League Club Directory's 2001 edition and pass trophies to a legend of the game, Kenny Dalglish, to present to those players and managers Tony felt had graced our level of the game that season.

Later that year, after helping him produce a couple of issues of Team Talk magazine, Tony suggested that I - rookie reporter and semi-professional centre-half - take over as editor. It was a publication he had published for many years with great knowledge, skill and passion for the game, so it was an honour.

Now, 16 years on, he asked me to pen a few words to kick-off the 39th edition of this bible of Non-League football. It is a pleasure to do so because I owe Tony an awful lot.

The magazine sadly perished 18 months into my editorship, not through anything Tony or I could have prevented, but the financial mismanagement of the chairman of the company that owned us at the time.

I continued to work on The NLP, which survived, until this summer when I left for pastures new when the biggest club I'd reported on for the paper, Luton Town, asked me to become their press and communications manager after two years in the editor's chair.

I have no doubt I would not have been able to enjoy doing such a fulfilling job without the belief Tony showed in me at the turn of the century, along with NLP editor-in-chief David Emery.

I've travelled the country being lucky enough to be paid to watch football, report on great up and coming players, tell their stories and make many friends. None more so than Tony, whose commitment to the grass-roots of this beautiful game never ceases to amaze me.

So it is a privilege to kick-off the 39th edition of a wonderful book that I still look forward to opening just as much as I did two decades ago when, as a teenage Arnold Town player, I couldn't wait to see how out team photo looked. Enjoy!

Stuart Hammonds
Former editor of The Non-League Paper

## WELL THAT WAS DIFFERENT!

Putting the Non-League Club Directory together is always a huge task which although can be maintained all season long, ends with a months worth of long days and nights. It is a work schedule that nine times out of ten leaves me with an aching back. Well, this year it would appear it's finally caught up with me, as two weeks from deadline day, I slipped a disc, not the best timing!

Still, I've never missed a deadline and I wasn't going to miss one now. So thanks to my sofa (my office for the past two weeks), a concoction of prescribed pain killers, which almost got rid of the pain and to all those who contributed, I still haven't missed a deadline.

Now I have to try and get off this sofa!

## PLANNING AHEAD

Can you believe next year's Directory will be the 40th edition!

The book has changed somewhat since 1978, hopefully for the better, and in next year's Directory Dad (Tony Williams) will be sharing with us what has happened in the Non-League game since he started the pocket sized annual.

But we would also like to include some of your thoughts. You don't have to have been around for the last 40 years, football seems to change on a season to season basis nowadays, so anything that you think has changed recently could get into the book too.

We'd also like to hear some of your stories/memories that will stay with you for life, be they funny, triumphant or even sad, we'd like to read about them, and maybe publish them next year.

Also, if you have any comments on the book, what you'd like to see more of, or less of, please get in touch. You can contact us either via tw.publications@btinternet.com

or by writing to NLD 2018, Rosebank, Kingsbridge TQ7 2NR

## SPECIAL ACKNOWLEDGMENTS


'OUR TEAM' OF PHOTOGRAPHERS

Peter Barnes, Keith Clayton, Alan Coomes, Jonathan Holloway,
'Uncle Eric' Marsh, Roger Turner, Bill Wheatcroft and Gordon Whittington.

FA COMPETITIONS DEPARTMENT

Chris Darnell and Scott Bolton

CONTRIBUTORS

Alan Constable. Mark Edmonds. Robin Flight. Kevin Hewitt. Ron Holpin. Stephen Hosmer.
Philip Smith. Kevin Wilmot. Nigel Wood.

Arthur Evans (Photographer & reports).
Richard Rundle (Football Club History Database).
Mike Simmonds (Schools).

Thank you one and all

*Mike Williams*

# THE EDITORS

**TONY WILLIAMS**
**Editor**

Educated at Malvern College, one of the country's best football schools in the late sixties, he represented England Under 18 against Scotland at Celtic Park before serving as an administrative officer in the Royal Air Force for five years.

He was on Reading's books from the age of 16 to 22, but also represented F.A. Amateur XI's and the R.A.F. while playing mainly in the old Isthmian League for Corinthian Casuals, Dulwich Hamlet and Kingstonian and joining Hereford United and Grantham during R.A.F. postings.

After taking an F.A. Coaching badge he coached at Harrow Borough, Epsom & Ewell and Hungerford Town and was asked to edit Jimmy Hill's Football Weekly after initial experience with the Amateur Footballer. Monthly Soccer and Sportsweek followed before he had the idea for a football Wisden and was helped by The Bagnall Harvey Agency to find a suitable generous sponsor in Rothmans.

After launching the Rothmans Football Yearbook in 1970 as its founder and co-compiler with Roy Peskett, he was asked to join Rothmans (although a non-smoker!) in the company's public relations department and was soon able to persuade the Marketing Director that Rothmans should become the first ever sponsor of a football league.

After a season's trial sponsoring the Hellenic and Isthmian Leagues, it was decided to go national with the Northern and Western Leagues and for four years he looked after the football department at Rothmans, with Jimmy Hill and Doug Insole presenting a brilliant sponsorship package which amongst many other innovations included three points for a win and goal difference.

So Non-League football led the way with league sponsorship and two, now well accepted, innovations.

Sportsmanship and goals were also rewarded in a sponsorship that proved a great success for football and for Rothmans. Indeed the sportsmanship incentives could be of great value to-day in the Football Association's bid to improve the game's image by ridding the game of dissent and cheating.

After the cigarette company pulled out of their sports sponsorship Tony produced the first Non-League Annual and later The Football League Club Directory, launching 'Non-League Football' magazine with "The Mail on Sunday" and then "Team Talk."

After his ten years with Hungerford Town, he moved West and served Yeovil Town as a Director for seven years but was thrilled when David Emery's plans for the exciting Non-League Media emerged and came into reality, thus giving the grass roots of the game the publicity and promotion that he and his team had been attempting to set up since the Annual (now Directory) was launched in 1978.

The aim of the company has always been to promote the non-league 'family,' its spirit and its general development. So a plaque from The Football Association inscribed 'To Tony Williams for his continued promotion of all that's good in football' was greatly appreciated as was the trophy to commemorate the thirtieth edition of the Directory and the recent GLS "Lifetime Award' for promoting non-league football.

**MIKE WILLIAMS**
**Editorial Manager**

What started out as a holiday job in 1988 helping put together (literally in those days) the Non-League Club Directory and League Club Directory, in the end forged a career which saw him work for Coventry City Football Club, e-comsport in London and finally return to TW Publications in 2003.

During his eight year spell with TW Publications he learned the ropes of all aspects of publishing culminating in the roll of production manager for the Non-League Club Directory, Team Talk Magazine, the League Club Directory and many more publications published by the company.

1995 saw the opportunity to take up the post of Publications Manager at Coventry City Football Club, and the transfer was made in the April of that year. Sky Blue Publications was formed and the League Club Directory became their leading title. Re-branded as the Ultimate Football Guide he was to deal with all aspects of the book, from design to sales and was also put on a steep learning curve into the world of Premiership programme production. The three years spent at the Midland's club gave him a great insight into all departments of a Premiership club, having produced publications for them all.

Leaving Coventry City F.C. in 1998, and after a spell working on a world wide football player database for e-comsport in London, he returned to the West Country in 2001 to set up his own design/publishing company, which incorporated working on the Directory again. 2009 saw the full time switch to TW Publications and the responsibilities of publishing the Directory.

Having gone to a rugby school his football playing career was delayed. However, becoming the youngest player to have played for the First XV and representing Torbay Athletics club at 100 and 200m proved his sporting pedigree. At the age of 20 he begun his football career which, at it's height, saw him playing for Chard Town in the Western League Premier Division.

Now enjoying his time helping run local side Loddiswell Athletic in the South Devon League, he relishes the challenge of maintaining the club's position in the Premier Division.

# All's Not Well At 'The Top'

In a year when emotions of football enthusiasts have been turned upside down, we are trying to concentrate on the positive aspects of the game we care for so much.

The wonderful example of Leicester City Football Club lifted morale across the country's football community, as we all realized it wasn't just obscene money that brought success at the highest level. The example of our Premier League champions has surely boosted morale at all levels of football in this country.

We had also been thrilled and inspired by the success of ex non-league player Jamie Vardy, which had encouraged the national media to underline others from the lower ranks. Suddenly the flow of so many unpronounceable foreign names joining our senior clubs were being matched by some home grown talent, that had previously appeared to be out of consideration.

**"For attitude, basic skills, character, tactics and general team work, our squad were completely outclassed"**

Two other uplifting and popular efforts by underdogs, saw relegated FC Halifax Town beat promoted Grimsby Town to win the FA Trophy at Wembley and Morpeth Town, after an incredibly tough FA Vase season, who beat the re-formed and presumably very sound, Salisbury in the Final.

So football had given many supporters a reason to be proud of their sport and had proved that it isn't always dominated by the bookies favourites.

But then the lives of England's supporters were turned upside down in the European Championship. A young, promising English squad were beaten by rank outsiders from Iceland, whose background and experience could not possibly be compared with England's best players.

For attitude, basic skills, character, tactics and general team work, our squad were completely outclassed on the night, by players whose statistics could not match England's in any way.

Our very best players had produced a sickening example for the rest of the country's sportsmen. England's national winter sport was in complete disarray. Young footballers and, in fact, everyone in the huge non-league family, had to face the fact that our leaders had let us down.

Yet our very close colleagues and rivals from Ireland and especially Wales did show the Leicester brand of confidence, spirit and actual ability that enabled them to take on and beat 'so called' senior opposition.

So let's benefit from the leadership and example of the uplifting performances of Leicester City, Iceland, Wales and the Irish who surely proved to us all that anything is possible for talented players with the right attitude and strength of character.

So good luck to our clubs in the English non-league football world. Hopefully they can prove they do possess the courage, skill and tactics to play football in an acceptable, positive and thoughtful way at their own particular level, giving an example to the youngsters who support them.

While considering the state of our game in Britain at non-league level, it's been interesting to look back over the 39 editions of our annual review of non-league football since 1978 and to consider the changes, good and not so good, that have affected the game.

The next issue of The Non-League Club Directory, will be our 40th, so we plan to look back over the changes we've seen in the country's non-league football world since we started. But before we discuss them, how about telling us how you feel about the game as it's changed in your life time and as it is to-day? What do you think?

*Tony Williams*

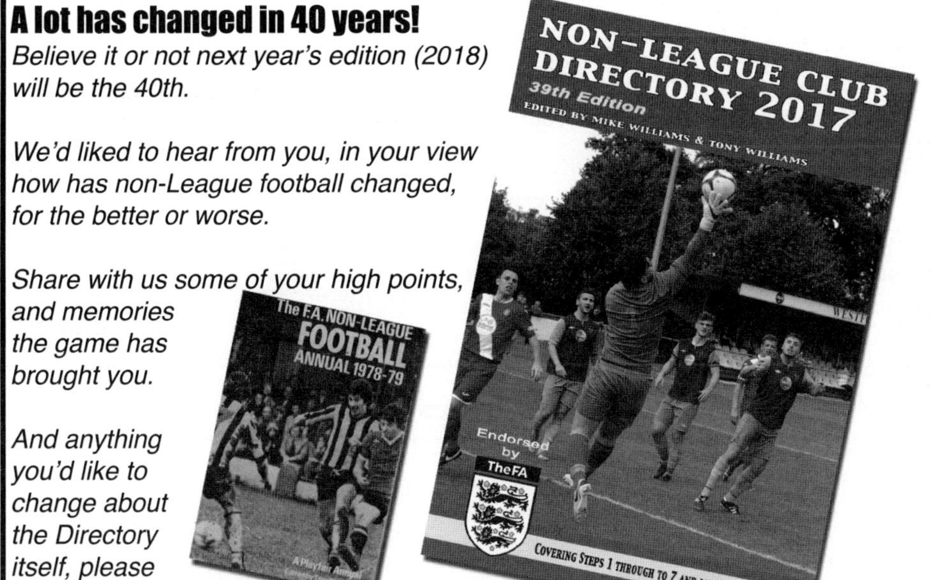

A lot has changed in 40 years!
Believe it or not next year's edition (2018) will be the 40th.
We'd liked to hear from you, in your view how has non-League football changed, for the better or worse.
Share with us some of your high points, and memories the game has brought you.
And anything you'd like to change about the Directory itself, please get in touch by emailing to
tw.publications@btinternet.com
NON-LEAGUE CLUB DIRECTORY 2017
39th Edition
EDITED BY MIKE WILLIAMS & TONY WILLIAMS
Endorsed by
The FA
COVERING STEPS 1 THROUGH TO 7 AND MORE....
The F.A. NON-LEAGUE FOOTBALL ANNUAL 1978-79

# Non-League Pyramid (Steps 1-7) 2016-17
# and it's 2015-16 Champions

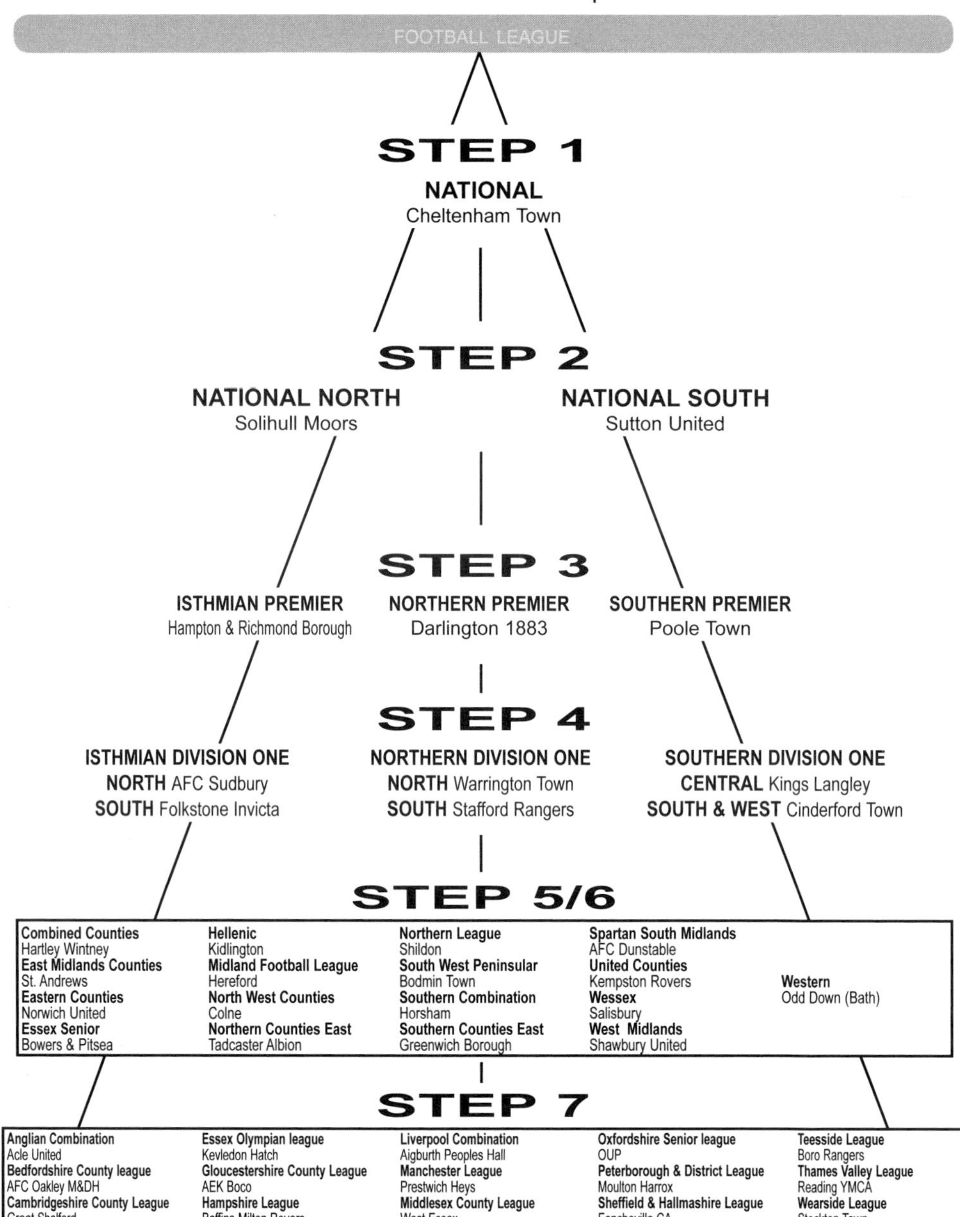

FOOTBALL LEAGUE
STEP 1
NATIONAL
Cheltenham Town
STEP 2
NATIONAL NORTH
Solihull Moors
NATIONAL SOUTH
Sutton United
STEP 3
ISTHMIAN PREMIER
Hampton & Richmond Borough
NORTHERN PREMIER
Darlington 1883
SOUTHERN PREMIER
Poole Town
STEP 4
ISTHMIAN DIVISION ONE
NORTH AFC Sudbury
SOUTH Folkstone Invicta
NORTHERN DIVISION ONE
NORTH Warrington Town
SOUTH Stafford Rangers
SOUTHERN DIVISION ONE
CENTRAL Kings Langley
SOUTH & WEST Cinderford Town
STEP 5/6
Combined Counties
Hartley Wintney
East Midlands Counties
St. Andrews
Eastern Counties
Norwich United
Essex Senior
Bowers & Pitsea
Hellenic
Kidlington
Midland Football League
Hereford
North West Counties
Colne
Northern Counties East
Tadcaster Albion
Northern League
Shildon
South West Peninsular
Bodmin Town
Southern Combination
Horsham
Southern Counties East
Greenwich Borough
Spartan South Midlands
AFC Dunstable
United Counties
Kempston Rovers
Wessex
Salisbury
West Midlands
Shawbury United
Western
Odd Down (Bath)
STEP 7
Anglian Combination
Acle United
Bedfordshire County league
AFC Oakley M&DH
Cambridgeshire County League
Great Shelford
Central Midlands League
(N) Glapwell (S) Selston
Cheshire Association League
Knutsford
Dorset Premier League
Shaftesbury Town
Essex & Suffolk Border League
Coggelshall Town
Essex Olympian league
Kevledon Hatch
Gloucestershire County League
AEK Boco
Hampshire League
Baffins Milton Rovers
Herts Senior County League
Standon & Puckeridge
Humber Premier League
Wawne United
Kent County League
Faversham Strike Force Seniors
Leicestershire League
Birstall United
Liverpool Combination
Aigburth Peoples Hall
Manchester League
Prestwich Heys
Middlesex County League
West Essex
North Berkshire League
Kintbury Rangers
Northamptonshire Combination
James King Blisworth
Northern Alliance
Blyth Town
Nottinghamshire Senior League
Ruddington Village
Oxfordshire Senior league
OUP
Peterborough & District League
Moulton Harrox
Sheffield & Hallmashire League
Fenchevilla CA
Somerset County League
Bishops Lyeard
Staffordshire League
Leek CSOB
Suffolk & Ipswich league
Crane Sports
Surrey Elite Intermediate
Horsley
Teesside League
Boro Rangers
Thames Valley League
Reading YMCA
Wearside League
Stockton Town
West Cheshire League
South Liverpool
West Lancashire League
Blackpool Wren Rovers
West Yorkshire League
Beeston St. Anthony's
Wiltshire league
Trowbridge Town

# CONFERENCE LEAGUE TABLE 2015-16

| | | P | W | D | L | F | A | GD | Pts |
|---|---|---|---|---|---|---|---|---|---|
| 1 | Cheltenham Town | 46 | 30 | 11 | 5 | 87 | 30 | 57 | 101 |
| 2 | Forest Green Rovers | 46 | 26 | 11 | 9 | 69 | 42 | 27 | 89 |
| 3 | Braintree Town | 46 | 23 | 12 | 11 | 56 | 38 | 18 | 81 |
| 4 | Grimsby Town | 46 | 22 | 14 | 10 | 82 | 45 | 37 | 80 |
| 5 | Dover Athletic | 46 | 23 | 11 | 12 | 75 | 53 | 22 | 80 |
| 6 | Tranmere Rovers | 46 | 22 | 12 | 12 | 61 | 44 | 17 | 78 |
| 7 | Eastleigh | 46 | 21 | 12 | 13 | 64 | 53 | 11 | 75 |
| 8 | Wrexham | 46 | 20 | 9 | 17 | 71 | 56 | 15 | 69 |
| 9 | Gateshead | 46 | 19 | 10 | 17 | 59 | 70 | -11 | 67 |
| 10 | Macclesfield Town | 46 | 19 | 9 | 18 | 60 | 48 | 12 | 66 |
| 11 | Barrow | 46 | 17 | 14 | 15 | 64 | 71 | -7 | 65 |
| 12 | Woking | 46 | 17 | 10 | 19 | 71 | 68 | 3 | 61 |
| 13 | Lincoln City | 46 | 16 | 13 | 17 | 69 | 68 | 1 | 61 |
| 14 | Bromley | 46 | 17 | 9 | 20 | 67 | 72 | -5 | 60 |
| 15 | Aldershot Town | 46 | 16 | 8 | 22 | 54 | 72 | -18 | 56 |
| 16 | Southport | 46 | 14 | 13 | 19 | 52 | 65 | -13 | 55 |
| 17 | Chester | 46 | 14 | 12 | 20 | 67 | 71 | -4 | 54 |
| 18 | Torquay United | 46 | 13 | 12 | 21 | 54 | 76 | -22 | 51 |
| 19 | Boreham Wood | 46 | 12 | 14 | 20 | 44 | 49 | -5 | 50 |
| 20 | Guiseley | 46 | 11 | 16 | 19 | 47 | 70 | -23 | 49 |
| 21 | FC Halifax Town | 46 | 12 | 12 | 22 | 55 | 82 | -27 | 48 |
| 22 | Altrincham | 46 | 10 | 14 | 22 | 48 | 73 | -25 | 44 |
| 23 | Kidderminster Harriers | 46 | 9 | 13 | 24 | 49 | 71 | -22 | 40 |
| 24 | Welling United | 46 | 8 | 11 | 27 | 35 | 73 | -38 | 35 |

**Play-Off Semi Finals:** Dover Athletic 0-1 Forest Green Roversovers / Forest Green Roversovers 1-1 Dover Athletic
Grimsby Town 0-1 Braintree Town / Braintree Town 0-2 Grimsby Town
**Final:** Forest Green Roversovers 1-3 Grimsby Town

| | | 1 | 2 | 3 | 4 | 5 | 6 | 7 | 8 | 9 | 10 | 11 | 12 | 13 | 14 | 15 | 16 | 17 | 18 | 19 | 20 | 21 | 22 | 23 | 24 |
|---|---|---|---|---|---|---|---|---|---|---|---|---|---|---|---|---|---|---|---|---|---|---|---|---|---|
| 1 | Aldershot Town | | 2-0 | 0-1 | 1-2 | 2-1 | 1-1 | 0-2 | 3-1 | 1-1 | 1-2 | 3-2 | 0-3 | 1-2 | 3-4 | 1-0 | 1-0 | 1-2 | 0-3 | 1-2 | 0-0 | 0-0 | 1-0 | 0-1 | 0-1 |
| 2 | Altrincham | 4-0 | | 1-0 | 1-0 | 0-4 | 0-0 | 2-1 | 0-3 | 1-2 | 1-1 | 1-3 | 0-1 | 2-3 | 2-1 | 1-1 | 2-2 | 3-3 | 0-0 | 1-1 | 1-1 | 2-1 | 5-0 | 3-1 | 1-1 |
| 3 | Barrow | 1-3 | 3-2 | | 0-0 | 2-0 | 1-1 | 1-2 | 3-2 | 2-1 | 1-0 | 4-1 | 2-2 | 0-0 | 1-3 | 1-1 | 1-1 | 1-0 | 1-1 | 1-0 | 4-0 | 3-4 | 1-1 | 2-1 | 2-0 |
| 4 | Boreham Wood | 0-1 | 0-1 | 0-2 | | 1-0 | 2-3 | 0-0 | 0-0 | 3-0 | 1-1 | 3-1 | 0-1 | 2-3 | 1-3 | 1-0 | 0-2 | 1-1 | 0-0 | 0-2 | 0-1 | 0-0 | 2-0 | 1-1 | 0-1 |
| 5 | Braintree Town | 1-2 | 3-0 | 1-1 | 0-2 | | 1-0 | 1-0 | 2-0 | 1-0 | 2-0 | 2-0 | 1-1 | 0-0 | 0-0 | 0-1 | 2-1 | 1-3 | 1-0 | 1-0 | 0-0 | 0-0 | 1-0 | 2-1 | 1-0 |
| 6 | Bromley | 1-3 | 1-3 | 5-0 | 1-2 | 1-2 | | 1-2 | 3-0 | 1-1 | 2-2 | 1-0 | 2-2 | 3-0 | 1-2 | 2-0 | 3-2 | 2-0 | 1-0 | 0-0 | 0-2 | 0-1 | 2-0 | 2-1 | 3-1 |
| 7 | Cheltenham Town | 0-0 | 1-0 | 2-1 | 4-1 | 1-1 | 4-1 | | 3-1 | 3-2 | 1-1 | 2-0 | 1-1 | 0-0 | 3-1 | 5-0 | 2-0 | 3-1 | 2-0 | 3-0 | 1-0 | 0-1 | 2-0 | 4-0 | 2-1 |
| 8 | Chester | 8-2 | 1-1 | 1-2 | 2-2 | 1-0 | 1-1 | 1-1 | | 1-1 | 1-0 | 2-1 | 1-2 | 4-2 | 1-1 | 1-1 | 3-1 | 2-3 | 0-2 | 0-0 | 4-1 | 0-1 | 4-0 | 1-2 | 3-2 |
| 9 | Dover Athletic | 5-2 | 2-1 | 3-1 | 2-1 | 0-0 | 2-3 | 1-2 | 0-0 | | 1-2 | 1-0 | 0-1 | 4-0 | 1-1 | 0-0 | 3-2 | 4-1 | 2-1 | 1-2 | 5-0 | 0-0 | 2-1 | 2-0 | 2-1 |
| 10 | Eastleigh | 1-1 | 2-0 | 3-1 | 1-0 | 0-2 | 2-0 | 1-0 | 1-0 | 2-5 | | 2-1 | 3-2 | 1-2 | 0-1 | 1-1 | 3-1 | 1-1 | 1-0 | 1-0 | 3-2 | 0-1 | 0-0 | 2-1 | 1-1 |
| 11 | FC Halifax Town | 0-2 | 1-0 | 3-1 | 3-2 | 3-6 | 2-2 | 1-7 | 0-1 | 4-2 | 0-0 | | 0-2 | 1-1 | 4-2 | 1-1 | 1-1 | 2-2 | 1-1 | 2-2 | 2-3 | 1-1 | 1-1 | 0-3 | 2-0 |
| 12 | Forest Green Rovers | 0-0 | 2-0 | 4-0 | 1-0 | 1-0 | 2-1 | 2-2 | 2-1 | 3-1 | 2-1 | 0-1 | | 0-1 | 0-1 | 3-0 | 3-0 | 3-1 | 2-1 | 2-1 | 3-1 | 0-2 | 1-0 | 1-2 | 0-0 |
| 13 | Gateshead | 3-2 | 2-2 | 1-1 | 2-1 | 2-3 | 3-1 | 1-1 | 1-0 | 2-3 | 2-1 | 1-4 | 0-1 | | 1-0 | 3-0 | 1-1 | 2-0 | 0-3 | 0-1 | 1-2 | 1-4 | 1-2 | 1-5 | 2-1 |
| 14 | Grimsby Town | 4-1 | 5-0 | 4-1 | 0-0 | 0-1 | 4-1 | 0-1 | 1-2 | 1-0 | 0-0 | 7-0 | 1-1 | 2-1 | | 1-1 | 1-0 | 2-0 | 0-2 | 1-0 | 2-2 | 1-1 | 3-1 | 3-1 | 1-0 |
| 15 | Guiseley | 0-4 | 1-0 | 3-1 | 1-1 | 1-1 | 2-0 | 0-2 | 3-3 | 0-1 | 1-4 | 2-1 | 0-1 | 0-2 | 2-2 | | 1-0 | 0-1 | 0-3 | 1-1 | 4-3 | 2-2 | 2-0 | 4-4 | 3-1 |
| 16 | Kidderminster Harriers | 2-0 | 1-1 | 0-0 | 1-1 | 0-1 | 0-1 | 1-2 | 2-2 | 1-1 | 3-2 | 1-0 | 0-2 | 0-1 | 2-2 | 0-1 | | 0-2 | 3-1 | 0-1 | 2-2 | 0-2 | 0-1 | 1-0 | 1-3 |
| 17 | Lincoln City | 2-0 | 1-1 | 2-2 | 3-1 | 2-0 | 0-1 | 1-1 | 2-1 | 2-3 | 3-0 | 0-1 | 0-1 | 1-1 | 1-1 | 1-0 | 1-2 | | 5-3 | 3-1 | 2-0 | 1-0 | 1-1 | 2-3 | 1-1 |
| 18 | Macclesfield Town | 0-2 | 3-0 | 1-2 | 0-0 | 3-1 | 2-0 | 0-1 | 1-2 | 0-0 | 1-2 | 0-1 | 4-1 | 1-0 | 2-1 | 1-0 | 2-1 | 1-1 | | 0-0 | 1-2 | 1-2 | 2-1 | 2-1 | 0-0 |
| 19 | Southport | 1-1 | 3-0 | 2-1 | 0-3 | 1-1 | 5-3 | 0-4 | 1-2 | 0-0 | 0-4 | 0-1 | 0-1 | 1-2 | 0-4 | 2-0 | 3-4 | 2-2 | 3-1 | | 0-1 | 2-2 | 3-3 | 2-2 | 3-2 |
| 20 | Torquay United | 0-2 | 2-0 | 2-2 | 1-2 | 0-0 | 3-7 | 0-3 | 2-0 | 2-3 | 0-1 | 0-0 | 4-1 | 0-2 | 1-1 | 1-1 | 3-2 | 1-3 | 1-0 | 1-0 | | 0-1 | 2-0 | 0-1 | 0-1 |
| 21 | Tranmere Rovers | 3-1 | 1-0 | 0-1 | 0-2 | 1-2 | 4-0 | 0-1 | 2-0 | 0-1 | 1-2 | 1-0 | 1-1 | 3-1 | 1-0 | 2-1 | 2-2 | 3-2 | 0-1 | 1-0 | 2-1 | | 1-2 | 1-0 | 1-2 |
| 22 | Welling United | 0-1 | 1-1 | 1-2 | 0-3 | 1-2 | 1-2 | 1-1 | 2-1 | 1-2 | 2-2 | 2-0 | 1-1 | 0-1 | 0-4 | 1-0 | 1-2 | 2-1 | 0-1 | 0-1 | 1-1 | 1-1 | | 2-1 | 0-2 |
| 23 | Woking | 2-1 | 2-0 | 2-2 | 0-0 | 1-1 | 2-0 | 0-1 | 5-2 | 0-1 | 2-1 | 1-1 | 2-1 | 1-1 | 1-3 | 0-1 | 1-1 | 3-1 | 2-5 | 1-2 | 2-2 | 4-1 | 2-0 | | 0-1 |
| 24 | Wrexham | 3-0 | 3-1 | 4-1 | 1-0 | 2-3 | 2-0 | 2-1 | 3-0 | 0-1 | 2-3 | 3-1 | 2-2 | 4-0 | 0-0 | 3-3 | 2-0 | 3-1 | 2-3 | 0-1 | 3-1 | 2-2 | 1-0 | 1-3 | |

# NATIONAL NORTH LEAGUE TABLE 2015-16

| | | P | W | D | L | F | A | GD | Pts |
|---|---|---|---|---|---|---|---|---|---|
| 1 | Solihull Moors | 42 | 25 | 10 | 7 | 84 | 48 | 36 | 85 |
| 2 | North Ferriby United | 42 | 22 | 10 | 10 | 82 | 49 | 33 | 76 |
| 3 | AFC Fylde | 42 | 22 | 9 | 11 | 76 | 53 | 23 | 75 |
| 4 | Harrogate Town | 42 | 21 | 9 | 12 | 73 | 46 | 27 | 72 |
| 5 | Boston United | 42 | 22 | 5 | 15 | 73 | 60 | 13 | 71 |
| 6 | Nuneaton Town | 42 | 20 | 13 | 9 | 71 | 46 | 25 | 70 |
| 7 | Tamworth | 42 | 16 | 15 | 11 | 55 | 45 | 10 | 63 |
| 8 | Chorley | 42 | 18 | 9 | 15 | 64 | 55 | 9 | 63 |
| 9 | Stockport County | 42 | 15 | 14 | 13 | 50 | 49 | 1 | 59 |
| 10 | Alfreton Town | 42 | 15 | 13 | 14 | 58 | 54 | 4 | 58 |
| 11 | Curzon Ashton | 42 | 14 | 15 | 13 | 55 | 52 | 3 | 57 |
| 12 | Stalybridge Celtic | 42 | 14 | 11 | 17 | 62 | 75 | -13 | 53 |
| 13 | FC United of Manchester | 42 | 15 | 8 | 19 | 60 | 75 | -15 | 53 |
| 14 | Bradford Park Avenue | 42 | 13 | 11 | 18 | 51 | 59 | -8 | 50 |
| 15 | Gloucester City | 42 | 12 | 14 | 16 | 39 | 49 | -10 | 50 |
| 16 | Gainsborough Trinity | 42 | 14 | 8 | 20 | 46 | 62 | -16 | 50 |
| 17 | Worcester City | 42 | 12 | 12 | 18 | 55 | 61 | -6 | 48 |
| 18 | AFC Telford United | 42 | 13 | 8 | 21 | 47 | 60 | -13 | 47 |
| 19 | Brackley Town | 42 | 11 | 13 | 18 | 45 | 54 | -9 | 46 |
| 20 | Lowestoft Town | 42 | 12 | 10 | 20 | 48 | 69 | -21 | 46 |
| 21 | Hednesford Town | 42 | 8 | 14 | 20 | 50 | 77 | -27 | 38 |
| 22 | Corby Town | 42 | 7 | 11 | 24 | 47 | 93 | -46 | 32 |

**Play-Off Semi Finals:** Boston United 2-0 North Ferriby United / North Ferriby United 3-0 Boston United
Harrogate Town 0-1 AFC Fylde / AFC Fylde 1-1 Harrogate Town
**Final:** North Ferriby United 2-1 AFC Fylde

| | | 1 | 2 | 3 | 4 | 5 | 6 | 7 | 8 | 9 | 10 | 11 | 12 | 13 | 14 | 15 | 16 | 17 | 18 | 19 | 20 | 21 | 22 |
|---|---|---|---|---|---|---|---|---|---|---|---|---|---|---|---|---|---|---|---|---|---|---|---|
| 1 | AFC Fylde | | 1-0 | 0-1 | 5-2 | 2-2 | 1-0 | 1-0 | 2-1 | 1-2 | 4-0 | 2-2 | 1-0 | 2-1 | 2-0 | 1-0 | 2-3 | 2-2 | 1-2 | 5-0 | 2-3 | 2-2 | 2-3 |
| 2 | AFC Telford United | 1-2 | | 1-1 | 2-2 | 2-0 | 3-1 | 2-0 | 3-0 | 0-0 | 5-1 | 0-2 | 0-1 | 0-4 | 1-3 | 1-0 | 1-1 | 1-5 | 0-3 | 2-0 | 0-1 | 1-0 | 2-0 |
| 3 | Alfreton Town | 1-2 | 2-3 | | 1-2 | 1-1 | 0-1 | 1-0 | 1-1 | 2-2 | 0-1 | 1-0 | 1-1 | 3-2 | 4-0 | 0-1 | 0-1 | 2-2 | 2-2 | 1-3 | 0-3 | 1-0 | 2-1 |
| 4 | Boston United | 0-3 | 1-0 | 2-1 | | 1-2 | 3-0 | 1-2 | 2-0 | 2-1 | 3-1 | 1-0 | 1-0 | 3-3 | 3-1 | 4-1 | 1-2 | 2-1 | 1-4 | 0-3 | 4-0 | 1-1 | 1-1 |
| 5 | Brackley Town | 0-0 | 0-0 | 1-4 | 1-3 | | 0-0 | 1-1 | 1-2 | 2-0 | 4-0 | 3-2 | 1-0 | 1-0 | 1-1 | 2-2 | 2-4 | 2-3 | 0-1 | 2-3 | 0-1 | 1-0 | 2-0 |
| 6 | Bradford Park Avenue | 1-2 | 1-0 | 2-2 | 1-2 | 1-0 | | 1-0 | 1-0 | 4-2 | 3-1 | 1-4 | 1-1 | 3-1 | 1-1 | 3-0 | 4-4 | 2-3 | 1-1 | 3-1 | 0-0 | 0-2 | 3-1 |
| 7 | Chorley | 3-2 | 2-1 | 1-2 | 2-0 | 1-0 | 2-2 | | 3-0 | 2-0 | 3-0 | 3-1 | 0-1 | 0-1 | 2-2 | 2-0 | 2-3 | 2-3 | 2-2 | 0-0 | 1-0 | 1-1 | 2-0 |
| 8 | Corby Town | 1-2 | 3-2 | 2-3 | 2-3 | 1-1 | 2-0 | 2-2 | | 0-4 | 2-3 | 1-2 | 3-1 | 0-3 | 0-0 | 3-5 | 1-4 | 1-3 | 1-3 | 0-3 | 0-4 | 2-0 | 0-3 |
| 9 | Curzon Ashton | 0-2 | 1-0 | 0-2 | 0-2 | 1-1 | 2-1 | 4-2 | 2-2 | | 0-0 | 3-0 | 1-1 | 1-2 | 3-2 | 4-1 | 0-3 | 1-0 | 1-3 | 0-0 | 0-0 | 2-0 | 3-1 |
| 10 | FC United of Manchester | 1-2 | 1-3 | 1-3 | 1-2 | 3-2 | 2-1 | 2-0 | 1-0 | 3-3 | | 1-2 | 1-2 | 4-3 | 1-1 | 6-1 | 3-2 | 3-2 | 2-2 | 0-1 | 1-2 | 1-1 | 0-2 |
| 11 | Gainsborough Trinity | 0-2 | 1-1 | 1-1 | 1-0 | 1-0 | 0-1 | 2-1 | 1-1 | 0-2 | 0-1 | | 3-3 | 2-1 | 3-1 | 1-1 | 2-0 | 1-0 | 1-6 | 3-1 | 0-1 | 0-2 | 1-1 |
| 12 | Gloucester City | 1-3 | 1-0 | 1-1 | 1-0 | 0-0 | 1-3 | 1-1 | 1-0 | 3-1 | 1-0 | 0-2 | | 0-1 | 2-2 | 0-1 | 3-2 | 0-1 | 0-2 | 3-0 | 0-0 | 1-2 | 0-1 |
| 13 | Harrogate Town | 2-2 | 0-1 | 1-2 | 0-0 | 1-0 | 2-1 | 2-4 | 5-0 | 1-1 | 5-0 | 3-1 | 0-0 | | 2-1 | 4-0 | 3-3 | 0-3 | 6-0 | 2-1 | 2-1 | 0-0 | 1-0 |
| 14 | Hednesford Town | 0-1 | 2-0 | 3-3 | 3-2 | 0-2 | 0-0 | 1-3 | 3-3 | 0-3 | 0-3 | 0-2 | 2-2 | 2-3 | | 2-1 | 1-1 | 2-4 | 0-0 | 2-1 | 1-2 | 2-1 | 0-1 |
| 15 | Lowestoft Town | 3-1 | 3-0 | 1-0 | 3-0 | 1-2 | 3-0 | 2-0 | 2-2 | 0-0 | 1-4 | 1-0 | 1-1 | 1-2 | 0-0 | | 0-3 | 0-1 | 2-2 | 0-2 | 2-2 | 0-4 | 2-1 |
| 16 | North Ferriby United | 3-0 | 2-0 | 0-1 | 4-3 | 2-1 | 1-0 | 4-0 | 5-0 | 0-0 | 1-0 | 4-0 | 3-0 | 0-1 | 1-1 | 0-0 | | 1-2 | 1-1 | 1-0 | 2-0 | 3-1 | 3-3 |
| 17 | Nuneaton Town | 1-1 | 0-0 | 2-0 | 1-3 | 1-0 | 1-0 | 2-2 | 0-0 | 0-1 | 2-2 | 2-0 | 0-1 | 0-0 | 3-0 | 1-0 | 3-1 | | 0-1 | 3-3 | 1-1 | 3-0 | 1-1 |
| 18 | Solihull Moors | 3-0 | 2-1 | 2-1 | 0-1 | 3-0 | 2-1 | 0-2 | 4-1 | 2-0 | 1-2 | 3-2 | 0-0 | 1-0 | 1-2 | 2-1 | 1-3 | 3-1 | | 4-1 | 1-0 | 1-2 | 3-0 |
| 19 | Stalybridge Celtic | 1-1 | 5-5 | 1-1 | 0-5 | 3-1 | 1-1 | 0-1 | 2-3 | 1-1 | 1-0 | 0-0 | 1-0 | 0-1 | 4-2 | 3-1 | 2-0 | 2-5 | 1-3 | | 1-1 | 3-5 | 3-1 |
| 20 | Stockport County | 0-4 | 0-1 | 1-0 | 2-1 | 1-1 | 2-0 | 1-3 | 2-2 | 0-0 | 1-2 | 2-0 | 3-0 | 1-2 | 3-0 | 0-2 | 1-1 | 1-1 | 2-4 | 0-3 | | 1-1 | 0-0 |
| 21 | Tamworth | 3-1 | 2-1 | 1-2 | 1-2 | 1-2 | 0-0 | 2-1 | 0-0 | 2-1 | 1-1 | 2-0 | 2-2 | 1-0 | 1-0 | 1-1 | 1-0 | 1-1 | 1-1 | 1-1 | 1-1 | | 3-0 |
| 22 | Worcester City | 2-2 | 3-0 | 1-1 | 2-1 | 0-0 | 3-1 | 2-3 | 1-2 | 2-2 | 0-0 | 2-0 | 1-2 | 0-0 | 1-4 | 2-1 | 2-0 | 0-1 | 2-2 | 5-0 | 2-3 | 1-2 | |

# NATIONAL SOUTH LEAGUE TABLE 2015-16

| | | P | W | D | L | F | A | GD | Pts |
|---|---|---|---|---|---|---|---|---|---|
| 1 | Sutton United | 42 | 26 | 12 | 4 | 83 | 32 | 51 | 90 |
| 2 | Ebbsfleet United | 42 | 24 | 12 | 6 | 73 | 36 | 37 | 84 |
| 3 | Maidstone United | 42 | 24 | 5 | 13 | 55 | 40 | 15 | 77 |
| 4 | Truro City | 42 | 17 | 14 | 11 | 62 | 55 | 7 | 65 |
| 5 | Whitehawk | 42 | 18 | 10 | 14 | 75 | 62 | 13 | 64 |
| 6 | Hemel Hempstead Town | 42 | 16 | 13 | 13 | 72 | 66 | 6 | 61 |
| 7 | Maidenhead United | 42 | 16 | 11 | 15 | 66 | 62 | 4 | 59 |
| 8 | Dartford | 42 | 16 | 11 | 15 | 58 | 56 | 2 | 59 |
| 9 | Gosport Borough | 42 | 15 | 11 | 16 | 53 | 63 | -10 | 56 |
| 10 | Concord Rangers | 42 | 15 | 10 | 17 | 66 | 68 | -2 | 55 |
| 11 | Bishop's Stortford | 42 | 15 | 10 | 17 | 56 | 63 | -7 | 55 |
| 12 | Oxford City | 42 | 13 | 15 | 14 | 70 | 60 | 10 | 54 |
| 13 | Wealdstone | 42 | 12 | 17 | 13 | 63 | 64 | -1 | 53 |
| 14 | Bath City | 42 | 14 | 11 | 17 | 50 | 61 | -11 | 53 |
| 15 | Chelmsford City | 42 | 15 | 7 | 20 | 66 | 64 | 2 | 52 |
| 16 | Weston-super-Mare | 42 | 14 | 9 | 19 | 63 | 76 | -13 | 51 |
| 17 | Eastbourne Borough | 42 | 13 | 11 | 18 | 60 | 63 | -3 | 50 |
| 18 | St Albans City | 42 | 13 | 10 | 19 | 58 | 65 | -7 | 49 |
| 19 | Margate | 42 | 13 | 8 | 21 | 51 | 73 | -22 | 47 |
| 20 | Havant & Waterlooville | 42 | 12 | 11 | 19 | 52 | 75 | -23 | 47 |
| 21 | Hayes & Yeading United | 42 | 11 | 13 | 18 | 51 | 76 | -25 | 46 |
| 22 | Basingstoke Town | 42 | 9 | 11 | 22 | 46 | 69 | -23 | 38 |

**Play-Off Semi Finals:** Truro City 0-2 Maidstone United / Maidstone United 1-0 Truro City
Whitehawk 1-2 Ebbsfleet United / Ebbsfleet United 1-2 Whitehawk (Ebbsfleet won 3-2 on pens)
**Final:** Ebbsfleet United 2-2 Maidstone United (Maidstone won 4-3 on pens aet)

| | | 1 | 2 | 3 | 4 | 5 | 6 | 7 | 8 | 9 | 10 | 11 | 12 | 13 | 14 | 15 | 16 | 17 | 18 | 19 | 20 | 21 | 22 |
|---|---|---|---|---|---|---|---|---|---|---|---|---|---|---|---|---|---|---|---|---|---|---|---|
| 1 | Basingstoke Town | | 1-2 | 1-1 | 1-2 | 0-2 | 0-1 | 1-5 | 1-2 | 0-1 | 1-1 | 1-0 | 2-0 | 2-1 | 0-1 | 0-0 | 2-0 | 2-2 | 1-2 | 2-0 | 1-1 | 2-2 | 3-1 |
| 2 | Bath City | 0-0 | | 2-2 | 2-0 | 0-1 | 0-0 | 1-0 | 1-1 | 0-1 | 5-0 | 2-3 | 1-1 | 2-1 | 0-2 | 2-0 | 1-3 | 1-0 | 1-3 | 0-3 | 2-1 | 2-1 | 0-3 |
| 3 | Bishop's Stortford | 1-2 | 3-2 | | 1-2 | 3-2 | 1-2 | 1-1 | 1-2 | 2-0 | 3-0 | 0-0 | 1-0 | 0-2 | 0-1 | 4-1 | 3-0 | 2-1 | 0-2 | 0-3 | 2-1 | 0-1 | 2-1 |
| 4 | Chelmsford City | 0-2 | 3-1 | 4-1 | | 5-2 | 0-1 | 0-3 | 0-0 | 6-1 | 2-2 | 4-0 | 0-1 | 4-1 | 3-0 | 2-3 | 0-4 | 2-1 | 0-2 | 1-2 | 0-2 | 2-3 | 4-3 |
| 5 | Concord Rangers | 5-0 | 1-2 | 2-2 | 1-0 | | 2-3 | 4-1 | 0-0 | 0-0 | 0-1 | 0-3 | 0-3 | 2-0 | 1-2 | 2-1 | 0-2 | 1-2 | 0-3 | 1-2 | 2-2 | 4-1 | 1-2 |
| 6 | Dartford | 0-0 | 4-1 | 3-1 | 1-1 | 1-2 | | 1-0 | 0-1 | 2-3 | 4-2 | 2-0 | 2-2 | 2-0 | 1-1 | 1-1 | 2-2 | 2-0 | 2-2 | 0-1 | 1-2 | 2-1 | 2-4 |
| 7 | Eastbourne Borough | 1-2 | 5-2 | 0-1 | 2-0 | 0-0 | 1-1 | | 1-2 | 3-0 | 2-2 | 2-0 | 2-3 | 1-2 | 1-0 | 1-4 | 1-1 | 1-0 | 1-1 | 0-0 | 3-0 | 3-3 | 1-1 |
| 8 | Ebbsfleet United | 1-0 | 0-1 | 4-2 | 3-1 | 4-2 | 1-1 | 4-2 | | 2-0 | 2-2 | 0-0 | 6-0 | 3-1 | 0-1 | 1-2 | 1-1 | 1-0 | 1-0 | 0-0 | 2-3 | 2-1 | 2-2 |
| 9 | Gosport Borough | 3-2 | 3-1 | 0-0 | 2-1 | 2-3 | 1-3 | 3-1 | 1-2 | | 2-1 | 2-5 | 2-6 | 2-1 | 0-0 | 1-2 | 0-0 | 0-0 | 0-2 | 3-1 | 1-1 | 1-0 | 2-2 |
| 10 | Havant & Waterlooville | 1-0 | 1-1 | 2-1 | 0-1 | 2-1 | 2-0 | 4-0 | 1-4 | 1-3 | | 1-0 | 1-2 | 3-1 | 2-1 | 2-0 | 2-1 | 1-1 | 0-2 | 0-0 | 1-2 | 1-1 | 2-3 |
| 11 | Hayes & Yeading United | 3-0 | 0-3 | 0-2 | 0-5 | 2-2 | 2-2 | 4-4 | 0-5 | 0-0 | 0-0 | | 1-1 | 2-5 | 1-0 | 0-2 | 2-1 | 1-3 | 1-3 | 2-2 | 0-0 | 1-1 | 3-4 |
| 12 | Hemel Hempstead Town | 2-2 | 1-1 | 1-2 | 1-1 | 1-2 | 1-0 | 1-0 | 1-2 | 1-0 | 2-0 | 4-0 | | 0-1 | 0-1 | 1-2 | 3-1 | 2-2 | 2-2 | 2-1 | 2-2 | 5-5 | 0-3 |
| 13 | Maidenhead United | 4-3 | 3-1 | 4-1 | 1-0 | 2-2 | 2-1 | 2-0 | 0-0 | 0-0 | 2-2 | 2-1 | 2-3 | | 0-2 | 3-1 | 2-1 | 0-1 | 1-1 | 0-0 | 1-1 | 2-0 | 3-0 |
| 14 | Maidstone United | 3-1 | 1-0 | 1-1 | 0-1 | 2-2 | 1-2 | 2-1 | 0-2 | 2-1 | 1-0 | 3-1 | 2-1 | 1-2 | | 2-1 | 0-1 | 1-0 | 1-2 | 2-1 | 1-0 | 3-1 | 0-1 |
| 15 | Margate | 2-1 | 1-1 | 1-1 | 4-1 | 0-1 | 0-2 | 0-1 | 0-2 | 1-0 | 4-1 | 1-2 | 4-3 | 3-2 | 1-0 | | 0-2 | 0-1 | 0-4 | 1-1 | 0-0 | 0-2 | 2-6 |
| 16 | Oxford City | 2-2 | 1-1 | 3-1 | 2-2 | 5-1 | 2-1 | 2-2 | 1-1 | 1-2 | 1-3 | 2-2 | 0-2 | 0-0 | 2-3 | 1-1 | | 4-1 | 0-1 | 1-2 | 3-2 | 3-0 | 0-0 |
| 17 | St Albans City | 3-0 | 0-1 | 1-1 | 1-1 | 2-2 | 4-0 | 3-1 | 0-2 | 1-3 | 6-0 | 1-1 | 2-2 | 3-2 | 1-2 | 3-0 | 1-3 | | 0-3 | 0-1 | 1-0 | 2-1 | 6-0 |
| 18 | Sutton United | 2-0 | 1-1 | 2-0 | 2-0 | 2-2 | 2-0 | 2-1 | 2-0 | 1-0 | 3-0 | 0-1 | 2-2 | 2-2 | 0-2 | 4-1 | 1-1 | 5-0 | | 2-2 | 5-2 | 0-0 | 2-2 |
| 19 | Truro City | 2-0 | 3-1 | 0-1 | 1-0 | 2-1 | 3-0 | 1-0 | 1-1 | 2-2 | 3-0 | 0-2 | 4-2 | 4-4 | 1-3 | 2-1 | 0-6 | 2-0 | 0-2 | | 1-2 | 1-3 | 1-1 |
| 20 | Wealdstone | 4-4 | 2-0 | 3-1 | 0-0 | 1-2 | 2-1 | 0-1 | 1-2 | 1-1 | 3-2 | 3-0 | 0-0 | 0-0 | 2-2 | 4-1 | 2-2 | 1-1 | 0-2 | 4-4 | | 2-3 | 2-2 |
| 21 | Weston-super-Mare | 2-1 | 1-1 | 1-1 | 0-3 | 0-3 | 2-1 | 1-2 | 2-1 | 0-4 | 3-2 | 0-2 | 2-4 | 2-0 | 1-2 | 1-0 | 5-2 | 4-1 | 0-2 | 2-2 | 1-2 | | 1-2 |
| 22 | Whitehawk | 1-0 | 0-1 | 2-3 | 4-2 | 0-2 | 0-1 | 1-2 | 0-1 | 3-0 | 1-1 | 1-3 | 0-1 | 3-2 | 1-0 | 2-2 | 2-0 | 6-0 | 2-0 | 0-0 | 3-0 | 0-2 | |

# ALDERSHOT TOWN

**Chairman:** Shahid Azeem

**Secretary:** Bob Green (T) 01252 320 211 (E) bob.green@theshots.co.uk

**Commercial Manager:** Mark Butler (T/E) mark.butler@theshots.co.uk

**Programme Editor:** Victoria Rogers (T/E) 07979 964 264

**Ground Address:** EBB Stadium, High street, Aldershot, GU11 1TW

(T) 01252 320 211 **Manager:** Gary Waddock

## Club Factfile

**Founded:** 1992 **Nickname:** Shots

**Previous Names:** None

**Previous Leagues:** Isthmian 1992-2003. Conference 2003-2008. Football League 2008-13.

**Club Colours (change):** Red/blue/red (Sky blue/navy blue/navy blue)

**Ground Capacity:** 7,500 **Seats:** 1,800 **Covered:** 6,850 **Clubhouse:** Yes **Shop:** Yes

**Directions**

Exit from the M3 at junction 4 and take the A331 to Aldershot , after 3 miles take the 4th exit off the A331 and take the Town Centre route to Aldershot.

1.25 miles from the A331 junction the ground will be on your right hand side. Located on the High Street in Aldershot.

**Previous Grounds:** None

**Record Attendance:** 7,500 v Brighton & Hove Albion, FA Cup 1st Round, 18/11/2000

**Record Victory:** 8-0 v Bishop's Stortford (A) Isthmian Premier 05/09/1998

**Record Defeat:** 0-6 v Worthing (A) Isthmian League Cup 02/03/99

**Record Goalscorer:** Mark Butler - 155 (1992-96)

**Record Appearances:** Jason Chewings - 400

**Additional Records:**

**Honours:**

Isthmian League Premier Division 2002-03. Conference 2007-08.

### 10 YEAR RECORD

| 06-07 | 07-08 | 08-09 | 09-10 | 10-11 | 11-12 | 12-13 | 13-14 | 14-15 | 15-16 |
|---|---|---|---|---|---|---|---|---|---|
| Conf 9 | Conf 1 | FL 2 15 | FL 2 6 | FL 2 14 | FL 2 11 | FL 2 24 | Conf 19 | Conf 18 | Nat 15 |

## ALDERSHOT TOWN MATCH RESULTS 2015-16

| Date | Comp | H/A | Opponents | Att: | Result | | Goalscorers | Pos | No. |
|---|---|---|---|---|---|---|---|---|---|
| Aug 8 | Nat Lge | H | Gateshead | 1749 | L | 1-2 | Browne 21 | 15 | 1 |
| 11 | Nat Lge | A | Cheltenham Town | 2552 | D | 0-0 | | 19 | 2 |
| 15 | Nat Lge | A | Wrexham | 4951 | L | 0-3 | | 21 | 3 |
| 18 | Nat Lge | H | Dover Athletic | 1559 | D | 1-1 | Brodie 37 | 21 | 4 |
| 22 | Nat Lge | A | Guiseley | 782 | **W** | 4-0 | Brodie 20 80 Stevenson 33 Alexander 49 | 14 | 5 |
| 29 | Nat Lge | H | Eastleigh | 1778 | L | 1-2 | C.Walker 64 | 18 | 6 |
| 31 | Nat Lge | A | Braintree Town | 707 | **W** | 2-1 | Harris 70 Brodie 86 | 13 | 7 |
| Sept 5 | Nat Lge | H | FC Halifax Town | 1603 | **W** | 3-2 | Stevenson 17 C.Walker 24 50 | 12 | 8 |
| 12 | Nat Lge | A | Grimsby Town | 3869 | L | 1-4 | C.Walker 30 | 14 | 9 |
| 15 | Nat Lge | H | Welling United | 1256 | **W** | 1-0 | Brodie 49 | 12 | 10 |
| 19 | Nat Lge | A | Barrow | 1564 | **W** | 3-1 | C.Walker 32 60 Alexander 66 | 11 | 11 |
| 22 | Nat Lge | A | Tranmere Rovers | 4126 | L | 1-3 | Hatton 5 | | 12 |
| 26 | Nat Lge | H | Macclesfield Town | 1579 | L | 0-3 | | 15 | 13 |
| Oct 3 | Nat Lge | A | Torquay United | 1946 | **W** | 2-0 | Hatton 21 C.Walker 34 | 13 | 14 |
| 6 | Nat Lge | H | Forest Green Rovers | 1353 | L | 0-3 | | 15 | 15 |
| 10 | Nat Lge | H | Altrincham | 1412 | **W** | 2-0 | Saville 33 Browne 63 | 14 | 16 |
| 13 | Nat Lge | A | Boreham Wood | 581 | **W** | 1-0 | C.Walker 10 | 12 | 17 |
| 17 | Nat Lge | H | Bromley | 1611 | D | 1-1 | C.Walker 38 | 12 | 18 |
| **24** | **FAC4Q** | **H** | **Sutton United** | **1471** | **W** | **1-0** | **Browne 71** | | 19 |
| 31 | Nat Lge | A | Southport | 845 | D | 1-1 | Stevenson 11 | 12 | 20 |
| **Nov 7** | **FAC1** | **H** | **Bradford City** | **2640** | **D** | **0-0** | | | 21 |
| 10 | Nat Lge | H | Lincoln City | 1367 | L | 1-2 | Akinyemi 65 | 13 | 22 |
| 14 | Nat Lge | A | Kidderminster Harriers | 1790 | L | 0-2 | | 13 | 23 |
| **18** | **FAC1r** | **A** | **Bradford City** | **2930** | **L** | **0-2** | | | 24 |
| 21 | Nat Lge | H | Wrexham | 1483 | L | 0-1 | | 15 | 25 |
| 28 | Nat Lge | H | Cheltenham Town | 1493 | L | 0-2 | | 17 | 26 |
| Dec 5 | Nat Lge | A | Dover Athletic | 1012 | L | 2-5 | Hatton 46 C. Walker 49 | 17 | 27 |
| **12** | **FAT1** | **H** | **Eastleigh** | **877** | **L** | **0-1** | | | 28 |
| 19 | Nat Lge | H | Guiseley | 1325 | **W** | 1-0 | Richards 79 | 16 | 29 |
| 26 | Nat Lge | H | Woking | 3150 | L | 0-1 | | 16 | 30 |
| 28 | Nat Lge | A | Eastleigh | 2107 | D | 1-1 | Hatton 26 (pen) | 16 | 31 |
| Jan 2 | Nat Lge | A | Woking | 3708 | L | 1-2 | Browne 74 | 17 | 32 |
| 9 | Nat Lge | H | Chester | 1617 | **W** | 3-1 | McGinty 50 Pavey 52 Stevenson 89 | 15 | 33 |
| 23 | Nat Lge | A | Macclesfield Town | 1515 | **W** | 2-0 | Pavey 19 Lathrope 65 | 14 | 34 |
| 30 | Nat Lge | H | Kidderminster Harriers | 1768 | **W** | 1-0 | C.Walker 50 | 13 | 35 |
| Feb 13 | Nat Lge | H | Tranmere Rovers | 1882 | D | 0-0 | | 13 | 36 |
| 20 | Nat Lge | A | Gateshead | 1074 | L | 2-3 | Browne 6 Gallagher 42 | 13 | 37 |
| 27 | Nat Lge | A | Welling United | 704 | **W** | 1-0 | Lafayette 76 (pen) | 13 | 38 |
| Mar 5 | Nat Lge | A | Lincoln City | 2398 | L | 0-2 | | 14 | 39 |
| 8 | Nat Lge | A | Chester City | 1425 | L | 2-8 | Lafayette 23 C.Walker 67 | 14 | 40 |
| 12 | Nat Lge | H | Torquay United | 1771 | D | 0-0 | | 15 | 41 |
| 19 | Nat Lge | A | Altrincham | 1292 | L | 0-4 | | 15 | 42 |
| 25 | Nat Lge | A | Forest Green Rovers | 2272 | D | 0-0 | | 15 | 43 |
| 28 | Nat Lge | H | Braintree Town | 1539 | **W** | 2-1 | Beckles 40 Ralph 69 | 15 | 44 |
| Apr 2 | Nat Lge | H | Barrow | 1488 | L | 0-1 | | 15 | 45 |
| 5 | Nat Lge | H | Grimsby Town | 1397 | L | 3-4 | C.Walker 32 Rasulo 43 Browne 70 | 15 | 46 |
| 9 | Nat Lge | A | FC HalifaxTown | 1714 | **W** | 2-0 | Stevenson 47 Browne 83 | 14 | 47 |
| 16 | Nat Lge | H | Boreham Wood | 1389 | L | 1-2 | Gallagher 11 | 15 | 48 |
| 23 | Nat Lge | H | Southport | 1456 | L | 1-2 | D.Walker 9 | 16 | 49 |
| 30 | Nat Lge | A | Bromley | 1445 | **W** | 3-1 | C.Walker 11 75 Francis 64 (og) | 15 | 50 |

| GOALSCORERS | Scoring Games | Consec Sco Games | Total |
|---|---|---|---|
| *2014-15 B. Williams* | | | *15* |
| C.Walker | 12 | 2 | 15 |
| Browne | 7 | 2 | 7 |
| Brodie | 4 | 2 | 5 |
| Stevenson | 5 | | 5 |
| Hatton | 4 | | 4 |
| Alexander | 2 | | 2 |
| Gallagher | 2 | | 2 |
| Lafayette | 2 | | 2 |
| Pavey | 2 | | 2 |
| Akinyemi | 1 | | 1 |
| Beckles | 1 | | 1 |
| Harris | 1 | | 1 |
| Lathrope | 1 | | 1 |
| McGinty | 1 | | 1 |
| Ralph | 1 | | 1 |
| Rasulo | 1 | | 1 |
| Richards | 1 | | 1 |
| Saville | 1 | | 1 |
| D.Walker | 1 | | 1 |
| Opponents | | | 1 |

# BARROW

**Chairman:** Paul Casson

**Secretary:** Russell Dodd **(T)** 07789 757 639 **(E)** secbafc@aol.com

**Commercial Manager:** Steven Casson **(T/E)** 07572 590 274

**Programme Editor:** Bob Herbert **(T/E)** 01229 829 133

**Ground Address:** Furness Building Society Stadium, Wilkie Road, Barrow-in-Furness LA14 5UW

**(T)** 01299 823 061 **Manager:** Paul Cox - 23.11.15

## Club Factfile

**Founded:** 1901 **Nickname:** Bluebirds

**Previous Names:** None

**Previous Leagues:** Lancashire Combination 1901-21. Football League 1921-72. Northern Premier 1972-79, 83-84, 86-89, 92-98, 99-04. Conference 1979-83, 84-86, 89-92, 98-99.

**Club Colours (change):** White/royal blue/white (Royal blue/white/royal blue)

**Ground Capacity:** 4,500 **Seats:** 1,000 **Covered:** 2,200 **Clubhouse:** Yes **Shop:** Yes

**Directions**
M6 Junction 36, onto A590 signposted Barrow. Follow A590 all the way to the outskirts of Barrow (approx. 27 miles) entering via Industrial route. In a further 2 miles you pass the Fire Station on the right hand side, take next left into Wilkie Road, the ground is on the right.

**Previous Grounds:** Strawberry & Little Park, Roose.

**Record Attendance:** 16,854 v Swansea Town - FA Cup 3rd Round 1954
**Record Victory:** 12-0 v Cleator - FA Cup 1920
**Record Defeat:** 1-10 v Hartlepool United - Football League Division 4 1959
**Record Goalscorer:** Colin Cowperthwaite - 282 (December 1977 - December 1992)
**Record Appearances:** Colin Cowperthwaite - 704
**Additional Records:** Paid £9,000 to Ashton United for Andy Whittaker (07/94)
Received £40,000 from Barnet for Kenny Lowe (01/91)

**Honours:**
Lancashire Senior Cup 1954-55. Lancashire Challenge Trophy 1980-81. Northern Premier League 1983-84, 88-89, 97-98.
FA Trophy 1989-90, 2009-10.
Conference North 2014-15.

### 10 YEAR RECORD

| 06-07 | 07-08 | 08-09 | 09-10 | 10-11 | 11-12 | 12-13 | 13-14 | 14-15 | 15-16 |
|---|---|---|---|---|---|---|---|---|---|
| Conf N 16 | Conf N 5 | Conf 20 | Conf 15 | Conf 18 | Conf 13 | Conf 22 | Conf N 11 | Conf N 1 | Nat 11 |

## BARROW MATCH RESULTS 2015-16

| Date | Comp | H/A | Opponents | Att: | Result | | Goalscorers | Pos | No. |
|---|---|---|---|---|---|---|---|---|---|
| Aug 8 | Nat Lge | H | Dover Athletic | 2285 | W | 2-1 | Cook 24 34 | 4 | 1 |
| 11 | Nat Lge | A | Grimsby Town | 5047 | L | 1-4 | Newby 90 | 15 | 2 |
| 15 | Nat Lge | A | Forest Green Rovers | 1217 | L | 0-4 | | 18 | 3 |
| 18 | Nat Lge | H | Guiseley | 1440 | D | 1-1 | Walker 36 | 17 | 4 |
| 22 | Nat Lge | A | Cheltenham Town | 2209 | L | 1-2 | Downes 44 (og) | 19 | 5 |
| 29 | Nat Lge | H | Southport | 1343 | W | 1-0 | Cook 39 | 16 | 6 |
| 31 | Nat Lge | A | Halifax Town | 1490 | L | 1-3 | Cook 53 | 18 | 7 |
| Sept 5 | Nat Lge | H | Eastleigh | 1448 | W | 1-0 | Walker 3 (pen) | 15 | 8 |
| 12 | Nat Lge | A | Braintree Town | 710 | D | 1-1 | Pilkington 81 | 15 | 9 |
| 15 | Nat Lge | H | Lincoln City | 1233 | W | 1-0 | Cook 56 | 13 | 10 |
| 19 | Nat Lge | H | Aldershot Town | 1564 | L | 1-3 | Walker 40 (pen) | 16 | 11 |
| 22 | Nat Lge | A | Macclesfield Town | 1215 | W | 2-1 | Cook 55 86 | 14 | 12 |
| 26 | Nat Lge | H | Kidderminster Harriers | 1323 | D | 1-1 | Cook 51 | 17 | 13 |
| Oct 3 | Nat Lge | A | Altrincham | 1384 | L | 0-1 | | 17 | 14 |
| 6 | Nat Lge | H | Chester City | 1345 | W | 3-2 | Howarth 35 47 Cowperthwaite 77 | 12 | 15 |
| 10 | Nat Lge | A | Bromley | 2455 | L | 0-5 | | 15 | 16 |
| 13 | Nat Lge | A | Tranmere Rovers | 4624 | W | 1-0 | Howarth 37 | 15 | 17 |
| 17 | Nat Lge | H | Welling United | 1327 | D | 1-1 | Cook 53 | 15 | 18 |
| **24** | **FAC4Q** | **A** | **AFC Fylde** | **901** | **L** | **0-1** | | | 19 |
| 31 | Nat Lge | A | Wrexham | 3892 | L | 1-4 | Symington 74 | 15 | 20 |
| Nov 6 | Nat Lge | A | Guiseley | 749 | L | 1-3 | Cook 45 (pen) | 16 | 21 |
| 10 | Nat Lge | H | Grimsby Town | 1255 | L | 1-3 | O'Khan 31 | 17 | 22 |
| 14 | Nat Lge | H | Torquay United | 1119 | W | 4-0 | O'Khan 9 41 Walker 63 Howarth 90 | 15 | 23 |
| 21 | Nat Lge | A | Dover Athletic | 847 | L | 1-3 | Cook 77 | 16 | 24 |
| 28 | Nat Lge | H | Woking | 1115 | W | 2-1 | Cook 4 S.Williams 73 | 14 | 25 |
| **Dec 12** | **FAT1** | **A** | **Sutton Coldfield Town** | **326** | **W** | **1-0** | **Van de Broek 79** | | 26 |
| 19 | Nat Lge | A | Lincoln City | 2540 | D | 2-2 | Walker 44 62 (pen) | 15 | 27 |
| 28 | Nat Lge | A | Southport | 1528 | L | 1-2 | O'Khan 26 | 16 | 28 |
| Jan 2 | Nat Lge | A | Gateshead | 692 | D | 1-1 | J.Williams 84 | 16 | 29 |
| 9 | Nat Lge | H | Tranmere Rovers | 1766 | L | 3-4 | Walker 67 (pen) Grand 82 Cook 87 | 18 | 30 |
| **19** | **FAT2** | **A** | **FC Halifax Town** | **673** | **L** | **0-1** | | | 31 |
| 23 | Nat Lge | A | Welling United | 542 | W | 2-1 | Livesey 45 Grimes 55 | 16 | 32 |
| 30 | Nat Lge | A | Woking | 1713 | D | 2-2 | Cook 28 Griffiths 18 (og) | 16 | 33 |
| Feb 2 | Nat Lge | H | Gateshead | 939 | D | 0-0 | | 16 | 34 |
| 6 | Nat Lge | H | Cheltenham Town | 1203 | L | 1-2 | Grand 77 | 16 | 35 |
| 27 | Nat Lge | H | Forest Green Rovers | 1233 | D | 2-2 | Livesey 73 J.Williams 83 | 17 | 36 |
| Mar 5 | Nat Lge | A | Boreham Wood | 332 | W | 2-0 | Tomlinson 13 Cook 45 | 15 | 37 |
| 8 | Nat Lge | H | Boreham Wood | 881 | D | 0-0 | | 16 | 38 |
| 12 | Nat Lge | H | Altrincham | 1019 | W | 3-2 | Livesey 44 Cook 61 Tomlinson 67 | 14 | 39 |
| 19 | Nat Lge | H | Bromley | 1123 | D | 1-1 | Walker 82 | 14 | 40 |
| 26 | Nat Lge | A | Chester City | 2020 | W | 2-1 | J.Williams 55 85 | 14 | 41 |
| 28 | Nat Lge | H | FC Halifax Town | 1466 | W | 4-1 | J.Williams 31Cook 48 Walker 81 Tomlinson 90 | 13 | 42 |
| Apr 2 | Nat Lge | A | Aldershot Town | 1488 | W | 1-0 | Cook 64 | 13 | 43 |
| 5 | Nat Lge | H | Braintree Town | 1039 | W | 2-0 | Walker 7 Cook 81 | 13 | 44 |
| 9 | Nat Lge | H | Macclesfield Town | 1526 | D | 1-1 | J.Williams 43 (pen) | 13 | 45 |
| 12 | Nat Lge | A | Eastleigh | 3292 | L | 1-3 | Cook 60 | 13 | 46 |
| 16 | Nat Lge | A | Kidderminster Harriers | 1517 | D | 0-0 | | 13 | 47 |
| 23 | Nat Lge | A | Torquay United | 2874 | D | 2-2 | Tomlinson 34 Cook 90 | 11 | 48 |
| 30 | Nat Lge | H | Wrexham | 1728 | W | 2-0 | Cook 43 77 | 11 | 49 |

| GOALSCORERS | Scoring Games | Consec Sco Games | Total | | Scoring Games | Consec Sco Games | Total |
|---|---|---|---|---|---|---|---|
| ***2014-15 Cook*** | | | ***23*** | Grimes | 1 | | 1 |
| Cook | 20 | 3 | 23 | Newby | 1 | | 1 |
| Walker | 9 | | 10 | Pilkington | 1 | | 1 |
| J.Williams | 6 | 2 | 6 | Symington | 1 | | 1 |
| Howarth | 4 | | 4 | Van de Bruek | 1 | | 1 |
| O'Khan | 3 | | 4 | S.Williams | 1 | | 1 |
| Tominson | 4 | | 4 | Opposition | | | 2 |
| Livesey | 3 | | 3 | | | | |
| Grand | 2 | | 2 | | | | |
| Cowperthwaite | 1 | | 1 | | | | |

# BOREHAM WOOD

**Chairman:** Danny Hunter
**Secretary:** Billy Hunter (T) 07758 253 537 (E) billy@borehamwoodfootballclub.co.uk
**Commercial Manager:** (T/E)
**Programme Editor:** Billy Hunter (T/E) 07758 253 537
**Ground Address:** Meadow Park, Broughinge Road, Boreham Wood WD6 5AL
(T) 0208 953 5097 **Manager:** Luke Garrard

## Club Factfile

**Founded:** 1948 **Nickname:** The Wood
**Previous Names:** Boreham Wood Rovers and Royal Retournez amalgamated in 1948 to form today's club
**Previous Leagues:** Mid Herts 1948-52, Parthenon 1952-57, Spartan 1956-66, Athenian 1966-74, Isthmian 1974-2004, Southern 2004-10

**Club Colours (change):** White/black/white (All sky blue)

**Ground Capacity:** 4,502 **Seats:** 600 **Covered:** 1,568 **Clubhouse:** Yes **Shop:** Yes

**Directions**
Leave A1 at A5135 and follow A5135 towards Borehamwood.
Cross two mini roundabouts then at large roundabout turn right (second exit) into Brook Road then take first right after car park for Broughinge Road.

**Previous Grounds:** Eldon Avenue 1948-63

**Record Attendance:** 4,030 v Arsenal - Friendly 13/07/2001
**Record Victory:** Not known - If you know please email tw.publications@btinternet.com
**Record Defeat:** Not known - If you know please email tw.publications@btinternet.com
**Record Goalscorer:** Mickey Jackson
**Record Appearances:** Dave Hatchett - 714
**Additional Records:** Received £5,000 from Dagenham & Redbridge for Steve Heffer

**Honours:**
Athenian League 1973-74. Isthmian League Division 2 1976-77, Division 1 1994-95, 2000-01.
Southern League East 2005-06, Premier Division Play-off 2009-10. Conference South Play-off 2014-15.
Herts Senior cup 1971-72, 98-99, 2001-02. London Challenge Cup 1997-98.

### 10 YEAR RECORD

| 06-07 | 07-08 | 08-09 | 09-10 | 10-11 | 11-12 | 12-13 | 13-14 | 14-15 | 15-16 |
|---|---|---|---|---|---|---|---|---|---|
| Isth P 7 | Isth P 19 | Isth P 18 | Isth P 4 | Conf S 14 | Conf S 8 | Conf S 9 | Conf S 13 | Conf S 2 | Nat 19 |

# BOREHAM WOOD MATCH RESULTS 2015-16

| Date | Comp | H/A | Opponents | Att: | Result | | Goalscorers | Pos | No. |
|---|---|---|---|---|---|---|---|---|---|
| Aug 8 | Nat Lge | H | Halifax Town | 701 | W | 3-1 | Shakes 37 Lucas 61 Crawford 90 | 2 | 1 |
| 11 | Nat Lge | A | Eastleigh | 1347 | L | 0-1 | | 2 | 2 |
| 15 | Nat Lge | A | Gateshead | 760 | L | 1-2 | Lucas 30 | 7 | 3 |
| 18 | Nat Lge | H | Forest Green Rovers | 464 | L | 0-1 | | 15 | 4 |
| 22 | Nat Lge | A | Tranmere Rovers | 4632 | W | 2-0 | Montgomery 58 Crawford 90 | 18 | 5 |
| 29 | Nat Lge | H | Woking | 601 | D | 1-1 | Morais 83 | 18 | 6 |
| 31 | Nat Lge | A | Dover Athletic | 1012 | L | 1-2 | Crawford 8 | 15 | 7 |
| Sept 5 | Nat Lge | H | Grimsby Town | 1293 | L | 1-3 | MacDonald 80 | 20 | 8 |
| 12 | Nat Lge | A | Lincoln City | 2272 | L | 1-3 | Whichelow 35 | 20 | 9 |
| 15 | Nat Lge | H | Bromley | 364 | L | 2-3 | Doe 57 Morais 90 | 20 | 10 |
| 19 | Nat Lge | H | Wrexham | 685 | L | 0-1 | | 21 | 11 |
| 22 | Nat Lge | A | Torquay United | 1725 | W | 2-1 | Montgomery 8 Tiryaki 55 | 20 | 12 |
| 26 | Nat Lge | H | Boreham Wood | 351 | L | 0-1 | | 20 | 13 |
| Oct 3 | Nat Lge | A | Macclesfield Town | 1186 | D | 0-0 | | 20 | 14 |
| 6 | Nat Lge | A | Kidderminster Harriers | 1294 | D | 1-1 | Clifford 77 | 20 | 15 |
| 10 | Nat Lge | H | Welling United | 543 | W | 2-0 | Lucas 19 Devera 64 | 20 | 16 |
| 13 | Nat Lge | H | Aldershot Town | 581 | L | 0-1 | | 20 | 17 |
| 17 | Nat Lge | A | Guiseley | 749 | D | 1-1 | Kamdjo | 20 | 18 |
| **24** | **FAC4Q** | **H** | **AFC Hornchurch** | **307** | **W** | **2-1** | **Tiryaki 38 Jeffrey 90** | | 19 |
| 31 | Nat Lge | H | Gateshead | 344 | L | 2-3 | Clifford 25 (pen) Vilhete 75 | 20 | 20 |
| **Nov 7** | **FAC1** | **A** | **Northwich Victoria** | **502** | **D** | **1-1** | **Morais 23** | | 21 |
| 10 | Nat Lge | A | Bromley | 939 | W | 2-1 | Howell 3 11 | 20 | 22 |
| 14 | Nat Lge | H | Chester | 589 | D | 0-0 | | 20 | 23 |
| **16** | **FAC1r** | **H** | **Northwich Victoria** | **512** | **L** | **1-2** | **MacDonald 90** | | 24 |
| 21 | Nat Lge | A | Altrincham | 1002 | L | 0-1 | | 20 | 25 |
| 25 | Nat Lge | H | Lincoln City | 661 | D | 1-1 | Kamdjo 26 | 20 | 26 |
| 28 | Nat Lge | H | Tranmere Rovers | 640 | D | 0-0 | | 20 | 27 |
| **Dec 12** | **FAT1** | **H** | **Woking** | **279** | **L** | **1-2** | **Tiryaki 8** | | 28 |
| 19 | Nat Lge | A | Forest Green Rovers | 1356 | L | 0-1 | | 21 | 29 |
| 26 | Nat Lge | H | Braintree Town | 443 | W | 1-0 | Jeffrey 7 | 20 | 30 |
| 28 | Nat Lge | A | Woking | 2097 | D | 0-0 | | 20 | 31 |
| Jan 9 | Nat Lge | H | Cheltenham Town | 647 | D | 0-0 | | 20 | 32 |
| 23 | Nat Lge | H | Eastleigh | 408 | D | 1-1 | Lucas 43 | 20 | 33 |
| Feb 7 | Nat Lge | H | Kidderminster Harriers | 366 | L | 0-2 | | 21 | 34 |
| 13 | Nat Lge | A | Grimsby Town | 3927 | D | 0-0 | | 21 | 35 |
| 16 | Nat Lge | A | Braintree Town | 628 | W | 2-0 | Doe 48 Howell 54 | 20 | 36 |
| 20 | Nat Lge | H | Torquay United | 555 | L | 0-1 | | 21 | 37 |
| 27 | Nat Lge | A | Southport | 815 | W | 3-0 | Howell 16 29 Stephens 75 | 19 | 38 |
| Mar 5 | Nat Lge | H | Barrow | 332 | L | 0-2 | | 19 | 39 |
| 8 | Nat Lge | A | Barrow | 881 | D | 0-0 | | 19 | 40 |
| 12t | Nat Lge | A | Wrexham | 3470 | L | 0-1 | | 21 | 41 |
| 19 | Nat Lge | H | Macclesfield Town | 306 | D | 0-0 | | 21 | 42 |
| 25 | Nat Lge | A | Cheltenham Town | 3242 | L | 1-4 | Haynes 63 | 21 | 43 |
| 28 | Nat Lge | H | Dover Athletic | 602 | W | 3-0 | Lucas 3 81 Haynes 45 | 19 | 44 |
| Apr 2 | Nat Lge | A | Chester | 1444 | D | 2-2 | Doe 16 White 90 | 19 | 45 |
| 5 | Nat Lge | A | FC Halifax Town | 1309 | L | 2-3 | White 55 Lucas 83 | 20 | 46 |
| 9 | Nat Lge | H | Southport | 434 | L | 0-2 | | 21 | 47 |
| 16 | Nat Lge | A | Aldershot Town | 1369 | W | 2-1 | Shakes 9 Clifford 77 (pen) | 20 | 48 |
| 23 | Nat Lge | H | Guiseley | 601 | W | 1-0 | Sam-Yorke 23 | 19 | 49 |
| 30 | Nat Lge | A | Welling United | 577 | W | 3-0 | Lokko 31 (og) Howell 41 Kamdjo 61 | 19 | 50 |

| GOALSCORERS | Scoring Games | Consec Sco Games | Total |
|---|---|---|---|
| *2014-15 Angol* | | | *29* |
| Lucas | 6 | | 7 |
| Howell | 4 | | 6 |
| Clifford | 3 | | 3 |
| Crawford | 3 | | 3 |
| Doe | 3 | | 3 |
| Kamdjo | 3 | | 3 |
| Morais | 3 | | 3 |
| Tiryaki | 3 | | 3 |
| Haynes | 2 | | 2 |
| Jeffrey | 2 | | 2 |
| MacDonald | 2 | | 2 |
| Montgomery | 2 | | 2 |
| Shakes | 2 | | 2 |
| White | 2 | | 2 |
| Devera | 1 | | 1 |
| Sam-Yorke | 1 | | 1 |
| Stephens | 1 | | 1 |
| Vilhete | 1 | | 1 |
| Whitchelow | 1 | | 1 |
| Opponents | | | 1 |

# BRAINTREE TOWN

**Chairman:** Lee Harding

**Secretary:** Tom Woodley (T) 07950 537 179 (E) tawoodley@talktalk.net

**Commercial Manager:** Mark Sansom (T/E) 07857 336 971

**Programme Editor:** Lee Harding (T/E) 07771 810 440

**Ground Address:** Cressing Road Stadium, off Clockhouse Way, Braintree CM7 3RD

**(T)** 01376 330 976 / 345 617 **Manager:** Jamie Day

## Club Factfile

**Founded:** 1898 **Nickname:** The Iron

**Previous Names:** Crittall Athletic > 1968, Braintree and Crittall Athletic > 1981, Braintree > 1983

**Previous Leagues:** N.Essex 1898-1925, Essex & Suffolk Border 1925-29, 55-64, Spartan 1928-35, Eastern Co. 1935-37, 38-39, 52-55, 70-91, Essex Co. 1937-38, London 1945-52, Gt London 1964-66, Met 1966-70, Southern 1991-96, Isthmian 1996-2006

**Club Colours (change):** Orange/blue/orange (Sky & white/white/white)

**Ground Capacity:** 4,222 **Seats:** 553 **Covered:** 1,288 **Clubhouse:** Yes **Shop:** Yes

**Directions**

Leave M11 at junction 8A (for Stansted Airport) and follow A120 towards Braintree and Colchester for 17 miles. At Gallows Corner roundabout (with WestDrive Kia on your right) take first exit into Cressing Road. Clockhouse Way and the entrance to the ground are three quarters of a mile on the left and are clearly sign-posted.

**Previous Grounds:** The Fiar Field 1898-1903, Spalding Meadow and Panfield Lane

**Record Attendance:** 4,000 v Tottenham Hotspur - Testimonial May 1952
**Record Victory:** 12-0 v Thetford - Eastern Counties League 1935-36
**Record Defeat:** 0-14 v Chelmsford City (A) - North Essex League 1923
**Record Goalscorer:** Chris Guy - 211 (1963-90)
**Record Appearances:** Paul Young - 524 (1966-77)
**Additional Records:** Gary Bennett scored 57 goals during season 1997-98
Received £10,000 from Brentford for Matt Metcalf and from Colchester United for John Cheesewright

**Honours:**
Eastern Counties League 1983-84, 84-85, Essex Senior Cup 1995-96. Isthmian League Premier Division 2005-06.
Conference South Champions 2010-11.
East Anglian Cup x3

**10 YEAR RECORD**

| 06-07 | 07-08 | 08-09 | 09-10 | 10-11 | 11-12 | 12-13 | 13-14 | 14-15 | 15-16 |
|---|---|---|---|---|---|---|---|---|---|
| Conf S 3 | Conf S 5 | Conf S 14 | Conf S 7 | Conf S 1 | Conf 12 | Conf 9 | Conf 6 | Conf 14 | Nat 3 |

# BRAINTREE TOWN MATCH RESULTS 2015-16

| Date | Comp | H/A | Opponents | Att: | Result | | Goalscorers | Pos | No. |
|---|---|---|---|---|---|---|---|---|---|
| Aug 8 | Nat Lge | H | Chester | 2256 | L | 0-1 | | 18 | 1 |
| 11 | Nat Lge | A | Halifax Town | 657 | L | 1-3 | Akinola 63 | 22 | 2 |
| 15 | Nat Lge | H | Tranmere Rovers | 838 | D | 0-0 | | 20 | 3 |
| 18 | Nat Lge | A | Bromley | 775 | W | 2-1 | Sparks 22 Akinola 48 | 16 | 4 |
| 22 | Nat Lge | H | Southport | 504 | W | 1-0 | Sparks 23 | 12 | 5 |
| 29 | Nat Lge | A | Welling United | 521 | W | 2-1 | Cheek 14 Sparks 76 | 9 | 6 |
| 31 | Nat Lge | H | Aldershot Town | 707 | L | 1-2 | Chiedozie 42 | 10 | 7 |
| Sept 5 | Nat Lge | A | Kidderminster Harriers | 1670 | W | 1-0 | Davis 43 (pen) | 6 | 8 |
| 12 | Nat Lge | H | Barrow | 710 | D | 1-1 | Akinola 56 | 9 | 9 |
| 15 | Nat Lge | A | Dover Athletic | 638 | D | 0-0 | | 9 | 10 |
| 19 | Nat Lge | A | Altrincham | 861 | W | 4-0 | Cheek 9 Davis 43 (pen) Edgar 90 Miles 90 | 7 | 11 |
| 22 | Nat Lge | H | Woking | 652 | W | 2-1 | Akinola 62 Cheek 74 | 5 | 12 |
| 26 | Nat Lge | H | Guiseley | 679 | L | 0-1 | | 9 | 13 |
| Oct 3 | Nat Lge | A | Eastleigh | 1330 | W | 2-0 | Davis 32 (pen) Cheek 60 | 6 | 14 |
| 6 | Nat Lge | A | Cheltenham Town | 2097 | D | 1-1 | Edgar 90 | 8 | 15 |
| 10 | Nat Lge | H | Grimsby Town | 1394 | D | 0-0 | | 9 | 16 |
| 13 | Nat Lge | H | Dover Athletic | 637 | W | 1-0 | Cheek 44 | 6 | 17 |
| 17 | Nat Lge | A | Lincoln City | 2565 | L | 0-2 | | 8 | 18 |
| **24** | **FAC4Q** | **H** | **Harlow Town** | **727** | **W** | **2-0** | **Cheek 14 90** | | 19 |
| 31 | Nat Lge | H | Macclesfield Town | 687 | W | 1-0 | Szmodics 75 | 5 | 20 |
| **Nov 7** | **FAC1** | **H** | **Oxford United** | **1248** | **D** | **1-1** | **Davis 62** | | 21 |
| 10 | Nat Lge | A | Woking | 1182 | D | 1-1 | Marks 23 | 7 | 22 |
| 14 | Nat Lge | A | FC Halifax Town | 1065 | W | 6-3 | Woodyard 4 CHEEK 3 (18 24 49) Davis 30 (pen) Szmodics 57 | 7 | 23 |
| **16** | **FAC1r** | **A** | **Oxford United** | **3265** | **L** | **1-3** | **Davis 33 (pen)** | | 24 |
| 28 | Nat Lge | H | Torquay United | 773 | D | 0-0 | | 9 | 25 |
| Dec 5 | Nat Lge | A | Tranmere Rovers | 4224 | W | 2-1 | Sparks 5 Akinola 24 | 9 | 26 |
| **22** | **FAT1** | **H** | **Bromley** | **204** | **W** | **1-0** | **Marks 89** | | 27 |
| 26 | Nat Lge | A | Boreham Wood | 443 | L | 0-1 | | 10 | 28 |
| **Jan 16** | **FAT2** | **H** | **Stourbridge** | **244** | **L** | **0-1** | | | 29 |
| 23 | Nat Lge | A | Forest Green Rovers | 1507 | L | 0-1 | | 13 | 30 |
| 26 | Nat Lge | H | Wrexham | 484 | W | 1-0 | Miles 76 | 10 | 31 |
| 30 | Nat Lge | H | Chester | 727 | W | 2-0 | Phillips 11 Paine 35 | 10 | 32 |
| Feb 2 | Nat Lge | H | Welling United | 461 | W | 1-0 | Sparks 8 | 7 | 33 |
| 13 | Nat Lge | A | Southport | 827 | D | 1-1 | Sparks 30 | 6 | 34 |
| 16 | Nat Lge | H | Boreham Wood | 628 | L | 0-2 | | 6 | 35 |
| 23 | Nat Lge | H | FC Halifax Town | 506 | W | 2-0 | Davis 1 Cheek 67 | 7 | 36 |
| 27 | Nat Lge | A | Guiseley | 788 | D | 1-1 | Cheek 42 | 6 | 37 |
| Mar 2 | Nat Lge | H | Kidderminster Harriers | 502 | W | 2-1 | Isaac 29 Paine 60 | 4 | 38 |
| 5 | Nat Lge | H | Eastleigh | 666 | W | 2-0 | Akinola 36 85 | 4 | 39 |
| 8 | Nat Lge | A | Torquay United | 1462 | D | 0-0 | | 4 | 40 |
| 15 | Nat Lge | H | Gateshead | 572 | D | 0-0 | | 5 | 41 |
| 19 | Nat Lge | H | Cheltenham Town | 1138 | W | 1-0 | Cheek 63 | 5 | 42 |
| 26 | Nat Lge | H | Bromley | 1321 | W | 1-0 | Akinola 40 | 4 | 43 |
| 28 | Nat Lge | A | Aldershot Town | 1539 | L | 1-2 | Akinola 63 | 6 | 44 |
| Apr 2 | Nat Lge | A | Macclesfield Town | 1222 | L | 1-3 | Akinola 76 | 6 | 45 |
| 5 | Nat Lge | A | Barrow | 1039 | L | 0-2 | | 6 | 46 |
| 9 | Nat Lge | H | Forest Green Rovers | 740 | D | 1-1 | Davis 34 (pen) | 6 | 47 |
| 12 | Nat Lge | A | Grimsby Town | 3010 | W | 1-0 | Miles 77 | 6 | 48 |
| 16 | Nat Lge | A | Gateshead | 588 | W | 3-2 | Miles 4 16 Brundle 48 | 5 | 49 |
| 23 | Nat Lge | A | Wrexham | 4507 | W | 3-2 | Cheek 3 43 Brundle 41 | 5 | 50 |
| 30 | Nat Lge | H | Altrincham | 1803 | W | 3-0 | Cheek 17 42 Brundle 63 | 3 | 51 |
| **May 5** | **PO SF1** | **A** | **Grimsby Town** | **5271** | **W** | **1-0** | **Davis 53 (pen)** | | 52 |
| **8** | **PO SF2** | **H** | **Grimsby Town** | **3102** | **L** | **0-2** | **(aet)** | | 53 |

| GOALSCORERS | Scoring Games | Consec Sco Games | Total | | Scoring Games | Consec Sco Games | Total |
|---|---|---|---|---|---|---|---|
| ***2014-15 Cox*** | | | ***12*** | Szmodics | 2 | | 2 |
| Cheek | 12 | 2 | 17 | Chiedozie | 1 | | 1 |
| Akinola | 9 | 3 | 10 | Isaac | 1 | | 1 |
| Davis | 7 | 2 | 9 | Phillips | 1 | | 1 |
| Sparks | 6 | 3 | 6 | Woodyard | 1 | | 1 |
| Miles | 4 | 2 | 5 | | | | |
| Brundle | 3 | 3 | 3 | | | | |
| Edgar | 2 | | 2 | | | | |
| Marks | 2 | | 2 | | | | |
| Paine | 2 | | 2 | | | | |

# BROMLEY

**Chairman:** Jerry Dolke
**Secretary:** Jeff Hutton (T) 07739 941 117 (E) secretary@bromleyfc.co.uk
**Commercial Manager:** Jerry Dolke (T/E) 020 8460 5291
**Programme Editor:** David Cooke (T/E) 07786 068 659
**Ground Address:** The Stadium, Hayes Lane, Bromley, Kent BR2 9EF
(T) 020 8460 5291 **Manager:** Neil Smith

Photo: Keith Clayton.

## Club Factfile

**Founded:** 1892 **Nickname:** The Lillywhites
**Previous Names:** None
**Previous Leagues:** South London, Southern, London, West Kent, South Surburban, Kent, Spartan 1907-08, Isthmian 1908-11, 52-2007, Athenian 1919-1952

**Club Colours (change):** White with black trim/black/black (All red)

**Ground Capacity:** 5,000 **Seats:** 1,300 **Covered:** 2,500 **Clubhouse:** Yes **Shop:** Yes

**Directions**
From M25 Motorway: Leaving the M25 at Junction 4, follow the A21 to Bromley and London, for approximately 4 miles and then fork left onto the A232 signposted Croydon/Sutton. At the 2nd set of traffic lights turn right into Baston Road (B265), following it for about 2 miles as it becomes Hayes Street and then Hayes Lane. Bromley FC is on right hand side of road just after a mini roundabout. From the Croydon/Surrey areas use the A232, turn left into Baston Road (B265), following it for about 2 miles as it becomes Hayes Street and then Hayes Lane. From West London use the South Circular Road as far as West Dulwich and then via Crystal Palace, Penge, Beckenham and Bromley South areas. From North and East London use the Blackwall Tunnel and then the A20 road as far as Sidcup. Then use the A232 to Keston Common, turn right into Baston Road (B265), following it for about 2 miles as it becomes Hayes Street and then Hayes Lane.

**Previous Grounds:** White Hart Field. Widmore Road. Plaistow Cricket Ground.

**Record Attendance:** 10,798 v Nigeria - 1950
**Record Victory:** 13-1 v Redhill - Athenian League 1945-46
**Record Defeat:** 1-11 v Barking - Athenian League 1933-34
**Record Goalscorer:** George Brown - 570 (1938-61)
**Record Appearances:** George Brown
**Additional Records:** Received £50,000 from Millwall for John Goodman

**Honours:**
Amateur Cup 1910-11, 37-38, 48-49.
Isthmian League 1908-09, 09-10, 53-54, 60-61. Athenian League 1922-23, 48-49, 50-51. Conference South 2014-15.
Kent Senior Cup 1949/50, 76-77, 91-92, 96-97, 2005-06, 06-07. Kent Amateur Cup x12. London Senior Cup x4

### 10 YEAR RECORD

| 06-07 | 07-08 | 08-09 | 09-10 | 10-11 | 11-12 | 12-13 | 13-14 | 14-15 | 15-16 |
|---|---|---|---|---|---|---|---|---|---|
| Isth P 2 | Conf S 11 | Conf S 13 | Conf S 12 | Conf S 11 | Conf S 17 | Conf S 15 | Conf S 3 | Conf S 1 | Nat 14 |

# BROMLEY MATCH RESULTS 2015-16

| Date | Comp | H/A | Opponents | Att: | Result | | Goalscorers | Pos | No. |
|---|---|---|---|---|---|---|---|---|---|
| Aug 8 | Nat Lge | H | Wrexham | 2083 | **W** | 3-1 | Francis 23 Wall 29 Emmanuel 42 | 3 | 1 |
| 11 | Nat Lge | A | Woking | 1570 | L | 0-2 | | 11 | 2 |
| 15 | Nat Lge | A | Grimsby Town | 4731 | L | 1-4 | Davies 40 | 17 | 3 |
| 18 | Nat Lge | H | Braintree Town | 775 | L | 1-2 | Emmanuel 67 | 20 | 4 |
| 22 | Nat Lge | A | Halifax Town | 1107 | D | 2-2 | Emmanuel 76 Joseph-Dubois 90 | 18 | 5 |
| 29 | Nat Lge | H | Dover Athletic | 1273 | D | 1-1 | Goldberg 88 | 19 | 6 |
| 31 | Nat Lge | A | Forest Green Rovers | 1764 | L | 1-2 | Wall 7 | 20 | 7 |
| Sept 5 | Nat Lge | H | Gateshead | 1411 | **W** | 3-0 | Emmanuel 76 90 Dennis 85 | 18 | 8 |
| 12 | Nat Lge | H | Macclesfield Town | 955 | **W** | 1-0 | May76 | 13 | 9 |
| 15 | Nat Lge | A | Boreham Wood | 364 | **W** | 3-2 | May 31 Emmanuel 53 Goldberg 63 | 11 | 10 |
| 19 | Nat Lge | A | Torquay United | 1653 | **W** | 7-3 | EMMANUEL 3 (7 13 29) Holland 59 Dennis 69 Cook 72 (pen) Fuseine 80 | 9 | 11 |
| 22 | Nat Lge | H | Kidderminster Harriers | 776 | **W** | 3-2 | Dennis 37 Emmanuel 48 Cook 59 (pen) | 8 | 12 |
| 26 | Nat Lge | H | Cheltenham Town | 1610 | **W** | 3-0 | Emmanuel 19 45 Dennis 29 | 4 | 13 |
| Oct 3 | Nat Lge | A | Tranmere R | 4817 | L | 0-4 | | 9 | 14 |
| 6 | Nat Lge | A | Welling United | 1127 | **W** | 2-1 | Fuseini 25 Holland 62 | 5 | 15 |
| 10 | Nat Lge | H | Barrow | 2455 | **W** | 5-0 | Holland 17 Cook 25 Prestedge 48 Emmanuel 64 Dennis 86 | 4 | 16 |
| 13 | Nat Lge | H | Cheltenham Town | 1500 | L | 1-2 | Cook 88 (pen) | 5 | 17 |
| 17 | Nat Lge | A | Lincoln City | 1617 | D | 1-1 | Holland 41 | 6 | 18 |
| **24** | **FAC4Q** | **H** | **Eastleigh** | **1110** | **L** | **1-2** | **Dennis 61** | | 19 |
| 31 | Nat Lge | A | Lincoln City | 2550 | **W** | 1-0 | Emmanual 81 | 4 | 20 |
| Nov 10 | Nat Lge | H | Boreham Wood | 939 | L | 1-2 | Emmanuel 39 | 6 | 21 |
| 14 | Nat Lge | H | Altrincham | 1737 | L | 1-3 | Emmanuel 37 | 6 | 22 |
| 21 | Nat Lge | A | Macclesfield Town | 1632 | L | 0-2 | | 11 | 23 |
| 28 | Nat Lge | A | Guiseley | 233 | L | 0-2 | | 12 | 24 |
| **Dec 12** | **FAT1** | **A** | **Braintree Town** | **204** | **L** | **0-1** | | | 25 |
| 19 | Nat Lge | A | Southport | 751 | L | 3-5 | Minshull 36 Swaine 45 Francis 76 | 13 | 26 |
| 26 | Nat Lge | H | Eastleigh | 1708 | D | 2-2 | Emmanuel 36 Rodgers 46 | 13 | 27 |
| 28 | Nat Lge | A | Dover Athletic | 1536 | **W** | 3-2 | Cunnington 37 Holland 65 Prestedge 79 | 13 | 28 |
| Jan 9 | Nat Lge | H | Southport | 1317 | D | 0-0 | | 13 | 29 |
| 23 | Nat Lge | H | Tranmere R | 2219 | L | 0-1 | | 13 | 30 |
| 30 | Nat Lge | A | Cheltenham Town | 2662 | L | 1-4 | Wall 85 | 14 | 31 |
| Feb 9 | Nat Lge | H | Grimsby Town | 1073 | L | 1-2 | Francis 6 | 14 | 32 |
| 13 | Nat Lge | A | Wrexham | 3511 | L | 0-2 | | 15 | 33 |
| 20 | Nat Lge | H | Woking | 1227 | **W** | 2-1 | Emmanuel 24 (pen) Cunnington 30 | 14 | 34 |
| 27 | Nat Lge | A | Kidderminster Harriers | 1539 | **W** | 1-0 | Anderson 86 | 14 | 35 |
| 29 | Nat Lge | H | Welling United | 1110 | **W** | 2-0 | Gordon 9 Emmanuel 55 (pen) | 13 | 36 |
| Mar 5 | Nat Lge | A | Chester | 2058 | D | 1-1 | Emmanual 53 | 13 | 37 |
| 8 | Nat Lge | H | FC Halifax Town | 706 | **W** | 1-0 | Cunnington 74 | 11 | 38 |
| 12 | Nat Lge | H | Guiseley | 1044 | **W** | 2-0 | Goldberg 70 83 | 11 | 39 |
| 15 | Nat Lge | A | Eastleigh | 1520 | L | 0-2 | | 11 | 40 |
| 21 | Nat Lge | A | Barrow | 1123 | D | 1-1 | Cunnington 57 | 11 | 41 |
| 25 | Nat Lge | A | Braintree Town | 1321 | L | 0-1 | | 11 | 42 |
| 28 | Nat Lge | H | Forest Green Rovers | 1455 | D | 2-2 | Joseph-Dubois 65 Holland 90 | 12 | 43 |
| Apr 2 | Nat Lge | H | Lincoln City | 1202 | **W** | 2-0 | Cunnington 33 Goldberg 75 | 11 | 44 |
| 9 | Nat Lge | A | Altrincham | 1035 | D | 0-0 | | 12 | 45 |
| 16 | Nat Lge | H | Torquay United | 2080 | L | 0-2 | | 13 | 46 |
| 23 | Nat Lge | A | Gateshead | 865 | L | 1-3 | Coombes 51 | 13 | 47 |
| 30 | Nat Lge | H | Aldershot Town | 1445 | L | 1-3 | Fuseini 16 | 14 | 48 |

| GOALSCORERS | Scoring Games | Consec Sco Games | Total |
|---|---|---|---|
| ***2014-15 Ademola*** | ***17*** | | |
| Emmanuel | 16 | 4 | 20 |
| Dennis | 6 | 3 | 6 |
| Holland | 6 | 2 | 6 |
| Cunnington | 5 | | 5 |
| Goldberg | 4 | | 5 |
| Cook | 4 | 2 | 4 |
| Francis | 3 | | 3 |
| Fusieni | 3 | | 3 |
| Wall | 3 | | 3 |
| Joseph-Dubois | 2 | | 2 |
| May | 2 | 2 | 2 |
| Prestedge | 2 | | 2 |
| Coombes | 1 | | 1 |
| Davies | 1 | | 1 |
| Gordon | 1 | | 1 |
| Minshull | 1 | | 1 |
| Rodgers | 1 | | 1 |
| Swaine | 1 | | 1 |

# CHESTER

**Chairman:** Simon Olorenshaw
**Secretary:** n/a (T) (E)
**Commercial Manager:** (T/E)
**Programme Editor:** Rob Ashcroft (T/E) 07925 340 476
**Ground Address:** Lookers Vauxhall Stadium, Bumpers Lane, Chester CH1 4LT
(T) 01244 371 376 **Manager:** Jon McCarthy

## Club Factfile

**Founded:** 1885 **Nickname:** Blues
**Previous Names:** Chester > 1983, Chester City 1983-2010
**Previous Leagues:** Cheshire 1919-31, Football League 1931-2000, 2004-09, Conference 2000-04, 09-10 (Did not finish the season)

**Club Colours (change):** Blue/blue/white (All yellow)

**Ground Capacity:** 6,012 **Seats:** 3,284 **Covered:** Yes **Clubhouse:** Yes **Shop:** Yes

**Directions**
Stay on the M56 until you reach a roundabout at the end of the motorway. Follow the signs to North Wales & Queensferry A5117. After around one and a half miles you will reach a set of traffic lights where you need to bear left on to the A550 (signposted North Wales & Queensferry). Then from the A550, take the A548 towards Chester. Head straight through the first set of traffic lights and after passing a Vauxhall and then a Renault garage on your left, turn right at the next lights into Sovereign Way. Continue to the end of Sovereign Way and then turn right into Bumpers Lane and the entrance to the Club car park is just down on the right.

**Previous Grounds:** Faulkner Street 1885-98, The Old Showground 98-99, Whipcord Lane 1901-06, Sealand Road 06-90, Macclesfield FC 90-92

**Record Attendance:** 20,378 v Chelsea - FA Cup 3rd Round replay 16/01/1952
**Record Victory:** 12-0 v York City - 01/02/1936
**Record Defeat:** Not known - If you know please email tw.publications@btinternet.com
**Record Goalscorer:** Stuart Rimmer - 135
**Record Appearances:** Ray Gill - 406 (1951-62)
**Additional Records:** Paid £100,000 to Rotherham for Gregg Blundell.
Received £300,000 from Liverpool for Ian Rush
**Honours:**
Conference 2003-04, Conference North 2012-13.
Cheshire Senior Cup 1894-95, 96-97, 1903-04, 07-08, 08-09, 30-31, 31-32, 2012-13. Herefordshire Senior Cup 1991-92 (shared).
Welsh Cup 1907-08, 32-33, 46-47. NPL Division One North 2010-11, Premier Division 2011-12.

### 10 YEAR RECORD

| 06-07 | 07-08 | 08-09 | 09-10 | 10-11 | 11-12 | 12-13 | 13-14 | 14-15 | 15-16 |
|---|---|---|---|---|---|---|---|---|---|
| FL 2 18 | FL 2 22 | FL 2 23 | Conf dnf | NP1N 1 | NP P 1 | Conf N 1 | Conf 21 | Conf 12 | Nat 17 |

# CHESTER MATCH RESULTS 2015-16

| Date | Comp | H/A | Opponents | Att: | Result | Goalscorers | Pos | No. |
|---|---|---|---|---|---|---|---|---|
| Aug 8 | Nat Lge | H | Braintree Town | 2256 | W 1-0 | Hunt 4 | 6 | 1 |
| 11 | Nat Lge | A | Halifax Town | 1732 | W 1-0 | Chappell 34 | 3 | 2 |
| 15 | Nat Lge | A | Dover Athletic | 801 | D 0-0 | | 5 | 3 |
| 18 | Nat Lge | H | Cheltenham Town | 2304 | D 1-1 | Hannah 8 | 8 | 4 |
| 22 | Nat Lge | A | Woking | 1503 | L 2-5 | Sharps 65 Rooney 89 | 10 | 5 |
| 29 | Nat Lge | A | Macclesfield Town | 2062 | W 2-1 | Peers 90 Hobson 90 | 7 | 6 |
| 31 | Nat Lge | H | Guiseley | 2304 | D 1-1 | Rooney 65 (pen) | 8 | 7 |
| Sept 5 | Nat Lge | H | Forest Green Rovers | 2163 | L 1-2 | George 62 | 11 | 8 |
| 12 | Nat Lge | A | Tranmere Rovers | 7433 | L 0-2 | | 12 | 9 |
| 15 | Nat Lge | H | Grimsby Town | 1964 | D 1-1 | Hannah 72 (pen) | 15 | 10 |
| 19 | Nat Lge | H | Eastleigh | 1922 | W 1-0 | Heneghan 7 | 13 | 11 |
| 22 | Nat Lge | A | Welling United | 564 | L 1-2 | Mahon 90 | 15 | 12 |
| 26 | Nat Lge | A | Bromley | 1610 | L 0-3 | | 17 | 13 14 |
| Oct 3 | Nat Lge | H | Wrexham | 3741 | W 3-2 | Rooney 34 Shaw 58 Richards 69 | 14 | 15 |
| 6 | Nat Lge | A | Barrow | 1345 | L 2-3 | Chapell 31 Shaw 73 | 16 | 16 |
| 10 | Nat Lge | H | Lincoln City | 2224 | L 2-3 | Chapell 26 Hannah 67 | 16 | 17 |
| 13 | Nat Lge | A | Southport | 1326 | W 2-1 | Kay 79 Mahon 84 | 16 | 18 |
| 17 | Nat Lge | H | FC Halifax Town | 2088 | W 2-1 | Roberts 44 Hunt 55 | 14 | 19 |
| **24** | **FAC4Q** | **A** | **Altrincham** | **1603** | **L 0-1** | | | 20 |
| 31 | Nat Lge | A | Forest Green Rovers | 1561 | L 1-2 | Hannah 11 | 14 | 21 |
| Nov 10 | Nat Lge | H | Kidderminster Harriers | 1956 | W 3-1 | Hannah 42 82 Rooney 46 | 14 | 22 |
| 14 | Nat Lge | A | Boreham Wood | 589 | D 0-0 | | 13 | 23 |
| 21 | Nat Lge | H | Woking | 1837 | L 1-2 | Hannah 90 | 13 | 24 |
| 24 | Nat Lge | H | Dover Athletic | 1479 | D 1-1 | Hannah 45 | 13 | 25 |
| 28 | Nat Lge | A | Gateshead | 842 | L 0-1 | | 15 | 26 |
| Dec 5 | Nat Lge | A | Cheltenham Town | 2501 | L 1-3 | Hannah 44 | 15 | 27 |
| **12** | **FAT1** | **A** | **AFC Telford Utd** | **850** | **W 2-0** | **Hannah 10 37** | | 28 |
| 19 | Nat Lge | H | Torquay United | 2160 | W 4-1 | HANNAH 3 (1 40 72) Higgins 38 | 14 | 29 |
| 28 | Nat Lge | H | Macclesfield Town | 2791 | L 0-2 | | 14 | 30 |
| Jan 2 | Nat Lge | H | Altrincham | 2155 | D 1-1 | Hannah 20 | 15 | 31 |
| 9 | Nat Lge | A | Aldershot Town | 1617 | L 1-3 | Rooney 78 | 16 | 32 |
| **16** | **FAT2** | **H** | **Hungerford Town** | **1276** | **W 4-0** | **Chapell 64 Hannah 83 Hunt 85 Gilchrist 90** | | 33 |
| 23 | Nat Lge | H | Southport | 2228 | D 0-0 | | 17 | 34 |
| 30 | Nat Lge | A | Braintree Town | 727 | L 0-2 | | 17 | 35 |
| **Feb 10** | **FAT3** | **A** | **FC Halifax Town** | **878** | **L 0-1** | | | 36 |
| 16 | Nat Lge | A | Altrincham | 1442 | W 3-0 | O'Brien 26 Astles 45 Hannah 76 | 16 | 37 |
| 20 | Nat Lge | A | Kidderminster Harriers | 2067 | D 2-2 | Hannah 66 (pen) Alabi 76 | 15 | 38 |
| 28 | Nat Lge | H | Tranmere Rovers | 3494 | L 0-1 | | 16 | 39 40 |
| Mar 5 | Nat Lge | H | Bromley | 2058 | D 1-1 | Hannah 16 | 17 | 41 |
| 8 | Nat Lge | H | Aldershot Town | 1425 | W 8-2 | ALABI 4 (13 35 42 45) Hughes 5 38 Hannah 54 74 | 15 | 42 |
| 12 | Nat Lge | A | Eastleigh | 1831 | L 0-1 | | 16 | 43 |
| 19 | Nat Lge | A | Wrexham | 6459 | L 0-3 | | 16 | 44 |
| 26 | Nat Lge | H | Barrow | 2020 | L 1-2 | Hannah 37 | 17 | 45 |
| 28 | Nat Lge | A | Guiseley | 1186 | D 3-3 | Hannah 39 Richards 83 Shaw 90 | 17 | 46 |
| Apr 2 | Nat Lge | H | Boreham Wood | 1444 | D 2-2 | Rooney 11 65 | 17 | 47 |
| 5 | Nat Lge | A | Torquay United | 1831 | L 0-2 | | 17 | 48 |
| 9 | Nat Lge | A | Lincoln City | 2001 | L 1-2 | Alabi 73 | 17 | 49 |
| 16 | Nat Lge | H | Welling United | 2237 | W 4-0 | Rooney 17 47 Richards 66 Shaw 84 | 17 | 50 |
| 23 | Nat Lge | A | Grimsby Town | 4575 | W 2-1 | Rooney 48 Astles 61 | 17 | 51 |
| 30 | Nat Lge | H | Gateshead | 2323 | W 4-2 | Richards 60 Higgins 62 Hannah 76 80 | 17 | 52 |

| GOALSCORERS | Scoring Games | Consec Sco Games | Total | | Scoring Games | Consec Sco Games | Total |
|---|---|---|---|---|---|---|---|
| ***2014-15 McConville*** | ***11*** | | | Mahon | 2 | | 2 |
| Hannah | 19 | 3 | 25 | George | 1 | | 1 |
| Rooney | 8 | | 10 | Gilchrist | 1 | | 1 |
| Alabi | 3 | | 6 | Heneghan | 1 | | 1 |
| Chappell | 4 | 2 | 4 | Hobson | 1 | | 1 |
| Richards | 4 | | 4 | Kay | 1 | | 1 |
| Shaw | 4 | 2 | 4 | O'Brien | 1 | | 1 |
| Hunt | 3 | | 3 | Peers | 1 | | 1 |
| Astles | 2 | | 2 | Roberts | 1 | | 1 |
| Higgins | 2 | | 2 | Sharps | 1 | | 1 |
| Hughes | 2 | | 2 | | | | |

For Dagenham & Redbridge go to page 62

# DOVER ATHLETIC

**Chairman:** Jim Parmenter
**Secretary:** Franke Clarke (T) 01304 822373 (3) (E) frank.clarke@doverathletic.com
**Commercial Manager:** Commercial Team (T/E) 01304 822 373
**Programme Editor:** Media Team (T/E) 01304 822 373
**Ground Address:** Crabble Athletic Ground, Lewisham Road, Dover, Kent CT17 0JB
(T) 01304 822 373 **Manager:** Chris Kinnear

## Club Factfile

**Founded:** 1983 **Nickname:** The Whites
**Previous Names:** Dover F.C. until club folded in 1983
**Previous Leagues:** Southern 1983-93, 2002-04, Conference 1993-2002, Isthmian 2004-2009

**Club Colours (change):** White/black/black (Blue/white/white)

**Ground Capacity:** 6,500 **Seats:** 1,000 **Covered:** 4,900 **Clubhouse:** Yes **Shop:** Yes

**Directions** From outside of Kent, find your way to the M25, then take the M2/A2 (following the signs to Canterbury, then from Canterbury follow signs to Dover) as far as the Whitfield roundabout (there is a McDonald's Drive-Thru on the left). Take the fourth exit at this roundabout, down Whitfield Hill. At the bottom of the hill turn left at the roundabout and follow this road until the first set of traffic lights. At the lights turn right (180 degrees down the hill) and follow the road under the railway bridge, the ground is a little further up the road on the left. There is no parking for supporters within the ground, although parking is available in the rugby ground, which is just inside the main entrance - stewards will direct you. If you have to take the M20/A20 leave the A20 in Folkestone (the exit immediately after the tunnel through the hill) and travel through the Alkham Valley (turn left at the roundabout at the end of the slip-road and then left again, following the signs for Alkham) which will eventually take you near Kearsney train station (turn right into Lower Road just before the railway bridge, before you get to the station).

**Previous Grounds:** None.

**Record Attendance:** 4,186 v Oxford United - FA Cup 1st Round November 2002
**Record Victory:** 7-0 v Weymouth - 03/04/1990
**Record Defeat:** 1-7 v Poole Town
**Record Goalscorer:** Lennie Lee - 160
**Record Appearances:** Jason Bartlett - 359
**Additional Records:** Paid £50,000 to Farnborough Town for David Lewworthy August 1993
Received £50,000 from Brentford for Ricky Reina 1997
**Honours:**
Southern League Southern Division 1987-88, Premier Division 1989-90, 92-93, Premier Inter League Cup 1990-91.
Kent Senior Cup 1990-91. Isthmian League Division 1 South 2007-08, Premier Division 2008-09.

### 10 YEAR RECORD

| 06-07 | | 07-08 | | 08-09 | | 09-10 | | 10-11 | | 11-12 | | 12-13 | | 13-14 | | 14-15 | | 15-16 | |
|---|---|---|---|---|---|---|---|---|---|---|---|---|---|---|---|---|---|---|---|
| Isth1S | 3 | Isth1S | 1 | Isth P | 1 | Conf S | 2 | Conf S | 7 | Conf S | 7 | Conf S | 3 | Conf S | 5 | Conf | 8 | Nat | 5 |

# DOVER ATHLETIC MATCH RESULTS 2015-16

| Date | Comp | H/A | Opponents | Att: | Result | | Goalscorers | Pos | No. |
|---|---|---|---|---|---|---|---|---|---|
| Aug 8 | Nat Lge | A | Barrow | 2285 | L | 1-2 | Deverdics 18 | 16 | 1 |
| 11 | Nat Lge | H | Kidderminster Harriers | 906 | W | 3-2 | Grimes 40 Miller 45 Payne 83 | 9 | 2 |
| 15 | Nat Lge | H | Chester | 801 | D | 0-0 | | 13 | 3 |
| 18 | Nat Lge | A | Aldershot Town | 1558 | D | 1-1 | Payne 7 | 13 | 4 |
| 22 | Nat Lge | H | Altrincham | 711 | W | 2-1 | Ofori-Acheampong 21 Raggett 90 | 15 | 5 |
| 29 | Nat Lge | A | Bromley | 1273 | D | 1-1 | Deverdics 70 | 12 | 6 |
| 31 | Nat Lge | H | Boreham Wood | 1012 | W | 2-1 | Parkinson 15 Grimes 17 | 7 | 7 |
| Sept 5 | Nat Lge | A | Southport | 957 | D | 0-0 | | 7 | 8 |
| 12 | Nat Lge | A | Cheltenham Town | 2021 | L | 2-3 | Deverdics 4 (pen) Payne 4 | 11 | 9 |
| 15 | Nat Lge | H | Braintree Town | 638 | D | 0-0 | | 10 | 10 |
| 19 | Nat Lge | H | Guiseley | 823 | D | 0-0 | | 14 | 11 |
| 22 | Nat Lge | A | Eastleigh | 1360 | W | 5-2 | Miller18 86 Deverdics 46 (pen) 63 (pen) Murphy 83 | 10 | 12 |
| 25 | Nat Lge | H | Woking | 864 | W | 2-0 | Payne 4 76 | 8 | 13 |
| Oct 3 | Nat Lge | A | Gateshead | 949 | W | 3-2 | Payne 5 Thomas 62 Parkinson 80 | 5 | 14 |
| 6 | Nat Lge | A | Torquay United | 1210 | W | 3-2 | Payne 14 90 Parkinson 68 | 4 | 15 |
| 10 | Nat Lge | H | Wrexham | 1253 | W | 2-1 | Miller 31 Ajala 51 | 3 | 16 |
| 13 | Nat Lge | A | Braintree Town | 637 | L | 0-1 | | 3 | 17 |
| 17 | Nat Lge | H | Macclesfield Town | 1012 | W | 2-1 | Payne 6 Deverdics 55 | 3 | 18 |
| **24** | **FAC4Q** | **A** | **Eastbourne Borough** | **821** | **W** | **2-1** | **Payne 3 Raggett 90** | | 19 |
| 31 | Nat Lge | A | Tranmere Rovers | 4486 | W | 1-0 | Miller 42 | 3 | 20 |
| **Nov 7** | **FAC1** | **H** | **Stourbridge** | **1392** | **L** | **1-2** | **Thomas 33** | | 21 |
| 10 | Nat Lge | H | Eastleigh | 913 | L | 1-2 | Modeste 62 | 3 | 22 |
| 14 | Nat Lge | A | Forest Green Rovers | 1661 | L | 1-3 | Deverdics 38 | 3 | 23 |
| 21 | Nat Lge | H | Barrow | 847 | W | 3-1 | Modeste 11 Orlu 19 Miller 35 | | 24 |
| 24 | Nat Lge | A | Chester | 1479 | D | 1-1 | Miller 37 | | 25 |
| 28 | Nat Lge | A | FC Halifax Town | 1067 | L | 2-4 | Miller 19 Payne 63 | 6 | 26 |
| Dec 5 | Nat Lge | H | Aldershot Town | 1012 | W | 5-2 | Deverdics 1 Parkinson 35 Payne 61 Raggett 70 75 | 3 | 27 |
| **12** | **FAT1** | **A** | **Whitehawk** | **372** | **W** | **3-1** | **Deverdics 55 Payne 88 90** | | 28 |
| 19 | Nat Lge | A | Grimsby Town | 4266 | L | 0-1 | | 5 | 29 |
| 26 | Nat Lge | A | Welling United | 1006 | W | 2-1 | Modeste 13 Deverdics 68 | 4 | 30 |
| 28 | Nat Lge | H | Bromley | 1536 | L | 2-3 | Miller 8 71 | 5 | 31 |
| Jan 9 | Nat Lge | A | Lincoln City | 2402 | W | 3-2 | Miller 43 65 Deverdics 55 (pen) | 4 | 32 |
| **16** | **FAT2** | **H** | **Southport** | **629** | **W** | **2-1** | **Raggett 42 Miller 64** | | 33 |
| 24 | Nat Lge | H | Cheltenham Town | 1184 | L | 1-2 | Deverdics 83 | 5 | 34 |
| **Feb 6** | **FAT3** | **H** | **Guiseley** | **687** | **D** | **2-2** | **Parkinson 60 Ofori-Acheampong 89** | | 35 |
| 13 | Nat Lge | H | Gateshead | 638 | W | 4-0 | Miller 24 45 Deverdics 31 Payne 56 | 5 | 36 |
| **15** | **FAT3r** | **A** | **Guiseley** | **476** | **W** | **3-0** | **Payne 31 89 Deverdics 78** | | 37 |
| **27** | **FAT4** | **A** | **Nantwich Town** | **892** | **L** | **1-2** | **Orlu 70** | | 38 |
| Mar 1 | Nat Lge | H | Southport | 588 | L | 1-2 | Miller 60 | 9 | 39 |
| 5 | Nat Lge | A | Woking | 1305 | W | 1-0 | Parkinson 35 | 7 | 40 |
| 8 | Nat Lge | H | Welling United | 726 | W | 2-1 | Payne 23 Raggett 50 | 6 | 41 |
| 12 | Nat Lge | H | Tranmere Rovers | 1460 | D | 0-0 | | 7 | 42 |
| 15 | Nat Lge | H | Lincoln City | 743 | W | 4-1 | Payne 3 60 Miller 58 72 | 4 | 43 |
| 19 | Nat Lge | A | Guiseley | 690 | W | 1-0 | Payne 6 | 4 | 44 |
| 26 | Nat Lge | H | Torquay United | 1367 | W | 5-0 | Modeste 34 Deverdics 39 (pen) Miller 41 Payne 4 Kinnear 85 | 4 | 45 |
| 28 | Nat Lge | A | Boreham Wood | 602 | L | 0-3 | | 5 | 46 |
| Apr 2 | Nat Lge | H | FC HalifaxTown | 1027 | W | 1-0 | Deverdics 8 | 4 | 47 |
| 5 | Nat Lge | A | Altrincham | 1007 | W | 2-1 | Miller 67 Payne 74 | 4 | 48 |
| 9 | Nat Lge | A | Wrexham | 4931 | W | 1-0 | Modeste 61 | 3 | 49 |
| 12 | Nat Lge | A | Macclesfield United | 1022 | D | 0-0 | | 3 | 50 |
| 15 | Nat Lge | H | Grimsby Town | 1957 | D | 1-1 | Parkinson 56 | 3 | 51 |
| 23 | Nat Lge | A | Kidderminster Harriers | 1410 | D | 1-1 | Miller 45 | 4 | 52 |
| 30 | Nat Lge | H | Forest Green Rovers | 1651 | L | 0-1 | | 5 | 53 |
| **May 4** | **PO SF1** | **H** | **Forest Green Rovers** | **2071** | **L** | **0-1** | | | 54 |
| **7** | **PO SF2** | **A** | **Forest Green Rovers** | **2755** | **D** | **1-1** | **Jefford 47 (og)** | | 55 |

| GOALSCORERS | Scoring Games | Consec Sco Games | Total |
|---|---|---|---|
| ***2014-15 Payne*** | | | ***17*** |
| Payne | 18 | 3 | 23 |
| Miller | 16 | 3 | 21 |
| Deverdics | 15 | 2 | 16 |
| Parkinson | 8 | 2 | 7 |
| Raggett | 5 | | 6 |
| Modeste | 5 | | 5 |
| Ofori-Acheampong | 2 | | 2 |
| Orlu | 2 | | 2 |
| Thomas | 2 | | 2 |

| | Scoring Games | Consec Sco Games | Total |
|---|---|---|---|
| Ajaja | 1 | | 1 |
| Grimes | 1 | | 1 |
| Kinnear | 1 | | 1 |
| Murphy | 1 | | 1 |
| Parkinson | 1 | | 1 |
| Opponents | | | 1 |

# EASTLEIGH

**Chairman:** Stewart Donald
**Secretary:** Ray Murphy (T) 07508 431 451 (E) rmurphy@eastleighfc.com
**Commercial Manager:** Mark Jewell (T/E) commercial@eastleighfc.com
**Programme Editor:** Ray Murphy (T/E) rmurphy@eastleighfc.com
**Ground Address:** Silverlake Stadium 'Ten Acres', Stoneham Lane, Eastleigh SO50 9HT
(T) 02380 613 361 **Manager:** Chris Todd

## Club Factfile

**Founded:** 1946 **Nickname:** The Spitfires
**Previous Names:** Swaythling Athletic 1946-59, Swaythling 1973-80
**Previous Leagues:** Southampton Junior & Senior 1946-59, Hampshire 1950-86, Wessex 1986-2003, Southern 2003-04, Isthmian 2004-05

**Club Colours (change):** Blue & white flash/white/blue (Red & white/red/red)

**Ground Capacity:** 3,000 **Seats:** 520 **Covered:** 520+ **Clubhouse:** Yes **Shop:** Yes

**Directions** From junction 13 of M3, turn right into Leigh Road, turn right at Holiday Inn, at mini roundabout take second exit, at the next mini roundabout take second exit, then next mini roundabout take first exit. Then take the first turning right (signposted) ground 200 metres on the left.

**Previous Grounds:** Southampton Common. Westfield >1957.

**Record Attendance:** 3,191 v Southampton - Friendly July 2007 - League Record: 2,283 v AFC Wimbledon, 28/03/2009
**Record Victory:** 12-1 v Hythe & Dibden (H) - 11/12/1948
**Record Defeat:** 0-11 v Austin Sports (A) - 01.01.1947
**Record Goalscorer:** Johnnie Williams - 177
**Record Appearances:** Ian Knight - 611
**Additional Records:** Paid £10,000 to Newport (I.O.W.) for Colin Matthews

**Honours:**
Southampton Senior League (West) 1949-50. Hampshire League Division Three 1950-51, 53-54, Division Two 1967-68.
Wessex League Division One 2002-03. Conference South 2013-14.
Hampshire: Intermediate Cup 1950-51, Senior Cup 2011-12.

### 10 YEAR RECORD

| 06-07 | 07-08 | 08-09 | 09-10 | 10-11 | 11-12 | 12-13 | 13-14 | 14-15 | 15-16 |
|---|---|---|---|---|---|---|---|---|---|
| Conf S 15 | Conf S 6 | Conf S 3 | Conf S 11 | Conf S 8 | Conf S 12 | Conf S 4 | Conf S 1 | Conf 4 | Nat 7 |

# EASTLEIGH MATCH RESULTS 2015-16

| Date | Comp | H/A | Opponents | Att: | Result | | Goalscorers | Pos | No. |
|---|---|---|---|---|---|---|---|---|---|
| Aug8 | Nat Lge | A | Southport | 1017 | W | 4-0 | Reason 42 Turley 53 Strevens 73 (pen) Constable 90 | 1 | 1 |
| 11 | Nat Lge | H | Boreham Wood | 1347 | W | 1-0 | Constable 90 | 1 | 2 |
| 15 | Nat Lge | H | Lincoln City | 1354 | D | 1-1 | Constable 77 | 3 | 3 |
| 18 | Nat Lge | A | Welling United | 545 | D | 2-2 | Constable 22 Strevens 78 | 6 | 4 |
| 22 | Nat Lge | H | Macclesfield Town | 1928 | W | 1-0 | Lafayette 66 | 4 | 5 |
| 29 | Nat Lge | A | Aldershot Town | 1778 | W | 2-1 | Constable 34 Cook 90 | 3 | 6 |
| 31 | Nat Lge | H | Torquay United | 1819 | W | 3-2 | Odubade 4 Cook 29 Payne 71 | 2 | 7 |
| Sept5 | Nat Lge | A | Barrow | 1448 | L | 0-1 | | 2 | 8 |
| 12 | Nat Lge | H | Gateshead | 2264 | L | 1-2 | Ramsden 79 log) | 6 | 9 |
| 15 | Nat Lge | A | Altrincham | 677 | D | 1-1 | Odubade 87 | 6 | 10 |
| 19 | Nat Lge | A | Chester | 1922 | L | 0-1 | | | 11 |
| 22 | Nat Lge | H | Dover Athletic | 1360 | L | 2-5 | Lafayette 30 Cook 50 | 11 | 12 |
| 26 | Nat Lge | A | Wrexham | 4708 | W | 3-2 | Reason 20 Drury 40 Strevens 87 | 10 | 13 |
| Oct3 | Nat Lge | H | Braintree Town | 1330 | L | 0-2 | | 11 | 14 |
| 10 | Nat Lge | A | Tranmere R | 5133 | W | 2-1 | Partington 47 Constable 54 | 14 | 15 |
| 13 | Nat Lge | H | Forest Green Rovers | 2884 | W | 3-2 | Odubade 2 50 Lafayette 90 | 8 | 16 |
| 17 | Nat Lge | A | Cheltenham Town | 1802 | D | 1-1 | Lafayette 77 | 10 | 17 |
| **24** | **FAC4Q** | **A** | **Bromley** | **1110** | **W** | **2-1** | **Odubade 2 Reason 77** | | 18 |
| 31 | Nat Lge | H | FC Halifax Town | 1890 | W | 2-1 | Drury 47 Payne 69 | 7 | 19 |
| **Nov7** | **FAC1** | **A** | **Crewe Alexandra** | **3008** | **W** | **1-0** | **Strevens 75 (pen)** | | 20 |
| 10 | Nat Lge | A | Dover Athletic | 913 | W | 2-1 | Constable 53 66 | 4 | 21 |
| 14 | Nat Lge | A | Guiseley | 699 | W | 4-1 | Drury 22 72 Partington 30 Reason 90 | | 22 |
| 21 | Nat Lge | H | Grimsby Town | 2057 | L | 0-1 | | 7 | 23 |
| 28 | Nat Lge | H | Southport | 1755 | W | 1-0 | Drury 84 | 5 | 24 |
| **Dec5** | **FAC2** | **A** | **Stourbridge** | **2086** | **W** | **2-0** | **Constable 59 Payne 77** | | 25 |
| 8 | Nat Lge | A | Macclesfield Town | 1087 | W | 2-1 | Constable 6 61 | 4 | 26 |
| **12th** | **FAT1** | **A** | **Aldershot Town** | **877** | **W** | **1-0** | **Lafayette 83** | | 27 |
| 19 | Nat Lge | H | Kidderminster Harriers | 1862 | W | 3-1 | Constable 42 Drury 72 Cook 85 | 3 | 28 |
| 26 | Nat Lge | A | Bromley | 1708 | D | 2-2 | Strevens 55 59 | 3 | 29 |
| 28 | Nat Lge | H | Aldershot Town | 2107 | D | 1-1 | Payne 8 (pen) | 4 | 30 |
| Jan9 | FAC3 | H | Bolton Wanderers | 5025 | D | 1-1 | Devile 55 (og) | | 31 |
| **16** | **FAT2** | **H** | **Gateshead** | **453** | **L** | **1-2** | **Constable 19** | | 32 |
| **19** | **FAC2r** | **A** | **Bolton Wanderers** | **8287** | **L** | **2-3** | **Partington 10 Mohamed 45** | | 33 |
| 23 | Nat Lge | A | Boreham Wood | 406 | D | 1-1 | Drury 90 | 4 | 34 |
| 30 | Nat Lge | H | Wrexham | 1901 | D | 1-1 | Drury 10 | 4 | 35 |
| Feb6 | Nat Lge | A | Lincoln City | 2085 | L | 0-3 | | 5 | 36 |
| 9th | Nat Lge | A | Kidderminster Harriers | 1335 | L | 2-3 | Constable 61 68 | 5 | 37 |
| 16 | Nat Lge | A | Gateshead | 648 | L | 1-2 | Payne 80 | 8 | 38 |
| 20 | Nat Lge | A | Forest Green Rovers | 2221 | L | 1-2 | Constable 65 | 10 | 39 |
| Mar2 | Nat Lge | H | Cheltenham Town | 1982 | W | 1-0 | Burgess 13 (og) | 8 | 40 |
| 5 | Nat Lge | A | Braintree Town | 666 | L | 0-2 | | 10 | 41 |
| 8 | Nat Lge | H | Woking | 1630 | W | 2-1 | Reason 68 Evans 90 | 9 | 42 |
| 12 | Nat Lge | H | Chester | 1831 | W | 1-0 | Tubbs 70 (pen) | 8 | 43 |
| 15 | Nat Lge | H | Bromley | 1520 | W | 2-0 | Odubade 24 Reason 34 | 5 | 44 |
| 25 | Nat Lge | H | Welling United | 2037 | D | 0-0 | | 7 | 45 |
| 28 | Nat Lge | A | Torquay United | 2081 | W | 1-0 | Cook 4 | 7 | 46 |
| Apr2 | Nat Lge | H | Guiseley | 1790 | D | 1-1 | Lockwood 2 (og) | 7 | 47 |
| 9 | Nat Lge | A | Grimsby Town | 4011 | D | 1-1 | | 7 | 48 |
| 13 | Nat Lge | H | Barrow | 3292 | W | 3-1 | Coulson 9 Constable 26 Strevens 90 (pen) | 7 | 49 |
| 16 | Nat Lge | H | Altrincham | 2034 | W | 2-0 | Reason 59 Coulson70 | 6 | 50 |
| 19 | Nat Lge | A | FC Halifax Town | 1337 | D | 0-0 | | 6 | 51 |
| 23 | Nat Lge | H | Tranmere Rovers | 3269 | L | 0-1 | | 7 | 52 |
| 30 | Nat Lge | A | Woking | 1853 | L | 1-2 | Tubbs 74 | 7 | 53 |

| GOALSCORERS | Scoring Games | Consec Sco Games | Total |
|---|---|---|---|
| ***2014-15 Constable*** | | | ***19*** |
| Constable | 14 | 4 | 17 |
| Drury | 7 | | 8 |
| Reason | 7 | | 7 |
| Strevens | 6 | | 7 |
| Odubade | 6 | | 6 |
| Cook | 5 | | 5 |
| Lafayette | 5 | | 5 |
| Payne | 5 | 2 | 5 |
| Partington | 3 | | 3 |
| Coulson | 2 | | 2 |
| Tubbs | 2 | | 2 |
| Evans | 1 | | 1 |
| Mohamed | 1 | | 1 |
| Turley | 1 | | 1 |
| Opponents | | | 4 |

# FOREST GREEN ROVERS

**Chairman:** Dale Vince OBE

**Secretary:** James Mooney **(T)** 01453 834 860 **(E)** james.mooney@fgrfc.com

**Commercial Manager:** **(T/E)** 01453 834 860

**Programme Editor:** **(T/E)** 01453 834 860

**Ground Address:** The New Lawn, Smiths Way, Nailsworth, Gloucestershire GL6 0FG

**(T)** 01453 834 860 **Manager:** Mark cooper

FA Cup 2nd Round tie which Forest Green Rovers narrowly lost to League Two's Oxford United 0-1. Played in front of 4,618 at the Kassam Stadium. Photo: Peter Barnes.

## Club Factfile

**Founded:** 1890 **Nickname:** Rovers

**Previous Names:** Stround FC 1980s-92.

**Previous Leagues:** Stroud & District 1890-1922, Gloucestershire Northern Senior 1922-67, Gloucestershire Senior 1967-73, Hellenic 1973-82, Southern 1982-89.

**Club Colours (change):** Green & black hoops/green/green & black hoops (All white)

**Ground Capacity:** 5,141 **Seats:** 2,000 **Covered:** 1,000 **Clubhouse:** Yes **Shop:** Yes

**Directions**

Nailsworth is on the A46 between Stroud and Bath. At mini roundabout in town turn up Spring Hill towards Forest Green (signposted) and the stadium is at the top of the hill after the second roundabout.

Satnav users should enter GL6 0ET and not the mail post code. Please note on Matchdays there is a Temporary Traffic Order in place on the highway around the stadium. Car parking is available inside the stadium at £3 per vehicle.

**Previous Grounds:** Moved to the New Lawn in 2006 - 400 meters away from the old Lawn ground.

**Record Attendance:** 4,836 v Derby County - FA Cup 3rd Round 03/01/2009

**Record Victory:** 8-0 v Fareham Town - Southern League Southern Division 1996-97

**Record Defeat:** 0-7 v Moor Green - Southern League Midland Division 1985-86

**Record Goalscorer:** Karl Bayliss

**Record Appearances:** Alex Sykes

**Additional Records:** Paid £20,000 to Salisbury City for Adrian Randall. Received £35,000 from Nuneaton Borough for Marc McGregor and from Oxford United for Wayne Hatswell.

**Honours:**

FA Vase 1981-82. Hellenic League 1981-82.

Gloucestershire Senior Cup 1984-85, 85-86, 86-87, 2015-16.

Gloucestershire Senior Professional Cup 1984-85, 86-86, 87-87.

### 10 YEAR RECORD

| 06-07 | 07-08 | 08-09 | 09-10 | 10-11 | 11-12 | 12-13 | 13-14 | 14-15 | 15-16 |
|---|---|---|---|---|---|---|---|---|---|
| Conf 14 | Conf 8 | Conf 18 | Conf 21 | Conf 20 | Conf 10 | Conf 10 | Conf 10 | Conf 5 | Nat 2 |

## FOREST GREEN ROVERSOVERS MATCH RESULTS 2015-16

| Date | Comp | H/A | Opponents | Att: | Result | | Goalscorers | Pos | No. |
|---|---|---|---|---|---|---|---|---|---|
| Aug 8 | Nat Lge | A | Altrincham | 975 | W | 1-0 | Parkin 74 | 7 | 1 |
| 11 | Nat Lge | H | Welling United | 1076 | W | 1-0 | O'Connor 45 | 1 | 2 |
| 15 | Nat Lge | H | Barrow | 1217 | W | 4-0 | O'Connor 19 (pen) 65 Guthrie 28 Racine 72 | 1 | 3 |
| 18 | Nat Lge | A | Boreham Wood | 464 | W | 1-0 | Guthrie 77 | 1 | 4 |
| 22 | Nat Lge | H | Lincoln City | 1385 | W | 3-1 | Jennings 24 O'Connor 40 Marsh-Brown 87 | 1 | 5 |
| 29 | Nat Lge | A | Kidderminster Harriers | 1905 | W | 2-0 | Marsh-Brown 64 Parkin 71 | 1 | 6 |
| 31 | Nat Lge | H | Bromley | 1764 | W | 2-1 | Racine 6 Sam-Yorke 43 | 1 | 7 |
| Sept 5 | Nat Lge | A | Chester | 2163 | W | 2-1 | Frear 40 O'Connor 78 | 1 | 8 |
| 12 | Nat Lge | H | Southport | 1535 | W | 2-1 | O'Connor 11 Marsh-Brown 21 | 1 | 9 |
| 15 | Nat Lge | A | Woiking | 1775 | L | 1-2 | Guthrie 74 | 1 | 10 |
| 19 | Nat Lge | A | Macclesfield Utd | 1311 | L | 1-4 | Parkin 2 | 1 | 11 |
| 22 | Nat Lge | H | Cheltenham Town | 3127 | D | 2-2 | Pipe 64 Guthrie 81 | 1 | 12 |
| 26 | Nat Lge | H | Gateshead | 1256 | L | 0-1 | | 1 | 13 |
| Oct 3 | Nat Lge | A | Grimsby Town | 5034 | D | 1-1 | Parkin 34 | 1 | 14 |
| 6 | Nat Lge | A | Aldershot Town | 1353 | W | 3-0 | Carter 38 Guthrie 43 O'Connor 85 | 1 | 15 |
| 10 | Nat Lge | H | Guiseley | 1749 | W | 3-0 | Frear 25 Parkin 57 (pen) O'Connor 78 | 1 | 16 |
| 13 | Nat Lge | A | Eastleigh | 2884 | L | 2-3 | O'Connor 21 Frear 45 | 1 | 17 |
| 17 | Nat Lge | H | Tranmere Rovers | 2133 | L | 0-2 | | 1 | 18 |
| **24** | **FAC4Q** | **A** | **Margate** | **1302** | **W** | **2-1** | **Marsh-Brown 40 Guthrie 72** | | 19 |
| 31 | Nat Lge | H | Chester | 1561 | W | 2-1 | Parkin 31 Marsh-Brown 33 | 1 | 20 |
| **Nov 7** | **FAC1** | **A** | **AFC Wimbledon** | **2465** | **W** | **2-1** | **Carter 6 Frear 90** | | 21 |
| 10 | Nat Lge | A | Welling United | 660 | D | 1-1 | Guthrie 82 | 2 | 22 |
| 14 | Nat Lge | H | Dover Athletic | 1661 | W | 3-1 | Jennings 53 Carter 58 Frear 71 | 1 | 23 |
| 21 | Nat Lge | A | Cheltenham Town | 5449 | D | 1-1 | Carter 70 | 2 | 24 |
| 28 | Nat Lge | H | Altrincham | 1292 | W | 2-0 | Parkin 1 19 | 2 | 25 |
| **Dec 6** | **FAC2** | **A** | **Oxford United** | **4618** | **L** | **0-1** | | | 26 |
| **12** | **FAT1** | **A** | **Havant & Waterlooville** | **266** | **L** | **0-2** | | | 27 |
| 19 | Nat Lge | H | Boreham Wood | 1356 | W | 1-0 | Guthrie 67 | 2 | 28 |
| 26 | Nat Lge | A | Torquay United | 2051 | L | 1-4 | Marsh-Brown 20 | 2 | 29 |
| 28 | Nat Lge | H | Kidderminster Harriers | 2110 | W | 3-0 | Parkin 16 (pen) Williams 58 Guthrie 90 | | 30 |
| Jan 1 | Nat Lge | H | Torquay United | 1907 | W | 3-1 | Carter 84 (pen) Gerring (og) 68 Marsh-Brown 90 | 2 | 31 |
| 16 | Nat Lge | A | Lincoln City | 1975 | W | 1-0 | Marsh-Brown 77 | 2 | 32 |
| 23 | Nat Lge | H | Braintree Town | 1507 | W | 1-0 | Parkin 52 | 1 | 33 |
| 26 | Nat Lge | A | Southport | 707 | W | 1-0 | Guthrie 90 | 1 | 34 |
| 30 | Nat Lge | H | Macclesfield Town | 1617 | W | 2-1 | Jennings 77 Clough 90 | 1 | 35 |
| Feb 6 | Nat Lge | A | Wrexham | 3891 | D | 2-2 | Carter 20 Williams 90 | 2 | 36 |
| 13 | Nat Lge | A | FC Halifax Town | 1329 | W | 2-0 | Parkin 20 Frear 30 | 2 | 37 |
| 20 | Nat Lge | H | Eastleigh | 2221 | W | 2-1 | Parkin 67 88 | 2 | 38 |
| 23 | Nat Lge | A | Guiseley | 550 | W | 1-0 | Williams 82 | 2 | 39 |
| 27 | Nat Lge | A | Barrow | 1233 | D | 2-2 | Moore 36 Marsh-Brown 60 | 2 | 40 |
| Mar 4 | Nat Lge | H | Grimsby Town | 2242 | L | 0-1 | | 2 | 41 |
| 12 | Nat Lge | A | Gateshead | 887 | W | 1-0 | Jennings 13 | 2 | 42 |
| 19 | Nat Lge | H | Tranmere Rovers | 5073 | D | 1-1 | Carter 5 | 2 | 43 |
| 25 | Nat Lge | H | Aldershot Town | 2272 | D | 0-0 | | 2 | 44 |
| 28 | Nat Lge | A | Bromley | 1455 | D | 2-2 | Guthrie 4 45 | 2 | 45 |
| Apr 2 | Nat Lge | H | Wrexham | 2246 | D | 0-0 | | 2 | 46 |
| 9 | Nat Lge | A | Braintree Town | 740 | D | 1-1 | Carter 37 | 2 | 47 |
| 16 | Nat Lge | H | Woking | 1605 | L | 1-2 | Moore 10 | 2 | 48 |
| 23 | Nat Lge | H | FCM Halifax Town | 1942 | L | 0-1 | | 2 | 49 |
| 30 | Nat Lge | A | Dover Athletic | 1651 | W | 1-0 | Williams 52 | 2 | 50 |
| **May 4** | **PO SF1** | **A** | **Dover Athletic** | **2071** | **W** | **1-0** | **Williams 35** | | 51 |
| **7** | **PO SF2** | **H** | **Dover Athletic** | **2755** | **D** | **1-1** | **Marsh-Brown 54** | | 52 |
| **15** | **PO Final** | **N** | **Grimsby Town** | **17198** | **L** | **1-3** | **Marsh-Brown 60** | | 53 |

| GOALSCORERS | Scoring Games | Consec Sco Games | Total |
|---|---|---|---|
| *2014-15 Parkin* | *30* | | |
| Parkin | 11 | 2 | 13 |
| Guthrie | 11 | 2 | 12 |
| Marsh-Brown | 10 | 2 | 11 |
| O'Connor | 9 | 2 | 9 |
| Carter | 8 | 2 | 8 |
| Frear | 6 | 2 | 6 |
| Williams | 5 | | 5 |
| Jennings | 4 | | 4 |
| Moore | 2 | | 2 |

| | Scoring Games | Consec Sco Games | Total |
|---|---|---|---|
| Racine | 2 | | 2 |
| Clough | 1 | | 1 |
| Pipe | 1 | | 1 |
| Sam-Yorke | 1 | | 1 |
| Opponents | | | 1 |

# GATESHEAD

**Chairman:** Richard Bennett
**Secretary:** 0191 478 3883 (T) (E) info@gateshead-fc.com
**Commercial Manager:** (T/E)
**Programme Editor:** (T/E)
**Ground Address:** International Stadium, Neilson Road, Gateshead NE10 0EF
(T) 0191 478 3883 **Manager:** Neil Aspin

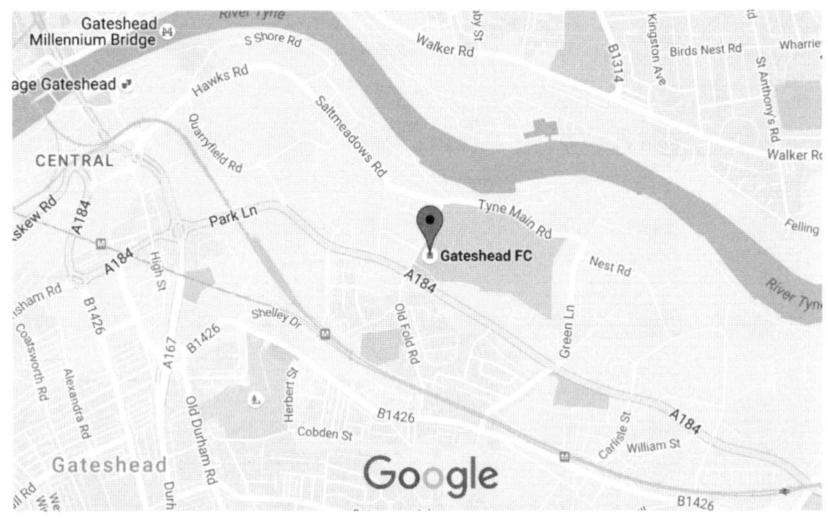


## Club Factfile

**Founded:** 1930 **Nickname:** Tynesiders, The Heed
**Previous Names:** Gateshead Town, Gateshead United.
**Previous Leagues:** Football League 1930-60, Northern Counties east 1960-62, North Regional 1962-68, Northern Premier 1968-70, 73-83, 85-86, 87-90, Wearside 1970-71, Midland 1971-72, Alliance/Conf 1983-85, 86-87, 90-98

**Club Colours (change):** White/black/black & white hoops (Sky blue with claret/sky blue/sky blue)

**Ground Capacity:** 11,795 **Seats:** 11,795 **Covered:** 7,271 **Clubhouse:** Yes **Shop:** Yes

**Directions**
Travelling up on the A1, turn off at the junction with the A194 just north of the Washington Services. Follow the A194 until the roundabout junction with the A184, turn left onto this road. The International Stadium is on the right after approximately 3 miles.

**Previous Grounds:** Redheugh Park 1930-71

**Record Attendance:** 11,750 v Newcastle United - Friendly 07/08/95
**Record Victory:** 8-0 v Netherfield - Northern Premier League
**Record Defeat:** 0-9 v Sutton United - Conference 22/09/90
**Record Goalscorer:** Paul Thompson - 130
**Record Appearances:** James Curtis - 506 (2003-present)
**Additional Records:** Record transfer fee paid; £9,000 - Paul Cavell, Dagenham & Redbridge 1994
Record transfer fee received; £150,000 Lee Novak, Huddersfield Town 2009
**Honours:**
Northern Premier League 1982-83, 85-86, Northern Premier League play-off 2007-08, Conference North play-off 2008-9, Durham Challenge Cup 2010-11

### 10 YEAR RECORD

| 06-07 | | 07-08 | | 08-09 | | 09-10 | | 10-11 | | 11-12 | | 12-13 | | 13-14 | | 14-15 | | 15-16 | |
|---|---|---|---|---|---|---|---|---|---|---|---|---|---|---|---|---|---|---|---|
| NP P | 9 | NP P | 3 | Conf N | 2 | Conf | 20 | Conf | 15 | Conf | 8 | Conf | 17 | Conf | 3 | Conf | 10 | Nat | 9 |

## GATESHEAD MATCH RESULTS 2015-16

| Date | Comp | H/A | Opponents | Att: | Result | | Goalscorers | Pos | No. |
|---|---|---|---|---|---|---|---|---|---|
| Aug 8 | Nat Lge | A | Aldershot T | 1749 | W | 2-1 | Bowman 77 80 | 5 | 1 |
| 11 | Nat Lge | H | Tranmere R | 1589 | L | 1-4 | Shaw 45 | 16 | 2 |
| 15 | Nat Lge | H | Boreham Wood | 760 | W | 2-1 | Bowman 67 81 | 10 | 3 |
| 18 | Nat Lge | A | Southport | 806 | W | 2-1 | Bowman 5 Gillies 69 (pen) | 5 | 4 |
| 22 | Nat Lge | H | Kidderminster Harriers | 800 | D | 1-1 | Bowman 83 | 6 | 5 |
| 29 | Nat Lge | A | Guiseley | 603 | W | 2-0 | Johnson 39 47 | 5 | 6 |
| 31 | Nat Lge | H | Lincoln City | 1248 | W | 2-0 | Curtis 40 Clark 80 | 4 | 7 |
| Sept 5 | Nat Lge | A | Bromley | 1411 | L | 0-3 | | 5 | 8 |
| 12 | Nat Lge | A | Eastleigh | 2264 | W | 2-1 | Johnson 20 Pattison 34 | 3 | 9 |
| 15 | Nat Lge | H | Wrexham | 1113 | W | 2-1 | Gillies 17 Bowman 58 | 2 | 10 |
| 19 | Nat Lge | H | Welling United | 822 | L | 1-2 | Buddle 36 | 4 | 11 |
| 22 | Nat Lge | A | FC Halifax Town | 1001 | D | 1-1 | Shaw 27 | 4 | 12 |
| 26 | Nat Lge | A | Forest Green Rovers | 1256 | W | 1-0 | Phillips 5 | 2 | 13 |
| Oct 3 | Nat Lge | H | Dover Athletic | 949 | L | 2-3 | Ramsden 16 Buddle 36 | 4 | 14 |
| 6 | Nat Lge | A | Grimsby Town | 3835 | L | 1-2 | Baxter 10 | 6 | 15 |
| 10 | Nat Lge | H | Cheltenham Town | 1238 | D | 1-1 | Cranston 35 | 6 | 16 |
| 13 | Nat Lge | A | Macclesfield Town | 1223 | L | 0-1 | | 9 | 17 |
| 17 | Nat Lge | H | Altrincham | 911 | D | 2-2 | Bowman 49 Phillips 90 | 11 | 18 |
| **24** | **FAC4** | **H** | **Worcester City** | **782** | **L** | **1-2** | **Bowman 55** | | 19 |
| 31 | Nat Lge | A | Boreham Wood | 344 | W | 3-2 | Mafuta 2 Johnson 11 Honeyman 77 | 8 | 20 |
| Nov 14 | Nat Lge | A | Wrexham | 4095 | L | 0-4 | | 9 | 21 |
| 21 | Nat Lge | H | FC Halifax Town | 853 | L | 1-4 | Bowman 37 (pen) | 12 | 22 |
| 28 | Nat Lge | H | Chester | 842 | W | 1-0 | Whitmore 83 (og) | 11 | 23 |
| Dec 5 | Nat Lge | A | Kidderminster Harriers | 1489 | W | 1-0 | McLaughlin 90 | 10 | 24 |
| 8 | Nat Lge | H | Southport | 582 | L | 0-1 | | 10 | 25 |
| **12** | **FAT1** | **H** | **Stocksbridge PS** | **199** | **W** | **4-1** | **Bowman 42 47 Mafuta 70 Johnson 80** | | 26 |
| 19 | Nat Lge | H | Woking | 573 | L | 1-5 | McLaughlin 17 | 12 | 27 |
| 29 | Nat Lge | H | Guiseley | 679 | W | 3-0 | Bowman 46 58 Johnson 88 | 12 | 28 |
| Jan 2 | Nat Lge | H | Barrow | 892 | D | 1-1 | Bowman 39 (pen) | 10 | 29 |
| **16** | **FAT2** | **A** | **Eastleigh** | **453** | **W** | **2-1** | **McLaughlin 49 Johnson 72** | | 30 |
| 23 | Nat Lge | A | Torquay United | 721 | W | 2-0 | Bowman 29 Johnson 52 | 9 | 31 |
| 30 | Nat Lge | H | Grimsby Town | 2173 | W | 1-0 | Johnson 39 47 | 9 | 32 |
| Feb 2 | Nat Lge | A | Barrow | 939 | D | 0-0 | | 9 | 33 |
| **6** | **FAT3** | **H** | **AFC Fylde** | **485** | **W** | **1-0** | **Bowman 73** | | 34 |
| 13 | Nat Lge | A | Dover Athletic | 638 | L | 0-4 | | 11 | 35 |
| 16 | Nat Lge | H | Eastleigh | 648 | W | 2-1 | McLaughlin 19 Bowman 24 | 6 | 36 |
| 20 | Nat Lge | H | Aldershot Town | 1074 | W | 3-2 | Bowman 35 Hamilton 37 McLaughlin 51 | 5 | 37 |
| 23 | Nat Lge | A | Cheltenham Town | 2201 | D | 0-0 | | 4 | 38 |
| **27** | **FAT4** | **A** | **FC Halifax Town** | **1431** | **D** | **0-0** | | | 39 |
| **Mar 2** | **FAT4r** | **H** | **FC Halifax Town** | **724** | **L** | **3-3** | **Gillies 3 119 Bowman 49 (lost 4-5 pens aet)** | | 40 |
| 5 | Nat Lge | A | Tranmere Rovers | 4668 | L | 1-3 | Johnson 68 | 9 | 41 |
| 8 | Nat Lge | A | Altrincham | 805 | W | 3-2 | Johnson 11 52 Hamilton 87 | 7 | 42 |
| 12 | Nat Lge | H | Forest Green Rovers | 887 | L | 0-1 | | 9 | 43 |
| 15 | Nat Lge | A | Braintree Town | 572 | D | 0-0 | | 9 | 44 |
| 19 | Nat Lge | A | Welling United | 500 | W | 1-0 | Whitmore 45 | 9 | 45 |
| 25 | Nat Lge | H | Macclesfield Town | 948 | L | 0-3 | | 9 | 46 |
| 28 | Nat Lge | A | Lincoln City | 2142 | D | 1-1 | Johnson 78 | 8 | 47 |
| Apr 2 | Nat Lge | H | Torquay United | 785 | L | 1-2 | Shaw 20 | 9 | 48 |
| 9 | Nat Lge | A | Woking | 1005 | D | 1-1 | Bowman 45 (pen) | 9 | 49 |
| 15 | Nat Lge | H | Braintree Town | 588 | L | 2-3 | Clark 13 Whitmore 64 | 10 | 50 |
| 23 | Nat Lge | H | Bromley | 865 | W | 3-1 | Johnson 12 GIllies 24 76 | 9 | 51 |
| 30 | Nat Lge | A | Chester | 2323 | L | 2-4 | Ramshaw 51 Johnson 86 | 9 | 52 |

| GOALSCORERS | Scoring Games | Consec Sco Games | Total | | Scoring Games | Consec Sco Games | Total |
|---|---|---|---|---|---|---|---|
| ***2014-15 Rodman and Wright*** | | | ***10*** | Phillips | 2 | | 2 |
| Bowman | 17 | 3 | 21 | Whitmore | 2 | | 2 |
| Johnson | 13 | 3 | 15 | Baxter | 1 | | 1 |
| Gillies | 4 | | 6 | Cranston | 1 | | 1 |
| McLaughlin | 5 | | 5 | Curtis | 1 | | 1 |
| Shaw | 3 | | 3 | Honeyman | 1 | | 1 |
| Buddle | 2 | | 2 | Pattison | 1 | | 1 |
| Clark | 2 | | 2 | Ramsden | 1 | | 1 |
| Hamilton | 2 | | 2 | Ramshaw | 1 | | 1 |
| Mafuta | 2 | | 2 | Opponents | | | 1 |

# GUISELEY

**Chairman:** Phil Rogerson
**Secretary:** Adrian Towers **(T)** 07946 388 739 **(E)** adie.towers@guiseleyafc.co.uk
**Commercial Manager:** **(T/E)**
**Programme Editor:** Rachel O'Connor **(T/E)** programme.editor@guiseleyafc.co.uk
**Ground Address:** Nethermoor Park, Otley Road, Guiseley, Leeds LS20 8BT
**(T)** 01943 873 223 (Office) 872 872 (Club) **Manager:** Mark Bower

## Club Factfile

**Founded:** 1909 **Nickname:** The Lions
**Previous Names:** None
**Previous Leagues:** Wharfedale, Leeds, West Riding Counties, West Yorkshire, Yorkshire 1968-82, Northern Counties East 1982-91, Northern Premier 1991-2010

**Club Colours (change):** White/navy/navy (All royal blue with white trim)

**Ground Capacity:** 3,000 **Seats:** 427 **Covered:** 1,040 **Clubhouse:** Yes **Shop:** Yes

**Directions** From the West M62, M606 then follow signs to A65 through Guiseley to Ground on Right. From South and East M1 and M621 towards Leeds City Centre. Continue on M621 to Junction 2, follow Headingly Stadium signs to A65 towards Ilkley then as above. From North West From Skipton, A65 Ilkley, via Burley By-pass A65 towards Leeds, Ground quarter of a mile on left after Harry Ramsden's roundabout From North/NE A1M, leave at A59, towards Harrogate, then A658 signed Leeds Bradford Airport, at Pool turn right onto A659 Otley, continue towards Bradford/Leeds, to Harry Ramsden roundabout then A65 Leeds ground quarter of a mile on left.

**Previous Grounds:** None

**Record Attendance:** 2,486 v Bridlington Town - FA Vase Semi-final 1st Leg 1989-90
**Record Victory:** Not known - If you know please email tw.publications@btinternet.com
**Record Defeat:** Not known - If you know please email tw.publications@btinternet.com
**Record Goalscorer:** Not known - If you know please email tw.publications@btinternet.com
**Record Appearances:** Not known - If you know please email tw.publications@btinternet.com
**Additional Records:**

**Honours:**
Northern Counties East 1990-91. FA Vase 1990-91.
Northern Premier League Division 1 1993-94, Premier Division 2009-10, Challenge Cup 2008-09. Conference North Play-off 2014-15.

### 10 YEAR RECORD

| 06-07 | 07-08 | 08-09 | 09-10 | 10-11 | 11-12 | 12-13 | 13-14 | 14-15 | 15-16 |
|---|---|---|---|---|---|---|---|---|---|
| NP P 6 | NP P 6 | NP P 3 | NP P 1 | Conf N 5 | Conf N 2 | Conf N 2 | Conf N 5 | Conf N 5 | Nat 20 |

# GUISELEY MATCH RESULTS 2015-16

| Date | Comp | H/A | Opponents | Att: | Result | Goalscorers | Pos | No. |
|---|---|---|---|---|---|---|---|---|
| Aug 8 | Nat Lge | A | Welling United | 505 | L 0-1 | | 19 | 1 |
| 11 | Nat Lge | H | Altrincham | 797 | W 1-0 | Atkinson 16 | 12 | 2 |
| 15 | Nat Lge | H | Kidderminster Harriers | 756 | W 1-0 | Boyes 85 | 8 | 3 |
| 18 | Nat Lge | A | Barrow | 1440 | D 1-1 | Boshell 45 | 10 | 4 |
| 22 | Nat Lge | H | Aldershot Town | 782 | L 0-4 | | 13 | 5 |
| 29 | Nat Lge | H | Gateshead | 603 | L 0-2 | | 15 | 6 |
| 31 | Nat Lge | A | Chester | 2304 | D 1-1 | Boyes 84 | 14 | 7 |
| Sept 5 | Nat Lge | A | Torquay United | 1558 | D 1-1 | Dickinson 28 (pen) | 17 | 8 |
| 12 | Nat Lge | H | Wokng | 643 | D 4-4 | Atkinson 33 Boshell 41 Craddock 67 Lawlor 90 | 17 | 9 |
| 15 | Nat Lge | H | FC Halifax Town | 1184 | W 2-1 | Hatfield 27 Dickinson 82 | 16 | 10 |
| 19 | Nat Lge | A | Dover Athletic | 823 | D 0-0 | | 15 | 11 |
| 22 | Nat Lge | H | Southport | 748 | D 1-1 | Dickinson 19 | 16 | 12 |
| 26 | Nat Lge | A | Braintree Town | 679 | W 1-0 | Craddock 80 | 13 | 13 |
| Oct 3 | Nat Lge | H | Lincoln City | 1279 | L 0-1 | | 13 | 14 |
| 6 | Nat Lge | H | Macclesfield Town | 653 | L 0-3 | | 18 | 15 |
| 10 | Nat Lge | A | Forest Green Rovers | 1749 | L 0-3 | | 18 | 16 |
| 13 | Nat Lge | A | Wrexham | 3633 | D 3-3 | Rothery 3 Dickinson 71 Boyes 84 | 18 | 17 |
| 17 | Nat Lge | H | Boreham Wood | 749 | D 1-1 | Boshell 90 (pen) | 18 | 18 |
| **24** | **FAC4Q** | **A** | **FC Halifax Town** | **1078** | **D 2-2** | **Boyes 73 78** | | 19 |
| **27** | **FAC4Qr** | **H** | **FC Halifax Town** | **948** | **L 1-2** | **Boyes 75 (aet)** | | 20 |
| 31 | Nat Lge | H | Welling United | 653 | W 2-0 | Dudley 10 43 | 17 | 21 |
| Nov 7 | Nat Lge | H | Barrow | 749 | W 3-1 | Boshall 5 Atkinson 36 Dudley 73 | 14 | 22 |
| 10 | Nat Lge | A | Cheltenham Town | 2237 | L 0-5 | | 15 | 23 |
| 14 | Nat Lge | H | Eastleigh | 699 | L 1-4 | Boyes 40 | 15 | 24 |
| 21 | Nat Lge | A | Tranmere Rovers | 4352 | L 1-2 | Boshell 24 | 18 | 25 |
| 28 | Nat Lge | H | Bromley | 787 | W 2-0 | Norburn 45 Dudley 89 | 16 | 26 |
| Dec 5 | Nat Lge | A | FC Halifax Town | 1355 | D 1-1 | Dudley 48 | 16 | 27 |
| **12** | **FAT1** | **A** | **Burscough** | **227** | **D 2-2** | **Craddock 20 Lowe 83** | | 28 |
| **15** | **FAT1r** | **H** | **Burscough** | **233** | **W 3-2** | **Rotherham 25 (pen) Devine 42 (og) Boshell 45** | **17** | 29 |
| 19 | Nat Lge | A | Aldershot Town | 1325 | L 0-1 | | 18 | 30 |
| 26 | Nat Lge | H | Grimsby Town | 679 | D 1-1 | Norburn 40 | 18 | 31 |
| 28 | Nat Lge | A | Gateshead | 679 | L 0-3 | | 18 | 32 |
| **Jan 16** | **FAT 2** | **A** | **Dulwich Hamlet** | **1949** | **W 2-1** | **Hurst 16 Dudley 29** | | 33 |
| 23 | Nat Lge | A | Kidderminster Harriers | 1431 | W 1-0 | Dickinson 79 | 18 | 34 |
| 30 | Nat Lge | A | Lincoln City | 2265 | L 0-1 | | 18 | 35 |
| **Feb 6** | **FAT3** | **A** | **Dover Athletic** | **667** | **D 2-2** | **Hatfield 36 Rothery 71** | | 36 |
| 13 | Nat Lge | A | Woking | 1182 | W 1-0 | Dickinson 9 | 17 | 37 |
| **15** | **FAT3r** | **H** | **Dover Athletic** | **476** | **L 0-3** | | | 38 |
| 20 | Nat Lge | A | Altrincham | 1137 | D 1-1 | Atkinson 56 | 17 | 39 |
| 23 | Nat Lge | H | Forest Green Rovers | 550 | L 0-1 | | 17 | 40 |
| 27 | Nat Lge | H | Braintree Town | 788 | D 1-1 | Norburn 73 | 18 | 41 |
| Mar 8 | Nat Lge | H | Tranmere Rovers | 1147 | D 2-2 | Dickenson 38 Hurst 60 | 18 | 42 |
| 12 | Nat Lge | A | Bromley | 1044 | L 0-2 | | 18 | 43 |
| 15 | Nat Lge | H | Grimsby Town | 1843 | D 2-2 | Atkinson 6 Boshell 51 | 18 | 44 |
| 19 | Nat Lge | H | Dover Athletic | 690 | L 0-1 | | 18 | 45 |
| 26 | Nat Lge | A | Southport | 983 | L 0-2 | | 18 | 46 |
| 28 | Nat Lge | H | Chester | 1186 | D 3-3 | Sinclair 74 90 Hatfield 81 | 18 | 47 |
| Apr 2 | Nat Lge | A | Eastleigh | 1790 | D 1-1 | Hurst 55 | 18 | 48 |
| 9 | Nat Lge | H | Cheltenham Town | 1058 | L 0-2 | | 19 | 49 |
| 12 | Nat Lge | H | Wrexham | 1046 | W 3-1 | Johnson 14 Boyes 16 26 | 18 | 50 |
| 16 | Nat Lge | A | Macclesfield Town | 1408 | L 0-1 | | 19 | 51 |
| 23 | Nat Lge | A | Boreham Wood | 601 | L 0-1 | | 21 | 52 |
| 30 | Nat Lge | H | Torquay United | 1915 | W 4-3 | Johnson 5 Hatfield 11 Dudley 30 73 | 20 | 53 |

| GOALSCORERS | Scoring Games | Consec Sco Games | Total |
|---|---|---|---|
| ***2014-15 Boyes*** | | | ***23*** |
| Boyes | 7 | 2 | 9 |
| Dudley | 7 | 2 | 8 |
| Boshall | 7 | | 7 |
| Dickenson | 7 | | 7 |
| Alkinson | 5 | | 5 |
| Hatfield | 4 | | 4 |
| Craddock | 3 | | 3 |
| Hurst | 3 | | 3 |
| Norburn | 3 | | 3 |
| Johnson | 2 | | 2 |
| Rothery | 2 | | 2 |
| Sinclair | 2 | | 2 |
| Lawlor | 1 | | 1 |
| Lowe | 1 | | 1 |
| Rotherham | 1 | | 1 |
| Opponents | | | 1 |

# LINCOLN CITY

**Chairman:** Bob Dorrian
**Secretary:** John Vickers (T) 01522 880 011 (E) john.vickers@lincolncityfc.co.uk
**Commercial Manager:** Ritchie Bates (T/E) ritchie.bates@lincolncityfc.co.uk
**Programme Editor:** John Vickers (T/E) 07881 913 249
**Ground Address:** Sincil Bank Stadium, Lincoln LN5 8LD
(T) 01522 880 011 **Manager:** Danny & Nick Cowley

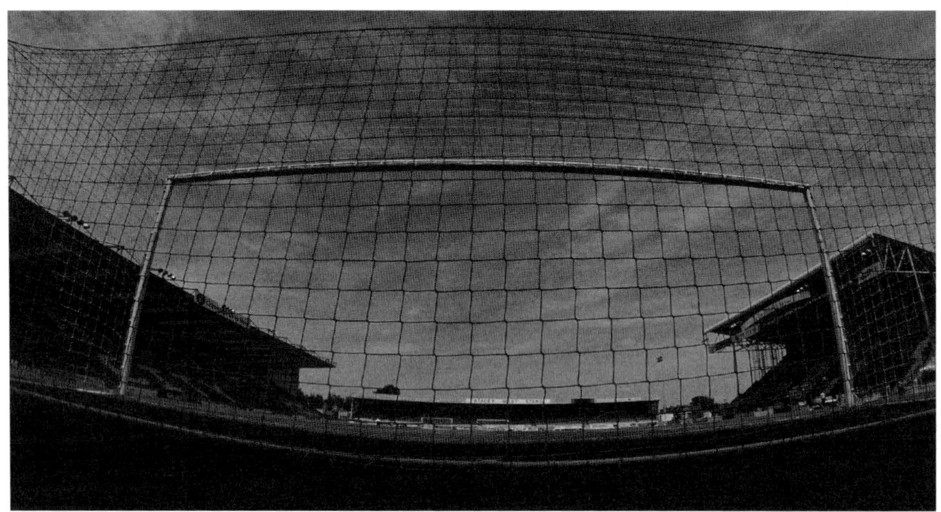

## Club Factfile

**Founded:** 1884 **Nickname:** Imps
**Previous Names:** None
**Previous Leagues:** Midland (Founder Member) 1889-91, 1908-09, 1911-12, 1920-21, Football Alliance 1891-92, Football League (Founder Member) 1892-1908, 1909-11, 1912-20, 1921-86, 1988-2011, Conference 1986-88.

**Club Colours (change):** Red & white stripes/black/red (Yellow/blue/yellow)

**Ground Capacity:** 9,800 **Seats:** Yes **Covered:** Yes **Clubhouse:** **Shop:** Yes

**Directions**
**From South:** Exit A1 at s/p 'Lincoln A46, Sleaford A17' onto the A46. At roundabout after 9.4 mile take 3rd exit (s/p Lincoln South A1434). Keep on A1434, following 'Lincoln and City Centre' signs for 4.3 miles. Then get into inside lane (s/p City Centre, Worksop A7) and go straight on (1st exit) at r'about into the High St. After 0.5 miles get in outside lane, and go straight on at lights (s/p City Ctre, Worksop A57). After 0.1 miles turn right into Scorer Street. **From North:** Exit A1(M) at the r'about after the Fina and Shell garages (s'p Lincoln A57, E. Markham) onto the A57. At junc. after 9.9 miles turn right (s/p Lincoln A57), remaining on A57 which here runs alongside the Foss Dyke. At r'about after 5.9 miles turn right (Lincoln South, Newark A46, Grantham A1) onto the A46. Straight on at r'about after 1.8 miles. At next r'about after 1.6 miles (by BP station) turn left (s/p) Lincoln South B1190, Doddington Ind.Est., into Doddington Rd, Sraight on for 2 miles to T-junction. Here, turn left (no signpost) onto Newark Rd A1434. Keep on A1434 following City Centre signs. Go straight on (1st exit) at r'about into the High St. After (0.5 miles get in outside lane, and go straight on at lights (s/p City Ctre, Worksop A57). After 0.1 miles turn right into Scorer St. Tip: Have some change ready for a small toll bridge (Dunham) en route.

**Previous Grounds:** John O'Gaunt's 1883-94.

**Record Attendance:** 23,196 v Derby County, League Cup 4th Round 15/11/1967
**Record Victory:** 11-1 v Crewe Alexandra, Division Three North 29/09/1951.
**Record Defeat:** 3-11 v Manchester City, Division Two 23/03/1895.
**Record Goalscorer:** (League) Andy Graver - 143, 1950-55, 58-61.
**Record Appearances:** (League) Grant Brown - 407, 1989-2002.
**Additional Records:** Paid, £75,000 for Tony Battersby from Bury, 08/1998.
Received, £500,000 for Gareth Anisworth from Port Vale, 09/1997.

**Honours:**
Midland League 1908-09, 20-21. Football League Division Three North 1931-32, 47-48, Division Four 1975-76.
Football Conference 1987-88.

### 10 YEAR RECORD

| 06-07 | | 07-08 | | 08-09 | | 09-10 | | 10-11 | | 11-12 | | 12-13 | | 13-14 | | 14-15 | | 15-16 | |
|---|---|---|---|---|---|---|---|---|---|---|---|---|---|---|---|---|---|---|---|
| FL 2 | 5 | FL 2 | 15 | FL 2 | 13 | FL 2 | 20 | FL 2 | 23 | Conf | 17 | Conf | 16 | Conf | 14 | Conf | 15 | Nat | 13 |

## LINCOLN CITY MATCH RESULTS 2015-16

| Date | Comp | H/A | Opponents | Att: | Result | | Goalscorers | Pos | No. |
|---|---|---|---|---|---|---|---|---|---|
| Aug 8 | Nat Lge | H | Cheltenham Town | 2767 | D | 1-1 | Hearn 73 | 14 | 1 |
| 11 | Nat Lge | A | Braintree Town | 657 | **W** | 3-1 | Rhead 47 73 (pen) Stanley 81 | 6 | 2 |
| 15 | Nat Lge | A | Eastleigh | 1354 | D | 1-1 | Muldoon 13 | 12 | 3 |
| 18 | Nat Lge | H | Macclesfield Town | 2320 | **W** | 5-3 | HEARN 3 (10 24 73) Rhead 26 49 | 7 | 4 |
| 22 | Nat Lge | A | Forest Green Rovers | 1385 | L | 1-3 | Simmons 70 | 9 | 5 |
| 29 | Nat Lge | A | Grimsby Town | 5849 | D | 1-1 | Rhead 32 (pen) | 11 | 6 |
| 31 | Nat Lge | A | Gateshead | 1248 | L | 0-2 | | 12 | 7 |
| Sept 5 | Nat Lge | H | Wrexham | 2678 | D | 1-1 | Rhead 70 | 13 | 8 |
| 12 | Nat Lge | H | Boreham Wood | 2272 | W | 3-1 | Rhead 64 (pen) 88 Simmons 90 | 10 | 9 |
| 15 | Nat Lge | A | Barrow | 1233 | L | 0-1 | | 14 | 10 |
| 19 | Nat Lge | A | Kidderminster Harriers | 1581 | **W** | 2-0 | Power 22 Muldoon 27 | 12 | 11 |
| 22 | Nat Lge | H | Altrincham | 1893 | D | 1-1 | Power 8 | 12 | 12 |
| 26 | Nat Lge | H | Torquay United | 2467 | W | 2-0 | Hearn 35 Rhead 39 | 12 | 13 |
| Oct 3 | Nat Lge | A | Guiseley | 1279 | **W** | 1-0 | Rhead 17 | 7 | 14 |
| 10 | Nat Lge | A | Chester | 2224 | **W** | 3-2 | Rhead 4 Everington 28 Power 54 | 16 | 15 |
| 13 | Nat Lge | A | Welling United | 702 | L | 1-2 | Hearn 58 | 10 | 16 |
| 17 | Nat Lge | H | Braintree Town | 2565 | **W** | 2-0 | Hawkridge 52 Hearn 54 | 7 | 17 |
| **24** | **FAC4Q** | **A** | **Tranmere Rovers** | **3729** | **D** | **0-0** | | | 18 |
| **27** | **FAC4Qr** | **H** | **Tranmere Rovers** | **2380** | **W** | **2-0** | **Hearn 80 Robinson 87** | | 19 |
| 31 | Nat Lge | H | Bromley | 2550 | L | 0-1 | | 11 | 20 |
| **Nov 7** | **FAC1** | **A** | **Whitehawk** | **1342** | **L** | **3-5** | **RHEAD 3 (45 pen 63 90)** | | 21 |
| 10 | Nat Lge | A | Aldershot Town | 1367 | **W** | 2-1 | Wootton 38 Muldoon 80 | 12 | 22 |
| 14 | Nat Lge | H | Tranmere Rovers | 3176 | **W** | 1-0 | Waterfall 44 | 12 | 23 |
| 21 | Nat Lge | A | Torquay United | 1752 | **W** | 3-1 | Waterfall 16 74 Hearn 25 | 5 | 24 |
| 25 | Nat Lge | A | Boreham Wood | 661 | D | 1-1 | Rhead 18 | 5 | 25 |
| 28 | Nat Lge | H | Welling United | 2528 | D | 1-1 | Muldoon 72 | 4 | 26 |
| Dec5 | Nat Lge | A | Woking | 1432 | L | 1-3 | Rhead 76 | 7 | 27 |
| 19 | Nat Lge | H | Barrow | 2540 | D | 2-2 | Rhead 28 43 | 7 | 28 |
| **21** | **FAT1** | **A** | **Bradford PA** | **360** | **L** | **1-2** | **Muldoon 90** | | 29 |
| 26 | Nat Lge | H | FC Halifax Town | 3558 | L | 0-1 | | 7 | 30 |
| 28 | Nat Lge | A | Grimsby Town | 7650 | L | 0-2 | | 9 | 31 |
| Jan 2 | Nat Lge | A | FC Halifax Town | 1932 | D | 2-2 | Stanley 16 Hearn 69 | 8 | 32 |
| 9 | Nat Lge | H | Dover Athletic | 2402 | L | 2-3 | Waterfall 36 Hearn 47 | 9 | 33 |
| 16 | Nat Lge | H | Forest Green Rovers | 1975 | L | 0-1 | | 9 | 34 |
| 23 | Nat Lge | A | Wrexham | 3853 | L | 1-3 | Rhead 14 (pen) | 11 | 35 |
| 30 | Nat Lge | H | Guiseley | 2265 | **W** | 1-0 | Bush 26 | 11 | 36 |
| Feb 6 | Nat Lge | H | Eastleigh | 2085 | **W** | 3-0 | Rhead 22 Caton 40 Muldoon 45 | 8 | 37 |
| 13 | Nat Lge | A | Altrincham | 1293 | D | 3-3 | Rhead 7 33 (pen) Muldoon 56 | 10 | 38 |
| 20 | Nat Lge | H | Southport | 2581 | **W** | 3-1 | Caton 31 59 McDaid 89 | 8 | 39 |
| Mar 5 | Nat Lge | H | Aldershot Town | 2398 | **W** | 2-0 | McCombe 8 Oastler 61 (og) | 8 | 40 |
| 12 | Nat Lge | A | Macclesfield Town | 1676 | D | 1-1 | McCombe 16 | 10 | 41 |
| 15 | Nat Lge | A | Dover Athletic | 743 | L | 1-4 | Muldoon 62 | 10 | 42 |
| 19 | Nat Lge | H | Kidderminster Harriers | 2178 | L | 1-2 | Muldoon 27 | 10 | 43 |
| 25 | Nat Lge | A | Tranmere Rovers | 5366 | L | 2-3 | Maris 41 McDaid 72 | 10 | 44 |
| 28 | Nat Lge | H | Gateshead | 2142 | D | 1-1 | Waterfall 37 | 11 | 45 |
| Apr 2 | Nat Lge | A | Bromley | 1202 | L | 0-2 | | 12 | 46 |
| 9 | Nat Lge | H | Chester | 2001 | **W** | 2-1 | McDaid 38 Maris 81 | 11 | 47 |
| 16 | Nat Lge | A | Southport | 961 | D | 2-2 | McDaid 45 Wood 89 | 11 | 48 |
| 23 | Nat Lge | H | Woking | 2518 | L | 2-3 | Rhead 7 Muldoon 48 | 12 | 49 |
| 30 | Nat Lge | A | Cheltenham Town | 5055 | L | 1-3 | Waterfall 45 | 13 | 50 |

| GOALSCORERS | Scoring Games | Consec Sco Games | Total | | Scoring Games | Consec Sco Games | Total |
|---|---|---|---|---|---|---|---|
| *2014-15 Tomlinson* | | | *14* | Simmons | 2 | | 2 |
| Rhead | 16 | 3 | 23 | Stanley | 2 | | 2 |
| Hearn | 9 | 2 | 11 | Bush | 1 | | 1 |
| Muldoon | 10 | | 10 | Everington | 1 | | 1 |
| Waterfall | 5 | 2 | 6 | Hawkridge | 1 | | 1 |
| McDaid | 4 | | 4 | Robinson | 1 | | 1 |
| Caton | 2 | | 3 | Wood | 1 | | 1 |
| Power | 3 | 2 | 3 | Wootton | 1 | | 1 |
| Maris | 2 | | 2 | Opponents | | | 1 |
| McCombe | 2 | | 2 | | | | |

# MACCLESFIELD TOWN

**Chairman:** Mark Blower
**Secretary:** Julie Briggs **(T)** 01625 264 686 **(E)** juliebriggs@mtfc.co.uk
**Commercial Manager:** Dan Ackerley **(T/E)** sales@mtfc.co.uk
**Programme Editor:** James Beckett **(T/E)** media@mtfc.co.uk
**Ground Address:** Moss Rose Ground, London Road, Macclesfield SK11 7SP
**(T)** 01625 264 686 **Manager:** John Askey

## Club Factfile

**Founded:** 1874 **Nickname:** The Silkmen
**Previous Names:** None
**Previous Leagues:** Manchester. Cheshire County. Northern Premier. Conference 1987-97. Football League 1997-2012.

**Club Colours (change):** Blue/white/blue (Red/white/black)

**Ground Capacity:** 6,335 **Seats:** 2,599 **Covered:** Yes **Clubhouse:** Yes **Shop:** Yes

**Directions**
From North (M6), Exit Junction 19, Knutsford. Follow the A537 to Macclesfield. Follow signs for the Town Centre. The follow signs A523 Leek, the ground is a mile out of town. The ground is sign-posted from the Town Centre
From South (M6), Exit Junction 17 Sandbach. Follow A534 to Congleton. Then A536 to Macclesfield. After passing the Rising Sun on the left, less than a mile, turn right into Moss Lane. Follow this around and it will bring you to the rear of the ground.

**Previous Grounds:** Rostron Field 1874-1891.

**Record Attendance:** 9,008 v Winsford United - Cheshire Senior Cup 04.02.1948.
**Record Victory:** 15-0 v Chester St Marys - Cheshire Senior Cup Second Round 16.02.1886.
**Record Defeat:** 1-13 v Tranmere Rovers Reserves - 03.05.1929.
**Record Goalscorer:** Not known - If you know please email tw.publications@btinternet.com
**Record Appearances:** Not known - If you know please email tw.publications@btinternet.com
**Additional Records:**

**Honours:**
Manchester League 1908-09, 10-11. Cheshire County League 1931-32, 32-33, 53-54, 60-61, 63-64, 67-68.
Northern Premier League 1968-69, 69-70, 86-87. Bob Lord Trophy 1993-94. Conference 1994-95, 96-97, Championship Shield 1996, 1997, 1998.
FA Trophy 1969-70, 95-96. Cheshire Senior cup x20 most recently 1999-2000.

**10 YEAR RECORD**

| 06-07 | 07-08 | 08-09 | 09-10 | 10-11 | 11-12 | 12-13 | 13-14 | 14-15 | 15-16 |
|---|---|---|---|---|---|---|---|---|---|
| FL 2 22 | FL 2 19 | FL 2 20 | FL 2 19 | FL 2 15 | FL 2 24 | Conf 11 | Conf 15 | Conf 6 | Nat 10 |

# MACCLESFIELD TOWN MATCH RESULTS 2015-16

| Date | Comp | H/A | Opponents | Att: | Result | Goalscorers | Pos | No. |
|---|---|---|---|---|---|---|---|---|
| Aug 8 | Nat Lge | A | Torquay United | 2066 | L 0-1 | | 20 | 1 |
| 11 | Nat Lge | H | Southport | 1472 | D 0-0 | | 20 | 2 |
| 15 | Nat Lge | H | Welling United | 1236 | W 2-1 | Whitaker 24 Dennis 46 | 14 | 3 |
| 18 | Nat Lge | A | Lincoln City | 2320 | L 3-5 | Dennis 2 90 Lewis 6 | 15 | 4 |
| 22 | Nat Lge | A | Eastleigh | 1928 | L 0-1 | | 17 | 5 |
| 29 | Nat Lge | H | Chester | 2062 | L 1-2 | Whitehead 52 | 21 | 6 |
| 31 | Nat Lge | A | Grimsby Town | 4251 | W 2-0 | Dennis 45 68 | 16 | 7 |
| Sept 5 | Nat Lge | H | Woking | 1285 | W 2-1 | Dennis 14 Byrne 62 | 14 | 8 |
| 12 | Nat Lge | A | Bromley | 955 | L 0-1 | | 16 | 9 |
| 15 | Nat Lge | A | Cheltenham Town | 1962 | L 0-2 | | 17 | 10 |
| 19 | Nat Lge | H | F.Green Rovers | 1311 | W 4-1 | Dennis 15 45 (pen) Lewis 62 Whitehead 83 | 17 | 11 |
| 22 | Nat Lge | H | Barrow | 1215 | L 1-2 | Lewis 58 | 17 | 12 |
| 26 | Nat Lge | A | Aldershot Town | 351 | W 3-0 | Rowe 3 41 Dennis 69 | 18 | 13 |
| Oct 3 | Nat Lge | H | Boreham Wood | 1186 | D 0-0 | | 14 | 14 |
| 6 | Nat Lge | A | Guiseley | 653 | W 3-0 | Turnbull 24 Whitehead 41 Whitaker 58 | | 15 |
| 10 | Nat Lge | H | Kidderminster Harriers | 1653 | W 2-1 | Diange 3 Rowe 38 | 13 | 16 |
| 13 | Nat Lge | H | Gateshead | 1223 | W 1-0 | Dennis 56 | 11 | 17 |
| 17 | Nat Lge | A | Dover Athletic | 1012 | L 1-2 | Whitehead 4 | 13 | 18 |
| **24** | **FAC4Q** | **H** | **Alfreton Town** | **1048** | **W 3-2** | **Dennis 5 37 Turnbull 7** | | 19 |
| 31 | Nat Lge | A | Braintree Town | 687 | L 0-1 | | 15 | 20 |
| **Nov 7** | **FAC1** | **A** | **Portsmouth** | **9,824** | **L 1-2** | **Dennis 15** | | 21 |
| 10 | Nat Lge | H | Altrincham | 1,801 | W 3-0 | Dennis 13 Whitaker 40 Holroyd 81 | 11 | 22 |
| 14 | Nat Lge | A | Woking | 1,324 | W 5-2 | Whitehead 13 DENNIS 3 ( 26 61 80) Byrne 49 | 11 | 23 |
| 21 | Nat Lge | H | Bromley | 1,632 | W 2-0 | Lewis 49 Dennis 80 | 9 | 24 |
| 28 | Nat Lge | A | Wrexham | 4,591 | W 3-2 | Dennis 23 48 Whitaker 71 | 7 | 25 |
| Dec 5 | Nat Lge | A | Southport | 861 | L 1-3 | Whitaker 45 (pen) | 9 | 26 |
| 8 | Nat Lge | H | Eastleigh | 1087 | L 1-2 | Diange 8 | 9 | 27 |
| 19 | Nat Lge | A | Welling United | 577 | W 1-0 | Dennis 6 | 6 | 28 |
| **22** | **FAT1** | **H** | **Ashton United** | **610** | **W 4-0** | **Dennis 14 (pen) Lewis 40 50 Whitehead 45** | | 29 |
| 26 | Nat Lge | H | Tranmere Rovers | 2037 | L 1-2 | Dennis 45 | 6 | 30 |
| 28 | Nat Lge | A | Chester | 2791 | W2-0 | Dennis 31 (pen) Sharps 25 (og) | 6 | 31 |
| Jan 2 | Nat Lge | A | Tranmere Rovers | 4923 | W 1-0 | Sampson 31 | 6 | 32 |
| 9 | Nat Lge | H | FC Halifax Town | 2055 | L 0-1 | | 7 | 33 |
| **16** | **FAT2** | **A** | **Truro City** | **665** | **D 2-2** | **Dennis 66 77** | | 34 |
| **19** | **FAT2r** | **H** | **Truro City** | **507** | **W 2-0** | **Whitaker 20 Dennis 77 (pen)** | | 35 |
| 24 | Nat Lge | H | Aldershot Town | 1515 | L 0-2 | | 7 | 36 |
| 30 | Nat Lge | A | Forest Green Rovers | 1617 | L 1-2 | Sampson 69 | 8 | 37 |
| **Feb 9** | **FAT3** | **A** | **Torquay United** | **838** | **D 3-3** | **Sampson 50 Turnbull 62 Dennis 78** | | 38 |
| 13 | Nat Lge | A | Kidderminster Harriers | 1693 | L 1-3 | Dennis 90 | 12 | 39 |
| **15** | **FAT3r** | **H** | **Torquay United** | **566** | **L 0-1** | | | 40 |
| 27 | Nat Lge | H | Wrexham | 2406 | D 0-0 | | 12 | 41 |
| Mar 2 | Nat Lge | H | Torquay Utd | 1082 | L 1-2 | Dennis 43 | 12 | 42 |
| 5 | Nat Lge | A | Altrincham | 2014 | D 0-0 | | 12 | 43 |
| 12 | Nat Lge | H | Lincoln City | 1676 | D 1-1 | Whitehead 50 | 12 | 44 |
| 19 | Nat Lge | A | Boreham Wood | 306 | D 0-0 | | 12 | 45 |
| 26 | Nat Lge | A | Gateshead | 948 | W 3-0 | STYCHE 3 (7 22 87) | 12 | 46 |
| 28 | Nat Lge | H | Grimsby Town | 2326 | W 2-1 | Sampson 25 Styche 68 | 10 | 47 |
| Apr 2 | Nat Lge | H | Braintree Town | 1222 | W 3-1 | Whittaker 25 (pen) Rowe 47 McCombe 65 | 10 | 48 |
| 9 | Nat Lge | A | Barrow | 1526 | D 1-1 | Whitehead 24 | 10 | 49 |
| 12 | Nat Lge | H | Dover Athletic | 1022 | D 0-0 | | 10 | 50 |
| 16 | Nat Lge | H | Guiseley | 1408 | W 1-0 | Lewis 76 | 9 | 51 |
| 23 | Nat Lge | H | Cheltenham Town | 1895 | L 0-1 | | 10 | 52 |
| 30 | Nat Lge | A | FC Halifax Town | 2943 | D 1-1 | Rowe 62 | 10 | 53 |

| GOALSCORERS | Scoring Games | Consec Sco Games | Total | | Scoring Games | Consec Sco Games | Total |
|---|---|---|---|---|---|---|---|
| *2014-15 Fairhurst* | *11* | | | Diange | 2 | | 2 |
| Dennis | 22 | 5 | 30 | Holroyd | 1 | | 1 |
| Whitehead | 8 | | 8 | McCombe | 1 | | 1 |
| Lewis | 6 | 2 | 7 | Opponents | | | 1 |
| Whittaker | 7 | 2 | 7 | | | | |
| Rowe | 5 | | 5 | | | | |
| Sampson | 4 | | 4 | | | | |
| Styche | 4 | | 4 | | | | |
| Turnbull | 3 | | 3 | | | | |
| Byrne | 2 | | 2 | | | | |

# MAIDSTONE UNITED

**Chairman:** Bill Williams (CEO)
**Secretary:** Ian Tucker (T) 07968 505 888 (E) itucker@maidstoneunited.co.uk
**Commercial Manager:** Simon Daniel (T/E) 01622 753 817
**Programme Editor:** Ian Tucker (T/E) 07968 505 888
**Ground Address:** The Gallagher Stadium, James Whatman Way, Maidstone, Kent ME14 1LQ
**(T)** 01622 753 817 **Manager:** Jay Saunders

## Club Factfile

**Founded:** 1992 **Nickname:** The Stones
**Previous Names:** None
**Previous Leagues:** Kent County, Kent. Isthmian 2006-15.

**Club Colours (change):** Amber/black/black & amber (All white)

**Ground Capacity:** **Seats:** Yes **Covered:** Yes **Clubhouse:** Yes **Shop:** Yes

**Directions**
M20 (junction 6) and M2 (junction 3).
Follow signs to Maidstone on the A229.
At the White Rabbit roundabout, take the third exit on to James Whatman Way.

**Previous Grounds:** London Road 1992-2001, Central Park (Sittingbourne) 2001-02 11-12, The Homelands 2002-11.

**Record Attendance:** 2,296 v Dulwich Hamlet, Isthmian League Premier Division 15/03/14
**Record Victory:** 12-1 v Aylesford - Kent League 1993-94
**Record Defeat:** 2-8 v Scott Sports - 1995-96
**Record Goalscorer:** Richard Sinden - 98
**Record Appearances:** Aaron Lacy - 187
**Additional Records:** Paid £2,000 for Steve Jones - 2000

**Honours:**
Kent League 2001-02, 05-06, League cup 2005-06. Isthmian Division 1 South 2006-07, Premier 2014-15.
National League South Play-offs 2015-16.
Kent Senior Trophy 2002-03.

**10 YEAR RECORD**

| 06-07 | 07-08 | 08-09 | 09-10 | 10-11 | 11-12 | 12-13 | 13-14 | 14-15 | 15-16 |
|---|---|---|---|---|---|---|---|---|---|
| Isth1S 1 | Isth P 17 | Isth P 15 | Isth P 18 | Isth P 20 | Isth1S 6 | Isth1S 2 | Isth P 7 | Isth P 1 | Nat S 3 |

# MAIDSTONE UNITED MATCH RESULTS 2015-16

| Date | Comp | H/A | Opponents | Att: | Result | | Goalscorers | Pos | No. |
|---|---|---|---|---|---|---|---|---|---|
| Aug 8 | Nat South | A | Sutton United | 1307 | W | 2-0 | Healy 58 Akrofi 88 | 3 | 1 |
| 11 | Nat South | H | Ebbsfleet United | 2363 | L | 0-2 | | 11 | 2 |
| 15 | Nat South | H | Oxford City | 2037 | L | 0-1 | | 15 | 3 |
| 18 | Nat South | A | Hemel Hempstead | 637 | W | 1-0 | May21 | 11 | 4 |
| 22 | Nat South | H | Hayes & Yeading | 1906 | W | 3-1 | May15 Akrofi 29 (pen) 71 | 5 | 5 |
| 29 | Nat South | A | Eastbourne Borough | 1011 | L | 0-1 | | 13 | 6 |
| 31 | Nat South | H | Chelmsford City | 2117 | L | 0-1 | | 14 | 7 |
| Sept 5 | Nat South | A | Gosport Borough | 633 | D | 0-0 | | 13 | 8 |
| 12 | Nat South | H | Havant & Waterlooville | 2054 | W | 1-0 | Birchall 6 | 12 | 9 |
| 15 | Nat South | A | Maidenhead United | 403 | W | 2-0 | May18 Healy 27 | 8 | 10 |
| 19 | Nat South | H | Bath City | 2098 | W | 1-0 | May6 | 6 | 11 |
| **26** | **FAC2Q** | **H** | **South Park** | **1169** | **W** | **6-2** | **May19 BODKIN 3 (40 60 87) Healy 43 Akrofi 81** | | 12 |
| Oct 3 | Nat South | A | Ebbsfleet United | 2157 | W | 1-0 | Healy 56 | 5 | 13 |
| **10** | **FAC3Q** | **H** | **Dunstable Town** | **1583** | **W** | **2-0** | **Osborn 71 May75** | | 14 |
| 17 | Nat South | H | St Albans City | 2103 | W | 1-0 | Flisher 76 | 4 | 15 |
| **24** | **FAC4Q** | **A** | **Chippenham Town** | **811** | **W** | **2-0** | **May 40 (pen) Taylor 90** | | 16 |
| 31 | Nat South | A | Concord Rangers | 516 | W | 2-1 | Akrofi 60 Rogers 63 | 3 | 17 |
| **Nov 7** | **FAC1** | **H** | **Yeovil Town** | **2811** | **L** | **0-1** | | | 18 |
| 14 | Nat South | A | Dartford | 1909 | D | 1-1 | Flisher 52 | 4 | 19 |
| 17 | Nat South | H | Wealdstone | 1812 | W | 1-0 | May28 | 3 | 20 |
| 21 | Nat South | A | Basingstoke Town | 611 | W | 1-0 | Smart 49 (og) | 2 | 21 |
| **28** | **FAT3Q** | **A** | **Hampton & Richmond** | **482** | **W** | **1-0** | **May90** | | 22 |
| Dec 1 | Nat South | H | Maidenhead United | 1731 | L | 1-2 | Collin 85 (pen) | 2 | 23 |
| 5 | Nat South | H | Truro City | 2002 | W | 2-1 | Coyle 74 May 79 | 2 | 24 |
| 8 | Nat South | H | Whitehawk | 1743 | L | 0-1 | | 2 | 25 |
| **12** | **FAT1** | **H** | **Bognor Regis Town** | **892** | **L** | **0-1** | | | 26 |
| 19 | Nat South | A | Hayes & Yeading | 302 | L | 0-1 | | 2 | 27 |
| 26 | Nat South | A | Margate | 1248 | L | 0-1 | | 2 | 28 |
| 28 | Nat South | H | Eastbourne Borough | 2691 | W | 2-1 | Karagiannis 32 Coyle 65 | 2 | 29 |
| Jan 2 | Nat South | H | Margate | 2609 | W | 2-1 | Healy 26 Karagiannis 58 | 2 | 30 |
| 9 | Nat South | A | Bath City | 710 | W | 2-0 | Sweeney 15 May77 | 2 | 31 |
| 30 | Nat South | H | Concord Rangers | 2355 | D | 2-2 | Healy 35 Karagiannis 65 (pen) | 2 | 32 |
| Feb 13 | Nat South | H | Gosport Borough | 1882 | W | 2-1 | Coyle 64 Flisher 90 | 2 | 33 |
| 20 | Nat South | A | Bishops Stortford | 652 | W | 1-0 | Dumaka 48 | 2 | 34 |
| 27 | Nat South | A | Havant & Waterlooville | 835 | L | 1-2 | Davies 60 | 3 | 35 |
| Mar 5 | Nat South | H | Basingstoke Town | 2076 | W | 3-1 | Rogers 4 Dumaka 47 Karagiannis 63 (pen) | 3 | 36 |
| 8 | Nat South | A | Oxford City | 225 | W | 3-2 | Davies 45 Flisher 78 Walker 68 (og) | 2 | 37 |
| 12 | Nat South | A | Wealdstone | 815 | D | 2-2 | Healy 11 Davies 40 | 2 | 38 |
| 15 | Nat South | A | Weston-s-Mare | 368 | W | 2-1 | Dumaka12 Karagiannis 90 (pen) | 2 | 39 |
| 19 | Nat South | H | Weston-s-Mare | 2143 | W | 3-1 | Karagiannis 15 (pen) 39 Dumaka 53 | 2 | 40 |
| 26 | Nat South | H | Hemel Hempstead Town | 2481 | W | 2-1 | Driver 17 Karagiannis 45 | 2 | 41 |
| 28 | Nat South | A | Chelmsford City | 891 | L | 0-3 | | 2 | 42 |
| Apr 2 | Nat South | A | St Albans City | 852 | W | 2-1 | Healy 8 Flisher 51 | 2 | 43 |
| 5 | Nat South | H | Sutton United | 3030 | L | 1-2 | Karagiannis 88 | 2 | 44 |
| 9 | Nat South | H | Dartford | 2602 | L | 1-2 | Wood 55 (og) | 3 | 45 |
| 16 | Nat South | A | Truro City | 841 | W | 3-1 | Dumaka 5 May35 61 | 3 | 46 |
| 23 | Nat South | A | Whitehawk | 770 | L | 0-1 | | 3 | 47 |
| 30 | Nat South | H | Bishops Stortford | 2549 | D | 1-1 | Healy 52 | 3 | 48 |
| **May 3** | **PO SF1** | **A** | **Truro City** | **1011** | **W** | **2-0** | **Healy 27 Flisher 56** | | 49 |
| **8** | **PO SF2** | **H** | **Truro City** | **2508** | **W** | **1-0** | **Flisher 73** | | 50 |
| **14** | **PO Final** | **A** | **Ebbsfleet United** | **3800** | **D** | **2-2** | **Taylor 47 Dumaka 121 (Won 4-3 on pens aet)** | | 51 |

| GOALSCORERS | Scoring Games | Consec Sco Games | Total | | Scoring Games | Consec Sco Games | Total |
|---|---|---|---|---|---|---|---|
| *2014-15 May* | | | *24* | Rogers | 2 | | 2 |
| May | 11 | 3 | 13 | Taylor | 2 | | 2 |
| Healy | 10 | 2 | 10 | Birchall | 1 | | 1 |
| Karadiannis | 8 | 3 | 9 | Collin | 1 | | 1 |
| Flisher | 7 | | 7 | Driver | 1 | | 1 |
| Dumaka | 6 | | 6 | Osborn | 1 | | 1 |
| Akrofi | 4 | | 5 | Sweeney | 1 | | 1 |
| Bodkin | 3 | | 3 | Opponents | 3 | | 3 |
| Coyle | 3 | | 3 | | | | |
| Davies | 3 | | 3 | | | | |

# NORTH FERRIBY UNITED

**Chairman:** Steve and Eman Forster
**Secretary:** Steve Tather **(T)** **(E)** steve.tather@northferribyunitedfc.co.uk
**Commercial Manager:** Denise Barrass **(T/E)** jamie.barwick@northferribyunitedfc.co.uk
**Programme Editor:** Jamie Barwick **(T/E)** 07725 460 921
**Ground Address:** Eon Visual Media Stadium, Grange Lane, Church Road, North Ferriby HU14 3AB
**(T)** 01482 634 601 **Manager:** Steve Housham

## Club Factfile

**Founded:** 1934 **Nickname:** United
**Previous Names:** None
**Previous Leagues:** East Riding Church, East Riding Amateur, Yorkshire 1969-82, Northern Counties East 1982-2000. Northern Premier 2000-13.

**Club Colours (change):** White with green trim/green/green (Yellow with green trim/yellow/yellow)

**Ground Capacity:** 3,000 **Seats:** 250 **Covered:** 1,000 **Clubhouse:** Yes **Shop:** Yes

**Directions**
Main Leeds to Hull road A63 or M62. North Ferriby is approx. 8 miles west of Hull.
Proceed through village past the Duke of Cumberland Hotel.
Turn right down Church Road. Ground mile down on left.

**Previous Grounds:** Not known - If you know please email tw.publications@btinternet.com

**Record Attendance:** 1,927 v Hull City - Charity game 2005
**Record Victory:** 9-0 v Hatfield Main - Northern Counties East 1997-98
**Record Defeat:** 1-7 v North Shields - Northern Counties East 1991
**Record Goalscorer:** Mark Tennison - 161
**Record Appearances:** Paul Sharp - 497 (1996-2006)
**Additional Records:** Andy Flounders scored 50 during season 1998-99
Received £60,000 from Hull City for Dean Windass
**Honours:**
Northern Counties East 1999-2000. Northern Premier League Division 1 2004-05, Premier Division 2012-13. National North Play-offs 2015-16.
East Riding Senior Cup 1970-71, 76-77, 77-78, 78-79, 90-91, 96-97, 97-98, 98-99, 99-2000, 00-01, 01-02, 02-03, 06-07, 07-08, 08-09, 09-10, 10-11, 12-13. FATrophy 2014-15.

## 10 YEAR RECORD

| 06-07 | 07-08 | 08-09 | 09-10 | 10-11 | 11-12 | 12-13 | 13-14 | 14-15 | 15-16 |
|---|---|---|---|---|---|---|---|---|---|
| NP P 13 | NP P 15 | NP P 10 | NP P 4 | NP P 5 | NP P 9 | NP P 1 | Conf N 2 | Conf N 10 | Nat N 2 |

# NORTH FERRIBY UNITED MATCH RESULTS 2015-16

| Date | Comp | H/A | Opponents | Att: | Result | | Goalscorers | Pos | No. |
|---|---|---|---|---|---|---|---|---|---|
| Aug 8 | Nat North | A | Tamworth | 791 | L | 0-1 | | 20 | 1 |
| 11 | Nat North | H | Chorley | 335 | **W** | 4-0 | BATESON 3 ( 36 82 84) Denton 86 | 6 | 2 |
| 15 | Nat North | H | Solihull Borough | 292 | D | 1-1 | Denton 37 | 8 | 3 |
| 18 | Nat North | A | Stockport County | 3140 | D | 1-1 | Bolder 90 | 9 | 4 |
| 22 | Nat North | H | Hednesford Town | 274 | D | 1-1 | Denton 85 | 11 | 5 |
| 29 | Nat North | A | Bradford PA | 226 | D | 4-4 | Bateson 16 28 Denton 30 Kendall 42 | 10 | 6 |
| 31 | Nat North | H | Lowestoft Town | 314 | D | 0-0 | | 11 | 7 |
| Sept 5 | Nat North | A | Brackley Town | 238 | **W** | 4-2 | Bateson 24 30 Kendall 49 68 | 8 | 8 |
| 12 | Nat North | H | Gloucester City | 266 | **W** | 3-0 | Denton 6 Clarke 13 Kendall 67 | 7 | 9 |
| 15 | Nat North | A | Harrogate Town | 397 | D | 3-3 | King 3 87 (pen) Emerton 90 | 9 | 10 |
| 19 | Nat North | A | AFC Telford United | 1250 | D | 1-1 | King 73 | 7 | 11 |
| **26** | **FAC2Q** | **A** | **Newton Aycliffe** | **254** | **D** | **0-0** | | | 12 |
| **29** | **FAC2Qr** | **H** | **Newton Aycliffe** | **186** | **W** | **3-0** | **Holte 30 Clarke 69 83** | | 13 |
| Oct 3 | Nat North | H | Corby Town | 443 | **W** | 5-0 | Clarke 2 Emerton 6 7 Palmer 50 King 71 (pen) | 6 | 14 |
| **10** | **FAC3Q** | **H** | **Nuneaton Town** | **531** | **W** | **2-1** | **Fry 20 King 74** | | 15 |
| 17 | Nat North | H | FC United | 951 | **W** | 1-0 | Clarke 90 | 5 | 16 |
| **24** | **FAC4Q** | **A** | **Stalybridge Celtic** | **417** | **D** | **1-1** | **Clarke 42** | | 17 |
| **28** | **FAC4Qr** | **H** | **Stalybridge Celtic** | **710** | **D** | **0-0** | **(Lost 7-8 on pens aet)** | | 18 |
| 31 | Nat North | A | Nuneaton Town | 637 | L | 1-3 | Bolder 52 | 8 | 19 |
| Nov 7 | Nat North | H | Boston United | 452 | **W** | 4-3 | King 29 55 Denton 73 Gray 79 | | 20 |
| 10 | Nat North | A | Alfreton Town | 473 | **W** | 1-0 | King 14 | 5 | 21 |
| 14 | Nat North | A | Curzon Ashton | 362 | **W** | 3-0 | King 22 52 Emerton 82 | | 22 |
| 21 | Nat North | H | AFC Fylde | 365 | **W** | 3-0 | Palmer 2 King 52 Denton 85 | 2 | 23 |
| 24 | Nat North | H | Nuneaton Town | 425 | L | 1-2 | Denton 46 | 3 | 24 |
| **28** | **FAT3Q** | **H** | **Stocksbridge PS** | **251** | **L** | **1-2** | **Denton 3** | | 25 |
| Dec 5 | Nat North | A | Chorley | 675 | **W** | 3-2 | Kendall 64 King 89 Bateson 90 | 2 | 26 |
| 19 | Nat North | H | Tanmworth | 367 | W | 3-1 | King 41 43 Brooksby 63 | 2 | 27 |
| 26 | Nat North | A | Gainsborough Trinity | 665 | L | 0-2 | | 3 | 28 |
| 28 | Nat North | H | Bradford PA | 539 | **W** | 1-0 | Denton 64 | 3 | 29 |
| Jan 2 | Nat North | H | Gainsborough Trinity | 612 | **W** | 4-0 | Emerton 30 Palmer 40 Bateson 53 Clarke 74 | 2 | 30 |
| 9 | Nat North | A | Solihull Moors | 684 | **W** | 3-1 | Denton 9 16 Bateson 50 | 2 | 31 |
| 23 | Nat North | H | Brackley Town | 406 | **W** | 2-1 | Clarke 20 Denton 48 | 2 | 32 |
| 30 | Nat North | A | Worcester City | 561 | L | 0-2 | | 2 | 33 |
| Feb 13 | Nat North | H | Harrogate Town | 509 | L | 0-1 | | 2 | 34 |
| 16 | Nat North | A | Hednesford Town | 251 | D | 1-1 | King 90 (pen) | 3 | 35 |
| 20 | Nat North | H | Curzon Ashton | 353 | D | 0-0 | | 3 | 36 |
| 27 | Nat North | A | FC United | 3419 | L | 2-3 | King 18 (pen) Denton 90 | 4 | 37 |
| Mar 5 | Nat North | A | Corby Town | 469 | **W** | 4-1 | Brooksby 1 Denton 5 34 Bateson 86 | 3 | 38 |
| 12 | Nat North | H | Stalybridge Celtic | 296 | **W** | 1-0 | Denton 21 | 3 | 39 |
| 19 | Nat North | A | Boston United | 1279 | **W** | 2-1 | Hone 24 Emerton 89 | 2 | 40 |
| 26 | Nat North | H | Stockport County | 926 | **W** | 2-0 | Brooksby 63 Denton 69 | 2 | 41 |
| Apr 2 | Nat North | H | Worcester Clty | 268 | D | 3-3 | King 45 (pen) Clarke 59 Denton 72 | 2 | 42 |
| 9 | Nat North | A | AFC Fylde | 511 | **W** | 3-2 | Hotte 41 King 43 Denton 55 | 2 | 43 |
| 12 | Nat North | A | Stalybridge Celtic | 173 | L | 0-2 | | 2 | 44 |
| 16 | Nat North | H | AFC Telford United | 488 | **W** | 2-0 | Clarke 55 Bateson 90 | 2 | 45 |
| 23 | Nat North | A | Gloucester City | 413 | L | 2-3 | Brooksby 60 Bateson 66 | 3 | 46 |
| 26 | Nat North | A | Lowestoft Town | 549 | **W** | 3-0 | Gray 12 Denton 38 Clarke 59 | 2 | 47 |
| 30 | Nat North | H | Alfreton Town | 484 | L | 0-1 | | 2 | 48 |
| **May 4** | **PO SF1** | **A** | **Boston United** | **2592** | **L** | **0-2** | | | 49 |
| **8** | **PO SF2** | **H** | **Boston United** | **2027** | **W** | **3-0** | **King 11 (pen) Denton 16 Clarke 54** | | 50 |
| **14** | **PO Final** | **H** | **AFC Fylde** | **1829** | **W** | **2-1** | **Brooksby 45 Hone 95 (aet)** | | 51 |

| GOALSCORERS | Scoring Games | Consec Sco Games | Total |
|---|---|---|---|
| *2014-15 Denton* | | | *23* |
| Denton | 20 | 3 | 22 |
| King | 15 | 4 | 19 |
| Bateson | 9 | 2 | 13 |
| Clarke | 11 | 2 | 12 |
| Emerton | 6 | | 6 |
| Brooksby | 4 | | 5 |
| Kendall | 5 | | 5 |
| Palmer | 3 | | 3 |
| Bolder | 2 | | 2 |
| Gray | 2 | | 2 |
| Hone | 2 | | 2 |
| Hotte | 2 | | 2 |
| Fry | 1 | | 1 |

# SOLIHULL MOORS

**Chairman:** Trevor Stevens
**Secretary:** Tim Delaney (T) 0121 705 6770 (E) sec.smfc@gmail.com
**Commercial Manager:** Ben Seifas (T/E) 0121 705 6770
**Programme Editor:** Ben Seifas (T/E) ben.seifas@solihullmoorsfc.co.uk
**Ground Address:** The Autotech Stadium, Damson Park, Damson Parkway, Solihull B91 2PP
(T) 0121 705 6770 **Manager:** Marcus Bignot

## Club Factfile

**Founded:** 2007 **Nickname:** Moors
**Previous Names:** Today's club was formed after the amalgamation of Solihull Borough and Moor Green in 2007
**Previous Leagues:** None

**Club Colours (change):** Blue & yellow hoops/blue/blue & yellow hoops (Red, white & black hoops/black/red & white hoops)

**Ground Capacity:** 3,050 **Seats:** 280 **Covered:** 1,000 **Clubhouse:** Yes **Shop:** Yes

**Directions**
Leave the M42 at Junction 6 and take the A45 towards Birmingham, after approximately 2 miles, at the traffic lights, take the left hand filter lane onto Damson Parkway. Follow the road for approximately 1 mile where the Autotech Stadium is situated on the right hand side, continue over the traffic lights (for the Land Rover factory entrance) to the traffic island and come back on yourself to find the entrance to the Football Club on the left just after the traffic lights. Use B92 9EJ as the postcode for SatNav purposes.

**Previous Grounds:** None

**Record Attendance:** 1,076 v Rushden & Diamonds - FA Cup 4th Qualifying Round 27/10/2007
**Record Victory:** 4-1 v Southport - Conference South 05/04/2008
**Record Defeat:** 1-6 v Kettering Town - Conference South 01/01/2008
**Record Goalscorer:** Not known - If you know please email tw.publications@btinternet.com
**Record Appearances:** Carl Motteram - 71 (2007-09)
**Additional Records:**

**Honours:**
National North 2015-16.
Birmingham Senior Cup 2015-16.

### 10 YEAR RECORD

| 06-07 | 07-08 | 08-09 | 09-10 | 10-11 | 11-12 | 12-13 | 13-14 | 14-15 | 15-16 |
|---|---|---|---|---|---|---|---|---|---|
| | Conf N 17 | Conf N 16 | Conf N 17 | Conf N 7 | Conf N 19 | Conf N 9 | Conf N 8 | Conf N 12 | Nat N 1 |

## SOLIHULL MOORS MATCH RESULTS 2015-16

| Date | Comp | H/A | Opponents | Att: | Result | | Goalscorers | Pos | No. |
|---|---|---|---|---|---|---|---|---|---|
| Aug8 | Nat North | H | AFC Fylde | 290 | W | 3-0 | Moore 18 (pen) 34 Hannigan 83 (og) | 2 | 1 |
| 11 | Nat North | A | Boston United | 1140 | W | 4-1 | Knights 28 50 Byrne 85 Asante 90 | 1 | 2 |
| 15 | Nat North | A | North Ferriby United | 292 | D | 1-1 | Armson 90 | 3 | 3 |
| 18 | Nat North | H | Worcester City | 525 | W | 3-0 | Moore 34 (pen) Knights 37 81 | 2 | 4 |
| 22 | Nat North | A | Stalybridge Celtic | 386 | W | 3-1 | Byrne 16 Daly 72 Knights 83 | 1 | 5 |
| 29 | Nat North | H | Alfreton Town | 425 | W | 2-1 | Knights 46 Nottingham 59 | 1 | 6 |
| 31 | Nat North | A | Corby Town | 760 | W | 3-1 | Armson 10 Asante 37 Moore 78 | 1 | 7 |
| Sept5 | Nat North | H | Harrogate Town | 806 | W | 1-0 | Brown 46 | 1 | 8 |
| 12 | Nat North | A | Bradford PA | 332 | D | 1-1 | Byrne 84 | 1 | 9 |
| 19 | Nat North | H | Curzon Ashton | 465 | W | 2-0 | Armson 60 Moore 68 | 1 | 10 |
| **26** | **FAC2Q** | **H** | **Oadby Town** | **341** | **W** | **3-1** | **Asante 77 86 Moore 90** | | 11 |
| Oct3 | Nat North | A | Chorley | 1205 | D | 2-2 | Asante 1 Armson 60 | 1 | 12 |
| **10** | **FAC3Q** | **H** | **Worcester City** | **923** | **D** | **1-1** | **Moore 45 (pen)** | | 13 |
| **13** | **FAC3Qr** | **A** | **Worcester City** | **652** | **L** | **0-1** | | | 14 |
| 17 | Nat North | A | Tamworth | 1007 | D | 1-1 | Brown 37 | 2 | 15 |
| 31 | Nat North | H | Stockport County | 1100 | W | 1-0 | Brown 31 | 2 | 16 |
| Nov7 | Nat North | A | Lowestoft Town | 438 | D | 2-2 | Moore 10 Armson 47 | 2 | 17 |
| 14 | Nat North | A | Hednesford Town | 562 | D | 0-0 | | 3 | 18 |
| 21 | Nat North | H | Gloucester City | 542 | D | 0-0 | | 3 | 19 |
| 24 | Nat North | A | Stockport County | 2437 | W | 4-2 | Asante 27 31 Moore 56 Knights 82 | 2 | 20 |
| **28** | **FAT3Q** | **H** | **Boston United** | **319** | **W** | **1-0** | **Gittings 81** | | 21 |
| Dec5 | Nat North | H | Boston United | 479 | L | 0-1 | | 3 | 22 |
| **12** | **FAT1** | **A** | **Grimsby Town** | **1071** | **D** | **1-1** | **Brown 46** | | 23 |
| 19 | Nat North | A | AFC Fylde | 581 | W | 2-1 | Moore 13 (pen) Knights 50 | 3 | 24 |
| **22** | **FAT2** | **H** | **Grimsby Town** | **479** | **L** | **2-3** | **Armson 62 Asante 80 (pen)** | | 25 |
| 26 | Nat North | H | Nuneaton Town | 1242 | W | 3-1 | Brown 60 Moore 62 Leslie 79 | 1 | 26 |
| 28 | Nat North | A | Alfreton Town | 546 | D | 2-2 | Knights 45 Armson 90 | 2 | 27 |
| Jan2 | Nat North | A | Nuneaton Town | 1306 | W | 1-0 | Byrne 69 | 1 | 28 |
| 5 | Nat North | H | Brackley Town | 410 | W | 3-0 | Moore 6 Daly 13 Asante 48 | 1 | 29 |
| 9 | Nat North | H | North Ferriby United | 684 | L | 1-3 | Knights 35 | 1 | 30 |
| 16 | Nat North | H | Stalybridge Celtic | 492 | W | 4-1 | Brown 6 Leslie 33 Daly 36 Byfield 86 | 1 | 31 |
| 23 | Nat North | A | Harrogate Town | 583 | L | 0-6 | | 1 | 32 |
| 30 | Nat North | A | Brackley Town | 334 | W | 1-0 | Asante 75 | 1 | 33 |
| Feb13 | Nat North | H | AFC Telford United | 670 | W | 2-1 | Beswick 18 Byrne 25 | 1 | 34 |
| 20 | Nat North | A | Gainsborough Trinity | 492 | W | 6-1 | Picton 25 (og) Beswick 31(pen) 45 Daly 67 Asante 80 90 | 1 | 35 |
| 27 | Nat North | H | Tamworth | 773 | L | 1-2 | Asante 52 | 1 | 36 |
| 29 | Nat North | A | Curzon Ashton | 229 | W | 3-1 | Asante 46 Brown 63 Armson 83 | 1 | 37 |
| Mar5 | Nat North | H | Gainsborough Trinity | 517 | W | 3-2 | Beswick 48 Nottingham 49 Brown 55 | 1 | 38 |
| 12 | Nat North | H | Lowestoft Town | 522 | W | 2-1 | Daly 18 Asante 46 | 1 | 39 |
| 15 | Nat North | H | FC United | 834 | L | 1-2 | Asante 47 | 1 | 40 |
| 19 | Nat North | A | Gloucester City | 411 | W | 2-0 | Asante 21 Knights 75 | 1 | 41 |
| 26 | Nat North | A | Worcester City | 828 | D | 2-2 | Brown 14 54 | 1 | 42 |
| 28 | Nat North | H | Corby Town | 828 | W | 4-1 | Nottingham 22 Cowan 36 Moore 5 65 (pen) | 1 | 43 |
| Apr2 | Nat North | H | Bradford PA | 569 | W | 2-1 | Nottingham 3 61 | 1 | 44 |
| 9 | Nat North | A | AFC Telford United | 1738 | W | 3-0 | ASANTE 3 (7 10 45) | 1 | 45 |
| 16 | Nat North | H | Hednesford Town | 972 | L | 1-2 | Byfield 90 | 1 | 46 |
| 23 | Nat North | H | Chorley | 952 | L | 0-2 | | 1 | 47 |
| 30 | Nat North | A | FC United | 3914 | D | 2-2 | Armson 11 18 | 1 | 48 |

| GOALSCORERS | Scoring Games | Consec Sco Games | Total |
|---|---|---|---|
| ***2014-15 Bogle*** | | | ***28*** |
| Asante | 17 | 3 | 20 |
| Moore | 12 | 2 | 14 |
| Knights | 9 | 3 | 11 |
| Armson | 9 | 2 | 10 |
| Brown | 9 | 2 | 10 |
| Byrne | 4 | | 5 |
| Daly | 5 | | 5 |
| Nottingham | 4 | | 5 |
| Beswick | 3 | | 4 |

| | Scoring Games | Consec Sco Games | Total |
|---|---|---|---|
| Byfield | 2 | | 2 |
| Leslie | 2 | | 2 |
| Cowan | 1 | | 1 |
| Gittings | 1 | | 1 |
| Opponents | | | 2 |

# SOUTHPORT

**Chairman:** Charles Clapham
**Secretary:** Ken Hilton (T) 01704 533 422 (E) secretary@southportfc.net
**Commercial Manager:** Haydn Preece (T/E) 01704 533 422
**Programme Editor:** Rob Urwin (T/E) 01704 533 422
**Ground Address:** Merseyrail Community Stadium, Haig Avenue, Southport, Merseyside PR8 6JZ
(T) 01704 533 422 **Manager:** Andy Bishop

## Club Factfile

**Founded:** 1881 **Nickname:** The Sandgrounders
**Previous Names:** Southport Central, Southport Vulcan
**Previous Leagues:** Preston & District, Lancashire 1889-1903, Lancashire comb. 1903-11, Central 1911-21, Football League 1921-78, Northern Premier 1978-93, 2003-04, Conference 1993-2003

**Club Colours (change):** Yellow/black/black (All green)

**Ground Capacity:** 6,008 **Seats:** 1,660 **Covered:** 2,760 **Clubhouse:** Yes **Shop:** Yes

**Directions**
Leave M6 at junction 26. Join M58 to junction 3. Join A570 signposted Southport, follow A570 through Ormskirk Town Centre following signs for Southport. At the big roundabout (McDonalds is on the left) take the fourth exit. Proceed along this road until you reach the 2nd set of pedstrian lights and take the next left into Haig Avenue.

**Previous Grounds:** Sussex Road Sports Ground, Scarisbrick New Road, Ash Lane (later named Haig Avenue)

**Record Attendance:** 20,010 v Newcastle United - FA Cup 1932
**Record Victory:** 8-1 v Nelson - 01/01/31
**Record Defeat:** 0-11 v Oldham Athletic - 26/12/62
**Record Goalscorer:** Alan Spence - 98
**Record Appearances:** Arthur Peat - 401 (1962-72)
**Additional Records:** Paid £20,000 to Macclesfield Town for Martin McDonald

**Honours:**
Lancashire Senior Cup 1904-05. Liverpool Senior Cup 1930-31, 31-32, 43-44, 62-63, 74-75, 90-91, 92-93, 98-99, Shared 57-58, 63-64. Football League Division 4 1972-73. Northern Premier League Challenge Cup 1990-91. Northern Premier League Premier Division 1992-93. Conference North 2004-05, 2009-10.

**10 YEAR RECORD**

| 06-07 | 07-08 | 08-09 | 09-10 | 10-11 | 11-12 | 12-13 | 13-14 | 14-15 | 15-16 |
|---|---|---|---|---|---|---|---|---|---|
| Conf 23 | Conf N 4 | Conf N 5 | Conf N 1 | Conf 21 | Conf 7 | Conf 20 | Conf 18 | Conf 19 | Nat 16 |

## SOUTHPORT MATCH RESULTS 2015-16

| Date | Comp | H/A | Opponents | Att: | Result | | Goalscorers | Pos | No. |
|---|---|---|---|---|---|---|---|---|---|
| Aug 8 | Nat Lge | H | Eastleigh | 1017 | L | 0-4 | | 24 | 1 |
| 11 | Nat Lge | A | Macclesfield Town | 1472 | D | 0-0 | | 21 | 2 |
| 15 | Nat Lge | A | Cheltenham Town | 2251 | L | 0-3 | | 22 | 3 |
| 18 | Nat Lge | H | Gateshead | 806 | L | 1-2 | Almond 39 | 23 | 4 |
| 22 | Nat Lge | A | Braintree Town | 504 | L | 0-1 | | 24 | 5 |
| 29 | Nat Lge | A | Barrow | 1343 | L | 0-1 | | 24 | 6 |
| 31 | Nat Lge | H | Altrincham | 1143 | **W** | 3-0 | Jones 12 (pen) Nolan 24 McCarthy 85 | 23 | 7 |
| Sept 5 | Nat Lge | H | Dover Athletic | 957 | D | 0-0 | | 22 | 8 |
| 12 | Nat Lge | A | Forest Green Rovers | 1535 | L | 1-2 | Wright 75 | 23 | 9 |
| 15 | Nat Lge | H | Tranmere Rovers | 2827 | D | 2-2 | Jones 15 Phenix 20 | 22 | 10 |
| 19 | Nat Lge | A | FC Halifax Town | 1211 | D | 2-2 | Brown 35 (og) Stockton 66 | 22 | 11 |
| 22 | Nat Lge | A | Guiseley | 748 | D | 1-1 | Almond 87 | 22 | 12 |
| 26 | Nat Lge | H | Grimsby Town | 1320 | L | 0-4 | | 22 | 13 |
| Oct 3 | Nat Lge | A | Woking | 1510 | **W** | 2-1 | Stockton 8 17 | 21 | 14 |
| 10 | Nat Lge | H | Torquay United | 1104 | L | 0-1 | | 22 | 15 |
| 13 | Nat Lge | H | Chester | 1326 | L | 1-2 | Almond 39 | 22 | 16 |
| 17 | Nat Lge | A | Kidderminster Harriers | 1593 | **W** | 1-0 | Bishop 83 | 22 | 17 |
| **24** | **FAC4Q** | **A** | **Salford City** | **1019** | **L** | **0-1** | | | 18 |
| 31 | Nat Lge | H | Aldershot Town | 845 | D | 1-1 | Foster 54 | 22 | 19 |
| Nov 14 | Nat Lge | H | Cheltenham Town | 947 | L | 0-4 | | 22 | 20 |
| 21 | Nat Lge | A | Welling United | 603 | **W** | 1-0 | Phenix 74 | 21 | 21 |
| 28 | Nat Lge | A | Eastleigh | 1755 | L | 0-1 | | 21 | 22 |
| Dec 5 | Nat Lge | H | Macclesfield Town | 861 | **W** | 3-1 | Almond 27 73 (pen) Thompson 77 | 21 | 23 |
| 8 | Nat Lge | A | Gateshead | 582 | **W** | 1-0 | Almond 56 | 20 | 24 |
| **15** | **FAT1** | **H** | **Worcester City** | **270** | **D** | **0-0** | | | 25 |
| 19 | Nat Lge | H | Bromley | 751 | **W** | 5-3 | Wright 20 Jones 45 Phenix 47 Almond 59 (pen) Allen 72 | 18 | 26 |
| **22** | **FAT1r** | **A** | **Worcester City** | **452** | **W** | **3-2** | **Almond 25 (pen) Wright 66 Thompson 90** | | 27 |
| 26 | Nat Lge | A | Wrexham | 5508 | **W** | 1-0 | Blakeman 19 | 17 | 28 |
| 28 | Nat Lge | H | Barrow | 1528 | **W** | 2-1 | Jones 23 Allen 50 | 15 | 29 |
| Jan 2 | Nat Lge | H | Wrexham | 2148 | **W** | 3-2 | Almond 40 84 (pen) Foster 51 | 14 | 30 |
| 9 | Nat Lge | A | Bromley | 1317 | D | 0-0 | | 14 | 31 |
| **16** | **FAT2** | **A** | **Dover Athletic** | **629** | **L** | **1-2** | **Ryan 25** | | 32 |
| 23 | Nat Lge | A | Chester | 2228 | D | 0-0 | | 15 | 33 |
| 26 | Nat Lge | H | Forest Green Rovers | 707 | L | 0-1 | | 15 | 34 |
| Feb 6 | Nat Lge | A | Tranmere Rovers | 5199 | L | 0-1 | | 15 | 35 |
| 13 | Nat Lge | H | Braintree Town | 827 | D | 1-1 | Almond 57 | 14 | 36 |
| 20 | Nat Lge | A | Lincoln City | 2581 | L | 1-3 | Almond 67 | 16 | 37 |
| 27 | Nat Lge | H | Boreham Wood | 815 | L | 0-3 | | 16 | 38 |
| 29 | Nat Lge | A | Dover Athletic | 588 | **W** | 2-1 | Allen 26 Bishop 73 | 16 | 39 |
| Mar 5 | Nat Lge | H | FC Halifax Town | 1148 | L | 0-1 | | 16 | 40 |
| 8 | Nat Lge | A | Grimsby Town | 3180 | L | 0-1 | | 17 | 41 |
| 12 | Nat Lge | H | Welling United | 746 | D | 3-3 | Phenix 37 Thompson 67 O'Brien 59 | 17 | 42 |
| 19 | Nat Lge | A | Torquay United | 1783 | L | 0-1 | | 17 | 43 |
| 26 | Nat Lge | H | Guiseley | 983 | **W** | 2-0 | Margetts 37 Westcott 66 | 16 | 44 |
| 28 | Nat Lge | A | Altrincham | 1480 | D | 1-1 | Jones 62 | 16 | 45 |
| Apr 2 | Nat Lge | H | Woking | 825 | D | 2-2 | Margetts 76 Westcott 84 | 16 | 46 |
| 9 | Nat Lge | A | Boreham Wood | 434 | **W** | 2-0 | Bishop 10 Browne 83 | 16 | 47 |
| 16 | Nat Lge | H | Lincoln City | 961 | D | 2-2 | Bishop 44 Allen 88 | 16 | 48 |
| 23 | Nat Lge | A | Aldershot Town | 1456 | **W** | 2-1 | Nolan 18 Wright 39 | 15 | 49 |
| 30 | Nat Lge | H | Kidderminster Harriers | 1473 | L | 3-4 | Almond 5 (pen) Phenix 63 Ryan 90 | 16 | 50 |

| GOALSCORERS | Scoring Games | Consec Sco Games | Total |
|---|---|---|---|
| ***2014-15 Brodie*** | | | ***14*** |
| Almond (Louis) | 11 | 2 | 13 |
| Jones | 5 | | 5 |
| Phenix | 5 | | 5 |
| Allen | 4 | | 4 |
| Bishop | 4 | | 4 |
| Wright | 4 | | 4 |
| Stockton | 3 | | 3 |
| Thompson | 3 | | 3 |
| Foster | 2 | | 2 |
| Margetts | 2 | | 2 |
| Nolan | 2 | | 2 |
| Ryan | 2 | | 2 |
| Westcott | 2 | | 2 |
| Blakeman | 1 | | 1 |
| Brown | 1 | | 1 |
| McCarthy | 1 | | 1 |
| O'Brien | 1 | | 1 |
| Opponents | | | 1 |

# SUTTON UNITED

**Chairman:** Bruce Elliott

**Secretary:** Ray Ward (T) 0208 644 4440 (E) honsec@suttonunited.net

**Commercial Manager:** Graham Baker (T/E) 0208 644 4440

**Programme Editor:** Lyall Reynolds (T/E) 0208 644 4440

**Ground Address:** Borough Sports Ground, Gander Green Lane, Sutton, Surrey SM1 2EY

(T) 0208 644 4440 **Manager:** Paul Doswell

## Club Factfile

**Founded:** 1898 **Nickname:** The U's

**Previous Names:** None

**Previous Leagues:** Sutton Junior, Southern Suburban, Athenian 1921-63, Isthmian 1963-86, 91-99, 2000-04, 2008-11, Conference 1999-2000, 04-08

**Club Colours (change):** All amber with chocolate trim (All white with chocolate trim)

**Ground Capacity:** 7,032 **Seats:** 765 **Covered:** 1,250 **Clubhouse:** Yes **Shop:** Yes

**Directions**

Travel along the M25 to junction 8. Then north on the A217 for about 15-20 minutes. Ignoring signs for Sutton itself, stay on the A217 to the traffic lights by the Gander Inn (on the left), turn right into Gander Green Lane. The Borough Sports Ground is about 200 yards up this road on the left hand side, if you reach West Sutton station you have gone too far.

**Previous Grounds:** Western Road, Manor Lane, London Road, The Find

**Record Attendance:** 14,000 v Leeds United - FA Cup 4th Round 24/01/1970

**Record Victory:** 11-1 v Clapton - 1966 and v Leatherhead - 1982-83 both Isthmian League

**Record Defeat:** 0-13 v Barking - Athenian League 1925-26

**Record Goalscorer:** Paul McKinnon - 279

**Record Appearances:** Larry Pritchard - 781 (1965-84)

**Additional Records:** Received £100,000 from AFC Bournemouth for Efan Ekoku 1990

**Honours:**

Athenian League 1927-28, 45-46, 57-58. Isthmian League 1966-67, 84-85, 98-99, 2010-11. National League South 2015-16.
London Senior Cup 1957-58, 82-83. Surrey Senior Cup 1945-46, 64-65, 67-68, 69-70, 79-80, 82-83, 83-84, 84-85, 85-86, 86-87, 87-88, 92-93, 94-95, 98-99, 2002-03. Anglo Italian Cup 1978-79. Bob Lord Trophy 1990-91.

**10 YEAR RECORD**

| 06-07 | 07-08 | 08-09 | 09-10 | 10-11 | 11-12 | 12-13 | 13-14 | 14-15 | 15-16 |
|---|---|---|---|---|---|---|---|---|---|
| Conf S 13 | Conf S 22 | Isth P 5 | Isth P 2 | Isth P 1 | Conf S 4 | Conf S 6 | Conf S 2 | Conf S 15 | Nat S 1 |

# SUTTON UNITED MATCH RESULTS 2015-16

| Date | Comp | H/A | Opponents | Att: | Result | | Goalscorers | Pos | No. |
|---|---|---|---|---|---|---|---|---|---|
| Aug 8 | Nat South | H | Maidstone United | 1307 | L | 0-2 | | 20 | 1 |
| 11 | Nat South | A | Havant & Waterlooville | 647 | W | 2-0 | Fitchett 37 Collins 70 | 12 | 2 |
| 15 | Nat South | A | Dartford | 910 | D | 2-2 | Spillane 36 Collins 85 | 11 | 3 |
| 17 | Nat South | H | Truro City | 746 | D | 2-2 | Fitchett 1 56 | 5 | 4 |
| 22 | Nat South | A | Maidenhead United | 446 | D | 1-1 | Dundas 46 | 14 | 5 |
| 29 | Nat South | H | Wealdstone | 803 | W | 5-2 | Collins 6 Fitchett 22 Spillane 26 Dundas 38 89 | 11 | 6 |
| 31 | Nat South | A | Whitehawk | 307 | L | 0-2 | | 13 | 7 |
| Sept 5 | Nat South | H | Concord Rangers | 730 | D | 2-2 | McAllister 44 Spencer 60 | 12 | 8 |
| 12 | Nat South | H | Gosport Borough | 767 | W | 1-0 | McAllister 23 | 11 | 9 |
| 15 | Nat South | A | Ebbsfleet United | 947 | L | 0-1 | | 12 | 10 |
| 19 | Nat South | A | Weston-s-Mare | 268 | W | 2-0 | Gomis 22 Bolarinwa 33 | 11 | 11 |
| **26** | **FAC2Q** | **A** | **Bishops Stortford** | **347** | **W** | **2-0** | **McAllister 39 Amankwaah 51** | | 12 |
| Oct 3 | Nat South | H | Hemel Hempstead Town | 949 | D | 2-2 | Fitchett 37 31 | 11 | 13 |
| **10** | **FAC3Q** | **A** | **Hemel Hempstead Town** | **707** | **D** | **1-1** | **Stearn 55** | | 14 |
| **12** | **FAC3Q r** | **H** | **Hemel Hempstead Town** | **418** | **W** | **2-1** | **Stearn 45 Wishart 86** | | 15 |
| 17 | Nat South | A | Bath City | 587 | W | 3-1 | Stearn 5 Eastmond 26 McAllister 65 | 10 | 16 |
| **24** | **FAC4Q** | **A** | **Aldershot Town** | **1471** | **L** | **0-1** | | | 17 |
| 31 | Nat South | A | Eastbourne Borough | 477 | D | 1-1 | Bolarinwa 18 | 9 | 18 |
| Nov 2 | Nat South | H | Oxford City | 809 | D | 1-1 | Aezamendi 57 (og) | 8 | 19 |
| 7 | Nat South | H | Hayes & Yeading | 758 | L | 0-1 | | 10 | 20 |
| 14 | Nat South | A | Bishop's Stortford | 349 | W | 2-0 | Dundas 18 Stearn 90 | 6 | 21 |
| 21 | Nat South | H | Havant & Waterlooville | 979 | W | 3-0 | McAllister 24 44 Dundas 80 | 5 | 22 |
| Dec 5 | Nat South | A | Concord Rangers | 307 | W | 3-0 | Dundas 82 Bolarinwa 86 90 | 5 | 23 |
| 12 | Nat South | A | Hayes & Yeading | 217 | W | 3-1 | Fitchett 13 22 Collins 77 | 4 | 24 |
| 19 | Nat South | H | Maidenhead United | 790 | D | 2-2 | Bolarinwa 41 McAllister 78 | 4 | 25 |
| **21** | **FAT3Q** | **H** | **Concord Rangers** | **251** | **W** | **2-0** | **Fitchett 40 Stearn 64** | | 26 |
| 26 | Nat South | H | Basingstoke Town | 932 | W | 2-0 | | 2 | 27 |
| **Jan 4** | **FAT1** | **H** | **Lowestoft Town** | **454** | **W** | **3-1** | **DUNDAS 3 (33 44 68)** | | 28 |
| 9 | Nat South | H | St Albans City | 916 | W | 5-0 | FITCHETT 3 (5 42 49) Stearn 19 Wright 79 | 3 | 29 |
| **16** | **FAT2** | **A** | **Curzon Ashton** | **605** | **W** | **1-0** | **Collins 20** | | 30 |
| 23 | Nat South | H | Dartford | 1075 | W | 2-0 | Fitchett 64 McAlister 70 | 3 | 31 |
| 30 | Nat South | A | Chelmsford City | 856 | W | 2-0 | Fitchett 4 68 | 3 | 32 |
| **Feb 6** | **FAT3** | **H** | **Bognor Regis Town** | **1258** | **D** | **0-0** | | | 33 |
| **9** | **FAT3r** | **A** | **Bognor Regis Town** | **941** | **L** | **1-2** | **Fitchett 58 (pen)** | | 34 |
| 13 | Nat South | H | Bath City | 815 | D | 1-1 | Stearn 2 | 3 | 35 |
| 16 | Nat South | A | Basingstoke Town | 470 | W | 2-1 | Stearn 32 Fitchett 50 (pen) | 3 | 36 |
| 20 | Nat South | A | Hemel Hempstead Town | 373 | D | 2-2 | Bolarinwa 9 Fitchett 57 | 3 | 37 |
| 27 | Nat South | H | Margate | 884 | W | 4-1 | Burge 15 Bolarinwa 35 Gomis 56 (pen) Flitchett 60 | 2 | 38 |
| Mar 5 | Nat South | A | St Albans City | 554 | W | 3-0 | Burge 3 56 Beckwith 62 | 2 | 39 |
| 12 | Nat South | H | Weston-s-Mare | 850 | D | 0-0 | | 3 | 40 |
| 19 | Nat South | A | Gosport Borough | 474 | W | 2-0 | Stearn 18 Wishart 42 | 3 | 41 |
| 21 | Nat South | A | Wealdstone | 631 | W | 2-0 | Gomis 32 (pen) John 81 | 3 | 42 |
| 26 | Nat South | A | Truro City | 750 | W | 2-0 | Stearn 27 Bolarinwa 83 | 3 | 43 |
| 28 | Nat South | H | Whitehawk | 1089 | D | 2-2 | Gomis 63 Fitchett 76 | 3 | 44 |
| Apr 2 | Nat South | H | Eastbourne Borough | 952 | W | 2-1 | Simpemba 54 (og) Gomis 59 | 3 | 45 |
| 5 | Nat South | A | Maidstone United | 3030 | W | 2-1 | Wishart 2 Eastmond 9 | 2 | 46 |
| 9 | Nat South | A | Margate | 576 | W | 4-0 | Bolarinwa 15 Gomis 25 (pen) Amankwaah 86 Wishart 90 | 2 | 47 |
| 11 | Nat South | H | Bishop's Stortford | 1061 | W | 2-0 | Eastmond 39 Collins 87 (pen) | 1 | 48 |
| 16 | Nat South | H | Ebbsfleet United | 3142 | W | 2-0 | Fitchett 25 Gomis 45 (pen) | 1 | 49 |
| 23 | Nat South | H | Chelmsford City | 1545 | W | 2-0 | Fitchett 26 Stearn 40 | 1 | 50 |
| 30 | Nat South | A | Oxford City | 503 | W | 1-0 | Bolarinwa 15 | 1 | 51 |

| GOALSCORERS | Scoring Games | Consec Sco Games | Total | | Scoring Games | Consec Sco Games | Total |
|---|---|---|---|---|---|---|---|
| ***2014-15 Fitchett*** | | | ***6*** | Eastmond | 3 | | 3 |
| Fitchett | 16 | 3 | 22 | Amankwaah | 2 | | 2 |
| Bolarinwa | 10 | 2 | 11 | Spillane | 2 | | 2 |
| Stearn | 11 | 3 | 11 | Beckwith | 1 | | 1 |
| Dundas | 8 | 2 | 10 | John | 1 | | 1 |
| McAllister | 7 | 2 | 8 | Spencer | 1 | | 1 |
| Gomis | 7 | | 7 | Wright | 1 | | 1 |
| Collins | 6 | 2 | 6 | Opponents | | | 2 |
| Wishart | 4 | | 4 | | | | |
| Burge | 2 | | 3 | | | | |

# TORQUAY UNITED

**Chairman:** David Phillips
**Secretary:** 01803 328 666 (T) (E) secretary@torquayunited.com
**Commercial Manager:** (T/E) commercial@torquayunited.com
**Programme Editor:** Andy Poole (T/E) andyppoole@aol.com
**Ground Address:** Plainmoor, Torquay, Devon TQ1 3PS
(T) 01803 328 666 **Manager:** Kevin Nicholson - 28.09.15

## Club Factfile

**Founded:** 1899 **Nickname:**
**Previous Names:** Torquay United & Ellacombe merged to form Torquay Town 1910, then merged with Babbacombe to form Torquay Utd in 1921
**Previous Leagues:** Western 1921-27. Football League 1927-2007, 09-14. Conference 2007-09.

**Club Colours (change):** All yellow (All white)

**Ground Capacity:** 6,500 **Seats:** Yes **Covered:** Yes **Clubhouse:** Yes **Shop:** Yes

**Directions**

BY ROAD FROM THE NORTH/EAST (A30/M5): At the junction of the A30/M5 take A38 signposted Plymouth. After 3 miles take left fork on A380 signposted Torquay. After a further 10 miles at Penn Inn roundabout take 2nd exit to Torquay. At Kerswell Gardens take the A3022 to Torquay. At Lowes Bridge turn left into Hele Rd (B3199) and continue until a double roundabout is reached. Turn left and immediately right into Westhill Road. Take the fifth turning on the right (St Marychurch Rd) then second left into St Paul's Rd. Continue on into St Paul's Crescent and the ground is on the left. Main entrance from Westlands Lane.
BY ROAD FROM THE WEST (A38): At Goodstone Junction on the A38 take exit marked Newton Abbot and join the A383. After 4.5 miles, at the Dyrons roundabout, take second exit on to the A382 signposted Totnes. At traffic lights turn right (A382) on the inner ring road until its junction with the A381. Turn left on the A381 signposted Torquay until the Penn Inn roundabout. Take the third exit signposted A380 to Torquay and follow the same directions as from the North/East.

**Previous Grounds:** Recreation Ground. Cricketfield Road > 1910.

**Record Attendance:** 21,908 v Huddersfield Town, FA Cup 4th Rnd, 29/01/1955.
**Record Victory:** 9-0 v Swindon Town, Division Three South, 08/03/1952
**Record Defeat:** 2-10 v Fulham, Division Three South, 07/09/1931
**Record Goalscorer:** Sammy Collins - 219 in 379 games (1948-58) Also scored 40 during the 1955-56 season.
**Record Appearances:** Dennis Lewis - 443 (1947-59)
**Additional Records:** Received £650,000 from Crewe for Rodney Jack (July 1998)

**Honours:**
**League:** Torquay & District 1909-09. Plymouth & District 1911-12. Southern Western Section 1926-27.
**FA/County Cups:** Devon Senior Cup 1910-11, 21-22. Devon Bowl/Devon St Luke's Bowl 1933-34, 34-35, 36-37,45-46, 47-48, 48-49, 54-55 (shared), 57-58, 60-61, 69-70, 70-71, 71-72, 95-96 (shared), 97-98, 2006-07.

### 10 YEAR RECORD

| 06-07 | 07-08 | 08-09 | 09-10 | 10-11 | 11-12 | 12-13 | 13-14 | 14-15 | 15-16 |
|---|---|---|---|---|---|---|---|---|---|
| FL 2 24 | Conf 3 | Conf 4 | FL 2 17 | FL 2 7 | FL 2 5 | FL 2 19 | FL 2 24 | Conf 13 | Nat 18 |

## TORQUAY UNITED MATCH RESULTS 2015-16

| Date | Comp | H/A | Opponents | Att: | Result | | Goalscorers | Pos | No. |
|---|---|---|---|---|---|---|---|---|---|
| Aug 8 | Nat Lge | H | Macclesfield Town | 2066 | **W** | 1-0 | Fisher 61 | 8 | 1 |
| 11 | Nat Lge | A | Wrexham | 4734 | L | 1-3 | Carnichael 42 | 14 | 2 |
| 15 | Nat Lge | A | FC Halifax Town | 1199 | **W** | 3-2 | MacDonald 20 Hurst 31 Fisher 63 | 9 | 3 |
| 18 | Nat Lge | H | Woking | 1936 | L | 0-1 | | 12 | 4 |
| 22 | Nat Lge | A | Grimsby Town | 4290 | D | 2-2 | Quigley 19 Robinson 33 (og) | 11 | 5 |
| 29 | Nat Lge | H | Cheltenham Town | 2018 | L | 0-3 | | 14 | 6 |
| 31 | Nat Lge | A | Eastleigh | 1819 | L | 2-3 | Hurst 84 Fisher 90 | 17 | 7 |
| Sept 5 | Nat Lge | H | Guiseley | 1558 | D | 1-1 | Geohaghon 34 | 19 | 8 |
| 12 | Nat Lge | A | Welling United | 659 | D | 1-1 | Butler | 18 | 9 |
| 15 | Nat Lge | A | Kidderminster Harriers | 1493 | D | 2-2 | Hurst 15 68 | 18 | 10 |
| 19 | Nat Lge | H | Bromley | 1653 | L | 3-7 | Hurst 5 Marsh 45 85 | 18 | 11 |
| 22 | Nat Lge | H | Boreham Wood | 1725 | L | 1-2 | Fisher 59 | 21 | 12 |
| 26 | Nat Lge | A | Lincoln City | 2467 | L | 0-2 | | 21 | 13 |
| Oct 3 | Nat Lge | H | Aldershot Town | 1946 | L | 0-2 | | 22 | 14 |
| 6 | Nat Lge | H | Dover Athletic | 1210 | L | 2-3 | Hurst 39 87 | 23 | 15 |
| 10 | Nat Lge | A | Southport | 1104 | **W** | 1-0 | Fisher 2 | 21 | 16 |
| 13 | Nat Lge | A | Woking | 1556 | D | 2-2 | Richards 47 Marsh 77 (pen) | 21 | 17 |
| 17 | Nat Lge | H | Grimsby Town | 2003 | D | 1-1 | Marsh 38 | 21 | 18 |
| **24** | **FAC4Q** | **A** | **Basingstoke Town** | **792** | **L** | **0-3** | | | 19 |
| 31 | Nat Lge | A | Altrincham | 1060 | D | 1-1 | Marsh 24 | 21 | 20 |
| Nov 14 | Nat Lge | A | Barrow | 1119 | L | 0-1 | | 21 | 21 |
| 21 | Nat Lge | H | Lincoln City | 1752 | L | 1-3 | Butler 75 | 22 | 22 |
| 28 | Nat Lge | A | Braintree Town | 773 | D | 0-0 | | 22 | 23 |
| Dec 5 | Nat Lge | H | Welling United | 1512 | L | 0-1 | | 22 | 24 |
| **13** | **FAT1** | **H** | **Chesham United** | **1130** | **D** | **0-0** | | | 25 |
| **15** | **FAT1r** | **A** | **Chesham United** | **123** | **W** | **2-0** | **Wright 25 27** | | 26 |
| 19 | Nat Lge | A | Chester | 2160 | L | 1-4 | Wright 68 | 23 | 27 |
| 26 | Nat Lge | H | Forest Green Rovers | 2051 | **W** | 4-1 | Marsh 22 37 Berry 83 Wright 88 | 23 | 28 |
| 28 | Nat Lge | A | Cheltenham Town | 3781 | L | 0-1 | | 23 | 29 |
| Jan 1 | Nat Lge | A | Forest Green Rovers | 1907 | L | 1-3 | Verma 48 | 23 | 30 |
| **16** | **FAT2** | **H** | **Wrexham** | **1361** | **W** | **1-0** | **Murombedzi 80** | | 31 |
| 23 | Nat Lge | H | Gateshead | 721 | L | 0-2 | | 23 | 32 |
| 30 | Nat Lge | A | Tranmere R | 5053 | L | 1-2 | Harrad 82 | 23 | 33 |
| **Feb9** | **FAT3** | **H** | **Macclesfield Town** | **838** | **D** | **3-3** | **Rees 32 Butler 60 Allen 83** | | 34 |
| **15** | **FAT 3r** | **A** | **Macclesfield Town** | **566** | **W** | **1-0** | **Smith 67** | | 35 |
| 20 | Nat Lge | A | Boreham Wood | 555 | **W** | 1-0 | Blissett 58 | 24 | 36 |
| 23 | Nat Lge | H | Welling United | 1341 | **W** | 2-0 | Smith 61 Allen 70 | 23 | 37 |
| **27** | **FAT4** | **A** | **Bognor Regis Town** | **1821** | **L** | **0-1** | | | 38 |
| Mar 2 | Nat Lge | A | Macclesfield Town | 1082 | **W** | 2-1 | Blissett 20 48 | 23 | 39 |
| 5 | Nat Lge | H | Kidderminster Harriers | 2021 | **W** | 3-2 | Smith 10 81 Blissett 42 | 22 | 40 |
| 8 | Nat Lge | H | Braintree Town | 1462 | D | 0-0 | | 22 | 41 |
| 12 | Nat Lge | A | Aldershot Town | 1771 | D | 0-0 | | 22 | 42 |
| 15 | Nat Lge | H | FC Halifax Town | 1664 | D | 0-0 | | 22 | 43 |
| 19 | Nat Lge | H | Southport | 1783 | **W** | 1-0 | Blissett 80 | 19 | 44 |
| 26 | Nat Lge | A | Dover Athletic | 1367 | L | 0-5 | | 21 | 45 |
| 28 | Nat Lge | H | Eastleigh | 2081 | L | 0-1 | | 22 | 46 |
| Apr 2 | Nat Lge | A | Gateshead | 785 | **W** | 2-1 | Allen 49 Wright 71 | 20 | 47 |
| 5 | Nat Lge | H | Chester | 1831 | **W** | 2-0 | Blissett 3 Allen 90 | 17 | 48 |
| 9 | Nat Lge | H | Tranmere Rovers | 2264 | L | 0-1 | | 18 | 49 |
| 12 | Nat Lge | H | Altrincham | 1995 | **W** | 2-0 | Young 17 Harrad 59 | 17 | 50 |
| 16 | Nat Lge | A | Bromley | 2080 | **W** | 2-0 | MacDonald 11 Richards 85 | 17 | 51 |
| 23 | Nat Lge | H | Barrow | 2874 | D | 2-2 | Richards 61 Blisset 81 | 18 | 52 |
| 30 | Nat Lge | A | Guiseley | 1915 | L | 3-4 | Blissett 53 Ajala 60 Harrad 77 | 18 | 53 |

| GOALSCORERS | Scoring Games | Consec Sco Games | Total |
|---|---|---|---|
| ***2014-15 Bowman*** | | | ***18*** |
| Blissett | 7 | | 8 |
| Hurst | 5 | 2 | 7 |
| Marsh | 5 | 2 | 7 |
| Allen | 4 | | 5 |
| Fisher | 5 | | 5 |
| Wright | 5 | | 5 |
| Smith | 3 | | 4 |
| Butler | 3 | | 3 |
| Harrad | 3 | | 3 |
| MacDonald | 2 | | 2 |
| Richards | 2 | | 2 |
| Ajala | 1 | | 1 |
| Berry | 1 | | 1 |
| Carmichael | 1 | | 1 |
| Geohaghon | 1 | | 1 |
| Murombedzi | 1 | | 1 |
| Quigley | 1 | | 1 |
| Rees | 1 | | 1 |
| Verma | 1 | | 1 |
| Young | 1 | | 1 |
| Opponents | | | 1 |

# TRANMERE ROVERS

**Chairman:** Mark Palios

**Secretary:** Tim Roberts (T) 03330 144 452 (E) timr@tranmererovers.co.uk

**Commercial Manager:** (T/E) commercial@tranmererovers.co.uk

**Programme Editor:** Tony Coombes (T/E) 0151 609 3334

**Ground Address:** Prenton Park, Prenton Road West, Birkenhead, Merseyside, CH42 9PY

(T) 03330 144 452 **Manager:** Gary Brabin

## Club Factfile

**Founded:** 1884 **Nickname:** Superwhite Army / Rovers

**Previous Names:** Belmont FC 1884-85.

**Previous Leagues:** West Lancashire. Lancashire Combination. Cheshire County. Central. Football League 1921-2015.

**Club Colours (change):** All white (Yellow/navy/yellow)

**Ground Capacity:** 16,567 **Seats:** Yes **Covered:** Yes **Clubhouse:** Yes **Shop:** Yes

**Directions**

North: From Liverpool city centre, travel through the Kingsway (Wallasey) Mersey Tunnel and after the toll booths (there is a £1.70 charge for cars), continue on the M53 to Junction 3. Take the first exit (signposted Birkenhead) and continue for approximately 1 mile passing Sainsbury's on the left hand side (keep in right hand lane). Turn right at the traffic lights at the Halfway House (pub), continue for 500 yards to the next set of traffic lights and turn left into Prenton Road West. The ground appears in front of you. South / East: M6, M56 and M53 to J4. Take the fourth exit from the roundabout onto the B5151 (Mount Road). Continue for 2.5 miles when Mount Road becomes Storeton Road and turn right onto Prenton Road West at traffic lights. The ground is on the righthand side in 200 yards.

**Previous Grounds:** Steeles Field 1884-87. Ravenshaws Field 1887-1920.

**Record Attendance:** 24,424, for an FA Cup tie against Stoke City on 5 February 1972

**Record Victory:** 13-4, against Oldham Athletic, on 26 December 1935

**Record Defeat:**

**Record Goalscorer:** Ian Muir - 180

**Record Appearances:** Ray Mathias - 637

**Additional Records:** 40 goals were scored in one season by both Bunny Bell (1934–35) and John Aldridge (1991–92)

**Honours:**

Lancashire Combination 1913-14, 18-19. League Division Three North 1937-38.

Welsh FACup 1934-35. Football League trophy 1989-90.

### 10 YEAR RECORD

| 06-07 | 07-08 | 08-09 | 09-10 | 10-11 | 11-12 | 12-13 | 13-14 | 14-15 | 15-16 |
|---|---|---|---|---|---|---|---|---|---|
| FL 1 9 | FL 1 11 | FL 1 7 | FL 1 19 | FL 1 17 | FL 1 12 | FL 1 11 | FL 1 21 | FL 2 24 | Nat 6 |

## TRANMERE ROVERS MATCH RESULTS 2015-16

| Date | Comp | H/A | Opponents | Att: | Result | | Goalscorers | Pos | No. |
|---|---|---|---|---|---|---|---|---|---|
| Aug 8 | Nat Lge | H | Woking | 5583 | W | 1-0 | Harris 58 | 9 | 1 |
| 11 | Nat Lge | A | Gateshead | 1589 | W | 4-1 | Ridehalgh 30 Sutton 40 Ihiekwe 44 Hil 66 | 2 | 2 |
| 15 | Nat Lge | A | Braintree Town | 838 | D | 0-0 | | 4 | 3 |
| 18 | Nat Lge | H | FC Halifax Town | 5235 | W | 1-0 | Mangan 74 | 2 | 4 |
| 22 | Nat Lge | H | Boreham Wood | 4,832 | L | 0-2 | | 5 | 5 |
| 29 | Nat Lge | A | Altrincham | 2,460 | L | 1-2 | Maynard 85 | 8 | 6 |
| 31 | Nat Lge | H | Kidderminster Harriers | 4,622 | D | 2-2 | Hogan 20 Mangan 26 | 9 | 7 |
| Sept 5 | Nat Lge | A | Welling United | 1,012 | D | 1-1 | Maynard 46 | 10 | 8 |
| 12 | Nat Lge | H | Chester | 7,433 | W | 2-0 | Hogan 6 Norwood 37 | 8 | 9 |
| 15 | Nat Lge | A | Southport | 2,827 | D | 2-2 | Harris 46 Norwood 57 | 8 | 10 |
| 19 | Nat Lge | A | Grimsby Town | 4,638 | D | 1-1 | Blissett 53 | 8 | 11 |
| 22 | Nat Lge | H | Aldershot Town | 4126 | W | 3-1 | Norwood 45 Mekki 69 Mangan 90 | 7 | 12 |
| 26 | Nat Lge | A | Cheltenham Town | 2556 | W | 1-0 | Mangan 90 | 6 | 13 |
| Oct 3 | Nat Lge | H | Bromley | 4817 | W | 4-0 | Mangan 28 80 (pen) Margetts 52 90 | 3 | 14 |
| 6 | Nat Lge | A | Wrexham | 6707 | D | 2-2 | Maynard 25 Mangan 52 | 3 | 15 |
| 10 | Nat Lge | H | Eastleigh | 5133 | L | 1-2 | Jennings 79 | 5 | 16 |
| 13 | Nat Lge | H | Barrow | 4624 | L | 0-1 | | 7 | 17 |
| 17 | Nat Lge | A | Forest Green Rovers | 2133 | W | 2-0 | Norwood 5 22 | 5 | 18 |
| **24** | **FAC4Q** | **H** | **Lincoln City** | **3729** | **D** | **0-0** | | | 19 |
| **27** | **FAC4Qr** | **A** | **Lincoln City** | **2380** | **L** | **0-2** | | | 20 |
| 31 | Nat Lge | H | Dover Athletic | 4486 | L | 0-1 | | 10 | 21 |
| Nov 14 | Nat Lge | A | Lincoln City | 3176 | L | 0-1 | | 10 | 22 |
| 21 | Nat Lge | H | Guiseley | 4352 | W | 2-1 | Norwood 45 90 (pen) | 10 | 23 |
| 24 | Nat Lge | A | Woking | 1477 | L | 1-4 | Norwood 90 | 10 | 24 |
| 28 | Nat Lge | A | Boreham Wood | 640 | D | 0-0 | | 10 | 25 |
| Dec 5 | Nat Lge | H | Braintree Town | 4224 | L | 1-2 | Mekki 3 | 12 | 26 |
| **12** | **FAT1** | **H** | **Wrexham** | **3397** | **L** | **2-4** | **Norwood 45 82** | | 27 |
| 19 | Nat Lge | A | FC Halifax Town | 1684 | D | 1-1 | Norwood 40 | 12 | 28 |
| 26 | Nat Lge | A | Macclesfield Town | 2037 | W | 2-1 | McNulty 5 Ihiekwe 77 | 11 | 29 |
| 28 | Nat Lge | H | Altrincham | 5,414 | W | 1-0 | Norwood 28 | 8 | 30 |
| Jan 2 | Nat Lge | H | Macclesfield Town | 4923 | L | 0-1 | | 9 | 31 |
| 9 | Nat Lge | A | Barrow | 1766 | W | 4-3 | Mekki 18 (pen) Maynard 89 Hughes 90 Kirby 90 | 8 | 32 |
| 23 | Nat Lge | A | Bromley | 2219 | W | 1-0 | Vaughan 54 | 8 | 33 |
| 30 | Nat Lge | H | Torquay United | 5053 | W | 2-1 | Taylor-Fletcher 37 Norwood 79 | 5 | 34 |
| Feb 6 | Nat Lge | H | Southport | 5199 | W | 1-0 | Norwood 63 (pen) | 4 | 35 |
| 13 | Nat Lge | A | Aldershot Town | 1882 | D | 0-0 | | 4 | 36 |
| 20 | Nat Lge | H | Cheltenham Town | 5418 | L | 0-1 | | 4 | 37 |
| 27 | Nat Lge | A | Chester | 3494 | W | 1-0 | Norwood 45 (pen) | 5 | 38 |
| Mar 5 | Nat Lge | H | Gateshead | 4668 | W | 3-1 | Norwood 26 (pen) 46 (pen) Higden 53 | 5 | 39 |
| 8 | Nat Lge | A | Guiseley | 1147 | D | 2-2 | Kirby 58 Atkinson 35 (og) | 5 | 40 |
| 12 | Nat Lge | A | Dover Athletic | 1460 | D | 0-0 | | 5 | 41 |
| 19 | Nat Lge | H | Forest Green Rovers | 5073 | D | 1-1 | Harris 48 | 5 | 42 |
| 24 | Nat Lge | H | Lincoln City | 5366 | W | 3-2 | Norwood 38 (pen) Kirby 45 Mekki 87 | 5 | 43 |
| 26 | Nat Lge | A | Kidderminster Harriers | 2744 | W | 2-0 | Norwood 14 90 | 4 | 44 |
| Apr 2 | Nat Lge | A | Welling United | 5173 | L | 1-2 | Vaughan 18 | 5 | 45 |
| 9 | Nat Lge | A | Torquay United | 2264 | W | 1-0 | Higdon 59 | 5 | 46 |
| 16 | Nat Lge | H | Wrexham | 7541 | L | 1-2 | Norwood 78 (pen) | 7 | 47 |
| 23 | Nat Lge | A | Eastleigh | 3269 | W | 1-0 | Norwood 87 | 9 | 48 |
| 30 | Nat Lge | H | Grimsby Town | 6637 | W | 1-0 | Jennings 22 | 6 | 49 |
| | | | | | | | | | 50 |

| GOALSCORERS | Scoring Games | Consec Sco Games | Total | | Scoring Games | Consec Sco Games | Total |
|---|---|---|---|---|---|---|---|
| Norwood | 17 | 2 | 22 | Margetts | 2 | | 2 |
| Mangan | 6 | 4 | 7 | Vaughan | 2 | | 2 |
| Maynard | 4 | | 4 | Blissett | 1 | | 1 |
| Mekki | 4 | | 4 | Hill | 1 | | 1 |
| Harris | 3 | | 3 | Hughes | 1 | | 1 |
| Kirby | 3 | | 3 | McNulty | 1 | | 1 |
| Higden | 2 | | 2 | Ridehalgh | 1 | | 1 |
| Hogan | 2 | | 2 | Sutton | 1 | | 1 |
| Ihiekwe | 2 | | 2 | Taylor-Fletcher | 1 | | 1 |
| Jennings | 2 | | 2 | Opponents | | | 1 |

# WOKING

**Chairman:** Rosemary Johnson
**Secretary:** Jane Spong (T) 01483 772 470 (E) community@wokingfc.co.uk
**Commercial Manager:** Elliot Machin (T/E) elliot.machin@wokingfc.co.uk
**Programme Editor:** Anthony Scott (T/E) 07769 114 476
**Ground Address:** Kingfield Stadium, Kingfield Road, Woking, Surrey GU22 9AA
(T) 01483 772 470 **Manager:** Garry Hill

## Club Factfile

**Founded:** 1889 **Nickname:** The Cards
**Previous Names:** None
**Previous Leagues:** Isthmian 1911-92.

**Club Colours (change):** Red and white halves/black/white (All yellow)

**Ground Capacity:** 6,000 **Seats:** 2,500 **Covered:** 3,900 **Clubhouse:** Yes **Shop:** Yes

**Directions**
Exit M25 Junction 10 and follow A3 towards Guildford. Leave at next junction onto B2215 through Ripley and join A247 to Woking. Alternatively exit M25 junction 11 and follow A320 to Woking Town Centre. The ground is on the outskirts of Woking opposite the Leisure Centre.

**Previous Grounds:** Wheatsheaf, Ive Lane (pre 1923)

**Record Attendance:** 6,000 v Swansea City - FA Cup 1978-79 and v Coventry City - FA Cup 1996-97
**Record Victory:** 17-4 v Farnham - 1912-13
**Record Defeat:** 0-16 v New Crusaders - 1905-06
**Record Goalscorer:** Charlie Mortimore - 331 (1953-65)
**Record Appearances:** Brian Finn - 564 (1962-74)
**Additional Records:** Paid £60,000 to Crystal Palace for Chris Sharpling
Received £150,000 from Bristol Rovers for Steve Foster
**Honours:**
Surrey Senior Cup 1912-13, 26-27, 55-56, 56-57, 71-72, 90-91, 93-94, 95-96, 99-2000, 2003-04, 2011-12, 2013-14. FA Amateur Cup 1957-58.
Isthmian League Cup 1990-91, Premier Division 1991-92. FA Trophy 1993-94, 94-95, 96-97.
Vauxhall Championship Shield 1994-95. GLS Conference Cup 2004-05. Conference South 2011-12.

### 10 YEAR RECORD

| 06-07 | 07-08 | 08-09 | 09-10 | 10-11 | 11-12 | 12-13 | 13-14 | 14-15 | 15-16 |
|---|---|---|---|---|---|---|---|---|---|
| Conf 15 | Conf 17 | Conf 21 | Conf S 5 | Conf S 5 | Conf S 1 | Conf 12 | Conf 9 | Conf 7 | Nat 12 |

## WOKING MATCH RESULTS 2015-16

| Date | Comp | H/A | Opponents | Att: | Result | | Goalscorers | Pos | No. |
|---|---|---|---|---|---|---|---|---|---|
| Aug 8 | Nat Lge | A | Tranmere Rovers | 5583 | L | 0-1 | | 21 | 1 |
| 11 | Nat Lge | H | Bromley | 1570 | W | 2-0 | Goddard 36 50 | 8 | 2 |
| 15 | Nat Lge | H | Altrincham | 1297 | W | 2-0 | Sole 32 Holman 75 | 7 | 3 |
| 18 | Nat Lge | A | Torquay United | 1936 | W | 1-0 | Yakubu 90 | 4 | 4 |
| 22 | Nat Lge | H | Chester | 1503 | W | 5-2 | Goddard 24 (pen) Holman 47 Daniel 53 Jones 76 Patty 90 | 2 | 5 |
| 29 | Nat Lge | A | Boreham Wood | 601 | D | 1-1 | Daniel 40 | 4 | 6 |
| 31 | Nat Lge | H | Welling United | 1675 | W | 2-0 | Goddard 62 Keohane 78 | 3 | 7 |
| Sept 5 | Nat Lge | A | Macclesfield Town | 1285 | L | 1-2 | Jones 86 | 3 | 8 |
| 12 | Nat Lge | A | Guiseley | 643 | D | 4-4 | Goddard 8 13 Saah 45 Holman 75 | 5 | 9 |
| 15 | Nat Lge | H | Forest Green Rovers | 1775 | W | 2-1 | Goddard 43 Keohane 70 | 4 | 10 |
| 19 | Nat Lge | H | Cheltenham Town | 2035 | L | 0-1 | | 5 | 11 |
| 22 | Nat Lge | A | Braintree Town | 652 | L | 1-2 | Murtagh 67 | 6 | 12 |
| 25 | Nat Lge | A | Dover Athletic | 864 | L | 0-2 | | 11 | 13 |
| Oct 3 | Nat Lge | H | Southport | 1510 | L | 1-2 | Murtagh 78 | 15 | 14 |
| 10 | Nat Lge | A | FC Halifax Town | 1155 | W | 3-0 | Holman 11 60 Goddard 58 | 12 | 15 |
| 13 | Nat Lge | H | Torquay United | 1556 | D | 2-2 | Daniel 2 Holman 85 | 13 | 16 |
| 17 | Nat Lge | H | Wrexham | 1778 | L | 0-1 | | 16 | 17 |
| **24** | **FAC4Q** | **A** | **Maidenhead United** | **867** | **L** | **0-3** | | | 18 |
| 31 | Nat Lge | A | Kidderminster Harriers | 1449 | L | 0-1 | | 16 | 19 |
| 10 | Nat Lge | H | Braintree Town | 1182 | D | 1-1 | Goddard 78 | 16 | 20 |
| 14 | Nat Lge | H | Macclesfield Town | 1324 | L | 2-5 | Holman 74 Jones 86 | 16 | 21 |
| 21 | Nat Lge | A | Chester | 1837 | W | 2-1 | Holman 15 Goddard 90 | 15 | 22 |
| 24 | Nat Lge | H | Tranmere Rovers | 1477 | W | 4-1 | Holman 27 55 Goddard 40 Quigley 73 | 13 | 23 |
| 28 | Nat Lge | A | Barrow | 1115 | L | 1-2 | Jones 48 | 13 | 24 |
| Dec 5 | Nat Lge | H | Lincoln City | 1432 | W | 3-1 | Holman 6 68 Quigley 40 | 11 | 25 |
| **12** | **FAT1** | **A** | **Boreham Wood** | **275** | **W** | **2-1** | **Saah 63 Sole 90** | | 26 |
| 19 | Nat Lge | A | Gateshead | 573 | W | 5-1 | Holman 3 41 Andrade 68 Robinson 77 Quigley 90 | 10 | 27 |
| 26 | Nat Lge | A | Aldershot Town | 3150 | W | 1-0 | Goddard 40 | 9 | 28 |
| 28 | Nat Lge | H | Boreham Wood | 2097 | D | 0-0 | | 9 | 29 |
| Jan 2 | Nat Lge | H | Aldershot Town | 3708 | W | 2-1 | Quigley 26 Goddard 45 | 7 | 30 |
| 9 | Nat Lge | A | Wrexham | 4030 | W | 3-1 | Taylor 13 (og) Quigley 50 Andrade 83 | | 31 |
| **16** | **FAT2** | **H** | **Maidenhead United** | **1006** | **W** | **6-1** | **Sole 47 Murtagh 61 66 Massey 8 (og) Quigley 64 Arthur 90** | | 32 |
| 23 | Nat Lge | H | FC Halifax Town | 1484 | D | 1-1 | Andrade 34 | 6 | 33 |
| 25 | Nat Lge | A | Altrincham | 826 | L | 1-3 | Sole 57 | 8 | 34 |
| 30 | Nat Lge | H | Barrow | 1713 | D | 2-2 | Goddard 21 Sole 45 | 6 | 35 |
| **Feb 6** | **FAT3** | **H** | **Oxford City** | **923** | **W** | **1-0** | **Quigley 40** | | 36 |
| 13 | Nat Lge | H | Guiseley | 1182 | L | 0-1 | | 9 | 37 |
| 20 | Nat Lge | A | Bromley | 1227 | L | 1-2 | Goddard 6 | 11 | 38 |
| 23 | Nat Lge | A | Grimsby Town | 2874 | L | 1-3 | Sole 34 | 11 | 39 |
| **27** | **FAT4** | **A** | **Grimsby Town** | **1675** | **L** | **0-2** | | | 40 |
| Mar 5 | Nat Lge | H | Dover Athletic | 1305 | L | 0-1 | | 11 | 41 |
| 8 | Nat Lge | A | Eastleigh | 1630 | L | 1-2 | Jones 25 | 12 | 42 |
| 12 | Nat Lge | A | Cheltenham Town | 2951 | L | 0-4 | | 13 | 43 |
| 26 | Nat Lge | H | Kidderminster Harriers | 1730 | D | 1-1 | Carr 14 | 13 | 44 |
| 28 | Nat Lge | A | Welling United | 550 | L | 1-2 | Gayle 55 (og) | 14 | 45 |
| Apr 2 | Nat Lge | A | Southport | 825 | D | 2-2 | Butcher 37 47 | 14 | 46 |
| 9 | Nat Lge | H | Gateshead | 1005 | D | 1-1 | Robinson 31 | 15 | 47 |
| 16 | Nat Lge | A | Forest Green Rovers | 1605 | W | 2-1 | Carr 69 (pen) Norman 90 | 14 | 48 |
| 19 | Nat Lge | H | Grimsby Town | 1394 | L | 1-3 | Andrade 70 | 14 | 49 |
| 23 | Nat Lge | A | Lincoln City | 2518 | W | 3-2 | Murtagh 20 Andrade 22 Goddard 87 | 14 | 50 |
| 30 | Nat Lge | H | Eastleigh | 1853 | W | 2-1 | Murtagh 13 Goddard 15 | 12 | 51 |

| GOALSCORERS | Scoring Games | Consec Sco Games | Total | | Scoring Games | Consec Sco Games | Total |
|---|---|---|---|---|---|---|---|
| ***2014-15 Rendell*** | | | ***24*** | Carr | 2 | | 2 |
| Goddard | 15 | 2 | 17 | Keohane | 2 | | 2 |
| Holman | 10 | 3 | 14 | Robinson | 2 | | 2 |
| Quigley | 7 | | 7 | Saah | 2 | | 2 |
| Murtagh | 6 | | 6 | Arthur | 1 | | 1 |
| Sole | 6 | | 6 | Norman | 1 | | 1 |
| Andrade | 5 | | 5 | Patty | 1 | | 1 |
| Jones | 5 | | 5 | Yakubu | 1 | | 1 |
| Daniel | 3 | | 3 | Opponents | | | 3 |
| Butcher | 1 | | 2 | | | | |

# WREXHAM

**Chairman:** Don Bircham (Chief Exe)
**Secretary:** Geraint Parry **(T)** 01978 891 864 **(E)** geraint.parry@wrexhamfc.tv
**Commercial Manager:** Geoff Scott **(T/E)** Geoff.Scott@wrexhamfc.tv
**Programme Editor:** **(T/E)**
**Ground Address:** Racecourse Ground, Mold road, Wrexham LL11 2AN
**(T)** 01978 891 864 **Manager:** Gary Mills

## Club Factfile

**Founded:** 1872 **Nickname:** The Robins
**Previous Names:** Wrexham Athletic for the 1882-83 season only
**Previous Leagues:** The Combination 1890-94, 1896-1906, Welsh League 1894-96, Birmingham & District 1906-21, Football League 1921-2008

**Club Colours (change):** Red/white/red (Yellow/yellow/blue)

**Ground Capacity:** 15,500 **Seats:** 10,100 **Covered:** 15,500 **Clubhouse:** Yes **Shop:** Yes

**Directions**
From Wrexham by-pass (A483) exit at Mold junction (A451).
Follow signs for Town Centre and football ground is half a mile on the left hand side.

**Previous Grounds:** Rhosddu Recreation Ground during the 1881-82 and 1882-83 seasons.

**Record Attendance:** 34,445 v Manchester United - FA Cup 4th Round 26/01/57
**Record Victory:** 10-1 v Hartlepool United - Division Four 03/03/62
**Record Defeat:** 0-9 v v Brentford - Division Three
**Record Goalscorer:** Tommy Bamford - 201 (1928-34)
**Record Appearances:** Arfon Griffiths - 592 (1959-79)
**Additional Records:** Paid £800,000 to Birmingham City for Bryan Hughes March 1997
Received £210,000 from Liverpool for Joey Jones October 1978
**Honours:**
Welsh FA Cup 1877-78, 81-82, 92-93, 96-97, 1902-03, 04-05, 08-09, 09-10, 10-11, 13-14, 14-15, 20-21, 23-24, 24-25, 30-31, 56-57, 57-58, 59-60, 71-72, 74-75, 77-78, 85-86, 94-95. Welsh Lge 1894-95, 95-96. Combination 1900-01, 01-02, 02-03, 04-05. Football Lge Div. 3 1977-78. FAW Prem. Cup 1997-98, 99-2000, 00-01, 02-03, 03-04. F. Lge Trophy 2004-05. FA Trophy 2012-13.

**10 YEAR RECORD**

| 06-07 | 07-08 | 08-09 | 09-10 | 10-11 | 11-12 | 12-13 | 13-14 | 14-15 | 15-16 |
|---|---|---|---|---|---|---|---|---|---|
| FL 2 19 | FL 2 24 | Conf 10 | Conf 11 | Conf 4 | Conf 2 | Conf 5 | Conf 17 | Conf 11 | Nat 8 |

## WREXHAM MATCH RESULTS 2015-16

| Date | Comp | H/A | Opponents | Att: | Result | | Goalscorers | Pos | No. |
|---|---|---|---|---|---|---|---|---|---|
| Aug 8 | Nat Lge | A | Bromley | 2083 | L | 1-3 | York 19 | 23 | 1 |
| 11 | Nat Lge | H | Torquay United | 4734 | W | 3-1 | Vose 57 Jennings 64 Gray 80 (pen) | 10 | 2 |
| 15 | Nat Lge | H | Aldershot Town | 4951 | W | 3-0 | York 20 Gray 52 Vose 90 (pen) | 6 | 3 |
| 18 | Nat Lge | A | Kidderminster Harriers | 2620 | W | 3-1 | M.Smith 20 Newton 55 A.Smith 90 | 3 | 4 |
| 22 | Nat Lge | H | Welling United | 5277 | W | 1-0 | Vose 90 | 3 | 5 |
| 29 | Nat Lge | H | F.C.Halifax Town | 5662 | W | 3-1 | Vidal 8 Vose 24 York 55 | 3 | 6 |
| 31 | Nat Lge | A | Cheltenham T | 2827 | L | 1-2 | Gray 54 | 6 | 7 |
| Sept 5 | Nat Lge | A | Lincoln City | 2678 | D | 1-1 | Gray 55 | 4 | 8 |
| 12 | Nat Lge | H | Altrincham | 4628 | W | 3-1 | Leather 20 (og) Hudson 43 Gray 58 | 2 | 9 |
| 15 | Nat Lge | A | Gateshead | 1113 | L | 1-2 | Newton 29 | 5 | 10 |
| 19 | Nat Lge | A | Boreham Wood | 685 | W | 1-0 | Jennings 12 | 4 | 11 |
| 22 | Nat Lge | H | Grimsby Town | 4818 | D | 0-0 | | 3 | 12 |
| 26 | Nat Lge | H | Eastleigh | 4708 | L | 2-3 | York 54 Newton 75 | 5 | 13 |
| Oct 3 | Nat Lge | A | Chester | 3741 | L | 2-3 | Vose 39 (pen) Jennings 90 | 7 | 14 |
| 6 | Nat Lge | H | Tranmere Rovers | 6707 | D | 2-2 | Evans 15 Quigley 82 | 9 | 15 |
| 10 | Nat Lge | A | Dover Athletic | 1253 | L | 1-2 | Jennings 39 (pen) | 10 | 16 |
| 14 | Nat Lge | H | Guiseley | 3633 | D | 3-3 | Vose 23 35 Jennings 90 | 9 | 17 |
| 17 | Nat Lge | A | Woking | 1778 | W | 1-0 | Jennings 28 | 9 | 18 |
| **24** | **FAC4Q** | **H** | **Gainsborough Trinity** | **1814** | **L** | **0-1** | | | 19 |
| 31 | Nat Lge | H | Barrow | 3892 | W | 4-1 | Jennings 45 90 York 58 78 | 8 | 20 |
| Nov 14 | Nat Lge | H | Gateshead | 4095 | W | 4-0 | Evans 55 Hudson 66 Vose 70 75 | 8 | 21 |
| 21 | Nat Lge | A | Aldershot Town | 1483 | W | 1-0 | York 63 | 6 | 22 |
| 28 | Nat Lge | H | Macclesfield Town | 4591 | L | 2-3 | Jennings 32 Gray 76 | 8 | 23 |
| Dec 5 | Nat Lge | A | Altrincham | 1512 | W | 1-0 | Carrington 78 | 5 | 24 |
| **12** | **FAT1** | **A** | **Tranmere Rovers** | **3397** | **W** | **3-2** | **York 4 Vose 44 Newton 60 M.Smith 66** | | 25 |
| 26 | Nat Lge | H | Southport | 5508 | L | 0-1 | | 8 | 26 |
| 28 | Nat Lge | A | FC Halifax Town | 2243 | L | 0-2 | | 10 | 27 |
| Jan 2 | Nat Lge | A | Southport | 2148 | L | 2-3 | York 16 Gray 70 | 11 | 28 |
| 9 | Nat Lge | H | Woking | 4030 | L | 1-3 | Vose 15 | 11 | 29 |
| **16** | **FAT2** | **A** | **Torquay United** | **1361** | **L** | **0-1** | | | 30 |
| 23 | Nat Lge | H | Lincoln City | 3853 | W | 3-1 | York 37 Jennings 48 Heslop 86 | 10 | 31 |
| 26 | Nat Lge | A | Braintree Town | 484 | L | 0-1 | | 11 | 32 |
| 30 | Nat Lge | A | Eastleigh | 1904 | D | 1-1 | Newton 18 | 12 | 33 |
| Feb 6 | Nat Lge | H | Forest Green Rovers | 3891 | D | 2-2 | Hudson 62 66 | 12 | 34 |
| 9 | Nat Lge | A | Altrincham | 1261 | D | 1-1 | Heslop 30 | 12 | 35 |
| 13 | Nat Lge | H | Bromley | 3511 | W | 2-0 | Fowler 31 Jennings 38 (pen) | 8 | 36 |
| 20 | Nat Lge | A | Welling United | 620 | W | 2-0 | Fowler 33 Jennings 44 (pen) | 6 | 37 |
| 23 | Nat Lge | H | Kidderminster Harriers | 3899 | W | 2-0 | Jackson 15 30 | 6 | 38 |
| 27 | Nat Lge | A | Macclesfield Town | 2406 | D | 0-0 | | 4 | 39 |
| Mar 2 | Nat Lge | H | Boreham Wood | 3470 | W | 1-0 | Jennings 12 (pen) | 6 | 40 |
| 19 | Nat Lge | H | Chester | 6459 | W | 3-0 | Jennings 64 (pen) Jackson 77 Evans 84 | 7 | 41 |
| 26 | Nat Lge | A | Grimsby Town | 4581 | L | 0-1 | | 8 | 42 |
| 28 | Nat Lge | H | Cheltenham Town | 4463 | W | 2-1 | Vidal 16 York 90 | 8 | 43 |
| Apr 2 | Nat Lge | A | Forest Green Rovers | 2246 | D | 0-0 | | 8 | 44 |
| 9 | Nat Lge | H | Dover Athletic | 4931 | L | 0-1 | | 8 | 45 |
| 12 | Nat Lge | A | Guiseley | 1046 | L | 1-3 | Newton 67 | 8 | 46 |
| 16 | Nat Lge | A | Tranmere Rovers | 7541 | W | 2-1 | Jackson 15 Newton 85 | 8 | 47 |
| 23 | Nat Lge | H | Braintree Town | 4507 | L | 2-3 | Heslop 11 Fowler 38 | 8 | 48 |
| 30 | Nat Lge | A | Barrow | 1728 | L | 0-2 | | 8 | 49 |

| GOALSCORERS | Scoring Games | Consec Sco Games | Total |
|---|---|---|---|
| ***2014-15 Moult*** | ***21*** | | |
| Jennings | 13 | 3 | 14 |
| Vose | 9 | 2 | 11 |
| York | 10 | | 11 |
| Gray | 7 | 3 | 7 |
| Newton | 6 | | 6 |
| Hudson | 3 | | 4 |
| Fowler | 3 | | 3 |
| Heslop | 3 | | 3 |
| Jackson | 3 | | 3 |
| M.Smith | 2 | | 2 |
| Vidal | 2 | | 2 |
| Carrington | 1 | | 1 |
| Evans | 1 | | 1 |
| Quigley | 1 | | 1 |
| A.Smith | 1 | | 1 |
| Opponents | | | 1 |

## CHELTENHAM TOWN MATCH RESULTS 2015-16

| Date | Comp | H/A | Opponents | Att: | Result | | | | No. |
|---|---|---|---|---|---|---|---|---|---|
| Aug 8 | Nat Lge | A | Lincoln City | 2767 | D | 1-1 | Munns 26 | 13 | 1 |
| 11 | Nat Lge | H | Aldershot Town | 2552 | D | 0-0 | | 17 | 2 |
| 15 | Nat Lge | H | Southport | 2251 | **W** | 3-0 | Downes 51 Morgan-Smith 76 82 | 11 | 3 |
| 18 | Nat Lge | A | Chester | 2304 | D | 1-1 | Storer 48 | 11 | 4 |
| 22 | Nat Lge | H | Barrow | 2209 | **W** | 2-1 | Storer 72 Dickie 88 | 7 | 5 |
| 29 | Nat Lge | A | Torquay United | 2018 | **W** | 3-0 | Downes 30 Wright 61 85 (pen) | 6 | 6 |
| 31 | Nat Lge | H | Wrexham | 2827 | **W** | 2-1 | Parslow 59 Morgan-Smith 84 | 5 | 7 |
| Sept 5 | Nat Lge | A | Altrincham | 1206 | L | 1-2 | Downes 82 | 6 | 8 |
| 12 | Nat Lge | H | Dover Athletic | 2021 | **W** | 3-2 | Waters 38 84 Wright 55 (pen) | 4 | 9 |
| 15 | Nat Lge | H | Macclesfield Town | 1962 | **W** | 2-0 | Pell 17 Wright 43 | 3 | 10 |
| 19 | Nat Lge | A | Woking | 2035 | **W** | 1-0 | Wright 67 | 2 | 11 |
| 22 | Nat Lge | A | Forest Green Rovers | 3127 | D | 2-2 | Morgan-Smith 45 Pell 77 | 2 | 12 |
| 26 | Nat Lge | H | Tranmere Rovers | 2556 | L | 0-1 | | 3 | 13 |
| Oct 3 | Nat Lge | A | FC Halifax Town | 1267 | **W** | 7-1 | MUNNS 3 (12 89 90) Morgan-Smith 40 Wright 47 Pell 58 Waters 80 | 2 | 14 |
| 6 | Nat Lge | H | Braintree Town | 2097 | D | 1-1 | Waters 90 | 1 | 15 |
| 10 | Nat Lge | A | Gateshead | 1238 | D | 1-1 | Wright 50 | 2 | 16 |
| 13 | Nat Lge | A | Bromley | 1500 | **W** | 2-1 | Waters 38 Hall 90 | 2 | 17 |
| 17 | Nat Lge | H | Eastleigh | 2802 | D | 1-1 | Munns 20 | 2 | 18 |
| **24** | **FAC4Q** | **A** | **Havant & Waterlooville** | **622** | **D** | **3-3** | **Wright 45 72 Downes 50** | | 19 |
| **28** | **FAC4Qr** | **H** | **Havant & Waterlooville** | **1638** | **W** | **1-0** | **Wright 46** | | 20 |
| 31 | Nat Lge | A | Grimsby Town | 5218 | **W** | 1-0 | Downes 68 | 2 | 21 |
| **Nov 7** | **FAC1** | **A** | **Hartlepool United** | **2287** | **L** | **0-1** | | | 22 |
| 10 | Nat Lge | H | Guiseley | 2237 | **W** | 5-0 | Waters 1 62 Dickie 9 Munns 81 Rowe 90 | 1 | 23 |
| 14 | Nat Lge | A | Southport | 947 | **W** | 4-0 | Pell 4 Waters 8 14 Parslow 53 | 1 | 24 |
| 21 | Nat Lge | H | Forest Green Rovers | 5449 | D | 1-1 | Pell 52 | 1 | 25 |
| 28 | Nat Lge | A | Aldershot Town | 1493 | **W** | 2-0 | Pell 7 Munns 28 | 1 | 26 |
| Dec 5 | Nat Lge | H | Chester | 2501 | **W** | 3-1 | Waters 18 60 Wright 87 | 1 | 27 |
| **12** | **FAT1** | **H** | **Chelmsford City** | **1124** | **W** | **3-1** | **DICKIE 3 ( 42 67 77)** | | 28 |
| 19 | Nat Lge | H | Altrincham | 2591 | **W** | 1-0 | Wright 56 (pen) | 1 | 29 |
| 26 | Nat Lge | A | Kidderminster Harriers | 3238 | **W** | 2-1 | Wright 26 Downes 67 | 1 | 30 |
| 28 | Nat Lge | H | Torquay United | 3781 | W | 1-0 | Munns 59 | 1 | 31 |
| Jan 9 | Nat Lge | A | Boreham Wood | 647 | D | 0-0 | | 1 | 32 |
| **16** | **FAT2** | **A** | **Oxford City** | **926** | **D** | **2-2** | **Rowe 82 Dale 90** | | 33 |
| 24 | Nat Lge | A | Dover Athletic | 1184 | **W** | 2-1 | Wright 88 (pen) 89 | 1 | 34 |
| **26** | **FAT2r** | **H** | **Oxford City** | **776** | **L** | **0-3** | | | 35 |
| 30 | Nat Lge | H | Bromley | 2662 | **W** | 4-1 | Holman 20 25 Rowe 49 Wright 63 | 1 | 36 |
| Feb 6 | Nat Lge | A | Barrow | 1202 | **W** | 2-1 | Wright 2 Hall 82 | 1 | 37 |
| 13 | Nat Lge | H | Welling United | 2549 | **W** | 2-0 | Wright 17 Holman 51 | 1 | 38 |
| 16 | Nat Lge | H | Kidderminster Harriers | 3387 | **W** | 2-0 | Wright 50 (pen) Holman 57 | 1 | 39 |
| 20 | Nat Lge | A | Tranmere Rovers | 5418 | **W** | 1-0 | Wright 3 | 1 | 40 |
| 23 | Nat Lge | H | Gateshead | 2201 | D | 0-0 | | 1 | 41 |
| Mar 2 | Nat Lge | A | Eastleigh | 1982 | L | 0-1 | | 1 | 42 |
| 5 | Nat Lge | A | Welling United | 604 | D | 1-1 | Holman 90 | 1 | 43 |
| 12 | Nat Lge | H | Woking | 2951 | **W** | 4-0 | HOLMAN 4 (32 38 58 64) | 1 | 44 |
| 19 | Nat Lge | A | Braintree Town | 1138 | L | 0-1 | | 1 | 45 |
| 25 | Nat Lge | H | Boreham Wood | 3242 | **W** | 4-1 | Wright 16 (pen) 51 (pen) Holman 41 90 | 1 | 46 |
| 28 | Nat Lge | A | Wrexham | 4463 | L | 1-2 | Dayton 41 | 1 | 47 |
| Apr 1 | Nat Lge | H | Grimsby Town | 4003 | **W** | 3-1 | Dayton 35 Pell 59 Wright 77 | 1 | 48 |
| 9 | Nat Lge | A | Guiseley | 1058 | **W** | 2-0 | Dickie 80 Holman 89 | 1 | 49 |
| 16 | Nat Lge | H | FC Halifax Town | 5245 | **W** | 2-0 | Holman 24 33 (pen) | 1 | 50 |
| 23 | Nat Lge | A | Macclesfield Town | 1895 | **W** | 1-0 | Holman 25 | 1 | 51 |
| 30 | Nat Lge | H | Lincoln City | 5055 | **W** | 3-1 | Wright 39 Storer 6 Holman 78 | 1 | 52 |

| GOALSCORERS | Scoring Games | Consec Sco Games | Total |
|---|---|---|---|
| Wright | 20 | 5 | 24 |
| Holman | 10 | 4 | 16 |
| Waters | 7 | 2 | 11 |
| Munns | 8 | | 8 |
| Pell | 7 | 3 | 7 |
| Dickie | 4 | | 6 |
| Downes | 6 | | 6 |
| Morgan-Smiith | 4 | | 5 |
| Rowe | 3 | | 3 |
| Storer | 3 | 2 | 3 |
| Dayton | 2 | | 2 |
| Hall | 2 | | 2 |
| Parslow | 2 | | 2 |
| Dale | 1 | | 1 |

## GRIMSBY TOWN MATCH RESULTS 2015-16

| Date | Comp | H/A | Opponents | Att: | Result | | Goalscorers | Pos | No. |
|---|---|---|---|---|---|---|---|---|---|
| Aug 8 | Nat Lge | A | Kidderminster Harriers | 3459 | D | 2-2 | Amond 32 Monkhouse 66 | 11 | 1 |
| 11 | Nat Lge | H | Barrow | 5047 | W | 4-1 | Monkhouse 16 59 Bogle 22 Nsiala 64 | 5 | 2 |
| 15 | Nat Lge | H | Bromley | 4731 | W | 4-1 | Amond 2 25 Bogle 7 (pen) Clay 89 | 2 | 3 |
| 18 | Nat Lge | A | Altrincham | 1680 | L | 1-2 | Bogle 42 | 9 | 4 |
| 22 | Nat Lge | H | Torquay United | 4290 | D | 2-2 | Robinson 68 Amond 80 | 8 | 5 |
| 29 | Nat Lge | A | Lincoln City | 5849 | D | 1-1 | Bogle 66 | 10 | 6 |
| 31 | Nat Lge | H | Macclesfield Town | 4251 | L | 0-2 | | 11 | 7 |
| Sept 5 | Nat Lge | A | Boreham Wood | 1293 | W | 3-1 | Doe 8 (og) Bogle 69 Amond 76 | 9 | 8 |
| 12 | Nat Lge | H | Aldershot Town | 3869 | W | 4-1 | Bogle 53 (pen) 81 Boshell 41 Lawlor 90 | 7 | 9 |
| 15 | Nat Lge | A | Chester | 1964 | D | 1-1 | Amond 90 | 7 | 10 |
| 19 | Nat Lge | H | Tranmere Rovers | 4636 | D | 1-1 | Pittman 8 | 7 | 11 |
| 22 | Nat Lge | A | Wrexham | 4818 | D | 0-0 | | 9 | 12 |
| 26 | Nat Lge | A | Southport | 1320 | W | 4-0 | Clay 18 Disley 29 Pittman 34 Gowling 46 | 7 | 13 |
| Oct 3 | Nat Lge | H | Forest Green Rovers | 5034 | D | 1-1 | Pittman 31 | 10 | 14 |
| 6 | Nat Lge | H | Gateshead | 3835 | W | 2-1 | Arnold 19 50 | 7 | 15 |
| 10 | Nat Lge | A | Braintree Town | 1394 | D | 0-0 | | 7 | 16 |
| 13 | Nat Lge | H | FC Halifax Town | 3806 | W | 7-0 | Bogle 10 42 AMOND 4( 35 45 76 82) Clay 55 | 4 | 17 |
| 17 | Nat Lge | A | Torquay United | 2003 | D | 1-1 | Bogle 79 (pen) | 4 | 18 |
| **24** | **FAC4Q** | **A** | **Harrogate Town** | **1920** | **W** | **4-1** | **Amond 34 70 Bogle 56 Arnold 57** | | 19 |
| 31 | Nat Lge | H | Cheltenham Town | 5218 | L | 0-1 | | 4 | 20 |
| **Nov 7** | **FAC1** | **H** | **St Albans City** | **2267** | **W** | **5-1** | **Townsend 39 Amond 45 90 Pittman 71 Marshall 84** | | 21 |
| 10 | Nat Lge | A | Barrow | 1255 | W | 3-1 | Amond 35 85 Gowling 60 | 5 | 22 |
| 14 | Nat Lge | H | Welling United | 4108 | W | 3-1 | Arnold 8 Townsend 12 Mackreth 90 | 5 | 23 |
| 21 | Nat Lge | A | Eastleigh | 2057 | W | 1-0 | Amond 29 | 3 | 24 |
| 28 | Nat Lge | H | Kidderminster Harriers | 3894 | W | 1-0 | Amond 66 | 3 | 25 |
| **Dec 7** | **FAC2** | **H** | **Shrewsbury Town** | **3366** | **D** | **0-0** | | | 26 |
| **12** | **FAT1** | **H** | **Solihull Moors** | **1071** | **D** | **1-1** | **Alabi 66** | | 27 |
| **15** | **FAC2r** | **A** | **Shrewsbury Town** | **2730** | **L** | **0-1** | | | 28 |
| 19 | Nat Lge | H | Dover Athletic | 4266 | W | 1-0 | Amond 90 (pen) | 4 | 29 |
| **22** | **FAT1r** | **A** | **Solihull Moors** | **479** | **W** | **3-2** | **Bogle 63 Alabi 66 (pen) Mackreth 67** | | 30 |
| 28 | Nat Lge | H | Lincoln City | 7650 | W | 2-0 | Amond 20 Arnold 79 | 3 | 31 |
| Jan 2 | Nat Lge | H | Guiseley | 5093 | D | 1-1 | Amond 71 | 3 | 32 |
| 9 | Nat Lge | A | Welling United | 1337 | W | 4-0 | AMOND 3 (63 69 77) Disley 82 | 3 | 33 |
| **16** | **FAT2** | **H** | **Weston-s-Mare** | **1230** | **W** | **3-1** | **Henderson 12 Bogle 44 Pittman 61** | **3** | 34 |
| 23 | Nat Lge | H | Altrincham | 4323 | W | 5-0 | Bogle 18 Monkhouse 2 52 Amond 62 Arnold 90 | 3 | 35 |
| 30 | Nat Lge | A | Gateshead | 2174 | L | 0-1 | | 3 | 36 |
| **Feb 6** | **FAT3** | **H** | **H & Waterloovile** | **1613** | **W** | **3-0** | **Pittman 73 Nolan 85 Swallow 90 (og)** | | 37 |
| 9 | Nat Lge | A | Bromley | 1073 | W | 2-1 | Nolan 32 Pittman 84 | 3 | 38 |
| 13 | Nat Lge | H | Boreham Wood | 3027 | D | 0-0 | | 3 | 39 |
| 20 | Nat Lge | A | FC Halifax Town | 3131 | L | 2-4 | Amond 88 Nolan 90 | 3 | 40 |
| 23 | Nat Lge | H | Woking | 2874 | W | 3-1 | Pittman 4 Amond 37 42 | 3 | 41 |
| 27 | FAT4 | H | Woking | 1675 | W | 2-0 | Arnold 10 35 | | 42 |
| Mar 4 | Nat Lge | A | Forest Green Rovers | 2242 | W | 1-0 | Disley 71 | 3 | 43 |
| 8 | Nat Lge | H | Southport | 3180 | W | 1-0 | Amond 1 | 3 | 44 |
| **12** | **FAT SF 1** | **A** | **Bognor Regis Town** | **2629** | **W** | **1-0** | **Arnold 71** | | 45 |
| 15 | Nat Lge | A | Guiseley | 1843 | D | 2-2 | Disley 20 Amond 55 | 3 | 46 |
| **19** | **FAT SF 2** | **H** | **Bognor Regis Town** | **2477** | **W** | **2-1** | **Amond 8 (pen) 78** | | 47 |
| 26 | Nat Lge | H | Wrexham | 4581 | W | 1-0 | Disley 7 | 3 | 48 |
| 28 | Nat Lge | A | Macclesfield Town | 2326 | L | 1-2 | Nolan 58 | 3 | 49 |
| Apr 2 | Nat Lge | A | Cheltenham Town | 4003 | L | 1-3 | Monkhouse 52 | 3 | 50 |
| 5 | Nat Lge | A | Aldershot Town | 1397 | W | 4-3 | Amond 53 Arnold 58 67 Nolan 88 | 3 | 51 |
| 9 | Nat Lge | H | Eastleigh | 4011 | D | 0-0 | | 4 | 52 |
| 12 | Nat Lge | H | Braintree Town | 3010 | L | 0-1 | | 4 | 53 |
| 15 | Nat Lge | A | Dover Athetic | 1957 | D | 1-1 | Bogle 17 (pen) | 4 | 54 |
| 19 | Nat Lge | A | Woking | 1394 | W | 3-1 | AMOND 3 (14 60 85) | 3 | 55 |
| 23 | Nat Lge | H | Chester | 4575 | L | 1-2 | Disley 83 | 3 | 56 |
| 30 | Nat Lge | A | Tranmere Rovers | 6637 | L | 0-1 | | 4 | 57 |
| **May 5** | **PO SF 1** | **H** | **Braintree Town** | **5271** | **L** | **0-1** | | | 58 |
| **8** | **PO SF 2** | **A** | **Braintree Town** | **3102** | **W** | **2-0** | **Amond 75 (pen) Bogle 110 (aet)** | | 59 |
| **15** | **PO Final** | **N** | **Forest Green Rovers** | **17198** | **W** | **3-1** | **Bogle 41 43 Arnold 90** | | 60 |
| **23** | **FAT Final** | **N** | **FC Halifax Town** | **46,781** | **L** | **0-1** | | | 61 |

| GOALSCORERS | Scoring Games | Consec Sco Games | Total | | Scoring Games | Consec Sco Games | Total |
|---|---|---|---|---|---|---|---|
| *2014-15 John-Lewis* | | | *20* | Gowling | 2 | | 2 |
| Amond | 24 | 3 | 37 | Mackreth | 2 | | 2 |
| Bogle | 15 | 3 | 18 | Townsend | 2 | | 2 |
| Arnold | 9 | | 12 | Boshell | 1 | | 1 |
| Pittman | 8 | 2 | 8 | Henderson | 1 | | 1 |
| Disley | 6 | | 6 | Lawlor | 1 | | 1 |
| Monkhouse | 5 | 2 | 6 | Marshall | 1 | | 1 |
| Nolan | 5 | | 5 | Nsiala | 1 | | 1 |
| Clay | 3 | | 3 | Robinson | 1 | | 1 |
| Alabi | 2 | | 2 | Opponents | | | 2 |

# Football Conference Play-off Final 2015-16

At Wembley, 15/05/16 - Att: 17,198

Forest Green Rovers 1-3 Grimsby Town

*Nathan Arnold (Grimsby) beats Steve Arnold (FGR) to score the third goal, whilst Danny East holds up a flag that says it all!*
*Photos: Keith Clayton*

*Photo: Peter Barnes*

*Photo: Peter Barnes*

## National Division Statistics 2015-16

| | NoS | GS | CTS | PS | CSG | MCGU | TCS | MCCS | CMWW | CD | FTS | CNG | TGC |
|---|---|---|---|---|---|---|---|---|---|---|---|---|---|
| Aldershot Town | 19+1 | 55 | 4 | 2 | 9 | 6 | 16 | 3 | 9 | 7 | 17 | 3 | 75 |
| Altrincham | 13 | 56 | 5 | 6 | 5 | 5 | 9 | 2 | 8 | 3 | 18 | 3 | 80 |
| Barrow | 15+2 | 65 | 4 | 6 | 11 | 10 | 13 | 2 | 5 | 4 | 8 | 1 | 73 |
| Boreham Wood | 19+1 | 49 | 3 | 2 | 6 | 3 | 16 | 3 | 7 | 5 | 20 | 4 | 55 |
| Braintree Town | 14 | 62 | 6 | 7 | 6 | 8 | 24 | 5 | 4 | 3 | 15 | 3 | 45 |
| Bromley | 19 | 68 | 7 | 5 | 11 | 6 | 12 | 2 | 6 | 6 | 12 | 3 | 75 |
| Cheltenham Town | 14 | 96 | 7 | 8 | 10 | 12 | 21 | 4 | 3 | 1 | 7 | 2 | 40 |
| Chester | 20 | 73 | 8 | 3 | 5 | 4 | 10 | First 3 | 7 | 3 | 14 | 3 | 73 |
| Dover Athletic | 14+1 | 90 | 5 | 5 | 12 | 7 | 15 | 2 | 4 | 3 | 11 | 2 | 64 |
| Eastleigh | 14+4 | 74 | 4 | 5 | 12 | 10 | 14 | 4 | 11 | 4 | 10 | 2 | 61 |
| FC Halifax Town | 15+2 | 76 | 5 | 4 | 14 | 13 | 13 | 2 | 7 | First 4 | 16 | 4 | 95 |
| Forest Green Rovers | 13+1 | 76 | 4 | 4 | 13 | 11 | 20 | First 4 | 7 | 2 | 8 | 2 | 51 |
| Gateshead | 18+1 | 70 | 4 | 4 | 8 | 7 | 14 | 4 | 6 | 2 | 11 | 2 | 77 |
| Grimsby Town | 18+2 | 111 | 7 | 8 | 12 | 12 | 20 | 4 | 4 | 1 | 12 | 2 | 55 |
| Guiseley | 16+1 | 59 | 4 | 3 | 6 | 7 | 8 | 2 | 12 | 3 | 19 | 2 | 84 |
| Kidderminster Harriers | 19 | 50 | 4 | 2 | 4 | 6* | 5 | 2 | First 19 | 8 | 17 | 3 | 76 |
| Lincoln City | 17+1 | 75 | 5 | 6 | 11 | 6 | 10 | 3 | 11 | 3 | 8 | 2 | 75 |
| Macclesfield Town | 12+1 | 75 | 5 | 6 | 12 | 9 | 19 | 3 | 10 | 2 | 15 | 2 | 58 |
| Southport | 17+1 | 56 | 5 | 6 | 7 | 9 | 12 | 2 | 7 | 4 | 20 | 3 | 70 |
| Torquay United | 20+1 | 61 | 4 | 1 | 6 | 6 | 16 | 4 | 12 | 5 | 18 | 3 | 83 |
| Tranmere Rovers | 19+1 | 63 | 4 | 9 | 11 | 9 | 19 | 2 | 5 | 3 | 12 | 4 | 50 |
| Welling United | 15+3 | 47 | 4 | 1 | 5 | 4 | 6 | 2 | 18 | 5 | 21 | 5 | 84 |
| Woking | 17+3 | 80 | 6 | 2 | 9 | 9 | 8 | 2 | 11 | 7 | 11 | 3 | 75 |
| Wrexham | 15+1 | 74 | 4 | 8 | 11 | 9 | 15 | 6 | 6 | 5 | 11 | 2 | 60 |

+ Denotes number of Own goals I * Denotes unfinished run
NoS - Number of Scorers I GS - Goals Scored I CTS - Club's Top Score I PS - Penalties Scored
CSG - Consecutive Scoring Games I MCGU - Most Consecutive Games Unbeaten I TCS - Total Clean Sheets
MCCS - Most Consecutive Clean Sheets I CMWW - Consecutive Matches Without a Win
CD - Consecutive Defeats I FTS - Failure to Score I CNG - Consecutive No Goals
I TGC - Total Goals Conceded

## National Division Leading goalscorers 2015-16

| Player | Club | Lge | FAC | FAT | Pens | HT | CSG | SG | Total |
|---|---|---|---|---|---|---|---|---|---|
| Padraig Amond | Grimsby Town | 30+1PO | 4 | 2 | 3 | 2 | 5 | 24 | 37 |
| Kristian Dennis | Macclesfield Town | 22 | 3 | 5 | 4 | 1 | 5 | 22 | 30 |
| Dan Holman | Woking & Cheltenham Town | 14+16 | | | 0+1 | | 3+3 | 10+10 | 30 |
| Ross Hannah | Chester | 22 | | 3 | 2 | | 3 | 19 | 25 |
| Danny Wright | Cheltenham Town | 22 | 3 | | 3 | | 3 | 20 | 25 |
| Andy Cook | Barrow | 23 | | | 1 | | 2 | 20 | 23 |
| Stefan Payne | Dover Athletic | 18 | 1 | 4 | | | 2 | 18 | 23 |
| Matt Rhead | Lincoln City | 20 | 3 | | 5 | | 3 | 16 | 23 |
| James Norwood | Tranmere Rovers | 20 | 2 | | 4 | | 2 | 17 | 22 |
| Ryan Bowman | Gateshead | 16 | 1 | 3 | 3 | | 3 | 17 | 21 |
| Ricky Miller | Dover Athletic | 20 | | 1 | | | 3 | 16 | 21 |
| Moses Emmanuel | Bromley | 19 | | | 1 | 1 | 4 | 16 | 20 |
| Omar Bogle | Grimsby Town | 12+3PO | 1 | 2 | 4 | | 3 | 15 | 18 |
| Jordan Burrow | FC Halifax Town | 14 | | 4 | 4 | | 3 | 14 | 18 |
| MIchael Cheek | Braintree Town | 15 | 2 | | | | 2 | 12 | 17 |
| James Constable | Eastleigh | 15 | 1 | 1 | | | 4 | 14 | 17 |
| Nick Deverdics | Dover Athletic | 14 | | 1 | 2 | | 2 | 14 | 15 |
| Charlie Walker | Aldershot Town | 15 | | | | | 2 | 13 | 15 |
| Johnson | Gateshead | 13 | | 2 | | | 3 | 13 | 15 |
| Louis Almond | Southport | 10 | | 1 | 5 | | 2 | 11 | 13 |
| Jon Parkin | Forest Green Rovers | 13 | | | | | 2 | 11 | 13 |
| Nathan Arnold | Grimsby Town | 7+1PO | 1 | 3 | | | | 9 | 12 |
| Kurtis Guthrie | Forest Green Rovers | 11 | 1 | | | | 2 | 11 | 12 |

HT - Hat-tricks I CSG - Consecutive Scoring Games I SG - Scoring Games I PO - Play-offs

# DAGENHAM & REDBRIDGE

**Chairman:** David Bennett
**Secretary:** (T) (E) info@daggers.co.uk
**Commercial Manager:** Stephen Thompson (T/E) steve@daggers.co.uk
**Programme Editor:** (T/E)
**Ground Address:** Chigwell Construction Stadium, Victoria Road, Dagenham Essex RM10 7XL
**(T)** 02 8592 1549 **Manager:** John Still

## Club Factfile

**Founded:** 1992 **Nickname:** The Daggers
**Previous Names:** Formed by the merger of Dagenham and Redbridge Forest
**Previous Leagues:** Football Conference 1992-96, 2000-2007. Isthmian 1996-2000. Football League 2007-16.

**Club Colours (change):** Red, blue & white/blue/blue (All white)

**Ground Capacity:** 6,078 **Seats:** **Covered:** **Clubhouse:** **Shop:**

**Directions** f you are coming from the **North or West**, follow the M25 Clockwise until junction 27 and take the M11 towards London. Proceed along the M11 and as the road splits at the end of the motorway follow the signs for A406 South & A13. There are speed cameras along this road and the speed limit is 50 mph. After 5 miles, take the slip road on the left signposted A13 Dagenham, Tilbury and Southend. Go under the underpass and over the flyover and with the leisure complex on your left bear left onto the A1306 signposted Dagenham East. At the fifth set of lights with McDonalds in front of you, tern left onto the A1112, Ballards Road. The speed limit is 30mph and there is a speed camera on your left. At the Bull Roundabout bear left and go past Dagenham East Tube Station. Victoria Road is the fifth turning on the left. **South & East Via Dartford Crossing:** Follow signs for A13 to Dagenham/ Central London. Proceed along this road and take the turn off signposted Elm Park & Dagenham East and turn right at the roundabout at the bottom of the slip road. Proceed to the set of lights and turn left onto a dual carriageway. After about half a mile you will see a McDonalds on your right. Get into the right hand filter lane and turn right onto the A1112 Ballards Road, then as above.

**Previous Grounds:**

**Record Attendance:** 5,949 v Ipswich Town (5/1/2002) FA Cup Thid Round
**Record Victory:** 8-1 v Woking, Football Conference, 19.04.94
**Record Defeat:** 0-9 v Hereford United, Football Conference, 27.02.04.
**Record Goalscorer:** Not known - If you know please email tw.publications@btinternet.com
**Record Appearances:** Not known - If you know please email tw.publications@btinternet.com
**Additional Records:** FA Cup: 4th Round, 2002-03. Transfer fee paid: Undisclosed, Oliver Hawkins from Hemel Hempstead.
Transfer fee received: £470,000 Dwight Gayle to Peterborough United

**Honours:**
Isthmian League Premier Division 1999-2000. Football Conference 2006-07. Football League Two Play-offs 2009-10.
Essex Senior Cup 1997-98, 2000-01.

### 10 YEAR RECORD

| 06-07 | | 07-08 | | 08-09 | | 09-10 | | 10-11 | | 11-12 | | 12-13 | | 13-14 | | 14-15 | | 15-16 | |
|---|---|---|---|---|---|---|---|---|---|---|---|---|---|---|---|---|---|---|---|
| Conf | 1 | FL 2 | 20 | FL 2 | 8 | FL 2 | 7 | FL 1 | 21 | FL 2 | 19 | FL 2 | 22 | FL 2 | 9 | FL 2 | 14 | FL 2 | 23 |

# YORK CITY

**Chairman:** Jason McGill

**Secretary:** Lisa Charlton **(T)** 01904 624 447 **(E)** lisa.charlton@yorkcityfootballclub.co.uk

**Commercial Manager:** Dave Hendry **(T/E)** commercial@yorkcityfootballclub.co.uk

**Programme Editor:** 01904 624 447 **(T/E)**

**Ground Address:** Bootham Crescent, York YO30 7AQ

**(T)** 01904 624 447 **Manager:** Jackie McNamara

## Club Factfile

**Founded:** 1922 **Nickname:** Minstermen

**Previous Names:** None

**Previous Leagues:** Football League

**Club Colours (change):** Red/blue/red (All sky blue)

**Ground Capacity:** 9,496 **Seats:** 1,844 **Covered:** 7,000 **Clubhouse:** Yes **Shop:** Yes

**Directions**

From Tadcaster (A64) take left turning onto A1237 (Outer Ringroad) continue for approx 5 miles to A19 and then turn right into York. Continue for just over 1 mile and turn left into Bootham Crescent opposite Grange Hotel.

**Previous Grounds:** Fulfordgate 1922-32

**Record Attendance:** 28,123 v Huddersfield Town - FA Cup 6th Round 1938

**Record Victory:** 9-1 v Southport - Division 3 North 1957

**Record Defeat:** 0-12 v Chester City - Division 3 North 1936

**Record Goalscorer:** Norman Wilkinson - 125 League (1954-66)

**Record Appearances:** Barry Jackson - 481 League (1958-70)

**Additional Records:** Paid £140,000 to Burnley for Adrian Randall December 1995
Received £1,000,000 from Manchester United for Jonathan Greening March 1998

**Honours:**
Football League Division 3 1983-84. FA Trophy 2011-12. Conference Premier Play-offs 2011-12.

**10 YEAR RECORD**

| 06-07 | 07-08 | 08-09 | 09-10 | 10-11 | 11-12 | 12-13 | 13-14 | 14-15 | 15-16 |
|---|---|---|---|---|---|---|---|---|---|
| Conf 4 | Conf 14 | Conf 17 | Conf 5 | Conf 8 | Conf 4 | FL 2 17 | FL 2 7 | FL 2 18 | FL 2 24 |

# AFC FYLDE

**Chairman:** David Haythornthwaite
**Secretary:** Martin Benson (T) 01772 682 593 (E) clubsecretary@afcfylde.co.uk
**Commercial Manager:** 01772 682 593 (T/E)
**Programme Editor:** 01772 682 593 (T/E)
**Ground Address:** Kellamergh Park, Bryning Lane, Warton, Preston PR4 1TN
(T) 01772 682 593 **Manager:** Dave Challinor

## Club Factfile

**Founded:** 1988 **Nickname:** The Coasters
**Previous Names:** Wesham FC and Kirkham Town amalgamated in 1988 to form Kirkham & Wesham > 2008
**Previous Leagues:** West Lancashire, North West Counties 2007-09. Northern Premier 2009-14.

**Club Colours (change):** All white (Orange with single black stripe/orange/orange)

**Ground Capacity:** 1,426 **Seats:** 282 **Covered:** 282 **Clubhouse:** Yes **Shop:** Yes

**Directions**
AFC Fylde is based in an area called 'The Fylde Coast' located between Blackpool and Preston. Kellamergh Park is located in WARTON. EXIT via Junction 3 M55 (signposted A585 Fleetwood/Kirkham). Up approach and turn left towards signs for Kirkham. In around 3/4 mile you will approach a roundabout. Then follow the signs for Wrea Green and Lytham St. Annes (2nd exit) B5259. After another 500 yards you will approach a new roundabout (go straight on) and 1/4 mile you will go over main Preston/Blackpool railway bridge and drop down almost immediately to a small mini roundabout (pub on left called Kingfisher). Carry on straight over this and up to main roundabout (another 200 yards) at junction of main Preston/Blackpool A583. Go straight over roundabout and drive on into Wrea Green Village. At 2nd mini roundabout in the centre of the village (Church on right and Primary School) take left turn into Bryning Lane, signposted on The Green (small white signpost) to Warton (2 miles).The Green will now be on your right as you exit out of the village and in around 1.8 miles you will come to the Birley Arms Pub on your left. Turn left at The Birley Arms Pub Car park and continue to drive through the car park down an access road and park in the Main Club Car Park.

**Previous Grounds:** Coronation Road > 2006

**Record Attendance:** 1,418 v FC United of Manchester, NPL P, 13/10/12.
**Record Victory:** 8-1 v Oxford City, Conference North, 06/09/14.
**Record Defeat:** Not known
**Record Goalscorer:** Not known
**Record Appearances:** Not known
**Additional Records:**

**Honours:**
West Lancashire League 1999-2000, 00-01, 01-02, 03-04, 04-05, 05-06, 06-07.
FA Vase 2007-08.
North West Counties League 2008-09. Northern Premier Division 1 North 2011-12. Lancashire FA Challenge Trophy 2011-12.

### 10 YEAR RECORD

| 06-07 | 07-08 | 08-09 | 09-10 | 10-11 | 11-12 | 12-13 | 13-14 | 14-15 | 15-16 |
|---|---|---|---|---|---|---|---|---|---|
| WYkP 1 | NWC2 2 | NWCP 1 | NP1N 13 | NP1N 5 | NP1N 1 | NP P 5 | NP P 2 | Conf N 2 | Nat N 3 |

## AFC FYLDE MATCH RESULTS 2015-16

| Date | Comp | H/A | Opponents | Att: | Result | | Goalscorers | Pos | No. |
|---|---|---|---|---|---|---|---|---|---|
| Aug 8 | Nat North | A | Solihull Moors | 290 | L | 0-3 | | 21 | 1 |
| 11 | Nat North | H | Hednesford Town | 355 | W | 2-0 | Finley 12 Lloyd 41 | 10 | 2 |
| 15 | Nat North | H | Gainsborough Town | 326 | D | 2-2 | Charles 13 27 | 12 | 3 |
| 18 | Nat North | A | Bradford PA | 303 | W | 2-1 | Charles 12 Stewart 43 (og) | 11 | 4 |
| 22 | Nat North | H | Lowestoft Town | 338 | W | 1-0 | Wilson 90 | 6 | 5 |
| 29 | Nat North | A | Curzon Ashton | 225 | W | 2-0 | Baker 7 (pen) Collins 20 | 4 | 6 |
| 31 | Nat North | H | Stockport County | 1077 | L | 2-3 | Baker 47 (pen) Rowe 85 | 5 | 7 |
| Sept 5 | Nat North | A | Gloucester City | 310 | W | 3-1 | Blinkhorn 12 Finley 27 Rowe 86 | 2 | 8 |
| 12 | Nat North | H | Tamworth | 353 | D | 2-2 | Charles 19 Blinkhorn 71 | 3 | 9 |
| 15 | Nat North | H | FC United | 821 | W | 4-0 | Finley 10 Baker 57 Charles 66 Rowe 88 | 2 | 10 |
| 19 | Nat North | A | Boston United | 1094 | W | 3-0 | Lloyd 59 Baker 61 (pen ) M.Hughes 64 | 2 | 11 |
| **26** | **FAC2Q** | **H** | **Stockport County** | **601** | **W** | **1-0** | **M Hughes 33** | | 12 |
| Oct 3 | Nat North | H | AFC Telford United | 504 | W | 1-0 | Wright 15 | 2 | 13 |
| **10** | **FAC3Q** | **H** | **Coleshill Town** | **390** | **W** | **9-0** | **Lloyd 4 51 M.HUGHES 3 (12 61 90) Charles 13 ROWE 3 (41 56 78)** | | 14 |
| 17 | Nat North | A | Corby Town | 515 | W | 2-1 | Baker 51 55 | 1 | 15 |
| **24** | **FAC4Q** | **A** | **Barrow** | **901** | **W** | **1-0** | **Charles 59** | | 16 |
| 31 | Nat North | H | Stalybridge Celtic | 472 | W | 5-0 | M.Hughes 14 Charles 39 Rowe 51 76 Lloyd 88 | 1 | 17 |
| **Nov 7** | **FAC1** | **A** | **Millwall** | **3445** | **L** | **1-3** | **Whittle 62** | | 18 |
| 14 | Nat North | H | Brackley Town | 345 | D | 2-2 | Rowe 29 Charles 57 | 2 | 19 |
| 21 | Nat North | A | North Ferriby United | 365 | L | 0-3 | | 4 | 20 |
| 24 | Nat North | A | Harrogate Town | 416 | D | 2-2 | Rowe 56 82 | 4 | 21 |
| **28** | **FAT3Q** | **A** | **Warrington Town** | **297** | **W** | **2-0** | **Lloyd 45 C.Hughes 70** | | 22 |
| Dec 5 | Nat North | A | Hednesford Town | 409 | W | 1-0 | M.Hughes 11 | 4 | 23 |
| 8 | Nat North | A | Alfreton Town | 433 | W | 2-1 | Hardy 68 M.Hughes 78 | 2 | 24 |
| **15** | **FAT1** | **H** | **Skelmersdale United** | **221** | **D** | **4-4** | **ROWE 3 (10 19 87) Lloyd-McGoldrick 47** | | 25 |
| 19 | Nat North | H | Solihull Moors | 581 | L | 1-2 | Charles 37 | 4 | 26 |
| 28 | Nat North | H | Curzon Ashton | 504 | L | 1-2 | Charles 29 | | 27 |
| Jan 2 | Nat North | A | Chorley | 903 | W | 1-0 | Rowe 84 | 5 | 28 |
| 9th | Nat North | A | Gainsborough Trinity | 406 | W | 2-0 | Finley 26 Rowe 58 | 4 | 29 |
| **13** | **FAT1r** | **A** | **Skelmersdale United** | **186** | **W** | **4-0** | **ROWE 3 (7 56 85) Blinkhorn 90** | | 30 |
| **16** | **FAT2** | **A** | **Eastbourne Borough** | **352** | **W** | **4-1** | **Langley 34 Lloyd 46 61 Rowe 83** | | 31 |
| 23 | Nat North | H | Worcester City | 511 | L | 2-3 | Charles 33 Rowe 49 | 4 | 32 |
| 30 | Nat North | A | AFC Telford United | 1035 | W | 2-1 | Rowe 7 Lloyd 40 | 4 | 33 |
| Feb 2 | Nat North | A | Chorley | 832 | L | 2-3 | Barnes 6 Rowe 9 | 4 | 34 |
| **6** | **FAT3Q** | **A** | **Gateshead** | **485** | **L** | **0-1** | | | 35 |
| 13 | Nat North | H | Gloucester City | 408 | W | 1-0 | Lloyd 10 | 3 | 36 |
| 16 | Nat North | A | Lowestoft Town | 438 | L | 1-3 | Rowe 36 | 4 | 37 |
| 27 | Nat North | H | Alfreton Town | 562 | L | 0-1 | | 6 | 38 |
| Mar 1 | Nat North | A | Nuneaton Town | 528 | D | 1-1 | Rowe 28 | 6 | 39 |
| 5 | Nat North | H | Boston United | 479 | W | 5-3 | Hughes 5 Hardy 45 Langley 61 Baker 69 Charles 90 | 4 | 40 |
| 8 | Nat North | H | Corby Town | 283 | W | 2-1 | Rowe 42 89 | 3 | 41 |
| 12 | Nat North | A | FC United | 3432 | W | 2-1 | Hannigan 32 Rowe 48 | 2 | 42 |
| 19 | Nat North | H | Nuneaton Town | 555 | D | 2-2 | Baker 81 Langley 89 | 3 | 43 |
| 28 | Nat North | A | Stockport County | 3399 | W | 4-0 | Hannigan 7 Charles 51 55 Rowe 82 | 3 | 44 |
| Apr 2 | Nat North | A | Brackley Town | 270 | D | 0-0 | | 3 | 45 |
| 5 | Nat North | A | Stalybridge Celtic | 234 | D | 1-1 | Finley 69 | 2 | 46 |
| 9 | Nat North | H | North Ferriby | 511 | L | 2-3 | Charles 45 Finley 83 | 3 | 47 |
| 11 | Nat North | H | Bradord PA | 406 | W | 1-0 | Crainey 44 | 2 | 48 |
| 16 | Nat North | A | Tamworth | 682 | L | 1-3 | Rowe 70 (pen) | 3 | 49 |
| 23 | Nat North | H | Harrogate Town | 660 | W | 2-1 | Rowe 41 Hardy 79 | 2 | 50 |
| 30 | Nat North | A | Worcester City | 689 | D | 2-2 | Rowe 31 33 | 3 | 51 |
| **May 3** | **PO SF1** | **A** | **Harrogate Town** | **1894** | **W** | **1-0** | **Rowe 53** | | 52 |
| **8** | **PO SF2** | **H** | **Harrogate Town** | **1384** | **D** | **1-1** | **Finley 11** | | 53 |
| **14** | **PO Final** | **A** | **North Ferriby United** | **1829** | **L** | **1-2** | **Finley 24** | | 54 |

| GOALSCORERS | Scoring Games | Consec Sco Games | Total |
|---|---|---|---|
| *2014-15 Rowe 30* | | | |
| Rowe | 24 | 7 | 34 |
| Charles | 14 | 2 | 16 |
| Lloyd | 8 | | 10 |
| M.Hughes | 6 | | 8 |
| Baker | 7 | 2 | 8 |
| Finley | 8 | | 8 |
| Blinkhorn | 3 | | 3 |
| Hardy | 3 | | 3 |
| Langley | 3 | | 3 |
| Hannigan | 2 | | 2 |
| C.Hughes | 2 | | 2 |
| Barnes | 1 | | 1 |
| Collins | 1 | | 1 |
| Crainey | 1 | | 1 |
| Lloyd-McGoldrick | 1 | | 1 |
| Whittle | 1 | | 1 |
| Wilson | 1 | | 1 |
| Wright | 1 | | 1 |
| Opposition | | | 1 |

# AFC TELFORD UNITED

**Chairman:** Ian Dosser
**Secretary:** Mrs Sharon Bowyer **(T)** 01952 640 064 **(E)** sharon.bowyer@telfordutd.co.uk
**Commercial Manager:** **(T/E)**
**Programme Editor:** **(T/E)**
**Ground Address:** New Bucks Head Stadium, Watling Street, Wellington, Telford TF1 2TU
**(T)** 01952 640 064 **Manager:** Rob Smith

## Club Factfile

**Founded:** 2004 **Nickname:** The Bucks
**Previous Names:** AFC Telford United was formed when Telford United folded in May 2004
**Previous Leagues:** As AFC Telford United: Northern Premier 2004-06
As Telford United: Southern 1969-79. Alliance/Conference 1979-2004
**Club Colours (change):** White/navy/white (Yellow/red/red)

**Ground Capacity:** 6,380 **Seats:** 2,200 **Covered:** 4,800 **Clubhouse:** Yes **Shop:** Yes

**Directions**
(Sat Nav follow TF1 2NW into Haybridge Road) From M54 Junction 6, A5223 towards Wellington, straight over first roundabout (retail park). Straight over second roundabout (B5067). Left at third roundabout (Furrows garage). Continue over railway bridge and follow road round to the right, then turn left into AFC Telford United Car Park.

**Previous Grounds:** None - Renovation of the old Bucks Head started in 2000 and was completed in 2003.

**Record Attendance:** 4,215 v Kendal Town - Northern Premier League play-off final
**Record Victory:** 7-0 v Runcorn (A) - Northern Premier League Division One 2005-06
**Record Defeat:** 3-6 v Bradford P.A. (H) - Northern Premier League Division One 2005-06
**Record Goalscorer:** Kyle Perry - 32 (2004-06)
**Record Appearances:** Stuart Brock - 132 (2004-09)
**Additional Records:** Paid £5,000 to Tamworth for Lee Moore 08/12/06
Received £33,000 from Burnley for Duane Courtney 31/08/05
**Honours:**
Northern Premier League Division 1 Play-off 2004-05, Premier Division Play-off 2006-07. Conference League Cup 2008-09.
Shropshire Senior Cup 2012-13. Conference North 2013-14.

**10 YEAR RECORD**

| 06-07 | 07-08 | 08-09 | 09-10 | 10-11 | 11-12 | 12-13 | 13-14 | 14-15 | 15-16 |
|---|---|---|---|---|---|---|---|---|---|
| NP P 3 | Conf N 2 | Conf N 4 | Conf N 11 | Conf N 2 | Conf 20 | Conf 24 | Conf N 1 | Conf 22 | Nat N 18 |

## AFC TELFORD UNITED MATCH RESULTS 2015-16

| Date | Comp | H/A | Opponents | Att: | Result | | Goalscorers | Pos | No. |
|---|---|---|---|---|---|---|---|---|---|
| Aug 8 | Nat North | A | Lowestoft Town | 539 | L | 0-3 | | 22 | 1 |
| 11 | Nat North | H | Curzon Ashton | 1180 | D | 0-0 | | 19 | 2 |
| 15 | Nat North | H | Stockport County | 1568 | L | 0-1 | | 21 | 3 |
| 18 | Nat North | A | Tamworth | 908 | L | 1-2 | Glover 47 (pen) | 22 | 4 |
| 22 | Nat North | H | Gainsborough Trinity | 1109 | L | 0-2 | | 22 | 5 |
| 29 | Nat North | A | Gloucester City | 425 | L | 0-1 | | 22 | 6 |
| 31 | Nat North | H | Brackley Town | 1212 | W | 2-0 | Clancy 12 Reid 23 | 22 | 7 |
| Sept 5 | Nat North | A | Bradford PA | 452 | L | 0-1 | | 22 | 8 |
| 12 | Nat North | H | Harrogate Town | 1173 | L | 0-4 | | 22 | 9 |
| 19 | Nat North | H | North Ferriby United | 1250 | D | 1-1 | Clancy 78 | 22 | 10 |
| **26** | **FAC2Q** | **A** | **Kettering Town** | **693** | **L** | **1-2** | **McCarthy 12** | **22** | **11** |
| Oct 3 | Nat North | A | AFC Fylde | 504 | L | 0-1 | | 22 | 12 |
| 10 | Nat North | A | Boston United | 1153 | L | 0-1 | | 22 | 13 |
| 17 | Nat North | H | Stalybridge Celtic | 1429 | W | 2-0 | Clancy 11 Hibbert 21 | 22 | 14 |
| 24 | Nat North | H | Boston United | 1158 | D | 2-2 | Paratore 7 Hibbert 36 | 22 | 15 |
| 31 | Nat North | H | Alfreton Town | 1107 | D | 1-1 | McCarthy 4 | 22 | 16 |
| Nov 3 | Nat North | A | FC United | 2781 | W | 3-1 | Clancy 20 Paratore 40 Hibbert 84 | 19 | 17 |
| 7 | Nat North | A | Corby Town | 612 | L | 2-3 | Hibbert 30 McCarthy 42 | 20 | 18 |
| 14 | Nat North | H | Nuneaton Town | 1416 | L | 1-5 | McCarthy 55 | 20 | 19 |
| 21 | Nat North | A | Worcester CIty | 726 | L | 0-3 | | 22 | 20 |
| **28** | **FAT3Q** | **A** | **FC United** | **1034** | **W** | **2-1** | **Tilt 11 Hassan 68** | | **21** |
| Dec 5 | Nat North | A | Curzon Ashton | 222 | L | 0-1 | | 22 | 22 |
| **12** | **FAT1** | **H** | **Chester** | **850** | **L** | **0-2** | | | **23** |
| 19 | Nat North | H | Lowestoft Town | 1136 | W | 1-0 | Samuels 63 | 22 | 24 |
| 26 | Nat North | A | Hednesford Town | 962 | L | 0-2 | | 22 | 25 |
| 28 | Nat North | H | Gloucester City | 1159 | L | 0-1 | | 22 | 26 |
| Jan 9 | Nat North | A | Stockport County | 2765 | W | 1-0 | Dawson 88 (pen) | 22 | 27 |
| 16 | Nat North | A | Gainsborough Trinity | 404 | D | 1-1 | Samuels 4 | 22 | 28 |
| 23 | Nat North | H | Bradford PA | 1080 | W | 3-1 | Bancessi 25 Cofie 45 Reid 88 | 22 | 29 |
| 26 | Nat North | H | Hednesford Town | 1257 | L | 1-3 | Hutchinson 28 | 22 | 30 |
| 30 | Nat North | H | AFC Fylde | 1016 | L | 1-2 | Cofie 14 | 22 | 31 |
| 9 | Nat North | H | FC United | 1323 | W | 5-1 | Cofie 40 Dawson 45 (pen) Hibbert 48 Samuels 79 Clancy 88 | 20 | 32 |
| Feb 13 | Nat North | A | Solihull Moors | 670 | L | 1-2 | Wilson 40 | 22 | 33 |
| 20 | Nat North | A | Stalybridge Celtic | 437 | D | 5-5 | Wilson 16 84 Wynter 45 McCarthy 63 90 | 22 | 34 |
| Mar 1 | Nat North | A | Alfreton Town | 547 | W | 3-2 | Wilson 65 79 McCarthy 83 | 20 | 35 |
| 5 | Nat North | H | Chorley | 1391 | W | 2-0 | Cofie 39 Dawson 45 (pen) | 19 | 36 |
| 12 | Nat North | A | Harrogate Town | 699 | W | 1-0 | Grogan 45 | 17 | 37 |
| 19 | Nat North | H | Corby Town | 1245 | W | 3-0 | Wilson 26 Dawson 64 (pen) Reid 78 | 17 | 38 |
| 26 | Nat North | H | Tamworth | 1508 | W | 1-0 | McCarthy 55 | 15 | 39 |
| Apr 2 | Nat North | A | Nuneaton Town | 754 | D | 0-0 | | 16 | 40 |
| 9 | Nat North | H | Solihull Moors | 1738 | L | 0-3 | | 17 | 41 |
| 16 | Nat North | A | North Ferriby United | 488 | L | 0-2 | | 18 | 42 |
| 19 | Nat North | A | Brackley Town | 360 | D | 0-0 | | 18 | 43 |
| 23 | Nat North | H | Worcester City | 1378 | W | 2-0 | Sharpe 77 (og) Clancy 90 | 17 | 44 |
| 30 | Nat North | A | Chorley | 1247 | L | 1-2 | Wilson 74 | 18 | 45 |

| GOALSCORERS | Scoring Games | Consec Sco Games | Total | | Scoring Games | Consec Sco Games | Total |
|---|---|---|---|---|---|---|---|
| *2014-15 Gray* | | | *19* | Bancessi | 1 | | 1 |
| McCarthy | 7 | 2 | 8 | Glover | 1 | | 1 |
| Wilson | 5 | | 7 | Grogan | 1 | | 1 |
| Clancy | 6 | | 6 | Hassan | 1 | | 1 |
| Hibbert | 5 | 2 | 5 | Hutchinson | 1 | | 1 |
| Cofie | 4 | | 4 | Tilt | 1 | | 1 |
| Dawson | 4 | | 4 | Wynter | 1 | | 1 |
| Reid | 3 | | 3 | Opponents | | | 1 |
| Samuels | 3 | | 3 | | | | |
| Paratore | 2 | | 2 | | | | |

# ALFRETON TOWN

**Chairman:** Wayne Bradley

**Secretary:** Bryan Rudkin **(T)** 07710 444 195 **(E)** bryanrudkin@hotmail.com

**Commercial Manager:** Rob Staniforth **(T/E)** 07986 236 225

**Programme Editor:** Lisa Towerzey **(T/E)** lisa@healthcaremedia.co.uk

**Ground Address:** Impact Arena, North Street, Alfreton, Derbyshire DE55 7FZ

**(T)** 01773 830 277 **Manager:** Nicky Law

The Hednesford 'keeper manages to deflect this corner away before the Alfreton duo can make an attempt on goal. Photo: Bill Wheatcroft.

## Club Factfile

**Founded:** 1959 **Nickname:** The Reds

**Previous Names:** Formed when Alfreton Miners Welfare and Alfreton United merged.

**Previous Leagues:** Central Alliance (pre reformation 1921-25) 59-61. Midland Combination 1925-27, 61-82. Northern Counties East 1982-87. Northern Premier 1987-99.

**Club Colours (change):** All red (All blue)

**Ground Capacity:** 3,600 **Seats:** 1,500 **Covered:** 2,600 **Clubhouse:** Yes **Shop:** Yes

**Directions**

From M1 Junction 28 Take A38 towards Derby for 2 miles.
Then take slip road onto B600 Turn right at Tjunction towards town centre.
At pedestrian crossing turn left into North Street and the ground is on the right hand side.

**Previous Grounds:** None

**Record Attendance:** 5,023 v Matlock Town - Central Alliance 1960

**Record Victory:** 15-0 v Loughbrough Midland League 1969-70

**Record Defeat:** 1-9 v Solihull - FAT 1997. 0-8 v Bridlington - 1992

**Record Goalscorer:** J Harrison - 303

**Record Appearances:** J Harrison - 560+

**Additional Records:** Paid £2,000 to Worksop Town for Mick Goddard
Received £7,000 from Ilkeston Town for Paul Eshelby

**Honours:**
Northern Counties East 1984-85, 2001-02. Northern Premier League Division 1 2002-03.
Conference North 2010-11.
Derbyshire Senior Cup x8 (Most recently 2015-16).

**10 YEAR RECORD**

| 06-07 | 07-08 | 08-09 | 09-10 | 10-11 | 11-12 | 12-13 | 13-14 | 14-15 | 15-16 |
|---|---|---|---|---|---|---|---|---|---|
| Conf N 14 | Conf N 16 | Conf N 3 | Conf N 3 | Conf N 1 | Conf 15 | Conf 13 | Conf 11 | Conf 21 | Nat N 10 |

## ALFRETON TOWN MATCH RESULTS 2015-16

| Date | Comp | H/A | Opponents | Att: | Result | | Goalscorers | Pos | No. |
|---|---|---|---|---|---|---|---|---|---|
| Aug 8 | Nat North | A | Bradford PA | 428 | D | 2-2 | Thanoj 64 Ironside 89 (pen) | 9 | 1 |
| 11 | Nat North | H | Lowestoft Town | 515 | L | 0-1 | | 15 | 2 |
| 15 | Nat North | H | Brackley Town | 612 | D | 1-1 | Austin 39 (og) | 16 | 3 |
| 18 | Nat North | A | Gloucester City | 372 | D | 1-1 | Allen 42 | 18 | 4 |
| 22 | Nat North | H | Curzon Ashton | 489 | D | 2-2 | Jones 15 Lesley 75 | 14 | 5 |
| 29 | Nat North | A | Solihull Moors | 425 | L | 1-2 | Jackson 44 | 18 | 6 |
| 31 | Nat North | H | Gainsborough Trinity | 576 | W | 1-0 | Allen 80 | 17 | 7 |
| Sept 5 | Nat North | A | Chorley | 1143 | W | 2-1 | Johnston 76 Robertson 77 | 17 | 8 |
| 12 | Nat North | H | Hednesford Town | 572 | W | 4-0 | Robertson 10 Jackson 62 Jones 73 82 | 9 | 9 |
| 15 | Nat North | H | Worcester City | 489 | W | 2-1 | Wilson 9 Robertson 20 | 6 | 10 |
| 19 | Nat North | A | Stockport County | 2839 | L | 0-1 | | 8 | 11 |
| **26** | **FAC2Q** | **A** | **Tamworth** | **663** | **W** | **3-2** | **Jackson 77 Robertson 89 (pen) Johnston 90** | | 12 |
| Oct 3 | Nat North | H | Stalybridge Celtic | 499 | L | 1-3 | Robertson 25 | 10 | 13 |
| **10** | **FAC3Q** | **A** | **Hednesford Town** | **569** | **W** | **4-2** | **ROBERTSON 3 (19 28 65) Bradley 21** | | 14 |
| 17 | Nat North | A | Boston United | 1126 | L | 1-2 | Jones 44 | 12 | 15 |
| **24** | **FAC4Q** | **A** | **Macclesfield Town** | **1048** | **L** | **2-3** | **Jones 39 Robertson 50** | | 16 |
| 31 | Nat North | A | AFCTelford United | 1107 | D | 1-1 | Jones 38 | 12 | 17 |
| Nov 7 | Nat North | A | Nuneaton Town | 654 | L | 0-2 | | 12 | 18 |
| 10 | Nat North | H | North Ferriby United | 473 | L | 0-1 | | 12 | 19 |
| 14 | Nat North | A | Harrogate Town | 607 | W | 2-1 | Thanoj 37 Johnson 54 | 12 | 20 |
| 21 | Nat North | H | Boston United | 602 | L | 1-2 | Ironside 83 | 12 | 21 |
| **28** | **FAT3Q** | **A** | **Nuneaton Town** | **467** | **L** | **0-2** | | | 22 |
| Dec 5 | Nat North | A | Lowestoft Town | 487 | L | 0-1 | | 14 | 23 |
| 8 | Nat North | H | AFC Fylde | 433 | L | 1-2 | Bradley 6 | 14 | 24 |
| 19 | Nat North | H | Bradford PA | 465 | L | 0-1 | | 16 | 25 |
| 26 | Nat North | A | Tamworth | 875 | W | 2-1 | Smith 5 Meikle 69 | 15 | 26 |
| 28 | Nat North | H | Solihull Moors | 546 | D | 2-2 | Smith 23 Bradley 73 (pen) | 16 | 27 |
| Jan 2 | Nat North | H | Tamworth | 626 | W | 1-0 | Bradley 89 | 13 | 28 |
| 9 | Nat North | A | Brackley Town | 375 | W | 4-1 | Jones 54 Bradley 56 Mills 75 (og) Wilson 76 | 12 | 29 |
| 23 | Nat North | H | Chorley | 605 | W | 1-0 | Meikle 82 | 11 | 30 |
| 30 | Nat North | H | Nuneaton Town | 610 | D | 2-2 | Jones 57 80 | 9 | 31 |
| Feb 1 | Nat North | A | Curzon Ashton | 271 | W | 2-0 | Jones 3 Jackson 49 | 9 | 32 |
| 13 | Nat North | A | FC United | 3338 | W | 3-1 | Meikle 60 Jones 69 Bradley 83 | 7 | 33 |
| 20 | Nat North | H | Corby Town | 573 | D | 1-1 | Jordan 19 | 9 | 34 |
| 27 | Nat North | A | AFC Fylde | 562 | W | 1-0 | Bradley 40 | 9 | 35 |
| Mar 1 | Nat North | H | AFC Telford United | 547 | L | 2-3 | Thanoj 58 Bradley 77 | 9 | 36 |
| 8 | Nat North | A | Worcester City | 351 | D | 1-1 | Jones 72 | 9 | 37 |
| 12 | Nat North | A | Hednesford Town | 421 | D | 3-3 | Heaton 32 Bradley 62 (pen) Smith 70 | 11 | 38 |
| 19 | Nat North | H | FC United | 1087 | L | 0-1 | | 11 | 39 |
| 26 | Nat North | H | Gloucester City | 513 | D | 1-1 | Smith 30 | 11 | 40 |
| 28 | Nat North | A | Gainsborough Trinity | 529 | D | 1-1 | Bradley 90 | 11 | 41 |
| Apr 2 | Nat North | A | Corby Town | 483 | W | 3-2 | Heaton 3 29 Leesley 89 | 10 | 42 |
| 9 | Nat North | H | Harrogate Town | 583 | W | 3-2 | Jordan 45 Jones 49 Jackson 74 | 9 | 43 |
| 19 | Nat North | A | Stalybridge Cletic | 252 | D | 1-1 | Jones 15 | 10 | 44 |
| 23 | Nat North | H | Stockport County | 837 | L | 0-3 | | 11 | 45 |
| 30 | Nat North | A | North Ferriby United | 484 | W | 1-0 | Smith 65 | 10 | 46 |

| GOALSCORERS | Scoring Games | Consec Sco Games | Total | | Scoring Games | Consec Sco Games | Total |
|---|---|---|---|---|---|---|---|
| ***2014-15 Hawley*** | | | ***10*** | Allen | 2 | | 2 |
| Jones | 12 | 3 | 14 | Ironside | 2 | | 2 |
| Bradley | 10 | 3 | 10 | Jordan | 2 | | 2 |
| Robertson | 7 | 3 | 9 | Leesley | 2 | | 2 |
| Jackson | 5 | | 5 | Wilson | 2 | | 2 |
| Smith | 5 | | 5 | Opponents | 1 | | 2 |
| Heaton | 2 | | 3 | | | | |
| Johnson | 3 | | 3 | | | | |
| Meikle | 3 | | 3 | | | | |
| Thanoj | 3 | | 3 | | | | |

# ALTRINCHAM

**Chairman:** Grahame Rowley

**Secretary:** Derek Wilshaw (T) 0161 928 1045 (E) dwilshaw@altrinchamfootballclub.co.uk

**Commercial Manager:** Matt Royle (T/E) 0161 928 1045

**Programme Editor:** Grahame Rowley (T/E) 0161 928 1045

**Ground Address:** The J Davidson Stadium, Moss Lane, Altrincham, Cheshire WA15 8AP

(T) 0161 928 1045 **Manager:** Neil Young - 02.05.16

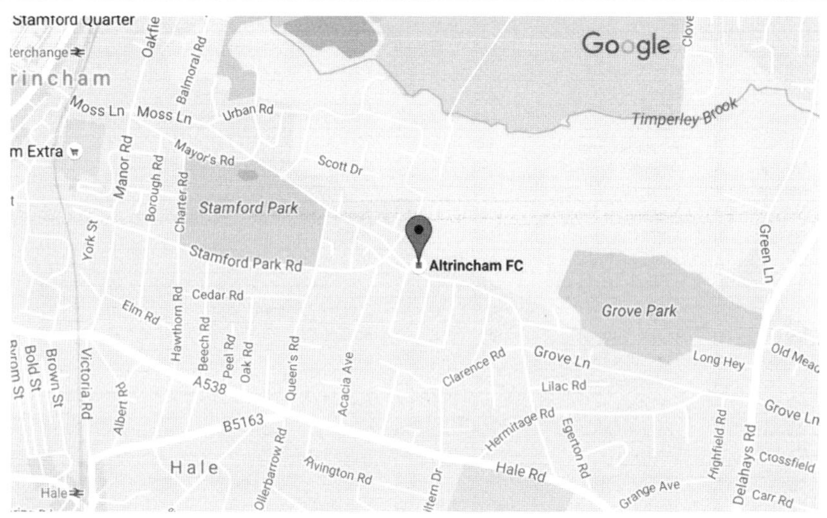


## Club Factfile

**Founded:** 1903 **Nickname:** The Robins

**Previous Names:** Broadheath FC 1893-1903.

**Previous Leagues:** Manchester 1903-11. Lancashire C. 1911-19. Cheshire C. 1919-68. Northern Premier 1968-79,97-99. Conference 1979-97, 99-

**Club Colours (change):** Red & white stripes/black/white. (Yellow/blue/yellow)

**Ground Capacity:** 6,085 **Seats:** 1,154 **Covered:** Yes **Clubhouse:** Yes **Shop:** Yes

**Directions**

From M6 junction19, turn right towards Altrincham into town centre (approx 15 minutes). Turn down Lloyd Street, past Sainsburys on the right. Tesco Extra on left. Then follow signs for Altrincham F.C.

**Previous Grounds:** Pollitts Field 1903-10.

**Record Attendance:** 10,275 - Altrincham Boys v Sunderland Boys English Schools Shield 1925.

**Record Victory:** 9-2 v Merthyr Tydfil - Conference 1990-91.

**Record Defeat:** 1-13 v Stretford (H) - 04.11.1893.

**Record Goalscorer:** Jack Swindells - 252 (1965-71).

**Record Appearances:** John Davison - 677 (1971-86).

**Additional Records:** Transfer fee paid - £15k to Blackpool for Keith Russell. Received - £50k from Leicester for Kevin Ellison.

**Honours:**

Cheshire Senior Cup Winners 1904-05, 33-34, 66-67, 81-82. F.A. Trophy Winners 1977-78, 85-86.
Football Alliance Champions 1979-80, 80-81. N.P.L. Premier Champions 1998-99.
Conference North & South Play-off Winners 2004-05.

**10 YEAR RECORD**

| 06-07 | 07-08 | 08-09 | 09-10 | 10-11 | 11-12 | 12-13 | 13-14 | 14-15 | 15-16 |
|---|---|---|---|---|---|---|---|---|---|
| Conf 21 | Conf 21 | Conf 15 | Conf 14 | Conf 22 | Conf N 8 | Conf N 4 | Conf N 3 | Conf 17 | Nat 22 |

# ALTRINCHAM MATCH RESULTS 2015-16

| Date | Comp | H/A | Opponents | Att: | Result | | Goalscorers | Pos | No. |
|---|---|---|---|---|---|---|---|---|---|
| Aug 8 | Nat Lge | H | Forest Green Rovers | 975 | L | 0 -1 | | 17 | 1 |
| 11 | Nat Lge | A | Guiseley | 797 | L | 0 -1 | | 21 | 2 |
| 15 | Nat Lge | A | Woking | 1297 | L | 0-2 | | 24 | 3 |
| 18 | Nat Lge | H | Grimsby Town | 1680 | W | 2-1 | Bowerman 13 60 | 19 | 4 |
| 22 | Nat Lge | A | Dover Athletic | 711 | L | 1-2 | Bowerman 41 | 21 | 5 |
| 29 | Nat Lge | H | Tranmere Rovers | 2460 | W | 2-1 | Bowerman 7 Rankine 29 | 17 | 6 |
| 31 | Nat Lge | A | Southport | 1143 | L | 0-3 | | 19 | 7 |
| Sept 5 | Nat Lge | H | Cheltenham Town | 1206 | W | 2-1 | Crowther 59 Heathcote 90 | 16 | 8 |
| 12 | Nat Lge | A | Wrexham | 4628 | L | 1-3 | Rankine 50 | 19 | 9 |
| 15 | Nat Lge | H | Eastleigh | 677 | D | 1-1 | Lawrie 29 | 19 | 10 |
| 19 | Nat Lge | H | Braintree Town | 861 | L | 0-4 | | 19 | 11 |
| 22 | Nat Lge | A | Lincoln City | 1893 | D | 1-1 | Crowther 16 | 19 | 12 |
| 26 | Nat Lge | A | Boreham Wood | 351 | W | 1-0 | Rankine 11 (pen) | 19 | 13 |
| Oct 3 | Nat Lge | H | Barrow | 1384 | W | 1-0 | Reeves 61 | 19 | 14 |
| 6 | Nat Lge | H | FC Halifax Town | 1119 | L | 1-3 | Reeves 58 | 19 | 15 |
| 10 | Nat Lge | A | Aldershot Town | 1412 | L | 0-2 | | 19 | 16 |
| 13 | Nat Lge | H | Kidderminster Harriers | 869 | D | 2-2 | Lawrie 21 Rankine 90 | 19 | 17 |
| 17 | Nat Lge | A | Gateshead | 911 | D | 2-2 | Rankine 77 Bowerman 79 | 19 | 18 |
| **24** | **FAC 4Q** | **H** | **Chester** | **1603** | **W** | **1-0** | **Reeves 51** | | 19 |
| 31 | Nat Lge | H | Torquay United | 1060 | D | 1-1 | Moult 66 | 19 | 20 |
| Nov 7 | FAC1 | H | Barnsley | 2571 | W | 1-0 | Reeves 46 | | 21 |
| 10 | Nat Lge | A | Macclesfield Town | 1801 | L | 0-3 | | 19 | 22 |
| 14 | Nat Lge | A | Bromley | 1737 | W | 3-1 | Reeves 18 51 O'Keefe 50 | | 23 |
| 21 | Nat Lge | H | Boreham Wood | 1002 | W | 1-0 | Clee 76 | 17 | 24 |
| 28 | Nat Lge | A | Forest Green Rovers | 1292 | L | 0-2 | | 18 | 25 |
| **Dec 5** | **FAC2** | **A** | **Colchester United** | **2592** | **L** | **2-3** | **Moult 3 Rankine 46** | | 26 |
| 15 | FAT1 | H | Leamington | 355 | D | 1-1 | Reeves 69 | | 27 |
| 19 | Nat Lge | A | Cheltenham Town | 2591 | L | 0-1 | | 19 | 28 |
| 28 | Nat Lge | A | Tranmere Rovers | 5414 | L | 0-1 | | | 29 |
| Jan 2 | Nat Lge | A | Chester | 2155 | D | 1-1 | Rankine 60 | 19 | 30 |
| **14** | **FAT1r** | **A** | **Leamington** | **332** | **W** | **2-1** | **Rankine 4 (pen) 100 (aet)** | | 31 |
| **16** | **FAT2** | **A** | **Bognor Regis Town** | **520** | **L** | **1-2** | **Lawrie 79** | | 32 |
| 23 | Nat Lge | A | Grimsby Town | 4323 | L | 0-5 | | 21 | 33 |
| 26 | Nat Lge | H | Woking | 826 | W | 3-1 | Rankine 12 (pen) Ginnelly 43 Margets 72 | 19 | 34 |
| Feb 6 | Nat Lge | A | Welling United | 551 | D | 1-1 | Rankine 58 | 19 | 35 |
| 9 | Nat Lge | H | Wrexham | 1261 | D | 1-1 | Ginnelly 11 | 19 | 36 |
| 13 | Nat Lge | H | Lincoln City | 1293 | D | 3-3 | Margetts 3 Ginnelly 11 Reeves 65 | 19 | 37 |
| 16 | Nat Lge | H | Chester | 1442 | L | 0-3 | | 19 | 38 |
| 20 | Nat Lge | H | Guiseley | 1137 | D | 1-1 | Rankine 41 | 19 | 39 |
| Mar 5 | Nat Lge | H | Macclesfield Town | 2014 | D | 0-0 | | 21 | 40 |
| 8 | Nat Lge | H | Gateshead | 805 | L | 2-3 | Holness 47 Moult 90 (pen) | 21 | 41 |
| 12 | Nat Lge | A | Barrow | 1019 | L | 2-3 | Sinnott 19 Lawrie 69 | 21 | 42 |
| 19 | Nat Lge | H | Aldershot Town | 1292 | W | 4-0 | Reeves 32 Ginnelly 47 Moult 61(Pen) Sinnott 69 | 20 | 43 |
| 26 | Nat Lge | A | FC Halifax Town | 1747 | L | 0-1 | | 20 | 44 |
| 28 | Nat Lge | H | Southport | 1480 | D | 1-1 | Ginnelly 60 | 21 | 45 |
| Apr 2 | Nat Lge | A | Kidderminster Harriers | 1402 | D | 1-1 | Reeves 9 | 21 | 46 |
| 5 | Nat Lge | H | Dover Athletic | 1007 | L | 1-2 | Rankine 35 | 22 | 47 |
| 9 | Nat Lge | H | Bromley | 1035 | D | 0-0 | | 22 | 48 |
| 12 | Nat Lge | A | Torquay United | 1995 | L | 0-2 | | 22 | 49 |
| 16 | Nat Lge | A | Eastleigh | 2054 | L | 0-2 | | 22 | 50 |
| 23 | Nat Lge | H | Welling United | 1396 | W | 5-0 | Sinnott 33 Rankine 45(pen) 90 Lawrie 50 Reeves 66 | 22 | 51 |
| 30 | Nat Lge | A | Braintree Town | 1803 | L | 0-3 | | 22 | 52 |

| GOALSCORERS | Scoring Games | Consec Sco Games | Total |
|---|---|---|---|
| ***2014-15 Reeves*** | | | ***21*** |
| Rankine | 13 | 2 | 15 |
| Reeves | 10 | 2 | 11 |
| Bowerman | 4 | 3 | 5 |
| Ginnelly | 5 | | 5 |
| Lawrie | 5 | | 5 |
| Moult | 4 | | 4 |
| Sinnott | 3 | | 3 |
| Crowther | 2 | | 2 |
| Margetts | 2 | | 2 |
| Clee | 1 | | 1 |
| Heathcote | 1 | | 1 |
| Holness | 1 | | 1 |
| O'Keefe | 1 | | 1 |

# BOSTON UNITED

**Chairman:** David Newton

**Secretary:** Craig Singleton (T) 07860 663 299 (E) craig.singleton@bufc.co.uk

**Commercial Manager:** Craig Singleton (T/E) 01205 364 406

**Programme Editor:** Craig Singleton (T/E) craig.singleton@bufc.co.uk

**Ground Address:** Jakemans Stadium, York Street, Boston PE21 6JN

(T) 01205 364 406 **Manager:** Dennis Greene

## Club Factfile

**Founded:** 1933 **Nickname:** The Pilgrims

**Previous Names:** Reformed as Boston United when Boston Town folded in 1933

**Previous Leagues:** Midland 1933-58, 62-64, Southern 1958-62, 98-2000, United Counties 1965-66, West Midlands 1966-68, Northern Premier 1968-79, 93-98, 2008-10, Alliance/Conference 1979-93, 2000-02, 07-08, Football League 2002-07

**Club Colours (change):** Amber and black halves/black/black (Green/white/green with white hoops)

**Ground Capacity:** 6,645 **Seats:** 5,711 **Covered:** 6,645 **Clubhouse:** Yes **Shop:** Yes

**Directions** A1 to A17 Sleaford to Boston-Over Boston Railway Station crossing, bear right at the Eagle Public House-To light over Haven Bridge-straight along John Adams Way(Dual Carriageway) -Turn right at traffic lights into main ridge, then right again into York Street(This is opposite Eagle Fisheries)-Ground is signposted after Railway crossing.

**Previous Grounds:** None

**Record Attendance:** 10,086 v Corby Town - Floodlights inauguration 1955

**Record Victory:** 12-0 v Spilsby Town - Grace Swan Cup 1992-93

**Record Defeat:** Not known.

**Record Goalscorer:** Chris Cook - 181

**Record Appearances:** Billy Howells - 500+

**Additional Records:** Paid £30,000 to Scarborough for Paul Ellender, 08/2001
Received £50,000 from Bolton Wanderers for David Norris 2000

**Honours:**
Central Alliance League 1961-62. United Counties League 1965-66. West Midlands League 1966-67, 67-68.
Northern Premier League 1972-73, 73-74, 76-77, 77-78, League Cup 1973-74, 75-76. Southern League 1999-2000. Conference 2001-02.

**10 YEAR RECORD**

| 06-07 | 07-08 | 08-09 | 09-10 | 10-11 | 11-12 | 12-13 | 13-14 | 14-15 | 15-16 |
|---|---|---|---|---|---|---|---|---|---|
| FL 2 23 | Conf N 10 | NP P 16 | NP P 3 | Conf N 3 | Conf N 11 | Conf N 16 | Conf N 6 | Conf N 3 | Nat N 5 |

## BOSTON UNITED MATCH RESULTS 2015-16

| Date | Comp | H/A | Opponents | Att: | Result | | Goalscorers | Pos | No. |
|---|---|---|---|---|---|---|---|---|---|
| Aug 8 | Nat North | A | Stockport County | 3396 | L | 1-2 | Southwell 59 | 16 | 1 |
| 11 | Nat North | H | Solihull Moors | 1140 | L | 1-4 | Southwell 82 (pen) | 21 | 2 |
| 15 | Nat North | H | Curzon Ashton | 1040 | W | 2-1 | Southwell 25 (pen) 43 (pen) | 16 | 3 |
| 18 | Nat North | A | Brackley Town | 311 | W | 3-1 | Piergianni 4 Jones 6 Rollins 74 | 8 | 4 |
| 22 | Nat North | H | Gloucester City | 990 | W | 1-0 | Southwell 69 | 8 | 5 |
| 29 | Nat North | A | Gainsborough Trinity | 846 | L | 0-1 | | 9 | 6 |
| 31 | Nat North | H | Tamworth | 1187 | D | 1-1 | Southwell 41 | 8 | 7 |
| Sept 5 | Nat North | A | Hednesford Town | 510 | L | 2-3 | Jones 61 Piergianni 80 | 14 | 8 |
| 12 | Nat North | H | Chorley | 1062 | L | 1-2 | Rollins 44 | 15 | 9 |
| 16 | Nat North | A | Corby Town | 613 | W | 3-2 | Southwell 12 50 Garner 88 | 11 | 10 |
| 19 | Nat North | H | AFC Fylde | 1094 | L | 0-3 | | 14 | 11 |
| **26** | **FAC2Q** | **A** | **Gainsborough Trinity** | **725** | **L** | **0-2** | | | 12 |
| Oct 3 | Nat North | A | Nuneaton Town | 774 | W | 3-1 | Robbins 18 Southwell 24 Garner 58 | 11 | 13 |
| 10 | Nat North | H | AFC Telford United | 1153 | W | 1-0 | Piergianni 48 | 8 | 14 |
| 17 | Nat North | H | Alfreton Town | 1126 | W | 2-1 | Roberts 31 Robbins 76 | 6 | 15 |
| 24 | Nat North | A | AFC Telford United | 1158 | D | 2-2 | Piergianni 56 Southwell 67 | 7 | 16 |
| 31 | Nat North | H | FC United | 1789 | W | 3-1 | Southwell 10 (pen) Richards 13 Piegianni 46 | 7 | 17 |
| Nov 7 | Nat North | A | North Ferriby United | 452 | L | 3-4 | Roberts 13 Piergianni 54 Dixon 83 | 7 | 18 |
| 10 | Nat North | H | Harrogate Town | 1074 | D | 3-3 | Southwell 36 Piergianni 63 Robbins 82 | 6 | 19 |
| 14 | Nat North | H | Corby Town | 1228 | W | 2-0 | Robbins 22 Felix 89 | 7 | 20 |
| 17 | Nat North | A | Worcester City | 307 | L | 1-2 | Southwell 50 | 7 | 21 |
| 21 | Nat North | A | Alfreton Town | 602 | W | 2-1 | Binco 2 62 | 6 | 22 |
| **28** | **FAT3Q** | **A** | **Solihull Moors** | **319** | **L** | **0-1** | | | 23 |
| Dec 5 | Nat North | A | Solihull Moors | 479 | W | 1-0 | Southwell 66 | 5 | 24 |
| 19 | Nat North | H | Stockport County | 1316 | W | 4-0 | Felix 19 Southwell 31 Jones 69 Hillard 73 | 5 | 25 |
| 26 | Nat North | A | Lowestoft Town | 696 | L | 0-3 | | 6 | 26 |
| 28 | Nat North | H | Gainsboroughfh Trinity | 1889 | W | 1-0 | Mills 46 | 4 | 27 |
| Jan 2 | Nat North | H | Lowestoft Town | 1491 | W | 4-1 | Sands 26 57 Hilliard 66 (pen) Jones 86 | 4 | 28 |
| 9 | Nat North | A | Curzon Ashton | 377 | W | 2-0 | Jones 49 Hilliard 70 | 3 | 29 |
| 23 | Nat North | H | Hednesford Town | 1269 | W | 3-1 | Roberts 15 Hilliard 84 Felix 88 | 3 | 30 |
| 31 | Nat North | A | Gloucester City | 657 | L | 0-1 | | 4 | 31 |
| Feb 13 | Nat North | H | Stalybridge Celtic | 1202 | L | 0-3 | | 5 | 32 |
| 24 | Nat North | A | Bradford PA | 402 | W | 2-1 | Rollins 1 Southwell 50 | 5 | 33 |
| 27 | Nat North | H | Worcester City | 1228 | D | 1-1 | Rollins 36 | 3 | 34 |
| Mar 5 | Nat North | A | AFC Fylde | 479 | L | 2-5 | Southwell 11 Jones 68 | 6 | 35 |
| 12 | Nat North | A | Chorley | 823 | L | 0-2 | | 6 | 36 |
| 19 | Nat North | H | North Ferriby United | 1279 | L | 1-2 | Southwell 22 | 7 | 37 |
| 26 | Nat North | H | Brackley Town | 1302 | L | 1-2 | Mills 90 | 7 | 38 |
| 28 | Nat North | A | Tamworth | 889 | W | 2-1 | Hilliard 40 Southwell 45 (Pen) | 5 | 39 |
| Apr 2 | Nat North | A | FC United | 3544 | W | 2-1 | Felix 2 Southwell 38 | 5 | 40 |
| 9 | Nat North | H | Bradford PA | 1370 | W | 3-0 | Piergianni 31 52 Southwell 68 | 5 | 41 |
| 16 | Nat North | A | Harrogate Town | 1027 | D | 0-0 | | 5 | 42 |
| 23 | Nat North | H | Nuneaton Town | 2037 | W | 2-1 | Felix 38 Rollins 50 | 5 | 43 |
| 30 | Nat North | A | Stalybridge Celtic | 945 | W | 5-0 | SOUTHWELL 3 (13 83 90) Rollins 40 Roberts 71 | 5 | 44 |
| **May 4** | **PO SF1** | **H** | **North Ferriby United** | **2592** | **W** | **2-0** | **Roberts 23 Mills 90** | | 45 |
| **8** | **PO SF1** | **A** | **North Ferriby United** | **2027** | **L** | **0-3** | | | 46 |

| GOALSCORERS | Scoring Games | Consec Sco Games | Total |
|---|---|---|---|
| *2014-15 Southwell* | | | *30* |
| Southwell | 20 | 3 | 24 |
| Piergianni | 8 | 4 | 8 |
| Jones | 6 | | 6 |
| Felix | 5 | | 5 |
| Hilliard | 5 | | 5 |
| Robbins | 5 | | 5 |
| Roberts | 4 | | 5 |
| Rollins | 5 | | 5 |
| Binco | 2 | 2 | 3 |
| Mills | 3 | | 3 |
| Garner | 2 | | 2 |
| Sands | 2 | | 2 |
| Dixon | 1 | | 1 |
| Richards | 1 | | 1 |

# BRACKLEY TOWN

**Chairman:** Francis Oliver
**Secretary:** Pat Ashby **(T)** 01280 704 077 **(E)** pat.ashby55@btinternet.com
**Commercial Manager:** Jan Butters **(T/E)** janenebutters@brackleytownfc.co.uk
**Programme Editor:** Steve Goodman **(T/E)** the-goodmans@o2.co.uk
**Ground Address:** St James Park, Churchill Way, Brackley NN13 7EJ
**(T)** 01280 704 077 **Manager:** Kevin Wilkin - Sept 2015

## Club Factfile

**Founded:** 1890 **Nickname:** Saints
**Previous Names:** None
**Previous Leagues:** Banbury & District, North Buckinghamshire, Hellenic 1977-83, 94-97, 99-2004, United Counties 1983-84, Southern 1997-99

**Club Colours (change):** Red and black stripes/black/black (Yellow with black trim/yellow/yellow with black top)

**Ground Capacity:** 3,500 **Seats:** 300 **Covered:** 1,500 **Clubhouse:** Yes **Shop:** Yes

**Directions**
Take A43 from Northampton or Oxford, or A422 from Banbury to large roundabout south of town. Take exit marked Brackley (South) and follow towards the town (Tesco store on left). Pass the Locomotive public house and take first turning right, signposted Football Club, into Churchill Way - road leads into Club car park.

**Previous Grounds:** Banbury Road, Manor Road, Buckingham Road > 1974

**Record Attendance:** 960 v Banbury United - 2005-06
**Record Victory:** Not known
**Record Defeat:** Not known
**Record Goalscorer:** Paul Warrington - 320
**Record Appearances:** Terry Muckelberg - 350
**Additional Records:** Received £2,000 from Oxford City for Phil Mason 1998

**Honours:**
Hellenic League Premier Division 1996-97, 2003-04, Division 1 Cup 1982-83. Southern League Division 1 Midlands 2006-07. Southern Premier Division 2011-12. Northamptonshire Senior Cup 2011-12, 14-15.

**10 YEAR RECORD**

| 06-07 | 07-08 | 08-09 | 09-10 | 10-11 | 11-12 | 12-13 | 13-14 | 14-15 | 15-16 |
|---|---|---|---|---|---|---|---|---|---|
| SthM 1 | SthP 8 | SthP 11 | SthP 5 | SthP 9 | SthP 1 | Conf N 3 | Conf N 7 | Conf N 18 | Nat N 19 |

## BRACKLEY TOWN MATCH RESULTS 2015-16

| Date | Comp | H/A | Opponents | Att: | Result | | Goalscorers | Pos | No. |
|---|---|---|---|---|---|---|---|---|---|
| Aug 8 | Nat North | H | Harrogate Town | 315 | W | 1-0 | Moyo 85 | 6 | 1 |
| 11 | Nat North | A | Nuneaton Town | 829 | L | 0-1 | | 9 | 2 |
| 15 | Nat North | A | Alfreton Town | 612 | D | 1-1 | Smith 70 | 11 | 3 |
| 18 | Nat North | H | Boston United | 311 | L | 1-3 | Graham 27 | 15 | 4 |
| 22 | Nat North | A | FC United | 2996 | L | 2-3 | Diggin 8 Moyo 83 | 15 | 5 |
| 29 | Nat North | H | Worcester City | 273 | W | 2-0 | Diggin 28 Mills 63 | 14 | 6 |
| 31 | Nat North | A | AFC Telford United | 1212 | L | 0-2 | | 19 | 7 |
| Sept 5 | Nat North | H | North Ferriby United | 238 | L | 2-4 | Whittall 33 Moyo 79 | 19 | 8 |
| 12 | Nat North | A | Stockport County | 2683 | D | 1-1 | Smith 64 | 18 | 9 |
| 15 | Nat North | H | Lowestoft Town | 208 | D | 2-2 | Diggin 1 45 | 18 | 10 |
| 19 | Nat North | H | Hednesford Town | 356 | D | 1-1 | Diggin 20 | 18 | 11 |
| **26** | **FAC2Q** | **A** | **Tooting & Mitcham** | **249** | **W** | **3-1** | **Smith 22 Whitall 63 Truelove 90** | | 12 |
| Oct 3 | Nat North | A | Bradford PA | 367 | L | 0-1 | | 21 | 13 |
| **10** | **FAC3Q** | **H** | **Rugby Town** | **409** | **D** | **1-1** | **Diggin 90** | | 14 |
| **13** | **FAC3Qr** | **A** | **Rugby Town** | **334** | **W** | **2-0** | **Batchelor 4 Diggin 80** | | 15 |
| 17 | Nat North | H | Gainsborough Trinity | 192 | W | 3-2 | Mills 25 78 Akinyunde 50 | 16 | 16 |
| **24** | **FAC4Q** | **H** | **Bamber Bridge** | **451** | **W** | **3-0** | **Diggin 17 78 Batchelor 83** | | 17 |
| 31 | Nat North | A | Chorley | 987 | L | 0-1 | | 18 | 18 |
| **Nov 7** | **FAC1** | **H** | **Newport County** | **1707** | **D** | **2-2** | **Graham 59 McDonald 90** | | 19 |
| 14 | Nat North | A | AFC Fylde | 345 | D | 2-2 | Diggin 41 Walker 56 | 19 | 20 |
| **17** | **FAC1r** | **A** | **Newport County** | **1511** | **L** | **1-4** | **Hawtin 39** | | 21 |
| 21 | Nat North | H | Stalybridge Celtic | 203 | L | 2-3 | Moyo 47 Diggin 50 | 21 | 22 |
| **28** | **FAT3Q** | **H** | **Worcester City** | **227** | **L** | **0-2** | | | 23 |
| Dec 1 | Nat North | H | Curzon Ashton | 174 | W | 2-0 | Diggin 25 Mills 62 | 17 | 24 |
| 5th | Nat North | H | Gloucester City | 240 | W | 1-0 | Diggin 84 | 15 | 25 |
| 19 | Nat North | A | Harrogate Town | 1534 | L | 0-1 | | 17 | 26 |
| 26 | Nat North | H | Corby Town | 475 | L | 1-2 | Smith 45 | 20 | 27 |
| 28 | Nat North | A | Worcester City | 647 | D | 0-0 | | 20 | 28 |
| Jan 2 | Nat North | A | Corby Town | 603 | D | 1-1 | Winters 69 | 20 | 29 |
| 5 | Nat North | A | Solihull Moors | 410 | L | 0-3 | | 20 | 30 |
| 9 | Nat North | H | Alfreton Town | 375 | L | 1-4 | Diggin 26 | 20 | 31 |
| 16 | Nat North | H | FC United | 660 | W | 4-0 | Walker 11 Moyo 39 Diggin 50 Winters 72 | 19 | 32 |
| 23 | Nat North | A | N. Ferriby United | 406 | L | 1-2 | Moyo 59 | 19 | 33 |
| 30 | Nat North | H | Solihull Moors | 334 | L | 0-1 | | 20 | 34 |
| Feb 8 | Nat North | A | Tamworth | 406 | W | 2-1 | Diggin 39 87 | 18 | 35 |
| 9 | Nat North | A | Gainsborough Trinity | 252 | L | 0-1 | | 18 | 36 |
| 13 | Nat North | H | Nuneaton Town | 365 | L | 2-3 | Lowe 1 Batchelor 62 | 18 | 37 |
| 20 | Nat North | H | Stockport County | 436 | L | 0-1 | | 20 | 38 |
| 27 | Nat North | A | Hednesford Town | 355 | W | 2-0 | Ndlovu 20 Diggin 39 | 19 | 39 |
| Mar 5 | Nat North | A | Lowestoft Town | 506 | W | 2-1 | Moyo 30 English 66 | 18 | 40 |
| 12 | Nat North | H | Bradford PA | 468 | D | 0-0 | | 19 | 41 |
| 19 | Nat North | A | Stalybridge Celtic | 401 | L | 1-2 | Wisdom 42 (og) | 20 | 42 |
| 26 | Nat North | A | Boston United | 1302 | W | 2-1 | Moyo 30 Batchelor 90 | 19 | 43 |
| Apr 2 | Nat North | H | ADC Fylde | 270 | D | 0-0 | | 19 | 44 |
| 9 | Nat North | A | Gloucester City | 364 | D | 0-0 | | 19 | 45 |
| 16 | Nat North | H | Chorley | 325 | D | 1-1 | Walker 20 | 19 | 46 |
| 19 | Nat North | H | AFC Telford United | 360 | D | 0-0 | | 19 | 47 |
| 23 | Nat North | A | Curzon Ashton | 184 | D | 1-1 | Moyo 53 | 20 | 48 |
| 30 | Nat North | H | Tamworth | 600 | W | 1-0 | Walker 52 | 19 | 49 |

| GOALSCORERS | Scoring Games | Consec Sco Games | Total |
|---|---|---|---|
| *2014-15 Rowe* | | | *9* |
| Diggin | 15 | 2 | 18 |
| Moyo | 9 | | 9 |
| Batchelor | 4 | | 4 |
| Mills | 4 | | 4 |
| Smith | 4 | | 4 |
| Walker | 4 | | 4 |
| Graham | 2 | | 2 |
| Whittall | 2 | | 2 |
| Winters | 2 | | 2 |
| Akinyunde | 1 | | 1 |
| English | 1 | | 1 |
| Hawtin | 1 | | 1 |
| Lowe | 1 | | 1 |
| McDonald | 1 | | 1 |
| Ndlovu | 1 | | 1 |
| Truelove | 1 | | 1 |
| Opponents | | | 1 |

# BRADFORD PARK AVENUE

**Chairman:** Dr. John Dean
**Secretary:** Colin Barker (T) 07863 180 787 (E) colin.barker1@tesco.net
**Commercial Manager:** Robin Eaves (T/E) 01274 604 578
**Programme Editor:** Joe Cockburn (T/E) joe.cockburn@bpafc.com
**Ground Address:** Horsfall Stadium, Cemetery Road, Bradford, West Yorkshire BD6 2NG
(T) 01274 604 578 **Manager:** Alex Meechan - July 2016

## Club Factfile

**Founded:** 1907 **Nickname:** Avenue
**Previous Names:** Reformed in 1988
**Previous Leagues:** Southern 1907-08, Football League 1908-70, Northern Premier 1970-74, West Riding Co.Am. 1988-89, Central Midlands 1989-90, North West Counties 1990-95

**Club Colours (change):** All white (Amber/black/red)

**Ground Capacity:** 5,000 **Seats:** 1,247 **Covered:** 2,000 **Clubhouse:** Yes **Shop:** Yes

**Directions**
M62 to junction 26. Join M606 leave at second junction. At the roundabout take 2nd exit (A6036 signposted Halifax) and pass Odsal Stadium on the left hand side. At next roundabout take the 3rd exit (A6036 Halifax, Horsfall Stadium is signposted). After approximately one mile turn left down Cemetery Road immediately before the Kings Head Public House. Ground is 150 yards on the left.

**Previous Grounds:** Park Ave. 1907-73, Valley Parade 1973-74, Manningham Mills 1988-89, McLaren Field 1985-93, Batley 1993-96

**Record Attendance:** 2,100 v Bristol City - FA Cup 1st Round 2003
**Record Victory:** 11-0 v Derby Dale - FA Cup 1908
**Record Defeat:** 0-7 v Barnsley - 1911
**Record Goalscorer:** Len Shackleton - 171 (1940-46)
**Record Appearances:** Tommy Farr - 542 (1934-50)
**Additional Records:** Paid £24,500 to Derby County for Leon Leuty 1950
Received £34,000 from Derby County for Kevin Hector 1966
**Honours:**
Football League Division 3 North 1928. North West Counties League 1994-95.
Northern Premier League Division 1 2000-01, Division 1 North 2007-08. Premier Division Play-offs 2011-12.
West Riding Senior Cup x9. West Riding County Cup 1990-91, 2014-15, 15-16.

**10 YEAR RECORD**

| 06-07 | | 07-08 | | 08-09 | | 09-10 | | 10-11 | | 11-12 | | 12-13 | | 13-14 | | 14-15 | | 15-16 | |
|---|---|---|---|---|---|---|---|---|---|---|---|---|---|---|---|---|---|---|---|
| NP 1 | 4 | NP1N | 1 | NP P | 7 | NP P | 2 | NP P | 3 | NP P | 4 | Conf N | 7 | Conf N | 10 | Conf N | 13 | Nat N | 14 |

# BRADFORD PARK AVENUE MATCH RESULTS 2015-16

| Date | Comp | H/A | Opponents | Att: | Result | | Goalscorers | Pos | No. |
|---|---|---|---|---|---|---|---|---|---|
| Aug 8 | Nat North | H | Alfreton Town | 428 | D | 2-2 | Potts 18 32 | 10 | 1 |
| 11 | Nat North | A | Stalybridge Celtic | 407 | D | 1-1 | Potts 40 | 12 | 2 |
| 15 | Nat North | A | Nuneaton Town | 765 | L | 0-1 | | 17 | 3 |
| 19 | Nat North | H | AFC Fylde | 303 | L | 1-2 | Walshaw 42 | 19 | 4 |
| 22 | Nat North | A | Corby Town | 609 | L | 0-2 | | 21 | 5 |
| 29 | Nat North | H | North Ferriby United | 226 | D | 4-4 | CHILAKA 3 (15 20 68) Marshall 56 | 20 | 6 |
| 31 | Nat North | A | Harrogate Town | 678 | L | 1-2 | Marshall 40 | 24 | 7 |
| Sept 5 | Nat North | H | AFC Telford United | 452 | W | 1-0 | Chilaka 60 | 22 | 8 |
| 12 | Nat North | H | Solihull Moors | 332 | D | 1-1 | Chilaka 6 | 20 | 9 |
| 19 | Nat North | A | Tamworth | 754 | D | 0-0 | | 20 | 10 |
| **26** | **FAC2Q** | **A** | **Consett** | **616** | **W** | **2-1** | **Chilaka 83 Marshall 90** | | 11 |
| Oct 3 | Nat North | H | Brackley Town | 367 | W | 1-0 | Dean 57 | 18 | 12 |
| **10** | **FAC3Q** | **A** | **Salford City** | **534** | **D** | **1-1** | **Marshall 60 (pen)** | | 13 |
| **14** | **FAC3Qr** | **H** | **Salford City** | **426** | **L** | **0-1** | **(aet)** | | 14 |
| 17 | Nat North | H | Gloucester City | 325 | D | 1-1 | Walshaw 35 (pen) | 17 | 15 |
| 24 | Nat North | A | Stockport County | 3234 | L | 0-2 | | 17 | 16 |
| 31 | Nat North | H | Lowestoft Town | 279 | W | 3-0 | Marshall 12 (pen) 46 Chilaka 29 | 14 | 17 |
| Nov 14 | Nat North | A | Chorley | 918 | D | 2-2 | Walshaw 72 90 | 15 | 18 |
| 21 | Nat North | H | Hednesford Town | 284 | D | 1-1 | St Juste 79 | 16 | 19 |
| 24 | Nat North | A | Gloucester City | 269 | W | 3-1 | Jones (og) 22 Chilaka 26 Marshall 62 pen) | 13 | 20 |
| Dec 5 | Nat North | H | Stalybridge Celtic | 319 | W | 3-1 | King 51 Marshall 65 Chilaka 89 | 13 | 21 |
| **8** | **FAT3Q** | **A** | **Buxton** | **208** | **W** | **2-1** | **Marshall 80 Chilaka 82** | | 22 |
| 19 | Nat North | A | Alfreton Town | 465 | W | 1-0 | King 15 | 12 | 23 |
| **21** | **FAT1** | **A** | **Lincoln City** | **360** | **W** | **2-1** | **Turner 30 King 75** | | 24 |
| 28 | Nat North | A | North Ferriby United | 539 | L | 0-1 | | 13 | 25 |
| Jan 2 | Nat North | A | FC United | 3370 | L | 1-2 | Colley 82 | 14 | 26 |
| **16** | **FAT2** | **H** | **Nantwich Town** | **207** | **D** | **1-1** | **Potts 73** | | 27 |
| 23 | Nat North | A | AFC Telford United | 1080 | L | 1-3 | Ainge 27 | 17 | 28 |
| **25** | **FAT2r** | **A** | **Nantwich Town** | **281** | **L** | **0-5** | | | 29 |
| 30 | Nat North | A | Guisborough Trinity | 431 | W | 1-0 | Chilaka 19 | 17 | 30 |
| Feb 13 | Nat North | H | Stockport County | 678 | D | 0-0 | | 17 | 31 |
| 17 | Nat North | H | FC United | 619 | W | 3-1 | Turner 13 Colley 67 Priestley 76 | 15 | 32 |
| 20 | Nat North | A | Lowestoft Town | 627 | L | 0-3 | | 15 | 33 |
| 24 | Nat North | H | Boston United | 402 | L | 1-2 | King 60 | 15 | 34 |
| 27 | Nat North | A | Curzon Ashton | 240 | L | 1-2 | Chippendale 23 | 17 | 35 |
| Mar 5 | Nat North | H | Curzon Ashton | 296 | W | 4-2 | Chilaka 53 65 Marshall 63 (pen) St Juste 83 | 16 | 36 |
| 12 | Nat North | A | Brackley Town | 468 | D | 0-0 | | 15 | 37 |
| 19 | Nat North | H | Tamworth | 296 | L | 0-2 | | 18 | 38 |
| 23 | Nat North | H | Chorley | 382 | W | 1-0 | Chilaka 55 | 16 | 39 |
| 28 | Nat North | H | Harrogate Town | 446 | W | 3-1 | Chilaka 12 Qualter 38 Mottley-Henry 89 | 14 | 40 |
| Apr 2 | Nat North | A | Solihull Moors | 569 | L | 1-2 | Marshall 41 | 15 | 41 |
| 5 | Nat North | A | Worcester City | 434 | L | 1-3 | Chilaka 23 | 16 | 42 |
| 9 | Nat North | H | Boston United | 1370 | L | 0-3 | | 16 | 43 |
| 11 | Nat North | A | AFC Fylde | 406 | L | 0-1 | | 16 | 44 |
| 13 | Nat North | H | Corby Town | 251 | W | 1-0 | Mottley-Henrym 78 | 14 | 45 |
| 16 | Nat North | H | Worcester City | 336 | W | 3-1 | WEBB-FOSTER 3 (19 35 42) | 12 | 46 |
| 23 | Nat North | A | Hednesford T | 287 | D | 0-0 | | 14 | 47 |
| 27 | Nat North | H | Nuneaton Town | 287 | L | 2-3 | Chilaka 64 87 | 14 | 48 |
| 30 | Nat North | H | Gainsborough Trinity | 345 | L | 1-4 | Colley 83 | 14 | 49 |

| GOALSCORERS | Scoring Games | Consec Sco Games | Total | | Scoring Games | Consec Sco Games | Total |
|---|---|---|---|---|---|---|---|
| *2014-15 Chilaka* | | | *15* | Turner | 2 | | 2 |
| Chilaka | 14 | 3 | 18 | Ainge | 1 | | 1 |
| Marshall | 10 | 3 | 11 | Chippendale | 1 | | 1 |
| King | 4 | | 4 | Dean | 1 | | 1 |
| Potts | 3 | 2 | 4 | Priestley | 1 | | 1 |
| Walshaw | 3 | | 4 | Qualter | 1 | | 1 |
| Colley | 3 | | 3 | Opponents | | | 1 |
| Webb-Foster | 1 | | 3 | | | | |
| Mottley-Henry | 2 | | 2 | | | | |
| St Juste | 2 | | 2 | | | | |

# CHORLEY

**Chairman:** Ken Wright
**Secretary:** Graham Watkinson (T) 0773 995 2167 (E) graham.watkinson@chorleyfc.com
**Commercial Manager:** John Derbyshire (T/E) 01257 230 007
**Programme Editor:** Josh Vosper (T/E) 01257 230 007
**Ground Address:** Victory Park Stadium, Duke Street, Chorley, Lancashire PR7 3DU
(T) 01257 230 007 **Manager:** Matt Jansen

## Club Factfile

**Founded:** 1883 **Nickname:** Magpies
**Previous Names:** None
**Previous Leagues:** Lancashire Alliance 1890-94, Lancashire 1894-1903, Lancashire Combination 1903-68, 69-70, Northern Premier 1968-69, 70-72, 82-88, Cheshire County 1970-82, Conference 1988-90

**Club Colours (change):** Black and white stripes/black/black (All green)

**Ground Capacity:** 4,100 **Seats:** 900 **Covered:** 2,800 **Clubhouse:** Yes **Shop:** Yes

**Directions**

M61 leave at junction 6, follow A6 to Chorley, going past the Yarrow Bridge Hotel on Bolton Road. Turn left at first set of traffic lights into Pilling Lane, first right into Ashley St. Ground 2nd entrance on left.

M6 junction 27, follow Chorley, turn left at lights, A49 continue for 2 ½ miles, turn right onto B5251. Drive through Coppull and into Chorley for about 2 miles. On entering Chorley turn right into Duke Street 200 yards past Plough Hotel. Turn right into Ashby Street after Duke Street school, and first right into Ground.

**Previous Grounds:** Dole Lane 1883-1901, Rangletts Park 1901-05, St George's Park 1905-20

**Record Attendance:** 9,679 v Darwen - FA Cup 1931-32
**Record Victory:** Not known
**Record Defeat:** Not known
**Record Goalscorer:** Peter Watson - 371 (158-66)
**Record Appearances:** Not known
**Additional Records:** Received £30,000 from Newcastle United for David Eatock 1996

**Honours:**
Lancashire Alliance 1892-93. Lancashire League 1896-97, 98-99. Lancashire Combination x11.
Cheshire County League 1975-76, 76-77, 81-82. Northern Premier League 1987-88.
Lancashire FA Trophy x17 (Record) Most recently 2015-16. Lancashire Combination League cup x3. Northern Premier Premier Division 2013-14.

### 10 YEAR RECORD

| 06-07 | 07-08 | 08-09 | 09-10 | 10-11 | 11-12 | 12-13 | 13-14 | 14-15 | 15-16 |
|---|---|---|---|---|---|---|---|---|---|
| NP 1 23 | NP1N 14 | NP1N 14 | NP1N 16 | NP1N 3 | NP P 3 | NP P 8 | NP P 1 | Conf N 4 | Nat N 8 |

# CHORLEY MATCH RESULTS 2015-16

| Date | Comp | H/A | Opponents | Att: | Result | | Goalscorers | Pos | No. |
|---|---|---|---|---|---|---|---|---|---|
| Aug 8 | Nat North | H | Nuneaton Town | 1011 | L | 2-3 | Carver 39 Hine 86 | 15 | 1 |
| 11 | Nat North | A | North Ferriby United | 335 | L | 0-4 | | 22 | 2 |
| 15 | Nat North | A | Corby Town | 759 | D | 2-2 | Whitham 25 Hine 43 | 22 | 3 |
| 18 | Nat North | H | FC United | 1876 | W | 3-0 | Hine 11 89 Stephenson 61 | 12 | 4 |
| 22 | Nat North | A | Worcester City | 575 | W | 3-2 | McDonald 46 (og) Stephenson 50 Guy 89 | 10 | 5 |
| 29 | Nat North | H | Harrogate Town | 1033 | L | 0-1 | | 15 | 6 |
| 31 | Nat North | A | Stalybridge Celtic | 577 | W | 1-0 | Hine 84 | 10 | 7 |
| Sept 5 | Nat North | H | Alfreton Town | 1142 | L | 1-2 | Bond 36 | 13 | 8 |
| 12 | Nat North | A | Boston United | 1062 | W | 2-1 | Hine 60 67 | 10 | 9 |
| 15 | Nat North | H | Stockport County | 1530 | W | 1-0 | Stephenson 26 | 7 | 10 |
| 19 | Nat North | A | Lowestoft Town | 588 | L | 0-2 | | 9 | 11 |
| 26 | FAC2Q | H | Frickley Athletic | 542 | W | 2-0 | Dean 60 (pen) 88 | | 12 |
| Oct 3 | Nat North | H | Solihull Moors | 1205 | D | 2-2 | Doyle 21 Daly 31 (og) | 9 | 13 |
| 10 | FAC3Q | A | Whitley Bay | 782 | W | 3-2 | Bond 48 Cottrell 51 Stephenson 79 | | 14 |
| 17 | Nat North | H | Hednesford Town | 1057 | D | 2-2 | Carver 80 Hine 83 | 10 | 15 |
| 23 | FAC4Q | A | Northwich Victoria | 534 | D | 0-0 | | | 16 |
| 27 | FAC4Qr | H | Northwich Victoria | 1020 | L | 1-2 | Bond 42 | | 17 |
| 31 | Nat North | H | Brackley Town | 987 | W | 1-0 | Stephenson 7 | 10 | 18 |
| Nov 7 | Nat North | A | Stockport County | 3408 | W | 3-1 | Cottrell 39 Stephenson 54 Hine 62 | | 19 |
| 14 | Nat North | H | Bradford PA | 918 | D | 2-2 | Stephenson 4 Doyle 15 | 9 | 20 |
| 21 | Nat North | A | Curzon Ashton | 425 | L | 2-4 | Bond 27 Lynch 59 | 9 | 21 |
| 24 | Nat North | A | Gainsborough Trinity | 353 | L | 1-2 | Jarvis 74 | 9 | 22 |
| 28 | FAT3Q | H | Skelmersdale United | 543 | D | 0-0 | | | 23 |
| Dec 1 | FAT3Qr | A | Skelmersdale United | 277 | L | 2-5 | Lynch 9 Whitham 42 | | 24 |
| 5 | Nat North | H | North Feriby United | 675 | L | 2-3 | Hine 37 Cottrell 38 | 10 | 25 |
| 19 | Nat North | A | Nuneaton Town | 620 | D | 2-2 | Teague 8 Stephenson 31 | 13 | 26 |
| 28 | Nat North | A | Harrogate Town | 642 | W | 4-2 | Stephenson 27 29 Teague 42 Ellis 66 (og) | 11 | 27 |
| Jan 2 | Nat North | A | AFC Fylde | 903 | L | 0-1 | | 11 | 28 |
| 9 | Nat North | H | Corby Town | 1011 | W | 3-0 | Hine 19 33 Roscoe 42 | 8 | 29 |
| 23 | Nat North | A | Alfreton Town | 605 | L | 0-1 | | 13 | 30 |
| 30 | Nat North | H | Tamworth | 918 | D | 1-1 | Stephenson 79 | 12 | 31 |
| Feb 2 | Nat North | H | AFC Fylde | 632 | W | 3-2 | Lynch 21 Connerton 34 Bond 68 | 9 | 32 |
| 13 | Nat North | H | Worcester City | 887 | W | 2-0 | Connerton 60 Whitham 64 | 10 | 33 |
| 16 | Nat North | H | Gloucester City | 668 | L | 0-1 | | 10 | 34 |
| 20 | Nat North | A | Hednesford Town | 404 | W | 3-1 | Connerton 30 71 Whitham 64 | 8 | 35 |
| 27 | Nat North | H | Nuneaton Town | 913 | W | 2-0 | Roscoe 26 Stephenson 90 | 8 | 36 |
| Mar 1 | Nat North | A | Gloucester City | 262 | D | 1-1 | Stephenson 39 | 8 | 37 |
| 5 | Nat North | A | AFC Telford United | 1391 | L | 0-2 | | 8 | 38 |
| 12 | Nat North | H | Boston United | 823 | W | 2-0 | Meppen-Walter 45 Stephenson 84 | 8 | 39 |
| 19 | Nat North | H | Curzon Ashton | 828 | W | 2-0 | Connerton 2 Roscoe 43 | 8 | 40 |
| 23 | Nat North | A | Bradford PA | 382 | L | 0-1 | | 8 | 41 |
| 26 | Nat North | A | FC United | 4150 | L | 0-2 | | 8 | 42 |
| 28 | Nat North | H | Stalybridge Celtic | 867 | D | 0-0 | | 8 | 43 |
| Apr 2 | Nat North | A | Tamworth | 641 | L | 1-2 | Stephenson 90 | 8 | 44 |
| 8 | Nat North | H | Gainsborough Trinity | 643 | W | 3-1 | Charnock 10 Evans 45 Stephenson 79 | 8 | 45 |
| 16 | Nat North | A | Brackley Town | 325 | D | 1-1 | Batchelor 68 (og) | 8 | 46 |
| 23 | Nat North | A | Solihull Moors | 952 | W | 2-0 | Stephenson 77 Whitham 87 | 8 | 47 |
| 30 | Nat North | H | AFC Telford United | 1247 | W | 2-1 | Stephenson 22 89 (pen) | 8 | 48 |

| GOALSCORERS | Scoring Games | Consec Sco Games | Total | | Scoring Games | Consec Sco Games | Total |
|---|---|---|---|---|---|---|---|
| *2014-15 Dean* | | | *24* | Dean | 2 | | 2 |
| Stephenson | 17 | 3 | 19 | Doyle | 2 | | 2 |
| Hine | 9 | 2 | 12 | Teague | 2 | | 2 |
| Bond | 5 | | 5 | Charnock | 1 | | 1 |
| Connerton | 4 | | 5 | Evans | 1 | | 1 |
| Whitham | 5 | | 5 | Guy | 1 | | 1 |
| Cottrell | 3 | | 3 | Jarvis | 1 | | 1 |
| Lynch | 3 | | 3 | Meppen-Walter | 1 | | 1 |
| Roscoe | 3 | | 3 | Opponents | | | 4 |
| Carver | 2 | | 2 | | | | |

# CURZON ASHTON

**Chairman:** Harry Twamley

**Secretary:** Robert Hurst **(T)** 0161 330 6033 **(E)** rob@curzon-ashton.co.uk

**Commercial Manager:** 0161 330 6033 **(T/E)**

**Programme Editor:** 0161 330 6033 **(T/E)**

**Ground Address:** Tameside Stadium, Richmond Street, Ashton-u-Lyme OL7 9HG

**(T)** 0161 330 6033 **Manager:** John Flanagan

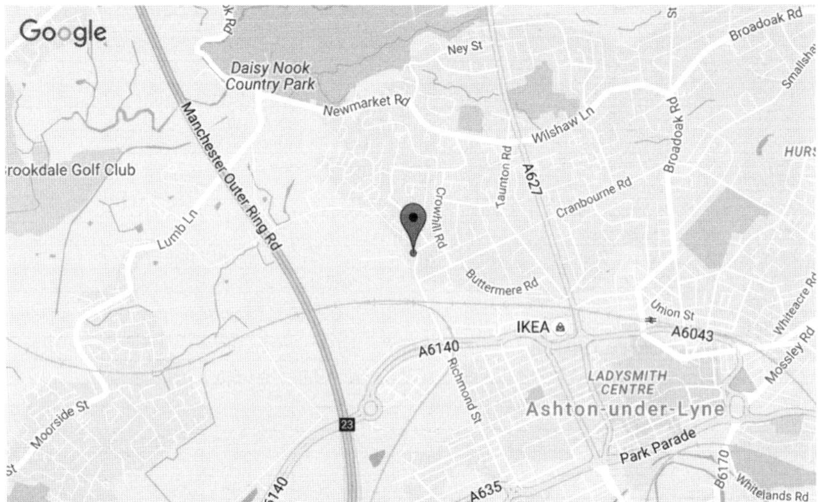


## Club Factfile

**Founded:** 1963 **Nickname:** Curzon

**Previous Names:** Club formed when Curzon Road and Ashton Amateurs merged.

**Previous Leagues:** Manchester Amateur, Manchester > 1978, Cheshire County 1978-82, North West Counties 1982-87, 98-2007, Northern Premier 1987-97, 2007-15, Northern Counties East 1997-98,

**Club Colours (change):** All royal blue (All red)

**Ground Capacity:** 4,000 **Seats:** 527 **Covered:** 1,100 **Clubhouse:** Yes **Shop:** Yes

**Directions** From Stockport (south) direction Leave the M60 at junc 23 (Ashton-U-Lyne). Turn left at the top of the slip road, go straight through the next set of lights, and bear right (onto Lord Sheldon Way) at the next set. Continue on this road until you come to a set of traffic lights with the Cineworld Cinema on your right. Turn left here onto Richmond St. Over the bridge, across the mini-roundabout and then first left down to the ground. From Oldham (north) direction Leave the M60 at junc 23 (Ashton-U-Lyne) and turn right at the top of the slip road signposted A635 Manchester. Turn right at the second set of traffic lights, sign posted Ashton Moss, and then follow directions as from the south.

**Previous Grounds:** Katherine Street > 204, Stalybridge Celtic FC 2004-06

**Record Attendance:** 1,826 v Stamford - FA Vase Semi-final

**Record Victory:** 7-0 v Ashton United

**Record Defeat:** 0-8 v Bamber Bridge

**Record Goalscorer:** Alan Sykes

**Record Appearances:** Alan Sykes

**Additional Records:**

**Honours:**

Northern Premier Division One North 2013-14, Premier Division Play-off 2014-15.

Manchester Premier Cup 1971-72, 72-73, 73-74, 81-82, 83-84, 85-86, 87-87, 89-90.

### 10 YEAR RECORD

| 06-07 | 07-08 | 08-09 | 09-10 | 10-11 | 11-12 | 12-13 | 13-14 | 14-15 | 15-16 |
|---|---|---|---|---|---|---|---|---|---|
| NWC1 2 | NP1N 4 | NP1N 4 | NP1N 3 | NP1N 4 | NP1N 2 | NP1N 7 | NP1N 1 | NP P 4 | Nat N 11 |

# CURZON ASHTON MATCH RESULTS 2015-16

| Date | Comp | H/A | Opponents | Att: | Result | | Goalscorers | Pos | No. |
|---|---|---|---|---|---|---|---|---|---|
| Aug 8 | Nat North | H | Corby Town | 212 | D | 2-2 | Burnett 30 49 | 12 | 1 |
| 11 | Nat North | A | AFC Telford United | 1180 | D | 0-0 | | 13 | 2 |
| 15 | Nat North | A | Boston United | 1040 | L | 1-2 | Burnett 2 | 18 | 3 |
| 17 | Nat North | H | Harrogate Town | 289 | L | 1-2 | Lakeland 39 | 20 | 4 |
| 22 | Nat North | A | Alfreton Town | 488 | D | 2-2 | Warburton 25 Brooke 37 | 20 | 5 |
| 29 | Nat North | H | AFC Fylde | 225 | L | 0-2 | | 21 | 6 |
| 31 | Nat North | A | FC United | 3830 | D | 3-3 | Brooke 1 Warburton 36 86 | 19 | 7 |
| Sept 5 | Nat North | H | Nuneaton Town | 337 | W | 1-0 | Warburton 17 | 18 | 8 |
| 12 | Nat North | A | Worcester City | 508 | D | 2-2 | Shaw 30 Wright 90 | 17 | 9 |
| 19 | Nat North | A | Solihull Moors | 465 | L | 0-2 | | 21 | 10 |
| **26** | **FAC2Q** | **A** | **Salford City** | **309** | **L** | **1-2** | **Warburton 16** | | 11 |
| Oct 3 | Nat North | H | Tamworth | 292 | W | 2-0 | Cummins 52 Guest 71 | 17 | 12 |
| 10 | Nat North | H | Lowestoft Town | 224 | W | 4-1 | Cummins 15 Wright 60 Rowney 67 Brown 90 | 14 | 13 |
| 17 | Nat North | H | Stockport County | 1442 | D | 0-0 | | 13 | 14 |
| 24 | Nat North | A | Corby Town | 499 | W | 4-0 | Cummins 17 41 Warburton 50 83 | 9 | 15 |
| 31 | Nat North | H | Gainsborough Trinity | 270 | W | 3-0 | Cummins 30 Wright 64 Brown 82 | 9 | 16 |
| Nov 14 | Nat North | H | North Ferriby United | 362 | L | 0-3 | | 12 | 17 |
| 21 | Nat North | H | Chorley | 425 | W | 4-2 | Warburton 17 Cummins 61 Brooke 78 81 | 10 | 18 |
| **28** | **FAT3Q** | **A** | **Harrogate Town** | **237** | **W** | **1-0** | **Wright 7** | | 19 |
| Dec 1 | Nat North | A | Brackley Town | 174 | L | 0-2 | | 10 | 20 |
| 5 | Nat North | H | AFC Telford United | 222 | W | 1-0 | Hunt 76 | 9 | 21 |
| **14** | **FAT1** | **H** | **Nuneaton Town** | **121** | **W** | **3-1** | **Wearden 4 Cummins 24 45** | | 22 |
| 28 | Nat North | A | AFC Fylde | 504 | W | 2-1 | Warburton 56 Brown 59 | 9 | 23 |
| Jan 1 | Nat North | A | Stalybridge Celtic | 716 | D | 1-1 | Brooke 54 | 9 | 24 |
| 9 | Nat North | H | Boston United | 372 | L | 0-2 | | 10 | 25 |
| 12 | Nat North | A | Gloucester City | 232 | L | 1-3 | Cummins 76 | 10 | 26 |
| **16** | **FAT2** | **A** | **Sutton United** | **605** | **L** | **0-1** | | | 27 |
| 23 | Nat North | A | Nuneaton Town | 702 | W | 1-0 | | 8 | 28 |
| 25 | Nat North | H | Stalybridge Celtic | 484 | D | 0-0 | | 8 | 29 |
| 30 | Nat North | A | Hednesford Town | 454 | W | 3-1 | Cummins 62 81 Cockerlime 90 | 8 | 30 |
| Feb 1 | Nat North | H | Alfreton Town | 271 | L | 0-2 | | 11 | 31 |
| 16 | Nat North | A | Tamworth | 544 | L | 1-2 | Brooke 90 | 12 | 32 |
| 20 | Nat North | A | North Ferriby United | 353 | D | 0-0 | | 11 | 33 |
| 27 | Nat North | H | Bradford PA | 240 | W | 2-1 | Cockerline 28 Cummins 67 | | 34 |
| 29 | Nat North | H | Solihull Moors | 229 | L | 1-3 | Cockerline 47 | 10 | 35 |
| Mar 5 | Nat North | A | Bradford PA | 296 | L | 2-4 | Warburton 8 14 | 11 | 36 |
| 8 | Nat North | A | Gainsborough Trinity | 291 | W | 2-0 | Brooke 4 Cummins 42 | 9 | 37 |
| 12 | Nat North | H | Worcester City | 206 | W | 3-1 | Rowney 72 Cockerline 81 Warburton 90 | 9 | 38 |
| 19 | Nat North | A | Chorley | 828 | L | 0-2 | | 10 | 39 |
| 26 | Nat North | A | Harrogate Town | 752 | D | 1-1 | Warburton 30 | 10 | 40 |
| 28 | Nat North | H | FC United | 1692 | D | 0-0 | | 10 | 41 |
| Apr 2 | Nat North | H | Hednesford Town | 329 | W | 3-2 | Wright 45 Brooke 51 Guest 85 | 9 | 42 |
| 9 | Nat North | A | Lowestoft Town | 477 | D | 0-0 | | 10 | 43 |
| 16 | Nat North | H | Gloucester City | 226 | D | 1-1 | Cummins 59 | 9 | 44 |
| 23 | Nat North | H | Brackley Town | 184 | D | 1-1 | Shaw 83 | 10 | 45 |
| 30 | Nat North | A | Stockport County | 3876 | D | 0-0 | | 11 | 46 |
| | | | | | | | | | 47 |
| | | | | | | | | | 48 |
| | | | | | | | | | 49 |
| | | | | | | | | | 50 |
| | | | | | | | | | 51 |
| | | | | | | | | | 52 |
| | | | | | | | | | 53 |
| | | | | | | | | | 54 |

| GOALSCORERS | Scoring Games | Consec Sco Games | Total | | Scoring Games | Consec Sco Games | Total |
|---|---|---|---|---|---|---|---|
| ***2014-15 Brooke*** | | | ***17*** | Hunt | 1 | | 1 |
| Cummins | 11 | 2 | 14 | Lakeland | 1 | | 1 |
| Warburton | 10 | 2 | 13 | Rowney | 2 | | 2 |
| Brooke | 8 | | 8 | Wearden | 1 | | 1 |
| Wright | 5 | | 5 | | | | |
| Brown | 3 | | 3 | | | | |
| Burnett | 2 | | 3 | | | | |
| Cockerline | 4 | | 4 | | | | |
| Shaw | 3 | | 3 | | | | |
| Guest | 2 | | 2 | | | | |

# DARLINGTON 1883

**Chairman:** Martin Jesper
**Secretary:** Jonathan Jowett **(T)** 01388 604 605 **(E)** commercial@dfc1883.co.uk
**Commercial Manager:** Anthony McMaster **(T/E)** 01388 604 605
**Programme Editor:** Ray Simpson **(T/E)** 01388 604 605
**Ground Address:** Bishop Auckland FC, Heritage Park, Bishop Auckland, Co. Durham DL14 9AE
**(T)** 01388 604 605 **Manager:** Martin Gray

Starting line-up before a 2015-16 pre-season friendly, a season that turned out to be a championship winning one.

## Club Factfile

**Founded:** 1883 **Nickname:** The Quakers
**Previous Names:** Darlington FC 1883-2012
**Previous Leagues:** Northern League 1883-1908, 2012-13, North Eastern 1908-21, Football League 1921-89, 91-2010, Conference 1989-90, 10-12.

**Club Colours (change):** Black & white hoops/black/black (All red)

**Ground Capacity:** 2,004 **Seats:** 250 **Covered:** 722 **Clubhouse:** Yes **Shop:** Yes

**Directions**
From Darlington South: From junction 58 from the A1, take the A68 towards Bishop Auckland. At the West Auckland by-pass, turn right at the roundabout. Go straight across at the next roundabout and the stadium is located 500 yards on your left.
From Darlington North: From junction 59 from the A1, take the A167 towards Aycliffe. Take the first left onto St.Andrews Way (B6444). Follow this to join the A6072 to Bishop Auckland, go through 3 roundabouts. Take first exit on to A688 and stadium will be on your right.
SATNAV: DL14 9TT

**Previous Grounds:** Feethams > 2003, Reynolds Arena, Hurworth Moor.

**Record Attendance:** **Record Att:** 21,023 v Bolton Wanderers - League Cup 3rd Round 14/11/1960
**Record Victory:** 9-2 v Lincoln City - Division 3 North 07/01/1928
**Record Defeat:** 0-10 v Doncaster Rovers - Division 4 25/01/1964
**Record Goalscorer:** Alan Walsh - 100, Jerry Best - 80
**Record Appearances:** Ron Greener - 490, John Peverell - 465, Brian Henderson - 463
**Additional Records:** Paid £95,000 to Motherwell for Nick Cusack January 1992.
Received £400,000 from Dundee United for Jason Devos October 1998
**Honours:**
Northern League 1895-96, 99-1900, 2012-13. North Eastern League 1912-13, 20-21. Football League Division 3 1924-25, Division 4 1990-91, Division 3 North Cup 1933-34. NPL Div.1 North Play-off 2014-15. NPL Premier Division 2015-16. Durham Senior Cup 1919-20. FA Trophy 2010-11.

**10 YEAR RECORD**

| 06-07 | 07-08 | 08-09 | 09-10 | 10-11 | 11-12 | 12-13 | 13-14 | 14-15 | 15-16 |
|---|---|---|---|---|---|---|---|---|---|
| FL 2 11 | FL 2 6 | FL 2 12 | FL 2 24 | Conf 7 | Conf 22 | NL 1 1 | NP1N 2 | NP1N 2 | NP P 1 |

# DARLINGTON 1883 MATCH RESULTS 2015-16

| Date | Comp | H/A | Opponents | Att: | Result | | Goalscorers | Pos | No. |
|---|---|---|---|---|---|---|---|---|---|
| Aug 15 | NPL | A | Buxton | 708 | L | 0-2 | | 21 | 1 |
| 18 | NPL | H | Frickley Athletic | 908 | W | 3-0 | Burgess 8 Portas 22 Cartman 33 | 10 | 2 |
| 22 | NPL | H | Barwell | 1243 | W | 3-1 | Armstrong 51 Cartman 53 Portas 90 | 6 | 3 |
| 25 | NPL | A | Workington | 684 | L | 1-2 | Armstrong 16 | 10 | 4 |
| 29 | NPL | A | Colwyn Bay | 386 | W | 4-2 | Burgess 22 White 33 44 Dowson 69 | 6 | 5 |
| 31 | NPL | H | Blyth Spartans | 1767 | W | 2-1 | Thompson 68 White 74 | 3 | 6 |
| Sept 5 | NPL | A | Halesowen Town | 649 | W | 3-0 | Armstrong 3 Burgess 69 Thompson 70 | 2 | 7 |
| 8 | NPL | H | Ramsbottom United | 1063 | W | 2-1 | Cartman 57 White 68 | 2 | 8 |
| **12** | **FAC1Q** | **H** | **Hyde United** | **902** | **L** | **1-3** | **Thompson 26** | | 9 |
| 19 | NPL | H | Hyde United | 1047 | L | 2-3 | Cartman 59 Dowson 63 | 2 | 10 |
| 21 | NPL | A | Ilkeston | 489 | D | 1-1 | Galbraith 47 | 1 | 11 |
| 26 | NPL | A | Ramsbottom United | 341 | W | 3-0 | Armstrong 13 Youhill 67 Cartman 90 | 1 | 12 |
| 29 | NPL | A | Skelmersdale United | 321 | D | 1-1 | Armstrong 90 | 3 | 13 |
| Oct 3 | NPL | H | Marine | 1171 | L | 0-1 | | 3 | 14 |
| 10 | NPL | A | Mickleover Sports | 456 | W | 5-1 | Cartman17 Thompson 35 GASKELL 3 (52 57 62) | 2 | 15 |
| 13 | NPL | A | Ashton United | 290 | W | 2-1 | Cartman 53 Armstrong 90 | | 16 |
| 17 | NPL | H | Stourbridge | 1141 | D | 1-1 | Thompson 4 | 2 | 17 |
| 20 | NPL | H | Workington | 1051 | W | 4-0 | Gaskell 8 65 Cartman 39 Scott 90 | 1 | 18 |
| 24 | NPL | H | Mickleover Sports | 1010 | W | 2-1 | Cartman 10 Mitchell 16 | 1 | 19 |
| **31** | **FAT1Q** | **H** | **Mossley** | **635** | **W** | **3-2** | **Nowakowski 28 Walton 62 Cartman 78 (pen)** | | 20 |
| **Nov 14** | **FAT2Q** | **A** | **Sutton Coldfield Town** | **414** | **L** | **0-1** | | | 21 |
| 28 | NPL | A | Barwell | 326 | L | 1-2 | Portas 65 | 4 | 22 |
| Dec 19 | NPL | A | Hyde United | 447 | W | 3-1 | GASKELL 3 (16 51 68) | 5 | 23 |
| 28 | NPL | A | Blyth Spartans | 1876 | W | 1-0 | Gaskell 35 | 5 | 24 |
| Jan 19 | NPL | H | Whitby Town | 940 | D | 2-2 | Thompson 13 Galbraith 31 | 6 | 25 |
| 23 | NPL | H | Colwyn Bay | 1077 | W | 3-0 | Galbraith 53 (pen) Burgess 56 82 | 6 | 26 |
| 30 | NPL | A | Marine | 552 | W | 1-0 | Burgess 36 | 6 | 27 |
| Feb 2 | NPL | H | Buxton | 857 | W | 3-1 | Gaskell 53 Cartman 62 Galbraith 83 | 4 | 28 |
| 9 | NPL | H | Matlock Town | 916 | W | 3-0 | Brown 16 Gaskell 62 Galbraith 90 | 3 | 29 |
| 13 | NPL | A | Salford City | 881 | W | 4-3 | Portas 59 Gaskell 70 76 Cartman 87 | 3 | 30 |
| 20 | NPL | A | Sutton Coldfield Town | 392 | W | 1-0 | Mitchell 30 | 3 | 31 |
| 23 | NPL | H | Ashton United | 961 | D | 1-1 | Portas 83 | 3 | 32 |
| 27 | NPL | A | Stourbridge | 818 | L | 0-1 | | 4 | 33 |
| Mar 1 | NPL | H | Salford City | 1587 | W | 3-2 | Galbraith 41 Scott 85 Hardy 90 | 2 | 34 |
| 8 | NPL | H | Ilkeston | 1021 | W | 3-1 | Cartman 10 Gaskell 22 Brown 33 | 3 | 35 |
| 12 | NPL | A | Matlock Town | 745 | W | 5-0 | Cartman 3 16 Burgess 39 Hardy 64 Thompson 74 | 2 | 36 |
| 15 | NPL | A | Stamford | 471 | W | 4-1 | Brown 60 Galbraith 63 Armstrong 76 Cartman 86 | 2 | 37 |
| 19 | NPL | H | Rushall Olympic | 1223 | W | 1-0 | Burgess 54 | 2 | 38 |
| 22 | NPL | A | Nantwich Town | 512 | W | 5-0 | Cartman 30 Portas 42 Galbraith 50 (Pen)62 Armstrong 72 | 2 | 39 |
| 26 | NPL | H | Halesowen Town | 1416 | W | 2-1 | Galbraith 55 Armstrong 78 | 2 | 40 |
| Apr 2 | NPL | H | Surron Coldfield Town | 1307 | W | 2-0 | Lycett 3 (og) Cartman 75 | 2 | 41 |
| 5 | NPL | A | Frickley Athletic | 740 | L | 1-3 | Armstrong 31 | 2 | 42 |
| 7 | NPL | H | Nantwich Town | 1268 | W | 2-1 | Thompson 39 Portas 73 | 2 | 43 |
| 9 | NPL | A | Grantham Town | 701 | W | 2-0 | Thompson 65 Hardy 87 | 2 | 44 |
| 13 | NPL | H | Skelmersdale United | 1296 | W | 3-0 | Burgess 28 Cartman 41 Thompson 62 | 1 | 45 |
| 17 | NPL | H | Stamford | 1707 | W | 2-1 | Burgess 44 Mitchell 70 | 1 | 46 |
| 19 | NPL | H | Grantham Town | 1734 | W | 2-0 | Scott 11 Purewal 24 | 2 | 47 |
| 21 | NPL | A | Whitby Town | 1804 | W | 7-1 | Thompson 3 Burgess 8 ARMSTRONG 3 (9 17 20) Galbraith 39(p) Scott 70 | 1 | 48 |
| 23 | NPL | A | Rushall Olympic | 709 | L | 0-1 | | 1 | 49 |

| GOALSCORERS | Scoring Games | Consec Sco Games | Total | | Scoring Games | Consec Sco Games | Total |
|---|---|---|---|---|---|---|---|
| Cartman | 18 | 3 | 19 | Hardy | 3 | | 3 |
| Gaskell | 8 | 3 | 14 | Mitchell | 3 | | 3 |
| Armstrong | 11 | 2 | 13 | Dowson | 2 | | 2 |
| Burgess | 11 | 2 | 11 | Nowakowski | 1 | | 1 |
| Galbraith | 9 | 2 | 11 | Pulewal | 1 | | 1 |
| Thompson | 11 | 3 | 11 | Walton | 1 | | 1 |
| Portas | 7 | 2 | 7 | Youhill | 1 | | 1 |
| Scott | 4 | 2 | 4 | Opponents | | | 1 |
| White | 4 | 2 | 4 | | | | |
| Brown | 3 | | 3 | | | | |

# FC HALIFAX TOWN

**Chairman:** David Bosomworth
**Secretary:** Mike Sharman (T) 01422 341 222 (E)
**Commercial Manager:** Ben Bottomley (T/E) 01422 341 222
**Programme Editor:** (T/E)
**Ground Address:** The Shay Stadium, Shay Syke, Halifax HX1 2YS
(T) 01422 341 222 **Manager:** Billy Heath

Picture says it all - 205-16 FA Trophy winners!
Photo: Peter Barnes

## Club Factfile

**Founded:** 1911 **Nickname:** Shaymen
**Previous Names:** Halifax Town 1911-2008 then reformed as F.C. Halifax Town
**Previous Leagues:** Yorkshire Combination 1911-12, Midland 1912-21, Football League 1921-93, 98-2002, Conference 1993-98, 2002-08

**Club Colours (change):** Blue/blue & white/blue & white (White/white & black/white & black)

**Ground Capacity:** 6,561 **Seats:** 2,330 **Covered:** 4,231 **Clubhouse:** Yes **Shop:** Yes

**Directions**
The Shay Stadium, Shay Syke, Halifax. HX1 2YS (PLEASE NOTE FOR SAT NAV use post code HX1 2YT) From the M62, Junction 26 (7.5 miles, 15 minutes by car. Head south east towards A58/Whitehall Road. Continue straight on to A58/Whitehall Road (signs for Halifax/A58). Continue to follow A58, at a roundabout, take first exit on to A629 Orange Street. Turn right at A629 Broad Street. Continue to follow A629. Go through one roundabout. Turn left at Shaw Hill. The Stadium will be on your left after 100 yards. From the M62, Junction 24 (4.5 miles, 9 minutes by car). Exit on to A629/Blackley New Road heading to Halifax. Continue on A629/Huddersfield Road heading towards Elland and Halifax.
Having gone down steep hill, traffic lights in dip, road inclines. Past Hospital on left, road levels, Athletics Track on right. Traffic lights. Filter right, Stadium on left in 100yds

**Previous Grounds:** Sandhall Lane 1911-15, Exley 1919-20

**Record Attendance:** 36,885 v Tottenham Hotspur - FA Cup 5th Round 14/02/1953
**Record Victory:** 12-0 v West Vale Ramblers - FA Cup 1st Qualifying Road 1913-14
**Record Defeat:** 0-13 v Stockport County - Division 3 North 1933-34
**Record Goalscorer:** Albert Valentine
**Record Appearances:** John Pickering
**Additional Records:**

**Honours:**
Conference 1997-98, Conference North Play-offs 2012-13. Northern Premier League Division 1 North 2009-10, Premier Division 2010-11.
West Riding County Cup 2012-13.

### 10 YEAR RECORD

| 06-07 | 07-08 | 08-09 | 09-10 | 10-11 | 11-12 | 12-13 | 13-14 | 14-15 | 15-16 |
|---|---|---|---|---|---|---|---|---|---|
| Conf 16 | Conf 20 | NP1N 8 | NP1N 1 | NP P 1 | Conf N 3 | Conf N 5 | Conf 5 | Conf 9 | Nat 21 |

# FC HALIFAX TOWN MATCH RESULTS 2015-16

| Date | Comp | H/A | Opponents | Att: | Result | Goalscorers | Pos | No. |
|---|---|---|---|---|---|---|---|---|
| Aug 8 | Nat Lge | A | Boreham Wood | 701 | L 1-3 | Burrow 45 (pen) | 22 | 1 |
| 11 | Nat Lge | H | Chester | 1732 | L 0-1 | | 23 | 2 |
| 15 | Nat Lge | H | Torquay United | 1199 | L 2-3 | Burrow 24 48 | 23 | 3 |
| 18 | Nat Lge | A | Tranmere Rovers | 5235 | L 0-1 | | 24 | 4 |
| 22 | Nat Lge | H | Bromley | 1107 | D 2-2 | Hughes 90 Burrow 90 (pen) | 23 | 5 |
| 29 | Nat Lge | A | Wrexham | 5662 | L 1-3 | Burrow 26 | 23 | 6 |
| 31 | Nat Lge | H | Barrow | 1490 | W 3-1 | Tuton 81 Hamilton 83 Burrow 90 | 21 | 7 |
| Sept 5 | Nat Lge | A | Aldershot Town | 1603 | L 2-3 | Hattersley 60 Brooks 83 | 23 | 8 |
| 12 | Nat Lge | H | Kidderminster Harriers | 1128 | D 1-1 | Hamilton 66 | 22 | 9 |
| 15 | Nat Lge | A | Guiseley | 1184 | L 1-2 | Hamilton 8 | 23 | 10 |
| 19 | Nat Lge | H | Southport | 1211 | D 2-2 | Burrow 74 (pen) 89 | 23 | 11 |
| 22 | Nat Lge | H | Gateshead | 1001 | D 1-1 | Bolton 53 | 23 | 12 |
| 26 | Nat Lge | A | Welling United | 653 | L 0-2 | | 23 | 13 |
| Oct 5 | Nat Lge | H | Cheltenham Town | 1267 | L 1-7 | James 29 | 23 | 14 |
| 6 | Nat Lge | A | Altrincham | 1119 | W 3-1 | Burrow 21 60 James 90 | 22 | 15 |
| 10 | Nat Lge | H | Woking | 1155 | L 0-3 | | 23 | 16 |
| 13 | Nat Lge | A | Grimsby Town | 3806 | L 0-7 | | 23 | 17 |
| 17 | Nat Lge | A | Chester | 2088 | L 1-2 | Burrow 73 | 23 | 18 |
| **24** | **FAC4Q** | **H** | **Guiseley** | **1078** | **D 2-2** | **Walker 14 James 44** | | **19** |
| **27** | **FAC4Qr** | **A** | **Guiseley** | **948** | **W 2-1** | **Walker 30 Bolton 114 (aet)** | | **20** |
| 31 | Nat Lge | A | Eastleigh | 1890 | L 1-2 | James 15 | 24 | 21 |
| **Nov 7** | **FAC1** | **H** | **Wycombe Wanderers** | **1789** | **L 0-4** | | | **22** |
| 14 | Nat Lge | H | Braintree Town | 1065 | L 3-6 | Burrrow 5 Tuton 32 42 | 24 | 23 |
| 21 | Nat Lge | A | Gateshead | 853 | W 4-1 | Smith 2 (og) James 39 Tuton 44 79 | 24 | 24 |
| 28 | Nat Lge | H | Dover Athletic | 1067 | W 4-2 | Tuton 7 75 Wroe 13 Burrow 42 | 23 | 25 |
| Dec5 | Nat Lge | H | Guiseley | 1355 | D 1-1 | Walker 84 | 23 | 26 |
| **12** | **FAT1** | **H** | **Tamworth** | **439** | **W 5-0** | **James 12 87 McDonald 28 Wroe 58 Hughes 735** | | **27** |
| 19 | Nat Lge | H | Tranmere Rovers | 1685 | D 1-1 | Wroe 44 | 22 | 28 |
| 26 | Nat Lge | A | Lincoln City | 3558 | W 1-0 | Walker 69 | 22 | 29 |
| 28 | Nat Lge | H | Wrexham | 2243 | W2-0 | Tuton 16 James 38 | 22 | 30 |
| Jan2 | Nat Lge | H | Lincoln City | 1932 | D 2-2 | Tuton 27 James 89 | 21 | 31 |
| 9 | Nat Lge | A | Macclesfield | 2055 | W 1-0 | Tuton 77 | 19 | 32 |
| **19** | **FAT2** | **H** | **Barrow** | **673** | **W 1-0** | **Tuton 68** | | **33** |
| 23 | Nat Lge | A | Woking | 1484 | D 1-1 | Walker 38 | 19 | 34 |
| 30 | Nat Lge | H | Welling United | 1407 | D 1-1 | James 56 | 19 | 35 |
| **Feb 10** | **FAT3** | **H** | **Chester** | **878** | **W 1-0** | **Burrow 45** | | **36** |
| 13 | Nat Lge | H | Forest Green Rovers | 1329 | L 0-2 | | 20 | 37 |
| 20 | Nat Lge | H | Grimsby Town | 3131 | W 4-2 | Whitehouse 9 Bolton 25 Wroe 28 Hibbs 89 | 20 | 38 |
| 23 | Nat Lge | A | Braintree Town | 506 | L 0-2 | | 20 | 39 |
| **27** | **FAT4** | **H** | **Gateshead** | **1431** | **D 0-0** | | | **40** |
| **Mar 2** | **FAT4r** | **A** | **Gateshead** | **724** | **W 3-3** | **James 22 Hughes 89 McDonald 93 (won 5-4 pens aet)** | | **41** |
| 5 | Nat Lge | A | Southport | 1148 | W 1-0 | McDonald 90 | 20 | 42 |
| 8 | Nat Lge | A | Bromley | 706 | L 0-1 | | 20 | 43 |
| **12** | **FAT SF 1** | **A** | **Nantwich Town** | **2078** | **W 4-2** | **McManus 3 Fairhurst 20 Burrow 46 61 (pen)** | | **44** |
| 15 | Nat Lge | A | Torquay United | 1664 | D 0-0 | | 20 | 45 |
| **19** | **FAT SF 2** | **H** | **Nantwich Town** | **3009** | **D 2-2** | **Burrow 3 White 89 (og)** | | **46** |
| 26 | Nat Lge | H | Altrincham | 1747 | W 1-0 | Hughes 68 | 19 | 47 |
| 28 | Nat Lge | A | Barrow | 1466 | L 1-4 | Hughes 87 | 20 | 48 |
| Apr 2 | Nat Lge | A | Dover Athletic | 1027 | L 0-1 | | 22 | 49 |
| 5 | Nat Lge | H | Boreham Wood | 1309 | W 3-2 | Burrow 20 Bolton 24 Hughes 90 | 20 | 50 |
| 9 | Nat Lge | H | Aldershot Town | 1714 | L 0-2 | | 20 | 51 |
| 12 | Nat Lge | A | Kidderminster Harriers | 1340 | L 0-1 | | 20 | 52 |
| 16 | Nat Lge | A | Cheltenham Town | 5245 | L 0-2 | | | 53 |
| 19 | Nat Lge | H | Eastleigh | 1337 | D 0-0 | | 20 | 54 |
| 23 | Nat Lge | A | Forest Green Rovers | 1942 | W 1-0 | McDonald 70 | 20 | 55 |
| 30 | Nat Lge | H | Macclesfield Town | 2943 | D 1-1 | McManus 45 | 21 | 56 |
| **May 23** | **FAT Final** | **N** | **Grimsby Town** | **46781** | **W 1-0** | **McManus 49** | | **57** |

| GOALSCORERS | Scoring Games | Consec Sco Games | Total | | Scoring Games | Consec Sco Games | Total |
|---|---|---|---|---|---|---|---|
| *2014-15 Piniket* | | | *13* | McManus | 3 | | 3 |
| Burrow | 14 | 3 | 18 | Brooks | 1 | | 1 |
| James | 9 | 2 | 11 | Fairhurst | 1 | | 1 |
| Tuton | 8 | 4 | 11 | Hattersley | 1 | | 1 |
| Hughes | 6 | | 6 | Hibbs | 1 | | 1 |
| Walker | 5 | | 5 | Whitehouse | 1 | | 1 |
| Bolton | 4 | | 4 | Opponents | | | 2 |
| McDonald | 4 | | 4 | | | | |
| Wroe | 4 | | 4 | | | | |
| Hamilton | 3 | 2 | 3 | | | | |

# FC UNITED OF MANCHESTER

**Chairman:** Andy Walsh (General Manager)
**Secretary:** John England (T) 07941 158 909 (E) johnengland@fc-utd.co.uk
**Commercial Manager:** Amanda Tudor (T/E) 07419 374 132
**Programme Editor:** John England (T/E) programme@fc-utd.co.uk
**Ground Address:** Broadhurst Park, 310 Lightbowne Road, Moston, Manchester, M40 0FJ
(T) 0161 769 2005 **Manager:** Karl Marginson

FC United celebrate scoring against Buxton, in the Third Qualifying Round of the FA Cup, to the obvious delight of the home crowd. Photo: Bill Wheatcroft.

## Club Factfile

**Founded:** 2005 **Nickname:** F.C.
**Previous Names:** None
**Previous Leagues:** North West Counties 2005-07. Northern Premier 2007-15.

**Club Colours (change):** Red/white/black (White/black/white)

**Ground Capacity:** 4,400 **Seats:** Yes **Covered:** Yes **Clubhouse:** Yes **Shop:** Yes

**Directions**
From South leave M60 at J21 turn left and immediately right to Manchester City Centre A663. After 350 yards bear right onto A6104 to Manchester. At Greengate roundabout take first exit onto Lightbowne Road. Ground is half a mile on the left From North leave M60 at J20, turn right onto A664 Blackley. After 700 yardsturn left at lights onto A6104 Oldham. After 1.5 miles take 4th exit off Greengate roundabout onto Lightbowne Road. Ground is half a mile on the left.

**Previous Grounds:** Gigg Lane(Bury FC) 2005-14.Bower Fold (Stalybridge Celtic FC) Aug-Dec'14. Tameside Stadium (Cuzon Ashton).

**Record Attendance:** 6,731 v Brighton & Hove Albion, FA Cup 2nd Round 08/12/2010 (Gigg Lane)
**Record Victory:** 10-2 v Castleton Gabriels 10/12/2005. 8-0 v Squires Gate 14/10/06, Glossop N.E. 28/10/06 & Nelson 05/09/10
**Record Defeat:** 0-5 v Harrogate Town, 20 February 2016
**Record Goalscorer:** Rory Patterson - 99 (2005-08)
**Record Appearances:** Jerome Wright - 364
**Additional Records:** Simon Carden scored 5 goals against Castleton Gabriels 10/12/2005.
Longest unbeaten run (League): 22 games 03/12/2006 - 18/08/2007.
**Honours:**
North West Counties League Division 2 2005-06, Division 1 2006-07.
Northern Premier League Division 1 North Play-off 2007-08, Premier Division 2014-15.

### 10 YEAR RECORD

| 06-07 | 07-08 | 08-09 | 09-10 | 10-11 | 11-12 | 12-13 | 13-14 | 14-15 | 15-16 |
|---|---|---|---|---|---|---|---|---|---|
| NWC1 1 | NP1N 2 | NP P 6 | NP P 13 | NP P 4 | NP P 6 | NP P 3 | NP P 2 | NP P 1 | Nat N 13 |

# FC UNITED OF MANCHESTER MATCH RESULTS 2015-16

| Date | Comp | H/A | Opponents | Att: | Result | | Goalscorers | Pos | No. |
|---|---|---|---|---|---|---|---|---|---|
| Aug 8 | Nat North | A | Gloucester City | 1451 | L | 0-1 | | 18 | 1 |
| 11 | Nat North | H | Stockport County | 3199 | L | 1-2 | Fallon 25 | 20 | 2 |
| 15 | Nat North | H | Tamworth | 3580 | D | 1-1 | Ashworth 28 | 20 | 3 |
| 18 | Nat North | A | Chorley | 1876 | L | 0-3 | | 21 | 4 |
| 22 | Nat North | H | Brackley Town | 2996 | W | 3-2 | Wolfendon 16 Madeley 25 Greaves 72 | 18 | 5 |
| 29 | Nat North | A | Hednesford Town | 927 | W | 3-0 | Lindfield 6 Bayunu 47 Cooke 85 | 12 | 6 |
| 31 | Nat North | H | Curzon Ashton | 3830 | D | 3-3 | Ashworth 56 Madeley 88 Fallon 90 | 14 | 7 |
| Sept 5 | Nat North | A | Lowestoft Town | 1154 | W | 4-1 | Greaves 8 18 Madeley 25 57 | 10 | 8 |
| 12 | Nat North | H | Corby Town | 3328 | W | 1-0 | Wolfenden 86 | 8 | 9 |
| 15 | Nat North | A | AFC Fylde | 821 | L | 0-4 | | 10 | 10 |
| 19 | Nat North | A | Stalybridge Celtic | 1775 | L | 0-1 | | 12 | 11 |
| **26** | **FAC2Q** | **H** | **Witton Albion** | **1648** | **W** | **3-1** | **Madeley 26 Lindfield 45 Fallon 65** | | 12 |
| Oct 3 | Nat North | H | Worcester City | 3619 | L | 0-2 | | 12 | 13 |
| **10** | **FAC3Q** | **H** | **Buxton** | **2357** | **D** | **1-1** | **Greaves 79** | | 14 |
| **13** | **FAC3Qr** | **A** | **Buxton** | **874** | **W** | **2-0** | **Daniels 75 Madeley 89** | | 15 |
| 17 | Nat North | A | North Ferriby United | 951 | L | 0-1 | | 15 | 16 |
| **24** | **FAC4Q** | **A** | **Sporting Khalsa** | **2252** | **W** | **3-1** | **Ashworth 25 Daniels 41 Lindfield 65** | | 17 |
| 31 | Nat North | A | Boston United | 1789 | L | 1-3 | Wolfenden 46 | 17 | 18 |
| Nov9 | Nat North | H | Nuneaton Town | 2781 | L | 1-3 | Greaves 74 | 17 | 19 |
| **9** | **FAC1** | **H** | **Chesterfield** | **2916** | **L** | **1-4** | **Ashworth 90** | | 20 |
| 14 | Nat North | H | Gainsborough Trinity | 3301 | L | 1-2 | Madeley 63 | 17 | 21 |
| 21 | Nat North | A | Nuneaton Town | 1167 | D | 2-2 | Greaves 12 Hunter 50 | 20 | 22 |
| **28** | **FAT3Q** | **H** | **AFC Telford United** | **1034** | **L** | **1-2** | **Thomson 90** | | 23 |
| Dec 5 | Nat North | A | Stockport County | 4797 | W | 2-1 | Fallon 45 Greaves 72 | 19 | 24 |
| 12 | Nat North | H | Nuneaton Town | 2781 | W | 3-2 | Madeley 15 Thomson 32 Clifton 60 (og) | 17 | 25 |
| 19 | Nat North | H | Gloucester City | 3187 | L | 1-2 | Thomson 37 | 15 | 26 |
| 28 | Nat North | H | Hednesford Town | 3421 | D | 1-1 | Wolfenden 28 | 19 | 27 |
| Jan 2 | Nat North | H | Bradford PA | 3370 | W | 2-1 | Wolfenden 3 Thomson 34 | 18 | 28 |
| 9 | Nat North | A | Tamworth | 1430 | D | 1-1 | Thomson 76 | 16 | 29 |
| 16 | Nat North | A | Brackley Town | 660 | L | 0-4 | | 17 | 30 |
| 23 | Nat North | H | Lowestoft Town | 3280 | W | 6-1 | Chantler 22 Lacey 46 Greaves 46 Madeley 63 Daniels 80 Lindfield 90 | 14 | 31 |
| 30 | Nat North | H | Harrogate Town | 3362 | W | 4-3 | Thomson 45 Sheridan 46 Greaves 55 Madeley 57 | 15 | 32 |
| Feb 8 | Nat North | A | AFC Telford United | 1323 | L | 1-5 | Thomson 82 | 15 | 33 |
| 13 | Nat North | H | Alfreton Town | 3338 | L | 1-3 | Madeley 45 | 15 | 34 |
| 17 | Nat North | A | Bradford PA | 619 | L | 1-3 | Thomson 5 | 15 | 35 |
| 20 | Nat North | A | Harrogate Town | 1357 | L | 0-5 | | 18 | 36 |
| 27 | Nat North | H | North Ferriby United | 3419 | W | 3-2 | Wolfenden 53 71 Lindfield 90 | 16 | 37 |
| Mar 5 | Nat North | A | Worcester City | 2133 | D | 0-0 | | 18 | 38 |
| 12 | Nat North | H | AFC Fylde | 3432 | L | 1-2 | Winter 72 | 18 | 39 |
| 15 | Nat North | A | Solihull Moors | 834 | W | 2-1 | Wright 1 Thomson 49 | 16 | 40 |
| 19 | Nat North | A | Alfreton Town | 1087 | W | 1-0 | Thomson 26 | 14 | 41 |
| 26 | Nat North | H | Chorley | 4150 | W | 2-0 | Wright 47 Johnson 86 | 12 | 42 |
| 28 | Nat North | A | Curzon Ashton | 1692 | D | 0-0 | | 12 | 43 |
| Apr 2 | Nat North | H | Boston United | 3544 | L | 1-2 | Sheridon 90 | 12 | 44 |
| 9 | Nat North | A | Corby Town | 1030 | W | 3-2 | Thomson 7 49 Ashworth 52 | 12 | 45 |
| 16 | Nat North | H | Stalybridge Celtic | 3451 | L | 0-1 | | 14 | 46 |
| 23 | Nat North | A | Gainsborough Trinity | 1021 | W | 1-0 | Wright 53 | 13 | 47 |
| 30 | Nat North | H | Solihull Moors | 3914 | D | 2-2 | Greaves 86 90 | 13 | 48 |

| GOALSCORERS | Scoring Games | Consec Sco Games | Total |
|---|---|---|---|
| ***2014-15 Greaves*** | | | ***25*** |
| Thomson | 11 | | 12 |
| Greaves | 9 | | 11 |
| Madeley | 10 | 2 | 11 |
| Wolfenden | 5 | | 7 |
| Ashworth | 5 | | 5 |
| Fallon | 4 | | 4 |
| Lindfield | 4 | | 4 |
| Daniels | 3 | | 3 |
| Wright | 3 | | 3 |
| Sheridan | 2 | | 2 |
| Bayunu | 1 | | 1 |
| Chantler | 1 | | 1 |
| Cooke | 1 | | 1 |
| Fitzwater | 1 | | 1 |
| Hunter | 1 | | 1 |
| Johnson | 1 | | 1 |
| Lacey | 1 | | 1 |
| Winter | 1 | | 1 |
| Opponents | | | 1 |

# GAINSBOROUGH TRINITY

**Chairman:** Richard Kane

**Secretary:** David Tinsley (T) 01427 613 295 (E) davidtinsley@yahoo.co.uk

**Commercial Manager:** John Myskiw (T/E) 01427 613 295

**Programme Editor:** Rob Hughes (T/E) 01427 613 295

**Ground Address:** The Northolme, Gainsborough, Lincolnshire DN21 2QW

(T) 01427 613 295 **Manager:** Dominic Roma

## Club Factfile

**Founded:** 1873 **Nickname:** The Blues

**Previous Names:** Trinity Recreationists

**Previous Leagues:** Midland Counties 1889-96, 1912-60, 61-68, Football League 1896-1912, Central Alliance 1960-61, Northern Premier 1968-2004

**Club Colours (change):** All blue (All lime)

**Ground Capacity:** 4,340 **Seats:** 504 **Covered:** 2,500 **Clubhouse:** Yes **Shop:** Yes

**Directions**

The Northolme is situated on the A159, Gainsborough to Scunthorpe road, approximately a third of a mile north of the Town Centre. Public Car Park on the right 150 yards before the Ground. Any person parked illegally in the Streets around the Ground will be issued with a ticket from the Police.

**Previous Grounds:** None

**Record Attendance:** 9,760 v Scunthorpe United - Midland League 1948

**Record Victory:** 7-0 v Fleetwood Town and v Great Harwood Town

**Record Defeat:** 1-7 v Stalybridge Celtic - Northern Premier 2000-01 and v Brentford - FA Cup 03-04.

**Record Goalscorer:** Not known

**Record Appearances:** Not known

**Additional Records:** Paid £3,000 to Buxton for Stuart Lowe
Received £30,000 from Lincoln City for Tony James

**Honours:**

Midland Counties League 1890-91, 1927-28, 48-49, 66-67
Lincolnshire Senior Cup x18

### 10 YEAR RECORD

| 06-07 | 07-08 | 08-09 | 09-10 | 10-11 | 11-12 | 12-13 | 13-14 | 14-15 | 15-16 |
|---|---|---|---|---|---|---|---|---|---|
| Conf N 12 | Conf N 11 | Conf N 13 | Conf N 14 | Conf N 18 | Conf N 4 | Conf N 8 | Conf N 16 | Conf N 17 | Nat N 18 |

## GAINSBOROUGH TRINITY MATCH RESULTS 2015-16

| Date | Comp | H/A | Opponents | Att: | Result | Goalscorers | Pos | No. |
|---|---|---|---|---|---|---|---|---|
| Aug 8 | Nat North | H | Worcester City | 402 | D 1-1 | Stamp 81 | 13 | 1 |
| 11 | Nat North | A | Harrogate Town | 390 | L 1-3 | Bignall 19 | 18 | 2 |
| 15 | Nat North | A | AFC Fylde | 326 | D 2-2 | Laryea 51 78 | 19 | 3 |
| 18 | Nat North | H | Stalybridge Celtic | 354 | W 3-1 | Jarman 36 Binns 74 Bignall 79 | 10 | 4 |
| 22 | Nat North | A | AFC Telford United | 1109 | W 2-0 | Jarman 6 Bignall 34 | 9 | 5 |
| 29 | Nat North | H | Boston United | 846 | W 1-0 | Bignall 56 | 6 | 6 |
| 31 | Nat North | A | Alfrton Town | 576 | L 0-1 | | 8 | 7 |
| Sept 5 | Nat North | H | Corby Town | 424 | D 1-1 | Bignall 15 | 7 | 8 |
| 12 | Nat North | A | Nuneaton Town | 625 | L 0-2 | | 11 | 9 |
| 15 | Nat North | H | Tamworth | 404 | L 0-2 | | 12 | 10 |
| 22 | Nat North | A | Gloucester City | 297 | W 2-0 | Jarman 12 28 | 11 | 11 |
| **26** | **FAC2Q** | **H** | **Boston United** | **725** | **W 2-0** | **Newsham 20 Jarman 39** | | 12 |
| Oct 3 | Nat North | H | Stockport County | 644 | L 0-1 | | 13 | 13 |
| **10** | **FAC3Q** | **A** | **Droylsden** | **306** | **W 4-3** | **Jarman 11 20 Newsham 45 Wilson 88** | | 14 |
| 17 | Nat North | A | Brackley Town | 192 | L 2-3 | Newsham 70 Davis 73 | 14 | 15 |
| **24** | **FAC4Q** | **A** | **Wrexham** | **1814** | **W 1-0** | **Jarman 74** | | 16 |
| 31 | Nat North | A | Curzon Ashton | 270 | L 0-3 | | 15 | 17 |
| **Nov 7** | **FAC1** | **H** | **ShrewsburyTown** | **2108** | **L 0-1** | | | 18 |
| 14 | Nat North | A | FC United | 3301 | W 2-1 | Russell 6 McKay 77 | 15 | 19 |
| 21 | Nat North | A | Tamworth | 632 | L 0-2 | | 15 | 20 |
| 24 | Nat North | H | Chorley | 353 | W 2-1 | Wilson 70 Davis 90 | 15 | 21 |
| **28** | **FAT3Q** | **H** | **Ashton United** | **307** | **D 0-0** | | | 22 |
| **Dec 1** | **FAT3Qr** | **A** | **Ashton United** | **106** | **L 1-3** | **Brogan 2** | | 23 |
| 5 | Nat North | H | Harrogate Town | 403 | W 2-1 | Jarman 56 Stamp 83 | 12 | 24 |
| 12 | Nat North | H | Hednesford Town | 361 | W 3-1 | Newsham 9 29 Davis 64 | 10 | 25 |
| 19 | Nat North | A | Worcester City | 530 | L 0-2 | | 11 | 26 |
| 26 | Nat North | H | North Ferriby United | 665 | W 2-0 | Jarman 51 Russell 57 | 9 | 27 |
| 28 | Nat North | A | Boston United | 1889 | L 0-1 | | 10 | 28 |
| Jan 2 | Nat North | A | North Ferriby United | 612 | L 0-4 | | 10 | 29 |
| 9 | Nat North | H | AFC Fylde | 406 | L 0-2 | | 12 | 30 |
| 16 | Nat North | H | AFC Telford United | 404 | D 1-1 | Reid 18 | 12 | 31 |
| 23 | Nat North | A | Corby Town | 541 | W 2-1 | Russell 43 (pen) Davis 46 | 10 | 32 |
| 30 | Nat North | H | Bradford PA | 431 | L 0-1 | | 11 | 33 |
| Feb 9 | Nat North | H | Brackley Town | 252 | W 1-0 | Stamp 55 | 10 | 34 |
| 13 | Nat North | A | Hednesford Town | 321 | W 2-0 | Russell 72 Picton 80 | 8 | 35 |
| 20 | Nat North | H | Solihull Moors | 492 | L 1-6 | Davis 62 | 10 | 36 |
| 27 | Nat North | A | Stockport County | 2990 | L 0-2 | | 13 | 37 |
| Mar 5 | Nat North | A | Solihull Moors | 517 | L 2-3 | Newsham 28 Reid 67 | 13 | 38 |
| 8 | Nat North | H | Curzon Ashton | 291 | L 0-2 | | 13 | 39 |
| 12 | Nat North | H | Nuneaton Town | 505 | W 1-0 | Jarman 90 | 12 | 40 |
| 19 | Nat North | A | Lowestoft Town | 530 | L 0-1 | | 12 | 41 |
| 26 | Nat North | A | Stalybridge Celtic | 448 | D 0-0 | | 13 | 42 |
| 28 | Nat North | H | Alfreton Town | 529 | D 1-1 | Picton 64 | 13 | 43 |
| Apr 2 | Nat North | H | Gloucester City | 502 | D 3-3 | Jarman 14 Newsham 56 Reid 80 | 13 | 44 |
| 9 | Nat North | A | Chorley | 643 | L 1-2 | Jarman 61 | 13 | 45 |
| 16 | Nat North | H | Lowestoft Town | 507 | D 1-1 | Jarman 23 | 16 | 46 |
| 23 | Nat North | H | FC United | 1021 | L 0-1 | | 18 | 47 |
| 30 | Nat North | A | Bradford PA | 345 | W 4-1 | Jarman 24 Russell 38 Newsham 44 53 | 18 | 48 |

| GOALSCORERS | Scoring Games | Consec Sco Games | Total |
|---|---|---|---|
| *2014-15 Beesley and Russell* | | *10* | |
| Jarman | 13 | 3 | 15 |
| Newsham | 7 | 2 | 9 |
| Bignall | 5 | 3 | 5 |
| Davis | 5 | | 5 |
| Russell | 5 | | 5 |
| Reid | 3 | | 3 |
| Stamp | 3 | | 3 |
| Laryea | 2 | | 2 |
| Picton | 2 | | 2 |

| | Scoring Games | Consec Sco Games | Total |
|---|---|---|---|
| Wilson | 2 | | 2 |
| Binnns | 1 | | 1 |
| Brogan | 1 | | 1 |
| McKay | 1 | | 1 |

# GLOUCESTER CITY

**Chairman:** Mike Dunstan, OBE
**Secretary:** Shaun Wetson (T) 07813 931 781 (E) secretary@gloucestercityafc.com
**Commercial Manager:** Tim Harris (T/E) 07767 415 415
**Programme Editor:** Mike Dunstan, OBE (T/E) chairman@gloucestercityafc.com
**Ground Address:** Cheltenham Town FC, The Abbey Business Stadium, Whaddon Road GL52 5NA
(T) 01242 573 558 (Cheltenham Town No.) **Manager:** Tim Harris

## Club Factfile

**Founded:** 1883 **Nickname:** The Tigers
**Previous Names:** Gloucester 1883-86,1889-1901, Gloucester Nomads 1888-89, Gloucester YMCA 1910-25, Gloucester City 1902-10,1925to date
**Previous Leagues:** Bristol & District (now Western) 1893-96, Gloucester & Dist. 1897-1907, North Gloucestershire 1907-10, Gloucestershire North Senior 1920-34, Birmingham Combination 1935-39, Southern 1939-2000

**Club Colours (change):** Yellow & black/black/black (All white)

**Ground Capacity:** 7,289 **Seats:** Yes **Covered:** Yes **Clubhouse:** Yes **Shop:** Yes

**Directions**
From the North (M5) leave at Jnctn 10, follow road A4019) towards Cheltenham, keep going straight through traffic lights until you reach a roundabout, PC World will be on your left and McDonalds on your right. Turn left here, after 500 yards you will then come to a double roundabout, go straight over, keep going for another 300 yards then turn right into Swindon Lane, follow the road over the level crossing and 2 mini roundabouts until you come to a large roundabout, go straight over, signposted Prestbury, continue past Racecourse and turn right into Albert Road, follow this to the end then turn left at roundabout into Prestbury Road, 200yards turn into Whaddon Road.

**Previous Grounds:** Budding's Field 1883-1886, 1889-1895, 1897-1898, 1902-1910; Avenue Road Ground, Tuffley Avenue 1895-1896, 1898 -1901, 1925-1927; Co-operative Field, India Road 1896-1897; Fielding and Platt Sports Ground, Llanthony 1910-1925; Sutgrove Park, Stroud Road 1927-1933; Bon Marche Ground, Estcourt Road 1933-1935; The Ground, Cheltenham Road, Longlevens 1935-1965; Horton Road Stadium 1965-1986; City Stadium, Meadow Park 1986-2007; The New Lawn, Forest Green 2007-2008; Corinium Stadium, Cirencester 2008-2010

**Previous Grounds:**

**Record Attendance:** Longlevens: 10,500 v Tottenham - Friendly 1952. Meadow Park: 4,000 v Dagenham & Red. - FAT 3rd Q Rnd 12/04/97
**Record Victory:** 10-1 v Sudbury Town (H) - FA Cup 3rd Qualifying Round 17/10/98
**Record Defeat:** 1-12 v Gillingham - 09/11/46
**Record Goalscorer:** Jerry Causon - 206 (1930-36)
**Record Appearances:** Tom Webb - 607 (2001 to date)
**Additional Records:** Paid £25,000 to Worcester City for Steve Ferguson 1990-91
Received £25,000 from AFC Bournemouth for Ian Hedges 1990

**Honours:**
Southern League Cup 1955-56, Midland Division 1988-89, Premier Division Play-off 2008-09.
Gloucestershire Senior Cup x19

### 10 YEAR RECORD

| 06-07 | 07-08 | 08-09 | 09-10 | 10-11 | 11-12 | 12-13 | 13-14 | 14-15 | 15-16 |
|---|---|---|---|---|---|---|---|---|---|
| SthP 10 | SthP 6 | SthP 3 | Conf N 18 | Conf N 14 | Conf N 14 | Conf N 11 | Conf N 17 | Conf N 14 | Nat N 15 |

# GLOUCESTER CITY MATCH RESULTS 2015-16

| Date | Comp | H/A | Opponents | Att: | Result | | Goalscorers | Pos | No. |
|---|---|---|---|---|---|---|---|---|---|
| Aug 8 | Nat North | H | FC United | 1451 | W | 1-0 | Anoruo 34 | 7 | 1 |
| 12 | Nat North | A | Corby Town | 650 | L | 1-3 | Anoruo 90 | 8 | 2 |
| 15 | Nat North | A | Stalybridge Celtic | 490 | L | 0-1 | | 14 | 3 |
| 18 | Nat North | H | Alfreton Town | 372 | D | 1-1 | Richards 83 | 16 | 4 |
| 22 | Nat North | A | Boston United | 990 | L | 0-1 | | 16 | 5 |
| 29 | Nat North | H | AFC Telford United | 425 | W | 1-0 | Anoruo 45 | 16 | 6 |
| 31 | Nat North | A | Nuneaton Town | 815 | W | 1-0 | Bowen 67 | 9 | 7 |
| Sept 5 | Nat North | H | AFC Fylde | 310 | L | 1-3 | Anorou 21 | 15 | 8 |
| 12 | Nat North | A | North Ferriby United | 266 | L | 0-3 | | 16 | 9 |
| 15 | Nat North | A | Hednesford Town | 410 | D | 2-2 | Bowen 51 Parker 87 | 15 | 10 |
| 19 | Nat North | H | Gainsborough Trinity | 297 | L | 0-2 | | 17 | 11 |
| **27** | **FA C2Q** | **H** | **Kidlington** | **393** | **W** | **4-2** | **Symons 26 Smith 41 Williams 45 Hall 68** | | 12 |
| Oct 3 | Nat North | H | Harrogate Town | 329 | L | 0-1 | | 20 | 13 |
| **10** | **FA C3Q** | **A** | **Leiston** | **329** | **W** | **3-1** | **Miller 28 (pen) Smith 50 Cooke 68** | | 14 |
| 17 | Nat North | A | Bradford PA | 325 | D | 1-1 | Miller 32 (pen) | 20 | 15 |
| **24** | **FAC4Q** | **A** | **Staines Town** | **417** | **L** | **1-2** | **Smith 66** | | 16 |
| 31 | Nat North | H | Corby Town | 312 | W | 1-0 | Cooke 66 | 16 | 17 |
| Nov 7 | Nat North | A | Tamworth | 759 | D | 2-2 | Smith 56 (pen) Cooke 90 | 14 | 18 |
| 14 | Nat North | H | Lowestoft Town | 364 | L | 0-1 | | 14 | 19 |
| 21 | Nat North | A | Solihull Moors | 542 | D | 0-0 | | 17 | 20 |
| 24 | Nat North | H | Bradford PA | 269 | L | 1-3 | Williams 66 | 17 | 21 |
| **28** | **FAT1** | **A** | **Chelmsford City** | **359** | **D** | **1-1** | **Hanks 6** | | 22 |
| **Dec 1** | **FAT1r** | **H** | **Chelmsford City** | **238** | **L** | **0-1** | | | 23 |
| 5 | Nat North | A | Brackley Town | 240 | L | 0-1 | | 21 | 24 |
| 19 | Nat North | A | FC United | 3187 | W | 2-1 | Parker 19 Williams 69 | 18 | 25 |
| 26 | Nat North | H | Worcester City | 662 | L | 0-1 | | 21 | 26 |
| 28 | Nat North | A | AFC Telford United | 1159 | W | 1-0 | Williams 87 | 18 | 27 |
| Jan 2 | Nat North | A | Worcester City | 812 | W | 2-1 | Williams 43 Jones 56 (pen) | 15 | 28 |
| 9 | Nat North | H | Stalybridge Celtic | 330 | W | 3-0 | HALL 3 ( 6 64 87) | 14 | 29 |
| 12 | Nat North | H | Curzon Ahton | 232 | W | 3-1 | Cundy 12 Hall 7 62 | 10 | 30 |
| 23 | Nat North | H | Stockport County | 791 | D | 0-0 | | 12 | 31 |
| 31 | Nat North | H | Boston United | 657 | W | 1-0 | Parker 62 | 12 | 32 |
| Feb 13 | Nat North | A | AFC Fylde | 408 | L | 0-1 | | 13 | 33 |
| 16 | Nat North | A | Chorley | 668 | W | 1-0 | Knowles 16 | 11 | 34 |
| 20 | Nat North | H | Tamworth | 406 | L | 1-2 | Parker 73 | 12 | 35 |
| 27 | Nat North | A | Harrogate Town | 802 | D | 0-0 | | 12 | 36 |
| Mar 1 | Nat North | H | Chorley | 262 | D | 1-1 | Jones 36 (pen) | 12 | 37 |
| 5 | Nat North | H | Hednesford Town | 350 | D | 2-2 | Parker 15 Sterling-James 26 | 12 | 38 |
| 12 | Nat North | A | Stockport County | 2830 | L | 0-3 | | 13 | 39 |
| 19 | Nat North | H | Solihull Moors | 411 | L | 0-2 | | 13 | 40 |
| 26 | Nat North | A | Alfreton Town | 513 | D | 1-1 | Webb 88 | 14 | 41 |
| Apr 2 | Nat North | A | Gainsborough Trinity | 502 | D | 3-3 | Robles 45 Hopper 84 90 | 14 | 42 |
| 9 | Nat North | H | Brackley Town | 364 | D | 0-0 | | 14 | 43 |
| 16 | Nat North | A | Curzon Ashton | 226 | D | 1-1 | Bishop 88 | 17 | 44 |
| 19 | Nat North | H | Nuneaton Town | 360 | L | 0-1 | | 17 | 45 |
| 23 | Nat North | H | North Ferriby United | 413 | W | 3-2 | Jones 13 (pen) Sterling-James 20 Knowles 40 | 15 | 46 |
| 30 | Nat North | A | Lowestoft Town | 935 | D | 1-1 | Robles 66 | 15 | 47 |

| GOALSCORERS | Scoring Games | Consec Sco Games | Total | | Scoring Games | Consec Sco Games | Total |
|---|---|---|---|---|---|---|---|
| *2014-15 Griffin and B.Jones* | | *9* | | Knowles | 2 | | 2 |
| Hall | 3 | 2 | 6 | Miller | 2 | 2 | 2 |
| Parker | 5 | | 5 | Robles | 2 | | 2 |
| Williams | 5 | 2 | 5 | Stirling-James | 2 | | 2 |
| Anoruro | 4 | 2 | 4 | Bishop | 1 | | 1 |
| Smith | 4 | | 4 | Cundy | 1 | | 1 |
| Cooke | 3 | | 3 | Hanks | 1 | | 1 |
| Jones | 3 | | 3 | Richards | 1 | | 1 |
| Bowen | 2 | | 2 | Symons | 1 | | 1 |
| Hopper | 2 | | 2 | Webb | 1 | | 1 |

# HARROGATE TOWN

**Chairman:** Irving Weaver

**Secretary:** Mike Bligh **(T)** 01423 21 0600 **(E)** mikebligh@harrogatetownafc.com

**Commercial Manager:** **(T/E)** enquiries@harrogatetownafc.com

**Programme Editor:** Mike Bligh **(T/E)** mikebligh@harrogatetownafc.com

**Ground Address:** The CNG Stadium, Wetherby Road, Harrogate HG2 7SA

**(T)** 01423 210 600 **Manager:** Simon Weaver

## Club Factfile

**Founded:** 1935 **Nickname:** Town

**Previous Names:** Harrogate Hotspurs 1935-48.

**Previous Leagues:** West Riding 1919-20, Yorkshire 1920-21, 22-31, 57-82, Midland 1921-22, Northern 1931-32, Harrogate & Dist. 1935-37, 40-46, W. Riding Co.Am. 1937-40, W. Yorks. 1946-57, N.C.E. 1982-87, N.P.L. 1987-2004

**Club Colours (change):** Yellow & black stripe/black/black (All blue)

**Ground Capacity:** 3,291 **Seats:** 502 **Covered:** 1,300 **Clubhouse:** Yes **Shop:** Yes

**Directions**
A61 to Harrogate, turn right on to A658, and at roundabout take A661, proceed through second set of lights (Woodlands pub) ground approx. 500 mtrs on the right. From A1 Wetherby. Leave A1 at Wetherby on to A661 to Harrogate. Stay on this road and when reaching Harrogate at Woodland pub lights, ground 500mtrs on the right.

**Previous Grounds:** None

**Record Attendance:** 4,280 v Railway Athletic - Whitworth Cup Final 1950

**Record Victory:** 13-0 v Micklefield

**Record Defeat:** 1-10 v Methley United - 1956

**Record Goalscorer:** Jimmy Hague - 135 (1956-58 and 1961-76)

**Record Appearances:** Paul Williamson - 428 (1980-81, 1982-85, and 1986-93)

**Additional Records:**

**Honours:**
West Riding County Cup 1962-63, 72-73, 85-86. Northern Premier League Division 1 2001-02.
West Riding Challenge Cup x2.

### 10 YEAR RECORD

| 06-07 | 07-08 | 08-09 | 09-10 | 10-11 | 11-12 | 12-13 | 13-14 | 14-15 | 15-16 |
|---|---|---|---|---|---|---|---|---|---|
| Conf N 6 | Conf N 6 | Conf N 9 | Conf N 21 | Conf N 12 | Conf N 15 | Conf N 6 | Conf N 9 | Conf N 15 | Nat N 4 |

# HARROGATE TOWN MATCH RESULTS 2015-16

| Date | Comp | H/A | Opponents | Att: | Result | | Goalscorers | Pos | No. |
|---|---|---|---|---|---|---|---|---|---|
| Aug 8 | Nat North | A | Brackley Town | 315 | L | 0-1 | | 19 | 1 |
| 11 | Nat North | H | Gainsborough Trinity | 390 | W | 3-1 | Knowles 59 Daniels 65 90 | 7 | 2 |
| 15 | Nat North | H | Hednesford Town | 345 | W | 2-1 | Daniels 43 Knowles 90 | 6 | 3 |
| 17 | Nat North | A | Curzon Ashton | 326 | W | 2-1 | Knowles 30 Shiels 60 | 1 | 4 |
| 22 | Nat North | H | Tamworth | 444 | D | 0-0 | | 5 | 5 |
| 29 | Nat North | A | Chorley | 225 | W | 1-0 | Clayton 38 | 3 | 6 |
| 31 | Nat North | H | Bradford PA | 678 | W | 2-1 | Daniels 49 75 | 2 | 7 |
| Sept 5 | Nat North | A | Solihull Moors | 806 | L | 0-1 | | 3 | 8 |
| 12 | Nat North | A | AFC Telford United | 1173 | W | 4-0 | Daniels 11 45 Thewlis 85 Knowles 88 | 2 | 9 |
| 16 | Nat North | H | North Ferriby United | 404 | D | 3-3 | Knowles 26 Daniels 52 Cayton 90 | 3 | 10 |
| 19 | Nat North | H | Nuneaton Town | 503 | L | 0-3 | | 4 | 11 |
| **26** | **FAC2Q** | **A** | **Workington** | **599** | **W** | **1-0** | **Daniels 82** | | **12** |
| Oct 3 | Nat North | A | Gloucester City | 329 | W | 1-0 | Daniels 89 (pen) | 3 | 13 |
| **10** | **FAC3Q** | **H** | **Burscough** | **513** | **W** | **3-0** | **Swain 12 Knowles 61 Devine (og) 65** | | **14** |
| 17 | Nat North | A | Lowestoft Town | 504 | W | 2-1 | Daniels 16 Emmett 84 | 3 | 15 |
| **24** | **FAC4Q** | **H** | **Grimsby Town** | **1920** | **L** | **1-4** | **Daniels 12** | | **16** |
| 31 | Nat North | H | Worcester City | 535 | W | 1-0 | McWilliams 58 | 4 | 17 |
| Nov 10 | Nat North | A | Boston United | 1074 | D | 3-3 | Yates 10 Knowles 57 Swain 67 | 4 | 18 |
| 14 | Nat North | H | Alfreton Town | 607 | L | 1-2 | Colbeck 20 | 4 | 19 |
| 21 | Nat North | A | Corby Town | 477 | W | 3-0 | Yates 28 63 Shiels 56 | 5 | 20 |
| 24 | Nat North | H | AFC Fylde | 416 | D | 2-2 | Thewlis 8 Daniels 57 | 5 | 21 |
| **28** | **FAT3Q** | **H** | **Curzon Ashton** | **237** | **L** | **0-1** | | | **22** |
| Dec 5 | Nat North | A | Gainsborough Trinity | 403 | L | 1-2 | Emmett 6 | 7 | 23 |
| 19 | Nat North | H | Brackley Town | 1534 | W | 1-0 | Thirlwell 90 | 6 | 24 |
| 26 | Nat North | A | Stockport County | 3326 | W | 2-1 | Yates 3 Thewlis 74 | 5 | 25 |
| 28 | Nat North | H | Chorley | 642 | L | 2-4 | Yates 55 Knowles 58 | 6 | 26 |
| Jan 9 | Nat North | A | Hednesford Town | 375 | W | 3-2 | Clayton 4 47 Emmett 8 | 6 | 27 |
| 23 | Nat North | H | Solihull Moors | 583 | W | 6-0 | BURRELL 3 (39 61 82) Kerry 56 Clayton 72 Colbeck 86 | 5 | 28 |
| 30 | Nat North | A | FC United | 3362 | L | 3-4 | Daniels 22 Kerry 29 Colbeck 36 | 6 | 29 |
| Feb 2 | Nat North | H | Stockport County | 570 | W | 2-1 | Clayton 49 Burrell 80 | 5 | 30 |
| 13 | Nat North | A | North Ferriby United | 509 | W | 1-0 | Kerry 28 | 4 | 31 |
| 16 | Nat North | A | Stalybridge Celtic | 244 | W | 1-0 | Ellis 41 | 2 | 32 |
| 20 | Nat North | A | FC United | 1357 | W | 5-0 | Daniels 10 Thewlis 21 Emmett 44 Clayton 71 Colbeck 90 | 2 | 33 |
| 27 | Nat North | H | Gloucester City | 802 | D | 0-0 | | 2 | 34 |
| Mar 8 | Nat North | A | Tamworth | 591 | L | 0-1 | | 2 | 35 |
| 12 | Nat North | H | AFC Telford United | 699 | L | 0-1 | | 4 | 36 |
| 19 | Nat North | A | Worcester City | 581 | D | 0-0 | | 4 | 37 |
| 26 | Nat North | H | Curzon Ashton | 752 | D | 1-1 | Daniels 63 | 4 | 38 |
| 28 | Nat North | A | Bradford PA | 446 | L | 1-3 | Daniels 90 | 4 | 39 |
| Apr 2 | Nat North | H | Stalybridge Celtic | 630 | W | 2-1 | Wright 30 (og) Daniels 90 | 4 | 40 |
| 5 | Nat North | H | Lowestoft Town | 546 | W | 4-0 | Daniels 47 80 Colbeck 52 Emmett 90 | 4 | 41 |
| 9 | Nat North | A | Alfreton Town | 583 | L | 2-3 | Thewlis 32 Daniels 76 | 4 | 42 |
| 12 | Nat North | A | Nuneaton Town | 612 | D | 0-0 | | 4 | 43 |
| 16 | Nat North | H | Boston United | 1027 | D | 0-0 | | 4 | 44 |
| 23 | Nat North | A | AFC Fylde | 660 | L | 1-2 | Burrell 90 | 4 | 45 |
| 30 | Nat North | H | Corby Town | 1025 | W | 5-0 | Daniels 3 (pen) 7 Kerry 16 Draper 66 (og) Emmett 81 | 4 | 46 |
| **May 4** | **PO SF1** | **H** | **AFC Fylde** | **1694** | **L** | **0-1** | | | **47** |
| **8** | **PO SF2** | **A** | **AFC Fylde** | **1384** | **D** | **1-1** | **Knowles 16** | | **48** |

| GOALSCORERS | Scoring Games | Consec Sco Games | Total | | Scoring Games | Consec Sco Games | Total |
|---|---|---|---|---|---|---|---|
| *2014-15 Walshaw* | | | *12* | Shiels | 2 | | 2 |
| Daniels | 18 | 5 | 23 | Swain | 2 | | 2 |
| Knowles | 9 | 3 | 9 | Ellis | 1 | | 1 |
| Clayton | 6 | | 7 | McWilliams | 1 | | 1 |
| Emmett | 6 | | 6 | Thirlwell | 1 | | 1 |
| Burrell | 3 | | 5 | Opponents | | | 3 |
| Colbeck | 5 | | 5 | | | | |
| Thewlis | 5 | | 5 | | | | |
| Yates | 4 | | 5 | | | | |
| Kerry | 4 | | 4 | | | | |

# KIDDERMINSTER HARRIERS

**Chairman:** Colin Gordon

**Secretary:** Helen MacDonald **(T)** 01562 823 931 **(E)** helen.macdonald@harriers.co.uk

**Commercial Manager:** Dave Pountney **(T/E)** dave.pountney@harriers.co.uk

**Programme Editor:** Matt Paddock **(T/E)** matt.wall@harriers.co.uk

**Ground Address:** Aggborough Stadium, Hoo Road, Kidderminster DY10 1NB

**(T)** 01562 823 931 **Manager:** John Eustace

## Club Factfile

**Founded:** 1886 **Nickname:** Harriers

**Previous Names:** Kidderminster > 1891

**Previous Leagues:** Birmingham 1889-90, 91-1939, 47-48, 60-62. Midland 1890-91. Southern 1939-45, 48-60, 72-83. Birmingham Comb. 1945-47. West Midlands 1962-72. Conference 1983-2000. Football League 2000-05.

**Club Colours (change):** Red & white halves/white/red & white (Yellow & blue/blue/yellow & blue)

**Ground Capacity:** 6,419 **Seats:** 3.175 **Covered:** 3,062 **Clubhouse:** Yes **Shop:** Yes

**Directions**

From North M5 Junc 3 onto A456 to Kidderminster, From South M5 Junc 6 onto A449 to Kidderminster. Alternatively M40/42 Junc 1 onto A38 to Bromsgrove/A448 to Kidderminster. (All routes follow Brown signs to (SVR) Steam Railway then follow signs to Aggborough). Aggborough is signposted at either end of Hoo Road.

**Previous Grounds:** None

**Record Attendance:** 9,155 v Hereford United - 27/11/48

**Record Victory:** 25-0 v Hereford (H) - Birmingham Senior Cup 12/10/1889

**Record Defeat:** 0-13 v Darwen (A) - FA Cup 1st Round 24/01/1891

**Record Goalscorer:** Peter Wassell - 432 (1963-74)

**Record Appearances:** Brendan Wassell - 686 (1962-74)

**Additional Records:** Paid £80,000 to Nuneaton Borough for Andy Ducros July 2000
Recieved £380,000 from W.B.A. for Lee Hughes July 1997

**Honours:**

FA Trophy 1986-87. Conference 1993-94, 1999-2000.
Worcestershire Senior Invitation Cup x26 1895-96, 1903-04, 20-21, 31-32, 34-35, 35-36, 36-37, 65-66, 66-67, 68-69, 70-71, 71-72, 78-79, 82-83, 83-84, 85-86, 88-89, 89-90, 90-91, 92-93, 97-98, 98-99, 99-2000, 01-02, 09-10, 14-15.

**10 YEAR RECORD**

| 06-07 | 07-08 | 08-09 | 09-10 | 10-11 | 11-12 | 12-13 | 13-14 | 14-15 | 15-16 |
|---|---|---|---|---|---|---|---|---|---|
| Conf 10 | Conf 13 | Conf 6 | Conf 13 | Conf 6 | Conf 6 | Conf 2 | Conf 7 | Conf 16 | Nat 23 |

# KIDDERMINSTER HARRIERS MATCH RESULTS 2015-16

| Date | Comp | H/A | Opponents | Att: | Result | | Goalscorers | Pos | No. |
|---|---|---|---|---|---|---|---|---|---|
| Aug 8 | Nat Lge | H | Grimsby Town | 3459 | D | 2-2 | Styche 59 Verma 90 | 12 | 1 |
| 11 | Nat Lge | A | Dover Athletic | 906 | L | 2-3 | Dawson 61 Singh 72 | 19 | 2 |
| 15 | Nat Lge | A | Guiseley | 756 | L | 0-1 | | 19 | 3 |
| 18 | Nat Lge | H | Wrexham | 2620 | L | 1-3 | Wright 80 | 22 | 4 |
| 22 | Nat Lge | A | Gateshead | 800 | D | 1-1 | Singh 26 | 22 | 5 |
| 29 | Nat Lge | H | Forest Green Rovers | 1905 | L | 0-2 | | 22 | 6 |
| 31 | Nat Lge | A | Tranmere R | 4622 | D | 2-2 | Singh 84 Styche 90 | 24 | 7 |
| Sept 5 | Nat Lge | H | Braintree Town | 1670 | L | 0-1 | | 24 | 8 |
| 12 | Nat Lge | A | FC Halifax Town | 1128 | D | 1-1 | Singh 11 | 24 | 9 |
| 15 | Nat Lge | H | Torquay United | 1493 | D | 2-2 | Verma 57 Styche 90 (pen) | 24 | 10 |
| 19 | Nat Lge | H | Lincoln City | 1581 | L | 0-2 | | 24 | 11 |
| 22 | Nat Lge | A | Bromley | 776 | L | 2-3 | Jones 20 65 | 24 | 12 |
| 26 | Nat Lge | A | Barrow | 1323 | D | 1-1 | Styche 5 | 24 | 13 |
| Oct 3 | Nat Lge | H | Welling United | 1438 | L | 0-1 | | 24 | 14 |
| 6 | Nat Lge | H | Boreham Wood | 1294 | D | 1-1 | Francis-Angol 8 | 24 | 15 |
| 10 | Nat Lge | A | Macclesfield Town | 1653 | L | 1-2 | Murphy 77 | 24 | 16 |
| 13 | Nat Lge | A | Altrincham | 869 | D | 2-2 | Hassan 35 Whitfield 75 | 24 | 17 |
| 17 | Nat Lge | H | Southport | 1593 | L | 0-1 | | 24 | 18 |
| **24** | **FAC4Q** | **A** | **Stourbridge** | **2022** | **L** | **0-3** | | | 19 |
| 31 | Nat Lge | H | Woking | 1449 | W | 1-0 | Murphy 77 | 23 | 20 |
| Nov 10 | Nat Lge | A | Chester | 1956 | L | 1-3 | Langmead 40 | 23 | 21 |
| 14 | Nat Lge | H | Aldershot Town | 1790 | W | 2-0 | McQuilkin 53 Whitfield 60 | 23 | 22 |
| 28 | Nat Lge | A | Grimsby Town | 3894 | L | 0-1 | | 24 | 23 |
| Dec 5 | Nat Lge | H | Gateshead | 1489 | L | 0-1 | | 24 | 24 |
| **12** | **FAT1** | **A** | **Stourbridge** | **902** | **L** | **1-2** | **Singh 54** | | 25 |
| 19 | Nat Lge | A | Eastleigh | 1862 | L | 1-3 | Whitfield 60 | 24 | 26 |
| 26 | Nat Lge | H | Cheltenham Town | 3238 | L | 1-2 | Hawkins 30 | 24 | 27 |
| 28 | Nat Lge | A | Forest Green Rovers | 2110 | L | 0-3 | | 24 | 28 |
| Jan 23 | Nat Lge | H | Guiseley | 1431 | L | 0-1 | | 24 | 29 |
| 30 | Nat Lge | A | Aldershot Town | 1768 | L | 0-1 | | 24 | 30 |
| Feb 7 | Nat Lge | A | Boreham Wood | 366 | W | 2-0 | Whitfield 20 Ngwatala 75 | 24 | 31 |
| 9 | Nat Lge | H | Eastleigh | 1335 | W | 3-2 | Maxwell 2 White 51 Gnahoua 72 | 23 | 32 |
| 13 | Nat Lge | H | Macclesfield Town | 1693 | W | 3-1 | Lowe 10 White 16 Gnahoua 23 | 23 | 33 |
| 16 | Nat Lge | A | Cheltenham Town | 3387 | L | 0-2 | | 23 | 34 |
| 20 | Nat Lge | H | Chester | 2067 | D | 2-2 | Gnahoua 22 White 26 (pen) | 23 | 35 |
| 23 | Nat Lge | A | Wrexham | 3899 | L | 0-2 | | 24 | 36 |
| 27 | Nat Lge | H | Bromley | 1539 | L | 0-1 | | 24 | 37 |
| 29 | Nat Lge | A | Braintree Town | 502 | L | 1-2 | Maxwell 49 | 24 | 38 |
| Mar 5 | Nat Lge | A | Torquay United | 2021 | L | 2-3 | Lamgmead 52 Gnahoua 62 | 24 | 39 |
| 19 | Nat Lge | A | Lincoln City | 2178 | W | 2-1 | McQuilkin 72 83 | 24 | 40 |
| 26 | Nat Lge | A | Woking | 1730 | D | 1-1 | McQuilkin 79 | 24 | 41 |
| 28 | Nat Lge | H | Tranmere Rovers | 2744 | L | 0-2 | | 24 | 42 |
| Apr 2 | Nat Lge | H | Altrincham | 1402 | D | 1-1 | Whitfield 89 | 24 | 43 |
| 9 | Nat Lge | A | Welling United | 565 | W | 2-1 | Langmead 82 McQuilkin 85 | 24 | 44 |
| 12 | Nat Lge | H | FC Halifax Town | 1340 | W | 1-0 | Whitfield 48 | 23 | 45 |
| 15 | Nat Lge | H | Barrow | 1517 | D | 0-0 | | 23 | 46 |
| 23 | Nat Lge | H | Dover Athletic | 1410 | D | 1-1 | Lowe 14 | 23 | 47 |
| 30 | Nat Lge | A | Southport | 1473 | W | 4-3 | McQuilkin 8 Ngwatala 38 Williams 75 Garnett 84 | 23 | 48 |

| GOALSCORERS | Scoring Games | Consec Sco Games | Total |
|---|---|---|---|
| ***2014-15 Johnson*** | | | ***10*** |
| McQuilkin | 6 | | 7 |
| Whitfield | 6 | | 6 |
| Singh | 4 | | 5 |
| Gnahoua | 4 | | 4 |
| Stitch | 4 | | 4 |
| Langmead | 3 | | 3 |
| White | 3 | | 3 |
| Jones | 2 | | 2 |
| Lowe | 2 | | 2 |
| Maxwell | 2 | | 2 |
| Murphy | 2 | | 2 |
| Ngwatala | 2 | | 2 |
| Verma | 2 | | 2 |
| Dawson | 1 | | 1 |
| Frances-Angol | 1 | | 1 |
| Garnett | 1 | | 1 |
| Hassan | 1 | | 1 |
| Hawkins | 1 | | 1 |
| Williams | 1 | | 1 |

# NUNEATON TOWN

**Chairman:** Lee Thorn
**Secretary:** John Mayne (T) 02476 385 738 (E)
**Commercial Manager:** Dave Sharpe (T/E) 02476 385 738
**Programme Editor:** Ben Shakespeare (T/E) 02476 385 738
**Ground Address:** Liberty Way, Nuneaton CV11 6RR
(T) 02476 385 738 **Manager:** Kevin Wilson

## Club Factfile

**Founded:** 2008 **Nickname:** The Boro
**Previous Names:** Nuneaton Borough 1937-2008
**Previous Leagues:** Central Amateur 1937-38, Birmingham Combination 1938-52, West Midlands 1952-58, Southern 1958-79 81-82, 88-90, 2003-04, 08-10, Conference 1979-81, 82-88, 99-03, 04-08

**Club Colours (change):** Blue & white hoops/white/blue (Red & black squares/black/red)

**Ground Capacity:** **Seats:** Yes **Covered:** Yes **Clubhouse:** Yes **Shop:** Yes

**Directions** From the South, West and North West, exit the M6 at Junction 3 and follow the A444 into Nuneaton. At the Coton Arches roundabout turn right into Avenue Road which is the A4254 signposted for Hinckley. Continue along the A4254 following the road into Garrett Street, then Eastboro Way, then turn left into Townsend Drive. Follow the road round before turning left into Liberty Way for the ground. From the North, exit the M1 at Junction 21 and follow the M69. Exit at Junction 1 and take the 4th exit at roundabout onto A5 (Tamworth, Nuneaton). At Longshoot Junction turn left onto A47, continue to roundabout and take the 1st exit onto A4254, Eastboro Way. Turn right at next roundabout into Townsend Drive, then right again into Liberty Way, CV11 6RR.

**Previous Grounds:** Manor Park

**Record Attendance:** 22,114 v Rotherham United - FA Cup 3rd Round 1967 (At Manor Park)
**Record Victory:** 11-1 - 1945-46 and 1955-56
**Record Defeat:** 1-8 - 1955-56 and 1968-69
**Record Goalscorer:** Paul Culpin - 201 (55 during season 1992-93)
**Record Appearances:** Alan Jones - 545 (1962-74)
**Additional Records:** Paid £35,000 to Forest green Rovers for Marc McGregor 2000
Received £80,000 from Kidderminster Harriers for Andy Ducros 2000
**Honours:**
Southern League Midland Division 1981-82, 92-93, Premier Division 1988-99, Premier Division Play-offs 2009-10.
Conference North Play-offs 2011-12.
Birmingham Senior Cup x7.

**10 YEAR RECORD**

| 06-07 | 07-08 | 08-09 | 09-10 | 10-11 | 11-12 | 12-13 | 13-14 | 14-15 | 15-16 |
|---|---|---|---|---|---|---|---|---|---|
| Conf N 10 | Conf N 7 | SthE 2 | SthP 2 | Conf N 6 | Conf N 5 | Conf 15 | Conf 13 | Conf 24 | Nat N 6 |

# NUNEATON TOWN MATCH RESULTS 2015-16

| Date | Comp | H/A | Opponents | Att: | Result | | Goalscorers | Pos | No. |
|---|---|---|---|---|---|---|---|---|---|
| Aug 8 | Nat North | A | Chorley | 1011 | W | 3-2 | Maguire 6 Williams 34 Morgan 77 | 3 | 1 |
| 11 | Nat North | H | Brackley Town | 829 | W | 1-0 | Harewood 4 | 3 | 2 |
| 15 | Nat North | H | Bradford PA | 765 | W | 1-0 | Reid 40 | 1 | 3 |
| 18 | Nat North | A | Lowestoft Town | 507 | W | 1-0 | Williams 60 | 1 | 4 |
| 22 | Nat North | H | Stockport County | 1047 | D | 1-1 | Harewood 81 | 2 | 5 |
| 29 | Nat North | A | Tamworth | 1436 | D | 1-1 | Williams 58 | 2 | 6 |
| 31 | Nat North | H | Gloucester City | 815 | L | 0-1 | | 3 | 7 |
| Sept 5 | Nat North | A | Curzon Ashton | 337 | L | 0-1 | | 6 | 8 |
| 12 | Nat North | H | Gainsborough Trinity | 625 | W | 2-0 | Williams 37 Byrne 61 | 4 | 9 |
| 15 | Nat North | H | Stalybridge Celtic | 613 | D | 3-3 | Williams 27 Clifton 36 43 | 5 | 10 |
| 19 | Nat North | A | Harrogate Town | 503 | W | 3-0 | Williams 8 Harewood 46 Whitehouse 66 | 3 | 11 |
| **26** | **FAC 2Q** | **A** | **Halesowen Town** | **549** | **W** | **2-0** | **Williams 63 Whitehouse 83** | | 12 |
| Oct 3 | Nat North | H | Boston United | 774 | L | 1-3 | Duffy 61 | 5 | 13 |
| **10** | **FAC 3Q** | **A** | **North Ferriby United** | **531** | **L** | **1-2** | **Williams 26** | | 14 |
| 18 | Nat North | A | Worcester City | 716 | W | 1-0 | Duffy 60 (pen) | 4 | 15 |
| 24 | Nat North | A | Hednesford Town | 525 | W | 4-2 | Daniels 8 Byrne 34 Duffy 66 89 | 3 | 16 |
| 31 | Nat North | H | North Ferriby United | 637 | W | 3-1 | Williams 5 22 Duffy 36 | 3 | 17 |
| Nov 7 | Nat North | H | Alfreton Town | 654 | W | 2-0 | Byrne 47 Williams78 | 1 | 18 |
| 14 | Nat North | A | AFC Telford United | 1416 | W | 5-1 | WHITEHOUSE 3 ( 5 31 73) Chettle 47 Williams 67 | 1 | 19 |
| 21 | Nat North | H | FC United | 1167 | D | 2-2 | Duffy 59 90 | 1 | 20 |
| 23 | Nat North | A | North Ferriby United | 425 | W | 2-1 | Chettle 29 Tshimanga 82 | 1 | 21 |
| **28** | **FAT3Q** | **H** | **Alfreton Town** | **467** | **W** | **2-0** | **Duffy 58 (pen) Chettle 90** | | 22 |
| Dec 5 | Nat North | H | Corby Town | 713 | D | 0-0 | | 1 | 23 |
| 9 | Nat North | A | FC United | 2781 | L | 2-3 | Duffy 40 Whitehouse 45 | 1 | 24 |
| **15** | **FAT1** | **A** | **Curzon Ashton** | **121** | **L** | **1-3** | **Harewood 48** | | 25 |
| 19 | Nat North | H | Chorley | 620 | D | 2-2 | Williams 10 80 | 1 | 26 |
| 26 | Nat North | A | Solihull Moors | 1242 | L | 1-3 | Harewood 87 (pen) | 2 | 27 |
| 28 | Nat North | H | Tamworth | 1165 | W | 3-0 | Harewod 8 17 Reid 67 | 1 | 28 |
| Jan 2 | Nat North | H | Solihull Moors | 1306 | L | 0-1 | | 3 | 29 |
| 16 | Nat North | A | Stockport County | 2823 | D | 1-1 | Duffy 22 | 5 | 30 |
| 23 | Nat North | H | Curzon Ashton | 702 | L | 0-1 | | 6 | 31 |
| 30 | Nat North | A | Alfreton Town | 610 | D | 2-2 | Harewood 49 Whitehouse 76 | 6 | 32 |
| Feb 13 | Nat North | A | Brackley Town | 365 | W | 3-2 | Byrne 12 Whitehouse 57 75 | 6 | 33 |
| 20 | Nat North | H | Worcester City | 825 | D | 1-1 | Morgan 82 | 5 | 34 |
| 27 | Nat North | A | Corby Town | 651 | W | 3-1 | Waite 1 Ironside 70 Whitehouse 80 | 5 | 35 |
| Mar 1 | Nat North | H | AFC Fylde | 528 | W | 1-1 | Whitehouse 49 | 4 | 36 |
| 12 | Nat North | A | Gainsborough Trinity | 505 | L | 0-1 | | 5 | 37 |
| 19 | Nat North | A | AFC Fylde | 555 | D | 2-2 | Clifton 2 Duffy 90 (pen) | 5 | 38 |
| 26 | Nat North | H | Lowestoft Town | 537 | W | 1-0 | Elliott 63 | 5 | 39 |
| Apr 2 | Nat North | H | AFC Telford United | 754 | D | 0-0 | | 7 | 40 |
| 9 | Nat North | A | Stalybridge Celtic | 324 | W | 5-2 | Duffy 28 Whitehouse 32 56 Harewood 73 Byrne 84 | 6 | 41 |
| 12 | Nat North | H | Harrogate Town | 612 | D | 0-0 | | 6 | 42 |
| 19 | Nat North | A | Gloucester City | 301 | W | 1-0 | Whitehouse 57 | 6 | 43 |
| 23 | Nat North | A | Boston United | 2037 | L | 1-2 | Sanogo 19 | 6 | 44 |
| 27 | Nat North | A | Bradford PA | 287 | W | 3-2 | Sanago 22 Harewood 30 Ironside 80 | 6 | 45 |
| 30 | Nat North | H | Hednesford Town | 866 | W | 3-0 | Byrne 4 Harewood 60 Reid 76 | 6 | 46 |

| GOALSCORERS | Scoring Games | Consec Sco Games | Total | | Scoring Games | Consec Sco Games | Total |
|---|---|---|---|---|---|---|---|
| ***2014-15 Brown*** | | | ***6*** | Sanago | 2 | | 2 |
| Williams | 12 | 4 | 14 | Ironside | 2 | | 2 |
| Whitehouse | 10 | 2 | 14 | Daniels | 1 | | 1 |
| Duffy | 10 | 3 | 12 | Elliott | 1 | | 1 |
| Harewood | 10 | 2 | 11 | Maguire | 1 | | 1 |
| Byrne | 6 | | 6 | Tshimanga | 1 | | 1 |
| Chettle | 3 | | 3 | Waite | 1 | | 1 |
| Clifton | 3 | | 3 | | | | |
| Reid | 3 | | 3 | | | | |
| Morgan | 2 | | 2 | | | | |

# SALFORD CITY

**Chairman:** Karen Baird

**Secretary:** Andrew Giblin **(T)** 07808 254 646 **(E)** andrewgiblin@aol.com

**Commercial Manager:** **(T/E)**

**Programme Editor:** Gareth Lyons **(T/E)** 0161 728 4572

**Ground Address:** Moor Lane, Kersal, Salford, Manchester M7 3OZ

**(T)** 0161 792 6287 **Manager:** Anthony Johnson & Bernard Morley

2015-16

## Club Factfile

**Founded:** 1940 **Nickname:** Ammies

**Previous Names:** Salford Central 1940-63, Salford Amateurs 1963 until merger with Anson Villa, Salford F.C. > 1990

**Previous Leagues:** Manchester 1963-80, Cheshire County 1980-82, North West Counties 1982-2008

**Club Colours (change):** Red/white/white (White/black/black)

**Ground Capacity:** 8,000 **Seats:** 260 **Covered:** 600 **Clubhouse:** Yes **Shop:** No

**Directions**

M62 to Junction 17 (Prestwich, Whitefield). Take A56 Bury New Road towards Manchester.
Continue through four sets of traffic lights.
Turn right into Moor Lane. Ground 500 yards on left.
Take first left after ground (Oaklands Road), first left again into Nevile Road and follow along to main entrance.

**Previous Grounds:**

**Record Attendance:** 3,000 v Whickham - FA Vase 1980

**Record Victory:** Not known - If you know please email tw.publications@btinternet.com

**Record Defeat:** Not known - If you know please email tw.publications@btinternet.com

**Record Goalscorer:** Not known - If you know please email tw.publications@btinternet.com

**Record Appearances:** Not known - If you know please email tw.publications@btinternet.com

**Additional Records:**

**Honours:**
Manchester League Premier Division 1975, 76, 77, 79. North West Counties League Cup 2006.
Northern Premier Division One North 2014-15, Premier Division Play-offs 2015-16.

### 10 YEAR RECORD

| 06-07 | | 07-08 | | 08-09 | | 09-10 | | 10-11 | | 11-12 | | 12-13 | | 13-14 | | 14-15 | | 15-16 | |
|---|---|---|---|---|---|---|---|---|---|---|---|---|---|---|---|---|---|---|---|
| NWC1 | 4 | NWC1 | 2 | NP1N | 20 | NP1N | 11 | NP1N | 12 | NP1N | 13 | NP1N | 16 | NP1N | 12 | NP1N | 1 | NP P | 3 |

# SALFORD CITY MATCH RESULTS 2015-16

| Date | Comp | H/A | Opponents | Att: | Result | | Goalscorers | Pos | No. |
|---|---|---|---|---|---|---|---|---|---|
| Aug 15 | NPL | H | Marine | 518 | D | 0-0 | | 16 | 1 |
| 18 | NPL | A | Matlock T | 344 | W | 2-1 | Seddon 49 Lynch 90 | 6 | 2 |
| 22 | NPL | A | Mickleover Sp. | 210 | W | 2-1 | Hulme 58 Webber 68 | 4 | 3 |
| 25 | NPL | H | Colwyn Bay | 461 | D | 2-2 | Webber 17 Hulme 38 | 7 | 4 |
| 29 | NPL | A | Buxton | 278 | W | 2-0 | Clark 24 Burton 51 | 2 | 5 |
| 31 | NPL | H | Hyde United | 636 | L | 0-1 | | 5 | 6 |
| Sept 5 | NPL | A | Barwell | 206 | W | 1-0 | Hulme 32 | 3 | 7 |
| 8 | NPL | H | Blyth Spartans | 500 | L | 0-1 | | 6 | 8 |
| **12** | **FAC1Q** | **H** | **Whitby Town** | **255** | **D** | **1-1** | **Smalley 55** | | 9 |
| **16** | **FAC1Qr** | **A** | **Whitby Town** | **244** | **W** | **5-0** | **POOLE 3 (19 21 48) Hulme 21 Kebbie 65** | | 10 |
| 19 | NPL | H | Rushall Olympic | 359 | L | 1-3 | Allen 51 (pen) | 10 | 11 |
| 23 | NPL | A | Whitby Town | 189 | W | 3-2 | Webber 6 43 Hulme 85 | 7 | 12 |
| **26** | **FAC2Q** | **H** | **Curzon Ashton** | **309** | **W** | **2-1** | **Webber 22 39** | | 13 |
| 29 | NPL | H | Halesowen T | 394 | W | 3-1 | Allen 3 37 Mwasile 90 | 5 | 14 |
| Oct 3 | NPL | A | Frickley Athletic | 280 | W | 1-0 | Hulme 31 | 4 | 15 |
| **10** | **FAC3Q** | **H** | **Bradford PA** | **534** | **D** | **1-1** | **Allen 8** | | 16 |
| **14** | **FAC3Qr** | **A** | **Bradford PA** | **426** | **W** | **1-0** | **Allen 94 (aet)** | | 17 |
| 17 | NPL | A | Sutton Coldfield T | 238 | W | 2-0 | Poole 13 Webber 25 | 5 | 18 |
| 20 | NPL | A | Colwyn Bay | 239 | W | 3-2 | Poole 12 26 Webber 90 | 4 | 19 |
| **24** | **FAC4Q** | **H** | **Southport** | **1019** | **W** | **1-0** | **Poole 76** | | 20 |
| 27 | NPL | H | Matlock Town | 427 | D | 2-2 | Poole 17 Allen 90 (pen) | 4 | 21 |
| **31** | **FAT 1Q** | **A** | **Nantwich Town** | **550** | **L** | **1-2** | **Howson 4** | | 22 |
| **Nov 6** | **FAC1** | **H** | **Notts County** | **1,400** | **W** | **2-0** | **Webber 46 Allan 73** | | 23 |
| 14 | NPL | A | Workington | 1.405 | W | 4-1 | Hulme 10 Webber 20 Burton 43 Allen 73 | 4 | 24 |
| 17 | NPL | H | Mickelover Sports | 690 | D | 1-1 | Allen 12 | 4 | 25 |
| 21 | NPL | H | Stamford | 1311 | W | 1-0 | Peers 44 | 3 | 26 |
| 28 | NPL | A | Grantham Town | 788 | L | 0-2 | | 3 | 27 |
| **Dec 4** | **FAC2** | **H** | **Hartlepool United** | **1,400** | **D** | **1-1** | **O'Halloran 23** | | 28 |
| **15** | **FAC2r** | **A** | **Hartlepool United** | **4,374** | **L** | **0-2** | **(aet)** | | 29 |
| 19 | NPL | A | Rushall Olympic | 538 | W | 3-2 | Allen 30 Poole 36 Hulme 55 | 4 | 30 |
| 28 | NPL | H | Hyde United | 866 | W | 2-1 | Poole 23 29 | 3 | 31 |
| Jan 2 | NPL | H | Barwell | 624 | W | 7-0 | Webber 13 POOLE 3 (16 56 86) Burton 30 Hulme 78 Mwasile 90 | 3 | 32 |
| 5 | NPL | A | Nantwich Town | 740 | D | 1-1 | Stopforth 48 | | 33 |
| 9 | NPL | H | Skelmersdale U | 660 | W | 4-0 | Johnston 5 35 Poole 15 Hulme 46 | 2 | 34 |
| 19 | NPL | H | Stourbridge | 574 | L | 0-1 | | 2 | 35 |
| 23 | NPL | H | Buxton | 707 | W | 2-0 | Hine 36 Johnston 45 | 2 | 36 |
| 26 | NPL | A | Blyth Spartans | 1432 | L | 1-2 | Hine 87 | 3 | 37 |
| 30 | NPL | H | Frickley Athletic | 547 | D | 2-2 | Allen 16 Hulme 60 | 3 | 38 |
| Feb 2 | NPL | H | Ramsbottom U | 551 | W | 4-0 | Allen 4 34 Seddon 41 Hine 83 | 3 | 39 |
| 13 | NPL | H | Darlington 1883 | 881 | L | 3-4 | Hine 27 Lynch 24 Webber 62 | 4 | 40 |
| 20 | NPL | A | Ilkeston | 999 | L | 1-2 | Webber 71 | 4 | 41 |
| 23 | NPL | A | Marine | 425 | W | 2-0 | Lynch 18 Clark 73 | 3 | 42 |
| 27 | NPL | H | Ilkeston | 889 | W | 2-0 | Webber 47 Hulme 62 | 3 | 43 |
| Mar 1 | NPL | A | Darkington 1883 | 1587 | L | 2-3 | Lynch 46 Hine 83 | 2 | 44 |
| 5 | NPL | H | Ashton United | 734 | W | 3-1 | Poole 18 Coo 51 (og) Allen 90 (pen) | 2 | 45 |
| 8 | NPL | H | Workington | 555 | W | 5-3 | LYNCH 3 ( 3 13 39) Allen 74 (pen) Webber 77 | 2 | 46 |
| 12 | NPL | A | Skelmersdale United | 370 | L | 1-3 | Webber 16 (pen) | 3 | 47 |
| 15 | NPL | A | Halesowen Town | 746 | W | 1-0 | Allen 64 | 3 | 48 |
| 19 | NPL | H | Sutton Coldfield T | 582 | W | 2-0 | Webber 13 Poole 69 | 3 | 49 |
| 26 | NPL | H | Whitby Town | 729 | D | 0-0 | | 3 | 50 |
| 28 | NPL | A | Ramsbottom United | 763 | W | 4-0 | Priestley 36 Stopforth 40 Smith (og) Hulme 86 | 3 | 51 |
| Apr 2 | NPL | H | Grantham Town | 760 | W | 5-0 | Poole 13 Webber 26 Hulme 65 77 Gumbs 85 | 3 | 52 |
| 5 | NPL | A | Ashton United | 383 | W | 3-0 | Hulme 6 Poole 15 Webber 45 | 3 | 53 |
| 9 | NPL | A | Stamford | 792 | D | 1-1 | Clark 90 | 3 | 54 |
| 16 | NPL | H | Nantwich Town | 667 | D | 1-1 | Allen 90 | 3 | 55 |
| 23 | NPL | A | Stourbridge | 1827 | W | 2-1 | Itela 10 72 | 3 | 56 |
| **26** | **PO SF** | **H** | **Ashton United** | **866** | **W** | **3-1** | **Hulme 25 Seddon 93 Poole 113 (aet)** | | 57 |
| **30** | **Final** | **H** | **Workington** | **1967** | **W** | **3-2** | **O'Halloran 14 Priestley 79 Hulme 87** | | 58 |

| GOALSCORERS | Scoring Games | Consec Sco Games | Total | | Scoring Games | Consec Sco Games | Total |
|---|---|---|---|---|---|---|---|
| Poole | 14 | 4 | 20 | Mwasile | 2 | | 2 |
| Webber | 17 | 2 | 19 | O'Halloran | 2 | | 2 |
| Hulme | 17 | 2 | 18 | Priestley | 2 | | 2 |
| Allen | 13 | 3 | 17 | Stopforth | 2 | | 2 |
| Lynch | 5 | | 7 | Gumbs | 1 | | 1 |
| Hine | 5 | | 5 | Howson | 1 | | 1 |
| Burton | 3 | | 3 | Kebbie | 1 | | 1 |
| Clark | 2 | | 3 | Peers | 1 | | 1 |
| Johnston | 3 | | 3 | Smalley | 1 | | 1 |
| Seddon | 3 | | 3 | Opponents | | | 2 |
| Itela | 1 | | 2 | | | | |

# STALYBRIDGE CELTIC

**Chairman:** Rob Gorski
**Secretary:** Martyn Torr **(T)** 07860 841 765 **(E)** office@stalybridgeceltic.co.uk
**Commercial Manager:** Syd White **(T/E)** office@stalybridgeceltic.co.uk
**Programme Editor:** Nick Shaw **(T/E)** programme@stalybridgeceltic.co.uk
**Ground Address:** Bower Fold, Mottram Road, Stalybridge, Cheshire SK15 2RT
**(T)** 0161 338 2828 **Manager:** Liam Watson

## Club Factfile

**Founded:** 1909 **Nickname:** Celtic
**Previous Names:** None
**Previous Leagues:** Lancashire Combination 1911-12, Central League 1912-21, Southern 1914-15, Football League 1921-23, Cheshire Co. 1923-82, North West Co. 1982-87, N.P.L. 1987-92, 98-2001, Conference 1992-98, 01-02

**Club Colours (change):** Royal blue/white/blue (Green/black/black)

**Ground Capacity:** 6,500 **Seats:** 1,500 **Covered:** 2,400 **Clubhouse:** Yes **Shop:** Yes

**Directions**
Leave the M6 at junction 19 (Northwich). At the roundabout at the end of the slip road turn right (exit 3 of 4) to join the A556 towards Altrincham. Stay on the A556 for 5 miles to a roundabout with the M56. Turn right at the roundabout (exit 3 of 4) onto the M56. Stay on the M56 for 6 1/2 miles to junction 3 (M60 signposted Sheffield, M67) Stay on the M60 for 7 miles to junction 24 (M67, Denton) At the roundabout turn right (exit 4 of 5) to join the M67. Stay on the M67 to the very end, Junction 4. At the roundabout turn left (exit 1 of 4) onto the A57 (Hyde Road). After 1/2 a mile you will reach a set of traffic lights (signposted Stalybridge). Turn left onto B6174 (Stalybridge Road). Almost immediately, there is a mini roundabout. Turn left (exit 1 of 5) onto Roe Cross Road (A6018). Follow this road for 1 3/4 miles passing the Roe Cross Inn on the right and through the cutting (the road is now called Mottram Road). When you pass the Dog and Partridge on the right, you will be almost there. Bower Fold is on the left opposite a sharp right turn next to the Hare and Hounds pub. If the car park is full (it usually is), parking can be found on the streets on the right of Mottram Road.

**Previous Grounds:** None

**Record Attendance:** 9,753 v West Bromwich Albion - FA Cup replay 1922-23
**Record Victory:** 16-2 v Manchester NE - 01/05/1926 and v Nantwich - 22/10/1932
**Record Defeat:** 1-10 v Wellington Town - 09/03/1946
**Record Goalscorer:** Harry Dennison - 215
**Record Appearances:** Kevan Keelan - 395
**Additional Records:** Cecil Smith scored 77 goals during the 1931-32 season
Paid £15,000 to Kettering Town for Ian Arnold 1995. Received £16,000 from Southport for Lee Trundle.

**Honours:**
Manchester Senior Cup 1922-23.
Northern Premier League Premier Division 1991-92, 2000-01.
Cheshire Senior Cup x2.

### 10 YEAR RECORD

| 06-07 | 07-08 | 08-09 | 09-10 | 10-11 | 11-12 | 12-13 | 13-14 | 14-15 | 15-16 |
|---|---|---|---|---|---|---|---|---|---|
| Conf N 18 | Conf N 2 | Conf N 6 | Conf N 9 | Conf N 10 | Conf N 6 | Conf N 13 | Conf N 19 | Conf N 19 | Nat N 12 |

# STALYBRIDGE CELTIC MATCH RESULTS 2015-16

| Date | Comp | H/A | Opponents | Att: | Result | Goalscorers | Pos | No. |
|---|---|---|---|---|---|---|---|---|
| Aug 8 | Nat North | A | Hednesford Town | 513 | L 1-2 | Shaw 75 | 17 | 1 |
| 11 | Nat North | H | Bradford PA | 407 | D 1-1 | Higgins 34 | 16 | 2 |
| 15 | Nat North | H | Gloucester City | 480 | W 1-0 | Simm 84 | 10 | 3 |
| 18 | Nat North | A | Gainsborough Trinity | 354 | L 1-3 | Farrell 81 | 14 | 4 |
| 22 | Nat North | H | Solihull Moors | 386 | L 1-3 | Dixon 45 | 14 | 5 |
| 29 | Nat North | A | Stockport County | 3628 | W 3-0 | Higgins 62 McKenna 71 Farrell 86 | 13 | 6 |
| 31 | Nat North | H | Chorley | 577 | L 0-1 | | 16 | 7 |
| Sept 5 | Nat North | A | Tamworth | 747 | D 1-1 | Dixon 45 | 13 | 8 |
| 12 | Nat North | H | Lowestoft Town | 318 | W 3-1 | Tames 4 12 Shaw 65 | 11 | 9 |
| 15 | Nat North | A | Nuneaton Town | 613 | D 3-3 | Chippendale 65 Johnson 68 Osei 87 | 11 | 10 |
| 19 | Nat North | H | FC United | 1775 | W 1-0 | Dixon 51 (pen) | 10 | 11 |
| **26** | **FAC2Q** | **A** | **Kendal Town** | **323** | **W 3-2** | **Tames 5 Johnson 77 Osei 82** | | 12 |
| Oct 3 | Nat North | A | Alfreton Town | 499 | W 3-1 | Tames 10 69 Johnson 83 | 8 | 13 |
| **10** | **FAC3Q** | **A** | **Chasetown** | **443** | **D 1-1** | **Tames 12** | | 14 |
| **13** | **FAC3Qr** | **H** | **Chasetown** | **318** | **W 2-0** | **Higgins 42 Farrell 87** | | 15 |
| 17 | Nat North | A | AFC Telford United | 1429 | L 0-2 | | 9 | 16 |
| **24** | **FAC4Q** | **H** | **North Ferriby United** | **547** | **D 1-1** | **Dixon 90** | | 17 |
| **28** | **FAC4Qr** | **A** | **North Ferriby United** | **710** | **D 0-0** | **(Won 8-7 on pens aet)** | | 18 |
| 31 | Nat North | A | AFC Fylde | 472 | L 0-5 | | 11 | 19 |
| **Nov 7** | **FAC1** | **A** | **Doncaster Rovers** | **3991** | **L 0-2** | | | 20 |
| 14 | Nat North | H | Worcester City | 479 | W 3-1 | Higgins 48 63 Simm 76 | 11 | 21 |
| 17 | Nat North | H | Corby Town | 205 | L 2-3 | Mudimu 15 Johnson 45 | 11 | 22 |
| 21 | Nat North | A | Brackley Town | 203 | W 3-2 | Farrell 8 Higgins 54 Dixon 68 (pen) | 11 | 23 |
| **28** | **FAT3Q** | **A** | **Sutton Coldfield** | **140** | **L 0-1** | | | 24 |
| Dec 5 | Nat North | A | Bradford PA | 219 | L 1-3 | Higgins 79 | 11 | 25 |
| 19 | Nat North | H | Hednesford Town | 408 | W 4-2 | Burns 45 Wright 48 Farrell 75 Shaw 83 | 10 | 26 |
| 28 | Nat North | H | Stockport County | 1516 | D 1-1 | Odejayl 90 (og) | 12 | 27 |
| Jan 2 | Nat North | H | Curzon Ashton | 716 | D 1-1 | Dixon 90 | 12 | 28 |
| 9 | Nat North | A | Gloucester City | 330 | L 0-3 | | 13 | 29 |
| 16 | Nat North | A | Solihull Moors | 492 | L 1-4 | Tames 73 | 14 | 30 |
| 23 | Nat North | H | Tamworth | 407 | L 3-5 | Higgins 46 Simm 53 Tames 62 | 15 | 31 |
| 25 | Nat North | A | Curzon Ashton | 484 | D 0-0 | | 14 | 32 |
| 30 | Nat North | A | Lowestoft Town | 570 | W 2-0 | Simm 13 Higgins 35 | 14 | 33 |
| Feb 13 | Nat North | A | Boston United | 1202 | W 3-0 | Simm 20 Tames 45 Wright 58 | 12 | 34 |
| 16 | Nat North | H | Harrogate Town | 244 | L 0-1 | | 13 | 35 |
| 23 | Nat North | A | Worcester City | 367 | L 0-5 | | 14 | 36 |
| 27 | Nat North | H | AFC Telford United | 437 | D 5-5 | Simm 20 37 Dixon 31 Higgins 50 Wisdom 55 | 14 | 37 |
| Mar 12 | Nat North | A | North Ferriby United | 296 | L 0-1 | | 16 | 38 |
| 19 | Nat North | H | Brackley Town | 401 | W 3-1 | Simm 15 Joyce 55 Mudimu 76 | 15 | 39 |
| 26 | Nat North | H | Gainsborough Trinity | 448 | D 0-0 | | 16 | 40 |
| 28 | Nat North | A | Chorley | 867 | D 0-0 | | 17 | 41 |
| Apr 2 | Nat North | A | Harrogate Town | 630 | L 1-2 | Simm 61 | 17 | 42 |
| 5 | Nat North | H | AFC Fylde | 234 | D 1-1 | Hughes 38 | 17 | 43 |
| 9 | Nat North | H | Nuneaton Town | 324 | L 2-5 | Farrell 69 Burns 90 | 18 | 44 |
| 12 | Nat North | H | North Ferriby United | 173 | W 2-0 | Chalmers 45 (pen) Simm 83 | 14 | 45 |
| 16 | Nat North | A | FC United | 3451 | W 1-0 | Wisdom 65 | 13 | 46 |
| 19 | Nat North | H | Alfreton Town | 252 | D 1-1 | Higgins 90 | 12 | 47 |
| 23 | Nat North | A | Corby Town | 476 | W 3-0 | Tames 54 Higgins 80 Mudimu 90 | 12 | 48 |
| 30 | Nat North | H | Boston United | 945 | L 0-5 | | 12 | 49 |

| GOALSCORERS | Scoring Games | Consec Sco Games | Total | | Scoring Games | Consec Sco Games | Total |
|---|---|---|---|---|---|---|---|
| *2014-15 Ennis* | | | *10* | Osie | 2 | | 2 |
| Higgins | 11 | 2 | 12 | Wisdom | 2 | | 2 |
| Simm | 9 | 2 | 10 | Wright | 2 | | 2 |
| Tames | 9 | 3 | 10 | Chalmers | 1 | | 1 |
| Dixon | 6 | | 7 | Chippendale | 1 | | 1 |
| Farrell | 6 | | 6 | Hughes | 1 | | 1 |
| Johnson | 4 | | 4 | Joyce | 1 | | 1 |
| Mudimu | 3 | | 3 | McKenna | 1 | | 1 |
| Shaw | 3 | | 3 | Opponents | 1 | | 1 |
| Burns | 2 | | 2 | | | | |

# STOCKPORT COUNTY

**Chairman:** Richard Park
**Secretary:** Mark Lockyear **(T)** 0161 266 2700 **(E)** mark.lockyear@stockportcounty.com
**Commercial Manager:** Simon Dawson **(T/E)** simon.dawson@stockportcounty.com
**Programme Editor:** **(T/E)**
**Ground Address:** Edgeley Park, Hardcastle Road, Stockport SK3 9DD
**(T)** 0161 286 8888 **Manager:** Jim Gannon

2015-16 Cheshire Senior Cup winners. Photo: Keith Clayton.

## Club Factfile

**Founded:** 1883 **Nickname:** County or Hatters
**Previous Names:** Heaton Norris Rovers 1883-88, Heaton Norris 1888-90.
**Previous Leagues:** Football League 1900-2011.

**Club Colours (change):** Blue & white hoops/white/white (Aqua/navy/navy)

**Ground Capacity:** 10,800 **Seats:** Yes **Covered:** Yes **Clubhouse:** **Shop:** Yes

**Directions**
**From The South** (M6): Exit the M6 at Junction 19 (sign-posted 'Manchester Airport, Stockport A55, M56 East') and at the r'about turn right onto the A556. At the Bowden r'about after 4.2 miles, turn right (sign-posted 'Manchester M56) onto the M56. Exit the M56 after 6.9 miles (sign-posted 'Stockport M60, Sheffield M67') onto the M60. Exit the M60 at Junction 1 ('sign-posted 'Stockport Town Centre and West'). At the r'about turn right and continue through to the second set of lights and turn left (ignoring the sign directing you to Stockport Co.) and follow the road to the left, which is Chestergate. At the lights turn right up King Street, past the fire station on the right to the top of the hill, turn right at the r'about signed Edgeley. Continue down Hardcastle street turning left after the bus stop signed Caroline Street. **From the North** (M62 from Leeds): Follow the M62 onto the M60 and continue south. Exit the M60 at Junction 1 ('sign-posted Stockport Town centre') At the roundabout turn right and continue through to the second set of lights and turn left (ignoring the sign directing you to Stockport Co.) and follow the road to the left, which is Chestergate. At the traffic lights turn right up King Street, past the fire station on the right to the top of the hill, turn right at the roundabout signed Edgeley. Continue down Hardcastle street turning left after the bus stop signed Caroline Street. At the end of Caroline St turn right where you will see the main car park on the left. (not available on Match Days)

**Previous Grounds:** Nursery Inn, Green Lane 1889-1902.

**Record Attendance:** 27,833 v Liverpool, FA Cup 5th Round 11/02/1950.
**Record Victory:** 13-0 v Halifax Town, Division Three North 06/01/1934.
**Record Defeat:** 1-8 v Chesterfield, Division Two 19/04/1902.
**Record Goalscorer:** (League) Jack Connor - 132, 1951-56.
**Record Appearances:** (League) Andy Thorpe - 489, 1978-86, 88-92.
**Additional Records:** Paid, £800,000 for Ian Moore from Nottingham Forest, 07/1998.
Received, £1,600,000 for Alun Armstrong from Middlesbrough, 02/1998.
**Honours:**
League Division Three North 1921-22, 36-37, Division Four 1966-67.
Cheshire Senior Cup 2015-16.

**10 YEAR RECORD**

| 06-07 | | 07-08 | | 08-09 | | 09-10 | | 10-11 | | 11-12 | | 12-13 | | 13-14 | | 14-15 | | 15-16 | |
|---|---|---|---|---|---|---|---|---|---|---|---|---|---|---|---|---|---|---|---|
| FL 2 | 8 | FL 2 | 4 | FL 1 | 18 | FL 1 | 24 | FL 2 | 24 | Conf | 16 | Conf | 21 | Conf N | 14 | Conf N | 11 | Nat N | 9 |

## STOCKPORT COUNTY MATCH RESULTS 2015-16

| Date | Comp | H/A | Opponents | Att: | Result | | Goalscorers | Pos | No. |
|---|---|---|---|---|---|---|---|---|---|
| Aug 8 | Nat North | H | Boston United | 3396 | **W** | 2-1 | Rule 34 Gavin 68 | 5 | 1 |
| 11 | Nat North | A | FC United | 3199 | **W** | 2-1 | Dyson 65 Odejayi 74 | 4 | 2 |
| 15 | Nat North | A | AFC Telford United | 1568 | **W** | 1-0 | Dyson 13 | 2 | 3 |
| 18 | Nat North | H | North Ferriby United | 3140 | D | 1-1 | Ledsham 87 | 2 | 4 |
| 22 | Nat North | A | Nuneaton Town | 1047 | D | 1-1 | Rule 70 | 3 | 5 |
| 29 | Nat North | H | Stalybridge Celtic | 3628 | L | 0-3 | | 7 | 6 |
| 31 | Nat North | A | AFC Fylde | 1077 | **W** | 3-2 | Baggie 41 (pen) Dyson 72 Kirby 90 | 4 | 7 |
| Sept 5 | Nat North | H | Worcester City | 3098 | D | 0-0 | | 4 | 8 |
| 12 | Nat North | H | Brackley Town | 2683 | D | 1-1 | Odejayi 57 | 5 | 9 |
| 15 | Nat North | A | Chorley | 1530 | L | 0-1 | | 8 | 10 |
| 19 | Nat North | H | Alfreton Town | 2839 | **W** | 1-0 | Ellison 3 | 6 | 11 |
| **26** | **FAC2Q** | **A** | **AFC Fylde** | **601** | **L** | **0-1** | | | 12 |
| Oct 3 | Nat North | A | Gainsborough Trinity | 644 | **W** | 1-0 | Evans 62 | 4 | 13 |
| 17 | Nat North | A | Curzon Ashton | 1443 | D | 0-0 | | 4 | 14 |
| 24 | Nat North | H | Bradford PA | 3234 | **W** | 2-0 | Evans 52 Dixon 67 | | 15 |
| 31 | Nat North | A | Solihull Moors | 1100 | L | 0-1 | | 6 | 16 |
| Nov 7 | Nat North | H | Chorley | 3408 | L | 1-3 | Kirby 41 | 6 | 17 |
| 14 | Nat North | H | Tamworth | 2905 | D | 1-1 | Kirby 37 | 8 | 18 |
| 21 | Nat North | A | Lowestoft Town | 629 | D | 2-2 | Kirby 3 Joyce 53 | 8 | 19 |
| 24 | Nat North | H | Solihull Moors | 2437 | L | 2-4 | O'Hanlon 36 Kirby 78 | 8 | 20 |
| **28** | **FAT3Q** | **H** | **Nantwich Town** | **1066** | **L** | **0-2** | | | 21 |
| Dec 5 | Nat North | H | FC United | 4797 | L | 1-2 | Margetts 56 | 8 | 22 |
| 12 | Nat North | A | Corby Town | 575 | **W** | 4-0 | Ledsham 48 Margetts 60 (pen) 73 (pen) Odejayi 67 | 8 | 23 |
| 19 | Nat North | A | Boston United | 1316 | L | 0-4 | | 8 | 24 |
| 26 | Nat North | H | Harrogate Town | 3326 | L | 1-2 | Brewster 12 | 8 | 25 |
| 28 | Nat North | A | Stalybridge Celtic | 1516 | D | 1-1 | Margetts 81 | 8 | 26 |
| Jan 9 | Nat North | H | AFC Telford United | 2765 | L | 0-1 | | 9 | 27 |
| 16 | Nat North | H | Nuneaton Town | 2823 | D | 1-1 | Brewster 86 | 8 | 28 |
| 23 | Nat North | A | Gloucester City | 791 | D | 0-0 | | 9 | 29 |
| Feb 2 | Nat North | A | Harrogate Town | 570 | L | 1-2 | Brodie 25 | 12 | 30 |
| 13 | Nat North | A | Bradford PA | 678 | D | 0-0 | | 14 | 31 |
| 20 | Nat North | A | Brackley Town | 436 | **W** | 1-0 | Anoruo 39 | 13 | 32 |
| 27 | Nat North | H | Gainsborough Trinity | 2990 | **W** | 2-0 | Marsden 5 80 | 11 | 33 |
| Mar 1 | Nat North | H | Hednesford Town | 2289 | **W** | 3-0 | Anorou 6 Brodie 44 Odejayi 83 | 10 | 34 |
| 5 | Nat North | A | Tamworth | 1016 | D | 1-1 | Marsden 31 | 9 | 35 |
| 12 | Nat North | H | Gloucester City | 2830 | **W** | 3-0 | Brodie 47 Marsden 57 Anouo 87 | 10 | 36 |
| 19 | Nat North | A | Hednesford Town | 572 | **W** | 2-1 | Anoruo 90 Odejayi 90 | 9 | 37 |
| 26 | Nat North | A | North Ferriby United | 926 | L | 0-2 | | 9 | 38 |
| 28 | Nat North | H | AFC Fylde | 3399 | L | 0-4 | | 9 | 39 |
| Apr 2 | Nat North | H | Lowestoft Town | 2396 | L | 0-2 | | 11 | 40 |
| 9 | Nat North | A | Worcester City | 705 | **W** | 3-2 | Odejayi 57 Smalley 82 Marsden 87 | 11 | 41 |
| 16 | Nat North | H | Corby Town | 2454 | D | 2-2 | Wilson 43 Connolly 59 | 10 | 42 |
| 23 | Nat North | A | Alfreton Town | 837 | **W** | 3-0 | Marsden 27 87 Brodie 85 | 9 | 43 |
| 30 | Nat North | H | Curzon Ashton | 3875 | D | 0-0 | | 9 | 44 |
| | | | | | | | | | 45 |
| | | | | | | | | | 46 |
| | | | | | | | | | 47 |
| | | | | | | | | | 48 |
| | | | | | | | | | 49 |

| GOALSCORERS | Scoring Games | Consec Sco Games | Total |
|---|---|---|---|
| ***2014-15 Dennis*** | | | ***15*** |
| Marsden | 5 | | 7 |
| Odejayi | 6 | 2 | 6 |
| Kirby | 4 | | 5 |
| Anoruo | 4 | | 4 |
| Brodie | 4 | | 4 |
| Margetts | 3 | | 4 |
| Dyson | 3 | 2 | 3 |
| Brewster | 2 | | 2 |
| Evans | 2 | | 2 |
| Ledsham | 2 | | 2 |
| Rule | 2 | | 2 |
| Baggie | 1 | | 1 |
| Connolly | 1 | | 1 |
| Dixon | 1 | | 1 |
| Ellison | 1 | | 1 |
| Gavin | 1 | | 1 |
| Joyce | 1 | | 1 |
| O'Hanlon | 1 | | 1 |
| Smalley | 1 | | 1 |
| Wilson | 1 | | 1 |

# TAMWORTH

**Chairman:** Bob Andrews

**Secretary:** George Delves (T) 07811 267 304 (E) georgedelves@thelambs.co.uk

**Commercial Manager:** David Morrell (T/E) commercial@thelambs.co.uk

**Programme Editor:** Terry Brumpton (T/E) terrybrumpton@yahoo.co.uk

**Ground Address:** The Lamb Ground, Kettlebrook, Tamworth, Staffordshire B77 1AA

(T) 01827 657 98 **Manager:** Andy Morrell

## Club Factfile

**Founded:** 1933 **Nickname:** The Lambs

**Previous Names:** None

**Previous Leagues:** Birmingham Combination 1933-54, West Midlands (originally Birmingham League) 1954-72, 84-88, Southern 1972-79, 83-84, 89-2003, Northern Premier 1979-83

**Club Colours (change):** All red (White/black/white)

**Ground Capacity:** 4,100 **Seats:** 518 **Covered:** 1,191 **Clubhouse:** Yes **Shop:** Yes

**Directions**
M42 Junction 10. Take A5/A51 to Town centre, then follow the signs for Kettlebrook and Tamworth FC.

**Previous Grounds:** Jolly Sailor Ground 1933-34

**Record Attendance:** 5,500 v Torquay United - FA Cup 1st Round 15/11/69

**Record Victory:** 14-4 v Holbrook Institue (H) - Bass Vase 1934

**Record Defeat:** 0-11 v Solihull (A) - Birmingham Combination 1940

**Record Goalscorer:** Graham Jessop - 195

**Record Appearances:** Dave Seedhouse - 869

**Additional Records:** Paid £7,500 to Ilkeston Town for David Hemmings December 2000
Received £7,500 from Telford United for Martin Myers 1990

**Honours:**
Birmingham Senior Cup 1960-61, 65-66, 68-69. West Midlands League 1964-65, 65-66, 71-72, 87-88. FA Vase 1988-89. Southern League Premier Division 2002-03. Conference North 2008-09.

**10 YEAR RECORD**

| 06-07 | 07-08 | 08-09 | 09-10 | 10-11 | 11-12 | 12-13 | 13-14 | 14-15 | 15-16 |
|---|---|---|---|---|---|---|---|---|---|
| Conf 22 | Conf N 15 | Conf N 1 | Conf 16 | Conf 19 | Conf 18 | Conf 19 | Conf 23 | Conf N 7 | Nat N 7 |

# TAMWORTH MATCH RESULTS 2015-16

| Date | Comp | H/A | Opponents | Att: | Result | | Goalscorers | Pos | No. |
|---|---|---|---|---|---|---|---|---|---|
| Aug8 | Nat North | H | North Ferriby United | 791 | W | 1-0 | Durrell 60 | 8 | 1 |
| 11 | Nat North | A | Worcester City | 668 | W | 2-1 | Clarke 22 Durrell 23 | 5 | 2 |
| 15 | Nat North | A | FC United | 3580 | D | 1-1 | Durrell 5 | 4 | 3 |
| 18 | Nat North | H | AFC Telford United | 908 | W | 2-1 | Clarke 7 70 | 4 | 4 |
| 22 | Nat North | A | Harrogate Town | 444 | D | 0-0 | | 4 | 5 |
| 29 | Nat North | H | Nuneaton Town | 1436 | D | 1-1 | Morrell 90 | 5 | 6 |
| 31 | Nat North | A | Boston United | 1187 | D | 1-1 | Dyer 46 | 6 | 7 |
| Sept5 | Nat North | H | Stalybridge Celtic | 747 | D | 1-1 | Dyer 90 | 5 | 8 |
| 12 | Nat North | A | AFC Fylde | 353 | D | 2-2 | Durrell 67 74 | 5 | 9 |
| 15 | Nat North | A | Gainsborough Trinity | 404 | W | 2-0 | Durrell 17 Warlow 36 | 4 | 10 |
| 19 | Nat North | H | Bradford PA | 754 | D | 0-0 | | 5 | 11 |
| **26** | **FAC2Q** | **H** | **Alfreton Town** | **663** | **L** | **2-3** | **Durrell 34 Newton 75** | | 12 |
| Oct3 | Nat North | A | Curzon Ashton | 292 | L | 0-2 | | 7 | 13 |
| 17 | Nat North | H | Solihull Moors | 1007 | D | 1-1 | Mettam 5 | 8 | 14 |
| 24 | Nat North | A | Lowestoft Town | 508 | W | 4-0 | Mettam 15 Newton 37 49 Racchi 49 | | 15 |
| 31 | Nat North | H | Hednesford Town | 871 | W | 1-0 | Newton 32 | 5 | 16 |
| Nov7 | Nat North | H | Gloucester City | 759 | D | 2-2 | Preston 42 Racchi 45 | | 17 |
| 14 | Nat North | A | Stockport County | 2904 | D | 1-1 | Durrell 62 | 6 | 18 |
| 21 | Nat North | H | Gainsborough Trinity | 632 | W | 2-0 | Preston 69 Dyer 90 | 7 | 19 |
| **28** | **FAT3Q** | **A** | **Corby Town** | **335** | **W** | **6-2** | **Durrell 1 Taylor 72 Strong 75 DYER 3 (78 80 90)** | | 20 |
| Dec5 | Nat North | H | Worcester City | 751 | W | 3-0 | Dyer 13 Clarke 47 Mettam 70 (oen) | 6 | 21 |
| **12** | **FAT1** | **A** | **FC Halifax Town** | **439** | **L** | **0-5** | | | 22 |
| 19 | Nat North | A | North Ferriby United | 367 | L | 1-3 | Strong 51 | 7 | 23 |
| 26 | Nat North | H | Alfreton Town | 875 | L | 1-2 | Strong 63 | 7 | 24 |
| 28 | Nat North | A | Nuneaton Town | 1165 | L | 0-3 | | 7 | 25 |
| Jan2 | Nat North | A | Alfreton Town | 626 | L | 0-1 | | 7 | 26 |
| 9 | Nat North | H | FC United | 1430 | D | 1-1 | Newton 90 | 7 | 27 |
| 23 | Nat North | A | Stalybridge Celtic | 407 | W | 5-3 | Durrell 18 NEWTON 4 ( 21 24 43 51) | 7 | 28 |
| 30 | Nat North | A | Chorley | 918 | D | 1-1 | Mettam 87 | 7 | 29 |
| Feb6 | Nat North | H | Brackley Town | 406 | L | 1-2 | Durrell 90 (pen) | 7 | 30 |
| 13 | Nat North | A | Corby Town | 539 | L | 0-2 | | 9 | 31 |
| 16 | Nat North | H | Curzon Ashton | 544 | W | 2-1 | Deeney 39 Dyer 54 | 7 | 32 |
| 20 | Nat North | A | Gloucester City | 408 | W | 2-1 | Taylor 70 Deeney 90 | 7 | 33 |
| 27 | Nat North | A | Solihull Moors | 773 | W | 2-1 | Dyer 6 Strong 24 | 7 | 34 |
| Mar5 | Nat North | H | Stockport County | 1016 | D | 1-1 | Durrell 61 | 7 | 35 |
| 8 | Nat North | H | Harrogate Town | 591 | W | 1-0 | Durrell 63 (pen) | 7 | 36 |
| 12 | Nat North | H | Corby Town | 616 | D | 0-0 | | 7 | 37 |
| 19 | Nat North | A | Bradford PA | 298 | W | 2-0 | Taylor 19 Durrell 79 | 6 | 38 |
| 26 | Nat North | A | AFC Telford United | 1508 | L | 0-1 | | 6 | 39 |
| 28 | Nat North | H | Boston Uited | 889 | L | 1-2 | Newton 57 | 7 | 40 |
| Apr2 | Nat North | H | Chorley | 641 | W | 2-1 | Dyer 54 Durrell 85 (pen) | 6 | 41 |
| 9 | Nat North | A | Hednesford Town | 601 | L | 1-2 | Mohamed 60 | 7 | 42 |
| 16 | Nat North | H | AFC Fylde | 683 | W | 3-1 | Mohammed 22 Newton 75 Taylor 77 | 6 | 43 |
| 23 | Nat North | H | Lowestoft Town | 1418 | D | 1-1 | Mohammed 43 | 7 | 44 |
| 30 | Nat North | A | Brackley Town | 600 | L | 0-1 | | 7 | 45 |

| GOALSCORERS | Scoring Games | Consec Sco Games | Total |
|---|---|---|---|
| ***2014-15 Clarke*** | | | ***9*** |
| Durrell | 14 | 3 | 15 |
| Newton | 7 | 3 | 11 |
| Dyer | 8 | 2 | 10 |
| Clarke | 2 | | 4 |
| Mettam | 4 | 2 | 4 |
| Strong | 4 | | 4 |
| Taylor | 4 | | 4 |
| Mohammed | 3 | | 3 |
| Deeney | 2 | | 2 |
| Preston | 2 | | 2 |
| Racchi | 2 | | 2 |
| Morrell | 1 | | 1 |
| Warlow | 1 | | 1 |

# WORCESTER CITY

**Chairman:** Anthony Hampson
**Secretary:** Joe Murphy (T) 01562 823 931 (E) joe.murphy@rpsgroup.com
**Commercial Manager:** n/a (T/E)
**Programme Editor:** Rob Bazley (T/E) 01562 823 931
**Ground Address:** c/o Kidderminster H., Aggborough Stadium, Hoo Road, Kidderminster, DY10 1NB
(T) 01562 823 931 **Manager:** Carl Heeley

## Club Factfile

**Founded:** 1902 **Nickname:** City
**Previous Names:**
**Previous Leagues:** West Midlands, Birmingham, Southern 1938-79, 85-2004, Alliance 1979-85

**Club Colours (change):** Blue & white stripes/blue/blue (Red/black/red)

**Ground Capacity:** 4,004 **Seats:** 1,125 **Covered:** 2,000 **Clubhouse:** Yes **Shop:** Yes

**Directions** NORTH - Take the M5 coming off at junction 3, follow signs for Severn Valley Railway, take the A456 to Kidderminster, turn left at traffic lights (opposite the Land Oak pub) onto the A449 to Worcester, at the next set of traffic lights turn right towards the Town Centre, then left onto Hoo Road (just before the roundabout at the bottom of hill), the ground should be 300 yards on the left hand side. SOUTH - Take the M5 to junction 6, follow A440 towards Kidderminster, turn right at the first island near McDonalds Drive Thru, take the first left into Hoo Road (opposite the Viaduct Pub), you should find the ground after half a mile on the right hand side.

**Previous Grounds:** Severn Terrace, Thorneloe, Flagge Meadow. St George's Lane 1905-2013.

**Record Attendance:** 17,042 v Sheffield United - FA Cup 4th Round 24/01/1959
**Record Victory:** 18-1 v Bilston - Birmingham League 21/11/1931
**Record Defeat:** 0-10 v Wellington - Birmingham League 29/08/1920
**Record Goalscorer:** John Inglis - 189 (1970-77)
**Record Appearances:** Bobby McEwan - 596 (1959-75)
**Additional Records:** Paid £8,500 to Telford United for Jim Williams 1981
Received £27,000 from Everton for John Barton
**Honours:**
Birmingham League 1913-14, 24-25, 28-29, 29-30.
Southern League Cup 1939-40, 2000-01, Division 1 1967-68, 76-77, Premier 1978-79.
Birmingham Senior Cup 1975-76. Worcestershire Senior Cup x26 (last win 1996-97)

**10 YEAR RECORD**

| 06-07 | 07-08 | 08-09 | 09-10 | 10-11 | 11-12 | 12-13 | 13-14 | 14-15 | 15-16 |
|---|---|---|---|---|---|---|---|---|---|
| Conf N 9 | Conf N 12 | Conf S 16 | Conf S 20 | Conf N 16 | Conf N 7 | Conf N 15 | Conf N 15 | Conf N 9 | Nat N 17 |

## WORCESTER CITY MATCH RESULTS 2015-16

| Date | Comp | H/A | Opponents | Att: | Result | | Goalscorers | Pos | No. |
|---|---|---|---|---|---|---|---|---|---|
| Aug8 | Nat North | A | Gainsborough Trinity | 402 | D | 1-1 | Rowe 65 | 14 | 1 |
| 11 | Nat North | H | Tamworth | 668 | L | 1-2 | Rowe 78 | 17 | 2 |
| 15 | Nat North | H | Lowestoft Town | 577 | W | 2-1 | Nti 41 Geddes 76 | 9 | 3 |
| 18 | Nat North | A | Solihull Moors | 525 | L | 0-3 | | 17 | 4 |
| 22 | Nat North | H | Chorley | 575 | L | 2-3 | Nti 35 76 | 17 | 5 |
| 29 | Nat North | A | Brackley Town | 273 | L | 0-2 | | 19 | 6 |
| 31 | Nat North | H | Hednesford Town | 576 | L | 1-4 | Geddes 81 | 20 | 7 |
| Sept5 | Nat North | A | Stockport County | 3098 | D | 0-0 | | 21 | 8 |
| 12 | Nat North | H | Curzon Ashton | 508 | D | 2-2 | Hughes 8 58 | 21 | 9 |
| 15 | Nat North | A | Alfreton Town | 489 | L | 1-2 | Hughes 71 | 21 | 10 |
| 19 | Nat North | A | Corby Town | 596 | W | 3-0 | Hughes 7 Miniham 12 Gater 78 | 19 | 11 |
| **26** | **FAC2Q** | **A** | **Holbeach United** | **396** | **D** | **1-1** | **Hughes 67** | | 12 |
| **29** | **FAC2Qr** | **H** | **Holbeach United** | **403** | **W** | **2-0** | **Nti 36 Burton 67** | | 13 |
| Oct3 | Nat North | A | FC United | 3619 | W | 2-0 | Hughes 25 Dunckley 89 | 16 | 14 |
| **10** | **FAC3Q** | **A** | **Solihull Moors** | **923** | **D** | **1-1** | **Burton 76** | | 15 |
| **13** | **FAC3Qr** | **H** | **Solihull Moors** | **652** | **W** | **1-0** | **Hughes 90** | | 16 |
| 18 | Nat North | H | Nuneaton Town | 716 | L | 0-1 | | 18 | 17 |
| **24** | **FAC4Q** | **A** | **Gateshead** | **782** | **W** | **2-1** | **Burton 24 70** | | 18 |
| 31 | Nat North | A | Harrogate Town | 535 | L | 0-1 | | 22 | 19 |
| **Nov7** | **FAC1** | **A** | **Sheffield United** | **11108** | **L** | **0-3** | | | 20 |
| 14 | Nat North | A | Stalybridge Celtic | 479 | L | 1-3 | Dunckley 87 | 22 | 21 |
| 17 | Nat North | H | Boston United | 307 | W | 2-1 | Smith 11 Brown 63 | 22 | 22 |
| 21 | Nat North | H | AFC Telford United | 726 | W | 3-0 | Thomas 62 Deeney 71 Burton 86 | 18 | 23 |
| **28** | **FAT3Q** | **A** | **Brackley Town** | **227** | **W** | **2-0** | **Nelson-Addy 60 Weir 88** | | 24 |
| Dec5 | Nat North | A | Tamworth | 751 | L | 0-3 | | 18 | 25 |
| **15** | **FAT1** | **A** | **Southport** | **270** | **D** | **0-0** | | | 26 |
| 19 | Nat North | H | Gainsborough Trinity | 430 | W | 2-0 | Hughes 38 Nelson-Addy 88 | 19 | 27 |
| 22 | FAT1r | H | Southport | 452 | L | 2-3 | Nti 3 Hughes 84 (pen) | | 28 |
| 26 | Nat North | A | Gloucester City | 662 | W | 1-0 | Burton 87 | 14 | 29 |
| 28 | Nat North | H | Brackley Town | 647 | D | 0-0 | | 15 | 30 |
| Jan2 | Nat North | H | Gloucester City | 812 | L | 1-2 | Burton 22 | 17 | 31 |
| 16 | Nat North | H | Corby Town | 597 | L | 1-2 | Donellan 87 | 18 | 32 |
| 23 | Nat North | A | AFC Fylde | 511 | W | 3-2 | Bakayoko 6 Nti 21 (pen) 83 | 16 | 33 |
| 30 | Nat North | H | North Ferriby Urd | 561 | W | 2-0 | Donnellan 4 25 | 16 | 34 |
| Feb13 | Nat North | A | Chorley | 887 | L | 0-2 | | 16 | 35 |
| 20 | Nat North | A | Nuneaton Town | 825 | D | 1-1 | Bakayoko 90 | 16 | 36 |
| 23 | Nat North | H | Stalybridge Celtic | 367 | W | 5-0 | NTI 3 ( 20 27 32) Bakayoko 55 Higgins 56 (og) | 15 | 37 |
| 27 | Nat North | A | Worcester City | 1228 | D | 1-1 | Murphy 46 | 15 | 38 |
| Mar5 | Nat North | H | FC United | 2133 | D | 0-0 | | 17 | 39 |
| 8 | Nat North | H | Alfreton Town | 351 | D | 1-1 | Hughes 90 | 14 | 40 |
| 12 | Nat North | A | Curzon Ashton | 208 | L | 1-3 | Donnellan 52 | 14 | 41 |
| 19 | Nat North | H | Harrogate Town | 581 | D | 0-0 | | 16 | 42 |
| 26 | Nat North | H | Solihull Borough | 828 | D | 2-2 | Burton 36 Hughes 89 | 18 | 43 |
| Apr2 | Nat North | A | North Ferriby United | 268 | D | 3-3 | Burton 7 Hughes 45 Murphy 88 | 18 | 44 |
| 5 | Nat North | H | Bradford PA | 434 | W | 3-1 | Nti 30 Hughes 9 45 | 15 | 45 |
| 9 | Nat North | H | Stockport County | 705 | L | 2-3 | Hughes 4 39 | 15 | 46 |
| 12 | Nat North | A | Hednesford Town | 333 | W | 1-0 | Murphy 5 | 15 | 47 |
| 16 | Nat North | A | Bradford PA | 336 | L | 1-3 | Perry 45 | 15 | 48 |
| 19 | Nat North | A | Lowestoft Town | 508 | L | 1-2 | Hughes 3 | 15 | 49 |
| 23 | Nat North | A | AFC Telford United | 1378 | L | 0-2 | | 16 | 50 |
| 30 | Nat North | H | AFC Fylde | 689 | D | 2-2 | Nti 66 Hughes 82 | 17 | 51 |

| GOALSCORERS | Scoring Games | Consec Sco Games | Total | | Scoring Games | Consec Sco Games | Total |
|---|---|---|---|---|---|---|---|
| *2014-15 Geddes* | | | *17* | Rowe | 2 | 2 | 2 |
| Hughes | 15 | 4 | 18 | Brown | 1 | | 1 |
| Nti | 8 | | 12 | Deeney | 1 | | 1 |
| Burton | 8 | | 9 | Gater | 1 | | 1 |
| Donnellan | 3 | | 4 | Minihan | 1 | | 1 |
| Bakayoko | 3 | | 3 | Perry | 1 | | 1 |
| Murphy | 3 | | 3 | Smith | 1 | | 1 |
| Dunckley | 2 | | 2 | Thomas | 1 | | 1 |
| Geddes | 2 | | 2 | Weir | 1 | | 1 |
| Nelson-Addy | 2 | | 2 | Opponents | | | 1 |

# BATH CITY

**Chairman:** Paul Williams
**Secretary:** Quentin Edwards **(T)** 01225 423 087 **(E)** qcath@blueyonder.co.uk
**Commercial Manager:** Bob Chester **(T/E)** 01225 423 087
**Programme Editor:** Mark Stillman **(T/E)** 01225 423 087
**Ground Address:** Twerton Park, Twerton, Bath, Somerset BA2 1DB
**(T)** 01225 423 087 **Manager:** Gary Owers

2014-15 Squad - Back row (l-r): Ashley Kington, Andy Watkins, Ross Stearn, Martin Slocombe, Dan Bowman, Chris Allen, Zak Evans, Pat Keary
Middle row: Jim Rollo (player-coach), Adi Britton (director of football), Elliott Gibbons, Sekani Simpson, David Pratt, Frankie Artus, Jason Mellor, Chas Hemmings, Andy Gallinagh, Ben Adelsbury, Dan Ball, Lee Williams (physio), John Freegard (coach)

## Club Factfile

**Founded:** 1889 **Nickname:** The Romans
**Previous Names:** Bath AFC 1889-92. Bath Railway FC 1902-05. Bath Amateurs 1913-23 (Reserve side)
**Previous Leagues:** Western 1908-21. Southern 1921-79, 88-90, 97-2007. Alliance/Conference 1979-88, 90-97.

**Club Colours (change):** Black & white/black/black (All red with white trim)

**Ground Capacity:** 8,840 **Seats:** 1,017 **Covered:** 4,800 **Clubhouse:** Yes **Shop:** Yes

**Directions:** Take Junction 18 off M4. 3rd exit off roundabout and follow A46 (10 miles) to Bath City Centre. Along Pulteney Road then right into Claverton Street and then follow A36 Lower Bristol Road (1.5 miles). Left under Railway bridge (signs Bath City FC) into Twerton High Street and ground is 2nd turning on left.

**Previous Grounds:** The Belvoir Ground 1889-92 & 1902-15. Lambridge Show Ground 1919-32.

**Record Attendance:** 18,020 v Brighton & Hove Albion - FA Cup 1960
**Record Victory:** 8-0 v Boston United - 1998-99
**Record Defeat:** 0-9 v Yeovil Town - 1946-47
**Record Goalscorer:** Paul Randall - 106
**Record Appearances:** David Mogg - 530
**Additional Records:** Paid £15,000 to Bristol City for Micky Tanner. Received £80,000 from Southampton for Jason Dodd.

**Honours:**
Southern Lge Western Div.2 1928-29. Southern Lge Western Division 1933-34. Southern League 1959-60, 77-78, 2006-07.
Southern League Cup 1978-79. Somerset Premier Cup 1951-52, 52-53, 57-58, 59-60, 65-66, 67-68, 69-70, 77-78, 80-81, 81-82, 83-84, 84-85, 85-86, 88-89, 89-90, 93-94, 94-95, 2007-08. Conference South Play-offs 2009-10.

### 10 YEAR RECORD

| 06-07 | 07-08 | 08-09 | 09-10 | 10-11 | 11-12 | 12-13 | 13-14 | 14-15 | 15-16 |
|---|---|---|---|---|---|---|---|---|---|
| SthP 1 | Conf S 8 | Conf S 8 | Conf S 4 | Conf 10 | Conf 23 | Conf S 11 | Conf S 7 | Conf S 14 | Nat S 14 |

# BATH CITY MATCH RESULTS 2015-16

| Date | Comp | H/A | Opponents | Att: | Result | | Goalscorers | Pos | No. |
|---|---|---|---|---|---|---|---|---|---|
| Aug 8 | Nat South | H | Wealdstone | 641 | W | 2-1 | Pratt 14 McCootie 81 | 5 | 1 |
| 11 | Nat South | A | Basingstoke Town | 547 | W | 2-1 | Nicholson 23 Kington 45 (pen) | 4 | 2 |
| 15 | Nat South | A | Whitehawk | 219 | W | 1-0 | McCootie 55 | 3 | 3 |
| 18 | Nat South | H | Maidenhead United | 648 | W | 2-1 | Artus 42 (pen) Coupe 88 | 1 | 4 |
| 22 | Nat South | A | St Albans City | 424 | W | 1-0 | Artus 32 | 1 | 5 |
| 29 | Nat South | H | Havant & Waterlooville | 769 | W | 5-0 | Pratt 12 65 Watkins 29 73 Artus 80 | 1 | 6 |
| 31 | Nat South | A | Weston-s-Mere | 720 | D | 1-1 | McCootie 40 | 1 | 7 |
| Sept 5 | Nat South | H | Dartford | 766 | D | 0-0 | | 1 | 8 |
| 12 | Nat South | H | Hemel Hempstead Town | 685 | D | 1-1 | Baldwin 58 | 2 | 9 |
| 15 | Nat South | A | Gosport Borough | 599 | L | 1-3 | Kington 81 | 3 | 10 |
| 19 | Nat South | A | Maidstone United | 2098 | L | 0-1 | | 4 | 11 |
| **26** | **FAC2Q** | **A** | **Bodmin Town** | **302** | **W** | **2-0** | **Artus 33 83** | | 12 |
| Oct 3 | Nat South | H | Basingstoke Town | 779 | D | 0-0 | | 4 | 13 |
| **10** | **FAC3Q** | **A** | **Harlow Town** | **606** | **D** | **2-2** | **Hemmings 11 Watkins 66** | | 14 |
| **13** | **FAC3Qr** | **H** | **Harlow Town** | **330** | **L** | **1-2** | **Pratt 88** | | 15 |
| 17 | Nat South | H | Sutton United | 587 | L | 1-3 | Artus 7 (pen) | 6 | 16 |
| 31 | Nat South | H | Chelmsford City | 478 | W | 2-0 | Adelsbury 17 Mohamed 46 | 6 | 17 |
| Nov 7 | Nat South | A | Bishops Stortford | 312 | L | 2-3 | Pratt 18 22 | | 18 |
| 14 | Nat South | H | Oxford City | 616 | L | 1-3 | McCootie 90 | 8 | 19 |
| 17 | Nat South | A | Margate | 362 | D | 1-1 | Mohamed 45 | | 20 |
| 21 | Nat South | A | Wealdstone | 602 | L | 0-2 | | 9 | 21 |
| **28** | **FAT3Q** | **A** | **Bognor Regis Town** | **362** | **L** | **0-1** | | | 22 |
| Dec 5 | Nat South | H | Hayes & Yeading | 432 | L | 2-3 | Watkins 56 Ball 83 | 10 | 23 |
| 19 | Nat South | A | Ebbsfleet United | 1115 | W | 1-0 | Mohamed 90 | 10 | 24 |
| 26 | Nat South | H | Truro City | 801 | L | 0-3 | | 10 | 25 |
| Jan 9 | Nat South | H | Maidstone United | 710 | L | 0-2 | | 11 | 26 |
| 16 | Nat South | A | Dartford | 923 | L | 1-4 | Pratt 63 | 13 | 27 |
| 23 | Nat South | H | Concord Rangers | 570 | L | 0-1 | | 15 | 28 |
| 30 | Nat South | A | Eastbourne Borough | 568 | L | 2-5 | Pratt 35 McCootie 44 | 17 | 29 |
| Feb 13 | Nat South | A | Sutton United | 815 | D | 1-1 | Richards 43 (pen) | 18 | 30 |
| 20 | Nat South | H | St Albans City | 757 | W | 1-0 | Watkins 21 | 16 | 31 |
| 23 | Nat South | A | Havant & Waterlooville | 424 | D | 1-1 | Watkins 90 | 16 | 32 |
| 27 | Nat South | A | Hemel Hempstead | 358 | D | 1-1 | Bowman 90 | 16 | 33 |
| Mar 1 | Nat South | H | Gosport Borough | 437 | L | 0-1 | | 16 | 34 |
| 5 | Nat South | A | Oxford City | 325 | D | 1-1 | Kelly 80 | 16 | 35 |
| 12 | Nat South | H | Ebbsfleet United | 558 | D | 1-1 | Kelly 88 (pen) | 18 | 36 |
| 15 | Nat South | A | Truro City | 472 | L | 1-3 | Pratt 8 | 18 | 37 |
| 19 | Nat South | H | Bishop's Stortford | 497 | D | 2-2 | Kelly 11 Pratt 79 | 18 | 38 |
| 25 | Nat South | A | Maidenhead United | 899 | L | 1-3 | Harvey 47 | 19 | 39 |
| 28 | Nat South | H | Weston-s-Mare | 827 | W | 2-1 | Harvey 89 (pen) 90 | 18 | 40 |
| Apr 2 | Nat South | A | Chelmsford City | 756 | L | 1-3 | Harvey 72 | 18 | 41 |
| 9 | Nat South | A | Concord Rangers | 232 | W | 2-1 | Watkins 11 Kelly 82 | 17 | 42 |
| 16 | Nat South | H | Eastbourne Borough | 533 | W | 1-0 | Batten 82 | 16 | 43 |
| 19 | Nat South | H | Whitehawk | 442 | L | 0-3 | | 17 | 44 |
| 23 | Nat South | A | Hayes & Yeading | 258 | W | 3-0 | Kelly 56 62 McCootie 71 | 17 | 45 |
| 30 | Nat South | H | Margate | 695 | W | 2-0 | McCootie 45 Watkins 80 | 14 | 46 |

| GOALSCORERS | Scoring Games | Consec Sco Games | Total |
|---|---|---|---|
| ***2014-15 Pratt*** | | | ***23*** |
| Pratt | 9 | 2 | 10 |
| Watkins | 8 | | 8 |
| McCootie | 7 | | 7 |
| Artus | 6 | 3 | 6 |
| Kelly | 5 | | 6 |
| Harvey | 4 | | 4 |
| Mohammed | 3 | | 3 |
| Kington | 2 | | 2 |
| Adelsbury | 1 | | 1 |
| Baldwin | 1 | | 1 |
| Ball | 1 | | 1 |
| Batten | 1 | | 1 |
| Bowman | 1 | | 1 |
| Coupe | 1 | | 1 |
| Hemmings | 1 | | 1 |
| Nicholson | 1 | | 1 |
| Richards | 1 | | 1 |

# BISHOP'S STORTFORD

**Chairman:** Ian Kettridge
**Secretary:** John Turner **(T)** 01279 306 456 **(E)** j.turner@bsfc.co.uk
**Commercial Manager:** John Turner **(T/E)** j.turner@bsfc.co.uk
**Programme Editor:** **(T/E)**
**Ground Address:** ProKit Uk Stadium, Woodside Park, Dunmow Road, Bishop's Stortford CM23 5RG
**(T)** 01279 306 456 **Manager:** Gordon Boateng

## Club Factfile

**Founded:** 1874 **Nickname:** Blues or Bishops
**Previous Names:** None
**Previous Leagues:** East Herts 1896-97, 1902-06, 19-21, Stansted & District 1906-19, Herts County 1921-25, 27-29, Herts & Essex Border 1925-27, Spartan 1929-51, Delphian 1951-63, Athenian 1963-73, Isthmian 1974-2004

**Club Colours (change):** Blue & white stripes/blue/blue (Red & black stripes/black/black)

**Ground Capacity:** 4,000 **Seats:** 298 **Covered:** 700 **Clubhouse:** Yes **Shop:** Yes

**Directions**
Woodside Park is situated 1/4 mile from Junction 8 of M11.
Follow A1250 towards Bishop's Stortford Town Centre, entrance to the ground is signposted through Woodside Park Industrial Estate.

**Previous Grounds:** Rhodes Avenue 1919-1997.

**Record Attendance:** 6,000 v Peterborough Town - FA Cup 2nd Round 1972-73 and v Middlesbrough - FA Cup 3rd Round replay 1982-83
**Record Victory:** 11-0 v Nettleswell & Buntwill - Herts Junior Cup 1911
**Record Defeat:** 0-13 v Cheshunt (H) - Herts Senior Cup 1926
**Record Goalscorer:** Post 1929 Jimmy Badcock - 123
**Record Appearances:** Phil Hopkins - 543
**Additional Records:**

**Honours:**
Athenian League 1969-70. FA Amateur Cup 1973-74. Isthmian League Division 1 1980-81. FA Trophy 1980-81.
London Senior Cup 1973-74. Premier Inter League Cup 1989-90. Herts Senior Cup x10 Most recently 2011-12.

**10 YEAR RECORD**

| 06-07 | 07-08 | 08-09 | 09-10 | 10-11 | 11-12 | 12-13 | 13-14 | 14-15 | 15-16 |
|---|---|---|---|---|---|---|---|---|---|
| Conf S 5 | Conf S 10 | Conf S 9 | Conf S 18 | Conf S 16 | Conf N 10 | Conf N 17 | Conf S 15 | Conf S 16 | Nat S 11 |

# BISHOP'S STORTFORD MATCH RESULTS 2015-16

| Date | Comp | H/A | Opponents | Att: | Result | | Goalscorers | Pos | No. |
|---|---|---|---|---|---|---|---|---|---|
| Aug 8 | Nat South | H | Havant & Waterlooville | 353 | **W** | 3-0 | BUCHANAN 3 (17 41 58) | 2 | 1 |
| 11 | Nat South | A | Maidenhead United | 354 | L | 1-4 | Buchanan 53 | 10 | 2 |
| 15 | Nat South | A | Basingstoke Town | 462 | D | 1-1 | Thalassitis 24 | 10 | 3 |
| 18 | Nat South | H | Chelmsford City | 662 | L | 1-2 | Buchanan 29 (pen) | 15 | 4 |
| 22 | Nat South | A | Truro City | 491 | **W** | 1-0 | Buchanan 52 | 12 | 5 |
| 29 | Nat South | H | Concord Rangers | 314 | **W** | 3-2 | BUCHANAN 3 ( 35 48 90 pen) | 10 | 6 |
| 31 | Nat South | A | Wealdstone | 663 | L | 1-3 | Church 68 | 11 | 7 |
| Sept 5 | Nat South | H | Weston-s-Mare | 348 | L | 0-1 | | 15 | 8 |
| 12 | Nat South | A | Hayes & Yeading | 176 | **W** | 2-0 | Smith 76 Sellears 83 | 13 | 9 |
| 19 | Nat South | A | Hemel Hempstead Town | 561 | **W** | 2-1 | Church 26 Buchanan 60 | 12 | 10 |
| **26** | **FAC2Q** | **H** | **Sutton United** | **347** | **L** | **0-2** | | | 11 |
| Oct 3 | Nat South | H | Maidenhead United | 332 | L | 0-2 | | 12 | 12 |
| 10 | Nat South | H | Hayes & Yeading | 313 | D | 0-0 | | 12 | 13 |
| 17 | Nat South | A | Eastbourne Borough | 424 | **W** | 1-0 | Sheringham 24 | 11 | 14 |
| 24 | Nat South | H | Dartford | 402 | L | 1-2 | Smith 40 | 11 | 15 |
| 31 | Nat South | A | Oxford City | 278 | L | 1-3 | Bywater 14 | 13 | 16 |
| Nov 7 | Nat South | H | Bath City | 322 | **W** | 3-2 | Ferrier 6 78 Buchanan 46 | 9 | 17 |
| 14 | Nat South | H | Sutton United | 349 | L | 0-2 | | 12 | 18 |
| 21 | Nat South | A | Ebbsfleet United | 1003 | L | 2-4 | Merryfield 73 Bywater 83 | 13 | 19 |
| **28** | **FAT3Q** | **A** | **Tilbury** | **132** | **L** | **0-3** | | | 20 |
| Dec 5 | Nat South | H | Basingstoke Town | 301 | L | 1-2 | Buchanan 78 | 15 | 21 |
| 19 | Nat South | A | Weston-s-Mare | 325 | D | 1-1 | Suarez 30 | 14 | 22 |
| 26 | Nat South | H | St Albans City | 514 | **W** | 2-1 | Bywater 54 Church 77 | 12 | 23 |
| 28 | Nat South | A | Concord Rangers | 260 | D | 2-2 | Buchanan 32 (pen) 65 | 12 | 24 |
| Jan 2 | Nat South | A | St Albans City | 520 | D | 1-1 | Ferrier 10 | 12 | 25 |
| 23 | Nat South | H | Gosport Borough | 312 | **W** | 2-0 | Wilmott 53 Buchanan 62 | 12 | 26 |
| 30 | Nat South | A | Margate | 723 | D | 1-1 | Buchanan 63 | 12 | 27 |
| Feb 2 | Nat South | H | Hemel Hempstead Town | 303 | **W** | 1-0 | Suarez 90 | 8 | 28 |
| 6 | Nat South | H | Ebbsfleet United | 504 | L | 1-2 | Ferrier 45 | 9 | 29 |
| 16 | Nat South | A | Havant & Waterlooville | 419 | L | 1-2 | Ferrier 81 | 10 | 30 |
| 20 | Nat South | H | Maidstone United | 652 | L | 0-1 | | 12 | 31 |
| 27 | Nat South | H | Truro City | 355 | L | 0-3 | | 13 | 32 |
| 29 | Nat South | A | Chelmsford City | 630 | L | 1-4 | Merryfield 4 | 13 | 33 |
| Mar 5 | Nat South | A | Whitehawk | 166 | **W** | 3-2 | Wilmott 5 Buchanan 20 32 | 13 | 34 |
| 12 | Nat South | H | Eastbourne Borough | 313 | D | 1-1 | Moore 26 | 13 | 35 |
| 15 | Nat South | H | Whitehawk | 249 | **W** | 2-1 | Buchanan 14 54 | 13 | 36 |
| 19 | Nat South | A | Bath City | 497 | D | 2-2 | Buchanan 58 (pen) 90 | 13 | 37 |
| 25 | Nat South | A | Dartford | 921 | L | 1-3 | Vint 15 (og) | 13 | 38 |
| Apr 2 | Nat South | H | Oxford City | 332 | **W** | 3-0 | Moore 32 Fortnam-Tomlinson 75 79 | 13 | 39 |
| 9 | Nat South | A | Gosport Borough | 327 | D | 0-0 | | 14 | 40 |
| 11 | Nat South | A | Sutton United | 1061 | L | 0-2 | | 14 | 41 |
| 16 | Nat South | H | Margate | 388 | **W** | 4-1 | BUCHANAN 4 ( 5 10 42 71_) | 13 | 42 |
| 19 | Nat South | H | Wealdstone | 337 | **W** | 2-1 | Church 22 Buchanan 60 | 11 | 43 |
| 30 | Nat South | A | Maidstone United | 2549 | D | 1-1 | Buchanan 3 (pen) | 11 | 44 |

| GOALSCORERS | Scoring Games | Consec Sco Games | Total |
|---|---|---|---|
| *2014-15 Church* | | | *8* |
| Buchanan | 17 | 3 | 28 |
| Ferrier | 5 | | 5 |
| Church | 4 | | 4 |
| Bywater | 3 | | 3 |
| Merryfield | 2 | | 2 |
| Suarez | 2 | | 2 |
| Smith | 2 | | 2 |
| Wilmott | 2 | | 2 |
| Fortnam-Thomlinson | 2 | | 2 |
| Moore | 2 | | 2 |
| Sellears | 1 | | 1 |
| Sheringham | 1 | | 1 |
| Thalassitis | 1 | | 1 |
| Opponents | | | 1 |

# CHELMSFORD CITY

**Chairman:** Trevor Smith
**Secretary:** Alan Brown (T) 07963 626 381 (E) algbrown@blueyonder.co.uk
**Commercial Manager:** Mick Hooker (T/E) 07957 814 639
**Programme Editor:** Scott Hatley (T/E) 07904 193 431
**Ground Address:** Melbourne Park Stadium, Salerno Way, Chelmsford CM1 2EH
(T) 01245 290 959 **Manager:** Rod Stringer

## Club Factfile

**Founded:** 1938 **Nickname:** City or Clarets
**Previous Names:** None
**Previous Leagues:** Southern League 1938-2004. Isthmian 2004-08

**Club Colours (change):** Claret/claret/white (All royal blue)

**Ground Capacity:** 3,000 **Seats:** 1,300 **Covered:** 1,300 **Clubhouse:** Yes **Shop:** Yes

**Directions**
Leave A12 at J15 and head towards Chelmsford. At the roundabout turn left into Westway. Turn left onto the A1060 signposted Sawbridgeworth. At the second set of traffic lights turn right into Chignal Road. Turn right into Melbourne Avenue. Salerno Way is on your left. At the end of the football pitches and immediately before the block of flats, turn left at the mini roundabout in Salerno Way to enter the Stadium car park.

**Previous Grounds:** New Writtle Street 1938-97, Maldon Town 1997-98, Billericay Town 1998-2005

**Record Attendance:** 16,807 v Colchester United - Southern League 10/09/1949. Salerno Way: 2,998 v Billericay Town - Isthmian Jan. 2006
**Record Victory:** 10-1 v Bashley (H) - Southern League 26/04/2000
**Record Defeat:** 1-10 v Barking (A) - FA Trophy 11/11/1978
**Record Goalscorer:** Tony Butcher - 287 (1957-71)
**Record Appearances:** Derek Tiffin - 550 (1950-63)
**Additional Records:** Paid £10,000 to Dover Athletic for Tony Rogers 1992
Received £50,000 from Peterborough United for David Morrison
**Honours:**
Southern League 1945-46, 67-68, 71-72, Southern Division 1988-89, League Cup 1945-46, 59-60, 90-91.
Essex Professional Cup 1957-58, 69-70, 70-71, 73-74, 74-75. Non-League Champions Cup 1971-72.
Essex Senior Cup 1985-86, 88-89, 92-93, 2002-03. Isthmian League Premier Division 2007-08.

## 10 YEAR RECORD

| 06-07 | | 07-08 | | 08-09 | | 09-10 | | 10-11 | | 11-12 | | 12-13 | | 13-14 | | 14-15 | | 15-16 | |
|---|---|---|---|---|---|---|---|---|---|---|---|---|---|---|---|---|---|---|---|
| Isth P | 3 | Isth P | 1 | Conf S | 5 | Conf S | 3 | Conf S | 4 | Conf S | 6 | Conf S | 5 | Conf S | 17 | Conf S | 10 | Nat S | 15 |

# CHELMSFORD CITY MATCH RESULTS 2015-16

| Date | Comp | H/A | Opponents | Att: | Result | | Goalscorers | Pos | No. |
|---|---|---|---|---|---|---|---|---|---|
| Aug 8 | Nat South | A | Oxford City | 253 | D | 2-2 | Skepelhorn 32 Henry 55 | 9 | 1 |
| 10 | Nat South | H | Hemel Hempstead Town | 723 | L | 0-1 | | 12 | 2 |
| 15 | Nat South | H | Hayes & Yeading | 559 | **W** | 4-0 | Nicholson 8 (og) Daley 31 Expiteta 73 Bricknell 81 | 8 | 3 |
| 18 | Nat South | A | Bishops Stortford | 662 | **W** | 2-1 | Expiteta 42 Hughes 56 | 5 | 4 |
| 22 | Nat South | A | Whitehawk | 231 | L | 2-4 | Morgan 55 Skepelhorn 70 (pen) | 10 | 5 |
| 29 | Nat South | H | St Albans City | 595 | **W** | 2-1 | Bricknell 43 60 | 8 | 6 |
| 31 | Nat South | A | Maidstone United | 2117 | **W** | 1-0 | Sawyer 38 (pen) | 7 | 7 |
| Sept 5 | Nat South | H | Havant & Waterlooville | 736 | D | 2-2 | Bricknell 43 Sawyer 46 | 6 | 8 |
| 12 | Nat South | A | Wealdstone | 803 | D | 0-0 | | 8 | 9 |
| 14 | Nat South | H | Concord Rangers | 617 | **W** | 5-2 | Bricknell 26 73 Adeloye 31 84 Palmer 65 | 4 | 10 |
| 19 | Nat South | A | Maidenhead United | 442 | L | 0-1 | | 8 | 11 |
| **26** | **FAC2Q** | **H** | **Ebbsfleet United** | **823** | **D** | **0-0** | | | 12 |
| **29** | **FAC2Qr** | **A** | **Ebbsfleet United** | **790** | **W** | **2-1** | **Skepelhorn 32 Henry 55** | | 13 |
| Oct 3 | Nat South | H | Oxford City | 988 | L | 0-4 | | 9 | 14 |
| **10** | **FAC3Q** | **A** | **Basingstoke Town** | **498** | **L** | **2-4** | **Palmer 31 Hughes 89** | | 15 |
| 17 | Nat South | A | Basingstoke Town | 453 | **W** | 2-1 | Whichelow 38 76 | 7 | 16 |
| 24 | Nat South | H | Ebbsfleet United | 858 | D | 0-0 | | 7 | 17 |
| 31 | Nat South | A | Bath City | 478 | L | 0-2 | | 8 | 18 |
| Nov 7 | Nat South | H | Truro City | 636 | L | 1-2 | Skepelhorn 7 | 11 | 19 |
| 14 | Nat South | A | Hayes & Yeading | 229 | **W** | 5-0 | Skepelhorn 20 54 Whichelow 39 Daley 50 Bricknell 80 | | 20 |
| 21 | Nat South | H | Eastbourne Borough | 778 | L | 0-3 | | 10 | 21 |
| **28** | **FAT3Q** | **H** | **Gloucester City** | **359** | **D** | **1-1** | **McAuley 87** | | 22 |
| **Dec 1** | **FAT3Qr** | **A** | **Gloucester City** | **238** | **W** | **1-0** | **Thalassitis 7** | | 23 |
| 5 | Nat South | A | Gosport Borough | 2132 | L | 1-2 | Thalassitis 78 | 12 | 24 |
| **12** | **FAT1** | **A** | **Cheltenham Town** | **1124** | **L** | **1-3** | **Bricknell 20** | | 25 |
| 19 | Nat South | H | Wealdstone | 873 | L | 0-2 | | 14 | 26 |
| 26 | Nat South | H | Dartford | 810 | L | 0-1 | | 14 | 27 |
| 28 | Nat South | A | St Albans City | 668 | D | 1-1 | Bricknell 77 | 14 | 28 |
| Jan 2 | Nat South | A | Dartford | 1205 | D | 1-1 | Bricknell 80 | 14 | 29 |
| 9 | Nat South | H | Weston-s-Mare | 737 | L | 2-3 | Hunt 39 Graham 41 | 15 | 30 |
| 16 | Nat South | A | Margate | 732 | L | 1-4 | Whichelow 37 | 15 | 31 |
| 23 | Nat South | H | Whitehawk | 697 | **W** | 4-3 | Lorraine 4 (og) Wiliams 28 Bridge 45 Bricknell 59 | 14 | 32 |
| 30 | Nat South | H | Sutton United | 856 | L | 0-2 | | 15 | 33 |
| Feb 20 | Nat South | H | Margate | 778 | L | 2-3 | Bridge 3 Williams 48 (pen) | 18 | 34 |
| 27 | Nat South | A | Weston-s-Mare | 406 | **W** | 3-0 | Williams 22 Bridge 69 Sawyer 90 | 18 | 35 |
| 29 | Nat South | H | Bishops Stortford | 630 | **W** | 4-1 | Haines 9 Bridge 45 Williams 5 Hughes 71 | 15 | 36 |
| Mar 5 | Nat South | A | Truro City | 512 | L | 0-1 | | 15 | 37 |
| 12 | Nat South | H | Maidenhead United | 1140 | **W** | 4-1 | Pentney 23 (og) Bridge 28 79 Daley 7 | 14 | 38 |
| 15 | Nat South | A | Hemel Hempstead Town | 423 | D | 1-1 | Bailey-Dennis 32 (og) | 14 | 39 |
| 19 | Nat South | A | Eastbourne Borough | 481 | L | 0-2 | | 17 | 40 |
| 26 | Nat South | A | Concord Rangers | 585 | L | 0-1 | | 18 | 41 |
| 28 | Nat South | H | Maidstone United | 691 | **W** | 3-0 | Williams 44 88 Daley 90 | 16 | 42 |
| Apr 2 | Nat South | H | Bath City | 756 | **W** | 3-1 | Bricknell 13 Graham 26 Hughes 49 | 14 | 43 |
| 5 | Nat South | A | Havant &Waterlooville | 588 | **W** | 1-0 | Prestedge 45 | 11 | 44 |
| 9 | Nat South | A | Ebbsfleet United | 2267 | L | 1-3 | Bricknell 1 | 11 | 45 |
| 16 | Nat South | H | Gosport Borough | 850 | **W** | 6-1 | BRICKNELL 4 (12 22 45 54) Graham 21 Bridge 90 | 11 | 46 |
| 23 | Nat South | A | Sutton United | 1545 | L | 0-2 | | 13 | 47 |
| 30 | Nat South | H | Basingstoke Town | 931 | L | 0-2 | | 15 | 48 |

| GOALSCORERS | Scoring Games | Consec Sco Games | Total |
|---|---|---|---|
| ***2014-15 Cheek*** | | | ***21*** |
| Bricknell | 12 | 2 | 17 |
| Bridge | 6 | 3 | 7 |
| Skelpelhorn | 5 | 2 | 6 |
| Williams | 5 | 3 | 6 |
| Daley | 4 | | 4 |
| Hughes | 4 | | 4 |
| Whichelow | 4 | | 4 |
| Graham | 3 | | 3 |
| Adeloye | 2 | | 2 |
| Expiteta | 2 | | 2 |
| Henry | 2 | | 2 |
| Palmer | 2 | | 2 |
| Sawyer | 2 | | 2 |
| Thalassitis | 2 | | 2 |
| Haines | 1 | | 1 |
| Hunt | 1 | | 1 |
| McAuley | 1 | | 1 |
| Morgan | 1 | | 1 |
| Prestedge | 1 | | 1 |
| Sawyer | 1 | | 1 |
| Opponents | | | 4 |

# CONCORD RANGERS

**Chairman:** Antony Smith
**Secretary:** Chris Crerie **(T)** 0790 952 8818 **(E)** concordrangers@btinternet.com
**Commercial Manager:** Chris Crerie **(T/E)** 0790 952 8818
**Programme Editor:** Alan Jessop-Peacock **(T/E)** 07492 062 804
**Ground Address:** Aspect Arena, Thames Road, Canvey Island, Essex SS8 0HH
**(T)** 01268 515 750 **Manager:** Adam Flanagan

## Club Factfile

**Founded:** 1967 **Nickname:** Beachboys
**Previous Names:** None
**Previous Leagues:** Southend & District, Southend Alliance, Essex Intermediate 1988-91, Essex Senior 1991-2008.

**Club Colours (change):** All yellow (All blue)

**Ground Capacity:** 1,500 **Seats:** Yes **Covered:** Yes **Clubhouse:** Yes **Shop:**

**Directions:** Take the A13 to Sadlers Farm at Benfleet, follow the road onto Canvey Way signposted Canvey Island ( A130 ) next roundabout (Waterside Farm ) take 3rd exit onto Canvey Island 1st exit, signposted seafront / Industrial area next roundabout 1st exit, next roundabout 1st exit. Next landmark is a set of traffic lights ( King Canute Pub on the left, carry on through to a mini r/bout passing a school on the right turn right into Thorney Bay Road, Thames Road is the 3rd turning on the right, Concord Rangers is approx 1 mile along Thames Road.

**Previous Grounds:** Waterside

**Record Attendance:** 1,500 v Lee Chapel North - FA Sunday Cup 1989-90
**Record Victory:** Not known - If you know please email tw.publications@btinternet.com
**Record Defeat:** Not known - If you know please email tw.publications@btinternet.com
**Record Goalscorer:** Not known - If you know please email tw.publications@btinternet.com
**Record Appearances:** Not known - If you know please email tw.publications@btinternet.com
**Additional Records:**

**Honours:**
Essex Intermediate League Division 2 1990-91. Essex Senior League 1997-98, 2003-04, 07-08.
Essex Senior Cup 2013-14, 14-15, 15-16.

## 10 YEAR RECORD

| 06-07 | | 07-08 | | 08-09 | | 09-10 | | 10-11 | | 11-12 | | 12-13 | | 13-14 | | 14-15 | | 15-16 | |
|---|---|---|---|---|---|---|---|---|---|---|---|---|---|---|---|---|---|---|---|
| ESen | 7 | ESen | 1 | Isth1N | 5 | Isth1N | 2 | Isth P | 8 | Isth P | 14 | Isth P | 4 | Conf S | 9 | Conf S | 7 | Nat S | 10 |

# CONCORD RANGERS MATCH RESULTS 2015-16

| Date | Comp | H/A | Opponents | Att: | Result | | Goalscorers | Pos | No. |
|---|---|---|---|---|---|---|---|---|---|
| Aug8 | Nat South | H | Weston-s-Mare | 267 | W | 4-1 | Stokes 1 Gardner 35 Cornhill 49 Cawley 62 (pen) | 1 | 1 |
| 10 | Nat South | A | Wealdstone | 664 | W | 2-1 | Cornhill 36 Greenhalgh 46 | 1 | 2 |
| 15 | Nat South | A | Truro City | 366 | L | 1-2 | Stokes 3 | 6 | 3 |
| 18 | Nat South | H | Dartford | 712 | L | 2-3 | Taaffe 2 60 | 9 | 4 |
| 22 | Nat South | H | Hemel Hempstead Town | 284 | L | 0-3 | | 15 | 5 |
| 29 | Nat South | A | Bishops Stortford | 314 | L | 2-3 | Gardner 6 King 78 | 16 | 6 |
| 31 | Nat South | H | Margate | 321 | W | 2-1 | White 23 Cawley 79 | 14 | 7 |
| Sept5 | Nat South | A | Sutton United | 730 | D | 2-2 | Cawley 52 Taaffe 61 | 14 | 8 |
| 12 | Nat South | H | Oxford City | 277 | L | 0-2 | | 15 | 9 |
| 14 | Nat South | A | Chelmsford City | 617 | L | 2-5 | Stokes 75 Cawley 78 | 15 | 10 |
| 19 | Nat South | H | Whitehawk | 236 | L | 1-2 | Cawley 6 (pen) | 17 | 11 |
| **26** | **FAC2Q** | **A** | **Wingate & Finchley** | **133** | **L** | **1-2** | **Stokes 1** | | 12 |
| Oct3 | Nat South | A | Eastbourne Borough | 401 | D | 0-0 | | 15 | 13 |
| 17 | Nat South | H | Hayes & Yeading | 234 | L | 0-3 | | 18 | 14 |
| 24 | Nat South | A | Hemel Hempstead Town | 375 | W | 2-1 | Cawley 30 Greenhalgh 36 | 16 | 15 |
| 31 | Nat South | H | Maidstone United | 516 | L | 1-2 | Greenhalgh 42 | 17 | 16 |
| Nov7 | Nat South | A | Weston-s-Mare | 369 | W | 3-0 | Taaffe 21 60 White 73 | | 17 |
| 14 | Nat South | H | Basingstoke Town | 286 | W | 5-0 | CAWLEY 3 (48 50 79 pen) Greenhalgh 67 Cornhill 89 | 14 | 18 |
| 21 | Nat South | A | Whitehawk | 372 | W | 2-0 | Bailey-Dennis 55 Cox 77 | 12 | 19 |
| 24 | Nat South | H | Maidenhead United | 226 | W | 2-0 | Greenhalgh 42 90 | 10 | 20 |
| Dec5 | Nat South | H | Sutton United | 307 | L | 0-3 | | 10 | 21 |
| 19 | Nat South | A | Havant & Waterlooville | 513 | L | 1-2 | White 47 | 12 | 22 |
| **21** | **FAT3Q** | **H** | **Sutton United** | **251** | **L** | **0-2** | | | 23 |
| 26 | Nat South | A | Ebbsfleet United | 1227 | L | 2-4 | Taaffe 51 Cawley 61 | 13 | 24 |
| 28 | Nat South | H | Bishops Stortford | 260 | D | 2-2 | Dowie 69 Bailey-Dennis 77 | 13 | 25 |
| Jan2 | Nat South | H | Ebbsfleet United | 767 | D | 0-0 | | 13 | 26 |
| 23 | Nat South | A | Bath City | 576 | W | 1-0 | White 14 | 13 | 27 |
| 30 | Nat South | A | Maidstone United | 2355 | D | 2-2 | Cawley 57 Easterford 90 | 13 | 28 |
| Feb6 | Nat South | H | Eastbourne Borough | 262 | W | 4-1 | Cawley 15 25 Bantick 40 Greenhalgh 90 | 11 | 29 |
| 13 | Nat South | A | St Albans City | 476 | D | 2-2 | Cawley 79 Bantick 89 | 9 | 30 |
| 20 | Nat South | H | Gosport Borough | 235 | D | 0-0 | | 9 | 31 |
| 27 | Nat South | A | Dartford | 925 | W | 2-1 | Cawley 23 White 73 | 9 | 32 |
| Mar5 | Nat South | H | Wealdstone | 276 | D | 2-2 | Cawley 14 King 61 | 11 | 33 |
| 12 | Nat South | A | Gosport Borough | 338 | W | 3-2 | Cawley 44 Easterford 80 King 90 | 9 | 34 |
| 19 | Nat South | H | St Albans City | 289 | L | 1-2 | King 18 | 11 | 35 |
| 22 | Nat South | A | Oxford City | 168 | L | 1-5 | Greenhalgh 76 | 11 | 36 |
| 26 | Nat South | H | Chelmsford City | 585 | W | 1-0 | Cawley 67 | 10 | 37 |
| 28 | Nat South | A | Margate | 469 | W | 1-0 | Cawley 14 | 8 | 38 |
| Apr2 | Nat South | A | Basingstoke Town | 444 | W | 2-0 | Carlos 40 Greenhalgh 54 | 8 | 39 |
| 9 | Nat South | H | Bath CIty | 232 | L | 1-2 | Taaffe 49 | 9 | 40 |
| 16 | Nat South | A | Hayes & Yeading | 149 | D | 2-2 | Carlos 58 Greenhalgh 90 | 10 | 41 |
| 19 | Nat South | H | Truro City | 216 | L | 1-2 | Greenhalgh 59 | 10 | 42 |
| 23 | Nat South | H | Havant & Waterlooville | 435 | L | 0-1 | | 11 | 43 |
| 30 | Nat South | A | Maidenhead United | 524 | D | 2-2 | Greenhalgh 31 56 | 10 | 44 |

| GOALSCORERS | Scoring Games | Consec Sco Games | Total |
|---|---|---|---|
| *2014-15 Cawley* | | | *15* |
| Cawley | 16 | 3 | 19 |
| Greenhalgh | 11 | 2 | 13 |
| Taaffe | 7 | | 7 |
| White | 5 | | 5 |
| King | 4 | 2 | 4 |
| Stokes | 4 | | 4 |
| Cornhill | 3 | 2 | 3 |
| Bailey-Dennis | 2 | | 2 |
| Bantick | 2 | | 2 |
| Carlos | 2 | | 2 |
| Easterford | 2 | | 2 |
| Gardner | 2 | | 2 |
| Cox | 1 | | 1 |
| Dowie | 1 | | 1 |

# DARTFORD

**Chairman:** Dave Skinner and Steve Irving

**Secretary:** Peter Martin (T) 01322 299 990 (E) secretary@dartfordfc.com

**Commercial Manager:** Lauren Webster (T/E) commercial@dartfordfc.com

**Programme Editor:** David Shafford (T/E) programme@dartfordfc.com

**Ground Address:** Princes Park Stadium, Grassbanks, Darenth Road, Dartford DA1 1RT

(T) 01322 299 990 **Manager:** Tony Burman

## Club Factfile

**Founded:** 1888 **Nickname:** The Darts

**Previous Names:** None

**Previous Leagues:** Kent League 1894-96, 97-98, 99-1902, 09-14, 21-26, 93-96, Southern 1996-2006

**Club Colours (change):** White/black/black (All blue)

**Ground Capacity:** 4,097 **Seats:** 640 **Covered:** Yes **Clubhouse:** Yes **Shop:** Yes

**Directions**

From M25 clockwise leave at Junction 1 B to roundabout controlled by traffic lights. Take third exit onto Princes Road, (A225) then second exit at next roundabout. Continue down hill to traffic lights (ground on your left), turn left into Darenth Road then second turning on your left into Grassbanks leading to car park. From M25 anti-clockwise leave at Junction 2 onto slip road A225 to roundabout, then first exit, second exit at next roundabout then down hill to traffic lights turn left into Darenth Road, then second turning on your left into Grassbanks leading to car park.

**Previous Grounds:** The Brent/Westgate House, Potters Meadow, Engleys Meadow, Summers Meadow, Watling Street

**Record Attendance:** 4,097 v Horsham YMCA - Isthmian Division 1 South 11/11/2006 and v Crystal Palace - Friendly 20/07/2007

**Record Victory:** Not known - If you know please email tw.publications@btinternet.com

**Record Defeat:** Not known - If you know please email tw.publications@btinternet.com

**Record Goalscorer:** Not known - If you know please email tw.publications@btinternet.com

**Record Appearances:** Steve Robinson - 692

**Additional Records:** Paid £6,000 to Chelmsford City for John Bartley
Received £25,000 from Redbridge Forest for Andy Hessenthaler

**Honours:**

Southern League Division 2 1896-97, Eastern Section 1930-31, 31-32, Southern Championship 30-31, 31-32, 73-74, 83-84, Southern Division 1980-81, League Cup 1976-77, 87-88, 88-89, Championship Shield 1983-84, 87-88, 88-89.
Isthmian League Division 1 North 2007-08, Premier Division 2009-10. Kent Senior Cup 1929-30, 34-35, 38-39, 69-70, 2015-16.

**10 YEAR RECORD**

| 06-07 | | 07-08 | | 08-09 | | 09-10 | | 10-11 | | 11-12 | | 12-13 | | 13-14 | | 14-15 | | 15-16 | |
|---|---|---|---|---|---|---|---|---|---|---|---|---|---|---|---|---|---|---|---|
| Isth1S | 7 | Isth1N | 1 | Isth P | 8 | Isth P | 1 | Conf S | 10 | Conf S | 2 | Conf | 8 | Conf | 22 | Conf | 23 | Nat S | 8 |

## DARTFORD MATCH RESULTS 2015-16

| Date | Comp | H/A | Opponents | Att: | Result | | Goalscorers | Pos | No. |
|---|---|---|---|---|---|---|---|---|---|
| Aug 8 | Nat South | A | Hemel Hempstead Town | 653 | L | 0-1 | | 19 | 1 |
| 11 | Nat South | H | Eastbourne Borough | 963 | **W** | 1-0 | T.Bradbrook 6 | 13 | 2 |
| 15 | Nat South | H | Sutton United | 910 | D | 2-2 | T.Bradbrook 15 69 | 12 | 3 |
| 18 | Nat South | A | Concord Rangers | 712 | **W** | 3-2 | Hammond 67 (og) Pugh 85 T.Bradbrook 90 | 7 | 4 |
| 22 | Nat South | H | Gosport Borough | 812 | L | 2-3 | E Bradbrook 65 T.Bradbrook 90 | 11 | 5 |
| 29 | Nat South | A | Margate | 996 | **W** | 2-0 | Noble 28 E.Bradbrook 70 | 9 | 6 |
| 31 | Nat South | H | Ebbsfleet United | 2251 | L | 0-1 | | 10 | 7 |
| Sept 5 | Nat South | A | Bath City | 766 | D | 0-0 | | 10 | 8 |
| 12 | Nat South | H | Weston-s-Mare | 802 | **W** | 2-1 | Harris 89 Noble 90 | 10 | 9 |
| 15 | Nat South | A | Oxford City | 283 | L | 1-2 | Pugh 35 | 10 | 10 |
| 19 | Nat South | H | Truro City | 850 | L | 0-1 | | 13 | 11 |
| **26** | **FAC2Q** | **H** | **Uxbridge** | **503** | **L** | **0-1** | | | 12 |
| Oct3 | Nat South | A | Wealdstone | 665 | L | 1-2 | T.Bradbrook 75 | 14 | 13 |
| 17 | Nat South | H | Hemel Hempstead Town | 844 | D | 2-2 | Harris 54 Hayes 90 | 14 | 14 |
| 24 | Nat South | A | Bishops Stortford | 402 | **W** | 2-1 | Cogan 12 E,Bradbrook 54 | | 15 |
| 31 | Nat South | H | Hayes & Yeading | 824 | **W** | 2-0 | T.Bradbrook 2 E Bradbrook 81 | 11 | 16 |
| Nov 14 | Nat South | H | Maidstone United | 1909 | D | 1-1 | E.Bradbrook 82 | 13 | 17 |
| **28** | **FAT3Q** | **H** | **Whitehawk** | **601** | **L** | **1-2** | **Ross 77 (og)** | | 18 |
| Dec 5 | Nat South | H | Havant & Waterlooville | 738 | **W** | 4-2 | E.Bradbrook 25 (pen) 56 Harris 45 Adams 66 | 11 | 19 |
| 12 | Nat South | A | Basingstoke Town | 531 | **W** | 1-0 | E.Brabrook | 8 | 20 |
| 19 | Nat South | A | Whitehawk | 347 | **W** | 1-0 | Pugh 35 | 7 | 21 |
| 26 | Nat South | A | Chelmsord City | 810 | **W** | 1-0 | Pugh 60 | 7 | 22 |
| 28 | Nat South | H | Margate | 1417 | D | 1-1 | E.Bradbrook 51 | 6 | 23 |
| Jan 2 | Nat South | H | Chelmsford City | 1205 | D | 1-1 | T.Bradbrook 90 | 6 | 24 |
| 16 | Nat South | H | Bath City | 923 | **W** | 4-1 | Pugh 11 35 Hayes 61 McNaughton 88 | 4 | 25 |
| 23 | Nat South | A | Sutton United | 1075 | L | 0-2 | | 5 | 26 |
| 26 | Nat South | H | Wealdstone | 853 | L | 1-2 | Pugh 51 | 5 | 27 |
| Feb 6 | Nat South | H | St Albans City | 931 | **W** | 2-0 | Pugh 56 90 | 5 | 28 |
| 20 | Nat South | A | Eastbourne Borough | 585 | D | 1-1 | Pugh 72 | 7 | 29 |
| 23 | Nat South | A | Gosport Borough | 386 | **W** | 3-1 | E.Bradbrook 61 76 Pugh 80 | 5 | 30 |
| 27 | Nat South | H | Concord Rangers | 925 | L | 1-2 | T.Bradbrook 18 | 6 | 31 |
| Mar 1 | Nat South | A | Hayes &Yeading | 177 | D | 2-2 | T.Bradbrook 39 E.Bradbrook 45 | 6 | 32 |
| 5 | Nat South | A | Weston-s-Mare | 436 | L | 1-2 | Sykes 44 | 6 | 33 |
| 12 | Nat South | H | Whitehawk | 906 | L | 2-4 | Pugh 45 (pen) 50 | 6 | 34 |
| 15 | Nat South | A | Maidenhead United | 313 | L | 1-2 | E.Bradbrook 12 | 6 | 35 |
| 19 | Nat South | A | Havant & Waterlooville | 661 | L | 0-2 | | 9 | 36 |
| 25 | Nat South | H | Bishops Stortford | 921 | **W** | 3-1 | Harris 6 Wood 26 T.Bradbrook 79 | 9 | 37 |
| 28 | Nat South | A | Ebbsfleet | 243 | D | 1-1 | Hayes 47 | 8 | 38 |
| Apr 4 | Nat South | H | Maidenhead United | 877 | **W** | 2-0 | Harris 33 E.Bradbrook 35 (pen) | 5 | 39 |
| 5 | Nat South | A | Truro City | 502 | L | 0-3 | | 5 | 40 |
| 9 | Nat South | A | Maidstone United | 2602 | **W** | 2-1 | E.Bradbrook 10 (pen) Ferguson 71 | 7 | 41 |
| 16 | Nat South | H | Basingstoke Town | 924 | D | 0-0 | | 7 | 42 |
| 23 | Nat South | H | Oxford City | 1190 | D | 2-2 | E.Bradbrook 54 90(pen) | 7 | 43 |
| 30 | Nat South | A | St Albans City | 1310 | L | 0-4 | | 8 | 44 |

| GOALSCORERS | Scoring Games | Consec Sco Games | Total |
|---|---|---|---|
| *2014-15 E.Bradbrook* | | | *10* |
| E.Bradbrook | 15 | 3 | 17 |
| Pugh | 10 | 3 | 13 |
| T.Bradbrook | 10 | 4 | 11 |
| Harris | 5 | | 5 |
| Hayes | 3 | | 3 |
| Noble | 2 | | 2 |
| Adama | 1 | | 1 |
| Cogan | 1 | | 1 |
| Ferguson | 1 | | 1 |
| McNaughton | 1 | | 1 |
| Sykes | 1 | | 1 |
| Wood | 1 | | 1 |
| Opponents | | | 2 |

# EAST THURROCK UNITED

**Chairman:** Brian Mansbridge
**Secretary:** Neil Speight (T) 07885 313 435 (E) speight.n@sky.com
**Commercial Manager:** (T/E)
**Programme Editor:** Neil Speight (T/E) 07885 313 435
**Ground Address:** Rookery Hill, Corringham, Essex SS17 9LB
(T) 01375 644 166 **Manager:** John Coventry

2015-16 Squad

## Club Factfile

**Founded:** 1969 **Nickname:** Rocks
**Previous Names:** Corringham Social > 1969 (Sunday side)
**Previous Leagues:** South Essex Combination, Greater London, Metropolitan 1972-75, London Spartan 1975-79, Essex Senior 1979-92, Isthmian 1992-2004, 05-16, Southern 2004-05.
**Club Colours (change):** Amber with black trim/black (Black & white stripes/white)

**Ground Capacity:** 3,500 **Seats:** 160 **Covered:** 1,000 **Clubhouse:** Yes **Shop:** Yes

**Directions**
From A13 London-Southend road,
take A1014 at Stanford-le-Hope for two and half miles,
Ground is on the left.

**Previous Grounds:** Billet, Stanford-le-Hope 1970-73, 74-76, Grays Athletic 1973-74, Tilbury FC 1977-82, New Thames Club 1982-84

**Record Attendance:** 1,215 v Woking FA Cup 2003
**Record Victory:** 7-0 v Coggeshall (H) - Essex Senior League 1984
**Record Defeat:** 0-9 v Eton Manor (A) - Essex Senior League 1982
**Record Goalscorer:** Graham Stewart - 102
**Record Appearances:** Glen Case - 600+
**Additional Records:** £22,000 from Leyton Orient for Greg Berry 1990

**Honours:**
Isthmian League Division Three 1999-2000, Division One North 2010-11, Premier Division Play-offs 2015-16.
East Anglian Cup 2002-03.

### 10 YEAR RECORD

| 06-07 | 07-08 | 08-09 | 09-10 | 10-11 | 11-12 | 12-13 | 13-14 | 14-15 | 15-16 |
|---|---|---|---|---|---|---|---|---|---|
| Isth P 16 | Isth P 20 | Isth1N 2 | Isth1N 5 | Isth1N 1 | Isth P 10 | Isth P 5 | Isth P 20 | Isth P 13 | Isth P 3 |

# EAST THURROCK UNITED MATCH RESULTS 2015-16

| Date | Comp | H/A | Opponents | Att: | Result | Goalscorers | Pos | No. |
|---|---|---|---|---|---|---|---|---|
| Aug 8 | IsthP | H | Billericay Town | 238 | D 1-1 | Higgins 45 (pen) | 9 | 1 |
| 11 | IsthP | A | Brentwood Town | 149 | W 3-1 | Smith 4 Bryant 45 Wraight 90 | 5 | 2 |
| 15 | IsthP | A | Hampton & Richmond B | 303 | L 1-2 | Higgins 2 | 14 | 3 |
| 24 | IsthP | A | Hendon | 169 | W 2-1 | Smith 25 90 | 8 | 4 |
| 29 | IsthP | H | Kingstonian | 171 | D 2-2 | Hustwick 74 (og) Smith 90 (pen) | 11 | 5 |
| 31 | IsthP | A | Enfield Town | 441 | D 1-1 | Wraight 67 | 11 | 6 |
| Sept 5 | IsthP | H | Leatherhead | 137 | D 4-4 | Smith 26 (pen) 39 Anderson 50 Honesty 90 | 13 | 7 |
| 8 | IsthP | H | Hendon | 143 | L 2-4 | Scott 5 Smith 52 (pen) | 15 | 8 |
| **15** | **FAC1Q** | **A** | **Yaxley** | **76** | **W 3-1** | **Higgins 31 52 Craddock 45** | | 9 |
| 19 | IsthP | A | Staines Town | 209 | L 2-3 | Smith 18 Higgins 78 (pen) | 13 | 10 |
| **26** | **FAC2Q** | **A** | **Carshalton Athletic** | **227** | **W 5-0** | **Smith 11 Higgins 25 Gilbey 36 Honesty 75 Walker 84** | | 11 |
| 29 | IsthP | H | Leiston | 163 | W 4-0 | Higgins 36 85 Smith 59 65 | 17 | 12 |
| Oct 3 | IsthP | A | Merstham | 503 | D 2-2 | Higgins 4 Scott 73 | 18 | 13 |
| **10** | **FAC3Q** | **H** | **Staines Town** | **263** | **L 3-6** | **Higgins 42 66 (pen) Smith 7** | | 14 |
| 14 | IsthP | A | Leiston | 147 | W 3-0 | HIGGINS 3 ( 57 75 80 pen) | 15 | 15 |
| 17 | IsthP | A | Bognor Regis Town | 364 | D 2-2 | Gilbey 41 Higgins 88 | 18 | 16 |
| 24 | IsthP | A | Billericay Town | 307 | L 1-3 | Scott 56 | 19 | 17 |
| 27 | IsthP | H | Brentwood Town | 185 | W 4-0 | Smith 23 45 (pen) Wraight 56 84 | 19 | 18 |
| **31** | **FAT1Q** | **H** | **South Park** | **68** | **W 4-0** | **Smith 3 Gilbey 9 Scott 33 Honesty 88** | | 19 |
| Nov 3 | IsthP | A | Needham Market | 152 | W 3-1 | Knott 25 Miller 58 Wraight 90 | 14 | 20 |
| 7 | IsthP | H | Hampton & Richmond B | 168 | W 2-1 | Scott 24 Honesty 45 | 13 | 21 |
| **14** | **FAT2Q** | **H** | **Tiverton Town** | **141** | **W 5-0** | **SMITH 3 (19 55 64 pen) Miller 87 Sammons 90** | | 22 |
| 17 | IsthP | H | Needham Market | 124 | L 1-2 | Honesty 56 | 13 | 23 |
| 21 | IsthP | H | Wingate & Finchley | 155 | D 1-1 | Wraight 88 | 13 | 24 |
| 24 | IsthP | H | Farnboorough | 120 | W 4-1 | Phillips 76 Yusuff 76 86 Wraight 84 | 11 | 25 |
| **28** | **FAT3Q** | **A** | **Merthyr Town** | **225** | **D 1-1** | **Newby 70** | | 26 |
| **Dec 1** | **FAT3Qr** | **H** | **Merthyr Town** | **162** | **W 3-1** | **Higgins 22 (pen) 74 Wraight 30** | | 27 |
| 5t | IsthP | H | Lewes | 154 | W 4-1 | Miller 48 Higgins 65 77 (pen) Yusuff 82 | 10 | 28 |
| **12** | **FAT1** | **H** | **Maidenhead Utd** | **150** | **L 1-4** | **Ruel 45** | | 29 |
| 19 | IsthP | A | Kingstonian | 272 | W 4-1 | Scott 13 Yusuff 49 Wraight 80 Higgins 84 | 10 | 30 |
| 26 | IsthP | H | Enfield Town | 238 | W 1-0 | Scott 15 | 9 | 31 |
| Jan 2 | IsthP | A | Grays Athletic | 255 | D 0-0 | | 9 | 32 |
| 5th | IsthP | A | VCD Athletic | 112 | W 3-1 | Wraight 30 81 Higgins 58 | 6 | 33 |
| 17 | IsthP | A | Tonbridge Angels | 553 | W 2-1 | Higgins 29 56 | 5 | 34 |
| 19 | IsthP | H | Burgess Hill Town | 143 | W 1-0 | Walker 67 | 4 | 35 |
| 23 | IsthP | H | Dulwich Hamlet | 311 | D 2-2 | Wraight 51 Higgins 77 | 3 | 36 |
| 26 | IsthP | H | Canvey Island | 215 | W 4-0 | HIGGINS 3 (10 25 73) Morgan 57 | 3 | 37 |
| 30 | IsthP | A | Burgess Hill Town | 412 | W 2-0 | Smith 72 Wraight 76 | 2 | 38 |
| Feb 2 | IsthP | A | Harrow Borough | 145 | W 5-2 | HIGGINS 3(13 46 86) Ellul 48 Wraight 86 | 2 | 39 |
| 6 | IsthP | H | Merstham | 251 | L 1-2 | Higgins 27 | 3 | 40 |
| 13 | IsthP | A | Canvey Island | 308 | W 4-2 | Higgins 26 (pen) 83 Smith 41 Wraight 70 | 2 | 41 |
| 16 | IsthP | H | Met Police | 155 | W 4-2 | Walker 13 30 Higgins 39 90 | 1 | 42 |
| 20 | IsthP | H | Bognor Regis Town | 320 | D 0-0 | | 1 | 43 |
| 27 | IsthP | A | Dulwich Hamlet | 1607 | D 2-2 | Higgins 34 Wraight 65 | 2 | 44 |
| 29 | IsthP | A | Farnborough | 182 | W 3-0 | Wraight 44 Higgins 54 Ellul 58 | 1 | 45 |
| Mar 5 | IsthP | H | Tonbridge Angels | 331 | W 3-0 | Higgins 12 Walker 32 Ruel 76 | 1 | 46 |
| 12 | IsthP | A | Leatherhead | 251 | L 1-2 | Higgins 3 (pen) | 2 | 47 |
| 19 | IsthP | H | Staines Town | 233 | D 0-0 | | 2 | 48 |
| 26 | IsthP | A | Met Police | 65 | W 3-0 | Sammons 3 Wraight 21 Marlow 77 | 2 | 49 |
| 28 | IsthP | H | Grays Athletic | 310 | W 3-0 | Higgins 15 25 Wraight 23 | 2 | 50 |
| Apr 2 | IsthP | A | Wingate & Finchley | 149 | W 3-1 | Higgins 45 65 (pen) Wraight 70 | 2 | 51 |
| 9 | IsthP | H | VCD Athletic | 159 | W 4-1 | Wraight 2 Newby 64 Ellul 78 84 | 2 | 52 |
| 16 | IsthP | H | Harrow Borough | 279 | W 2-0 | Higgins 4 Wraight 87 | 2 | 53 |
| 23 | IsthP | A | Lewes | 505 | D 1-1 | Higgins 9 | 3 | 54 |
| **26** | **PO SF** | **H** | **Tonbridge Angels** | **849** | **W 2-0** | **Hayles 8 Marlow 45** | | 55 |
| **May 1** | **PO Final** | **H** | **Dulwich Hamlet** | **1661** | **W 3-1** | **Craddock 11 Hayles 19 35** | | 56 |

| GOALSCORERS | Scoring Games | Consec Sco Games | Total |
|---|---|---|---|
| ***2014-15 Higgins*** | | | ***44*** |
| Higgins | 28 | 8 | 45 |
| Wraight | 20 | 4 | 22 |
| Smith, Lewis | 14 | 3 | 20 |
| Scott | 7 | | 7 |
| Honesty | 5 | | 5 |
| Walker | 4 | | 5 |
| Ellul | 3 | | 4 |
| Yusuff | 3 | | 4 |
| Craddock | 3 | | 3 |
| Gilbey | 3 | | 3 |
| Miller | 3 | | 3 |
| Hales | 2 | | 2 |
| Marlow | 2 | | 2 |
| Newby | 2 | | 2 |
| Ruel | 2 | | 2 |
| Sammons | 2 | | 2 |
| Anderson | 1 | | 1 |
| Bryant | 1 | | 1 |
| Knott | 1 | | 1 |
| Morgan | 1 | | 1 |
| Phillips | 1 | | 1 |
| Opponents | | | 1 |

# EASTBOURNE BOROUGH

**Chairman:** Paul Maynard
**Secretary:** Mrs Jan Field **(T)** 01323 766 265 **(E)** janfield38@sky.com
**Commercial Manager:** Sharon Hind **(T/E)** 07850 582 434
**Programme Editor:** Anthony Scott **(T/E)** 07769 114 476
**Ground Address:** Langney Sports Club, Priory Lane, Eastbourne BN23 7QH
**(T)** 01323 766 265 **Manager:** Tommy Widdrington

## Club Factfile

**Founded:** 1966 **Nickname:** Borough
**Previous Names:** Langney Sports > 2001
**Previous Leagues:** Eastbourne & Hastings, Sussex County, Southern

**Club Colours (change):** Red/black/red & black hoops (All yellow)

**Ground Capacity:** 4,151 **Seats:** 542 **Covered:** 2,500 **Clubhouse:** Yes **Shop:** Yes

**Directions**
From M25 take M23/A23 eastbound to A27 Polegate by pass pick up and follow signs for crematorium 50yds past crematorium turn right at mini roundabout into Priory Road Stadium 100yds on left.

**Previous Grounds:** None

**Record Attendance:** 3,770 v Oxford United - FA Cup 1st Round 05/11/05
**Record Victory:** 10-1 v Haywards Heath Town - Sussex County Division One 1991-92
**Record Defeat:** 0-8 v Sheppey United (A) - FA Vase 09/10/93 and v Peachaven & Tels (A) - Sussex Co. Div.1 09/11/93
**Record Goalscorer:** Nigel Hole - 146
**Record Appearances:** Darren Baker - 689
**Additional Records:** Paid £1,800 to Yeovil Town for Yemi Odoubade.
Received £15,000 from Oxford United for Yemi Odoubade.

**Honours:**
Sussex County League 1999-2000, 02-03.
Sussex Senior Cup 2001-02, 15-16.

### 10 YEAR RECORD

| 06-07 | 07-08 | 08-09 | 09-10 | 10-11 | 11-12 | 12-13 | 13-14 | 14-15 | 15-16 |
|---|---|---|---|---|---|---|---|---|---|
| Conf S 7 | Conf S 2 | Conf 13 | Conf 19 | Conf 23 | Conf S 18 | Conf S 12 | Conf S 10 | Conf S 11 | Nat S 17 |

## EASTBOURNE BOROUGH MATCH RESULTS 2015-16

| Date | Comp | H/A | Opponents | Att: | Result | | Goalscorers | Pos | No. |
|---|---|---|---|---|---|---|---|---|---|
| Aug 8 | Nat South | H | Maidenhead United | 551 | L | 1-2 | Worrall 54 (pen) | 16 | 1 |
| 11 | Nat South | A | Dartford | 963 | L | 0-1 | | 20 | 2 |
| 15 | Nat South | A | Wealdstone | 581 | W | 1-0 | Pinney 90 | 14 | 3 |
| 18 | Nat South | H | St Albans City | 437 | W | 1-0 | Romain 28 | 10 | 4 |
| 22 | Nat South | A | Weston-s-Mare | 326 | W | 2-1 | Pinney 54 Lok 66 | 6 | 5 |
| 29 | Nat South | H | Maidstone United | 1011 | W | 1-0 | Collier 30 | 5 | 6 |
| 31 | Nat South | A | Havant & Waterlooville | 620 | L | 0-4 | | 9 | 7 |
| Sept 5 | Nat South | H | Truro City | 532 | D | 0-0 | | 9 | 8 |
| 12 | Nat South | A | Basingstoke Town | 432 | W | 5-1 | Baptista 32 Romain 65 Evans 69 McCallum 87 Haysman 90 | 6 | 9 |
| 15 | Nat South | H | Margate | 438 | L | 1-4 | Baptista 87 | 9 | 10 |
| 19 | Nat South | A | Oxford City | 228 | D | 2-2 | Pinney 15 McCallum 53 | 10 | 11 |
| **26** | **FAC2Q** | **H** | **AFC Sudbury** | **404** | **W** | **2-1** | **Pinney 36 46** | | 12 |
| Oct 3 | Nat South | H | Concord Rangers | 401 | D | 0-0 | | 10 | 13 |
| **10** | **FAC3Q** | **H** | **Hartley Wintney** | **491** | **W** | **3-2** | **Lok 15 Kane 56 Pinney 90** | | 14 |
| 17 | Nat South | H | Bishops Stortford | 424 | L | 0-1 | | 12 | 15 |
| **24** | **FAC4Q** | **A** | **Dover Athletic** | **821** | **L** | **1-2** | **McCallum 77** | | 16 |
| 31 | Nat South | H | Sutton United | 477 | D | 1-1 | Pinney 58 | 14 | 17 |
| Nov 14 | Nat South | H | Ebbsfleet United | 581 | L | 1-2 | Haysman 90 | 15 | 18 |
| 21 | Nat South | A | Chelmsford City | 778 | W | 3-0 | Pinney 33 53 Romain 90 | | 19 |
| **29** | **FAT3Q** | **A** | **Hayes & Yeading** | **158** | **D** | **2-2** | **Evans 39 Collier 86** | | 20 |
| **Dec 1** | **FAT3Qr** | **H** | **Hayes & Yeading** | **204** | **W** | **4-0** | **Simpemba 3 McCallum 36 Collier 47 Pinney 90** | | 21 |
| 5 | Nat South | H | Oxford City | 422 | D | 1-1 | Worrall 66 (pen) | 14 | 22 |
| **12** | **FAT1** | **H** | **Hemel Hempstead Town** | **317** | **W** | **7-4** | **Watt 15 (og) Romain 17 20 Evans 77 90 McCallum 80 Pinney 83** | | 23 |
| 19 | Nat South | A | Truro City | 339 | L | 0-1 | | 17 | 24 |
| 26 | Nat South | H | Whitehawk | 783 | D | 1-1 | Pinney 90 | 17 | 25 |
| 28 | Nat South | A | Maidstone United | 2691 | L | 1-2 | Lok 60 | 18 | 26 |
| Jan 9 | Nat South | H | Basingstoke Town | 478 | L | 1-2 | Haysman 46 | 19 | 27 |
| **16** | **FAT2** | **H** | **AFC Fylde** | **352** | **L** | **1-4** | **Collier 28** | | 28 |
| 23 | Nat South | H | Wealdstone | 431 | W | 3-0 | Pinney 11 Haysman 24 Evans 71 | 16 | 29 |
| 30 | Nat South | H | Bath City | 568 | W | 5-2 | Evans 5 53 (pen) Pinney 22 48 Simpemba 81 | 14 | 30 |
| Feb 2 | Nat South | A | Gosport Borough | 357 | L | 1-3 | Taylor 16 | 14 | 31 |
| 6 | Nat South | A | Concord Rangers | 262 | L | 1-4 | Pinney 28 (pen) | 14 | 32 |
| 9 | Nat South | A | Hayes & Yeading | 113 | D | 4-4 | Pinney 7 Beale 54 Evans 62 Simpemba 90 | 14 | 33 |
| 13 | Nat South | H | Weston-s-Mare | 351 | D | 3-3 | Beale 32 Taylor 46 86 | 14 | 34 |
| 16 | Nat South | A | Whitehawk | 340 | W | 2-1 | Romain 2 Pinney 16 | 12 | 35 |
| 20 | Nat South | H | Dartford | 565 | D | 1-1 | Pinney 25 | 11 | 36 |
| 23 | Nat South | A | Margate | 557 | W | 1-0 | Beale 86 | 9 | 37 |
| 27 | Nat South | A | Maidenhead Urd | 424 | L | 0-2 | | 11 | 38 |
| Mar 5 | Nat South | H | Hayes & Yeading | 454 | W | 2-0 | Romain 8 Evans 90 | 10 | 39 |
| 8 | Nat South | A | Hemel Hempstead Town | 263 | L | 0-1 | | 10 | 40 |
| 12 | Nat South | A | Bishops Stortford | 313 | D | 1-1 | Haysman 48 | 12 | 41 |
| 19 | Nat South | H | Chelmsford City | 481 | W | 2-0 | Pinney 50 Lok 84 | 10 | 42 |
| 26 | Nat South | A | St Albans City | 663 | L | 1-3 | McCallum 3 | 11 | 43 |
| 28 | Nat South | H | Havant&Waterlooville | 614 | D | 2-2 | Stone 71 McCallum 90 | 11 | 44 |
| Apr 2 | Nat South | A | Sutton United | 962 | L | 1-2 | Pinney 27 | 12 | 45 |
| 9 | Nat South | H | Hemel Hempstead Town | 578 | L | 2-3 | Lok 41 Collier 84 | 15 | 46 |
| 16 | Nat South | A | Bath City | 533 | L | 0-1 | | 15 | 47 |
| 23 | Nat South | H | Gosport Borough | 592 | W | 3-0 | Shephard 51 Taylor 64 77 | 14 | 48 |
| 30 | Nat South | A | Ebbsfleet United | 1348 | L | 2-4 | Pinney 53 72 | 17 | 49 |

| GOALSCORERS | Scoring Games | Consec Sco Games | Total |
|---|---|---|---|
| ***2014-15 Lok*** | | | ***10*** |
| Pinney | 19 | 2 | 23 |
| Evans | 7 | | 9 |
| McCallum | 7 | | 7 |
| Romain | 6 | | 7 |
| Collier | 5 | | 5 |
| Haysman | 5 | | 5 |
| Lok | 5 | | 5 |
| Taylor | 3 | | 5 |
| Beale | 3 | | 3 |
| Simpemba | 3 | | 3 |
| Baptista | 2 | 2 | 2 |
| Worrall | 2 | | 2 |
| Kane | 1 | | 1 |
| Sheppard | 1 | | 1 |
| Stone | 1 | | 1 |
| Opponents | | | 1 |

# EBBSFLEET UNITED

**Chairman:** Dr Abdulla M.S. Al-Humaidi
**Secretary:** Peter Danzey (T) 01474 533 796 (E) peter.danzey@eufc.co.uk
**Commercial Manager:** Dave Archer (T/E) 01474 533 796
**Programme Editor:** Ed Miller (T/E) 01474 533 796
**Ground Address:** Stonebridge Road, Northfleet, Kent DA11 9GN
(T) 01474 533 796 **Manager:** Daryl McMahon

## Club Factfile

**Founded:** 1946 **Nickname:** The Fleet
**Previous Names:** Gravesend United and Northfleet United merged in 1946 to form Gravesend and Northfleet > 2007
**Previous Leagues:** Southern 1946-79, 80-96. Alliance 1979-80, Isthmian 1997-2001

**Club Colours (change):** Red/white/red (Yellow/black/black)

**Ground Capacity:** 4,184 **Seats:** 500 **Covered:** 3,000 **Clubhouse:** Yes **Shop:** Yes

**Directions**
A2 to Ebbsfleet/Eurostar International Junction.
Follow Brown signs to 'The Fleet'.

**Previous Grounds:** Gravesend United: Central Avenue

**Record Attendance:** 12,036 v Sunderland - FA Cup 4th Round 12/02/1963
**Record Victory:** 8-1 v Clacton Town - Southern League 1962-63
**Record Defeat:** 0-9 v Trowbridge Town - Southern League Premier DIvision 1991-92
**Record Goalscorer:** Steve Portway - 152 (1992-94, 97-2001)
**Record Appearances:** Ken Burrett - 537
**Additional Records:** Paid £8,000 to Wokingham Town for Richard Newbery 1996 and to Tonbridge for Craig Williams 1997
Received £35,000 from West Ham United for Jimmy Bullard 1998
**Honours:**
Southern League 1956-57, Division 1 South 1974-75, Southern Division 1994-95. Isthmian League Premier 2001-02.
FA Trophy 2007-08. Kent Senior Cup 1948-49, 52-53, 80-81, 99-00, 00-01, 01-02.

### 10 YEAR RECORD

| 06-07 | 07-08 | 08-09 | 09-10 | 10-11 | 11-12 | 12-13 | 13-14 | 14-15 | 15-16 |
|---|---|---|---|---|---|---|---|---|---|
| Conf 7 | Conf 11 | Conf 14 | Conf 22 | Conf S 3 | Conf 14 | Conf 23 | Conf S 4 | Conf S 8 | Nat S 2 |

# EBBSFLEET UNITED MATCH RESULTS 2015-16

| Date | Comp | H/A | Opponents | Att: | Result | | Goalscorers | Pos | No. |
|---|---|---|---|---|---|---|---|---|---|
| Aug 8 | Nat South | H | Basingstoke Town | 888 | W | 1-0 | Kedwell 51 | 7 | 1 |
| 11 | Nat South | A | Maidstone United | 2363 | W | 2-0 | Parkes 40 82 | 3 | 2 |
| 15 | Nat South | A | St Albans City | 602 | W | 2-0 | Kedwell 50 (pen) Clark 76 | 1 | 3 |
| 22 | Nat South | A | Wealdsone | 764 | W | 2-1 | Parkes 51 Kedwell 62 | 3 | 4 |
| 29 | Nat South | H | Whitehawk | 972 | D | 2-2 | Godden 54 Haynes 79 | 2 | 5 |
| 31 | Nat South | A | Dartford | 2251 | W | 1-0 | Parkes 7 | 2 | 6 |
| Sept 5 | Nat South | H | Maidenhead United | 1016 | W | 3-1 | Godden 18 70 Parkes 30 | 2 | 7 |
| 12 | Nat South | A | Margate | 1017 | W | 2-0 | Clark 44 Parkes 78 | 1 | 8 |
| 15 | Nat South | H | Sutton United | 947 | W | 1-0 | Parkes 54 | 1 | 9 |
| 19 | Nat South | A | Havant & Waterlooville | 751 | W | 4-1 | Godden 21 64 Parkes 56 Haynes 90 | 1 | 10 |
| 22 | Nat South | H | Weston-s-Mare | 2045 | W | 2-1 | Kedwell 21 Bonner 49 | 1 | 11 |
| **26** | **FAC2Q** | **A** | **Chelmsford City** | **823** | **D** | **0-0** | | | 12 |
| **29** | **FAC2Qr** | **H** | **Chelmsford City** | **790** | **L** | **1-2** | **Godden 24** | | 13 |
| Oct 3 | Nat South | H | Maidstone United | 2157 | L | 0-1 | | 1 | 14 |
| 17 | Nat South | A | Gosport Borough | 563 | W | 2-1 | Godden 27 Kedwell 57 | 1 | 15 |
| 24 | Nat South | A | Chelmsford City | 858 | D | 0-0 | | 1 | 16 |
| 31 | Nat South | H | Wealdstone | 1121 | L | 2-3 | Haynes 14 Godden 51 | 1 | 17 |
| Nov 7 | Nat South | H | Oxford City | 1098 | D | 1-1 | Godden 45 | 1 | 18 |
| 14 | Nat South | A | Eastbourne Borough | 581 | W | 2-1 | Godden 8 Beale 33 (og) | | 19 |
| 21 | Nat South | H | Bishops Stortford | 103 | W | 4-2 | GODDEN 3 ( 6 42 71) Bonner 23 | 1 | 20 |
| **28** | **FAT3Q** | **Hy** | **Molesey** | **672** | **W** | **4-1** | **Godden 5 13 Kedwell 9 West 7410** | | 21 |
| Dec 5 | Nat South | A | Hemel Hempstead Town | 571 | W | 2-1 | Godden 89 Kedwell 90 | 1 | 22 |
| **12** | **FAT1** | **A** | **Oxford City** | **425** | **L** | **1-2** | **Godden 15** | | 23 |
| 19 | Nat South | H | Bath City | 1115 | L | 0-1 | | 1 | 24 |
| 26 | Nat South | H | Concord Rangers | 1227 | W | 4-2 | Kedwell 30 Parkes 40 49 Godden 90 | 1 | 25 |
| 28 | Nat South | A | Whitehawk | 2691 | W | 1-0 | Godden 75 | 1 | 26 |
| Jan 2 | Nat South | A | Concord Rangers | 767 | D | 0-0 | | 1 | 27 |
| 9 | Nat South | H | Truro City | 1185 | D | 0-0 | | 1 | 28 |
| 23 | Nat South | H | Margate | 1462 | L | 1-2 | Kedwell 46 | 1 | 29 |
| 30 | Nat South | A | Basingstoke Town | 608 | W | 2-1 | Cook 68 McLean 90 | 1 | 30 |
| Feb 6 | Nat South | A | Bishops Stortford | 504 | W | 2-1 | McLean 11 36 | 1 | 31 |
| 13 | Nat South | A | Oxford City | 390 | D | 1-1 | McLean 18 | 1 | 32 |
| 16 | Nat South | H | St Albans City | 1089 | W | 1-0 | McLean 44 | 1 | 33 |
| 20 | Nat South | A | Truro City | 786 | D | 1-1 | Acheampong 59 | 1 | 34 |
| 27 | Nat South | H | Hayes & Yeading | 950 | D | 0-0 | | 1 | 35 |
| Mar 1 | Nat South | H | Havant & Waterlooville | 854 | D | 2-2 | Kissock 25 Godden 55 | 1 | 36 |
| 5 | Nat South | H | Gosport Borough | 932 | W | 2-0 | Kedwell 14 (pen) Harding 33 (og) | 1 | 37 |
| 8 | Nat South | A | Maidenhead United | 448 | D | 0-0 | | 1 | 38 |
| 12 | Nat South | A | Bath City | 558 | D | 1-1 | Parkes 76 | 1 | 39 |
| 19 | Nat South | H | Hemel Hempstead Town | 1021 | W | 6-0 | Kedwell 25 Lewis 49 Clark 62 Fish 66 Parkes 71 Shields 73 | 1 | 40 |
| 25 | Nat South | A | Weston-s-Mare | 604 | L | 1-2 | Godden 77 | 1 | 41 |
| 28 | Nat South | H | Dartford | 2435 | D | 1-1 | Godden 38 | 1 | 42 |
| Apr 2 | Nat South | A | Hayes & Yeading | 287 | W | 5-0 | GODDEN 4 (7 45 63 76) Sheringham 87 | 1 | 43 |
| 9 | Nat South | H | Chelmsford City | 2267 | W | 3-1 | Shields 53 Kedwell 56 Godden 70 | 1 | 44 |
| 16 | Nat South | A | Sutton United | 3142 | L | 0-2 | | 2 | 45 |
| 30 | Nat South | H | Eastbourne Borough | 1348 | W | 4-2 | GODDEN 3 (12 34 80) Sheringham 35 | 2 | 46 |
| **May 4** | **PO SF1** | **A** | **Whitehawk** | **1055** | W | **2-1** | **Lewis 29 Kedwell 74** | | 47 |
| **8** | **PO SF2** | **H** | **Whitehawk** | **1942** | **L** | **1-2** | **Clark 24 (Won 3-2 on pens)** | | 48 |
| **14** | **PO Final** | **H** | **Maidstone United** | **3800** | **D** | **2-2** | **Kedwell 20 (pen) 108 (pen) (Lost 3-4 on pens aet)** | | 49 |

| GOALSCORERS | Scoring Games | Consec Sco Games | Total |
|---|---|---|---|
| *2014-15 Godden* | | | *12* |
| Godden | 20 | 7 | 30 |
| Kedwell | 14 | 2 | 15 |
| Parkes | 10 | 5 | 12 |
| McLean | 4 | 4 | 5 |
| Clark | 4 | | 4 |
| Haynes | 3 | | 3 |
| Bonner | 2 | | 2 |
| Lewis | 2 | | 2 |
| Sheringham | 2 | | 2 |

| | Scoring Games | Consec Sco Games | Total |
|---|---|---|---|
| Shields | 2 | | 2 |
| Acheampong | 1 | | 1 |
| Cook | 1 | | 1 |
| Fish | 1 | | 1 |
| Kissock | 1 | | 1 |
| West | 1 | | 1 |
| Opponents | | | 2 |

# GOSPORT BOROUGH

**Chairman:** Mark Hook
**Secretary:** Brian Cosgrave (T) 07984 960 537 (E) brian.cosgrave@hotmail.co.uk
**Commercial Manager:** Natasha Hook (T/E) 07581 441 675
**Programme Editor:** (T/E)
**Ground Address:** GDL Stadium, Privett Park, Privett Road, Gosport, Hampshire PO12 0SX
**(T)** 023 9250 1042 (Match days only) **Manager:** Alex Pike

## Club Factfile

**Founded:** 1944 **Nickname:** The 'Boro'
**Previous Names:** Gosport Borough Athletic
**Previous Leagues:** Portsmouth 1944-45, Hampshire 1945-78, Southern 1978-92, Wessex 1992-2007

**Club Colours (change):** Yellow & blue/blue/blue (Orange & black/black & orange/orange)

**Ground Capacity:** 4,500 **Seats:** 450 **Covered:** 600 **Clubhouse:** Yes **Shop:** Yes

**Directions**
Exit M27 at J11. TakeA32 Fareham to Gosport road.
After 3 miles take the 3rd exit at Brockhurst r/a, into Military Road.
At next r/a take 1st exit into Privett Road. Ground is approx. 400 yards on left.

**Previous Grounds:** None

**Record Attendance:** 4,770 v Pegasus - FA Amateur Cup 1951
**Record Victory:** 14-0 v Cunliffe Owen - Hampshire League 1945-46
**Record Defeat:** 0-9 v Gloucester City - Southern Premier Division 1989-90 and v Lymington & N.M. - Wessex Lge 99-2000
**Record Goalscorer:** Justin Bennett- 257
**Record Appearances:** Tony Mahoney - 765
**Additional Records:**

**Honours:**
Hampshire League 1945-46, 76-77, 77-78. Hampshire Senior Cup 1987-88, 2014-15. Wessex League Cup 1992-93.
Wessex League 2006-07. Southern Division 1 South & West Play-offs 2011-12, Premier Division Play-offs 2012-13.

**10 YEAR RECORD**

| 06-07 | 07-08 | 08-09 | 09-10 | 10-11 | 11-12 | 12-13 | 13-14 | 14-15 | 15-16 |
|---|---|---|---|---|---|---|---|---|---|
| WexP 1 | Sthsw 11 | Sthsw 12 | Sthsw 8 | Sthsw 13 | Sthsw 3 | SthP 5 | Conf S 12 | Conf S 6 | Nat S 9 |

## GOSPORT BOROUGH MATCH RESULTS 2015-16

| Date | Comp | H/A | Opponents | Att: | Result | | Goalscorers | Pos | No. |
|---|---|---|---|---|---|---|---|---|---|
| Aug8 | Nat South | H | Basingstoke Town | 389 | D | 0-0 | | 13 | 1 |
| 11 | Nat South | A | Maidstone United | 349 | **W** | 4-0 | BENNETT 4 ( 12 14 70 87) | 6 | 2 |
| 15 | Nat South | A | St Albans City | 458 | D | 0-0 | | 7 | 3 |
| 18 | Nat South | H | Weston-s-Mare | 412 | D | 2-2 | Bennett 71 Williams 90 | 8 | 4 |
| 22 | Nat South | A | Wealdstone | 812 | **W** | 3-2 | Bennett 43 64 Wort 88 | 4 | 5 |
| 29 | Nat South | H | Whitehawk | 530 | **W** | 3-1 | Poole 35 Harding 64 Wooden 66 | 3 | 6 |
| 31 | Nat South | A | Dartford | 534 | **W** | 1-0 | Woodford 89 | 3 | 7 |
| Sept5 | Nat South | H | Maidstone United | 633 | D | 0-0 | | 3 | 8 |
| 12 | Nat South | A | Sutton United | 787 | L | 0-1 | | 4 | 9 |
| 15 | Nat South | H | Bath City | 599 | **W** | 3-1 | BENNETT 3 (31 70 90) | 4 | 10 |
| 19 | Nat South | H | Margate | 564 | L | 1-2 | Bennett 75 (pen) | 5 | 11 |
| **26** | **FAC2Q** | **H** | **Bideford** | **325** | **W** | **7-0** | **BENNETT 4 (10 22 80 91) Dunford 14 Woodford 45 Ramsey 89** | | 12 |
| Oct3 | Nat South | A | Hayes & Yeading United | 182 | D | 0-0 | | 6 | 13 |
| **10** | **FAC3Q** | **A** | **Whitehawk** | **410** | **D** | **2-2** | **Barker 71 Bennett 73** | | 14 |
| **13** | **FAC3Qr** | **H** | **Whitehawk** | **330** | **L** | **1-2** | **Barker 10** | | 15 |
| 17 | Nat South | H | Ebbsfleet United | 563 | L | 1-2 | Bennett 54 | 9 | 16 |
| 24 | Nat South | A | Truro City | 401 | D | 2-2 | Bennett 17 Vine 46 | 8 | 17 |
| 31 | Nat South | H | Hemel Hempstead Town | 431 | L | 2-6 | Vine 67 Wort 68 | 10 | 18 |
| Nov14 | Nat South | H | Weston-s-Mare | 387 | **W** | 1-0 | Bennett 76 | 9 | 19 |
| 21 | Nat South | A | Oxford City | 349 | **W** | 2-1 | Vine 15 Bennett 87 | 6 | 20 |
| 24 | Nat South | A | St Albans City | 258 | **W** | 3-1 | Barker 34 Dunford 60 Woodford 80 | 4 | 21 |
| **28** | **FAT3Q** | **A** | **Cirencester Town** | **88** | **L** | **1-2** | **Poate** | | 22 |
| Dec5 | Nat South | H | Chelmsford City | 2132 | **W** | 2-1 | Wooden 49 Barker 84 | 4 | 23 |
| 19 | Nat South | A | Margate | 540 | L | 0-1 | | 6 | 24 |
| 26 | Nat South | H | Havant & Waterlooville | 1313 | **W** | 2-1 | Wooden 12 Molyneux 31 (og) | 5 | 25 |
| Jan9 | Nat South | H | Wealdstone | 593 | D | 1-1 | Bennett 32 (pen) | 4 | 26 |
| 18 | Nat South | A | Wealdstone | 506 | D | 1-1 | Wooden 90 | 5 | 27 |
| 23 | Nat South | A | Bishops Stortford | 312 | L | 0-2 | | 6 | 28 |
| Feb2 | Nat South | H | Eastbourne Borough | 357 | **W** | 3-1 | Wort 23 32 Bennett 52 | 4 | 29 |
| 6 | Nat South | H | Maidenhead United | 354 | **W** | 2-1 | Bennett 72 75 | 4 | 30 |
| 10 | Nat South | A | Havant & Waterlooville | 731 | **W** | 3-1 | Cummings 22 (og) Wooden 53 Bennett 60 | | 31 |
| 13 | Nat South | A | Maidstone United | 1882 | L | 1-2 | Taylor 81 (og) | 4 | 32 |
| 20 | Nat South | A | Concord Rangers | 235 | D | 0-0 | | 4 | 33 |
| 23 | Nat South | H | Dartford | 386 | L | 1-3 | Wooden 17 | 4 | 34 |
| 27 | Nat South | H | Oxford City | 323 | D | 0-0 | | 4 | 35 |
| Mar1 | Nat South | A | Bath City | 427 | **W** | 1-0 | Williams 19 | 4 | 36 |
| 5 | Nat South | A | Ebbsfleet United | 932 | L | 0-2 | | 4 | 37 |
| 12 | Nat South | H | Concord Rangers | 338 | L | 2-3 | Wooden 32 Poole 86 | 4 | 38 |
| 19 | Nat South | H | Sutton United | 474 | L | 0-2 | | 5 | 39 |
| 26 | Nat South | A | Whitehawk | 375 | L | 0-3 | | 7 | 40 |
| Apr2 | Nat South | A | Hemel Hempstead Town | 472 | L | 0-1 | | 10 | 41 |
| 9 | Nat South | H | Bishops Stortford | 327 | D | 0-0 | | 10 | 42 |
| 14 | Nat South | H | Basingstoke Town | 298 | **W** | 3-2 | Wooden 20 Bennett 48 Wilde 73 | 8 | 43 |
| 16 | Nat South | A | Chelmsford City | 850 | L | 1-6 | Bennett 45 (pen) | 8 | 44 |
| 23 | Nat South | A | Eastbourne Borough | 592 | L | 0-3 | | 9 | 45 |
| 30 | Nat South | H | Hayes & Yeading United | 503 | L | 2-5 | Wooden 12 Bennett 59 | 9 | 46 |

| GOALSCORERS | Scoring Games | Consec Sco Games | Total |
|---|---|---|---|
| *2014-15 Bennett* | | | *30* |
| Bennett | 17 | 3 | 28 |
| Wooden | 8 | | 9 |
| Barker | 3 | 2 | 4 |
| Wort | 3 | | 4 |
| Vine | 3 | 2 | 3 |
| Woodford | 3 | | 3 |
| Dunford | 2 | | 2 |
| Poole | 2 | | 2 |
| Williams | 2 | | 2 |
| Harding | 1 | | 1 |
| Poate | 1 | | 1 |
| Ramsey | 1 | | 1 |
| Wilde | 1 | | 1 |
| Opponents | | | 2 |

# HAMPTON & RICHMOND BOROUGH

**Chairman:** Steve McPherson

**Secretary:** Nick Hornsey **(T)** 0208 8979 2456 **(E)** secretary@hamptonfc.net

**Commercial Manager:** **(T/E)**

**Programme Editor:** Rob Overfield **(T/E)** 0208 8979 2456

**Ground Address:** Accord Beveree Stadium, Beaver Close, Station Road, Hampton TW12 2BX

**(T)** 0208 8979 2456 **Manager:** Alan Dowson - 15/09/14

## Club Factfile

**Founded:** 1921 **Nickname:** Beavers or Borough

**Previous Names:** Hampton > 1999

**Previous Leagues:** Kingston & District, South West Middlesex, Surrey Senior 1959-64, Spartan 1964-71, Athenian 1971-73, Isthmian 1973-2007, 12-16. Conference 2007-12.

**Club Colours (change):** Red & blue (Sky blue & white)

**Ground Capacity:** 3,000 **Seats:** 300 **Covered:** 800 **Clubhouse:** Yes **Shop:** Yes

**Directions**

From M25; Exit M25 at Junction 10 (M3 Richmond). Exit M3 at Junction 1 and take 4th exit (Kempton Park, Kingston). After approximately 3 miles turn left in to High Street, Hampton. Immediately turn left on to Station Road. The entrance to the ground is 200 yards on the right hand side.

**Previous Grounds:** None

**Record Attendance:** 2,520 v AFC Wimbledon - 11/10/2005

**Record Victory:** 11-1 v Eastbourne United - Isthmian League Division 2 South 1991-92

**Record Defeat:** 0-13 v Hounslow Town - Middlesex Senior Cup 1962-63

**Record Goalscorer:** Peter Allen - 176 (1964-73)

**Record Appearances:** Tim Hollands - 750 (1977-95)

**Additional Records:** Paid £3,000 to Chesham United for Matt Flitter June 2000
Received £40,000 from Queens Park Rangers for Leroy Phillips

**Honours:**

Isthmian League Premier Division 2006-07, 2015-16.
Spartan League x4. London Senior Cup x2. Middlesex Senior Challenge Cup 2011-12.

**10 YEAR RECORD**

| 06-07 | 07-08 | 08-09 | 09-10 | 10-11 | 11-12 | 12-13 | 13-14 | 14-15 | 15-16 |
|---|---|---|---|---|---|---|---|---|---|
| Isth P 1 | Conf S 3 | Conf S 2 | Conf S 14 | Conf S 18 | Conf S 21 | Isth P 13 | Isth P 12 | Isth P 15 | Isth P 1 |

# HAMPTON & RICHMOND BOROUGH MATCH RESULTS 2015-16

| Date | Comp | H/A | Opponents | Att: | Result | | Goalscorers | Pos | No. |
|---|---|---|---|---|---|---|---|---|---|
| Aug8 | IsthP | A | Harrow Borough | 189 | D | 1-1 | Moone 18 | 11 | 1 |
| 11 | IsthP | H | Wingate & Finchley | 331 | L | 1-2 | Sinclair 40 | 14 | 2 |
| 15 | IsthP | H | E Thurrock United | 303 | W | 2-1 | Kabamba 26 Kamara 36 | 12 | 3 |
| 22 | IsthP | A | VCD Athletic | 101 | D | 1-1 | Kabamba 21 | 13 | 4 |
| 26 | IsthP | A | Lewes | 349 | D | 1-1 | Diarra 13 | 15 | 5 |
| 29 | IsthP | H | Met Police | 298 | W | 1-0 | Casey 45 | 8 | 6 |
| 31 | IsthP | A | Staines Town | 402 | W | 2-1 | Jelley 90 Moone 90 | 7 | 7 |
| Sept 5 | IsthP | H | Burgess Hill | 382 | D | 1-1 | Moone 66 | 7 | 8 |
| 8 | IsthP | H | Lewes | 330 | L | 0-4 | | 10 | 9 |
| **12** | **FAC1Q** | **H** | **Dulwich Hamlet** | **404** | **L** | **0-1** | | | 10 |
| 19 | IsthP | A | Billericay Town | 261 | W | 1-0 | Kabamba 25 | 9 | 11 |
| 22 | IsthP | A | Dulwich Hamlet | 555 | D | 3-3 | Moone 14 Sinclair 43 (pen) Pacquette 50 | 10 | 12 |
| 26 | IsthP | H | Merstham | 291 | W | 2-1 | Rose 80 Pacquette 88 | 8 | 13 |
| Oct 3 | IsthP | A | Leiston | 197 | L | 1-3 | Kabamba 34 | 11 | 14 |
| 10 | IsthP | H | Hendon | 475 | W | 5-0 | Diarra 9 47 Sinclair 49 Moone 81 Taylor 90 | 9 | 15 |
| 13 | IsthP | A | Merstham | 164 | W | 6-1 | Kiernan 2 Jelley 15 Kabamba 39 Diarra 52 72 Sinclair 90 | 6 | 16 |
| 17 | IsthP | A | Needham Market | 230 | D | 1-1 | Sinclair 65 | 7 | 17 |
| 20 | IsthP | H | Dulwich Hamlet | 442 | W | 2-1 | Diarra 59 Sinclair 75 (pen) | 5 | 18 |
| 24 | IsthP | H | Harrow Borough | 244 | D | 2-2 | Casey 31 53 | 4 | 19 |
| 27 | IsthP | A | Wingate & Finchley | 129 | W | 3-1 | Kiernan 18 80 Moone 68 | 2 | 20 |
| **31** | **FAT1Q** | **A** | **Lewes** | **325** | **D** | **0-0** | | | 21 |
| **Nov 3** | **FAT1Qr** | **H** | **Lewes** | **171** | **W** | **2-1** | **Moone 70 90** | | 22 |
| 7 | IsthP | A | East Thurrock Utd | 168 | L | 1-2 | Peddie 46 (og) | 4 | 23 |
| **14** | **FAT2Q** | **H** | **AFC Sudbury** | **212** | **W** | **3-1** | **Lowe 34 Jelley 61 Moone 68** | | 24 |
| **28** | **FAT3Q** | **H** | **Maidstone United** | **482** | **L** | **0-1** | | | 25 |
| Dec 5 | IsthP | A | Enfield Town | 292 | W | 3-2 | Jelley 50 (pen) Federico 90 Sinclair 90 | 7 | 26 |
| 12 | IsthP | H | Grays Athletic | 404 | W | 3-1 | Kabamba 59 89 Diarra 79 | 5 | 27 |
| 15 | IsthP | H | Bognor Regis Town | 202 | W | 2-1 | Lowe 21 45 | 2 | 28 |
| 19 | IsthP | A | Metropolitan Police | 228 | W | 3-0 | Kabamba 32 Sinclair 49 (pen) Lowe 84 | 2 | 29 |
| 26 | IsthP | H | Staines Town | 646 | W | 3-2 | Federico 23 Lowe 47 Kiernan 80 | 2 | 30 |
| Jan 9 | IsthP | H | Kingstonian | 808 | W | 3-1 | Kabamba 78 Murphy 83 Moone 89 | 2 | 31 |
| 16 | IsthP | A | Canvey Island | 298 | W | 4-0 | Lowe 17 21 Hutchinson 63 Gough 78 (og) | 1 | 32 |
| 23 | IsthP | H | Tonbridge Angels | 691 | D | 2-2 | Kabamba 22 Federico 53 | 1 | 33 |
| 30 | IsthP | A | Bognor Regis Town | 620 | L | 0-1 | | 3 | 34 |
| Feb 2 | IsthP | H | Farnborough | 301 | W | 3-1 | Kabamba 17 (pen) 88 Keirnan 76 | 2 | 35 |
| 6 | IsthP | H | Leiston | 342 | W | 4-3 | Diarra 18 Lowe 29 44 Kabamba 81 | 1 | 36 |
| 10 | IsthP | A | Leatherhead | 367 | D | 2-2 | Kabamba 68 Diarra 90 | 1 | 37 |
| 13 | IsthP | A | Hendon | 218 | D | 1-1 | Lowe 48 | 1 | 38 |
| 20 | IsthP | H | Needham Market | 436 | W | 5-0 | Kabamba 2 Diarra 9 Murphy 25 Beere 36 Lowe 57 | 1 | 39 |
| 23 | IsthP | H | VCD Athletic | 285 | W | 4-0 | Federico 31 43 Beere 38 Kiernan 48 | 2 | 40 |
| 27 | IsthP | A | Tonbridge Angels | 559 | L | 0-1 | | 3 | 41 |
| Mar 5 | IsthP | H | Canvey Island | 414 | W | 5-0 | Casey 25 KABAMBA 3 ( 35 39 61) Beere 45 | 2 | 42 |
| 8 | IsthP | A | Brentwood Town | 123 | W | 3-0 | Hutchinson 4 Lowe 17 68 | 1 | 43 |
| 12 | IsthP | A | Burgess Hill Town | 412 | W | 2-1 | Jelley 20 (pen) Kiernan 52 | 1 | 44 |
| 19 | IsthP | H | Billericay Town | 505 | W | 2-1 | Kiernan 47 Diarra 78 | 1 | 45 |
| 26 | IsthP | A | Kingstonian | 724 | L | 1-4 | Diarra 22 | 1 | 46 |
| 28 | IsthP | H | Leatherhead | 707 | W | 2-0 | Kabamba 66 Lowe 86 | 1 | 47 |
| Apr 2 | IsthP | H | Brentwood Town | 727 | W | 5-1 | Soloman 23 Lowe 28 Kiernan 45 Beere 78 Moone 85 | 1 | 48 |
| 9 | IsthP | A | Farnborough | 348 | W | 3-0 | Hutchinson 14 Kiernan 38 Diarra 47 | 1 | 49 |
| 16 | IsthP | A | Grays Athletic | 255 | W | 3-0 | Diarra 27 Kiernan 50 51 | 1 | 50 |
| 23 | IsthP | H | Enfield Town | 2376 | D | 0-0 | | 1 | 51 |

| GOALSCORERS | Scoring Games | Consec Sco Games | Total | | Scoring Games | Consec Sco Games | Total |
|---|---|---|---|---|---|---|---|
| *2014-15 Moone* | | | *19* | Casey | 4 | | 4 |
| Kabamba | 14 | 2 | 19 | Hutchinson | 3 | | 3 |
| Lowe | 11 | 3 | 15 | Murphy | 2 | | 2 |
| Diarra | 13 | 3 | 14 | Pacquette | 2 | | 2 |
| Kiernan | 10 | | 12 | Kamara | 1 | | 1 |
| Moone | 10 | 2 | 11 | Rose | 1 | | 1 |
| Sinclair | 8 | 4 | 8 | Soloman | 1 | | 1 |
| Federico | 4 | | 5 | Taylor | 1 | | 1 |
| Jelley | 5 | | 5 | Opponents | | | 2 |
| Beere | 4 | | 4 | | | | |

# HEMEL HEMPSTEAD TOWN

**Chairman:** David Boggins
**Secretary:** Dean Chance **(T)** 01442 251 251 **(E)** dean.chance@ntlworld.com
**Commercial Manager:** (T/E)
**Programme Editor:** (T/E)
**Ground Address:** Vauxhall Road, Adeyfield Road, Hemel Hempstead HP2 4HW
**(T)** 01442 251 251 **Manager:** Dean Brennan

## Club Factfile

**Founded:** 1885 **Nickname:** The Tudors
**Previous Names:** Hemel Hempstead FC
**Previous Leagues:** Spartan 1922-52, Delphian 1952-63, Athenian 1963-77, Isthmian 1977-2004

**Club Colours (change):** All red (All green)

**Ground Capacity:** 3,152 **Seats:** 300 **Covered:** 900 **Clubhouse:** Yes **Shop:** Yes

**Directions**
Leave M1 at Junction 8 - follow dual carriageway over two roundabouts.
Get into outside lane and after 100 yards turn right.
Follow road to mini-roundabout turn left, next large roundabout take third exit into ground car park.

**Previous Grounds:** Crabtree Lane

**Record Attendance:** 3,500 v Tooting & Mitcham - Amateur Cup 1962 (Crabtree Lane)
**Record Victory:** Not known - If you know please email tw.publications@btinternet.com
**Record Defeat:** Not known - If you know please email tw.publications@btinternet.com
**Record Goalscorer:** Dai Price
**Record Appearances:** John Wallace - 1012
**Additional Records:**

**Honours:**
Isthmian League Division 3 1998-99. Herts Senior Cup x9 Most recently 2014-15. Herts Charity Cup x6.
Southern Premier Division 2013-14.

### 10 YEAR RECORD

| 06-07 | 07-08 | 08-09 | 09-10 | 10-11 | 11-12 | 12-13 | 13-14 | 14-15 | 15-16 |
|---|---|---|---|---|---|---|---|---|---|
| SthP 5 | SthP 7 | SthP 5 | SthP 20 | SthP 15 | SthP 19 | SthP 4 | SthP 1 | Conf S 9 | Nat S 6 |

# HEMEL HEMPSTEAD TOWN MATCH RESULTS 2015-16

| Date | Comp | H/A | Opponents | Att: | Result | | Goalscorers | Pos | No. |
|---|---|---|---|---|---|---|---|---|---|
| Aug 8 | Nat South | H | Dartford | 653 | W | 1-0 | Hawkins 31 | 8 | 1 |
| 10 | Nat South | A | Chelmsford City | 723 | W | 1-0 | Slabber 15 | 2 | 2 |
| 15 | Nat South | A | Weston-s-Mare | 368 | W | 4-2 | Potton 3 Hawkins 5 Spring 62 71 | 2 | 3 |
| 18 | Nat South | H | Maidstone United | 637 | L | 0-1 | | | 4 |
| 22 | Nat South | A | Concord Rangers | 264 | W | 3-0 | Slabber 9 60 Herd 90 | 2 | 5 |
| 29 | Nat South | H | Maidenhead United | 416 | L | 0-1 | | 4 | 6 |
| 31 | Nat South | A | St Albans City | 860 | D | 2-2 | Hawkins 45 (pen) Lowe 88 | 6 | 7 |
| Sept 5 | Nat South | H | Basingstoke Town | 414 | D | 2-2 | Harriott 8 Slabber 86 | 5 | 8 |
| 12 | Nat South | A | Bath City | 685 | D | 1-1 | Hawkins 15 | 7 | 9 |
| 15 | Nat South | H | Hayes & Yeading | 395 | W | 4-0 | Forbes 39 Smith 64 Spring 72 Harriott 78 | 6 | 10 |
| 19 | Nat South | H | Bishops Stortford | 561 | L | 1-2 | Sharif 90 | 7 | 11 |
| **26** | **FAC2Q** | **A** | **Bury Town** | **408** | **W** | **3-0** | **Hawkins 31(pen) Oli 5 Harriott 71** | | 12 |
| Oct 3 | Nat South | A | Sutton United | 949 | D | 2-2 | Potton 71 Herd 76 (pen) | 8 | 13 |
| **10** | **FAC3Q** | **H** | **Sutton United** | **707** | **D** | **1-1** | **Potton 26** | | 14 |
| **12** | **FAC3Qr** | **A** | **Sutton United** | **418** | **L** | **1-2** | **Herd 90** | | 15 |
| 17 | Nat South | A | Dartford | 844 | D | 2-2 | Gnahore 17 Husin 41 | 8 | 16 |
| 24 | Nat South | H | Concord Rangers | 375 | L | 1-2 | Herd 87 | 9 | 17 |
| 31 | Nat South | A | Gosport Borough | 431 | W | 6-2 | Spring 31 Husin 33 90 SLABBER 3 (36 38 73) | 8 | 18 |
| Nov 21 | Nat South | H | Margate | 453 | L | 1-2 | Hawkins 22 (pen) | 11 | 19 |
| **28** | **FAT3Q** | **H** | **Weymouth** | **349** | **W** | **1-0** | **Slabber 18** | | 20 |
| Dec 5 | Nat South | H | Ebbsfleet United | 571 | L | 1-2 | Richens 82 | 13 | 21 |
| **12** | **FAT1** | **A** | **Eastbourne Borough** | **317** | **L** | **4-7** | **Hawkins 45 53 Banton 62 Slabber 73** | | 22 |
| 19 | Nat South | A | Oxford City | 310 | W | 2-0 | Montgomery 54 Hawkins 81 | 12 | 23 |
| 26 | Nat South | H | Wealdstone | 751 | D | 2-2 | Hawkins 73 Slabber 88 | 11 | 24 |
| 28 | Nat South | A | Maidenhead United | 492 | W | 3-2 | Montgomery 8 Hawkins 34 Slabber 43 | 10 | 25 |
| Jan 9 | Nat South | H | Havant & Waterlooville | 348 | W | 2-0 | John 35 Obi 90 | 9 | 26 |
| 16 | Nat South | A | Basingstoke Town | 547 | L | 0-2 | | 9 | 27 |
| 23 | Nat South | H | Hayes & Yeading | 171 | D | 1-1 | Slabber 51 | 8 | 28 |
| 31 | Nat South | A | Weston s Mare | 408 | D | 5-5 | Potton 6 27 Thomas 11 Montgomery 46 79 | 8 | 29 |
| Feb 2 | Nat South | A | Bishops Stortford | 303 | L | 0-1 | | 9 | 30 |
| 13 | Nat South | A | Truro City | 626 | L | 2-4 | Slabber 23 Potton 85 | 10 | 31 |
| 20 | Nat South | H | Sutton United | 373 | D | 2-2 | Richens 89 Butler 90 | 10 | 32 |
| 27 | Nat South | H | Bath City | 358 | D | 1-1 | Montgomery 6 | 12 | 33 |
| Mar 5 | Nat South | A | Havant & Waterlooville | 573 | W | 2-1 | Potten 15 Hickford 90 | 12 | 34 |
| 8 | Nat South | H | Eastbourne Borough | 263 | W | 1-0 | Shields 45 | 12 | 35 |
| 12 | Nat South | H | Truro City | 563 | W | 2-1 | Montgomery 13 76 | 8 | 36 |
| 15 | Nat South | H | Chelmsford City | 423 | D | 1-1 | Potton 90 | 7 | 37 |
| 19 | Nat South | A | Ebbsfleet United | 1021 | L | 0-6 | | 8 | 38 |
| 22 | Nat South | A | Whitehawk | 209 | W | 1-0 | Todorov 43 | 6 | 39 |
| 26 | Nat South | A | Maidstone United | 2481 | L | 1-2 | Wellard 6 | 8 | 40 |
| Apr 2 | Nat South | H | Gosport Borough | 472 | W | 1-0 | Herd 42 | 7 | 41 |
| 4 | Nat South | A | Wealdstone | 753 | D | 0-0 | | | 42 |
| 9 | Nat South | A | Eastbourne Borough | 578 | W | 3-2 | Ferrier 56 Sekajja 57 Herd 90 | 5 | 43 |
| 12 | Nat South | H | St Albans City | 972 | D | 2-2 | Sekajja 70 Bailey-Dennis 90 | 5 | 44 |
| 16 | Nat South | H | Oxford City | 546 | W | 3-1 | Ferrier 44 Montgomery 45 Richens 56 | 4 | 45 |
| 23 | Nat South | A | Margate | 823 | L | 3-4 | Montgomery 38 81 Connolly 68 | 5 | 46 |
| 30 | Nat South | H | Whitehawk | 1138 | L | 0-3 | | 6 | 47 |

| GOALSCORERS | Scoring Games | Consec Sco Games | Total |
|---|---|---|---|
| ***2014-15 Parkes*** | | | ***23*** |
| Slabber | 10 | 2 | 13 |
| Hawkins | 10 | 4 | 11 |
| Montgomery | 7 | 2 | 10 |
| Potton | 7 | 2 | 8 |
| Herd | 6 | | 6 |
| Spring | 3 | | 4 |
| Harriott | 3 | | 3 |
| Husin | 3 | | 3 |
| Richens | 3 | | 3 |
| Ferrier | 2 | | 2 |
| Sekajja | 2 | | 2 |
| Bailey-Dennis | 1 | | 1 |
| Banton | 1 | | 1 |
| Butler | 1 | | 1 |
| Connolly | 1 | | 1 |

| | Scoring Games | Consec Sco Games | Total |
|---|---|---|---|
| Forbes | 1 | | 1 |
| Gnahore | 1 | | 1 |
| Hickford | 1 | | 1 |
| John | 1 | | 1 |
| Lowe | 1 | | 1 |
| Obi | 1 | | 1 |
| Oli | 1 | | 1 |
| Shariff | 1 | | 1 |
| Shields | 1 | | 1 |
| Smith | 1 | | 1 |
| Thomas | 1 | | 1 |
| Todorov | 1 | | 1 |
| Wellard | 1 | | 1 |

# HUNGERFORD TOWN

**Chairman:** Steve Skipworth
**Secretary:** Mike Hall (T) 07714 953 784 (E)
**Commercial Manager:** (T/E)
**Programme Editor:** Mike Hall (T/E) mike.hall0@talk21.com
**Ground Address:** Bulpitt Lane, Hungerford RG17 0AY
**(T)** 01488 682 939 **Manager:** Bobby Wilkinson

## Club Factfile

**Founded:** 1886 **Nickname:** The Crusaders
**Previous Names:** None
**Previous Leagues:** Newbury & District, Swindon & District, Hellenic 1958-78, 2003-09, Isthmian 1978-2003. Southern 2009-16.

**Club Colours (change):** White/white/white (All red)

**Ground Capacity:** 2,500 **Seats:** 170 **Covered:** 400 **Clubhouse:** Yes **Shop:** Yes

**Directions**
From M4 Junction, take A338 to Hungerford. First Roundabout turn right on to A4, next roundabout first left, 100 yards roundabout 1st left up High Street, go over three roundabouts, at fourth roundabout turn first left signposted 'Football Club'. Take second left into Bulpitt Lane, go over crossroads, ground on left.

**Previous Grounds:** None

**Record Attendance:** 1,684 v Sudbury Town - FA Vase Semi-final 1988-89
**Record Victory:** Not known - If you know please email tw.publications@btinternet.com
**Record Defeat:** Not known - If you know please email tw.publications@btinternet.com
**Record Goalscorer:** Ian Farr - 268
**Record Appearances:** Dean Bailey and Tim North - 400+
**Additional Records:** Paid £4,000 to Yeovil Town for Joe Scott
Received £3,800 from Barnstaple Town for Joe Scott
**Honours:**
Hellenic Division 1 1970-71, Premier Division 2008-09, League Cup 2006-07, 07-08. Southern Premier Play-offs 2015-16.
Berks & Bucks Senior Cup 1981-82. Basingstoke Senior Cup 2012-13.
Isthmian representatives in Anglo Italian Cup 1981.

### 10 YEAR RECORD

| 06-07 | 07-08 | 08-09 | 09-10 | 10-11 | 11-12 | 12-13 | 13-14 | 14-15 | 15-16 |
|---|---|---|---|---|---|---|---|---|---|
| Hel P 3 | Hel P 3 | Hel P 1 | Sthsw 17 | Sthsw 7 | Sthsw 5 | Sthsw 2 | SthP 6 | SthP 4 | SthP 5 |

# HUNGERFORD TOWN MATCH RESULTS 2015-16

| Date | Comp | H/A | Opponents | Att: | Result | | Goalscorers | Pos | No. |
|---|---|---|---|---|---|---|---|---|---|
| Aug 8 | SPL | A | Paulton Rovers | 186 | D | 0-0 | | 13 | 1 |
| 10 | SPL | H | Poole Town | 246 | D | 0-0 | | 10 | 2 |
| 15 | SPL | H | Dorchester Town | 193 | L | 2-3 | Jarvis 29 42 | 18 | 3 |
| 17 | SPL | A | Redditch United | 205 | D | 2-2 | Bossman 9 34 | 15 | 4 |
| 22 | SPL | H | Biggleswade Town | 129 | W | 2-0 | Jarvis 23 Rusby 54 | 14 | 5 |
| 29 | SPL | A | Bedworth Town | 165 | W | 2-0 | Tyler 8 Day 51 | 10 | 6 |
| 31 | SPL | H | Chippenham Town | 231 | W | 1-0 | O'Brien 81 | 7 | 7 |
| Sept 5 | SPL | A | Bideford | 178 | W | 2-1 | Brown 43 Milton 88 (og) | 4 | 8 |
| **12** | **FAC1Q** | **H** | **Bradford Town** | **132** | **D** | **1-1** | **Draycott 73** | | 9 |
| **16** | **FAC1Qr** | **A** | **Bradford Town** | **131** | **L** | **0-2** | | | 10 |
| 19 | SPL | H | St Neots Town | 116 | D | 3-3 | Tyler 14 Jarvis 36 Goodger 84 | 6 | 11 |
| 22 | SPL | A | Chesham United | 223 | D | 2-2 | Jones 2 Stow 86 | 7 | 12 |
| 26 | SPL | A | Weymouth | 484 | L | 1-2 | Cooper 47 Kelly 54 | 8 | 13 |
| 28 | SPL | H | Hitchin Town | 127 | D | 1-1 | Clark 54 | 9 | 14 |
| Oct 3 | SPL | A | Kettering Town | 588 | L | 1-2 | Draycott 90 (pen) | 9 | 15 |
| 10 | SPL | H | Bedworth United | 128 | W | 5-1 | JARVIS 3 (27 38 57) Preen 39 Collins 47 | 7 | 16 |
| 17 | SPL | A | Cambridge City | 190 | L | 1-3 | Stow 75 | 9 | 17 |
| 19 | SPL | H | Chesham United | 123 | W | 3-1 | Brown 8 Stewart 32 (og) Jarvis 52 (pen)_ | 6 | 18 |
| 24 | SPL | H | Histon | 98 | W | 1-0 | Tyler 90 | 6 | 19 |
| 27 | SPL | A | Merthyr Town | 373 | L | 1-4 | Brown 68 | 6 | 20 |
| **31** | **FAT1Q** | **H** | **Banbury United** | **138** | **D** | **0-0** | | | 21 |
| **Nov 3** | **FAT1Qr** | **A** | **Banbury United** | **170** | **W** | **3-0** | **Day 36 Draycott 41 Jones 89** | | 22 |
| 7 | SPL | A | Frome Town | 224 | W | 2-0 | Brown 7 10 | 5 | 23 |
| **14** | **FAT2Q** | **A** | **St Neots Town** | **207** | **W** | **2-1** | **Preen 55 Brown 77** | | 24 |
| 16 | SPL | H | Redditch United | 126 | D | 0-0 | | 5 | 25 |
| 21 | SPL | A | Dorchester Town | 333 | W | 1-0 | Day 39 | 5 | 26 |
| 23 | SPL | H | Kings Lynn Town | 112 | W | 2-1 | Brown 15 Jarvis 22 | 4 | 27 |
| **28** | **FAT3Q** | **H** | **Thamesmead Town** | **120** | **W** | **3-0** | **Brown 12 Draycott 84 O'Brien 90** | | 28 |
| Dec 5 | SPL | A | Cirencester Town | 101 | W | 3-2 | Jarvis 13 84 Brown 79 | 3 | 29 |
| 8 | SPL | A | Poole Town | 369 | D | 0-0 | | 3 | 30 |
| **12** | **FAT1** | **A** | **Corinthian-Casuals** | **162** | **W** | **2-1** | **Jarvis 43 Draycott 71** | | 31 |
| 26 | SPL | A | Chippenham Town | 449 | D | 1-1 | Jones 75 | 3 | 32 |
| Jan 9 | SPL | A | Dunstable Town | 161 | L | 0-1 | | 6 | 33 |
| **16** | **FAT2** | **A** | **Chester** | **1275** | **L** | **0-4** | | | 34 |
| 23 | SPL | A | Biggleswade Town | 145 | W | 4-1 | Brown 26 39 Tyler 55 80 | 7 | 35 |
| 30 | SPL | H | Kettering Town | 249 | W | 2-1 | Jarvis 36 Brown 69 (pen) | 6 | 36 |
| Feb 1 | SPL | H | Stratford Town | 120 | D | 0-0 | | 6 | 37 |
| 6 | SPL | A | St Neots Town | 234 | W | 2-0 | Clark 10 Jarvis 29 | | 38 |
| 15 | SPL | H | Leamington | 137 | L | 1-2 | Brown 64 | 5 | 39 |
| 20 | SPL | A | Hitchin Town | 431 | L | 1-2 | Preen 50 | 6 | 40 |
| 23 | SPL | H | Cambridge City | 100 | W | 2-0 | Clark 12 Draycott 39 | 6 | 41 |
| 25 | SPL | H | Bideford | 114 | W | 2-0 | Jones 73 Jarvis 75 | 5 | 42 |
| Mar 7 | SPL | H | Paulton Rovers | 113 | W | 3-1 | O'Brien 1 Jarvis 7 31 | 5 | 43 |
| 12 | SPL | H | Cirencester Town | 111 | L | 1-2 | Jarvis 49 | 6 | 44 |
| 14 | SPL | H | Slough Town | 147 | W | 1-0 | Rusby 13 | 5 | 45 |
| 19 | SPL | A | Stratford Town | 179 | W | 2-0 | Brown 43 Rusby 70 | 4 | 46 |
| 21 | SPL | H | Weymouth | 208 | L | 0-1 | | 4 | 47 |
| 26 | SPL | H | Dunstable Town | 125 | L | 2-3 | Clark 43 Draycott 54 (pen) | 6 | 48 |
| 28 | SPL | A | Slough Town | 319 | W | 2-0 | Preen 39 Draycott 68 | 5 | 49 |
| Apr 2 | SPL | H | Merthyr Town | 191 | W | 1-0 | Herring 86 | 4 | 50 |
| 12 | SPL | A | Kings Lynn | 287 | W | 1-0 | Herring 90 | 5 | 51 |
| 16 | SPL | H | Frome Town | 186 | W | 4-0 | Horgan 34 65 Jones 51 Tyler 62 | 4 | 52 |
| 19 | SPL | A | Histon | 154 | W | 3-0 | Brown 57 61 Goodger 75 | 2 | 53 |
| 23 | SF | A | Leamington | 721 | D | 0-0 | | 5 | 54 |
| **27** | **PO SF** | **A** | **Hitchin Town** | **1305** | **W** | **3-2** | **Rees 64 Clark75 Brown 84** | | 55 |
| **May 2** | **PO Final** | **H** | **Leamington** | **1363** | **W** | **2-1** | **Brown 64 Jones 85** | | 56 |

| GOALSCORERS | Scoring Games | Consec Sco Games | Total |
|---|---|---|---|
| *2014-15 Draycott* | | | *24* |
| Jarvis | 13 | 3 | 18 |
| Brown | 14 | 3 | 17 |
| Draycott | 8 | 2 | 8 |
| Tyler | 5 | | 6 |
| Clark | 5 | | 5 |
| Jones | 5 | | 5 |
| Preen | 4 | | 4 |
| Day | 3 | | 3 |
| O'Brien | 3 | | 3 |
| Rusby | 3 | 2 | 3 |
| Bosman | 1 | | 2 |
| Goodger | 2 | | 2 |
| Herring | 2 | 2 | 2 |
| Horgan | 2 | | 2 |
| Stow | 2 | | 2 |
| Collins | 1 | | 1 |
| Cooper | 1 | | 1 |
| Rees | 1 | | 1 |
| Opponents | | | 2 |

# MAIDENHEAD UNITED

**Chairman:** Peter Griffin
**Secretary:** Ken Chandler **(T)** 07863 183 872 **(E)** kenneth.chandler@btinternet.com
**Commercial Manager:** n/a **(T/E)**
**Programme Editor:** **(T/E)**
**Ground Address:** York Road, Maidenhead, Berkshire SL6 1SF
**(T)** 01628 636 314 **Manager:** Alan Devonshire

## Club Factfile

**Founded:** 1870 **Nickname:** Magpies
**Previous Names:** Maidenhead F.C and Maidenhead Norfolkians merged to form today's club
**Previous Leagues:** Southern 1894-1902, 2006-07, West Berkshire 1902-04, Gr. West Suburban 1904-22, Spartan 1922-39, Gr. West Comb. 1939-45, Corinthian 1945-63, Athenian 1963-73, Isthmian 1973-2004, Conf. 2004-06

**Club Colours (change):** Black & white stripes/black/white (Yellow/blue/yellow)

**Ground Capacity:** 4,500 **Seats:** 400 **Covered:** 2,000 **Clubhouse:** Yes **Shop:** Yes

**Directions**
The Ground is in the town centre.
200 yards from the station and two minutes walk from the High Street.
Access from M4 Junctions 7 or 8/9.

**Previous Grounds:** Kidwells Park (Norfolkians)

**Record Attendance:** 7,920 v Southall - FA Amateur Cup Quarter final 07/03/1936
**Record Victory:** 14-1 v Buckingham Town - FA Amateur Cup 06/09/1952
**Record Defeat:** 0-14 v Chesham United (A) - Spartan League 31/03/1923
**Record Goalscorer:** George Copas - 270 (1924-35)
**Record Appearances:** Bert Randall - 532 (1950-64)
**Additional Records:** Received £5,000 from Norwich City for Alan Cordice 1979

**Honours:**
Corinthian League 1957-58, 60-61, 61-62. Berks & Bucks Senior Cup1894-95, 1895-96, 1911-12, 1927-28, 1929-30, 1930-31, 1931-32, 1938-39, 1945-46, 1955-56, 1956-57, 1960-61, 1962-63, 1965-66, 1969-70, 1997-98, 1998-99, 2001-02, 2002-03, 2009-10, 2014-15.
Southern League Premier Division Play-offs 2006-07.

### 10 YEAR RECORD

| 06-07 | 07-08 | 08-09 | 09-10 | 10-11 | 11-12 | 12-13 | 13-14 | 14-15 | 15-16 |
|---|---|---|---|---|---|---|---|---|---|
| SthP 4 | Conf S 17 | Conf S 6 | Conf S 16 | Conf S 19 | Conf S 20 | Conf S 19 | Conf S 18 | Conf S 18 | Nat S 7 |

# MAIDENHEAD UNITED MATCH RESULTS 2015-16

| Date | Comp | H/A | Opponents | Att: | Result | | Goalscorers | Pos | No. |
|---|---|---|---|---|---|---|---|---|---|
| Aug 8 | Nat South | A | Eastbourne Borough | 551 | W | 2-1 | Wright 57 (pen) Reid 86 | 6 | 1 |
| 11 | Nat South | H | Bishops Stortford | 354 | W | 4-1 | Wright 9 (pen) 67 Reid 45 Barrett 81 | 2 | 2 |
| 15 | Nat South | H | Gosport Borough | 458 | D | 0-0 | | 4 | 3 |
| 18 | Nat South | A | Bath City | 648 | L | 1-2 | Wright 23 | 6 | 4 |
| 22 | Nat South | H | Sutton United | 446 | D | 1-1 | Tarpey 10 | 7 | 5 |
| 29 | Nat South | A | Hemel Hempstead Town | 418 | W | 1-0 | Tarpey 44 | 7 | 6 |
| 31 | Nat South | H | Hayes & Yeading | 532 | W | 2-1 | Wright 11 18 | 5 | 7 |
| Sept 5 | Nat South | A | Ebbsfleet United | 1016 | L | 1-3 | Tarpey 58 | 7 | 8 |
| 12 | Nat South | A | Whitehawk | 194 | L | 2-3 | Wright 28 Forbes 47 | 9 | 9 |
| 15 | Nat South | H | Maidstone United | 403 | L | 0-2 | | | 10 |
| 19 | Nat South | H | Chelmsford City | 442 | W | 1-0 | Wright 80 | 9 | 11 |
| **26** | **FAC2Q** | **A** | **Winchester City** | **245** | **D** | **1-1** | **James 89** | | 12 |
| **29** | **FAC 2Qr** | **H** | **Winchester City** | **256** | **W** | **4-2** | **Tarpey 32 43 Reid 59 60** | | 13 |
| Oct 3 | Nat South | A | Bishops Stortford | 332 | W | 2-0 | Inman 36 Reid 66 | 7 | 14 |
| **10** | **FAC3Q** | **A** | **Blackfield & Langley** | **189** | **W** | **1-0** | **Wright 56** | | 15 |
| 17 | Nat South | H | Weston-s-Mare | 432 | W | 2-0 | Wright 10 58 | 5 | 16 |
| **24** | **FAC4Q** | **H** | **Woking** | **867** | **W** | **3-0** | **Forbes 5 Pritchard 55 Tarpey 60** | | 17 |
| 31 | Nat South | H | Basingstoke Town | 456 | W | 4-3 | TARPEY 3 (20 55 83) Wright 35 | 5 | 18 |
| **Nov 8** | **FAC1** | **A** | **Port Vale** | **3977** | **D** | **1-1** | **Mulley 90** | | 19 |
| 14 | Nat South | A | Havant & Waterlooville | 550 | L | 1-3 | Reid 12 | 5 | 20 |
| **19** | **FAC1r** | **H** | **Port Vale** | **2212** | **L** | **1-3** | **Massey 15** | | 21 |
| 24 | Nat South | A | Concord Rangers | 226 | L | 0-2 | | 8 | 22 |
| **28** | **FAT3Q** | **H** | **Bideford** | **262** | **W** | **4-0** | **Pritchard 32 46 Smith 85 Wright 90** | | 23 |
| Dec 1 | Nat South | A | Maidstone United | 1731 | W | 2-1 | Wright 25 (pen) Reid 45 | 6 | 24 |
| **12** | **FAT1** | **A** | **East Thurrock United** | **156** | **W** | **4-1** | **Nisbet 31Tarpey 57 Reid 72 83** | | 25 |
| 15 | Nat South | A | St Albans City | 613 | L | 2-3 | Inman 19 Mulley 44 | 6 | 26 |
| 19 | Nat South | A | Sutton United | 790 | D | 2-2 | Mulley 63 Tarpey 66 | 9 | 27 |
| 26 | Nat South | A | Oxford City | 283 | D | 0-0 | | 9 | 28 |
| 28 | Nat South | H | Hemel Hempstead Town | 492 | L | 2-3 | Barrett 75 Tarpey 78 | 9 | 29 |
| Jan 9 | Nat South | A | Margate | 618 | L | 2-3 | Barrett 47 50 | 10 | 30 |
| **16** | **FAT2** | **A** | **Woking** | **1006** | **L** | **1-6** | **Tarpey 30** | | 31 |
| 23 | Nat South | A | Truro City | 390 | D | 4-4 | TARPEY 4 (42 54 81 90) | 11 | 32 |
| 30 | Nat South | H | Havant & Waterlooville | 707 | D | 2-2 | Wright 9 Tarpey 23 | 11 | 33 |
| Feb 6 | Nat South | A | Gosport Borough | 354 | L | 1-2 | Pritchard 38 | 13 | 34 |
| 13 | Nat South | H | Wealdstone | 524 | D | 1-1 | Smith 57 | 13 | 35 |
| 20 | Nat South | A | Basingstoke Town | 482 | L | 1-2 | Pritchard 48 | 15 | 36 |
| 23 | Nat South | H | Oxford City | 305 | W | 2-1 | Pritchard 51 Reid 70 | 11 | 37 |
| 27 | Nat South | H | Eastbourne Borough | 424 | W | 2-0 | Pritchard 42 Barrett 90 | 10 | 38 |
| Mar 5 | Nat South | H | Margate | 438 | W | 3-1 | Reid 3 Mulley 48 Tarpey 63 | 9 | 39 |
| 8 | Nat South | H | Ebbsfleet United | 448 | D | 0-0 | | 8 | 40 |
| 12 | Nat South | A | Chelmsford City | 1140 | L | 1-4 | Comley 59 | 10 | 41 |
| 15 | Nat South | H | Dartford | 313 | W | 2-1 | Upward 4 Wright 41 | 7 | 42 |
| 19 | Nat South | H | Truro City | 517 | D | 0-0 | | 7 | 43 |
| 25 | Nat South | H | Bath City | 899 | W | 3-1 | Mulley 16 65 Pritchard 57 | 7 | 44 |
| 28 | Nat South | A | Hayes & Yeading | 520 | W | 5-2 | Nisbet 5 Tarpey 29 Upward 33 Reid 90 Mulley 90 | 5 | 45 |
| Apr 2 | Nat South | A | Dartford | 877 | L | 0-2 | | 6 | 46 |
| 5 | Nat South | H | Whitehawk | 441 | W | 3-0 | REID 3 ( 62 73 79) | 5 | 47 |
| 9th | Nat South | H | St Albans City | 567 | L | 0-1 | | 6 | 48 |
| 16 | Nat South | A | Wealdstone | 800 | D | 0-0 | | 6 | 49 |
| 23 | Nat South | A | Weston-s-Mare | 491 | L | 0-2 | | 8 | 50 |
| 30 | Nat South | H | Concord Rangers | 524 | D | 2-2 | Tarpey 15 Inman 45 | 7 | 51 |

| GOALSCORERS | Scoring Games | Consec Sco Games | Total |
|---|---|---|---|
| *2014-15 Tarpey* | | | *22* |
| Tarpey | 16 | 2 | 21 |
| Wright | 15 | 2 | 16 |
| Reid | 12 | 2 | 15 |
| Pritchard | 8 | | 8 |
| Mulley | 7 | | 7 |
| Barrett | 4 | | 5 |
| Inman | 3 | | 3 |
| Forbbes | 2 | | 2 |
| Nisbet | 2 | | 2 |
| Smith | 2 | | 2 |
| Upward | 2 | | 2 |
| Comley | 1 | | 1 |
| James | 1 | | 1 |
| Massey | 1 | | 1 |

# MARGATE

**Chairman:** John Webb
**Secretary:** Ken Tomlinson (T) 01843 221 769 (E) ken.tomlinson@margate-fc.com
**Commercial Manager:** Ryan Day (T/E) 01843 221 769
**Programme Editor:** Ryan Day (T/E) 07806 755 227
**Ground Address:** Hartsdown Park, Hartsdown Road, Margate, Kent CT9 5QZ
(T) 01843 221 769 **Manager:** Nikki Bull

## Club Factfile

**Founded:** 1896 **Nickname:** The Gate
**Previous Names:** None
**Previous Leagues:** Kent 1911-23, 24-28, 29-33, 37-38, 46-59. Southern 1933-37, 59-2001, Conference 2001-04

**Club Colours (change):** All blue (Yellow/yellow/black)

**Ground Capacity:** 3,000 **Seats:** 350 **Covered:** 1,750 **Clubhouse:** Yes **Shop:** Yes

**Directions**
From M25 continue onto M26 merge onto M20, at junction 7, exit onto Sittingbourne Rd/A249 toward Sheerness/Canterbury/Ramsgate, continue to follow A249, take the ramp onto M2, continue onto A299 (signs for Margate/Ramsgate) keep right at the fork, at the roundabout, take the 2nd exit onto Canterbury Rd (Birchington)/A28 continue to follow A28, turn right onto The Square/A28 continue to follow A28, turn right onto George V Ave/B2052, turn right onto Hartsdown Rd/B2052, ground will be on the left.

**Previous Grounds:** At least six before moving to Hartsdown in 1939.

**Record Attendance:** 14,500 v Tottenham Hotspur - FA Cup 3rd Round 1973
**Record Victory:** 8-0 v Tunbridge Wells (H) - 1966-67, v Chatham Town (H) - 1987-88 and v Stalybridge Celtic (H) - 2001-02
**Record Defeat:** 0-11 v AFC Bournemouth (A) - FA Cup 20/11/1971
**Record Goalscorer:** Jack Palethorpe scored 66 during 1929-30
**Record Appearances:** Bob Harrop
**Additional Records:** Paid £5,000 to Dover Athletic for Steve Cuggy

**Honours:**
Southern League Premier Division 1935-36, 2000-01, Division 1 1962-63, Division 1 South 1977-78.
Isthmian Premier Play-off 2014-15.

### 10 YEAR RECORD

| 06-07 | 07-08 | 08-09 | 09-10 | 10-11 | 11-12 | 12-13 | 13-14 | 14-15 | 15-16 |
|---|---|---|---|---|---|---|---|---|---|
| Isth P 6 | Isth P 9 | Isth P 19 | Isth P 19 | Isth P 16 | Isth P 15 | Isth P 9 | Isth P 11 | Isth P 2 | Nat S 19 |

# MARGATE MATCH RESULTS 2015-16

| Date | Comp | H/A | Opponents | Att: | Result | | Goalscorers | Pos | No. |
|---|---|---|---|---|---|---|---|---|---|
| Aug 8 | Nat South | H | Truro City | 752 | D | 1-1 | D.Green 50 | 11 | 1 |
| 10 | Nat South | A | Whitehawk | 288 | D | 2-2 | D.Green 46 Ladapo 68 (pen) | 14 | 2 |
| 15 | Nat South | A | Havant & Waterlooville | 613 | L | 0-2 | | 18 | 3 |
| 18 | Nat South | H | Wealdstone | 677 | D | 0-0 | | 18 | 4 |
| 22 | Nat South | A | Basingstoke Town | 471 | D | 0-0 | | 17 | 5 |
| 29 | Nat South | H | Dartford | 996 | L | 0-2 | | 18 | 6 |
| 31 | Nat South | A | Concord Rangers | 321 | L | 1-2 | Taiwo 66 | 19 | 7 |
| Sept 5 | Nat South | H | St Albans City | 635 | L | 0-1 | | 21 | 8 |
| 12 | Nat South | H | Ebbsfleet United | 1017 | L | 0-2 | | 20 | 9 |
| 15 | Nat South | A | Eastbourne Borough | 438 | **W** | 4-1 | J.Taylor 6 22 Wills 30 Ladapo 57 | 19 | 10 |
| 19 | Nat South | A | Gosport Borough | 554 | **W** | 2-1 | Moore 29 Ladapo 67 | 16 | 11 |
| **26** | **FA2Q** | **A** | **Potters Bar Town** | **213** | **W** | **5-1** | **Wassmer 60 Wills 74 90 D.Green 84 Moss 90.** | | 12 |
| Oct 3 | Nat South | H | Weston-s Mare | 650 | L | 0-2 | | 18 | 13 |
| **10** | **FAC3Q** | **H** | **Truro City** | **550** | **W** | **4-0** | **D.Green 44 Ladapo 45 B.Johnson 61J.Taylor 87** | | 14 |
| 17 | Nat South | A | Oxford City | 311 | D | 1-1 | J.Taylor 49 | 17 | 15 |
| **24** | **FAC4Q** | **H** | **Forest Green Rovers** | **1302** | **L** | **1-2** | **Moore 60** | | 16 |
| 31 | Nat South | A | Truro City | 418 | L | 1-2 | Wills 70 | 19 | 17 |
| Nov 7 | Nat South | H | Havant & Waterlooville | 607 | **W** | 4-1 | Ladapo 47 53 Taiwo 54 Moore 90 | 18 | 18 |
| 14 | Nat South | H | Whitehawk | 590 | L | 2-6 | Wills 20 Ladapo 40 | 19 | 19 |
| 17 | Nat South | H | Bath City | 362 | D | 1-1 | Goodman 87 | | 20 |
| 21 | Nat South | A | Hemel Hempstead Town | 453 | **W** | 2-1 | Ladapo 17 Wills 79 | 17 | 21 |
| **28** | **FAT3Q** | **A** | **Dulwich Hamlet** | **1479** | **L** | **0-2** | | | 22 |
| Dec 5 | Nat South | A | St Albans City | 421 | L | 0-3 | | 19 | 23 |
| 19 | Nat South | H | Gosport Borough | 540 | **W** | 1-0 | Ladapo 67 | 18 | 24 |
| 26 | Nat South | H | Maidstone United | 1248 | **W** | 1-0 | Ladapo 60 | 18 | 25 |
| 28 | Nat South | A | Dartford | 1417 | D | 1-1 | Ladapo 38 | 15 | 26 |
| Jan 2 | Nat South | A | Maidstone United | 2609 | L | 1-2 | Goodman 37 | 15 | 27 |
| 9 | Nat South | H | Maidenhead United | 618 | **W** | 3-2 | Shields 23 M.Johnson 40 Jolley 85 | | 28 |
| 16 | Nat South | H | Chelmsford City | 732 | **W** | 4-1 | L.Taylor 3 ( 5 (pen) 15 (pen) 71) D Green 43 | 11 | 29 |
| 23 | Nat South | A | Whitehawk | 1462 | **W** | 2-1 | Wills 9 L.Taylor 90 | 10 | 30 |
| 30 | Nat South | H | Bishops Stortford | 723 | D | 1-1 | L.Taylor 84 (pen) | 9 | 31 |
| Feb 6 | Nat South | A | Hayes & Yeading | 185 | W | 2-0 | Wassmer 13 Moore 34 | 8 | 32 |
| 13 | Nat South | H | Basingstoke Town | 632 | **W** | 2-1 | Akendayini 16 39 | 6 | 33 |
| 20 | Nat South | A | Chelmsford City | 778 | **W** | 3-2 | N.Green 10 Ladapo 24 Wilson 64 | 6 | 34 |
| 23 | Nat South | H | Eastbourne Borough | 557 | L | 0-1 | | 6 | 35 |
| 27 | Nat South | A | Sutton United | 884 | L | 1-4 | Jolley 88 | 7 | 36 |
| Mar 5 | Nat South | A | Maidenhead united | 438 | L | 1-3 | Cundle 20 | 7 | 37 |
| 12 | Nat South | H | Oxford City | 669 | L | 0-2 | | 11 | 38 |
| 19 | Nat South | H | Hayes & Yeading | 557 | L | 1-2 | Ladapo 32 (pen) | 12 | 39 |
| 26 | Nat South | A | Wealdstone | 750 | L | 1-4 | D.Green 17 | 15 | 40 |
| 28 | Nat South | H | Concord Rangers | 469 | L | 0-1 | | 15 | 41 |
| Apr 2 | Nat South | A | Weston-s-Mare | 416 | L | 0-1 | | 16 | 42 |
| 9 | Nat South | H | Sutton United | 576 | L | 0-4 | | 18 | 43 |
| 16 | Nat South | A | Bishops Stortford | 388 | L | 1-4 | D.Green 55 | 19 | 44 |
| 23 | Nat South | H | Hemel Hempstead Town | 823 | **W** | 4-3 | Hunt 1 M.Johnson 26 D.Green 41 Moore 52 | 18 | 45 |
| 30 | Nat South | A | Bath City | 695 | L | 0-2 | | 19 | 46 |

| GOALSCORERS | Scoring Games | Consec Sco Games | Total | | Scoring Games | Consec Sco Games | Total |
|---|---|---|---|---|---|---|---|
| ***2014-15 Moss*** | | | ***24*** | Jolley | 2 | | 2 |
| Ladapo | 12 | 2 | 13 | Taiwo | 2 | | 2 |
| D.Green | 8 | 2 | 8 | Wassmer | 2 | | 2 |
| Wills | 6 | | 7 | Cundle | 1 | | 1 |
| Moore | 5 | | 5 | N.Green | 1 | | 1 |
| L.Taylor | 2 | 3 | 5 | Hunt | 1 | | 1 |
| J.Taylor | 3 | 2 | 4 | B.Johnson | 1 | | 1 |
| Akendayini | 2 | | 2 | Moss | 1 | | 1 |
| Goodman | 2 | | 2 | Shields | 1 | | 1 |
| M.Johnson | 2 | | 2 | Wilson | 1 | | 1 |

# OXFORD CITY

**Chairman:** Brian Cox
**Secretary:** John Shepperd (T) 01865 744 493 (E) shepoxf@tiscali.co.uk
**Commercial Manager:** Colin Taylor (T/E) 07817 885 396
**Programme Editor:** Colin Taylor (T/E) 07817 885 396
**Ground Address:** Court Place Farm, Marsh Lane, Marston, Oxford OX3 0NQ
(T) 01865 744 493 **Manager:** Justin Merritt

## Club Factfile

**Founded:** 1882 **Nickname:** City
**Previous Names:** None
**Previous Leagues:** Isthmian 1907-88, 94-2005, South Midlands 1990-93, Spartan South Midlands 2005-06

**Club Colours (change):** Blue and white hoops/blue/blue (All yellow)

**Ground Capacity:** 3,000 **Seats:** 300 **Covered:** 400 **Clubhouse:** Yes **Shop:** Yes

**Directions** From the South - Travel north from Newbury on the A34 past Abingdon and take the Oxford Ring Road toward London (East). Stay on Ring Road over 5 roundabouts following signs for London & M40 East. At the last Headington roundabout go straightover North towards Banbury & Northampton on A40. Within a mile a flyover is visible as the exit from the Ring Road. Turn left under the flyover and left again toward Marsh Lane. Turn right at the T Junction and the ground is on your left just before the Pedestrian Crossing. From the East - Leave the M40 at Junction 8 and follow the A40 to the Headington roundabout going straightover towards Banbury & Northampton A40. Within a mile a flyover is visible as the exit from the Ring Road. Turn left under the flyover and left again toward Marsh Lane. Turn right at the T Junction and the ground is on your left just before the Pedestrian Crossing. From the North - Leave the M40 at Junction 9 along the A34 toward Oxford. After 5 miles leave A34 following signs for Londan A40 for the next two roundabouts. Leave the A40 at the Marston slip road just before the flyover. Go over the A40 on the flyover into Marsh Lane and the ground is on your left before the Pedestrian Crossing.

**Previous Grounds:** Grandpont 1884-1900, The White House 11900-1988, Cuttleslowe Park 1990-91, Pressed Steel 1991-93

**Record Attendance:** 9,500 v Leytonstone - FA Amateur Cup - 1950
**Record Victory:** Not known - If you know please email tw.publications@btinternet.com
**Record Defeat:** Not known - If you know please email tw.publications@btinternet.com
**Record Goalscorer:** John Woodley
**Record Appearances:** John Woodley
**Additional Records:** Paid £3,000 to Woking for S Adams
Received £15,000 from Yeovil Town for Howard Forinton

**Honours:**
FA Amateur Cup 1905-06. Oxford Senior Cup x3
Spartan South Midlands League Premier Division 2005-06. Southern Premier Play-offs 2011-12.

**10 YEAR RECORD**

| 06-07 | 07-08 | 08-09 | 09-10 | 10-11 | 11-12 | 12-13 | 13-14 | 14-15 | 15-16 |
|---|---|---|---|---|---|---|---|---|---|
| SthW 12 | SthW 4 | SthP 6 | SthP 13 | SthP 14 | SthP 2 | Conf N 10 | Conf N 20 | Conf N 6 | Nat S 12 |

# OXFORD CITY MATCH RESULTS 2015-16

| Date | Comp | H/A | Opponents | Att: | Result | Goalscorers | Pos | No. |
|---|---|---|---|---|---|---|---|---|
| Aug 8 | Nat South | H | Chelmsford City | 253 | D 2-2 | Adrian 34 Bubb 56 | 10 | 1 |
| 10 | Nat South | A | St Albans City | 481 | W 3-1 | Isaac 21 Alamo 70 Bubb 90 | 7 | 2 |
| 15 | Nat South | A | Maidstone United | 2037 | W 1-0 | Lapoujade 60 | 5 | 3 |
| 18 | Nat South | H | Basingstoke Town | 255 | D 2-2 | Santiago 32 Bubb 72 (pen) | 4 | 4 |
| 22 | Nat South | A | Havant & Waterlooville | 552 | L 1-2 | Coulson 82 | 9 | 5 |
| 29 | Nat South | H | Weston-s-Mare | 202 | W 3-0 | Bubb 26 Santiagp 67 Coulson 90 | 6 | 6 |
| 31 | Nat South | A | Truro City | 541 | W 6-0 | Bubb 20 MUKENDI 3 (54 56 65) Sterling-James 89 Coulson 89 | 4 | 7 |
| Sept 5 | Nat South | H | Whitehawk | 361 | D 0-0 | | 4 | 8 |
| 12 | Nat South | A | Concord Rangers | 277 | W 2-0 | Lafuente 35 Cornhill 40 (og) | 3 | 9 |
| 15 | Nat South | H | Dartford | 283 | W 2-1 | Lafuente 51 Isaac 80 | 2 | 10 |
| 19 | Nat South | H | Eastbourne Borough | 228 | D 2-2 | Bubb 59 Lafuente 67 | 2 | 11 |
| **26** | **FAC2Q** | **H** | **Shortwood United** | **201** | **W 3-1** | **Bubb 29 (pen) Stirling-Jones 53 62** | | 12 |
| Oct 3 | Nat South | A | Chelmsford City | 988 | W 4-0 | Bubb 50 (pen) Isaac 74 Coulson 80 Lafuente 83 | 2 | 13 |
| **10** | **FAC3Q** | **A** | **Bognor Regis Town** | **515** | **L 2-4** | **Bubb 12 Lapoujade 44** | | 14 |
| 17 | Nat South | H | Margate | 311 | D 1-1 | Isaac 5 | 2 | 15 |
| 31 | Nat South | H | Bishops Stortford | 278 | W 3-1 | Bubb 5 Isaac 64 Coulson 85 | 2 | 16 |
| Nov 2 | Nat South | A | Sutton United | 809 | D 1-1 | Isaac 36 | 2 | 17 |
| 7 | Nat South | A | Ebbsfleet United | 1098 | D 1-1 | Coulson 29 | | 18 |
| 10 | Nat South | H | Havant & Waterlooville | 353 | L 1-3 | McDonagh 49 | | 19 |
| 14 | Nat South | A | Bath City | 616 | W 3-1 | McDonagh 12 Pond 30 Pifarre 51 | 2 | 20 |
| 21 | Nat South | H | Gosport Borough | 349 | L 1-2 | Pond 10 | 3 | 21 |
| **28** | **FAT3Q** | **H** | **Marlow** | **177** | **W 6-2** | **Bubb 12 76 Fleet 28 Isaac 58 Jackson 64 84** | | 22 |
| Dec 5 | Nat South | A | Eastbourne Borough | 422 | D 1-1 | Bubb 32 | 3 | 23 |
| **12** | **FAT1** | **H** | **Ebbsfleet United** | **425** | **W 3-1** | **Coulson 27 Benjamin 50 57** | | 24 |
| 19 | Nat South | H | Hemel Hempstead Town | 310 | L 0-2 | | 3 | 25 |
| 26 | Nat South | H | Maidenhead United | 283 | D 0-0 | | 4 | 26 |
| **Jan 16** | **FAT2** | **H** | **Cheltenham Town** | **928** | **D 2-2** | **Bubb 65 Jackson 86** | | 27 |
| 23 | Nat South | H | St Albans City | 247 | W 4-1 | Bubb 60 Pond 58 McDonagh 71 Jackson 75 | 4 | 28 |
| **26** | **FAT2r** | **A** | **Cheltenham Town** | **776** | **W 3-0** | **Jackson 30 Bubb 54 Pond 77** | | 29 |
| **Feb 6** | **FAT3** | **A** | **Woking** | **923** | **L 0-1** | | | 30 |
| 10 | Nat South | A | Weston-s-Mare | 280 | L 2-5 | Lapoujade 44 Whichelow 72 | 7 | 31 |
| 13 | Nat South | H | Ebbsfleet United | 390 | D 1-1 | Bubb 90 (pen) | 7 | 32 |
| 15 | Nat South | A | Wealdstone | 663 | D 2-2 | Bubb 34 (pen) Whichelow 88 | 6 | 33 |
| 20 | Nat South | A | Hayes & Yeading | 152 | L 1-2 | Bubb 10 | 8 | 34 |
| 23 | Nat South | A | Maidenhead United | 305 | L 1-2 | Lapoujade 62 | 9 | 35 |
| 27 | Nat South | A | Gosport Borough | 323 | D 0-0 | | 8 | 36 |
| Mar 5 | Nat South | H | Bath City | 325 | D 1-1 | Bubb 86 (pen) | 8 | 37 |
| 8 | Nat South | H | Maidstone United | 225 | L 2-3 | Bubb 30 Patterson 90 | 9 | 38 |
| 12 | Nat South | A | Margate | 669 | W 2-0 | Whitchelow 39 Bevans 84 | 7 | 39 |
| 19 | Nat South | H | Wealdstone | 393 | W 3-2 | Isaac 42 Bubb 47 McDonough 57 | 6 | 40 |
| 22 | Nat South | H | Concord Rangers | 168 | W 5-1 | Arzamendi 4 Fleet 16 Benjamin 16 64 McDonagh 61 | 5 | 41 |
| 26 | Nat South | A | Basingstoke Town | 515 | L 0-2 | | 5 | 42 |
| 30 | Nat South | H | Turom City | 235 | L 1-2 | Jackson 44 | 5 | 43 |
| Apr 2 | Nat South | A | Bishop's Stortford | 332 | L 0-3 | | 9 | 44 |
| 9 | Nat South | H | Hayes & Yeading | 235 | D 2-2 | Lapoujade 46 Bubb 56 | 8 | 45 |
| 12 | Nat South | A | Whitehawk | 193 | L 0-2 | | 8 | 46 |
| 16 | Nat South | A | Hemel Hempstead Town | 546 | L 1-3 | Henderson 69 | 11 | 47 |
| 23 | Nat South | A | Dartford | 1190 | D 2-2 | Bubb 44 Lafuente 55 | 10 | 48 |
| 30 | Nat South | H | Sutton United | 503 | L 0-1 | | 12 | 49 |

| GOALSCORERS | Scoring Games | Consec Sco Games | Total | | Scoring Games | Consec Sco Games | Total |
|---|---|---|---|---|---|---|---|
| *2014-15 Yussuf* | | | *31* | Sterling-James | 3 | | 3 |
| Bubb | 23 | 4 | 24 | Whichelow | 3 | | 3 |
| Isaac | 8 | 3 | 8 | Fleet | 2 | | 2 |
| Coulson | 7 | 2 | 7 | Santiago | 2 | | 2 |
| Jackson | 6 | 3 | 6 | Adrian | 1 | | 1 |
| Lafuente | 5 | 3 | 5 | Alamo | 1 | | 1 |
| Lapoujade | 5 | | 5 | Arzamendi | 1 | | 1 |
| McDonagh | 5 | | 5 | Bevans | 1 | | 1 |
| Benjamin | 3 | | 4 | Henderson | 1 | | 1 |
| Pond | 4 | | 4 | Patterson | 1 | | 1 |
| Mukendi | 1 | | 3 | Pifarre | 1 | | 1 |
| | | | | Opponents | | | 1 |

# POOLE TOWN

**Chairman:** Clive Robbins
**Secretary:** Bill Reid **(T)** 01794 517 991 **(E)** secretary@pooletownfc.co.uk
**Commercial Manager:** Mark Bumford **(T/E)**
**Programme Editor:** Ben Bonsey **(T/E)** jackamey94@hotmail.co.uk
**Ground Address:** Tatnam Ground, Oakdale School, School Lane, Poole BH15 3JR
**(T)** 07771 604 289 (Match days) **Manager:** Tommy Killick

2015-16 Squad

## Club Factfile

**Founded:** 1880 **Nickname:** The Dolphins
**Previous Names:** Poole Rovers 1884, Poole Hornets 1886 - amalgamated on 20.09.1890 to form Town. Know as Poole & St. Mary's 1919-20.
**Previous Leagues:** Dorset 1896-1903, 04-05, 10-11. Hampshire 1903-04, 05-10, 11-23, 34-35, 96-2004. Western 1923-26, 30-34, 35-57. Southern 1926-30, 57-96, 2011-16. Wessex 2004-11.

**Club Colours (change):** Red & white halves/red/red & white (Sky blue/navy blue/navy blue)

**Ground Capacity:** 2,000 **Seats:** 154 **Covered:** 200 **Clubhouse:** Yes **Shop:** Yes

**Directions**
Follow the A35 into Poole and at the roundabout by the fire station take the second exit into Holes Bay Road (A350). At next roundabout take 1st exit onto Broadstone Way (A349) and turn right at Wessex Gate East traffic lights into Willis Way. Turn right into Fleets Way and continue until you see Poole Motor Cycles. Turn left into Palmer Road opposite Poole Motor Cycles and take first right into School Lane which will take you into the Club/School car park. The ground is on the right hand side. Nearest Railway Station: Poole (3/4 mile)

**Previous Grounds:** Ye Old Farm Ground. Wimborne Road Rec > 1933. Poole Stadium 1933-94. Hamworthy Utd FC 1994-96. Holt Utd 1996.

**Record Attendance:** **Att:** 10,224 v Queens Park Rangers, FA Cup 1st Rnd Replay, 1946 (at Poole Stadium).
**Record Victory:** 11-0 v Horndean (A) Hampshire League 11/02/1998
**Record Defeat:** 1-8 v East Cowes VA (A) Hampshire League 01/05/2001.
**Record Goalscorer:** Not known - If you know please email tw.publications@btinternet.com
**Record Appearances:** Not known - If you know please email tw.publications@btinternet.com
**Additional Records:** Got to 3rd Round of FA Cup in 1926 v Everton. Transfer fee paid £5,000 for Nicky Dent 1990. Transfer fee received £70,000 for Charlie Austin from Swindon Town 2009.
**Honours:**
Western League 1956-57. Dorset Senior Cup x13 Most recently 2012-13.
Wessex League Champions 2008-09, 09-10, 10-11. Southern Division One South & West 2012-13, Premier 2015-16.

### 10 YEAR RECORD

| 06-07 | 07-08 | 08-09 | 09-10 | 10-11 | 11-12 | 12-13 | 13-14 | 14-15 | 15-16 |
|---|---|---|---|---|---|---|---|---|---|
| WexP 4 | WexP 4 | WexP 1 | WexP 1 | WexP 1 | Sthsw 2 | Sthsw 1 | SthP 7 | SthP 2 | SthP 1 |

# POOLE TOWN MATCH RESULTS 2015-16

| Date | Comp | H/A | Opponents | Att: | Result | | Goalscorers | Pos | No. |
|---|---|---|---|---|---|---|---|---|---|
| Aug 8 | SPL | H | Kettering Town | 399 | W | 1-0 | Gillespie 3 | 9 | 1 |
| 10 | SPL | A | Hungerford Town | 246 | D | 0-0 | | 1 | 2 |
| 15 | SPL | A | St Neots Town | 366 | W | 3-2 | Emerson 38 Roberts 74 Burbidge 70 | 5 | 3 |
| 18 | SPL | H | Chippenham Town | 473 | L | 1-3 | Devlin 76 (pen) | 11 | 4 |
| 22 | SPL | H | Merthyr Town | 355 | D | 2-2 | Brooks 54 Roberts 86 | 11 | 5 |
| 29 | SPL | A | Slough Town | 304 | W | 3-1 | Devlin 48 Gillespie 65 Brooks 90 | 6 | 6 |
| 31 | SPL | H | Frome Town | 425 | W | 5-0 | Gillespie 6 87 Devlin 26 (pen) Brooks 32 Whisken 81 | 3 | 7 |
| Sept 5 | SPL | A | Kings Lynn Town | 525 | L | 2-3 | Miller 71 (og) Roberts 76 | 6 | 8 |
| **12** | **FAC1Q** | **H** | **Barnstaple Town** | **306** | **W** | **1-0** | **Devlin 23 (pen)** | | 9 |
| 19 | SPL | A | Biggleswade | 202 | W | 1-0 | Holmes 26 | 3 | 10 |
| 22 | SPL | H | Dorchester Town | 509 | D | 0-0 | | 3 | 11 |
| **26** | **FAC 2Q** | **A** | **Hayes & Yeading** | **185** | **W** | **3-2** | **Walker 11 Gillespie 39 Spetch 52** | | 12 |
| 29 | SPL | A | Bideford | 158 | W | 2-1 | Devlin 40 Walker 85 | 4 | 13 |
| Oct3 | SPL | H | Redditch United | 305 | W | 2-1 | Devlin 36 (pen) Moore 44 | 3 | 14 |
| 6 | SPL | H | Paulton Rovers | 298 | W | 2-1 | Roberts 62 Connell 78 (pen) | 1 | 15 |
| **10** | **FAC 3Q** | **A** | **Hastings United** | **735** | **W** | **2-0** | **Whisken 3 Brooks 44** | | 16 |
| 17 | SPL | H | Cirencester Town | 358 | W | 3-0 | Devlin 60 77 Holmes 85 | 2 | 17 |
| 20 | SPL | A | Dorchester Town | 556 | W | 5-1 | Spetch 15 Whyte 35 58 Walker 39 Roberts 73 | 1 | 18 |
| **24** | **FAC4Q** | **A** | **Whitehawk** | **450** | **L** | **0-2** | | | 19 |
| 27 | SPL | A | Chesham United | 282 | L | 1-3 | Burbidge 25 | 1 | 20 |
| **31** | **FAT 1Q** | **A** | **Merthyr Town** | **270** | **L** | **0-1** | | | 21 |
| Nov 7 | SPL | A | Dunstable Town | 152 | D | 1-1 | Burbidge 90 | 3 | 22 |
| 14 | SPL | H | Cambridge City | 357 | W | 2-1 | Roberts 17 73 | 1 | 23 |
| 17 | SPL | A | Chippenham Town | 257 | W | 1-0 | Dickson 10 | | 24 |
| 21 | SPL | H | St Neots Town | 355 | W | 3-0 | Spetch 5 Burbidge 51 Wallker 72 | 1 | 25 |
| 24 | SPL | A | Histon | 170 | W | 7-0 | Dickson 2 Devlin 10,12(ps) Burbidge 12 Trotman 17 (og) Holmes 57 90 | 1 | 26 |
| 28 | SPL | A | Kettering Town | 525 | L | 0-1 | | 1 | 27 |
| Dec 5 | SPL | H | Leamington | 382 | W | 1-0 | Brooks 20 | 1 | 28 |
| 8 | SPL | H | Hungerford Town | 369 | D | 0-0 | | 1 | 29 |
| 12 | SPL | A | Bedworth United | 204 | W | 2-0 | Brooks 38 Wort 81 | 1 | 30 |
| 19 | SPL | H | Slough Town | 429 | D | 3-3 | Dickson 5 Spetch 26 Wort 68 | 1 | 31 |
| 26 | SPL | A | Frome Town | 354 | D | 0-0 | | 1 | 32 |
| Jan 16 | SPL | H | Kings Lynn Town | 355 | D | 1-1 | Gillespie 78 | 1 | 33 |
| 23 | SPL | A | Merthyr Town | 494 | D | 1-1 | Spetch 86 | 1 | 34 |
| Feb2 | SPL | H | Weymouth | 676 | W | 2-0 | Brooks 63 Roberts 76 | 1 | 35 |
| 16 | SPL | H | Biggleswade Town | 266 | D | 2-2 | Roberts 35 Brooks 45 | 1 | 36 |
| 23 | SPL | H | Hitchin Town | 329 | W | 1-0 | Roberts 28 | 1 | 37 |
| 27 | SPL | A | Cirencester Town | 128 | L | 0-3 | | 1 | 38 |
| Mar 1 | SPL | A | Redditch United | 501 | D | 0-0 | | 1 | 39 |
| 5 | SPL | H | Histon | 359 | W | 3-0 | Burbidge 2 60 Lee 18 | 1 | 40 |
| 12 | SPL | A | Leamington | 502 | L | 0-1 | | 1 | 41 |
| 19 | SPL | H | Bedworth United | 392 | W | 5-0 | Roberts 8 56 Burbidge 16 Holgate 76 Lee 82 | 1 | 42 |
| 26 | SPL | H | Stratford Town | 407 | L | 1-2 | Devlin 69 | 2 | 43 |
| 28 | SPL | A | Weymouth | 1205 | W | 1-0 | Brooks 37 | 2 | 44 |
| Apr 2 | SPL | H | Chesham United | 456 | W | 3-0 | Brooks 6 25 Roberts 52 | 1 | 45 |
| 5 | SPL | A | Paulton Rovers | 275 | W | 4-0 | Roberts 47 Brooks 54 63 Lee 72 | 1 | 46 |
| 9 | SPL | A | Hitchin Town | 712 | D | 0-0 | | 1 | 47 |
| 12 | SPL | A | Stratford Town | 232 | W | 1-0 | Burbidge 19 | 1 | 48 |
| 16 | SPL | H | Dunstable Town | 1057 | W | 3-0 | BROOKS 3 (3 57 82pen) | 1 | 49 |
| 19 | SPL | H | Bideford | 550 | W | 3-0 | Brooks 61 Connell 71 Burbidge 82 | 1 | 50 |
| 23 | SPL | A | Cambridge City | 250 | W | 2-1 | Roberts 66 Lindsay 82 | 1 | 51 |

| GOALSCORERS | Scoring Games | Consec Sco Games | Total | | Scoring Games | Consec Sco Games | Total |
|---|---|---|---|---|---|---|---|
| ***2014-15 Burbridge & Devlin*** | | | ***16*** | Lee | 3 | | 3 |
| Brooks | 12 | 3 | 17 | Connell | 2 | | 2 |
| Roberts | 13 | 2 | 15 | Whisken | 2 | | 2 |
| Devlin | 10 | 2 | 11 | Whyte | 2 | | 2 |
| Burbidge | 10 | | 10 | Wort | 2 | | 2 |
| Gillespie | 5 | 2 | 6 | Emerson | 1 | | 1 |
| Spetch | 5 | 2 | 5 | Holgate | 1 | | 1 |
| Holmes | 3 | | 4 | Lindsay | 1 | | 1 |
| Walker | 4 | 2 | 4 | Moore | 1 | | 1 |
| Dickson | 3 | | 3 | Opponents | 2 | | 2 |

# ST ALBANS CITY

**Chairman:** Lawrence Levy & John McGowan
**Secretary:** Tom Norman **(T)** 01727 848 914 **(E)** tom.norman@stalbanscityfc.com
**Commercial Manager:** **(T/E)**
**Programme Editor:** **(T/E)**
**Ground Address:** Clarence Park, York Road, St. Albans, Herts AL1 4PL
**(T)** 01727 848 914 **Manager:** Ian Allinson

## Club Factfile

**Founded:** 1908 **Nickname:** The Saints
**Previous Names:** None
**Previous Leagues:** Herts County 1908-10, Spartan 1908-20, Athenian 1920-23, Isthmian 1923-2004, Conference 2004-11. Southern 2011-14.

**Club Colours (change):** Yellow/blue/white (Blue/white/blue)

**Ground Capacity:** 5,007 **Seats:** 667 **Covered:** 1,900 **Clubhouse:** Yes **Shop:** Yes

**Directions**
From the M25 (Clockwise) Exit M25 at junction 21A(A405). Follow signs to St. Albans from slip road. At Noke Hotel roundabout (Shell garage will be straight ahead), bear right on A405 and stay on A405 until London Colney roundabout (traffic light controlled). Turn left onto A1081. Follow road for approx 1 mile until mini roundabout (Great Northern pub on left). Turn right into Alma Road. At traffic lights turn right into Victoria Street and continue to junction with Crown pub. Go straight across into Clarence Road, ground is first on left about 50 yards past junction or take the next turning on the left into York Road, ground entrance is at the end of the road on the left. From the M25 (Counter-clockwise) Exit M25 at junction 22 (A1081). Follow signs to St. Albans from slip road. At London Colney roundabout (traffic light controlled) exit onto A1081. Follow road for approx 1 mile until mini roundabout (Great Northern pub on left). Turn right into Alma Road. At traffic lights turn right into Victoria Street and continue to junction with Crown pub. Go straight across into Clarence Road, ground is first on left about 50 yards past junction or take the next turning on the left into York Road, ground entrance is at the end of the road on the left.

**Previous Grounds:** None

**Record Attendance:** 9,757 v Ferryhill Athletic - FA Amateur Cup 1926
**Record Victory:** 14-0 v Aylesbury United (H) - Spartan League 19/10/1912
**Record Defeat:** 0-11 v Wimbledon (H) - Isthmian League 1946
**Record Goalscorer:** Billy Minter - 356 (Top scorer for 12 consecutive season from 1920-32)
**Record Appearances:** Phil Wood - 900 (1962-85)
**Additional Records:** Paid £6,000 to Yeovil Town for Paul Turner August 1957
Received £92,759 from Southend United for Dean Austin 1990
**Honours:**
Athenian League 1920-21, 21-22. Isthmian League 1923-24, 26-27, 27-28.
London Senior Cup 1970-71.

### 10 YEAR RECORD

| 06-07 | 07-08 | 08-09 | 09-10 | 10-11 | 11-12 | 12-13 | 13-14 | 14-15 | 15-16 |
|---|---|---|---|---|---|---|---|---|---|
| Conf 24 | Conf S 19 | Conf S 12 | Conf S 13 | Conf S 22 | SthP 8 | SthP 11 | SthP 4 | Conf S 13 | Nat S 18 |

## ST ALBANS CITY MATCH RESULTS 2015-16

| Date | Comp | H/A | Opponents | Att: | Result | | Goalscorers | Pos | No. |
|---|---|---|---|---|---|---|---|---|---|
| Aug 8 | Nat South | A | Gosport Borough | 389 | D | 0-0 | | 14 | 1 |
| 10 | Nat South | H | Oxford City | 481 | L | 1-3 | Theophanous 23 | 18 | 2 |
| 15 | Nat South | H | Ebbsfleet United | 602 | L | 0-2 | | 20 | 3 |
| 18 | Nat South | A | Eastbourne Borough | 437 | L | 0-1 | | 21 | 4 |
| 22 | Nat South | H | Bath City | 424 | L | 0-1 | | 21 | 5 |
| 29 | Nat South | A | Chelmsford City | 595 | L | 1-2 | Theophanous 56 | 21 | 6 |
| 31 | Nat South | H | Hemel Hempstead Town | 860 | D | 2-2 | Thomas 1 Krans 71 | 21 | 7 |
| Sept 5 | Nat South | A | Margate | 635 | **W** | 1-0 | Theophanous 52 | 19 | 8 |
| 12 | Nat South | A | Truro City | 413 | L | 0-2 | | 19 | 9 |
| 14 | Nat South | H | Basingstoke Town | 315 | **W** | 3-0 | Theophanous 13 62 Hilliard 56 | 18 | 10 |
| 19 | Nat South | H | Hayes & Yeading | 518 | D | 1-1 | Theophanous 40 | 18 | 11 |
| **26** | **FAC2Q** | **H** | **Deal Town** | **351** | **W** | **2-1** | **Theophanous 4 Allen 62** | | 12 |
| Oct 3 | Nat South | A | Whitehawk | 228 | L | 0-6 | | 20 | 13 |
| **10** | **FAC3Q** | **A** | **Petersfield Town** | **370** | **W** | **1-0** | **Martin 43** | | 14 |
| 17 | Nat South | A | Maidstone United | 2103 | L | 0-1 | | 20 | 15 |
| **24** | **FAC4Q** | **H** | **Weston-s-Mare** | **629** | **W** | **2-1** | **Montgomery 45 Chappell 78** | | 16 |
| 31 | Nat South | A | Havant & Waterlooville | 557 | D | 1-1 | Crawford 29 | 21 | 17 |
| **Nov 7** | **FAC1** | **A** | **Grimsby Town** | **2267** | **L** | **1-5** | **Theophanous 62** | **21** | 18 |
| 14 | Nat South | H | Wealdstone | 708 | **W** | 1-0 | Martin 25 | 20 | 19 |
| 21 | Nat South | A | Weston-s-Mare | 398 | L | 1-4 | Theophanous 73 | 20 | 20 |
| 24 | Nat South | H | Gosport Borough | 258 | L | 1-3 | Krans 90 | 21 | 21 |
| **28** | **FAT3Q** | **A** | **Lowestoft Town** | **420** | **L** | **0-4** | | **21** | 22 |
| Dec 5 | Nat South | H | Margate | 421 | **W** | 3-0 | Theophanous 56 Crawford 59 Corcoran 89 | 21 | 23 |
| 15 | Nat South | H | Maidenhead United | 613 | **W** | 3-2 | Meade 5 Martin 41 Edwards 90 | 19 | 24 |
| 19 | Nat South | A | Basingstoke Town | 455 | D | 2-2 | Bender 72 Oshodi 87 | 21 | 25 |
| 26 | Nat South | A | Bishops Stortford | 514 | L | 1-2 | Oshodi 61 | 21 | 26 |
| 28 | Nat South | H | Chelmsford City | 668 | D | 1-1 | Oshodi 41 | 20 | 27 |
| Jan 2 | Nat South | H | Bishops Stortford | 520 | D | 1-1 | Theophanous 55 | 20 | 28 |
| 9 | Nat South | A | Sutton United | 916 | L | 0-5 | | 20 | 29 |
| 23 | Nat South | A | Oxford City | 247 | L | 1-4 | MacDonald 11 | 22 | 30 |
| 30 | Nat South | H | Truro City | 686 | L | 0-1 | | 22 | 31 |
| Feb 6 | Nat South | A | Dartford | 931 | L | 0-2 | | 22 | 32 |
| 13 | Nat South | H | Concord Rangers | 476 | D | 2-2 | Oshodi 30 Thalassitis 52 | 21 | 33 |
| 16 | Nat South | A | Ebbsfleet United | 1089 | L | 0-1 | | 21 | 34 |
| 20 | Nat South | A | Bath City | 757 | L | 0-1 | | 22 | 35 |
| 27 | Nat South | H | Whitehawk | 470 | **W** | 6-0 | MacDONALD 4 (8 27pen 32 75) Theophanous 72 Edwards 90 | 21 | 36 |
| Mar 5 | Nat South | H | Sutton United | 554 | L | 0-3 | | 21 | 37 |
| 8 | Nat South | H | Weston-s-Mare | 300 | **W** | 2-1 | Thalassitis 67 Theophanous 82 | 21 | 38 |
| 12 | Nat South | A | Hayes & Yeading | 188 | **W** | 3-1 | MacDonald 8 Thaliassitis 33 Anderson 57 | 21 | 39 |
| 19 | Nat South | A | Concord Rangers | 289 | **W** | 2-1 | Martin 39 Theophanous 89 | 20 | 40 |
| 26 | Nat South | H | Eastbourne Borough | 663 | **W** | 3-1 | MacDonald 22 Oshodi 68 Theophanous 78 | 20 | 41 |
| Apr 2 | Nat South | H | Maidstone United | 652 | L | 1-3 | Theophanous 27 | 21 | 42 |
| 9 | Nat South | A | Maidenhead United | 567 | **W** | 1-0 | Thalassitis 85 | 21 | 43 |
| 12 | Nat South | A | Hemel Hempstead Town | 972 | D | 2-2 | Thalassitis 55 Connolly 39 (og) | 21 | 44 |
| 16 | Nat South | H | Havant & Waterlooville | 702 | **W** | 6-0 | Martin 3 Theophanpous14Thalassitis 23 89 MacDonald 40Corcoran 68 | 18 | 45 |
| 23 | Nat South | A | Wealdstone | 777 | D | 1-1 | Theophanous 4 | 19 | 46 |
| 30 | Nat South | H | Dartford | 1310 | **W** | 4-0 | Kaloczi 17 85 Dembele 51 (og) Theophanus 88 | 18 | 47 |

| GOALSCORERS | Scoring Games | Consec Sco Games | Total | | Scoring Games | Consec Sco Games | Total |
|---|---|---|---|---|---|---|---|
| ***2014-15 Frendo*** | | | ***11*** | Krans | 2 | | 2 |
| Theophanous | 18 | 3 | 19 | Allen | 1 | | 1 |
| MacDonald | 5 | | 8 | Anderson | 1 | | 1 |
| Thalassitis | 6 | | 7 | Bender | 1 | | 1 |
| Martin | 5 | | 5 | Chappell | 1 | | 1 |
| Oshodi | 5 | | 5 | Hilliard | 1 | | 1 |
| Corcoran | 2 | | 2 | Meade | 1 | | 1 |
| Crawford | 2 | | 2 | Montgomery | 1 | | 1 |
| Edwards | 2 | | 2 | Thomas | 1 | | 1 |
| Kaloczi | 1 | | 2 | Opponents | | | 2 |

# TRURO CITY

**Chairman:** Peter Masters
**Secretary:** Ian Rennie (T) 07881 498 916 (E) ianrennie@trurocityfc.net
**Commercial Manager:** Colin Bradbury (T/E) 07974 561 933
**Programme Editor:** Steve Rogers (T/E) 07776 214 300
**Ground Address:** Treyew Road, Truro, Cornwall TR1 2TH
(T) 01872 225 400 / 278 853 (Social Club) **Manager:** Lee Hodges

Photo: Keith Clayton.

## Club Factfile

**Founded:** 1889 **Nickname:** City, White Tigers, The Tinmen
**Previous Names:** None
**Previous Leagues:** Cornwall County, Plymouth & District, South Western, Western 2006-08, Southern 2008-11, 13-15. Conference 2011-13.

**Club Colours (change):** All white (All orange)

**Ground Capacity:** 3,500 **Seats:** 1,675 **Covered:** Yes **Clubhouse:** Yes **Shop:**

**Directions**
On arriving at Exeter, leave the M5 at junction 31 and join the A30. Travel via Okehampton, Launceston, and Bodmin.. At the end of the dual carriageway (windmills on right hand side) take left hand turning signposted Truro. After approximately 7 miles turn right at traffic lights, travel downhill crossing over three roundabouts, following signs for Redruth. Approximately 500 metres after third roundabout signed 'Arch Hill', ground is situated on left hand side.

**Previous Grounds:** None

**Record Attendance:** 1,400 v Aldershot - FA Vase
**Record Victory:** Not known - If you know please email tw.publications@btinternet.com
**Record Defeat:** Not known - If you know please email tw.publications@btinternet.com
**Record Goalscorer:** Not known - If you know please email tw.publications@btinternet.com
**Record Appearances:** Not known - If you know please email tw.publications@btinternet.com
**Additional Records:** 115 points & 185 goals, Western League Division One (42 games) 2006-07.
Became first British club to achieve five promotions in six seasons.

**Honours:**
South Western League 1960-61, 69-70, 92-93, 95-96, 97-98. Western League Division 1 2006-07, Premier Division 07-08.
FA Vase 2006-07. Southern League Division 1 South & West 2008-09, Premier Division 2010-11, Premier Play-off 2014-15.
Cornwall Senior Cup x15

### 10 YEAR RECORD

| 06-07 | 07-08 | 08-09 | 09-10 | 10-11 | 11-12 | 12-13 | 13-14 | 14-15 | 15-16 |
|---|---|---|---|---|---|---|---|---|---|
| West1 1 | WestP 1 | Sthsw 1 | SthP 11 | SthP 1 | Conf S 14 | Conf S 22 | SthP 17 | SthP 3 | Nat S 4 |

# TRURO CITY MATCH RESULTS 2015-16

| Date | Comp | H/A | Opponents | Att: | Result | | Goalscorers | Pos | No. |
|---|---|---|---|---|---|---|---|---|---|
| Aug 8 | Nat South | A | Margate | 752 | D | 1-1 | Dawson 65 | 12 | 1 |
| 11 | Nat South | H | Hayes & Yeading | 503 | L | 0-2 | | 17 | 2 |
| 15 | Nat South | H | Concord Rangers | 366 | W | 2-1 | White 47 (pen) Wright 51 | 13 | 3 |
| 17 | Nat South | A | Sutton United | 746 | D | 2-2 | White 9 (pen) Pugh 90 | 14 | 4 |
| 22 | Nat South | H | Bishops Stortford | 491 | L | 0-1 | | 16 | 5 |
| 29 | Nat South | A | Gosport Borough | 530 | L | 1-3 | Wright 27 | 17 | 6 |
| 31 | Nat South | H | Oxford City | 541 | L | 0-6 | | 17 | 7 |
| Sept 5 | Nat South | A | Eastbourne Borough | 532 | D | 0-0 | | 17 | 8 |
| 12 | Nat South | H | St Albans City | 413 | W | 2-0 | Riley-Lowe12 Dawson 28 | 16 | 9 |
| 15 | Nat South | A | Weston-s-Mare | 360 | D | 2-2 | Pugh 79 Cooke 81 | 16 | 10 |
| 19 | Nat South | A | Dartford | 850 | W | 1-0 | Vassell 86 | 14 | 11 |
| **26** | **FAC2Q** | **A** | **Taunton Town** | **481** | **D** | **2-2** | **Duff 9 Wright 18** | | 12 |
| **29** | **FAC2Qr** | **H** | **Taunton Town** | **236** | **W** | **3-1** | **Brett 31 Wright 47 Pugh 69** | | 13 |
| Oct 3 | Nat South | H | Havant & Waterlooville | 478 | W | 3-0 | Reid 11 Richards 52 Vassell 75 | 14 | 14 |
| **10** | **FAC3Q** | **A** | **Margate** | **550** | **L** | **1-4** | **Duff 8** | | 15 |
| 17 | Nat South | A | Whitehawk | 256 | D | 0-0 | | 13 | 16 |
| 24 | Nat South | H | Gosport Borough | 401 | D | 2-2 | Richards 8 Reid 19 | | 17 |
| 31 | Nat South | H | Margate | 418 | W | 2-1 | Cooke 24 Duff 33 | 12 | 18 |
| Nov 7 | Nat South | A | Chelmsford City | 636 | W | 2-1 | Reid 23 Brett 31 | 7 | 19 |
| 17 | Nat South | H | Basingstoke Town | 285 | W | 2-0 | Riley-Lowe 21 Cooke 89 | 5 | 20 |
| 22 | Nat South | A | Hayes & Yeading | 293 | D | 2-2 | Afful 73 Ash 90 | 6 | 21 |
| **28** | **FAT3Q** | **A** | **Kingstonian** | **316** | **W** | **3-0** | **Green 9 Wright 26 Vassell 83** | | 22 |
| Dec 5 | Nat South | A | Maidstone United | 2002 | L | 1-2 | White 86 | 8 | 23 |
| **12** | **FAT1** | **H** | **Cirencester Town** | **302** | **D** | **2-2** | **Vassell 42 Pugh 45** | | 24 |
| **15** | **FAT1r** | **A** | **Cirencester Town** | **123** | **W** | **1-0** | **White 86 (pen)** | | 25 |
| 19 | Nat South | H | Eastbourne Borough | 339 | W | 1-0 | White 41 (pen) | 8 | 26 |
| 26 | Nat South | A | Bath City | 801 | W | 3-0 | Green 38 Vassell 40 Brett 47 | 8 | 27 |
| Jan 10 | Nat South | A | Ebbsfleet United | 1186 | D | 0-0 | | 7 | 28 |
| **16** | **FAT2** | **H** | **Macclesfield Town** | **665** | **D** | **2-2** | **Knowles 60 Vassell 87** | | 29 |
| **19** | **FAT2r** | **A** | **Macclesfield Town** | **507** | **L** | **0-2** | | | 30 |
| 23 | Nat South | H | Maidenhead United | 390 | D | 4-4 | Green 9 Jay 15 Vassell 45 55 | 7 | 31 |
| 30 | Nat South | A | St Albans City | 686 | W | 1-0 | Vassell 61 | 6 | 32 |
| Feb 6 | Nat South | H | Wealdstone | 606 | D | 4-4 | Vassell 58 Pugh 80 Ash 87 Brett 90 | 6 | 33 |
| 16 | Nat South | H | Hemel Hempstead Town | 626 | W | 4-2 | Vassell 16 Brett 28 (pen) Green 39 Cooke 74 | 5 | 34 |
| 20 | Nat South | H | Ebbsfleet United | 786 | D | 1-1 | Acheampong 45 (og) | 5 | 35 |
| 27 | Nat South | A | Bishops Stortford | 355 | W | 3-0 | Vassell 4 Brett 51 Jay 63 | 5 | 36 |
| Mar 5 | Nat South | H | Chelmsford City | 512 | W | 1-0 | Duff 68 | 5 | 37 |
| 12 | Nat South | A | Hemel Hempstead Town | 583 | L | 1-2 | Green 44 | 5 | 38 |
| 15 | Nat South | H | Bath City | 472 | W | 3-1 | White 63 Afful 81 90 | 4 | 39 |
| 19 | Nat South | A | Maidenhead United | 517 | D | 0-0 | | 4 | 40 |
| 26 | Nat South | H | Sutton United | 613 | L | 0-2 | | 4 | 41 |
| 30 | Nat South | A | Oxford City | 235 | W | 2-1 | Vassell 7 Wright 14 | 4 | 42 |
| Apr 5 | Nat South | H | Dartford | 502 | W | 3-0 | Knowles 28 Green 38 Jay 87 | 4 | 43 |
| 12 | Nat South | H | Weston-s-Mare | 472 | L | 1-3 | Jay 83 | 4 | 44 |
| 16 | Nat South | H | Maidstone United | 841 | L | 1-3 | Brett 24 | 5 | 45 |
| 19 | Nat South | A | Concord Rangers | 216 | W | 2-1 | Jay 23 White 39 (pen) | 4 | 46 |
| 23 | Nat South | A | Basingstoke Town | 463 | L | 0-2 | | 4 | 47 |
| 26 | Nat South | H | Whitehawk | 402 | D | 1-1 | Jay 45 | 4 | 48 |
| 28 | Nat South | A | Havant & Waterlooville | 620 | D | 0-0 | | 4 | 49 |
| 30 | Nat South | H | Wealdstone | 719 | L | 1-2 | Afful 71 | 4 | 50 |
| **May 4** | **PO SF1** | **H** | **Maidstone United** | **1011** | **L** | **0-2** | | | 51 |
| **8** | **PO SF2** | **A** | **Maidstone United** | **2508** | **L** | **0-1** | | | 52 |

| GOALSCORERS | Scoring Games | Consec Sco Games | Total | | Scoring Games | Consec Sco Games | Total |
|---|---|---|---|---|---|---|---|
| ***2014-15 Duff*** | | | ***19*** | Duff | 4 | | 4 |
| Vassell | 12 | 4 | 13 | Reid | 3 | | 3 |
| Brett | 7 | | 7 | Ash | 2 | | 2 |
| White | 7 | 2 | 7 | Dawson | 2 | | 2 |
| Green | 6 | | 6 | Knowles | 2 | | 2 |
| Jay | 6 | | 6 | Richards | 2 | | 2 |
| Wright | 6 | 2 | 6 | Riley-Lowe | 2 | | 2 |
| Pugh | 5 | | 5 | Opponents | | | 1 |
| Afful | 3 | | 4 | | | | |
| Cooke | 4 | | 4 | | | | |

# WEALDSTONE

**Chairman:** Peter Marsden
**Secretary:** Paul Fruin **(T)** 0779 003 8095 **(E)** clubsecretary@wealdstonefc.com
**Commercial Manager:** Kevin Tye **(T/E)** kevintye@wealdstonefc.com
**Programme Editor:** Mark Hyde **(T/E)** wfcprogramme@googlemail.com
**Ground Address:** St. Georges Stadium, Grosvenor Vale, Ruislip, Middlesex HA4 6JQ
**(T)** 07790 038 095 - 01895 637 487 (SC) **Manager:** Gordon Bartlett

## Club Factfile

**Founded:** 1899 **Nickname:** The Stones
**Previous Names:** None
**Previous Leagues:** Willesden & District 1899-1906, 08-13, London 1911-22, Middlesex 1913-22, Spartan 1922-28, Athenian 1928-64, Isthmian 1964-71, 95-2006, 2007-14. Southern 1971-79, 81-82, 88-95, Conference 1979-81, 82-88

**Club Colours (change):** Royal blue/white/royal blue (All yellow)

**Ground Capacity:** 2,300 **Seats:** 300 **Covered:** 450 **Clubhouse:** Yes **Shop:**

**Directions**
**From the M1:** Follow Signs for Heathrow Airport on the M25. Come off at Junction 16 onto the A40, come off at The Polish War Memorial junction A4180 sign posted to Ruislip, continue on West End Road, right into Grosvenor Vale after approx 1.5 miles, the ground is at the end of the road.
**From the M25:** Follow Take Junction 16 Off M25 onto A40. Then come off at The Polish War Memorial junction A4180 sign posted to Ruislip, continue on West End Road, right into Grosvenor Vale after approx 1.5 miles, the ground is at the end of the road.
**From the M4:** Junction 4B, take the M25 towards Watford, come off Junction 16 and join A40, come off at The Polish War Memorial junction A4180 sign posted to Ruislip, continue on West End Road, right into Grosvenor Vale after approx 1.5 miles, the ground is at the end of the road.

**Previous Grounds:** Lower Mead Stadium, Watford FC, Yeading FC, Northwood FC

**Record Attendance:** 13,504 v Leytonstone - FA Amateur Cup 4th Round replay 05/03/1949 (at Lower Mead Stadium)
**Record Victory:** 22-0 v The 12th London Regiment (The Rangers) - FA Amateur Cup 13/10/1923
**Record Defeat:** 0-14 v Edgware Town (A) - London Senior Cup 09/12/1944
**Record Goalscorer:** George Duck - 251
**Record Appearances:** Charlie Townsend - 514
**Additional Records:** Paid £15,000 to Barnet for David Gipp
Received £70,000 from Leeds United for Jermaine Beckford
**Honours:**
Athenian League 1951-52. Southern League Division 1 South 1973-74, Southern Division 1981-82. Conference 1984-85.
Isthmian League Division 3 1996-97, Premier 2013-14. FA Amateur Cup 1965-66. London Senior Cup 1961-62. FA Trophy 1984-85.
Middlesex Senior Cup x11

## 10 YEAR RECORD

| 06-07 | 07-08 | 08-09 | 09-10 | 10-11 | 11-12 | 12-13 | 13-14 | 14-15 | 15-16 |
|---|---|---|---|---|---|---|---|---|---|
| SthP 19 | Isth P 13 | Isth P 7 | Isth P 6 | Isth P 12 | Isth P 4 | Isth P 3 | Isth P 1 | Conf S 12 | Nat S 13 |

# WEALDSTONE MATCH RESULTS 2015-16

| Date | Comp | H/A | Opponents | Att: | Result | | Goalscorers | Pos | No. |
|---|---|---|---|---|---|---|---|---|---|
| Aug 8 | Nat South | A | Bath City | 641 | L | 1-2 | Wright 36 | 17 | 1 |
| 10 | Nat South | H | Concord Rangers | 664 | L | 1-2 | Godfrey 45 | 20 | 2 |
| 15 | Nat South | H | Eastbourne Borough | 561 | L | 0-1 | | 21 | 3 |
| 18 | Nat South | A | Margate | 677 | D | 0-0 | | 20 | 4 |
| 22 | Nat South | H | Ebbsfleet United | 764 | L | 1-2 | Hudson-Odoi 41 | 20 | 5 |
| 29 | Nat South | A | Sutton United | 803 | L | 2-5 | Spence 33 (og) Hudson-Odoi 49 | 20 | 6 |
| 31 | Nat South | H | Bishops Stortford | 663 | W | 3-1 | Hamblin 15 Hutchinson 75 Louis 90 | 18 | 7 |
| Sept 5 | Nat South | A | Hayes & Yeading | 359 | D | 0-0 | | 18 | 8 |
| 12 | Nat South | H | Chelmsford City | 803 | D | 0-0 | | 18 | 9 |
| 19 | Nat South | A | Basingstoke Town | 536 | D | 1-1 | Ball 11 | 20 | 10 |
| **26** | **FAC2Q** | **H** | **Biggleswade Town** | **320** | **D** | **1-1** | **Ball 41** | | 11 |
| **29** | **FAC2Q r** | **A** | **Biggleswadw Town** | **264** | **W** | **2-0** | **Louis 62 Lucien 75** | | 12 |
| Oct 3 | Nat South | H | Dartford | 665 | W | 2-1 | Hamblin 43 Lucien 56 | 17 | 13 |
| **10** | **FAC3Q** | **A** | **Brockenhurst** | **477** | **W** | **5-1** | **Louis 13 Hamblin 52 Nwachuckwu (og) 72 Davies 89 Wright 90** | | 14 |
| 17 | Nat South | A | Havant & Waterlooville | 736 | W | 2-1 | Hudson-Odie 19 Louis 39 | 16 | 15 |
| **24** | **FAC4Q** | **H** | **Bognor Regis Town** | **847** | **W** | **2-1** | **Hudson-Odie 14 Hamblin 61** | | 16 |
| 31 | Nat South | A | Ebbsfleet United | 1121 | W | 3-2 | Harriott 2 44 Louis 61 | 15 | 17 |
| **Nov 7** | **FAC1** | **H** | **Colchester United** | **2469** | **L** | **2-6** | **Louis 31 (pen) Hudson-Odie 38** | | 18 |
| 14 | Nat South | A | St Albans City | 708 | L | 0-1 | | 18 | 19 |
| 17 | Nat South | A | Maidstone United | 1812 | L | 0-1 | | 18 | 20 |
| 21 | Nat South | H | Bath City | 602 | W | 2-0 | Louis 3 Ball 87 | 16 | 21 |
| 24 | Nat South | H | Whichelow | 545 | D | 2-2 | Wright 17 Hutchinson 90 | 16 | 22 |
| **28** | **FAT3Q** | **A** | **Met Police** | **152** | **W** | **2-0** | **Hudson-Odie 34 Wright 46** | | 23 |
| Dec 5 | Nat South | H | Weston-s-Mare | 534 | L | 2-3 | Wright 5 Jefferson 85 | 17 | 24 |
| 19 | Nat South | A | Chelmsford City | 873 | W | 2-0 | Parker 15 Hudson 46 | 16 | 25 |
| 26 | Nat South | A | Hemel Hempstead | 751 | D | 2-2 | Parker 31 Wright 77 | 19 | 26 |
| Jan 9 | Nat South | A | Gosport Borough | 593 | D | 1-1 | Louis 35 (pen) | 16 | 27 |
| **13** | **FAT1** | **A** | **Weston-s-Mare** | **155** | **L** | **2-3** | **Hudson-Odie 42 75** | **16** | 28 |
| 18 | Nat South | H | Gosport Borough | 506 | D | 1-1 | Hudson-Odie 46 | 16 | 29 |
| 23 | Nat South | A | Eastbourne Borough | 431 | L | 0-3 | | 17 | 30 |
| 26 | Nat South | A | Dartford | 853 | W | 2-1 | McGleish 76 Louis 82 | 15 | 31 |
| Feb 6 | Nat South | H | Truro City | 606 | D | 4-4 | Ball 5 Louis 37 Harriott 42 Pugh 48 (og) | 15 | 32 |
| 13 | Nat South | A | Maidenhead United | 524 | D | 1-1 | Parker 24 | 15 | 33 |
| 15 | Nat South | H | Oxford City | 663 | D | 2-2 | Hudson-Odie 38 63 | 15 | 34 |
| 20 | Nat South | A | Weston-s-Mare | 455 | W | 2-1 | Morgan 24 Davies 53 | 14 | 35 |
| 27 | Nat South | H | Basingstoke Town | 641 | D | 4-4 | Harriott 4 74 Wright 60 Hudson-Odie 90 | 14 | 36 |
| Mar 5 | Nat South | A | Concord Rangers | 276 | D | 2-2 | Louis 69 Davies 78 | 14 | 37 |
| 12 | Nat South | H | Maidstone United | 815 | D | 2-2 | Harriott 35 Wright 56 | 16 | 38 |
| 14 | Nat South | H | Hayes &Yeading | 638 | W | 3-0 | Louis 8 Davies 12 Harriott 21 | 13 | 39 |
| 19 | Nat South | A | Oxford City | 393 | L | 2-3 | Hudson-Odie 26 46 | 15 | 40 |
| 21 | Nat South | H | Sutton United | 631 | L | 0-2 | | 15 | 41 |
| 26 | Nat South | H | Margate | 750 | W | 4-1 | Parker 5 Wright 33 Hudson-Odie 51 Hamblin 82 | 13 | 42 |
| Apr 2 | Nat South | H | Havant & Waterlooville | 646 | W | 3-2 | Louis 67 Demetriou74 Wright 65 | 11 | 43 |
| 4 | Nat South | H | Hemel Hempsead | 753 | D | 0-0 | | 11 | 44 |
| 9 | Nat South | A | Whitehawk | 424 | L | 0-3 | | 13 | 45 |
| 16 | Nat South | H | Maidenhead United | 800 | D | 0-0 | | 14 | 46 |
| 19 | Nat South | A | Bishops Stortford | 337 | L | 1-2 | Lucien 54 | 14 | 47 |
| 23 | Nat South | H | St Albans City | 777 | D | 1-1 | Kalczim 38 (og) | 15 | 48 |
| 30 | Nat South | A | Truro City | 719 | W | 2-1 | Louis 73 82 (pen) | 13 | 49 |

| GOALSCORERS | Scoring Games | Consec Sco Games | Total |
|---|---|---|---|
| ***2014-15 Louis and McGleish*** | | | ***10*** |
| Hudson-Odie | 12 | 2 | 16 |
| Louis | 13 | 2 | 14 |
| Wright | 10 | 3 | 10 |
| Hamblin | 5 | 2 | 5 |
| Harriott | 4 | | 5 |
| Ball | 4 | 2 | 4 |
| Davies | 4 | | 4 |
| Parker | 4 | | 4 |
| Lucien | 3 | 2 | 3 |
| Louis | 3 | | 3 |
| Hurchinson | 2 | | 2 |
| Demetriou | 1 | | 1 |
| Godfrey | 1 | | 1 |
| Jefferson | 1 | | 1 |
| McGleish | 1 | | 1 |
| Morgan | 1 | | 1 |
| Opposition | | | 4 |

# WELLING UNITED

**Chairman:** Paul Websdale
**Secretary:** Barrie Hobbins (T) 0208 301 1196 (E) wufcsecretary@hotmail.com
**Commercial Manager:** Paul White (T/E) commercial@wellingunited.com
**Programme Editor:** (T/E)
**Ground Address:** Park View Road Ground, Welling, Kent DA16 1SY
(T) 0208 301 1196 **Manager:** Mark Goldberg

## Club Factfile

**Founded:** 1963 **Nickname:** The Wings
**Previous Names:** None
**Previous Leagues:** Eltham & District 1963-71, London Spartan 1971-77, Athenian 1978-81, Southern 1981-86, 2000-04, Conference 1986-2000

**Club Colours (change):** Red/red/white (Sky blue & navy/navy & sky blue/navy)

**Ground Capacity:** 4,000 **Seats:** 1,070 **Covered:** 1,500 **Clubhouse:** Yes **Shop:** Yes

**Directions**
M25 to Dartford then A2 towards London.
Take Bexleyheath/Blackfen/Sidcup,turn off (six miles along A2) then follow A207 signed welling.
Ground is 1 mile From A2 on main road towards Welling High Street.

**Previous Grounds:** Butterfly Lane, Eltham 1963-78

**Record Attendance:** 4,100 v Gillingham - FA Cup
**Record Victory:** 7-1 v Dorking - 1985-86
**Record Defeat:** 0-7 v Welwyn Garden City - 1972-73
**Record Goalscorer:** Not known - If you know please email tw.publications@btinternet.com
**Record Appearances:** Not known - If you know please email tw.publications@btinternet.com
**Additional Records:** Paid £30,000 to Enfield for Gary Abbott
Received £95,000 from Birmingham City for Steve Finnan 1995
**Honours:**
Southern League 1985-86. Conference South 2012-13.
Kent Senior Cup 1985-86, 98-99, 2008-09. London Senior Cup 1989-90. London Challenge Cup 1991-92.

**10 YEAR RECORD**

| 06-07 | 07-08 | 08-09 | 09-10 | 10-11 | 11-12 | 12-13 | 13-14 | 14-15 | 15-16 |
|---|---|---|---|---|---|---|---|---|---|
| Conf S 8 | Conf S 16 | Conf S 7 | Conf S 9 | Conf S 6 | Conf S 3 | Conf S 1 | Conf 16 | Conf 20 | Nat 24 |

# WELLING UNITED MATCH RESULTS 2015-16

| Date | Comp | H/A | Opponents | Att: | Result | | Goalscorers | Pos | No. |
|---|---|---|---|---|---|---|---|---|---|
| Aug 8 | Nat Lge | H | Guiseley | 505 | **W** | 1-0 | Kabba 40 | 10 | 1 |
| 11 | Nat Lge | A | Forest Green Rovers | 1076 | L | 0-1 | | 13 | 2 |
| 15 | Nat Lge | A | Macclesfield Town | 1236 | L | 1-2 | Kabba 90 | 16 | 3 |
| 18 | Nat Lge | H | Eastleigh | 545 | D | 2-2 | Partington 31 (og) Vidal 71 | 14 | 4 |
| 22 | Nat Lge | A | Wrexham | 4277 | L | 0-1 | | 16 | 5 |
| 29 | Nat Lge | H | Braintree Town | 521 | L | 1-2 | Obafemi 6 | 20 | 6 |
| 31 | Nat Lge | A | Woking | 1675 | L | 0-2 | | 21 | 7 |
| Sept 5 | Nat Lge | H | Tranmere Rovers | 1012 | D | 1-1 | Vidal 9 | 21 | 8 |
| 12 | Nat Lge | H | Torquay United | 659 | D | 1-1 | Corne 87 | 21 | 9 |
| 15 | Nat Lge | A | Aldershot Town | 1256 | L | 0-1 | | 20 | 10 |
| 19 | Nat Lge | A | Gateshead | 822 | **W** | 2-1 | Russell 24 (og) Vidal 29 | 18 | 11 |
| 22 | Nat Lge | H | Chester | 564 | **W** | 2-1 | Harris 43 Wellard 70 | 18 | 12 |
| 26 | Nat Lge | H | FC Halifax Town | 653 | **W** | 2-0 | Kabba 44 45 | 18 | 13 |
| Oct 3 | Nat Lge | A | Kidderminster Harriers | 1438 | **W** | 1-0 | Porter 49 | 15 | 14 |
| 6 | Nat Lge | H | Bromley | 1127 | L | 1-2 | Chambers 4 | 17 | 15 |
| 10 | Nat Lge | A | Boreham Wood | 543 | L | 0-2 | | 17 | 16 |
| 13 | Nat Lge | H | Lincoln City | 702 | **W** | 2-1 | Corne 42 Obafemi 85 | 17 | 17 |
| 17 | Nat Lge | A | Barrow | 1327 | D | 1-1 | Williams (og) 42 | 17 | 18 |
| **25** | **FAC4Q** | **A** | **Grays Athletic** | **512** | **D** | **1-1** | **Corne 83** | | 19 |
| **27** | **FAC4Qr** | **H** | **Grays Athletic** | **733** | **W** | **4-0** | **VIDAL 4 ( 24 53 70 82)** | | 20 |
| 31 | Nat Lge | A | Guiseley | 653 | L | 0-2 | | 18 | 21 |
| **Nov 7** | **FAC1** | **A** | **Barwell** | **843** | **W** | **2-0** | **Wellard 34 Bakare 90** | | 22 |
| 10 | Nat Lge | H | Forest Green Rovers | 660 | D | 1-1 | Bakare 63 | 18 | 23 |
| 14 | Nat Lge | A | Grimsby Town | 4108 | L | 1-3 | Come 7 | 18 | 24 |
| 21 | Nat Lge | H | Southport | 603 | L | 0-1 | | 19 | 25 |
| 28 | Nat Lge | A | Lincoln City | 2528 | D | 1-1 | Harris 45 | | 26 |
| **Dec 5** | **FAC2** | **H** | **Carlisle United** | **2028** | **L** | **0-5** | | | 27 |
| **12** | **FAT1** | **A** | **Tilbury** | **186** | **W** | **4-3** | **St Aimie 7 Porter 33 42 Wellard 90** | | 28 |
| 19 | Nat Lge | H | Macclesfield Town | 577 | L | 0-1 | | 20 | 29 |
| 26 | Nat Lge | H | Dover Athletic | 1006 | L | 1-2 | Corne 90 | 21 | 30 |
| Jan 9 | Nat Lge | H | Grimsby Town | 1337 | L | 0-4 | | 22 | 31 |
| **16** | **FAT2** | **A** | **Havant & Waterlooville** | **371** | **L** | **1-2** | **Harris 19** | | 32 |
| 23 | Nat Lge | H | Barrow | 542 | L | 1-2 | Vidal 28 (pen) | 22 | 33 |
| 30 | Nat Lge | A | FC Halifax Town | 1407 | D | 1-1 | Daniel 79 | 22 | 34 |
| Feb 2 | Nat Lge | A | Braintree Town | 461 | L | 0-1 | | 22 | 35 |
| 6 | Nat Lge | H | Altrincham | 551 | D | 1-1 | Kabba 90 | 22 | 36 |
| 13 | Nat Lge | A | Cheltenham Town | 2549 | L | 0-2 | | 22 | 37 |
| 20 | Nat Lge | H | Wrexham | 620 | L | 0-2 | | 22 | 38 |
| 23 | Nat Lge | A | Torquay United | 1341 | L | 0-2 | | 22 | 39 |
| 27 | Nat Lge | H | Aldershot Town | 704 | L | 0-1 | | 22 | 40 |
| 29 | Nat Lge | A | Bromley | 1110 | L | 0-2 | | 22 | 41 |
| Mar 5 | Nat Lge | H | Cheltenham Town | 604 | D | 1-1 | Wanadio 90 | 23 | 42 |
| 8 | Nat Lge | A | Dover Athletic | 726 | L | 1-2 | Bakare 2 | 23 | 43 |
| 12 | Nat Lge | A | Southport | 746 | D | 3-3 | Bakare 74 Kabba 82 Gayle 89 | 23 | 44 |
| 19 | Nat Lge | H | Gateshead | 500 | L | 0-1 | | 23 | 45 |
| 25 | Nat Lge | A | Eastleigh | 2037 | D | 0-0 | | 23 | 46 |
| 28 | Nat Lge | H | Woking | 550 | **W** | 2-1 | Lokko 28 Nortey 62 | 23 | 47 |
| Apr 2 | Nat Lge | A | Tranmere Rovers | 5173 | **W** | 2-1 | Gayle 20 Daniel 72 | 23 | 48 |
| 9 | Nat Lge | H | Kidderminster Harriers | 565 | L | 1-2 | Daniel 7 | 23 | 49 |
| 16 | Nat Lge | A | Chester | 2737 | L | 0-4 | | 24 | 50 |
| 23 | Nat Lge | A | Altrincham | 1396 | L | 0-5 | | 24 | 51 |
| 30 | Nat Lge | H | Boreham Wood | 577 | L | 0-3 | | 24 | 52 |

| GOALSCORERS | Scoring Games | Consec Sco Games | Total |
|---|---|---|---|
| ***2014-15 Beautyman*** | ***11*** | | |
| Vidal | 5 | | 8 |
| Kabba | 5 | | 6 |
| Corne | 5 | | 5 |
| Bakare | 4 | 2 | 4 |
| Daniel | 3 | | 3 |
| Harris | 3 | | 3 |
| Porter | 2 | | 3 |
| Wellard | 3 | | 3 |
| Gayle | 2 | | 2 |
| Obafemi | 2 | | 2 |
| Chambers | 1 | | 1 |
| Lokko | 1 | | 1 |
| Nortey | 1 | | 1 |
| St Aimie | 1 | | 1 |
| Wanadio | 1 | | 1 |
| Opponents | | | 3 |

# WESTON-SUPER-MARE

**Chairman:** Paul Bliss
**Secretary:** Richard Sloane **(T)** 01934 621 618 **(E)** wsmsecretary@gmail.com
**Commercial Manager:** Neil Keeling **(T/E)** 01934 621 618
**Programme Editor:** **(T/E)**
**Ground Address:** Woodspring Stadium, Winterstoke Road, Weston-super-Mare BS24 9AA
**(T)** 01934 621 618 **Manager:** Ryan Northmore

## Club Factfile

**Founded:** 1899 **Nickname:** Seagulls
**Previous Names:** Borough or Weston-super-Mare
**Previous Leagues:** Somerset Senior, Western League

**Club Colours (change):** White & black halves/black/white & black (Navy blue & red halves/red/navy blue & red)

**Ground Capacity:** 3,000 **Seats:** 278 **Covered:** 2,000 **Clubhouse:** Yes **Shop:** Yes

**Directions**
Leave the M5 at Junction 21, take the dual carriageway A370 and continue straight until the 4th roundabout with ASDA on the right.
Turn left into Winterstoke Road, bypassing a mini roundabout and continue for 1/2 mile.
Woodspring Stadium is on the right.

**Previous Grounds:** Langford Road, Winterstoke Road

**Record Attendance:** 2,623 v Woking - FA Cup 1st Round replay 23/11/1993 (At Winterstoke Road)
**Record Victory:** 11-0 v Paulton Rovers
**Record Defeat:** 1-12 v Yeovil Town Reserves
**Record Goalscorer:** Matt Lazenby - 180
**Record Appearances:** Harry Thomas - 740
**Additional Records:** Received £20,000 from Sheffield Wednesday for Stuart Jones

**Honours:**
Somerset Senior Cup 1923-24, 26-67.
Western League 1991-92.

### 10 YEAR RECORD

| 06-07 | 07-08 | 08-09 | 09-10 | 10-11 | 11-12 | 12-13 | 13-14 | 14-15 | 15-16 |
|---|---|---|---|---|---|---|---|---|---|
| Conf S 21 | Conf S 20 | Conf S 17 | Conf S 21 | Conf S 12 | Conf S 13 | Conf S 7 | Conf S 11 | Conf S 17 | Nat S 16 |

# WESTON-SUPER-MARE MATCH RESULTS 2015-16

| Date | Comp | H/A | Opponents | Att: | Result | | Goalscorers | Pos | No. |
|---|---|---|---|---|---|---|---|---|---|
| Aug 8 | Nat South | A | Concord Rangers | 267 | L | 1-4 | Plummer 75 (pen) | 21 | 1 |
| 11 | Nat South | H | Gosport Borough | 349 | L | 0-4 | | 22 | 2 |
| 15 | Nat South | H | Hemel Hempstead Town | 368 | L | 2-4 | Fortune 64 Withey 78 | 22 | 3 |
| 22 | Nat South | H | Eastbourne Borough | 326 | L | 1-2 | Grubb 18 | 22 | 4 |
| 29 | Nat South | A | Oxford City | 202 | L | 0-3 | | 22 | 5 |
| 31 | Nat South | H | Bath City | 720 | D | 1-1 | Barnes 86 | 22 | 6 |
| Sept 5 | Nat South | A | Bishops Stortford | 348 | W | 1-0 | Wilson 45 | 22 | 7 |
| 12 | Nat South | A | Dartford | 802 | L | 1-2 | Grubb 81 | 22 | 8 |
| 15 | Nat South | H | Truro City | 360 | D | 2-2 | Barnes 47 Wilson 88 | 21 | 9 |
| 19 | Nat South | H | Sutton United | 368 | L | 0-2 | | 22 | 10 |
| 22 | Nat South | A | Ebbsfleet United | 2045 | L | 1-2 | Filipov 65 | 22 | 11 |
| **26** | **FAC2Q** | **A** | **Hook Norton** | **533** | **W** | **2-0** | **Ash 79 (pen) Wilson 85** | | **12** |
| Oct 3 | Nat South | A | Margate | 650 | W | 2-0 | Ash 10 19 | 21 | 13 |
| **10** | **FAC3Q** | **A** | **Wingate &Finchley** | **337** | **W** | **3-1** | **Ash 9 52 Mawford 27** | | **14** |
| 17 | Nat South | A | Maidenhead United | 432 | L | 0-2 | | 21 | 15 |
| **24** | **FAC4Q** | **A** | **St Albans City** | **829** | **L** | **1-2** | **Withey 56** | | **16** |
| 31 | Nat South | A | Whitehawk | 282 | W | 2-0 | Ash 6 31 | 20 | 17 |
| Nov 7 | Nat South | H | Concord Rangers | 369 | L | 0-3 | | 20 | 18 |
| 14 | Nat South | A | Gosport Borough | 387 | L | 0-1 | | 21 | 19 |
| 21 | Nat South | H | St Albans City | 398 | W | 4-1 | ASH 3 ( 51 52 71 ) Wilson 90 | | 20 |
| 24 | Nat South | H | Havant & Waterlooville | 329 | W | 3-2 | Barnes 20 Ash 37 Wilson 78 | 20 | 21 |
| **28** | **FAT3Q** | **H** | **Hitchin Town** | **175** | **W** | **4-0** | **Wilson 12 McClennon 25 Mawford 64 Ash 74** | | **22** |
| Dec 5 | Nat South | A | Wealdstone | 534 | W | 3-2 | McClennan 47 Ash 55 Fortune 90 | 18 | 23 |
| 19 | Nat South | H | Bishops Stortford | 320 | D | 1-1 | Wilson 72 | 19 | 24 |
| 26 | Nat South | A | Hayes & Yeading | 175 | D | 1-1 | Wilson 48 | 19 | 25 |
| Jan 9 | Nat South | A | Chelmsford City | 737 | W | 3-2 | Cane 26 Grubb 48 60 | | 26 |
| **13** | **FAT1** | **H** | **Wealdstone** | **155** | **W** | **3-2** | **WILSON 3 (17 23 90)** | | **27** |
| **16** | **FAT2** | **A** | **Grimsby Town** | **1230** | **L** | **1-3** | **Grubb 22** | | **28** |
| 30 | Nat South | A | Hemel Hempstead Town | 408 | D | 5-5 | GRUBB 3 (40 47 66) Herd 43 (og) Plummer 89 | 18 | 29 |
| Feb 10 | Nat South | H | Oxford City | 280 | W | 5-2 | Plummer 9 Withey 19 Wilson 32 87 Cooper 76 | | 30 |
| 13 | Nat South | A | Eastbourne Borough | 351 | D | 3-3 | Plummer 68 Grubb 79 Varokakis 90 | 17 | 31 |
| 16 | Nat South | H | Hayes & Yeading | 340 | L | 0-2 | | 18 | 32 |
| 20 | Nat South | H | Wealdstone | 455 | L | 1-2 | McClennon 8 | 19 | 33 |
| 27 | Nat South | H | Chelmsford City | 406 | L | 0-3 | | 20 | 34 |
| Mar 5 | Nat South | H | Dartford | 436 | W | 2-1 | Wilson 12 32 | 20 | 35 |
| 8 | Nat South | A | St Albans City | 300 | L | 1-2 | Wilson 36 | 20 | 36 |
| 12 | Nat South | A | Sutton United | 850 | D | 0-0 | | 20 | 37 |
| 15 | Nat South | H | Maidstone United | 368 | L | 1-2 | Wilson 79 (pen) | 20 | 38 |
| 19 | Nat South | A | Maidstone United | 2143 | L | 1-3 | Wilson 24 | 21 | 39 |
| 25 | Nat South | H | Ebbsfleet United | 604 | W | 2-1 | Grubb 55 66 | 20 | 40 |
| 28 | Nat South | A | Bath City | 827 | L | 1-2 | Wilson 90 | 21 | 41 |
| Apr 2 | Nat South | H | Margate | 416 | W | 1-0 | Mawford 83 | 20 | 42 |
| 5 | Nat South | H | Basingstoke Town | 396 | W | 2-1 | Grubb 60 77 | 16 | 43 |
| 9 | Nat South | A | Basingstoke Town | 400 | D | 2-2 | Barnes 64 Wilson 78 | 17 | 44 |
| 12 | Nat South | A | Truro City | 472 | W | 3-1 | Wilson 9 McClennan 75 Mawford 90 | 17 | 45 |
| 16 | Nat South | H | Whitehawk | 565 | L | 1-2 | Varouxakis 89 | 17 | 46 |
| 23 | Nat South | H | Maidenhead United | 491 | W | 2-0 | Wilson 52 (pen) Grubb 78 | 16 | 47 |
| 30 | Nat South | A | Havant & Waterlooville | 885 | D | 1-1 | Wilson 73 | 16 | 48 |

| GOALSCORERS | Scoring Games | Consec Sco Games | Total | | Scoring Games | Consec Sco Games | Total |
|---|---|---|---|---|---|---|---|
| ***2014-15 Grubb*** | | | ***13*** | Varouxakis | 2 | | 2 |
| Wilson | 18 | 3 | 23 | Cane | 1 | | 1 |
| Grubb | 9 | 2 | 14 | Cooper | 1 | | 1 |
| Ash | 8 | 3 | 13 | Filipov | 1 | | 1 |
| Barnes | 4 | | 4 | Opponents | | | 1 |
| Mawford | 4 | | 4 | | | | |
| McClennon | 4 | | 4 | | | | |
| Plummer | 4 | | 4 | | | | |
| Withey | 3 | | 3 | | | | |
| Fortune | 2 | | 2 | | | | |

# WHITEHAWK

**Chairman:** John Summers
**Secretary:** John Rosenblatt **(T)** 07724 519 370 **(E)** johnrosenblatt@whitehawkfc.com
**Commercial Manager:** Adam Ross **(T/E)** 07422 502 780
**Programme Editor:** **(T/E)**
**Ground Address:** The Enclosed Ground, East Brighton Park, Wilson Avenue, Brighton BN2 5TS
**(T)** 01273 601 244 **Manager:** Pablo Asensio - Feb 2016

## Club Factfile

**Founded:** 1945 **Nickname:** Hawks
**Previous Names:** Whitehawk & Manor Farm Old Boys untill 1958.
**Previous Leagues:** Brighton & Hove District, Sussex County > 2010. Isthmian 2010-13.

**Club Colours (change):** All red (All blue)

**Ground Capacity:** 3,000 **Seats:** Yes **Covered:** 500 **Clubhouse:** Yes **Shop:** No

**Directions**
From N (London) on M23/A23 – after passing Brighton boundary sign & twin pillars join A27 (sp Lewes); immediately after passing Sussex University (on L) leave A27 via slip rd at sp B2123, Falmer, Rottingdean; at roundabout at top of slip rd turn R onto B2123 (sp Falmer, Rottingdean); in 2m at traffic lights in Woodingdean turn R by Downs Hotel into Warren Road; in about 1m at traffic lights turn L into Wilson Ave, crossing racecourse; in 1¼m turn L at foot of hill (last turning before traffic lights) into East Brighton Park; follow lane for the ground.

**Previous Grounds:** None

**Record Attendance:** 2,100 v Bognor Regis Town - FA Cup 1988-89
**Record Victory:** Not known - If you know please email tw.publications@btinternet.com
**Record Defeat:** Not known - If you know please email tw.publications@btinternet.com
**Record Goalscorer:** Billy Ford
**Record Appearances:** Ken Powell - 1,103
**Additional Records:**

**Honours:**
Sussex County League Division 1 1961-62, 63-64, 83-84, 2009-10. Division 2 1967-68, 80-81.
Isthmian League Division 1 South 2011-12, Premier Division 2012-13.
Sussex Senior Cup 1950-51, 61-62, 2011-12, 14-15. Sussex RUR Charity Cup x3.

### 10 YEAR RECORD

| 06-07 | | 07-08 | | 08-09 | | 09-10 | | 10-11 | | 11-12 | | 12-13 | | 13-14 | | 14-15 | | 15-16 | |
|---|---|---|---|---|---|---|---|---|---|---|---|---|---|---|---|---|---|---|---|
| SxC1 | 2 | SxC1 | 2 | SxC1 | 13 | SxC1 | 1 | Isth1S | 3 | Isth1S | 1 | Isth P | 1 | Conf S | 19 | Conf S | 4 | Nat S | 5 |

## WHITEHAWK MATCH RESULTS 2015-16

| Date | Comp | H/A | Opponents | Att: | Result | | Goalscorers | Pos | No. |
|---|---|---|---|---|---|---|---|---|---|
| Aug 8 | Nat South | A | Hayes & Yeading | 189 | W | 4-3 | Robinson 33 Torres 45 Mills 54 56 | 4 | 1 |
| 11 | Nat South | H | Margate | 288 | D | 2-2 | Robinson 12 40 | 8 | 2 |
| 15 | Nat South | H | Bath City | 219 | L | 0-1 | | 9 | 3 |
| 18 | Nat South | A | Gosport Borough | 412 | D | 2-2 | Neilson 48 Deering 53 | 12 | 4 |
| 22 | Nat South | H | Chelmsford City | 231 | W | 4-2 | Neilson 5 14 Deering 22 Mills 65 | 8 | 5 |
| 29 | Nat South | A | Ebbsfleet United | 972 | D | 2-2 | Ijaha 21 Deering 37 | 12 | 6 |
| 31 | Nat South | H | Sutton United | 307 | W | 2-0 | Mills 13 Fenelon 14 | 8 | 7 |
| Dept 5 | Nat South | A | Oxford City | 361 | D | 0-0 | | 8 | 8 |
| 12 | Nat South | H | Maidenhead United | 197 | W | 3-2 | Fenelon 58 Mills 76 Rose 90 | 5 | 9 |
| 15 | Nat South | A | Havant & Waterlooville | 539 | W | 3-2 | Mills 13 Robinson 84 Neilson 90 | 5 | 10 |
| 19 | Nat South | A | Concord Rangers | 236 | W | 2-1 | Robinson 41 Mills 75 | 3 | 11 |
| **26** | **FAC2Q** | **H** | **Dulwich Hamlet** | **355** | **W** | **4-2** | **Deering 8 (pen) MILLS 3 ( 37 57 90)** | | 12 |
| Oct 3 | Nat South | H | St Albans City | 228 | W | 6-0 | Mills 16 Deering 43 90 Martin 65 Arnold 70 Ngamvoulou 85 | 3 | 13 |
| **10** | **FAC3Q** | **H** | **Gosport Borough** | **410** | **D** | **2-2** | **Mills 2 90** | | 14 |
| **13** | **FAC3Qr** | **A** | **Gosport Borough** | **330** | **W** | **2-1** | **Neilson 53 Robinson 82** | | 15 |
| 17 | Nat South | H | Truro City | 256 | D | 0-0 | | 3 | 16 |
| **24** | **FAC4Q** | **H** | **Poole Town** | **450** | **W** | **2-0** | **Mills 47 Deering 90** | | 17 |
| 27 | Nat South | A | Basingstoke Town | 518 | L | 1-3 | Deering 50 | 3 | 18 |
| 31 | Nat South | H | Weston-s-Mare | 282 | L | 0-2 | | 4 | 19 |
| **Nov 7** | **FAC1** | **H** | **Lincoln City** | **1342** | **W** | **5-3** | **Mills 6 Robinson 27 Deering 58 90 (pen) Martin 86** | | 20 |
| 14 | Nat South | A | Margate | 590 | W | 6-2 | Mendy 5 Rose 28 60 NEILSON 3 ( 52 55 74) | 4 | 21 |
| 21 | Nat South | H | Concord Rangers | 372 | L | 0-2 | | 4 | 22 |
| 23 | Nat South | A | Wealdstone | 545 | D | 2-2 | Mills 59 66 | 4 | 23 |
| **28** | **FAT3Q** | **A** | **Dartford** | **601** | **W** | **2-1** | **Deering 75 Stevens 84** | | 24 |
| **Dec 5** | **FAC2** | **A** | **Dagenham & Redbridge** | **1983** | **D** | **1-1** | **Rose 90** | | 25 |
| 8 | Nat South | A | Maidstone United | 1743 | W | 1-0 | Martin 45 | 4 | 26 |
| **12** | **FAT1** | **H** | **Dover Athletic** | **372** | **L** | **1-3** | **Neilson 87** | | 27 |
| **16** | **FAC2r** | **H** | **Dagenham & Redbridge** | **2174** | **L** | **2-3** | **Mills 32 Gotta 90 (aet)** | | 28 |
| 19 | Nat South | H | Dartford | 347 | L | 0-1 | | 5 | 29 |
| 26 | Nat South | A | Eastbourne Borough | 783 | D | 1-1 | Mills 28 | 6 | 30 |
| 29 | Nat South | H | Ebbsfleet United | 639 | L | 0-1 | | 7 | 31 |
| Jan 23 | Nat South | A | Chelmsford City | 697 | L | 3-4 | Robinson 41 Torres 79 Mills 90 | 9 | 32 |
| 16 | Nat South | H | Eastbourne Borough | 295 | L | 1-2 | Neilson 90 | 11 | 33 |
| Feb 20 | Nat South | H | Havant & Waterlooville | 308 | D | 1-1 | Robinson 68 | 13 | 34 |
| 27 | Nat South | A | St Albans City | 470 | L | 0-6 | | 15 | 35 |
| Mar 5 | Nat South | H | Bishops Stortford | 166 | L | 2-3 | Vanderhyde 16 (og) Mills 18 | 17 | 36 |
| 8 | Nat South | H | Hays & Yeading | 96 | L | 1-3 | Leacock 53 | 17 | 37 |
| 12 | Nat South | A | Dartford | 906 | W | 4-2 | MILLS 3 (54 81 90) Neilson 90 | 15 | 38 |
| 15 | Nat South | A | Bishops Stortford | 249 | L | 1-2 | Mills 33 | 15 | 39 |
| 19 | Nat South | H | Basingstoke Town | 301 | W | 1-0 | Robinson 27 | 14 | 40 |
| 22 | Nat South | H | Hemel Hempstead | 209 | L | 0-1 | | 14 | 41 |
| 26 | Nat South | H | Gosport Borough | 375 | W | 3-0 | Mills 32 Osborn 67 Robinson 83 | 12 | 42 |
| 28 | Nat South | A | Sutton United | 1089 | D | 2-2 | Arnold 45 Osborn 61 | 15 | 43 |
| Apr 5 | Nat South | A | Maidenhead United | 441 | L | 0-3 | | 15 | 44 |
| 9 | Nat South | H | Wealdstone | 424 | W | 3-0 | West 10 Mills 18 Martin 74 | 12 | 45 |
| 12 | Nat South | H | Oxford City | 193 | W | 2-0 | Rose 45 78 | 11 | 46 |
| 16 | Nat South | A | Weston-s-Mare | 565 | W | 2-1 | Mills 26 64 | 9 | 47 |
| 19 | Nat South | A | Bath City | 442 | W | 3-0 | Osborn 7 Rose 53 West 59 | 9 | 48 |
| 23 | Nat South | H | Maidstone United | 770 | W | 1-0 | Ijaha 43 | 6 | 49 |
| 26 | Nat South | A | Truro City | 402 | D | 1-1 | Mills 90 | 5 | 50 |
| 30 | Nat South | A | Hemel Hempstead Town | 1138 | W | 3-0 | Martin 25 65 Mills 41 | 5 | 51 |
| **May 3** | **PO SF1** | **H** | **Ebbsfleet United** | **1055** | **L** | **1-2** | **Mills 82** | | 52 |
| **8** | **PO SF2** | **A** | **Ebbsfleet United** | **1942** | **W** | **2-1** | **Arnold 4 Mills 51 (Lost 2-3 on pens)** | | 53 |

| GOALSCORERS | Scoring Games | Consec Sco Games | Total | | Scoring Games | Consec Sco Games | Total |
|---|---|---|---|---|---|---|---|
| *2014-15 Robinson* | | | *21* | Ijaha | 2 | | 2 |
| Mills | 25 | 6 | 33 | Torres | 2 | | 2 |
| Deering | 9 | 3 | 11 | West | 2 | | 2 |
| Robinson | 10 | 2 | 11 | Gotta | 1 | | 1 |
| Neilson | 8 | 2 | 11 | Leacock | 1 | | 1 |
| Rose | 6 | | 7 | Mandy | 1 | | 1 |
| Martin | 4 | | 6 | Ngamvoulou | 1 | | 1 |
| Arnold | 3 | | 3 | Stevens | 1 | | 1 |
| Osborn | 3 | | 3 | Opponents | | | 1 |
| Fenelon | 2 | | 2 | | | | |

## National Division North Statistics 2015-16

| | NoS | GS | CTS | PS | CSG | MCGU | TCS | MCCS | CMWW | CD | FTS | CNG | TGC |
|---|---|---|---|---|---|---|---|---|---|---|---|---|---|
| AFC Fylde | 18+1 | 105 | 9 | 4 | 18 | 10 | 20 | 5 | 3 | 2 | 5 | 1 | 66 |
| AFC Telford United | 16 | 50 | 5 | 5 | 13 | 7 | 12 | 5 | 6 | 4 | 18 | 4 | 65 |
| Alfreton Town | 14+2 | 67 | 4 | 4 | 13 | 10 | 7 | 1 | 6 | 5 | 9 | 2 | 63 |
| Boston United | 14 | 75 | 5 | 6 | 10 | 7 | 11 | 2 | 5 | 4 | 10 | 2 | 66 |
| Brackley Town | 16+1 | 57 | 4 | 0 | 5 | 6 | 14 | 2 | 6 | 3 | 15 | 2 | 63 |
| Bradford PA | 15+1 | 59 | 4 | 5 | 8 | 7 | 11 | 2 | 7 | 4 | 14 | 2 | 70 |
| Chorley | 18+3 | 72 | 4 | 2 | 6 | 5 | 14 | 2 | 6 | 2 | 12 | 3 | 64 |
| Corby Town | 13+2 | 51 | 3 | 7 | 8 | First 6 | 5 | 1 | 14 | 5 | 16 | 3 | 103 |
| Curzon Ashton | 13 | 60 | 4 | 0 | 5 | 7 | 15 | 3 | 7 | 3 | 16 | 3 | 57 |
| FC Utd of Manchester | 18+1 | 71 | 6 | 0 | 13 | 5 | 8 | 3 | 6 | 4 | 11 | 2 | 84 |
| Gainsborough | 13 | 54 | 4 | 1 | 6 | 4 | 11 | 2 | 4 | 4 | 17 | 3 | 68 |
| Gloucester City | 20 | 48 | 4 | 6 | 5 | 6 | 12 | 2 | 11 | 2 | 17 | 2 | 56 |
| Harrogate Town | 14+2 | 79 | 6 | 2 | 11 | 6 | 19 | 4 | 6 | 2 | 12 | 4 | 53 |
| Hednesford Town | 20 | 56 | 4 | 4 | 7 | 4 | 6 | 1 | 12 | 4 | 15 | 3 | 85 |
| Lowestoft Town | 13+3 | 54 | 4 | 4 | 8 | 5 | 12 | 2 | 8 | 6 | 13 | 2 | 74 |
| North Ferriby | 13 | 94 | 4 | 6 | 9 | 16 | 18 | 3 | 5 | 2 | 10 | 2 | 56 |
| Nuneaton Town | 16 | 77 | 5 | 4 | 14 | 9 | 16 | 3 | 5 | 2 | 8 | 2 | 51 |
| Solihull Moors | 13+2 | 92 | 6 | 7 | 14 | 13 | 13 | 2 | 4 | 2 | 6 | 2 | 55 |
| Stalybridge Celtic | 16+1 | 69 | 5 | 3 | 8 | 7 | 13 | 3 | 6 | 3 | 14 | 3 | 82 |
| Stockport County | 20 | 50 | 4 | 3 | 6 | 7 | 15 | 4 | 8 | 3 | 15 | 3 | 52 |
| Tamworth | 13 | 63 | 6 | 4 | 8 | 11 | 11 | 3 | 6 | 5 | 9 | 2 | 55 |
| Worcester City | 17+1 | 66 | 5 | 2 | 8 | 6 | 16 | 2 | 7 | 3 | 13 | 4 | 70 |

+ Denotes number of Own goals I * Denotes unfinished run
NoS - Number of Scorers I GS - Goals Scored I CTS - Club's Top Score I PS - Penalties Scored
CSG - Consecutive Scoring Games I MCGU - Most Consecutive Games Unbeaten I TCS - Total Clean Sheets
MCCS - Most Consecutive Clean Sheets I CMWW - Consecutive Matches Without a Win
CD - Consecutive Defeats I FTS - Failure to Score I CNG - Consecutive No Goals
I TGC - Total Goals Conceded

## National Division North Leading goalscorers 2015-16

| Player | Club | Lge | FAC | FAT | Pens | HT | CSG | SG | Total |
|---|---|---|---|---|---|---|---|---|---|
| Darren Stephenson | Chorley | 18 | 1 | | 1 | | 3 | 17 | 19 |
| Greg Mills | Corby Town | 17 | | 2 | 7 | 1 | 2 | 14 | 19 |
| Dayle Southwell | Boston United | 19 | | | 4 | | 3 | 16 | 19 |
| Chib Chilaka | Bradford PA | 16 | 1 | 1 | | 1 | 2 | 12 | 18 |
| Steve Diggin | Brackley Town | 14 | 4 | | | | 2 | 15 | 18 |
| Liam King | North Ferriby Utd | 16 | 1 | | 2 | | 4 | 13 | 17 |
| Dion Charles | AFC Fylde | 14 | 2 | | | | 2 | 14 | 16 |
| Jake Reed | Lowestoft Town | 15 | | 1 | 1 | | 2 | 14 | 16 |
| Chib Chilaka | Bradford PA | 14 | 1 | | | 1 | 2 | 12 | 15 |
| Elliott Durrell | Tamworth | 14 | 1 | 1 | 3 | | 3 | 14 | 15 |
| Nathan Jarman | Gainsborough Trinity | 11 | 4 | | | | 2 | 12 | 15 |
| Niall Cummins | Curzon Ashton | 12 | | 2 | | | 2 | 11 | 14 |
| Sam Jones | Alfreton Town | 13 | 1 | | | | 3 | 12 | 14 |
| Stefan Moore | Solihull Moors | 12 | 2 | | 5 | | 2 | 12 | 14 |
| Aaron Williams | Nuneaton Town | 12 | 2 | | | | 4 | 12 | 14 |
| Elliott Whitehouse | Nuneaton Town | 13 | 1 | | | | 2 | 10 | 14 |
| Curtis Bateson | North Ferriby United | 13 | | | | | 2 | 9 | 13 |
| Matt Warburton | Curzon Ashton | 12 | 1 | | | | 2 | 10 | 13 |
| Danny Clarke | North Ferriby United | 9 | 3 | | | | 2 | 11 | 12 |
| Rob Duffy | Nuneaton Town | 11 | | 1 | | | 3 | 10 | 12 |
| Jack Higgins | Stalybridge Celtic | 11 | 1 | | | | 2 | 11 | 12 |
| Josh Hine | Chorley | 12 | | | | | 2 | 9 | 12 |
| Daniel Nti | Worcester City | 10 | 1 | 1 | 1 | 1 | | 8 | 12 |
| George Thomson | FC United of Manchester | 11 | | 1 | | | 2 | 11 | 12 |

HT - Hat-tricks I CSG - Consecutive Scoring Games I SG - Scoring Games I PO - Play-offs

## National Division South Statistics 2015-16

| | NoS | GS | CTS | PS | CSG | MCGU | TCS | MCCS | CMWW | CD | FTS | CNG | TGC |
|---|---|---|---|---|---|---|---|---|---|---|---|---|---|
| Basingstoke Town | 19 | 58 | 4 | 2 | 7 | 4 | 9 | Last3 | First11 | 6 | 16 | 4 | 76 |
| Bath City | 17 | 55 | 5 | 6 | 9 | First 9 | 12 | 2 | 8 | 5 | 10 | 2 | 66 |
| Bishops Stortford | 13+1 | 56 | 4 | 5 | 10 | 7 | 9 | 2 | 5 | 5 | 10 | 3 | 68 |
| Chelmsford City | 20+4 | 73 | 6 | 3 | 6 | 5 | 10 | 1 | 8 | 4 | 16 | 2 | 73 |
| Concord Rangers | 14 | 67 | 4 | 3 | 11 | 10 | 11 | 4 | 7 | 4 | 9 | 2 | 72 |
| Dartford | 12+2 | 59 | 4 | 5 | 13 | 7 | 10 | 3 | 6 | 4 | 10 | 2 | 59 |
| Eastbourne Borough | 14+1 | 80 | 7 | 4 | 13 | 5 | 11 | 1 | 5 | 3 | 8 | 2 | 78 |
| Ebbsfleet United | 15+2 | 84 | 6 | 4 | 10 | First 11 | 16 | 3 | 3 | 2 | 9 | 2 | 46 |
| Gosport Borough | 13+2 | 64 | 7 | 3 | 10 | First 8 | 12 | 3 | 6 | 5 | 15 | 4 | 69 |
| Havant & Waterlooville | 14 | 68 | 4 | 4 | 12 | 5 | 7 | 2 | 5 | 3 | 13 | 2 | 87 |
| Hayes & Yeading | 18+2 | 53 | 5 | 5 | 4 | 5 | 11 | 3 | 8 | 3 | 18 | 3 | 83 |
| Hemel Hempstead T | 28 | 82 | 6 | 4 | 20 | 6 | 12 | 2 | 7 | 2 | 6 | 1 | 76 |
| Maidenhead United | 14 | 86 | 5 | 3 | 11 | 9 | 14 | 4 | 11 | 3 | 10 | 3 | 76 |
| Maidstone United | 16+3 | 70 | 6 | 7 | 13 | 9 | 17 | 4 | 4 | 4 | 12 | 4 | 44 |
| Margate | 19 | 61 | 5 | 5 | 11 | 7 | 6 | 2 | 10 | 10 | 15 | 4 | 78 |
| Oxford City | 21+1 | 89 | 6 | 6 | 16 | 8 | 10 | 4 | 9 | 3 | 9 | 2 | 71 |
| St Albans City | 18+2 | 64 | 6 | 1 | 10* | 5 | 10 | 1 | 11 | 5 | 14 | 3 | 77 |
| Sutton United | 16+2 | 95 | 5 | 7 | 11* | 17* | 23 | 5x3 | 4 | 1 | 8 | 1 | 38 |
| Truro City | 16+1 | 76 | 4 | 6 | 11 | 7 | 17 | 4 | 5 | 3 | 13 | 2 | 71 |
| Wealdstone | 16+4 | 79 | 5 | 3 | 10 | 11 | 10 | 2 | First 6 | 3 | 11 | 3 | 7 |
| Weston-s-Mare | 13+1 | 77 | 5 | 4 | 12 | 8 | 8 | 2 | First 6 | First 5 | 9 | 2 | 84 |
| Whitehawk | 17+1 | 99 | 6 | 2 | 9* | 14 | 12 | 2 | 11 | 3 | 10 | 1 | 80 |

+ Denotes number of Own goals I * Denotes unfinished run

NoS - Number of Scorers I GS - Goals Scored I CTS - Club's Top Score I PS - Penalties Scored
CSG - Consecutive Scoring Games I MCGU - Most Consecutive Games Unbeaten I TCS - Total Clean Sheets
MCCS - Most Consecutive Clean Sheets I CMWW - Consecutive Matches Without a Win
CD - Consecutive Defeats I FTS - Failure to Score I CNG - Consecutive No Goals
I TGC - Total Goals Conceded

## National Division South Leading goalscorers 2015-16

| Player | Club | Lge | FAC | FAT | Pens | HT | CSG | SG | Total |
|---|---|---|---|---|---|---|---|---|---|
| Danny Mills | Whitehawk | 23+2PO | 8 | | | 2 | 6 | 25 | 33 |
| Matt Godden | Ebbsfleet United | 26 | 1 | 3 | | 3 | 7 | 19 | 30 |
| Justin Bennett | Gosport Borough | 23 | 5 | | 2 | 3 | 3 | 18 | 28 |
| Elliott Buchanan | Bishop's Stortford | 28 | | | 5 | 3 | 3 | 17 | 28 |
| Bradley Bubb | Oxford City | 18 | 2 | 4 | 5 | | 4 | 22 | 24 |
| Nat Pinney | Eastbourne Borough | 18 | 3 | 2 | 1 | | 2 | 17 | 23 |
| Scott Wilson | Weston-s-Mare | 18 | 1 | 4 | 2 | 1 | 3 | 19 | 23 |
| Dan Fitchett | Sutton United | 20 | | 2 | 2 | 1 | 3 | 16 | 22 |
| Dave Tarpey | Maidenhead United | 16 | 3 | 2 | | 2 | 2 | 14 | 21 |
| Elliott Brabrook | Dartford | 17 | | | 3 | | 3 | 15 | 17 |
| Louie Theophanous | St Albans City | 15 | 2 | | | | 1 | 9 | 17 |
| Bradley Hudson-Odei | Wealdstone | 11 | 2 | 3 | | | 2 | 12 | 16 |
| Ben Wright | Maidenhead United | 14 | 1 | 1 | 3 | | 2 | 13 | 16 |
| Billy Bricknell | Chelmsford City | 14 | | 1 | | | 3 | 9 | 15 |
| Danny Kedwell | Ebbsfleet United | 12+2PO | | 1 | 2 | | 2 | 8 | 15 |
| Scott Donnelly | Havant & Waterlooville | 12 | 1 | 1 | 3 | | 3 | 11 | 14 |
| Dayle Grubb | Weston-s-Mere | 13 | | 1 | | 1 | 2 | 9 | 14 |
| James Hayter | Havant & Waterlooville | 10 | 2 | 2 | | | 4 | 12 | 14 |
| Jefferson Louis | Wealdstone | 11 | 3 | | 3 | | 2 | 13 | 14 |
| Bradley Ash | Weston-s-Mere | 9 | 3 | 1 | 1 | 1 | 3 | 8 | 13 |
| Chris Flood | Basingstoke Town | 7 | 6 | | | 1 | 2 | 10 | 13 |
| Ben Greenhalgh | Concord Rangers | 12 | | | | | 2 | 11 | 13 |
| Andy Pugh | Dartford | 13 | | | 1 | | 3 | 10 | 13 |
| Freddie Ladapo | Margate | 12 | 1 | | 2 | | 2 | 12 | 13 |
| Jay May | Maidstone United | 9 | 3 | 1 | 1 | | 3 | 11 | 13 |
| Jamie Slabber | Hemel Hempstead Town | 11 | | 2 | | 1 | 2 | 10 | 13 |
| Liam Enver-Marum | Basingstoke Town | 9 | 2 | 1 | 2 | | 2 | 10 | 12 |
| Jordan Parkes | Ebbsfleet United | 12 | | | | | 5 | 10 | 12 |

HT - Hat-tricks I CSG - Consecutive Scoring Games I SG - Scoring Games I PO - Play-offs

# NORTHERN PREMIER LEAGUE PREMIER DIVISION LEAGUE TABLE 2015-16

| | | P | W | D | L | F | A | GD | Pts |
|---|---|---|---|---|---|---|---|---|---|
| 1 | Darlington | 46 | 33 | 5 | 8 | 106 | 42 | 64 | 104 |
| 2 | Blyth Spartans | 46 | 32 | 3 | 11 | 89 | 41 | 48 | 99 |
| 3 | Salford City | 46 | 27 | 9 | 10 | 94 | 48 | 46 | 90 |
| 4 | Ashton United | 46 | 26 | 9 | 11 | 90 | 52 | 38 | 87 |
| 5 | Workington | 46 | 25 | 11 | 10 | 78 | 50 | 28 | 86 |
| 6 | Stourbridge | 46 | 25 | 9 | 12 | 90 | 63 | 27 | 84 |
| 7 | Frickley Athletic | 46 | 22 | 11 | 13 | 69 | 46 | 23 | 77 |
| 8 | Nantwich Town | 46 | 20 | 15 | 11 | 94 | 62 | 32 | 75 |
| 9 | Barwell | 46 | 23 | 4 | 19 | 82 | 66 | 16 | 73 |
| 10 | Rushall Olympic | 46 | 19 | 12 | 15 | 74 | 61 | 13 | 69 |
| 11 | Buxton | 46 | 21 | 4 | 21 | 71 | 74 | -3 | 67 |
| 12 | Sutton Coldfield Town | 46 | 17 | 11 | 18 | 59 | 66 | -7 | 62 |
| 13 | Halesowen Town | 46 | 17 | 11 | 18 | 53 | 63 | -10 | 62 |
| 14 | Ilkeston | 46 | 15 | 9 | 22 | 61 | 79 | -18 | 54 |
| 15 | Marine | 46 | 12 | 17 | 17 | 53 | 61 | -8 | 53 |
| 16 | Skelmersdale United | 46 | 14 | 11 | 21 | 66 | 82 | -16 | 53 |
| 17 | Matlock Town | 46 | 14 | 10 | 22 | 59 | 79 | -20 | 52 |
| 18 | Grantham Town | 46 | 13 | 12 | 21 | 51 | 85 | -34 | 51 |
| 19 | Whitby Town | 46 | 12 | 11 | 23 | 60 | 79 | -19 | 47 |
| 20 | Mickleover Sports | 46 | 11 | 13 | 22 | 50 | 74 | -24 | 46 |
| 21 | Stamford | 46 | 12 | 9 | 25 | 71 | 97 | -26 | 45 |
| 22 | Hyde United | 46 | 11 | 7 | 28 | 53 | 90 | -37 | 40 |
| 23 | Colwyn Bay | 46 | 10 | 8 | 28 | 51 | 95 | -44 | 38 |
| 24 | Ramsbottom United | 46 | 5 | 11 | 30 | 43 | 112 | -69 | 26 |

**Play-Off Semi Finals:** Blyth Spartans 3-4 Workington I Salford City 3-1 Ashton United (aet)
**Final:** Salford City 3-2 Workington

| | PREMIER DIVISION | 1 | 2 | 3 | 4 | 5 | 6 | 7 | 8 | 9 | 10 | 11 | 12 | 13 | 14 | 15 | 16 | 17 | 18 | 19 | 20 | 21 | 22 | 23 | 24 |
|---|---|---|---|---|---|---|---|---|---|---|---|---|---|---|---|---|---|---|---|---|---|---|---|---|---|
| 1 | Ashton United | | 2-0 | 0-2 | 3-1 | 1-2 | 1-2 | 2-0 | 2-0 | 3-0 | 3-0 | 2-1 | 3-2 | 4-4 | 0-0 | 4-2 | 6-0 | 2-3 | 0-3 | 5-0 | 1-0 | 2-3 | 3-0 | 2-0 | 0-1 |
| 2 | Barwell | 0-1 | | 0-1 | 1-0 | 3-0 | 2-1 | 1-0 | 3-1 | 6-0 | 2-0 | 4-0 | 1-1 | 4-0 | 2-4 | 0-4 | 2-1 | 2-3 | 0-1 | 3-1 | 0-1 | 3-1 | 2-0 | 2-1 | 0-1 |
| 3 | Blyth Spartans | 1-1 | 4-0 | | 1-0 | 3-0 | 0-1 | 2-3 | 1-0 | 0-1 | 3-0 | 1-0 | 1-2 | 1-0 | 4-0 | 1-1 | 5-0 | 3-0 | 2-1 | 1-2 | 4-3 | 4-3 | 1-2 | 3-2 | 3-0 |
| 4 | Buxton | 2-1 | 5-1 | 0-4 | | 2-0 | 2-0 | 0-2 | 3-0 | 1-1 | 2-1 | 3-1 | 2-3 | 3-0 | 4-1 | 3-1 | 2-1 | 1-2 | 0-2 | 2-1 | 3-1 | 2-3 | 2-2 | 3-2 | 0-2 |
| 5 | Colwyn Bay | 0-2 | 0-4 | 1-3 | 3-2 | | 2-4 | 0-2 | 0-1 | 1-1 | 2-0 | 0-2 | 0-3 | 1-4 | 1-2 | 1-1 | 4-1 | 1-2 | 2-3 | 1-4 | 2-1 | 0-2 | 3-0 | 1-4 | 0-2 |
| 6 | Darlington | 1-1 | 3-1 | 2-1 | 3-1 | 3-0 | | 3-0 | 2-0 | 2-1 | 2-3 | 3-1 | 0-1 | 3-0 | 2-1 | 2-1 | 2-1 | 1-0 | 3-2 | 3-0 | 2-1 | 1-1 | 2-0 | 2-2 | 4-0 |
| 7 | Frickley Athletic | 0-0 | 1-0 | 2-3 | 5-1 | 1-0 | 3-1 | | 3-1 | 1-2 | 3-0 | 3-1 | 0-1 | 1-2 | 2-0 | 1-0 | 3-0 | 0-2 | 0-1 | 3-0 | 3-1 | 2-1 | 3-1 | 2-2 | 1-1 |
| 8 | Grantham Town | 3-3 | 0-5 | 2-3 | 0-3 | 0-0 | 0-2 | 1-0 | | 2-0 | 2-0 | 1-2 | 0-0 | 2-1 | 2-0 | 0-3 | 0-4 | 2-2 | 2-0 | 2-2 | 3-1 | 2-2 | 2-1 | 1-0 | 0-1 |
| 9 | Halesowen Town | 1-2 | 1-1 | 0-1 | 1-1 | 1-0 | 0-3 | 1-1 | 3-0 | | 1-1 | 2-0 | 1-0 | 3-2 | 1-1 | 1-1 | 2-1 | 1-3 | 0-1 | 2-1 | 1-3 | 2-0 | 2-2 | 0-0 | 2-0 |
| 10 | Hyde United | 0-4 | 1-0 | 0-4 | 2-1 | 3-2 | 1-3 | 1-1 | 2-2 | 0-1 | | 1-3 | 0-2 | 2-2 | 0-1 | 0-4 | 5-0 | 2-2 | 1-2 | 1-1 | 7-1 | 0-2 | 1-2 | 2-1 | 0-4 |
| 11 | Ilkeston | 1-1 | 1-0 | 3-4 | 3-1 | 0-0 | 1-1 | 0-2 | 2-1 | 1-3 | 3-1 | | 0-0 | 0-1 | 0-2 | 3-1 | 3-0 | 4-1 | 2-1 | 1-3 | 0-3 | 4-3 | 1-1 | 2-1 | 0-3 |
| 12 | Marine | 0-0 | 1-2 | 0-2 | 1-2 | 2-2 | 0-1 | 1-1 | 1-1 | 0-3 | 2-3 | 3-1 | | 2-1 | 3-3 | 1-2 | 3-0 | 1-1 | 0-2 | 2-2 | 1-1 | 1-3 | 2-1 | 2-1 | 1-2 |
| 13 | Matlock Town | 1-0 | 1-3 | 0-2 | 1-2 | 1-1 | 0-5 | 3-0 | 3-1 | 0-3 | 2-1 | 1-0 | 0-0 | | 2-0 | 1-1 | 2-0 | 1-0 | 1-2 | 1-2 | 0-1 | 1-1 | 2-2 | 1-0 | 0-1 |
| 14 | Mickleover Sports | 1-3 | 1-3 | 0-2 | 2-0 | 1-2 | 1-5 | 0-1 | 2-3 | 2-0 | 1-0 | 1-1 | 1-1 | 2-0 | | 1-1 | 3-1 | 1-1 | 1-2 | 2-1 | 0-1 | 1-3 | 0-1 | 1-0 | 1-2 |
| 15 | Nantwich Town | 2-2 | 2-1 | 1-2 | 1-2 | 3-2 | 0-5 | 1-0 | 6-2 | 3-0 | 3-0 | 1-1 | 1-1 | 2-2 | 1-1 | | 7-1 | 3-3 | 1-1 | 1-0 | 6-3 | 1-0 | 4-1 | 1-2 | 2-0 |
| 16 | Ramsbottom United | 0-2 | 1-3 | 0-0 | 0-1 | 2-2 | 0-3 | 0-2 | 2-2 | 0-2 | 1-4 | 4-0 | 1-1 | 0-3 | 1-1 | 1-4 | | 2-1 | 0-4 | 0-3 | 1-1 | 1-2 | 0-1 | 4-1 | 1-1 |
| 17 | Rushall Olympic | 0-2 | 2-0 | 0-1 | 0-1 | 2-1 | 1-0 | 0-1 | 4-0 | 0-0 | 2-0 | 2-2 | 3-0 | 2-3 | 1-1 | 1-0 | 2-0 | | 2-3 | 0-0 | 5-1 | 1-2 | 0-1 | 3-1 | 1-1 |
| 18 | Salford City | 3-1 | 7-0 | 0-1 | 2-0 | 2-2 | 3-4 | 2-2 | 5-0 | 3-1 | 0-1 | 2-0 | 0-0 | 2-2 | 1-1 | 1-1 | 4-0 | 1-3 | | 4-0 | 1-0 | 0-1 | 2-0 | 0-0 | 5-3 |
| 19 | Skelmersdale United | 1-2 | 3-3 | 2-1 | 2-1 | 3-4 | 1-1 | 1-1 | 0-1 | 1-0 | 2-1 | 2-1 | 2-3 | 3-2 | 1-1 | 0-1 | 1-1 | 4-1 | 3-1 | | 1-4 | 1-2 | 1-2 | 0-0 | 2-0 |
| 20 | Stamford | 3-4 | 1-2 | 0-1 | 2-4 | 2-3 | 1-4 | 1-0 | 1-3 | 1-2 | 2-1 | 1-1 | 0-0 | 2-0 | 2-0 | 0-4 | 3-3 | 2-3 | 1-1 | 5-2 | | 2-2 | 3-3 | 2-2 | 1-2 |
| 21 | Stourbridge | 1-2 | 2-3 | 3-0 | 3-0 | 2-0 | 1-0 | 1-1 | 1-1 | 3-2 | 5-1 | 1-2 | 2-0 | 4-1 | 2-1 | 4-3 | 2-3 | 2-2 | 1-2 | 3-1 | 2-0 | | 2-0 | 2-0 | 0-0 |
| 22 | Sutton Coldfield Town | 0-1 | 1-5 | 1-0 | 0-0 | 5-0 | 0-1 | 2-2 | 2-0 | 3-0 | 0-0 | 0-2 | 4-2 | 2-2 | 2-0 | 0-1 | 2-2 | 2-1 | 0-2 | 3-1 | 2-0 | 2-3 | | 1-0 | 0-2 |
| 23 | Whitby Town | 0-2 | 2-1 | 0-2 | 1-0 | 2-0 | 1-7 | 1-1 | 1-1 | 2-1 | 0-3 | 4-2 | 1-0 | 2-1 | 4-1 | 3-3 | 1-1 | 1-3 | 2-3 | 1-1 | 3-5 | 4-0 | 0-1 | | 1-0 |
| 24 | Workington | 5-2 | 1-1 | 2-0 | 5-0 | 1-2 | 2-1 | 1-3 | 1-1 | 3-0 | 2-0 | 3-2 | 1-0 | 4-1 | 2-2 | 1-1 | 4-0 | 1-1 | 1-4 | 2-1 | 2-0 | 1-1 | 1-1 | 3-1 | |

# NORTHERN PREMIER LEAGUE DIVISION ONE NORTH LEAGUE TABLE 2015-16

| | | P | W | D | L | F | A | GD | Pts |
|---|---|---|---|---|---|---|---|---|---|
| 1 | Warrington Town | 42 | 34 | 4 | 4 | 121 | 36 | 85 | 106 |
| 2 | Spennymoor Town | 42 | 27 | 10 | 5 | 113 | 35 | 78 | 91 |
| 3 | Northwich Victoria | 42 | 29 | 5 | 8 | 102 | 41 | 61 | 83 |
| 4 | Glossop North End | 42 | 24 | 9 | 9 | 78 | 41 | 37 | 81 |
| 5 | Burscough | 42 | 25 | 5 | 12 | 81 | 50 | 31 | 80 |
| 6 | Lancaster City | 42 | 18 | 15 | 9 | 74 | 57 | 17 | 69 |
| 7 | Clitheroe | 42 | 22 | 3 | 17 | 90 | 86 | 4 | 69 |
| 8 | Trafford | 42 | 19 | 8 | 15 | 78 | 51 | 27 | 65 |
| 9 | Farsley | 42 | 18 | 9 | 15 | 82 | 50 | 32 | 63 |
| 10 | Ossett Albion | 42 | 20 | 3 | 19 | 56 | 63 | -7 | 63 |
| 11 | Witton Albion | 42 | 18 | 7 | 17 | 85 | 72 | 13 | 61 |
| 12 | Bamber Bridge | 42 | 16 | 12 | 14 | 73 | 55 | 18 | 60 |
| 13 | Mossley | 42 | 18 | 6 | 18 | 80 | 76 | 4 | 60 |
| 14 | Brighouse Town | 42 | 17 | 8 | 17 | 75 | 72 | 3 | 59 |
| 15 | Kendal Town | 42 | 14 | 10 | 18 | 62 | 80 | -18 | 52 |
| 16 | Prescot Cables | 42 | 13 | 7 | 22 | 66 | 99 | -33 | 46 |
| 17 | Ossett Town | 42 | 12 | 7 | 23 | 51 | 94 | -43 | 43 |
| 18 | Radcliffe Borough | 42 | 11 | 7 | 24 | 54 | 75 | -21 | 40 |
| 19 | Droylsden | 42 | 11 | 6 | 25 | 68 | 139 | -71 | 39 |
| 20 | Scarborough Athletic | 42 | 10 | 8 | 24 | 40 | 64 | -24 | 38 |
| 21 | Harrogate Railway Athletic | 42 | 6 | 8 | 28 | 52 | 115 | -63 | 26 |
| 22 | New Mills | 42 | 0 | 3 | 39 | 26 | 156 | -130 | 3 |

**Play-Off Semi Finals:** Spennymoor Town 3-1 Burscough I Northwich Victoria 2-1 Glossop North End
**Final:** Spennymoor Town 2-0 Northwich Victoria

| | DIVISION ONE NORTH | 1 | 2 | 3 | 4 | 5 | 6 | 7 | 8 | 9 | 10 | 11 | 12 | 13 | 14 | 15 | 16 | 17 | 18 | 19 | 20 | 21 | 22 |
|---|---|---|---|---|---|---|---|---|---|---|---|---|---|---|---|---|---|---|---|---|---|---|---|
| 1 | Bamber Bridge | | 3-0 | 3-5 | 0-1 | 5-1 | 1-1 | 2-3 | 5-0 | 1-1 | 2-2 | 4-1 | 3-0 | 1-0 | 2-0 | 0-1 | 1-1 | 1-3 | 0-0 | 2-2 | 1-0 | 2-2 | 1-4 |
| 2 | Brighouse Town | 0-1 | | 1-0 | 3-4 | 8-0 | 2-1 | 0-0 | 3-1 | 4-2 | 2-2 | 3-1 | 6-1 | 1-2 | 1-3 | 1-2 | 5-3 | 1-0 | 2-1 | 0-4 | 1-1 | 0-2 | 1-5 |
| 3 | Burscough | 1-0 | 2-1 | | 6-1 | 3-1 | 0-0 | 0-3 | 3-2 | 2-0 | 1-2 | 3-2 | 2-0 | 1-1 | 2-0 | 1-2 | 0-1 | 1-0 | 3-0 | 0-2 | 4-1 | 4-1 | 2-3 |
| 4 | Clitheroe | 1-4 | 3-4 | 0-2 | | 6-1 | 2-5 | 3-0 | 3-0 | 0-0 | 4-2 | 2-0 | 5-1 | 2-0 | 1-3 | 1-2 | 3-1 | 2-1 | 4-2 | 0-1 | 2-4 | 2-5 | 2-0 |
| 5 | Droylsden | 4-0 | 4-3 | 2-4 | 1-5 | | 0-4 | 2-1 | 2-3 | 3-4 | 1-1 | 1-1 | 4-1 | 1-6 | 1-2 | 1-3 | 4-3 | 3-3 | 4-2 | 1-3 | 1-3 | 0-9 | 1-4 |
| 6 | Farsley | 2-1 | 0-1 | 0-3 | 2-0 | 6-0 | | 1-3 | 3-1 | 0-3 | 0-0 | 1-2 | 4-0 | 1-2 | 1-0 | 3-0 | 3-0 | 2-1 | 3-1 | 1-1 | 2-0 | 0-1 | 7-0 |
| 7 | Glossop North End | 2-2 | 2-0 | 0-1 | 4-1 | 6-0 | 2-1 | | 5-1 | 2-0 | 3-1 | 5-1 | 2-0 | 0-2 | 2-3 | 2-1 | 2-1 | 2-1 | 0-0 | 1-1 | 2-1 | 0-1 | 1-0 |
| 8 | Harrogate Railway Athletic | 1-2 | 1-1 | 1-2 | 1-3 | 1-1 | 1-1 | 2-4 | | 1-3 | 1-3 | 2-0 | 4-1 | 0-1 | 1-3 | 1-2 | 2-1 | 4-1 | 0-6 | 0-4 | 0-5 | 0-7 | 2-2 |
| 9 | Kendal Town | 1-2 | 1-3 | 2-1 | 1-3 | 0-1 | 1-1 | 0-3 | 3-1 | | 2-2 | 3-1 | 3-0 | 0-5 | 1-3 | 2-0 | 5-5 | 3-2 | 1-0 | 0-0 | 0-2 | 0-3 | 1-1 |
| 10 | Lancaster City | 1-1 | 2-1 | 1-0 | 1-2 | 1-1 | 2-2 | 1-1 | 1-0 | 3-1 | | 0-3 | 2-0 | 2-2 | 6-1 | 3-2 | 5-0 | 4-1 | 1-1 | 0-3 | 0-1 | 2-1 | 3-2 |
| 11 | Mossley | 2-1 | 1-2 | 2-3 | 3-0 | 5-1 | 3-3 | 1-0 | 5-3 | 3-2 | 2-0 | | 3-0 | 2-3 | 0-0 | 2-1 | 0-1 | 4-1 | 1-0 | 1-3 | 0-0 | 2-3 | 4-0 |
| 12 | New Mills | 0-7 | 1-1 | 1-2 | 2-3 | 1-4 | 1-4 | 0-3 | 0-3 | 0-2 | 1-3 | 2-7 | | 1-5 | 1-4 | 0-2 | 1-7 | 0-5 | 0-3 | 0-9 | 0-4 | 0-5 | 3-3 |
| 13 | Northwich Victoria | 2-0 | 1-0 | 4-0 | 0-0 | 8-2 | 0-5 | 0-1 | 1-1 | 3-0 | 2-1 | 5-1 | 2-0 | | 2-0 | 5-0 | 5-2 | 4-0 | 0-1 | 3-0 | 1-2 | 3-2 | 2-1 |
| 14 | Ossett Albion | 0-1 | 1-2 | 1-1 | 6-1 | 1-0 | 1-0 | 0-0 | 2-1 | 1-3 | 1-3 | 4-3 | 2-0 | 0-3 | | 1-0 | 0-1 | 0-2 | 1-0 | 0-4 | 2-1 | 0-3 | 4-0 |
| 15 | Ossett Town | 1-1 | 1-1 | 2-2 | 1-5 | 2-3 | 2-5 | 1-3 | 2-1 | 1-1 | 2-2 | 2-2 | 2-0 | 0-4 | 2-3 | | 1-1 | 1-2 | 2-0 | 1-5 | 1-0 | 0-4 | 0-5 |
| 16 | Prescot Cables | 1-1 | 2-1 | 0-3 | 1-1 | 3-2 | 2-0 | 0-4 | 4-2 | 2-2 | 2-3 | 0-2 | 5-2 | 0-2 | 4-0 | 1-3 | | 0-1 | 1-1 | 0-1 | 4-1 | 0-3 | 0-6 |
| 17 | Radcliffe Borough | 1-1 | 2-2 | 2-2 | 1-6 | 1-3 | 3-1 | 0-1 | 0-0 | 0-1 | 1-1 | 0-2 | 4-0 | 1-2 | 1-0 | 4-0 | 3-0 | | 2-1 | 1-4 | 0-3 | 1-3 | 2-2 |
| 18 | Scarborough Athletic | 0-3 | 0-1 | 0-3 | 1-3 | 2-4 | 1-0 | 0-0 | 2-2 | 2-1 | 0-1 | 0-2 | 2-1 | 0-3 | 1-2 | 2-1 | 0-3 | 1-0 | | 1-1 | 1-0 | 0-1 | 2-3 |
| 19 | Spennymoor Town | 1-0 | 1-3 | 3-1 | 5-0 | 5-0 | 0-4 | 2-2 | 1-1 | 6-1 | 1-1 | 4-1 | 9-0 | 2-0 | 3-0 | 5-0 | 3-0 | 1-0 | 2-2 | | 2-2 | 2-3 | 3-0 |
| 20 | Trafford | 3-1 | 2-2 | 1-0 | 2-0 | 1-1 | 3-0 | 1-1 | 6-0 | 2-2 | 2-1 | 2-1 | 3-2 | 2-2 | 0-1 | 4-0 | 8-0 | 2-0 | 0-1 | 0-2 | | 1-2 | 1-2 |
| 21 | Warrington Town | 1-0 | 2-0 | 1-3 | 5-0 | 5-1 | 1-1 | 3-0 | 6-3 | 3-0 | 1-1 | 5-0 | 1-0 | 4-2 | 1-0 | 2-1 | 6-1 | 2-0 | 1-0 | 1-0 | 4-1 | | 4-2 |
| 22 | Witton Albion | 2-4 | 4-1 | 0-2 | 2-3 | 4-0 | 2-1 | 3-0 | 5-0 | 2-3 | 0-1 | 1-1 | 2-2 | 1-2 | 1-0 | 3-1 | 1-2 | 2-0 | 1-0 | 1-2 | 2-0 | 1-1 | |

# NORTHERN PREMIER LEAGUE DIVISION ONE SOUTH LEAGUE TABLE 2015-16

| | | P | W | D | L | F | A | GD | Pts |
|---|---|---|---|---|---|---|---|---|---|
| 1 | Stafford Rangers | 42 | 29 | 8 | 5 | 79 | 31 | 48 | 95 |
| 2 | Shaw Lane Aquaforce | 42 | 28 | 10 | 4 | 95 | 40 | 55 | 94 |
| 3 | Coalville Town | 42 | 25 | 10 | 7 | 81 | 46 | 35 | 85 |
| 4 | Basford United | 42 | 22 | 10 | 10 | 67 | 42 | 25 | 76 |
| 5 | Lincoln United | 42 | 21 | 11 | 10 | 70 | 46 | 24 | 74 |
| 6 | Stocksbridge Park Steels | 42 | 20 | 9 | 13 | 72 | 53 | 19 | 69 |
| 7 | Chasetown | 42 | 19 | 11 | 12 | 68 | 49 | 19 | 68 |
| 8 | Leek Town | 42 | 18 | 9 | 15 | 61 | 56 | 5 | 63 |
| 9 | Rugby Town | 42 | 17 | 9 | 16 | 73 | 68 | 5 | 60 |
| 10 | Romulus | 42 | 18 | 6 | 18 | 76 | 74 | 2 | 60 |
| 11 | Market Drayton Town | 42 | 16 | 10 | 16 | 65 | 65 | 0 | 58 |
| 12 | Spalding United | 42 | 14 | 14 | 14 | 52 | 54 | -2 | 56 |
| 13 | Belper Town | 42 | 15 | 9 | 18 | 66 | 65 | 1 | 54 |
| 14 | Newcastle Town | 42 | 15 | 8 | 19 | 65 | 68 | -3 | 53 |
| 15 | Kidsgrove Athletic | 42 | 12 | 14 | 16 | 81 | 78 | 3 | 50 |
| 16 | Gresley | 42 | 16 | 2 | 24 | 58 | 75 | -17 | 50 |
| 17 | Sheffield | 42 | 13 | 8 | 21 | 61 | 71 | -10 | 47 |
| 18 | Carlton Town | 42 | 14 | 5 | 23 | 60 | 72 | -12 | 47 |
| 19 | Goole AFC | 42 | 10 | 8 | 24 | 51 | 87 | -36 | 38 |
| 20 | Loughborough Dynamo | 42 | 10 | 5 | 27 | 60 | 108 | -48 | 35 |
| 21 | Daventry Town | 42 | 10 | 3 | 29 | 43 | 113 | -70 | 33 |
| 22 | Tividale | 42 | 5 | 11 | 26 | 52 | 95 | -43 | 26 |

**Play-Off Semi Finals:** Coalville Town 5-0 Basford United I Shaw Lane Aquaforce 3-2 Lincoln United
**Final:** Shaw Lane Aquaforce 1-3 Coalville Town

| | DIVISION ONE SOUTH | 1 | 2 | 3 | 4 | 5 | 6 | 7 | 8 | 9 | 10 | 11 | 12 | 13 | 14 | 15 | 16 | 17 | 18 | 19 | 20 | 21 | 22 |
|---|---|---|---|---|---|---|---|---|---|---|---|---|---|---|---|---|---|---|---|---|---|---|---|
| 1 | Basford United | | 3-0 | 1-2 | 2-0 | 0-1 | 3-1 | 1-0 | 2-0 | 1-0 | 2-1 | 0-1 | 3-2 | 2-2 | 1-1 | 0-1 | 3-0 | 1-1 | 1-2 | 2-2 | 1-1 | 1-2 | 4-2 |
| 2 | Belper Town | 0-2 | | 1-3 | 0-0 | 1-0 | 2-0 | 2-3 | 5-2 | 1-1 | 2-0 | 0-0 | 1-2 | 2-0 | 3-3 | 2-0 | 0-2 | 0-2 | 0-3 | 1-1 | 0-1 | 2-1 | 3-0 |
| 3 | Carlton Town | 0-1 | 1-2 | | 2-3 | 1-1 | 5-2 | 0-0 | 0-1 | 1-4 | 1-3 | 2-3 | 1-0 | 3-2 | 1-3 | 0-2 | 1-3 | 0-3 | 2-0 | 0-0 | 0-2 | 3-2 | 5-2 |
| 4 | Chasetown | 0-1 | 1-3 | 2-0 | | 1-3 | 2-1 | 1-1 | 2-1 | 1-1 | 2-2 | 2-2 | 9-1 | 0-1 | 3-0 | 1-1 | 3-1 | 1-2 | 1-3 | 3-1 | 1-0 | 0-1 | 2-1 |
| 5 | Coalville Town | 0-1 | 3-2 | 2-1 | 1-1 | | 5-0 | 6-2 | 1-0 | 0-0 | 1-1 | 0-1 | 3-0 | 0-0 | 1-0 | 3-2 | 5-4 | 3-2 | 3-2 | 2-1 | 1-1 | 2-1 | 3-1 |
| 6 | Daventry Town | 0-2 | 0-6 | 1-0 | 1-0 | 1-4 | | 2-3 | 0-7 | 0-5 | 0-4 | 0-5 | 1-0 | 1-3 | 1-3 | 3-0 | 0-4 | 0-1 | 1-4 | 0-1 | 1-2 | 1-3 | 1-1 |
| 7 | Goole AFC | 2-1 | 3-3 | 0-1 | 0-1 | 0-0 | 2-0 | | 0-2 | 3-3 | 0-0 | 0-1 | 2-1 | 0-4 | 0-5 | 2-3 | 3-4 | 0-3 | 3-2 | 0-1 | 0-1 | 1-2 | 2-2 |
| 8 | Gresley | 0-1 | 2-1 | 0-2 | 2-1 | 1-3 | 1-4 | 2-1 | | 2-0 | 0-1 | 2-1 | 3-3 | 2-3 | 0-2 | 1-4 | 1-3 | 0-3 | 0-0 | 2-0 | 0-1 | 0-3 | 2-1 |
| 9 | Kidsgrove Athletic | 1-4 | 2-2 | 3-3 | 1-2 | 2-5 | 1-2 | 1-2 | 3-1 | | 1-1 | 2-2 | 0-2 | 1-1 | 2-1 | 4-2 | 1-1 | 3-5 | 3-0 | 2-0 | 0-3 | 2-2 | 4-0 |
| 10 | Leek Town | 2-2 | 1-0 | 1-0 | 0-1 | 4-1 | 5-1 | 3-5 | 3-0 | 3-3 | | 1-2 | 3-1 | 0-0 | 1-4 | 1-1 | 1-0 | 0-1 | 1-0 | 0-3 | 2-0 | 2-1 | 3-1 |
| 11 | Lincoln United | 1-0 | 2-2 | 1-1 | 0-0 | 0-1 | 2-2 | 2-1 | 1-3 | 4-0 | 1-2 | | 3-1 | 0-0 | 4-0 | 0-2 | 3-1 | 3-2 | 2-1 | 1-0 | 0-1 | 0-0 | 4-0 |
| 12 | Loughborough Dynamo | 0-1 | 2-5 | 3-2 | 2-3 | 1-4 | 2-0 | 2-0 | 1-3 | 2-6 | 4-0 | 2-1 | | 0-1 | 0-3 | 0-3 | 6-1 | 1-2 | 1-0 | 2-2 | 0-2 | 1-5 | 3-3 |
| 13 | Market Drayton Town | 1-4 | 1-0 | 1-2 | 0-3 | 2-2 | 4-0 | 2-1 | 3-0 | 0-3 | 1-2 | 4-3 | 2-3 | | 4-1 | 2-0 | 2-1 | 0-3 | 1-0 | 1-1 | 2-3 | 4-1 | 3-0 |
| 14 | Newcastle Town | 1-1 | 0-2 | 2-1 | 1-2 | 2-1 | 2-3 | 3-2 | 2-0 | 2-0 | 2-1 | 1-3 | 0-0 | 1-1 | | 2-3 | 2-2 | 3-2 | 2-3 | 0-1 | 0-0 | 2-0 | 2-0 |
| 15 | Romulus | 0-4 | 2-3 | 1-3 | 1-2 | 0-2 | 4-0 | 5-0 | 0-2 | 0-5 | 2-0 | 1-2 | 5-1 | 4-0 | 2-1 | | 1-5 | 1-5 | 4-3 | 1-1 | 1-3 | 1-1 | 2-0 |
| 16 | Rugby Town | 1-0 | 0-0 | 2-1 | 2-3 | 2-0 | 3-1 | 2-0 | 2-1 | 3-3 | 1-0 | 1-1 | 4-1 | 3-1 | 2-1 | 0-2 | | 1-2 | 2-0 | 1-1 | 0-1 | 1-2 | 1-1 |
| 17 | Shaw Lane Aquaforce | 5-0 | 1-0 | 1-0 | 1-1 | 0-0 | 3-3 | 3-3 | 4-2 | 2-2 | 3-1 | 0-2 | 4-1 | 3-0 | 0-0 | 3-0 | 3-2 | | 1-1 | 5-0 | 2-0 | 1-0 | 3-2 |
| 18 | Sheffield | 1-2 | 1-3 | 1-2 | 0-4 | 1-3 | 0-1 | 2-1 | 3-1 | 4-0 | 0-2 | 3-1 | 2-2 | 3-1 | 2-1 | 0-4 | 1-1 | 1-1 | | 2-2 | 0-2 | 2-3 | 3-3 |
| 19 | Spalding United | 2-3 | 2-1 | 5-3 | 1-1 | 1-0 | 1-2 | 4-0 | 0-3 | 2-1 | 1-1 | 0-0 | 2-0 | 1-0 | 5-0 | 1-0 | 1-1 | 0-3 | 0-0 | | 1-2 | 0-2 | 2-1 |
| 20 | Stafford Rangers | 0-0 | 6-0 | 3-0 | 2-1 | 2-2 | 4-1 | 3-0 | 3-1 | 0-3 | 1-0 | 4-1 | 5-2 | 0-0 | 2-1 | 2-2 | 4-0 | 0-1 | 3-2 | 2-0 | | 1-1 | 3-0 |
| 21 | Stocksbridge Park Steels | 2-2 | 2-1 | 2-1 | 2-0 | 0-1 | 3-2 | 1-2 | 2-3 | 3-1 | 3-0 | 0-1 | 5-0 | 3-2 | 1-0 | 4-4 | 1-0 | 1-1 | 0-1 | 2-1 | 1-2 | | 1-1 |
| 22 | Tividale | 1-1 | 4-2 | 0-3 | 1-1 | 1-2 | 1-2 | 0-1 | 0-2 | 3-1 | 1-2 | 1-3 | 3-2 | 3-3 | 5-3 | 0-2 | 4-3 | 1-2 | 0-2 | 1-1 | 0-1 | 0-0 | |

# THE DOODSON SPORT LEAGUE CUP 2015-16

**HOLDERS:** WARRINGTON TOWN

### PRELIMINARY ROUND

| | | | |
|---|---|---|---|
| Belper Town | v | Rugby Town | 3-4 |
| Shaw Lane Aquaforce | v | Sheffield FC | 4-1 |
| Tividale | v | Stafford Rangers | 2-2, 1-4p |
| Bamber Bridge | v | New Mills | 4-0 |

### ROUND ONE

| | | | |
|---|---|---|---|
| Harrogate Railway Athletic | v | Stocksbridge Park Steels | 2-3 |
| Ashton United | v | Nantwich Town | 0-3 |
| Barwell | v | Loughborough Dynamo | 2-2, 5-4p |
| Rugby Town | v | Ilkeston | 0-2 |
| Blyth Spartans | v | Darlington 1883 | 1-2 |
| Buxton | v | Gresley | 2-0 |
| Coalville Town | v | Stamford | 0-1 |
| Daventry Town | v | Newcastle Town | 3-2 |
| Farsley Celtic | v | Shaw Lane Aquaforce | 2-0 |
| Goole AFC | v | Ossett Town | 0-2 |
| Grantham Town | v | Frickley Athletic | 0-2 |
| Halesowen Town | v | Leek Town | 2-1 |
| Lincoln United | v | Mickleover Sports | 1-1, 5-4p |
| Marine | v | Glossop North End | 2-1 |
| Market Drayton Town | v | Stourbridge | 1-1, 4-3p |
| Ossett Albion | v | Mossley | 3-2 |
| Romulus | v | Sutton Coldfield Town | 0-1 |
| Salford City | v | Trafford | 1-2 |
| Scarborough Athletic | v | Whitby Town | 2-2, 4-3p |
| Skelmersdale United | v | Northwich Victoria | 1-6 |
| Spalding United | v | Matlock Town | 0-0, 3-4p |
| Spennymoor Town | v | Brighouse Town | 2-0 |
| Stafford Rangers | v | Rushall Olympic | 1-0 |
| Witton Albion | v | Burscough | 3-2 |
| Droylsden | v | Radcliffe Borough | 2-3 |
| Workington | v | Kendal Town | 3-0 |
| Carlton Town | v | Basford United | 2-1 |
| Kidsgrove Athletic | v | Chasetown | 2-1 |
| Clitheroe | v | Prescot Cables | 6-0 |
| Ramsbottom United | v | Warrington Town | 2-0 |
| Hyde United | v | Colwyn Bay | 1-1, 3-4p |
| Lancaster City | v | Bamber Bridge | 0-1 |

### ROUND TWO

| | | | |
|---|---|---|---|
| Farsley Celtic | v | Stocksbridge Park Steels | 6-0 |
| Frickley Athletic | v | Darlington 1883 | 2-3 |
| Halesowen Town | v | Sutton Coldfield Town | 0-2 |
| Matlock Town | v | Daventry Town | 1-3 |
| Nantwich Town | v | Market Drayton Town | 3-1 |
| Scarborough Athletic | v | Ossett Albion | 2-0 |
| Trafford | v | Northwich Victoria | 2-0 |
| Carlton Town | v | Barwell | 3-2 |
| Stafford Rangers | v | Kidsgrove Athletic | 2-2, 4-5p |
| Ilkeston | v | Lincoln United | 5-1 |
| Spennymoor Town | v | Ossett Town | 0-1 |
| Marine | v | Ramsbottom United | 2-1 |
| Witton Albion | v | Bamber Bridge | 1-2 |
| Workington | v | Clitheroe | 2-0 |
| Stamford | v | Buxton | 4-1 |
| Radcliffe Borough | v | Colwyn Bay | 0-1 |

### ROUND THREE

| | | | |
|---|---|---|---|
| Stamford | v | Carlton Town | 1-3 |
| Sutton Coldfield Town | v | Kidsgrove Athletic | 2-2, 2-4p |
| Colwyn Bay | v | Trafford | 1-1, 5-4p |
| Farsley Celtic | v | Scarborough Athletic | 1-1, 4-5p |
| Marine | v | Workington | 3-2 |
| Ossett Town | v | Darlington 1883 | 3-1 |
| Ilkeston | v | Daventry Town | 3-0 |
| Nantwich Town | v | Bamber Bridge | 5-1 |

### QUARTER-FINALS

| | | | |
|---|---|---|---|
| Scarborough Athletic | v | Carlton Town | 4-0 |
| Marine | v | Ossett Town | 1-0 |
| Nantwich Town | v | Colwyn Bay | 3-4 |
| Kidsgrove Athletic | v | Ilkeston | 0-2 |

### SEMI-FINALS

| | | | |
|---|---|---|---|
| Scarborough Athletic | v | Ilkeston | 1-1, 5-3p |
| Marine | v | Colwyn Bay | 4-1 |

### FINAL

| | | | |
|---|---|---|---|
| Scarborough Athletic | v | Marine | 1-2 |

## Northern Premier League Premier Division South Statistics 2015-16

| | NoS | GS | CTS | PS | CSG | MCGU | TCS | MCCS | CMWW | CD | FTS | CNG | TGC |
|---|---|---|---|---|---|---|---|---|---|---|---|---|---|
| Ashton United | 17+3 | 108 | 6 | 6 | 13 | 13 | 23 | 4 | 4 | 3 | 11 | 2 | 70 |
| Barwell | 20 | 96 | 6 | 4 | 11 | 10 | 13 | 3 | 6 | 4 | 14 | 3 | 77 |
| Blyth Spartans | 15 | 100 | 5 | 9 | 13 | 6 | 26 | 4 | 4 | 2 | 6 | 2 | 51 |
| Buxton | 18+1 | 88 | 6 | 10 | 10 | 6 | 8 | 3 | 6 | 4 | 13 | 2 | 83 |
| Colwyn Bay | 20+1 | 51 | 4 | 3 | 5 | 3* | 4 | 1 | 9 | 5 | 21 | 4 | 101 |
| Darlington 1883 | 17+1 | 110 | 7 | 3 | 14* | 10 | 15 | 3 | 3 | 2 | 4 | | 48 |
| Frickley Athletic | 15+2 | 72 | 5 | 3 | 9 | 8 | 15 | 2 | 5 | 3 | 12 | 3 | 49 |
| Grantham Town | 17+2 | 52 | 3 | 6 | 8 | 8 | 9 | 2 | 9 | 6 | 16 | 4 | 91 |
| Halesowen Town | 20+2 | 56 | 3 | 1 | 8 | 5 | 13 | 2 | 6 | 4 | 14 | 2 | 68 |
| Hyde United | 13 | 60 | 7 | 2 | 7 | 6 | 5 | 2 | 16 | 7* | 20 | 4 | 96 |
| Ilkeston | 22+3 | 67 | 4 | 3 | 10 | 9 | 7 | 2 | 9 | 9 | 13 | 3 | 86 |
| Marine | 16+2 | 68 | 3 | 9 | 13 | 7 | 14 | 2 | 11 | 6 | 15 | 4 | 74 |
| Matlock Town | 13 | 70 | 4 | 2 | 8 | 6 | 12 | 2 | 9 | 7 | 14 | 2 | 87 |
| Mickelover Sports | 18 | 51 | 4 | 0 | 12 | 5 | 8 | 2 | 12 | 4 | 12 | 2 | 77 |
| Nantwich Town | 15+1 | 118 | 7 | 14 | 23 | 10 | 16 | 4 | 6 | 2 | 4 | | 72 |
| Ramsbottom United | 24+2 | 48 | 4 | 3 | 5 | 3 | 3 | 1 | 21 | 6 | 20 | 4 | 118 |
| Rushall Olympic | 17+1 | 84 | 5 | 4 | 12 | 7 | 13 | 2 | 7 | 3 | 13 | 4 | 68 |
| Salford City | 20+2 | 112 | 7 | 5 | 18 | 10 | 21 | 6 | 3 | 2 | 7 | | 57 |
| Skelmersdale United | 19+3 | 86 | 5 | 6 | 10 | 7 | 7 | 2 | 8 | 5 | 12 | 2 | 101 |
| Stamford | 22+3 | 75 | 5 | 6 | 11 | 3 | 8 | 2 | 8 | 8 | 9 | 2 | 103 |
| Stourbridge | 16 | 111 | 5 | 8 | 17 | 10 | 17 | 4 | 4 | 2 | 6 | | 72 |
| Sutton Coldfield Town | 22+1 | 63 | 5 | 1 | 7 | 7 | 16 | 2 | 4 | 4 | 16 | 3 | 68 |
| Whitby Town | 17 | 64 | 4 | 7 | 6 | 6 | 9 | 4 | 11 | 5 | 15 | 2 | 86 |
| Workington | 17+1 | 87 | 5 | 1 | 14 | 6 | 18 | 5 | 3 | 2 | 9 | 2 | 57 |

+ Denotes number of Own goals I * Denotes unfinished run

NoS - Number of Scorers I GS - Goals Scored I CTS - Club's Top Score I PS - Penalties Scored
CSG - Consecutive Scoring Games I MCGU - Most Consecutive Games Unbeaten I TCS - Total Clean Sheets
MCCS - Most Consecutive Clean Sheets I CMWW - Consecutive Matches Without a Win
CD - Consecutive Defeats I FTS - Failure to Score I CNG - Consecutive No Goals
I TGC - Total Goals Conceded

## Northern Premier League Premier Leading goalscorers 2015-16

| Player | Club | Lge | FAC | FAT | Pens | HT | CSG | SG | Total |
|---|---|---|---|---|---|---|---|---|---|
| Karl Hawley | Stourbridge | 27 | 2 | 2 | 4 | | 4 | 28 | 31 |
| Martin Pilkington | Ashton United | 25 | 2 | 2 | 1 | | 2 | 22 | 29 |
| Robbie Dale | Blyth Spartans | 23 | | 2 | 5 | 1 | 3 | 18 | 25 |
| Liam Hardy | Buxton | 19 | 4 | 1 | 7 | 3 | 4 | 16 | 24 |
| Daniel Mitchley | Skelmersdale United & Marine | 9+13 | | 0+1 | 2+3 | | 7+4 | 9+14 | 23 |
| Michael Roberts | Whitby Town | 23 | | | 7 | 1 | 3 | 18 | 23 |
| Scott Spencer | Hyde United | 18 | 3 | | 1 | 3 | 6 | 13 | 23 |
| Luke Benbow | Rushall Olympic | 20 | 1 | 1 | 2 | | 6 | 17 | 22 |
| Scott Allison | Workington | 18 | 3 | | | 1 | 2 | 11 | 21 |
| Jacob Hazel | Frickley Athletic | 19 | 1 | | 1 | 1 | 3 | 17 | 20 |
| Alex Reid | Rushall Olympic | 16 | 3 | 1 | | 1 | 3 | 16 | 20 |
| Liam Shotton | Nantwich Town | 16 | | 4 | | 2 | 3 | 16 | 20 |
| Nathan Cartman | Darlington 1883 | 18 | | 1 | 1 | | 2 | 17 | 19 |
| James Poole | Salford City | 15 | 4 | | | 2 | 4 | 12 | 19 |
| Danny Webber | Salford City | 16 | 3 | | 1 | | 2 | 16 | 19 |
| Chris Almond | Skelmersdale United | 15 | | 3 | 2 | 1 | 2 | 12 | 18 |
| Elliott Osborne | Nantwich Town | 13 | | 5 | 8 | | | 16 | 18 |
| Richie Allen | Salford City | 15 | 2 | | 4 | | 2 | 14 | 17 |
| Brady Hickey | Barwell | 13 | 4 | | | 1 | | 11 | 17 |
| Anthony Carney | Barwell | 12 | 3 | 1 | 1 | 1 | 3 | 11 | 16 |
| Jordan Hulme | Salford City | 15 | 1 | | | | 2 | 13 | 16 |
| Chris Lait | Stourbridge | 11 | 3 | 2 | | | 3 | 15 | 16 |
| Joel Purkiss | Matlock Town | 14 | 1 | 1 | | | 2 | 13 | 16 |
| Sean Reid | Blyth Spartans | 15 | | | | | 3 | 12 | 15 |
| Justin Richards | Stourbridge | 12 | 2 | 1 | | | 3 | 14 | 15 |
| Steve Jones | Nantwich Town | 12 | | 2 | | | 2 | 13 | 14 |
| Graeme Armstrong | Darlington 1883 | 13 | | | | 1 | 2 | 11 | 13 |
| Ayrton Bevins | Hyde United | 12 | 1 | | | 1 | 2 | 8 | 13 |
| Lee Gaskell | Darlington 1883 | 13 | | | | 2 | 3 | 7 | 13 |
| Josh Hancock | Nantwich Town | 11 | | 2 | | | 2 | 11 | 13 |
| Daniel Maguire | Blyth Spartans | 12 | | 1 | | 1 | 2 | 11 | 13 |
| Alex Tomkinson | Barwell | 12 | 1 | | 1 | | 2 | 13 | 13 |
| Matthew Bell | Nantwich Town | 11 | | 1 | | | 3 | 11 | 12 |
| Matty Kosylo | Nantwich Town | 11 | | 1 | | | | 8 | 12 |
| Niall McManus | Matlock Town | 11 | | 1 | | | 4 | 12 | 12 |
| Lee Ndlovu | Grantham Town & Ilkeston | 4+7 | 0+1 | | | | | 4+8 | 12 |

HT - Hat-tricks I CSG - Consecutive Scoring Games I SG - Scoring Games I PO - Play-offs

# ASHTON UNITED

**Chairman:** Terry Hollis
**Secretary:** Andy Finnigan (T) 07866 360 200 (E) secretary@ashtonutd.com
**Commercial Manager:** (T/E)
**Programme Editor:** (T/E)
**Ground Address:** Hurst Cross, Surrey Street, Ashton-u-Lyne OL6 8DY
(T) 0161 339 4158 **Manager:** Paul Phillips & Steve Halford

2015-16 Squad

## Club Factfile

**Founded:** 1878 **Nickname:** Robins
**Previous Names:** Hurst 1878-1947
**Previous Leagues:** Manchester, Lancashire Combination 1912-33, 48-64, 66-68, Midland 1964-66, Cheshire County 1923-48, 68-82, North West Counties 1982-92

**Club Colours (change):** Red and white halves/red/red (Blue & black halves/blue/blue)

**Ground Capacity:** 4,500 **Seats:** 250 **Covered:** 750 **Clubhouse:** Yes **Shop:** Yes

**Directions**
From the M62 (approx 7.5 miles) Exit at Junction 20, take A627M to Oldham exit (2.5 miles) Take A627 towards Oldham town centre At King Street Roundabout take Park Road Continue straight onto B6194 Abbey Hills Road Follow B6194 onto Lees Road Turn right at the stone cross memorial and 1st right into the ground. From the M60 (approx 2.5 miles); Exit at Junction 23, take A635 for Ashton town centre Follow by-pass to B6194 Mossley Road. At traffic lights turn left into Queens Road Continue onto B6194 Lees Road Turn left at the stone cross memorial and 1st right into the ground.

**Previous Grounds:** Rose HIll 1878-1912

**Record Attendance:** 11,000 v Halifax Town - FA Cup 1st Round 1952
**Record Victory:** 11-3 v Stalybridge Celtic - Manchester Intermediate Cup 1955
**Record Defeat:** 1-11 v Wellington Town - Cheshire League 1946-47
**Record Goalscorer:** Not known
**Record Appearances:** Micky Boyle - 462
**Additional Records:** Paid £9,000 to Netherfield for Andy Whittaker 1994
Received £15,000 from Rotherham United for Karl Marginson 1993
**Honours:**
Manchester League 1911-12. Lancs Comb. 1916-17. NWCL Div. Two 1987-88, Div. One 1991-92, League cup 1991-92, Challenge Cup 1991-92. Manchester Challenge Shield 1992-93. Northern Premier League Division 1 Cup 1994-95, 96-97, 98-99, League Challenge Cup 2010-11. Manchester Senior Cup 1894-95, 1913-14, 75-76, 77-78. Manchester Premier Cup 1979-80, 82-83, 91092, 2000-01, 01-02, 02-03.

### 10 YEAR RECORD

| 06-07 | 07-08 | 08-09 | 09-10 | 10-11 | 11-12 | 12-13 | 13-14 | 14-15 | 15-16 |
|---|---|---|---|---|---|---|---|---|---|
| NP P 18 | NP P 10 | NP P 9 | NP P 12 | NP P 14 | NP P 12 | NP P 10 | NP P 5 | NP P 3 | NP P 3 |

# ASHTON UNITED MATCH RESULTS 2015-16

| Date | Comp | H/A | Opponents | Att: | Result | | Goalscorers | Pos | No. |
|---|---|---|---|---|---|---|---|---|---|
| Aug 15 | NPL | H | Mickleover Sports | 126 | D | 0-0 | | 13 | 1 |
| 18 | NPL | A | Marine | 294 | D | 0-0 | | 16 | 2 |
| 22 | NPL | A | Stamford | 255 | **W** | 4-3 | Morning 18 Baguley 71(pen) Connor 83 Mason 90 | 10 | 3 |
| 25 | NPL | H | Blyth Spartans | 163 | L | 0-2 | | 12 | 4 |
| 29 | NPL | A | Grantham Town | 163 | D | 3-3 | Baguley 37 Johnson 63 Pilkington 84 | 15 | 5 |
| 31 | NPL | H | Colwyn Bay | 186 | L | 1-2 | Johnson 65 | 18 | 6 |
| Sept 5 | NPL | A | Ilkeston | 497 | D | 1-1 | Baguley 43 (pen) | 18 | 7 |
| 8 | NPL | H | Whitby Town | 125 | **W** | 2-0 | Baguley 48 Burns 83 | 15 | 8 |
| **12** | **FAC1Q** | **H** | **Guisborough Town** | **133** | **D** | **0-0** | | | 9 |
| **16** | **FAC1Qr** | **A** | **Guisborough Town** | **220** | **W** | **3-2** | **Chadwick 11 Pilkington 21 (pen) 71** | | 10 |
| 19 | NPL | H | Skelmersdale United | 157 | **W** | 5-0 | Pilkington 16 Morning 72 Gorton 74 Banim 85 Johnson 8913 | | 11 |
| 22 | NPL | A | Buxton | 304 | L | 1-2 | Baguley 66 (pen) | 16 | 12 |
| **26** | **FAC2Q** | **A** | **Abbey Hey** | **240** | **W** | **5-0** | **JOHNSON 3 (4 40 90) Burns 70 Melia 79** | | 13 |
| 29 | NPL | H | Frickley Athletic | 143 | **W** | 2-0 | Morning 29 Chadwick 90 | 10 | 14 |
| Oct 3 | NPL | A | Matlock Town | 282 | L | 0-1 | | 12 | 15 |
| **10** | **FAC3Q** | **A** | **AFC Rushden & Diamonds** | **630** | **L** | **0-2** | | | 16 |
| 13 | NPL | H | Darlington 1883 | 290 | L | 1-2 | Pilkington 35 | 15 | 17 |
| 17 | NPL | A | Halesowen Town | 340 | **W** | 2-1 | Pilkington 56 Johnson 65 | 14 | 18 |
| 20 | NPL | A | Blyth Spartans | 525 | D | 1-1 | Gee 13 | 15 | 19 |
| 24 | NPL | H | Stamford | 116 | **W** | 1-0 | Gorton 26 | 15 | 20 |
| 27 | NPL | H | Marine | 152 | **W** | 3-2 | Baguley 27 44 Burns 59 | 11 | 21 |
| **31** | **FAT1Q** | **H** | **Ramsbottom United** | **138** | **D** | **2-2** | **Gorton 17 Pilkington 65** | | 22 |
| **Nov 3** | **FAT1Qr** | **A** | **Ramsbottom United** | **151** | **D** | **2-2** | **Chadwick 8 Morning 47 (Won 10-9 on pens aet)** | | 23 |
| 7 | NPL | A | Mickleover Sports | 208 | **W** | 3-1 | King 12 Pilkington 15 34 | 6 | 24 |
| **14** | **FAT2Q** | **H** | **Stratford Town** | **112** | **W** | **2-1** | **King 33 Charles 43 (og)** | | 25 |
| 21 | NPL | H | Nantwich Town | 155 | **W** | 4-2 | Pilkington 51 Toner 66 Chadwick 86 90 | 5 | 26 |
| **28** | **FAT3Q** | **A** | **Gainsborough Trinity** | **307** | **D** | **0-0** | | | 27 |
| **Dec 1** | **FAT3Qr** | **H** | **Gainsborough Trinity** | **106** | **W** | **3-1** | **Pilkington 6 Mason 44 King 78** | | 28 |
| 5 | NPL | H | Sutton Coldfield Town | 120 | **W** | 3-0 | Pilkington 9 90 Chadwick 62 | 6 | 29 |
| 19 | NPL | A | Skelmersdale United | 204 | **W** | 2-1 | Morning 44 Connor 45 | 6 | 30 |
| **23** | **FAT1** | **A** | **Macclesfield Town** | **610** | **L** | **0-4** | | | 31 |
| 29 | NPL | A | Colwyn Bay | 196 | **W** | 2-0 | Toner 43 Gorton 74 | 6 | 32 |
| Jan 2 | NPL | H | Buxton | 236 | **W** | 3-1 | Gorton 18 Mason 69 Baguley 70 | 4 | 33 |
| 9 | NPL | A | Workington | 441 | L | 2-5 | Pilkington 50 Toner 90 | 5 | 34 |
| 12 | NPL | H | Ramsbottom United | 174 | **W** | 6-0 | Mason 21 63 Morning 56 Toner 54 Johnson 67 Connor 85 | 4 | 35 |
| 23 | NPL | H | Grantham Town | 144 | **W** | 2-0 | Baguley 2 Pilkington 86 | 4 | 36 |
| 30 | NPL | H | Matlock Town | 162 | D | 4-4 | Mornng 48 57 Pilkington 50 66 | 4 | 37 |
| 13 | NPL | H | Rushall Olympic | 154 | L | 2-3 | Gorton 22 Morning 53 | 8 | 38 |
| 23 | NPL | A | Darlington 1883 | 961 | D | 1-1 | Toner 90 | 7 | 39 |
| 27 | NPL | H | Hyde United | 302 | **W** | 3-0 | Gee 20 (pen) Pilkington 72 Chadwick 87 | 7 | 40 |
| Mar 1 | NPL | A | Whitby Town | 185 | **W** | 2-0 | Pilkington 25 88 | 7 | 41 |
| 5 | NPL | A | Salford City | 734 | L | 1-3 | O'Halloran 68 (og) | 7 | 42 |
| 8 | NPL | A | Ramsbottom United | 142 | **W** | 2-0 | Pilkington 11 Lindfield 21 | 7 | 43 |
| 12 | NPL | H | Barwell | 133 | **W** | 2-0 | Lindfield 5 Pilkington 72 | 7 | 44 |
| 15 | NPL | A | Frickley Athletic | 222 | D | 0-0 | | 7 | 45 |
| 19 | NPL | A | Barwell | 228 | **W** | 1-0 | Pilkington 49 | 5 | 46 |
| 21 | NPL | A | Stourbridge | 448 | **W** | 2-1 | Baguley 29 (pen) Dean 42 | 4 | 47 |
| 26 | NPL | H | Ilkeston | 207 | **W** | 2-1 | Chadwick 21 Baguley 38 | 4 | 48 |
| 28 | NPL | H | Hyde United | 446 | **W** | 4-0 | Dean 61 Baguley 70 Chadwick 85 88 | 4 | 49 |
| Apr 2 | NPL | H | Stourbridge | 205 | L | 2-3 | Green 62 (og) Pilkington 83 | 4 | 50 |
| 5 | NPL | H | Salford City | 383 | L | 0-3 | | 4 | 51 |
| 9 | NPL | A | Nantwich Town | 274 | D | 2-2 | Pilkington 30 78 | 5 | 52 |
| 13 | NPL | H | Ashton United | 171 | **W** | 2-0 | Dean 5 Pilkington 49 | 5 | 53 |
| 16 | NPL | H | Workington | 212 | L | 0-1 | | 5 | 54 |
| 19 | NPL | H | Halesowen Town | 185 | **W** | 3-0 | Pilkington 18 Gorton 35 Baguley 80 | 4 | 55 |
| 23 | NPL | A | Sutton Coldfield Town | 162 | **W** | 1-0 | Pilkington 34 | 4 | 56 |
| **26** | **PO SF** | **A** | **Salford City** | **866** | **L** | **1-3** | **Haining 69** | | 57 |

| GOALSCORERS | Scoring Games | Consec Sco Games | Total | | Scoring Games | Consec Sco Games | Total |
|---|---|---|---|---|---|---|---|
| ***2014-15 Pilkington*** | | | ***16*** | Connor | 3 | | 3 |
| Pilkington | 22 | 2 | 29 | Dean | 3 | | 3 |
| Baguley | 11 | 2 | 13 | King | 3 | | 3 |
| Chadwick | 8 | | 10 | Gee | 2 | | 2 |
| Morning | 8 | | 9 | Lindfield | 2 | | 2 |
| Johnson | 6 | 2 | 8 | Banim | 1 | | 1 |
| Gorton | 7 | | 7 | Haining | 1 | | 1 |
| Mason | 5 | | 5 | Melia | 1 | | 1 |
| Toner | 5 | 2 | 5 | Opponents | | | 3 |
| Burns | 3 | | 3 | | | | |

# BARWELL

**Chairman:** David Laing
**Secretary:** Mrs Shirley Brown **(T)** 07961 905 141 **(E)** shirley.brown16@ntlworld.com
**Commercial Manager:** Contact secretary **(T/E)**
**Programme Editor:** James Tomlin **(T/E)** 07738 134 565
**Ground Address:** Kirkby Road Sports Ground, Kirkby Road, Barwell LE9 8FQ
**(T)** 07961 905 141 **Manager:** Jimmy Ginnelly

## Club Factfile

**Founded:** 1992 **Nickname:** Canaries
**Previous Names:** Barwell Athletic FC and Hinckley FC amalgamated in 1992.
**Previous Leagues:** Midland Alliance 1992-2010, Northern Premier League 2010-11. Southern 2011-13.

**Club Colours (change):** Yellow with green yolk/green/yellow (Green/black/green)

**Ground Capacity:** 2,500 **Seats:** 256 **Covered:** 750 **Clubhouse:** Yes **Shop:** Yes

**Directions**

**FROM M6 NORTH/M42/A5 NORTH:** From M6 North join M42 heading towards Tamworth/Lichfield, leave M42 at Junction 10(Tamworth Services) and turn right onto A5 signposted Nuneaton. Remain on A5 for approx 11 miles, straight on at traffic lights at Longshoot Motel then at next roundabout take first exit signposted A47 Earl Shilton. In about 3 miles at traffic lights go straight on and in 1 mile at roundabout take first exit signposted Barwell. In about 1.5 miles, centre of village, go straight over mini roundabout and then in 20 metres turn right into Kirkby Road. Entrance to complex is 400 metres on right opposite park.

**FROM M1 SOUTH:** From M1 South Take M69 )Signposted Coventry) Take Junction 2 Off M69 (Signposted Hinckley) Follow signs to Hinckley . Go straight on at traffic lights with Holywell Pub on the right. The road bears to the right at next traffic lights turn right signposted Earl Shilton/Leicester. Keep on this road past golf club on right at Hinckley United Ground on left and at large roundabout take second exit signposted Barwell. In about 1.5 miles, centre of village, go straight over mini roundabout and then in 20 metres turn right into Kirkby Road. Entrance to complex is 400 metres on right opposite park.

**Previous Grounds:** None

**Record Attendance:** 1,279 v Whitley Bay, FA Vase Semi-Final 2009-10.
**Record Victory:** Not known
**Record Defeat:** Not known
**Record Goalscorer:** Andy Lucas
**Record Appearances:** Adrian Baker
**Additional Records:**

**Honours:**
Midland Alliance League Cup 2005-06, Champions 2009-10.
Northern Premier Division One South 2010-11.
Leicestershire Challenge Cup 2014-15.

### 10 YEAR RECORD

| 06-07 | | 07-08 | | 08-09 | | 09-10 | | 10-11 | | 11-12 | | 12-13 | | 13-14 | | 14-15 | | 15-16 | |
|---|---|---|---|---|---|---|---|---|---|---|---|---|---|---|---|---|---|---|---|
| MidAl | 6 | MidAl | 10 | MidAl | 2 | MidAl | 1 | NP1S | 1 | SthP | 9 | SthP | 7 | NP P | 14 | NP P | 8 | NP P | 9 |

# BARWELL MATCH RESULTS 2015-16

| Date | Comp | H/A | Opponents | Att: | Result | | Goalscorers | Pos | No. |
|---|---|---|---|---|---|---|---|---|---|
| Aug 15 | NPL | H | Blyth Spartans | 227 | L | 0-1 | | 18 | 1 |
| 18 | NPL | A | Sutton Coldfield Town | 148 | W | 5-1 | Kay 10 Brennan 24 Thornton 42 Hickey 54 Towers 86 | 8 | 2 |
| 22 | NPL | A | Darlington 1883 | 1243 | L | 1-3 | Tomkinson 86 | 9 | 3 |
| 25 | NPL | H | Grantham Town | 207 | W | 3-1 | Christie 32 Lavery 52 Hickey 89 | 8 | 4 |
| 29 | NPL | H | Marine | 178 | D | 1-1 | Tomkinson 74 | 10 | 5 |
| 31 | NPL | A | Mickleover Sports | 202 | W | 3-1 | Towers 37 Woodward 58 Hickey 73 | 7 | 6 |
| Sept 5 | NPL | H | Salford City | 206 | L | 0-1 | | 11 | 7 |
| 8 | NPL | A | Stourbridge | 377 | W | 3-2 | Hickey 9 60 Carney 34 | 4 | 8 |
| **12** | **FAC1Q** | **H** | **Westfields** | **122** | **W** | **4-1** | **Carney 16 90 Gaunt 50 Tomkinson 71** | | 9 |
| 19 | NPL | A | Workington | 463 | D | 1-1 | Towers 54 | 6 | 10 |
| 22 | NPL | H | Nantwich Town | 168 | L | 0-4 | | 12 | 11 |
| **26** | **FAC2Q** | **H** | **Cogenhoe United** | **128** | **W** | **5-0** | **HICKEY 3 ( 3 56 90) Nisevic 5 Towers 37** | | 12 |
| Oct 3 | NPL | A | Ramsbottom United | 176 | W | 3-1 | Carney 28 (pen) 66 Christie 86 | 10 | 13 |
| 5 | NPL | A | Ilkeston | 404 | L | 0-1 | | 15 | 14 |
| **10** | **FAC3Q** | **H** | **Kings Lynn Town** | **292** | **W** | **1-0** | **Towers 76** | | 15 |
| 13 | NPL | H | Halesowen Town | 165 | W | 6-0 | Christie 12 55 CARNEY 3 ( 27 37 44) Kay 50 | 10 | 16 |
| 17 | NPL | A | Hyde United | 295 | L | 0-1 | | 11 | 17 |
| 20 | NPL | A | Grantham Town | 163 | W | 5-0 | Purcicoe 2 Powell 6 Tomkinson 17 Hickey 66 70 | 10 | 18 |
| **24** | **FAC4Q** | **H** | **AFC Rushden & Diamonds** | **819** | **D** | **2-2** | **Carney 11 Lavery 76** | | 19 |
| **28** | **FAC4Qr** | **A** | **AFC Rushden & Diamonds** | **1162** | **W** | **1-0** | **Hickey 82** | | 20 |
| **31** | **FAT1Q** | **A** | **Leamington** | **291** | **L** | **1-6** | **Carney 75** | | 21 |
| **Nov 7** | **FAC1** | **H** | **Welling United** | **843** | **L** | **0-2** | | | 22 |
| 14 | NPL | A | Halesowen Town | 254 | D | 1-1 | Carney 27 | 16 | 23 |
| 28 | NPL | H | Darlington 1883 | 326 | W | 2-1 | Tomkinson 45 Towers 50 | 14 | 24 |
| Dec 5 | NPL | A | Matlock Town | 246 | W | 3-1 | Tomkinson 10 Towers 14 Carney 90 (pen) | 11 | 25 |
| 8 | NPL | H | Sutton Coldfield Town | 131 | W | 2-0 | Story 29 Hickey 90 | 9 | 26 |
| 12 | NPL | A | Blyth Spartans | 432 | L | 0-4 | | 9 | 27 |
| 15 | NPL | A | Buxton | 130 | L | 1-5 | Tomkinson 55 | 9 | 28 |
| 19 | NPL | H | Workington | 203 | L | 0-1 | | 10 | 29 |
| 26 | NPL | A | Stamford | 405 | W | 2-1 | Barlone 13 45 | 9 | 30 |
| 28 | NPL | H | Mickleover Sports | 175 | L | 2-4 | Tomkinson 45 Story 75 | 10 | 31 |
| Jan 2 | NPL | A | Salford City | 624 | L | 0-7 | | 12 | 32 |
| 5 | NPL | H | Rushall Olympic | 136 | L | 2-3 | Carney 79 Barlone 81 | 10 | 33 |
| 9 | NPL | H | Ilkeston | 247 | W | 4-0 | Carney 9 Tomkinson 45 Lavery 69 Towers 76 | 9 | 34 |
| 19 | NPL | H | Buxton | 109 | W | 1-0 | Carney 47 | 8 | 35 |
| 23 | NPL | A | Marine | 335 | W | 2-1 | Story 10 Towers 51 | 7 | 36 |
| 25 | NPL | H | Stourbridge | 174 | W | 3-1 | Tomkinson 43 Barlone 52 Hickey 78 | 5 | 37 |
| 30 | NPL | H | Ramsbottom United | 217 | W | 2-1 | Story 45 Towers 89 | 5 | 38 |
| Feb 13 | NPL | H | Hyde United | 154 | W | 2-0 | Towers 30 Ballinger 5 | 5 | 39 |
| 20 | NPL | A | Colwyn Bay | 205 | W | 4-0 | Towers 17 39 Hickey 43 49 | 5 | 40 |
| 27 | NPL | H | Frickley Athletic | 203 | W | 1-0 | Tomkinson 66 (pen) | 6 | 41 |
| Mar 5 | NPL | H | Whitby Town | 226 | W | 2-1 | Tomkinson 66 Kay 90 | 5 | 42 |
| 8 | NPL | H | Skelmersdale United | 126 | W | 3-1 | Carney 44 (pen) Lavery 59 72 | 5 | 43 |
| 12 | NPL | A | Ashton United | 133 | L | 0-2 | | 6 | 44 |
| 15 | NPL | A | Rushall Olympic | 207 | L | 0-2 | | 6 | 45 |
| 19 | NPL | H | Ashton United | 228 | L | 0-1 | | 7 | 46 |
| 26 | NPL | A | Nantwich Town | 302 | L | 1-2 | Towers 56 | 7 | 47 |
| 29 | NPL | H | Stamford | 149 | L | 0-1 | | 7 | 48 |
| Apr 2 | NPL | A | Skelmersdale United | 196 | D | 3-3 | Lavery 12 Eddington 77 Boothe 90 | 7 | 49 |
| 9 | NPL | H | Colwyn Bay | 156 | W | 3-0 | Tomkinson 2 Lavery 33 Towers 44 | 7 | 50 |
| 16 | NPL | A | Frickley Athletic | 248 | L | 0-1 | | 8 | 51 |
| 19 | NPL | A | Whitby Town | 191 | L | 1-2 | Hollis 30 | 9 | 52 |
| 23 | NPL | H | Matlock Town | 151 | W | 4-0 | Hickey 3 51 Towers 10 37 | 9 | 53 |

| GOALSCORERS | Scoring Games | Consec Sco Games | Total |
|---|---|---|---|
| **2014-15 *Carney*** | | | ***20*** |
| Hickey | 12 | | 17 |
| Towers | 15 | 2 | 17 |
| Carney | 12 | 3 | 16 |
| Tomkinson | 13 | 2 | 13 |
| Lavery | 6 | | 7 |
| Barlone | 4 | | 4 |
| Christie | 4 | | 4 |
| Story | 4 | | 4 |
| Kay | 3 | | 3 |
| Ballinger | 1 | | 1 |

| | Scoring Games | Consec Sco Games | Total |
|---|---|---|---|
| Boothe | 1 | | 1 |
| Brennan | 1 | | 1 |
| Eddington | 1 | | 1 |
| Gaunt | 1 | | 1 |
| Hollis | 1 | | 1 |
| Nisevic | 1 | | 1 |
| Powell | 1 | | 1 |
| Purcicoe | 1 | | 1 |
| Thornton | 1 | | 1 |
| Woodward | 1 | | 1 |

# BLYTH SPARTANS

**Chairman:** Tony Platten
**Secretary:** Ian Evans (T) 07905 984 308 (E) generalmanager@blythspartans.com
**Commercial Manager:** Contact secretary (T/E)
**Programme Editor:** Matt Riggs (T/E) 07933 916 245
**Ground Address:** Croft Park, Blyth, Northumberland NE24 3JE
(T) 01670 352 373 **Manager:** Tom Wade

**NORTHERN PREMIER LEAGUE PREMIER DIVISION ACTION**
Matlock Town v Buxton - Photo: Bill Wheatcroft.

## Club Factfile

**Founded:** 1899 **Nickname:** Spartans
**Previous Names:** None
**Previous Leagues:** Northumberland 1901-07, Northern All. 1907-13, 46-47, North Eastern 1913-39, Northern Com. 1945-46, Midland 1958-60, Northern Counties 1960-62, Northern 1962-94, Northern Premier 1994-2006. Conference 2006-13.
**Club Colours (change):** Green & white stripes/black/black (Yellow with red sash/red/red)

**Ground Capacity:** 4,435 **Seats:** 563 **Covered:** 1,000 **Clubhouse:** Yes **Shop:** Yes

**Directions**
From the Tyne Tunnel, take the A19 signposted MORPETH. At second roundabout take the A189 signposted ASHINGTON. From A189 take A1061 signposted BLYTH. At 1st roundabout follow signs A1061 to BLYTH. Go straight across next two roundabouts following TOWN CENTRE/SOUTH BEECH. At next roundabout turn left onto A193 go straight across next roundabout, and at the next turn right into Plessey Rd and the ground is situated on your left. Team coach should the turn left into William St (3rd left) and reverse up Bishopton St to the designated parking spot.

**Previous Grounds:** None

**Record Attendance:** 10,186 v Hartlepool United - FA Cup 08/12/1956
**Record Victory:** 18-0 v Gateshead Town - Northern Alliance 28/12/1907
**Record Defeat:** 0-10 v Darlington - North Eastern League 12/12/1914
**Record Goalscorer:** Not known.
**Record Appearances:** Eddie Alder - 605 (1965-68)
**Additional Records:** Received £30,000 from Hull City for Les Mutrie

**Honours:**
North Eastern League 1935-36. Northern League 1972-73, 74-75, 75-76, 79-80, 80-81, 81-82, 82-83, 83-84, 86-87, 87-88.
Northern League Division 1 1994-95. Northern Premier League Premier Division 2005-06.
Northumberland Senior Cup 2014-15.

### 10 YEAR RECORD

| 06-07 | 07-08 | 08-09 | 09-10 | 10-11 | 11-12 | 12-13 | 13-14 | 14-15 | 15-16 |
|---|---|---|---|---|---|---|---|---|---|
| Conf N 7 | Conf N 18 | Conf N 15 | Conf N 13 | Conf N 9 | Conf N 21 | NP P 16 | NP P 8 | NP P 6 | NP P 2 |

# BLYTH SPARTANS MATCH RESULTS 2015-16

| Date | Comp | H/A | Opponents | Att: | Result | | Goalscorers | Pos | No. |
|---|---|---|---|---|---|---|---|---|---|
| Aug 15 | NPL | A | Barwell | 227 | W | 1-0 | Turnbull 86 | 7 | 1 |
| 18 | NPL | H | Whitby Town | 403 | W | 3-2 | Maguire 13 Dale 63 76 | 4 | 2 |
| 22 | NPL | H | Buxton | 546 | W | 1-0 | Maguire 90 | 2 | 3 |
| 25 | NPL | A | Ashton United | 163 | W | 2-0 | Richardson 12 Wade 33 | 1 | 4 |
| 29 | NPL | H | Nantwich Town | 492 | D | 1-1 | Dale 59 | 1 | 5 |
| 31 | NPL | A | Darlington 1883 | 1767 | L | 1-2 | Dale 48 | 1 | 6 |
| Sept 5 | NPL | H | Stamford | 550 | W | 4-3 | Nicholson 7 DALE 3 (23 54 85) | 1 | 7 |
| 8 | NPL | A | Salford City | 500 | W | 1-0 | Wearmouth 90 | 1 | 8 |
| **12** | **FAC1Q** | **A** | **Spennymoor Town** | **132** | **L** | **1-2** | **Turnbull 62 (pen)** | | 9 |
| 19 | NPL | A | Stourbridge | 609 | L | 0-3 | | 1 | 10 |
| 22 | NPL | H | Mickleover Sports | 445 | W | 4-0 | Reid 7 60 Dale 56 Robinson 90 | 2 | 11 |
| 29 | NPL | H | Hyde United | 517 | W | 3-0 | Dale 22 Reid 31 Maguire 68 | 1 | 12 |
| Oct 3 | NPL | A | Grantham Town | 311 | W | 3-2 | Nicholson 8 Dale 17 Reid 63 | 1 | 13 |
| 6 | NPL | A | Ramsbottom Town | 170 | D | 0-0 | | 1 | 14 |
| 10 | NPL | H | Sutton Coldfield | 643 | L | 1-2 | Maguire 69 | 1 | 15 |
| 17 | NPL | A | Colwyn Bay | 234 | W | 3-1 | Parker 70 Richardson 79 Nicholson 89 | 1 | 16 |
| 20 | NPL | H | Ashton United | 525 | D | 1-1 | Reid 59 | 2 | 17 |
| 24 | NPL | A | Buxton | 278 | W | 4-0 | MAGUIRE 3 (14 30 61) Mullen 58 | 2 | 18 |
| 28 | NPL | A | Whitby Town | 367 | W | 2-0 | Maguire 59 75 | 1 | 19 |
| **31** | **FAT1Q** | **H** | **Kendal Town** | **442** | **W** | **4-0** | **Dale 31 86 Wade 35 Richardson 52** | | 20 |
| **Nov 14** | **FAT2Q** | **H** | **Whitby Town** | **643** | **W** | **1-0** | **Mullen 58** | | 21 |
| 21 | NPL | A | Skelmersdale United | 248 | L | 1-2 | Richardson 9 | 2 | 22 |
| **28** | **FAT3Q** | **A** | **Matlock Town** | **303** | **L** | **2-4** | **Maguire 6 Cartwright 61** | | 23 |
| Dec 5 | NPL | A | Marine | 414 | W | 2-0 | Maguire 25 Richardson 79 | 1 | 24 |
| 12 | NPL | H | Barwell | 432 | W | 4-0 | Reid 21 65 Richardson 48 Parker 53 | 1 | 25 |
| 15 | NPL | A | Frickley Athletic | 215 | W | 3-2 | Maguire 12 Dale 27 (pen) Reid 73 | 1 | 26 |
| 19 | NPL | H | Stourbridge | 523 | W | 4-3 | Reid 33 Dale 39 Turnbull 68 (pen) NIcholson 90 | 1 | 27 |
| 28 | NPL | H | Darlington 1883 | 1876 | L | 0-1 | | 1 | 28 |
| Jan 9 | NPL | A | Halesowen Town | 461 | W | 1-0 | Dale 66 (pen) | 1 | 29 |
| 23 | NPL | H | Nantwich Town | 464 | W | 2-1 | Buddle 23 Hutchinson 84 | 1 | 30 |
| 26 | NPL | H | Salford City | 1432 | W | 2-1 | Mullen 5 (pen) Kneeshaw 85 | 1 | 31 |
| 30 | NPL | H | Grantham Town | 821 | W | 1-0 | Dale 59 | 1 | 32 |
| Feb 2 | NPL | A | Workington | 774 | L | 0-2 | | 1 | 33 |
| 9 | NPL | H | Ilkeston | 571 | W | 1-0 | Dale 44 (pen) | 1 | 34 |
| 13 | NPL | H | Ramsbottom United | 550 | W | 5-0 | KNEESHAW 5 ( 6 13 83 85 90) | 1 | 35 |
| 20 | NPL | A | Rushall Olympic | 358 | W | 1-0 | Dale 44 (pen) | 1 | 36 |
| 23 | NPL | H | Frickley Athletic | 613 | L | 2-3 | Dale 68 (pen) 85 (pen) | 1 | 37 |
| 27 | NPL | H | Colwyn Bay | 681 | W | 3-0 | Richardson 39 Kneeshaw 62 Dale 89 | 1 | 38 |
| Mar 1 | NPL | A | Mickleover Sports | 228 | W | 2-0 | Nicholson 38 Wearmouth 90 | 1 | 39 |
| 7 | NPL | A | Sutton Coldfield | 256 | L | 0-1 | | 1 | 40 |
| 12 | NPL | H | Halesowen Town | 745 | L | 0-1 | | 1 | 41 |
| 19 | NPL | H | Matlock Town | 567 | W | 1-0 | Buddle 63 | 1 | 42 |
| 26 | NPL | A | Stamford | 485 | W | 1-0 | McGuire 60 | 1 | 43 |
| 28 | NPL | H | Workington | 1009 | W | 3-0 | Buddle 10 Dale 29 49 | 1 | 44 |
| Apr 2 | NPL | A | Ilkeston | 404 | W | 4-3 | Reid 45 89 Dale 57 90 | 1 | 45 |
| 4 | NPL | A | Hyde United | 338 | W | 4-0 | Reid 47 50 Robinson 58 Kneeshaw 70 | 1 | 46 |
| 9 | NPL | H | Skelmersdale United | 787 | L | 1-2 | Kneeshaw 68 | 1 | 47 |
| 16 | NPL | A | Matlock Town | 227 | W | 2-0 | Reid 6 Mullen 57 | 1 | 48 |
| 19 | NPL | H | Rushall Olympic | 403 | W | 3-0 | Reid 18 Maguire 35 Richardson 64 | 1 | 49 |
| 23 | NPL | H | Marine | 546 | L | 1-2 | Robinson 27 | 2 | 50 |
| **26** | **PO SF** | **H** | **Workington** | **1124** | **L** | **3-4** | **Reid 45 Morse 74 Maguire 85** | | 51 |

| GOALSCORERS | Scoring Games | Consec Sco Games | Total | | Scoring Games | Consec Sco Games | Total |
|---|---|---|---|---|---|---|---|
| **2014-15 *Maguire*** | | | ***28*** | Turnbull | 3 | | 3 |
| Dale | 18 | 3 | 25 | Parker | 2 | | 2 |
| Reid | 13 | 3 | 16 | Wade | 1 | | 2 |
| Maguire | 12 | 2 | 15 | Wearmouth | 2 | | 2 |
| Kneeshaw | 5 | 2 | 9 | Baguley | 1 | | 1 |
| Richardson | 8 | 2 | 8 | Cartwright | 1 | | 1 |
| Nicholson | 5 | | 5 | Morse | 1 | | 1 |
| Mullen | 4 | | 4 | | | | |
| Buddle | 3 | | 3 | | | | |
| Robinson | 3 | | 3 | | | | |

# BUXTON

**Chairman:** David Hopkins
**Secretary:** Don Roberts (T) 07967 822 448 (E) admin@buxtonfc.co.uk
**Commercial Manager:** Contact secretary (T/E)
**Programme Editor:** Danny Hopkins (T/E) 07891 973 656
**Ground Address:** The Silverlands, Buxton, Derbyshire SK17 6QH
(T) 01298 23197 **Manager:** Martin McIntosh

## Club Factfile

**Founded:** 1877 **Nickname:** The Bucks
**Previous Names:** None
**Previous Leagues:** Combination 1891-99, Manchester 1899-1932, Cheshire County 1932-40, 46-73, Northern Premier 1973-98, Northern Counties East 1998-2006

**Club Colours (change):** All royal blue (All red)

**Ground Capacity:** 4,000 **Seats:** 490 **Covered:** 2,500 **Clubhouse:** Yes **Shop:** Yes

**Directions**
FROM STOCKPORT (A6): Turn left at first roundabout after dropping down the hill into the town, turn right at next roundabout, right at traffic lights (London Road pub) to Buxton Market Place. After two sets of pedestrian lights turn right at Royles shop then turn immediate left and follow road approx 500 metres to ground (opposite police station.)
FROM BAKEWELL (A6): Turn left at roundabout on to Dale Road and follow road to traffic lights then as above.
FROM MACCLESFIELD/CONGLETON/LEEK: Follow road to Burbage traffic lights and take right fork in the road at the Duke of York pub (Macclesfield Road.) Then at next traffic lights turn left (London Road pub) and follow as above.
FROM ASHBOURNE (A515): Go straight on at first traffic lights (London Road pub) and follow directions as above.

**Previous Grounds:** The Park (Cricket Club) 1877-78. Fields at Cote Heath and Green Lane 1878-84.

**Record Attendance:** 6,000 v Barrow - FA Cup 1st Round 1961-62
**Record Victory:** Not known
**Record Defeat:** Not known
**Record Goalscorer:** Mark Reed - 236 (in 355 + 46 sub appearances 2002-07, 2009-)
**Record Appearances:** David Bainbridge - 642
**Additional Records:** Paid £5,000 to Hyde United for Gary Walker 1989
Received £16,500 from Rotherham for Ally Pickering 1989

**Honours:**
Manchester League 1931-32, Lge cup 1925-26, 26-27. Cheshire Co. League 1972-73, Lge Cup 1956-57, 57-58, 68-69.
N.C.E. League 2005-06, Presidents Cup 2004-05, 05-06. N.P.L. Division 1 2006-07, President's Cup 1981-82, 2006-07.
Derbyshire Senior Cup 1938-39, 45-46, 56-57, 59-60, 71-72, 80-81, 85-86, 86-87, 2008-09.

### 10 YEAR RECORD

| 06-07 | 07-08 | 08-09 | 09-10 | 10-11 | 11-12 | 12-13 | 13-14 | 14-15 | 15-16 |
|---|---|---|---|---|---|---|---|---|---|
| NP 1 1 | NP P 5 | NP P 14 | NP P 8 | NP P 6 | NP P 13 | NP P 7 | NP P 13 | NP P 10 | NP P 11 |

# BUXTON MATCH RESULTS 2015-16

| Date | Comp | H/A | Opponents | Att: | Result | | Goalscorers | Pos | No. |
|---|---|---|---|---|---|---|---|---|---|
| Aug 15 | NPL | H | Darlington 1883 | 708 | W | 2-0 | Burbeary 18 Hardy 47 | 3 | 1 |
| 18 | NPL | A | Ramsbottom United | 209 | W | 1-0 | Hardy 10 | 3 | 2 |
| 22 | NPL | A | Blyth Spartans | 546 | L | 0-1 | | 7 | 3 |
| 25 | NPL | H | Skelmersdale United | 205 | W | 2-1 | Burrell 14 Hardy 66 (pen) | 4 | 4 |
| 29 | NPL | H | Salford City | 278 | L | 0-2 | | 8 | 5 |
| 31 | NPL | A | Nantwich Town | 394 | W | 2-1 | Hardy 89 (pen) 90 | 4 | 6 |
| Sept 5 | NPL | H | Stourbridge | 308 | L | 2-3 | Hardy 20 (pen) Buckley 58 | 6 | 7 |
| 8 | NPL | A | Stamford | 268 | W | 4-2 | Barraclough 45 Gascoigne 53 Hardy 72 85 | 3 | 8 |
| **12** | **FAC1Q** | **H** | **Ramsbottom United** | **207** | **W** | **2-1** | **Hardy 3 (pen) Barraclough 59** | | 9 |
| 19 | NPL | A | MIckleover Sports | 304 | L | 0-2 | | 4 | 10 |
| 22 | NPL | H | Ashton United | 204 | W | 2-1 | Burbeary 39 Hardy 90 (pen) | 4 | 11 |
| **26** | **FAC2Q** | **A** | **Armthorpe Welfare** | **253** | **W** | **6-1** | **Doran 38 HARDY 3 ( 34 pen 46 75) Young 57 Belezika 82** | | 12 |
| 29 | NPL | H | Colwyn Bay | 208 | W | 2-0 | Hardy 47 (pen) Taylor 53 | 4 | 13 |
| Oct 3 | NPL | A | Sutton Coldfield | 208 | D | 0-0 | | 5 | 14 |
| 6 | NPL | A | Grantham Town | 186 | W | 3-0 | Hardy 27 Bembo-Leta 56 Wiles 79 | 3 | 15 |
| **10** | **FAC3Q** | **A** | **FC United** | **2357** | **D** | **1-1** | **Burrell 45** | | 16 |
| **14** | **FAC3Qr** | **H** | **FC United** | **874** | **L** | **0-2** | | | 17 |
| 17 | NPL | A | Ilkeston | 495 | L | 1-3 | Barraclough 32 | 7 | 18 |
| 20 | NPL | A | Skelmersdale United | 222 | L | 1-2 | Doran 43 | 8 | 19 |
| 24 | NPL | H | Blyth Spartans | 278 | L | 0-4 | | 10 | 20 |
| 27 | NPL | H | Ramsbottom United | 181 | W | 2-1 | Burbeary 43 (pen) Barraclough 67 | 8 | 21 |
| **31** | **FAT1Q** | **H** | **Frick;ey Athletic** | **151** | **W** | **2-1** | **Barraclough 10 Wiles 59** | | 22 |
| **14** | **FAT2Q** | **H** | **Radcliffe Borough** | **183** | **W** | **5-1** | **Doran 28 Bembo-Leta 30 Burbeary 54 McKenzie 56 (og) Hardy 82** | | 23 |
| Dec 5 | NPL | H | Workington | 211 | L | 0-2 | | 14 | 24 |
| **8** | **FAT3Q** | **H** | **Bradford PA** | **208** | **L** | **1-2** | **Taylor 48** | | 25 |
| 15 | NPL | H | Barwell | 130 | W | 5-1 | Barraclough 11 90 HARDY 3 ( 44 45 46) | 12 | 26 |
| 19 | NPL | H | Mickleover Sports | 241 | W | 4-1 | HARDY 3 ( 26 72 87) Barraclough 45 | 9 | 27 |
| 26 | NPL | A | Matlock Town | 651 | W | 2-1 | Hardy 33 Barraclough 84 | 7 | 28 |
| 28 | NPL | H | Nantwich Town | 292 | W | 3-1 | Burbeary 2 Bembo-Leta 40 Burrell 70 | 7 | 29 |
| Jan 2 | NPL | A | Ashton United | 236 | L | 1-3 | Young 65 | 7 | 30 |
| 19 | NPL | A | Barwell | 109 | L | 0-1 | | 9 | 31 |
| 23 | NPL | A | Salford City | 707 | L | 0-2 | | 11 | 32 |
| 30 | NPL | H | Sutton Coldfield Town | 245 | D | 2-2 | Taylor 31 Barraclough 36 | 12 | 33 |
| Feb 2 | NPL | A | Darlington 1883 | 857 | L | 1-3 | Hardy 49 | 12 | 34 |
| 9 | NPL | A | Frickley Athletic | 259 | L | 1-5 | Barraclough 20 | 12 | 35 |
| 13 | NPL | H | Grantham Town | 233 | W | 3-0 | Wiles 5 Green 15 Worsfold 39 | 12 | 36 |
| 20 | NPL | A | Halesowen Town | 401 | D | 1-1 | Burbeary 79 (pen) | 11 | 37 |
| 23 | NPL | H | Rushall Olympic | 181 | L | 1-2 | Doran 60 | 11 | 38 |
| 27 | NPL | H | Halesowen Town | 300 | D | 1-1 | Grayson 33 | 11 | 39 |
| 29 | NPL | A | Hyde United | 266 | L | 1-2 | Taylor 22 | 11 | 40 |
| Mar 12 | NPL | H | Stamford | 211 | W | 3-1 | Salt 21 Barraclough 70 73 | 12 | 41 |
| 15 | NPL | A | Marine | 319 | W | 2-1 | Doran 21 Harris 78 | 12 | 42 |
| 19 | NPL | A | Whitby Town | 224 | L | 0-1 | | 11 | 43 |
| 22 | NPL | A | Colwyn Bay | 125 | L | 2-3 | Barraclough 54 Young 73 | 11 | 44 |
| 26 | NPL | A | Stourbridge | 506 | L | 0-3 | | 11 | 45 |
| 28 | NPL | H | Matlock Town | 353 | W | 3-0 | Barraclough 37 Walker 41 69 | 11 | 46 |
| 31 | NPL | H | Marine | 183 | L | 2-3 | Worsfold 64 68 (pen) | 11 | 47 |
| Apr 2 | NPL | H | Whitby Town | 232 | W | 3-2 | Barraclough 8 Harris 30 Walker 69 | 11 | 48 |
| 9 | NPL | A | Rushall Olympic | 212 | W | 1-0 | Barraclough 51 | 11 | 49 |
| 12 | NPL | H | Ilkeston | 228 | W | 3-1 | WORSFOLD 3 (2 18 38) | 11 | 50 |
| 16 | NPL | H | Hyde United | 236 | W | 2-1 | Bembo-Leta 17 Harris 81 | 10 | 51 |
| 19 | NPL | H | Frickley Athletic | 178 | L | 0-2 | | 10 | 52 |
| 23 | NPL | A | Workington | 583 | L | 0-5 | | 11 | 53 |

| GOALSCORERS | Scoring Games | Consec Sco Games | Total | | Scoring Games | Consec Sco Games | Total |
|---|---|---|---|---|---|---|---|
| ***2014-15 Hardy*** | ***26*** | | | Harris | 3 | | 3 |
| Hardy | 16 | 4 | 24 | Wiles | 3 | | 3 |
| Barraclough | 15 | 3 | 17 | Young | 3 | | 3 |
| Burbeary | 6 | | 6 | Belezika | 1 | | 1 |
| Worsfield | 4 | | 6 | Buckley | 1 | | 1 |
| Doran | 5 | | 5 | Gascoigne | 1 | | 1 |
| Bembo-Leta | 4 | | 4 | Grayson | 1 | | 1 |
| Taylor | 4 | | 4 | Green | 1 | | 1 |
| Walker | 4 | | 4 | Salt | 1 | | 1 |
| Burrell | 3 | | 3 | | | | |

# COALVILLE TOWN

**Chairman:** Glyn Rennocks
**Secretary:** Steve Cartwright (T) 07496 792 650 (E) info@coalvilletownfc.co.uk
**Commercial Manager:** (T/E)
**Programme Editor:** Wayne McDermott (T/E) 07876 140 248
**Ground Address:** Owen Street Sports Ground, Owen St, Coalville LE67 3DA
(T) 01530 833 365 **Manager:** Tommy Brookbanks

2015-16 Squad

## Club Factfile

**Founded:** 1994 **Nickname:** The Ravens
**Previous Names:** Ravenstoke Miners Ath. 1926-58. Ravenstoke FC 1958-95. Coalville 1995-98.
**Previous Leagues:** Coalville & Dist. Amateur. North Leicester. Leicestershire Senior. Midland Alliance > 2011.

**Club Colours (change):** Black & white stripes/black/white (Red & yellow stripes/red/yellow)

**Ground Capacity:** 2,000 **Seats:** 240 **Covered:** 240 **Clubhouse:** Yes **Shop:** Yes

**Directions**
From the M42/A42 take the exit signposted Ashby and follow A511 to Coalville and Leicester. After approx. 3 miles and at the first roundabout take the second exit (A511). At the next roundabout take the 3rd exit into Coalville Town Centre. At the traffic lights go straight over to mini-roundabout then straight on for 50 meters before turning right into Owen Street. Ground is at the top of Owen Street on the left.

**Previous Grounds:** None

**Record Attendance:** 1,500.
**Record Victory:** Not known
**Record Defeat:** Not known
**Record Goalscorer:** Not known
**Record Appearances:** Nigel Simms.
**Additional Records:** 153 goals scored during 2010-11 season.

**Honours:**
Leicestershire Senior Cup 1999-00. Leicestershire Senior 2001-02, 02-03. Midland Football Alliance 2010-11.
Northern Premier League Division One South Play-offs 2015-16.
Leicestershire Challenge Cup 2012-13.

### 10 YEAR RECORD

| 06-07 | 07-08 | 08-09 | 09-10 | 10-11 | 11-12 | 12-13 | 13-14 | 14-15 | 15-16 |
|---|---|---|---|---|---|---|---|---|---|
| MidAl 18 | MidAl 8 | MidAl 3 | MidAl 2 | MidAl 1 | NP1S 14 | NP1S 2 | NP1S 2 | NP1S 10 | NP1S 3 |

*Northern Premier League Premier Division action between Matlock Town and Buxton.*
*Photos: Bill Wheatcroft.*

# CORBY TOWN

**Chairman:** Stevie Noble
**Secretary:** Gerry Lucas (T) 07932 6333 43 (E) gerry21@gmail.com
**Commercial Manager:** (T/E)
**Programme Editor:** (T/E)
**Ground Address:** Steel Park, Jimmy Kane Way, Rockingham Road, Corby NN17 2AE
(T) 01536 406 640 **Manager:** Tommy Wright

## Club Factfile

**Founded:** 1947 **Nickname:** The Steelmen
**Previous Names:** Stewart & Lloyds (Corby) > 1947
**Previous Leagues:** United Counties 1935-52. Midland 1952-58. Southern 1958-2009, 13-15. Football Conference 2009-13, 15-16.

**Club Colours (change):** White & black stripes/black/black (All purple)

**Ground Capacity:** 3,893 **Seats:** 577 **Covered:** 1,575 **Clubhouse:** Yes **Shop:** Yes

**Directions**
From A14, Exit at Jnc 7, Keep left, at first roundabout take A6003 Oakham/Uppingham stay on this road for approx. 7 miles (ignore signs for Corby to your right en route) straight over two roundabouts at second B.P. petrol station on right. At next roundabout approx 1 mile ahead turn right onto A6116 for 300 yards entrance to Ground between Rugby Club and Rockingham Forest Hotel (Great Western).

**Previous Grounds:** Occupation Road 1948-85.

**Record Attendance:** 2,240 v Watford - Friendly 1986-87
**Record Victory:** Not known
**Record Defeat:** Not known
**Record Goalscorer:** David Holbauer - 159 (1984-95)
**Record Appearances:** Derek Walker - 601
**Additional Records:** Paid £2,700 to Barnet for Elwun Edwards 1981
Received £20,000 from Oxford United for Matt Murphy 1993
**Honours:**
United Counties League 1950-51, 51-52. Southern League Premier Division 2008-09, 2014-15.
Northants Senior Cup x7 Most recently 2012-13.

## 10 YEAR RECORD

| 06-07 | 07-08 | 08-09 | 09-10 | 10-11 | 11-12 | 12-13 | 13-14 | 14-15 | 15-16 |
|---|---|---|---|---|---|---|---|---|---|
| SthP 20 | SthP 16 | SthP 1 | Conf N 6 | Conf N 13 | Conf N 17 | Conf N 20 | SthP 11 | SthP 1 | Nat N 22 |

# CORBY TOWN MATCH RESULTS 2015-16

| Date | Comp | H/A | Opponents | Att: | Result | | Goalscorers | Pos | No. |
|---|---|---|---|---|---|---|---|---|---|
| Aug 8 | Nat North | A | Curzon Ashton | 212 | D | 2-2 | Sammons 1 77 | 11 | 1 |
| 12 | Nat North | H | Gloucester City | 650 | W | 3-1 | Tshimanga 12 Sammons 21 Mills 24 (pen) | 6 | 2 |
| 15 | Nat North | H | Chorley Town | 759 | D | 2-2 | Sammons 27 37 | 7 | 3 |
| 18 | Nat North | A | Hednesford Town | 462 | D | 3-3 | TSHIMANGA 3 (48 52 57) | 6 | 4 |
| 22 | Nat North | H | Bradford PA | 609 | W | 2-0 | Tshimanga 18 Weir-Daley 85 | 6 | 5 |
| 29 | Nat North | A | Lowesroft Town | 635 | D | 2-2 | Weir-Daley 15 Sammons 42 | 6 | 6 |
| 31 | Nat North | H | Solihull Moors | 760 | L | 1-3 | Weir-Daley 28 | 7 | 7 |
| Sept 5 | Nat North | A | Gainsborough Trinity | 424 | D | 1-1 | Mills 56 | 9 | 8 |
| 12 | Nat North | A | FC United | 3326 | L | 0-1 | | 12 | 9 |
| 16 | Nat North | H | Boston United | 613 | L | 2-3 | Weir-Daley 52 Mills 66 (pen) | 15 | 10 |
| 19 | Nat North | A | Worcester City | 596 | L | 0-3 | | 18 | 11 |
| **26** | **FAC2Q** | **H** | **Rushall Olympic** | **439** | **D** | **1-1** | **Calnes 76 (og)** | | 12 |
| **29** | **FAC2Qr** | **A** | **Rushall Olympic** | **168** | **L** | **1-2** | **Carruthers 62** | | 13 |
| Oct 3 | Nat North | A | North Ferriby United | 443 | L | 0-5 | | 19 | 14 |
| 17 | Nat North | H | AFC Fylde | 515 | L | 1-2 | Courtney 86 | 21 | 15 |
| 24 | Nat North | H | Curzon Ashton | 499 | L | 0-4 | | 21 | 16 |
| 31 | Nat North | A | Gloucester City | 312 | L | 0-1 | | | 17 |
| Nov 7 | Nat North | H | AFC Telford United | 612 | W | 3-2 | Ball 16 McDonald 37 Mills 61 | 18 | 18 |
| 14 | Nat North | A | Boston United | 1228 | L | 0-2 | | 18 | 19 |
| 17 | Nat North | A | Stalybridge Celtic | 205 | W | 3-2 | MILLS 3 (7 69 88) | 17 | 20 |
| 21 | Nat North | H | Harrogate Town | 477 | L | 0-3 | | 19 | 21 |
| **28** | **FAT3Q** | **H** | **Tamworth** | **335** | **L** | **2-6** | **Mills 24 41 (pen)** | | 22 |
| Dec 5 | Nat North | A | Nuneaton Town | 713 | D | 0-0 | | 20 | 23 |
| 12 | Nat North | H | Stockport County | 575 | L | 0-4 | | 20 | 24 |
| 26 | Nat North | A | Brackley Town | 475 | W | 2-1 | Mills 39 89 (pen) | 19 | 25 |
| 28 | Nat North | H | Lowestoft Town | 616 | L | 3-5 | McDonald 17 Mills 8 88 (pen) | 21 | 26 |
| Jan 2 | Nat North | H | Brackley Town | 603 | D | 1-1 | Thomas 85 | 21 | 27 |
| 9 | Nat North | A | Chorley | 1011 | L | 0-3 | | 21 | 28 |
| 16 | Nat North | A | Worcester City | 597 | W | 2-1 | Courtney 44 Ross 90 (og) | 20 | 29 |
| 23 | Nat North | H | Gainsborough Trinity | 541 | L | 1-2 | Mills 69 (pen) | 20 | 30 |
| Feb 13 | Nat North | H | Tamworth | 539 | W | 2-0 | Mills 6 Appleton 36 | 19 | 31 |
| 20 | Nat North | A | Alfreton Town | 573 | D | 1-1 | Milnes 90 | 19 | 32 |
| 27 | Nat North | H | Nuneaton Town | 651 | L | 1-3 | Mills 57 | 20 | 33 |
| Mar 5 | Nat North | H | North Ferriby United | 469 | L | 1-4 | Mills 7 | 22 | 34 |
| 8 | Nat North | A | AFC Fylde | 283 | L | 1-2 | Thomas 90 | 22 | 35 |
| 12 | Nat North | A | Tamworth | 616 | D | 0-0 | | 22 | 36 |
| 19 | Nat North | A | AFC Telford United | 1245 | L | 0-3 | | 22 | 37 |
| 26 | Nat North | H | Hednesford Town | 566 | D | 0-0 | | 22 | 38 |
| 28 | Nat North | A | Solihull Moors | 828 | L | 1-4 | Milnes 13 | 22 | 39 |
| Apr 2 | Nat North | H | Alfreton Town | 483 | L | 2-3 | Brown 6 McKenzie 35 | 22 | 40 |
| 9 | Nat North | H | FC United | 1030 | L | 2-3 | Milnes 24 Mills 90 (pen) | 22 | 41 |
| 13 | Nat North | A | Bradford PA | 251 | L | 0-2 | | 22 | 42 |
| 16 | Nat North | A | Stockport County | 2454 | D | 2-2 | Milnes 81 Mills 90 | 22 | 43 |
| 23 | Nat North | H | Stalybridge Celtic | 475 | L | 0-3 | | 22 | 44 |
| 30 | Nat North | A | Harrogate Town | 1025 | L | 0-5 | | 22 | 45 |
| | | | | | | | | | 46 |
| | | | | | | | | | 47 |

| GOALSCORERS | Scoring Games | Consec Sco Games | Total |
|---|---|---|---|
| ***2014-15 Wear-Daley*** | | | ***22*** |
| Mills | 14 | 2 | 19 |
| Sammons | 6 | 3 | 6 |
| Tshimanga | 4 | 2 | 5 |
| Milnes | 4 | | 4 |
| Weir-Daley | 4 | 3 | 4 |
| Courtney | 2 | | 2 |
| McDonald | 2 | | 2 |
| Thomas | 2 | | 2 |
| Appleton | 1 | | 1 |
| Ball | 1 | | 1 |
| Brown | 1 | | 1 |
| Carruthers | 1 | | 1 |
| McKenzie | 1 | | 1 |
| Opponents | | | 2 |

# FRICKLEY ATHLETIC

**Chairman:** Gareth Dando
**Secretary:** David Knight **(T)** **(E)**
**Commercial Manager:** **(T/E)**
**Programme Editor:** Gareth Dando **(T/E)** 07709 098 469
**Ground Address:** Westfield Lane, South Elmsall, Pontefract WF9 2EQ
**(T)** 01977 642 460 **Manager:** Karl Rose

2015-16 Squad

## Club Factfile

**Founded:** 1910 **Nickname:** The Blues
**Previous Names:** Frickley Colliery
**Previous Leagues:** Sheffield, Yorkshire 1922-24, Midland Counties 1924-33, 34-60, 70-76, Cheshire County 1960-70, Northern Premier 1976-80, Conference 1980-87

**Club Colours (change):** All royal blue (All yellow)

**Ground Capacity:** 2,087 **Seats:** 490 **Covered:** 700 **Clubhouse:** Yes **Shop:** Yes

**Directions**

From North : Leave A1 to join A639, go over flyover to junction. Turn left and immediately right, signed South Elmsall. Continue to roundabout and take 2nd exit to traffic lights and turn left onto Mill Lane (B6474). Turn right at the T-junction and continue down hill to next T-junction. Turn right and immediately left up Westfield Lane. The ground is signposted to the left after about half a mile.

From South : Exit M18 at J2 onto A1 (North). Leave A1 for A638 towards Wakefield. Continue on A638, going straight on at the first roundabout and turn left at next roundabout to traffic lights. Continue as above from traffic lights.

**Previous Grounds:** None

**Record Attendance:** 6,500 v Rotherham United - FA Cup 1st Round 1971
**Record Victory:** Not known
**Record Defeat:** Not known
**Record Goalscorer:** K Whiteley
**Record Appearances:** Not known
**Additional Records:** Received £12,500 from Boston United for Paul Shirtliff and from Northampton Town for Russ Wilcox

**Honours:**
Sheffield & Hallamshire Senior Cup x14 Most recently 2015-16.

### 10 YEAR RECORD

| 06-07 | 07-08 | 08-09 | 09-10 | 10-11 | 11-12 | 12-13 | 13-14 | 14-15 | 15-16 |
|---|---|---|---|---|---|---|---|---|---|
| NP P 16 | NP P 14 | NP P 11 | NP P 15 | NP P 18 | NP P 19 | NP P 18 | NP P 21 | NP P 19 | NP P 7 |

# FRICKLEY ATHLETIC MATCH RESULTS 2015-16

| Date | Comp | H/A | Opponents | Att: | Result | | Goalscorers | Pos | No. |
|---|---|---|---|---|---|---|---|---|---|
| Aug 15 | NPL | H | Matlock Town | 236 | L | 1-2 | Ible 77 | 17 | 1 |
| 18 | NPL | A | Darlington 1883 | 908 | L | 0-3 | | 24 | 2 |
| 22 | NPL | A | Sutton Coldfield Town | 132 | D | 2-2 | Williams 73 Cyrus 89 | 22 | 3 |
| 25 | NPL | H | Mickleover Sports | 179 | **W** | 2-0 | Hinsley 38 Johnson 82 | 16 | 4 |
| 29 | NPL | A | Ramsbottom United | 176 | **W** | 2-0 | Thomas 15 Williams 80 | 11 | 5 |
| 31 | NPL | H | Whitby Town | 264 | D | 2-2 | Hazel 35 Thomas 66 | 12 | 6 |
| Sept 5 | NPL | A | Colwyn Bay | 262 | **W** | 2-0 | Hazel 6 Parkinson 54 | 8 | 7 |
| 8 | NPL | H | Ilkeston | 237 | **W** | 3-1 | THOMAS 3 ( 5 (pen) 20 27) | 5 | 8 |
| **12** | **FAC1Q** | **A** | **Maltby Main** | **202** | **W** | **2-0** | **Johnson 21 Hazel 31** | | 9 |
| 19 | NPL | H | Halesowen Town | 267 | L | 1-2 | Hazel 34 | 8 | 10 |
| 22 | NPL | A | Rushall Olympic | 157 | **W** | 1-0 | Hazel 9 | 6 | 11 |
| **26** | **FAC2Q** | **A** | **Chorley** | **542** | **L** | **0-2** | | | 12 |
| 29 | NPL | A | Ashton United | 143 | L | 0-2 | | 8 | 13 |
| Oct 3 | NPL | H | Salford City | 280 | L | 0-1 | | 11 | 14 |
| 10 | NPL | A | Skelmersdale United | 231 | D | 1-1 | Wood 90 | 13 | 15 |
| 17 | NPL | H | Marine | 224 | L | 0-1 | | 18 | 16 |
| 20 | NPL | A | Mickleover Sports | 154 | **W** | 1-0 | Cyrus 53 | 14 | 17 |
| 24 | NPL | H | Sutton Coldfield Town | 218 | **W** | 3-1 | Thomas 35 Grayson 60 70 | 14 | 18 |
| **31** | **FAT1Q** | **A** | **Buxton** | **151** | **L** | **1-2** | **Hinsley 30** | | 19 |
| Nov 7 | NPL | A | Matlock Town | 369 | L | 0-3 | | 15 | 20 |
| 14 | NPL | H | Stamford | 212 | **W** | 3-1 | McGowan 51 (og) Grayson 70 Lenighan 88 | | 21 |
| 21 | NPL | H | Workington | 240 | D | 1-1 | Cyrus 7 | 12 | 22 |
| 28 | NPL | A | Hyde United | 286 | D | 1-1 | Davie 48 | 11 | 23 |
| Dec 15 | NPL | H | Blyth Spartans | 215 | L | 2-3 | Hazel 45 Williams 66 | 11 | 24 |
| 19 | NPL | A | Halesowen Town | 301 | D | 1-1 | Grayson 80 | 14 | 25 |
| 26 | NPL | H | Grantham Town | 273 | **W** | 3-1 | HAZEL 3 ( 6 42 67) | 12 | 26 |
| 28 | NPL | A | Whitby Town | 311 | D | 1-1 | Hazel 11 | 12 | 27 |
| Jan 2 | NPL | H | Rushall Olympic | 240 | L | 0-2 | | 14 | 28 |
| 23 | NPL | H | Ramsbottom United | 217 | **W** | 3-0 | Hazel 17 Walshaw 46 Williams 63 | 14 | 29 |
| 25 | NPL | A | Ilkeston Town | 339 | **W** | 2-0 | Hazel 52 Walshaw 62 | 11 | 30 |
| 30 | NPL | A | Salford City | 547 | D | 2-2 | Davie 45 58 | 11 | 31 |
| Feb 9 | NPL | H | Buxton | 259 | **W** | 5-1 | Akeroys 1 Walshaw 52 80 Davie 60 Hinsley 66 | 11 | 32 |
| 13 | NPL | A | Stamford | 259 | L | 0-1 | | 11 | 33 |
| 20 | NPL | H | Skelmersdale United | 202 | **W** | 3-0 | Hinsley 18 Grayson 67 Hazel 80 | 10 | 34 |
| 22 | NPL | A | Blyth Spartans | 613 | **W** | 3-2 | Grayson 17 38 Hazel 65 | 9 | 35 |
| 27 | NPL | A | Barwell | 203 | L | 0-1 | | 10 | 36 |
| Mar 12 | NPL | A | Stourbridge | 619 | D | 1-1 | Hinsley 24 | 10 | 37 |
| 15 | NPL | H | Ashton United | 222 | D | 0-0 | | 10 | 38 |
| 26 | NPL | H | Colwyn Bay | 237 | **W** | 1-0 | Hazel 61 | 10 | 39 |
| 28 | NPL | A | Grantham Town | 241 | L | 0-1 | | 10 | 40 |
| 30 | NPL | H | Nantwich Town | 232 | **W** | 1-0 | Hazel 10 | 10 | 41 |
| Apr 2 | NPL | H | Hyde United | 222 | **W** | 3-0 | Hinsley 23 Gooda 28 Fitton 50 (og) | 10 | 42 |
| 5 | NPL | H | Darlington 1883 | 740 | **W** | 3-1 | Williams 53 Davie 73 Hazel 83 | 9 | 43 |
| 9 | NPL | A | Workington | 418 | **W** | 3-1 | Cyrus 4 2 Hazel 79 | 8 | 44 |
| 13 | NPL | A | Marine | 286 | D | 1-1 | Hazel 17 | 8 | 45 |
| 16 | NPL | H | Barwell | 248 | **W** | 1-0 | Cyrus 22 | 7 | 46 |
| 19 | NPL | A | Buxton | 178 | **W** | 2-0 | Davie 34 Williams 58 | 7 | 47 |
| 21 | NPL | H | Stourbridge | 269 | **W** | 2-1 | Hazel 87 (pen) Davie 80 (pen) | 7 | 48 |
| 23 | NPL | A | Nantwich Town | 349 | L | 0-1 | | 7 | 49 |

| GOALSCORERS | Scoring Games | Consec Sco Games | Total |
|---|---|---|---|
| **2014-15 *Allott*** | | | ***23*** |
| Hazel | 17 | 3 | 20 |
| Grayson | 7 | | 7 |
| Davie | 6 | | 7 |
| Cyrus | 5 | | 6 |
| Thomas | 6 | 2 | 6 |
| Hinsley | 6 | | 6 |
| Williams | 6 | | 6 |
| Walshaw | 4 | | 4 |
| Johnson | 2 | | 2 |
| Akeroys | 1 | | 1 |
| Gooda | 1 | | 1 |
| Ible | 1 | | 1 |
| Lenighan | 1 | | 1 |
| Parkinson | 1 | | 1 |
| Wood | 1 | | 1 |
| Opponents | | | 2 |

# GRANTHAM TOWN

**Chairman:** Peter Railton

**Secretary:** Patrick Nixon **(T)** 07747 136 033 **(E)** psnixon@hotmail.com

**Commercial Manager:** (T/E)

**Programme Editor:** (T/E)

**Ground Address:** South Kesteven Sports Stadium, Trent Road, Gratham NG31 7XQ

**(T)** 01476 591 818 (office) **Manager:** Adam Stevens

2015-16 Squad - **Back Row Left to Right** - Gio Carchedi, Lee Ndlovu, Michael Emmett, Lawrence Gorman, Jake Turner, Rhys Lewis, Michael Hollingsworth, Stefan Bilyk, Lee Beeson, Danny Meadows.
**Middle Row:** - Ian Death (Supporters Club), Jack Beckett, Brad McGowan, Ellis Storey, Aiden Kirby, Lee Shaw, Liam Read, Ben Saunders. **Front Row:** Ian Howard, Main Sponsor ( Managing Partner JMP), Pat Nixon (Club Secretary), Barry Palmer (Director), Danny Martin (Assistant Manager), Adam Stevens (Manager), Dennis Rhule (Coach), Nigel Marshall (Physio), Roger Booth (President), Yvonne Carratt, Main Sponsor ( Partner JMP), Keith Horton (Chief Executive)

## Club Factfile

**Founded:** 1874 **Nickname:** Gingerbreads

**Previous Names:** Not known

**Previous Leagues:** Midland Amateur Alliance, Central Alliance 1911-25, 59-61, Midland Counties 1925-59, 61-72, Southern 1972-79, 85-2006, Northern Premier 1979-85

**Club Colours (change):** Black & white stripes/black/black & white (Orange & black/orange/orange & black)

**Ground Capacity:** 7,500 **Seats:** 750 **Covered:** 1,950 **Clubhouse:** Yes **Shop:** Yes

**Directions**

FROM A1 NORTH Leave A1 At A607 Melton Mowbray exit. Turn left at island on slip road into Swingbridge Lane. At T junction turn left into Trent Road ground is 100yds on right.

FROM A52 NOTTINGHAM. Pass over A1 and at first island turn right into housing estate & Barrowby Gate. Through housing estate to T junction. Turn right and then immediately left into Trent road ground is 100 yards on the left.

FROM A607 MELTON MOWBRAY. Pass under A1 and take next left A1 South slip road. At island turn right into Swingbridge Road then as for A1 North above. From all directions follow brown signs for Sports Complex, which is immediately behind the stadium.

**Previous Grounds:** London Road

**Record Attendance:** 3,695 v Southport - FA Trophy 1997-98

**Record Victory:** 13-0 v Rufford Colliery (H) - FA Cup 15/09/1934

**Record Defeat:** 0-16 v Notts County Rovers (A) - Midland Amateur Alliance 22/10/1892

**Record Goalscorer:** Jack McCartney - 416

**Record Appearances:** Chris Gardner - 664

**Additional Records:** Received £20,000 from Nottingham Forest for Gary Crosby

**Honours:**
Southern League Midland Division 1997-98. Lincolnshire Senior Cup x21 Most recently 2011-12.
Northern Premier Division 1 South 2011-12.

### 10 YEAR RECORD

| 06-07 | 07-08 | 08-09 | 09-10 | 10-11 | 11-12 | 12-13 | 13-14 | 14-15 | 15-16 |
|---|---|---|---|---|---|---|---|---|---|
| NP P 22 | NP 1 6 | NP1S 13 | NP1S 11 | NP1S 5 | NP1S 1 | NP P 19 | NP P 15 | NP P 12 | NP P 18 |

# GRANTHAM TOWN MATCH RESULTS 2015-16

| Date | Comp | H/A | Opponents | Att: | Result | | Goalscorers | Pos | No. |
|---|---|---|---|---|---|---|---|---|---|
| Aug 15 | NPL | A | Hyde United | 509 | D | 2-2 | Ndlovu 51 Humble 80 | 9 | 1 |
| 18 | NPL | H | Ilkeston Town | 228 | L | 1-2 | Ndlovu 1 | 18 | 2 |
| 22 | NPL | H | Rushall Olympic | 170 | D | 2-2 | Beeson 4 Ndlovu 67 | 18 | 3 |
| 25 | NPL | A | Barwell | 207 | L | 1-3 | Ndlovu 50 | 22 | 4 |
| 29 | NPL | H | Ashton United | 163 | D | 3-3 | Saunders 2 Read 89 (pen) Hollingsworth 90 | 22 | 5 |
| Sept 5 | NPL | H | Marine | 207 | D | 0-0 | | 23 | 6 |
| **12** | **FAC1Q** | **A** | **Chasetown** | **191** | **L** | **0-3** | | **23** | **7** |
| 15 | NPL | A | Sutton Coldfield | 105 | L | 0-2 | | 23 | 8 |
| 19 | NPL | A | Nantwich Town | 288 | L | 2-6 | Meadows 21 Lewis 30 | 23 | 9 |
| 26 | NPL | H | Matlock Town | 183 | **W** | 2-1 | Lewis 87 McGowan 90 | 22 | 10 |
| 29 | NPL | A | Stourbridge | 331 | D | 1-1 | Saunders 66 | 22 | 11 |
| Oct 3 | NPL | H | Blyth Spartans | 311 | L | 2-3 | McGhee 29 Shaw 81 | 22 | 12 |
| 6 | NPL | H | Buxton | 186 | L | 0-3 | | 22 | 13 |
| 10 | NPL | A | Whitby Town | 253 | D | 1-1 | Smith 47 | 22 | 14 |
| 13 | NPL | A | Mickleover Sports | 159 | **W** | 3-2 | Lewis 37 Wiley (og) 45 Emmott 89 | 21 | 15 |
| 17 | NPL | H | Skelmersdale United | 203 | D | 2-2 | Smith 16 Beeson 62 (pen) | 21 | 16 |
| 20 | NPL | H | Barwell | 163 | L | 0-5 | | 21 | 17 |
| 24 | NPL | A | Ilkeston | 484 | L | 1-2 | Saunders 82 | 22 | 18 |
| **31** | **FAT1Q** | **A** | **Basford United** | **162** | **L** | **1-3** | **Meadows 15 (pen)** | | **19** |
| Nov 7 | NPL | H | Hyde United | 292 | **W** | 2-0 | Smith 76 Meadows 87 (pen) | 21 | 20 |
| 14 | NPL | H | Mickleover Sports | 200 | **W** | 2-0 | Smith 74 Saunders 78 | 20 | 21 |
| 24 | NPL | A | Stamford | 383 | **W** | 3-1 | Meadows 24 Harris 47 Shaw 63 | 20 | 22 |
| 28 | NPL | H | Salford City | 788 | **W** | 2-0 | Lewis 69 81 | | 23 |
| 8 | NPL | A | Rushall Olympic | 213 | L | 0-4 | | 17 | 24 |
| 12 | NPL | H | Halesowen Town | 260 | **W** | 2-0 | Hollingsworth 29 Bilyk 90 | 15 | 25 |
| 19 | NPL | H | Nantwich Town | 202 | L | 0-3 | | 17 | 26 |
| 26 | NPL | A | Frickley Athletic | 273 | L | 1-3 | Lewis 59 | 17 | 27 |
| 28 | NPL | H | Stamford | 457 | **W** | 3-1 | Lewis 4 Shaw 22 Bilyk 90 | 17 | 28 |
| Jan 9 | NPL | H | Ramsbottom United | 210 | L | 0-4 | | 17 | 29 |
| 16 | NPL | H | Workington | 235 | L | 0-1 | | 17 | 30 |
| 23 | NPL | A | Ashton United | 144 | L | 0-2 | | 17 | 31 |
| 30 | NPL | A | Blyth Spartans | 821 | L | 0-1 | | 17 | 32 |
| Feb 2 | NPL | A | Matlock Town | 320 | L | 1-3 | McGhee 26 | 17 | 33 |
| 13 | NPL | A | Buxton | 233 | L | 0-3 | | 18 | 34 |
| 20 | NPL | H | Whitby Town | 225 | **W** | 1-0 | Meadows 74 (pen) | 17 | 35 |
| 27 | NPL | A | Skelmersale United | 239 | **W** | 1-0 | Shaw 15 | 17 | 36 |
| Mar 5 | NPL | A | Workington | 476 | D | 1-1 | Meadows 90 (pen) | 18 | 37 |
| 8 | NPL | H | Sutton Coldfield Town | 142 | **W** | 2-1 | Shaw 89 Ryan 84 | 16 | 38 |
| 12 | NPL | A | Ramsbottom Uunited | 171 | D | 2-2 | Edghill 24 (og) Lewis 57 | 17 | 39 |
| 15 | NPL | H | Stourbridge | 152 | D | 2-2 | Shaw 14 22 | 16 | 40 |
| 19 | NPL | A | Colwyn Bay | 162 | **W** | 1-0 | Shaw 25 | 14 | 41 |
| 28 | NPL | H | Frickley Athletic | 241 | **W** | 1-0 | Burns 70 | 14 | 42 |
| Apr 2 | NPL | A | Salford City | 760 | L | 0-5 | | 14 | 43 |
| 7 | NPL | A | Marine | 254 | D | 1-1 | Ryan 53 | 14 | 44 |
| 9 | NPL | H | Darlington 1883 | 701 | L | 0-2 | | 16 | 45 |
| 16 | NPL | A | Halesowen Town | 428 | L | 0-3 | | 18 | 46 |
| 19 | NPL | A | Darlington 1883 | 1734 | L | 0-2 | | 18 | 47 |
| 23 | NPL | H | Colwyn Bay | 193 | D | 0-0 | | 18 | 48 |

| GOALSCORERS | Scoring Games | Consec Sco Games | Total |
|---|---|---|---|
| **2014-15 *Simmons*** | | | ***11*** |
| Lewis | 7 | 2 | 8 |
| Shaw | 7 | 2 | 8 |
| Meadows | 6 | 2 | 6 |
| Ndlovu | 4 | 4 | 4 |
| Saunders | 4 | | 4 |
| Smith | 4 | 2 | 4 |
| Beeson | 2 | | 2 |
| Bilyk | 2 | | 2 |
| Hollingsworth | 2 | | 2 |
| McGhee | 2 | | 2 |
| Ryan | 2 | | 2 |
| Burns | 1 | | 1 |
| Emmott | 1 | | 1 |
| Harris | 1 | | 1 |
| Humble | 1 | | 1 |
| McGowan | 1 | | 1 |
| Read | 1 | | 1 |
| Opposition | | | 2 |

# HALESOWEN TOWN

**Chairman:** Chris Lambert (CEO)
**Secretary:** Andrew While **(T)** 07976 769 972 **(E)** secretary@ht-fc.com
**Commercial Manager:** Paul Guest **(T/E)** paulguest@ht-fc.com
**Programme Editor:** Rob Edmonds **(T/E)** programme@ht-fc.com
**Ground Address:** The Grove, Old Hawne Lane, Halesowen B63 3TB
**(T)** 0121 550 9433 **Manager:** John Hill

## Club Factfile

**Founded:** 1873 **Nickname:** Yeltz
**Previous Names:** None
**Previous Leagues:** West Midlands 1892-1905, 06-11, 46-86, Birmingham Combination 1911-39

**Club Colours (change):** Blue/blue/white (Purple/white/white)

**Ground Capacity:** 3,150 **Seats:** 525 **Covered:** 930 **Clubhouse:** Yes **Shop:** Yes

**Directions**
Leave M5 at Junction 3, follow A456 Kidderminster to first island and turn right (signposted A459 Dudley).
Turn left at next island (signposted A458 Stourbridge).
At next island take third exit into Old Hawne Lane.
Ground about 400 yards on left.

**Previous Grounds:** None

**Record Attendance:** 5,000 v Hendon - FA Cup 1st Round Proper 1954
**Record Victory:** 13-1 v Coventry Amateurs - Birmingham Senior cup 1956
**Record Defeat:** 0-8 v Bilston - West Midlands League 07/04/1962
**Record Goalscorer:** Paul Joinson - 369
**Record Appearances:** Paul Joinson - 608
**Additional Records:** Paid £7,250 to Gresley Rovers for Stuart Evans
Received £40,000 from Rushden & Diamonds for Jim Rodwell
**Honours:**
FA Vase 1984-85, 85-86 (R-up 1982-83). Southern League Midland Division 1989-90, Western Division 2001-02.
Birmingham Senior Cup 1983-84, 97-98. Staffordshire Senior Cup 1988-89.
Worcestershire Senior Cup 1951-52, 61-62, 2002-03, 04-05. Northern Premier Division One South 2013-14.

**10 YEAR RECORD**

| 06-07 | 07-08 | 08-09 | 09-10 | 10-11 | 11-12 | 12-13 | 13-14 | 14-15 | 15-16 |
|---|---|---|---|---|---|---|---|---|---|
| SthP 6 | SthP 3 | SthP 10 | SthP 8 | SthP 21 | Sthsw 12 | NP1S 7 | NP1S 1 | NP P 11 | NP P 13 |

# HALESOWEN TOWN MATCH RESULTS 2015-16

| Date | Comp | H/A | Opponents | Att: | Result | | Goalscorers | Pos | No. |
|---|---|---|---|---|---|---|---|---|---|
| Aug15 | NPL | H | Colwyn Bay | 471 | **W** | 1-0 | Fagbola 16 (og) | 8 | 1 |
| 18 | NPL | A | Mickleover Sports | 208 | L | 0-2 | | 14 | 2 |
| 22 | NPL | A | Skelmersdale United | 248 | L | 0-1 | | 17 | 3 |
| 25 | NPL | H | Stamford | 262 | L | 1-3 | Griffiths 65 | 20 | 4 |
| 29 | NPL | H | Workington | 337 | **W** | 2-0 | Pearson 8 Cooper 73 | 16 | 5 |
| 31 | NPL | A | Sutton Coldfield Town | 320 | L | 0-3 | | 20 | 6 |
| Sept5 | NPL | H | Darlington 1883 | 649 | L | 0-3 | | 22 | 7 |
| 8 | NPL | A | Matlock Town | 271 | **W** | 3-0 | Reffell 45 Pearson 68 Griffiths 81 | 18 | 8 |
| **12** | **FAC1Q** | **H** | **Mickleover Sports** | **252** | **W** | **2-1** | **Griffiths 43 Collins 89** | | 9 |
| 19 | NPL | A | Frickley Athletic | 267 | **W** | 2-1 | Rafell 84 87 | 17 | 10 |
| 22 | NPL | H | Marine | 259 | W | 1-0 | Hales 61 | 9 | 11 |
| **26** | **FAC2Q** | **H** | **Nuneaton Town** | **549** | **L** | **0-2** | | | 12 |
| 29 | NPL | A | Salford City | 394 | L | 1-3 | Bragoli 64 | 12 | 13 |
| Oct3 | NPL | H | Whitby Town | 377 | D | 0-0 | | 14 | 14 |
| 6 | NPL | H | Nantwich Town | 268 | D | 1-1 | Cooper 48 | 14 | 15 |
| 10 | NPL | H | Matlock Town | 450 | **W** | 3-2 | Hull 47 Bragoli 53 Pearson 87 | 10 | 16 |
| 13 | NPL | A | Barwell | 165 | L | 0-6 | | 12 | 17 |
| 17 | NPL | H | Ashton United | 340 | L | 1-2 | Bragoli 45 | 13 | 18 |
| 20 | NPL | A | Stamford | 237 | **W** | 2-1 | Bragoli 53 Gueyes 74 | 12 | 19 |
| 24 | NPL | H | Skelmersdale United | 303 | **W** | 2-1 | Daniels 14 Hales 72 | | 20 |
| 27 | NPL | H | Mickleover Sports | 248 | D | 1-1 | Daniels 36 | 10 | 21 |
| **31** | **FAT1Q** | **H** | **Stourbridge** | **808** | **L** | **1-2** | **Daniels 34** | | 22 |
| Nov7 | NPL | A | Colwyn Bay | 235 | D | 1-1 | Hales 87 | 11 | 23 |
| 14 | NPL | H | Barwell | 254 | D | 1-1 | Raffell 62 | 9 | 24 |
| 21 | NPL | H | Ramsbottom United | 323 | **W** | 2-1 | Hales 58 Raffell 82 | 7 | 25 |
| 28 | NPL | A | Rushall Olympic | 241 | D | 0-0 | | 12 | 26 |
| Dec5 | NPL | H | Hyde United | 287 | D | 1-1 | Bragoli 71 | 8 | 27 |
| 12 | NPL | A | Grantham Town | 260 | L | 0-2 | | 8 | 28 |
| 19 | NPL | H | Frickley Athletic | 301 | D | 1-1 | Waite 48 | 8 | 29 |
| 26 | NPL | A | Stourbridge | 1813 | L | 2-3 | Turner 7 Anderson 51 | 11 | 30 |
| 28 | NPL | H | Sutton Coldfield Town | 445 | D | 2-2 | Anderson 46 89 | 11 | 31 |
| Jan2 | NPL | A | Marine | 409 | **W** | 3-0 | Anderson 13 Parsons-Smith 56 Melvin 83 | 8 | 32 |
| 9 | NPL | H | Blyth Spartans | 481 | L | 0-1 | | 10 | 33 |
| 23 | NPL | A | Workington | 470 | L | 0-3 | | 12 | 34 |
| 30 | NPL | A | Whitby Town | 276 | L | 1-2 | Anderson 57 | 14 | 35 |
| Feb13 | NPL | A | Nantwich Town | 320 | L | 0-3 | | 15 | 36 |
| 20 | NPL | H | Buxton | 401 | D | 1-1 | Ravenhill 10 (og) | 15 | 37 |
| 27 | NPL | A | Buxton | 300 | D | 1-1 | Sweeney 39 | 17 | 38 |
| Mar4 | NPL | H | Ilkeston | 457 | **W** | 2-0 | Clarke 69 Melvin 74 (pen) | 15 | 39 |
| 12 | NPL | A | Blyth Spartans | 745 | **W** | 1-0 | Clarke 35 | 13 | 40 |
| 15 | NPL | H | Salford City | 746 | L | 0-1 | | 13 | 41 |
| 19 | NPL | A | Ilkeston | 344 | **W** | 3-1 | Anderson 8 27 Parsons-Smith 34 | 13 | 42 |
| 26 | NPL | A | Darlington 83 | 1416 | L | 1-2 | Turner 53 | 13 | 43 |
| 28 | NPL | H | Stourbridge | 2107 | **W** | 2-0 | Sweeney 38 Chiriac 80 | 12 | 44 |
| Apr2 | NPL | H | Rushall Olympic | 411 | L | 1-3 | Sweeney 90 | 13 | 45 |
| 9 | NPL | A | Ramsbottom United | 182 | **W** | 2-0 | Mole 12 Anderson 43 | 13 | 46 |
| 16 | NPL | H | Grantham Town | 428 | **W** | 3-0 | Clarke 9 Denny 44 Griffiths 78 | 13 | 47 |
| 19 | NPL | A | Ashton United | 185 | L | 0-3 | | 13 | 48 |
| 23 | NPL | A | Hyde United | 359 | **W** | 1-0 | Clarke 54 | 13 | 49 |

| GOALSCORERS | Scoring Games | Consec Sco Games | Total | | Scoring Games | Consec Sco Games | Total |
|---|---|---|---|---|---|---|---|
| **2014-15 *Christie*** | | | ***20*** | Melvin | 2 | | 2 |
| Anderson | 6 | 3 | 8 | Parsons-Smith | 2 | | 2 |
| Bragoli | 5 | 2 | 5 | Turner | 2 | | 2 |
| Raffell | 3 | 2 | 5 | Chiriac | 1 | | 1 |
| Clarke | 4 | | 4 | Collins | 1 | | 1 |
| Griffiths | 4 | 2 | 4 | Denny | 1 | | 1 |
| Hales | 4 | | 4 | Gueyes | 1 | | 1 |
| Daniels | 3 | 3 | 3 | Hull | 1 | | 1 |
| Pearson | 3 | | 3 | Mole | 1 | | 1 |
| Sweeney | 3 | | 3 | ***Waite*** | ***1*** | | ***1*** |
| Cooper | 2 | | 2 | ***Opponents*** | | | ***2*** |

# HEDNESFORD TOWN

**Chairman:** Stephen Price
**Secretary:** Terry McMahon **(T)** 07901 822 040 **(E)** mcmahon64@gmail.com
**Commercial Manager:** Terry McMahon **(T/E)** 07901 822 040
**Programme Editor:** Scott Smith **(T/E)** 07518 144 801
**Ground Address:** Keys Park, Park Road, Hednesford, Cannock WS12 2DZ
**(T)** 01543 422 870 **Manager:** Liam McDonald

## Club Factfile

**Founded:** 1880 **Nickname:** The Pitmen
**Previous Names:** Hednesford 1938-74
**Previous Leagues:** Walsall & District, Birmingham Comb. 1906-15, 45-53, West Mids 1919-39, 53-72, 74-84, Midland Counties 1972-74, Southern 1984-95, 2001-2005, 2009-11, Conference 1995-2001, 05-06, 13-16. Northern Premier 2006-09, 11-13.

**Club Colours (change):** White & black/white/white & black (Red & yellow/red/red & yellow)

**Ground Capacity:** 6,039 **Seats:** 1,011 **Covered:** 5,335 **Clubhouse:** Yes **Shop:** Yes

**Directions**
Leave M6 at J11 and follow the signs for Cannock. At the next island take the third exit towards Rugeley (A460). On reaching the A5 at Churchbridge island, rejoin the A460 signposted Rugeley and follow this road over five traffic islands. At the sixth traffic island, by a Texaco petrol station, turn right past a McDonalds restaurant and follow this road to the next island which is 'Cross Keys Island'. Go over this island to the next small island and turn right. Keys Park football ground is on left.

**Previous Grounds:** The Tins 1880-1903. The Cross Keys 1903-95.

**Record Attendance:** 3,169 v York City - FA Cup 3rd Round 13/01/1997
**Record Victory:** 12-1 v Redditch United - Birmingham Combination 1952-53
**Record Defeat:** 0-15 v Burton - Birmingham Combination 1952-53
**Record Goalscorer:** Joe O'Connor - 230 in 430 games
**Record Appearances:** Kevin Foster - 463
**Additional Records:** Paid £12,000 to Macclesfield Town for Steve Burr
Received £50,000 from Blackpool for Kevin Russell
**Honours:**
Southern League Premier Division 1994-95. FA Trophy 2004-05.
Staffordshire Senior Cup x3 Most recently 2012-13. Birmingham Senior Cup 1935-36, 2012-13.

**10 YEAR RECORD**

| 06-07 | 07-08 | 08-09 | 09-10 | 10-11 | 11-12 | 12-13 | 13-14 | 14-15 | 15-16 |
|---|---|---|---|---|---|---|---|---|---|
| NP P 7 | NP P 8 | NP P 8 | SthP 4 | SthP 2 | NP P 5 | NP P 2 | Conf N 4 | Conf N 8 | Nat N 21 |

## HEDNESFORD TOWN MATCH RESULTS 2015-16

| Date | Comp | H/A | Opponents | Att: | Result | | Goalscorers | Pos | No. |
|---|---|---|---|---|---|---|---|---|---|
| Aug 8 | Nat North | H | Stalybridge Celtic | 513 | **W** | 2-1 | Tilt 16 Modest 76 | 4 | 1 |
| 11 | Nat North | A | AFC Fylde | 355 | L | 0-2 | | 11 | 2 |
| 15 | Nat North | A | Harrogate Town | 345 | L | 1-2 | Todd 61 | 13 | 3 |
| 18 | Nat North | H | Corby Town | 462 | D | 3-3 | Tilt 2 Williams 10 Modest 62 | 13 | 4 |
| 22 | Nat North | A | North Ferriby United | 274 | D | 1-1 | Digie 60 | 13 | 5 |
| 29 | Nat North | H | FC United | 927 | L | 0-3 | | 17 | 6 |
| 31 | Nat North | A | Worcester City | 576 | **W** | 4-1 | Thorley 20 Obeng 38 Williams 51 Bailey 64 | 15 | 7 |
| Sept 5 | Nat North | H | Boston United | 510 | **W** | 3-2 | Obeng 31 Williams 34 90 | 11 | 8 |
| 12 | Nat North | A | Alfreton Town | 572 | L | 0-4 | | 14 | 9 |
| 15 | Nat North | H | Gloucester City | 410 | D | 2-2 | Perry 35 (pen) 59 | 13 | 10 |
| 19 | Nat North | A | Brackley Town | 356 | D | 1-1 | Perry 32 | 13 | 11 |
| **26** | **FAC2Q** | **H** | **Bedworth United** | **100** | **W** | **2-0** | **Todd 71 Thorley 82** | | 12 |
| Oct 3 | Nat North | H | Lowestoft Town | 378 | **W** | 2-1 | Williams 35 Thorley 51 | 12 | 13 |
| **10** | **FAC3Q** | **H** | **Alfreton Town** | **569** | **L** | **2-4** | **Obeng 12 Disney 74 (pen)** | | 14 |
| 17 | Nat North | A | Chorley | 1057 | D | 2-2 | Thomas 64 Digie 86 | 11 | 15 |
| 24 | Nat North | H | Nuneaton Town | 525 | L | 2-4 | Johnson 58 Perry 61 | 12 | 16 |
| 31 | Nat North | A | Tamworth | 871 | L | 0-1 | | 13 | 17 |
| Nov 14 | Nat North | H | Solihull Moors | 562 | D | 0-0 | | 13 | 18 |
| 21 | Nat North | A | Bradford PA | 284 | D | 1-1 | Thomas 3 | 13 | 19 |
| **28** | **FAT3Q** | **A** | **Leamington** | **306** | **L** | **2-4** | **Todd 14 Bailey 71** | | 20 |
| Dec 5 | Nat North | H | AFC Fylde | 409 | L | 0-1 | | 17 | 21 |
| 12 | Nat North | A | Gainsborough Trinity | 361 | L | 1-3 | Perry 86 | 18 | 22 |
| 19 | Nat North | A | Stalybridge Celtic | 408 | L | 2-4 | Peers 19 Bailey 88 | | 23 |
| 26 | Nat North | H | AFC Telford United | 962 | **W** | 2-0 | Perry 42 Thomas 45 | 17 | 24 |
| 28 | Nat North | A | FC United | 3421 | D | 1-1 | Thomas 65 | 17 | 25 |
| Jan 9 | Nat North | H | Harrogate Town | 375 | L | 2-3 | Ngamvoulou 77 Payne 90 | 19 | 26 |
| 23 | Nat North | A | Boston United | 1269 | L | 1-3 | Ngamvoulou 11 | 21 | 27 |
| 26 | Nat North | A | AFC Telford United | 1257 | **W** | 3-1 | Perry 53 Thomas 73 James 90 | 18 | 28 |
| 30 | Nat North | H | Curzon Ashton | 454 | L | 0-3 | | 18 | 29 |
| Feb 13 | Nat North | H | Gainsborough Trinity | 321 | L | 0-2 | | 20 | 30 |
| 16 | Nat North | H | North Ferriby United | 251 | D | 1-1 | Payne 19 | 21 | 31 |
| 20 | Nat North | H | Chorley | 404 | L | 1-3 | Thomas 56 | 21 | 32 |
| 23 | Nat North | A | Lowestoft Town | 465 | D | 0-0 | | 21 | 33 |
| 27 | Nat North | H | Brackley Town | 355 | L | 0-2 | | 21 | 34 |
| Mar 1 | Nat North | A | Stockport County | 2289 | L | 0-3 | | 21 | 35 |
| 5 | Nat North | A | Gloucester City | 350 | D | 2-2 | Digie 18 65 | 21 | 36 |
| 12 | Nat North | H | Alfreton Town | 421 | D | 3-3 | Payne 13 (pen) 24(pen) Fitzwater 37 | 21 | 37 |
| 19 | Nat North | H | Stockport County | 572 | L | 1-2 | Bailey 72 | 21 | 38 |
| 26 | Nat North | A | Corby Town | 566 | D | 0-0 | | 21 | 39 |
| Apr 2 | Nat North | A | Curzon Ashton | 329 | L | 2-3 | Ennis 69 Royle 51 | 21 | 40 |
| 9 | Nat North | H | Tamworth | 601 | **W** | 2-1 | Peers 69 76 | 21 | 41 |
| 12 | Nat North | H | Worcester City | 333 | L | 0-1 | | 21 | 42 |
| 16 | Nat North | A | Solihull Moors | 972 | **W** | 2-1 | Thomas 17 Glover 51 | 21 | 43 |
| 23 | Nat North | H | Bradford PA | 287 | D | 0-0 | | 21 | 44 |
| 30 | Nat North | A | Nuneaton Town | 866 | L | 0-3 | | 21 | 45 |

| GOALSCORERS | Scoring Games | Consec Sco Games | Total | | Scoring Games | Consec Sco Games | Total |
|---|---|---|---|---|---|---|---|
| ***2014-15 Glover*** | | | ***11*** | Modest | 2 | | 2 |
| Perry | 7 | 2 | 7 | Ngamvoulou | 2 | | 2 |
| Thomas | 7 | | 7 | Tilt | 2 | | 2 |
| Williams | 5 | 2 | 5 | Disney | 1 | | 1 |
| Bailey | 4 | 2 | 4 | Ennis | 1 | | 1 |
| Digie | 4 | 2 | 4 | Fitzwater | 1 | | 1 |
| Payne | 3 | | 4 | Glover | 1 | | 1 |
| Obeng | 3 | | 3 | James | 1 | | 1 |
| Peers | 2 | | 3 | Johnson | 1 | | 1 |
| Thorley | 3 | | 3 | Royal | 1 | | 1 |
| Todd | 3 | | 3 | | | | |

# ILKESTON

**Chairman:** Nigel Harrop
**Secretary:** Andrew Raisin **(T)** 07813 357 393 **(E)** a.raisin@ilkestonfc.co.uk
**Commercial Manager:** **(T/E)**
**Programme Editor:** Declan Harrop **(T/E)** 07446 976 265
**Ground Address:** New Manor Ground, Awsworth Road, Ilkeston, Derbyshire DE7 8JF
**(T)** 0115 944 428 **Manager:** Paul Holland

## Club Factfile

**Founded:** 2010 **Nickname:** The Robins
**Previous Names:** None
**Previous Leagues:** None

**Club Colours (change):** Red & blue/white/white (Blue & white /white/white)

**Ground Capacity:** 3,029 **Seats:** 550 **Covered:** 2,000 **Clubhouse:** Yes **Shop:** Yes

**Directions**
M1 Junction 26, take the A610 signed Ripley, leave at the first exit on to the A6096 signed Awsworth / Ilkeston, at the next island take the A6096 signed Ilkeston, keep on this road for about half a mile, then turn right into Awsworth Road, Signed Cotmanhay (Coaches can get down this road) the ground is about half a mile on the left hand side down this road. Car Parking available at the ground £1 per car.

**Previous Grounds:** None.

**Record Attendance:** 2,680 v Chelsea - pre-season friendly July 2013. Competitive: 1,670 v Leek Town - NPL Divi.1S P-Off Final 28.4.2012.
**Record Victory:** 7-0 v Sheffield FC - Evo-Stik League D1S P-Off SF 23.4.2012 & v Heanor Town (H) Derbys Sen Cup 2012-13.
**Record Defeat:** 1-5 v Northwich Victoria (H) - FA Trophy Third Qualifying Round 28.11.2011.
**Record Goalscorer:** Gary Ricketts - 32
**Record Appearances:** Ryan Wilson - 88
**Additional Records:**

**Honours:**
Northern Premier League Division One South Play-Off 2011-12.
Derbyshire Senior Challenge Cup 2012-13, 13-14.

**10 YEAR RECORD**

| 06-07 | 07-08 | 08-09 | 09-10 | 10-11 | 11-12 | 12-13 | 13-14 | 14-15 | 15-16 |
|---|---|---|---|---|---|---|---|---|---|
| | | | | | NP1S 3 | NP P 12 | NP P 17 | NP P 5 | NP P 14 |

# ILKESTON MATCH RESULTS 2015-16

| Date | Comp | H/A | Opponents | Att: | Result | | Goalscorers | Pos | No. |
|---|---|---|---|---|---|---|---|---|---|
| Aug 15 | NPL | H | Skelmersdale United | 505 | L | 1-3 | Harness 6 | 20 | 1 |
| 18 | NPL | A | Grantham Town | 228 | W | 2-1 | Hughes 29 Baker 86 | 16 | 2 |
| 22 | NPL | A | Colwyn Bay | 300 | W | 2-0 | Edwards 34 Hughes 50 | 8 | 3 |
| 24 | NPL | H | Stourbridge | 454 | W | 4-3 | Coulson 12 Edwards 24 Luto 56 Hughes 62 | 3 | 4 |
| 29 | NPL | H | Sutton Coldfield Town | 457 | D | 1-1 | Harness 60 | 4 | 5 |
| 31 | NPL | A | Matlock Town | 529 | L | 0-1 | | 9 | 6 |
| Sept 5 | NPL | H | Ashton United | 497 | D | 1-1 | Garton 3 (og) | 9 | 7 |
| 8 | NPL | A | Frickley Athletic | 237 | L | 1-3 | Blake 86 | 12 | 8 |
| **12** | **FAC1Q** | **H** | **Rugby Town** | **417** | **L** | **2-3** | **Ndlovu 2 Williams 75** | | 9 |
| 19 | NPL | A | Marine | 398 | L | 1-3 | Williams 89 (pen) | 19 | 10 |
| 21 | NPL | H | Darlington 1883 | 489 | D | 1-1 | Blake 11 | 19 | 11 |
| 30 | NPL | A | Whitby Town | 246 | L | 2-4 | Ndlovu 5 Blake 77 | 19 | 12 |
| Oct 3 | NPL | H | Nantwich Town | 455 | W | 3-1 | Ndlovu 55 75 Marshall 68 | 17 | 13 |
| 6 | NPL | H | Barwell | 404 | W | 1-0 | Marshall 81 (pen) | 9 | 14 |
| 10 | NPL | A | Colwyn Bay | 534 | D | 0-0 | | 11 | 15 |
| 13 | NPL | A | Stamford | 332 | D | 1-1 | Udoh 39 | 11 | 16 |
| 17 | NPL | H | Buxton | 495 | W | 3-1 | Williams 62 70 Atkinson 80 | | 17 |
| 20 | NPL | A | Stourbridge | 503 | W | 2-1 | Udoh 65 Atkinson 7 | 6 | 18 |
| 24 | NPL | H | Colwyn Bay | 484 | W | 2-1 | Coulson 28 Burgess 45 | 5 | 19 |
| **31** | **FAT1Q** | **A** | **Cambridge City** | **232** | **W** | **1-0** | **Coulson 45** | | 20 |
| **14** | **FAT2Q** | **H** | **Stocksbridge PS** | **406** | **D** | **1-1** | **Burgess 65** | | 21 |
| **17** | **FAT2Qr** | **A** | **Stocksbridge PS** | **108** | **L** | **2-3** | **Blake 41 Patterson 49 (og)** | | 22 |
| 21 | NPL | H | Hyde United | 454 | W | 3-1 | Ndlovu 55 Udoh 62 90 | 6 | 23 |
| 28 | NPL | A | Workington | 333 | L | 2-3 | Ndlovu 38 Doyle-Charles 58 | 8 | 24 |
| Dec 5 | NPL | H | Ramsbottom United | 432 | W | 3-0 | Ndlovu 76 Williams 81 Udoh 84 | 7 | 25 |
| 19 | NPL | H | Marine | 405 | D | 0-0 | | 7 | 26 |
| 26 | NPL | A | Mickleover Sports | 441 | D | 1-1 | Baker 5 | 8 | 27 |
| 28 | NPL | H | Matlock Town | 593 | L | 0-1 | | 9 | 28 |
| Jan 9 | NPL | A | Barwell | 247 | L | 0-4 | | 13 | 29 |
| 19 | NPL | A | Rushall Olympic | 217 | D | 2-2 | Williams 74 Ndlovu 80 | 12 | 30 |
| 23 | NPL | A | Sutton Coldfield | 203 | W | 2-0 | Blake 19 Atkinson 90 | 10 | 31 |
| 25 | NPL | H | Frickley Athletic | 338 | L | 0-2 | | 10 | 32 |
| 30 | NPL | A | Nantwich Town | 429 | D | 1-1 | Ndlovu 39 | 10 | 33 |
| Feb 9 | NPL | A | Blyth Spartans | 571 | L | 0-1 | | 10 | 34 |
| 13 | NPL | A | Skelmersdale United | 234 | L | 1-2 | Williams 47 | 13 | 35 |
| 20 | NPL | H | Salford City | 999 | W | 2-1 | Baker 18 Burrows 55 | 12 | 36 |
| 22 | NPL | H | Stamford | 352 | L | 0-3 | | 12 | 37 |
| 27 | NPL | A | Salford City | 889 | L | 0-2 | | 12 | 38 |
| Mar 5 | NPL | A | Halesowen Town | 457 | L | 0-2 | | 13 | 39 |
| 8 | NPL | A | Darlington 1883 | 1021 | L | 1-3 | Udoh 90 | 13 | 40 |
| 12 | NPL | H | Workington | 402 | L | 0-3 | | 14 | 41 |
| 19 | NPL | H | Halesowen Town | 344 | L | 1-3 | Atkinson 74 | 15 | 42 |
| 26 | NPL | A | Ashton United | 207 | L | 1-2 | Lee 87 | 16 | 43 |
| 28 | NPL | H | Mickleover Sports | 431 | L | 0-2 | | 16 | 44 |
| Apr 2 | NPL | H | Blyth Spartans | 404 | L | 3-4 | Nicholson 10 (og) Goddard 31 Rose 37 | 16 | 45 |
| 4 | NPL | H | Whitby Town | 345 | W | 2-1 | Williams 26 (pen) 38 | 16 | 46 |
| 9 | NPL | A | Hyde United | 340 | W | 3-1 | Thornberry 1 Gordon 18 Burrows 90 | 15 | 47 |
| 13 | NPL | A | Buxton | 228 | L | 1-3 | Atkinson 43 | 15 | 48 |
| 16 | NPL | H | Rushall Olympic | 435 | W | 4-1 | Atkinson 14 Gordon 65 Lee 82 Tyrell 87 | 14 | 49 |
| 23 | NPL | A | Ramsbottom United | 233 | L | 0-4 | | 14 | 50 |

| GOALSCORERS | Scoring Games | Consec Sco Games | Total |
|---|---|---|---|
| **2014-15 *Duffy*** | | | ***20*** |
| Williams | 7 | 2 | 9 |
| Ndlovu | 8 | 2 | 9 |
| Atkinson | 6 | 2 | 6 |
| Blake | 5 | 2 | 5 |
| Udoe | 5 | | 5 |
| Coulson | 3 | 2 | 3 |
| Hughes | 3 | 2 | 3 |
| Baker | 3 | | 3 |
| Burgess | 2 | | 2 |
| Burrows | 2 | | 2 |
| Edwards | 2 | 2 | 2 |
| Gordon | 2 | | 2 |
| Harness | 2 | | 2 |
| Lee | 2 | | 2 |
| Marshall | 2 | | 2 |
| Doyle-Charles | 1 | | 1 |
| Goddard | 1 | | 1 |
| Luto | 1 | | 1 |
| Marshall | 1 | | 1 |
| Rose | 1 | | 1 |
| Thornberry | 1 | | 1 |
| Tyrell | 1 | | 1 |
| Opponents | | | 3 |

# MARINE

**Chairman:** Paul Leary
**Secretary:** Richard Cross (T) 07762 711 714 (E) richard@marinefc.com
**Commercial Manager:** contact secretary (T/E)
**Programme Editor:** Dave McMillan (T/E) 07949 483 003
**Ground Address:** The Marine Travel Arena, College Road, Crosby, Liverpool L23 3AS
(T) 0151 924 1743 **Manager:** Sean Hessey

2015-16 Squad - Back Row (L-R) – Connor Willis, Chad Whyte, Matty Cooper, Jack Stanford, Llloyd Ellams, James Foley, Jonathan Goulding
Middle Row (L-R) – Gary Trowler (Kit Manager), Andy Nicholas, Liam Willis, Andy Owens, Brian Lawlor (Committee), Richard Cross (Club Secretary), Paul Eustace (Committee), Barry Godfrey (Committee), Mitch Duggan, James Short, Thomas Owens
Front Row (L-R) – Estelle Riley (Physio), Sean Myler, Steven Wainwright, Lewis Codling, Phil Hackney (Assistant Manger), Sean Hessey (Manager), Dave McMillan (Vice Chairman), Carl Peers, Jamie Menagh, Karl Clair, Phil Fisher (Goalkeeper Coach)

## Club Factfile

**Founded:** 1894 **Nickname:** Mariners
**Previous Names:** None
**Previous Leagues:** Liverpool Zingari, Liverpool County Combination, Lancashire Combination 1935-39, 46-69, Cheshire County 1969-79

**Club Colours (change):** White/black/white & black hoops (Yellow/green/green & white hoops)

**Ground Capacity:** 3,185 **Seats:** 400 **Covered:** 1,400 **Clubhouse:** Yes **Shop:** Yes

**Directions**
From the East & South: Leave the M62 at junction 6 and take the M57 to Switch Island at the end. At the end of the M57 take the A5036 (signposted Bootle & Docks). At the roundabout, at the end of the road (by Docks), turn right onto the A565 following signs for 'Crosby' and 'Marine AFC' and follow this road for 1 mile. After passing the Tesco Express on your right, turn left at the traffic lights (by Merchant Taylors' School) into College Road. The ground is half a mile on your left
From the North: Leave the M6 at junction 26 and join the M58. Travel along the M58 to Switch Island at the end. Take the A5036 (signposted Bootle & Docks) and follow directions above.

**Previous Grounds:** Waterloo Park 1894-1903

**Record Attendance:** 4,000 v Nigeria - Friendly 1949
**Record Victory:** 14-0 v Sandhurst - FA Cup 1st Qualifying Round 01/10/1938
**Record Defeat:** 2-11 v Shrewsbury Town - FA Cup 1st Round 1995
**Record Goalscorer:** Paul Meachin - 200
**Record Appearances:** Peter Smith 952
**Additional Records:** Paid £6,000 to Southport for Jon Penman October 1985
Received £20,000 from Crewe Alexandra for Richard Norris 1996
**Honours:**
Northern Premier League Premier Division 1993-94, 84-95.
Lancashire Junior Cup 1978-79, Lancashire Trophy x3. Lancashire Amateur Cup x5. Lancashire Senior Cup x6.
Liverpool Non-League Cup x3. Liverpool Challenge Cup x3.

### 10 YEAR RECORD

| 06-07 | 07-08 | 08-09 | 09-10 | 10-11 | 11-12 | 12-13 | 13-14 | 14-15 | 15-16 |
|---|---|---|---|---|---|---|---|---|---|
| NP P 4 | NP P 7 | NP P 13 | NP P 9 | NP P 9 | NP P 7 | NP P 11 | NP P 20 | NP P 21 | NP P 15 |

# MARINE MATCH RESULTS 2015-16

| Date | Comp | H/A | Opponents | Att: | Result | Goalscorers | Pos | No. |
|---|---|---|---|---|---|---|---|---|
| Aug 15 | NPL | A | Salford City | 518 | D 0-0 | | 14 | 1 |
| 18 | NPL | H | Ashton United | 294 | D 0-0 | | 17 | 2 |
| 22 | NPL | H | Nantwich Town | 345 | L 1-2 | Codling 51 | 19 | 3 |
| 24 | NPL | A | Hyde United | 414 | W 2-0 | Peers 11 Ollerenshaw 88 (og) | 11 | 4 |
| 29 | NPL | A | Barwell | 178 | D 1-1 | Hickey 27 (og) | 13 | 5 |
| 31 | NPL | H | Skelmersdale United | 486 | D 2-2 | Codling 63 Peers 82 | 15 | 6 |
| Sept 5 | NPL | A | Grantham | 207 | D 0-0 | | 15 | 7 |
| 8 | NPL | H | Rushall Olympic | 301 | D 1-1 | Ellams 8 (pen) | 16 | 8 |
| **12** | **FAC1Q** | **H** | **Clitheroe** | **237** | **W 2-0** | **Peers 30 Clair 90** | | 9 |
| 19 | NPL | H | Ilkeston | 398 | W 3-1 | Owens 5 (pen) 84 Whyte 35 | 16 | 10 |
| 22 | NPL | A | Halesowen Town | 259 | L 0-1 | | 18 | 11 |
| **26** | **FAC2Q** | **H** | **Washington** | **293** | **D 3-3** | **Ellams 12 (pen) 27 Codling 68** | | 12 |
| **29** | **FAC2Q r** | **A** | **Washington** | **318** | **W 3-2** | **Ellams 74 Peers 108 120 (aet)** | | 13 |
| Oct 3 | NPL | A | Darlington 1883 | 1171 | W 1-0 | Ellams 76 (pen) | 16 | 14 |
| **13** | **FAC3Q** | **H** | **Northwich Victoria** | **417** | **L 2-4** | **Owens 51 Whyte 83** | | 15 |
| 17 | NPL | A | Frickley Athletic | 224 | W 1-0 | Mitchley 39 | | 16 |
| 20 | NPL | H | Hyde United | 290 | L 2-3 | Holden 63 Mitchley 65 | 19 | 17 |
| 24 | NPL | A | Nantwich Town | 335 | D 1-1 | Mitchley 45 | 18 | 18 |
| 27 | NPL | A | Ashton United | 152 | L 2-3 | Mitchley 60 Owens 78 | 19 | 19 |
| **31** | **FAT1Q** | **H** | **Sheffield** | **259** | **W 1-0** | **Owens 82** | | 20 |
| Nov 7 | NPL | H | Whitby Town | 435 | W 2-1 | Willis 1 Owens 12 | 17 | 21 |
| **14** | **FAT2Q** | **H** | **Kidsgrove Athletic** | **274** | **D 2-2** | **Nicholas 59 Whyte 69** | | 22 |
| 21 | NPL | H | Stourbridge | 333 | L 1-3 | Whyte 75 | 19 | 23 |
| **Dec 1** | **FAT2Qr** | **A** | **Kidsgrove Athletic** | **156** | **W 1-0** | **Whyte 47** | | 24 |
| 5 | NPL | H | Blyth Spartans | 414 | L 0-2 | | 20 | 25 |
| **8** | **FAT3Q** | **H** | **Burscough** | **294** | **L 1-2** | **Mitchley 62** | | 26 |
| 15 | NPL | H | Workington | 276 | L 1-2 | Willis 81 | 22 | 27 |
| 19 | NPL | A | Ilkeston | 405 | D 0-0 | | 19 | 28 |
| Jan 2 | NPL | H | Halesowen Town | 409 | L 0-3 | | 19 | 29 |
| 23 | NPL | H | Barwell | 335 | L 1-2 | Mitchley 41 | 20 | 30 |
| 26 | NPL | A | Rushall Olympic | 161 | L 0-3 | | 20 | 31 |
| 30 | NPL | H | Darlington 1883 | 552 | L 0-1 | | 21 | 32 |
| Feb 1 | NPL | A | Stourbridge | 387 | L 0-2 | | 21 | 33 |
| 6 | NPL | A | Workington | 470 | L 0-1 | | | 34 |
| 9 | NPL | H | Colwyn Bay | 328 | D 2-2 | Codling 33 Nicholas 71 | 21 | 35 |
| 13 | NPL | H | Matlock Town | 286 | W 2-1 | Mitchley 89 (pen) Codling 90 | 21 | 36 |
| 20 | NPL | A | Matlock Town | 323 | D 0-0 | | 21 | 37 |
| 23 | NPL | H | Salford City | 425 | L 0-2 | | 21 | 38 |
| 27 | NPL | H | Sutton Coldfield Town | 376 | W 2-1 | Mitchley 58 Nicholas | 19 | 39 |
| Mar 1 | NPL | A | Skelmersdale United | 257 | W 3-2 | Mitchley 15 18 (pen) Wainwright 50 | 19 | 40 |
| 12 | NPL | A | Mickleover Sports | 180 | D 1-1 | Willis 64 | 19 | 41 |
| 15 | NPL | H | Buxton | 319 | L 1-2 | Sharp 33 | 19 | 42 |
| 19 | NPL | A | Stamford | 407 | D 0-0 | | 19 | 43 |
| 22 | NPL | A | Ramsbottom United | 192 | D 1-1 | Codling 23 | 18 | 44 |
| 28 | NPL | A | Colwyn Bay | 305 | W 3-0 | Mitchley 7 Short 22 Barnett 65 | 19 | 45 |
| 31 | NPL | A | Buxton | 183 | W 3-2 | Mitchley 51 Owens 89 (pen) 90 (pen) | 18 | 46 |
| Apr 2 | NPL | H | Stamford | 329 | D 1-1 | Sharp 18 | 17 | 47 |
| 5 | NPL | H | Mickleover Sports | 297 | D 3-3 | Barnett 52 Nicholas 69 Owens 81 | 16 | 48 |
| 7 | NPL | H | Grantham Town | 254 | D 1-1 | Hebson 80 | 15 | 49 |
| 9 | NPL | A | Whitby Town | 249 | L 0-1 | | 18 | 50 |
| 13 | NPL | H | Frickley Athletic | 286 | D 1-1 | Barnett 5 | 18 | 51 |
| 16 | NPL | H | Ramsbottom United | 425 | W 3-0 | Mitchley 27 (pen) 67 Goulding 62 | 17 | 52 |
| 19 | NPL | A | Sutton Coldfield | 121 | L 2-4 | Codling 27 Whyte 29 | 17 | 53 |
| 23 | NPL | A | Blyth Spartans | 636 | W 2-1 | Bellew 49 Mitchley 82 | 15 | 54 |

| GOALSCORERS | Scoring Games | Consec Sco Games | Total |
|---|---|---|---|
| **2014-15 *Ellams*** | | | ***12*** |
| Mitchley | 13 | 4 | 15 |
| Owens | 8 | | 9 |
| Codling | 7 | 2 | 7 |
| Whyte | 5 | 3 | 6 |
| Ellams | 4 | 3 | 5 |
| Peers | 4 | | 5 |
| Nicholas | 4 | | 4 |
| Barnett | 3 | | 3 |
| Willis | 3 | | 3 |
| Sharp | 2 | | 2 |
| Bellew | 1 | | 1 |
| Clair | 1 | | 1 |
| Goulding | 1 | | 1 |
| Hebson | 1 | | 1 |
| Holden | 1 | | 1 |
| Short | 1 | | 1 |
| Wainwright | 1 | | 1 |
| Opponents | | | 2 |

# MATLOCK TOWN

**Chairman:** Tom Wright
**Secretary:** Keith Brown (T) 07831 311 427 (E) clubshop@matlocktownfc.com
**Commercial Manager:** Tom Wright (T/E) 07850 065 968
**Programme Editor:** Tom Wright (T/E) 07850 065 968
**Ground Address:** Autoworld Arena, Causeway Lane, Matlock, Derbyshire DE4 3AR
(T) 01629 583 866 **Manager:** Craig Hopkins & Glen Kirkwood

Photo: Bill Wheatcroft

## Club Factfile

**Founded:** 1885 **Nickname:** The Gladiators
**Previous Names:** None
**Previous Leagues:** Midland Combination 1894-96, Matlock and District, Derbyshire Senior, Central Alliance 1924-25, 47-61, Central Combination 1934-35, Chesterfield & District 1946-47, Midland Counties 1961-69

**Club Colours (change):** All royal blue (All yellow)

**Ground Capacity:** 5,500 **Seats:** 560 **Covered:** 1,200 **Clubhouse:** Yes **Shop:** Yes

**Directions**
On A615, ground is 500 yards from Town Centre and Matlock BR. Sat Nav users can enter DE4 3AR

**Previous Grounds:** None

**Record Attendance:** 5,123 v Burton Albion - FA Trophy 1975
**Record Victory:** 10-0 v Lancaster City (A) - 1974
**Record Defeat:** 0-8 v Chorley (A) - 1971
**Record Goalscorer:** Peter Scott
**Record Appearances:** Mick Fenoughty
**Additional Records:** Paid £2,000 for Kenny Clark 1996
Received £10,000 from York City for Ian Helliwell
**Honours:**
FA Trophy 1974-75. Anglo Italian Non-League Cup 1979.
Derbyshire Senior Cup x7.

**10 YEAR RECORD**

| 06-07 | 07-08 | 08-09 | 09-10 | 10-11 | 11-12 | 12-13 | 13-14 | 14-15 | 15-16 |
|---|---|---|---|---|---|---|---|---|---|
| NP P 5 | NP P 16 | NP P 15 | NP P 7 | NP P 11 | NP P 14 | NP P 17 | NP P 12 | NP P 14 | NP P 17 |

# MATLOCK TOWN MATCH RESULTS 2015-16

| Date | Comp | H/A | Opponents | Att: | Result | | Goalscorers | Pos | No. |
|---|---|---|---|---|---|---|---|---|---|
| Aug 15 | NPL | A | Frickley Athletic | 236 | **W** | 2-1 | Harcourt 86 Purkiss 90 | 6 | 1 |
| 18 | NPL | H | Salford City | 344 | L | 1-2 | Purkiss 84 | 12 | 2 |
| 22 | NPL | H | Whitby Town | 256 | **W** | 1-0 | McManus 89 | 9 | 3 |
| 25 | NPL | A | Rushall Olympic | 181 | **W** | 3-2 | Purkiss 14 McManus 20 Forbes 55 | 6 | 4 |
| 29 | NPL | A | Hyde United | 310 | D | 2-2 | McManus 48 Coates 55 | 5 | 5 |
| 31 | NPL | H | Ilkeston Town | 529 | **W** | 1-0 | McManus 31 | 2 | 6 |
| Sept 5 | NPL | A | Skelmersdale United | 236 | L | 2-3 | Holland 36 Cribley 63 | 5 | 7 |
| 8 | NPL | H | Halesowen Town | 271 | L | 0-3 | | 9 | 8 |
| **12** | **FAC1Q** | **H** | **Whitley Bay** | **287** | **D** | **0-0** | | | 9 |
| **15** | **FAC1Qr** | **A** | **Whitley Bay** | **338** | **L** | **3-3** | **Purkiss 65 Holland 83 Siddall 99 (Lost 2-4 on pens aet)** | | 10 |
| 19 | NPL | H | Colwyn Bay | 302 | D | 1-1 | Cribley 25 | 13 | 11 |
| 26 | NPL | A | Grantham Town | 183 | L | 1-2 | Wilson 12 | 14 | 12 |
| 29 | NPL | A | Mickleover Sports | 272 | L | 0-2 | | 17 | 13 |
| Oct 3 | NPL | H | Ashton United | 282 | **W** | 1-0 | Holland 19 | 12 | 14 |
| 6 | NPL | H | Marine | 237 | **W** | 1-0 | Nelthorpe 57 | 9 | 15 |
| 10 | NPL | A | Stourbridge | 450 | L | 2-3 | Holland 69 90 | 9 | 16 |
| 13 | NPL | A | Nantwich Town | 307 | D | 2-2 | McManus 11 Holland 14 | 9 | 17 |
| 17 | NPL | H | Stamford | 336 | L | 0-1 | | 10 | 18 |
| 24 | NPL | A | Whitby Town | 276 | L | 1-2 | Purkiss 72 | 16 | 19 |
| 27 | NPL | A | Salford City | 427 | D | 2-2 | Wilson 37 Holland 90 | 16 | 20 |
| **31** | **FAT 1Q** | **H** | **Gresley** | **242** | **W** | **2-0** | **Purkiss 40 Wilson 89 (pen)** | | 21 |
| Nov 7 | NPL | H | Frickley Athletic | 369 | **W** | 3-0 | Purkiss 27 36 McManus 90 | 14 | 22 |
| **14** | **FAT 2Q** | **A** | **Shaw Lane Aquaforce** | **232** | **W** | **2-1** | **Travis 51 Holland 59** | | 23 |
| 21 | NPL | H | Sutton Coldfield Town | 266 | D | 2-2 | Purkiss 4 Cribley 61 | 15 | 24 |
| **28** | **FAT3Q** | **H** | **Blyth Spartans** | **303** | **W** | **4-2** | **Holland 12 27 Siddall 76 McManus 83** | | 25 |
| Dec 5 | NPL | H | Barwell | 246 | L | 1-3 | Needham 45 | 16 | 26 |
| **12** | **FAT1** | **A** | **Nantwich Town** | **423** | **L** | **0-2** | | | 27 |
| 19 | NPL | A | Colwyn Bay | 148 | **W** | 4-1 | Purkiss 5 Wilson13 Cribley 79 McManus 86 | 16 | 28 |
| 26 | NPL | H | Buxton | 651 | L | 1-2 | Nelthorpe 23 | 16 | 29 |
| 28 | NPL | A | Ilkeston | 593 | **W** | 1-0 | Dawes 40 | 14 | 30 |
| Jan 23 | NPL | H | Hyde United | 364 | **W** | 2-1 | Wilson 44 McManus 77 | 15 | 31 |
| 30 | NPL | A | Ashton United | 162 | D | 4-4 | McManus 10 Wilson 36 Purkiss 66 80 | 15 | 32 |
| Feb 2 | NPL | H | Grantham Town | 220 | **W** | 3-1 | Wilson 25 Purkiss 50 Travis 63 | 13 | 33 |
| 9 | NPL | A | Darlington 1883 | 916 | L | 0-3 | | | 34 |
| 13 | NPL | A | Marne | 286 | L | 1-2 | Wilson 59 | 14 | 35 |
| 16 | NPL | H | Mickleover Sports | 282 | **W** | 2-0 | McManus 17 Wilson 69 | 14 | 36 |
| 20 | NPL | H | Marine | 323 | D | 0-0 | | 14 | 37 |
| 23 | NPL | H | Nantwich Town | 223 | D | 1-1 | Purkiss 37 | 14 | 38 |
| 27 | NPL | A | Stamford | 316 | L | 0-2 | | 14 | 39 |
| Mar 6 | NPL | A | Stourbridge | 344 | L | 1-4 | Needham 87 | 14 | 40 |
| 12 | NPL | H | Darlington 1983 | 745 | L | 0-5 | | 15 | 41 |
| 19 | NPL | A | Blyth Spartans | 567 | L | 0-1 | | 16 | 42 |
| 26 | NPL | H | Skelmersdale United | 259 | L | 1-2 | Wilson 14 (pen) | 17 | 43 |
| 28 | NPL | A | Buxton | 353 | L | 0-3 | | 17 | 44 |
| Apr 2 | NPL | H | Workington | 257 | L | 0-1 | | 18 | 45 |
| 5 | NPL | H | Ramsbottom United | 266 | **W** | 2-0 | McManus 9 Holland 10 | 17 | 46 |
| 9 | NPL | A | Sutton Coldfield | 192 | D | 2-2 | Dawes 32 Ball 49 | 17 | 47 |
| 12 | NPL | H | Stourbridge | 226 | D | 1-1 | Siddall 90 | 17 | 48 |
| 14 | NPL | A | Ramsbottom United | 132 | **W** | 3-0 | Purkiss 1 58 Dawes 12 | 16 | 49 |
| 16 | NPL | H | Blyth Spartans | 586 | L | 0-2 | | 16 | 50 |
| 19 | NPL | A | Workington | 394 | L | 1-4 | Dawes 40 | 16 | 51 |
| 23 | NPL | A | Barwell | 151 | L | 0-4 | | 17 | 52 |

| GOALSCORERS | Scoring Games | Consec Sco Games | Total | | Scoring Games | Consec Sco Games | Total |
|---|---|---|---|---|---|---|---|
| **2014-15 *Holland*** | | | ***18*** | Travis | 2 | | 2 |
| Purkiss | 13 | 2 | 16 | Ball | 1 | | 1 |
| McManus | 12 | 4 | 12 | Coates | 1 | | 1 |
| Holland | 9 | 2 | 11 | Forbes | 1 | | 1 |
| Wilson | 10 | 2 | 10 | Harcourt | 1 | | 1 |
| Cribley | 4 | | 4 | | | | |
| Dawes | 4 | | 4 | | | | |
| Siddall | 3 | | 3 | | | | |
| Needham | 2 | | 2 | | | | |
| Nelthorpe | 2 | | 2 | | | | |

# MICKLEOVER SPORTS

**Chairman:** Don Arnott
**Secretary:** Tony Shaw (T) 07966 197 246 (E)
**Commercial Manager:** (T/E)
**Programme Editor:** James Edge (T/E) 07964 217 945
**Ground Address:** Don Arnott Arena, Mickleover Sports Club, Station Rd, Mickleover Derby DE3 9JG
**(T)** 01332 521 167 **Manager:** Craig Hopkins

## Club Factfile

**Founded:** 1948 **Nickname:** Sports
**Previous Names:** Mickleover Old Boys 1948-93
**Previous Leagues:** Central Midlands 1993-99, Northern Counties East 1999-2009

**Club Colours (change):** Red and black stripes/black/red (All blue)

**Ground Capacity:** 1,500 **Seats:** 280 **Covered:** 500 **Clubhouse:** Yes **Shop:** Yes

**Directions**

M1 NORTH - J28. A38 to Derby. At Markeaton Island right A52 Ashbourne, 2nd left Radbourne Lane, 3rd Left Station Road 50 yds.

M1 SOUTH – J25. A52 to Derby. Follow signs for Ashbourne, pick up A52 at Markeaton Island (MacDonalds) then as above.

FROM STOKE A50 – Derby. A516 to A38 then as above.

**Previous Grounds:** None

**Record Attendance:** Not known
**Record Victory:** Not known
**Record Defeat:** Not known
**Record Goalscorer:** Not known
**Record Appearances:** Not known
**Additional Records:** Won 16 consecutive League matches in 2009-10 - a Northern Premier League record

**Honours:**
Central Midlands Supreme Division 1998-99. Northern Counties East Division One 2002-03, Premier Division 2008-09.
Northern Premier League Division One South 2009-10, 14-15.

### 10 YEAR RECORD

| 06-07 | 07-08 | 08-09 | 09-10 | 10-11 | 11-12 | 12-13 | 13-14 | 14-15 | 15-16 |
|---|---|---|---|---|---|---|---|---|---|
| NCEP 7 | NCEP 14 | NCEP 1 | NP1S 1 | NP P 15 | NP P 21 | NP1S 21 | NP1S 5 | NP1S 1 | NP P 20 |

# MICKLEOVER SPORTS MATCH RESULTS 2015-16

| Date | Comp | H/A | Opponents | Att: | Result | Goalscorers | Pos | No. |
|---|---|---|---|---|---|---|---|---|
| Aug 15 | NPL | A | Ashton United | 126 | D 0-0 | | 15 | 1 |
| 18 | NPL | H | Halesowen Town | 208 | W 2-0 | Degirolamo 42 Dales 75 | 5 | 2 |
| 22 | NPL | H | Salford City | 210 | L 1-2 | Degirolamo 59 | 5 | 3 |
| 25 | NPL | A | Frickley Ath | 179 | L 0-2 | | 6 | 4 |
| 29 | NPL | A | Rushall Olympic | 208 | D 1-1 | Broadhead 53 | 18 | 5 |
| 31 | NPL | H | Barwell | 202 | L 1-3 | Cisse 42 | 22 | 6 |
| Sept 5 | NPL | A | Hyde United | 362 | W 1-0 | Griffiths-Junior 45 | 17 | 7 |
| 8 | NPL | H | Skelmersdale United | 167 | W 2-1 | Dawes 74 Dales 90 | 13 | 8 |
| **12** | **FAC1Q** | **A** | **Halesowen Town** | **252** | **L 1-2** | **O'Neill-Dwyer 80** | | 9 |
| 19 | NPL | H | Buxton | 304 | W 2-0 | McDonald 43 McGrath 45 | 9 | 10 |
| 22 | NPL | A | Blyth Spartans | 445 | L 0-4 | | 15 | 11 |
| 29 | NPL | H | Matlock Town | 272 | W 2-0 | McDonald 49 Dwyer 90 | 9 | 12 |
| Oct 3 | NPL | A | Workington | 122 | D 2-2 | McDonald 4 Griffiths-Junior 14 | 11 | 13 |
| 6 | NPL | A | Sutton Coldfield Town | 122 | L 0-2 | | 14 | 14 |
| 10 | NPL | H | Darlington 1883 | 456 | L 1-5 | Dales 55 | 14 | 15 |
| 13 | NPL | H | Grantham Town | 159 | L 2-3 | McDonald 8 Dales 50 | | 16 |
| 17 | NPL | A | Ramsbottom United | 184 | D 1-1 | Bennett 16 | 15 | 17 |
| 20 | NPL | H | Frickley Ath | 154 | L 0-1 | | 17 | 18 |
| 24 | NPL | A | Darlington 1883 | 1010 | L 1-2 | Oshoboke 25 | | 19 |
| 27 | NPL | A | Halesowen Town | 248 | D 1-1 | Dales 81 | 18 | 20 |
| **31** | **FAT1Q** | **A** | **Rushall Olympic** | **101** | **L 0-1** | | | 21 |
| Nov 7 | NPL | H | Ashton United | 208 | L 1-3 | Bennett 61 | 19 | 22 |
| 14 | NPL | A | Grantham Town | 200 | L 0-2 | | 19 | 23 |
| 17 | NPL | A | Salford City | 690 | D 1-1 | Griffiths-Junior 28 | 18 | 24 |
| 21 | NPL | H | Whitby Town | 125 | W 1-0 | Dwyer 89 | 17 | 25 |
| 28 | NPL | A | Whitby Town | 201 | L 1-4 | Degirolamo 53 | 18 | 26 |
| Dec 5 | NPL | H | Stamford | 223 | L 0-1 | | 18 | 27 |
| 19 | NPL | A | Buxton | 241 | L 1-4 | Griffiths-Junior 7 | 18 | 28 |
| 26 | NPL | H | Ilkeston | 441 | D 1-1 | Green 23 | 18 | 29 |
| 28 | NPL | A | Barwell | 175 | W 4-2 | THOMAS 3 ( 12 67 80) McGrath 87 | 18 | 30 |
| Jan 23 | NPL | H | Rushall Olympic | 257 | D 1-1 | Dales 53 | 18 | 31 |
| Feb 13 | NPL | H | Sutton Coldfield Town | 167 | L 0-1 | | 20 | 32 |
| 16 | NPL | A | Matlock Town | 282 | L 0-2 | | 20 | 33 |
| 20 | NPL | A | Stourbridge | 531 | L 1-2 | Degirolamo 19 | 20 | 34 |
| Mar 1 | NPL | H | Blyth Spartans | 228 | L 0-2 | | 20 | 35 |
| 12 | NPL | H | Marine | 180 | D 1-1 | Olukanmi 55 | 22 | 36 |
| 15 | NPL | H | Colwyn Bay | 162 | L 1-2 | Bennett 64 | 22 | 37 |
| 19 | NPL | H | Ramsbotham United | 164 | W 3-1 | Green 29 Thompson 79 Dinanga 87 | 22 | 38 |
| 22 | NPL | H | Workington | 231 | L 1-2 | McGrath 22 | 22 | 39 |
| 26 | NPL | H | Hyde United | 219 | W 1-0 | McGrath 19 | 21 | 40 |
| 28 | NPL | A | Ilkeston | 431 | W 2-0 | Thompson 80 McGrath 87 | 21 | 41 |
| 31 | NPL | A | Colwyn Bay | 286 | W 2-1 | Green 66 Dales 73 | 20 | 42 |
| Apr 2 | NPL | H | Nantwich Town | 234 | D 1-1 | McGarr 22 | 19 | 43 |
| 5 | NPL | A | Marine | 297 | D 3-3 | Thomas 27 Dinanga 44 63 | 18 | 44 |
| 9 | NPL | H | Stourbridge | 273 | L 1-3 | Thomas 61 | 17 | 45 |
| 16 | NPL | A | Skelmersdale United | 206 | D 1-1 | Dales1 | 19 | 46 |
| 20 | NPL | A | Nantwich Town | 202 | D 1-1 | Green 22 | 19 | 47 |
| 23 | NPL | A | Stamford | 366 | L 0-2 | | 20 | 48 |

| GOALSCORERS | Scoring Games | Consec Sco Games | Total |
|---|---|---|---|
| Dales | 8 | 2 | 8 |
| McGrath | 5 | | 5 |
| Thomas | 3 | | 5 |
| Degirolamo | 4 | | 4 |
| Green | 4 | | 4 |
| Griffiths-Junior | 4 | | 4 |
| McDonald | 4 | 2 | 4 |
| Bennett | 3 | | 3 |
| Dinanga | 2 | | 3 |
| Dwyer | 2 | | 2 |
| Thompson | 2 | | 2 |
| Broadhead | 1 | | 1 |
| Cisse | 1 | | 1 |
| Dawes | 1 | | 1 |
| McGarr | 1 | | 1 |
| Olukanmi | 1 | | 1 |
| O'Neill-Dwyer | 1 | | 1 |
| Oshoboke | 1 | | 1 |

# NANTWICH TOWN

**Chairman:** Tony Davison
**Secretary:** Bernard Lycett (T) 07876 230 280 (E) secretary@nantwichtownfc.com
**Commercial Manager:** Jon Gold (T/E) jon.gold@nantwichtownfc.com
**Programme Editor:** Steve Sharman (T/E) 07519 144 766
**Ground Address:** Weaver Stadium, Waterlode, Kingsley Fields, Nantwich, CW5 5BS
**(T)** 01270 621 771 **Manager:** Phil Parkinson - 04/02/15

2015-16 Squad.

## Club Factfile

**Founded:** 1884 **Nickname:** Dabbers
**Previous Names:** Nantwich
**Previous Leagues:** Shropshire & Dist. 1891-92, Combination 1892-94, 1901-10, Cheshire Junior 1894-95, Crewe & Dist. 1895-97, North Staffs & Dist. 1897-1900, Cheshire 1900-01, Manchester 1910-12, 65-68, Lancs. Com. 1912-14, Cheshire Co. 1919-38, 68-82, Crewe & Dist. 1938-39, 47-48, Crewe Am. Comb. 1946-47, Mid-Cheshire 1948-65, North West Co. 1982-2007
**Club Colours (change):** All green (Orange/black/black)

**Ground Capacity:** 3,500 **Seats:** 350 **Covered:** 495 **Clubhouse:** Yes **Shop:** Yes

**Directions**
M6 Jun 16 A500 towards Nantwich. Over 4 roundabouts onto A51 towards Nantwich Town Centre, through traffic lights and over railway crossing. Over next r/bout then left at next r/bout past Morrisons supermarket on right. Continue over r/bout through traffic lights. Ground on right at next set of traffic lights.
SATNAV Postcode: CW5 5UP

**Previous Grounds:** London Road/Jackson Avenue (1884-2007)

**Record Attendance:** 5,121 v Winsford United - Cheshire Senior Cup 2nd Round 1920-21
**Record Victory:** 20-0 v Whitchurch Alexandra (home) 1900/01 Cheshire League Division 1, 5 April 1901
**Record Defeat:** 2-16 v Stalybridge Celtic (away) 1932/33 Cheshire County League, 22 Oct 1932
**Record Goalscorer:** John Scarlett 161 goals (1992/3 to 2005/6). **Goals in a season:** Bobby Jones 60 goals (1946/7)
**Record Appearances:** Not known
**Additional Records:** Gerry Duffy scored 42 during season 1961-62
Record Fee Received undisclosed fee from Crewe Alexandra for Kelvin Mellor - Feb 2008
**Honours:**
FA Vase Winners 2005/06. Cheshire Senior Cup Winners 1932/33, 1975/76, 2007/08 & 2011/12. Cheshire County League Champions 1980/81. Mid-Cheshire League Champions 1963/64. North West Counties League Challenge Cup Winners 1994/95.
Cheshire Amateur Cup Winners 1895/96 & 1963/64.

**10 YEAR RECORD**

| 06-07 | 07-08 | 08-09 | 09-10 | 10-11 | 11-12 | 12-13 | 13-14 | 14-15 | 15-16 |
|---|---|---|---|---|---|---|---|---|---|
| NWC1 3 | NP1S 3 | NP P 3 | NP P 10 | NP P 17 | NP P 10 | NP P 14 | NP P 19 | NP P 15 | NP P 8 |

# NANTWICH TOWN MATCH RESULTS 2015-16

| Date | Comp | H/A | Opponents | Att: | Result | | Goalscorers | Pos | No. |
|---|---|---|---|---|---|---|---|---|---|
| Aug 15 | NPL | H | Stamford | 302 | W | 6-3 | Hancock 44 Hudson 53 Osborne 71 (pen) 90 (pen) Jones 81 Shotton 90 | 2 | 1 |
| 18 | NPL | A | Stourbridge | 387 | L | 3-4 | Bell 15 Thornton 50 Kosylo 75 (pen) | 9 | 2 |
| 22 | NPL | A | Marine | 345 | W | 2-1 | Bell 54 75 | 5 | 3 |
| 25 | NPL | H | Sutton Coldfield Town | 274 | W | 4-1 | Hancock 47Jones 50 Kosylo 51 Osborne 75 | 2 | 4 |
| 29 | NPL | A | Blyth Spartans | 492 | D | 1-1 | Jones 69 | 3 | 5 |
| 31 | NPL | H | Buxton | 394 | L | 1-2 | Osborne 90 (pen) | 6 | 6 |
| Sept 5 | NPL | A | Whitby Town | 232 | D | 3-3 | Short 12 Hall 69 Kosylo 75 | 7 | 7 |
| 8 | NPL | H | Colwyn Bay | 218 | W | 3-2 | Osborne 45 (pen) Hancock 47 Jones 79 | 4 | 8 |
| **12** | **FAC1Q** | **A** | **Spalding United** | **157** | **L** | **0-1** | | | 9 |
| 19 | NPL | H | Grantham Town | 288 | W | 6-2 | Jones 29 60 Kosylo 47 Hancock 61 90 Shotton 76 | 3 | 10 |
| 22 | NPL | A | Barwell | 168 | W | 4-0 | Gordon 50 SHOTTON 3 (73 88 90) | 1 | 11 |
| 26 | NPL | A | Colwyn Bay | 272 | D | 1-1 | Jones 71 | 3 | 12 |
| 29 | NPL | H | Ramsbottom United | 246 | W | 7-1 | KOSYLO 3 (1 11 50 pen) Short 39 Hancock 47 Osborne 58 (pen) Jones 88 | 2 | 13 |
| Oct 3 | NPL | A | Ilkeston | 455 | L | 1-3 | Hancock 40 | 2 | 14 |
| 6 | NPL | A | Halesowen Town | 268 | D | 1-1 | Kosylo 90 | 2 | 15 |
| 13 | NPL | H | Matlock Town | 307 | D | 2-2 | Bell 5 Shotton 6 | 4 | 16 |
| 17 | NPL | A | Workington | 445 | D | 1-1 | Gordon 65 | 4 | 17 |
| 20 | NPL | A | Sutton Coldfield Town | 153 | W | 1-0 | Short 88 | 3 | 18 |
| 24 | NPL | H | Marine | 335 | D | 1-1 | Bell 14 | 3 | 19 |
| 27 | NPL | H | Stourbridge | 257 | W | 1-0 | Shotton 90 | 4 | 20 |
| **31** | **FAT 1Q** | **H** | **Salford City** | **550** | **W** | **2-1** | **Osborne 17 Jones 37** | | 21 |
| Nov 7 | NPL | A | Stamford | 405 | W | 4-0 | Bailey 45 Osborne 49 Gordon 77 Short 87 | 2 | 22 |
| **14** | **FAT 2Q** | **H** | **Kings Lynn Town** | **359** | **W** | **5-1** | **Jones 10 SHOTTON 3 (60 79 82pen) Short 77** | | 23 |
| 17 | NPL | H | Hyde United | 221 | W | 3-0 | Shotton 79 Osborne 85 Gordon 87 | 1 | 24 |
| 21 | NPL | A | Ashton United | 155 | L | 2-4 | Shotton 48 Jones 88 | 1 | 25 |
| **28** | **FAT3Q** | **A** | **Stockport County** | **1066** | **W** | **2-0** | **White 81 Shotton 90** | | 26 |
| **Dec 12** | **FAT1** | **H** | **Matlock Town** | **423** | **W** | **2-0** | **Hancock 25 Osborne 69 (pen)** | | 27 |
| 19 | NPL | A | Grantham Town | 202 | W | 3-0 | Bell 55 Hancock 56 Cooke 90 | 2 | 28 |
| 26 | NPL | H | Skelmersdale United | 605 | W | 1-0 | Kosylo 88 (pen) | 2 | 29 |
| 29 | NPL | A | Buxton | 292 | L | 1-3 | Weight 45 (og) | 2 | 30 |
| Jan 2 | NPL | H | Whitby Town | 340 | L | 1-2 | Osborne 51 (pen) | 2 | 31 |
| 5 | NPL | H | Salford City | 740 | D | 1-1 | Bell 30 | 3 | 32 |
| 9 | NPL | A | Rushall Olympic | 236 | L | 0-1 | | 3 | 33 |
| **20** | **FAT2** | **A** | **Bradford PA** | **207** | **D** | **1-1** | **Hancock 56** | | 34 |
| 23 | NPL | H | Blyth Spartans | 464 | L | 1-2 | White 6 | 5 | 35 |
| **26** | **FAT2r** | **H** | **Bradford PA** | **281** | **W** | **5-0** | **Bell 38 Hall 46 Osborne 63 65 (pen) Kosylo 90** | | 36 |
| 30 | NPL | H | Ilkeston | 429 | D | 1-1 | Jones 72 | 7 | 37 |
| Feb 13 | NPL | H | Halesowen Town | 320 | W | 3-0 | Cooke 12 Osborne 44 (pen) Bell 60 | 7 | 38 |
| **16** | **FAT3** | **H** | **Stourbridge** | **510** | **W** | **1-0** | **Jones 89** | | 39 |
| 20 | NPL | A | Matlock Town | 223 | D | 1-1 | Kosylo 47 | 7 | 40 |
| **27** | **FAT4** | **H** | **Dover Athletic** | **892** | **W** | **2-1** | **Osborne 55 Shotton 90** | | 41 |
| **Mar 12** | **FAT SF1** | **H** | **FC HalifaxTown** | **2078** | **L** | **2-4** | **Cooke 43 Kosylo 77** | | 42 |
| 15 | NPL | A | Ramsbottom United | 167 | W | 4-1 | Bailey 12 Osborne 46 Jones 53 Gordon 71 | 9 | 43 |
| **19** | **FAT SF2** | **A** | **FC Halifax Town** | **3009** | **D** | **2-2** | **Shotton 10 Bailey 31** | | 44 |
| 22 | NPL | H | Darlington1883 | 512 | L | 0-5 | | 9 | 45 |
| 26 | NPL | H | Barwell | 302 | W | 2-1 | Hancock 30 Harrop 89 | 9 | 46 |
| 28 | NPL | A | Skelmersdale United | 204 | W | 1-0 | Osborne 90 (pen) | 8 | 47 |
| 30 | NPL | A | Frickley Athletic | 232 | L | 0-1 | | 8 | 48 |
| Apr 2 | NPL | A | Mickleover Sports | 234 | D | 1-1 | Bell 86 | 9 | 49 |
| 5 | NPL | H | Rushall Olympic | 243 | D | 3-3 | Shotton 18 Osborne 22 Bell 77 | 9 | 50 |
| 7 | NPL | A | Darlington 1883 | 1268 | L | 1-2 | Bell 47 | 9 | 51 |
| 9 | NPL | H | Ashton United | 274 | D | 2-2 | Cooke 67 68 | 10 | 52 |
| 13 | NPL | H | Workington | 235 | W | 2-0 | Shotton 41 Hancock 56 | 8 | 53 |
| 16 | NPL | A | Salford City | 667 | D | 1-1 | Hancock 24 | 9 | 54 |
| 18 | NPL | A | Hyde United | 299 | W | 4-0 | Gordon 39 Shotton 73 Fisher 84 Cooke 86 | 7 | 55 |
| 20 | NPL | H | Mickleover Sports | 202 | D | 1-1 | Shotton 15 | 7 | 56 |
| 23 | NPL | H | Frickley Athletic | 349 | W | 1-0 | Shotton 70 | 8 | 57 |

| GOALSCORERS | Scoring Games | Consec Sco Games | Total |
|---|---|---|---|
| **2014-15 *Burns*** | | | ***13*** |
| Shotton | 16 | 4 | 20 |
| Osborne | 16 | 2 | 18 |
| Jones | 11 | 2 | 14 |
| Hancock | 10 | 2 | 13 |
| Bell | 11 | 3 | 12 |
| Kosylo | 9 | | 12 |
| Cooke | 5 | | 6 |
| Gordon | 6 | | 6 |
| Short | 5 | | 5 |
| Bailey | 3 | | 3 |
| Hall | 2 | | 2 |
| White | 2 | | 2 |
| Fisher | 1 | | 1 |
| Harrop | 1 | | 1 |
| Hudson | 1 | | 1 |
| Thornton | 1 | | 1 |
| Opponents | | | 1 |

# RUSHALL OLYMPIC

**Chairman:** John C Allen
**Secretary:** Peter Athersmith (T) 07771 361 002 (E) rushallolympic@yahoo.co.uk
**Commercial Manager:** Darren Stockall (T/E) 07870 236 013
**Programme Editor:** Darren Stockall (T/E) 07870 236 013
**Ground Address:** Dales Lane off Daw End Lane, Rushall, Nr Walsall WS4 1LJ
(T) 01922 641 021 **Manager:** Richard Sneekes

2015-16 Squad

## Club Factfile

**Founded:** 1951 **Nickname:** The Pics
**Previous Names:** None
**Previous Leagues:** Walsall Amateur 1952-55, Staffordshire County (South) 1956-78, West Midlands 1978-94, Midland Alliance 1994-2005, Southern 2005-08
**Club Colours (change):** Gold and black/black/black (Red with white trim/red/red)

**Ground Capacity:** 2,500 **Seats:** 200 **Covered:** 200 **Clubhouse:** Yes **Shop:** Yes

**Directions**
M6 J10 follow signs for Walsall stay on this dual carriage way for about four miles until you come to the Walsall Arboretum and turn left following signs for Lichfield A461. Go under the bridge and you will come to McDonald's on your right, turn right into Daw End Lane. Go over the canal bridge and turn right opposite the Royal Oak Public House and the ground is on the right.
Alternative: From the A38 to it's junction with the A5 (Muckley Corner Hotel) take the A461 to Walsall after about five miles you will reach some traffic lights in Rushall by Mcdonald's, turn left into Daw End Lane go over the canal bridge and turn right opposite The Royal Oak Public House the ground is on the right.

**Previous Grounds:** Rowley Place 1951-75, Aston University 1976-79

**Record Attendance:** 2,000 v Leeds United Ex players
**Record Victory:** Not known
**Record Defeat:** Not known
**Record Goalscorer:** Graham Wiggin
**Record Appearances:** Alan Dawson - 400+
**Additional Records:**

**Honours:**
West Midlands League 1979-80. Midland Alliance 2004-05.
Staffordshire Senior Cup 2015-16. Walsall Senior Cup 2015-16.

### 10 YEAR RECORD

| 06-07 | 07-08 | 08-09 | 09-10 | 10-11 | 11-12 | 12-13 | 13-14 | 14-15 | 15-16 |
|---|---|---|---|---|---|---|---|---|---|
| SthM 15 | SthM 5 | NP1S 5 | NP1S 12 | NP1S 3 | NP P 8 | NP P 6 | NP P 7 | NP P 9 | NP P 10 |

# RUSHALL OLYMPIC MATCH RESULTS 2015-16

| Date | Comp | H/A | Opponents | Att: | Result | | Goalscorers | Pos | No. |
|---|---|---|---|---|---|---|---|---|---|
| Aug 15 | NPL | H | Ramsbottom United | 237 | W | 2-0 | Taylor 3 Reid 47 | 5 | 1 |
| 18 | NPL | A | Stamford | 489 | W | 3-2 | Benbow 4 Duggan 71 Yafal 79 | 2 | 2 |
| 22 | NPL | A | Grantham Town | 170 | D | 2-2 | Benbow 27 Taylor 51 | 3 | 3 |
| 25 | NPL | H | Matlock Town | 181 | L | 2-3 | Benbow 26 53 | 8 | 4 |
| 29 | NPL | H | Mickleover Sports | 208 | D | 1-1 | Benbow 28 | 9 | 5 |
| 31 | NPL | A | Stourbridge | 512 | D | 2-2 | Benbow 71 Duggan 88 | 10 | 6 |
| Sept 5 | NPL | H | Workington | 239 | D | 1-1 | Benbow 64 | 12 | 7 |
| 8 | NPL | A | Marine | 301 | D | 1-1 | Duggan 70 | 11 | 8 |
| **12** | **FAC1Q** | **A** | **Shepshed Dynamo** | **212** | **D** | **0-0** | | | 9 |
| **15** | **FAC1Qr** | **H** | **Shepshed Dynamo** | **151** | **W** | **4-1** | **Roberts 37 REID 3 (40 50 58)** | | 10 |
| 19 | NPL | A | Salford City | 359 | W | 3-1 | Benbow 41 90 Reid 42 | 7 | 11 |
| 22 | NPL | H | Frickley Athletic | 157 | L | 0-1 | | 11 | 12 |
| **26** | **FAC2Q** | **A** | **Corby Town** | **439** | **D** | **1-1** | **Benbow 70** | | 13 |
| **29** | **FAC2Qr** | **H** | **Corby Town** | **168** | **W** | **2-1** | **Duggan 6 69** | | 14 |
| Oct 3 | NPL | H | Skelmersdale United | 209 | D | 0-0 | | 15 | 15 |
| 6 | NPL | H | Matlock Town | 237 | L | 0-1 | | 17 | 16 |
| **10** | **FAC3Q** | **A** | **Stourbridge** | **773** | **L** | **0-1** | | | 17 |
| 17 | NPL | H | Whitby Town | 207 | W | 3-1 | McDonald 21 37 Palmer 31 | 16 | 18 |
| 24 | NPL | H | Colwyn Bay | 181 | W | 2-1 | Benbow 58 90 | | 19 |
| 27 | NPL | H | Stamford | 202 | W | 5-1 | Heath11 77 Benbow 20 McDonald 56 Taylor 84 | 13 | 20 |
| **31** | **FAT1Q** | **H** | **Mickleover Sports** | **101** | **W** | **1-0** | **Benbow 27 (pen)** | | 21 |
| Nov 7 | NPL | A | Ramsbottom United | 203 | L | 1-2 | Benbow 54 | 12 | 22 |
| **14** | **FAT2Q** | **A** | **Leamington** | **290** | **D** | **0-0** | | | 23 |
| 21 | NPL | A | Colwyn Bay | 209 | W | 2-1 | Benbow 16 Reid 67 | 10 | 24 |
| **24** | **FAT2Qr** | **H** | **Leamington** | **181** | **L** | **2-3** | **Reid 74 Wright 85 (aet)** | | 25 |
| 28 | NPL | H | Halesowen Town | 241 | D | 0-0 | | 12 | 26 |
| Dec 8 | NPL | H | Grantham Town | 213 | W | 4-0 | Benbow 27 50 Reid 60 85 | 9 | 27 |
| 19 | NPL | H | Salford City | 538 | L | 2-3 | Heath 50 Lavell-Moore 81 | 10 | 28 |
| 26 | NPL | A | Sutton Coldfield United | 243 | L | 1-2 | Benbow 19 (pen) | 14 | 29 |
| 28 | NPL | H | Stourbridge | 369 | L | 1-2 | Lavell-Moore 6 | 15 | 30 |
| Jan 2 | NPL | A | Frickley Athletic | 240 | W | 2-0 | Benbow 41 Reid 42 | 13 | 31 |
| 5th | NPL | A | Barwell | 136 | W | 3-2 | McKenzie 46 90 Reid 48 | 7 | 32 |
| 9 | NPL | H | Nantwich Town | 236 | W | 1-0 | Reid 36 | 7 | 33 |
| 19 | NPL | H | Ilkeston | 217 | D | 2-2 | McKenzie 43 Heath 71 (pen) | 8 | 34 |
| 23 | NPL | A | Mickleover Sports | 257 | D | 1-1 | Reid 63 | 9 | 35 |
| 26 | NPL | H | Marine | 161 | W | 3-0 | Spencer 17 Heath 51 Morris 52 | 9 | 36 |
| Feb 13 | NPL | A | Ashton United | 154 | W | 3-2 | Reid 59 Spencer 68 75 | 9 | 37 |
| 16 | NPL | A | Skelmersdale United | 185 | L | 1-4 | Fitzpatrick 84 | 9 | 38 |
| 20 | NPL | H | Blyth Spartans | 358 | L | 0-1 | | 9 | 39 |
| 23 | NPL | A | Buxton | 181 | W | 2-1 | Reid 27 44 | 9 | 40 |
| 27 | NPL | A | Whitby Town | 233 | W | 3-1 | McKenzie 25 Reid 46 Pell 50 (og) | 8 | 41 |
| Mar 5 | NPL | H | Hyde United | 202 | W | 2-0 | Duggan 59 61 | 8 | 42 |
| 15 | NPL | H | Barwell | 207 | W | 2-0 | Reid 25 Duggan 72 | 8 | 43 |
| 18 | NPL | A | Darlington 1883 | 1223 | L | 0-1 | | 8 | 44 |
| 21 | NPL | A | Hyde United | 252 | D | 2-2 | Reid 47 Brown 55 | 8 | 45 |
| 28 | NPL | H | Sutton Coldfield Town | 302 | L | 0-1 | | 9 | 46 |
| Apr 2 | NPL | A | Halesowen Town | 411 | W | 3-1 | Tolley 14 Reid 34 Taylor 89 | 9 | 47 |
| 5 | NPL | A | Nantwich Town | 243 | D | 3-3 | Heath 70 Benbow 84 (pen) 90 | 8 | 48 |
| 7 | NPL | A | Wokington | 358 | D | 1-1 | Brown 55 | 8 | 49 |
| 9 | NPL | H | Buxton | 212 | L | 0-1 | | 9 | 50 |
| 13 | NPL | H | Ashton United | 171 | L | 0-2 | | 9 | 51 |
| 16 | NPL | A | Ilkeston | 435 | L | 1-4 | Brown 88 | 11 | 52 |
| 19 | NPL | A | Blyth Spartans | 469 | L | 0-3 | | 11 | 53 |
| 23 | NPL | H | Darlington 1883 | 709 | W | 1-0 | Caines 36 | 10 | 54 |

| GOALSCORERS | Scoring Games | Consec Sco Games | Total | | Scoring Games | Consec Sco Games | Total |
|---|---|---|---|---|---|---|---|
| ***2014-15 Williams*** | | | ***34*** | Lavell-Moore | 2 | | 2 |
| Benbow | 18 | 6 | 22 | Caines | 1 | | 1 |
| Reid | 16 | 2 | 20 | Fitzpatrick | 1 | | 1 |
| Duggan | 6 | | 8 | Morris | 1 | | 1 |
| Heath | 5 | | 6 | Palmer | 1 | | 1 |
| McKenzie | 4 | | 4 | Roberts | 1 | | 1 |
| Taylor | 4 | | 4 | Tolley | 1 | | 1 |
| Brown | 3 | | 3 | Wright | 1 | | 1 |
| McDonald | 1 | | 3 | Yafal | 1 | | 1 |
| Spencer | 2 | | 3 | Opponents | | | 1 |

# SKELMERSDALE UNITED

**Chairman:** Paul Griffiths
**Secretary:** Bryn Jones (T) 07904 911 234 (E) skemsaint@sky.com
**Commercial Manager:** Norman Fenney (T/E)
**Programme Editor:** Kevin Panther (T/E) 01695 731 624
**Ground Address:** Stormy Corner, Selby Place, Statham Road WN8 8EF
(T) 01695 722 123 **Manager:** Tommy Lawson

## Club Factfile

**Founded:** 1882 **Nickname:** Skem
**Previous Names:** None
**Previous Leagues:** Liverpool County Combination, Lancashire Combination 1891-93, 1903-07, 21-24, 55-56, 76-78, Cheshire County 1968-71, 78-82, Northern Premier 1971-76, North West Counties 1983-2006

**Club Colours (change):** All royal blue (All bright red)

**Ground Capacity:** 2,300 **Seats:** 240 **Covered:** 500 **Clubhouse:** Yes **Shop:** Yes

**Directions**
Exit M58 J4 (signposted Skelmersdale), carry straight on at next roundabout (Hope Island) into Glenburn Road, left at next roundabout (Half Mile Island) into Neverstitch Road (signposted Stanley Industrial Estate). Immediately right at next roundabout into Staveley Road and then left into Statham Road. Ground is 500 yards on left in Selby Place.

**Previous Grounds:** None

**Record Attendance:** 7,000 v Slough Town - FA Amateur Cup Semi-final 1967
**Record Victory:** Not known
**Record Defeat:** Not known
**Record Goalscorer:** Stuart Rudd - 230
**Record Appearances:** Robbie Holcroft - 422 including 398 consecutively
**Additional Records:** Paid £2,000 for Stuart Rudd
Received £4,000 for Stuart Rudd
**Honours:**
FA Amateur Cup 1970-71. Barassi Anglo-Italian Cup 1970-71.
Northern Premier Division One North 2013-14.
Lancashire Junior Cup x2. Lancashire Non-League Cup x2. Liverpool Senior Cup 2014-15.

### 10 YEAR RECORD

| 06-07 | 07-08 | 08-09 | 09-10 | 10-11 | 11-12 | 12-13 | 13-14 | 14-15 | 15-16 |
|---|---|---|---|---|---|---|---|---|---|
| NP 1 15 | NP1N 3 | NP1N 2 | NP1N 5 | NP1N 2 | NP1N 7 | NP1N 1 | NP P 6 | NP P 7 | NP P 16 |

# SKELMERSDALE UNITED MATCH RESULTS 2015-16

| Date | Comp | H/A | Opponents | Att: | Result | | Goalscorers | Pos | No. |
|---|---|---|---|---|---|---|---|---|---|
| Aug 15 | NPL | A | Ilkeston Town | 505 | W | 3-1 | Burton 54 83 Mitchley 56 | 3 | 1 |
| 18 | NPL | H | Workington | 217 | W | 2-0 | Rendell 53 Mitchley 72 | 1 | 2 |
| 22 | NPL | H | Halesowen Town | 248 | W | 1-0 | Mitchley 29 | 1 | 3 |
| 25 | NPL | A | Buxton | 205 | L | 1-2 | Mitchley 24 | 3 | 4 |
| 29 | NPL | H | Stourbridge | 215 | L | 1-2 | Mitchley 74 (pen) | 7 | 5 |
| 31 | NPL | A | Marine | 486 | D | 2-2 | Mitchley 34 (pen) 44 | 8 | 6 |
| Sept 5 | NPL | H | Matlock Town | 236 | W | 3-2 | Mitchley 50 Almond 55 Corrigan 60 | 4 | 7 |
| 8 | NPL | A | Mickleover Sports | 167 | L | 1-2 | Strickland 76 | 8 | 8 |
| **12** | **FAC1Q** | **A** | **Glossop North End** | **339** | **D** | **1-1** | **Parker (og) 90** | | 9 |
| **15** | **FAC1Qr** | **H** | **Glossop North End** | **248** | **W** | **2-1** | **Kinsella 22 Donnelly 93 (aet)** | | 10 |
| 19 | NPL | A | Ashton United | 157 | L | 0-5 | | 15 | 11 |
| 22 | NPL | H | Sutton Coldfield Town | 209 | L | 1-2 | Mitchley 50 | 17 | 12 |
| **26** | **FAC 2Q** | **A** | **Bamber Bridge** | **281** | **L** | **0-2** | | | 13 |
| 29 | NPL | H | Darlington 1883 | 321 | D | 1-1 | Burton 43 | 16 | 14 |
| Oct 3 | NPL | A | Rushall Olympic | 209 | D | 0-0 | | 18 | 15 |
| 10 | NPL | H | Frickley Athletic | 231 | D | 1-1 | Kusaloka 56 | 17 | 16 |
| 13 | NPL | H | Colwyn Bay | 208 | L | 3-4 | Strickland 31 Almond 71 McIntosh 85 | 16 | 17 |
| 17 | NPL | A | Grantham Town | 203 | D | 2-2 | Kinsella 53 Strickland 84 (pen) | 19 | 18 |
| 20 | NPL | H | Buxton | 222 | W | 2-1 | Kinsella 4 Ince 35 | 16 | 19 |
| 24 | NPL | A | Halesowen Town | 303 | L | 1-2 | McIntosh 87 | 17 | 20 |
| 27 | NPL | A | Workington | 439 | L | 1-2 | Kinsella 40 | 17 | 21 |
| **31** | **FAT1Q** | **H** | **Hyde United** | **209** | **D** | **3-3** | **Ince 17 Kinsella 51 Rendell 90** | | 22 |
| **Nov 4** | **FAT1Qr** | **A** | **Hyde United** | **224** | **W** | **1-0** | **Wilkinson 24 (og)** | **18** | 23 |
| **14** | **FAT 2Q** | **H** | **Lincoln United** | **185** | **W** | **4-2** | **Kinsella 54 Almond 56 Rendell 62 79** | | 24 |
| 21 | NPL | H | Blyth Spartans | 248 | W | 2-1 | Rendell 24 Kinsella 34 | 18 | 25 |
| **28** | **FAT3Q** | **A** | **Chorley** | **543** | **D** | **0-0** | | | 26 |
| **Dec 1** | **FAT3Qr** | **H** | **Chorley** | **277** | **W** | **5-2** | **Almond 34 74 Holden 62 Kinsella 77 Ince 79** | | 27 |
| **15** | **FAT1** | **A** | **AFC Fylde** | **221** | **D** | **4-4** | **Gyimah 64 Ince 69 Woolcott 80 Almond 83** | | 28 |
| 19 | NPL | H | Ashton United | 204 | L | 1-2 | McIntosh 76 | 20 | 29 |
| 26 | NPL | A | Nantwich Town | 605 | L | 0-1 | | 20 | 30 |
| Jan 2 | NPL | A | Sutton Coildfield Town | 234 | L | 1-3 | Almond 36 | 20 | 31 |
| 9 | NPL | A | Salford City | 660 | L | 0-4 | | 20 | 32 |
| **13** | **FAT1r** | **H** | **AFC Fylde** | **186** | **L** | **0-4** | | | 33 |
| 19 | NPL | A | Colwyn Bay | 176 | W | 4-1 | ALMOND 3 (19 pen 52 64) Hazeldine 77 | 19 | 34 |
| 23 | NPL | A | Stourbridge | 458 | L | 1-3 | Hazeldine 25 | 19 | 35 |
| 26 | NPL | H | Ramsbottom United | 151 | D | 1-1 | Hazeldine 50 | 19 | 36 |
| Feb 2 | NPL | H | Hyde United | 162 | W | 2-1 | Hazeldine 18 20 | 18 | 37 |
| 13 | NPL | H | IlkestonTown | 234 | W | 2-1 | Vassallo 9 Booth 78 | 16 | 38 |
| 16 | NPL | H | Rushall Olympic | 185 | W | 4-1 | Booth 16 Hazeldine 38 44 Vassello 69 | 16 | 39 |
| 20 | NPL | A | Frickley Athletic | 202 | L | 0-3 | | 16 | 40 |
| 23 | NPL | A | Ramsbottom United | 151 | W | 3-0 | ALMOND 3 ( 24 47 90) | 16 | 41 |
| 27 | NPL | H | Grantham Town | 239 | L | 0-1 | | 16 | 42 |
| Mar 1 | NPL | H | Marine | 257 | L | 2-3 | Corrigan 28 Almond 44 | 16 | 43 |
| 5 | NPL | A | Stamford | 325 | L | 2-5 | Hazeldine 13 Tuck 86 | 16 | 44 |
| 8 | NPL | A | Barwell | 126 | L | 1-3 | Tuck 57 | 17 | 45 |
| 12 | NPL | H | Salford City | 370 | W | 3-1 | HAZELDINE 3 (1 42 71) | 16 | 46 |
| 19 | NPL | A | Hyde United | 273 | D | 1-1 | Almond 5 | 17 | 47 |
| 22 | NPL | H | Whitby Town | 193 | D | 0-0 | | 17 | 48 |
| 26 | NPL | A | Matlock Town | 259 | W | 2-1 | McIntosh 41 Burgin 78(og) | 14 | 49 |
| 28 | NPL | H | Nantwich Town | 204 | L | 0-1 | | 15 | 50 |
| Apr 2 | NPL | H | Barwell | 196 | D | 3-3 | Almond 33 (pen) 50 (pen) Hazeldine 79 | 15 | 51 |
| 9 | NPL | A | Blyth Spartans | 787 | W | 2-1 | Hazeldine 36 Bakkor 54 | 14 | 52 |
| 13 | NPL | A | Darlington 1883 | 1296 | L | 0-3 | | 14 | 53 |
| 16 | NPL | H | Mickleover Sports | 206 | D | 1-1 | Almond 63 | 15 | 54 |
| 19 | NPL | H | Stamford | 183 | L | 1-4 | Hazeldine 2 | 15 | 55 |
| 23 | NPL | A | Whitby Town | 232 | D | 1-1 | Hazeldine 45 | 16 | 56 |

| GOALSCORERS | Scoring Games | Consec Sco Games | Total | | Scoring Games | Consec Sco Games | Total |
|---|---|---|---|---|---|---|---|
| **2014-15 *Mitchley*** | | | ***21*** | Corrigan | 2 | | 2 |
| Almond | 13 | 2 | 18 | Tucker | 2 | | 2 |
| Hazeldine | 11 | 4 | 15 | Vassello | 2 | | 2 |
| Mitchley | 8 | 7 | 9 | Bakkor | 1 | | 1 |
| Kinsella | 8 | 2 | 8 | Donnelly | 1 | | 1 |
| Rendell | 4 | | 5 | Gyimah | 1 | | 1 |
| Ince | 4 | | 4 | Holden | 1 | | 1 |
| McIntosh | 4 | | 4 | Kusaloka | 1 | | 1 |
| Burton | 3 | | 3 | Woolcott | 1 | | 1 |
| Strickland | 3 | 2 | 3 | Opponents | | | 3 |
| Booth | 2 | | 2 | | | | |

# SPENNYMOOR TOWN

**Chairman:** Bradley Groves (Chief Executive)
**Secretary:** Steven Lawson **(T)** 07871 206 474 **(E)** stevenlawson_16@hotmail.co.uk
**Commercial Manager:** B Beasley & C Ponfret **(T/E)** spennymoortownfc@aol.com
**Programme Editor:** **(T/E)** spennymoortownfc@aol.com
**Ground Address:** The Brewery Field, Durham Road, Spennymoor DL16 6JN
**(T)** 01388 827 248 **Manager:** Jason Ainsley

## Club Factfile

**Founded:** 1904 **Nickname:** Moors
**Previous Names:** Amalgamation of Evenwood Town & Spennymoor United in 2005-06.
**Previous Leagues:** Northern League 2005-14.

**Club Colours (change):** Black & white stripes/black/white (All red)

**Ground Capacity:** 3,000 **Seats:** 224 **Covered:** 800 **Clubhouse:** Yes **Shop:** Yes

**Directions** Leave the A1(M) at junction 59, then at roundabout take the 1st exit onto the A167. At roundabout take the 2nd exit onto the A167 At Rushyford roundabout take the 3rd exit onto the A167. At roundabout take the 3rd exit onto the A167. At Thinford Roundabout take the 1st exit onto the A688. At roundabout take the 1st exit onto the A688. At roundabout take the 3rd exit onto Saint Andrew's Lane. At roundabout take the 1st exit onto Saint Andrew's Lane. At mini roundabout take 2nd exit onto King Street. At mini roundabout take 2nd exit onto King Street/Durham Road. Bear right onto Durham Road. Take 3rd exit on left onto Wood Vue.

**Previous Grounds:**

**Record Attendance:** 2,670 v Darlington, Northern League 2012-13.
**Record Victory:** 10-0 v Billingham Town (H), Northern League Division One, 18/03/2014
**Record Defeat:** 2-8 v Clitheroe (A), FA Cup 2nd Qualifying Round, 29/09/2007
**Record Goalscorer:** Gavin Cpgdon - 103
**Record Appearances:** Lewis Dodds - 227
**Additional Records:** Northern League record points tally of 109 during 2012-13.

**Honours:**
**League:** Northern League Division Two 2006-07, Division One 2009-10, 2010-11, 2011-12, 2013-14.
**FA/County Cups:** Durham Challange Cup 2011-12, FA Vase 2012-13.

### 10 YEAR RECORD

| 06-07 | 07-08 | 08-09 | 09-10 | 10-11 | 11-12 | 12-13 | 13-14 | 14-15 | 15-16 |
|---|---|---|---|---|---|---|---|---|---|
| NL 2 1 | NL 1 12 | NL 1 4 | NL 1 1 | NL 1 1 | NL 1 1 | NL 1 2 | NL 1 1 | NP1N 5 | NP1N 2 |

# STAFFORD RANGERS

**Chairman:** John Bromley

**Secretary:** Robbie Mullin **(T)** 01785 602 431 **(E)** robbie.mullin@staffordrangersfc.co.uk

**Commercial Manager:** **(T/E)** 01785 602 431

**Programme Editor:** **(T/E)**

**Ground Address:** Marston Road, Stafford ST16 3BX (Sat Nav ST16 3UF)

**(T)** 01785 602 430 **Manager:** Neil Kitching

2015-16 Squad

## Club Factfile

**Founded:** 1876 **Nickname:** Rangers

**Previous Names:** None

**Previous Leagues:** Shropshire 1891-93, Birmingham 1893-96, N. Staffs. 1896-1900, Cheshire 1900-01, Birmingham Comb. 1900-12, 46-52, Cheshire County 1952-69, N.P.L. 1969-79, 83-85, Alliance 1979-83, Conf. 1985-95, 2005-11. Southern >2005.

**Club Colours (change):** Black & white stripes/black/black (All red)

**Ground Capacity:** 6,000 **Seats:** 4,264 **Covered:** 3,500 **Clubhouse:** Yes **Shop:** Yes

**Directions**

M6 Junction 14. Follow signs for Uttoxeter and Stone. Straight over at 1st and 2nd (A34) islands, 3rd right sign posted Common Road and Astonfields Road Ind. Estate. The ground is straight ahead after three quarters of a mile. The route from the Motorway is highlighted by the standard football road signs.
*Sat Nav ST16 3UF

**Previous Grounds:** None

**Record Attendance:** 8,536 v Rotherham United - FA Cup 3rd Round 1975

**Record Victory:** 14-0 v Kidsgrove Athletic - Staffordshire Senior Cup 2003

**Record Defeat:** 0-12 v Burton Town - Birmingham League 1930

**Record Goalscorer:** M. Cullerton - 176

**Record Appearances:** Jim Sargent

**Additional Records:** Paid £13,000 to VS rugby for S. Butterworth
Received £100,000 from Crystal Palace for Stan Collymore

**Honours:**

Northern Premier League 1971-72, 84-85, Division One South 2015-16.
FA trophy 1971-72.
Staffordshire Senior Cup x8 Most recently 2014-15.

### 10 YEAR RECORD

| 06-07 | 07-08 | 08-09 | 09-10 | 10-11 | 11-12 | 12-13 | 13-14 | 14-15 | 15-16 |
|---|---|---|---|---|---|---|---|---|---|
| Conf 20 | Conf 23 | Conf N 18 | Conf N 16 | Conf N 20 | NP P 16 | NP P 15 | NP P 22 | NP1S 6 | NP1S 1 |

# STOURBRIDGE

**Chairman:** Andy Pountney
**Secretary:** Clive Eades (T) 07958 275 986 (E) clive.eades2@capita.co.uk
**Commercial Manager:** (T/E)
**Programme Editor:** Terry Brumpton & Ian Binner (T/E) 01543 426 413
**Ground Address:** War Memorial Athletic Ground, High Street, Amblecote DY8 4HN
(T) 01384 394 040 **Manager:** Gary Hackett

2015-16 Squad

## Club Factfile

**Founded:** 1876 **Nickname:** The Glassboys
**Previous Names:** Stourbridge Standard 1876-87
**Previous Leagues:** West Midlands (Birmingham League) 1892-1939, 54-71, Birmingham Combination 1945-53, Southern 1971-2000. Midland Alliance 2000-06. Southern 2006-14.

**Club Colours (change):** Red and white stripes/red/red (Yellow/green/yellow)

**Ground Capacity:** 2,000 **Seats:** 250 **Covered:** 750 **Clubhouse:** Yes **Shop:** Yes

**Directions**

**From M6:** Leave the M5 Southbound at Junction 3 and take the A456 towards Kidderminster. Upon entering Hagley (following a long downhill approach), take the right hand filter lane at the traffic lights (Signposted A491 Stourbridge). Continue to follow the A491 towards Stourbridge Town Centre and continue to follow the Ring Road (watching the Speed Camera), and take the A491 exit now signposted Wolverhampton. The ground is on the left hand side of the road immediately after the 3rd set of traffic lights (approximately 500 yards) and opposite the Vets for Pets. Please note that Parking is Extremely Limited on the Ground.

**From M42:** Leave the M5 Northbound at Junction 4 and follow the A491 towards Stourbridge and in Hagley, take the left hand filter lane to continue on the A491 and proceed as above.

**Previous Grounds:** None

**Record Attendance:** 5,726 v Cardiff City - Welsh Cup Final 1st Leg 1974
**Record Victory:** Not known
**Record Defeat:** Not known
**Record Goalscorer:** Ron Page - 269
**Record Appearances:** Ron Page - 427
**Additional Records:** Received £20,000 from Lincoln City for Tony Cunningham 1979

**Honours:**
Southern League Division 1 North 1973-74, Midland Division 90-91, League Cup 92-93. Midland Alliance 2001-02, 02-03.
Worcestershire Junior Cup 1927-28. Hereford Senior Cup 1954-55. Birmingham Senior Cup x3.
Worcestershire Senior Cup x11 Most recently 2012-13.

## 10 YEAR RECORD

| 06-07 | 07-08 | 08-09 | 09-10 | 10-11 | 11-12 | 12-13 | 13-14 | 14-15 | 15-16 |
|---|---|---|---|---|---|---|---|---|---|
| SthM 7 | SthM 3 | SthP 16 | SthP 9 | SthP 8 | SthP 6 | SthP 2 | SthP 5 | NP P 16 | NP P 6 |

# STOURBRIDGE MATCH RESULTS 2015-16

| Date | Comp | H/A | Opponents | Att: | Result | | Goalscorers | Pos | No. |
|---|---|---|---|---|---|---|---|---|---|
| Aug 15 | NPL | A | Whitby Town | 241 | L | 0-4 | | 24 | 1 |
| 18 | NPL | H | Nantwich Town | 387 | W | 4-3 | Hawley 38 51 Dodd 59 (pen) Brown 68 | 9 | 2 |
| 22 | NPL | H | Workington | 415 | D | 0-0 | | 13 | 3 |
| 24 | NPL | A | Ilkeston | 454 | L | 3-4 | Brown 48 Scarr 51 Hawley 69 | 14 | 4 |
| 29 | NPL | A | Skelmersdale United | 215 | W | 2-1 | Broadhurst 20 70 | 12 | 5 |
| 31 | NPL | H | Rushall Olympic | 512 | D | 2-2 | Lait 50 Brown 80 | 14 | 6 |
| Sept 5 | NPL | A | Buxton | 308 | W | 3-2 | Lait 41 Pierpoint 73 Hawley 81 (pen) | 10 | 7 |
| 8 | NPL | H | Barwell | 377 | L | 2-3 | Lait 5 Brown 69 | 10 | 8 |
| **12** | **FAC1Q** | **A** | **Tividale** | **237** | **W** | **1-0** | **Pierpoint 26** | | 9 |
| 19 | NPL | H | Blyth Spartans | 609 | W | 3-0 | Dodd 23 (pen) Richards 66 Hawley 75 | 11 | 10 |
| 22 | NPL | A | Ramsbottom United | 210 | W | 2-1 | Hawley 48 Lait 90 | 7 | 11 |
| **26** | **FAC2Q** | **H** | **Dunkirk** | **322** | **W** | **3-1** | **Lait 7 Hawley 34 Pierpoint 64** | | 12 |
| 28 | NPL | H | Grantham Town | 331 | D | 1-1 | Richards 6 | 7 | 13 |
| Oct 3 | NPL | A | Hyde United | 351 | W | 2-0 | Hawley 13 Dodd 77 (pen) | 6 | 14 |
| 6 | NPL | A | Colwyn Bay | 175 | W | 2-0 | Hawley 66 (pen) Richards 88 | 4 | 15 |
| **10** | **FAC3Q** | **H** | **Rushall Olympic** | **773** | **W** | **1-0** | **Richards 9** | | 16 |
| 12 | NPL | H | Sutton Coldfield | 428 | W | 2-0 | Hawley 28 Richards 39 | 2 | 17 |
| 17 | NPL | A | Darlington 1884 | 1141 | D | 1-1 | Hawley 30 | 3 | 18 |
| 20 | NPL | H | Ilkeston | 503 | L | 1-2 | Billingham 28 | 3 | 19 |
| **24** | **FAC4Q** | **H** | **Kidderminster Harriers** | **2032** | **W** | **3-0** | **Dodd 6 Richards 16 Lait 52** | | 20 |
| 27 | NPL | A | Nantwich Town | 257 | L | 0-1 | | 5 | 21 |
| **31** | **FAT1Q** | **A** | **Halesowen Town** | **808** | **W** | **2-1** | **Pierpoint 28 Hawley 79** | | 22 |
| **Nov 7** | **FAC1** | **A** | **Dover Athletic** | **1392** | **W** | **2-1** | **Lait 8 Hawley 69 (pen)** | | 23 |
| **14** | **FAT2Q** | **H** | **Carlton Town** | **428** | **W** | **2-0** | **Hawley 66 Lait 76** | | 24 |
| 21 | NPL | A | Marine | 333 | W | 3-1 | Hawley 10 90 Tonks 43 | 8 | 25 |
| **28** | **FAT3Q** | **H** | **Spennymoor Town** | **393** | **W** | **4-2** | **Wright 37 87 Pierpoint 65 Richards 68** | | 26 |
| **Dec 5** | **FAC2** | **H** | **Eastleigh** | **2086** | **L** | **0-2** | | | 27 |
| **12** | **FAT1** | **H** | **Kidderminster Harriers** | **902** | **W** | **2-1** | **Lait 66 Scarr 68** | | 28 |
| 19 | NPL | A | Blyth Spartans | 523 | L | 3-4 | Pierpoint 13 Richards 16 Hawley 41 | 12 | 29 |
| 26 | NPL | H | Halesowen Town | 1813 | W | 3-2 | Hawley 12 Scarr 53 Broadhurst 86 | 11 | 30 |
| 28 | NPL | A | Rushall Olympic | 369 | W | 2-1 | Smikle 24 Richards 64 | 8 | 31 |
| Jan 2 | NPL | H | Ramsbottom United | 665 | L | 2-3 | Broadhurst 75 Richards 89 | 9 | 32 |
| 9 | NPL | A | Stamford | 348 | D | 2-2 | Hawley 27 Lait 61 | 11 | 33 |
| **16** | **FAT2** | **A** | **Braintree Town** | **244** | **W** | **1-0** | **Dodd 54** | **11** | 34 |
| 19 | NPL | A | Salford City | 574 | W | 1-0 | Richards 69 | 9 | 35 |
| 23 | NPL | H | Skelmersdale United | 458 | W | 3-1 | Hawley 43 Dodd 35 Scarr 61 | 8 | 36 |
| 26 | NPL | A | Barwell | 174 | L | 1-3 | Geddes 32 | 8 | 37 |
| 30 | NPL | H | Hyde United | 438 | W | 5-1 | Hawley 4 Lait 23 Dodd 31 Richards 52 Vincent 79 | 8 | 38 |
| Feb 1 | NPL | H | Marine | 387 | W | 2-0 | Hawley 19 Lait 50 | 6 | 39 |
| 13 | NPL | H | Colwyn Bay | 479 | W | 2-0 | Scarr 75 Vincent 90 | 6 | 40 |
| **16** | **FAT3** | **A** | **Nantwich Town** | **510** | **L** | **0-1** | | **7** | 41 |
| 20 | NPL | H | Mickleover Sports | 531 | W | 2-1 | Green 16 Hawley 40 (pen) | 5 | 42 |
| 23 | NPL | A | Sutton Coldfield Town | 258 | W | 3-2 | Hawley 44 64 Lait 57 | 5 | 43 |
| 27 | NPL | H | Darlington 1884 | 818 | W | 1-0 | Broadhurst 60 | 5 | 44 |
| Mar 6 | NPL | H | Matlock | 344 | W | 4-1 | Lait 14 Green 23 Dodd 51 (pen) Broadhurst 74 | 5 | 45 |
| 12 | NPL | H | Frickley Athletic | 619 | D | 1-1 | Hawley 46 | 5 | 46 |
| 15 | NPL | A | Grantham Town | 152 | D | 2-2 | Hawley 41 Scarr 78 | 5 | 47 |
| 19 | NPL | A | Workington | 510 | D | 1-1 | Geddes 39 | 6 | 48 |
| 21 | NPL | H | Ashton United | 448 | L | 1-2 | Smikle 77 | 6 | 49 |
| 26 | NPL | H | Buxton | 506 | W | 3-0 | Richards 61 Hawley 71 Scarr 87 | 6 | 50 |
| 28 | NPL | A | Halesowen Town | 2107 | L | 0-2 | | 6 | 51 |
| Apr 2 | NPL | A | Ashton United | 205 | W | 3-2 | Bowerman 4 Scarr 10 Hawley 35 | 6 | 52 |
| 4 | NPL | H | Stamford | 476 | W | 2-0 | Lait 36 Vincent 87 | 5 | 53 |
| 9 | NPL | A | Mickleover Sports | 273 | W | 3-1 | Richards 23 24 Green 30 | 4 | 54 |
| 13 | NPL | A | Matlock Town | 226 | D | 1-1 | Hawley 65 | 4 | 55 |
| 16 | NPL | H | Whitby Town | 536 | W | 2-0 | Lait 61 Richards 72 | 4 | 56 |
| 21 | NPL | A | Frickley Athletic | 269 | L | 1-2 | Hawley 75 | 4 | 57 |
| 23 | NPL | H | Salford City | 1827 | L | 1-2 | Pierpoint 20 | 6 | 58 |

| GOALSCORERS | Scoring Games | Consec Sco Games | Total |
|---|---|---|---|
| **2014-15 *Brown*** | | | ***13*** |
| Hawley | 28 | 4 | 31 |
| Lait | 16 | 3 | 16 |
| Richards | 15 | 3 | 16 |
| Dodd | 8 | | 8 |
| Scarr | 8 | | 8 |
| Pierpoint | 7 | | 7 |
| Broadhurst | 6 | 2 | 6 |
| Brown | 4 | | 4 |
| Green | 3 | | 3 |
| Vincent | 3 | | 3 |
| Geddes | 2 | | 2 |
| Smikle | 2 | | 2 |
| Wright | 2 | | 2 |
| Billingham | 1 | | 1 |
| Bowerman | 1 | | 1 |
| Tonks | 1 | | 1 |

# SUTTON COLDFIELD TOWN

**Chairman:** Nick Thurston

**Secretary:** Neil Murrall (T) 0121 354 2997 (E)

**Commercial Manager:** (T/E)

**Programme Editor:** (T/E)

**Ground Address:** Central Ground, Coles Lane, Sutton Coldfield B72 1NL

**(T)** 0121 354 2997 **Manager:** Neil Tooth

## Club Factfile

**Founded:** 1897 **Nickname:** Royals

**Previous Names:** Sutton Coldfield F.C. 1879-1921

**Previous Leagues:** Central Birmingham, Walsall Senior, Staffordshire County, Birmingham Combination 1950-54, West Midlands (Regional) 1954-65, 79-82, Midlands Combination 1965-79

**Club Colours (change):** All blue (Yellow/black/black)

**Ground Capacity:** 4,500 **Seats:** 200 **Covered:** 500 **Clubhouse:** Yes **Shop:** Yes

**Directions**

From M42 Junc 9, take A4097 [Minworth sign]. At island, follow signs to Walmley Village. At traffic lights turn right [B4148]. After shops turn left at traffic lights into Wylde Green Road. Over railway bridge turn right into East View Road, which becomes Coles Lane.

**Previous Grounds:** Meadow Plat 1879-89, Coles Lane 1890-1919

**Record Attendance:** 2,029 v Doncaster Rovers - FA Cup 1980-81

**Record Victory:** Not known

**Record Defeat:** Not known

**Record Goalscorer:** Eddie Hewitt - 288

**Record Appearances:** Andy Ling - 550

**Additional Records:** Paid £1,500 to Gloucester for Lance Morrison, to Burton Albion for Micky Clarke and to Atherstone United for Steve Farmer 1991. Received £25,000 from West Bromwich Albion for Barry Cowdrill 1979

**Honours:**

West Midlands League 1979-80. Midland Combination x2.
NPL Div.1 South Play-off 2014-15.

### 10 YEAR RECORD

| 06-07 | 07-08 | 08-09 | 09-10 | 10-11 | 11-12 | 12-13 | 13-14 | 14-15 | 15-16 |
|---|---|---|---|---|---|---|---|---|---|
| SthM 12 | SthM 4 | SthM 6 | SthM 6 | NP1S 6 | NP1S 12 | NP1S 6 | NP1S 6 | NP1S 4 | NP P 12 |

# SUTTON COLDFIELD TOWN MATCH RESULTS 2015-16

| Date | Comp | H/A | Opponents | Att: | Result | | Goalscorers | Pos | No. |
|---|---|---|---|---|---|---|---|---|---|
| Aug 15 | NPL | A | Workington | 488 | D | 1-1 | Richards 34 | 11 | 1 |
| 18 | NPL | H | Barwell | 148 | L | 1-5 | Pace 85 | 21 | 2 |
| 22 | NPL | H | Frickley Atletic | 132 | D | 2-2 | Trainer 2 Richards 44 | 21 | 3 |
| 25 | NPL | A | Nantwich Town | 274 | L | 1-4 | Trainer 45 | 23 | 4 |
| 29 | NPL | A | Ilkeston | 457 | D | 1-1 | Bell 43 | 23 | 5 |
| 31 | NPL | H | Halesowen Town | 320 | **W** | 3-0 | Diop 34 60 Forde 75 | 19 | 6 |
| Sept 5 | NPL | A | Ramsbottom United | 218 | **W** | 1-0 | Nicholson 78 | 14 | 7 |
| **12** | **FAC1Q** | **H** | **Oadby Town** | **140** | **L** | **0-1** | | | 8 |
| 15 | NPL | H | Grantham Town | 105 | **W** | 2-0 | Rodgers 58 70 | 17 | 9 |
| 19 | NPL | H | Whitby Town | 124 | **W** | 1-0 | Diop 69 | 5 | 10 |
| 22 | NPL | A | Skelmersdale United | 209 | **W** | 2-1 | Diop 30 Bryant 71 | | 11 |
| 29 | NPL | A | Stamford | 278 | D | 3-3 | O'Callaghan 11 Diop 16 Melvin 27 | 6 | 12 |
| Oct 3 | NPL | H | Buxton | 208 | D | 0-0 | | 7 | 13 |
| 6 | NPL | H | Mickleover Sports | 122 | **W** | 2-0 | Rodgers 45 Forde 53 | 7 | 14 |
| 10 | NPL | A | Marine | 643 | **W** | 2-1 | Kettle 38 Lilly 83 | 3 | 15 |
| 13 | NPL | A | Stourbridge | 428 | L | 0-2 | | 4 | 16 |
| 17 | NPL | H | Salford City | 238 | L | 0-2 | | 6 | 17 |
| 20 | NPL | H | Nantwich Town | 153 | L | 0-1 | | 7 | 18 |
| 24 | NPL | A | Frickley Athletic | 219 | L | 1-3 | Rodgers 74 | 10 | 19 |
| **31** | **FAT1Q** | **H** | **Coalville Town** | **138** | **W** | **2-0** | **Forde 15 74** | | 20 |
| Nov 7 | NPL | H | Workington | 228 | L | 0-2 | | 13 | 21 |
| **14** | **FAT2Q** | **H** | **Darlington 1883** | **414** | **W** | **1-0** | **Goddard 14** | | 22 |
| 21 | NPL | A | Matlock Town | 266 | D | 2-2 | Rodgers 12 Edmunds 44 | 14 | 23 |
| **28** | **FAT3Q** | **H** | **Stalybridge Celtic** | **140** | **W** | **1-0** | **Stephens 5** | | 24 |
| Dec 5 | NPL | A | Ashton United | 120 | L | 0-3 | | 15 | 25 |
| 8 | NPL | A | Barwell | 131 | L | 0-2 | | 15 | 26 |
| **12** | **FAT1** | **H** | **Barrow** | **326** | **L** | **0-1** | | | 27 |
| 19 | NPL | A | Whitby Town | 231 | **W** | 1-0 | Goddard 38 | 15 | 28 |
| 26 | NPL | H | Rushall Olympic | 243 | **W** | 2-1 | Forde 9 O'Callaghan 55 | 13 | 29 |
| 28 | NPL | A | Halesowen Town | 445 | D | 2-2 | Edmunds 4 Christie 68 | 13 | 30 |
| Jan 2 | NPL | H | Skelmersdale United | 234 | **W** | 3-1 | Rodgers 24 O'Callaghan 44 Edmunds 90 | 11 | 31 |
| 9 | NPL | H | Hyde United | 162 | D | 0-0 | | 12 | 32 |
| 23 | NPL | H | Ilkeston | 203 | L | 0-2 | | 13 | 33 |
| 30 | NPL | A | Buxton | 245 | D | 2-2 | Farquarson 87 Kettle 89 | 13 | 34 |
| Feb 6 | NPL | H | Stamford | 185 | **W** | 2-0 | Lilly 8 48 (pen) | 11 | 35 |
| 13 | NPL | A | Mickleover Sports | 187 | **W** | 1-0 | Forde 51 | 10 | 36 |
| 20 | NPL | H | Darlington 1883 | 392 | L | 0-1 | | 13 | 37 |
| 23 | NPL | H | Stourbridge | 258 | L | 2-3 | Forde 38 Edmunds 69 | 13 | 38 |
| 27 | NPL | A | Marine | 376 | L | 1-2 | Lillly 62 | 13 | 39 |
| Mar 5 | NPL | H | Blyth Spartans | 256 | **W** | 1-0 | Forde 21 | 11 | 40 |
| 8 | NPL | A | Grantham Town | 142 | L | 1-2 | Rodgers 69 | 11 | 41 |
| 12 | NPL | A | Hyde United | 243 | **W** | 2-1 | Kettle 72 Edmunds 90 | 11 | 42 |
| 19 | NPL | A | Salford City | 582 | L | 0-2 | | 12 | 43 |
| 26 | NPL | H | Ramsbotom United | 178 | D | 2-2 | Gayle 61 Gueyes 90 | 12 | 44 |
| 28 | NPL | A | Rushall Olympic | 302 | **W** | 1-0 | | 11 | 45 |
| Apr 2 | NPL | A | Darlington 1883 | 1307 | L | 0-2 | | 12 | 46 |
| 5 | NPL | H | Colwyn Bay | 118 | **W** | 5-0 | O'Callaghan 6 83 Forde 73 Gueyes 78 87 | 12 | 47 |
| 9 | NPL | H | Matlock Town | 192 | D | 2-2 | Rodgers 33 Gayle 71 | 12 | 48 |
| 16 | NPL | A | Colwyn Bay | 182 | L | 0-3 | | 12 | 49 |
| 19 | NPL | H | Marine | 121 | **W** | 4-2 | Goulding 50 (og) Forde 56 O'Callaghan 67 Beresford 84 | 12 | 50 |
| 23 | NPL | H | Ashton United | 162 | L | 0-1 | | 12 | 51 |

| GOALSCORERS | Scoring Games | Consec Sco Games | Total |
|---|---|---|---|
| Forde | 9 | | 10 |
| Rodgers | 6 | | 8 |
| O'Callaghan | 5 | | 6 |
| Diop | 5 | 3 | 5 |
| Edmunds | 5 | | 5 |
| Lily | 4 | | 4 |
| Gueyes | 2 | | 3 |
| Kettle | 3 | | 3 |
| Gayle | 2 | | 2 |
| Goddard | 2 | | 2 |
| Richards | 2 | | 2 |
| Trainer | 2 | 2 | 2 |
| Bell | 1 | | 1 |
| Beresford | 1 | | 1 |
| Bryant | 1 | | 1 |
| Christie | 1 | | 1 |
| Farquarson | 1 | | 1 |
| Melvin | 1 | | 1 |
| Nicholson | 1 | | 1 |
| Pace | 1 | | 1 |
| Stephens | 1 | | 1 |
| Bryant | 1 | | 1 |
| Opponents | | | 1 |

# WARRINGTON TOWN

**Chairman:** Toby Macormac
**Secretary:** Chris Henshall **(T)** 07969 123 786 **(E)** info@warringtontownfc.co.uk
**Commercial Manager:** (T/E)
**Programme Editor:** (T/E)
**Ground Address:** Cantilever Park, Common Lane, Latchford, Warrington WA4 2RS
**(T)** 01925 653 044 **Manager:** Lee Smith & Stuart Mellish

Warrington's Danny O'Donnell tries to get the ball of Witton's Alex Titchiner during 'Town's' visit in the league last season. Photo: Keith Clayton

## Club Factfile

**Founded:** 1948 **Nickname:** The Town
**Previous Names:** Stockton Heath Albion 1949-61
**Previous Leagues:** Warrington & District 1949-52, Mid Cheshire 1952-78, Cheshire County 1978-82, North West Counties 1982-90 Northern Premier 1990-97

**Club Colours (change):** Yellow and blue/blue/yellow (Blue & white/white/blue)

**Ground Capacity:** 2,000 **Seats:** 350 **Covered:** 650 **Clubhouse:** Yes **Shop:** Yes

**Directions**
From M62 Junction 9 Warrington Town Centre: Travel 1 mile south on A49, turn left at traffic lights into Loushers Lane, ground ½ mile on right hand side. From M6 North or South Junction 20: Follow A50 (Warrington signs) for 2 miles, cross Latchford Swingbridge, turn immediate left into Station Road, ground on left.

**Previous Grounds:** London Road 1948-65

**Record Attendance:** 2,600 v Halesowen Town - FA Vase Semi-final 1st leg 1985-86
**Record Victory:** Not known
**Record Defeat:** Not known
**Record Goalscorer:** Steve Hughes - 167
**Record Appearances:** Neil Whalley
**Additional Records:** Paid £50,000 to Preston North End for Liam Watson Received £60,000 from P.N.E. for Liam Watson
Players to progress - Roger Hunt, Liverpool legend and 1966 World Cup winner.
**Honours:**
North West Counties 1989-90, Division 2 2000-01, League Cup 1985-86, 87-88, 88-89.
Northern Premier League Division One North 2015-16.

## 10 YEAR RECORD

| 06-07 | 07-08 | 08-09 | 09-10 | 10-11 | 11-12 | 12-13 | 13-14 | 14-15 | 15-16 |
|---|---|---|---|---|---|---|---|---|---|
| NP 1 22 | NP1S 13 | NP1N 19 | NP1N 9 | NP1N 9 | NP1N 11 | NP1N 10 | NP1N 3 | NP1N 9 | NP1N 1 |

## ATTENDANCES STATISTICS

There is no doubt that of the three 'Step Three' competitions, The Northern Premier League attracted larger attendances than their Southern and Isthmian counterparts last season.

This is not surprising as their large independent towns have less local opposition and they have also enjoyed traditional local support. Whereas many Isthmian's are surrounded by League clubs in all London's home counties while the Southern League members are spread right across the South of England from Cornwall to the Eastern Counties
The most popular visitors turned out to be the eventual NPL Champions, as Darlington 1883 attracted the biggest crowds of the season to 10 of their league rivals, while the glamorous Salford City club also proved popular.

Once again Cup ties attracted large attendances, especially if the ties were also 'local derbys', but full marks to the NPL clubs whose best crowds averaged over a thousand.

### ISTHMIAN PREMIER

| | | | | | | |
|---|---|---|---|---|---|---|
| Total Best Attendances | 18,389 | | Home Wins | 10 | **Most Popular** | |
| Average Best Attendance | 766 | | Drawn Game | 7 | **Away Clubs** | |
| | | | Away Wins | 7 | Dulwich Hamlet | 4 |
| **Best 3 Attendances** | | | | | Enfield Town | 2 |
| Bognor Regis Town | 2629 | v | Grimsby T (FAT) | 0-1 | Lewes | 2 |
| Dulwich Hamlet | 2467 | v | Lewes | 2-1 | Tonbridge Angels | 2 |
| Hampton & Richmond | 2376 | v | Enfield Town | 0-0 | | |

### NORTHERN PREMIER

| | | | | | | |
|---|---|---|---|---|---|---|
| Total Best Attendances | 24.617 | | Home Wins | 13 | **Most Popular** | |
| Average Best Attendance | 1,025 | | Drawn Game | 1 | **Away Clubs** | |
| | | | Away Wins | 10 | Darlington 1883 | 10 |
| **Best 3 Attendances** | | | | | Salford City | 5 |
| Stourbridge | 2032 | v | Kidderminster H (FAC) | 3-0 | | |
| Halesowen Town | 2107 | v | Stourbridge | 2-2 | | |
| Nantwich Town | 2078 | v | FC Halifax T (FAT) | 2-4 | | |

### SOUTHERN PREMIER

| | | | | | | |
|---|---|---|---|---|---|---|
| Total Best Attendances | 17,652 | | Away Wins | 11 | **Most Popular** | |
| Average Best Attendance | 735 | | Drawn Games | 7 | **Away Clubs** | |
| | | | Home Wins | 6 | Kettering Town | 4 |
| **Best 3 Attendances** | | | | | Hitchin Town | 2 |
| Weymouth | 1,808 | v | Dorchester Town | 2-2 | Hungerford Town | 2 |
| Dorchester Town | 1.357 | v | Weymouth | 1-0 | Leamington | 2 |
| Hitchin Town | 1,305 | v | Hungerford T(PO S-F) | 2-3 | | |

### NATIONAL LEAGUE

| | | | | | | |
|---|---|---|---|---|---|---|
| Total Best Attendances | 82,265 | | Home Wins | 9 | **Most Popular** | |
| Average Best Attendance | 3,428 | | Away Wins | 7 | **Away Clubs** | |
| | | | Drawn Games | 8 | FC Utd of Manchester | 9 |
| **Best 3 Attendances** | | | | | Nuneaton Town | 3 |
| Grimsby Town | 7,650 | v | Lincoln City | 2-0 | Solihull Moors | 2 |
| Wrexham | 6,707 | v | Tranmere Rovers | 2-2 | | |
| Cheltenham Town | 5,449 | v | Forest Green Rovers | 1-1 | | |

### NATIONAL NORTH

| | | | | | | |
|---|---|---|---|---|---|---|
| Total Best Attendances | 38,614 | | Home Wins | 8 | **Most Popular** | |
| Average Best Attendance | 1755 | | Away Wins | 8 | **Away Clubs** | |
| | | | Drawn Games | 6 | Griimsby Town | 6 |
| **Best 3 Attendances** | | | | | Barrow | 3 |
| Stockport County | 4,797 | v | FC Utd of Manchester | 1-2 | Tranmere Rovers | 3 |
| FC Utd of Manchester | 4,150 | v | Chorley | 2-0 | | |
| Worcester City | 2,133 | v | FC Utd of Manchester | 1-2 | | |

### NATIONAL SOUTH

| | | | | | | |
|---|---|---|---|---|---|---|
| Total Best Attendances | 31,790 | | Away Wins | 10 | **Most Popular** | |
| Average Best Attendance | 1,445 | | Home Wins | 8 | **Away Clubs** | |
| | | | Drawn Games | 4 | Dartford | 3 |
| **Best 3 Attendances** | | | | | Chelmsford City | 2 |
| Sutton United | 3,142 | v | Ebbsfleet United | 2-0 | Maidenhead U | 2 |
| Maidstone United | 3,030 | v | Sutton United | 1-2 | Maidstone U | 2 |
| Wealdstone | 2,469 | v | Colchester U (FAC) | 2-6 | Weston-s-Mare | 2 |

# WHITBY TOWN

**Chairman:** Graham Manser
**Secretary:** Peter Tyreman **(T)** 07899 762 690 **(E)** agm_wtfc@hotmail.com
**Commercial Manager:** **(T/E)**
**Programme Editor:** **(T/E)**
**Ground Address:** Turnbull Ground, Upgang Lane, Whitby, North Yorks YO21 3HZ
**(T)** Office: 01947 604847 CH: 01947 605 153 **Manager:** Chris Hardy

2015-16 Squad

## Club Factfile

**Founded:** 1926 **Nickname:** Seasiders
**Previous Names:** Whitby United (pre 1950)
**Previous Leagues:** Northern League 1926-97

**Club Colours (change):** All royal blue (All white)

**Ground Capacity:** 2,680 **Seats:** 622 **Covered:** 1,372 **Clubhouse:** Yes **Shop:** Yes

**Directions**
On entering Whitby from both the A169 and A171 roads, take the first fork and follow signs for the "West Cliff".
Then turn left at the Spa Shop and Garage, along Love Lane to junction of the A174.
Turn right and the ground is 600 yards on the left.

**Previous Grounds:** None

**Record Attendance:** 4,000 v Scarborough - North Riding Cup 18/04/1965
**Record Victory:** 11-2 v Cargo Fleet Works - 1950
**Record Defeat:** 3-13 v Willington - 24/03/1928
**Record Goalscorer:** Paul Pitman - 382
**Record Appearances:** Paul Pitman - 468
**Additional Records:** Paid £2,500 to Newcastle Blue Star for John Grady 1990
Received £5,000 from Gateshead for Graham Robinson 1997
**Honours:**
Rothmans National Cup 1975-76, 77-78. Northern League 1992-93, 96-97. FA Vase 1996-97.
Northern Premier League Division 1 1997-98.
North Riding Senior Cup x5.

## 10 YEAR RECORD

| 06-07 | 07-08 | 08-09 | 09-10 | 10-11 | 11-12 | 12-13 | 13-14 | 14-15 | 15-16 |
|---|---|---|---|---|---|---|---|---|---|
| NP P 11 | NP P 12 | NP P 19 | NP P 14 | NP P 16 | NP P 17 | NP P 13 | NP P 9 | NP P 13 | NP P 19 |

# WHITBY TOWN MATCH RESULTS 2015-16

| Date | Comp | H/A | Opponents | Att: | Result | | Goalscorers | Pos | No. |
|---|---|---|---|---|---|---|---|---|---|
| Aug 15 | NPL | H | Stourbridge | 241 | W | 4-0 | Waters 6 Gardner 53 Roberts 64 Brown 90 | 1 | 1 |
| 18 | NPL | A | Blyth Spartans | 403 | L | 2-3 | Roberts 24 (pen) 57 | 7 | 2 |
| 22 | NPL | A | Matlock Town | 256 | L | 0-1 | | 14 | 3 |
| 26 | NPL | H | Ramsbottom United | 263 | D | 1-1 | Roberts 60 | 14 | 4 |
| 29 | NPL | H | Stamford | 237 | L | 3-5 | McCarthy 6 45 Mason 90 | 20 | 5 |
| 31 | NPL | A | Frickley Athletic | 264 | D | 2-2 | Mason 52 Roberts 84 (pen) | 21 | 6 |
| Sept 5 | NPL | H | Natwich Town | 232 | D | 3-3 | Roberts 10 Waters 45 Gell 88 | 20 | 7 |
| 8 | NPL | A | Ashton United | 125 | L | 0-2 | | 21 | 8 |
| **12** | **FAC1Q** | **A** | **Salford City** | **255** | **D** | **1-1** | **Gell 39** | | 9 |
| **16** | **FAC1Qr** | **H** | **Salford City** | **244** | **L** | **0-5** | | | 10 |
| 19 | NPL | A | Sutton Coldfield Town | 124 | L | 0-1 | | 22 | 11 |
| 23 | NPL | H | Salford City | 189 | L | 2-3 | Mason 45 Waters 75 | 22 | 12 |
| 26 | NPL | H | Ilkeston | 246 | W | 4-2 | ROBERTS 3 (11 59 58) McTiernan 45 | 20 | 13 |
| Oct 3 | NPL | A | Halesowen Town | 377 | D | 0-0 | | 21 | 14 |
| 6 | NPL | A | Workington | 461 | D | 1-3 | Bullock 18 | 21 | 15 |
| 10 | NPL | H | Grantham Town | 253 | D | 1-1 | Brobbel 31 | 22 | 16 |
| 14 | NPL | H | Hyde United | 201 | L | 0-3 | | | 17 |
| 17 | NPL | A | Rushall Olympic | 207 | L | 1-3 | Mason 43 | 23 | 18 |
| 20 | NPL | A | Ramsbottom United | 147 | L | 1-4 | Roberts 65 (pen) | 23 | 19 |
| 24 | NPL | H | Matlock Town | 276 | W | 2-1 | Waters 34 Roberts 42 (pen) | | 20 |
| 28 | NPL | H | Blyth Spartans | 367 | L | 0-2 | | 23 | 21 |
| **31** | **FAT1Q** | **A** | **Workington** | **343** | **W** | **3-0** | **Waters 45 Mason 44 Brobbel 65** | | 22 |
| Nov 7 | NPL | A | Marine | 435 | L | 1-2 | Brobbel 84 | 22 | 23 |
| **14** | **FAT2Q** | **A** | **Blyth Spartans** | **643** | **L** | **0-1** | | | 24 |
| 21 | NPL | A | Mickleover Sports | 125 | L | 0-1 | | 22 | 25 |
| 28 | NPL | H | Mickleover Sports | 201 | W | 4-1 | Roberts 42 McTiernan 50 Hopson 57 Weledji 85 | 21 | 26 |
| Dec 19 | NPL | H | Sutton Coldfield Town | 231 | L | 0-1 | | 21 | 27 |
| 28 | NPL | H | Frickley Athletic | 311 | D | 1-1 | Roberts 45 (pen) | 21 | 28 |
| Jan 2 | NPL | A | Nantwich Town | 340 | W | 2-1 | Roberts 16 Brobbel 35 | 21 | 29 |
| 19 | NPL | A | Darlington 1883 | 940 | D | 2-2 | Waters 6 Hopson 74 | 21 | 30 |
| 23 | NPL | A | Stamford | 385 | D | 2-2 | Roberts 11 Waters 14 | 21 | 31 |
| 30 | NPL | H | Halesowen Town | 276 | W | 2-1 | Roberts 51 59 | 20 | 32 |
| Feb 13 | NPL | H | Workington | 329 | W | 1-0 | Roberts 49 | 19 | 33 |
| 20 | NPL | A | Grantham Town | 225 | L | 0-1 | | 19 | 34 |
| 22 | NPL | A | Hyde United | 249 | L | 1-2 | McTiernan 16 | 19 | 35 |
| 27 | NPL | H | Rushall Olympic | 233 | L | 1-3 | Waters 33 | 21 | 36 |
| Mar 1 | NPL | H | Ashton United | 185 | L | 0-2 | | 21 | 37 |
| 5 | NPL | A | Barwell | 226 | L | 1-2 | Poole 4 | 21 | 38 |
| 12 | NPL | H | Colwyn Bay | 223 | W | 2-0 | McTiernan 5 McWilliams 37 | 21 | 39 |
| 19 | NPL | H | Buxton | 224 | W | 1-0 | Roberts 88 (pen) | 20 | 40 |
| 22 | NPL | A | Skelmersdale United | 193 | D | 0-0 | | 20 | 41 |
| 26 | NPL | A | Salford City | 729 | D | 0-0 | | 20 | 42 |
| Apr 2 | NPL | A | Buxton | 232 | L | 2-3 | Roberts 82 Martin 87 | 22 | 43 |
| 4 | NPL | A | Ilkeston | 345 | L | 1-2 | Roberts 66 (pen) | 22 | 44 |
| 9 | NPL | H | Marine | 249 | W | 1-0 | Hopson 58 | 20 | 45 |
| 13 | NPL | A | Colwyn Bay | 192 | W | 4-1 | Pell 13 Roberts 57 88 Hume 81 | 20 | 46 |
| 16 | NPL | A | Stourbridge | 536 | L | 0-2 | | 20 | 47 |
| 19 | NPL | H | Barwell | 191 | W | 2-1 | Hopson 58 Gell 63 | 19 | 48 |
| 21 | NPL | H | Darlington 1883 | 1804 | L | 1-7 | Hopson 81 | 19 | 49 |
| 23 | NPL | H | Skelmersdale United | 232 | D | 1-1 | Hopson 87 | 19 | 50 |

| GOALSCORERS | Scoring Games | Consec Sco Games | Total |
|---|---|---|---|
| **2014-15 *McTiernan*** | | | ***11*** |
| Roberts | 18 | 3 | 23 |
| Waters | 8 | 2 | 8 |
| Hopson | 6 | 3 | 6 |
| Mason | 5 | 2 | 5 |
| Brobbel | 4 | 2 | 4 |
| McTiernan | 4 | | 4 |
| Gell | 3 | | 3 |
| McCarthy | 2 | | 2 |
| Brown | 1 | | 1 |
| Bullock | 1 | | 1 |
| Gardner | 1 | | 1 |
| Hume | 1 | | 1 |
| Martin | 1 | | 1 |
| McWilliams | 1 | | 1 |
| Pell | 1 | | 1 |
| Thompson | 1 | | 1 |
| Weledji | 1 | | 1 |

# WORKINGTON

**Chairman:** Glenn Heathcote
**Secretary:** Alec Graham (T) 07788 537 811 (E) workington.reds@tiscali.co.uk
**Commercial Manager:** (T/E)
**Programme Editor:** Paul Armstrong (T/E) 07951 243 717
**Ground Address:** Borough Park, Workington, Cumbria CA14 2DT
(T) 01900 602 871 **Manager:** Derek Townsley

2016-17 Squad - Back row: Alan Clark (Kit Man), Gari Rowntree, Rob McCartney, Scott Allison, Josh calvert, Jonny Jamieson, Alex Mitchell, Kyle May, James Earl, Jake Simpson, Anthony Wright, Alice Simpson (Physio)
Front Row: Conor Tinnion, Gareth Arnison, Adam Telfer, Sam Smith, Lee Andrews (Ass. Manager), Derek Townsley (Manager), Alex Salmon, Matty Tymon, Phil McCluckie, Steven Rudd.

## Club Factfile

**Founded:** 1884 **Nickname:** Reds
**Previous Names:** None
**Previous Leagues:** Cumberland Assoc. 1890-94, Cumberland Senior 1894-1901, 03-04. Lancashire 1901-03, Lancashire Comb. 1904-10, North Eastern 1910-11, 21-51, Football League 1951-77, N.P.L. 1977-2005. Conference 2005-14.
**Club Colours (change):** Red with two white diagonal bands/white/red (Yellow with two red diagonal bands/yellow/yellow)

**Ground Capacity:** 2,500 **Seats:** 500 **Covered:** 1,000 **Clubhouse:** Yes **Shop:** Yes

**Directions**
A66 into Workington. At traffic lights at bottom of hill (HSBC opposite), turn left towards town centre. Approach traffic lights in centre lane (Washington Central Hotel on your right) and turn right. Continue on this road, passing over a mini roundabout, a pedestrian crossing and a further set of traffic lights. You will come to the Railway Station (facing you), carry on through the junction and bear right, passing the Derwent Park Stadium (Rugby League/speedway), then left and Borough Park becomes visible ahead of you.

**Previous Grounds:** Various 1884-1921, Lonsdale Park 1921-37

**Record Attendance:** 21,000 v Manchester United - FA Cup 3rd round 04/01/1958
**Record Victory:** 17-1 v Cockermouth Crusaders - Cumberland Senior League 19/01/1901
**Record Defeat:** 0-9 v Chorley (A) - Northern Premier League 10/11/1987
**Record Goalscorer:** Billy Charlton - 193
**Record Appearances:** Bobby Brown - 419
**Additional Records:** Paid £6,000 to Sunderland for Ken Chisolm 1956
Received £33,000 from Liverpool for Ian McDonald 1974

**Honours:**
North West Counties League 1998-99
Cumberland County Cup x24 (Most recently 2015-16.

### 10 YEAR RECORD

| 06-07 | 07-08 | 08-09 | 09-10 | 10-11 | 11-12 | 12-13 | 13-14 | 14-15 | 15-16 |
|---|---|---|---|---|---|---|---|---|---|
| Conf N 3 | Conf N 14 | Conf N 12 | Conf N 4 | Conf N 11 | Conf N 13 | Conf N 14 | Conf N 22 | NP P 2 | NP P 5 |

# WORKINGTON MATCH RESULTS 2015-16

| Date | Comp | H/A | Opponents | Att: | Result | Goalscorers | Pos | No. |
|---|---|---|---|---|---|---|---|---|
| Aug 15 | NPL | H | Sutton Coldfield | 488 | D 1-1 | Allison 55 | 12 | 1 |
| 18 | NPL | A | Skelmersdale United | 217 | L 0-2 | | 20 | 2 |
| 22 | NPL | A | Stourbridge | 415 | D 0-0 | | 20 | 3 |
| 26 | NPL | H | Darlington 1883 | 684 | **W** 2-1 | Tinnion 15 84 | 17 | 4 |
| 29 | NPL | A | Halesowen Town | 337 | L 0-2 | | 19 | 5 |
| 31 | NPL | H | Ramsbottom United | 484 | **W** 4-0 | McGee 10 ALLISON 3 (12 24 86) | 11 | 6 |
| Sept 5 | NPL | A | Rushall Olympic | 239 | D 1-1 | Allison 81 | 13 | 7 |
| 8 | NPL | H | Hyde United | 457 | **W** 2-0 | McGee 16 Calvert 63 | 10 | 8 |
| **12** | **FAC1Q** | **H** | **Colwyn Bay** | **438** | **W 5-0** | **ALLISON 3 ( 31 39 85) May 43 McCartney 89** | | 9 |
| 19 | NPL | H | Barwell | 463 | D 1-1 | Tinnion 60 | 14 | 10 |
| 22 | NPL | A | Colwyn Bay | 172 | **W** 2-0 | Tyman 40 Tinnion 83 | 8 | 11 |
| **26** | **FAC2Q** | **H** | **Harrogate Town** | **599** | **L 0-1** | | | 12 |
| Oct 3 | NPL | H | Mickleover Sports | 460 | D 2-2 | Tymon 35 Smith 72 | 9 | 13 |
| 6 | NPL | H | Whitby Town | 461 | **W** 3-1 | Tymon 10 McGee 66 Arnison 87 | 8 | 14 |
| 10 | NPL | A | Stamford | 431 | **W** 2-1 | McGee 28 McLuckie 75 | 7 | 15 |
| 17 | NPL | H | Nantwich Town | 445 | D 1-1 | Tinnion 12 | 8 | 16 |
| 20 | NPL | A | Darlington 1886 | 1051 | L 0-4 | | 9 | 17 |
| 27 | NPL | H | Skelmersdale United | 439 | **W** 2-1 | Arnison 77 Rowntree 86 | 9 | 18 |
| **31** | **FAT1Q** | **H** | **Whitby Town** | **343** | **L 0-3** | | | 19 |
| Nov 7 | NPL | A | Sutton Coldfield | 228 | **W** 2-0 | Tymon 7 Simpson 16 | 5 | 20 |
| 14 | NPL | H | Salford City | 1405 | L 1-4 | McGee 29 | 5 | 21 |
| 21 | NPL | A | Frickley Athletic | 240 | D 1-1 | Arnison 58 | 9 | 22 |
| 28 | NPL | H | Ilkeston | 333 | **W** 3-2 | McGee 57 Arnison 76 (pen) 90 | 5 | 23 |
| Dec 5 | NPL | A | Buxton | 211 | **W** 2-0 | McGee 17 Arnison 90 | 4 | 24 |
| 15 | NPL | A | Marine | 276 | **W** 2-1 | Cameron 3 McCartney 46 | 4 | 25 |
| 19 | NPL | A | Barwell | 203 | **W** 1-0 | May65 | 3 | 26 |
| Jan 2 | NPL | H | Colwyn Bay | 564 | L 1-2 | Tinnion 36 | 5 | 27 |
| 9 | NPL | H | Ashton United | 441 | **W** 5-2 | TINNION 3 (16 30 73) Allison 77 86 | 4 | 28 |
| 16 | NPL | A | Grantham Town | 235 | **W** 1-0 | Tinnion 11 | 3 | 29 |
| 23 | NPL | H | Halesowen Town | 470 | **W** 3-0 | Simpson 19 Arnison 25 Tinnion 88 | 3 | 30 |
| 25 | NPL | A | Hyde United | 256 | **W** 4-0 | May 34 Earl 44 Arnison 55 McLuckie 62 | 2 | 31 |
| Feb 2 | NPL | H | Blyth Spartans | 774 | **W** 2-0 | Simpson 75 Allison 84 | 2 | 32 |
| 6 | NPL | H | Marine | 470 | **W** 1-0 | Smith 26 | 2 | 33 |
| 13 | NPL | A | Whitley Bay | 329 | L 0-1 | | 2 | 34 |
| 20 | NPL | H | Stamford | 347 | **W** 2-0 | Tymon 31 McGee 73 | 2 | 35 |
| 27 | NPL | A | Ramsbottom United | 213 | D 1-1 | McGrath 6 (og) | 2 | 36 |
| Mar 5 | NPL | H | Grantham Town | 476 | D 1-1 | Allison 64 | 3 | 37 |
| 8 | NPL | A | Salford City | 555 | L 3-5 | Smith 22 McGee 36 May 90 | 4 | 38 |
| 12 | NPL | A | Ilkeston | 402 | **W** 3-0 | Wright 28 Allison 61 67 | 4 | 39 |
| 19 | NPL | H | Stourbridge | 510 | D 1-1 | McGee 50 | 4 | 40 |
| 22 | NPL | A | Mickleover Sports | 231 | **W** 2-1 | Allison 23 78 | 4 | 41 |
| 28 | NPL | A | Blyth Spartans | 1009 | L 0-3 | | 5 | 42 |
| Apr 2 | NPL | A | Matlock Town | 257 | **W** 1-0 | Tymon 88 | 5 | 43 |
| 7 | NPL | H | Rushall Olympic | 358 | D 1-1 | Hebson 80 | 5 | 44 |
| 9 | NPL | H | Frickley Athletic | 418 | L 1-3 | May 37 | 6 | 45 |
| 13 | NPL | A | Nantwich Town | 235 | L 0-2 | | 6 | 46 |
| 16 | NPL | A | Ashton United | 212 | **W** 1-0 | Allison 80 | 6 | 47 |
| 19 | NPL | H | Matlock Town | 394 | **W** 4-1 | ALLISON 4 (33 38 43 89) | 6 | 48 |
| 23 | NPL | H | Buxton | 583 | **W** 5-0 | May4 Arnison 5 Tinnion 11 79 Wilson 24 | 5 | 49 |
| **26** | **PO SF** | **A** | **Blyth Spartans** | **1124** | **W 4-3** | **ALLISON 3 (34 56 68) Wilson 90** | | 50 |
| **30** | **PO Final** | **A** | **Salford City** | **1967** | **L 2-3** | **May 6 Arnison 20** | | 51 |

| GOALSCORERS | Scoring Games | Consec Sco Games | Total |
|---|---|---|---|
| **2014-15 *Tymon*** | | | ***15*** |
| Allison | 12 | 2 | 24 |
| Tinnion | 8 | 4 | 13 |
| Arnison | 9 | 3 | 10 |
| McGee | 9 | 2 | 10 |
| May | 7 | | 7 |
| Tymon | 6 | 2 | 6 |
| Simpson | 3 | | 3 |
| Smith | 3 | | 3 |
| McCartney | 2 | | 2 |
| McLuckie | 2 | | 2 |
| Wilson | 2 | | 2 |
| Calvert | 1 | | 1 |
| Cameron | 1 | | 1 |
| Earl | 1 | | 1 |
| Hebson | 1 | | 1 |
| Rowntree | 1 | | 1 |
| Wright | 1 | | 1 |
| Opponents | | | 1 |

# BAMBER BRIDGE

**Chairman:** Frank Doyle
**Secretary:** George Halliwell **(T)** 07970 042 954 **(E)** geohalli@blueyonder.co.uk
**Commercial Manager:** **(T)**
**Programme Editor:** **(T)**
**Ground Address:** Sir Tom Finney Stadium, Brownedge Road, Bamber Bridge PR5 6UX
**(T)** 01772 909 690 **Manager:** Neil Reynolds

**Founded:** 1952 **Nickname:** Brig
**Previous Names:** None
**Previous Leagues:** Preston & District 1952-90, North West Counties 1990-93

**Club Colours (change):** White/black/black (All red)

**Ground Capacity:** 3,000 **Seats:** 554 **Covered:** 800 **Clubhouse:** Yes **Shop:** Yes
**Previous Grounds:** King George V, Higher Wallton 1952-86

**Record Attendance:** 2,300 v Czech Republic - Pre Euro '96 friendly
**Record Victory:** 8-0 v Curzon Ashton - North West Counties 1994-95
**Record Defeat:** Not known - if you know please email tw.publications@btinternet.com
**Record Goalscorer:** Not known - if you know please email tw.publications@btinternet.com
**Record Appearances:** Not known - if you know please email tw.publications@btinternet.com
**Additional Records:** Paid £10,000 to Horwich RMI for Mark Edwards
Received £15,000 from Wigan Athletic for Tony Black 1995
**Senior Honours:**
ATDC Lancashire Trophy 1994-95.
Northern Premier League Premier Division 1995-96, Challenge Cup 1995-96.

**10 YEAR RECORD**

| 06-07 | 07-08 | 08-09 | 09-10 | 10-11 | 11-12 | 12-13 | 13-14 | 14-15 | 15-16 |
|---|---|---|---|---|---|---|---|---|---|
| NP 1 13 | NP1N 5 | NP1N 11 | NP1N 14 | NP1N 7 | NP1N 10 | NP1N 9 | NP1N 4 | NP1N 3 | NP1N 12 |

# BRIGHOUSE TOWN

**Chairman:** Ray McLaughlin
**Secretary:** Malcolm Taylor **(T)** 07884 182 970 **(E)** malctay@blueyonder.co.uk
**Commercial Manager:** **(T)**
**Programme Editor:** **(T)**
**Ground Address:** Dual Seal Stadium, St Giles Rd, Hove Edge, Brighouse, HD6 2PN
**(T)** 01484 380 088 **Manager:** Paul Quinn

**Founded:** 1963 **Nickname:** Town
**Previous Names:** Blakeborough
**Previous Leagues:** Huddersfield Works. 1963-75. West Riding County Amateur 1975-08.

**Club Colours (change):** Orange/black/orange (All green)

**Ground Capacity:** 1,000 **Seats:** 100 **Covered:** 200 **Clubhouse:** Yes **Shop:**
**Previous Grounds:** Green Lane.

**Record Attendance:** Not known - if you know please email tw.publications@btinternet.com
**Record Victory:** Not known - if you know please email tw.publications@btinternet.com
**Record Defeat:** Not known - if you know please email tw.publications@btinternet.com
**Record Goalscorer:** Not known - if you know please email tw.publications@btinternet.com
**Record Appearances:** Not known - if you know please email tw.publications@btinternet.com
**Additional Records:** FA Cup: Second Qualifying Round 2013-14 FA Trophy: First Qualifying Round 2015-16
FA Vase: Fourth Round 2012–13
**Senior Honours:**
West Riding County Amateur League: Prem Div - 1990/91 1994/95 1995/96 2000/01 2001/02, Prem Cup - 1993/94, 95/96 98/99, 00/01; Div 1 - 1988/89. Northern Counties East Premier 2013-14.

**10 YEAR RECORD**

| 06-07 | 07-08 | 08-09 | 09-10 | 10-11 | 11-12 | 12-13 | 13-14 | 14-15 | 15-16 |
|---|---|---|---|---|---|---|---|---|---|
| WRCP 3 | WRCP 8 | NCE1 15 | NCE1 2 | NCEP 16 | NCEP 4 | NCEP 2 | NCEP 1 | NP1N 14 | NP1N 14 |

# BURSCOUGH

**Chairman:** Mike Swift
**Secretary:** Stan Petheridge **(T)** 07815 954 304 **(E)** stanpeth@fsmail.net
**Commercial Manager:** **(T)**
**Programme Editor:** Stuart Rood **(T)** 07478 728 503
**Ground Address:** Victoria Park, Bobby Langton Way, Mart Lane, Burscough L40 0SD
**(T)** 01704 896 776 **Manager:** Dave Powell

**Founded:** 1946 **Nickname:** Linnets
**Previous Names:** None
**Previous Leagues:** Liverpool County Combination 1946-53, Lancashire Combination 1953-70, Cheshire County 1970-82, North West Counties 1982-98, Northern Premier League 1998-2007, Conference 2007-09
**Club Colours (change):** All green (Sky blue/navy/sky blue)

**Ground Capacity:** 2,500 **Seats:** 270 **Covered:** 1,000 **Clubhouse:** Yes **Shop:** Yes
**Previous Grounds:** None

**Record Attendance:** 4,798 v Wigan Athletic - FA Cup 3rd Qualifying Round 1950-51
**Record Victory:** 10-0 v Cromptons Rec - 1947 and v Nelson - 1948-49 both Lancashire Combination
**Record Defeat:** 0-9 v Earltown - Liverpool County Combination 1948-49
**Record Goalscorer:** Wes Bridge - 188
**Record Appearances:** Not known - if you know please email tw.publications@btinternet.com
**Additional Records:** Johnny Vincent scored 60 goals during the 1953-64 season
Louis Bimpson scored 7 goals in one game.
**Senior Honours:**
North West Counties League Division 1 1982-83. FA Trophy 2002-03. Northern Premier League Premier Division 2006-07.
Liverpool Challenge Cup x3. Liverpool Non-League Senior Cup x2.

**10 YEAR RECORD**

| 06-07 | 07-08 | 08-09 | 09-10 | 10-11 | 11-12 | 12-13 | 13-14 | 14-15 | 15-16 |
|---|---|---|---|---|---|---|---|---|---|
| NP P 1 | Conf N 8 | Conf N 21 | NP P 16 | NP P 19 | NP P 22 | NP1N 11 | NP1N 14 | NP1N 15 | NP1N 5 |

# CLITHEROE

**Chairman:** Anne Barker
**Secretary:** Chris Musson **(T)** 07503 240 629 **(E)** clitheroefc@hotmail.com
**Commercial Manager:** Tony Alveston **(T)** 07837 386 755
**Programme Editor:** Chris Musson **(T)** 01254 245 461
**Ground Address:** Shawbridge, off Pendle Road, Clitheroe, Lancashire BB7 1LZ
**(T)** 01200 423 344 **Manager:** Simon Haworth

**Founded:** 1877 **Nickname:** The Blues
**Previous Names:** Clitheroe Central 1877-1903.
**Previous Leagues:** Blackburn & District, Lancashire Combination 1903-04, 05-10, 25-82, North West Counties 1982-85
**Club Colours (change):** All blue (Red/black/red)

**Ground Capacity:** 2,400 **Seats:** 250 **Covered:** 1,400 **Clubhouse:** Yes **Shop:**
**Previous Grounds:** None

**Record Attendance:** 2,050 v Mangotsfield - FA Vase Semi-final 1995-96
**Record Victory:** Not known - if you know please email tw.publications@btinternet.com
**Record Defeat:** Not known - if you know please email tw.publications@btinternet.com
**Record Goalscorer:** Don Francis
**Record Appearances:** Lindsey Wallace - 670
**Additional Records:** Received £45,000 from Crystal Palace for Carlo Nash
**Senior Honours:**
North West Counties League 1984-85, 2003-04.
Lancashire Challenge Trophy 1984-85. East Lancashire Floodlit Trophy 1994-95.

**10 YEAR RECORD**

| 06-07 | 07-08 | 08-09 | 09-10 | 10-11 | 11-12 | 12-13 | 13-14 | 14-15 | 15-16 |
|---|---|---|---|---|---|---|---|---|---|
| NP 1 16 | NP1N 13 | NP1N 12 | NP1N 8 | NP1N 6 | NP1N 19 | NP1N 8 | NP1N 17 | NP1N 13 | NP1N 7 |

# COLNE

**Chairman:** Shaun O'Neill
**Secretary:** Edward Lambert **(T)** 01282 862 545 **(E)**
**Commercial Manager:** **(T)**
**Programme Editor:** Ben Metcalfe **(T)**
**Ground Address:** The XLCR Stadium, Harrison Drive, Colne, Lancashire. BB8 9SL
**(T)** 01282 862 545 **Manager:** Steve Cunningham

**Founded:** 1996 **Nickname:**
**Previous Names:** None
**Previous Leagues:** North West Counties 1996-2016.

**Club Colours (change):** All Red. (White/black/black).

**Ground Capacity:** 1,800 **Seats:** 160 **Covered:** 1,000 **Clubhouse:** Yes **Shop:** Yes
**Previous Grounds:**

**Record Attendance:** **Att:** 1,742 v AFC Sudbury F.A. Vase SF 2004 **Goalscorer:** Geoff Payton **App:** Richard Walton
**Record Victory:** Not known - if you know please email tw.publications@btinternet.com
**Record Defeat:** Not known - if you know please email tw.publications@btinternet.com
**Record Goalscorer:** Not known - if you know please email tw.publications@btinternet.com
**Record Appearances:** Not known - if you know please email tw.publications@btinternet.com
**Additional Records:**

**Senior Honours:**
BEP Cup Winners 1996-97. North West Counties League Division Two 2003-04, Premier Division 2015-16.

**10 YEAR RECORD**

| 06-07 | 07-08 | 08-09 | 09-10 | 10-11 | 11-12 | 12-13 | 13-14 | 14-15 | 15-16 |
|---|---|---|---|---|---|---|---|---|---|
| NWC1 11 | NWC1 5 | NWCP 18 | NWCP 8 | NWCP 5 | NWCP 8 | NWCP 8 | NWCP 9 | NWCP 4 | NWCP 1 |

# COLWYN BAY

**Chairman:** Mr D Titcher
**Secretary:** Paul Edwards **(T)** 07990 730 323 **(E)** Pauledwards@colwynbayfc.co.uk
**Commercial Manager:** **(T)**
**Programme Editor:** Paul Edwards&Tim Channon **(T)** Pauledwards@colwynbayfc.co.uk
**Ground Address:** Llanelian Road, Old Colwyn, North Wales LL29 8UN
**(T)** 01492 514 680 **Manager:** Paul Moore

**Founded:** 1885 **Nickname:** The Bay / Seagulls
**Previous Names:** None
**Previous Leagues:** North Wales Coast 1901-21, 33-35, Welsh National 1921-30, North Wales Combination 1930-31, Welsh League (North) 1945-84, North West Counties 1984-91. Northern Premier 1991-2011. Football Conference 2011-15.
**Club Colours (change):** Sky blue and claret/sky blue/claret (Yellow/mid blue/yellow)

**Ground Capacity:** 2,500 **Seats:** 250 **Covered:** 700 **Clubhouse:** Yes **Shop:** Yes
**Previous Grounds:** Eirias Park

**Record Attendance:** 5,000 v Borough United at Eirias Park 1964
**Record Victory:** Not known - if you know please email tw.publications@btinternet.com
**Record Defeat:** Not known - if you know please email tw.publications@btinternet.com
**Record Goalscorer:** Peter Donnelly
**Record Appearances:** Bryn A Jones
**Additional Records:**

**Senior Honours:**
Northern League Division 1 1991-92, Division 1 Play-off 2009-10

**10 YEAR RECORD**

| 06-07 | 07-08 | 08-09 | 09-10 | 10-11 | 11-12 | 12-13 | 13-14 | 14-15 | 15-16 |
|---|---|---|---|---|---|---|---|---|---|
| NP 1 5 | NP1S 7 | NP1N 4 | NP1N 4 | NP P 2 | Conf N 12 | Conf N 18 | Conf N 12 | Conf N 20 | NP P 23 |

# DROYLSDEN

**Chairman:** David Pace
**Secretary:** Bryan Pace (T) 07763 318 860 (E) alphagroup@jlservices.co.uk
**Commercial Manager:** (T)
**Programme Editor:** Bryan Pace (T) 07763 318 860
**Ground Address:** The Butchers Arms Ground, Market Street, Droylsden, M43 7AY
(T) 0161 370 1426 **Manager:** David Pace

**Founded:** 1892 **Nickname:** The Bloods
**Previous Names:** None
**Previous Leagues:** Manchester, Lancashire Combination 1936-39, 50-68, Cheshire County 1939-50, 68-82, North West Counties 1982-87, Northern Premier 1986-2004
**Club Colours (change):** All red (Yellow/blue/blue)

**Ground Capacity:** 3,000 **Seats:** 500 **Covered:** 2,000 **Clubhouse:** Yes **Shop:** Yes
**Previous Grounds:** None

**Record Attendance:** 4,250 v Grimsby, FA Cup 1st Round 1976.
**Record Victory:** 13-2 v Lucas Sports Club
**Record Defeat:** Not known - if you know please email tw.publications@btinternet.com
**Record Goalscorer:** E. Gillibrand - 275 (1931-35)
**Record Appearances:** Paul Phillips - 326
**Additional Records:** Received £11,000 from Crewe Alexandra for Tony Naylor 1990

**Senior Honours:**
Northern Premier League Division 1 1998-99. Conference North 2006-07.
Manchester Premier Cup x3. Manchester Senior Cup x3.

**10 YEAR RECORD**

| 06-07 | 07-08 | 08-09 | 09-10 | 10-11 | 11-12 | 12-13 | 13-14 | 14-15 | 15-16 |
|---|---|---|---|---|---|---|---|---|---|
| Conf N 1 | Conf 24 | Conf N 7 | Conf N 5 | Conf N 8 | Conf N 9 | Conf N 21 | NP P 24 | NP1N 10 | NP1N 19 |

# FARSLEY CELTIC

**Chairman:** John Palmer
**Secretary:** Joshua Greaves (T) 07725 999 758 (E) office@farsleyceltic.com
**Commercial Manager:** Michael Binns (T)
**Programme Editor:** Mark Rawlinson (T)
**Ground Address:** Throstle Nest, Newlands, Pudsey, Leeds, LS28 5BE
(T) 0113 255 7292 **Manager:** John Deacy & Neil Parsley

**Founded:** 2010 **Nickname:** The Villagers
**Previous Names:** Farsley Celtic > 2010. Farsley AFC 2010-15.
**Previous Leagues:** Northern Counties East 2010-11.

**Club Colours (change):** All blue (All yellow)

**Ground Capacity:** 4,000 **Seats:** 300 **Covered:** 1,500 **Clubhouse:** Yes **Shop:** Yes
**Previous Grounds:** None

**Record Attendance:**
**Record Victory:** 8-0 v Arnold Town (H) Northern Counties East Premier 2010-11.
**Record Defeat:** 5-1 v Tadcaster Albion, President's Cup Final 27/04/11.
**Record Goalscorer:** Not known - if you know please email tw.publications@btinternet.com
**Record Appearances:** Not known - if you know please email tw.publications@btinternet.com
**Additional Records:** None

**Senior Honours:**
Northern Counties East Premier Division 2010-11.

**10 YEAR RECORD**

| 06-07 | 07-08 | 08-09 | 09-10 | 10-11 | 11-12 | 12-13 | 13-14 | 14-15 | 15-16 |
|---|---|---|---|---|---|---|---|---|---|
| | | | | NCEP 1 | NP1N 4 | NP1N 14 | NP1N 7 | NP1N 12 | NP1N 9 |

# GLOSSOP NORTH END

**Chairman:** David Atkinson
**Secretary:** Peter Hammond (T) 07733 170 778 (E) gnefc@hotmail.com
**Commercial Manager:** (T)
**Programme Editor:** Neil Rimmer (T) 07841 408 376
**Ground Address:** Surrey Street, Glossop, Derbys SK13 7AJ
(T) 01457 855 469 **Manager:** Chris Willcox

**Founded:** 1886 **Nickname:** Hillmen
**Previous Names:** Glossop North End1886-1896 and Glossop FC 1898-1992. Reformed in 1992.
**Previous Leagues:** The Football League. Cheshire County. Manchester. Lancashire Comb. North West Counties >2015.

**Club Colours (change):** All royal blue (Orange/black/orange).

**Ground Capacity:** 2,374 **Seats:** 209 **Covered:** 509 **Clubhouse:** Yes **Shop:** Yes
**Previous Grounds:**

**Record Attendance:** **Att:** 10,736 v Preston North End F.A. Cup 1913-1914
**Record Victory:** Not known - if you know please email tw.publications@btinternet.com
**Record Defeat:** Not known - if you know please email tw.publications@btinternet.com
**Record Goalscorer:** Not known - if you know please email tw.publications@btinternet.com
**Record Appearances:** Not known - if you know please email tw.publications@btinternet.com
**Additional Records:**

**Senior Honours:**
Manchester League 1927-28. Derbyshire Senior Cup 2000-01.
North West Counties League Premier Division 2014-15.

**10 YEAR RECORD**

| 06-07 | 07-08 | 08-09 | 09-10 | 10-11 | 11-12 | 12-13 | 13-14 | 14-15 | 15-16 |
|---|---|---|---|---|---|---|---|---|---|
| NWC1 9 | NWC1 7 | NWCP 5 | NWCP 7 | NWCP 14 | NWCP 6 | NWCP 13 | NWCP 3 | NWCP 1 | NP1N 4 |

# GOOLE AFC

**Chairman:** Richard & Andy Norman
**Secretary:** Andrew Morris (T) 07751 457 254 (E)
**Commercial Manager:** Anthony Whiteley (T) 07557 400 990
**Programme Editor:** Graeme Wilson (T) 07960 414 630
**Ground Address:** Victoria Pleasure Gardens, Marcus Road, Goole DN14 6TN
(T) 01405 762 794 (Match days) **Manager:** Lee Morris

**Founded:** 1997 **Nickname:** The Badgers
**Previous Names:** Goole Town > 1996.
**Previous Leagues:** Central Midlands 1997-98.
Northern Counties East 2000-04.
**Club Colours (change):** Red & black stripes/red/red (Dark & light blue/dark blue/dark blue)

**Ground Capacity:** 3,000 **Seats:** 200 **Covered:** 800 **Clubhouse:** Yes **Shop:** Yes
**Previous Grounds:** None

**Record Attendance:** 976 v Leeds United - 1999
**Record Victory:** Not known - if you know please email tw.publications@btinternet.com
**Record Defeat:** Not known - if you know please email tw.publications@btinternet.com
**Record Goalscorer:** Kevin Severn (1997-2001)
**Record Appearances:** Phil Dobson - 187 (1999-2001)
**Additional Records:**

**Senior Honours:**
Central Midlands 1997-98.
Northern Counties East Division 1 1999-2000, Premier Division 2003-04.

**10 YEAR RECORD**

| 06-07 | 07-08 | 08-09 | 09-10 | 10-11 | 11-12 | 12-13 | 13-14 | 14-15 | 15-16 |
|---|---|---|---|---|---|---|---|---|---|
| NP 1 7 | NP 1 9 | NP1S 18 | NP1S 18 | NP1S 13 | NP1S 10 | NP1N 21 | NP1S 13 | NP1S 16 | NP1S 19 |

# HYDE UNITED

**Chairman:** Peter Ainger (CEO)
**Secretary:** Mark Worthington **(T)** 07515 676 392 **(E)**
**Commercial Manager:** Alan Hackney **(T)** 07803 555 124
**Programme Editor:** **(T)**
**Ground Address:** Ewen Fields, Walker Lane, Hyde SK14 5PL
**(T)** 0161 367 7273 **Manager:** Darren Kelly

**Founded:** 1885 **Nickname:** The Tigers
**Previous Names:** Hyde F.C. 1885-1917, Hyde United 1919-2010, Hyde F.C. 2010-15.
**Previous Leagues:** Lancashire & Cheshire 1919-21, Manchester 1921-30, Cheshire County 1930-68, 1970-82, Northern Premier 1968-70, 1983-2004. Football Conference 2004-15.
**Club Colours (change):** Red/white/red (Yellow & black stripes/black/black)

**Ground Capacity:** 4,250 **Seats:** 530 **Covered:** 4,073 **Clubhouse:** Yes **Shop:** Yes
**Previous Grounds:** None

**Record Attendance:** 7,600 v Nelson - FA Cup 1952
**Record Victory:** 14-0 v Prestwich – Manchester League 06/04/1901
**Record Defeat:** 0-26 v Preston North End - FA Cup 15/10/1887
**Record Goalscorer:** Jack Cheetham – 161 (1930-1933)
**Record Appearances:** Steve Johnson - 623 (1975-1988)
**Additional Records:** Paid £8,000 to Mossley for Jim McCluskie 1989
Received £50,000 from Crewe Alexandra for Colin Little 1995
**Senior Honours:**
Northern Premier League Division 1 2003-04, Premier Division 2004-05, League Cup x3. Conference North 2011-12.
Cheshire Senior Cup x6. Manchester Premier cup x6.

**10 YEAR RECORD**

| 06-07 | 07-08 | 08-09 | 09-10 | 10-11 | 11-12 | 12-13 | 13-14 | 14-15 | 15-16 |
|---|---|---|---|---|---|---|---|---|---|
| Conf N 8 | Conf N 9 | Conf N 20 | Conf N 15 | Conf N 19 | Conf N 1 | Conf 18 | Conf 24 | Conf N 22 | NP P 22 |

# KENDAL TOWN

**Chairman:** George Gudgeon
**Secretary:** Linda Gudgeon **(T)** 07712 119 162 **(E)** info@kendaltownfootballclub.co.uk
**Commercial Manager:** Linda Stott **(T)** 07914 379 606
**Programme Editor:** Merrill Tummey **(T)** 07733 135 796
**Ground Address:** Pye Motors Stadium, Parkside Road, Kendal, Cumbria LA9 7BL
**(T)** 01539 738 818 **Manager:** David Foster

**Founded:** 1919 **Nickname:** Town
**Previous Names:** Netherfield AFC 1919-2000
**Previous Leagues:** Westmorland, North Lancashire Combination 1945-68, Northern Premier 1968-83, North West Counties 1983-87
**Club Colours (change):** Black and white stripes/black/red (Light blue/navy/navy)

**Ground Capacity:** 2,490 **Seats:** 450 **Covered:** 1000 **Clubhouse:** Yes **Shop:** Yes
**Previous Grounds:** None

**Record Attendance:** 5,184 v Grimsby Town - FA Cup 1st Round 1955
**Record Victory:** 11-0 v Great Harwood - 22/03/1947
**Record Defeat:** 0-10 v Stalybridge Celtic - 01/09/1984
**Record Goalscorer:** Tom Brownlee
**Record Appearances:** Not known - if you know please email tw.publications@btinternet.com
**Additional Records:** Received £10,250 from Manchester City for Andy Milner 1995
**Senior Honours:**
Westmorlands Senior Cup x12. Lancashire Senior Cup 2002-03.

**10 YEAR RECORD**

| 06-07 | 07-08 | 08-09 | 09-10 | 10-11 | 11-12 | 12-13 | 13-14 | 14-15 | 15-16 |
|---|---|---|---|---|---|---|---|---|---|
| NP P 19 | NP P 11 | NP P 5 | NP P 5 | NP P 8 | NP P 11 | NP P 21 | NP1N 10 | NP1N 16 | NP1N 15 |

# LANCASTER CITY

**Chairman:** Stuart Houghton
**Secretary:** Graham Dockerty (T) 01524 382 238 (E)
**Commercial Manager:** Jim Johnstone (T)
**Programme Editor:** Andrew Satterthwaite (T) 07947 145 915
**Ground Address:** Giant Axe, West Road, Lancaster LA1 5PE
(T) 01524 382 238 **Manager:** Phil Brown

**Founded:** 1905 **Nickname:** Dolly Blues
**Previous Names:** None
**Previous Leagues:** Lancashire Combination 1905-70, Northern Premier League 1970-82, 87-2004, North West Counties 1982-87, Conference 2004-07
**Club Colours (change):** Blue & white hoops/blue/blue (Yellow/blue/yellow)

**Ground Capacity:** 3,064 **Seats:** 513 **Covered:** 900 **Clubhouse:** Yes **Shop:** Yes
**Previous Grounds:** None

**Record Attendance:** 7,500 v Carlisle United - FA Cup 1936
**Record Victory:** 8-0 v Leyland Motors (A) - 1983-84
**Record Defeat:** 0-10 v Matlock Town - Northern Premier League Division 1 1973-74
**Record Goalscorer:** David Barnes - 130
**Record Appearances:** Edgar J Parkinson - 591
**Additional Records:** Paid £6,000 to Droylsden for Jamie Tandy
Received £25,000 from Birmingham City for Chris Ward
**Senior Honours:**
Lancashire Junior Cup (ATS Challenge Trophy) 1927-28, 28-29, 30-31, 33-34, 51-52, 74-75.
Northern Premier League Division 1 1995-96.

**10 YEAR RECORD**

| 06-07 | 07-08 | 08-09 | 09-10 | 10-11 | 11-12 | 12-13 | 13-14 | 14-15 | 15-16 |
|---|---|---|---|---|---|---|---|---|---|
| Conf N 24 | NP1N 11 | NP1N 7 | NP1N 2 | NP1N 8 | NP1N 6 | NP1N 13 | NP1N 6 | NP1N 11 | NP1N 6 |

# MOSSLEY

**Chairman:**
**Secretary:** Harry Hulmes (T) 07944 856 343 (E) harry.hulmes@btinternet.com
**Commercial Manager:** (T)
**Programme Editor:** John Cawthorne (T) mossleyweb@hotmail.com
**Ground Address:** Seel Park, Market Street, Mossley, Lancashire OL5 0ES
(T) 01457 832 369 **Manager:** Peter Band & Lloyd Morrison

**Founded:** 1903 **Nickname:** Lilywhites
**Previous Names:** Park Villa 1903-04, Mossley Juniors
**Previous Leagues:** Ashton, South East Lancashire, Lancashire Combination 1918-19, Cheshire County 1919-72, Northern Premier 1972-95, North West Counties 1995-2004
**Club Colours (change):** White/black/white (Orange/black/black)

**Ground Capacity:** 4,000 **Seats:** 200 **Covered:** 1,500 **Clubhouse:** Yes **Shop:** Yes
**Previous Grounds:** None

**Record Attendance:** 7,000 v Stalybridge Celtic 1950
**Record Victory:** 9-0 v Urmston, Manchester Shield, 1947
**Record Defeat:** 2-13 v Witton Albion, Cheshire League, 1926
**Record Goalscorer:** David Moore - 235 (1974-84)
**Record Appearances:** Jimmy O'Connor - 613 (1972-87)
**Additional Records:** Paid £2,300 to Altrincham for Phil Wilson
Received £25,000 from Everton for Eamonn O'Keefe
**Senior Honours:**
Northern Premier League 1978-79, 79-80, Challenge Cup 78-79, Division 1 2005-06.
Manchester Premier Cup 1937-38, 48-49, 60-61, 66-67, 67-68, 88-89, 90-91, 2011-12, 12-13, 14-15, 15-16.
Manchester Challenge Trophy 2011-12.

**10 YEAR RECORD**

| 06-07 | 07-08 | 08-09 | 09-10 | 10-11 | 11-12 | 12-13 | 13-14 | 14-15 | 15-16 |
|---|---|---|---|---|---|---|---|---|---|
| NP P 20 | NP1N 15 | NP1N 10 | NP1N 7 | NP1N 15 | NP1N 14 | NP1N 5 | NP1N 15 | NP1N 7 | NP1N 13 |

# OSSETT ALBION

**Chairman:** Dominic Riordan
**Secretary:** Stephen Hanks **(T)** 07792 221 088 **(E)** ossettalbion@sky.com
**Commercial Manager:** **(T)**
**Programme Editor:** Stephen Hanks **(T)** 07792 221 088
**Ground Address:** Queens Terrace, Dimple Wells, Ossett, Yorkshire WF5 8JU
**(T)** 01924 273 746 **Manager:** Richard Tracey

**Founded:** 1944 **Nickname:** Albion
**Previous Names:** Not known
**Previous Leagues:** Heavy Woollen Area 1944-49, West Riding County Amateur 1949-50, West Yorkshire 1950-57, Yorkshire 1957-82, Northern Counties East 1982-2004
**Club Colours (change):** Gold/black/black (Claret & sky/claret & sky/claret)

**Ground Capacity:** 3,000 **Seats:** Yes **Covered:** 750 **Clubhouse:** Yes **Shop:** Yes
**Previous Grounds:** Fearn House

**Record Attendance:** 1,200 v Leeds United - Opening of floodlights 1986
**Record Victory:** 12-0 v British Ropes (H) - Yorkshire League Division 2 06/05/1959
**Record Defeat:** 2-11 v Swillington (A) - West Yorkshire League Division 1 25/04/1956
**Record Goalscorer:** John Balmer
**Record Appearances:** Peter Eaton - 800+ (22 years)
**Additional Records:**
**Senior Honours:**
Northern Counties East League Division 1 1986-87, Premier Division 1998-99, 2003-04, League Cup 1983-84, 2002-03.
West Riding County Cup x4.

**10 YEAR RECORD**

| 06-07 | 07-08 | 08-09 | 09-10 | 10-11 | 11-12 | 12-13 | 13-14 | 14-15 | 15-16 |
|---|---|---|---|---|---|---|---|---|---|
| NP 1 11 | NP1N 6 | NP1N 6 | NP1N 21 | NP1N 22 | NP1N 18 | NP1N 20 | NP1N 21 | NP1N 17 | NP1N 10 |

# OSSETT TOWN

**Chairman:** James Rogers
**Secretary:** Neil Spofforth **(T)** 07818 400 808 **(E)**
**Commercial Manager:** **(T)**
**Programme Editor:** Neil Spofforth **(T)** 07818 400 808
**Ground Address:** The 4G Voice & Data Stadium,Ingfield, Prospect Road, Ossett, Wakefield WF5 9HA
**(T)** 01924 272 960 **Manager:** Grant Black

**Founded:** 1936 **Nickname:** Town
**Previous Names:** None
**Previous Leagues:** Leeds 1936-39, Yorkshire 1945-82, Northern Counties East 1983-99
**Club Colours (change):** All red (All blue)

**Ground Capacity:** 4,000 **Seats:** 360 **Covered:** 1,000 **Clubhouse:** Yes **Shop:** Yes
**Previous Grounds:** Wakefield Road 1936-39. Back Lane.

**Record Attendance:** 2,600 v Manchester United - Friendly 1989
**Record Victory:** 10-1 v Harrogate RA (H) - Northern Counties East 27/04/1993
**Record Defeat:** 0-7 v Easington Colliery - FA Vase 08/10/1983
**Record Goalscorer:** Dave Leadbitter
**Record Appearances:** Steve Worsfold
**Additional Records:** Received £1,350 from Swansea Town for Dereck Blackburn
**Senior Honours:**
West Riding County Cup 1958-59, 81-82

**10 YEAR RECORD**

| 06-07 | 07-08 | 08-09 | 09-10 | 10-11 | 11-12 | 12-13 | 13-14 | 14-15 | 15-16 |
|---|---|---|---|---|---|---|---|---|---|
| NP P 10 | NP P 18 | NP P 12 | NP P 19 | NP P 21 | NP1N 17 | NP1N 12 | NP1N 8 | NP1N 18 | NP1N 17 |

# PRESCOT CABLES

**Chairman:** Tony Zeverona
**Secretary:** Doug Lace **(T)** 07753 143 273 **(E)** prescotcables@hotmail.com
**Commercial Manager:** **(T)**
**Programme Editor:** Paul Watkinson **(T)** 0151 426 4593
**Ground Address:** Valerie Park, Eaton Street, Prescot L34 6HD
**(T)** 0151 430 0507 **Manager:** Andy Paxton

**Founded:** 1884 **Nickname:** Tigers
**Previous Names:** Prescot > 1995
**Previous Leagues:** Liverpool County Combination, Lancashire Combination 1897-98, 1918-20, 27-33, 36-76, Mid Cheshire 1976-78, Cheshire County 1978-82, North West Counties 1982-2003
**Club Colours (change):** Amber/black/black (All red)

**Ground Capacity:** 3,000 **Seats:** 500 **Covered:** 600 **Clubhouse:** Yes **Shop:** Yes
**Previous Grounds:** None

**Record Attendance:** 8,122 v Ashton National - 1932
**Record Victory:** 18-3 v Great Harwood - 1954-55
**Record Defeat:** 1-12 v Morecambe - 1936-37
**Record Goalscorer:** Freddie Crampton
**Record Appearances:** Harry Grisedale
**Additional Records:**
**Senior Honours:**
Lancashire Combination 1956-57. North West Counties League 2002-03.
Liverpool Non-League Cup x4. Liverpool Challenge Cup x6.

**10 YEAR RECORD**

| 06-07 | 07-08 | 08-09 | 09-10 | 10-11 | 11-12 | 12-13 | 13-14 | 14-15 | 15-16 |
|---|---|---|---|---|---|---|---|---|---|
| NP P 14 | NP P 13 | NP P 22 | NP1N 15 | NP1N 21 | NP1N 16 | NP1N 17 | NP1N 20 | NP1N 20 | NP1N 16 |

# RADCLIFFE BOROUGH

**Chairman:** David Chalmers (Chief Executive)
**Secretary:** Ric Fielding **(T)** 07877 696 097 **(E)** rbfc@hotmail.co.uk
**Commercial Manager:** Ben Hiard **(T)**
**Programme Editor:** Matthew Bostock **(T)** 07597 384 616
**Ground Address:** Stainton Park, Pilkington Road, Radcliffe, Lancashire M26 3OE
**(T)** 0161 724 8346 **Manager:** Bill Prendergast

**Founded:** 1949 **Nickname:** Boro
**Previous Names:** None
**Previous Leagues:** South East Lancashire, Manchester 1953-63, Lancashire Combination 1963-71, Cheshire County 1971-82, North West Counties 1982-97
**Club Colours (change):** Royal blue & white hoops/royal blue/white (Black & red hoops/black/black)

**Ground Capacity:** 3,100 **Seats:** 350 **Covered:** 1,000 **Clubhouse:** Yes **Shop:** Yes
**Previous Grounds:** Ashworth Street. Bright Street > 1970.

**Record Attendance:** 2,495 v York City - FA Cup 1st Round 2000-01
**Record Victory:** Not known - if you know please email tw.publications@btinternet.com
**Record Defeat:** Not known - if you know please email tw.publications@btinternet.com
**Record Goalscorer:** Ian Lunt - 147
**Record Appearances:** David Bean - 401
**Additional Records:** Paid £5,000 to Buxton for Gary Walker 1991
Received £20,000 from Shrewsbury Town for Jody Banim 2003
**Senior Honours:**
North West Counties 19984-85. Northern Premier League Division 1 1996-97.

**10 YEAR RECORD**

| 06-07 | 07-08 | 08-09 | 09-10 | 10-11 | 11-12 | 12-13 | 13-14 | 14-15 | 15-16 |
|---|---|---|---|---|---|---|---|---|---|
| NP P 21 | NP1N 16 | NP1N 16 | NP1N 10 | NP1N 18 | NP1N 15 | NP1N 15 | NP1N 18 | NP1N 19 | NP1N 18 |

# RAMSBOTTOM UNITED

**Chairman:** Harry Williams
**Secretary:** Tony Cunningham **(T)** 07973 416 580 **(E)** secretary@rammyunited.co.uk
**Commercial Manager:** **(T)**
**Programme Editor:** Rob Moss **(T)** 07944 038 512
**Ground Address:** The Harry Williams Stadium, Acrebottom (off Bridge Street) BL0 0BS.
**(T)** 01706 822 799 **Manager:** Paul Fildes & Mark fell

**Founded:** 1966 **Nickname:** The Rams
**Previous Names:** None
**Previous Leagues:** Bury Amateur, Bolton Combination & Manchester League

**Club Colours (change):** Blue/blue/white (Red/black/red).

**Ground Capacity:** **Seats:** Yes **Covered:** Yes **Clubhouse:** Yes **Shop:** No
**Previous Grounds:**

**Record Attendance:** **Att:** 1,653 v FC United of Manchester 07.04.2007.
**Record Victory:** 9-0 v Stantondale (Home, NWCFL Division Two, 9th November 1996)
**Record Defeat:** 0-7 v Salford City (Away, NWCFL Division One, 16th November 2002)
**Record Goalscorer:** Russell Brierley - 176 (1996-2003). **Record in a season:** Russell Brierley - 38 (1999-2000)
**Record Appearances:** Not known
**Additional Records:**

**Senior Honours:**
North West Counties Division Two 1996-97, Premier Division 2011-12.

**10 YEAR RECORD**

| 06-07 | 07-08 | 08-09 | 09-10 | 10-11 | 11-12 | 12-13 | 13-14 | 14-15 | 15-16 |
|---|---|---|---|---|---|---|---|---|---|
| NWC1 8 | NWC1 16 | NWCP 14 | NWCP 4 | NWCP 2 | NWCP 1 | NP1N 6 | NP1N 5 | NP P 17 | NP P 24 |

# SCARBOROUGH ATHLETIC

**Chairman:**
**Secretary:** Wendy Danby **(T)** 07545 878 467 **(E)** club.secretary@scarboroughathletic.com
**Commercial Manager:** Andy Troughton **(T)** andy.troughton@scarboroughathletic.com
**Programme Editor:** Nick Finch **(T)** 07800 635 273
**Ground Address:** Bridlington Town FC, Queensgate, Bridlington, East Yorks YO16 7LN
**(T)** 07545 878 467 **Manager:** Steve Kittrick - Jan 2016

**Founded:** 2007 **Nickname:** The Seadogs
**Previous Names:** Formed after Scarborough F.C. folded in 2007.
**Previous Leagues:** Northern Counties East 2007-13.

**Club Colours (change):** Red & white hoops/red/red (Sky blue & white stripes/white/white).

**Ground Capacity:** 3000 **Seats:** 500 **Covered:** 1,200 **Clubhouse:** Yes **Shop:** No
**Previous Grounds:** None

**Record Attendance:** **Att:** 791 v Leeds Carnegie N.C.E. Div.1 - 25.04.09.
**Record Victory:** 13-0 v Brodsworth, Northern Counties East, 2009-10.
**Record Defeat:** Not known - if you know please email tw.publications@btinternet.com
**Record Goalscorer:** Not known - if you know please email tw.publications@btinternet.com
**Record Appearances:** Not known - if you know please email tw.publications@btinternet.com
**Additional Records:**

**Senior Honours:**
Northern Counties East Division One 2008-09, Premier 2012-13.

**10 YEAR RECORD**

| 06-07 | 07-08 | 08-09 | 09-10 | 10-11 | 11-12 | 12-13 | 13-14 | 14-15 | 15-16 |
|---|---|---|---|---|---|---|---|---|---|
| | NCE1 5 | NCE1 1 | NCEP 5 | NCEP 10 | NCEP 3 | NCEP 1 | NP1S 7 | NP1N 6 | NP1N 20 |

# TADCASTER ALBION

**Chairman:** Matthew Gore
**Secretary:** Ian Nottingham **(T)** 07910 779 313 **(E)** ian.nottingham@enterizi.com
**Commercial Manager:** **(T)**
**Programme Editor:** Mark Murphy **(T)**
**Ground Address:** i2i Stadium, Ings Lane, Tadcaster LS24 9AY
**(T)** 01904 606 000 **Manager:** Billy Miller

**Founded:** 1892 **Nickname:** The Brewers
**Previous Names:** None
**Previous Leagues:** York, Harrogate, Yorkshire 1973-82. Northern Counties East 1982-2016.

**Club Colours (change):** White/blue/white (All yellow)

**Ground Capacity:** 1,500 **Seats:** 150 **Covered:** 400 **Clubhouse:** Yes **Shop:** No
**Previous Grounds:**

**Record Attendance:** **Att:** 1,200 v Winterton FA Vase 4th Round 1996-97
**Record Victory:** 13-0 v Blidworth Welfare, NCEL Division One, 1997-98
**Record Defeat:** 10-2 v Thackley, 1984-85
**Record Goalscorer:** Not known - if you know please email tw.publications@btinternet.com
**Record Appearances:** Not known - if you know please email tw.publications@btinternet.com
**Additional Records:** FA Cup: Third Qualifying Round: 2012-13, knocked out by Boston Utd 2-0.
FA Vase: Fifth Round: 1977-78, knocked out by Frenchville Community 2-1.
**Senior Honours:**
Northern Counties East Division 1 2009-10, Premier Division 2015-16.

**10 YEAR RECORD**

| 06-07 | 07-08 | 08-09 | 09-10 | 10-11 | 11-12 | 12-13 | 13-14 | 14-15 | 15-16 |
|---|---|---|---|---|---|---|---|---|---|
| NCE1 7 | NCE1 12 | NCE1 17 | NCE1 1 | NCEP 4 | NCEP 8 | NCEP 6 | NCEP 2 | NCEP 3 | NCEP 1 |

# TRAFFORD

**Chairman:** John Eadie
**Secretary:** Graham Foxall **(T)** 07796 864 151 **(E)** davem@traffordfc.co.uk
**Commercial Manager:** **(T)**
**Programme Editor:** Dave Murray **(T)** 07551 982 299
**Ground Address:** Shawe View, Pennybridge Lane, Flixton Urmston M41 5AQ
**(T)** 0161 747 1727 **Manager:** Tom Baker

**Founded:** 1990 **Nickname:** The North
**Previous Names:** North Trafford 1990-94
**Previous Leagues:** Mid Cheshire 1990-92, North West Counties 1992-97, 2003-08, Northern Premier 1997-2003

**Club Colours (change):** All white (Yellow & blue/blue/blue)

**Ground Capacity:** 2,500 **Seats:** 292 **Covered:** 740 **Clubhouse:** Yes **Shop:** Yes
**Previous Grounds:** Not known

**Record Attendance:** 803 v Flixton - Northern Premier League Division 1 1997-98
**Record Victory:** 10-0 v Haslingden St.Mary's (Lancs Amt Shield 1991)
**Record Defeat:** Not known - if you know please email tw.publications@btinternet.com
**Record Goalscorer:** Scott Barlow - 100
**Record Appearances:** Lee Southwood - 311
**Additional Records:** NWC League Record: 18 consecutive league wins in 2007-08
Most Points In One Season: 95 points from 38 games 2007-08
**Senior Honours:**
North West Counties Division 1 1996-97, 2007-08.
Manchester Challenge Trophy 2004-05. Northern Premier President's Cup 2008-09.

**10 YEAR RECORD**

| 06-07 | 07-08 | 08-09 | 09-10 | 10-11 | 11-12 | 12-13 | 13-14 | 14-15 | 15-16 |
|---|---|---|---|---|---|---|---|---|---|
| NWC1 5 | NWC1 1 | NP1N 15 | NP1N 12 | NP1N 14 | NP1N 12 | NP1N 4 | NP P 10 | NP P 23 | NP1N 8 |

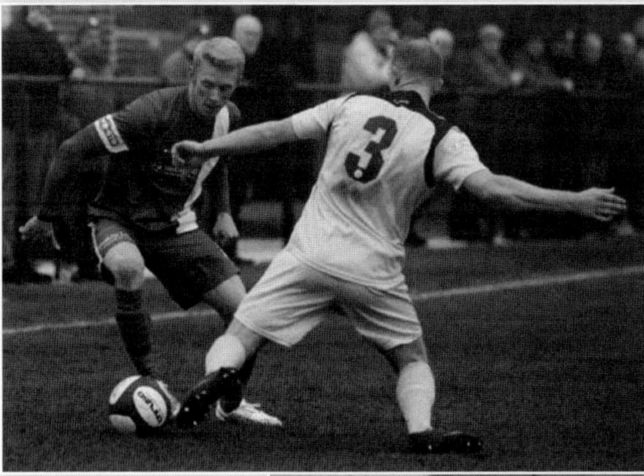

Northern Premier League Division One North action between Glossop and Trafford. Photos: Keith Clayton.

**Left:** Reed (Glossop) gets past Neville (Trafford).

Mark Reed (Glosop) knocks the winner past Russell Saunders in the Trafford goal.

Most look for shelter under Glossop's coverd terrace.

Moran (Glossop) blocks Davies (Trafford).

# AFC RUSHDEN & DIAMONDS

**Chairman:** Ralph Burditt
**Secretary:** James Waller **(T)** **(E)** secretary@afcdiamonds.com
**Commercial Manager:** John Gregory **(T)** marketing@afcdiamonds.com
**Programme Editor:** Miss Stephanie Webb **(T)** afcstephanie@gmail.com
**Ground Address:** The Dog and Duck, London Road, Wellingborough, Northants NN8 2DP
**(T)** 01933 441 388 **Manager:** Andy Peaks

**Founded:** 2011 **Nickname:**
**Previous Names:** None
**Previous Leagues:** United Counties 2012-15. Southern 2015-16.

**Club Colours (change):** White/blue/white (Yellow/black/yellow)

**Ground Capacity:** **Seats:** Yes **Covered:** Yes **Clubhouse:** Yes **Shop:**
**Previous Grounds:** None

**Record Attendance:** 1157 Rushden & Higham Utd (A) 6/10/12 UCL Division One
**Record Victory:** 9-0 v Buckingham Town (A) 15/12/12 and v Desborough Town (A) 21/02/15
**Record Defeat:** Not known - if you know please email tw.publications@btinternet.com
**Record Goalscorer:** Alfie Taylor - 50, 18/08/12 - 22/03/14
**Record Appearances:** Sam Brown - 126, 18/08/12 - current
**Additional Records:**

**Senior Honours:**
United Counties Premier Division 2014-15.
Northamptonshire Senior Cup 2015-16.

**10 YEAR RECORD**

| 06-07 | 07-08 | 08-09 | 09-10 | 10-11 | 11-12 | 12-13 | 13-14 | 14-15 | 15-16 |
|---|---|---|---|---|---|---|---|---|---|
| | | | | | | UCL 1 2 | UCL P 3 | UCL P 1 | SthC 5 |

# BASFORD UNITED

**Chairman:** Chris Munroe
**Secretary:** Tracie Witton **(T)** 07973 702 588 **(E)** info@basfordunitedfc.co.uk
**Commercial Manager:** **(T)**
**Programme Editor:** Neil McCowen **(T)** 07817 941 136
**Ground Address:** Greenwich Avenue, off Bagnall Road, Basford, Nottingham NG6 0LD
**(T)** 0115 924 4491 **Manager:** Martin Carruthers

**Founded:** 1900 **Nickname:** None
**Previous Names:** None
**Previous Leagues:** Notts Alliance 1905-39, 1946-2004. Notts Amateur League 1939-46. Notts Amateur Alliance 2004-06. Notts Senior 2006-11. Central Midlands 2011-12. East Midlands Counties 2012-13. Northern Counties East 2013-14. Midland League 2014-15.
**Club Colours (change):** Yellow/black/yellow (White/royal blue/royal blue)

**Ground Capacity:** **Seats:** **Covered:** Yes **Clubhouse:** Yes **Shop:**
**Previous Grounds:** Old Peer Tree Inn, Dolly Tub > 1903, Catchems Corner 1903-30, Vernon Avenue 1930-34, Mill Street 1934-91.

**Record Attendance:** 3,500 v Grantham United, FACup 1937.
**Record Victory:** Not known - if you know please email tw.publications@btinternet.com
**Record Defeat:** Not known - if you know please email tw.publications@btinternet.com
**Record Goalscorer:** Not known - if you know please email tw.publications@btinternet.com
**Record Appearances:** Not known - if you know please email tw.publications@btinternet.com
**Additional Records:** Former club secretary, Wallace Brownlow, who took up the post when 19 in 1907, remained in the position until his death in 1970 - a world record of 63 years.
**Senior Honours:**
Notts Alliance 1905-06, 07-08, 19-20, Division One 1997-98. Central Midlands Southern 2011-12. East Midland Counties 2012-13.
Midland Football League Premier Division 2014-15.
Notts Senior Cup 1946-47, 87-88, 2014-15, 15-16.

**10 YEAR RECORD**

| 06-07 | 07-08 | 08-09 | 09-10 | 10-11 | 11-12 | 12-13 | 13-14 | 14-15 | 15-16 |
|---|---|---|---|---|---|---|---|---|---|
| NottS 3 | NottS 5 | NottS 3 | NottS 2 | NottS 2 | CMSth 1 | EMC 1 | NCEP 5 | MFLP 1 | NP1S 4 |

# BEDWORTH UNITED

**Chairman:** Neill Rayson-Randle
**Secretary:** Andy Stickley (T) 07740 869 757 (E) andrew.stickley@live.co.uk
**Commercial Manager:** (T)
**Programme Editor:** Barry Walker (T) bedworthunitededitor@gmail.com
**Ground Address:** The Oval, Coventry Road, Bedworth CV12 8NN
(T) 02476 314 752 **Manager:** Stuart Storer

**Founded:** 1896 **Nickname:** Greenbacks
**Previous Names:** Bedworth Town 1947-68
**Previous Leagues:** Birmingham Combination 1947-54, Birmingham/West Midlands 1954-72. Southern 1972-2013, 14-16. Northern Premier 2013-14.
**Club Colours (change):** All green (Gold/black/gold)

**Ground Capacity:** 7,000 **Seats:** 300 **Covered:** 300 **Clubhouse:** Yes **Shop:** Yes
**Previous Grounds:** British Queen Ground 1911-39

**Record Attendance:** 5,172 v Nuneaton Borough - Southern League Midland Division 23/02/1982
**Record Victory:** Not known - if you know please email tw.publications@btinternet.com
**Record Defeat:** Not known - if you know please email tw.publications@btinternet.com
**Record Goalscorer:** Peter Spacey - 1949-69
**Record Appearances:** Peter Spacey - 1949-69
**Additional Records:** Paid £1,750 to Hinckley Town for Colin Taylor 1991-92
Received £30,000 from Plymouth Argyle for Richard Landon
**Senior Honours:**
Birmingham Combination x2. Birmingham Senior Cup x3. Midland Floodlit Cup 1981-82, 92-93.
Southern Division 1 Central Play-offs 2011-12, 14-15.

**10 YEAR RECORD**

| 06-07 | 07-08 | 08-09 | 09-10 | 10-11 | 11-12 | 12-13 | 13-14 | 14-15 | 15-16 |
|---|---|---|---|---|---|---|---|---|---|
| SthM 16 | SthM 15 | SthM 14 | SthM 16 | SthC 15 | SthC 3 | SthP 21 | NP1S 20 | SthC 4 | SthP 21 |

# BELPER TOWN

**Chairman:** Alan Benfield
**Secretary:** Ian Wright (T) 07768 948 506 (E) info@belpertownfc.co.uk
**Commercial Manager:** (T)
**Programme Editor:** David Laughlin (T) 07768 010 604
**Ground Address:** The Marstons Stadium, Christchurch Meadow, Bridge Street, Belper DE56 1BA
(T) 01773 825 549 **Manager:** Charlie Palmer

**Founded:** 1883 **Nickname:** Nailers
**Previous Names:** None
**Previous Leagues:** Central Alliance 1957-61, Midland Counties 1961-82, Northern Counties East 1982-97

**Club Colours (change):** Yellow/black/black (All white)

**Ground Capacity:** 2,650 **Seats:** 500 **Covered:** 850 **Clubhouse:** Yes **Shop:** Yes
**Previous Grounds:** Acorn Ground > 1951

**Record Attendance:** 3,200 v Ilkeston Town - 1955
**Record Victory:** 15-2 v Nottingham Forest 'A' - 1956
**Record Defeat:** 0-12 v Goole Town - 1965
**Record Goalscorer:** Mick Lakin - 231
**Record Appearances:** Craig Smithurst - 678
**Additional Records:** Paid £2,000 to Ilkeston Town for Jamie Eaton 2001
Received £2,000 from Hinckley United for Craig Smith
**Senior Honours:**
Central Alliance League 1958-59, Derbyshire Senior Cup 1958-59, 60-61, 62-63, 79-80.
Midland Counties 1979-80. Northern Counties East 1984-85.

**10 YEAR RECORD**

| 06-07 | 07-08 | 08-09 | 09-10 | 10-11 | 11-12 | 12-13 | 13-14 | 14-15 | 15-16 |
|---|---|---|---|---|---|---|---|---|---|
| NP 1 19 | NP 1 8 | NP1S 2 | NP1S 6 | NP1S 14 | NP1S 6 | NP1S 3 | NP1S 4 | NP P 24 | NP1S 13 |

# CARLTON TOWN

**Chairman:** Michael Garton
**Secretary:** Paul Shelton **(T)** 07854 586 875 **(E)** info@carltontownfc.co.uk
**Commercial Manager:** Brian Dennett **(T)**
**Programme Editor:** Daniel Lord **(T)** 07858 970 023
**Ground Address:** Bill Stokeld Stadium, Stoek Lane, Gedling NG4 2QS (Sat Nav NG4 2QW)
**(T)** 0115 940 3192 **Manager:** Wayne Scott

**Founded:** 1904 **Nickname:** Town
**Previous Names:** Sneinton
**Previous Leagues:** Notts Alliance, Central Midlands, Northern Counties East

**Club Colours (change):** Yellow with royal blue trim/royal blue with white trim/royal blue (Red with white trim/red with white trim/red)

**Ground Capacity:** 1,500 **Seats:** 164 **Covered:** 100 **Clubhouse:** Yes **Shop:** No
**Previous Grounds:**

**Record Attendance:** 1,000 - Radio Trent Charity Match
**Record Victory:** Not known - if you know please email tw.publications@btinternet.com
**Record Defeat:** Not known - if you know please email tw.publications@btinternet.com
**Record Goalscorer:** Not known - if you know please email tw.publications@btinternet.com
**Record Appearances:** Not known - if you know please email tw.publications@btinternet.com
**Additional Records:**

**Senior Honours:**
Notts Alliance League Division 2 1984-85, Division 1 1992-93. Central Midlands Supreme Division 2002-03.
Northern Counties East Division 1 2005-06.
Notts Senior Cup 2012-13.

**10 YEAR RECORD**

| 06-07 | 07-08 | 08-09 | 09-10 | 10-11 | 11-12 | 12-13 | 13-14 | 14-15 | 15-16 |
|---|---|---|---|---|---|---|---|---|---|
| NCEP 3 | NP 1 10 | NP1S 4 | NP1S 9 | NP1S 8 | NP1S 2 | NP1S 12 | NP1S 10 | NP1S 18 | NP1S 18 |

# CHASETOWN

**Chairman:** John Donnelly
**Secretary:** John Richards **(T)** 07866 902 093 **(E)** chasetown@googlemail.com
**Commercial Manager:** **(T)**
**Programme Editor:** Lauren Lincoln **(T)** 07807 421 710
**Ground Address:** The Scholars, Church Street, Chasetown, Walsall WS7 3QL
**(T)** 01543 682 222 **Manager:** Dave Stringer

**Founded:** 1954 **Nickname:** The Scholars
**Previous Names:** Chase Terrace Old Scholars 1954-72
**Previous Leagues:** Cannock Youth 1954-58, Lichfield & District 1958-61, Staffordshire County 1961-72, West Midlands 1972-94, Midland Alliance 1994-2006, Southern 2006-09
**Club Colours (change):** Royal blue/royal blue/white (All bright red)

**Ground Capacity:** 2,000 **Seats:** 151 **Covered:** 220 **Clubhouse:** Yes **Shop:** Yes
**Previous Grounds:** Burntwood Recreation

**Record Attendance:** 2,420 v Cardiff City - FA Cup 3rd Round January 2008
**Record Victory:** 14-1 v Hanford - Walsall Senior Cup 1991-92
**Record Defeat:** 1-8 v Telford United Reserves - West Midlands League
**Record Goalscorer:** Tony Dixon - 197
**Record Appearances:** Not known - if you know please email tw.publications@btinternet.com
**Additional Records:**

**Senior Honours:**
West Midlands League 1978, League Cup x2.
Midland Alliance 2005-06.
Walsall Senior Cup x2.

**10 YEAR RECORD**

| 06-07 | 07-08 | 08-09 | 09-10 | 10-11 | 11-12 | 12-13 | 13-14 | 14-15 | 15-16 |
|---|---|---|---|---|---|---|---|---|---|
| SthM | SthM 7 | SthM 4 | NP1S 2 | NP P 10 | NP P 20 | NP1S 5 | NP1S 12 | NP1S 13 | NP1S 7 |

# GRESLEY

**Chairman:** Barry North
**Secretary:** Ian Collins **(T)** 07733 055 212 **(E)** office@gresleyfc.com
**Commercial Manager:** **(T)**
**Programme Editor:** Robin Mansfield **(T)** 07855 847 337
**Ground Address:** The Moat Ground, Moat Street, Church Gresley, Derbyshire DE11 9RE
**(T)** 01283 215 316 **Manager:** Damion Beckford-Quailey

**Founded:** 2009 **Nickname:**
**Previous Names:** Gresley Rovers
**Previous Leagues:** East Midlands 2009-11. Midland Football Alliance 2011-12.

**Club Colours (change):** All red (Blue/navy blue/navy blue)

**Ground Capacity:** **Seats:** Yes **Covered:** Yes **Clubhouse:** Yes **Shop:** Yes
**Previous Grounds:** None

**Record Attendance:** 861 v Whitehawk (FA Vase Quarter Final 27th Feb 2010)
**Record Victory:** 9-0 v Anstey Nomads 30th August 2010 (EMCL)
**Record Defeat:** 1-5 v Westfields (MFA)
**Record Goalscorer:** Royce Turville - 61
**Record Appearances:** Jamie Barrett - 142
**Additional Records:**
**Senior Honours:**
East Midlands Counties League 2010-11. Midland Alliance 2011-12.

**10 YEAR RECORD**

| 06-07 | 07-08 | 08-09 | 09-10 | 10-11 | 11-12 | 12-13 | 13-14 | 14-15 | 15-16 |
|---|---|---|---|---|---|---|---|---|---|
| | | | EMC 2 | EMC 1 | MidAl 1 | NP1S 11 | NP1S 9 | NP1S 5 | NP1S 16 |

# KIDSGROVE ATHLETIC

**Chairman:** Mick Fitzjohn
**Secretary:** Robin Grey (Press O) **(T)** 075221 48082 **(E)**
**Commercial Manager:** **(T)**
**Programme Editor:** Mark Lovatt-Harris **(T)** 07896 949 719
**Ground Address:** The Novus Stadium, Hollinwood Road, Kidsgrove, Staffs ST7 1DH
**(T)** 01782 782 412 **Manager:** Peter Ward & Ant Buckle

**Founded:** 1952 **Nickname:** The Grove
**Previous Names:** None
**Previous Leagues:** Buslem and Tunstall 1953-63, Staffordshire County 1963-66, Mid Cheshire 1966-90, North West Counties 1990-2002
**Club Colours (change):** All blue (All red)

**Ground Capacity:** 4,500 **Seats:** 1,000 **Covered:** 800 **Clubhouse:** Yes **Shop:** Yes
**Previous Grounds:** Vickers and Goodwin 1953-60

**Record Attendance:** 1,903 v Tiverton Town - FA Vase Semi-final 1998
**Record Victory:** 23-0 v Cross Heath W.M.C. - Staffordshire Cup 1965
**Record Defeat:** 0-15 v Stafford Rangers - Staffordshire Senior Cup 20/11/2001
**Record Goalscorer:** Scott Dundas - 53 (1997-98)
**Record Appearances:** Not known - if you know please email tw.publications@btinternet.com
**Additional Records:** Paid £10,000 to Stevenage Borough for Steve Walters
Received £3,000 for Ryan Baker 2003-04
**Senior Honours:**
Mid Cheshire League x4, League Cup x3.
North West Counties Division 1 1997-98, 2001-02, Challenge Cup 1997-98.
Staffordshire Senior Cup 2010-11.

**10 YEAR RECORD**

| 06-07 | 07-08 | 08-09 | 09-10 | 10-11 | 11-12 | 12-13 | 13-14 | 14-15 | 15-16 |
|---|---|---|---|---|---|---|---|---|---|
| NP 1 8 | NP 1 17 | NP1S 15 | NP1S 4 | NP1S 7 | NP1S 13 | NP1S 18 | NP1S 21 | NP1S 20 | NP1S 15 |

# LEEK TOWN

**Chairman:** Jon Eeles
**Secretary:** Brain Wain **(T)** 07967 204 470 **(E)**
**Commercial Manager:** **(T)**
**Programme Editor:** Tracy Reynolds **(T)** 07540 161 017
**Ground Address:** Harrison Park, Macclesfield Road, Leek, Cheshire ST13 8LD
**(T)** 01538 399 278 **Manager:** Anthony Danylyk

**Founded:** 1946 **Nickname:** The Blues
**Previous Names:** None
**Previous Leagues:** Staffordshire Co., Manchester 1951-54, 57-73, West Midlands (B'ham) 1954-56,Cheshire Co. 1973-82, North West Counties 1982-87, N.P.L. 1987-94, 95-97, Southern 1994-95, Conference 1997-99
**Club Colours (change):** All blue (Amber & black/black/amber)

**Ground Capacity:** 3,000 **Seats:** 650 **Covered:** 3,000 **Clubhouse:** Yes **Shop:** Yes
**Previous Grounds:** None

**Record Attendance:** 5,312 v Macclesfield Town - FA Cup 1973-74
**Record Victory:** Not known - if you know please email tw.publications@btinternet.com
**Record Defeat:** Not known - if you know please email tw.publications@btinternet.com
**Record Goalscorer:** Dave Sutton - 144
**Record Appearances:** Gary Pearce - 447
**Additional Records:** Paid £2,000 to Sutton Town for Simon Snow
Received £30,000 from Barnsley for Tony Bullock
**Senior Honours:**
Northern Premier League 1996-97. Staffordshire Senior Cup 1995-96.

**10 YEAR RECORD**

| 06-07 | 07-08 | 08-09 | 09-10 | 10-11 | 11-12 | 12-13 | 13-14 | 14-15 | 15-16 |
|---|---|---|---|---|---|---|---|---|---|
| NP P 17 | NP P 19 | NP1S 9 | NP1S 8 | NP1S 16 | NP1S 5 | NP1S 10 | NP1S 3 | NP1S 2 | NP1S 8 |

# LINCOLN UNITED

**Chairman:** Ian Beaumont
**Secretary:** Malcolm Cowling **(T)** 07985 599 529 **(E)** Malcolm.cowling@btinernet.com
**Commercial Manager:** Allen Crombie **(T)** 07967 755 520
**Programme Editor:** Allen Crombie **(T)** 07967 755 520
**Ground Address:** Sun Hat Stadium, Ashby Avenue, Hartsholme, Lincoln LN6 0DY
**(T)** 01522 690 674 or 07985 599 529 **Manager:** Sam Wilkinson

**Founded:** 1938 **Nickname:** United
**Previous Names:** Lincoln Amateurs > 1954
**Previous Leagues:** Lincolnshire 1945-46, 60-67, Lincoln 1946-60, Yorkshire 1967-82, Northern Counties East 1982-86, 92-95, Central Midlands 1982-92
**Club Colours (change):** All white with black trim (Claret & light blue/light blue/light blue)

**Ground Capacity:** 2,714 **Seats:** 400 **Covered:** 1,084 **Clubhouse:** Yes **Shop:** Yes
**Previous Grounds:** Skew Bridge 1940s, Co-op Sports Ground > 1960s, Hartsholme Cricket Club > 1982

**Record Attendance:** 2,000 v Crook Town - FA Amateur Cup 1st Round 1968
**Record Victory:** 12-0 v Pontefract Colliery - 1995
**Record Defeat:** 0-7 v Huddersfield Town - FA Cup 1st Round 16/11/1991
**Record Goalscorer:** Tony Simmons - 215
**Record Appearances:** Steve Carter - 447
**Additional Records:** Paid £1,000 to Hucknall Town for Paul Tomlinson December 2000
Received £3,000 from Charlton Athletic for Dean Dye July 1991
**Senior Honours:**
Northern Counties East Division 1 1985-86, 92-93, Premier Division 1994-95.

**10 YEAR RECORD**

| 06-07 | 07-08 | 08-09 | 09-10 | 10-11 | 11-12 | 12-13 | 13-14 | 14-15 | 15-16 |
|---|---|---|---|---|---|---|---|---|---|
| NP P 15 | NP P 20 | NP1S 10 | NP1S 19 | NP1S 12 | NP1S 18 | NP1S 20 | NP1S 17 | NP1S 9 | NP1S 5 |

# LOUGHBOROUGH DYNAMO

**Chairman:** Frank Fall
**Secretary:** Brian Pugh **(T)** 07716 846 626 **(E)** contact@loughboroughdynamofc.co.uk
**Commercial Manager:** **(T)**
**Programme Editor:** Brian Pugh **(T)** 07716 846 626
**Ground Address:** Nanpantan Sports Ground, Nanpantan Road, Loughborough LE11 3YE
**(T)** 01509 237 148 **Manager:** Wayne Hallcro

**Founded:** 1955 **Nickname:** Dynamo
**Previous Names:** None
**Previous Leagues:** Loughborough Alliance 1957-66, Leicestershire & District 1966-71, East Midlands 1971-72, Central Alliance 1972-89, Leicestershire Senior 1989-2004, Midland Alliance 2004-08
**Club Colours (change):** Gold/black/gold (Blue with red shoulder flash/blue/red)

**Ground Capacity:** 1,500 **Seats:** 250 **Covered:** Yes **Clubhouse:** Yes **Shop:** No
**Previous Grounds:** None

**Record Attendance:** Not known - if you know please email tw.publications@btinternet.com
**Record Victory:** Not known - if you know please email tw.publications@btinternet.com
**Record Defeat:** Not known - if you know please email tw.publications@btinternet.com
**Record Goalscorer:** Not known - if you know please email tw.publications@btinternet.com
**Record Appearances:** Not known - if you know please email tw.publications@btinternet.com
**Additional Records:**

**Senior Honours:**
Leicestershire Senior League Division 1 2001-02, Premier Division 2003-04.
Leicestershire Senior Cup 2002-03, 03-04.

**10 YEAR RECORD**

| 06-07 | 07-08 | 08-09 | 09-10 | 10-11 | 11-12 | 12-13 | 13-14 | 14-15 | 15-16 |
|---|---|---|---|---|---|---|---|---|---|
| MidAl 9 | MidAl 2 | NP1S 14 | NP1S 14 | NP1S 17 | NP1S 8 | NP1S 16 | NP1S 14 | NP1S 14 | NP1S 20 |

# MARKET DRAYTON TOWN

**Chairman:** Ben Cockram
**Secretary:** Rod Pope **(T)** 07572 283 090 **(E)** opoe2nt@btinternet.com
**Commercial Manager:** **(T)**
**Programme Editor:** Rod Pope **(T)** 07904 786 497
**Ground Address:** Greenfields Sports Ground, Greenfields Lane, Market Drayton TF9 3SL
**(T)** 01630 661 780 **Manager:** Martyn Davies

**Founded:** 1969 **Nickname:**
**Previous Names:** Little Drayton Rangers > 2003
**Previous Leagues:** West Midlands (Regional) 1969-2006, Midland Alliance 2006-09

**Club Colours (change):** All red (All blue)

**Ground Capacity:** **Seats:** **Covered:** **Clubhouse:** Yes **Shop:** Nk
**Previous Grounds:** Not known

**Record Attendance:** 440 vs. AFC Telford, Friendly 11/07/09. 229 vs. Witton Albion, Unibond South 25/08/09
**Record Victory:** (League) 9-0 Home vs. Racing Club Warwick 10/03/09
**Record Defeat:** Not known - if you know please email tw.publications@btinternet.com
**Record Goalscorer:** Not known - if you know please email tw.publications@btinternet.com
**Record Appearances:** Not known - if you know please email tw.publications@btinternet.com
**Additional Records:**

**Senior Honours:**
West Midlands (Regional) League 2005-06. Midland Alliance 2008-09.

**10 YEAR RECORD**

| 06-07 | 07-08 | 08-09 | 09-10 | 10-11 | 11-12 | 12-13 | 13-14 | 14-15 | 15-16 |
|---|---|---|---|---|---|---|---|---|---|
| MidAl 13 | MidAl 3 | MidAl 1 | NP1S 13 | NP1S 18 | NP1S 16 | NP1S 15 | NP1S 19 | NP1S 19 | NP1S 11 |

# NEWCASTLE TOWN

**Chairman:** Jeffrey Harrall
**Secretary:** Ray Tatton (T) 07792 292 849 (E) rftatton@tiscali.co.uk
**Commercial Manager:** (T)
**Programme Editor:** Ray Tatton (T) 07792 292 849
**Ground Address:** Lyme Valley Stadium, Buckmaster Avenue, Clayton, ST5 3BX
(T) 01782 662 350 **Manager:** Ivan Lodge

**Founded:** 1964 **Nickname:** Castle
**Previous Names:** Parkway Hanley, Clayton Park & Parkway Clayton. Merged as NTFC in 1986.
**Previous Leagues:** Newcatle & District, Staffs Co & Mid Cheshire, North West Counties

**Club Colours (change):** Blue/blue/white (White/black/red)

**Ground Capacity:** 4,000 **Seats:** 300 **Covered:** 1,000 **Clubhouse:** Yes **Shop:** Yes
**Previous Grounds:** None

**Record Attendance:** 3,948 v Notts County - FA Cup 1996
**Record Victory:** Not known - if you know please email tw.publications@btinternet.com
**Record Defeat:** Not known - if you know please email tw.publications@btinternet.com
**Record Goalscorer:** Andy Bott - 149
**Record Appearances:** Dean Gillick - 632
**Additional Records:**

**Senior Honours:**
Mid Cheshire League 1985-86. Walsall Senior Cup 1993-94, 94-95.

**10 YEAR RECORD**

| 06-07 | 07-08 | 08-09 | 09-10 | 10-11 | 11-12 | 12-13 | 13-14 | 14-15 | 15-16 |
|---|---|---|---|---|---|---|---|---|---|
| NWC1 12 | NWC1 3 | NWCP 3 | NWCP 1 | NP1S 2 | NP1S 15 | NP1S 17 | NP1S 8 | NP1S 3 | NP1S 14 |

# NORTHWICH VICTORIA

**Chairman:** Derek Nuttall
**Secretary:** Dave Thomas (T) 07798 564 596 (E) dave.thomas@northwichvics.co.uk
**Commercial Manager:** (T)
**Programme Editor:** Jamie Dewsbury (T) 07828 035 622
**Ground Address:** Wincham Park, Chapel Street, Northwich CW9 6DA
(T) 01606 45144 **Manager:** Adam Lakeland

**Founded:** 1874 **Nickname:** Vics, Greens or Trickies
**Previous Names:** None
**Previous Leagues:** The Combination 1890-92, 1894-98, Football League 1892-94, Cheshire 1898-1900, Manchester 1900-12 Lancashire 1912-19, Cheshire County 1919-68, Northern Premier 1968-79, Conference 1979-2010
**Club Colours (change):** Green and white hoops/white/white (Yellow/green/green)

**Ground Capacity:** 6,000 **Seats:** 4,264 **Covered:** 3,500 **Clubhouse:** Yes **Shop:** Yes
**Previous Grounds:** The Drill Field. Victoria Stadium. Stafford Rangers FC.

**Record Attendance:** 11,290 v Witton Albion - Cheshire League Good Friday 1949
**Record Victory:** 17-0 v Marple Association 1883
**Record Defeat:** 3-10 v Port Vale - 1931
**Record Goalscorer:** Peter Burns - 160 (1955-65)
**Record Appearances:** Ken Jones - 970 (1969-85)
**Additional Records:** Paid £12,000 to Hyde United for Malcolm O'Connor August 1988. Received £50,000 from Leyton Orient for Gary Fletcher June 1921 and from Chester City for Neil Morton October 1990.
**Senior Honours:**
FA Trophy 1983-84.
Conference North 2005-06.
Cheshire Senior Cup x16 Most recent 2013-14. Staffordshire Senior Cup x3.

**10 YEAR RECORD**

| 06-07 | 07-08 | 08-09 | 09-10 | 10-11 | 11-12 | 12-13 | 13-14 | 14-15 | 15-16 |
|---|---|---|---|---|---|---|---|---|---|
| Conf 13 | Conf 19 | Conf 22 | Conf N 12 | NP P 12 | NP P 2 | NP1S 8 | NP1N 9 | NP1N 4 | NP1N 3 |

# ROMULUS

**Chairman:** Richard Evans
**Secretary:** Peter Lowe **(T)** 07738 604 391 **(E)** peterwloweuk@yahoo.co.uk
**Commercial Manager:** **(T)**
**Programme Editor:** Paul Dockerill **(T)** 07711 856 551
**Ground Address:** Sutton Coldfield FC, Central Ground, Coles Lane B72 1NL
**(T)** 0121 354 2997 **Manager:** Richard Evans

**Founded:** 1979 **Nickname:** The Roms
**Previous Names:** None
**Previous Leagues:** Midland Combination 1999-2004, Midland Alliance 2004-07, Southern 2007-2010

**Club Colours (change):** Red and white stripes/red/red (Yellow & black stripes/yellow/black)

**Ground Capacity:** 4,500 **Seats:** 200 **Covered:** 500 **Clubhouse:** Yes **Shop:** Yes
**Previous Grounds:** Penns Lane.

**Record Attendance:** Not known - if you know please email tw.publications@btinternet.com known
**Record Victory:** Not known - if you know please email tw.publications@btinternet.com
**Record Defeat:** Not known - if you know please email tw.publications@btinternet.com
**Record Goalscorer:** Not known - if you know please email tw.publications@btinternet.com
**Record Appearances:** Not known - if you know please email tw.publications@btinternet.com
**Additional Records:** Players who have progress: Dean Sturridge, Stuart Bowen, Luke Rogers, Darius Vassell and Zat Knight.
**Senior Honours:**
Midland Combination Division One 1999-00, Premier Division 2003-04, Challenge Cup 03-04.

**10 YEAR RECORD**

| 06-07 | 07-08 | 08-09 | 09-10 | 10-11 | 11-12 | 12-13 | 13-14 | 14-15 | 15-16 |
|---|---|---|---|---|---|---|---|---|---|
| MidAl 2 | SthM 10 | SthM 11 | SthM 8 | NP1S 10 | NP1S 20 | NP1S 19 | NP1S 11 | NP1S 12 | NP1S 10 |

# RUGBY TOWN

**Chairman:** Brian Melvin
**Secretary:** Doug Wilkins **(T)** 07976 284 614 **(E)** rugbytown@melbros.com
**Commercial Manager:** **(T)**
**Programme Editor:** Neil Melvin & Chris Peters **(T)** 07795 242 656
**Ground Address:** Butlin Road, Rugby, Warwicks CV21 3SD
**(T)** 01788 844 806 **Manager:** James Jepson

**Founded:** 1956 **Nickname:** The Valley
**Previous Names:** Valley Sports 1956-71, Valley Sport Rugby 1971-73, VS Rugby 1973-2000, Rugby United 2000-05
**Previous Leagues:** Rugby & District 1956-62, Coventry & Partnership, North Warwickshire 1963-69, United Counties 1969-75
West Midlands 1975-83. Southern 1983-2015.
**Club Colours (change):** Sky blue/white/sky blue (Red/navy blue/navy blue)

**Ground Capacity:** 6,000 **Seats:** 750 **Covered:** 1,000 **Clubhouse:** Yes **Shop:** Yes
**Previous Grounds:** None

**Record Attendance:** 3,961 v Northampton Town - FA Cup 1984
**Record Victory:** 10-0 v Ilkeston Town - FA Trophy 04/09/1985
**Record Defeat:** 1-11 v Ilkeston Town (A) - 18/04/1998
**Record Goalscorer:** Danny Conway - 124
**Record Appearances:** Danny Conway - 374
**Additional Records:** Paid £3,500 for R Smith, I Crawley and G Bradder
Received £15,000 from Northampton Town for Terry Angus
**Senior Honours:**
FA Vase 1982-83. Southern League Midland Division 1986-87. Midland Combination Division 1 2001-02.
Birmingham Senior Cup 1988-89, 91-92

**10 YEAR RECORD**

| 06-07 | 07-08 | 08-09 | 09-10 | 10-11 | 11-12 | 12-13 | 13-14 | 14-15 | 15-16 |
|---|---|---|---|---|---|---|---|---|---|
| SthP 17 | SthP 15 | SthP 17 | SthP 22 | SthC 6 | SthC 6 | SthC 2 | SthC 2 | SthC 6 | NP1S 9 |

# SHAW LANE AFC

**Chairman:** Craig Wood
**Secretary:** David Exley (T) 07939 558 124 (E) dave.exley50@hotmail.co.uk
**Commercial Manager:** (T)
**Programme Editor:** Karen Parton (T) 07740 012 056
**Ground Address:** Shaw Lane Sports Club, Shaw Lane, Barnsley, S70 6HZ
(T) 01226 203 509 **Manager:** Craig Elliot

**Founded:** 1991 **Nickname:** The Ducks
**Previous Names:** Shaw Lane 1991-2004. Merged with Worsbrough Common to form Aquaforce Barnsley. 04-07. Merged with Barugh FC to form Shaw Lane Aquaforce.
**Previous Leagues:** Sheffield & Hallamshire County 2011-13. Northern Counties East 2013-15.

**Club Colours (change):** Blue & white stripes/black/black (Cherry/midnight blue/cherry)

**Ground Capacity:** 2,000 **Seats:** 200 **Covered:** Yes **Clubhouse:** Yes **Shop:**
**Previous Grounds:** None

**Record Attendance:** 904 v Athersley Rec NECL Prem League
**Record Victory:** v Grimsby Borough 13-0 1/4/2013 NECL Div 1
**Record Defeat:** v Athersley Rec 6-3 Sheffield Senior Cup 2014/15
**Record Goalscorer:** Not known - if you know please email tw.publications@btinternet.com
**Record Appearances:** Not known - if you know please email tw.publications@btinternet.com
**Additional Records:** FA Vase: Quarter-final, 2014-15. FA Trophy: Second Round Qualifying, 2015-16
FA Cup: Preliminary Round, 2015-16
**Senior Honours:**
Sheffield & Hallamshire County Senior League 2012-13.
Northern Counties East Premier Division 2014-15.

**10 YEAR RECORD**

| 06-07 | 07-08 | 08-09 | 09-10 | 10-11 | 11-12 | 12-13 | 13-14 | 14-15 | 15-16 |
|---|---|---|---|---|---|---|---|---|---|
| | SHS1 7 | SHS1 4 | SHS1 8 | SHS1 9 | SHS1 2 | SHSP 1 | NCE1 2 | NCEP 1 | NP1S 2 |

# SHEFFIELD

**Chairman:** Richard Tims
**Secretary:** Bill Towning (T) 07557 107 158 (E) bill@sheffieldfc.com
**Commercial Manager:** (T)
**Programme Editor:** Stuart James (T) 07709 225 110
**Ground Address:** Home of Football Stadium, Sheffield Road, Dronfield S18 2GD
(T) 0114 362 7016 **Manager:** James Colliver - Feb 2016

**Founded:** 1857 **Nickname:** Not known
**Previous Names:** None
**Previous Leagues:** Yorkshire 1949-82

**Club Colours (change):** Red/black/black (All blue)

**Ground Capacity:** 1,456 **Seats:** 250 **Covered:** 500 **Clubhouse:** Yes **Shop:** Yes
**Previous Grounds:** Abbeydale Park, Dore 1956-89, Sheffield Amateur Sports Stadium, Hillsborough Park 1989-91, Don Valley Stadium 1991-97

**Record Attendance:** 2,000 v Barton Rovers - FA Vase Semi-final 1976-77
**Record Victory:** Not known - if you know please email tw.publications@btinternet.com
**Record Defeat:** Not known - if you know please email tw.publications@btinternet.com
**Record Goalscorer:** Not known - if you know please email tw.publications@btinternet.com
**Record Appearances:** Not known - if you know please email tw.publications@btinternet.com
**Additional Records:** Paid £1,000 to Arnold Town for David Wilkins. Received £1,000 from Alfreton for Mick Godber 2002.
World's first ever Football Club.
**Senior Honours:**
FA Amateur Cup 1902-03. Northern Counties East Division 1 1988-89, 90-91, League Cup 2000-01, 04-05.
Sheffield and Hallamshire Senior Cup 1993-94, 2004-05, 05-06.

**10 YEAR RECORD**

| 06-07 | 07-08 | 08-09 | 09-10 | 10-11 | 11-12 | 12-13 | 13-14 | 14-15 | 15-16 |
|---|---|---|---|---|---|---|---|---|---|
| NCEP 2 | NP 1 4 | NP1S 11 | NP1S 5 | NP1S 11 | NP1S 4 | NP1S 9 | NP1S 16 | NP1S 15 | NP1S 17 |

# SPALDING UNITED

**Chairman:** Andrew Gay
**Secretary:** Louise Maplethorpe **(T)** 07590 928 907 **(E)** tulips@uk2.net
**Commercial Manager:** **(T)**
**Programme Editor:** Ray Tucker **(T)** 01775 725 253
**Ground Address:** Sir Halley Stewart Playing Fields, Winfrey Avenue, Spalding PE11 1DA
**(T)** 01775 712 047 **Manager:** David Frecklington

**Founded:** 1921 **Nickname:** Tulips
**Previous Names:** Not known
**Previous Leagues:** Peterborough, United Counties 1931-55,68-78,86-88,91-99,03-04, 11-14 Eastern Counties 1955-60, Central Alliance 1960-61, Midland Co. 1961-68, Northern Counties East 1982-86, Southern 1988-91, 99-03. NPL 2003-11.
**Club Colours (change):** All royal blue (Orange/black/black)

**Ground Capacity:** 2,700 **Seats:** 300 **Covered:** 500 **Clubhouse:** Yes **Shop:** Yes
**Previous Grounds:** Not known

**Record Attendance:** 6,972 v Peterborough - FA Cup 1982
**Record Victory:** Not known - if you know please email tw.publications@btinternet.com
**Record Defeat:** Not known - if you know please email tw.publications@btinternet.com
**Record Goalscorer:** Not known - if you know please email tw.publications@btinternet.com
**Record Appearances:** Not known - if you know please email tw.publications@btinternet.com
**Additional Records:**

**Senior Honours:**
United Counties League 1954-55, 75-75, 87-88, 98-99, 2003-04, 13-14. Northern Counties East 1983-84.
Lincolnshire Senior Cup 1952-53.

**10 YEAR RECORD**

| 06-07 | 07-08 | 08-09 | 09-10 | 10-11 | 11-12 | 12-13 | 13-14 | 14-15 | 15-16 |
|---|---|---|---|---|---|---|---|---|---|
| SthM 19 | NP 1 18 | NP1S 17 | NP1S 21 | NP1S 22 | UCL P 13 | UCL P 3 | UCL P 1 | NP1S 7 | NP1S 12 |

# STAMFORD

**Chairman:** Robert Feetham
**Secretary:** Phil Bee **(T)** 07772 646 776 **(E)** phil.bee1947@hotmail.co.uk
**Commercial Manager:** Paul Pepper **(T)**
**Programme Editor:** Richard Curtis **(T)** 07754 490 318
**Ground Address:** Zeeco Stadium, Ryhall Road, Stamford. PE9 1US
**(T)** 01780 751 471 **Manager:** Graham Drury

**Founded:** 1894 **Nickname:** The Daniels
**Previous Names:** Stamford Town and Rutland Ironworks amalgamated in 1894 to form Rutland Ironworks > 1896
**Previous Leagues:** Peterborough, Northants (UCL) 1908-55, Central Alliance 1955-61, Midland counties 1961-72, United Counties 1972-98, Southern 1998-2007
**Club Colours (change):** All red (Yellow/blue/yellow)

**Ground Capacity:** 2,000 **Seats:** 250 **Covered:** 1,250 **Clubhouse:** Yes **Shop:** Yes
**Previous Grounds:** None

**Record Attendance:** 4,200 v Kettering Town - FA Cup 3rd Qualifying Round 1953
**Record Victory:** 13-0 v Peterborough Reserves - Northants League 1929-30
**Record Defeat:** 0-17 v Rothwell - FA Cup 1927-28
**Record Goalscorer:** Bert Knighton - 248
**Record Appearances:** Dick Kwiatkowski - 462
**Additional Records:**

**Senior Honours:**
FA Vase 1979-80. United Counties League x7. Lincolnshire Senior Cup, Senior Shield. Lincolnshire Senior 'A' Cup x3.

**10 YEAR RECORD**

| 06-07 | 07-08 | 08-09 | 09-10 | 10-11 | 11-12 | 12-13 | 13-14 | 14-15 | 15-16 |
|---|---|---|---|---|---|---|---|---|---|
| SthP 8 | NP P 20 | NP1S 7 | NP1S 10 | NP1S 19 | NP1S 7 | NP1S 4 | NP P 18 | NP P 20 | NP P 21 |

# STOCKSBRIDGE PARK STEELS

**Chairman:** Allen Bethel
**Secretary:** Michael Grimmer **(T)** 07801 626 725 **(E)** mickgrimmer@gmail.com
**Commercial Manager:** Roger Gissing **(T)**
**Programme Editor:** Philip Burkenshaw **(T)** sheffprint@aol.com
**Ground Address:** Look Local Stadium, Bracken Moor Lane, Stocksbridge, Sheffield S36 2AN
**(T)** 0114 288 8305 (Match days) **Manager:** Chris Hilton

**Founded:** 1986 **Nickname:** Steels
**Previous Names:** Stocksbridge Works and Oxley Park merged in 1986
**Previous Leagues:** Northern Counties East 1986-96

**Club Colours (change):** Yellow/royal blue/yellow (All red)

**Ground Capacity:** 3,500 **Seats:** 400 **Covered:** 1,500 **Clubhouse:** Yes **Shop:** Yes
**Previous Grounds:** Stonemoor 1949-51, 52-53

**Record Attendance:** 2,050 v Sheffield Wednesday - opening of floodlights October 1991
**Record Victory:** 17-1 v Oldham Town - FA Cup 2002-03
**Record Defeat:** 0-6 v Shildon
**Record Goalscorer:** Trevor Jones - 145
**Record Appearances:** Not known - if you know please email tw.publications@btinternet.com
**Additional Records:** Paul Jackson scored 10 v Oldham Town in the 2002-03 FA Cup - a FA Cup record
Received £15,000 from Wolverhampton Wanderers for Lee Mills
**Senior Honours:**
Northern Counties East Division 1 1991-92, Premier Division 1993-94, League Cup 1994-95.
Sheffield Senior Cup 1951-52, 92-93, 95-96, 98-99

**10 YEAR RECORD**

| 06-07 | 07-08 | 08-09 | 09-10 | 10-11 | 11-12 | 12-13 | 13-14 | 14-15 | 15-16 |
|---|---|---|---|---|---|---|---|---|---|
| NP 1 6 | NP1S 5 | NP1S 3 | NP P 11 | NP P 13 | NP P 18 | NP P 20 | NP P 23 | NP1S 17 | NP1S 6 |

# WITTON ALBION

**Chairman:** Mark Harris
**Secretary:** Glynis McDonough **(T)** **(E)** secretary@wittonalbion.com
**Commercial Manager:** **(T)**
**Programme Editor:** Stephen Yoxall **(T)** programme@wittonalbion.com
**Ground Address:** Wincham Park, Chapel Street, Wincham, CW9 6DA
**(T)** 01606 430 08 **Manager:** Carl Macauley - 19/10/15

**Founded:** 1887 **Nickname:** The Albion
**Previous Names:** None
**Previous Leagues:** Lancashire Combination, Cheshire County > 1979, Northern Premier 1979-91, Conference 1991-94

**Club Colours (change):** Red & white stripes/navy/red (All orange)

**Ground Capacity:** 4,500 **Seats:** 650 **Covered:** 2,300 **Clubhouse:** Yes **Shop:** Yes
**Previous Grounds:** Central Ground (1910-1989)

**Record Attendance:** 3,940 v Kidderminster Harries - FA Trophy Semi-final 13/04/1991
**Record Victory:** 13-0 v Middlewich (H)
**Record Defeat:** 0-9 v Macclesfield Town (A) - 18/09/1965
**Record Goalscorer:** Frank Fidler - 175 (1947-50)
**Record Appearances:** Brian Pritchard - 729
**Additional Records:** Paid £12,500 to Hyde United for Jim McCluskie 1991
Received £11,500 from Chester City for Peter Henderson
**Senior Honours:**
Northern Premier League Premier Division 1990-91, Division 1 North Play-offs 2011-12. Cheshire Senior Cup x7.

**10 YEAR RECORD**

| 06-07 | 07-08 | 08-09 | 09-10 | 10-11 | 11-12 | 12-13 | 13-14 | 14-15 | 15-16 |
|---|---|---|---|---|---|---|---|---|---|
| NP P 2 | NP P 2 | NP P 20 | NP1S 7 | NP1N 10 | NP1N 3 | NP1N 4 | NP P 16 | NP P 22 | NP1N 11 |

# SOUTHERN LEAGUE PREMIER DIVISION LEAGUE TABLE 2015-16

| | | P | W | D | L | F | A | GD | Pts |
|---|---|---|---|---|---|---|---|---|---|
| 1 | Poole Town | 46 | 27 | 12 | 7 | 86 | 35 | 51 | 93 |
| 2 | Redditch United | 46 | 24 | 15 | 7 | 82 | 37 | 45 | 84 |
| 3 | Hitchin Town | 46 | 24 | 12 | 10 | 78 | 50 | 28 | 84 |
| 4 | Hungerford Town | 46 | 24 | 11 | 11 | 73 | 43 | 30 | 83 |
| 5 | Leamington | 46 | 23 | 12 | 11 | 59 | 38 | 21 | 81 |
| 6 | Kettering Town | 46 | 24 | 8 | 14 | 83 | 53 | 30 | 80 |
| 7 | Weymouth | 46 | 21 | 14 | 11 | 63 | 39 | 24 | 77 |
| 8 | Chippenham Town | 46 | 21 | 13 | 12 | 76 | 53 | 23 | 76 |
| 9 | King's Lynn Town | 46 | 21 | 7 | 18 | 58 | 54 | 4 | 70 |
| 10 | Merthyr Town | 46 | 19 | 9 | 18 | 69 | 58 | 11 | 66 |
| 11 | Chesham United | 46 | 18 | 10 | 18 | 72 | 70 | 2 | 64 |
| 12 | Dunstable Town | 46 | 17 | 11 | 18 | 68 | 68 | 0 | 62 |
| 13 | Dorchester Town | 46 | 18 | 8 | 20 | 67 | 69 | -2 | 62 |
| 14 | Biggleswade Town | 46 | 17 | 9 | 20 | 76 | 82 | -6 | 60 |
| 15 | Cirencester Town | 46 | 18 | 6 | 22 | 67 | 76 | -9 | 60 |
| 16 | Frome Town | 46 | 14 | 16 | 16 | 51 | 73 | -22 | 58 |
| 17 | Slough Town | 46 | 16 | 9 | 21 | 67 | 77 | -10 | 57 |
| 18 | Cambridge City | 46 | 15 | 7 | 24 | 63 | 80 | -17 | 52 |
| 19 | Stratford Town | 46 | 13 | 11 | 22 | 59 | 68 | -9 | 50 |
| 20 | St Neots Town | 46 | 10 | 18 | 18 | 69 | 78 | -9 | 48 |
| 21 | Bedworth United | 46 | 12 | 8 | 26 | 58 | 107 | -49 | 44 |
| 22 | Histon | 46 | 11 | 7 | 28 | 63 | 98 | -35 | 40 |
| 23 | Bideford | 46 | 8 | 13 | 25 | 38 | 88 | -50 | 37 |
| 24 | Paulton Rovers | 46 | 8 | 12 | 26 | 38 | 89 | -51 | 36 |

**Play-Off Semi Finals:** Hitchin Town 2-3 Hungerford Town I Redditch United 1-1, 1-3p Leamington (aet)

**Final:** Hungerford Town 2-1 Leamington

| | PREMIER DIVISION | 1 | 2 | 3 | 4 | 5 | 6 | 7 | 8 | 9 | 10 | 11 | 12 | 13 | 14 | 15 | 16 | 17 | 18 | 19 | 20 | 21 | 22 | 23 | 24 |
|---|---|---|---|---|---|---|---|---|---|---|---|---|---|---|---|---|---|---|---|---|---|---|---|---|---|
| 1 | Bedworth United | | 2-2 | 2-4 | 4-3 | 3-1 | 0-2 | 0-1 | 1-0 | 1-2 | 2-2 | 3-2 | 1-2 | 0-2 | 1-1 | 3-0 | 2-0 | 1-2 | 1-1 | 0-2 | 1-2 | 2-1 | 0-6 | 0-4 | 3-2 |
| 2 | Bideford | 2-1 | | 0-0 | 1-1 | 0-0 | 0-1 | 1-1 | 2-3 | 0-0 | 2-0 | 0-5 | 0-0 | 1-2 | 2-0 | 0-5 | 1-1 | 0-1 | 0-1 | 1-2 | 0-5 | 2-1 | 4-4 | 1-1 | 0-2 |
| 3 | Biggleswade Town | 4-1 | 0-2 | | 3-2 | 2-2 | 0-1 | 1-0 | 1-0 | 3-3 | 3-0 | 2-1 | 3-5 | 1-4 | 1-3 | 2-4 | 3-2 | 0-3 | 4-1 | 0-1 | 1-1 | 5-1 | 5-2 | 4-3 | 1-1 |
| 4 | Cambridge City | 4-2 | 2-0 | 2-2 | | 1-0 | 0-3 | 1-2 | 0-3 | 1-1 | 2-1 | 1-2 | 0-1 | 3-1 | 0-4 | 1-3 | 1-2 | 1-0 | 2-0 | 1-2 | 0-2 | 4-2 | 1-4 | 2-0 | 1-0 |
| 5 | Chesham United | 4-2 | 3-1 | 1-1 | 1-3 | | 1-0 | 1-3 | 3-4 | 5-1 | 5-1 | 2-0 | 1-1 | 2-2 | 0-3 | 2-0 | 3-0 | 0-1 | 2-1 | 3-1 | 3-0 | 1-1 | 3-1 | 2-0 | 1-0 |
| 6 | Chippenham Town | 5-0 | 2-0 | 3-2 | 1-3 | 2-2 | | 0-1 | 3-1 | 4-1 | 1-1 | 3-0 | 1-1 | 1-1 | 0-2 | 4-1 | 4-3 | 1-0 | 3-0 | 0-1 | 0-3 | 3-3 | 1-1 | 2-1 | 1-1 |
| 7 | Cirencester Town | 2-3 | 3-4 | 2-1 | 1-1 | 3-0 | 1-4 | | 4-3 | 1-5 | 1-1 | 1-2 | 0-0 | 2-3 | 1-0 | 0-1 | 1-2 | 1-0 | 3-0 | 3-0 | 0-2 | 1-3 | 2-5 | 3-0 | 0-3 |
| 8 | Dorchester Town | 3-2 | 1-2 | 0-1 | 3-0 | 2-1 | 1-1 | 1-1 | | 0-0 | 0-0 | 3-0 | 0-1 | 0-1 | 1-4 | 2-0 | 0-1 | 1-1 | 6-0 | 1-5 | 1-5 | 1-2 | 1-0 | 3-1 | 1-0 |
| 9 | Dunstable Town | 1-2 | 5-0 | 2-1 | 3-1 | 1-1 | 1-2 | 0-2 | 1-0 | | 3-2 | 4-2 | 0-0 | 1-0 | 4-0 | 0-2 | 0-2 | 2-1 | 1-2 | 1-1 | 1-2 | 1-3 | 3-0 | 3-1 | 2-1 |
| 10 | Frome Town | 2-1 | 3-0 | 2-1 | 0-4 | 1-1 | 1-0 | 3-2 | 0-3 | 4-3 | | 2-2 | 0-4 | 0-2 | 1-2 | 1-0 | 0-0 | 1-1 | 1-0 | 0-0 | 1-1 | 2-1 | 3-2 | 2-0 | 1-1 |
| 11 | Histon | 4-1 | 3-2 | 1-2 | 2-3 | 3-1 | 0-0 | 3-3 | 0-1 | 3-1 | 1-3 | | 5-1 | 0-3 | 3-1 | 1-2 | 0-3 | 0-2 | 1-1 | 0-7 | 0-0 | 1-2 | 0-0 | 0-2 | 1-4 |
| 12 | Hitchin Town | 3-1 | 0-0 | 3-0 | 4-2 | 5-1 | 1-1 | 2-0 | 3-2 | 4-1 | 1-2 | 3-2 | | 2-1 | 2-1 | 2-0 | 2-2 | 2-0 | 2-0 | 0-0 | 1-2 | 3-1 | 2-0 | 2-3 | 1-0 |
| 13 | Hungerford Town | 5-1 | 2-0 | 2-0 | 2-0 | 3-1 | 1-0 | 1-2 | 2-3 | 2-3 | 4-0 | 1-0 | 1-1 | | 2-1 | 2-1 | 1-2 | 1-0 | 3-1 | 0-0 | 0-0 | 1-0 | 3-3 | 0-0 | 0-1 |
| 14 | Kettering Town | 0-1 | 7-0 | 2-1 | 0-0 | 3-0 | 1-2 | 4-3 | 3-0 | 3-1 | 1-1 | 5-4 | 1-1 | 2-1 | | 2-1 | 1-1 | 3-2 | 2-0 | 1-0 | 0-0 | 1-0 | 1-1 | 3-1 | 0-1 |
| 15 | King's Lynn Town | 3-0 | 0-1 | 2-1 | 1-0 | 2-0 | 2-0 | 2-0 | 1-2 | 1-1 | 1-0 | 4-2 | 1-0 | 0-1 | 0-3 | | 0-1 | 2-3 | 0-0 | 3-2 | 1-0 | 2-1 | 1-1 | 2-1 | 0-0 |
| 16 | Leamington | 0-0 | 2-1 | 0-1 | 1-2 | 1-0 | 2-2 | 2-0 | 3-0 | 1-0 | 2-0 | 2-1 | 0-1 | 0-0 | 3-2 | 1-1 | | 1-0 | 2-0 | 1-0 | 0-1 | 3-0 | 2-2 | 1-0 | 0-0 |
| 17 | Merthyr Town | 2-2 | 3-0 | 1-2 | 2-1 | 1-2 | 2-0 | 0-1 | 2-4 | 1-3 | 1-1 | 3-0 | 5-1 | 4-1 | 1-1 | 2-0 | 0-2 | | 1-1 | 1-1 | 2-1 | 2-0 | 1-1 | 3-0 | 1-3 |
| 18 | Paulton Rovers | 0-0 | 0-0 | 3-2 | 2-1 | 2-0 | 0-1 | 1-4 | 1-1 | 1-2 | 2-1 | 0-2 | 2-1 | 0-0 | 0-1 | 1-3 | 1-1 | 1-2 | | 0-4 | 0-5 | 3-3 | 2-5 | 2-1 | 1-1 |
| 19 | Poole Town | 5-0 | 3-0 | 2-2 | 2-1 | 3-0 | 1-3 | 3-0 | 0-0 | 3-0 | 5-0 | 3-0 | 1-0 | 0-0 | 1-0 | 1-1 | 1-0 | 2-2 | 2-1 | | 2-1 | 3-3 | 3-0 | 1-2 | 2-0 |
| 20 | Redditch United | 8-1 | 4-1 | 2-2 | 0-0 | 1-0 | 6-2 | 0-1 | 2-0 | 0-0 | 1-1 | 1-0 | 3-2 | 2-2 | 2-1 | 2-0 | 0-0 | 3-1 | 1-1 | 0-0 | | 1-0 | 1-1 | 3-2 | 1-1 |
| 21 | Slough Town | 1-2 | 2-1 | 2-0 | 3-1 | 0-1 | 1-0 | 1-0 | 4-1 | 1-0 | 0-0 | 7-1 | 1-0 | 0-2 | 1-3 | 2-0 | 1-3 | 3-1 | 2-1 | 1-3 | 0-2 | | 2-2 | 2-4 | 0-0 |
| 22 | St Neots Town | 2-2 | 3-1 | 2-0 | 1-1 | 2-4 | 0-4 | 1-2 | 1-0 | 1-0 | 2-2 | 1-1 | 1-2 | 0-2 | 0-1 | 0-1 | 1-0 | 1-2 | 1-0 | 2-3 | 1-3 | 0-0 | | 2-2 | 1-1 |
| 23 | Stratford Town | 2-0 | 0-0 | 3-0 | 5-2 | 1-1 | 1-1 | 2-1 | 1-2 | 0-0 | 0-1 | 1-2 | 1-1 | 0-2 | 2-1 | 1-1 | 0-1 | 0-3 | 4-0 | 0-1 | 1-0 | 1-1 | 2-1 | | 1-1 |
| 24 | Weymouth | 1-0 | 1-0 | 0-1 | 1-0 | 1-4 | 1-1 | 3-1 | 2-2 | 0-0 | 2-0 | 1-0 | 0-2 | 2-1 | 3-2 | 2-0 | 1-0 | 3-0 | 4-1 | 0-1 | 2-0 | 6-1 | 1-1 | 2-1 | |

## SOUTHERN LEAGUE DIVISION ONE CENTRAL LEAGUE TABLE 2015-16

| | | P | W | D | L | F | A | GD | Pts |
|---|---|---|---|---|---|---|---|---|---|
| 1 | Kings Langley | 42 | 27 | 6 | 9 | 83 | 44 | 39 | 87 |
| 2 | Royston Town | 42 | 25 | 8 | 9 | 99 | 46 | 53 | 83 |
| 3 | Egham Town | 42 | 26 | 5 | 11 | 80 | 39 | 41 | 83 |
| 4 | St Ives Town | 42 | 22 | 12 | 8 | 72 | 38 | 34 | 78 |
| 5 | AFC Rushden & Diamonds | 42 | 23 | 8 | 11 | 81 | 44 | 37 | 77 |
| 6 | Chalfont St Peter | 42 | 23 | 2 | 17 | 76 | 71 | 5 | 71 |
| 7 | Northwood | 42 | 20 | 9 | 13 | 62 | 49 | 13 | 69 |
| 8 | Aylesbury | 42 | 20 | 8 | 14 | 72 | 52 | 20 | 68 |
| 9 | Beaconsfield SYCOB | 42 | 19 | 10 | 13 | 77 | 54 | 23 | 67 |
| 10 | Godalming Town | 42 | 19 | 10 | 13 | 51 | 45 | 6 | 67 |
| 11 | Ware | 42 | 19 | 6 | 17 | 67 | 69 | -2 | 63 |
| 12 | Potters Bar Town | 42 | 16 | 10 | 16 | 62 | 64 | -2 | 58 |
| 13 | Petersfield Town | 42 | 16 | 7 | 19 | 71 | 80 | -9 | 55 |
| 14 | Bedford Town | 42 | 12 | 13 | 17 | 57 | 60 | -3 | 49 |
| 15 | Uxbridge | 42 | 13 | 9 | 20 | 59 | 71 | -12 | 48 |
| 16 | Arlesey Town | 42 | 14 | 5 | 23 | 48 | 87 | -39 | 47 |
| 17 | Fleet Town | 42 | 12 | 9 | 21 | 55 | 78 | -23 | 45 |
| 18 | Barton Rovers | 42 | 9 | 15 | 18 | 51 | 75 | -24 | 42 |
| 19 | Aylesbury United | 42 | 11 | 7 | 24 | 45 | 81 | -36 | 40 |
| 20 | Hanwell Town | 42 | 10 | 9 | 23 | 38 | 64 | -26 | 39 |
| 21 | Leighton Town | 42 | 9 | 8 | 25 | 47 | 86 | -39 | 35 |
| 22 | North Greenford United | 42 | 6 | 6 | 30 | 51 | 107 | -56 | 24 |

**Play-Off Semi Finals:** Egham Town 2-2, 2-4p St Ives Town (aet) I Royston Town 1-2 AFC Rushen & Diamonds
**Final:** St Ives Town 2-1 AFC Rushen & Diamonds

| | DIVISION ONE CENTRAL | 1 | 2 | 3 | 4 | 5 | 6 | 7 | 8 | 9 | 10 | 11 | 12 | 13 | 14 | 15 | 16 | 17 | 18 | 19 | 20 | 21 | 22 |
|---|---|---|---|---|---|---|---|---|---|---|---|---|---|---|---|---|---|---|---|---|---|---|---|
| 1 | AFC Rushden & Diamonds | | 6-1 | 1-0 | 2-1 | 4-0 | 1-1 | 2-0 | 3-1 | 0-1 | 5-2 | 2-0 | 1-0 | 0-1 | 7-1 | 8-1 | 0-0 | 1-1 | 3-2 | 1-4 | 2-0 | 1-2 | 3-0 |
| 2 | Arlesey Town | 2-1 | | 0-2 | 0-0 | 1-0 | 2-5 | 1-1 | 3-2 | 0-7 | 4-1 | 1-1 | 1-3 | 0-3 | 0-2 | 5-0 | 0-1 | 1-0 | 0-2 | 1-3 | 0-1 | 1-1 | 1-3 |
| 3 | Aylesbury | 2-4 | 3-0 | | 2-2 | 3-1 | 3-1 | 2-1 | 2-0 | 1-0 | 3-3 | 2-0 | 2-2 | 0-3 | 0-0 | 3-1 | 0-0 | 4-0 | 4-4 | 2-3 | 0-2 | 2-1 | 6-0 |
| 4 | Aylesbury United | 0-4 | 1-0 | 0-1 | | 0-0 | 1-2 | 1-5 | 0-4 | 0-3 | 0-1 | 1-2 | 1-1 | 1-4 | 2-1 | 3-0 | 1-1 | 2-6 | 1-0 | 0-4 | 2-4 | 2-2 | 0-3 |
| 5 | Barton Rovers | 1-3 | 1-2 | 0-3 | 2-2 | | 1-1 | 1-1 | 0-1 | 0-1 | 1-8 | 0-0 | 0-1 | 0-2 | 2-0 | 3-1 | 0-3 | 2-2 | 2-2 | 2-2 | 1-1 | 2-2 | 4-1 |
| 6 | Beaconsfield SYCOB | 4-0 | 3-1 | 2-1 | 3-0 | 1-1 | | 2-2 | 2-0 | 1-2 | 3-0 | 0-2 | 3-1 | 2-0 | 0-2 | 5-0 | 4-1 | 5-0 | 3-0 | 0-2 | 1-1 | 2-1 | 1-1 |
| 7 | Bedford Town | 1-2 | 1-0 | 1-0 | 3-0 | 1-0 | 3-2 | | 4-0 | 4-3 | 2-2 | 0-3 | 1-1 | 1-3 | 2-1 | 1-1 | 1-2 | 2-2 | 1-1 | 0-0 | 0-0 | 0-1 | 3-2 |
| 8 | Chalfont St Peter | 2-0 | 3-0 | 4-3 | 3-2 | 3-0 | 5-1 | 1-1 | | 0-1 | 1-2 | 4-1 | 3-0 | 2-3 | 4-2 | 3-2 | 0-3 | 2-1 | 1-0 | 0-2 | 1-4 | 1-3 | 3-2 |
| 9 | Egham Town | 2-0 | 2-1 | 1-0 | 2-1 | 0-2 | 1-1 | 1-4 | 1-0 | | 2-2 | 0-1 | 3-0 | 1-0 | 1-2 | 3-1 | 1-1 | 4-1 | 4-0 | 3-1 | 0-1 | 2-2 | 3-2 |
| 10 | Fleet Town | 0-0 | 1-2 | 0-1 | 2-1 | 0-2 | 1-1 | 1-1 | 2-1 | 2-1 | | 2-1 | 0-1 | 0-0 | 4-2 | 2-1 | 1-3 | 3-2 | 0-1 | 1-2 | 0-2 | 2-0 | 1-1 |
| 11 | Godalming Town | 1-0 | 0-2 | 1-0 | 1-0 | 1-2 | 2-0 | 2-1 | 0-3 | 1-3 | 2-0 | | 1-0 | 0-1 | 2-2 | 3-1 | 2-1 | 4-1 | 0-1 | 1-0 | 1-1 | 2-2 | 0-1 |
| 12 | Hanwell Town | 1-2 | 0-3 | 1-2 | 0-1 | 1-3 | 1-4 | 2-1 | 0-1 | 0-4 | 0-0 | 1-2 | | 2-1 | 2-1 | 3-2 | 0-1 | 2-2 | 2-2 | 0-1 | 0-1 | 1-0 | 0-1 |
| 13 | Kings Langley | 1-1 | 1-2 | 2-0 | 1-0 | 6-1 | 1-3 | 3-1 | 3-1 | 2-1 | 2-0 | 1-1 | 3-3 | | 2-1 | 2-0 | 2-0 | 2-0 | 4-1 | 4-4 | 1-1 | 3-1 | 4-2 |
| 14 | Leighton Town | 0-1 | 1-3 | 1-2 | 1-2 | 4-3 | 1-0 | 1-1 | 0-1 | 0-1 | 1-0 | 0-0 | 1-1 | 0-2 | | 3-2 | 0-3 | 2-2 | 0-2 | 1-2 | 1-4 | 1-1 | 1-2 |
| 15 | North Greenford United | 1-3 | 3-1 | 2-3 | 2-4 | 0-0 | 0-0 | 3-1 | 6-2 | 1-2 | 2-4 | 2-1 | 0-3 | 1-3 | 2-1 | | 0-1 | 1-2 | 1-1 | 1-1 | 1-6 | 1-1 | 0-2 |
| 16 | Northwood | 2-2 | 5-0 | 1-1 | 1-3 | 2-2 | 2-1 | 1-2 | 0-1 | 0-2 | 2-1 | 2-2 | 2-0 | 2-0 | 2-4 | 1-0 | | 2-1 | 2-1 | 0-4 | 1-1 | 3-1 | 1-2 |
| 17 | Petersfield Town | 0-1 | 1-2 | 3-2 | 0-2 | 2-2 | 1-2 | 2-1 | 7-0 | 1-0 | 3-1 | 1-1 | 2-0 | 0-1 | 4-3 | 1-0 | 1-0 | | 4-1 | 0-4 | 2-0 | 2-1 | 2-3 |
| 18 | Potters Bar Town | 1-0 | 2-2 | 1-0 | 1-2 | 2-1 | 4-0 | 1-0 | 1-1 | 0-1 | 3-0 | 1-2 | 1-1 | 3-1 | 0-1 | 2-1 | 1-2 | 3-1 | | 3-1 | 0-1 | 3-1 | 3-3 |
| 19 | Royston Town | 1-0 | 4-1 | 0-2 | 4-1 | 1-1 | 2-2 | 3-1 | 1-2 | 1-1 | 4-0 | 0-1 | 2-0 | 2-1 | 6-0 | 7-1 | 1-2 | 2-3 | 4-1 | | 2-0 | 1-1 | 3-1 |
| 20 | St Ives Town | 2-2 | 6-0 | 0-0 | 0-1 | 2-3 | 3-1 | 1-0 | 2-4 | 0-1 | 2-0 | 1-1 | 1-0 | 2-0 | 5-0 | 2-1 | 1-0 | 3-0 | 1-1 | 0-3 | | 1-1 | 1-0 |
| 21 | Uxbridge | 0-1 | 4-0 | 2-3 | 1-0 | 0-1 | 0-2 | 2-0 | 0-2 | 0-7 | 4-2 | 0-1 | 1-0 | 0-2 | 3-0 | 2-1 | 0-3 | 3-4 | 4-1 | 3-1 | 2-4 | | 3-1 |
| 22 | Ware | 1-1 | 0-1 | 1-0 | 2-1 | 2-1 | 1-0 | 1-0 | 1-3 | 2-1 | 6-1 | 2-1 | 0-1 | 1-2 | 1-1 | 3-4 | 2-0 | 3-1 | 1-2 | 1-4 | 1-1 | 2-0 | |

# SOUTHERN LEAGUE DIVISION ONE SOUTH & WEST LEAGUE TABLE 2015-16

| | | P | W | D | L | F | A | GD | Pts |
|---|---|---|---|---|---|---|---|---|---|
| 1 | Cinderford Town | 42 | 29 | 9 | 4 | 80 | 29 | 51 | 96 |
| 2 | Banbury United | 42 | 28 | 10 | 4 | 97 | 38 | 59 | 94 |
| 3 | Taunton Town | 42 | 27 | 8 | 7 | 94 | 34 | 60 | 89 |
| 4 | Swindon Supermarine | 42 | 27 | 6 | 9 | 81 | 42 | 39 | 87 |
| 5 | Winchester City | 42 | 24 | 11 | 7 | 97 | 49 | 48 | 83 |
| 6 | Evesham United | 42 | 24 | 9 | 9 | 92 | 38 | 54 | 81 |
| 7 | Shortwood United | 42 | 24 | 6 | 12 | 88 | 59 | 29 | 78 |
| 8 | Tiverton Town | 42 | 20 | 13 | 9 | 76 | 44 | 32 | 73 |
| 9 | North Leigh | 42 | 21 | 5 | 16 | 79 | 53 | 26 | 68 |
| 10 | Didcot Town | 42 | 18 | 10 | 14 | 82 | 57 | 25 | 64 |
| 11 | Larkhall Athletic | 42 | 15 | 10 | 17 | 62 | 65 | -3 | 55 |
| 12 | Bishops Cleeve | 42 | 14 | 13 | 15 | 55 | 66 | -11 | 55 |
| 13 | Marlow | 42 | 15 | 7 | 20 | 68 | 79 | -11 | 52 |
| 14 | Mangotsfield United | 42 | 12 | 12 | 18 | 59 | 65 | -6 | 48 |
| 15 | AFC Totton | 42 | 14 | 6 | 22 | 73 | 81 | -8 | 48 |
| 16 | Yate Town | 42 | 12 | 11 | 19 | 48 | 62 | -14 | 47 |
| 17 | Wimborne Town | 42 | 12 | 8 | 22 | 65 | 80 | -15 | 44 |
| 18 | Slimbridge | 42 | 10 | 12 | 20 | 46 | 57 | -11 | 42 |
| 19 | Bridgwater Town | 42 | 9 | 7 | 26 | 42 | 83 | -41 | 34 |
| 20 | Wantage Town | 42 | 8 | 5 | 29 | 45 | 100 | -55 | 29 |
| 21 | Burnham | 42 | 6 | 6 | 30 | 39 | 99 | -60 | 24 |
| 22 | Bashley | 42 | 0 | 2 | 40 | 13 | 201 | -188 | 2 |

**Play-Off Semi Finals:** Banbury United 1-0 Winchester City I Taunton Town 2-1 Swindon Supermarine
**Final:** Banbury United 2-0 Taunton Town

| | DIVISION ONE SOUTH & WEST | 1 | 2 | 3 | 4 | 5 | 6 | 7 | 8 | 9 | 10 | 11 | 12 | 13 | 14 | 15 | 16 | 17 | 18 | 19 | 20 | 21 | 22 |
|---|---|---|---|---|---|---|---|---|---|---|---|---|---|---|---|---|---|---|---|---|---|---|---|
| 1 | AFC Totton | | 0-4 | 4-0 | 7-0 | 2-0 | 0-1 | 1-2 | 1-3 | 2-2 | 2-1 | 0-1 | 2-2 | 2-1 | 0-2 | 2-0 | 1-5 | 0-2 | 2-2 | 2-2 | 1-2 | 2-0 | 2-1 |
| 2 | Banbury United | 3-0 | | 8-0 | 1-1 | 2-1 | 1-0 | 0-1 | 2-1 | 0-0 | 5-0 | 3-1 | 2-1 | 3-1 | 2-1 | 3-1 | 0-3 | 2-0 | 0-0 | 8-1 | 2-0 | 2-1 | 2-0 |
| 3 | Bashley | 0-4 | 0-5 | | 1-2 | 0-4 | 0-2 | 1-10 | 0-3 | 1-4 | 1-5 | 0-0 | 2-5 | 0-8 | 0-1 | 0-0 | 0-4 | 0-5 | 0-2 | 1-3 | 1-4 | 0-3 | 1-2 |
| 4 | Bishops Cleeve | 0-0 | 0-2 | 6-0 | | 1-0 | 1-1 | 0-2 | 5-0 | 2-1 | 1-1 | 1-1 | 2-2 | 2-0 | 2-1 | 0-1 | 0-1 | 1-1 | 1-1 | 2-0 | 2-2 | 1-1 | 3-1 |
| 5 | Bridgwater Town | 0-5 | 1-4 | 5-1 | 0-1 | | 4-1 | 0-1 | 0-1 | 1-5 | 1-1 | 0-1 | 1-0 | 2-1 | 1-2 | 2-2 | 0-3 | 1-2 | 0-0 | 1-1 | 1-0 | 2-4 | 0-2 |
| 6 | Burnham | 1-5 | 0-5 | 5-1 | 1-2 | 0-1 | | 2-3 | 1-2 | 0-5 | 0-4 | 1-1 | 2-3 | 0-1 | 1-2 | 0-2 | 0-2 | 1-3 | 0-0 | 2-1 | 1-3 | 1-4 | 0-3 |
| 7 | Cinderford Town | 3-0 | 3-3 | 6-0 | 3-1 | 1-0 | 2-0 | | 1-1 | 3-1 | 1-0 | 1-0 | 4-3 | 2-1 | 1-1 | 1-0 | 4-1 | 2-0 | 3-2 | 4-1 | 0-0 | 2-2 | 1-0 |
| 8 | Didcot Town | 1-4 | 0-1 | 7-0 | 5-1 | 3-0 | 5-0 | 0-1 | | 1-1 | 5-1 | 1-0 | 5-3 | 2-3 | 2-2 | 3-1 | 0-1 | 0-2 | 1-2 | 2-0 | 0-2 | 1-2 | 1-1 |
| 9 | Evesham United | 6-0 | 2-2 | 7-0 | 2-0 | 5-0 | 4-0 | 3-0 | 0-1 | | 5-2 | 3-0 | 1-1 | 1-0 | 0-0 | 1-1 | 0-1 | 0-3 | 3-2 | 2-1 | 3-1 | 1-0 | 0-1 |
| 10 | Larkhall Athletic | 2-0 | 2-2 | 5-0 | 1-0 | 1-1 | 3-0 | 0-0 | 1-3 | 3-0 | | 2-0 | 1-2 | 0-2 | 0-3 | 2-0 | 1-1 | 1-2 | 1-0 | 4-0 | 0-2 | 1-4 | 1-0 |
| 11 | Mangotsfield United | 1-1 | 0-1 | 5-0 | 3-2 | 5-1 | 0-3 | 0-2 | 3-2 | 1-4 | 1-2 | | 0-0 | 0-2 | 0-0 | 1-1 | 1-0 | 1-3 | 3-4 | 1-1 | 3-1 | 2-2 | 1-1 |
| 12 | Marlow | 2-1 | 1-1 | 5-0 | 2-0 | 3-1 | 1-2 | 0-2 | 0-5 | 0-3 | 3-0 | 3-1 | | 3-2 | 2-3 | 2-1 | 0-1 | 0-1 | 3-1 | 0-1 | 3-3 | 0-3 | 2-0 |
| 13 | North Leigh | 5-0 | 1-1 | 4-1 | 1-3 | 3-1 | 1-0 | 0-0 | 3-1 | 1-2 | 3-0 | 0-4 | 5-4 | | 1-3 | 4-2 | 1-2 | 1-0 | 2-0 | 1-0 | 3-1 | 1-2 | 1-1 |
| 14 | Shortwood United | 5-3 | 0-0 | 6-0 | 2-0 | 3-2 | 5-3 | 2-0 | 1-3 | 3-2 | 3-1 | 4-1 | 1-2 | 0-2 | | 2-0 | 1-5 | 1-2 | 0-1 | 5-2 | 4-1 | 1-1 | 3-2 |
| 15 | Slimbridge | 3-0 | 1-3 | 6-0 | 0-2 | 3-0 | 2-0 | 0-2 | 0-0 | 0-0 | 1-1 | 1-1 | 2-0 | 1-1 | 1-3 | | 0-1 | 2-3 | 1-1 | 1-2 | 0-1 | 1-1 | 0-4 |
| 16 | Swindon Supermarine | 2-0 | 2-2 | 5-0 | 1-2 | 3-1 | 2-0 | 0-2 | 0-0 | 0-2 | 2-1 | 3-2 | 3-1 | 2-1 | 2-0 | 1-2 | | 1-1 | 2-2 | 3-1 | 2-0 | 2-1 | 2-0 |
| 17 | Taunton Town | 3-2 | 7-1 | 11-0 | 3-0 | 0-0 | 2-2 | 0-0 | 1-1 | 0-1 | 1-2 | 3-0 | 3-0 | 2-1 | 1-2 | 4-1 | 0-0 | | 1-0 | 5-0 | 2-1 | 2-1 | 3-1 |
| 18 | Tiverton Town | 2-1 | 0-1 | 9-0 | 1-1 | 1-1 | 2-2 | 2-1 | 5-1 | 2-3 | 0-0 | 1-3 | 2-0 | 2-1 | 4-1 | 1-0 | 2-1 | 1-0 | | 4-0 | 2-1 | 1-1 | 4-0 |
| 19 | Wantage Town | 0-4 | 0-2 | 9-0 | 7-1 | 0-1 | 3-2 | 0-2 | 0-0 | 0-5 | 2-3 | 0-3 | 1-0 | 0-2 | 3-1 | 0-1 | 1-4 | 1-2 | 0-4 | | 0-0 | 0-3 | 0-4 |
| 20 | Wimborne Town | 2-5 | 0-2 | 6-1 | 2-2 | 1-2 | 2-0 | 1-0 | 1-1 | 0-1 | 3-3 | 0-3 | 2-3 | 0-4 | 1-4 | 0-3 | 1-2 | 2-2 | 2-3 | 3-0 | | 5-6 | 2-0 |
| 21 | Winchester City | 3-1 | 4-0 | 4-0 | 4-1 | 7-2 | 6-1 | 0-0 | 1-5 | 2-1 | 1-1 | 2-1 | 6-1 | 0-0 | 2-1 | 2-1 | 3-1 | 0-3 | 0-0 | 3-0 | 2-1 | | 3-0 |
| 22 | Yate Town | 4-2 | 0-4 | 2-0 | 0-0 | 1-0 | 0-0 | 0-1 | 3-3 | 0-0 | 2-1 | 3-3 | 0-0 | 1-3 | 0-3 | 0-0 | 5-2 | 0-3 | 0-1 | 2-1 | 1-3 | 0-0 | |

# RED INSURE LEAGUE CUP 2015-16

**HOLDERS:** POOLE TOWN

**PRELIMINARY ROUND**

| | | | |
|---|---|---|---|
| Hitchin Town | v | Aylesbury | 1-0 |
| Frome Town | v | Larkhall Athletic | 1-1, 5-6p |
| Kings Langley | v | Chalfont St Peter | 0-0, 1-3p |

**ROUND ONE**

| | | | |
|---|---|---|---|
| Redditch United | v | Aylesbury United | 1-1, 3-4p |
| Shortwood United | v | Bridgwater Town | 0-1 |
| AFC Rushden & Diamonds | v | Histon | 1-4 |
| Barton Rovers | v | King's Lynn Town | 1-3 |
| Bedworth United | v | Evesham United | 2-1 |
| Biggleswade Town | v | Royston Town | 3-2 |
| Chippenham Town | v | Larkhall Athletic | 4-1 |
| Cirencester Town | v | Hungerford Town | 0-1 |
| Dorchester Town | v | Poole Town | 1-3 |
| Dunstable Town | v | Cambridge City | 1-3 |
| Godalming Town | v | Burnham | 6-0 |
| Leamington | v | Bishops Cleeve | 2-0 |
| Leighton Town | v | Arlesey Town | 0-2 |
| Marlow | v | Hanwell Town | 2-1 |
| North Greenford United | v | Beaconsfield SYCOB | 1-5 |
| Paulton Rovers | v | Banbury United | 2-1 |
| Potters Bar Town | v | Fleet Town | 3-0 |
| Slough Town | v | Chesham United | 3-0 |
| St Neots Town | v | St Ives Town | 2-1 |
| Tiverton Town | v | Taunton Town | 0-0, 0-3p |
| Uxbridge | v | Egham Town | 0-1 |
| Ware | v | Northwood | 2-2, 3-4p |
| Wimborne Town | v | Weymouth | 1-1, 1-4p |
| Cinderford Town | v | Merthyr Town | 3-3, 4-5p |
| North Leigh | v | Swindon Supermarine | 4-1 |
| Petersfield Town | v | Winchester City | 2-4 |
| Slimbridge | v | Yate Town | 3-3, 1-4p |
| AFC Totton | v | Bashley | 7-2 |
| Wantage Town | v | Didcot Town | 4-1 |
| Hitchin Town | v | Bedford Town | 3-2 |
| Stratford Town | v | Kettering Town | 3-3, 5-4p |

**ROUND TWO**

| | | | |
|---|---|---|---|
| Hitchin Town | v | Stratford Town | 2-2, 4-2p |
| Hungerford Town | v | North Leigh | 4-4, 4-1p |
| AFC Totton | v | Winchester City | 2-5 |
| Biggleswade Town | v | Arlesey Town | 1-1, 6-5p |
| Bridgwater Town | v | Chippenham Town | 1-4 |
| King's Lynn Town | v | Histon | 2-2, 4-5p |
| Leamington | v | Bedworth United | 3-0 |
| Marlow | v | Slough Town | 3-6 |
| Northwood | v | Chalfont St Peter | 5-1 |
| St Neots Town | v | Cambridge City | 2-2, 2-3p |
| Weymouth | v | Poole Town | 2-1 |
| Yate Town | v | Merthyr Town | 1-3 |
| Paulton Rovers | v | Taunton Town | 2-0 |
| Potters Bar Town | v | Beaconsfield SYCOB | 4-2 |
| Egham Town | v | Godalming Town | 1-2 |
| Aylesbury United | v | Wantage Town | 4-0 |

**ROUND THREE**

| | | | |
|---|---|---|---|
| Merthyr Town | v | Chippenham Town | 3-1 |
| Weymouth | v | Paulton Rovers | 0-1 |
| Cambridge City | v | Histon | 1-0 |
| Hitchin Town | v | Biggleswade Town | 2-0 |
| Hungerford Town | v | Winchester City | 0-2 |
| Potters Bar Town | v | Slough Town | 2-2, 3-1p |
| Aylesbury United | v | Leamington | 1-0 |
| Godalming Town | v | Northwood | 0-2 |

**QUARTER-FINALS**

| | | | |
|---|---|---|---|
| Merthyr Town | V | Paulton Rovers | 0-0, 5-3p |
| Cambridge City | v | Hitchin Town | 1-0 |
| Aylesbury United | v | Potters Bar Town | 0-3 |
| Winchester City | v | Northwood | 0-1 |

**SEMI-FINALS**

| | | | |
|---|---|---|---|
| Potters Bar Town | v | Cambridge City | 0-1 |
| Northwood | v | Merthyr Town | 0-0, 2-4p |

**FINAL**

| | | | |
|---|---|---|---|
| Merthyr Town | v | Cambridge City | 5-1 |
| Cambridge City | v | Merthyr Town | 0-2 |

## Southern League Premier Division South Statistics 2015-16

| | NoS | GS | CTS | PS | CSG | MCGU | TCS | MCCS | CMWW | CD | FTS | CNG | TGC |
|---|---|---|---|---|---|---|---|---|---|---|---|---|---|
| Bedworth United | 17+2 | 62 | 4 | 3 | 5 | 4 | 7 | 2 | 14 | 4 | 15 | 6 | 113 |
| Bideford | 19 | 47 | 4 | 3 | 11 | 7 | 11 | 1 | 15 | 5 | 25 | 6 | 105 |
| Biggleswade Town | 18+1 | 80 | 5 | 6 | 12 | 6 | 8 | 2 | 8 | 5 | 11 | | 87 |
| Cambridge City | 16+1 | 64 | 4 | 5 | 7 | 4 | 9 | 3 | 5 | 5 | 12 | 3 | 83 |
| Chesham United | 15+1 | 89 | 5 | 7 | 13 | 8 | 14 | 3 | 6 | 3 | 15 | 2 | 81 |
| Chippenham Town | 18+4 | 84 | 5 | 6 | 13 | 7 | 15 | 3 | 7 | 4 | 13 | 2 | 59 |
| Cirencester Town | 18 | 80 | 4 | 6 | 8* | 4 | 12 | 2 | 4 | 3 | 11 | | 86 |
| Dorchester Town | 18+1 | 74 | 6 | 3 | 6 | 4 | 12 | 2 | 4 | 4 | 14 | 3 | 78 |
| Dunstable Town | 17+2 | 73 | 5 | 6 | 9 | 7 | 12 | 3 | 8* | 3 | 14 | 2 | 74 |
| Frome Town | 21+1 | 57 | 4 | 4 | 14 | 8 | 11 | 1 | 11 | 4 | 17 | 4 | 79 |
| Histon | 17+1 | 65 | 5 | 5 | 8 | 4 | 6 | 2 | 10 | 7 | 18 | 2 | 107 |
| Hitchin Town | 15+2 | 93 | 4 | 3 | 12 | 7 | 20 | 4 | 5 | 3 | 10 | 2 | 62 |
| Hungerford Town | 18+2 | 87 | 5 | 4 | 10 | 12 | 25 | 6 | 7 | 2 | 11 | 2 | 54 |
| Kettering Town | 23+2 | 94 | 7 | 7 | 20 | 11 | 16 | 3 | 3 | 2 | 10 | 2 | 61 |
| Kings Lynn Town | 17 | 70 | 5 | 4 | 12 | 5 | 15 | 2 | 3 | 2 | 16 | 3 | 63 |
| Leamington | 16+1 | 77 | 6 | 4 | 9 | 8 | 22 | 5 | 8 | 2 | 14 | 2 | 50 |
| Merthyr Town | 18+1 | 76 | 5 | 3 | 12 | 5 | 10 | 1 | 7 | 5 | 9 | 2 | 64 |
| Paulton Rovers | 18 | 42 | 3 | 1 | 7 | 5 | 6 | 3 | 11 | 5 | 20 | 3 | 95 |
| Poole Town | 18+2 | 92 | 7 | 8 | 8 | 10 | 27 | 7 | 4 | 3 | 11 | | 39 |
| Redditch United | 20+1 | 83 | 8 | 12 | 7 | 7 | 18 | 3 | 5 | 2 | 13 | 2 | 40 |
| Slough Town | 16 | 75 | 7 | 5 | 13 | 4 | 11 | 2 | 7 | 4 | 11 | 3 | 83 |
| St Neots Town | 23+2 | 80 | 6 | 6 | 15 | 8 | 9 | 2 | 11 | 5 | 9 | | 85 |
| Stratford Town | 13 | 64 | 4 | 3 | 6 | 4 | 10 | 2 | 12 | 4 | 16 | 5 | 73 |
| Weymouth | 13+1 | 70 | 6 | 4 | 7 | 6 | 17 | 3 | 4 | 3 | 13 | 2 | 45 |

+ Denotes number of Own goals I * Denotes unfinished run

NoS - Number of Scorers I GS - Goals Scored I CTS - Club's Top Score I PS - Penalties Scored

CSG - Consecutive Scoring Games I MCGU - Most Consecutive Games Unbeaten I TCS - Total Clean Sheets

MCCS - Most Consecutive Clean Sheets I CMWW - Consecutive Matches Without a Win

CD - Consecutive Defeats I FTS - Failure to Score I CNG - Consecutive No Goals

I TGC - Total Goals Conceded

## Southern League Premier Leading goalscorers 2015-16

| Player | Club | Lge | FAC | FAT | Pens | HT | CSG | SG | Total |
|---|---|---|---|---|---|---|---|---|---|
| Charlie Griffin | Cirencester Town | 20 | 2 | 3 | 1 | 1 | 3 | 18 | 25 |
| Tom Meechan | St Neots Town | 22 | 2 | | 3 | 1 | 4 | 16 | 24 |
| Andy Sandell | Chippenham Town | 22 | 1 | | 5 | | 4 | 15 | 23 |
| Ben Mackey | Leamington | 16 | | 6 | | | 3 | 18 | 22 |
| Nat Jarvis | Hungerford Town | 17 | | 1 | 1 | 1 | | 13 | 18 |
| Marvin Brooks | Poole Town | 16 | 1 | | | | 3 | 13 | 17 |
| Jonny McNamara | Hitchin Town | 16 | 1 | | | | 2 | 15 | 17 |
| Dave Pearce | Chesham United | 14 | 2 | 1 | 6 | | 2 | 13 | 17 |
| Ryan Blake | Chesham United | 10 | 4 | 2 | | | 2 | 12 | 16 |
| Inih Effiong | Biggleswade Town | 15 | | | | 1 | 3 | 10 | 15 |
| Sam Merson | Biggleswade Town | 14 | 1 | | | | 3 | 13 | 15 |
| Charlie Mpi | Slough Town | 12 | | 1 | | | 4 | 13 | 14 |
| Jordan Nicholson | Histon | 14 | | | | 1 | 2 | 10 | 14 |
| Ian Traylor | Merthyr Town | 13 | | 1 | 3 | | 3 | 13 | 14 |
| Stefan Brown | Hungerford Town | 11 | | 2 | 1 | | 3 | 12 | 13 |
| Rob Burns | Hitchin Town | 9 | 4 | | | | 4 | 11 | 13 |
| Tony Burnett | Biggleswade Town | 12 | | | 2 | 1 | 2 | 9 | 12 |
| Luke Roberts | Poole Town | 12 | | | | | 2 | 11 | 12 |
| Ashley Sammons | Redditch United | 12 | | | 2 | | 2 | 10 | 12 |

HT - Hat-tricks I CSG - Consecutive Scoring Games I SG - Scoring Games I PO - Play-offs

# BANBURY UNITED

**Chairman:** Ronnie Jackson
**Secretary:** Barry Worlsey **(T)** 07941 267 567 **(E)** bworsley@btinternet.com
**Commercial Manager:** **(T/E)**
**Programme Editor:** David Shadbolt **(T/E)** 07944 671 214
**Ground Address:** The Banbury Plant Hire Community Stadium, off Station Road, Banbury OX16 5AD
**(T)** 01295 263 354 **Manager:** Mike Ford

## Club Factfile

**Founded:** 1931 **Nickname:** Puritans
**Previous Names:** Spencer Villa 1931-34. Banbury Spencer. Club reformed in 1965 as Banbury United
**Previous Leagues:** Banbury Junior 1933-34, Oxon Senior 1934-35, Birmingham Combination 1935-54, West Midlands 1954-66, Southern 1966-90, Hellenic 1991-2000

**Club Colours (change):** Red/gold/red (Gold/red/gold)

**Ground Capacity:** 6,500 **Seats:** 250 **Covered:** 250 **Clubhouse:** Yes **Shop:** Yes

**Directions**
From M40, Junction 11, head towards Banbury, over first roundabout, left at next roundabout into Concorde Avenue. Straight on at next roundabout, taking left hand lane, and turn left at traffic lights, turn first right into Station Approach. At station forecourt and car park, take narrow single track road on extreme right and follow to Stadium.(Direct SatNav to OX16 5AB).

**Previous Grounds:** Middleton Road 1931-34.

**Record Attendance:** 7,160 v Oxford City - FA Cup 3rd Qualifying Round 30/10/1948
**Record Victory:** 12-0 v RNAS Culham - Oxon Senior Cup 1945-46
**Record Defeat:** 2-11 v West Bromwich Albion 'A' - Birmingham Combination 1938-39
**Record Goalscorer:** Dick Pike and Tony Jacques - 222 (1935-48 and 1965-76 respectively)
**Record Appearances:** Jody McKay - 576
**Additional Records:** Paid £2,000 to Oxford United for Phil Emsden
Received £20,000 from Derby County for Kevin Wilson 1979

**Honours:**
Hellenic Premier 1999-2000. Oxford Senior Cup 1978-79, 87-88, 2003-04, 14-15.
Southern League Division One South & West Play-offs 2015-16.

### 10 YEAR RECORD

| 06-07 | 07-08 | 08-09 | 09-10 | 10-11 | 11-12 | 12-13 | 13-14 | 14-15 | 15-16 |
|---|---|---|---|---|---|---|---|---|---|
| SthP 13 | SthP 9 | SthP 19 | SthP 12 | SthP 16 | SthP 16 | SthP 16 | SthP 19 | SthP 21 | Sthsw 2 |

# HAT TRICKS BRING VICTORIES AND HEADLINES

Scoring a hat trick in competitive football at any level will always be remembered by the marksman. Usually the goals will have helped his club to a victory and of course the goalscorer usually personally hits the headlines. In fact in the 62 goalscorers with Hat Tricks listed for the three National Divisions, only Matt Rhead of Lincoln City finished on the losing side, as Whitehawk achieved a fine 5-3 away FA Cup replay victory.

The three National divisions produced some consistent marksmen, but it was National South that provided nearly twice as many Hat Tricks as their senior National Division.

Three Southern clubs benefitted from a marksman who registered three hat tricks each. Gosport Borough's Justin Bennett had claimed his three match winning efforts before the end of September and his club achieved an impressive goal tally of 14-1 for the three victories.

Bishop Stortford's Elliott Buchanan consistently served his club well throughout the campaign, with a hat trick in the first league game, another before the end of August and his third in the last two weeks of the season.

Ebbsfleet United have kept a constant challenge at the top of the division, thanks to Matt Godden's 30 goals including his three excellent hat tricks.

The National North division was dominated by AFC Fylde as far as hat tricks were concerned. They produced four, of which Danny Rowe included three within his impressive season's total of 34 goals.

Coleshill Town certainly caught Fylde on top form and they conceded two hat tricks in their 0-9 FA Cup defeat. Danny Rowe certainly knew how to make a club suffer, as he scored hat tricks in both FA Trophy ties against Skelmersdale United.

In the senior division, Grimsby Town's Padraig Amond's wonderful season's tally of 37 goals was boosted by three hat tricks spaced throughout the campaign, along with his steady scoring which helped his club to two Wembley appearances.

A sad end to the season for Gosport Borough after claiming three hat tricks in a great start earlier in the campaign, they finished the season conceding a hat trick to Hayes & Yeading in their last game of the season.

On checking the hat tricks in the Step Three Leagues, it looks as if, either the **Southern League** defences are good and perhaps hat tricks by their senior marksmen are similar to those in The National Premier Division, where goals have to be fought for against tough defences.

| 2015-2016 Hat Tricks | Scored |
|---|---|
| Isthmian Premier Division | 37 |
| N.P.L. Premier Division | 36 |
| National South | 29 |
| National North | 18 |
| National Prem | 15 |
| Southern Premier Division | 14 |

The Isthmian and North Premier League supporters have had plenty of goals to celebrate and the entertainment value has been appreciated. Heroes in those leagues are the Bognor Regis Town top striker Jason Prior, with four hat tricks within a wonderful season's total of 42.

In the North East, Workington thrilled their supporters with a competitive season and 83 goals. Ace goalscorer Scott Allison produced two hat tricks in their last three games (within his total of 24 goals including 4 hat tricks) and four consecutive victories confirmed a place in the play-off Final.

# BASINGSTOKE TOWN

**Chairman:** Rafi Razzak
**Secretary:** Richard Trodd **(T)** 07887 507 447 **(E)** richard.trodd@ntlworld.com
**Commercial Manager:** **(T/E)**
**Programme Editor:** Peter Grinham **(T/E)**
**Ground Address:** Camrose Ground, Western Way, Basingstoke RG22 6EZ
**(T)** 01256 327 575 **Manager:** Terry Brown

## Club Factfile

**Founded:** 1896 **Nickname:** Dragons
**Previous Names:** None
**Previous Leagues:** Hampshire 1900-40, 45-71, Southern 1971-87, Isthmian 1987-2004. Conference 2004-16.

**Club Colours (change):** All blue (All white)

**Ground Capacity:** 6,000 **Seats:** 651 **Covered:** 2,000 **Clubhouse:** Yes **Shop:** Yes

**Directions**
Leave M3 at junction 6 and turn left onto South Ringway which is the A30.
Straight over first roundabout. At second roundabout turn left into Winchester Road.
Proceed past ground on right to roundabout.
Take fifth exit into Western Way. Ground on right.

**Previous Grounds:** Castle Field 1896-1947

**Record Attendance:** 5,085 v Wycombe Wanderers - FA Cup 1st Round replay 1997-98
**Record Victory:** 10-1 v Chichester City (H) - FA Cup 1st Qualifying Round 1976
**Record Defeat:** 0-8 v Aylesbury United - Southern League April 1979
**Record Goalscorer:** Paul Coombs - 159 (1991-99)
**Record Appearances:** Billy Coomb
**Additional Records:** Paid £4,750 to Gosport Borough for Steve Ingham

**Honours:**
Hampshire League 1967-68, 69-70, 70-71. Southern League Southern Division 1984-85.
Hampshire Senior Cup 1970-71, 89-90, 95-96, 2007-08.

### 10 YEAR RECORD

| 06-07 | 07-08 | 08-09 | 09-10 | 10-11 | 11-12 | 12-13 | 13-14 | 14-15 | 15-16 |
|---|---|---|---|---|---|---|---|---|---|
| Conf S 19 | Conf S 15 | Conf S 18 | Conf S 15 | Conf S 13 | Conf S 5 | Conf S 14 | Conf S 14 | Conf S 3 | Nat S 22 |

# BASINGSTOKE TOWN MATCH RESULTS 2015-16

| Date | Comp | H/A | Opponents | Att: | Result | | Goalscorers | Pos | No. |
|---|---|---|---|---|---|---|---|---|---|
| Aug 8 | Nat South | A | Ebbsfleet United | 888 | L | 0-1 | | 18 | 1 |
| 12 | Nat South | H | Bath City | 547 | L | 1-2 | Smart 29 | 19 | 2 |
| 15 | Nat South | H | Bishops Stortford | 462 | D | 1-1 | Flood 87 | 19 | 3 |
| 18 | Nat South | A | Oxford City | 255 | D | 2-2 | Macklin 20 Soares 66 | 19 | 4 |
| 22 | Nat South | H | Margate | 471 | D | 0-0 | | 19 | 5 |
| 29 | Nat South | A | Hayes & Yeading | 182 | L | 0-3 | | 19 | 6 |
| 31 | Nat South | H | Gosport Borough | 534 | L | 0-1 | | 20 | 7 |
| Sept 5 | Nat South | A | Hemel Hempstead Town | 414 | D | 2-2 | Flood 37 Enver-Marum 87 (pen) | 20 | 8 |
| 12 | Nat South | H | Eastbourne Borough | 432 | L | 1-5 | Flood 71 | 21 | 9 |
| 14 | Nat South | A | St Albans City | 315 | L | 0-3 | | 21 | 10 |
| 19 | Nat South | H | Wealdstone | 536 | D | 1-1 | Gilkes 30 | 21 | 11 |
| **26** | **FAC2Q** | **H** | **Slough Town** | **369** | **W** | **4-2** | **FLOOD 3 (6 50 53) Macklin 90** | | 12 |
| Oct 3 | Nat South | A | Bath City | 779 | D | 0-0 | | 22 | 13 |
| **10** | **FAC3Q** | **H** | **Chelmsford City** | **498** | **W** | **4-2** | **Williams 11 Flood 23 Enver-Marum 60 81** | | 14 |
| 17 | Nat South | H | Chelmsford City | 453 | L | 1-2 | Enver-Marum 57 | 22 | 15 |
| **24** | **FAC4Q** | **H** | **Torquay United** | **792** | **W** | **3-0** | **Salmon 3 Flood 34 60** | | 16 |
| 27 | Nat South | H | Whitehawk | 518 | W | 3-1 | Flood 12 Dunn 89 Macklin 90 | 21 | 17 |
| 31 | Nat South | A | Maidenhead United | 456 | L | 3-4 | McAuley 15 Soares 41 Ray 76 | 22 | 18 |
| **Nov 7** | **FAC1** | **A** | **Cambridge United** | **2974** | **L** | **0-1** | | | 19 |
| 14 | Nat South | A | Concord Rangers | 286 | L | 0-5 | | 22 | 20 |
| 17 | Nat South | A | Truro City | 285 | L | 0-2 | | 22 | 21 |
| 21 | Nat South | H | Maidstone United | 611 | L | 0-1 | | 22 | 22 |
| **28** | **FAT3Q** | **A** | **Havant & Waterlooville** | **277** | **L** | **1-2** | **Enver-Marum 27 (pen)** | | 23 |
| Dec 5 | Nat South | A | Bishops Stortford | 301 | W | 2-1 | Gasson 39 Hyam 90 | 22 | 24 |
| 12 | Nat South | H | Dartford | 531 | L | 0-1 | | 22 | 25 |
| 19 | Nat South | H | St Albans City | 455 | D | 2-2 | Vine 8 Flood 82 | 22 | 26 |
| 26 | Nat South | A | Sutton United | 932 | L | 0-2 | | 22 | 27 |
| 28 | Nat South | H | Hayes & Yeading | 530 | W | 1-0 | Williams 48 | 22 | 28 |
| Jan 9 | Nat South | A | Eastbourne United | 478 | W | 2-1 | Williams 89 90 | 22 | 29 |
| 16 | Nat South | H | Hemel Hempstead Town | 547 | W | 2-0 | Flood 49 Soares 77 | 20 | 30 |
| 23 | Nat South | A | Havant & Waterlooville | 617 | L | 0-1 | | 20 | 31 |
| 30 | Nat South | H | Ebbsfleet United | 608 | L | 1-2 | Deaman 41 | 21 | 32 |
| Feb 13 | Nat South | A | Margate | 632 | L | 1-2 | McLean 18 | 22 | 33 |
| 16 | Nat South | H | Sutton United | 470 | L | 1-2 | Macklin 90 | 22 | 34 |
| 20 | Nat South | H | Maidenhead United | 482 | W | 2-1 | Enver-Marum 35 90 | 21 | 35 |
| 27 | Nat South | A | Wealdstone | 641 | D | 4-4 | Enver-Marum 9 Williams 22 Deaman 45 Southam 65 | 21 | 36 |
| Mar 5 | Nat South | A | Maidstone United | 2076 | L | 1-3 | Gasson 25 | 22 | 37 |
| 12 | Nat South | H | Havant & Waterlooville | 523 | D | 1-1 | Connolly 70 | 22 | 38 |
| 19 | Nat South | A | Whitehawk | 301 | L | 0-1 | | 22 | 39 |
| 26 | Nat South | H | Oxford City | 515 | W | 2-0 | Enver-Marum 55 76 | 22 | 40 |
| Apr 2 | Nat South | H | Concord Rangers | 444 | L | 0-2 | | 22 | 41 |
| 5 | Nat South | A | Weston-s-Mare | 396 | L | 1-2 | Soares 87 | 22 | 42 |
| 9 | Nat South | H | Weston-s-Mare | 400 | D | 2-2 | Flood 6 Enver-Marum 27 | 22 | 43 |
| 12 | Nat South | A | Gosport Borough | 298 | L | 2-3 | Enver-Marum 55 Williams 75 | 22 | 44 |
| 16 | Nat South | A | Dartford | 924 | D | 0-0 | | 22 | 45 |
| 23 | Nat South | H | Truro City | 463 | W | 2-0 | Dunn 8 Williams 90 | 22 | 46 |
| 30 | Nat South | A | Chelmsford City | 931 | W | 2-0 | Soares 30 Bennett 37 | 22 | 47 |

| GOALSCORERS | Scoring Games | Consec Sco Games | Total | | Scoring Games | Consec Sco Games | Total |
|---|---|---|---|---|---|---|---|
| ***2014-15 Flood*** | | | ***18*** | Connolly | 1 | | 1 |
| Flood | 10 | 2 | 13 | Gilkes | 1 | | 1 |
| Enver-Marum | 10 | 2 | 12 | Hyam | 1 | | 1 |
| Williams | 6 | | 7 | McAuley | 1 | | 1 |
| Soares | 6 | | 5 | McLean | 1 | | 1 |
| Macklin | 4 | | 4 | Ray | 1 | | 1 |
| Deaman | 2 | | 2 | Salmon | 1 | | 1 |
| Dunn | 2 | | 2 | Southam | 1 | | 1 |
| Gasson | 2 | | 2 | Smart | 1 | | 1 |
| Bennett | 1 | | 1 | Vine | 1 | | 1 |

# BIGGLESWADE TOWN

**Chairman:** Maurice Dorrington
**Secretary:** Mike Draxter (T) (E) michaeldraxler@hotmail.com
**Commercial Manager:** (T/E)
**Programme Editor:** David Simpson (T/E) simpson_david@hotmail.co.uk
**Ground Address:** The Carlsberg Stadium, Langford Road, Biggleswade SG18 9JT
**(T)** 01767 318 202 (Matchdays) **Manager:** Chris Nunn

## Club Factfile

**Founded:** 1874 **Nickname:** The Waders
**Previous Names:** Biggleswade FC
**Previous Leagues:** Biggleswade & District, Bedford & District, Spartan South Midlands 1951-55, 80-2009, Eastern Counties 1955-63, United Counties 1963-80

**Club Colours (change):** White with green trim/green/green (Blue & black stripes/black/blue & black)

**Ground Capacity:** 3,000 **Seats:** 300 **Covered:** 400 **Clubhouse:** Yes **Shop:**

**Directions**
From the south – up the A1, past the first roundabout (Homebase) signposted Biggleswade. At next roundabout (Sainsburys) turn right onto A6001. As you approach the Town Centre, go straight over the mini roundabout following signs for Langford (Teal Road). At traffic lights, turn right (still heading towards Langford). Continue along Hitchin Street over two mini roundabouts and as you pass under the A1, the ground entrance is 200 yards on the right. From the north – exit A1 at the Sainsburys roundabout and follow instructions as above.

**Previous Grounds:** Fairfield

**Record Attendance:** 2,000
**Record Victory:** Not known
**Record Defeat:** Not known
**Record Goalscorer:** Not known
**Record Appearances:** Not known
**Additional Records:**

**Honours:**
Spartan South Midlands Premier Division 2008-09. Bedfordshire Premier Cup 2009. Bedfordshire Senior Challenge Cup 2012-13.

### 10 YEAR RECORD

| 06-07 | 07-08 | 08-09 | 09-10 | 10-11 | 11-12 | 12-13 | 13-14 | 14-15 | 15-16 |
|---|---|---|---|---|---|---|---|---|---|
| SSM P 18 | SSM P 3 | SSM P 1 | SthM 12 | SthC 4 | SthC 8 | SthC 4 | SthP 9 | SthP 19 | SthP 14 |

# BIGGLESWADE TOWN MATCH RESULTS 2015-16

| Date | Comp | H/A | Opponents | Att: | Result | | Goalscorers | Pos | No. |
|---|---|---|---|---|---|---|---|---|---|
| Aug 8 | SPL | A | Bedworth United | 185 | W | 4-2 | Hill 24 Daniel 45 Davies 59 Merson 84 | 2 | 1 |
| 11 | SPL | H | Slough Town | 165 | W | 5-1 | BURNETT 3 (12 49 52) Hoye 18 Daniel 47 | 1 | 2 |
| 15 | SPL | H | Redditch United | 163 | D | 1-1 | Merson 60 | 2 | 3 |
| 18 | SPL | A | Dunstable Town | 124 | L | 1-2 | Coulson 88 | 6 | 4 |
| 22 | SPL | A | Hungerford Town | 120 | L | 0-2 | | 12 | 5 |
| 29 | SPL | H | Leamington | 255 | W | 3-2 | Burnett 56 Iwediouno 75 Hill 90 | 7 | 6 |
| 31 | SPL | A | St Neots Town | 456 | L | 0-2 | | 12 | 7 |
| Sept 5 | SPL | H | Paulton Rovers | 146 | W | 4-1 | Merson 32 51 Daniel 56 York 66 | 10 | 8 |
| **12** | **FAC1Q** | **A** | **Brantham Athletic** | **108** | **W** | **2-0** | **Daniel 70 88** | | 9 |
| 19 | SPL | H | Poole Town | 202 | L | 0-1 | | 12 | 10 |
| **26** | **FAC2Q** | **A** | **Wealdstone** | **320** | **D** | **1-1** | **Merson 64** | | 11 |
| **29** | **FAC2Qr** | **H** | **Wealdstone** | **264** | **L** | **0-2** | | | 12 |
| Oct 3 | SPL | A | Merthyr Town | 409 | W | 2-1 | Bradley 40 (og) Davies 62 | 10 | 13 |
| 6 | SPL | A | Stratford Town | 137 | L | 0-3 | | 12 | 14 |
| 10 | SPL | H | Frome Town | 165 | W | 3-0 | Rees 69 Daniel 67 Burnett 89 | 9 | 15 |
| 17 | SPL | A | Weymouth | 537 | W | 1-0 | Merson 75 | 6 | 16 |
| 20 | SPL | H | Kettering Town | 249 | L | 1-3 | Merson 34 | 7 | 17 |
| 27 | SPL | A | Kings Lynn Town | 415 | L | 1-2 | Merson 17 | 15 | 18 |
| **31** | **FAT1Q** | **A** | **Grays Athletic** | **151** | **L** | **1-2** | **Hilliard 48** | | 19 |
| Nov 3 | SPL | A | Kettering Town | 429 | L | 1-2 | Marsh 52 | 18 | 20 |
| 7 | SPL | A | Hitchin Town | 417 | L | 0-3 | | 18 | 21 |
| 17 | SPL | H | Dunstable Town | 115 | D | 3-3 | Frater 53 90 Burnett 88 | 15 | 22 |
| 21 | SPL | A | Redditch United | 245 | D | 2-2 | Merson 15 Hill 65 (pen) | 15 | 23 |
| 24 | SPL | H | Chippenham Town | 99 | L | 0-1 | | 15 | 24 |
| 28 | SPL | H | Bedworth United | 125 | W | 4-1 | Hill 5 (pen) Effiong 50 60 Allinson79 | 14 | 25 |
| Dec 1 | SPL | A | Slough Town | 242 | L | 0-2 | | 15 | 26 |
| 12 | SPL | H | Dorchester Town | 108 | W | 1-0 | Effiong 72 | 16 | 27 |
| 19 | SPL | A | Leamington | 403 | W | 1-0 | Effiong 24 | 13 | 28 |
| 26 | SPL | H | St Neots Town | 328 | W | 5-2 | EFFIONG 3 (4 pen15 pen 32) Burnett 6 Daniel | 11 | 29 |
| 29 | SPL | H | Cambridge City | 274 | W | 3-2 | Marsh 9 52 Burnett 15 | | 30 |
| Jan 2 | SPL | A | Histon | 250 | W | 2-1 | Effiong 4 Merson 73 | 5 | 31 |
| 16 | SPL | A | Paulton Rovers | 137 | L | 2-3 | Merson 23 Effiong 41 | 9 | 32 |
| 23 | SPL | H | Hungerford Town | 145 | L | 1-4 | Rees 26 | 10 | 33 |
| 30 | SPL | H | Merthyr Town | 201 | L | 0-3 | | 11 | 34 |
| Feb 9 | SPL | A | Chesham United | 178 | D | 1-1 | York 4 | 10 | 35 |
| 13 | SPL | H | Stratford Town | 135 | W | 4-3 | Rees 49 Daniel 60 Effiong 70 89 | 10 | 36 |
| 16 | SPL | A | Poole Town | 266 | D | 2-2 | Daniel 67 Effiong 74 | 9 | 37 |
| 20 | SPL | A | Cambridge City | 206 | D | 2-2 | Effiong 51 Merson 87 | 11 | 38 |
| 27 | SPL | H | Weymouth | 175 | D | 1-1 | Effiong 20 | 11 | 39 |
| Mar 1 | SPL | H | Cirencester Town | 98 | W | 1-0 | Effiong 44 | 10 | 40 |
| 5 | SPL | A | Frome Town | 143 | L | 1-2 | Burnett 78 | 12 | 41 |
| 12 | SPL | H | Chesham United | 147 | D | 2-2 | Burnett 26 89 (pen) | 12 | 42 |
| 19 | SPL | A | Cirencester Town | 78 | L | 1-2 | Rees 78 | 12 | 43 |
| 26 | SPL | A | Dorchester Town | 329 | W | 1-0 | Burnett 30 (pen) | 12 | 44 |
| 28 | SPL | H | Histon | 201 | W | 2-1 | Key 19 40 | 11 | 45 |
| Apr 2 | SPL | H | Kings Lynn Town | 181 | L | 2-4 | Daniel 7 Freeman 59 | 12 | 46 |
| 6 | SPL | H | Bideford | 147 | L | 0-2 | | 12 | 47 |
| 9 | SPL | A | Chippenham Town | 263 | L | 2-3 | Daniel 9 Hoyle 47 | 12 | 48 |
| 16 | SPL | H | Hitchin Town | 461 | L | 3-5 | Freeman 27 Vincent 69 Rees 87 | 13 | 49 |
| 23 | SPL | A | Bideford | 169 | D | 0-0 | | 14 | 50 |

| GOALSCORERS | Scoring Games | Consec Sco Games | Total | | Scoring Games | Consec Sco Games | Total |
|---|---|---|---|---|---|---|---|
| ***2014-15 Bossman*** | ***14*** | | | Freeman | 2 | | 2 |
| Effiong | 12 | 4 | 15 | Hoyle | 2 | | 2 |
| Burnett | 10 | 2 | 12 | Key | 1 | | 2 |
| Merson | 11 | 3 | 12 | York | 2 | | 2 |
| Daniel | 10 | 2 | 11 | Allinson | 1 | | 1 |
| Rees | 5 | | 5 | Coulson | 1 | | 1 |
| Hill | 4 | | 4 | Hilliard | 1 | | 1 |
| Marsh | 2 | | 3 | Iwediouno | 1 | | 1 |
| Davies | 2 | | 2 | Vincent | 1 | | 1 |
| Frater | 2 | | 2 | Opponents | | | 1 |

# CAMBRIDGE CITY

**Chairman:** Kevin Satchell

**Secretary:** Andy Dewey (T) 07720 678 585 (E) andy@cambridgecityfc.com

**Commercial Manager:** (T/E) 07887 748 002

**Programme Editor:** Chris Farrington (T/E) ccfc.editor@googlemail.com

**Ground Address:** St Ives Town FC, Westwood Road, St Ives, Cambridgeshire PE27 6DT

(T) 01223 233 226 **Manager:** Dan Gleeson & Neil Midgley

An artist's impression of how the 'Lilywhites' new stadium in Sawston will look, and with work starting back up again the future looks good for all involved.

## Club Factfile

**Founded:** 1908 **Nickname:** Lilywhites

**Previous Names:** Cambridge Town 1908-51

**Previous Leagues:** Bury & District 1908-13, 19-20, Anglian 1908-10, Southern Olympian 1911-14, Southern Amateur 1913-35, Spartan 1935-50, Athenian 1950-58, Southern 1958-2004

**Club Colours (change):** White/black/black & white hoops (All light blue)

**Ground Capacity:** 2,722 **Seats:** 526 **Covered:** 220 **Clubhouse:** Yes **Shop:** Yes

**Directions**

From the A14 (Junction 26) continue along London Road (A1096). On entering the Town of St Ives (avoiding Town Centre), continue over the first roundabout and over the by-pass (Harrison Way), continue over the next two roundabouts (still on Harrison Way). Turn left at the next two mini- roundabouts onto the A1123 (Needingworth Road/St Audrey Lane). Turn left at the cross roads onto Ramsey Road where Westwood Road can be found on the right hand side (opposite the Fire Station). Continue to the bottom of the road where the turning for the football club can be found on the right hand side before the St Ives Recreation Centre.

**Previous Grounds:** City Ground.

**Record Attendance:** 12,058 v Leytonstone - FA Amateur Cup 1st Round 1949-50

**Record Victory:** Not known

**Record Defeat:** Not known

**Record Goalscorer:** Gary Grogan

**Record Appearances:** Mal Keenan

**Additional Records:** Paid £8,000 to Rushden & Diamonds for Paul Coe
Received £100,000 from Millwall for Neil Harris 1998

**Honours:**

Southern League 1962-63, Southern Division 1985-86.
Suffolk Senior Cup 1909-10. East Anglian x9. Cambridgeshire Professional Cup 2012-13, 14-15, Invitational Cup 2014-15.

## 10 YEAR RECORD

| 06-07 | 07-08 | 08-09 | 09-10 | 10-11 | 11-12 | 12-13 | 13-14 | 14-15 | 15-16 |
|---|---|---|---|---|---|---|---|---|---|
| Conf S 13 | Conf S 14 | SthP 4 | SthP 6 | SthP 4 | SthP 5 | SthP 8 | SthP 3 | SthP 13 | SthP 18 |

## CAMBRIDGE CITY MATCH RESULTS 2015-16

| Date | Comp | H/A | Opponents | Att: | Result | | Goalscorers | Pos | No. |
|---|---|---|---|---|---|---|---|---|---|
| Aug 8 | SPL | H | Weymouth | 240 | W | 1-0 | Kelly 23 | 6 | 1 |
| 11 | SPL | A | Kings Lynn Town | 642 | L | 0-1 | | 10 | 2 |
| 15 | SPL | A | Frome Town | 168 | W | 4-0 | Reynolds 43 Malcolm 53 Murray 75 Serrano 86 | 6 | 3 |
| 19 | SPL | H | Chesham United | 214 | W | 1-0 | Malcolm 41 | 3 | 4 |
| 22 | SPL | A | Redditch United | 218 | D | 0-0 | | 3 | 5 |
| 29 | SPL | H | Cirencester Town | 209 | L | 1-2 | Malcolm 83 | 8 | 6 |
| 31 | SPL | A | Histon | 556 | W | 3-2 | Malcolm 7 69 Chaffey 49 | 4 | 7 |
| Sept 5 | SPL | H | Dorchester Town | 191 | L | 0-3 | | 3 | 8 |
| **12** | **FAC1Q** | **A** | **AFC Hornchurch** | **235** | **L** | **1-2** | **Kelly 23** | | 9 |
| 19 | SPL | A | Bideford | 169 | D | 1-1 | Malcolm 42 | 11 | 10 |
| 23 | SPL | H | Leamington | 151 | L | 1-2 | Dawkin 28 | 12 | 11 |
| Oct3 | SPL | H | Dunstable Town | 232 | D | 1-1 | Kelly 71 | 14 | 12 |
| 7 | SPL | H | Bedworth Town | 146 | W | 4-2 | Harradine 3 Pepper 30 Kelly 32 Malcolm 60 | 10 | 13 |
| 17 | SPL | H | Hungerford Town | 190 | W | 3-1 | Serrano 17 Kelly 48 66 | 10 | 14 |
| 24 | SPL | A | Slough Town | 292 | L | 1-3 | Norris 90 | 14 | 15 |
| **31** | **FAT1Q** | **H** | **Ilkeston** | **232** | **L** | **0-1** | | | 16 |
| Nov 3 | SPL | A | Leamington | 251 | W | 2-1 | Kaye 27 Malcolm 90 | 10 | 17 |
| 14 | SPL | A | Poole Town | 357 | L | 1-2 | Malcolm 61 | 13 | 18 |
| 25 | SPL | H | St Neots Town | 237 | L | 1-4 | Dawkin 2 (pen) | 14 | 19 |
| Dec5 | SPL | A | Kettering Town | 552 | D | 0-0 | | 16 | 20 |
| 8 | SPL | A | Chippenham Town | 242 | W | 3-1 | Dawkin 1 (pen) Norris 32 Lewis 71 | 15 | 21 |
| 12 | SPL | H | Merthyr Town | 152 | W | 1-0 | Gleeson 69 | 14 | 22 |
| 19 | SPL | A | Cirencester Town | 106 | D | 1-1 | Lewis 57 | 15 | 23 |
| 29 | SPL | A | Biggleswade Town | 274 | L | 2-3 | Reynolds 40 Harradine 48 | 16 | 24 |
| Jan 15 | SPL | A | Dorchester Town | 427 | L | 0-3 | | 17 | 25 |
| 19 | SPL | A | Weymouth | 346 | L | 0-1 | | 17 | 26 |
| 23 | SPL | H | Redditch United | 153 | L | 0-2 | | 18 | 27 |
| 27 | SPL | H | Frome Town | 153 | W | 2-1 | Harradine 41 45 | 16 | 28 |
| 30 | SPL | A | Dunstable Town | 151 | L | 1-3 | Harradine 5 | 18 | 29 |
| Feb 6 | SPL | H | Bideford | 138 | W | 2-0 | Felumi 56 Hall 81 | 16 | 30 |
| 10 | SPL | H | HIston | 229 | L | 1-2 | Kelly 70 (pen) | 16 | 31 |
| 13 | SPL | A | Bedworth Town | 178 | L | 3-4 | Hall 15 Serano 72 Woolfe 86 | 18 | 32 |
| 20 | SPL | H | Biggleswade Town | 206 | D | 2-2 | Murray 3 Hall 31 | 17 | 33 |
| 23 | SPL | A | Chesham United | 202 | W | 3-1 | Kelly 32 54 Hall 62 | 15 | 34 |
| 27 | SPL | A | Hungerford Town | 100 | L | 0-2 | | 15 | 35 |
| Mar 7 | SPL | A | Hitchin Town | 374 | L | 2-4 | Woolfe 7 Norris 90 | 19 | 36 |
| 12 | SPL | H | Kettering Town | 333 | L | 0-4 | | 19 | 37 |
| 19 | SPL | A | Merthyr Town | 327 | L | 1-2 | Lewis 46 | 20 | 38 |
| 28 | SPL | H | Hitchiin Town | 222 | L | 0-1 | | 20 | 39 |
| 30 | SPL | H | Stratford Town | 134 | W | 2-0 | Harradine 43 Robertsm 47 (og) | 20 | 40 |
| Apr 2 | SPL | A | St Neots Town | 351 | D | 1-1 | Hall 61 (pen) | 20 | 41 |
| 8 | SPL | H | Slough Town | 188 | W | 4-2 | HALL 3 ( 22 81 83 pen) Harradine 52 | 18 | 42 |
| 12 | SPL | A | Paulton Rovers | 77 | L | 1-2 | Hall 64 | 18 | 43 |
| 14 | SPL | H | Chippenham Town | 121 | L | 0-3 | | 18 | 44 |
| 18 | SPL | H | Paulton Rovers | 107 | W | 2-0 | Harradine 15 Hall 90 | 18 | 45 |
| 20 | SPL | H | Kings Lynn Town | 135 | L | 1-3 | Hall 38 | 18 | 46 |
| 23 | SPL | H | Poole Town | 250 | L | 1-2 | Harradine 30 | 18 | 47 |
| 26 | SPL | A | Stratford Town | 183 | L | 2-5 | Hall 36 Midgley 80 | 18 | 48 |

| GOALSCORERS | Scoring Games | Consec Sco Games | Total | | Scoring Games | Consec Sco Games | Total |
|---|---|---|---|---|---|---|---|
| *2014-15 Phillips* | *21* | | | Reynolds | 2 | | 2 |
| Hall | 10 | 3 | 12 | Woolfe | 2 | | 2 |
| Harradine | 8 | | 9 | Chaffey | 1 | | 1 |
| Kelly | 8 | 2 | 9 | Felumi | 1 | | 1 |
| Malcolm | 7 | 3 | 9 | Gleeson | 1 | | 1 |
| Dawkin | 3 | | 3 | Kaye | 1 | | 1 |
| Lewis | 3 | | 3 | Midgley | 1 | | 1 |
| Norris | 3 | | 3 | Pepper | 1 | | 1 |
| Serrano | 3 | | 3 | Opponents | | | 1 |
| Murray | 2 | | 2 | | | | |

# CHESHAM UNITED

**Chairman:** Brian McCarthy
**Secretary:** Alan Lagden (T) (E) secretary@cheshamunited.co.uk
**Commercial Manager:** (T/E)
**Programme Editor:** Steve Doman (T/E) cufcprogramme@talktalk.net
**Ground Address:** The Meadow, Amy Lane, Amersham Road, Chesham HP5 1NE
(T) 01494 783 964 **Manager:** Andy Leese

## Club Factfile

**Founded:** 1917 **Nickname:** The Generals
**Previous Names:** Chesham Town and Chesham Generals merged in 1917 to form Chesham United.
**Previous Leagues:** Spartan 1917-47, Corinthian 1947-63, Athenian 1963-73, Isthmian 1973-2004

**Club Colours (change):** Claret & blue/claret/claret (Yellow/black/yellow)

**Ground Capacity:** 5,000 **Seats:** 284 **Covered:** 2,500 **Clubhouse:** Yes **Shop:** Yes

**Directions**
From M25 Junction 20 take A41 (Aylesbury), leave A41 at turn-off for Chesham (A416), pass through Ashley Green into Chesham. Follow signs to Amersham, still on A416 pass two petrol stations opposite each other and at next roundabout take third exit into ground.
From M1 Junction 8 follow signs for Hemel Hempstead then joining the A41 for Aylesbury, then as above.

**Previous Grounds:** None

**Record Attendance:** 5,000 v Cambridge United - FA Cup 3rd Round 05/12/1979
**Record Victory:** Not known
**Record Defeat:** Not known
**Record Goalscorer:** John Willis
**Record Appearances:** Martin Baguley - 600+
**Additional Records:** Received £22,000 from Oldham Athletic for Fitz Hall

**Honours:**
Isthmian League 1992-93, Division 1 1986-87, 97-97. Berks & Bucks Senior Cup x12.

### 10 YEAR RECORD

| 06-07 | | 07-08 | | 08-09 | | 09-10 | | 10-11 | | 11-12 | | 12-13 | | 13-14 | | 14-15 | | 15-16 | |
|---|---|---|---|---|---|---|---|---|---|---|---|---|---|---|---|---|---|---|---|
| Sthsw | 15 | SthM | 6 | SthM | 5 | SthM | 4 | SthP | 6 | SthP | 4 | SthP | 3 | SthP | 2 | SthP | 12 | SthP | 13 |

# CHESHAM UNITED MATCH RESULTS 2015-16

| Date | Comp | H/A | Opponents | Att: | Result | | Goalscorers | Pos | No. |
|---|---|---|---|---|---|---|---|---|---|
| Aug 8 | SPL | A | Leamington | 487 | L | 0-1 | | 18 | 1 |
| 11 | SPL | H | Hitchin Town | 351 | D | 1-1 | Youngs 80 | 17 | 2 |
| 15 | SPL | A | Cirencester Town | 242 | W | 2-1 | Youngs 56 Pearce 59 | 12 | 3 |
| 19 | SPL | A | Cambridge City | 214 | L | 0-1 | | 15 | 4 |
| 22 | SPL | H | Frome Town | 241 | W | 5-1 | Blake 25 Wadkins 35 74 Hayles 66 90 | 13 | 5 |
| 29 | SPL | A | Stratford Town | 210 | D | 1-1 | Wadkins 18 | 12 | 6 |
| 31 | SPL | H | Slough Town | 439 | D | 1-1 | Pearce 62 | 15 | 7 |
| Sept 5 | SPL | A | Merthyr Town | 486 | W | 2-1 | Youngs 33 Hayles 83 | 15 | 8 |
| **12** | **FAC1Q** | **H** | **Aylesbury** | **336** | **D** | **0-0** | | | 9 |
| **15** | **FAC1Qr** | **A** | **Aylesbury** | **163** | **W** | **2-1** | **Blake 17 Hayles 38** | | 10 |
| 19 | SPL | A | Cirencester Town | 137 | L | 0-3 | | 14 | 11 |
| 22 | SPL | H | Hungerford Town | 223 | D | 2-2 | Wilson 9 Beasant 72 | 14 | 12 |
| **26** | **FAC 2Q** | **A** | **Paulton Rovers** | **123** | **W** | **2-0** | **Blake 64 72** | | 13 |
| 29 | SPL | A | Histon | 207 | L | 1-3 | Pearce 64 | | 14 |
| Oct 3 | SPL | H | Dorchester Town | 273 | L | 3-4 | Bossman 15 Taylor 67 Fenton 83 | 18 | 15 |
| 6 | SPL | A | Redditch United | 207 | W | 3-0 | Wadkins 19 Pearce 34 63 (pen) | 13 | 16 |
| **10** | **FAC3Q** | | **North Leigh** | **290** | **W** | **2-0** | **Pearce 83 (pen) 86** | | 17 |
| 17 | SPL | H | Bideford | 243 | W | 3-1 | Bossman 32 Wadkins 54 Taylor 62 | 15 | 18 |
| 19 | SPL | A | Hungerford Town | 123 | L | 1-3 | Bossman 5 | | 19 |
| **24** | **FAC4Q** | **H** | **Enfield Town** | **759** | **W** | **2-1** | **Ujar 19 Little 45** | | 20 |
| 27 | SPL | H | Poole Town | 262 | W | 3-1 | Bossman 21 (pen) Pearce 75 81 (pen) | 14 | 21 |
| **31** | **FAT1Q** | **A** | **Billericay Town** | **271** | **W** | **2-0** | **Blake 16 67** | | 22 |
| **Nov 7** | **FAC1** | **A** | **Bristol Rovers** | **5181** | **W** | **1-0** | **Blake 71** | | 23 |
| **14** | **FAT2Q** | **A** | **Swindon Super** | **187** | **W** | **3-2** | **Little 19 Fenton 30 Bossman 69** | | 24 |
| 21 | SPL | A | Paulton Rovers | 127 | L | 0-2 | | 18 | 25 |
| 24 | SPL | A | Kettering Town | 401 | L | 0-3 | | 19 | 26 |
| **28** | **FAT3Q** | **A** | **Frome Town** | **133** | **D** | **1-1** | **Youngs 22** | | 27 |
| **Dec 1** | **FAT3Qr** | **H** | **Frome Town** | **214** | **W** | **2-1** | **Pearce 53 (pen) Fenton 90** | | 28 |
| **5** | **FAC2** | **A** | **Bradford City** | **6047** | **L** | **0-4** | | | 29 |
| 8 | SPL | A | Bedworth United | 129 | L | 1-3 | Fenton 55 | 20 | 30 |
| **13** | **FAT1** | **A** | **Torquay United** | **1130** | **D** | **0-0** | | | 31 |
| **15** | **FAT1r** | **H** | **Torquay United** | **356** | **L** | **0-2** | | | 32 |
| 19 | SPL | H | Stratford Town | 303 | W | 2-0 | Pearce 21 (pen) 36 | 20 | 33 |
| 26 | SPL | A | Slough Town | 438 | W | 1-0 | Blake 34 | 18 | 34 |
| Jan 5 | SPL | H | St Neots Town | 245 | W | 3-1 | Blake 44 73 Smith 80 | 17 | 35 |
| 9 | SPL | A | Kings Lynn Town | 490 | L | 0-2 | | 19 | 36 |
| 30 | SPL | A | Dorchester Town | 434 | L | 1-2 | Gator 10 | 19 | 37 |
| Feb 2 | SPL | H | Dunstable Town | 222 | W | 5-1 | Head 26 (og) Gater 37 Ujar 70 Taylor 53 Blake 89 | 19 | 38 |
| 6 | SPL | H | Cirencester Town | 285 | L | 1-3 | Ujar 89 | 19 | 39 |
| 9 | SPL | H | Biggleswade Town | 178 | D | 1-1 | Taylor 48 | 18 | 40 |
| 13 | SPL | H | Redditch United | 244 | L | 0-1 | | 19 | 41 |
| 16 | SPL | A | Weymouth | 448 | W | 4-1 | Gater 9 Ujah 43 Bossman 78 Hayles 86 | 19 | 42 |
| 23 | SPL | H | Cambridge City | 202 | L | 1-3 | Pearce 70 | 19 | 43 |
| 27 | SPL | A | Bideford | 169 | D | 0-0 | | 18 | 44 |
| Mar 1 | SPL | H | Histon | 172 | W | 2-0 | Youngs 40 68 | 17 | 45 |
| 5 | SPL | H | Bedworth United | 240 | W | 4-2 | Bossman 11 Blake 27 71 Pearce 90 (pen) | 15 | 46 |
| 12 | SPL | A | Biggleswade Town | 147 | D | 2-2 | Youngs 7 34 | 16 | 47 |
| 15 | SPL | A | Chippenham Town | 266 | D | 2-2 | Blake 18 Bossman 42 | 16 | 48 |
| 19 | SPL | H | Chippenham Town | 260 | W | 1-0 | Hamilton-Forbes 22 | 16 | 49 |
| 22 | SPL | H | Leamington | 264 | W | 3-0 | Youngs 6 11 Pearce 52 | 12 | 50 |
| 26 | SPL | H | Kings Lynn | 351 | W | 2-0 | Pearce 29 Blake 36 | 11 | 51 |
| Apr 2 | SPL | A | Poole Town | 459 | L | 0-3 | | 14 | 52 |
| 6 | SPL | A | Frome Town | 147 | D | 1-1 | Ujar 55 | 13 | 53 |
| 9 | SPL | H | Kettering Town | 429 | L | 0-3 | | 15 | 54 |
| 11 | SPL | A | Hirchin Town | 366 | L | 1-5 | Taylor 90 | 15 | 55 |
| 19 | SPL | H | Merthyr Town | 203 | L | 0-1 | | 15 | 56 |
| 21 | SPL | A | Dunstable Town | 126 | D | 1-1 | Blake 10 | 15 | 57 |
| 23 | SPL | H | Weymouth | 382 | W | 1-0 | Bossman 82 | 13 | 58 |
| 26 | SPL | A | St Neots Town | 208 | W | 4-2 | Pearce 3 Bossman 6 80 Little 35 | 13 | 59 |

| GOALSCORERS | Scoring Games | Consec Sco Games | Total | | Scoring Games | Consec Sco Games | Total |
|---|---|---|---|---|---|---|---|
| *2014-15 Blake* | | | *17* | Gater | 3 | | 3 |
| Pearce | 13 | 2 | 17 | Little | 3 | | 3 |
| Blake | 12 | 2 | 16 | Beasant | 1 | | 1 |
| Bossman | 12 | 2 | 11 | Hamilton-Forbes | 1 | | 1 |
| Youngs | 7 | 2 | 10 | Smith | 1 | | 1 |
| Hayles | 4 | | 5 | Wilson | 1 | | 1 |
| Taylor | 5 | | 5 | Opponents | | | 1 |
| Ujar | 5 | | 5 | | | | |
| Wadkins | 5 | 2 | 5 | | | | |
| Fenton | 4 | | 4 | | | | |

# CHIPPENHAM TOWN

**Chairman:** Neil Blackmore
**Secretary:** Derek Crisp (T) (E)
**Commercial Manager:** (T/E)
**Programme Editor:** Will Hulbert (T/E)
**Ground Address:** Hardenhuish Park, Bristol Road, Chippenham SN14 6LR
**(T)** 01249 650 400 **Manager:** Mark Collier

2015-16 Squad

## Club Factfile

**Founded:** 1873 **Nickname:** The Bluebirds
**Previous Names:** None
**Previous Leagues:** Hellenic, Wiltshire Senior, Wiltshire Premier, Western

**Club Colours (change):** All royal blue (Lime green/grey/black)

**Ground Capacity:** 3,000 **Seats:** 300 **Covered:** 1,000 **Clubhouse:** Yes **Shop:** Yes

**Directions**
Exit 17 from M4. Follow A350 towards Chippenham for three miles to first roundabout, take second exit (A350); follow road to third roundabout (junction with A420). Turn left and follow signs to town centre. Ground is 1km on left hand side adjacent to pedestrian controlled traffic lights. Car/Coach park next to traffic lights.

**Previous Grounds:** Played at four different locations before moving in to Hardenhuish on 24/09/1919.

**Record Attendance:** 4,800 v Chippenham United - Western League 1951
**Record Victory:** 9-0 v Dawlish Town (H) - Western League
**Record Defeat:** 0-10 v Tiverton Town (A) - Western League
**Record Goalscorer:** Dave Ferris
**Record Appearances:** Ian Monnery
**Additional Records:**

**Honours:**
Western League 1951-52. Les Phillips Cup 1999-2000. Wiltshire Senior Cup. Wiltshire Senior Shield x4.

**10 YEAR RECORD**

| 06-07 | 07-08 | 08-09 | 09-10 | 10-11 | 11-12 | 12-13 | 13-14 | 14-15 | 15-16 |
|---|---|---|---|---|---|---|---|---|---|
| SthP 7 | SthP 4 | SthP 8 | SthP 3 | SthP 7 | SthP 11 | SthP 15 | SthP 18 | SthP 11 | SthP 8 |

# CHIPPENHAM TOWN MATCH RESULTS 2015-16

| Date | Comp | H/A | Opponents | Att: | Result | | Goalscorers | Pos | No. |
|---|---|---|---|---|---|---|---|---|---|
| Aug 8 | SPL | A | Dunstable Town | 107 | W | 2-1 | Reynolds 12 (og) Sandell 90 | 5 | 1 |
| 11 | SPL | H | Bideford | 235 | W | 2-0 | Sandell 4 88 | 3 | 2 |
| 15 | SPL | H | Bedworth Town | 312 | W | 5-0 | Sandell 6 29 Ferguson 54 Campbell 68 Preece 84 | 1 | 3 |
| 18 | SPL | A | Poole Town | 473 | W | 3-1 | Sandell 6 (pen) 30 (pen) Smith 90 | 1 | 4 |
| 22 | SPL | A | Histon | 169 | D | 0-0 | | 1 | 5 |
| 29 | SPL | H | Dorchester Town | 380 | W | 3-1 | Phillips 44 Ferguson 67 Campbell 90 | 1 | 6 |
| 31 | SPL | A | Hungerford Town | 231 | L | 0-1 | | 1 | 7 |
| Sept 5 | SPL | H | St Neots Town | 382 | D | 1-1 | Guthrie 10 | 1 | 8 |
| **11** | **FAC1Q** | **A** | **Frome Town** | **370** | **D** | **0-0** | | | 9 |
| **15** | **FAC1Qr** | **H** | **Frome Town** | **278** | **W** | **1-0** | **Ballinger 59** | | 10 |
| 19 | SPL | H | Merthyr Town | 387 | W | 1-0 | Taylor 77 | 1 | 11 |
| 22 | SPL | A | Weymouth | 516 | D | 1-1 | Taylor 45 | | 12 |
| **26** | **FAC2Q** | **A** | **Bradford Town** | **393** | **W** | **3-2** | **Smith 13 Preece 44 Phillips 80** | **1** | 13 |
| 29 | SPL | H | Frome Town | 364 | D | 1-1 | Smith 57 | 2 | 14 |
| Oct 3 | SPL | A | Kings Lynn Town | 425 | L | 0-2 | | 4 | 15 |
| 6 | SPL | H | Kettering Town | 423 | W | 2-1 | Tindle 42 Sandell 65 | 2 | 16 |
| **10** | **FAC3Q** | **A** | **Uxbridge** | **379** | **W** | **3-0** | **Holgate 15 Ferguson 49 Sandell 82** | | 17 |
| 17 | SPL | A | Stratford Town | 189 | D | 1-1 | Holgate 2 | 3 | 18 |
| 20 | SPL | H | Weymouth | 349 | D | 1-1 | Cooper 61 | 5 | 19 |
| **24** | **FAC4Q** | **H** | **Maidstone United** | **811** | **L** | **0-2** | | | 20 |
| 27 | SPL | H | Slough Town | 334 | D | 3-3 | Allen 7 Taylor 47 Sandell 59 | 5 | 21 |
| **31** | **FAT1Q** | **A** | **Dorchester Town** | **250** | **L** | **1-2** | **Jones 73** | | 22 |
| Nov 7 | SPL | H | Redditch United | 359 | L | 0-3 | | 6 | 23 |
| 17 | SPL | H | Poole Town | 257 | L | 0-1 | | 6 | 24 |
| 21 | SPL | A | Bedworth Town | 147 | W | 2-0 | Holgate 36 Smith 80 | 6 | 25 |
| 24 | SPL | A | Biggleswade Town | 99 | W | 1-0 | Sandell 31 | 6 | 26 |
| 28 | SPL | H | Dunstable Town | 325 | W | 4-1 | Sandell 23 (pen) 45 Ferguson 45 Guthrie 49 | 4 | 27 |
| Dec 1 | SPL | A | Bideford | 123 | W | 1-0 | Griffin 20 | 2 | 28 |
| 5 | SPL | A | Hitchin Town | 290 | D | 1-1 | Smith 48 | 2 | 29 |
| 8 | SPL | H | Cambridge City | 242 | L | 1-3 | Smith 74 | 2 | 30 |
| 19 | SPL | A | Dorchester Town | 369 | D | 1-1 | Sandell 89 (pen) | 2 | 31 |
| 26 | SPL | H | Hungerford Town | 449 | D | 1-1 | Griffin 24 | 2 | 32 |
| Jan 2 | SPL | A | Cirencester Town | 321 | W | 4-1 | Sandell 16 43 Guthrie 31 Griffin 58 | 2 | 33 |
| 9 | SPL | H | Leamington | 395 | W | 4-3 | Sandell 35 Griffin 37 77 Ferguson 72 | 2 | 34 |
| 16 | SPL | A | St Neots Town | 272 | W | 4-0 | Smith 15 Sandell 44 (pen) Burton 54 (og) Tann 90(og) | 2 | 35 |
| 23 | SPL | H | Histon | 364 | W | 3-0 | Sandell 29 72 Guthrie 80 | 2 | 36 |
| 30 | SPL | H | Kings Lynn Town | 427 | W | 4-1 | Sandell 37 82 Griffin 55 Taylor 86 | 1 | 37 |
| Feb 13 | SPL | H | Kettering Town | 527 | L | 0-2 | | 2 | 38 |
| 16 | SPL | A | Paulton Rovers | 220 | W | 1-0 | Taylor 82 | 2 | 39 |
| 20 | SPL | A | Frome Town | 272 | L | 0-1 | | 2 | 40 |
| 27 | SPL | H | Stratford Town | 378 | W | 2-1 | Malpass 12 Sandell 32 | 2 | 41 |
| Mar 1 | SPL | A | Merthyr Town | 302 | L | 0-2 | | 2 | 42 |
| 12 | SPL | H | Hitchin Town | 338 | D | 1-1 | Ferguson 45 | 3 | 43 |
| 15 | SPL | H | Chesham United | 266 | D | 2-2 | Griffin 46 Tindall 67 | 3 | 44 |
| 6 | SPL | A | Chesham United | 260 | L | 0-1 | | 6 | 45 |
| 26 | SPL | A | Leamington | 463 | D | 2-2 | Toundry 38 (og) Griffin 62 | 5 | 46 |
| 28 | SPL | H | Cirencester Town | 446 | L | 0-1 | | 6 | 47 |
| April 2 | SPL | A | Slough Town | 255 | L | 0-1 | | 6 | 48 |
| 9 | SPL | H | Biggleswade Town | 263 | W | 3-2 | Fiddes 66 Smith 67 Jones 76 | 8 | 49 |
| 14 | SPL | A | Cambridge City | 121 | W | 3-0 | Whtehead 48 (pen) Taylor 63 Smith 78 | 7 | 50 |
| 20 | SPL | A | Redditch United | 295 | L | 2-6 | Whitehead 7 88 | 8 | 51 |
| 23 | SPL | H | Paulton Rovers | 317 | W | 3-0 | Griffin 53 Ferguson 57 58 | 8 | 52 |

| GOALSCORERS | Scoring Games | Consec Sco Games | Total | | Scoring Games | Consec Sco Games | Total |
|---|---|---|---|---|---|---|---|
| ***2014-15 Ferguson*** | | | ***9*** | Jones | 2 | | 2 |
| Sandell | 16 | 5 | 23 | Phillips | 2 | | 2 |
| Griffin | 8 | 3 | 9 | Preece | 2 | | 2 |
| Smith | 9 | 2 | 9 | Tindle | 2 | | 2 |
| Ferguson | 7 | | 8 | Allen | 1 | | 1 |
| Taylor | 6 | 2 | 6 | Ballinger | 1 | | 1 |
| Guthrie | 4 | | 4 | Cooper | 1 | | 1 |
| Holgate | 3 | 2 | 3 | Fiddes | 1 | | 1 |
| Whitehead | 2 | | 3 | Malpass | 1 | | 1 |
| Campbell | 2 | | 2 | Opponents | | | 4 |

# CINDERFORD TOWN

**Chairman:** Stuart Tait
**Secretary:** Rob Maskell (T) 07835 511 774 (E) maskellbilly@yahoo.co.uk
**Commercial Manager:** (T/E)
**Programme Editor:** Rob Maskell (T/E) maskellbilly@yahoo.co.uk
**Ground Address:** The Causeway, Hildene, Cinderford, Gloucestershire GL14 2QH
(T) 07896 887 162 **Manager:** Alan Gough & Chris Burns

Photo: Peter Holloway

## Club Factfile

**Founded:** 1922 **Nickname:** The Foresters
**Previous Names:** None
**Previous Leagues:** Gloucestershire Northern Senior 1922-39, 60-62, Western 1946-59, Warwickshire Combination 1963-64, West Midlands 1965-69, Gloucestershire Co. 1970-73, 85-89, Midland Comb. 1974-84, Hellenic 1990-95

**Club Colours (change):** White/black/black (Green & black stripes/green/green)

**Ground Capacity:** 3,500 **Seats:** 250 **Covered:** 1,000 **Clubhouse:** Yes **Shop:** Yes

**Directions**
Take A40 west out of Gloucester, then A48 for 8 miles. Turn right at Elton Garage onto A4151 (Forest of Dean). Continue through Littledean, climb steep hill, turn right at crossroads (football ground), then second left into Latimer Road. Or if coming from Severn Bridge take A48 Chepstow through Lydney, Newnham then left at Elton Garage – then as above.

**Previous Grounds:** Mousel Lane, Royal Oak

**Record Attendance:** 4,850 v Minehead - Western League 1955-56
**Record Victory:** 13-0 v Cam Mills - 1938-39
**Record Defeat:** 0-10 v Sutton Coldfield - 1978-79
**Record Goalscorer:** Not known
**Record Appearances:** Russel Bowles - 528
**Additional Records:**

**Honours:**
Western League Division 2 1956-57. Midland Combination 1981-82. Hellenic Premier Division 1994-95, League Cup 94-95.
Southern League Division One South & West 2015-16.
Gloucestershire Senior Amateur Cup North x6. Gloucestershire Junior Cup North 1980-81. Gloucestershire Senior Cup 2000-01.

### 10 YEAR RECORD

| 06-07 | 07-08 | 08-09 | 09-10 | 10-11 | 11-12 | 12-13 | 13-14 | 14-15 | 15-16 |
|---|---|---|---|---|---|---|---|---|---|
| SthM 9 | SthM 16 | SthM 11 | Sthsw 16 | Sthsw 12 | Sthsw 10 | Sthsw 10 | Sthsw 15 | Sthsw 9 | Sthsw 1 |

*Cinderford Town v Shortwood United - Southern League South & West*
*Easter Monday 2016 @ the Causeway.*
*score 1-1*
*attendance 261*
*Photos: Peter Barnes*

# CIRENCESTER TOWN

**Chairman:** Stephen Abbley
**Secretary:** Scott Griffin (T) 01285 654 543 (E) scott.griffin@cirentownfc.plus.com
**Commercial Manager:** (T/E)
**Programme Editor:** Scott Griffin (T/E) scott.griffin@cirentownfc.plus.com
**Ground Address:** The Corinium Stadium, Kingshill Lane, Cirencester GL7 1HS
(T) 01285 654 543 **Manager:** Brian Hughes

Action from Cirencester's FA Trophy match at home to North Leigh.
Photo: Peter Barnes.

## Club Factfile

**Founded:** 1889 **Nickname:** Centurions
**Previous Names:** None
**Previous Leagues:** Hellenic

**Club Colours (change):** Red & black stripes/black/red (Amber/white/Amber)

**Ground Capacity:** 4,500 **Seats:** 550 **Covered:** 1,250 **Clubhouse:** Yes **Shop:** Yes

**Directions** Go along the dual carriageway, the Cirencester North-South outer bypass which links the M4 at Junction 15, Swindon, with the M5 at Junction 11a, Gloucester. That road is identified on the road signs and road maps as A419(T) from Swindon or A417(T) from the M5. It is about 20 or so minutes road time from both the M4 and the M5 junctions, traffic permitting. Come off the bypass at the Burford Road Junction (named on the road signs). There is a big services located there - fuel, food and a Travelodge. At that junction, go up the slip road to a roundabout. At the roundabout, turn away from Cirencester Town Centre, (If you are coming from the south, go over the bypass and straight over another roundabout) and up to the traffic lights. Turn right at the traffic lights and follow the road to a T-junction. Turn right, the road takes you back over the bypass, and then turn first left into Kingshill Lane. The Ground is half a mile on the right, past Kingshill School and the Council Playing Fields - See more at: http://www.southern-football-league.co.uk/clubs/cirencester-town#sthash.6fp1KGuA.dpuf

**Previous Grounds:** Smithfield Stadium

**Record Attendance:** 2,600 v Fareham Town - 1969
**Record Victory:** Not known
**Record Defeat:** Not known
**Record Goalscorer:** Not known
**Record Appearances:** Not known
**Additional Records:** Paid £4,000 to Gloucester City for Lee Smith

**Honours:**
Hellenic League Premier Division 1995-96. Southern Division One South & West 2013-14.
Gloucestershire Senior Amateur Cup 1989-90. Gloucestershire Senior Challenge Cup 1995-96, 2014-15.

### 10 YEAR RECORD

| 06-07 | 07-08 | 08-09 | 09-10 | 10-11 | 11-12 | 12-13 | 13-14 | 14-15 | 15-16 |
|---|---|---|---|---|---|---|---|---|---|
| SthP 21 | SthP 21 | Sthsw 14 | Sthsw 5 | SthP 13 | SthP 22 | Sthsw 11 | Sthsw 1 | SthP 8 | SthP 15 |

# CIRENCESTER TOWN MATCH RESULTS 2015-16

| Date | Comp | H/A | Opponents | Att: | Result | | Goalscorers | Pos | No. |
|---|---|---|---|---|---|---|---|---|---|
| Aug 8 | SPL | A | Redditch United | 302 | W | 1-0 | Kotwica 74 | 7 | 1 |
| 11 | SPL | H | Dorchester Town | 110 | W | 4-3 | Griffin 2 Jones 62 Parsons 64 84 (pen) | 4 | 2 |
| 15 | SPL | H | Hitchin Town | 125 | D | 0-0 | | 4 | 3 |
| 18 | SPL | A | Paulton Rovers | 38 | W | 4-1 | Brown 3 Dunton 24 Hooper 52 Kotwica 90 | 2 | 4 |
| 22 | SPL | H | Kings Lynn Town | 126 | L | 0-1 | | 4 | 5 |
| 29 | SPL | A | Cambridge City | 209 | W | 2-1 | Griffin 49 Kotwica 55 | 2 | 6 |
| 31 | SPL | H | Merthyr Town | 224 | W | 1-0 | Griffin 82 | 2 | 7 |
| Sept 5 | SPL | A | Slough Town | 260 | L | 0-1 | | 3 | 8 |
| **12** | **FAC1Q** | **A** | **Dorchester Town** | **320** | **D** | **1-1** | **Griffin 40 (pen)** | | 9 |
| **15** | **FAC1Qr** | **H** | **Dorchester Town** | **103** | **W** | **3-1** | **Jones 34 Kotwica 64 Henry 84** | | 10 |
| 19 | SPL | H | Chesham United. | 137 | W | 3-0 | Henry 48 Brown 60 Hooper 69 | 2 | 11 |
| 22 | SPL | A | Stratford Town | 180 | L | 1-2 | Parsons 76 | 2 | 12 |
| **26** | **FAC2Q** | **A** | **Petersfield United** | **152** | **L** | **1-2** | **Griffin 46** | | 13 |
| 29 | SPL | H | Weymouth | 156 | L | 0-3 | | 7 | 14 |
| Oct 3 | SPL | A | St Neots Town | 306 | W | 2-1 | Kotwica 49 Griffin 75 | 6 | 15 |
| 7 | SPL | A | Frome Town | 145 | L | 2-3 | Thompson 38 Connolly 90 | 6 | 16 |
| 17 | SPL | A | Poole Town | 358 | L | 0-3 | | 8 | 17 |
| 24 | SPL | H | Dunstable Town | 86 | L | 1-5 | Griffin 53 | 13 | 18 |
| 27 | SPL | A | Bideford | 214 | D | 1-1 | Griffin 25 | 9 | 19 |
| **31** | **FAT1Q** | **H** | **North Leigh** | **85** | **W** | **2-1** | **Griffin 26 Henry 50** | | 20 |
| Nov 7 | SPL | A | Leamington | 405 | L | 0-2 | | 15 | 21 |
| **14** | **FAT2Q** | **A** | **Tonbridge Angels** | **372** | **W** | **2-1** | **Kotwica 4 73** | | 22 |
| 21 | SPL | A | Hitchin Town | 306 | L | 0-2 | | 17 | 23 |
| **28** | **FAT3Q** | **H** | **Gosport Borough** | **88** | **W** | **2-1** | **Griffin 3 27** | | 24 |
| Dec 5 | SPL | H | Hungerford Town | 101 | L | 2-3 | Mortimer-Jones 21 Langworthy 48 | 18 | 25 |
| 8 | SPL | H | Kettering Town | 225 | W | 1-0 | Langworthy 66 | 16 | 26 |
| **12** | **FAT1** | **A** | **Truro City** | **302** | **D** | **2-2** | **Reid 65 (pen) Kotwica 90** | | 27 |
| **15** | **FAT1r** | **H** | **Truro City** | **123** | **L** | **0-1** | | | 28 |
| 19 | SPL | H | Cambridge City | 106 | D | 1-1 | Knight 48 | 18 | 29 |
| 26 | SPL | A | Merthyr Town | 438 | W | 1-0 | Knight 80 | 17 | 30 |
| Jan 2 | SPL | H | Chippenham Town | 321 | L | 1-4 | Bennett 22 | 17 | 31 |
| 5 | SPL | H | Histon | 92 | L | 1-2 | Kotwica 74 | 19 | 32 |
| 9 | SPL | A | Bedworth United | 182 | W | 1-0 | Griffin 7 | 16 | 33 |
| 12 | SPL | H | Stratford Town | 126 | W | 3-0 | Hooper 8 Griffin 46 Kotwica 66 | 14 | 34 |
| 23 | SPL | A | Kings Lynn Town | 515 | L | 0-2 | | 15 | 35 |
| 30 | SPL | H | St Neots Town | 93 | L | 2-5 | Griffin 65 83 | 16 | 36 |
| Feb 2 | SPL | A | Chesham United | 285 | W | 3-1 | Langworthy 72 Knight 80 Brown 90 (pen) | 15 | 37 |
| 9 | SPL | A | Dorchester Town | 266 | D | 1-1 | Pritchett 26 | 14 | 38 |
| 13 | SPL | H | Frome Town | 105 | D | 1-1 | Kotwica 63 (pen) | 14 | 39 |
| 16 | SPL | H | Slough Town | 112 | L | 1-3 | Pritchett 78 | 15 | 40 |
| 23 | SPL | H | Paulton Rovers | 54 | W | 3-0 | Griffin 58 Dunton 72 Knight 86 | 14 | 41 |
| 27 | SPL | H | Poole Town | 128 | W | 3-0 | Knight 20 Hooper 45 Langworthy 47 | 13 | 42 |
| Mar 1 | SPL | A | Biggleswade Town | 98 | L | 0-1 | | 13 | 43 |
| 5 | SPL | A | Kettering Town | 489 | L | 3-4 | GRIFFIN 3 (33 44 82 pen) | 14 | 44 |
| 12 | SPL | A | Hungerford Town | 111 | W | 2-1 | Griffin 20 45 | 14 | 45 |
| 15 | SPL | H | Redditch United | 107 | L | 0-2 | | 14 | 46 |
| 19 | SPL | H | Biggleswade Town | 78 | W | 2-1 | Hooper 26 Liddiard 90 | 13 | 47 |
| 26 | SPL | H | Bedworth United | 125 | L | 2-3 | Langworthy 75 Griffin 80 | 15 | 48 |
| 28 | SPL | A | Chippenham Town | 446 | W | 1-0 | Connolly 90 | 15 | 49 |
| Apr 3 | SPL | H | Bideford Town | 136 | L | 3-4 | Mortimer-Jones 22 Kotwica 36 Griffin 45 | 15 | 50 |
| 9 | SPL | A | Dunstable Town | 102 | W | 2-0 | Liddiard 48 83 | 13 | 51 |
| 16 | SPL | H | Leamington | 318 | L | 1-2 | Dunmore 90 | 14 | 52 |
| 19 | SPL | A | Weymouth | 556 | L | 1-3 | Griffin 56 | 14 | 53 |
| 23 | SPL | A | Histon | 153 | D | 3-3 | Griffin 80 85 Bennett 90 | 15 | 54 |

| GOALSCORERS | Scoring Games | Consec Sco Games | Total | | Scoring Games | Consec Sco Games | Total |
|---|---|---|---|---|---|---|---|
| Griffin | 19 | 3 | 26 | Connolly | 2 | | 2 |
| Kotwica | 11 | | 12 | Dunton | 2 | | 2 |
| Hooper | 5 | | 5 | Jones | 2 | | 2 |
| Knight | 5 | 2 | 5 | Mortimer-Jones | 2 | | 2 |
| Langworthy | 5 | | 5 | Pritchett | 2 | | 2 |
| Brown | 3 | | 3 | Dunmore | 1 | | 1 |
| Henry | 3 | 2 | 3 | Reid | 1 | | 1 |
| Liddiard | 3 | | 3 | Thompson | 1 | | 1 |
| Parsons | 2 | | 3 | | | | |
| Bennett | 2 | | 2 | | | | |

# DORCHESTER TOWN

**Chairman:** Matt Lucas
**Secretary:** Dave Ring (T) 01305 262 451 (E) david.ring@dorchestertownfc.com
**Commercial Manager:** (T/E)
**Programme Editor:** Melvin Cross (T/E) melvin.cross@btinterent.com
**Ground Address:** The Avenue Stadium, Weymouth Avenue, Dorchester DT1 2RY
(T) 01305 262 451 **Manager:** Mark Jermyn - 18/01/15

## Club Factfile

**Founded:** 1880 **Nickname:** The Magpies
**Previous Names:** None
**Previous Leagues:** Dorset, Western 1947-72

**Club Colours (change):** Black & white/black/black (Yellow/blue/yellow)

**Ground Capacity:** 5,009 **Seats:** 710 **Covered:** 2,846 **Clubhouse:** Yes **Shop:** Yes

**Directions**
The stadium is located at the junction of A35 Dorchester Bypass and the A354 to Weymouth, adjacent to Tesco. There is a coach bay for the team coach at the front of the stadium. Any supporters coach should park on the railway embankment side of the stadium.

**Previous Grounds:** Council Recreation Ground, Weymouth Avenue 1908-1929, 1929-90, The Avenue Ground 1929

**Record Attendance:** 4,159 v Weymouth - Southern Premier 1999
**Record Victory:** 7-0 v Canterbury (A) - Southern League Southern Division 1986-87
**Record Defeat:** 0-13 v Welton Rovers (A) - Western League 1966
**Record Goalscorer:** Not known
**Record Appearances:** Mark Jermyn - 600+ over 14 seasons
**Additional Records:** Denis Cheney scored 61 goals in one season. Paid £12,000 to Gloucester City for Chris Townsend 1990. Received £35,000 from Portsmouth for Trevor Sinclair.
**Honours:**
Western League 19954-55. Southern League 1985-86, Division 1 East 2002-03. Dorset Senior Cup x8 Most recently 2011-12.

**10 YEAR RECORD**

| 06-07 | 07-08 | 08-09 | 09-10 | 10-11 | 11-12 | 12-13 | 13-14 | 14-15 | 15-16 |
|---|---|---|---|---|---|---|---|---|---|
| Conf S 17 | Conf S 21 | Conf S 19 | Conf S 17 | Conf S 17 | Conf S 11 | Conf S 8 | Conf S 22 | SthP 17 | SthP 12 |

# DORCHESTER TOWN MATCH RESULTS 2015-16

| Date | Comp | H/A | Opponents | Att: | Result | | Goalscorers | Pos | No. |
|---|---|---|---|---|---|---|---|---|---|
| Aug 8 | SPL | H | Histon | 100 | W | 3-0 | Lee 22 Ayunga 63 Davis 84 | 1 | 1 |
| 11 | SPL | A | Cirencester Town | 110 | L | 3-4 | Ayunga 40 Lee 45 Oldring 79 | 8 | 2 |
| 15 | SPL | A | Hungerford Town | 193 | W | 3-2 | Dillon 47 Hanger 56 Morgan 58 | 7 | 3 |
| 18 | SPL | H | Frome Town | 341 | D | 0-0 | | 8 | 4 |
| 22 | SPL | A | Chesham United | 228 | D | 0-0 | | 8 | 5 |
| 29 | SPL | A | Chippenham Town | 380 | L | 1-3 | Ayunga 1 | 13 | 6 |
| 31 | SPL | H | Weymouth | 1357 | W | 1-0 | Jermyn 72 | 11 | 7 |
| Sept 5 | SPL | A | Cambridge City | 191 | W | 3-0 | Davis 9 Dillon 47 Tarbuck 57 | 7 | 8 |
| **12** | **FAC1Q** | **H** | **Cirencester Town** | **320** | **D** | **1-1** | **Smeeton 15** | | 9 |
| **15** | **FAC1Qr** | **A** | **Cirencester Town** | **103** | **L** | **1-3** | **Oldring 11** | | 10 |
| 19 | SPL | H | Stratford Town | 322 | W | 3-1 | Walker 20 Davis 43 Watson 66 | 4 | 11 |
| 22 | SPL | A | Poole Town | 509 | D | 0-0 | | 4 | 12 |
| 29 | SPL | H | Merthyr Town | 307 | D | 1-1 | Davis 57 (pen) | 5 | 13 |
| Oct 3 | SPL | A | Chesham United | 273 | W | 4-3 | Morgan 14 Tarbuck 35 40 Ayunga 90 | 5 | 14 |
| 6 | SPL | A | Kings Lynn Town | 243 | L | 1-4 | Tarbuck 78 | 5 | 15 |
| 10 | SPL | H | Hitchin Town | 313 | L | 0-1 | | 7 | 16 |
| 20 | SPL | H | Poole Town | 556 | L | 1-5 | Tarbuck 90 | 9 | 17 |
| 24 | SPL | A | Redditch United | 280 | L | 0-2 | | 11 | 18 |
| 27 | SPL | H | Paulton Rovers | 270 | W | 6-0 | Davis 5 Ayunga 45 WATSON 3 ( 47 50 67) Tarbuck 88 | 12 | 19 |
| **31** | **FAT1Q** | **H** | **Chippenham Town** | **250** | **W** | **2-1** | **Watson 85 Oldring 88** | | 20 |
| Nov 7 | SPL | H | Bedworth United | 292 | W | 3-2 | Tarbuck 21 Watson 26 Davis 72 (pen) | 7 | 21 |
| **14** | **FAT2Q** | **H** | **Kingstonian** | **312** | **D** | **2-2** | **Goode 4 (og) Oldring 82** | | 22 |
| **17** | **FAT2Qr** | **A** | **Kingstonian** | **221** | **L** | **1-2** | **Martin 13** | | 23 |
| 21 | SPL | H | Hungerford Town | 333 | L | 0-1 | | 10 | 24 |
| 24 | SPL | A | Hitchin Town | 283 | L | 0-1 | | 11 | 25 |
| 28 | SPL | A | Histon | 156 | W | 1-0 | Sayers 6 | 9 | 26 |
| Dec 5 | SPL | H | Kings Lynn Town | 285 | W | 2-0 | Ayunga 69 Walker 81 | 8 | 27 |
| 12 | SPL | A | Biggleswade Town | 108 | L | 0-1 | | 10 | 28 |
| 19 | SPL | H | Chippenham Town | 369 | D | 1-1 | Davis 68 (pen) | 11 | 29 |
| 26 | SPL | A | Weymouth | 1808 | D | 2-2 | Walker 15 Clarke 90 | 10 | 30 |
| Jan 6 | SPL | A | Frome Town | 259 | W | 3-0 | Hanger 40 Ayunga 67 Sayers 78 | 10 | 31 |
| 16 | SPL | H | Cambridge City | 427 | W | 3-0 | Davis 49 Ayunga 57 Martin 78 | 7 | 32 |
| 23 | SPL | A | Dunstable Town | 159 | L | 0-1 | | 9 | 33 |
| 30 | SPL | H | Chesham United | 434 | W | 2-1 | L.Holmes 3 Walker 62 | 8 | 34 |
| Feb 9 | SPL | H | Cirencester Town | 266 | D | 1-1 | L.Holmes 15 | 9 | 35 |
| 13 | SPL | H | Slough Town | 447 | L | 1-2 | Oldring 90 | 9 | 36 |
| 20 | SPL | A | Merthyr Town | 362 | W | 4-2 | Walker 8 L.Holmes 32 T.Holmes 81 Sayers 90 | 9 | 37 |
| 23 | SPL | H | Kettering Town | 342 | L | 0-3 | | 9 | 38 |
| 27 | SPL | H | St Neots Town | 360 | W | 1-0 | Tarbuck 64 | 9 | 39 |
| Mar 5 | SPL | A | Hitchin Town | 366 | L | 2-3 | T.Holmes 25 Watson 71 | 11 | 40 |
| 8 | SPL | H | Bideford | 251 | L | 1-2 | Walker 10 | 11 | 41 |
| 12 | SPL | A | KIngs Lynn Town | 523 | W | 2-1 | Walker 44 89 | 11 | 42 |
| 15 | SPL | A | Leamington | 312 | L | 0-3 | | 11 | 43 |
| 19 | SPL | H | Leamington | 342 | L | 0-1 | | 11 | 44 |
| 26 | SPL | H | Biggleswade Town | 329 | L | 0-1 | | 13 | 45 |
| 28 | SPL | A | Bideford | 233 | W | 3-2 | Brooks 10 Davis 65 Walker 67 | 12 | 46 |
| Apr 2 | SPL | A | Paulton Rovers | 120 | D | 1-1 | Tarbuck 68 | 11 | 47 |
| 9 | SPL | H | Redditch United | 378 | L | 1-5 | Walker 1 | 11 | 48 |
| 16 | SPL | A | Bedworth United | 145 | L | 0-1 | | 12 | 49 |
| 19 | SPL | A | Stratford Town | 196 | W | 2-1 | Davis 19 T.Holmes 34 | 12 | 50 |
| 23 | SPL | H | Kettering Town | 507 | L | 1-4 | T.Holmes 16 | 12 | 51 |

| GOALSCORERS | Scoring Games | Consec Sco Games | Total | | Scoring Games | Consec Sco Games | Total |
|---|---|---|---|---|---|---|---|
| *2014-15 Walker* | | | *11* | Dillon | 2 | | 2 |
| Davis | 10 | 2 | 10 | Hanger | 2 | | 2 |
| Walker | 9 | 2 | 10 | Lee | 2 | | 2 |
| Tarbuck | 9 | 2 | 9 | Martin | 2 | | 2 |
| Ayunga | 8 | 2 | 8 | Morgan | 2 | | 2 |
| Watson | 5 | 3 | 7 | Brooks | 1 | | 1 |
| Oldring | 5 | | 5 | Clarke | 1 | | 1 |
| T.Holmes | 4 | | 4 | Jermyn | 1 | | 1 |
| L.Holmes | 3 | | 3 | Smeeton | 1 | | 1 |
| Sayers | 3 | | 3 | Opponents | | | 1 |

# DUNSTABLE TOWN

**Chairman:** John McLoughlin
**Secretary:** Malcolm Aubrey (T) (E) dunstabletown.secretary@gmail.com
**Commercial Manager:** (T/E)
**Programme Editor:** Paul Harris (T/E) hpauljharris@aol.com
**Ground Address:** Creasey Park Stadium, Brewers Hill Rd, Dunstable LU6 1BB
(T) 01582 603 336 **Manager:** Tony Fontanelle - 25/02/15

## Club Factfile

**Founded:** 1883 **Nickname:** The Duns / The Blues
**Previous Names:** Dunstable Town 1883-1976. Dunstable FC 1976-98.
**Previous Leagues:** Metropolitan & District 1950-61, 64-65. United Counties 1961-63. Southern 1965-76, 2004-09. Spartan South Midlands 1998-2003, 09-13. Isthmian 2003-04.
**Club Colours (change):** Blue & white (Red & white)

**Ground Capacity:** 3,500 **Seats:** 350 **Covered:** 1000 **Clubhouse:** Yes **Shop:** Yes

**Directions** From the south: When travelling on the A5, go straight across the lights in the centre of Dunstable. Turn left at the next main set of lights into Brewers Hill Road. You will immediately pass the Fire Station on your left. Carry on until you hit the first roundabout, Go over the roundabout and take the immediate right into Creasey Park Drive. From the north: When travelling south on the A5, go through the chalk cutting and over the first set of traffic lights. At the next set of lights, turn right into Brewers Hill Road. Then proceed as above. From the East: Turn right at the traffic lights in the centre of Dunstable. Turn left at the next main set of traffic lights into Brewers Hill Road. Then proceed as above. From the east: When coming into Dunstable, go straight across the first roundabout you come to. Then turn left at the double mini-roundabout into Drovers Way. Follow this road for about 1/2 mile as it bears to the right and becomes Brewers Hill Road. Go over two mini-roundabouts and just before you hit the larger roundabout, turn left into Creasey Park Drive.

**Previous Grounds:** Kingsway 1950-58.

**Record Attendance:** 10,000 (approx) v Manchester United, friendly, July 1974
**Record Victory:** 12-0 v Welwyn Garden City, Spartan South Midlands League 2009-10.
**Record Defeat:** 0-13 v Arsenal, Metropolitan League
**Record Goalscorer:** Not known
**Record Appearances:** Not known
**Additional Records:** Received £25,000 from Reading for Kerry Dixon 1980.

**Honours:**
Spartan South Midlands Division One 1999-00, Premier 2002-03, 12-13. Southern Division One Central 2013-14.
Bedfordshire Senior Cup 1895–96, 1956–57, 59–60, 79–80, 82–83, 85–86, 86–87, 87–88, 88–89, 2002–03, 06–07, 08–09.
Bedforshire Premier Cup 1980–81, 82–83, 90–91, 2006–07, 11-12.

### 10 YEAR RECORD

| 06-07 | | 07-08 | | 08-09 | | 09-10 | | 10-11 | | 11-12 | | 12-13 | | 13-14 | | 14-15 | | 15-16 | |
|---|---|---|---|---|---|---|---|---|---|---|---|---|---|---|---|---|---|---|---|
| SthM | 11 | SthM | 13 | SthM | 21 | SSM P | 7 | SSM P | 7 | SSM P | 2 | SSM P | 1 | SthC | 1 | SthP | 14 | SthP | 11 |

# DUNSTABLE TOWN MATCH RESULTS 2015-16

| Date | Comp | H/A | Opponents | Att: | Result | | Goalscorers | Pos | No. |
|---|---|---|---|---|---|---|---|---|---|
| Aug 8 | SPL | H | Chippenham Town | 107 | L | 1-2 | Talbot 88 | 17 | 1 |
| 11 | SPL | A | Histon | 283 | L | 1-3 | Marsh 6 | 23 | 2 |
| 15 | SPL | A | Weymouth | 533 | D | 0-0 | | 22 | 3 |
| 18 | SPL | H | Biggleswade Town | 124 | **W** | 2-1 | Marsh 69 (pen) Blackett 90 | 17 | 4 |
| 22 | SPL | A | Dorchester Town | 228 | D | 0-0 | | 17 | 5 |
| 29 | SPL | H | Redditch United | 135 | L | 1-2 | Watkins 12 | 20 | 6 |
| 31 | SPL | A | Hitchin Town | 360 | L | 1-4 | Wharton 61 | 20 | 7 |
| Sept 5 | SPL | H | Leamington | 177 | L | 0-2 | | 20 | 8 |
| 12 | FAC1Q | H | Barton Rovers | 181 | **W** | 2-1 | Talbot 21 Keenlyside 52 | | 9 |
| 19 | SPL | H | Frome Town | 123 | **W** | 3-2 | Gregory 20 Watkins 32 Wharton 72 | 20 | 10 |
| 26 | FAC2Q | H | Kingstonian | 173 | **W** | 2-0 | Talbot 53 75 | | 11 |
| 29 | SPL | H | Kettering Town | 212 | **W** | 4-0 | Kaloczi 3 Osobu 35 Pennell 37 Kenleyside 46 | | 12 |
| Oct 3 | SPL | A | Cambridge City | 232 | D | 1-1 | Pennell 73 | 19 | 13 |
| 6 | SPL | A | Kings Lynn Town | 459 | D | 1-1 | Kaloczi 58 | 20 | 14 |
| 10 | FAC3Q | A | Maidstone United | 1583 | L | 0-2 | | | 15 |
| 17 | SPL | A | Merthyr Town | 290 | **W** | 3-1 | Kaloczi 20 Calcutt 45 Wharton 90 | 18 | 16 |
| 20 | SPL | H | St Neots Town | 156 | **W** | 3-0 | Watkins 23 Pennell 73 Wharton 76 | 17 | 17 |
| 24 | SPL | A | Cirencester Town | 86 | **W** | 5-1 | Osubo 13 Calcutt 15 Keenleyside 44 Vardy 87 Roache 90 | 8 | 18 |
| 31 | FAT1Q | H | Haringey Boro | 76 | L | 1-3 | Reynolds 90 | | 19 |
| Nov 3 | SPL | A | St Neots Town | 197 | L | 0-1 | | 15 | 20 |
| 7 | SPL | H | Poole Town | 152 | D | 1-1 | Watkins 4 | 14 | 21 |
| 14 | SPL | A | Bedworth U | 177 | **W** | 2-1 | Wales 62 Watkins 82 | 8 | 22 |
| 17 | SPL | A | Biggleswade Town | 115 | D | 3-3 | Vardy 31 Calcutt 33 Talbot 43 | 8 | 23 |
| 21 | SPL | H | Weymouth | 151 | **W** | 2-1 | Talbot 17 Kaloczi 61 | 7 | 24 |
| 24 | SPL | H | Slough Town | 142 | L | 1-3 | Calcutt 15 | 8 | 25 |
| 28 | SPL | A | Histon | 116 | **W** | 4-2 | Wharton 1 Keenleyside 9 48 Gregory 23 | | 26 |
| Dec 1 | SPL | A | Chippenham Town | 325 | L | 1-4 | Tindle 57 (og) | 10 | 27 |
| 5 | SPL | H | Bideford | 106 | **W** | 5-0 | Kaloczi 40 Wharton 45 CALCUTT 3 ( 4 pen 61 90) | 6 | 28 |
| 12 | SPL | A | Paulton Rovers | 138 | **W** | 2-1 | Wales 40 Calcutt 68 | 6 | 29 |
| 24 | SPL | H | Hitchin Town | 291 | D | 0-0 | | 6 | 30 |
| Jan 9 | SPL | H | Hungerford Town | 161 | **W** | 1-0 | Keenleyside 90 | 4 | 31 |
| 23 | SPL | H | Dorchester Town | 159 | **W** | 1-0 | Vardy 8 | 6 | 32 |
| 25 | SPL | H | Stratford Town | 101 | **W** | 3-1 | Watkins 33 Talbot 70 (pen) Wharton 87 | 4 | 33 |
| 30 | SPL | H | Cambridge City | 151 | **W** | 3-1 | Talbot 7 33 Wales 65 | 3 | 34 |
| Feb 2 | SPL | A | Chesham United | 222 | L | 1-5 | Talbot 28 | 3 | 35 |
| 13 | SPL | H | Kings Lynn Town | 139 | L | 0-2 | | 6 | 36 |
| 23 | SPL | A | Leamington | 275 | L | 0-1 | | 7 | 37 |
| 27 | SPL | H | Merthyr Town | 149 | **W** | 2-1 | Talbot 1 9 (pen) | 7 | 38 |
| Mar 5 | SPL | A | Slough Town | 226 | L | 0-1 | | 8 | 39 |
| 12 | SPL | A | Bideford | 159 | D | 0-0 | | 9 | 40 |
| 19 | SPL | H | Paulton Rovers | 101 | L | 1-2 | Kaloczi 59 | 9 | 41 |
| 26 | SPL | A | Hungerford Town | 125 | **W** | 3-2 | Wales 47 (pen) 88 Longe-King 4 | 9 | 42 |
| Apr 2 | SPL | A | Stratford Town | 141 | D | 0-0 | | 10 | 43 |
| 4 | SPL | A | Redditch Town | 327 | D | 0-0 | | 10 | 44 |
| 6 | SPL | A | Kettering Town | 470 | L | 1-3 | Vardy 53 | 10 | 45 |
| 9 | SPL | H | Cirencester Town | 102 | L | 0-2 | | 10 | 46 |
| 13 | SPL | A | Frome Town | 104 | L | 3-4 | Edwards 60 Calcutt 73 Roberts 82 (og) | 10 | 47 |
| 16 | SPL | A | Poole Town | 1057 | L | 0-3 | | 10 | 48 |
| 21 | SPL | H | Chesham United | 126 | D | 1-1 | Calcutt 77 (pen) | 10 | 49 |
| 23 | SPL | H | Bedworth United | 103 | L | 1-2 | Calcutt 16 | 11 | 50 |

| GOALSCORERS | Scoring Games | Consec Sco Games | Total |
|---|---|---|---|
| ***2014-15 McKenzie-Lowe*** | | | ***13*** |
| Talbot | 9 | 3 | 12 |
| Calcutt | 9 | 2 | 11 |
| Wharton | 7 | 2 | 7 |
| Kaloczi | 6 | | 6 |
| Keenleyside | 6 | | 6 |
| Watkins | 6 | | 6 |
| Wales | 4 | | 5 |
| Vardy | 4 | | 4 |
| Pennell | 3 | 2 | 3 |
| Gregory | 2 | | 2 |
| Marsh | 2 | | 2 |
| Osobu | 2 | | 2 |
| Blackett | 1 | | 1 |
| Edwards | 1 | | 1 |
| Long-King | 1 | | 1 |
| Reynolds | 1 | | 1 |
| Roache | 1 | | 1 |
| Opponents | | | 2 |

# FROME TOWN

**Chairman:** Jeremy Alderman
**Secretary:** Gary Collinson (T) (E) gary@frometownfc.co.uk
**Commercial Manager:** Brian Stevens (T/E) info@frometownfc.co.uk
**Programme Editor:** Gary Collinson (T/E) gary@frometownfc.co.uk
**Ground Address:** Blindmans Brewery Stadium, Badgers Hill, Berkley Road, Frome BA11 2EH
**(T)** 01373 464 087 **Manager:** Adrian Foster

## Club Factfile

**Founded:** 1904 **Nickname:** The Robins
**Previous Names:** None
**Previous Leagues:** Wiltshire Premier 1904, Somerset Senior 1906-19, Western 1919, 63-2009

**Club Colours (change):** Red with white flash/red/red (Yellow with blue flash/blue/yellow)

**Ground Capacity:** 2,200 **Seats:** 575 **Covered:** 575 **Clubhouse:** Yes **Shop:** Yes

**Directions**
From Bath, take A36 and then A361. At third roundabout, follow A361 and at fourth roundabout take A3098. Take first right and ground is one mile on left hand side. From south follow A36 (Warminster) and take A3098 to Frome. At T Junction turn right and take second exit at roundabout. Ground is first right and follow road for one mile on left hand side.

**Previous Grounds:** None

**Record Attendance:** 8,000 v Leyton Orient - FA Cup 1st Round 1958
**Record Victory:** Not Known
**Record Defeat:** Not Known
**Record Goalscorer:** Not Known
**Record Appearances:** Not Known
**Additional Records:**

**Honours:**
Somerset County League 1906-07, 08-09, 10-11.
Western League Division 1 1919-20, 2001-02, Premier Division 1962-63, 78-79.
Somerset Senior Cup 1932-33, 33-34, 50-51 Somerset Premier Cup 1966-67, 68-69 (shared), 82-83, 2008-09.

## 10 YEAR RECORD

| 06-07 | 07-08 | 08-09 | 09-10 | 10-11 | 11-12 | 12-13 | 13-14 | 14-15 | 15-16 |
|---|---|---|---|---|---|---|---|---|---|
| WestP 3 | WestP 4 | WestP 2 | Sthsw 6 | Sthsw 4 | SthP 12 | SthP 18 | SthP 14 | SthP 20 | SthP 16 |

## FROME TOWN MATCH RESULTS 2015-16

| Date | Comp | H/A | Opponents | Att: | Result | | Goalscorers | Pos | No. |
|---|---|---|---|---|---|---|---|---|---|
| Aug 8 | SPL | A | Slough Town | 275 | D | 0-0 | | 12 | 1 |
| 12 | SPL | H | Merthyr Town | 279 | D | 1-1 | Thomson 43 | 14 | 2 |
| 15 | SPL | H | Cambridge City | 168 | L | 0-4 | | 21 | 3 |
| 18 | SPL | A | Dorchester Town | 341 | D | 0-0 | | 20 | 4 |
| 22 | SPL | A | Chesham United | 241 | L | 1-5 | Taylor 4 | 23 | 5 |
| 29 | SPL | H | Kettering Town | 212 | L | 1-2 | Hobbs 58 | 23 | 6 |
| 31 | SPL | A | Poole Town | 425 | L | 0-5 | | 23 | 7 |
| Sept 5 | SPL | H | Hitchin Town | 151 | L | 0-4 | | 23 | 8 |
| **11** | **FAC1Q** | **H** | **Chippenham Town** | **370** | **D** | **0-0** | | | 9 |
| **15** | **FAC1Qr** | **A** | **Chippenham Town** | **278** | **L** | **0-1** | | | 10 |
| 19 | SPL | A | Dunstable Town | 123 | L | 2-3 | Sibbick 74 Monelle 82 | 24 | 11 |
| 23 | SPL | H | Bideford | 131 | **W** | 3-0 | Monelle 27 Sibbick 45 Tumelty 90 | 22 | 12 |
| 29 | SPL | A | Chippenham Town | 364 | D | 1-1 | Hobbs 75 | 22 | 13 |
| Oct 3 | SPL | H | Leamington | 209 | D | 0-0 | | 21 | 14 |
| 7 | SPL | H | Cirencester Town | 145 | **W** | 3-2 | Monelle 37 Miller 44 Haldene 60 | 21 | 15 |
| 10 | SPL | A | Biggleswade Town | 165 | L | 0-3 | | 21 | 16 |
| 17 | SPL | H | Bedworth Town | 202 | **W** | 2-1 | Davies 29 90 | 20 | 17 |
| 20 | SPL | A | Bideford | 199 | L | 0-2 | | 21 | 18 |
| 24 | SPL | A | Stratford Town | 176 | **W** | 1-0 | Sibbick 89 (pen) | 20 | 19 |
| 28 | SPL | H | Weymouth | 472 | D | 1-1 | Sibbick 38 | 21 | 20 |
| **31** | **FAT1Q** | **A** | **Egham Town** | **72** | **W** | **2-1** | **Moore 25 Sibbick 38** | | 21 |
| Nov 7 | SPL | H | Hungerford Town | 224 | L | 0-2 | | 20 | 22 |
| 14 | FAT2Q | H | Slough Town | 151 | **W** | 2-1 | Page 9 Jefferies 33 | | 23 |
| **28** | **FAT3Q** | **H** | **Chesham United** | **133** | **D** | **1-1** | **Hulbert 71** | | 24 |
| **Dec 1** | **FAT3Qr** | **A** | **Chesham United** | **214** | **L** | **1-2** | **Page 45** | | 25 |
| 5 | SPL | H | Histon | 142 | D | 2-2 | Hobbs 59 Sibbick 67 | 21 | 26 |
| 12 | SPL | A | Kings Lynn Town | 376 | L | 0-1 | | 21 | 27 |
| 26 | SPL | H | Poole Town | 354 | D | 0-0 | | 21 | 28 |
| Jan 6 | SPL | H | Dorchester Town | 259 | L | 0-3 | | 21 | 29 |
| 16 | SPL | A | Hitchin Town | 572 | **W** | 2-1 | Page 43 MIller 90 | 21 | 30 |
| 26 | SPL | A | Cambridge City | 153 | L | 1-2 | Miller 7 (pen) | 21 | 31 |
| 30 | SPL | A | Leamington | 405 | L | 0-2 | | 21 | 32 |
| Feb 9 | SPL | A | Merthyr Town | 283 | D | 1-1 | Fitzgibbon 17 | 22 | 33 |
| 13 | SPL | A | Cirencester Town | 106 | D | 1-1 | Cleverley 70 | 22 | 34 |
| 16 | SPL | A | Kettering Town | 425 | D | 1-1 | Miller 75 (pen) | 21 | 35 |
| 20 | SPL | H | Chippenham Town | 272 | **W** | 1-0 | Miller 71 | 21 | 36 |
| 27 | SPL | A | Bedworth United | 159 | D | 2-2 | Page 55 Teale 59 | 21 | 37 |
| Mar 1 | SPL | A | Paulton Rovers | 302 | L | 1-2 | Davies 25 | 21 | 38 |
| 5 | SPL | H | Biggleswade Town | 143 | **W** | 2-1 | Cleverley 23 Davies 35 (pen) | 21 | 39 |
| 9 | SPL | H | Slough Town | 102 | **W** | 2-1 | Hulbert 20 Teale 64 | 20 | 40 |
| 12 | SPL | A | Histon | 202 | **W** | 3-1 | Hobbs 61 Jackson 79 90 | 20 | 41 |
| 16 | SPL | H | St Neots Town | 123 | **W** | 3-2 | Hobbs 45 Page 50 Teale 85 | 20 | 42 |
| 19 | SPL | H | King's Lynn | 145 | **W** | 1-0 | Jefferies 56 | 17 | 43 |
| 21 | SPL | A | Redditch United | 282 | D | 1-1 | Mapstone 45 | 17 | 44 |
| 26 | SPL | A | St Neots Town | 262 | D | 2-2 | Jefferies 21 Page 67 | 17 | 45 |
| 28 | SPL | H | Paulton Rovers | 328 | **W** | 1-0 | Miller 89 | 17 | 46 |
| Apr 2 | SPL | A | Weymouth | 561 | L | 0-2 | | 17 | 47 |
| 6 | SPL | H | Chesham United | 147 | D | 1-1 | Jefferies 28 | 17 | 48 |
| 9 | SPL | H | Stratford Town | 261 | **W** | 2-0 | Cleverley 55 Simpson 67 (og) | 17 | 49 |
| 13 | SPL | H | Dunstable Town | 103 | **W** | 4-3 | Bryant 10 28 Davies 71 McPhee 90 | 17 | 50 |
| 16 | SPL | A | Hungerford Town | 186 | L | 0-4 | | 17 | 51 |
| 23 | SPL | H | Redditch United | 280 | D | 1-1 | Jackson 67 | 16 | 52 |

| GOALSCORERS | Scoring Games | Consec Sco Games | Total | | Scoring Games | Consec Sco Games | Total |
|---|---|---|---|---|---|---|---|
| ***2014-15 Haldine*** | | | 7 | Bryant | 1 | | 2 |
| MIller | 6 | 3 | 6 | Hulbert | 2 | | 2 |
| Page | 6 | | 6 | Fitzgibbon | 1 | | 1 |
| Sibbick | 6 | 2 | 6 | Haldene | 1 | | 1 |
| Davies | 4 | 2 | 5 | Mapstone | 1 | | 1 |
| Hobbs | 4 | 2 | 5 | McPhee | 1 | | 1 |
| Jefferies | 4 | | 4 | Moore | 1 | | 1 |
| Cleverley | 3 | | 3 | Taylor | 1 | | 1 |
| Jackson | 3 | | 3 | Thomson | 1 | | 1 |
| Monnelle | 3 | 2 | 3 | Tumelty | 1 | | 1 |
| Teale | 3 | | 3 | Opponents | | | 1 |

# HAYES & YEADING UNITED

**Chairman:** Tony O'Driscoll
**Secretary:** Derrick Matthews **(T)** 07816 123 418 **(E)** GM@hyufc.com
**Commercial Manager:** **(T/E)** commercial@hyufc.com
**Programme Editor:** Anthony Scott **(T/E)** programme@hyufc.com
**Ground Address:** SKYex Community Stadium, Beaconsfield Road, Hayes UB4 0SL
**(T)** 0208 573 2075 **Manager:** Micky Lewis

Photo courtesy: www.hyufc.com

## Club Factfile

**Founded:** 2007 **Nickname:**
**Previous Names:** Hayes - Botwell Mission 1909-29. Hayes and Yeading merged to form today's club in 2007
**Previous Leagues:** Isthmian. Conference 2007-16.

**Club Colours (change):** Red/black/black (All blue)

**Ground Capacity:** 6,000 **Seats:** 2,500 **Covered:** 3,900 **Clubhouse:** Yes **Shop:** Yes

**Directions**
From the M40/A40(M) Head eastbound towards London, take the Target Roundabout exit signposted Northolt, Harrow & Hayes. At the top of the slip road take the fourth exit (the first after the exit towards London) onto the A312 towards Hayes. The next roundabout (The White Hart) is about is about 1 mile and a half on. Here ignore signs to Yeading (third exit) instead take the second exit towards Hayes & Heathrow to stay on the A312 (Hayes-By - Pass). At the next roundabout again ignore signs to Yeading and carry straight over. Take the next exit signposted Southall and Uxbridge (A4020 Uxbridge Road). At the top of the slip road take the first exit towards Southall and follow the directions below Head eastbound along the (A4020) Uxbridge Road. Head eastbound along the (A4020) Uxbridge Road signposted towards Southall. Get into the far right hand lane as soon as you can and turn right into Springfield Road at the next set of Traffic Lights (There is a petrol station and a retail development with a Wickes on the corner of Springfield Road). Follow the road to the School, the Road bears left into Beaconsfield Road, and about 100 yards on your right is the entrance to the ground.

**Previous Grounds:** Kingfield Stadium (Woking FC) 2012-13.

**Record Attendance:** 1,881 v Luton Town - Conference Premier 06/03/2010
**Record Victory:** 8-2 v Hillingdon Borough (A) - Middlesex Senior Cup 11/11/08
**Record Defeat:** 0-8 v Luton Town (A) - Conference Premier 27/03/10
**Record Goalscorer:** Josh Scott - 40 (2007-09)
**Record Appearances:** James Mulley - 137 (2007-10)
**Additional Records:**

**Honours:**
Conference South Play-offs 2008-09

## 10 YEAR RECORD

| 06-07 | 07-08 | 08-09 | 09-10 | 10-11 | 11-12 | 12-13 | 13-14 | 14-15 | 15-16 |
|---|---|---|---|---|---|---|---|---|---|
| | Conf S 13 | Conf S 4 | Conf 17 | Conf 16 | Conf 21 | Conf S 17 | Conf S 20 | Conf S 19 | Nat S 21 |

# HAYES & YEADING MATCH RESULTS 2015-16

| Date | Comp | H/A | Opponents | Att: | Result | | Goalscorers | Pos | No. |
|---|---|---|---|---|---|---|---|---|---|
| Aug 8 | Nat South | H | Whitehawk | 189 | L | 3-4 | Benyon 3 Ehui 23 Williams 45 | 15 | 1 |
| 11 | Nat South | A | Truro City | 503 | W | 2-0 | Ehui 12 (pen) 50 | 9 | 2 |
| 15 | Nat South | A | Chelmsford City | 559 | L | 0-4 | | 17 | 3 |
| 18 | Nat South | H | Havant & Waterlooville | 194 | D | 0-0 | | 16 | 4 |
| 22 | Nat South | A | Maidstone United | 1906 | L | 1-3 | Ehui 90 | 18 | 5 |
| 29 | Nat South | H | Basingstoke Town | 182 | W | 3-0 | Benyon 7 Nicholson 25 Osborn 75 | 14 | 6 |
| 31 | Nat South | A | Maidenhead United | 532 | L | 1-2 | Osborn 56 | 16 | 7 |
| Sept 5 | Nat South | H | Wealdstone | 359 | D | 0-0 | | 16 | 8 |
| 12 | Nat South | H | Bishops Stortford | 178 | L | 0-2 | | 17 | 9 |
| 15 | Nat South | A | Hemel Hempstead Town | 395 | L | 0-4 | | 18 | 10 |
| 19 | Nat South | A | St Albans City | 518 | D | 1-1 | Benyon 47 | 19 | 11 |
| 26 | FA Cup 2Q | H | Poole Town | 185 | L | 2-3 | Scott 56 Ehui 76 | | 12 |
| Oct 3 | Nat South | H | Gosport Borough | 182 | D | 0-0 | | 19 | 13 |
| 10 | Nat South | A | Bishop's Stortford | 313 | D | 0-0 | | | 14 |
| 17 | Nat South | A | Concord Rangers | 234 | W | 3-0 | Scott 29 (pen) 84 Benyon 56 | 15 | 15 |
| 31 | Nat South | A | Dartford | 824 | L | 0-2 | | 16 | 16 |
| Nov 7 | Nat South | A | Sutton United | 758 | W | 1-0 | Scott 69 | 16 | 17 |
| 14 | Nat South | H | Chelmsford City | 229 | L | 0-5 | | 17 | 18 |
| 22 | Nat South | H | Truro City | 293 | D | 2-2 | Salmon 27 May 37 | 18 | 19 |
| 28 | FAT3Q | H | Eastbourne Borough | 204 | L | 0-4 | | | 20 |
| Dec 5 | Nat South | A | Bath City | 432 | W | 3-2 | Jay 9 Williams 25 Benyon 90 | 16 | 21 |
| 12 | Nat South | H | Sutton United | 217 | L | 1-3 | McKain 25 | 16 | 22 |
| 19 | Nat South | H | Maidstone United | 302 | W | 1-0 | Benyon 39 | 15 | 23 |
| 26 | Nat South | H | Weston-s-Mare | 176 | D | 1-1 | Benyon 67 | 15 | 24 |
| 28 | Nat South | A | Basingstoke Town | 530 | L | 0-1 | | 16 | 25 |
| Jan 23 | Nat South | H | Hemel Hempstead | 171 | D | 1-1 | Lodge 34 | 18 | 26 |
| Feb 6 | Nat South | H | Margate | 185 | L | 0-2 | | 19 | 27 |
| 9 | Nat South | H | Eastbourne Borough | 113 | D | 4-4 | Williams 25 McKain 42 Benyon 66 (pen) Lodge 88 (pen) | | 28 |
| 16 | Nat South | A | Weston-s-Mare | 262 | W | 2-0 | Worsfold 28 54 | 18 | 29 |
| 20 | Nat South | H | Oxford City | 152 | W | 2-1 | Benyon 57 Walker 89 (og) | 17 | 30 |
| 27 | Nat South | A | Ebbsfleet United | 950 | D | 0-0 | | 17 | 31 |
| Mar 1 | Nat South | H | Dartford | 177 | D | 2-2 | Benyon 21 Murombedzi 28 | 17 | 32 |
| 5 | Nat South | A | Eastbourne Borough | 454 | L | 0-2 | | 18 | 33 |
| 8 | Nat South | A | Whitehawk | 96 | W | 3-1 | Lodge 56 Benyon 71 Ehui 90 | 14 | 34 |
| 12 | Nat South | H | St Albans City | 188 | L | 1-3 | Ehui 79 | 17 | 35 |
| 14 | Nat South | A | Wealdstone | 638 | L | 0-3 | | 17 | 36 |
| 19 | Nat South | A | Margate | 557 | W | 2-1 | Benyon 40 (pen) Cronin 47 | 16 | 37 |
| 25 | Nat South | A | Havant & Waterlooville | 747 | L | 0-1 | | 17 | 38 |
| 28 | Nat South | H | Maidenhead United | 520 | L | 2-5 | Harper 71 Purse 85 | 19 | 39 |
| Apr 2 | Nat South | H | Ebbsfleet United | 287 | L | 0-5 | | 19 | 40 |
| 9 | Nat South | N | Oxford City | 235 | D | 2-2 | Arzamendi 31 (og) Worsfold 37 | 20 | 41 |
| 16 | Nat South | H | Concord Rangers | 148 | D | 2-2 | Monthe 85 Benyon 90 | 20 | 42 |
| 23 | Nat South | H | Bath City | 258 | L | 0-3 | | 20 | 43 |
| 30 | Nat South | A | Gosport Borough | 503 | W | 5-2 | BENYON 3 (9 69 87) Kearney 74 84 | 21 | 44 |

| GOALSCORERS | Scoring Games | Consec Sco Games | Total | | Scoring Games | Consec Sco Games | Total |
|---|---|---|---|---|---|---|---|
| ***2014-15 Cox*** | | | ***7*** | Cronin | 1 | | 1 |
| Benyon | 14 | | 16 | Harper | 1 | | 1 |
| Ehui | 6 | 2 | 7 | Jay | 1 | | 1 |
| Scott | 3 | | 4 | May | 1 | | 1 |
| Lodge | 3 | | 3 | Monthe | 1 | | 1 |
| Williams | 3 | | 3 | Murombedzi | 1 | | 1 |
| Worsfold | 3 | | 3 | Nicholson | 1 | | 1 |
| Kearney | 2 | | 2 | Purse | 1 | | 1 |
| McKane | 2 | | 2 | Salmon | 1 | | 1 |
| Osborn | 2 | 2 | 2 | Opponents | | | 2 |

# HITCHIN TOWN

**Chairman:**
**Secretary:** Roy Izzard **(T)** 07803 202 498 **(E)** roy.izzard@outlook.com
**Commercial Manager:** **(T/E)**
**Programme Editor:** Mick Docking **(T/E)** mickdocking@gmail.com
**Ground Address:** Top Field, Fishponds Road, Hitchin SG5 1NU
**(T)** 01462 459 028 (match days only) **Manager:** Mark Burke

2015-16 Squad.

## Club Factfile

**Founded:** 1865 **Nickname:** Canaries
**Previous Names:** Hitchin FC 1865-1911. Re-formed in 1928
**Previous Leagues:** Spartan 1928-39, Herts & Middlesex 1939-45, Athenian 1945-63, Isthmian 1964-2004

**Club Colours (change):** Yellow/green/green (All green)

**Ground Capacity:** 5,000 **Seats:** 500 **Covered:** 1,250 **Clubhouse:** Yes **Shop:** Yes

**Directions**
From East A1 to J8 onto A602 to Hitchin.
At Three Moorhens Pub roundabout, take third exit (A600) towards Bedford, over next roundabout and lights, turn right at next roundabout, turnstiles on left, parking 50 yards on.

**Previous Grounds:** None

**Record Attendance:** 7,878 v Wycombe Wanderers - FA Amateur Cup 3rd Round 08/02/1956
**Record Victory:** 13-0 v Cowley and v RAF Uxbridge - both Spartan League 1929-30
**Record Defeat:** 0-10 v Kingstonian (A) and v Slough Town (A) - 1965-66 and 1979-80 respectively
**Record Goalscorer:** Paul Giggle - 214 (1968-86)
**Record Appearances:** Paul Giggle - 769 (1968-86)
**Additional Records:** Paid £2,000 to Potton United for Ray Seeking
Received £30,000 from Cambridge United for Zema Abbey, January 2000
**Honours:**
AFA Senior Cup 1931-32. London Senior Cup 1969-70. Isthmian League Division 1 1992-93.
Herts Senior Cup x13 Most recently 2015-16.

### 10 YEAR RECORD

| 06-07 | 07-08 | 08-09 | 09-10 | 10-11 | 11-12 | 12-13 | 13-14 | 14-15 | 15-16 |
|---|---|---|---|---|---|---|---|---|---|
| SthP 11 | SthP 18 | SthP 20 | SthC 2 | SthC 2 | SthP 14 | SthP 13 | SthP 13 | SthP 9 | SthP 3 |

## HITCHIN TOWN MATCH RESULTS 2015-16

| Date | Comp | H/A | Opponents | Att: | Result | | Goalscorers | Pos | No. |
|---|---|---|---|---|---|---|---|---|---|
| Aug 8 | SPL | H | Stratford Town | 278 | L | 2-3 | Martin 45 Bickerstaff 63 | 16 | 1 |
| 11 | SPL | A | Chesham United | 351 | D | 1-1 | McNamara 65 | 16 | 2 |
| 15 | SPL | A | Cirencester Town | 125 | D | 0-0 | | 17 | 3 |
| 17 | SPL | H | Kings Lynn | 351 | W | 2-0 | McNamara 22 Burns 74 | 9 | 4 |
| 22 | SPL | H | Slough Town | 319 | W | 3-1 | Smith 27 McNamara 70 82 | 9 | 5 |
| 29 | SPL | A | Merthyr Town | 497 | L | 1-5 | Martin 21 | 14 | 6 |
| 31 | SPL | H | Dunstable Town | 360 | W | 4-1 | Burns 12 Kirkpatrick 17.Smith 55 Lench 90 | 10 | 7 |
| Sept 5 | SPL | A | Frome Town | 151 | W | 4-0 | Burns 16 17 Ann 25 McNamara 63 | 5 | 8 |
| **12** | **FAC1Q** | **A** | **Peterborough Sports** | **187** | **D** | **1-1** | **Burns 55** | | 9 |
| **14** | **FAC1Qr** | **H** | **Peterborough Sports** | **198** | **W** | **4-2** | **Burns 24 Smith 44 118 McNamara 108 (aet)** | | 10 |
| 19 | SPL | A | Histon | 318 | L | 1-5 | Lench 27 | 10 | 11 |
| 21 | SPL | H | Bedworth Town | 264 | W | 3-1 | Rolfe 45 (pen) McNamara 46 Kirkpatrick 88 | 6 | 12 |
| **26** | **FAC2Q** | **A** | **Kirkley & Pakefield** | **217** | **W** | **2-0** | **Lench 3 Burns 73** | | 13 |
| 28 | SPL | A | Hungerford Town | 127 | D | 1-1 | McNamara 3 | 8 | 14 |
| Oct 5 | SPL | H | Leamington | 311 | D | 2-2 | Frendo 52 Burns 75 | 7 | 15 |
| **10** | **FAC3Q** | **A** | **Enfield Town** | **883** | **D** | **0-0** | | | 16 |
| **12** | **FAC3Qr** | **H** | **Enfield Town** | **486** | **L** | **1-2** | **Burns 40** | | 17 |
| 17 | SPL | H | Redditch United | 211 | L | 1-2 | McNamara 87 | 14 | 18 |
| 24 | SPL | H | Kettering Town | 379 | W | 2-1 | Kirkpatrick 79 McNamara 89 | 13 | 19 |
| **31** | **FAT1Q** | **H** | **Burgess Hill Town** | **190** | **W** | **3-2** | **Pearson 58 (og) Boyd 81 C.Donnelly 89** | | 20 |
| Nov 7 | SPL | H | Biggleswade Town | 417 | W | 3-0 | C.Donnelly 37 Burns 71 McNamara 85 | 9 | 21 |
| **14** | **FAT2Q** | **A** | **Haringey Borough** | **119** | **D** | **1-1** | **Scott 72 (og)** | | 22 |
| **16** | **FAT2Qr** | **H** | **Haringey Borough** | **109** | **W** | **3-0** | **B.Donnelly 4 83 Smith 26** | | 23 |
| 21 | SPL | H | Cirencester Town | 304 | W | 2-0 | Lench 77 Burns 81 | 9 | 24 |
| 24 | SPL | A | Dorchester Town | 283 | W | 1-0 | B.Donnelly 29 | 7 | 25 |
| **28** | **FAT3Q** | **A** | **Weston-s-Mare** | **175** | **L** | **0-4** | | | 26 |
| Dec 5 | SPL | H | Chippenham Town | 290 | D | 1-1 | Ann 2 | 10 | 27 |
| 7 | SPL | H | Paulton Rovers | 235 | W | 2-0 | B.Donnelly 51 Ann61 | 8 | 28 |
| 12 | SPL | A | Bideford | 150 | D | 0-0 | | 8 | 29 |
| 19 | SPL | H | Merthyr Town | 402 | W | 2-0 | Kirkpatrick 1 Ann 90 | 6 | 30 |
| 26 | SPL | A | Dunstable Town | 291 | D | 0-0 | | 5 | 31 |
| Jan 5 | SPL | A | Bedworth United | 155 | W | 2-1 | Lench 8 48 | 3 | 32 |
| 9 | SPL | A | Weymouth | 494 | W | 2-0 | Lench 15 Ann 78 | 3 | 33 |
| 16 | SPL | H | Frome Town | 572 | L | 1-2 | McNamara 45 | 4 | 34 |
| 23 | SPL | A | Slough Town | 314 | L | 0-1 | | 5 | 35 |
| 30 | SPL | A | Paulton Rovers | 189 | L | 1-2 | B.Donnelly 4 | 7 | 36 |
| Feb 6 | SPL | H | Histon | 401 | W | 3-2 | McNamara 26 Burns 79 C.Donnelly 88 | 7 | 37 |
| 13 | SPL | A | Leamington | 345 | W | 1-0 | C.Donnelly 10 | 5 | 38 |
| 16 | SPL | A | St Neots Town | 298 | W | 2-1 | Smith 58 McNamara 72 | 4 | 39 |
| 20 | SPL | H | Hungerford Town | 431 | W | 2-1 | Webb 11 B.Donnelly 31 | 4 | 40 |
| 23 | SPL | A | Poole Town | 329 | L | 0-1 | | 4 | 41 |
| 27 | SPL | A | Redditch United | 381 | L | 2-3 | McNamara 47 C.Donnelly 90 | 4 | 42 |
| Mar 5 | SPL | H | Dorchester Town | 366 | W | 3-2 | B.Donnelly 26 Ann 66 McNamara 79 | 4 | 43 |
| 7 | SPL | H | Cambridge City | 374 | W | 4-2 | C.Donnelly 15 Kirkpatrick 35 72 McNamara 51 | 3 | 44 |
| 12 | SPL | A | Chippenham Town | 338 | D | 1-1 | Rolfe 64 (pen) | 4 | 45 |
| 15 | SPL | A | Stratford Town | 156 | D | 1-1 | B.Donnelly 27 | 4 | 46 |
| 19 | SPL | H | Bideford | 490 | D | 0-0 | | 5 | 47 |
| 22 | SPL | A | Kings Lynn Town | 366 | L | 0-1 | | 5 | 48 |
| 25 | SPL | H | Weymouth | 578 | W | 1-0 | McNamara 79 | 4 | 49 |
| 28 | SPL | A | Cambridge City | 222 | W | 1-0 | Kirkpatrick 84 | 3 | 50 |
| Apr 2 | SPL | A | Kettering Town | 673 | D | 1-1 | C.Donnelly 52 | 3 | 51 |
| 9 | SPL | H | Poole United | 712 | D | 0-0 | | 4 | 52 |
| 11 | SPL | H | Chesham United | 366 | W | 5-1 | Walster 3 (pen) B.Donnelly 57 70 Webb 72 Burns 76 | 2 | 53 |
| 16 | SPL | A | Biggleswade Town | 461 | W | 5-3 | B.DONNELLY 3 (12 60 73) Bickerstaff 36 Burns 54 | 2 | 54 |
| 23 | SPL | H | St Neots Town | 1184 | W | 2-0 | Smith 49 Burns 71 | 3 | 55 |
| **27** | **PO SF** | **H** | **Hungerford Town** | **1305** | **L** | **2-3** | **B.Donnelly 56 Burns 59** | | 56 |

| GOALSCORERS | Scoring Games | Consec Sco Games | Total | | Scoring Games | Consec Sco Games | Total |
|---|---|---|---|---|---|---|---|
| *2014-15 Donnelly* | | | *12* | Martin | 2 | | 2 |
| McNamara | 17 | 3 | 18 | Rolfe | 2 | | 2 |
| Burns | 15 | 4 | 16 | Webb | 2 | | 2 |
| B.Donnelly | 11 | 2 | 15 | Boyd | 1 | | 1 |
| C.Donnelly | 7 | 2 | 7 | Frendo | 1 | | 1 |
| Kirkpatrick | 6 | | 7 | Walster | 1 | | 1 |
| Lench | 7 | 2 | 7 | Opponents | | | 2 |
| Ann | 6 | | 6 | | | | |
| Smith | 6 | | 6 | | | | |
| Bickerstaff | 2 | | 2 | | | | |

# KETTERING TOWN

**Chairman:** Ritchie Jeune
**Secretary:** Neil Griffin (T) 01536 217 006 (E) neil.griffin@ketteringtownfc.com
**Commercial Manager:** Martin Bellamy (T/E) martin.bellamy@ketteringtownfc.com
**Programme Editor:** Paul Cooke (T/E) companioncooke@btinternet.com
**Ground Address:** Latimer Park, Burton Latimer, Kettering NN15 5PS
(T) 01536 217 006 **Manager:** Marcus Law

## Club Factfile

**Founded:** 1872 **Nickname:** The Poppies
**Previous Names:** Kettering > 1924
**Previous Leagues:** Midland 1892-1900, also had a team in United Counties 1896-99, Southern 1900-30, 1950-79, 2001-02, Birmingham 1930-50, Alliance/Conference 1979-2001, 02-03, Isthmian 2003-04
**Club Colours (change):** Red & black stripes/black/red (Blue & white stripes/white/blue)

**Ground Capacity:** **Seats:** Yes **Covered:** Yes **Clubhouse:** Yes **Shop:**

**Directions**
From Junction 10 of the A14 turn due South at the roundabout onto Kettering Road (signposted Burton Latimer). After 200 yards turn right at the roundabout onto Attendiez Way. Go over the next roundabout and follow the road around Morrison's warehouse. The road becomes Polwell Lane and the entrance to Latimer Park is on the left just after Morrison's warehouse.
If approaching from the South, take the A6 to its junction with the A14 and follow the directions above or, if travelling up the A509 turn right at the roundabout just after Isham (signposted Burton Latimer) onto Station Road and continue for half a mile past the Weetabix and Alumasc factories before turning left onto Polwell Lane. The entrance to Latimer Park is on the right after 50 yards.

**Previous Grounds:** North Park, Green Lane, Rockingham Road > 2011. Nene Park 2011-13.

**Record Attendance:** 11,536 v Peterborough - FA Cup 1st Round replay 1958-59
**Record Victory:** 16-0 v Higham YMCI - FA Cup 1909
**Record Defeat:** 0-13 v Mardy - Southern League Division Two 1911-12
**Record Goalscorer:** Roy Clayton - 171 (1972-81)
**Record Appearances:** Roger Ashby
**Additional Records:** Paid £25,000 to Macclesfield for Carl Alford 1994. Recieved £150,000 from Newcastle United for Andy Hunt

**Honours:**
Southern League 1927-28, 56-57, 72-73, 2001-02, Division One Central 2014-15. Conference North 2007-08.

**10 YEAR RECORD**

| 06-07 | 07-08 | 08-09 | 09-10 | 10-11 | 11-12 | 12-13 | 13-14 | 14-15 | 15-16 |
|---|---|---|---|---|---|---|---|---|---|
| Conf N 2 | Conf N 1 | Conf 8 | Conf 6 | Conf 14 | Conf 24 | SthP 22 | SthC 3 | SthC 1 | SthP 6 |

## KETTERING TOWN MATCH RESULTS 2015-16

| Date | Comp | H/A | Opponents | Att: | Result | | Goalscorers | Pos | No. |
|---|---|---|---|---|---|---|---|---|---|
| Aug 8 | SPL | A | Poole Town | 399 | L | 0-1 | | 19 | 1 |
| 11 | SPL | H | Redditch United | 626 | D | 0-0 | | 18 | 2 |
| 15 | SPL | H | Merthyr Town | 579 | **W** | 3-2 | Solkhon 24 Sandy 49 Baker-Richardson 83 | 13 | 3 |
| 18 | SPL | A | Leamington | 545 | L | 2-3 | Williams 48 Gooding 52 (pen) | 14 | 4 |
| 22 | SPL | H | Weymouth | 581 | L | 0-1 | | 19 | 5 |
| 29 | SPL | A | Frome Town | 313 | **W** | 2-1 | Williams 51 Sandy 82 | 16 | 6 |
| 31 | SPL | H | Kings Lynn Town | 618 | **W** | 2-1 | Gooding 23 Wright 64 | 14 | 7 |
| Sept 5 | SPL | A | Stratford Town | 410 | L | 1-2 | Mulligan 18 | 16 | 8 |
| **12** | **FAC1Q** | **A** | **Market Drayton Town** | **221** | **W** | **5-0** | **Gooding 17(p) 37(p) Baker-Richardson 27 Grocott 51 Brown 87** | | 9 |
| 19 | SPL | A | Paulton Rovers | 222 | **W** | 1-0 | Baker-Richardson 12 | 13 | 10 |
| **26** | **FAC2Q** | **H** | **AFC Telford United** | **693** | **W** | **2-1** | **Baker-Richardson 49 59** | | 11 |
| 29 | SPL | A | Dunstable Town | 212 | L | 0-4 | | 17 | 12 |
| Oct 3 | SPL | H | Hungerford Town | 588 | **W** | 2-1 | Mulligan 10 Baker-Richardson 79 | 12 | 13 |
| 6 | SPL | H | Chippenham Town | 423 | L | 1-2 | Ogbonna 74 | 15 | 14 |
| **10** | **FAC3Q** | **H** | **Bamber Bridge** | **696** | **D** | **1-1** | **Canavan 61** | | 15 |
| **13** | **FAC3Qr** | **A** | **Bamber Bridge** | **478** | **L** | **2-3** | **Grocott 51 Ogbonna 59** | | 16 |
| 17 | SPL | H | Histon | 562 | **W** | 5-4 | Canavan 7 Solkhon 26 Ogbonna 38 (pen) Grocott 54 Bryan 73 | 16 | 17 |
| 20 | SPL | A | Biggleswade Town | 249 | **W** | 3-1 | Grocott 7 Canavan 15 Obeng 86 | 10 | 18 |
| 24 | SPL | A | Hitchin Town | 379 | L | 1-2 | Ogbonna 30 | 12 | 19 |
| **30** | **FAT1Q** | **A** | **St Ives Town** | **325** | **W** | **1-0** | **Mulligan 74** | | 20 |
| Nov 3 | SPL | H | Biggleswde Town | 429 | **W** | 2-1 | Solkhon 64 Iwelino 86 (og) | 9 | 21 |
| 7 | SPL | A | Bideford | 209 | L | 0-2 | | 11 | 22 |
| **14** | **FAT2Q** | **H** | **Burscough** | **435** | **L** | **0-3** | | | 23 |
| 21 | SPL | A | Merthyr Town | 469 | D | 1-1 | Carvalho 90 | 11 | 24 |
| 24 | SPL | H | Chesham United | 401 | **W** | 3-0 | Carvalho 20 Brighton 24 Howe 34 | | 25 |
| 28 | SPL | H | Poole Town | 525 | **W** | 1-0 | Carvalho 64 | 7 | 26 |
| Dec 5 | SPL | H | Cambridge City | 552 | D | 0-0 | | 9 | 27 |
| 8 | SPL | A | Cirencester Town | 225 | L | 0-1 | | 9 | 28 |
| 12 | SPL | A | St Neots Town | 438 | **W** | 1-0 | Howe 20 | 9 | 29 |
| 26 | SPL | A | Kings Lynn Town | 816 | **W** | 3-0 | Brighton 43 Carvalho 62 80 | 9 | 30 |
| Jan 2 | SPL | A | Bedworth United | 448 | D | 1-1 | Canavan 85 | 9 | 31 |
| 23 | SPL | A | Weymouth | 637 | L | 2-3 | Langdon 40 Canavan 42 | 12 | 32 |
| 30 | SPL | A | Hungerfprd Town | 249 | L | 1-2 | Canavan 63 | 12 | 33 |
| Feb 13 | SPL | A | Chippenham Town | 527 | **W** | 2-0 | Weir-Daley 4 Carvalho 90 | 12 | 34 |
| 16 | SPL | H | Frome Town | 425 | D | 1-1 | Carvalho 18 (pen) | 13 | 35 |
| 23 | SPL | H | Dorchester Town | 342 | **W** | 3-0 | Grocott 24 Weir-Daley 49 Howe 68 | 12 | 36 |
| 27 | SPL | A | Histon | 436 | L | 1-3 | Weir-Daley 58 | 12 | 37 |
| Mar 1 | SPL | A | Slough Town | 294 | **W** | 3-1 | Howell 7 Weir-Daley 34 Carvalho 45 | 12 | 38 |
| 5 | SPL | H | Cirencester Town | 489 | **W** | 4-3 | Solkhon 11 Howe 18 Stephens 19 Carvalho 88 | 10 | 39 |
| 12 | SPL | A | Cambridge City | 333 | **W** | 4-0 | Howe 1 Brighton 7 28 Weir-Daley 43 | 8 | 40 |
| 15 | SPL | H | Paulton Rovers | 408 | **W** | 2-0 | Canavan 89 Obeng 90 | 8 | 41 |
| 19 | SPL | H | St Neots Town | 561 | D | 1-1 | Roberts 47 | 8 | 42 |
| 22 | SPL | H | Stratford Town | 467 | **W** | 3-1 | Popa 56 Weir-Dale 67 Carvalho 82 (pen) | 7 | 43 |
| 26 | SPL | H | SloughTown | 637 | **W** | 1-0 | Carvalho 61 | 7 | 44 |
| Apr 2 | SPL | H | Hitchin Town | 673 | D | 1-1 | Weir-Daley 3 | 8 | 45 |
| 7 | SPL | H | Dunstable Town | 470 | **W** | 3-1 | Popa 6 15 Solkhon 84 | 6 | 46 |
| 9 | SPL | A | Chesham United | 429 | **W** | 3-0 | Howe 13 Baker 15 Stephens | 5 | 47 |
| 12 | SPL | H | Leamington | 669 | D | 1-1 | Canavan 14 | 5 | 48 |
| 14 | SPL | H | Bedworth United | 529 | L | 0-1 | | 6 | 49 |
| 18 | SPL | A | Redditch United | 452 | L | 1-2 | Carvalho 67(pen) | 7 | 50 |
| 21 | SPL | H | Bideford Town | 447 | **W** | 7-0 | Brighton 49 90 Obeng 50 58 Howe 67 Stephens 85 Baker 88 | 7 | 51 |
| 23 | SPL | A | Dorchester Town | 507 | **W** | 4-1 | Lander 5 (og) Brighton 15 Howe 39 Solkhon 81 | 6 | 52 |

| GOALSCORERS | Scoring Games | Consec Sco Games | Total | | Scoring Games | Consec Sco Games | Total |
|---|---|---|---|---|---|---|---|
| Carvalho | 11 | | 12 | Popa | 3 | | 3 |
| Canavan | 8 | 2 | 8 | Stephens | 3 | | 3 |
| Howe | 8 | | 8 | Baker | 2 | | 2 |
| Brighton | 5 | | 7 | Sandy | 2 | | 2 |
| Weir-Daley | 7 | | 7 | Williams | 2 | | 2 |
| Baker-Richardson | 5 | 3 | 6 | Brown | 1 | | 1 |
| Solkhon | 6 | | 6 | Bryan | 1 | | 1 |
| Grocutt | 5 | 2 | 5 | Howell | 1 | | 1 |
| Gooding | 3 | | 4 | Langdon | 1 | | 1 |
| Obeng | 3 | | 4 | Roberts | 1 | | 1 |
| Ogbanna | 4 | 2 | 4 | Wright | 1 | | 1 |
| Mulligan | 3 | | 3 | Opponents | | | 2 |

# KING'S LYNN TOWN

**Chairman:** Stephen Cleeve
**Secretary:** Norman Cesar (T) 07887 373 956 (E) ncesar1947@yahoo.co.uk
**Commercial Manager:** (T/E)
**Programme Editor:** Norman Cesar (T/E) ncesar1947@yahoo.co.uk
**Ground Address:** The Walks Stadium, Tennyson Road, King's Lynn PE30 5PB
(T) 01553 760 060 **Manager:** Gary Setchell

## Club Factfile

**Founded:** 1879 **Nickname:** Linnets
**Previous Names:** King's Lynn > 2010
**Previous Leagues:** N'folk & Suffolk, Eastern Co. 1935-39, 48-54, UCL 1946-48, 2010-12, Midland Co. 1954-58, NPL 1980-81, 2012-15, Southern >2008, Conference 2008-09.

**Club Colours (change):** Yellow/blue/yellow (All purple)

**Ground Capacity:** 8,200 **Seats:** 1,200 **Covered:** 5,000 **Clubhouse:** Yes **Shop:** Yes

**Directions** At the roundabout, at the junction of A47 and the A17, follow the A47, signposted King's Lynn and Norwich. Travel along the dual carriageway for approx. one and a half miles branching off left, following the signs for Town Centre, onto the Hardwick roundabout. Take the first exit, following the signs for Town Centre, travel through two sets of traffic lights until reaching a further set of traffic lights at the Southgates roundabout. Take the fourth exit onto Vancouver Avenue, and travel for approx. 300 metres, going straight across a mini roundabout, The Walks is a further 200 metres along on the left hand side, with car parking outside the ground. The changing rooms and hospitality suite are located at the rear of the main stand.

**Previous Grounds:** None

**Record Attendance:** **Att:** 12,937 v Exeter City FAC 1st Rnd 1950-51.
**Record Victory:** Not known
**Record Defeat:** Not known
**Record Goalscorer:** Malcolm Lindsey 321.
**Record Appearances:** Mick Wright 1,152 (British Record)
**Additional Records:**

**Honours:**
Southern League Division 1 East 2003-04, Premier Division 2007-08, League Cup 2004-05.
Northern Premier Division One South 2012-13.

### 10 YEAR RECORD

| 06-07 | | 07-08 | | 08-09 | | 09-10 | | 10-11 | | 11-12 | | 12-13 | | 13-14 | | 14-15 | | 15-16 | |
|---|---|---|---|---|---|---|---|---|---|---|---|---|---|---|---|---|---|---|---|
| SthP | 3 | SthP | 1 | Conf N | 17 | NP P | dnf | UCL P | 2 | UCL P | 2 | NP1S | 1 | NP P | 11 | NP P | 18 | SthP | 9 |

# KING'S LYNN MATCH RESULTS 2015-16

| Date | Comp | H/A | Opponents | Att: | Result | Goalscorers | Pos | No. |
|---|---|---|---|---|---|---|---|---|
| Aug 8 | SPL | A | Merthyr Town | 509 | L 0-2 | | 23 | 1 |
| 11 | SPL | H | Cambridge City | 642 | W 1-0 | Hurst 47 | 13 | 2 |
| 15 | SPL | H | Bideford | 572 | L 0-1 | | 15 | 3 |
| 17 | SPL | A | Hitchin Town | 351 | L 0-2 | | 16 | 4 |
| 22 | SPL | A | Cirencester Town | 126 | W 1-0 | Clunan 35 | 15 | 5 |
| 29 | SPL | H | Paulton Rovers | 487 | D 0-0 | | 17 | 6 |
| 31 | SPL | A | Kettering Town | 618 | L 1-2 | Fryatt 45 | 17 | 7 |
| Sept 5 | SPL | H | Poole Town | 525 | W 3-2 | Fryatt 22 Clunan 56 Mulready 78 | 17 | 8 |
| **12** | **FAC1Q** | **H** | **Wroxham** | **614** | **W 4-1** | **Miller 3 38 Stevenson 24 28** | | **9** |
| 19 | SPL | A | Redditch United | 277 | L 0-2 | | 18 | 10 |
| 22 | SPL | H | Histon | 466 | W 4-2 | Mulready 45 83 Hurst 70 Yong 72 | 16 | 11 |
| **26** | **FAC2Q** | **H** | **Witham Town** | **571** | **W 1-0** | **Clunan 15 (pen)** | | **12** |
| 29 | SPL | A | Bedworth United | 202 | L 0-3 | | 18 | 13 |
| Oct 3 | SPL | H | Chippenham Town | 425 | W 2-0 | Mulready 17 71 | 13 | 14 |
| 6 | SPL | A | Dunstable Town | 459 | D 1-1 | Hilliard 45 | 11 | 15 |
| **10** | **FAC3Q** | **A** | **Barwell** | **292** | **L 0-1** | | | **16** |
| 17 | SPL | H | Leamington | 578 | L 0-1 | | 17 | 17 |
| 20 | SPL | A | Histon | 259 | W 2-1 | Bridges 69 Fryatt 83 | 15 | 18 |
| 24 | SPL | A | Weymouth | 468 | L 0-2 | | 17 | 19 |
| 27 | SPL | H | Biggleswade Town | 415 | W 2-1 | Stevenson 23 90 | 10 | 20 |
| **31** | **FAT1Q** | **A** | **Belper Town** | **238** | **D 1-1** | **Fryatt 27** | | **21** |
| **Nov 3** | **FAT1Qr** | **H** | **Belper Town** | **376** | **W 5-1** | **Smith 20 Clunan 50 (pen) Hurst 65 Hilliard 83 90** | | **22** |
| 7 | SPL | H | Slough Town | 480 | W 2-1 | Hurst 38 Chilton 90 | 8 | 23 |
| **14** | **FAT2Q** | **A** | **Nantwich Town** | **359** | **L 1-5** | **Gaughran 71** | | **24** |
| 21 | SPL | A | Bideford | 168 | W 5-0 | Stevenson 15 25 Zielonka 41 Bridges 60 Hilliard 84 | 8 | 25 |
| 23 | SPL | A | Hungerford Town | 112 | L 1-2 | Stevenson 84 | 8 | 26 |
| 5 | SPL | A | Dorchester Town | 285 | L 0-2 | | 14 | 27 |
| 12 | SPL | H | Frome Town | 376 | W 1-0 | Edge 82 | 12 | 28 |
| 19 | SPL | A | Paulton Rovers | 119 | W 3-1 | Zielonka 20 Hilliard 49 Bridges 53 | 12 | 29 |
| 26 | SPL | H | Kettering Town | 816 | L 0-3 | | 13 | 30 |
| Jan 2 | SPL | A | St Neots Town | 520 | W 1-0 | Bridges 85 | 11 | 31 |
| 5 | SPL | H | Merthyr Town | 391 | L 2-3 | Clunan 69 (pen) Stevenson 90 | 11 | 32 |
| 9 | SPL | H | Chesham United | 490 | W 2-0 | Clunan 12 Mulready 32 | 9 | 33 |
| 16 | SPL | A | Poole Town | 365 | D 1-1 | Mulready 32 | 10 | 34 |
| 23 | SPL | H | Cirencester Town | 516 | W 2-0 | Smith 29 Hilliard 90 | 8 | 35 |
| 30 | SPL | A | Cheltenham Town | 427 | L 1-4 | Stevenson 74 | 9 | 36 |
| Feb 6 | SPL | H | Redditch United | 498 | W 1-0 | Stevenson 76 | 8 | 37 |
| 13 | SPL | A | Dunstable Town | 139 | W 2-0 | Hurst 16 Stevenson 76 | 7 | 38 |
| 17 | SPL | A | Stratford Town | 217 | D 1-1 | Friend 89 | 7 | 39 |
| 20 | SPL | H | Bedworth United | 579 | W 3-0 | Zielonka 32 Hilliard 75 Fryatt 81 | 5 | 40 |
| 27 | SPL | A | Leamington | 541 | D 1-1 | Gaughan 24 | 5 | 41 |
| Mar 12 | SPL | H | Dorchester Town | 523 | L 1-2 | Zielonka 71 | 10 | 42 |
| 19 | SPL | A | Frome Town | 145 | L 0-1 | | 10 | 43 |
| 22 | SPL | H | Hitchin Town | 366 | W 1-0 | Sands 70 | 9 | 44 |
| 26 | SPL | A | Chesham United | 351 | L 0-2 | | 10 | 45 |
| 30 | SPL | H | St Neots Town | 354 | D 1-1 | Fryatt 17 | 9 | 46 |
| Apr 2 | SPL | A | Biggleswade Town | 181 | W 4-2 | Clunan 14 (pen) Sands 20 23 Hilliard 52 | 9 | 47 |
| 9 | SPL | H | Weymouth | 514 | D 0-0 | | 9 | 48 |
| 12 | SPL | H | Hungerford Town | 287 | L 0-1 | | 9 | 49 |
| 16 | SPL | A | Slough Town | 338 | L 0-2 | | 9 | 50 |
| 20 | SPL | A | Cambridge City | 135 | W 3-1 | Sands15 Stevenson 28 45 | 9 | 51 |
| 23 | SPL | H | Stratford Town | 466 | W 2-1 | Smith 49 Burns 71 | 9 | 52 |

| GOALSCORERS | Scoring Games | Consec Sco Games | Total |
|---|---|---|---|
| *2014-15 Thomson* | | | *20* |
| Stevenson | 9 | 2 | 13 |
| Hilliard | 7 | | 8 |
| Mulready | 5 | | 7 |
| Clunan | 6 | | 7 |
| Fryatt | 6 | 2 | 6 |
| Hurst | 5 | | 5 |
| Bridges | 4 | | 4 |
| Sands | 4 | | 4 |
| Zielonka | 4 | | 4 |
| Smith | 3 | | 3 |
| Gaughan | 2 | | 2 |
| Miller | 2 | | 2 |
| Burns | 1 | | 1 |
| Chilton | 1 | | 1 |
| Edge | 1 | | 1 |
| Friend | 1 | | 1 |
| Yong | 1 | | 1 |

# KINGS LANGLEY

**Chairman:** Derry Edgar

**Secretary:** Andy Mackness (T) 07976 692 801 (E) andymackness@yahoo.co.uk

**Commercial Manager:** Darren Eliot (T/E) 07861 897 089

**Programme Editor:** Roy Mitchard (T/E) kingfisher@mitchard3.freeserve.co.uk

**Ground Address:** Gaywood Park, Hempstead Road, Kings Langley Herts WD4 8BS

(T) 07976 692 801 **Manager:** Ritchie Hanlon & Paul Hughes

2016-17 Squad proudly shows off last season's collection of trophies.

## Club Factfile

**Founded:** 1886 **Nickname:** Kings

**Previous Names:** None

**Previous Leagues:** Hertfordshire County 1946-52, 55-2001. Parthenon 1952-55. Spartan South Midlands 1955-2015.

**Club Colours (change):** White & black/white/white

**Ground Capacity:** **Seats:** **Covered:** **Clubhouse:** Yes **Shop:**

**Directions**

From M25 leave at Junction 20. Take A4251 to Kings Langley. Go over first roundabout and through village, past 'Young Pretender' Pub & restaurant on left. Go past Coniston Road on left and immediately indicate and move into 'turn right lane' in middle of road. Turn RIGHT into Ground. If car park is full, use lay-byes on road outside ground. Total distance from junction 20 :- 1.4 miles approx. From Hemel Hempstead, take A4251 through Apsley. Continue under railway bridge and ground is approx. a quarter of a mile on LEFT, immediately before lay-bye.

**Previous Grounds:**

**Record Attendance:** Not known
**Record Victory:** Not known
**Record Defeat:** Not known
**Record Goalscorer:** Not known
**Record Appearances:** Not known
**Additional Records:** 47 consecutive matches unbeaten in all competitions between 15-09-07 and 15-10-08.

**Honours:**
Hertfordshrie County 1949-50, 51-52, 65-66, 66-67, Division One 1975-76.
Spartan South Midlands Division Two 2007-08, Premier Division 2014-15. Southern League Division One Central 2015-16.

**10 YEAR RECORD**

| 06-07 | | 07-08 | | 08-09 | | 09-10 | | 10-11 | | 11-12 | | 12-13 | | 13-14 | | 14-15 | | 15-16 | |
|---|---|---|---|---|---|---|---|---|---|---|---|---|---|---|---|---|---|---|---|
| SSM2 | 2 | SSM2 | 1 | SSM1 | 2 | SSM1 | 7 | SSM1 | 3 | SSM1 | 4 | SSM1 | 6 | SSM1 | 2 | SSM P | 1 | SthC | 1 |

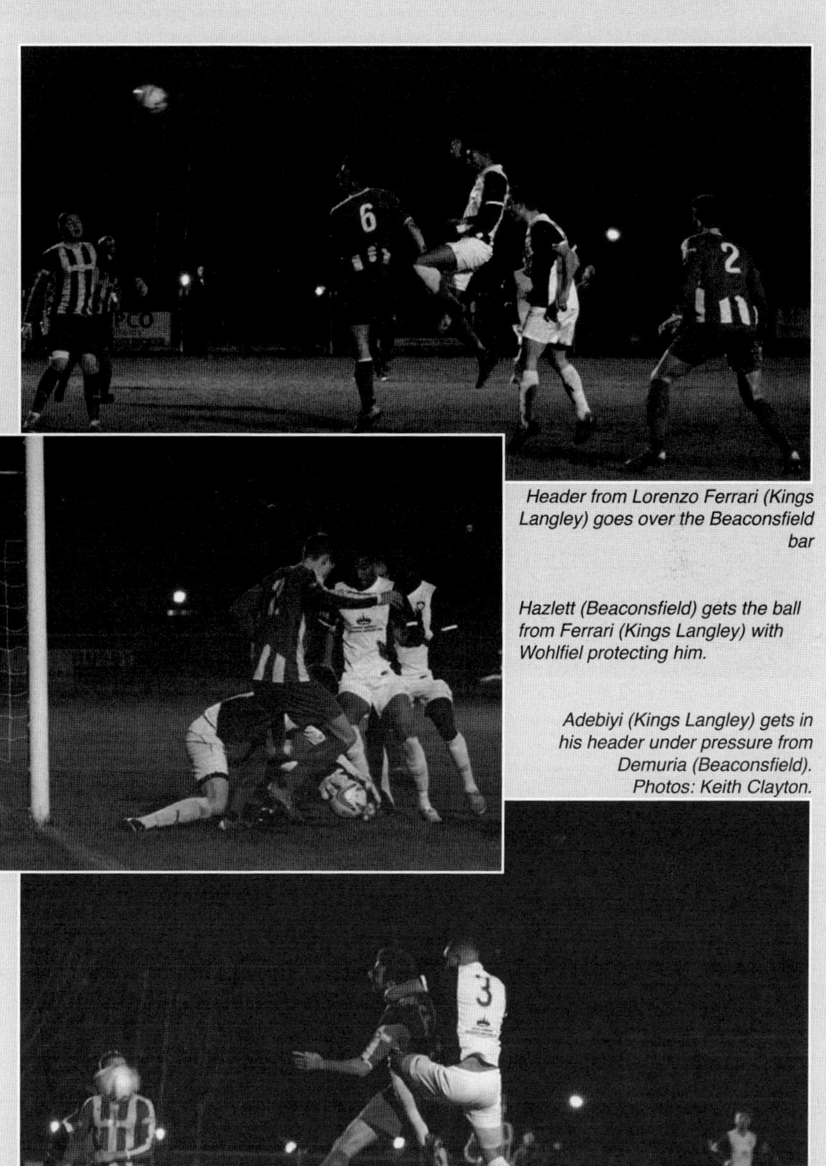

Header from Lorenzo Ferrari (Kings Langley) goes over the Beaconsfield bar

Hazlett (Beaconsfield) gets the ball from Ferrari (Kings Langley) with Wohlfiel protecting him.

Adebiyi (Kings Langley) gets in his header under pressure from Demuria (Beaconsfield). Photos: Keith Clayton.

# LEAMINGTON

**Chairman:** Jim Scott
**Secretary:** Richard Edy (T) 07508 207 053 (E) matchsecretary@leamingtonfc.co.uk
**Commercial Manager:** Nic Sproul (T/E) 07710 112 292
**Programme Editor:** Sally Ellis (T/E) programme@leamingtonfc.co.uk
**Ground Address:** Phillips 66 Community Stadium, Harbury Lane, Whitmarsh, Leamington CV33 9QB
(T) 01926 430 406 **Manager:** Paul Holleran

## Club Factfile

**Founded:** 1892 **Nickname:** The Brakes
**Previous Names:** Leamington Town 1892-1937, Lockheed Borg & Beck 1944-46 , Lockheed Leamington 1946-73, AP Leamington 1973-88
**Previous Leagues:** Birmingham Combination, Birmingham & District, West Midlands Regional, Midland Counties, Southern, Midland Combination, Midland Alliance 2005-07. Southern 2007-13. Football Conference 2013-15.

**Club Colours (change):** Gold with black trim/black /gold (Blue with yellow trim/blue/blue)

**Ground Capacity:** 5,000 **Seats:** 120 **Covered:** 720 **Clubhouse:** Yes **Shop:** Yes

**Directions**
From West and North – M40 Southbound – Exit J14 and take A452 towards Leamington. Ahead at 1st island. Next island take 2nd exit A452 (Europa Way). Next island take 4th exit (Harbury Lane) signposted Harbury and Bishops Tachbrook. Next island take 3rd exit (Harbury Lane). At traffic lights continue straight ahead Harbury Lane. Ground is 1.5 miles on left.
From South – M40 northbound – Exit J13. Turn right onto A452 towards Leamington. At 1st island take 3rd exit A452 (Europa Way) and follow as above (Europa Way onwards).

**Previous Grounds:** Old Windmill Ground

**Record Attendance:** 1,380 v Retford United - 17/02/2007
**Record Victory:** Not known
**Record Defeat:** Not known
**Record Goalscorer:** Josh Blake - 166
**Record Appearances:** Josh Blake - 314
**Additional Records:**

**Honours:**
Birmingham & District 1961-62. West Midlands Regional 1962-63. Midland Counties 1964-65.
Southern League 1982-83, 2012-13, Division 1 Midlands 2008-09.
Midland Combination Division 2 2000-01, Premier Division 2004-05. Midland Alliance 2006-07, League cup 2005-06.

### 10 YEAR RECORD

| 06-07 | 07-08 | 08-09 | 09-10 | 10-11 | 11-12 | 12-13 | 13-14 | 14-15 | 15-16 |
|---|---|---|---|---|---|---|---|---|---|
| MidAl 1 | SthM 2 | SthM 1 | SthP 10 | SthP 5 | SthP 7 | SthP 1 | Conf N 13 | Conf N 21 | SthP 3 |

# LEAMINGTON MATCH RESULTS 2015-16

| Date | Comp | H/A | Opponents | Att: | Result | | Goalscorers | Pos | No. |
|---|---|---|---|---|---|---|---|---|---|
| Aug 8 | SPL | H | Chesham United | 487 | W | 1-0 | Mackey 28 | 8 | 1 |
| 11 | SPL | A | St Neots Town | 368 | L | 0-1 | | 11 | 2 |
| 15 | SPL | A | Histon | 294 | W | 3-0 | Moore 37 Ogleby 75 Mace 83 | 8 | 3 |
| 18 | SPL | H | Kettering Town | 545 | W | 3-2 | Edwards 4 Taundry 35 Mackey 62 | 4 | 4 |
| 22 | SPL | H | Bideford | 482 | W | 2-1 | Moore 29 Ogleby 56 | 2 | 5 |
| 29 | SPL | A | Biggleswade | 255 | L | 2-3 | Mackey 15 67 | 3 | 6 |
| 31 | SPL | H | Bedworth United | 454 | D | 0-0 | | 5 | 7 |
| Sept 5 | SPL | A | Dunstable Town | 177 | W | 2-0 | Edwards 5 Green 90 | 2 | 8 |
| **12** | **FAC1Q** | **H** | **Stamford** | **401** | **D** | **1-1** | **Chilton 78** | | 9 |
| **15** | **FAC1Qr** | **A** | **Stamford** | **204** | **L** | **1-2** | **Mace 86** | | 10 |
| 19 | SPL | H | Weymouth | 453 | D | 0-0 | | 5 | 11 |
| 23 | SPL | A | Cambridge City | 151 | W | 2-1 | Mackey 35 41 | 2 | 12 |
| 29 | SPL | H | Slough Town | 411 | W | 3-0 | Edwards 10 36 Mackey 25 | | 13 |
| Oct 3 | SPL | A | Frome Town | 209 | D | 0-0 | | 2 | 14 |
| 5 | SPL | A | Hitchin Town | 311 | D | 2-2 | Mackey 31 Edwards 31 | 1 | 15 |
| 10 | SPL | H | Merthyr Town | 623 | W | 1-0 | Mackey 86 | 1 | 16 |
| 17 | SPL | A | Kings Lynn Town | 578 | W | 1-0 | Mackey 45 | 1 | 17 |
| 24 | SPL | A | Paulton Rovers | 190 | D | 1-1 | Oulton 90 | | 18 |
| 27 | SPL | H | Redditch United | 471 | L | 0-1 | | 2 | 19 |
| **31** | **FAT1Q** | **H** | **Barwell** | **291** | **W** | **6-1** | **Edwards 9 Chilton 29 81 Mackey 35 65 Green 86** | | 20 |
| Nov 3 | SPL | H | Cambridge City | 251 | L | 1-2 | Ogleby 39 | 2 | 21 |
| 7th | SPL | H | Cirencester Town | 405 | W | 2-0 | Halsall 38 Chilton 90 | 1 | 22 |
| **14** | **FAT2Q** | **H** | **Rushall Olympic** | **296** | **D** | **0-0** | | | 23 |
| 21 | SPL | H | Histon | 312 | W | 2-1 | Chilton 20 Mackay 70 | 2 | 24 |
| **24** | **FAT2Qr** | **A** | **Rushall Olympic** | **181** | **W** | **3-2** | **Hood 47 Moore 81 Mackey 102** | | 25 |
| **28** | **FAT3Q** | **H** | **Hednesford Town** | **308** | **W** | **4-2** | **Ogleby 22 Taundry 58 Mackey 70 74 (pen)** | | 26 |
| Dec 1 | SPL | H | St Neots Town | 302 | D | 2-2 | Moore 12 Ogleby 73 | 2 | 27 |
| 5 | SPL | A | Poole Town | 382 | L | 0-1 | | 4 | 28 |
| **15** | **FAT1** | **A** | **Altrincham** | **355** | **D** | **1-1** | **Ogleby 75** | | 29 |
| 19 | SPL | H | Biggleswade Town | 403 | L | 0-1 | | 7 | 30 |
| 26 | SPL | A | Bedworth Town | 347 | L | 0-2 | | 8 | 31 |
| Jan 9 | SPL | A | Chippenham Town | 395 | L | 3-4 | Edwards 63 Mackay 67 Tank 84 | 12 | 32 |
| **16** | **FAT1r** | **H** | **Altrincham** | **332** | **L** | **1-2** | **Mackey 89 (aet)** | | 33 |
| 23 | SPL | A | Bideford | 191 | D | 1-1 | Chilton 38 | 11 | 34 |
| 30 | SPL | H | Frome Town | 405 | W | 2-0 | Gudger 63 Mackey 79 | 10 | 35 |
| Feb 13 | SPL | H | Hitchin Town | 345 | L | 0-1 | | 11 | 36 |
| 15 | SPL | A | Hungerford Town | 147 | W | 2-1 | Baker-Richardson 83 90 | 10 | 37 |
| 20 | SPL | A | Slough Town | 286 | W | 3-1 | Stonehouse 15 (og) Ogleby 80 Austin 90 | 10 | 38 |
| 23 | SPL | H | Dunstable Town | 275 | W | 1-0 | Edwards 75 | 8 | 39 |
| 27 | SPL | H | Kings Lynn Town | 541 | D | 1-1 | Mackey 58 | 8 | 40 |
| Mar 1 | SPL | H | Stratford Town | 434 | W | 1-0 | Baker-Richardson 32 | 5 | 41 |
| 5 | SPL | A | Merthyr Town | 407 | W | 2-0 | Edwards 13 Baker-Richardson 77 | 5 | 42 |
| 12 | SPL | H | Poole Town | 502 | W | 1-0 | Mackay 57 | 5 | 43 |
| 15 | SPL | H | Dorchester Town | 312 | W | 3-0 | Austin 9 54 George 74 | 4 | 44 |
| 19 | SPL | A | Dorchester Town | 342 | W | 1-0 | Austin 36 | 3 | 45 |
| 22 | SPL | A | Chesham United | 264 | L | 0-3 | | 3 | 46 |
| 26 | SPL | H | Chippenham Town | 463 | D | 2-2 | Edwards 73 86 | 4 | 47 |
| 28 | SPL | A | Stratford Town | 576 | W | 1-0 | Austin 3 (pen) | 4 | 48 |
| Apr 2 | SPL | A | Redditch United | 742 | D | 0-0 | | 5 | 49 |
| 5 | SPL | A | Weymouth | 591 | L | 0-1 | | 6 | 50 |
| 9 | SPL | H | Paulton Rovers | 443 | W | 2-0 | Austin 11(pen) Mackey 87 | 3 | 51 |
| 12 | SPL | A | Kettering Town | 669 | D | 1-1 | Austin 43 (pen) | 3 | 52 |
| 16 | SPL | A | Cirencester Town | 318 | W | 2-1 | Edwards 11 Baker-Richardson 75 | 3 | 53 |
| 23 | SPL | H | Hungerford Town | 721 | D | 0-0 | | 3 | 54 |
| **27** | **PO SF** | **A** | **Redditch United** | **1303** | **D** | **1-1** | **Baker-Richardson 90 (Won 3-1 pens)** | | 55 |
| **May 2** | **PO Final** | **A** | **Hungerford Town** | **1363** | **L** | **1-2** | **Baker-Richardson 20** | | 56 |

| GOALSCORERS | Scoring Games | Consec Sco Games | Total |
|---|---|---|---|
| *2014-15 Newton* | | | *18* |
| Mackey | 18 | 3 | 22 |
| Edwards | 11 | | 12 |
| Baker-Richardson | 7 | 2 | 7 |
| Chilton | 6 | | 7 |
| Ogleby | 6 | | 7 |
| Austin | 5 | | 6 |
| Moore | 3 | | 4 |
| Green | 2 | | 2 |
| Mace | 2 | | 2 |
| Taundry | 2 | | 2 |
| George | 1 | | 1 |
| Gudger | 1 | | 1 |
| Halsall | 1 | | 1 |
| Hood | 1 | | 1 |
| Oulton | 1 | | 1 |
| Tank | 1 | | 1 |
| Opponents | | | 1 |

THE MARTYRS
M.T.F.C.

# MERTHYR TOWN

**Chairman:** Meurig Price
**Secretary:** Jamie Mack (T) 07823 776 422 (E) merthysec@gmail.com
**Commercial Manager:** Brent Carter (T/E) 07983 615 504
**Programme Editor:** Malcolm Johnson (T/E) malcjohnson@hotmail.com
**Ground Address:** Miller Argent Community Stadium, Penydarren Park, Park Terrace CF47 8RF
(T) 0772 567 302 **Manager:** Steve Jenkins

## Club Factfile

**Founded:** 2010 **Nickname:** Martyrs
**Previous Names:** None
**Previous Leagues:** Western League 2010-12.

**Club Colours (change):** White/black/black (All red)

**Ground Capacity:** **Seats:** Yes **Covered:** Yes **Clubhouse:** Yes **Shop:**

**Directions**
Leave the M4 at Junction 32 and join the A470 to Merthyr Tydfil. After approx 22 miles at the fourth roundabout take 3rd exit. At next roundabout go straight on and go straight on through two sets of traffic lights. At third set turn left (ground signposted Merthyr Tydfil FC from here). After 50 yards take first right, then first right just after Catholic Church into Park Terrace. The ground is at the end of the road approx. 200 yards on.

**Previous Grounds:** None

**Record Attendance:** Not known
**Record Victory:** Not known
**Record Defeat:** Not known
**Record Goalscorer:** Not known
**Record Appearances:** Not known
**Additional Records:**

**Honours:**
Western League Division One 2010-11, Premier Division 2011-12.
Southern Division One South & West 2014-15.

### 10 YEAR RECORD

| 06-07 | 07-08 | 08-09 | 09-10 | 10-11 | 11-12 | 12-13 | 13-14 | 14-15 | 15-16 |
|---|---|---|---|---|---|---|---|---|---|
| | | | | West1 1 | WestP 1 | Sthsw 3 | Sthsw 2 | Sthsw 1 | SthP 10 |

# MERTHYR TOWN MATCH RESULTS 2015-16

| Date | Comp | H/A | Opponents | Att: | Result | | Goalscorers | Pos | No. |
|---|---|---|---|---|---|---|---|---|---|
| Aug 8 | SPL | H | Kings Lynn | 509 | W | 2-0 | McLaggon 5 Evans 32 | 3 | 1 |
| 12 | SPL | A | Frome Town | 279 | D | 1-1 | Prosser 71 | 5 | 2 |
| 15 | SPL | A | Ketttering Town | 579 | L | 2-3 | Green 39 Prosser 90 | 10 | 3 |
| 18 | SPL | H | Stratford Town | 511 | W | 3-0 | Traylor 31 Bowen 88 Prosser 90 | 7 | 4 |
| 22 | SPL | A | Poole Town | 355 | D | 2-2 | Bauza 19 Scotcher 76 | 7 | 5 |
| 29 | SPL | H | Hitchin Town | 497 | W | 5-1 | McLaggon 35 Bauza 40 Traylor 47 Scotcher 59 Wright 79 | 4 | 6 |
| 31 | SPL | A | Cirencester Town | 224 | L | 0-1 | | 5 | 7 |
| Sept 5 | SPL | H | Chesham United | 486 | L | 1-2 | Prosser 52 | 8 | 8 |
| **12** | **FAC1Q** | **A** | **Plymouth Parkway** | **221** | **W** | **2-0** | **McLaggon 12 48** | | 9 |
| 19 | SPL | A | Chippenham Town | 387 | L | 0-1 | | 16 | 10 |
| 22 | SPL | A | Paulton Rovers | 401 | D | 1-1 | Prosser 53 | 17 | 11 |
| **26** | **FAC2Q** | **H** | **Hartley Wintney** | **280** | **L** | **0-1** | | | 12 |
| 29 | SPL | A | Dorchester Town | 307 | D | 1-1 | Buaza 51 | 13 | 13 |
| Oct 3 | SPL | H | Biggleswade Town | 409 | L | 1-2 | Traylor 65 | 17 | 14 |
| 10 | SPL | A | Leamington | 623 | L | 0-1 | | 19 | 15 |
| 17 | SPL | H | Dunstable Town | 290 | L | 1-3 | Belle 17 | 21 | 16 |
| 20 | SPL | A | Paulton Rovers | 172 | W | 2-1 | Grimshaw 33 (og) Evans 66 | 19 | 17 |
| 24 | SPL | A | St Neots Town | 280 | W | 2-1 | Prosser 4 16 | 18 | 18 |
| 27 | SPL | H | Hungerford Town | 373 | W | 4-1 | Wright 2 17 Traylor 74 Bauza 90 | 11 | 19 |
| **31** | **FAT1Q** | **H** | **Poole Town** | **220** | **W** | **1-0** | **Jones 85** | | 20 |
| Nov 7 | SPL | H | Weymouth | 474 | L | 1-3 | Jenkins 54 | 16 | 21 |
| **17** | **FAT2Q** | **A** | **Hastings United** | **150** | **W** | **2-1** | **Jenkins 32 Crabb 90** | | 22 |
| 21 | SPl | H | Kettering Town | 469 | D | 1-1 | Prosser 21 | 19 | 23 |
| **28** | **FAT3Q** | **H** | **East Thurrock United** | **225** | **D** | **1-1** | **Jones 46** | | 24 |
| **Dec 1** | **FAT3Qr** | **A** | **East Thurrock United** | **162** | **L** | **1-3** | **Traylor 18 (pen)** | | 25 |
| 5 | SPL | H | Bedworth United | 381 | D | 2-2 | Prosser 23 Traylor 35 | 17 | 26 |
| 8 | SPL | H | Bideford | 274 | W | 3-0 | Evans 49 Prosser 53 Jenkins 59 | 16 | 27 |
| 12 | SPL | A | Cambridge City | 152 | L | 0-1 | | 17 | 28 |
| 15 | SPL | A | Slough Town | 225 | L | 1-3 | McLaggon 64 | 17 | 29 |
| 19 | SPL | H | Hitchin Town | 402 | L | 0-2 | | 17 | 30 |
| 26 | SPL | H | Cirencester Town | 535 | L | 0-1 | | 19 | 31 |
| Jan 2 | SPL | A | Redditch United | 307 | L | 1-3 | Bagridge 83 | 19 | 32 |
| 5 | SPL | A | Kings Lynn Town | 391 | W | 3-2 | Prosser 17 Traylor 79 McLaggon 36 | 18 | 33 |
| 9 | SPL | H | Histon | 453 | W | 3-0 | Traylor 66 (pen) 71 Morgan 90 | 15 | 34 |
| 23 | SPL | H | Poole Town | 494 | D | 1-1 | Reffell 15 | 16 | 35 |
| 30 | SPL | A | Biggleswade Town | 201 | W | 3-0 | Jenkins 2 Traylor 65 Reffell 85 | 15 | 36 |
| Feb 9 | SPL | H | Frome Town | 282 | D | 1-1 | Wright 45 | 16 | 37 |
| 20 | SPL | H | Dorchester Town | 362 | L | 2-4 | Traylor 33 Baggridge 90 | 17 | 38 |
| 23 | SPL | A | Stratford Town | 145 | W | 3-0 | McLaggon 31 Traylor 43 Jenkins 67 | 16 | 39 |
| 27 | SPL | A | Dunstable Town | 149 | L | 1-2 | Traylor 70 (pen) | 16 | 40 |
| Mar 1 | SPL | H | Chippenham Town | 302 | W | 2-0 | Traylor 2 Prosser 90 | 15 | 41 |
| 5 | SPL | H | Leamington | 407 | L | 0-2 | | 16 | 42 |
| 12 | SPL | A | Bedworth United | 191 | W | 2-1 | Jones 20 McLaggon 36 | 15 | 43 |
| 19 | SPL | H | Cambridge City | 327 | W | 2-1 | Reffell 37 McLaggon 58 | 14 | 44 |
| 26 | SPL | A | Histon | 236 | W | 2-0 | Reffell 72 Bloom 88 | 14 | 45 |
| 28 | SPL | H | Redditch United | 512 | W | 2-1 | McLaggon 33 Brown 42 | 13 | 46 |
| Apr 2 | SPL | A | Hungerford Town | 191 | L | 0-1 | | 13 | 47 |
| 9 | SPL | H | St Neots Town | 551 | D | 1-1 | McLaggon 13 | 14 | 48 |
| 12 | SPL | A | Bideford | 152 | W | 1-0 | Prosser 65 | 11 | 49 |
| 16 | SPL | A | Weymouth | 646 | L | 0-3 | | 11 | 50 |
| 19 | SPL | A | Chesham United | 203 | W | 1-0 | Reffell 74 | 10 | 51 |
| 22 | SPL | H | Slough Town | 514 | W | 2-0 | Reffell 65 Baggridge 69 | 10 | 52 |

| GOALSCORERS | Scoring Games | Consec Sco Games | Total | | Scoring Games | Consec Sco Games | Total |
|---|---|---|---|---|---|---|---|
| Traylor | 13 | 3 | 14 | Scotcher | 2 | | 2 |
| Prosser | 12 | 3 | 13 | Belle | 1 | | 1 |
| McLaggon | 10 | | 11 | Bloom | 1 | | 1 |
| Reffell | 6 | | 6 | Bowen | 1 | | 1 |
| Jenkins | 5 | | 5 | Brown | 1 | | 1 |
| Bauza | 4 | 2 | 4 | Crabb | 1 | | 1 |
| Wright | 3 | | 4 | Green | 1 | | 1 |
| Baggridge | 3 | | 3 | Morgan | 1 | | 1 |
| Evans | 3 | | 3 | Opponents | | | 1 |
| Jones | 3 | | 3 | | | | |

# REDDITCH UNITED

**Chairman:** Chris Swan
**Secretary:** Julian Workman (T) (E) julian.workman@hotmail.com
**Commercial Manager:** Kerry Poulton (T/E)
**Programme Editor:** Julian Workman (T/E) julian.workman@hotmail.com
**Ground Address:** Valley Stadium, Bromsgrove Road, Redditch B97 4RN
**(T)** 01527 67450 **Manager:**

## Club Factfile

**Founded:** 1891 **Nickname:** The Reds
**Previous Names:** Redditch Town
**Previous Leagues:** Birmingham combination 1905-21, 29-39, 46-53, West Midlands 1921-29, 53-72, Southern 1972-79, 81-2004, Alliance 1979-80. Conference 2004-11.

**Club Colours (change):** Red/black/black (All blue)

**Ground Capacity:** 5,000 **Seats:** 400 **Covered:** 2,000 **Clubhouse:** Yes **Shop:** Yes

**Directions**
M42 J2, at island first exit onto the A441 for 2 miles, next island first exit onto Birmingham Road A441 for 1.2 miles then at island third exit onto Middlehouse Lane B4184 for 0.3 miles. At traffic lights (next to the fire station) turn left onto Birmingham Road for 0.2 miles then turn right into Clive Road for 0.3 miles. At island take first exit onto Hewell Road for 0.2 miles then at 'T' junction right onto Windsor Street for 0.1 miles. At traffic lights (next to bus station) continue straight ahead onto Bromsgrove Road for 0.3 miles and at the brow of the hill, turn right into the ground's entrance.

**Previous Grounds:** HDA Sports Ground, Millsborough Road

**Record Attendance:** 5,500 v Bromsgrove Rovers - Wets Midlands League 1954-55
**Record Victory:** Not known
**Record Defeat:** Not known
**Record Goalscorer:** Not known
**Record Appearances:** Not known
**Additional Records:** Paid £3,000 to Halesowen Town for Paul Joinson. Received £40,000 from Aston Villa for David Farrell. Played nine games in nine days at the end of the 1997-98 season.
**Honours:**
Worcestershire Senior Cup 1893-94, 29-30, 74-75, 76-76, 2007-08, 13-14.
Birmingham Senior Cup 1924-25, 31-32, 38-39, 76-77, 2004-05.
Southern League Division 1 North 1975-76, Western Division 2003-04. Staffordshire Senior Cup 1990-91.

### 10 YEAR RECORD

| 06-07 | 07-08 | 08-09 | 09-10 | 10-11 | 11-12 | 12-13 | 13-14 | 14-15 | 15-16 |
|---|---|---|---|---|---|---|---|---|---|
| Conf N 19 | Conf N 13 | Conf N 14 | Conf N 19 | Conf N 21 | SthP 15 | SthP 19 | SthP 10 | SthP 6 | SthP 2 |

# REDDITCH UNITED MATCH RESULTS 2015-16

| Date | Comp | H/A | Opponents | Att: | Result | | Goalscorers | Pos | No. |
|---|---|---|---|---|---|---|---|---|---|
| Aug 8 | SPL | H | Cirencester Town | 302 | L | 0-1 | | 20 | 1 |
| 11 | SPL | A | Kettering Town | 626 | D | 0-0 | | 19 | 2 |
| 15 | SPL | A | Biggleswade | 165 | D | 1-1 | Archer 14 | 19 | 3 |
| 17 | SPL | H | Hungerford Town | 205 | D | 2-2 | Carline 40 Osborne 45 | 16 | 4 |
| 22 | SPL | H | Cambridge City | 218 | D | 0-0 | | 18 | 5 |
| 29 | SPL | A | Dunstable T | 135 | **W** | 2-1 | Dubitat 29 70 (pen) | 16 | 6 |
| 31 | SPL | H | Stratford Town | 385 | **W** | 3-2 | Archer 63 (pen) Dubitat 63 (pen) 75 | 13 | 7 |
| Sept 5 | SPL | A | Bedworth United | 202 | **W** | 2-1 | Dubitat 68 Carline 90 | 12 | 8 |
| **12** | **FAC1Q** | **A** | **Hinckley AFC** | **295** | **L** | **1-2** | **Bunn 41** | | 9 |
| 19 | SPL | H | Kings Lynn Town | 277 | **W** | 2-0 | Ashmore 26 Shearer 52 | 7 | 10 |
| 22 | SPL | A | Slough Town | 250 | **W** | 2-0 | Dubidat 7 Molyneux 77 | 3 | 11 |
| 28 | SPL | H | St Neots Town | 305 | L | 1-2 | Carline 47 | | 12 |
| Oct 3 | SPL | A | Poole Town | 207 | L | 0-3 | | 8 | 13 |
| 6 | SPL | A | Chesham United | 368 | D | 1-1 | Osborne 45 | 8 | 14 |
| 17 | SPL | A | Hitchin Town | 211 | **W** | 2-1 | Dubitat 14 Carline 18 | 5 | 15 |
| 19 | SPL | H | Slough Town | 219 | **W** | 1-0 | Richards 62 | 5 | 16 |
| 24 | SPL | H | Dorchester Town | 280 | **W** | 2-0 | Shearer 75 (pen) Carline 83 | 4 | 17 |
| 27 | SPL | A | Leamington | 471 | **W** | 1-0 | Shearer 17 | 3 | 18 |
| **31** | **FAT1Q** | **A** | **Evesham United** | **302** | **L** | **0-1** | | | 19 |
| Nov 7 | SPL | A | Chippenham Town | 359 | **W** | 3-0 | Sammons 56 Shearer 68 (pen) Loveridge 82 | 2 | 20 |
| 16 | SPL | A | Hungerford Town | 126 | D | 0-0 | | 2 | 21 |
| 21 | SPL | H | Biggleswade Town | 245 | D | 2-2 | Dubidat 27 Carline 60 | 3 | 22 |
| 28 | SPL | H | St Neots Town | 192 | D | 1-1 | Maye 52 | 3 | 23 |
| Dec 5 | SPL | H | Paulton Rovers | 205 | D | 1-1 | Shearer 55 (pen) | 5 | 24 |
| 12 | SPL | A | Histon | 178 | D | 0-0 | | 4 | 25 |
| 26 | SPL | A | Stratford Town | 408 | L | 0-1 | | 7 | 26 |
| Jan 2 | SPL | H | Merthyr Town | 307 | **W** | 3-1 | Luckie 2 33 Young 90 | 3 | 27 |
| 16 | SPL | H | Bedworth United | 216 | **W** | 8-1 | Loveridge 25 Luckie 36 65 Carline 41 Osborne 45 Cullinane-Liburd 73 Sammons 81 84 | 3 | 28 |
| 23 | SPL | A | Cambridge City | 153 | **W** | 2-0 | Carline 25 Thompson-Brown 56 | 4 | 29 |
| Feb 6 | SPL | A | Kings Lynn Town | 498 | L | 0-1 | | 6 | 30 |
| 13 | SPL | H | Chesham United | 244 | **W** | 1-0 | Sammons 86 (pen) | 3 | 31 |
| 17 | SPL | A | Bideford | 138 | **W** | 5-0 | Mutton 26 Sammons 70 77 Shearer 77 88 (pen) | 3 | 32 |
| 20 | SPL | A | St Neots Town | 226 | **W** | 3-1 | Osborne 29 Cullinane-Liburd 32 Luckie 84 | 3 | 33 |
| 27 | SPL | H | Hitchin Town | 381 | **W** | 3-2 | Sammons 56 Johnson 80 90 | 3 | 34 |
| Mar 1 | SPL | H | Poole Town | 501 | D | 0-0 | | 3 | 35 |
| 5 | SPL | A | Weymouth | 536 | L | 0-2 | | 3 | 36 |
| 12 | SPL | A | Paulton Roverrs | 110 | **W** | 5-0 | Luckie 17 Sammons 39 Cullinane-Liburd 48 Hallahan 76 Molyneux 84 | 2 | 37 |
| 15 | SPL | A | Cirencester Town | 107 | **W** | 2-0 | Luckie 58 Shearer 85 | 2 | 38 |
| 19 | SPL | H | Histon | 452 | **W** | 1-0 | Carline 86 | 2 | 39 |
| 21 | SPL | H | Frome Town | 282 | D | 1-1 | Shearer 89 (pen) | 1 | 40 |
| 26 | SPL | H | Bideford | 401 | **W** | 4-1 | Carline 26 Thompson-Brown 38 Merson 64 Shearer 90 (pen) | 1 | 41 |
| 28 | SPL | A | Merthyr Town | 512 | L | 1-2 | Merson 31 | 1 | 42 |
| Apr 2 | SPL | H | Leamington | 742 | D | 0-0 | | 2 | 43 |
| 4 | SPL | H | Dunstable Town | 327 | D | 0-0 | | 2 | 44 |
| 9 | SPL | A | Dorchester Town | 378 | **W** | 5-1 | Martin18 (og) Shearer 20 Merson 49 Carline 72 Richards 78 | 2 | 45 |
| 18 | SPL | H | Kettering Town | 453 | **W** | 2-1 | Sammons 8 (pen) 44 (pen) | 3 | 46 |
| 20 | SPL | H | Chippenham Town | 295 | **W** | 6-2 | Sammons 20 Mutton 34 Richards 45 Merson 69 81 Thompson-Brown 77 | 2 | 47 |
| 23 | SPL | A | Frome Town | 280 | D | 1-1 | Merson 15 | 2 | 48 |
| **27** | **PO SF** | **H** | **Leamington** | **1303** | **D** | **1-1** | **Sammons 35 (Lost 1-3 on pens aet)** | | 49 |

| GOALSCORERS | Scoring Games | Consec Sco Games | Total |
|---|---|---|---|
| *2014-15 Sammons* | | | *20* |
| Sammons | 10 | 2 | 12 |
| Carline | 11 | 2 | 11 |
| Shearer | 10 | 2 | 11 |
| Dubitat | 6 | 3 | 8 |
| Luckie | 6 | | 7 |
| Merson | 5 | | 6 |
| Osborne | 4 | | 4 |
| Cullinane-Liburd | 3 | | 3 |
| Richards | 3 | | 3 |
| Thompson-Brown | 3 | | 3 |
| Archer | 2 | | 2 |
| Johnson | 1 | | 2 |
| Loveridge | 2 | | 2 |
| Molyneux | 2 | | 2 |
| Mutton | 2 | | 2 |
| Ashmore | 1 | | 1 |
| Bunn | 1 | | 1 |
| Hallahan | 1 | | 1 |
| Maye | 1 | | 1 |
| Young | 1 | | 1 |
| Opponents | | | 1 |

# SLOUGH TOWN

**Chairman:** Steve Easterbrook
**Secretary:** Kath Lathey **(T)** 07792 126 124 **(E)** kay.lathey@gmail.com
**Commercial Manager:** Pauk Lillywhite **(T/E)**
**Programme Editor:** Steve Chapman **(T/E)** sc014b6636@blueyonder.co.uk
**Ground Address:** Beaconsffield SYCOB FC, Holloways Park, Slough Road, Beaconsfield HP9 2SG
**(T)** 07792 126 124 **Manager:** Neil Baker & Jon Underwood

The club are hopeful of moving to Arbour Park (Stoke Road, Slough SL2 5AY), possibly as early as 29th August but until then Beaconsfield SYCOB remains their home.

## Club Factfile

**Founded:** 1890 **Nickname:** The Rebels
**Previous Names:** None
**Previous Leagues:** Southern Alliance 1892-93, Berks & Bucks 1901-05, Gt Western Suburban 1909-19, Spartan 1920-39, Herts & Middx 1940-45, Corinthian 1946-63, Athenian 1963-73, Isthmian 1973-90, 94-95, Conf. 1990-94

**Club Colours (change):** Amber/navy blue/amber (All purple)

**Ground Capacity:** 3,500 **Seats:** 200 **Covered:** Yes **Clubhouse:** Yes **Shop:** Yes

**Directions**
Leave M40 at Junction 2, take A355 towards Slough, only 50 yards off the roundabout on the A355 is slip road on right with sign giving Club name. Turn right through gate and clubhouse is 200 metres on the right. The ground is 'signposted' from both sides of the carriageway (A355).

**Previous Grounds:**

**Record Attendance:** 8,000 v Liverpool - Schoolboys 1976
**Record Victory:** 17-0 v Railway Clearing House - 1921-22
**Record Defeat:** 1-11 v Chesham Town - 1909-10
**Record Goalscorer:** Tony Norris - 84 (1925-26)
**Record Appearances:** Terry Reardon - 458 (1964-81)
**Additional Records:** Paid £18,000 to Farnborough Town for Colin Fielder
Received £22,000 from Wycombe Wanderers for Steve Thompson
**Honours:**
Isthmian League 1980-81, 89-90. Athenian League x3. Berks & Bucks Senior Cup x10.

### 10 YEAR RECORD

| 06-07 | 07-08 | 08-09 | 09-10 | 10-11 | 11-12 | 12-13 | 13-14 | 14-15 | 15-16 |
|---|---|---|---|---|---|---|---|---|---|
| Isth P 22 | Sthsw 21 | Sthsw 16 | SthM 5 | SthC 5 | SthC 2 | SthC 6 | SthC 5 | SthP 16 | SthP 17 |

# SLOUGH TOWN MATCH RESULTS 2015-16

| Date | Comp | H/A | Opponents | Att: | Result | | Goalscorers | Pos | No. |
|---|---|---|---|---|---|---|---|---|---|
| Aug 8 | SPL | H | Frome Town | 275 | D | 0-0 | | 15 | 1 |
| 11 | SPL | A | Biggleswade | 165 | L | 1-5 | Webb 90 | 22 | 2 |
| 15 | SPL | A | Stratford Town | 308 | D | 1-1 | Harris 90 | 20 | 3 |
| 18 | SPL | H | Histon | 270 | W | 7-1 | PUTMAN 3 (5 23 85) HARRIS 3 (36,40 62) Martin 44 | 12 | 4 |
| 22 | SPL | A | Hitchin Town | 316 | L | 1-3 | Harris 29 | 16 | 5 |
| 29 | SPL | H | Poole Town | 315 | L | 1-3 | Smith 47 | 19 | 6 |
| 31 | SPL | A | Chesham United | 439 | D | 1-1 | Mpi 84 | 19 | 7 |
| Sept 5 | SPL | H | Cirencester Town | 260 | W | 1-0 | Mpi 47 | 18 | 8 |
| **12** | **FAC1Q** | **A** | **Dorking Wanderers** | **184** | **W** | **1-0** | **Martin 90 (pen)** | | 9 |
| 19 | SPL | A | Bedworth United | 212 | L | 1-2 | Hicks 86 | 19 | 10 |
| 22 | SPL | H | Slough Town | 250 | L | 0-2 | | 19 | 11 |
| **26** | **FAC 2Q** | **A** | **Basingstoke Town** | **369** | **L** | **2-4** | **Martin 29 (pen) Harris 78** | | 12 |
| 29 | SPL | A | Leamington | 411 | L | 0-3 | | 20 | 13 |
| Oct 3 | SPL | H | Bideford | 236 | W | 2-1 | Mpi 59 61 | 20 | 14 |
| 6 | SPL | H | Dorchester Town | 243 | W | 4-1 | Harris 23 Putman 26 Strutton 59 Mpi 90 | 17 | 15 |
| 10 | SPL | A | Dunstable Town | 258 | W | 2-1 | Putman 42 Mpi 65 | 13 | 16 |
| 17 | SPL | H | Paulton Rovers | 244 | W | 2-1 | Mpi 3 Benjamin 25 | 11 | 17 |
| 19 | SPL | A | Redditch United | 219 | L | 0-1 | | 11 | 18 |
| 24 | SPL | H | Cambridge City | 292 | W | 3-2 | Rumbold 48 Strutton 68 Clayton 78 | 7 | 19 |
| 27 | SPL | A | Chippenham Town | 334 | D | 3-3 | Strutton 37 76 Harris 58 | 8 | 20 |
| **Nov 1** | **FAT1Q** | **A** | **Romford** | **134** | **W** | **4-0** | **Sear 6 HIcks 28 Mpi 52 Putman 74** | | 21 |
| 7 | SPL | A | Kings Lynn Town | 480 | L | 1-2 | Mpi 14 | 10 | 22 |
| **14** | **FAT2Q** | **A** | **Frome Town** | **151** | **L** | **1-2** | **Putman 5** | | 23 |
| 21 | SPL | H | Stratford Town | 261 | L | 2-4 | Mpi 7 Putman 55 | 12 | 24 |
| 24 | SPL | A | Dunstable Town | 142 | W | 3-1 | Strutton 52 Harris 72 Mpi 80 | 12 | 25 |
| Dec 1 | SPL | A | Biggleswade Town | 242 | W | 2-0 | Smith 63 Mpi 71 | 10 | 26 |
| 5 | SPL | H | St Neots Town | 280 | D | 2-2 | Smith 45 (pen) Mpi 73 | 11 | 27 |
| 12 | SPL | A | Weymouth | 532 | L | 1-6 | Smith 78 | 12 | 28 |
| 15 | SPL | H | Merthyr Town | 325 | W | 3-1 | Harris 13 Putman 24 Smith 45 (pen) | | 29 |
| 19 | SPL | A | Poole Town | 429 | D | 3-3 | Hallahan 47 88 Jepson 57 | 10 | 30 |
| 23 | SPL | H | Hitchin Town | 314 | W | 1-0 | Putman 43 | 10 | 31 |
| 26 | SPL | H | Chesham United | 438 | L | 0-1 | | 12 | 32 |
| Feb 6 | SPL | H | Bedworth United | 247 | L | 1-2 | Mpi 50 | 14 | 33 |
| 13 | SPL | A | Dorchester Town | 447 | W | 2-1 | Smith 30 N.Webb 45 | 13 | 34 |
| 16 | SPL | A | Cirencester Town | 112 | W | 3-1 | Barney 27 58 Smith 48 | 12 | 35 |
| 20 | SPL | H | Leamington | 286 | L | 1-3 | Harris 52 | 12 | 36 |
| 27 | SPL | A | Paulton Rovers | 208 | D | 3-3 | Smith 16 Putman 58 Barney 61 | 13 | 37 |
| Mar 1 | SPL | H | Kettering Town | 294 | L | 1-3 | N.Webb 36 | 14 | 38 |
| 5 | SPL | H | Dunstable Town | 226 | W | 1-0 | Smith 82 (pen) | 13 | 39 |
| 9 | SPL | A | Frome Town | 102 | L | 1-2 | Putman 27 | 13 | 40 |
| 12 | SPL | A | St Neots Town | 266 | D | 0-0 | | 13 | 41 |
| 14 | SPL | A | Hungerford Town | 147 | L | 0-1 | | 13 | 42 |
| 19 | SPL | H | Weymouth | 320 | D | 0-0 | | 14 | 43 |
| 22 | SPL | A | Bideford | 131 | L | 1-2 | Grant 78 | 14 | 44 |
| 26 | SPL | A | Kettering Town | 637 | L | 0-1 | | 16 | 45 |
| 28 | SPL | H | Hungerford Town | 319 | L | 0-2 | | 16 | 46 |
| Apr 2 | SPL | H | Chippenham Town | 255 | W | 1-0 | Barney 34 | 16 | 47 |
| 9 | SPL | A | Cambridge City | 188 | L | 2-4 | Harris 18 Barney 35 | 16 | 48 |
| 16 | SPL | H | Kings Lynn Town | 338 | W | 2-0 | Barney 31 90 | 16 | 49 |
| 23 | SPL | A | Merthyr Town | 514 | L | 0-2 | | 17 | 50 |

| GOALSCORERS | Scoring Games | Consec Sco Games | Total |
|---|---|---|---|
| **2014-15 E.Smith** | | | **20** |
| Mpi | 13 | 4 | 14 |
| Harris | 10 | 3 | 12 |
| Putman | 10 | 2 | 12 |
| Smith | 9 | 3 | 9 |
| Barney | 5 | 3 | 7 |
| Strutton | 4 | 2 | 5 |
| Martin | 4 | | 3 |
| Webb | 3 | | 3 |
| Hallahan | 1 | | 2 |
| Hicks | 2 | | 2 |
| Benjamin | 1 | | 1 |
| Clayton | 1 | | 1 |
| Grant | 1 | | 1 |
| Jepson | 1 | | 1 |
| Rumbold | 1 | | 1 |
| Sear | 1 | | 1 |

# ST. IVES TOWN

**Chairman:** Gary Clarke
**Secretary:** Marina Howlett (T) 01480 463 207 (E) sitfcsecretary@aol.com
**Commercial Manager:** Mark Taylor (T/E)
**Programme Editor:** David Hook (T/E) hooklevi@aol.com
**Ground Address:** Pro-Edge Stadium, Westwood Road, St. Ives PE27 6WU
(T) 01480 463 207 **Manager:** Ricky Marheineke

## Club Factfile

**Founded:** 1887 **Nickname:** Saints
**Previous Names:** None
**Previous Leagues:** Cambridgeshire, Central Amateur, Hunts, Peterborough & District. United Counties > 2013.

**Club Colours (change):** Black & white stripes/black/black (All red)

**Ground Capacity:** **Seats:** Yes **Covered:** Yes **Clubhouse:** Yes **Shop:** No

**Directions:** From A1123 Houghton Road rurn right at traffic lights into Ramsey Road. After Fire Station turn right into Westwood Road. Ground at end of road on right hand side immediately before St Ivo Recreation Centre Car Park.

**Previous Grounds:** Meadow Lane.

**Record Attendance:** 767 v Needham Market, FA Vase 5th Rnd 2007-08. 801 v Cambridge United, pre-season friendly, 2009-10.
**Record Victory:** Not known
**Record Defeat:** Not known
**Record Goalscorer:** Not known
**Record Appearances:** Not known
**Additional Records:**

**Honours:**
Hunts Senior Cup 1900/01, 11-12, 22-23, 25-26, 29-30, 81-82, 86-87, 87-88, 2006-07, 08-09, 11-12, 15-16. Hunts Premier Cup 2006-07, 08-09. United Counties League Cup 2009-10. Southern Division One Central Play-offs 2015-16.

**10 YEAR RECORD**

| 06-07 | 07-08 | 08-09 | 09-10 | 10-11 | 11-12 | 12-13 | 13-14 | 14-15 | 15-16 |
|---|---|---|---|---|---|---|---|---|---|
| UCL P 10 | UCL P 5 | UCL P 6 | UCL P 10 | UCL P 11 | UCL P 3 | UCL P 2 | SthC 13 | SthC 9 | SthC 4 |

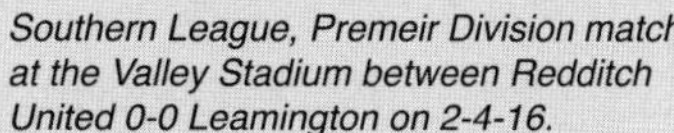

*Southern League, Premeir Division match at the Valley Stadium between Redditch United 0-0 Leamington on 2-4-16.*

*Here we see Leamington's keeper, Tony Breeden punching the ball clear from a Redditch United corner.*

*Jordan Cullinane-Liburd looks to cross the ball despite the attentions of Leamington's Richard Taundry.*

*Header from Lorenzo Ferrari (Kings Langley) goes over the Beaconsfield bar Photos: Keith Clayton.*

*Redditch United forward (left) leaps highest but loses out in this aerial duel against Leamington at the Valley Stadium.*
*Photos: Jonathan Holloway.*

# ST. NEOTS TOWN

**Chairman:** Lee Kearns
**Secretary:** Gary Wilson **(T)** 01480 470 012 **(E)** garygwilson@sky.com
**Commercial Manager:** Mark Davies **(T/E)**
**Programme Editor:** Lee Kearns **(T/E)** leekearns4@gmail.com
**Ground Address:** Rowley Park, Kester Way, Cambridge Road, St Neots, PE19 6SN
**(T)** 01480 470 012 **Manager:** Andy Davies

## Club Factfile

**Founded:** 1879 **Nickname:** Saints
**Previous Names:** St Neots 1879-1924. St. Neots & District 1924-1951.
**Previous Leagues:** S Midlands, Cent. Alliance, UCL, Eastern Co., Hunts, United Counties > 2011.

**Club Colours (change):** All dark blue

**Ground Capacity:** 3,000 **Seats:** 250 **Covered:** 850 **Clubhouse:** Yes **Shop:** No

**Directions** From St Neots town centre, take the B1428 Cambridge Road, after going under the railway bridge, turn left at the first roundabout into Dramsell Rise. Follow the road up the hill to Kester Way and the ground. If approaching from Cambridge on the A428, turn right at the first roundabout as you approach St Neots onto the Cambridge Road. At the second roundabout, turn right into Dramsell Rise and follow as above. If travelling via the A1, follow signs for the A428 Cambridge. Go straight over roundabout with Tescos on left hand side, then turn left at next roundabout. Follow final instructions above as if approaching from Cambridge.

**Previous Grounds:** Rowley Park >2008.

**Record Attendance:** **Att:** 2,000 v Wisbech 1966
**Record Victory:** Not known
**Record Defeat:** Not known
**Record Goalscorer:** Not known
**Record Appearances:** Not known
**Additional Records:** 105 points obtained in the 2010-11 season - a United Counties record.

**Honours:**
United Counties League 1967-68, 2010-11. Division One 1994-95.Southern League Division 1 Central 2011-12.
Huntingdonshire Senior Cup x37 Most recently 2013-14. Huntingdonshire Premier Cup 2001-02.

### 10 YEAR RECORD

| 06-07 | 07-08 | 08-09 | 09-10 | 10-11 | 11-12 | 12-13 | 13-14 | 14-15 | 15-16 |
|---|---|---|---|---|---|---|---|---|---|
| UCL P 17 | UCL P 8 | UCL P 17 | UCL P 2 | UCL P 1 | SthC 1 | SthP 12 | SthP 16 | SthP 5 | SthP 20 |

## ST. NEOTS TOWN MATCH RESULTS 2015-16

| Date | Comp | H/A | Opponents | Att: | Result | | Goalscorers | Pos | No. |
|---|---|---|---|---|---|---|---|---|---|
| Aug 8 | SPL | A | Bideford | 233 | D | 4-4 | MEECHAN 3 (10 13 80) Gordon 48 | 11 | 1 |
| 11 | SPL | H | Leamington | 368 | W | 1-0 | Meechan 48 | 6 | 2 |
| 15 | SPL | H | Poole Town | 366 | L | 2-3 | Gordon 67 Hall 86 | 11 | 3 |
| 18 | SPL | A | Bedworth United | 193 | W | 6-0 | Meechan 25 50 Ward 34 Clarke 37 Hall 33 Mailancol 49 | 5 | 4 |
| 22 | SPL | H | Stratford Town | 293 | D | 2-2 | Meechan 64 73 | 6 | 5 |
| 29 | SPL | A | Weymouth | 608 | D | 1-1 | Meechan 77 | 9 | 6 |
| 31 | SPL | H | Biggleswade Town | 456 | W | 2-0 | Hawkins 36 Meechan 64 | 6 | 7 |
| Sept 5 | SPL | A | Chippenham Town | 382 | D | 1-1 | Frater 83 | 6 | 8 |
| 19 | SPL | A | Hungerford Town | 116 | D | 3-3 | Meechan 58 (pen) Mitchell-King 64 Anton 90 | 9 | 9 |
| **23** | **FAC1Qr** | **H** | **Tilbury** | **97** | **W** | **5-2** | **Meechan 25 88 Ward 17 Hawkins 85 Hobbs 90** | | 10 |
| **26** | **FAC 2Q** | **H** | **Worthing** | **342** | **D** | **1-1** | **Vieira 70** | | 11 |
| Oct 3 | SPL | H | Cirencester Town | 306 | L | 1-2 | Hawkins 40 | 16 | 12 |
| **6** | **FAC2Qr** | **A** | **Worthing** | **403** | **D** | **2-2** | **Hawkins 28 Clarke 64 (lost 5-6 on pens aet)** | | 13 |
| 10 | SPL | A | Paulton Rovers | 180 | W | 5-2 | Meechan 20 (pen) 58 Hawkins 32 73 Beech 84 | 14 | 14 |
| 17 | SPL | H | Dorchester Town | 313 | W | 1-0 | Meechan 70 | 12 | 15 |
| 20 | SPL | A | Dunstable Town | 256 | L | 0-3 | | 13 | 16 |
| 24 | SPL | H | Merthyr Town | 280 | L | 1-2 | Mitchel-King 83 | 15 | 17 |
| **31** | **FAT1Q** | **H** | **Bedworth** | **216** | **W** | **2-0** | **Mitchel-King 26 Blackett 86** | | 18 |
| Nov 3 | SPL | H | Dunstable Town | 197 | W | 1-0 | Meechan 38 | 11 | 19 |
| **14** | **FAT2Q** | **H** | **Hungerford Town** | **207** | **L** | **1-2** | **Boardman 64 (og)** | | 20 |
| 17 | SPL | H | Bedworth United | 171 | D | 2-2 | Meechan 21 (pen) Horne 45 | 13 | 21 |
| 21 | SPL | A | Poole Town | 355 | L | 0-3 | | 13 | 22 |
| 25 | SPL | A | Cambridge City | 237 | W | 4-1 | Hawkins 20 Roberts 44 Meechan 48 (pen) Galliford 90 | 12 | 23 |
| 28 | SPL | A | Redditch United | 192 | D | 1-1 | Clarke 80 | 12 | 24 |
| Dec 1 | SPL | A | Leamington | 302 | D | 2-2 | Clarke 25 Mitchell-King 86 | 11 | 25 |
| 5 | SPL | A | Slough Town | 280 | D | 2-2 | Frater 27 Gilliard 63 | 13 | 26 |
| 8 | SPL | H | Histon | 312 | D | 1-1 | Galliford 31 (pen) | 12 | 27 |
| 12 | SPL | H | Kettering Town | 438 | L | 0-1 | | 13 | 28 |
| 19 | SPL | H | Weymouth | 299 | D | 1-1 | Mitchel-King 27 | 14 | 29 |
| 26 | SPL | A | Biggleswade Town | 328 | L | 2-5 | Meechan 47 52 | 15 | 30 |
| Jan 2 | SPL | H | Kings Lynn Town | 520 | L | 0-1 | | 15 | 31 |
| 5 | SPL | A | Chesham United | 245 | L | 1-3 | Meechan 22 | 16 | 32 |
| 16 | SPL | H | Chippenham Town | 272 | L | 0-4 | | 18 | 33 |
| 23 | SPL | A | Stratford Town | 224 | L | 1-2 | Meechan 44 | | 34 |
| 30 | SPL | A | Cirencester Town | 93 | W | 5-2 | Casey 4 Meechan 21 Dawkins 34 Clarke 56 90 | 17 | 35 |
| Feb 6 | SPL | H | Hungerford Town | 234 | L | 0-2 | | 18 | 36 |
| 9 | SPL | A | Bideford | 167 | W | 3-1 | Akinyemi 50 Longden 54 McGrath 76 (og) | 16 | 37 |
| 13 | SPL | A | Histon | 293 | D | 0-0 | | 16 | 38 |
| 16 | SPL | H | Hitchin Town | 298 | L | 1-2 | Roberts 2 (pen) | 16 | 39 |
| 20 | SPL | H | Redditch United | 226 | L | 1-3 | Tann 22 | 16 | 40 |
| 27 | SPL | A | Dorchester Town | 360 | L | 0-1 | | 19 | 41 |
| Mar 5 | SPL | H | Paulton Rovers | 260 | W | 1-0 | Clarke 87 | 18 | 42 |
| 12 | SPL | H | Slough Town | 266 | D | 0-0 | | 17 | 43 |
| 16 | SPL | A | Frome Town | 123 | L | 2-3 | Ward 64 Gordon 69 | 18 | 44 |
| 19 | SPL | A | Kettering Town | 561 | D | 1-1 | Roberts 47 | 18 | 45 |
| 26 | SPL | H | Frome Town | 262 | D | 2-2 | Gordon 5 64 | 19 | 46 |
| 30 | SPL | A | Kings Lynn Town | 354 | D | 1-1 | Roberts 65 | 18 | 47 |
| Apr 2 | SPL | H | Cambridge City | 351 | D | 1-1 | Roberts 15 | 18 | 48 |
| 9 | SPL | A | Merthyr Town | 551 | D | 1-1 | Bloom 23 (og) | 19 | 49 |
| 23 | SPL | A | Hitchin Town | 1184 | L | 0-2 | | 19 | 50 |
| 26 | SPL | H | Chesham United | 208 | L | 2-4 | Roberts 21 66 | 20 | 51 |

| GOALSCORERS | Scoring Games | Consec Sco Games | Total |
|---|---|---|---|
| ***2014-15 Roberts*** | | | ***26*** |
| Meechan | 17 | 4 | 24 |
| Clarke | 6 | 2 | 7 |
| Hawkins | 6 | 3 | 7 |
| Roberts | 5 | 2 | 6 |
| Gordon | 4 | | 5 |
| Mitchel-King | 5 | 2 | 5 |
| Ward | 3 | | 3 |
| Frater | 2 | | 2 |
| Galliford | 2 | | 2 |
| Hall | 2 | 2 | 2 |
| Anton | 1 | | 1 |
| Akinyemi | 1 | | 1 |

| | Scoring Games | Consec Sco Games | Total |
|---|---|---|---|
| Beech | 1 | | 1 |
| Blackett | 1 | | 1 |
| Casey | 1 | | 1 |
| Dawkins | 1 | | 1 |
| Gilliard | 1 | | 1 |
| Hobbs | 1 | | 1 |
| Home | 1 | | 1 |
| Longden | 1 | | 1 |
| Mailancol | 1 | | 1 |
| Tann | 1 | | 1 |
| Vieira | 1 | | 1 |
| Opponents | | | 3 |

# STRATFORD TOWN

**Chairman:** Melanie Tweddle
**Secretary:** Brian Rose (T) 07833 776 834 (E) brian_rose@nfumutual.co.uk
**Commercial Manager:** Melanie Tweedle (T/E) 07968 600 300
**Programme Editor:** Paul Eden (T/E) info@stratfordtownfc.org
**Ground Address:** The DCS Stadium, Knights Lane, Tiddington, Stratford Upon Avon CV37 7BZ
**(T)** 01789 269 336 **Manager:** Carl Adams

## Club Factfile

**Founded:** 1943 **Nickname:** The Town
**Previous Names:** Straford Rangers 1943-49. Stratford Town Amateurs 1964-70.
**Previous Leagues:** Worcestershire/Midland Comb. Birmingham & Dist. W.Mid (Reg). Hellenic. Midland Alliance > 2013.

**Club Colours (change):** All blue. (Tangerine/black/tangerine)

**Ground Capacity:** **Seats:** Yes **Covered:** Yes **Clubhouse:** Yes **Shop:** Yes

**Directions**
From Town Centre follow signs for Banbury (A422) and Oxford (A3400). Cross Clopton Bridge and turn immediately left onto B4086 towards Wellesbourne. After approx 1 mile you enter the village of Tiddington. Turn 1st right into Knights Lane. Ground is approx 800 yards on right (100 yards after school).

**Previous Grounds:** A number of pitches before Alcester Road by the late 1940s.

**Record Attendance:** **Att:** 1,078 v Aston Villa, Birmingham Senior Cup, Oct. 1996.
**Record Victory:** Not known
**Record Defeat:** Not known
**Record Goalscorer:** Not known
**Record Appearances:** Not known
**Additional Records:**

**Honours:**
Worcestershire/Midland Combination 1956-57, 86-87.
Birmingham Senior Cup 1962-63. Midland Alliance 2012-13, League Cup 2002-03, 03-04, 10-11. Southern Div.1 S&W Play-off 2014-15.

### 10 YEAR RECORD

| 06-07 | 07-08 | 08-09 | 09-10 | 10-11 | 11-12 | 12-13 | 13-14 | 14-15 | 15-16 |
|---|---|---|---|---|---|---|---|---|---|
| MidAl 4 | MidAl 7 | MidAl 6 | MidAl 3 | MidAl 5 | MidAl 8 | MidAl 1 | Sthsw 10 | Sthsw 3 | SthP 19 |

# STRATFORD TOWN MATCH RESULTS 2015-16

| Date | Comp | H/A | Opponents | Att: | Result | | Goalscorers | Pos | No. |
|---|---|---|---|---|---|---|---|---|---|
| Aug 8 | SPL | A | Hitchin Town | 278 | W | 3-2 | Gregory 13 Angus 36 Halsall 57 | 4 | 1 |
| 11 | SPL | H | Bedworth United | 288 | W | 2-0 | Thompson-Brown 52 Halsall 63 | 2 | 2 |
| 15 | SPL | H | Slough Town | 308 | D | 1-1 | Thompson-Brown 2 | 3 | 3 |
| 18 | SPL | A | Merthyr Town | 511 | L | 0-3 | | 10 | 4 |
| 22 | SPL | A | St Neots Town | 293 | D | 2-2 | Thompson-Brown 54 Halsall 72 | 10 | 5 |
| 29 | SPL | H | Chesham United | 210 | D | 1-1 | Fagan 53 | 11 | 6 |
| 31 | SPL | A | Redditch United | 385 | L | 2-3 | Ahenkorah 25 30 | 16 | 7 |
| Sept 5 | SPL | H | Kettering Town | 410 | W | 2-1 | Ahenkorah 22 (pen) Thompson-Brown 62 | 14 | 8 |
| **12** | **FAC1Q** | **A** | **Holbeach United** | **239** | **L** | **0-2** | | | 9 |
| 19 | SPL | A | Dorchester Town | 322 | L | 1-3 | Ahenkorah 54 | 15 | 10 |
| 22 | SPL | H | Cirencester Town | 180 | W | 2-1 | Westwood 44 Angus 55 | 10 | 11 |
| Oct 3 | SPL | H | Histon | 241 | L | 1-2 | Ahenkorah 31 | 15 | 12 |
| 6 | SPL | H | Biggleswade Town | 137 | W | 3-0 | Ahenkorah 4 29 McGrath | 10 | 13 |
| 10 | SPL | A | Bideford | 185 | D | 1-1 | Sheldon 60 | 11 | 14 |
| 17 | SPL | H | Chippenham Town | 189 | D | 1-1 | Ahenkorah 32 | 13 | 15 |
| 24 | SPL | H | Frome Town | 176 | L | 0-1 | | 16 | 16 |
| **31** | **FAT1Q** | **A** | **Histon** | **187** | **D** | **0-0** | | | 17 |
| **Nov 3** | **FAT1Qr** | **H** | **Histon** | **133** | **W** | **4-1** | **Gregory 23 SHELDON 3 ( 48 52 54)** | | 18 |
| **14** | **FAT2Q** | **A** | **Ashton United** | **112** | **L** | **1-2** | **Ahenkorah 38** | | 19 |
| 21 | SPL | A | Slough Town | 261 | W | 4-2 | McGrath 14 Sheldon 38 Ahenkorah 43 Gregory 64 | 16 | 20 |
| 28 | SPL | H | Poulton Rovers | 140 | W | 4-0 | McGrath 10 Sheldon 17 Angus 31 Moses-Garvey 67 | 15 | 21 |
| Dec 1 | SPL | A | Bedworth Town | 189 | W | 4-0 | Moses-Garvey 2 Sheldon 9 Tulloch 29 Angus 58 | 12 | 22 |
| 5 | SPL | H | Weymouth | 209 | D | 1-1 | Sheldon 80 | 12 | 23 |
| 19 | SPL | A | Chesham United | 303 | L | 0-2 | | 16 | 24 |
| 26 | SPL | H | Redditch United | 408 | W | 1-0 | McGrath 15 | 14 | 25 |
| Jan 12 | SPL | A | Cirencester Town | 126 | L | 0-3 | | 14 | 26 |
| 23 | SPL | A | St Neots Town | 224 | W | 2-1 | Gregory 18 65 (pen) | 14 | 27 |
| 26 | SPL | A | Dunstable Town | 101 | L | 1-3 | Fagan 90 | 14 | 28 |
| 30 | SPL | A | Histon | 217 | W | 2-0 | Stringfellow 11 McGrath 20 | 13 | 29 |
| Feb 1 | SPL | A | Hungerford Town | 120 | D | 0-0 | | 12 | 30 |
| 13 | SPL | A | Biggleswade Town | 125 | L | 3-4 | Gregory 11 Fagan 46 Angus 86 | 13 | 31 |
| 16 | SPL | H | Kings Lynn Town | 217 | D | 1-1 | Westwood 84 | 12 | 32 |
| 20 | SPL | A | Paulton Rovers | 105 | L | 1-2 | Magee 58 | 14 | 33 |
| 23 | SPL | H | Merthyr Town | 145 | L | 0-3 | | 16 | 34 |
| 27 | SPL | A | Chippenham Town | 378 | L | 1-2 | Magee 20 | 17 | 35 |
| Mar 1 | SPL | A | Leamington | 434 | L | 0-1 | | 18 | 36 |
| 5 | SPL | H | Bideford | 194 | D | 0-0 | | 17 | 37 |
| 12 | SPL | A | Weymouth | 567 | L | 1-2 | Gregory 5 (pen) | 18 | 38 |
| 15 | SPL | H | Hitchin Town | 156 | D | 1-1 | Fagan 16 | 17 | 39 |
| 19 | SPL | H | Hungerford Town | 179 | L | 0-2 | | 19 | 40 |
| 22 | SPL | A | Kettering Town | 467 | L | 1-3 | McGrath 84 | 19 | 41 |
| 26 | SPL | A | Poole Town | 407 | W | 2-1 | Westwood 16 Fagan 7 | 18 | 42 |
| 28 | SPL | H | Leamington | 576 | L | 0-1 | | 18 | 43 |
| 30 | SPL | A | Cambridge City | 134 | L | 0-2 | | 18 | 44 |
| Apr 2 | SPL | H | Dunstable Town | 141 | D | 0-0 | | 19 | 45 |
| 9 | SPL | A | Frome Town | 102 | L | 0-2 | | 20 | 46 |
| 12 | SPL | H | Poole Town | 232 | L | 0-1 | | 20 | 47 |
| 19 | SPL | H | Dorchester Town | 196 | L | 1-2 | Gregory 88 | 20 | 48 |
| 23 | SPL | A | Kings Lynn Town | 460 | L | 1-2 | Gregory 68 | 20 | 49 |
| 26 | SPL | H | Cambridge City | 183 | W | 5-2 | Sheldon 3 Gregory 3(13 59 86) Magee 87 | 19 | 50 |

| GOALSCORERS | Scoring Games | Consec Sco Games | Total |
|---|---|---|---|
| Gregory | 9 | 3 | 12 |
| Ahenkorah | 8 | 1 | 10 |
| Sheldon | 7 | 3 | 9 |
| McGrath | 6 | | 6 |
| Angus | 5 | | 5 |
| Fagan | 5 | | 5 |
| Thompson-Brown | 4 | 2 | 4 |
| Halsall | 3 | 2 | 3 |
| Magee | 3 | | 3 |
| Westwood | 3 | | 3 |
| Moses-Garvey | 2 | | 2 |
| Stringfellow | 1 | | 1 |
| Tulloch | 1 | | 1 |

# WEYMOUTH

**Chairman:** Chris Pugsley
**Secretary:** Pete Saxby (T) 01305 785 558 (E) secretary@theterras.co.uk
**Commercial Manager:** (T/E)
**Programme Editor:** Ian White (T/E) whiteij7544@btinterneti.com
**Ground Address:** Bob Lucas Stadium, Radipole Lane, Weymouth DT4 9XJ
**(T)** 01305 785 558 **Manager:** Jason Matthews

## Club Factfile

**Founded:** 1890 **Nickname:** The Terras
**Previous Names:** None
**Previous Leagues:** Dorset, Western 1907-23, 28-49, Southern 1923-28, 49-79, 89-2005, Alliance/Conference 1979-89, 2005-10

**Club Colours (change):** Claret & blue/white/claret (Yellow/blue/blue)

**Ground Capacity:** 6,600 **Seats:** 800 **Covered:** Yes **Clubhouse:** Yes **Shop:** Yes

**Directions**
Approach Weymouth from Dorchester on the A354.
Turn right at first roundabout onto Weymouth Way, continue to the next roundabout then turn right (signposted Football Ground).
At the next roundabout take third exit into the ground.

**Previous Grounds:** Recreation Ground > 1987.

**Record Attendance:** 4,995 v Manchester United - Ground opening 21/10/97
**Record Victory:** Not known
**Record Defeat:** Not known
**Record Goalscorer:** W 'Farmer' Haynes - 275
**Record Appearances:** Tony Hobsons - 1,076
**Additional Records:** Paid £15,000 to Northwich Victoria for Shaun Teale
Received £100,000 from Tottenham Hotspur for Peter Guthrie 1988
**Honours:**
Southern League 1964-65, 65-66. Conference South 2005-06.
Dorset Senior Cup x29 Most recent 2015-16.

### 10 YEAR RECORD

| 06-07 | 07-08 | 08-09 | 09-10 | 10-11 | 11-12 | 12-13 | 13-14 | 14-15 | 15-16 |
|---|---|---|---|---|---|---|---|---|---|
| Conf 11 | Conf 18 | Conf 23 | Conf S 22 | SthP 18 | SthP 17 | SthP 9 | SthP 12 | SthP 7 | SthP 7 |

# WEYMOUTH MATCH RESULTS 2015-16

| Date | Comp | H/A | Opponents | Att: | Result | Goalscorers | Pos | No. |
|---|---|---|---|---|---|---|---|---|
| Aug 8 | SPL | A | Cambridge City | 240 | L 0-1 | | 21 | 1 |
| 11 | SPL | H | Paulton Rovers | 643 | **W** 4-1 | Yetton 42 Copp 59 (pen) 63 (pen) Molesley 81 | 9 | 2 |
| 15 | SPL | H | Dunstable Town | 533 | D 0-0 | | 9 | 3 |
| 18 | SPL | H | Bideford | 543 | **W** 1-0 | Yetton 89 | 9 | 4 |
| 22 | SPL | A | Kettering Town | 581 | **W** 1-0 | Yetton 47 | 5 | 5 |
| 29 | SPL | H | St Neots Town | 608 | D 1-1 | McPhee 88 | 5 | 6 |
| 31 | SPL | A | Dorchester Town | 1357 | L 0-1 | | 9 | 7 |
| Sept 5 | SPL | H | Histon | 538 | **W** 1-0 | Sibanda 89 (og) | 8 | 8 |
| **12** | **FAC1Q** | **A** | **Petersfield Town** | **201** | **L 1-3** | **Yetton 72** | | 9 |
| 19 | SPL | A | Leamington | 453 | D 0-0 | | 8 | 10 |
| 22 | SPL | H | Chippenham Town | 516 | D 1-1 | Thomson 15 | 9 | 11 |
| 26 | SPL | H | Hungerford Town | 484 | **W** 2-1 | Cooper 47 Kelly 54 | 5 | 12 |
| 29 | SPL | A | Cirencester Town | 156 | **W** 3-0 | Thomson 38 Wannell 53 Shephard 78 | 3 | 13 |
| Oct 3 | SPL | H | Bedworth United | 578 | **W** 1-0 | Thomson 78 | 1 | 14 |
| 10 | SPL | A | Redditch United | 368 | D 1-1 | Evans 9 | 3 | 15 |
| 17 | SPL | H | Biggleswade Town | 537 | L 0-1 | | 4 | 16 |
| 20 | SPL | A | Chippenham Town | 349 | D 1-1 | Cooper 69 | 4 | 17 |
| 24 | SPL | H | Kings Lynn Town | 468 | **W** 2-0 | Yetton 19 Copp 64 | | 18 |
| 28 | SPL | A | Frome Town | 472 | D 1-1 | Yetton 70 | 4 | 19 |
| **31** | **FAT1Q** | **A** | **Winchester City** | **349** | **W 2-1** | **Evans 46 Copp** | | 20 |
| Nov 7 | SPL | A | Merthyr Town | 474 | **W** 3-1 | Shephard 58 77 Kelly 68 | 4 | 21 |
| **14** | **FAT2Q** | **A** | **Bedford Town** | **229** | **W 4-1** | **Kelly 16 Yetton 38 55 Shephard 45** | | 22 |
| 21 | SPL | A | Dunstable Town | 151 | L 1-2 | Evans 73 | 4 | 23 |
| **28** | **FAT3Q** | **A** | **Hemel Hempstead Town** | **349** | **L 0-1** | | | 24 |
| Dec 5 | SPL | A | Stratford Town | 209 | D 1-1 | Shephard 90 | 7 | 25 |
| 12 | SPL | H | Slough Town | 532 | **W** 6-1 | Evans 29 Thomson 31 34 Shephard 47 Cooper 57 Rigg 67 | 7 | 26 |
| 19 | SPL | A | St Neots Town | 299 | D 1-1 | Shephard 77 | 5 | 27 |
| 26 | SPL | H | Dorchester Town | 1808 | D 2-2 | Shephard 29 (pen) Yetton 45 | 4 | 28 |
| Jan 6 | SPL | A | Paulton Rovers | 275 | D 1-1 | Evans 72 | 6 | 29 |
| 9 | SPL | H | Hitchin Town | 494 | L 0-2 | | 8 | 30 |
| 16 | SPL | A | Histon | 219 | **W** 4-1 | Rigg 2 75 Thomson 50 Shephard 78 | 5 | 31 |
| 19 | SPL | H | Cambridge City | 346 | **W** 1-0 | Evans 23 | | 32 |
| 23 | SPL | H | Kettering Town | 637 | **W** 3-2 | Shephard 3 Thomson 71 Kelly 77 | 3 | 33 |
| 30 | SPL | A | Bedworth United | 156 | L 2-3 | Surridge 70 Kelly 90 | 4 | 34 |
| Feb 2 | SPL | A | Poole Town | 676 | L 0-2 | | 5 | 35 |
| 16 | SPL | H | Chesham United | 448 | L 1-4 | Thomson 56 | 8 | 36 |
| 27 | SPL | A | Biggleswade Town | 175 | D 1-1 | Yetton 36 | 10 | 37 |
| Mar 5 | SPL | H | Redditch United | 536 | **W** 2-0 | Yetton 59 Wannell 90 | 9 | 38 |
| 12 | SPL | H | Stratford Town | 567 | **W** 2-1 | Thomson 62 75 | 7 | 39 |
| 15 | SPL | A | Bideford | 153 | **W** 2-0 | Copp 60 Yetton 89 | 7 | 40 |
| 19 | SPL | A | Slough Town | 320 | D 0-0 | | 7 | 41 |
| 21 | SPL | A | Hungerford Town | 208 | **W** 1-0 | Sills 50 | 7 | 42 |
| 25 | SPL | A | Hitchin Town | 578 | L 0-1 | | 7 | 43 |
| 28 | SPL | H | Poole Town | 1205 | L 0-1 | | 8 | 44 |
| Apr 2 | SPL | H | Frome Town | 561 | **W** 2-0 | Rigg 55 Thomson 89 | 7 | 45 |
| 5 | SPL | H | Leamington | 591 | **W** 1-0 | Wannell 64 | 6 | 46 |
| 9 | SPL | A | Kings Lynn Town | 514 | D 0-0 | | 7 | 47 |
| 16 | SPL | H | Merthyr Town | 646 | **W** 3-0 | Copp 15 Shephard 25 Cooper 83 | 6 | 48 |
| 19 | SPL | H | Cirencester Town | 556 | **W** 3-1 | Shephard 28 (pen) Molesley 48 Thomson 88 | 6 | 49 |
| 23 | SPL | A | Chesham United | 382 | L 0-1 | | 7 | 50 |

| GOALSCORERS | Scoring Games | Consec Sco Games | Total |
|---|---|---|---|
| ***2014-15 Yetton*** | | | ***33*** |
| Yetton | 11 | 2 | 12 |
| Shephard | 10 | 4 | 12 |
| Thomson | 10 | 2 | 12 |
| Copp | 6 | | 6 |
| Evans | 6 | | 6 |
| Kelly | 5 | 2 | 5 |
| Cooper | 4 | | 4 |
| Rigg | 4 | | 4 |
| Wannell | 3 | | 3 |

| | Scoring Games | Consec Sco Games | Total |
|---|---|---|---|
| Molesey | 2 | | 2 |
| McPhee | 1 | | 1 |
| Sills | 1 | | 1 |
| Surridge | 1 | | 1 |
| | | | |
| Opponents | | | 1 |

# AFC DUNSTABLE

**Chairman:** Simon Bullard
**Secretary:** Craig Renfrew **(T)** 07707 058 416 **(E)** afcdunstable2016@gmail.com
**Commercial Manager:** **(T)**
**Programme Editor:** Craig Renfrew **(T)** afcdunstable2016@gmail.com
**Ground Address:** Creasey Park, Creasey Pk Dr, Brewers Hill Road LU6 1BB
**(T)** 01582 891 433 **Manager:** Steve Heath

**Founded:** 1981 **Nickname:** Od's
**Previous Names:** Old Dunstablians 1981- 2004.
**Previous Leagues:** Spartan South Midlands >2016.

**Club Colours (change):** Royal blue/royal blue/blue (All red)

**Ground Capacity:** 3,200 **Seats:** 350 **Covered:** 1,000 **Clubhouse:** Yes **Shop:** Yes
**Previous Grounds:**

**Record Attendance:** Not known - if you know please email tw.publications@btinternet.com
**Record Victory:** Not known - if you know please email tw.publications@btinternet.com
**Record Defeat:** Not known - if you know please email tw.publications@btinternet.com
**Record Goalscorer:** Not known - if you know please email tw.publications@btinternet.com
**Record Appearances:** Not known - if you know please email tw.publications@btinternet.com
**Additional Records:**

**Senior Honours:**
Spartan South Midlands Division Two 2003-04, 06-07, Premier Division 2015-16.
Bedfordshire Junior Cup 1989-90. Bedfordshire Senior Trophy 2006-07.

**10 YEAR RECORD**

| 06-07 | 07-08 | 08-09 | 09-10 | 10-11 | 11-12 | 12-13 | 13-14 | 14-15 | 15-16 |
|---|---|---|---|---|---|---|---|---|---|
| SSM2 1 | SSM2 4 | SSM2 3 | SSM1 5 | SSM1 2 | SSM P 3 | SSM P 8 | SSM P 9 | SSM P 3 | SSM P 1 |

# ARLESEY TOWN

**Chairman:** John Morrell
**Secretary:** Chris Sterry **(T)** **(E)** chris.sterry@ntlworld.com
**Commercial Manager:** **(T)**
**Programme Editor:** Steve Hazelwood **(T)** hazelwood1972@virginmedia.com
**Ground Address:** New Lamb Meadow, Hitchin Road, Arlesey SG15 6RS
**(T)** 01462 734 504 **Manager:** Zema & Nathan Abbey - 11/02/15

**Founded:** 1891 **Nickname:** The Blues
**Previous Names:** None
**Previous Leagues:** Biggleswade & Dist., Bedfordshire Co. (South Midlands) 1922-26, 27-28, Parthenon, London 1958-60, United Co. 1933-36, 82-92, Spartan South Mid. 1992-2000, Isthmian 2000-04, 06-08, Southern 2004-07

**Club Colours (change):** Light blue/dark blue/dark blue (Cherry & black/black/black)

**Ground Capacity:** 2,920 **Seats:** 150 **Covered:** 600 **Clubhouse:** Yes **Shop:** Yes
**Previous Grounds:** The Bury. Lamb Meadow.

**Record Attendance:** 2,000 v Luton Town Reserves - Bedfordshire Senior Cup 1906
**Record Victory:** Not known - if you know please email tw.publications@btinternet.com
**Record Defeat:** Not known - if you know please email tw.publications@btinternet.com
**Record Goalscorer:** Not known - if you know please email tw.publications@btinternet.com
**Record Appearances:** Gary Marshall
**Additional Records:** FA Cup: First Round, 2011-12, 2012-13 FA Trophy: Fifth Round, 2003-04
FA Vase: Winners, 1994-95

**Senior Honours:**
South Midlands Premier Division x5. United Counties Premier Division 1984-85. FA Vase 1994-95.
Isthmian League Division 3 2000-01. Southern League Division 1 Central 2010-11.
Bedfordshire Senior Cup 1965-66, 78-79, 96-97, 2010-11.

**10 YEAR RECORD**

| 06-07 | 07-08 | 08-09 | 09-10 | 10-11 | 11-12 | 12-13 | 13-14 | 14-15 | 15-16 |
|---|---|---|---|---|---|---|---|---|---|
| Isth1N 18 | Isth1N 15 | SthC 18 | SthC 9 | SthC 1 | SthP 18 | SthP 6 | SthP 15 | SthP 22 | SthC 16 |

# ASHFORD TOWN (MIDDLESEX)

**Chairman:** Dave Baker
**Secretary:** Geoff Knock **(T)** 07928 792 792 **(E)** geoff.knock@btinternet.com
**Commercial Manager:** **(T)**
**Programme Editor:** Geoff Knock **(T)** geoff.knock@btinternet.com
**Ground Address:** Robert Parker Stadium, Stanwell, Staines TW19 7BH
**(T)** 01784 245 908 **Manager:** Ben Murray

**Founded:** 1958 **Nickname:** Ash Trees
**Previous Names:** Ashford Albion 1958-64.
**Previous Leagues:** Hounslow & District 1964-68, Surrey Intermediate 1968-82, Surrey Premier 1982-90, Combind Counties 1990-2000, 14-16, Isthmian 20 00-04, 06-10, Southern 2004-06, 10-14.
**Club Colours (change):** Tangerine and white stripes/black/tangerine

**Ground Capacity:** 2,550 **Seats:** 250 **Covered:** 250 **Clubhouse:** Yes **Shop:** No
**Previous Grounds:** Clockhouse Lane Recreation 1958-85.

**Record Attendance:** 992 v AFC Wimbledon - Isthmian League Premier Division 26/09/2006
**Record Victory:** Not known - if you know please email tw.publications@btinternet.com
**Record Defeat:** Not known - if you know please email tw.publications@btinternet.com
**Record Goalscorer:** Andy Smith
**Record Appearances:** Alan Constable - 650
**Additional Records:** Received £10,000 from Wycombe Wanderers for Dannie Bulman 1997
**Senior Honours:**
Surrey Premier League 1982-90. Combined Counties League 1994-95, 95-96, 96-97, 97-98.
Middlesex Charity Cup 2000-01. Middlesex Premier Cup 2006-07. Isthmian League Cup 2006-07.

**10 YEAR RECORD**

| 06-07 | 07-08 | 08-09 | 09-10 | 10-11 | 11-12 | 12-13 | 13-14 | 14-15 | 15-16 |
|---|---|---|---|---|---|---|---|---|---|
| Isth P 17 | Isth P 6 | Isth P 10 | Isth P 20 | SthC 16 | SthC 9 | SthC 10 | SthC 22 | CCP 3 | CCP 2 |

# AYLESBURY

**Chairman:** Danny Martone
**Secretary:** April Benson **(T)** **(E)** apriljbenson@googlemail.com
**Commercial Manager:** **(T)**
**Programme Editor:** Mike Farquharson **(T)** mikefarquharson@gmail.com
**Ground Address:** Haywood Way, Aylesbury, Bucks. HP19 9WZ
**(T)** 01296 421 101 **Manager:** Daniel Gordon & Gareth Risbridger

**Founded:** 1930 **Nickname:** The Moles
**Previous Names:** Negretti & Zambra FC 1930-54, Stocklake 1954-2000, Haywood United > 2000, Haywood FC 2000-06, Aylesbury Vale 2006-09.
**Previous Leagues:** Aylesbury District. Wycombe & District. Chiltern, Spartan South Midlands

**Club Colours (change):** Red & black/black/red (Silver & white/maroon/maroon)

**Ground Capacity:** **Seats:** Yes **Covered:** Yes **Clubhouse:** Yes **Shop:** No
**Previous Grounds:** Negretti & Zambra King's Cross 1930-49. Stocklake Industrial Estate 1949-87.

**Record Attendance:** Not known - if you know please email tw.publications@btinternet.com
**Record Victory:** Not known - if you know please email tw.publications@btinternet.com
**Record Defeat:** Not known - if you know please email tw.publications@btinternet.com
**Record Goalscorer:** Not known - if you know please email tw.publications@btinternet.com
**Record Appearances:** Not known - if you know please email tw.publications@btinternet.com
**Additional Records:** FA Cup: Fourth qualifying round, 2009-10 FA Trophy: First qualifying round, 2010-11, 2011-12
FA Vase: Third round, 2008-09
**Senior Honours:**
Spartan South Midlands League Division 1 2003-04, Premier Division 2009-10.
Wycombe Senior Cup 1994-95. Berks & Bucks Senior Cup 2015-16.

**10 YEAR RECORD**

| 06-07 | 07-08 | 08-09 | 09-10 | 10-11 | 11-12 | 12-13 | 13-14 | 14-15 | 15-16 |
|---|---|---|---|---|---|---|---|---|---|
| SSM P 5 | SSM P 9 | SSM P 15 | SSM P 1 | SthC 8 | SthC 20 | SthC 12 | SthC 16 | SthC 3 | SthC 8 |

# AYLESBURY UNITED

**Chairman:** Graham Read
**Secretary:** Steve Baker (T) 07768 353 265 (E) stevepb42@hotmail.com
**Commercial Manager:** (T)
**Programme Editor:** Warren Sheward (T) w.sheward@sky.com
**Ground Address:** Thame United FC, The ASM Stadium, Meadow View Park, Thame OX9 3RN
(T) 01296 487 367 (Office) **Manager:** Glyn Creaser

**Founded:** 1897 **Nickname:** The Ducks
**Previous Names:** None
**Previous Leagues:** Post War: Spartan >1951, Delphian 51-63, Athenian 63-76, Southern 76-88, 2004-10, Conf. 88-89, Isthmian 89-2004. Spartan South Midlands 2010-13.
**Club Colours (change):** Green/white/white (All orange)

**Ground Capacity:** 2,800 **Seats:** 155 **Covered:** 300 **Clubhouse:** Yes **Shop:** No
**Previous Grounds:** Turnfurlong Lane. Buckingham Road >2006

**Record Attendance:** Turnfurlong Lane - 7,440 v Watford FAC 1st Rnd 1951-52. Buckingham Road - 6,031 v England 04/06/1988.
**Record Victory:** 10-0 v Hornchurch & Upminster (H), Delphain League 17/04/1954
**Record Defeat:** 0-9 v Bishop's Stortford (A), Delphain League 08/10/1955
**Record Goalscorer:** Cliff Hercules - 301 (1984-2002)
**Record Appearances:** Cliff Hercules - 651+18 (1984-2002)
**Additional Records:**

**Senior Honours:**
Southern League 1987-88. Berks & Bucks Senior Cup x5 2012-13. Isthmian Cup 1994-95.

**10 YEAR RECORD**

| 06-07 | 07-08 | 08-09 | 09-10 | 10-11 | 11-12 | 12-13 | 13-14 | 14-15 | 15-16 |
|---|---|---|---|---|---|---|---|---|---|
| SthM 6 | SthM 8 | SthM 10 | SthM 22 | SSM P 6 | SSM P 4 | SSM P 2 | SthC 12 | SthC 13 | SthC 19 |

# BARTON ROVERS

**Chairman:** Darren Whiley
**Secretary:** Darren Whiley (T) (E) bartonrovers@talktalk.net
**Commercial Manager:** (T)
**Programme Editor:** Pete Burr (T) programme@bartonrovers.com
**Ground Address:** Luton Road, Barton-le-Clay, Bedford MK45 4SD
(T) 01582 707 772 **Manager:** James Gray - June 2016

**Founded:** 1898 **Nickname:** Rovers
**Previous Names:** None
**Previous Leagues:** Luton & district 1947-54, South Midlands 1954-79, Isthmian 1979-2004
**Club Colours (change):** All royal blue (Yellow/black/yellow)

**Ground Capacity:** 4,000 **Seats:** 160 **Covered:** 1,120 **Clubhouse:** Yes **Shop:** Yes
**Previous Grounds:** None

**Record Attendance:** 1,900 v Nuneaton Borough - FA Cup 4th Qualifying Round 1976
**Record Victory:** Not known - if you know please email tw.publications@btinternet.com
**Record Defeat:** Not known - if you know please email tw.publications@btinternet.com
**Record Goalscorer:** Richard Camp - 152 (1989-98)
**Record Appearances:** Tony McNally - 598 (1988-2005)
**Additional Records:** Paid £1,000 to Hitchin Town for B. Baldry 1980
Received £1,000 from Bishop's Stortford for B. Baldry 1981

**Senior Honours:**
South Midlands League 1970-71, 71-72, 72-73, 74-75, 75-76, 76-77.
Bedfordshire Senior Cup 1971-72, 72-73, 80-81, 81-82, 89-90, 97-98, 98-99, Premier Cup 1995-96, Senior Challenge Cup 2015-16.

**10 YEAR RECORD**

| 06-07 | 07-08 | 08-09 | 09-10 | 10-11 | 11-12 | 12-13 | 13-14 | 14-15 | 15-16 |
|---|---|---|---|---|---|---|---|---|---|
| SthM 20 | SthM 11 | SthM 17 | SthM 21 | SthC 12 | SthC 11 | SthC 14 | SthC 6 | SthC 5 | SthC 18 |

## BEACONSFIELD SYCOB

**Chairman:** Paul Hughes
**Secretary:** Robin Woolman (T) 01753 853 607 (E) robin.woolman@btinternet.com
**Commercial Manager:** (T)
**Programme Editor:** Graham White (T) grassrootscommunications@btinternet.com
**Ground Address:** Holloways Park, Windsor Road, Beaconsfield, Bucks HP9 2SE
(T) 01494 676 868 **Manager:** Geoff Warner - July 2015

**Founded:** 1994 **Nickname:** The Rams
**Previous Names:** Slough YCOB and Beaconsfield United merged in 1994
**Previous Leagues:** Spartan South Midlands 1004-2004, 07-08, Southern 2004-07

**Club Colours (change):** Red and white quarters/red/red (Yellow/royal blue/yellow)

**Ground Capacity:** 3,500 **Seats:** **Covered:** **Clubhouse:** Yes **Shop:**
**Previous Grounds:** None

**Record Attendance:** Not known - if you know please email tw.publications@btinternet.com
**Record Victory:** Not known - if you know please email tw.publications@btinternet.com
**Record Defeat:** Not known - if you know please email tw.publications@btinternet.com
**Record Goalscorer:** Allan Arthur
**Record Appearances:** Allan Arthur
**Additional Records:** FA Cup: 2nd Round Qualifying, 1998-99, 99-2000, 00-01, 02-03,004-05, 11-12
FA Trophy: 1st Round Qualifying, 2005-06, 09-10, 10-11 FA Vase: 2nd Round, 2003-04
**Senior Honours:**
Spartan South Midlands 2000-01, 03-04, 07-08. Berks and Bucks Senior Trophy 2003-04

**10 YEAR RECORD**

| 06-07 | 07-08 | 08-09 | 09-10 | 10-11 | 11-12 | 12-13 | 13-14 | 14-15 | 15-16 |
|---|---|---|---|---|---|---|---|---|---|
| Sthsw 22 | SSM P 1 | Sthsw 4 | SthM 19 | SthC 22 | SthC 5 | SthC 5 | SthC 8 | SthC 20 | SthC 9 |

## BEDFORD TOWN

**Chairman:** David Howell
**Secretary:** James Smiles (T) 07986 714 418 (E) james.smiles@bedfordeagles.net
**Commercial Manager:** (T)
**Programme Editor:** Chris Lathey (T) chris@lathey.net
**Ground Address:** The Eyrie, Meadow Lane, Cardington, Bedford MK44 3SB
(T) 01234 831 558 **Manager:** Jon Taylor

**Founded:** 1989 **Nickname:** The Eagles
**Previous Names:** Original Bedford Town founded in 1908 folded in 1982
**Previous Leagues:** South Midlands 1989-94, Isthmian 1994-2004, Southern 2004-06, Conference 2006-07

**Club Colours (change):** Blue with white trim/blue/blue (Gold with black trim/black/black)

**Ground Capacity:** 3,000 **Seats:** 300 **Covered:** 1,000 **Clubhouse:** Yes **Shop:** Yes
**Previous Grounds:** Allen Park, Queens Park, Bedford Park Pitch 1991-93

**Record Attendance:** 3,000 v Peterborough United - Ground opening 06/08/1993
**Record Victory:** 9-0 v Ickleford and v Cardington
**Record Defeat:** 0-5 v Hendon
**Record Goalscorer:** Jason Reed
**Record Appearances:** Eddie Lawley
**Additional Records:**
**Senior Honours:**
Isthmian League Division 2 1998-99. Bedfordshire Senior Cup 1994-95. Southern League Play-offs 2005-06.

**10 YEAR RECORD**

| 06-07 | 07-08 | 08-09 | 09-10 | 10-11 | 11-12 | 12-13 | 13-14 | 14-15 | 15-16 |
|---|---|---|---|---|---|---|---|---|---|
| Conf S 22 | SthP 19 | SthP 15 | SthP 18 | SthP 17 | SthP 10 | SthP 10 | SthP 22 | SthC 17 | SthC 14 |

# CHALFONT ST PETER

**Chairman:** Denis Mair
**Secretary:** Colin Finch **(T)** 07748 837 526 **(E)** colin@crmfinch.freeserve.co.uk
**Commercial Manager:** **(T)**
**Programme Editor:** Ian Doorbar **(T)** doors8jz@hotmail.com
**Ground Address:** Mill Meadow, Gravel Hill, Amersham Road, Chalfont St Peter SL9 9QX
**(T)** 01753 885 797 **Manager:** Danny Edwards

**Founded:** 1926 **Nickname:** Saints
**Previous Names:** None
**Previous Leagues:** G W Comb. Parthernon. London. Spartan. L Spartan. Athenian. Isthmian, Spartan South Midlands 2006-11.

**Club Colours (change):** Red/green/red. (Yellow/black/black).

**Ground Capacity:** 4,500 **Seats:** 220 **Covered:** 120 **Clubhouse:** Yes **Shop:** Yes
**Previous Grounds:** None

**Record Attendance:** **Att:** 2,550 v Watford benefit match 1985 **App:** Colin Davies
**Record Victory:** 10-1 v Kentish Town (away) Spartan League Premier Division 23 Dec 2008
**Record Defeat:** 0-13 v Lewes (away) Isthmian Division 3, 7 Nov 2000
**Record Goalscorer:** Not known - if you know please email tw.publications@btinternet.com
**Record Appearances:** Not known - if you know please email tw.publications@btinternet.com
**Additional Records:** FA Cup: 3rd Qualifying Round 1998-99, 2012-13, 14-15
FA Trophy: 3rd Qualifying Round 1989-90, 91-92 FA Vase: Semi Finalists 2008-9
**Senior Honours:**
Isthmian Lge Div 2 87-88, Berks & Bucks Intermediate Cup 52-53.
Spartan South Midlands Premier Division 2010-11.

**10 YEAR RECORD**

| 06-07 | 07-08 | 08-09 | 09-10 | 10-11 | 11-12 | 12-13 | 13-14 | 14-15 | 15-16 |
|---|---|---|---|---|---|---|---|---|---|
| SSM P 6 | SSM P 2 | SSM P 3 | SSM P 2 | SSM P 1 | SthC 12 | SthC 16 | SthC 14 | SthC 16 | SthC 6 |

# EGHAM TOWN

**Chairman:** Patrick Bennett
**Secretary:** Daniel Bennett **(T)** 07932 612 424 **(E)** danielbennett1974@yahoo.co.uk
**Commercial Manager:** **(T)**
**Programme Editor:** Mark Ferguson **(T)** markeghamtownfc@yahoo.co.uk
**Ground Address:** Runnymead Stadium, Tempest Road, Egham TW20 8XD
**(T)** 01784 435 226 **Manager:** Gary Meakin

**Founded:** 1877 **Nickname:** Sarnies
**Previous Names:** Runnymead Rovers 1877-1905. Egham F.C. 05-63.
**Previous Leagues:** Spartan. Athenian. Isthmian. Southern. Combined Counties 2006-13.

**Club Colours (change):** Red with diagonal white stripe/red/red (Green/black/black)

**Ground Capacity:** 5500 **Seats:** 262 **Covered:** 3300 **Clubhouse:** Yes **Shop:** No
**Previous Grounds:** Moved to Recreation Ground - now Runnymead Stadium - in 1963.

**Record Attendance:** 1400 v Wycombe Wanderers, FAC 2nd Qual. 1972-73.
**Record Victory:** Not known - if you know please email tw.publications@btinternet.com
**Record Defeat:** Not known - if you know please email tw.publications@btinternet.com
**Record Goalscorer:** Mark Butler (153).
**Record Appearances:** Dave Jones (850+).
**Additional Records:**
**Senior Honours:**
Spartan League Champions 1971-72. Athenian League Division 2 Champions.
Combined Counties League 2012-13.

**10 YEAR RECORD**

| 06-07 | 07-08 | 08-09 | 09-10 | 10-11 | 11-12 | 12-13 | 13-14 | 14-15 | 15-16 |
|---|---|---|---|---|---|---|---|---|---|
| CCP 10 | CCP 12 | CCP 13 | CCP 4 | CCP 13 | CCP 4 | CCP 1 | SthC 11 | SthC 15 | SthC 3 |

# FARNBOROUGH

**Chairman:** Simon Gardener
**Secretary:** Jim Hardy (T) 07722 504 278 (E) clubsecretary@farnboroughfc.co.uk
**Commercial Manager:** (T)
**Programme Editor:** Dominic Lloyd (T) webadmin@farnboroughfc.co.uk
**Ground Address:** Rushmoor Community Stadium, Cherrywood Road, Farnborough, Hants GU14 8DU
(T) 01252 541 469 **Manager:** Spencer Day

**Founded:** 1967 **Nickname:** Boro
**Previous Names:** Farnborough Town 1967-2007
**Previous Leagues:** Surrey Senior 1968-72, Spartan 1972-76, Athenian 1976-77, Isthmian 1977-89, 99-2001, 15-16. Alliance/Conference 1989-90, 91-93, 94-99, 2010-15. Southern 1990-91, 93-94, 2007-10.
**Club Colours (change):** Yellow & blue/blue/yellow (All white)

**Ground Capacity:** 7,000 **Seats:** 627 **Covered:** 1,350 **Clubhouse:** Yes **Shop:** Yes
**Previous Grounds:** None as Farnborough. Queens Road as Farnborough Town

**Record Attendance:** 2,230 v Corby Town - Southern Premier 21/03/2009
**Record Victory:** 7-0 v Newport (I.O.W.) (A) - Southern League Division 1 South & West 01/12/2007
**Record Defeat:** 0-4 v Hednesford Town (A) - Southern League Premier Division 04/03/2010
**Record Goalscorer:** Dean McDonald - 35 (in 53+3 Appearances 2009-10)
**Record Appearances:** Nic Ciardini - 147 (2007-10)
**Additional Records:**

**Senior Honours:**
Southern League Division 1 South & West 2007-08, Premier Division 2009-10.
Farnborough Town: Southern League Premier Division 1990-91, 93-94. Isthmian League Division 1 1984-85, Premier Division 2000-01.
Hampshire Senior Cup 1974-75, 81-82, 83-84, 85-86, 90-91, 2003-04.

**10 YEAR RECORD**

| 06-07 | 07-08 | 08-09 | 09-10 | 10-11 | 11-12 | 12-13 | 13-14 | 14-15 | 15-16 |
|---|---|---|---|---|---|---|---|---|---|
| Conf S 11 | SthW 1 | SthP 2 | SthP 1 | Conf S 2 | Conf S 16 | Conf S 13 | Conf S 16 | Conf S 20 | Isth P 18 |

# FLEET TOWN

**Chairman:** Steve Cantle
**Secretary:** Richard Whittingdon (T) (E) rcwhittington@virginmedia.com
**Commercial Manager:** (T)
**Programme Editor:** Martin Griffiths (T) mgriffiths@ntlworld.com
**Ground Address:** Calthorpe Park, Crookham Road, Fleet, Hants GU51 5FA
(T) 01252 623 804 Match day only **Manager:** Craig Davis

**Founded:** 1890 **Nickname:** The Blues
**Previous Names:** Fleet FC 1890-1963
**Previous Leagues:** Hampshire 1961-77, Athenian, Combined Counties, Chiltonian, Wessex 1989-95, 2000-02, Southern 1995-2000, 02-04, 07-08, Isthmian 2004-07, 2008-11.
**Club Colours (change):** Blue with white stripe/blue/blue (Yellow & black/black/black)

**Ground Capacity:** 2,000 **Seats:** 250 **Covered:** 250 **Clubhouse:** Yes **Shop:** Yes
**Previous Grounds:** Watsons Meadow > 1923.

**Record Attendance:** 1,336 v AFC Wimbledon, Isthmian League 08/01/2005
**Record Victory:** 15-0 v Petersfield , Wessex League 26/12/1994
**Record Defeat:** 0-7 v Bashley, Southern League 12/04/2004
**Record Goalscorer:** Mark Frampton - 428
**Record Appearances:** Mark Frampton - 250
**Additional Records:** Paid £3,000 to Aldershot for Mark Russell

**Senior Honours:**
Wessex League 1994-95.
Aldershot Senior Cup 1993, 95, 96, 2000, 08, 09, 10. Basingstoke Senior Cup 2006, 08, 10. Hampshire Senior Cup 2009.

**10 YEAR RECORD**

| 06-07 | 07-08 | 08-09 | 09-10 | 10-11 | 11-12 | 12-13 | 13-14 | 14-15 | 15-16 |
|---|---|---|---|---|---|---|---|---|---|
| Isth1S 5 | Sthsw 2 | Isth1S 3 | Isth1S 6 | Isth1S 13 | SthC 21 | SthC 18 | Sthsw 21 | Sthsw 19 | SthC 17 |

# HANWELL TOWN

**Chairman:** Bob Fisher
**Secretary:** Clive Cooke (T) 07791 314 689 (E) clivecooke2@sky.com
**Commercial Manager:** (T)
**Programme Editor:** Bob Fisher (T) bob.fisher@hanwelltfc.plus.com
**Ground Address:** Reynolds Field, Preivale Lane, Perivale, Greenford, UB6 8TL
(T) 020 8998 1701 **Manager:** Ray Duffy

**Founded:** 1920 **Nickname:** Magpies
**Previous Names:** None
**Previous Leagues:** Dauntless. Wembley & Dist. Middlesex. London Spartan. Southern.

**Club Colours (change):** Black & white stripes/black/black (Red/white/red)

**Ground Capacity:** 1,250 **Seats:** 175 **Covered:** 600 **Clubhouse:** Yes **Shop:** No
**Previous Grounds:** Moved to Reynolds Field in 1981.

**Record Attendance:** **Att:** 600 v Spurs, floodlight switch on, 1989.
**Record Victory:** Not known - if you know please email tw.publications@btinternet.com
**Record Defeat:** Not known - if you know please email tw.publications@btinternet.com
**Record Goalscorer:** Keith Rowlands
**Record Appearances:** Phil Player 617 (20 seasons)
**Additional Records:**

**Senior Honours:**
London Spartan Senior Div. 83-84. London Senior Cup 1991-92, 92-93.
Spartan South Midlands Premier 2013-14.

**10 YEAR RECORD**

| 06-07 | 07-08 | 08-09 | 09-10 | 10-11 | 11-12 | 12-13 | 13-14 | 14-15 | 15-16 |
|---|---|---|---|---|---|---|---|---|---|
| SthS 21 | SSM P 9 | SSM P 7 | SSM P 13 | SSM P 15 | SSM P 21 | SSM P 6 | SSM P 1 | SthC 7 | SthC 20 |

# HISTON

**Chairman:** John Hall
**Secretary:** Howard Wilkins (T) 01223 237 373 (E) howard.wilkins@histonfc.co.uk
**Commercial Manager:** (T)
**Programme Editor:** Howard Wilkins (T) howard.wilkins@histonfc.co.uk
**Ground Address:** The Glass World Stadium, Bridge Road, Impington, Cambridge CB24 9PH
(T) 01223 237 373 **Manager:** Steve Fallon

**Founded:** 1904 **Nickname:** The Stutes
**Previous Names:** Histon Institute
**Previous Leagues:** Cambridgeshire 1904-48, Spartan 1948-60, Delphian 1960-63, Eastern Counties 1966-2000, Southern 2000-05. Conference 2005-14.
**Club Colours (change):** Red and black stripes/black/black (Blue & white stripes/blue/blue)

**Ground Capacity:** 3,250 **Seats:** 450 **Covered:** 1,800 **Clubhouse:** Yes **Shop:** Yes
**Previous Grounds:** None

**Record Attendance:** 6,400 v King's Lynn - FA Cup 1956
**Record Victory:** 11-0 v March Town - Cambridgeshire Invitation Cup 15/02/01
**Record Defeat:** 1-8 v Ely City - Eastern Counties Division One 1994
**Record Goalscorer:** Neil Kennedy - 292
**Record Appearances:** Neil Andrews and Neil Kennedy
**Additional Records:** Paid £6,000 to Chelmsford City for Ian Cambridge 2000. Received £30,000 from Manchester United for Guiliano Maiorana.
**Senior Honours:**
Eastern Counties League Cup 1990-91, Eastern Counties League 1999-2000, Southern League Premier 2004-05, Conference South 2006-07.
Cambridgeshire Professional Cup 2012-13, 15-16.

**10 YEAR RECORD**

| 06-07 | 07-08 | 08-09 | 09-10 | 10-11 | 11-12 | 12-13 | 13-14 | 14-15 | 15-16 |
|---|---|---|---|---|---|---|---|---|---|
| Conf S 1 | Conf 7 | Conf 3 | Conf 18 | Conf 24 | Conf N 16 | Conf N 19 | Conf N 21 | SthP 18 | SthP 22 |

# KEMPSTON ROVERS

**Chairman:** Russell Shreeves
**Secretary:** Kevin Howlett **(T)** 07721 849 671 **(E)** howlett.home@btinternet.com
**Commercial Manager:** **(T)**
**Programme Editor:** Mark Kennett **(T)** markkennett@hotmail.com
**Ground Address:** Hillgrounds Leisure, Hillgrounds Road, Kempston, Bedford MK42 8SZ
**(T)** 01234 852 346 **Manager:** Jimmy Stoyles & Gary Flinn

**Founded:** 1884 **Nickname:** Walnut Boys
**Previous Names:** None
**Previous Leagues:** South Midlands 1927-53. United Counties 1957-2016.

**Club Colours (change):** Red & white stripes/black/black

**Ground Capacity:** 2,000 **Seats:** 100 **Covered:** 250 **Clubhouse:** Yes **Shop:**
**Previous Grounds:**

**Record Attendance:** Not known - if you know please email tw.publications@btinternet.com
**Record Victory:** Not known - if you know please email tw.publications@btinternet.com
**Record Defeat:** Not known - if you know please email tw.publications@btinternet.com
**Record Goalscorer:** Not known - if you know please email tw.publications@btinternet.com
**Record Appearances:** Not known - if you know please email tw.publications@btinternet.com
**Additional Records:** FA Cup: Fourth qualifying round, 1978-79
FA Vase: Fifth round 1974-75, 1980-81
**Senior Honours:**
United Counties League Premier Division 1973-74, 2015-16, Division One 1957-58, 85-86, 2010-11, Division Two 1955-56,
United Counties KO Cup 1955-56, 57-58, 59-60, 74-75, 76-77.
Beds Senior Cup 1908-09, 37-38, 76-77, 91-92. Hinchingbrooke Cup 2010-11.

**10 YEAR RECORD**

| 06-07 | 07-08 | 08-09 | 09-10 | 10-11 | 11-12 | 12-13 | 13-14 | 14-15 | 15-16 |
|---|---|---|---|---|---|---|---|---|---|
| UCL 1 3 | UCL P 12 | UCL 1 5 | UCL 1 5 | UCL 1 1 | UCL P 10 | UCL P 17 | UCL P 12 | UCL P 8 | UCL P 1 |

# KIDLINGTON

**Chairman:** Nick Duval
**Secretary:** David Platt **(T)** 07956 531 185 **(E)** dplatt45@hotmail.co.uk
**Commercial Manager:** **(T)**
**Programme Editor:** Donna Conelly **(T)** donna.con7@gmail.com
**Ground Address:** Yarnton Road, Kidlington, Oxford OX5 1AT
**(T)** 01865 849 777 **Manager:** Martin Wilkinson

**Founded:** 1909 **Nickname:** Greens
**Previous Names:** None.
**Previous Leagues:** Oxford Senior.

**Club Colours (change):** All green

**Ground Capacity:** 1,500 **Seats:** Yes **Covered:** Yes **Clubhouse:** Yes **Shop:** No
**Previous Grounds:**

**Record Attendance:** **Att:** 2,500 v Showbiz XI, 1973.
**Record Victory:** Not known - if you know please email tw.publications@btinternet.com
**Record Defeat:** Not known - if you know please email tw.publications@btinternet.com
**Record Goalscorer:** Not known - if you know please email tw.publications@btinternet.com
**Record Appearances:** Not known - if you know please email tw.publications@btinternet.com
**Additional Records:** F.A Cup: First Qualifying Round 2009-10
F.A. Vase: Fifth Round 1976-77
**Senior Honours:**
Hellenic League Premier Division 2015-16.

**10 YEAR RECORD**

| 06-07 | 07-08 | 08-09 | 09-10 | 10-11 | 11-12 | 12-13 | 13-14 | 14-15 | 15-16 |
|---|---|---|---|---|---|---|---|---|---|
| Hel P 9 | Hel P 15 | Hel P 9 | Hel P 11 | Hel P 7 | Hel P 18 | Hel P 13 | Hel P 6 | Hel P 4 | Hel P 1 |

# MARLOW

**Chairman:** Terry Staines
**Secretary:** Terry Staines (T) (E) terry.staines@ntlworld.com
**Commercial Manager:** (T)
**Programme Editor:** Terry Staines (T) terry.staines@ntlworld.com
**Ground Address:** Alfred Davies Memorial Ground, Oak tree Road, Marlow SL7 3ED
(T) 01628 483 970 **Manager:** Mark Bartley

**Founded:** 1870 **Nickname:** The Blues
**Previous Names:** Great Marlow
**Previous Leagues:** Reading & District, Spartan 1908-10, 28-65, Gt Western Suburban, Athenian 1965-84, Isthmian 1984-2004. Southern 2004-12. Hellenic 2012-13.
**Club Colours (change):** All royal blue (All red)

**Ground Capacity:** 3,000 **Seats:** 250 **Covered:** 600 **Clubhouse:** Yes **Shop:**
**Previous Grounds:** Crown ground 1870-1919, Star Meadow 1919-24

**Record Attendance:** 3,000 v Oxford United - FA Cup 1st Round 1994
**Record Victory:** Not known - if you know please email tw.publications@btinternet.com
**Record Defeat:** Not known - if you know please email tw.publications@btinternet.com
**Record Goalscorer:** Kevin Stone
**Record Appearances:** Mick McKeown - 500+
**Additional Records:** Paid £5,000 to Sutton United for Richard Evans
Received £8,000 from Slough Town for David Lay
**Senior Honours:**
Isthmian League Division 1 1987-88, League Cup 92-93. Hellenic League Premier Division 2012-13.
Berks & Bucks Senior Cup x11

**10 YEAR RECORD**

| 06-07 | 07-08 | 08-09 | 09-10 | 10-11 | 11-12 | 12-13 | 13-14 | 14-15 | 15-16 |
|---|---|---|---|---|---|---|---|---|---|
| Sthsw 7 | Sthsw 9 | SthM 9 | SthM 15 | SthC 11 | SthC 22 | Hel P 1 | SthC 17 | SthC 11 | SthC 13 |

# NORTHWOOD

**Chairman:** Ian Barry
**Secretary:** Alan Evans (T) 07960 744 349 (E) alan.evansnfc@btopenworld.com
**Commercial Manager:** (T)
**Programme Editor:** Terry Brumpton (T) terrybrumpton@yahoo.co.uk
**Ground Address:** Northwood Park, Chestnut Avenue, Northwood, Middlesex HA6 1HR
(T) 01923 827 148 **Manager:** Mark Burgess

**Founded:** 1926 **Nickname:** Woods
**Previous Names:** Northwood United 1926-1945.
**Previous Leagues:** Harrow & Wembley 1932-69, Middlesex 1969-78, Hellenic 1979-84, London Spartan 1984-93, Isthmian 1993-2005, 2007-10, Southern 2005-07
**Club Colours (change):** All red (Yellow/black/black)

**Ground Capacity:** 3,075 **Seats:** 308 **Covered:** 932 **Clubhouse:** Yes **Shop:** No
**Previous Grounds:** Northwood Recreation Ground 1926-1928. Northwood Playing Fields 1928-1971.

**Record Attendance:** 1,642 v Chlesea - Friendly July 1997
**Record Victory:** 15-0 v Dateline (H) - Middlesex Intermediate Cup 1973
**Record Defeat:** 0-8 v Bedfont - Middlesex League 1975
**Record Goalscorer:** Not known - if you know please email tw.publications@btinternet.com
**Record Appearances:** Chris Gell - 493+
**Additional Records:** Lawrence Yaku scored 61 goals during season 1999-2000
**Senior Honours:**
Isthmian League Division 1 North 2002-03, Charity Shield 2002.
Middlesex Premier Cup 1994-95. Middlesex Senior Cup 2015-16.

**10 YEAR RECORD**

| 06-07 | 07-08 | 08-09 | 09-10 | 10-11 | 11-12 | 12-13 | 13-14 | 14-15 | 15-16 |
|---|---|---|---|---|---|---|---|---|---|
| SthP 22 | Isth1N 10 | Isth1N 6 | Isth1N 10 | SthC 20 | SthC 7 | SthC 13 | SthC 9 | SthC 10 | SthC 7 |

# PETERSFIELD TOWN

**Chairman:** Gaeme Moir
**Secretary:** Mark Nicoll (T) 07949 328 240 (E) secretary.petersfieldtownfc@outlook.com
**Commercial Manager:** (T)
**Programme Editor:** Graeme Moir (T) graememoir@petersfieldpost.co.uk
**Ground Address:** Love Lane, Petersfield, Hampshire GU31 4BW
(T) 01730 233 416 **Manager:** TBC

**Founded:** 1993 **Nickname:** Rams
**Previous Names:** Petersfield United folded in 1993. Petersfield Town reformed 1993 to join Wessex League.
**Previous Leagues:** Hampshire 1980-84. Isthmian 1984-93. Wessex 1993-2015.

**Club Colours (change):** Red & black stripes/black/red & black (Green/green/green & white)

**Ground Capacity:** 3000 **Seats:** 250 **Covered:** 250 **Clubhouse:** Yes **Shop:**
**Previous Grounds:** None

**Record Attendance:** Not known - if you know please email tw.publications@btinternet.com
**Record Victory:** Not known - if you know please email tw.publications@btinternet.com
**Record Defeat:** Not known - if you know please email tw.publications@btinternet.com
**Record Goalscorer:** Not known - if you know please email tw.publications@btinternet.com
**Record Appearances:** Not known - if you know please email tw.publications@btinternet.com
**Additional Records:**

**Senior Honours:**
Wessex League Division One 2013-14, Premier Division 2014-15.

**10 YEAR RECORD**

| 06-07 | 07-08 | 08-09 | 09-10 | 10-11 | 11-12 | 12-13 | 13-14 | 14-15 | 15-16 |
|---|---|---|---|---|---|---|---|---|---|
| Wex1 17 | Wex1 8 | Wex1 4 | Wex1 8 | Wex1 11 | Wex1 12 | Wex1 6 | Wex1 1 | WexP 1 | SthC 13 |

# POTTERS BAR TOWN

**Chairman:** Peter Waller
**Secretary:** Jeff Barnes (T) (E) jeff@jeffbarnes.co.uk
**Commercial Manager:** Jeff Barnes (T) 07785 765 793
**Programme Editor:** Jeff Barnes (T) jeff@jeffbarnes.co.uk
**Ground Address:** Pakex Stadium, Parkfield, Watkins Rise, Potters Bar EN6 1QB
(T) 01707 654 833 **Manager:** Steve Ringrose - 21/02/15

**Founded:** 1960 **Nickname:** Grace or Scholars
**Previous Names:** None
**Previous Leagues:** Barnet & District 1960-65, North London Combination 1965-68, Herts Senior County 1968-91, Spartan South Midlands 1991-2005, Southern 2005-06. Isthmian 2006-13.
**Club Colours (change):** Maroon/white/white (All yellow)

**Ground Capacity:** 2,000 **Seats:** 150 **Covered:** 250 **Clubhouse:** Yes **Shop:** Yes
**Previous Grounds:** None

**Record Attendance:** 268 v Wealdstone - FA Cup 1998 (4,000 watched a charity match in 1997)
**Record Victory:** Not known - if you know please email tw.publications@btinternet.com
**Record Defeat:** Not known - if you know please email tw.publications@btinternet.com
**Record Goalscorer:** Not known - if you know please email tw.publications@btinternet.com
**Record Appearances:** Not known - if you know please email tw.publications@btinternet.com
**Additional Records:**

**Senior Honours:**
Spartan South Midlands League Premier 1996-97, 2004-05.

**10 YEAR RECORD**

| 06-07 | 07-08 | 08-09 | 09-10 | 10-11 | 11-12 | 12-13 | 13-14 | 14-15 | 15-16 |
|---|---|---|---|---|---|---|---|---|---|
| Isth1N 14 | Isth1N 17 | Isth1N 19 | Isth1N 14 | Isth1N 13 | Isth1N 12 | Isth1N 10 | SthC 15 | SthC 14 | SthC 12 |

# ROYSTON TOWN

**Chairman:** Steve Jackson
**Secretary:** Terry McKinnell **(T)** 07772 086 709 **(E)** terry.mckinnell@talktalk.net
**Commercial Manager:** **(T)**
**Programme Editor:** Kelly Taylor **(T)** info@abaconsultants.com
**Ground Address:** Garden Walk, Royston, Herts, SG8 7HP
**(T)** 01763 241 204 **Manager:** Steve Castle

**Founded:** 1872 **Nickname:** Crows
**Previous Names:** None
**Previous Leagues:** Cambridgeshire & Herts Co. Isthmian

**Club Colours (change):** White/black/black (Red & black/blue/blue)

**Ground Capacity:** **Seats:** Yes **Covered:** Yes **Clubhouse:** Yes **Shop:**
**Previous Grounds:** Royston Heath, Mackerell Hall and Newmarket Road before acquiring Garden Walk in 1931.

**Record Attendance:** **Att:** 876 v Aldershot Town, 1993-94.
**Record Victory:** Not known - if you know please email tw.publications@btinternet.com
**Record Defeat:** Not known - if you know please email tw.publications@btinternet.com
**Record Goalscorer:** Not known - if you know please email tw.publications@btinternet.com
**Record Appearances:** Not known - if you know please email tw.publications@btinternet.com
**Additional Records:**
**Senior Honours:**
Herts County Champions 1976-77. South Midlands Div.1 1978-79, 2008-09, Premier Division 2011-12.

**10 YEAR RECORD**

| 06-07 | 07-08 | 08-09 | 09-10 | 10-11 | 11-12 | 12-13 | 13-14 | 14-15 | 15-16 |
|---|---|---|---|---|---|---|---|---|---|
| SSM P 20 | SSM1 5 | SSM1 1 | SSM P 4 | SSM P 3 | SSM P 1 | SthC 7 | SthC 7 | SthC 2 | SthC 2 |

# UXBRIDGE

**Chairman:** Alan Holloway
**Secretary:** Roger Stevens **(T)** 0777 513 405 **(E)** sec@uxbridgefc.co.uk
**Commercial Manager:** **(T)**
**Programme Editor:** Sharon Madigan **(T)** program.editor@uxbridgefc.co.uk
**Ground Address:** Honeycroft Road, West Drayton, Middlesex UB7 8HX
**(T)** 01895 443 557 **Manager:** Tony Choules

**Founded:** 1871 **Nickname:** The Reds
**Previous Names:** Uxbridge Town 1923-45
**Previous Leagues:** Southern 1894-99, Gt Western Suburban 1906-19, 20-23, Athenian 1919-20, 24-37, 63-82, Spartan 1937-38, London 1938-46, Gt Western Comb. 1939-45, Corinthian 1946-63, Isthmian
**Club Colours (change):** Red/white/red (Sky blue/navy/navy)

**Ground Capacity:** 3,770 **Seats:** 339 **Covered:** 760 **Clubhouse:** Yes **Shop:**
**Previous Grounds:** RAF Stadium 1923-48, Cleveland Road 1948-78

**Record Attendance:** 1,000 v Arsenal - Opening of the floodlights 1981
**Record Victory:** Not known - if you know please email tw.publications@btinternet.com
**Record Defeat:** Not known - if you know please email tw.publications@btinternet.com
**Record Goalscorer:** Phil Duff - 153
**Record Appearances:** Roger Nicholls - 1,054
**Additional Records:**
**Senior Honours:**
Middlesex Senior Cup 1893-94, 95-96, 1950-51, 2000-01. London Challenge Cup 1993-94, 96-97, 98-99.

**10 YEAR RECORD**

| 06-07 | 07-08 | 08-09 | 09-10 | 10-11 | 11-12 | 12-13 | 13-14 | 14-15 | 15-16 |
|---|---|---|---|---|---|---|---|---|---|
| Sthsw 8 | Sthsw 5 | Sthsw 13 | Sthsw 15 | SthC 13 | SthC 4 | SthC 11 | SthC 10 | SthC 12 | SthC 15 |

# AFC TOTTON

**Chairman:** Andy Straker
**Secretary:** Shaun Hinton **(T)** **(E)** secretary.afctotton@gmail.com
**Commercial Manager:** **(T)**
**Programme Editor:** Andy Straker **(T)** strakes1@gmail.com
**Ground Address:** Testwood Stadium, Salisbury Road, Calmore, Totton SO40 2RW
**(T)** 02380 868 981 **Manager:** Steve Hollick

**Founded:** 1886 **Nickname:** Stags
**Previous Names:** Totton FC until merger with Totton Athletic in 1975
**Previous Leagues:** Hampshire 1982-86, Wessex 1986-2008

**Club Colours (change):** All dark blue (All yellow)

**Ground Capacity:** 3,000 **Seats:** 500 **Covered:** 500 **Clubhouse:** Yes **Shop:** Yes
**Previous Grounds:** South testwood Park 1886-1933.

**Record Attendance:** 600 v Windsor & Eton - FA Cup 4th Qualifying Round 1982-83
**Record Victory:** Not known - if you know please email tw.publications@btinternet.com
**Record Defeat:** Not known - if you know please email tw.publications@btinternet.com
**Record Goalscorer:** Not known - if you know please email tw.publications@btinternet.com
**Record Appearances:** James Sherlington
**Additional Records:**

**Senior Honours:**
Hampshire League 1981-82, 84-85. Wessex League Premier Division 2007-08.
Southern League Division South & West 2010-11.
Hampshire Senior Cup 2010-11.

**10 YEAR RECORD**

| 06-07 | 07-08 | 08-09 | 09-10 | 10-11 | 11-12 | 12-13 | 13-14 | 14-15 | 15-16 |
|---|---|---|---|---|---|---|---|---|---|
| WexP 2 | WexP 1 | Sthsw 3 | Sthsw 2 | Sthsw 1 | SthP 3 | SthP 14 | SthP 21 | Sthsw 15 | Sthsw 15 |

# BARNSTAPLE TOWN

**Chairman:** Jasmine Chesters
**Secretary:** Jane Huxtable **(T)** 07773 668 461 **(E)** jane@barnstapletownfc.com
**Commercial Manager:** **(T)**
**Programme Editor:** Daniel Roulstone **(T)** daniel.roulstone@googlemail.com
**Ground Address:** Mill Road, Barnstaple, North Devon EX31 1JQ
**(T)** 01271 343 469 **Manager:** Barry Yeo

**Founded:** 1906 **Nickname:** Barum
**Previous Names:** Pilton Yeo Vale
**Previous Leagues:** North Devon, Devon & Exeter, South Western. Western >2016.

**Club Colours (change):** All red. (All blue)

**Ground Capacity:** 5,000 **Seats:** 250 **Covered:** 1,000 **Clubhouse:** Yes **Shop:** Yes
**Previous Grounds:**

**Record Attendance:** **Att:** 6,200 v Bournemouth FA Cup 1st Round 51-52 **App:** Ian Pope
**Record Victory:** 12-1 v Tavistock, F.A. Cup 3rd Qualifying Round 1954
**Record Defeat:** 1-10 v Mangotsfield United, Western League 1990-91
**Record Goalscorer:** Not known - if you know please email tw.publications@btinternet.com
**Record Appearances:** Not known - if you know please email tw.publications@btinternet.com
**Additional Records:** F.A Cup: First Round 1951-52, 1954-55, 1959-60, 1972-73
F.A. Trophy: Second Round 1971-72 F.A. Vase: Fourth Round 1994-95

**Senior Honours:**
Western Champions 1952-53, 79-80, Devon Pro Cup (12), Devon Senior Cup 1992-93.
Western League Division One 1993-94, 2014-15.

**10 YEAR RECORD**

| 06-07 | 07-08 | 08-09 | 09-10 | 10-11 | 11-12 | 12-13 | 13-14 | 14-15 | 15-16 |
|---|---|---|---|---|---|---|---|---|---|
| WestP 7 | WestP 12 | WestP 18 | WestP 15 | WestP 11 | WestP 15 | WestP 20 | West1 3 | West1 1 | WestP 2 |

# BIDEFORD

**Chairman:** Kevin Tyrrell
**Secretary:** Kevin Tyrrell (T) 07929 078 613 (E) k.tyrell@talktalk.net
**Commercial Manager:** (T)
**Programme Editor:** Ian Knight (T) ianknight699@yahoo.com
**Ground Address:** The Sports Ground, Kingsley Road, Bideford EX39 2LH
(T) 01237 474 974 **Manager:** Sean Joyce

**Founded:** 1946 **Nickname:** The Robins
**Previous Names:** Bideford Town
**Previous Leagues:** Devon & Exeter 1947-49, Western 1949-72, 75-2010, Southern 1972-75

**Club Colours (change):** All red (All blue)

**Ground Capacity:** 6,000 **Seats:** 375 **Covered:** 1,000 **Clubhouse:** Yes **Shop:**
**Previous Grounds:** None

**Record Attendance:** 5,975 v Gloucester City - FA Cup 4th Qualifying Round 1949
**Record Victory:** 16-1 v Soundwell, 1950-51
**Record Defeat:** 1-10 v Taunton Town, 1998-99
**Record Goalscorer:** Tommy Robinson - 259
**Record Appearances:** Derek May - 527
**Additional Records:**

**Senior Honours:**
Western League 1963-64, 70-71, 71-72, 81-82, 82-83, 2001-02, 03-04, 04-05, 05-06, 09-10, Division 1 1951-52, Division 3 1949-50.
Southern Division 1 South & West 2011-12.
Devon Senior Cup 1979-80

**10 YEAR RECORD**

| 06-07 | 07-08 | 08-09 | 09-10 | 10-11 | 11-12 | 12-13 | 13-14 | 14-15 | 15-16 |
|---|---|---|---|---|---|---|---|---|---|
| WestP 4 | WestP 6 | WestP 6 | WestP 1 | Sthsw 10 | Sthsw 1 | SthP 20 | SthP 8 | SthP 15 | SthP 23 |

# BISHOP'S CLEEVE

**Chairman:** David Walker
**Secretary:** Nigel Green (T) 07919 518 880 (E) themitres@outlook.com
**Commercial Manager:** (T)
**Programme Editor:** John Hunt (T) cheltenhamleague@aol.com
**Ground Address:** Kayte Lane, Bishop's Cleeve, Cheltenham GL52 3PD
(T) 01242 676 166 **Manager:** Stephen Cleal

**Founded:** 1892 **Nickname:** The Mitres
**Previous Names:**
**Previous Leagues:** Cheltenham, North Gloucestershire, Hellenic 1983-2006

**Club Colours (change):** Green/black/green (Blue/blue/white & blue)

**Ground Capacity:** 1,500 **Seats:** 50 **Covered:** 50 **Clubhouse:** Yes **Shop:** Yes
**Previous Grounds:** Stoke Road and ground shared with Moreton Town, Wollen Sports, Highworth Town and Forest Green Rovers

**Record Attendance:** 1,300 v Cheltenham Town - July 2006
**Record Victory:** Not known - if you know please email tw.publications@btinternet.com
**Record Defeat:** Not known - if you know please email tw.publications@btinternet.com
**Record Goalscorer:** Kevin Slack
**Record Appearances:** John Skeen
**Additional Records:**

**Senior Honours:**
Hellenic League Division 1 1986-87, Premier League Cup 1988.
Gloucestershire Junior Cup North. Gloucestershire Senior Amateur Cup North x3.

**10 YEAR RECORD**

| 06-07 | 07-08 | 08-09 | 09-10 | 10-11 | 11-12 | 12-13 | 13-14 | 14-15 | 15-16 |
|---|---|---|---|---|---|---|---|---|---|
| SthM 13 | SthM 12 | Sthsw 18 | Sthsw 11 | Sthsw 15 | Sthsw 11 | Sthsw 21 | Sthsw 20 | Sthsw 21 | Sthsw 12 |

# BRIDGWATER TOWN 1984

**Chairman:** Adrian Byrne
**Secretary:** Ian Barber (T) (E) ianbarber4@gmail.com
**Commercial Manager:** (T)
**Programme Editor:** Ian Barber (T) ianbarber4@gmail.com
**Ground Address:** Fairfax Park, College Way, Bath Road, Bridgwater, Somerset TA6 4TZ
(T) 01278 446 899 **Manager:** Craig Laird

**Founded:** 1984 **Nickname:** The Robins
**Previous Names:** Bridgwater Town
**Previous Leagues:** Somerset Senior, Western

**Club Colours (change):** Red & white stripes/black/red (Yellow/blue/blue)

**Ground Capacity:** 2,500 **Seats:** 128 **Covered:** 500 **Clubhouse:** Yes **Shop:** Yes
**Previous Grounds:** None

**Record Attendance:** 1,112 v Taunton Town - 26/02/1997
**Record Victory:** Not known - if you know please email tw.publications@btinternet.com
**Record Defeat:** Not known - if you know please email tw.publications@btinternet.com
**Record Goalscorer:** Not known - if you know please email tw.publications@btinternet.com
**Record Appearances:** Not known - if you know please email tw.publications@btinternet.com
**Additional Records:**

**Senior Honours:**
Somerset Senior League x3. Somerset Senior Cup 1993-94, 95-96. Western League Division 1 1995-96.

**10 YEAR RECORD**

| 06-07 | 07-08 | 08-09 | 09-10 | 10-11 | 11-12 | 12-13 | 13-14 | 14-15 | 15-16 |
|---|---|---|---|---|---|---|---|---|---|
| WestP 2 | Sthsw 6 | Sthsw 7 | Sthsw 3 | Sthsw 18 | Sthsw 15 | Sthsw 19 | Sthsw 14 | Sthsw 12 | Sthsw 19 |

# DIDCOT TOWN

**Chairman:** John Bailey
**Secretary:** Jaquelyn Chalk (T) (E) jaquelyn-dtc@virginmedia.com
**Commercial Manager:** (T)
**Programme Editor:** Pat Horsman (T) patrickhorsman@icloud.com
**Ground Address:** Draycott Engineering Loop Meadow Stadium, Bowmont Water, Didcot OX11 7GA
(T) 01235 813 138 **Manager:** Andy Ballard

**Founded:** 1907 **Nickname:** Railwaymen
**Previous Names:** Didcot Village and Northbourne Wanderers amalgamated to form Didcot Town in 1907.
**Previous Leagues:** Metropolitan 1957-63, Hellenic 1963-2006

**Club Colours (change):** Red & white/red/red & white (All blue & gold)

**Ground Capacity:** 5,000 **Seats:** 250 **Covered:** 200 **Clubhouse:** Yes **Shop:** Yes
**Previous Grounds:** Fleet Meadow. Edmonds Park. Cow Lane. Haydon Road. Station Road 1923-99.

**Record Attendance:** 2,707 - v Exeter City, FA Cup 1st Round, 08.11.2015
**Record Victory:** Not known - if you know please email tw.publications@btinternet.com
**Record Defeat:** Not known - if you know please email tw.publications@btinternet.com
**Record Goalscorer:** Ian Concanon
**Record Appearances:** Not known - if you know please email tw.publications@btinternet.com
**Additional Records:**

**Senior Honours:**
Hellenic League Premier Division 1953-54, 2005-06, Division 1 1976-77, 87-88, League Cup x6.
FA Vase 2004-05. Berks & Bucks Senior Trophy 2001-02, 02-03, 05-06.

**10 YEAR RECORD**

| 06-07 | 07-08 | 08-09 | 09-10 | 10-11 | 11-12 | 12-13 | 13-14 | 14-15 | 15-16 |
|---|---|---|---|---|---|---|---|---|---|
| Sthsw 10 | Sthsw 3 | Sthsw 5 | SthP 15 | SthP 19 | Sthsw 16 | Sthsw 17 | Sthsw 12 | Sthsw 7 | Sthsw 10 |

# EVESHAM UNITED

**Chairman:** Jim Cockerton
**Secretary:** Mike Peplow (T) 07889 011 539 (E) eveshamunitedsecretary@hotmail.com
**Commercial Manager:** (T)
**Programme Editor:** Mike Peplow (T) eveshamunitedsecretary@hotmail.com
**Ground Address:** Jubilee Stadium, Cheltenham Rd, Evesham WR11 2LZ
**(T)** 01386 442 303 **Manager:** Paul Collicut

**Founded:** 1945 **Nickname:** The Robins
**Previous Names:** Not known
**Previous Leagues:** Worcester, Birmingham Combination, Midland Combination 1951-55, 65-92, West Midlands (Regional) 1955-62
**Club Colours (change):** Red and white stripes/black/black (Blue and white stripes/blue/blue)

**Ground Capacity:** **Seats:** Yes **Covered:** Yes **Clubhouse:** Yes **Shop:** Yes
**Previous Grounds:** The Crown Meadow > 1968, Common Reed 1968-2006. Ground shared with Worcester City 2006-12.

**Record Attendance:** 2,338 v West Bromwich Albion - Friendly 18/07/1992
**Record Victory:** 11-3 v West Heath United
**Record Defeat:** 1-8 v Ilkeston Town
**Record Goalscorer:** Sid Brain
**Record Appearances:** Rob Candy
**Additional Records:** Paid £1,500 to Hayes for Colin Day 1992
Received £5,000 from Cheltenham Town for Simon Brain
**Senior Honours:**
Midland Combination Premier Division 1991-92, Division 1 1965-66, 67-68, 68-69.
Southern League Division 1 Midlands 2007-08.
Worcestershire Senior Urn x2

**10 YEAR RECORD**

| 06-07 | 07-08 | 08-09 | 09-10 | 10-11 | 11-12 | 12-13 | 13-14 | 14-15 | 15-16 |
|---|---|---|---|---|---|---|---|---|---|
| SthM 5 | SthM 1 | SthP 9 | SthP 16 | SthP 12 | SthP 20 | Sthsw 14 | Sthsw 16 | Sthsw 2 | Sthsw 6 |

# HEREFORD

**Chairman:** Jon Hale
**Secretary:** Martin Watson (T) 07572 102 621 (E) fd@herefordfc.co.uk
**Commercial Manager:** (T)
**Programme Editor:** Jamie Griffiths (T) media@herefordfc.co.uk
**Ground Address:** Edgar Street, Hereford HR4 9JU
**(T)** 01432 268 257 **Manager:** Pete Beadle

**Founded:** 2014 **Nickname:** The Bulls
**Previous Names:** Formed in 2014 after the demise of Hereford United who folded during the 2014-15 season.
**Previous Leagues:** Midland 2015-16.

**Club Colours (change):** White/black/white

**Ground Capacity:** 8,843 **Seats:** 2,761 **Covered:** 6,082 **Clubhouse:** Yes **Shop:**
**Previous Grounds:**

**Record Attendance:**
**Record Victory:** 8-0 v Heanor Town - Midland League 23/04/16.
**Record Defeat:** 4-5 v Coleshill Town - Midland League 2015-16.
**Record Goalscorer:** John Mills - 52 - 2015-16.
**Record Appearances:** Not known - if you know please email tw.publications@btinternet.com
**Additional Records:**
**Senior Honours:**
Midland League 2015-16.
Herefordshire Challenge Cup 2015-16.

**10 YEAR RECORD**

| 06-07 | 07-08 | 08-09 | 09-10 | 10-11 | 11-12 | 12-13 | 13-14 | 14-15 | 15-16 |
|---|---|---|---|---|---|---|---|---|---|
| | | | | | | | | | MidL 1 |

# LARKHALL ATHLETIC

**Chairman:** Paul Rankin
**Secretary:** Dr Tracey Hill **(T)** 07825 774 683 **(E)** larkhallathletic@gmail.com
**Commercial Manager:** Dr Tracey Hill **(T)** 07825 774 683
**Programme Editor:** Andy Meadon **(T)** ampcfootball@hotmail.com
**Ground Address:** Plain Ham, Charlcombe Lane, Larkhall, Bath BA1 8DJ
**(T)** 01225 334 952 **Manager:** Wayne Thorne

**Founded:** 1914 **Nickname:** Larks
**Previous Names:** None
**Previous Leagues:** Somerset Senior. Western 1976-2014.

**Club Colours (change):** All royal blue (All yellow)

**Ground Capacity:** 1,000 **Seats:** Yes **Covered:** 50 **Clubhouse:** Yes **Shop:**
**Previous Grounds:** None

**Record Attendance:** 280 v Tunbridge Wells, FA Vase, Feb 2013
**Record Victory:** 8-0 v Oldland Abbotonians, 2007
**Record Defeat:** 1-6 v Exmouth Town, 2001
**Record Goalscorer:** Ben Highmore scored 52 goals during the 2008-09 season.
**Record Appearances:** Luke Scott - 600+ (as at July 2014)
**Additional Records:**
**Senior Honours:**
Somerset Senior Cup 1975-76, 2003-04. Somerset Senior Champions. Western Division One 1988-89, 93-94, 94-95, 08-09.
Western Premier Division 2010-11, 13-14. Les Phillips Cup 2013-14.

**10 YEAR RECORD**

| 06-07 | 07-08 | 08-09 | 09-10 | 10-11 | 11-12 | 12-13 | 13-14 | 14-15 | 15-16 |
|---|---|---|---|---|---|---|---|---|---|
| West1 5 | West1 3 | West1 1 | WestP 14 | WestP 1 | WestP 3 | WestP 5 | WestP 1 | Sthsw 5 | Sthsw 11 |

# MANGOTSFIELD UNITED

**Chairman:** Mike Richardson
**Secretary:** David Jones **(T)** 07903 655 723 **(E)** davidj693@hotmail.co.uk
**Commercial Manager:** **(T)**
**Programme Editor:** Bob Smale **(T)** bob_smale@yahoo.co.uk
**Ground Address:** Cossham Street, Mangotsfield, Bristol BS16 9EN
**(T)** 0117 956 0119 **Manager:** David Mehew

**Founded:** 1950 **Nickname:** The Field
**Previous Names:** None
**Previous Leagues:** Bristol & District 1950-67. Avon Premier Combination 1967-72. Western 1972-2000.

**Club Colours (change):** Maroon/sky blue/sky blue (yellow/black/yellow)

**Ground Capacity:** 2,500 **Seats:** 300 **Covered:** 800 **Clubhouse:** Yes **Shop:** Yes
**Previous Grounds:** None

**Record Attendance:** 1,253 v Bath City - F.A. Cup 1974
**Record Victory:** 17-0 v Hanham Sports (H) - 1953 Bristol & District League
**Record Defeat:** 3-13 v Bristol City United - Bristol & District League Division 1
**Record Goalscorer:** John Hill
**Record Appearances:** John Hill - 600+
**Additional Records:** In the last 10 matches of the 2003/04 season, the club went 738 minutes (just over 8 games) without scoring and then finished the campaign with 13 goals in the last two, which included a 9-0 away win.
**Senior Honours:**
Gloucestershire Senior Cup 1968-69, 75-76, 2002-03, 12-13. Somerset Premier Cup 1987-88. Western League 1990-91.
Southern League Division One West 2004-05. Gloucestershire F.A. Trophy x6.

**10 YEAR RECORD**

| 06-07 | 07-08 | 08-09 | 09-10 | 10-11 | 11-12 | 12-13 | 13-14 | 14-15 | 15-16 |
|---|---|---|---|---|---|---|---|---|---|
| SthP 9 | SthP 14 | SthP 22 | Sthsw 9 | Sthsw 3 | Sthsw 14 | Sthsw 13 | Sthsw 11 | Sthsw 10 | Sthsw 14 |

# NORTH LEIGH

**Chairman:** Peter King
**Secretary:** Keith Huxley (T) 01993 851 497 (E) huxley893@btinternet.com
**Commercial Manager:** (T)
**Programme Editor:** Mike Burnell (T) michael.burnell1@ntlworld.com
**Ground Address:** Eynsham Hall Park, North Leigh, Witney, Oxon OX29 6SL
(T) 07583 399 577 **Manager:** John Brough

**Founded:** 1908 **Nickname:** The Millers
**Previous Names:** None
**Previous Leagues:** Witney & District, Hellenic 1990-2008

**Club Colours (change):** Yellow with black trim/black/yellow (All red)

**Ground Capacity:** 2,000 **Seats:** 100 **Covered:** 200 **Clubhouse:** Yes **Shop:** No
**Previous Grounds:** None

**Record Attendance:** 426 v Newport County - FA Cup 3rd Qualifying Round 16/10/2004
**Record Victory:** Not known - if you know please email tw.publications@btinternet.com
**Record Defeat:** Not known - if you know please email tw.publications@btinternet.com
**Record Goalscorer:** P Coles
**Record Appearances:** P King
**Additional Records:**

**Senior Honours:**
Hellenic Premier Division 2001-02, 02-03, 07-08. Oxon Charity Cup x2.
Oxfordshire Senior Cup 2011-12.

**10 YEAR RECORD**

| 06-07 | 07-08 | 08-09 | 09-10 | 10-11 | 11-12 | 12-13 | 13-14 | 14-15 | 15-16 |
|---|---|---|---|---|---|---|---|---|---|
| Hel P 2 | Hel P 1 | Sthsw 8 | Sthsw 10 | Sthsw 6 | Sthsw 6 | Sthsw 9 | Sthsw 7 | Sthsw 8 | Sthsw 9 |

# PAULTON ROVERS

**Chairman:** David Bissex
**Secretary:** Andy Harris (T) 07760 377 302 (E) footballsecretary.prfc@gmail.com
**Commercial Manager:** (T)
**Programme Editor:** Andy Harris (T) footballsecretary.prfc@gmail.com
**Ground Address:** Athletic Ground, Winterfield Road, Paulton, Bristol BS39 7RF
(T) 01761 412 907 **Manager:** Tony Ricketts

**Founded:** 1881 **Nickname:** The Robins or Rovers
**Previous Names:** Not known
**Previous Leagues:** Wiltshire Premier, Somserset Senior, Western

**Club Colours (change):** All maroon (Blue with yellow trim/blue/blue)

**Ground Capacity:** 5,000 **Seats:** 253 **Covered:** 2,500 **Clubhouse:** Yes **Shop:** Yes
**Previous Grounds:** Chapel Field, Cricket Ground, Recreation Ground

**Record Attendance:** 2,000 v Crewe Alexandra - FA Cup 1906-07
**Record Victory:** Not known - if you know please email tw.publications@btinternet.com
**Record Defeat:** Not known - if you know please email tw.publications@btinternet.com
**Record Goalscorer:** Graham Colbourne
**Record Appearances:** Steve Tovey
**Additional Records:**

**Senior Honours:**
Somerset Senior Cup x12.
Somerset Premier Cup 2012-13.

**10 YEAR RECORD**

| 06-07 | 07-08 | 08-09 | 09-10 | 10-11 | 11-12 | 12-13 | 13-14 | 14-15 | 15-16 |
|---|---|---|---|---|---|---|---|---|---|
| Sthsw 2 | Sthsw 7 | Sthsw 10 | Sthsw 7 | Sthsw 11 | Sthsw 7 | Sthsw 5 | Sthsw 4 | SthP 10 | SthP 24 |

# SALISBURY

**Chairman:** David Phillips
**Secretary:** Douglas Ferraro **(T)** **(E)** douglasj71@virginmedia.com
**Commercial Manager:** **(T)**
**Programme Editor:** Alec Hayter **(T)** alechayter@gmail.com
**Ground Address:** Raymond McEnhill Stadium, Partridge Way, Old Sarum SP4 6PU
**(T)** 07803 247 874 **Manager:** Steve Claridge

**Founded:** 2015 **Nickname:** The Whites
**Previous Names:** None
**Previous Leagues:** Wessex 2015-16.

**Club Colours (change):** White with black trim/black/white (Navy blue with sky blue trim/navy/navy)

**Ground Capacity:** 5,000 **Seats:** 500 **Covered:** 2,247 **Clubhouse:** Yes **Shop:**
**Previous Grounds:**

**Record Attendance:**
**Record Victory:** 9-1 v Bournemouth - Wessex Premier 25/08/15.
**Record Defeat:** 4-1 v AFC Porchester - Wessex Premier 30/04/16.
**Record Goalscorer:** Sam Wilson - 40 - 2015-16.
**Record Appearances:** Thomas Whelan - 54 - 2015-16.
**Additional Records:**
**Senior Honours:**
Wessex League Premier Division 2015-16.

**10 YEAR RECORD**

| 06-07 | 07-08 | 08-09 | 09-10 | 10-11 | 11-12 | 12-13 | 13-14 | 14-15 | 15-16 |
|---|---|---|---|---|---|---|---|---|---|
| | | | | | | | | | WexP 1 |

# SHORTWOOD UNITED

**Chairman:** Peter Webb
**Secretary:** Mark Webb **(T)** 07792 323784 **(E)** squish.shortwoodfc@live.co.uk
**Commercial Manager:** **(T)**
**Programme Editor:** Jim Cunneen **(T)** jimcunneen1951@btinternet.com
**Ground Address:** Meadowbank, Shortwood, Nailsworth GL6 0SJ
**(T)** 01453 833 936 **Manager:** John Evans

**Founded:** 1900 **Nickname:** The Wood
**Previous Names:** None.
**Previous Leagues:** Gloucestershire County. Hellenic >2012.

**Club Colours (change):** Red & white/black/black (All royal blue)

**Ground Capacity:** 2,000 **Seats:** 50 **Covered:** 150 **Clubhouse:** Yes **Shop:** No
**Previous Grounds:** Played at Nailsworth Playing Field, Table Land and Wallow Green before moving to Meadowbank in 1972.

**Record Attendance:** **Att:** 1,000 v Forest Green Rovers, FA Vase 5th Rnd 1982.
**Record Victory:** Not known - if you know please email tw.publications@btinternet.com
**Record Defeat:** Not known - if you know please email tw.publications@btinternet.com
**Record Goalscorer:** Peter Grant.
**Record Appearances:** Peter Grant.
**Additional Records:** Gloucestershire Lge Champions 1981-82.
**Senior Honours:**
Hellenic League Champions 1984-85, 91-92.
Gloucestershire Senior Cup (x 2).

**10 YEAR RECORD**

| 06-07 | 07-08 | 08-09 | 09-10 | 10-11 | 11-12 | 12-13 | 13-14 | 14-15 | 15-16 |
|---|---|---|---|---|---|---|---|---|---|
| Hel P 8 | Hel P 5 | Hel P 2 | Hel P 2 | Hel P 6 | Hel P 2 | Sthsw 8 | Sthsw 6 | Sthsw 11 | Sthsw 7 |

# SLIMBRIDGE

**Chairman:** Barry Gay
**Secretary:** Colin Gay (T) (E) colin.gay@slimbridgeafc.co.uk
**Commercial Manager:** (T)
**Programme Editor:** Tim Blake (T) purtongas@mac.com
**Ground Address:** Thornhill Park, Cambridge, Glos GL2 7AF
(T) 07702 070 229 **Manager:** Leon Sterling

**Founded:** 1899 **Nickname:** The Swans
**Previous Names:** None
**Previous Leagues:** Stroud & District. Gloucester Northern. Gloucestershire County >2009. Hellenic 2009-2013. Western 2013-15.

**Club Colours (change):** All blue (Red/black/black)

**Ground Capacity:** **Seats:** Yes **Covered:** Yes **Clubhouse:** Yes **Shop:** Yes
**Previous Grounds:**

**Record Attendance:** All records recorded since 2002-03. **Att:** 525 v Shortwood United, Hellenic Prem. 24.08.03.
**Record Victory:** 12-1 v Cheltenham Civil Service, Reg Davis Cup, 18.08.2007
**Record Defeat:** 1-6 v North Leigh, Hellenic Premier, 06.11.2004
**Record Goalscorer:** Julian Freeman - 79 (in 122 appearances)
**Record Appearances:** Fred Ward - 207
**Additional Records:**

**Senior Honours:**
Stroud & District League Division Three 1951-52, Division Two 1952-53, Division one 1953-54, 98-99, Division Four 1989-90.
Hellenic League Division 1 West 2002-03, 09-10, Premier 2006-07. Gloucester Northern League 2007-08.
Gloucestershire County League 2008-09. Gloucester Challenge Trophy 2003-04, 05-06, 06-07. Glos Northern Senior Cup 2000-01.

**10 YEAR RECORD**

| 06-07 | 07-08 | 08-09 | 09-10 | 10-11 | 11-12 | 12-13 | 13-14 | 14-15 | 15-16 |
|---|---|---|---|---|---|---|---|---|---|
| Hel P 1 | GlN1 1 | GlCo 1 | Hel1W 1 | Hel P 5 | Hel P 5 | Hel P 6 | WestP 16 | WestP 3 | Sthsw 18 |

# SWINDON SUPERMARINE

**Chairman:** Jez Webb
**Secretary:** Keith Yeomans (T) (E) supermarinefc@aol.com
**Commercial Manager:** (T)
**Programme Editor:** Keith Yeomans (T) supermarinefc@aol.com
**Ground Address:** The Webbs Wood Stadium, South Marston, Swindon SN3 4BZ
(T) 01793 828 778 **Manager:** Dave Webb

**Founded:** 1992 **Nickname:** Marine
**Previous Names:** Club formed after the amalgamation of Swindon Athletic and Supermarine
**Previous Leagues:** Wiltshire, Hellenic1992-2001.

**Club Colours (change):** All blue (All red)

**Ground Capacity:** 3,000 **Seats:** 300 **Covered:** 300 **Clubhouse:** Yes **Shop:** Yes
**Previous Grounds:** Supermarine: Vickers Airfield > Mid 1960s

**Record Attendance:** 1,550 v Aston Villa
**Record Victory:** Not known - if you know please email tw.publications@btinternet.com
**Record Defeat:** Not known - if you know please email tw.publications@btinternet.com
**Record Goalscorer:** Damon York - 136 (1990-98)
**Record Appearances:** Damon York - 314 (1990-98)
**Additional Records:** Paid £1,000 to Hungerford Town for Lee Hartson

**Senior Honours:**
Hellenic League Premier Division 1997-98, 2000-01, Challenge Cup 97-97, 99-2000.

**10 YEAR RECORD**

| 06-07 | 07-08 | 08-09 | 09-10 | 10-11 | 11-12 | 12-13 | 13-14 | 14-15 | 15-16 |
|---|---|---|---|---|---|---|---|---|---|
| Sthsw 4 | SthP 12 | SthP 13 | SthP 14 | SthP 10 | SthP 21 | Sthsw 4 | Sthsw 5 | Sthsw 14 | Sthsw 4 |

# TAUNTON TOWN

**Chairman:** Kevin Sturmey
**Secretary:** Andy Power (T) 07769 695 192 (E) admin@tauntontown.com
**Commercial Manager:** Kevin Sturmey (T) 07778 434 055
**Programme Editor:** Andy Power (T) admin@tautontown.com
**Ground Address:** The Viridor Stadium, Wordsworth Drive, Taunton, Somerset TA1 2HG
(T) 01823 254 909 / 278 191 **Manager:** Leigh Robinson

**Founded:** 1947 **Nickname:** The Peacocks
**Previous Names:** None
**Previous Leagues:** Western 1954-77, 83-2002, Southern 1977-83

**Club Colours (change):** Claret/sky blue/sky blue (Yellow/blue/yellow)

**Ground Capacity:** 2,500 **Seats:** 300 **Covered:** 1,000 **Clubhouse:** Yes **Shop:** Yes
**Previous Grounds:** None

**Record Attendance:** 3,284 v Tiverton Town - FA Vase Semi-final 1999
**Record Victory:** 12-0 v Dawlish Town (A) - FA Cup Preliminary Round 28/08/1993
**Record Defeat:** 0-8 v Cheltenham Town (A) - FA Cup 2nd Qualifying Round 28/09/1991
**Record Goalscorer:** Tony Payne
**Record Appearances:** Tony Payne
**Additional Records:** Reg Oram scored 67 in one season

**Senior Honours:**
Western League 1968-69, 89-90, 95-96, 98-99, 99-2000, 2000-01. FA Vase 2000-01.
Somerset Premier Cup 2002-03, 05-06, 13-14, 14-15.

**10 YEAR RECORD**

| 06-07 | 07-08 | 08-09 | 09-10 | 10-11 | 11-12 | 12-13 | 13-14 | 14-15 | 15-16 |
|---|---|---|---|---|---|---|---|---|---|
| Sthsw 5 | Sthsw 18 | Sthsw 20 | Sthsw 19 | Sthsw 9 | Sthsw 17 | Sthsw 18 | Sthsw 8 | Sthsw 4 | Sthsw 3 |

# TIVERTON TOWN

**Chairman:** Pete Buxton
**Secretary:** Ramsey Findlay (T) 07761 261 990 (E) ramsayfindlay@hotmail.co.uk
**Commercial Manager:** Jamie Gibson (T) 07773 776 715
**Programme Editor:** Simon Ellis (T) s.ellis85@btinternet.com
**Ground Address:** Ladysmead, Bolham Road, Tiverton, Devon EX16 6SG
(T) 01884 252 397 **Manager:** Martyn Rogers

**Founded:** 1913 **Nickname:** Tivvy
**Previous Names:** None
**Previous Leagues:** Devon and Exeter, Western

**Club Colours (change):** All yellow (All white)

**Ground Capacity:** 3,500 **Seats:** 520 **Covered:** 2,300 **Clubhouse:** Yes **Shop:** Yes
**Previous Grounds:** None

**Record Attendance:** 3,000 v Leyton Orient - FA Cup 1st Round Proper 1994-95
**Record Victory:** 10-0 v Exmouth Town, Devon St Lukes Cup 16/02/1994
**Record Defeat:** 2-6 v Stafford Rangers (A) - Southern League 2001-02 & Heavitree United, Les Philips Cup 29/11/1997
**Record Goalscorer:** Phil Everett
**Record Appearances:** Not known
**Additional Records:**

**Senior Honours:**
FA Vase 1997-98, 98-99. Western League x5. Southern League Cup 2006-07.
Devon Senior Cup 1955-56, 65-66. East Devon Senior Cup x7.

**10 YEAR RECORD**

| 06-07 | 07-08 | 08-09 | 09-10 | 10-11 | 11-12 | 12-13 | 13-14 | 14-15 | 15-16 |
|---|---|---|---|---|---|---|---|---|---|
| SthP 15 | SthP 17 | SthP 12 | SthP 19 | SthP 20 | Sthsw 9 | Sthsw 16 | Sthsw 3 | Sthsw 16 | Sthsw 8 |

# WANTAGE TOWN

**Chairman:** Tony Woodward
**Secretary:** David Heggie **(T)** **(E)** daveheggie.wcfc@live.co.uk
**Commercial Manager:** **(T)**
**Programme Editor:** Toni Cooper **(T)** tonicooper1@aol.com
**Ground Address:** Alfredian Park, Manor Road, Wantage OX12 8DW
**(T)** 01235 764 781 **Manager:** Stuart Cattell

**Founded:** 1892 **Nickname:** Alfredians
**Previous Names:** None.
**Previous Leagues:** Swindon & District. North Berkshire. Reading & District. Hellenic > 2014.

**Club Colours (change):** Green & white/white/green with white hoops

**Ground Capacity:** 1,500 **Seats:** 50 **Covered:** 300 **Clubhouse:** Yes **Shop:** No
**Previous Grounds:**

**Record Attendance:** **Att:** 550 v Oxford United, July 2003.
**Record Victory:** Not known - if you know please email tw.publications@btinternet.com
**Record Defeat:** Not known - if you know please email tw.publications@btinternet.com
**Record Goalscorer:** Not known - if you know please email tw.publications@btinternet.com
**Record Appearances:** Not known - if you know please email tw.publications@btinternet.com
**Additional Records:**

**Senior Honours:**
Hellenic Division 1 East 1980-81, 03-04, Premier Division 2010-11, 13-14.
Oxon Senior Cup 1982-83.

**10 YEAR RECORD**

| 06-07 | 07-08 | 08-09 | 09-10 | 10-11 | 11-12 | 12-13 | 13-14 | 14-15 | 15-16 |
|---|---|---|---|---|---|---|---|---|---|
| Hel P 11 | Hel P 12 | Hel P 11 | Hel P 5 | Hel P 1 | Hel P 12 | Hel P 2 | Hel P 1 | Sthsw 20 | Sthsw 20 |

# WIMBORNE TOWN

**Chairman:** Paula Henley
**Secretary:** Peter Barham **(T)** **(E)** barhamp@hotmail.co.uk
**Commercial Manager:** **(T)**
**Programme Editor:** Graham Dunn **(T)** magpies.graham@gmail.com
**Ground Address:** Cowgrove Road, Wimborne, Dorset, BH21 4EL
**(T)** 01202 884 821 **Manager:** Steve Cuss - May 2011

**Founded:** 1878 **Nickname:** Magpies
**Previous Names:** None
**Previous Leagues:** Dorset, Dorset Combination, Western 1981-86, Wessex 1986-2010

**Club Colours (change):** Black and white stripes/black/black (Sky blue/navy blue/navy blue)

**Ground Capacity:** 3,250 **Seats:** 275 **Covered:** 425 **Clubhouse:** Yes **Shop:** Yes
**Previous Grounds:** None

**Record Attendance:** 3,250 v Bamber Bridge
**Record Victory:** Not known - if you know please email tw.publications@btinternet.com
**Record Defeat:** Not known - if you know please email tw.publications@btinternet.com
**Record Goalscorer:** Jason Lovell
**Record Appearances:** James Sturgess
**Additional Records:**

**Senior Honours:**
FA Vase 1991-92. Wessex League 1991-92, 93-94, 99-2000.
Dorset Senior Amateur Cup 1936-37, 63-64.

**10 YEAR RECORD**

| 06-07 | 07-08 | 08-09 | 09-10 | 10-11 | 11-12 | 12-13 | 13-14 | 14-15 | 15-16 |
|---|---|---|---|---|---|---|---|---|---|
| WexP 6 | WexP 3 | WexP 4 | WexP 2 | Sthsw 19 | Sthsw 19 | Sthsw 12 | Sthsw 13 | Sthsw 13 | Sthsw 17 |

# WINCHESTER CITY

**Chairman:** Paul Murray
**Secretary:** Martin Moody **(T)** 07768 848 905 **(E)** secretary.wcfc@gmail.com
**Commercial Manager:** Scott Balaam **(T)**
**Programme Editor:** John Moody **(T)** johnmoody45@gmail.com
**Ground Address:** The Denplan City Ground, Hillier Way, Winchester SO23 7SR
**(T)** 07768 848 905 **Manager:** Ian Saunders

**Founded:** 1884 **Nickname:** The Capitals
**Previous Names:** None
**Previous Leagues:** Hampshire 1898-71, 73-03. Southern 1971-73, 2006-09, 2012-13. Wessex 2003-06. 2009-12, 13-15.

**Club Colours (change):** Red & black stripes/red/red (Blue & black stripes/blue/blue)

**Ground Capacity:** 2,500 **Seats:** 200 **Covered:** 275 **Clubhouse:** Yes **Shop:** Yes
**Previous Grounds:**

**Record Attendance:** 1,818 v Bideford, FA Vase Semi-final.
**Record Victory:** Not known - if you know please email tw.publications@btinternet.com
**Record Defeat:** Not known - if you know please email tw.publications@btinternet.com
**Record Goalscorer:** Andy Forbes.
**Record Appearances:** Ian Mancey.
**Additional Records:**

**Senior Honours:**
Hants Senior Cup 1932, 2005. Southampton Senior Cup 2000-01.
Hampshire Premier Division 2002-03. Wessex Division One 2003-04, 05-06, Premier Division 2011-12. FA Vase 2004.

**10 YEAR RECORD**

| 06-07 | 07-08 | 08-09 | 09-10 | 10-11 | 11-12 | 12-13 | 13-14 | 14-15 | 15-16 |
|---|---|---|---|---|---|---|---|---|---|
| SthW 13 | SthW 17 | SthW 22 | WexP 11 | WexP 3 | WexP 1 | SthC 22 | WexP 5 | WexP 2 | Sthsw 5 |

# YATE TOWN

**Chairman:** Colin Pick
**Secretary:** Terry Tansley **(T)** 07875 272 126 **(E)** admin@yatetownfc.com
**Commercial Manager:** **(T)**
**Programme Editor:** Terry Tansley **(T)** admin@yatetownfc.com
**Ground Address:** Jelf Stadium, Lodge Road, Yate, Bristol BS37 7LE
**(T)** 01454 228 103 **Manager:** Paul Britton

**Founded:** 1906 **Nickname:** The Bluebells
**Previous Names:** Yate Rovers 1906-1930s. Yate YMCA 1933-58.
**Previous Leagues:** Bristol Premier Combination > 1968, Gloucestershire County 1968-83, Hellenic 1983-89, 2000-03, Southern 1989-2000

**Club Colours (change):** White/blue navy/white (All yellow)

**Ground Capacity:** 2,000 **Seats:** 236 **Covered:** 400 **Clubhouse:** Yes **Shop:** Yes
**Previous Grounds:** Yate Aerodrome 1954-60. Sunnyside Lane 1960-84.

**Record Attendance:** 2,000 v Bristol Rovers v Bristol Rovers Past XI - Vaughan Jones testimonial 1990
**Record Victory:** 13-3 v Clevedon - Bristol Premier Combination 1967-68
**Record Defeat:** Not known - if you know please email tw.publications@btinternet.com
**Record Goalscorer:** Kevin Thaws
**Record Appearances:** Gary Hewlett
**Additional Records:** Paid £2,000 to Chippenham Town for Matt Rawlings 2003
Received £15,000 from Bristol Rovers for Mike Davis

**Senior Honours:**
Hellenic League 1987-88, 88-89. Gloucestershire Senior Cup 2004-05, 05-06.

**10 YEAR RECORD**

| 06-07 | 07-08 | 08-09 | 09-10 | 10-11 | 11-12 | 12-13 | 13-14 | 14-15 | 15-16 |
|---|---|---|---|---|---|---|---|---|---|
| SthP 14 | SthP 10 | SthP 21 | Sthsw 13 | Sthsw 14 | Sthsw 13 | Sthsw 6 | Sthsw 9 | Sthsw 6 | Sthsw 16 |

Action from the Southern League Division One South & West match between Shootwood United and Burnham on the 16th January. Photos: Peter Barnes.

# ISTHMIAN PREMIER LEAGUE TABLE 2015-16

| | | P | W | D | L | F | A | GD | Pts |
|---|---|---|---|---|---|---|---|---|---|
| 1 | Hampton & Richmond Borough | 46 | 28 | 11 | 7 | 105 | 52 | 53 | 95 |
| 2 | Bognor Regis Town | 46 | 29 | 7 | 10 | 95 | 42 | 53 | 94 |
| 3 | East Thurrock United | 46 | 26 | 13 | 7 | 107 | 53 | 54 | 91 |
| 4 | Tonbridge Angels | 46 | 24 | 13 | 9 | 90 | 49 | 41 | 85 |
| 5 | Dulwich Hamlet | 46 | 23 | 12 | 11 | 93 | 58 | 35 | 81 |
| 6 | Enfield Town | 46 | 24 | 8 | 14 | 74 | 47 | 27 | 80 |
| 7 | Kingstonian | 46 | 21 | 10 | 15 | 78 | 64 | 14 | 73 |
| 8 | Leiston | 46 | 20 | 12 | 14 | 72 | 57 | 15 | 72 |
| 9 | Billericay Town | 46 | 18 | 17 | 11 | 76 | 53 | 23 | 71 |
| 10 | Merstham | 46 | 18 | 8 | 20 | 74 | 80 | -6 | 62 |
| 11 | Leatherhead | 46 | 18 | 8 | 20 | 67 | 81 | -14 | 62 |
| 12 | Metropolitan Police | 46 | 17 | 10 | 19 | 60 | 79 | -19 | 61 |
| 13 | Wingate & Finchley | 46 | 17 | 9 | 20 | 66 | 70 | -4 | 60 |
| 14 | Canvey Island | 46 | 17 | 9 | 20 | 69 | 89 | -20 | 60 |
| 15 | Grays Athletic | 46 | 15 | 12 | 19 | 63 | 74 | -11 | 57 |
| 16 | Staines Town | 46 | 15 | 10 | 21 | 53 | 74 | -21 | 55 |
| 17 | Harrow Borough | 46 | 15 | 9 | 22 | 66 | 80 | -14 | 54 |
| 18 | Farnborough | 46 | 16 | 5 | 25 | 65 | 88 | -23 | 53 |
| 19 | Hendon | 46 | 13 | 13 | 20 | 68 | 85 | -17 | 52 |
| 20 | Needham Market | 46 | 13 | 12 | 21 | 51 | 76 | -25 | 51 |
| 21 | Burgess Hill Town | 46 | 12 | 14 | 20 | 57 | 73 | -16 | 50 |
| 22 | Brentwood Town | 46 | 10 | 10 | 26 | 51 | 80 | -29 | 40 |
| 23 | Lewes | 46 | 6 | 16 | 24 | 48 | 87 | -39 | 34 |
| 24 | VCD Athletic | 46 | 8 | 10 | 28 | 46 | 103 | -57 | 34 |

**Play-Off Semi Finals:** Bognor Regis Town 0-1 Dulwich Hamlet I East Thurrock United 2-0 Tonbridge Angels
**Final:** East Thurrock United 3-1 Dulwich Hamlet

| | PREMIER DIVISION | 1 | 2 | 3 | 4 | 5 | 6 | 7 | 8 | 9 | 10 | 11 | 12 | 13 | 14 | 15 | 16 | 17 | 18 | 19 | 20 | 21 | 22 | 23 | 24 |
|---|---|---|---|---|---|---|---|---|---|---|---|---|---|---|---|---|---|---|---|---|---|---|---|---|---|
| 1 | Billericay Town | | 2-0 | 1-1 | 0-0 | 0-3 | 4-1 | 3-1 | 3-0 | 2-3 | 1-1 | 0-1 | 2-1 | 3-1 | 0-0 | 2-0 | 4-1 | 1-1 | 1-1 | 6-0 | 1-1 | 2-3 | 1-1 | 1-1 | 4-0 |
| 2 | Bognor Regis Town | 3-1 | | 3-1 | 2-1 | 5-0 | 2-3 | 2-2 | 1-1 | 4-1 | 3-0 | 1-0 | 1-0 | 4-0 | 0-0 | 5-0 | 3-0 | 4-0 | 4-3 | 2-1 | 2-1 | 3-0 | 0-5 | 2-0 | 6-0 |
| 3 | Brentwood Town | 1-1 | 0-1 | | 1-1 | 3-3 | 1-2 | 1-3 | 1-2 | 1-1 | 1-2 | 0-3 | 2-1 | 4-1 | 0-0 | 4-1 | 0-2 | 0-1 | 1-2 | 2-2 | 1-0 | 7-0 | 0-1 | 2-0 | 0-1 |
| 4 | Burgess Hill Town | 1-1 | 0-4 | 1-1 | | 3-2 | 3-2 | 0-2 | 1-0 | 3-1 | 1-2 | 1-2 | 0-5 | 0-1 | 1-3 | 1-2 | 1-1 | 2-1 | 5-1 | 4-2 | 2-2 | 0-2 | 0-0 | 2-0 | 0-1 |
| 5 | Canvey Island | 0-2 | 1-1 | 1-0 | 3-3 | | 1-2 | 2-4 | 2-0 | 1-0 | 0-3 | 0-4 | 1-0 | 3-2 | 2-1 | 3-1 | 1-1 | 5-2 | 0-2 | 0-3 | 1-2 | 2-3 | 1-1 | 2-1 | 2-1 |
| 6 | Dulwich Hamlet | 1-0 | 2-0 | 4-0 | 1-1 | 3-0 | | 2-2 | 2-0 | 2-2 | 1-1 | 3-3 | 4-0 | 4-2 | 5-1 | 1-0 | 1-1 | 2-1 | 4-0 | 1-2 | 0-1 | 1-2 | 2-1 | 5-2 | 2-1 |
| 7 | East Thurrock United | 1-1 | 0-0 | 4-0 | 1-0 | 4-0 | 2-2 | | 1-0 | 4-1 | 3-0 | 2-1 | 2-0 | 2-4 | 2-2 | 4-4 | 4-0 | 4-1 | 1-2 | 4-2 | 1-2 | 0-0 | 3-0 | 4-1 | 1-1 |
| 8 | Enfield Town | 2-2 | 2-1 | 2-1 | 1-0 | 2-1 | 2-2 | 1-1 | | 4-1 | 2-0 | 2-3 | 3-0 | 2-0 | 4-0 | 4-0 | 0-2 | 2-1 | 2-2 | 2-0 | 3-0 | 2-1 | 0-1 | 3-0 | 2-0 |
| 9 | Farnborough | 0-2 | 2-1 | 3-0 | 1-0 | 2-6 | 1-4 | 0-3 | 0-0 | | 5-0 | 0-3 | 2-1 | 1-0 | 3-2 | 1-3 | 3-0 | 5-1 | 0-3 | 0-1 | 1-1 | 2-3 | 1-2 | 3-0 | 2-1 |
| 10 | Grays Athletic | 2-0 | 0-2 | 4-0 | 2-0 | 2-0 | 1-2 | 0-0 | 1-0 | 3-1 | | 0-3 | 3-2 | 1-1 | 1-3 | 0-2 | 0-2 | 4-0 | 1-3 | 3-3 | 0-2 | 1-1 | 1-1 | 0-1 | 0-0 |
| 11 | Hampton & Rich' Boro' | 2-1 | 2-1 | 5-1 | 1-1 | 5-0 | 2-1 | 2-1 | 0-0 | 3-1 | 3-1 | | 2-2 | 5-0 | 3-1 | 2-0 | 4-3 | 0-4 | 2-1 | 1-0 | 5-0 | 3-2 | 2-2 | 4-0 | 1-2 |
| 12 | Harrow Borough | 2-1 | 1-2 | 1-0 | 1-0 | 1-2 | 1-0 | 2-5 | 1-2 | 3-1 | 3-0 | 1-1 | | 5-5 | 1-3 | 2-2 | 0-0 | 4-1 | 0-2 | 0-3 | 0-2 | 1-0 | 1-1 | 1-2 | 1-0 |
| 13 | Hendon | 1-1 | 1-1 | 1-1 | 1-0 | 2-2 | 1-1 | 1-2 | 1-0 | 3-0 | 2-2 | 1-1 | 0-1 | | 1-1 | 2-3 | 2-4 | 2-0 | 2-2 | 0-2 | 0-2 | 2-0 | 0-3 | 3-1 | 4-3 |
| 14 | Kingstonian | 2-2 | 2-1 | 4-0 | 1-0 | 2-1 | 0-3 | 1-4 | 1-0 | 1-2 | 2-1 | 4-1 | 5-2 | 1-0 | | 0-3 | 1-0 | 2-2 | 3-1 | 7-0 | 4-2 | 0-1 | 1-3 | 3-0 | 2-1 |
| 15 | Leatherhead | 4-1 | 0-3 | 1-0 | 3-2 | 4-4 | 1-0 | 2-1 | 0-3 | 0-1 | 3-0 | 2-2 | 1-2 | 2-5 | 0-0 | | 3-2 | 3-0 | 0-2 | 1-3 | 2-2 | 3-0 | 0-2 | 2-0 | 0-0 |
| 16 | Leiston | 1-1 | 0-2 | 2-0 | 1-1 | 1-1 | 1-1 | 0-3 | 2-0 | 4-2 | 1-2 | 3-1 | 2-0 | 2-0 | 2-1 | 3-1 | | 3-1 | 3-1 | 1-2 | 3-0 | 3-1 | 1-2 | 3-0 | 0-1 |
| 17 | Lewes | 2-3 | 0-2 | 1-5 | 1-2 | 3-1 | 3-1 | 1-1 | 0-2 | 1-0 | 1-1 | 1-1 | 1-1 | 2-2 | 1-2 | 3-4 | 1-1 | | 1-0 | 1-2 | 0-0 | 2-2 | 0-1 | 2-2 | 0-0 |
| 18 | Merstham | 0-2 | 3-2 | 1-3 | 1-2 | 1-0 | 0-2 | 2-2 | 0-4 | 1-1 | 2-2 | 1-6 | 0-1 | 1-0 | 3-1 | 1-2 | 0-2 | 2-2 | | 1-0 | 2-0 | 5-1 | 2-2 | 6-1 | 0-2 |
| 19 | Metropolitan Police | 1-0 | 1-0 | 0-0 | 1-1 | 0-1 | 1-3 | 0-3 | 2-2 | 1-2 | 2-4 | 0-3 | 3-2 | 3-0 | 2-1 | 1-0 | 0-3 | 0-0 | 2-3 | | 1-0 | 0-0 | 0-3 | 1-1 | 1-3 |
| 20 | Needham Market | 1-3 | 0-1 | 4-0 | 1-2 | 2-3 | 2-1 | 1-3 | 2-3 | 0-2 | 0-0 | 1-1 | 2-4 | 0-3 | 0-0 | 1-0 | 2-2 | 1-0 | 1-0 | 1-1 | | 0-1 | 2-1 | 0-3 | 1-3 |
| 21 | Staines Town | 0-1 | 0-1 | 0-1 | 2-2 | 2-2 | 1-3 | 3-2 | 0-1 | 2-0 | 0-4 | 1-2 | 1-1 | 1-3 | 0-2 | 1-0 | 2-2 | 3-0 | 2-0 | 3-1 | 0-2 | | 1-1 | 1-0 | 1-2 |
| 22 | Tonbridge Angels | 2-2 | 1-3 | 4-0 | 2-3 | 2-0 | 1-1 | 1-2 | 3-1 | 2-0 | 2-3 | 1-0 | 3-3 | 3-1 | 1-1 | 4-0 | 0-1 | 1-0 | 3-2 | 0-1 | 3-3 | 2-0 | | 7-0 | 4-3 |
| 23 | VCD Athletic | 2-3 | 1-1 | 0-2 | 2-2 | 0-1 | 3-2 | 1-3 | 3-2 | 2-1 | 4-2 | 1-1 | 2-3 | 2-3 | 0-3 | 0-1 | 0-0 | 0-0 | 1-3 | 3-3 | 1-1 | 0-3 | 0-3 | | 2-1 |
| 24 | Wingate & Finchley | 0-1 | 1-3 | 2-1 | 5-1 | 1-2 | 1-1 | 1-3 | 1-2 | 4-3 | 3-2 | 1-3 | 3-1 | 1-1 | 2-1 | 1-1 | 1-0 | 1-1 | 1-3 | 1-3 | 6-0 | 0-0 | 0-1 | 2-0 | |

# ISTHMIAN DIVISION ONE NORTH LEAGUE TABLE 2015-16

| | | P | W | D | L | F | A | GD | Pts |
|---|---|---|---|---|---|---|---|---|---|
| 1 | AFC Sudbury | 46 | 33 | 6 | 7 | 90 | 49 | 41 | 105 |
| 2 | Thurrock | 46 | 30 | 6 | 10 | 99 | 52 | 47 | 96 |
| 3 | Harlow Town | 46 | 29 | 9 | 8 | 92 | 47 | 45 | 96 |
| 4 | Cray Wanderers | 46 | 27 | 9 | 10 | 98 | 52 | 46 | 90 |
| 5 | AFC Hornchurch | 46 | 25 | 11 | 10 | 87 | 35 | 52 | 86 |
| 6 | Cheshunt | 46 | 22 | 14 | 10 | 88 | 50 | 38 | 80 |
| 7 | Maldon & Tiptree | 46 | 22 | 12 | 12 | 89 | 66 | 23 | 78 |
| 8 | Brightlingsea Regent | 46 | 22 | 11 | 13 | 76 | 55 | 21 | 77 |
| 9 | Dereham Town | 46 | 21 | 11 | 14 | 82 | 61 | 21 | 74 |
| 10 | Thamesmead Town | 46 | 21 | 11 | 14 | 74 | 63 | 11 | 74 |
| 11 | Tilbury | 46 | 20 | 9 | 17 | 85 | 66 | 19 | 69 |
| 12 | Aveley | 46 | 20 | 8 | 18 | 84 | 71 | 13 | 68 |
| 13 | Bury Town | 46 | 16 | 14 | 16 | 74 | 68 | 6 | 62 |
| 14 | Phoenix Sports | 46 | 16 | 8 | 22 | 60 | 74 | -14 | 56 |
| 15 | Haringey Borough | 46 | 12 | 14 | 20 | 61 | 76 | -15 | 50 |
| 16 | Romford | 46 | 12 | 12 | 22 | 59 | 83 | -24 | 48 |
| 17 | Soham Town Rangers | 46 | 13 | 9 | 24 | 61 | 90 | -29 | 48 |
| 18 | Great Wakering Rovers | 46 | 12 | 11 | 23 | 69 | 103 | -34 | 47 |
| 19 | Witham Town | 46 | 12 | 9 | 25 | 59 | 96 | -37 | 45 |
| 20 | Heybridge Swifts | 46 | 12 | 8 | 26 | 59 | 87 | -28 | 44 |
| 21 | Waltham Abbey | 46 | 11 | 8 | 27 | 54 | 80 | -26 | 41 |
| 22 | Wroxham | 46 | 10 | 10 | 26 | 50 | 89 | -39 | 40 |
| 23 | Barkingside | 46 | 9 | 10 | 27 | 55 | 97 | -42 | 37 |
| 24 | Redbridge | 46 | 8 | 4 | 34 | 46 | 141 | -95 | 28 |

**Play-Off Semi Finals:** Harlow Town 3-0 Cray Wanderers I Thurrock 0-2 AFC Hornchurch

**Final:** Harlow Town 3-1 AFC Hornchurch

| | DIVISION ONE NORTH | 1 | 2 | 3 | 4 | 5 | 6 | 7 | 8 | 9 | 10 | 11 | 12 | 13 | 14 | 15 | 16 | 17 | 18 | 19 | 20 | 21 | 22 | 23 | 24 |
|---|---|---|---|---|---|---|---|---|---|---|---|---|---|---|---|---|---|---|---|---|---|---|---|---|---|
| 1 | AFC Hornchurch | | 1-1 | 1-2 | 5-1 | 2-0 | 3-0 | 0-2 | 2-1 | 3-0 | 0-0 | 4-1 | 0-0 | 2-1 | 1-3 | 1-0 | 6-0 | 0-1 | 2-1 | 1-1 | 0-0 | 0-0 | 2-0 | 2-0 | 3-0 |
| 2 | AFC Sudbury | 1-1 | | 3-1 | 1-0 | 1-3 | 2-0 | 0-0 | 2-6 | 2-1 | 5-1 | 2-0 | 0-1 | 4-2 | 0-2 | 1-0 | 5-1 | 5-2 | 5-2 | 2-0 | 0-4 | 3-0 | 0-2 | 2-1 | 2-1 |
| 3 | Aveley | 1-3 | 0-1 | | 1-0 | 2-4 | 3-2 | 3-1 | 1-1 | 2-2 | 1-1 | 1-1 | 1-2 | 1-0 | 0-0 | 2-4 | 6-1 | 1-1 | 3-1 | 0-2 | 0-2 | 0-4 | 3-2 | 3-0 | 1-0 |
| 4 | Barkingside | 1-2 | 1-3 | 0-5 | | 0-0 | 0-1 | 3-3 | 2-5 | 2-1 | 2-1 | 0-1 | 1-2 | 0-0 | 2-2 | 0-1 | 0-1 | 4-0 | 1-1 | 2-5 | 0-4 | 0-3 | 2-4 | 3-2 | 2-1 |
| 5 | Brightlingsea Regent | 1-1 | 1-1 | 0-0 | 1-2 | | 2-2 | 3-2 | 1-2 | 1-0 | 4-1 | 1-1 | 0-1 | 1-0 | 1-0 | 0-3 | 1-3 | 3-1 | 3-0 | 2-1 | 2-2 | 1-4 | 4-1 | 4-0 | 0-1 |
| 6 | Bury Town | 1-1 | 1-1 | 5-1 | 4-1 | 0-1 | | 0-0 | 1-1 | 1-2 | 2-0 | 5-3 | 0-3 | 1-3 | 1-2 | 0-0 | 4-1 | 5-1 | 1-1 | 1-1 | 2-3 | 2-0 | 3-4 | 4-4 | 1-0 |
| 7 | Cheshunt | 1-2 | 0-1 | 1-1 | 4-0 | 2-2 | 1-1 | | 0-1 | 1-0 | 3-0 | 1-0 | 2-0 | 4-2 | 1-0 | 1-0 | 4-2 | 2-0 | 1-1 | 2-0 | 3-0 | 3-2 | 3-1 | 1-1 | 3-3 |
| 8 | Cray Wanderers | 0-2 | 1-2 | 3-1 | 4-0 | 2-3 | 3-3 | 2-0 | | 0-1 | 3-1 | 4-2 | 3-1 | 2-4 | 1-1 | 5-0 | 5-0 | 0-1 | 6-1 | 1-0 | 1-2 | 3-2 | 2-1 | 1-0 | 3-1 |
| 9 | Dereham Town | 0-3 | 0-1 | 0-2 | 2-1 | 5-1 | 1-1 | 0-4 | 2-2 | | 5-1 | 3-3 | 2-2 | 1-0 | 3-2 | 1-2 | 5-0 | 1-0 | 1-0 | 3-0 | 2-2 | 4-2 | 1-0 | 2-2 | 2-0 |
| 10 | Great Wakering Rovers | 0-5 | 1-2 | 3-2 | 1-4 | 0-0 | 0-1 | 0-0 | 0-0 | 1-5 | | 1-1 | 2-2 | 3-2 | 1-2 | 1-0 | 1-0 | 2-3 | 2-0 | 2-3 | 1-4 | 6-1 | 3-2 | 2-0 | 3-4 |
| 11 | Haringey Borough | 0-3 | 1-3 | 3-1 | 2-3 | 2-2 | 2-3 | 0-4 | 0-0 | 0-0 | 3-1 | | 2-3 | 1-0 | 0-2 | 1-2 | 2-0 | 1-1 | 2-2 | 1-1 | 2-2 | 0-2 | 1-2 | 2-3 | 1-3 |
| 12 | Harlow Town | 3-1 | 1-2 | 4-1 | 3-1 | 0-1 | 2-0 | 2-0 | 1-1 | 2-0 | 3-1 | 0-0 | | 3-1 | 2-1 | 4-0 | 4-0 | 1-1 | 3-0 | 1-0 | 4-1 | 3-2 | 2-1 | 5-2 | 4-0 |
| 13 | Heybridge Swifts | 1-0 | 1-1 | 2-0 | 1-0 | 1-5 | 2-1 | 1-8 | 0-1 | 0-2 | 2-3 | 1-4 | 1-2 | | 1-2 | 2-0 | 2-2 | 1-1 | 1-3 | 1-2 | 2-4 | 2-1 | 3-3 | 2-2 | 1-0 |
| 14 | Maldon & Tiptree | 1-1 | 0-2 | 2-1 | 3-0 | 1-0 | 3-1 | 3-3 | 1-2 | 2-2 | 2-3 | 1-2 | 1-1 | 4-0 | | 2-3 | 3-3 | 3-1 | 3-0 | 4-3 | 2-2 | 4-4 | 0-3 | 3-0 | 5-4 |
| 15 | Phoenix Sports | 2-4 | 1-4 | 0-3 | 0-2 | 1-0 | 0-1 | 1-2 | 2-1 | 3-2 | 3-3 | 0-3 | 2-2 | 3-1 | 1-2 | | 4-1 | 0-0 | 2-0 | 1-1 | 0-2 | 1-2 | 1-2 | 1-2 | 1-2 |
| 16 | Redbridge | 0-6 | 0-4 | 1-4 | 2-2 | 0-3 | 0-1 | 1-1 | 2-4 | 0-5 | 1-2 | 0-1 | 0-1 | 1-0 | 3-2 | 0-3 | | 1-6 | 3-1 | 3-4 | 0-4 | 1-5 | 1-0 | 2-1 | 0-2 |
| 17 | Romford | 2-0 | 0-1 | 0-5 | 2-1 | 0-2 | 3-3 | 1-3 | 2-3 | 1-2 | 2-1 | 0-1 | 4-3 | 2-0 | 0-2 | 0-0 | 3-0 | | 1-2 | 2-3 | 1-1 | 0-3 | 2-0 | 1-0 | 0-0 |
| 18 | Soham Town Rangers | 1-0 | 0-1 | 3-1 | 1-0 | 2-1 | 0-3 | 1-1 | 0-2 | 2-3 | 2-2 | 2-1 | 1-0 | 2-4 | 1-2 | 1-1 | 4-1 | 4-2 | | 2-2 | 1-2 | 1-4 | 2-1 | 1-2 | 1-0 |
| 19 | Thamesmead Town | 1-1 | 1-2 | 0-2 | 1-1 | 0-2 | 1-0 | 1-2 | 1-2 | 1-0 | 3-2 | 1-0 | 2-1 | 0-0 | 2-2 | 3-2 | 5-2 | 2-1 | 3-0 | | 1-0 | 2-1 | 4-3 | 3-2 | 0-0 |
| 20 | Thurrock | 2-1 | 5-1 | 2-1 | 3-1 | 1-0 | 2-1 | 1-0 | 0-1 | 1-2 | 4-1 | 3-2 | 1-2 | 3-1 | 2-0 | 0-1 | 3-1 | 3-1 | 3-0 | 1-4 | | 3-1 | 2-1 | 1-2 | 5-1 |
| 21 | Tilbury | 0-1 | 0-1 | 0-2 | 1-1 | 0-1 | 3-1 | 4-3 | 0-0 | 2-2 | 4-0 | 0-0 | 3-1 | 1-0 | 0-0 | 5-3 | 4-1 | 3-1 | 2-2 | 1-0 | 0-1 | | 2-1 | 4-0 | 1-0 |
| 22 | Waltham Abbey | 1-0 | 0-3 | 1-2 | 3-3 | 1-2 | 0-1 | 0-0 | 2-1 | 2-1 | 2-2 | 1-1 | 0-2 | 0-3 | 1-2 | 0-2 | 2-0 | 1-1 | 0-4 | 0-0 | 1-3 | 0-0 | | 0-1 | 2-1 |
| 23 | Witham Town | 0-4 | 1-2 | 0-5 | 3-2 | 0-3 | 0-1 | 3-2 | 1-2 | 1-1 | 2-2 | 2-3 | 1-2 | 1-1 | 1-3 | 1-2 | 3-0 | 3-3 | 3-2 | 1-3 | 0-3 | 2-0 | 1-0 | | 2-1 |
| 24 | Wroxham | 0-4 | 1-2 | 2-5 | 1-1 | 3-3 | 1-1 | 0-3 | 0-4 | 0-2 | 2-4 | 0-1 | 1-1 | 0-3 | 0-2 | 1-1 | 3-4 | 1-1 | 3-2 | 1-0 | 1-0 | 3-2 | 1-0 | 0-0 | |

# ISTHMIAN DIVISION ONE SOUTH LEAGUE TABLE 2015-16

| | | P | W | D | L | F | A | GD | Pts |
|---|---|---|---|---|---|---|---|---|---|
| 1 | Folkestone Invicta | 46 | 36 | 6 | 4 | 102 | 34 | 68 | 114 |
| 2 | Dorking Wanderers | 46 | 27 | 9 | 10 | 99 | 56 | 43 | 90 |
| 3 | Worthing | 46 | 27 | 7 | 12 | 96 | 56 | 40 | 88 |
| 4 | Hythe Town | 46 | 27 | 6 | 13 | 74 | 49 | 25 | 87 |
| 5 | Faversham Town | 46 | 25 | 8 | 13 | 76 | 45 | 31 | 83 |
| 6 | Corinthian-Casuals | 46 | 26 | 7 | 13 | 75 | 52 | 23 | 82 |
| 7 | Hastings United | 46 | 25 | 6 | 15 | 99 | 64 | 35 | 81 |
| 8 | Herne Bay | 46 | 22 | 10 | 14 | 79 | 54 | 25 | 76 |
| 9 | Molesey | 46 | 23 | 6 | 17 | 87 | 83 | 4 | 75 |
| 10 | Carshalton Athletic | 46 | 21 | 9 | 16 | 83 | 74 | 9 | 72 |
| 11 | South Park | 46 | 21 | 9 | 16 | 78 | 71 | 7 | 72 |
| 12 | Ramsgate | 46 | 21 | 8 | 17 | 92 | 76 | 16 | 71 |
| 13 | Guernsey | 46 | 21 | 5 | 20 | 94 | 88 | 6 | 68 |
| 14 | Three Bridges | 46 | 20 | 6 | 20 | 59 | 67 | -8 | 66 |
| 15 | Whyteleafe | 46 | 19 | 5 | 22 | 69 | 77 | -8 | 62 |
| 16 | Walton Casuals | 46 | 18 | 6 | 22 | 74 | 85 | -11 | 60 |
| 17 | Tooting & Mitcham United | 46 | 16 | 10 | 20 | 66 | 71 | -5 | 58 |
| 18 | Sittingbourne | 46 | 16 | 6 | 24 | 63 | 77 | -14 | 54 |
| 19 | Chatham Town | 46 | 13 | 7 | 26 | 61 | 70 | -9 | 46 |
| 20 | East Grinstead Town | 46 | 12 | 7 | 27 | 55 | 84 | -29 | 43 |
| 21 | Chipstead | 46 | 11 | 6 | 29 | 54 | 92 | -38 | 39 |
| 22 | Walton & Hersham | 46 | 9 | 6 | 31 | 50 | 113 | -63 | 30 |
| 23 | Whitstable Town | 46 | 8 | 2 | 36 | 52 | 118 | -66 | 26 |
| 24 | Peacehaven & Telscombe | 46 | 6 | 7 | 33 | 48 | 129 | -81 | 25 |

**Play-Off Semi Finals:** Dorking Wanderers 1-2 Faversham Town I Worthing 7-0 Hythe Town
**Final:** Worthing 3-0 Faversham Town

| | DIVISION ONE SOUTH | 1 | 2 | 3 | 4 | 5 | 6 | 7 | 8 | 9 | 10 | 11 | 12 | 13 | 14 | 15 | 16 | 17 | 18 | 19 | 20 | 21 | 22 | 23 | 24 |
|---|---|---|---|---|---|---|---|---|---|---|---|---|---|---|---|---|---|---|---|---|---|---|---|---|---|
| 1 | Carshalton Athletic | | 1-1 | 1-2 | 1-1 | 0-4 | 2-2 | 3-0 | 1-1 | 4-1 | 3-1 | 1-3 | 0-1 | 3-2 | 4-0 | 5-2 | 3-0 | 1-1 | 4-1 | 1-0 | 2-3 | 3-1 | 2-1 | 1-2 | 2-3 |
| 2 | Chatham Town | 0-1 | | 0-1 | 1-2 | 2-3 | 1-0 | 0-1 | 0-1 | 4-1 | 2-1 | 0-2 | 1-2 | 1-1 | 1-1 | 1-2 | 1-1 | 1-2 | 2-3 | 1-3 | 4-0 | 2-1 | 1-2 | 1-2 | 0-3 |
| 3 | Chipstead | 1-3 | 0-1 | | 1-1 | 0-1 | 2-3 | 0-2 | 2-2 | 4-1 | 1-1 | 1-2 | 1-2 | 1-4 | 2-1 | 2-3 | 0-0 | 1-4 | 1-1 | 0-2 | 1-1 | 0-1 | 3-1 | 3-2 | 1-2 |
| 4 | Corinthian-Casuals | 2-0 | 4-0 | 3-1 | | 1-2 | 1-0 | 3-1 | 0-1 | 1-0 | 2-2 | 1-2 | 1-0 | 1-2 | 3-1 | 2-1 | 1-0 | 1-2 | 1-0 | 0-2 | 5-1 | 0-1 | 4-2 | 0-1 | 2-0 |
| 5 | Dorking Wanderers | 1-0 | 0-0 | 5-0 | 4-1 | | 5-3 | 5-1 | 1-0 | 4-0 | 1-2 | 4-2 | 1-3 | 1-2 | 2-2 | 1-0 | 0-0 | 1-5 | 3-1 | 1-3 | 3-0 | 2-1 | 2-0 | 1-2 | 2-2 |
| 6 | East Grinstead Town | 2-3 | 2-1 | 0-2 | 1-1 | 0-2 | | 2-1 | 0-1 | 2-1 | 0-1 | 0-0 | 2-2 | 2-1 | 0-1 | 0-2 | 0-2 | 0-2 | 2-0 | 1-2 | 4-0 | 0-1 | 3-1 | 1-2 | 2-4 |
| 7 | Faversham Town | 1-1 | 2-0 | 2-1 | 1-2 | 2-1 | 2-1 | | 2-2 | 0-2 | 3-0 | 0-1 | 4-0 | 3-1 | 2-0 | 1-1 | 1-0 | 1-2 | 3-1 | 2-1 | 1-1 | 7-0 | 2-1 | 1-0 | 0-0 |
| 8 | Folkestone Invicta | 3-1 | 2-1 | 2-1 | 4-0 | 1-1 | 3-0 | 0-2 | | 5-2 | 1-0 | 4-0 | 3-0 | 3-1 | 3-1 | 2-2 | 3-1 | 1-0 | 1-0 | 3-1 | 6-0 | 2-1 | 3-0 | 3-0 | 1-0 |
| 9 | Guernsey | 2-1 | 3-1 | 2-1 | 2-4 | 2-1 | 3-1 | 1-2 | 1-2 | | 1-4 | 0-0 | 3-1 | 4-2 | 6-1 | 3-0 | 3-0 | 2-3 | 1-0 | 6-2 | 4-1 | 6-2 | 2-0 | 2-1 | 1-1 |
| 10 | Hastings United | 0-1 | 1-0 | 6-0 | 3-3 | 2-3 | 5-2 | 1-4 | 1-4 | 2-0 | | 1-2 | 3-1 | 4-2 | 6-0 | 3-2 | 2-0 | 5-1 | 0-1 | 2-0 | 2-0 | 1-0 | 6-1 | 2-0 | 1-3 |
| 11 | Herne Bay | 1-1 | 1-2 | 4-1 | 0-1 | 0-0 | 1-1 | 1-1 | 1-3 | 1-1 | 2-0 | | 0-2 | 3-1 | 7-0 | 1-2 | 3-1 | 3-2 | 2-1 | 0-0 | 3-0 | 4-0 | 0-2 | 1-0 | 3-4 |
| 12 | Hythe Town | 3-0 | 3-1 | 3-0 | 1-1 | 0-3 | 2-0 | 2-0 | 2-1 | 1-1 | 1-1 | 0-2 | | 0-0 | 0-1 | 4-2 | 2-0 | 3-0 | 1-0 | 2-1 | 4-0 | 0-3 | 2-1 | 0-0 | 3-0 |
| 13 | Molesey | 2-1 | 2-1 | 2-0 | 0-1 | 2-2 | 1-0 | 1-5 | 0-1 | 4-0 | 2-1 | 3-2 | 1-3 | | 4-2 | 3-2 | 2-1 | 2-2 | 1-2 | 3-2 | 6-2 | 4-1 | 2-0 | 1-3 | 1-4 |
| 14 | Peacehaven & Tels' | 2-4 | 0-4 | 1-3 | 0-1 | 2-4 | 1-1 | 1-0 | 2-4 | 2-1 | 0-4 | 0-3 | 0-3 | 1-2 | | 2-3 | 2-6 | 1-0 | 2-0 | 1-1 | 1-2 | 1-1 | 0-2 | 1-3 | 0-2 |
| 15 | Ramsgate | 7-1 | 1-1 | 3-0 | 3-2 | 1-1 | 4-0 | 1-0 | 2-1 | 2-1 | 2-2 | 1-0 | 1-3 | 2-1 | 8-1 | | 1-3 | 2-3 | 4-0 | 0-1 | 1-1 | 2-0 | 2-3 | 3-0 | 1-1 |
| 16 | Sittingbourne | 1-2 | 2-1 | 1-6 | 1-2 | 1-2 | 2-1 | 2-1 | 1-2 | 3-2 | 1-3 | 1-2 | 0-2 | 1-1 | 3-1 | 4-0 | | 2-1 | 1-2 | 0-3 | 2-2 | 1-2 | 1-0 | 3-2 | 0-2 |
| 17 | South Park | 1-0 | 0-0 | 2-0 | 1-1 | 2-0 | 1-3 | 0-2 | 0-4 | 4-4 | 1-1 | 0-4 | 1-0 | 6-2 | 1-1 | 1-3 | 1-1 | | 0-2 | 1-0 | 1-1 | 1-2 | 2-0 | 3-1 | 0-1 |
| 18 | Three Bridges | 2-3 | 2-1 | 3-1 | 0-1 | 0-6 | 1-1 | 1-0 | 0-1 | 1-2 | 3-2 | 0-3 | 3-0 | 0-2 | 3-3 | 2-0 | 1-0 | 1-4 | | 2-2 | 1-0 | 2-1 | 3-0 | 0-0 | 2-0 |
| 19 | Tooting & Mitcham Utd | 3-0 | 2-7 | 0-1 | 0-3 | 3-0 | 4-0 | 1-1 | 0-2 | 4-1 | 0-2 | 1-1 | 0-1 | 2-2 | 2-0 | 3-0 | 0-1 | 4-1 | 0-2 | | 1-1 | 0-3 | 2-2 | 1-1 | 1-1 |
| 20 | Walton & Hersham | 1-3 | 1-2 | 0-1 | 0-3 | 1-4 | 1-3 | 0-1 | 0-3 | 1-2 | 2-4 | 1-4 | 1-3 | 2-3 | 3-2 | 3-2 | 0-2 | 2-3 | 0-2 | 2-1 | | 3-2 | 4-1 | 1-2 | 1-3 |
| 21 | Walton Casuals | 2-2 | 1-2 | 3-2 | 2-3 | 2-2 | 2-1 | 1-1 | 1-1 | 1-5 | 0-2 | 2-0 | 2-1 | 1-2 | 3-1 | 1-2 | 5-3 | 0-1 | 3-1 | 2-3 | 1-0 | | 1-0 | 1-2 | 2-2 |
| 22 | Whitstable Town | 1-2 | 0-2 | 3-1 | 0-2 | 0-1 | 2-3 | 0-4 | 0-1 | 3-1 | 1-2 | 2-2 | 0-3 | 1-2 | 4-3 | 2-4 | 0-5 | 1-6 | 1-3 | 3-0 | 1-2 | 0-8 | | 2-4 | 0-1 |
| 23 | Whyteleafe | 1-3 | 2-5 | 3-1 | 1-0 | 0-2 | 0-1 | 0-2 | 1-3 | 4-3 | 4-1 | 2-0 | 1-2 | 2-0 | 3-2 | 2-2 | 1-2 | 0-2 | 1-1 | 0-1 | 1-2 | 4-1 | 4-2 | | 1-2 |
| 24 | Worthing | 2-2 | 2-0 | 2-0 | 3-0 | 2-4 | 5-2 | 0-1 | 1-2 | 0-2 | 1-3 | 3-0 | 2-0 | 1-2 | 5-0 | 2-1 | 3-0 | 3-1 | 0-2 | 5-1 | 2-0 | 1-2 | 5-3 | 5-1 | |

# ROBERT DYAS LEAGUE CUP 2015-16

**HOLDERS:** HENDON

## PRELIMINARY ROUND

| | | | |
|---|---|---|---|
| Barkingside | v | AFC Hornchurch | 0-9 |
| AFC Sudbury | v | Brightlingsea Regent | 1-5 |
| Billericay Town | v | Aveley | 1-2 |

## FIRST ROUND

| | | | |
|---|---|---|---|
| Brentwood Town | v | Enfield Town | 1-2 |
| Bury Town | v | Leiston | 0-3 |
| Canvey Island | v | Grays Athletic | 2-2, 1-3p |
| Chipstead | v | Walton & Hersham | 1-2 |
| Corinthian-Casuals | v | South Park | 4-0 |
| Dorking Wanderers | v | Peacehaven & Telscombe | 2-1 |
| Dulwich Hamlet | v | Thamesmead Town | 2-0 |
| Folkestone Invicta | v | Ramsgate | 2-0 |
| Haringey Borough | v | Metropolitan Police | 2-2, 3-4p |
| Harrow Borough | v | Kingstonian | 2-3 |
| Hastings United | v | Hythe Town | 3-2 |
| Merstham | v | Sittingbourne | 1-2 |
| Molesey | v | Hendon | 0-2 |
| Redbridge | v | Cheshunt | 0-3 |
| Staines Town | v | Hampton & Richmond Borough | 2-0 |
| Three Bridges | v | Leatherhead | 1-1, 11-10p |
| Tibury | v | Great Wakering Rovers | 1-3 |
| Tonbridge Angels | v | Herne Bay | 2-0 |
| Tooting & Mitcham United | v | Phoenix Sports | 5-1 |
| VCD Athletic | v | Chatham Town | 1-2 |
| Whitstable Town | v | Faversham Town | 1-1, 4-5p |
| Whyteleafe | v | Carshalton Athletic | 1-1, 4-5p |
| Wingate & Finchley | v | Harlow Town | 1-0 |
| Witham Town | v | Maldon & Tiptree | 2-3 |
| Worthing | v | Burgess Hill Town | 2-2, 3-4p |
| Romford | v | East Thurrock United | 0-3 |
| Walton Casuals | v | East Grinstead Town | 4-0 |
| Soham Town Rangers | v | Brightlingsea Regent | 0-3 |
| Waltham Abbey | v | AFC Hornchurch | 1-1, 4-3p |
| Thurrock | v | Aveley | 2-1 |
| Needham Market | v | Heybridge Swifts | 5-0 |
| Farnborough | v | Lewes | 3-2 |

## SECOND ROUND

| | | | |
|---|---|---|---|
| Corinthian-Casuals | v | Carshalton Athletic | 3-1 |
| Dorking Wanderers | v | Burgess Hill Town | 3-1 |
| Dulwich Hamlet | v | Staines Town | 2-1 |
| Enfield Town | v | Cheshunt | 1-0 |
| Hendon | v | Kingstonian | 2-2, 1-3p |
| Maldon & Tiptree | v | Leiston | 0-3 |
| Tooting & Mitcham United | v | Metropolitan Police | 4-1 |
| Waltham Abbey | v | Wingate & Finchley | 3-4 |
| Great Wakering Rovers | v | Thurrock | 5-1 |
| Grays Athletic | v | East Thurrock United | 2-2, 3-2p |
| Walton Casuals | v | Walton & Hersham | 2-5 |
| Chatham Town | v | Sittingbourne | 0-1 |
| Faversham Town | v | Folkestone Invicta | 2-1 |
| Tonbridge Angels | v | Hastings United | 2-2, 0-3p |
| Needham Market | v | Brightlingsea Regent | 1-3 |
| Farnborough | v | Three Bridges | 4-0 |

## THIRD ROUND

| | | | |
|---|---|---|---|
| Kingstonian | v | Farnborough | 2-1 |
| Wingate & Finchley | v | Grays Athletic | 5-4 |
| Hastings United | v | Sittingbourne | 1-1, 3-4p |
| Dulwich Hamlet | v | Faversham Town | 1-2 |
| Leiston | v | Great Wakering Rovers | 2-1 |
| Walton & Hersham | v | Dorking Wanderers | 0-2 |
| Tooting & Mitcham United | v | Corinthian-Casuals | 2-1 |
| Brightlingsea Regent | v | Enfield Town | 1-2 |

## QUARTER-FINALS

| | | | |
|---|---|---|---|
| Faversham Town | v | Dorking Wanderers | 1-0 |
| Leiston | v | Kingstonian | 0-2 |
| Sittingbourne | v | Corinthian-Casuals | 2-1 |
| Enfield Town | v | Wingate & Finchley | 1-3 |

## SEMI-FINALS

| | | | |
|---|---|---|---|
| Kingstonian | v | Wingate & Finchley | 2-2, 4-2p |
| Faversham Town | v | Sittingbourne | 3-0 |

## FINAL

| | | | |
|---|---|---|---|
| Faversham Town | v | Kingstonian | 0-5 |

## Isthmian League Premier Division South Statistics 2015-16

| | NoS | GS | CTS | PS | CSG | MCGU | TCS | MCCS | CMWW | CD | FTS | CNG | TGC |
|---|---|---|---|---|---|---|---|---|---|---|---|---|---|
| Billericay Town | 16 | 77 | 6 | 6 | 13 | 9 | 12 | 2 | 7 | 3 | 10 | 2 | 58 |
| Bognor Regis Town | 18+2 | 117 | 5 | 7 | 18 | 12 | 25 | 4 | 3 | 2 | 8 | 2 | 56 |
| Brentwood Town | 21+1 | 65 | 7 | 4 | 5 | 4 | 10 | 2 | 9 | 3 | 20 | 3 | 90 |
| Burgess Hill Town | 17 | 60 | 5 | 5 | 5 | 4 | 4 | 1 | 13* | 3 | 14 | 2 | 78 |
| Canvey Island | 21+1 | 71 | 6 | 1 | 11 | 7 | 9 | 2 | 5 | 4 | 14 | 3 | 90 |
| Dulwich Hamlet | 19+2 | 108 | 5 | 11 | 27* | 6 | 13 | 4 | 6 | 2 | 3 | 1 | 69 |
| East Thurrock United | 20+1 | 137 | 5 | 14 | 31 | 10 | 19 | 3 | 4 | 1 | 2 | 2 | 67 |
| Enfield Town | 15+1 | 85 | 4 | 3 | 7* | 10 | 20 | 4 | 6 | 3 | 15 | 3 | 53 |
| Farnborough | 24 | 71 | 5 | 4 | 16 | 5 | 9 | 1 | 8 | 6 | 10 | 2 | 95 |
| Grays Athletic | 13+3 | 81 | 6 | 5 | 10 | 10 | 15 | 4 | 10* | 9* | 18 | 4 | 82 |
| Hampton & Richmond | 16+2 | 110 | 6 | 6 | 10 | 8 | 14 | | 3 | 2 | 7 | 2 | 56 |
| Harrow Borough | 12+1 | 66 | 5 | 4 | 7 | 6 | 10 | 2 | 7 | 6 | 8 | 3 | 84 |
| Hendon | 24+3 | 69 | 5 | 7 | 8 | 8 | 6 | 1 | 6 | 6 | 12 | 3 | 89 |
| Kingstonian | 20 | 91 | 7 | 3 | 9 | 9 | 14 | 2 | 5* | 3 | 10 | 2 | 77 |
| Leatherhead | 20+1 | 70 | 4 | 4 | 7 | 5 | 11 | 2 | 8 | 3 | 15 | 2 | 90 |
| Leiston | 17+1 | 81 | 4 | 6 | 13 | 7 | 16 | 5 | 6 | 4 | 9 | 2 | 63 |
| Lewes | 23 | 49 | 4 | 5 | 5 | 6* | 7 | 2 | 18 | 9 | 16 | 3 | 91 |
| Merstham | 17 | 77 | 6 | 8 | 9 | 3 | 7 | 2 | 7 | 3 | 11 | 2 | 88 |
| Met Police | 22 | 65 | 3 | 4 | 12 | 6 | 15 | 2 | 7 | 3 | 17 | 2 | 84 |
| Needham Market | 14+1 | 52 | 4 | 4 | 8 | 6 | 11 | 3 | 14 | 4 | 16 | 2 | 82 |
| Staines Town | 18 | 69 | 6 | 7 | 12 | 10 | 12 | 2 | 3 | 7 | 16 | 3 | 89 |
| Tonbridge Angels | 16 | 98 | 7 | 4 | 29 | 9 | 19 | 3 | 5 | 2 | 3 | 0 | 57 |
| VCD Athletic | 17 | 52 | 3 | 7 | 9 | 5 | 5 | 2 | 20 | 4 | 21 | 3 | 111 |
| Wingate & Finchley | 16+1 | 73 | 6 | 5 | 9 | 6 | 11 | 3 | 7 | 2 | 10 | 2 | 76 |

+ Denotes number of Own goals I * Denotes unfinished run

NoS - Number of Scorers I GS - Goals Scored I CTS - Club's Top Score I PS - Penalties Scored
CSG - Consecutive Scoring Games I MCGU - Most Consecutive Games Unbeaten I TCS - Total Clean Sheets
MCCS - Most Consecutive Clean Sheets I CMWW - Consecutive Matches Without a Win
CD - Consecutive Defeats I FTS - Failure to Score I CNG - Consecutive No Goals
I TGC - Total Goals Conceded

## Isthmian League Premier Leading goalscorers 2015-16

| Player | Club | Lge | FAC | FAT | Pens | HT | CSG | SG | Total |
|---|---|---|---|---|---|---|---|---|---|
| Sam Higgins | East Thurrock United | 38 | 5 | 2 | 9 | 3 | 8 | 28 | 45 |
| Jason Prior | Bognor Regis Town | 35 | 2 | 4 | 7 | 4 | 5 | 25 | 41 |
| Nathan Elder | Tonbridge Angels | 24 | 2 | 1 | | | 4 | 22 | 27 |
| Pat Cox | Staines Town | 17 | 8 | 1 | 7 | 2 | 4 | 17 | 26 |
| Martin Tuohy | Canvey Island | 24 | | | | | 3 | 19 | 24 |
| Corey Whitely | Enfield Town | 21 | | 2 | 2 | 1 | 4 | 16 | 23 |
| Luke Blewden | Tonbridge Angels | 20 | | 2 | 2 | 1 | 4 | 16 | 22 |
| Billy Healey | Wingate & Finchley | 20 | 2 | | 3 | | 3 | 15 | 22 |
| Tom Wraight | East Thurrock United | 21 | | 1 | | | 2 | 20 | 22 |
| Dumebi Dumaka | Grays Athletic | 17 | 4 | | 1 | 1 | 3 | 12 | 21 |
| Lewis Smith | East Thurrock United | 14 | 2 | 4 | 5 | 1 | 2 | 14 | 20 |
| Marc Charles-Smith | Harrow Borough | 19 | | | 2 | 1 | 2 | 13 | 19 |
| Brad Fortnam-Tomlinson | Grays Athletic | 15 | 3 | 1 | 1 | 2 | 3 | 13 | 19 |
| Bobby Devyne | Enfield Town | 15 | 1 | 1 | | | 3 | 16 | 17 |
| Charlie Penny | Merstham | 17 | | | 3 | 2 | 3 | 10 | 17 |
| Ashley Carew | Dulwich Hamlet | 13 | 2 | 1 | 10 | | 2 | 15 | 16 |
| Alfie Rutherford | Bognor Regis Town | 15 | | 1 | | 1 | 2 | 11 | 16 |
| Christie Finch | Leiston | 15 | | | 2 | | 2 | 11 | 15 |
| Nyren Clunis | Dulwich Hamlet | 12 | | 2 | | | 2 | 13 | 14 |
| Fabio Saraiva | Merstham | 14 | | | 2 | | 2 | 12 | 14 |
| Charlie Collins | Metropolitan Police | 10 | | 3 | 2 | | | 11 | 13 |
| Vas Karagiannis | Leatherhead | 13 | | | 1 | 2 | 2 | 6 | 13 |
| Dan Bennett | Kingstonian | 8 | 1 | 3 | | 1 | 2 | 9 | 12 |
| Pelayo Gomez-Pico | Kingstonian | 10 | | 2 | 2 | | 2 | 11 | 12 |
| Gareth Heath | Leiston | 12 | | | | | 2 | 11 | 12 |
| Keiran Hughes-Mason | Leatherhead | 10 | 1 | 1 | 1 | | 2 | 11 | 12 |
| Chris Smith | Burgess Hill Town | 10 | | 2 | | | 2 | 11 | 12 |
| Joe Turner | Metropolitan Police | 11 | | 1 | 1 | | 2 | 10 | 12 |

HT - Hat-tricks I CSG - Consecutive Scoring Games I SG - Scoring Games I PO - Play-offs

# AFC SUDBURY

**Chairman:** Philip Turner
**Secretary:** Davis Webb **(T)** 07885 327 510 **(E)** dave-afc@supanet.com
**Commercial Manager:** **(T/E)**
**Programme Editor:** Darren Theobald **(T/E)** theobaldd@hotmail.co.uk
**Ground Address:** Wardale Williams Stadium, Brundon Lane, Sudbury CO10 7HN
**(T)** 01787 376 213 **Manager:** Jamie Godbold - 12/01/15

## Club Factfile

**Founded:** 1999 **Nickname:** Yellows
**Previous Names:** Sudbury Town (1874) and Sudbury Wanderers (1958) merged in 1999
**Previous Leagues:** Eastern Counties 1999-2006, Isthmian 2006-08, Southern 2008-10.

**Club Colours (change):** Yellow/blue/yellow (All red)

**Ground Capacity:** 2,500 **Seats:** 200 **Covered:** 1,500 **Clubhouse:** Yes **Shop:** Yes

**Directions**

From Braintree: Take A131 through Halstead to Sudbury. On descending hill into Sudbury turn left at first set of traffic lights (Kings Head), and then take the first right into Brundon Lane. The road narrows before reaching ground on the right hand side.

From Colchester, Bury St Edmunds and Ipswich: Enter Sudbury and follow signs for Halstead/Chelmsford. Go aross the river bridge and go under the old rail bridge, then turn right at the traffic lights (Kings Head) into Bulmer Road and the first right again into Brundon Lane. The road narrows before reaching ground on the right hand side.

**Previous Grounds:** The Priory Stadium

**Record Attendance:** 1,800
**Record Victory:** Not known
**Record Defeat:** Not known
**Record Goalscorer:** Gary Bennett - 172
**Record Appearances:** Paul Betson - 376
**Additional Records:**

**Honours:**
Eastern Counties League 2000-01, 01-02, 02-03, 03-04, 04-05. Isthmian League Division One North 2015-16.
Suffolk Premier Cup 2002, 2003, 2004.

### 10 YEAR RECORD

| 06-07 | 07-08 | 08-09 | 09-10 | 10-11 | 11-12 | 12-13 | 13-14 | 14-15 | 15-16 |
|---|---|---|---|---|---|---|---|---|---|
| Isth1N 5 | Isth1N 2 | SthM | SthM 14 | Isth1N 7 | Isth1N 8 | Isth1N 17 | Isth1N 10 | Isth1N 3 | Isth1N 1 |

# Most Goals - For & Against

| | League | GF | GA | Total | Lg Pos | Number of Scorers |
|---|---|---|---|---|---|---|
| **East Thurrock United** | **Isthmian Premier** | **137** | **67** | **204** | **3** | **20+1og** |
| Nantwich Town | N.P.L. Premier | 118 | 72 | 190 | 8 | 15+1og |
| Skelmersdale United | N.P.L. Premier | 86 | 101 | 187 | 16 | 19+3ogs |
| Stourbridge | N.P.L. Premier | 111 | 72 | 183 | 6 | 16 |
| Whitehawk | National South | 99 | 81 | 180 | 5 | 17+1og |
| Ashton United | N.P.L. Premier | 108 | 70 | 178 | 4 | 17+3ogs |
| Stamford | N.P.L. Premier | 75 | 103 | 178 | 21 | 22+3ogs |
| **Dulwich Hamlet** | **Isthmian Premier** | **108** | **69** | **177** | **5** | **19+2og** |
| Bedworth United | Southern Premier | 62 | 113 | 175 | 21 | 17+2ogs |
| Barwell | N.P.L. Premier | 96 | 77 | 173 | 9 | 20 |
| **Bognor Regis Town** | **Isthmian Premier** | **117** | **56** | **173** | **2** | **18+2og** |
| Histon | Southern Premier | 65 | 107 | 172 | 22 | 17+1og |
| AFC Fylde | National North | 105 | 66 | 171 | 3 | 18+1og |
| Buxton | N.P.L. Premier | 88 | 83 | 171 | 11 | 18+1ig |
| FC Halifax Town | National Premier | 75 | 96 | 171 | 21 | 15+2ogs |
| Chesham United | Southern Premier | 89 | 81 | 170 | 13 | 15+1og |
| Salford City | N.P.L. Premier | 112 | 57 | 169 | 3 | 20+2ogs |
| **Kingstonian** | **Isthmian Premier** | **91** | **77** | **168** | **7** | **20** |
| Biggleswade United | Southern Premier | 80 | 87 | 167 | 14 | 18+1og |
| **Farnborough** | **Isthmian Premier** | **71** | **95** | **166** | **18** | **24** |
| Grimsby Town | National League | 111 | 55 | 166 | 4 | 18+2og |
| **Hampton & Richmond** | **Isthmian Premier** | **110** | **56** | **166** | **1** | **16+2og** |
| Ramsbottom United | N.P.L. Premier | 48 | 118 | 166 | 24 | 24+2og |
| **Merstham** | **Isthmian Premier** | **77** | **88** | **165** | **10** | **17** |
| St Neots Town | Southern Premier | 80 | 85 | 165 | 19 | 23+2ogs |
| **Grays Athletic** | **Isthmian Premier** | **81** | **82** | **163** | **15** | **13+3og** |
| **VCD Athletic** | **Isthmian Premier** | **52** | **111** | **163** | **24** | **17+2ogs** |
| Maidenhead United | National South | 86 | 76 | 162 | 7 | 14 |
| **Canvey Island** | **Isthmian Premier** | **71** | **90** | **161** | **14** | **21+1og** |
| Oxford City | National South | 89 | 71 | 160 | 12 | 21+1og |

# BILLERICAY TOWN

**Chairman:** Steve Kent
**Secretary:** Ian Ansell (T) 07958 978 154 (E) secretary@billericaytownfc.co.uk
**Commercial Manager:** (T/E)
**Programme Editor:** Gary Clark (T/E) 07957 004 930
**Ground Address:** New Lodge, Blunts Wall Road, Billericay CM12 9SA
(T) 01277 652 188 **Manager:** Craig Edwards

## Club Factfile

**Founded:** 1880 **Nickname:** Town or Blues
**Previous Names:** None
**Previous Leagues:** Romford & District 1890-1914, Mid Essex 1918-47, South Essex Combination 1947-66, Essex Olympian 1966-71, Essex Senior 1971-77, Athenian 1977-79. Isthmian 1979-2012. Conference 2012-13.

**Club Colours (change):** Blue & white

**Ground Capacity:** 3,500 **Seats:** 424 **Covered:** 2,000 **Clubhouse:** Yes **Shop:** Yes

**Directions**
From the M25 (J29) take the A127 to the Basildon/Billericay (A176) turn-off, (junction after the Old Fortune of War r'about). Take second exit at r'about (Billericay is signposted). Then straight over (2nd exit) at the next roundabout. Continue along that road until you enter Billericay. At the first r'about take the first available exit. At the next r'about (with Billericay School on your left) go straight over (1st exit). At yet another r'about!, turn left into the one-way system. Keep in the left-hand lane and go straight over r'about. At first set of lights, turn left. Blunts Wall Road is the second turning on your right.

**Previous Grounds:** None

**Record Attendance:** 3,841 v West Ham United - Opening of Floodlights 1977
**Record Victory:** 11-0 v Stansted (A) - Essex Senior League 05/05/1976
**Record Defeat:** 3-10 v Chelmsford City (A) - Essex Senior Cup 04/01/1993
**Record Goalscorer:** Freddie Claydon - 273
**Record Appearances:** J Pullen - 418
**Additional Records:** Leon Gutzmore scored 51 goals during the 1997-98 season.
Received £22,500+ from West Ham United for Steve Jones November 1992
**Honours:**
FA Vase 1975-76, 76-77, 78-79. Essex Senior Cup 1975-76. Athenian League 1978-79. Isthmian Premier Division 2011-12.
Essex Senior Trophy x2.

## 10 YEAR RECORD

| 06-07 | 07-08 | 08-09 | 09-10 | 10-11 | 11-12 | 12-13 | 13-14 | 14-15 | 15-16 |
|---|---|---|---|---|---|---|---|---|---|
| Isth P 4 | Isth P 10 | Isth P 11 | Isth P 13 | Isth P 11 | Isth P 1 | Conf S 21 | Isth P 10 | Isth P 8 | Isth P 9 |

# BILLERICAY TOWN MATCH RESULTS 2015-16

| Date | Comp | H/A | Opponents | Att: | Result | | Goalscorers | Pos | No. |
|---|---|---|---|---|---|---|---|---|---|
| Aug 6 | IsthP | A | East Thurrock Utd | 238 | D | 1-1 | Beavon 90 | 8 | 1 |
| 11 | IsthP | H | Needham Market | 248 | D | 1-1 | Derry 30 | 11 | 2 |
| 15 | IsthP | H | Enfield Town | 343 | W | 3-0 | Derry 17 Beavon 45 Sodje 57 (pen) | 8 | 3 |
| 22 | IsthP | A | Grays Athletic | 263 | L | 0-2 | | 11 | 4 |
| 25 | IsthP | H | Merstham | 208 | D | 1-1 | Sodje 16 | 13 | 5 |
| 29 | IsthP | A | Bognor Regis Town | 312 | L | 1-3 | Derry 3 | 16 | 6 |
| 31 | IsthP | H | Canvey Island | 471 | L | 0-3 | | 18 | 7 |
| Sept 5 | IsthP | A | Dulwich Hamlet | 1547 | L | 0-1 | | 19 | 8 |
| 8 | IsthP | A | Merstham | 153 | W | 2-0 | Stamp 29 Cojocarel 74 | 19 | 9 |
| **12** | **FAC1Q** | **H** | **Enfield Town** | **333** | **D** | **1-1** | **Sodje13** | | 10 |
| **15** | **FAC1Qr** | **A** | **Enfield Town** | **309** | **L** | **0-2** | | | 11 |
| 19 | IsthP | H | Hampton & Richmond B | 261 | L | 0-1 | | 19 | 12 |
| 22 | IsthP | H | Met Police | 171 | W | 6-0 | FondopTalom 12 Nesbitt 41Akurang 57 Stephenson 71 Sodjie 85 Cojocarel 90 | 13 | 13 |
| 26 | IsthP | A | Lewes | 351 | W | 3-2 | Fondop Talom 29 61 Sodje 82 | 13 | 14 |
| 29 | IsthP | A | VCD Athletic | 105 | W | 3-2 | Fondop Talom 24 84 Nesbitt 67 | | 15 |
| Oct 3 | IsthP | H | Staines Town | 401 | L | 2-3 | Fondop Talom 22 Hazelwood 89 | 13 | 16 |
| 10 | IsthP | A | Kingstonian | 333 | D | 2-2 | Fondop Talom 38 Derry 83 | 13 | 17 |
| 13 | IsthP | H | VCD Athletic | 193 | D | 1-1 | Fondop Talom 81 | 12 | 18 |
| 17 | IsthP | H | Leatherhead | 271 | W | 2-0 | Ellul 5 Hazelwood 60 | 11 | 19 |
| 20 | IsthP | A | Met Police | 83 | L | 0-1 | | 11 | 20 |
| 24 | IsthP | H | East Thurrock United | 307 | W | 3-1 | Derry 15 18 Nesbitt 90 | | 21 |
| 27 | IsthP | A | Needham Market | 355 | W | 3-1 | NESBITT 3 ( 4 26 86 pen) | 8 | 22 |
| **31** | **FAT1Q** | **H** | **Chesham United** | **271** | **L** | **0-2** | | | 23 |
| Nov 7 | IsthP | A | Enfield Town | 309 | D | 2-2 | Nesbitt 62 Stephenson 90 | 10 | 24 |
| 14 | IsthP | H | Harrow Borough | 265 | W | 2-1 | Hubble 32 Akurang 52 | 7 | 25 |
| 21 | IsthP | A | Burgess Hill Town | 356 | D | 1-1 | Sodje 53 | 8 | 26 |
| 28 | IsthP | H | Tonbridge Angels | 375 | D | 1-1 | Monville 5 | 8 | 27 |
| Dec 6 | IsthP | A | Wingate & Finchley | 139 | W | 1-0 | Nesbitt 84 | 6 | 28 |
| 12 | IsthP | H | Hendon | 278 | W | 3-1 | Ellul 13 Nesbitt 59 Sodje 87 | 4 | 29 |
| 19 | IsthP | H | Bognor Regis Town | 281 | W | 2-0 | Ellul 11 Fondop Talom 90 | 3 | 30 |
| 26 | IsthP | A | Canvey Island | 621 | W | 2-0 | Nesbitt 45 Derry 68 | 3 | 31 |
| Jan 16 | IsthP | H | Brentwood Town | 551 | D | 1-1 | Nesbit 61 | 4 | 32 |
| 23 | IsthP | A | Harrow Borough | 161 | L | 1-2 | Cox 4 | 6 | 33 |
| Feb 2 | IsthP | H | Grays Athletic | 216 | D | 1-1 | Hubble 52 | 7 | 34 |
| 6 | IsthP | A | Staines Town | 209 | W | 1-0 | Sodje 22 | 7 | 35 |
| 10 | IsthP | H | Leiston | 164 | W | 4-1 | Cox 16 20 Derry 49 84 | 6 | 36 |
| 13 | IsthP | H | Kingstonian | 338 | D | 0-0 | | 6 | 37 |
| 15 | IsthP | A | Farnborough | 178 | W | 2-0 | Poole 21 (pen) Sodje 79 | 4 | 38 |
| Mar 5 | IsthP | A | Brentwood Town | 220 | D | 1-1 | Hubble 34 | 6 | 39 |
| 8 | IsthP | H | Lewes | 175 | D | 1-1 | Stephenson 48 | 6 | 40 |
| 12 | IsthP | H | Dulwich Hamlet | 424 | W | 4-1 | COX 3 (15 56pen 66) Poole 35 (pen) | 6 | 41 |
| 19 | IsthP | A | Hampton & Richmond B | 505 | L | 1-2 | Poole 71 (pen) | 8 | 42 |
| 26 | IsthP | H | Farnborough | 329 | L | 2-3 | Cox 61 90 | 8 | 43 |
| 28 | IsthP | A | Leiston | 201 | D | 1-1 | Derry 54 | 9 | 44 |
| Apr 2 | IsthP | H | Burgess Hill Town | 52 | D | 0-0 | | 9 | 45 |
| 6 | IsthP | A | Leatherhead | 227 | L | 1-4 | Fondop Talom 50 | 9 | 46 |
| 9 | IsthP | A | Tonbridge Angels | 512 | D | 2-2 | Cox 14 35 | 9 | 47 |
| 18 | IsthP | A | Hendon | 135 | D | 1-1 | Derry 39 | 9 | 48 |
| 23 | IsthP | H | Wingate & Finchley | 473 | W | 4-0 | DERRY 3(2 9 26) Hubble 83 | 9 | 49 |

| GOALSCORERS | Scoring Games | Consec Sco Games | Total |
|---|---|---|---|
| *2014-15 Sappleton* | | | *17* |
| Derry | 10 | 2 | 14 |
| Nesbitt | 9 | 2 | 11 |
| Cox | 5 | | 10 |
| Fondop Talom | 8 | 6 | 10 |
| Sodje | 7 | 2 | 9 |
| Hubble | 4 | | 4 |
| Ellul | 3 | | 3 |
| Poole | 3 | | 3 |
| Stephenson | 3 | | 3 |

| | Scoring Games | Consec Sco Games | Total |
|---|---|---|---|
| Akurang | 2 | | 2 |
| Beavon | 2 | | 2 |
| Cojocarel | 2 | | 2 |
| Hazelwood | 2 | | 2 |
| Monville | 1 | | 1 |
| Stamp | 1 | | 1 |

# BOGNOR REGIS TOWN

**Chairman:** Dominic Reynolds
**Secretary:** Simon Cook (T) 07527 455 167 (E) sajcook2@aol.com
**Commercial Manager:** (T/E)
**Programme Editor:** Rob Garforth (T/E) 07791 591 375
**Ground Address:** Nyewood Lane, Bognor Regis PO21 2TY
(T) 01243 822 325 **Manager:** Jamie Howell

## Club Factfile

**Founded:** 1883 **Nickname:** The Rocks
**Previous Names:** None
**Previous Leagues:** West Sussex 1896-1926, Brighton & Hove District 1926-27, Sussex County 1927-72, Southern League 1972-81, Isthmian 1982-2004, Conference 2004-09

**Club Colours (change):** White & green (Yellow & black)

**Ground Capacity:** 4,100 **Seats:** 350 **Covered:** 2,600 **Clubhouse:** Yes **Shop:** Yes

**Directions**
West along sea front from pier past Aldwick shopping centre then turn right into Nyewood Lane.

**Previous Grounds:** None

**Record Attendance:** 3,642 v Swnsea City - FA Cup 1st Round replay 1984
**Record Victory:** 24-0 v Littlehampton - West Sussex League 1913-14
**Record Defeat:** 0-19 v Shoreham - West Sussex League 1906-07
**Record Goalscorer:** Kevin Clements - 206. On 16/12/14 Jason Prior scored his 100th goal for the club making it the fastest century of goals.
**Record Appearances:** Mick Pullen - 967 (20 seasons)
**Additional Records:** Paid £2,000 for Guy Rutherford 1995-96. Received £10,500 from Brighton & Hove for John Crumplin and Geoff Cooper, and from Crystal Palace for Simon Rodger.
**Honours:**
Sussex Professional Cup 1973-74. Sussex Senior Cup x9.
Isthmian League Division 1 South Play-offs 2011-12.

### 10 YEAR RECORD

| 06-07 | 07-08 | 08-09 | 09-10 | 10-11 | 11-12 | 12-13 | 13-14 | 14-15 | 15-16 |
|---|---|---|---|---|---|---|---|---|---|
| Conf S 12 | Conf S 18 | Conf S 21 | Isth P 22 | Isth1S 2 | Isth1S 2 | Isth P 14 | Isth P 3 | Isth P 14 | Isth P 2 |

# BOGNOR REGIS TOWN MATCH RESULTS 2015-16

| Date | Comp | H/A | Opponents | Att: | Result | | Goalscorers | Pos | No. |
|---|---|---|---|---|---|---|---|---|---|
| Aug 8 | IsthP | H | Merstham | 420 | W | 4-3 | PRIOR 3 (4 34 68) Charman 49 | 3 | 1 |
| 11 | IsthP | A | Staines Town | 313 | W | 1-0 | Crane 54 | 3 | 2 |
| 15 | IsthP | A | Canvey Island | 312 | D | 1-1 | Prior 90 | 3 | 3 |
| 22 | IsthP | H | Tonbridge Angels | 360 | L | 0-5 | | 9 | 4 |
| 25 | IsthP | A | Met Police | 129 | L | 0-1 | | 10 | 5 |
| 29 | IsthP | H | Billericay Town | 312 | W | 3-1 | Green 19 Ellul 23 (og) Prior 55 | 6 | 6 |
| 31 | IsthP | A | Lewes | 568 | W | 2-0 | Prior 11 21 | 5 | 7 |
| Sept 5 | IsthP | H | Enfield | 444 | D | 1-1 | Pearce 88 | 6 | 8 |
| 8 | IsthP | H | Met Police | 301 | W | 2-1 | Prior 47 (pen) Rutherford 68 | 6 | 9 |
| 12 | FAC1Q | H | Merstham | 299 | W | 2-1 | Robson 68 Charman 89 | | 10 |
| 19 | IsthP | A | Grays Athletic | 207 | W | 2-0 | Prior 45 (pen) Rutherford 74 | 5 | 11 |
| 22 | Isth P | H | Kingstonian | 351 | D | 0-0 | | 4 | 12 |
| 26 | FAC2Q | H | Lowestoft Town | 396 | W | 2-1 | Beck 76 Pearce 83 | | 13 |
| 28 | IsthP | A | Farmborough | 255 | L | 1-2 | Nilsen 47 | 4 | 14 |
| Oct 3 | IsthP | H | Harrow Borough | 372 | W | 1-0 | El-Abd 48 | 6 | 15 |
| 10 | FAC3Q | H | Oxford City | 515 | W | 4-2 | Prior 41 (pen) 85 Parsons 72 75 | | 16 |
| 13 | IsthP | H | Farnborough | 323 | W | 4-1 | Rutherford 10 62 Nilsen 28 Parsons 84 | 5 | 17 |
| 17 | IsthP | H | East Thurrock United | 364 | D | 2-2 | Rutherford 19 82 | 4 | 18 |
| 24 | FAC4Q | A | Wealdstone | 847 | L | 1-2 | Field 89 | | 19 |
| 27 | IsthP | H | Staines Town | 340 | W | 3-0 | Prior 43 51 Tuck 66 | 6 | 20 |
| 31 | FAT1Q | A | East Grinstead Town | 249 | W | 3-0 | El Abd 14 White 31 Prior 64 | | 21 |
| Nov 7 | IsthP | H | Canvey Island | 335 | W | 5-0 | PRIOR 3 ( 8 29 57) Kandi 23 31 | 3 | 22 |
| 14 | FAT2Q | A | Taunton Town | 351 | W | 4-1 | Pearce 22 Kandi 23 Prior 75 Rutherford 78 | | 23 |
| 17 | IsthP | A | Brentwood Town | 88 | W | 1-0 | Pearce 84 | 2 | 24 |
| 21 | IsthP | H | Dulwich Hamlet | 770 | L | 2-3 | White 32 Nilsen 77 | 2 | 25 |
| 24 | IsthP | A | Merstham | 153 | L | 2-3 | Prior 10 Kandi 43 | 3 | 26 |
| 28 | FAT3Q | H | Bath City | 362 | W | 1-0 | Prior 90 (pen) | | 27 |
| Dec 5 | IsthP | A | Hendon | 144 | D | 1-1 | El-Abd 79 | 7 | 28 |
| 12 | FAT1 | A | Maidstone Utd | 892 | W | 1-0 | Kandi 17 | | 29 |
| 15 | IsthP | A | Hampton & Richmond B | 202 | L | 1-2 | Robson 69 | 8 | 30 |
| 19 | IsthP | A | Bllericay Town | 261 | L | 0-2 | | 8 | 31 |
| 26 | IsthP | H | Lewes | 705 | W | 4-0 | PRIOR 3 (13 16 61) Pearce 90 | 8 | 32 |
| Jan 9 | IsthP | H | Needham Market | 492 | W | 2-1 | Kandi 4 85 | 7 | 33 |
| 16 | IsthP | H | VCD Athletic | 477 | W | 2-0 | Prior 4 50 | 6 | 34 |
| 19 | FAT2 | H | Altrincham | 520 | W | 2-1 | Robson 75 Crane 83 | | 35 |
| 23 | IsthP | A | Wingate & Finchley | 130 | W | 3-1 | Robson 38 78 Prior 79 (pen) | 4 | 36 |
| 30 | IsthP | H | Hampton & Richmond B | 620 | W | 1-0 | Rutherford 74 | 4 | 37 |
| Feb 2 | IsthP | H | Leiston | 372 | W | 3-0 | Rutherford 19 Nilsen 38 Prior 90 | 4 | 38 |
| 6 | FAT3 | A | Sutton United | 1258 | D | 0-0 | | | 39 |
| 9 | FAT3r | H | Sutton United | 941 | W | 2-1 | Prior 18 Beckwith 104 (og) (aet) | | 40 |
| 20 | IsthP | A | East Thurrock United | 320 | D | 0-0 | | 6 | 41 |
| 23 | IsthP | A | Tonbridge Angels | 377 | W | 3-1 | Prior 26 29 Rutherford 5 | 5 | 42 |
| Mar 5 | IsthP | A | VCD Athletic | 135 | D | 1-1 | Prior 17 | 5 | 43 |
| 12 | FAT SF1 | H | Grimsby Town | 2620 | L | 0-1 | | | 44 |
| 16 | IsthP | A | Leatherhead | 265 | W | 3-0 | Charman 14 Pearce 49 69 | 6 | 45 |
| 19 | FAT SF2 | A | Grimsby Town | 2477 | L | 1-2 | Beck 31 | | 46 |
| 22 | IsthP | A | Harrow Borough | 169 | W | 2-1 | Crane 4 Robson 45 | 5 | 47 |
| 24 | IsthP | H | Grays Athletic | 451 | W | 3-0 | RUTHERFORD 3 (31 33 62) | 4 | 48 |
| 26 | IsthP | A | Needham Market | 310 | W | 1-0 | Crane 76 | 4 | 49 |
| 28 | IsthP | H | Burgess Hill Town | 702 | W | 2-1 | Prior 25 86 (pen) | 4 | 50 |
| 31 | IsthP | A | Enfield Town | 406 | L | 1-2 | Prior 26 | 4 | 51 |
| Apr 2 | IsthP | A | Dulwich Hamlet | 1914 | L | 0-2 | | 4 | 52 |
| 4 | IsthP | A | Kingstonian | 447 | L | 1-2 | Pearce 34 | 4 | 53 |
| 6 | IsthP | A | Burgess Hill Town | 510 | W | 4-0 | Prior 19 (pen) 24 Wollers 31 Crane 55 | 4 | 54 |
| 9 | IsthP | H | Leatherhead | 421 | W | 5-0 | El-Abd 30 Green 38 Crane 53 Pearce 56 84 | 3 | 55 |
| 13 | IsthP | H | Wingate & Finchley | 391 | W | 6-0 | Rutherford 10 57 PRIOR 3 (29 53 83) Green 85 | 3 | 56 |
| 16 | IsthP | A | Leiston | 285 | W | 2-0 | Tighe 49 Rutherford 51 | 3 | 57 |
| 19 | IsthP | H | Brentwood Town | 407 | W | 3-1 | Prior 13 Tighe 47 Nilsen 90 | 2 | 58 |
| 23 | IsthP | H | Hendon | 510 | W | 4-0 | Prior 3 40 Rutherford 25 Tighe 89 | 2 | 59 |
| 28 | PO SF | H | Dulwich Hamlet | 1403 | L | 0-1 | | | 60 |

| GOALSCORERS | Scoring Games | Consec Sco Games | Total |
|---|---|---|---|
| *2014-15 Pearce* | | | *17* |
| Prior | 26 | 4 | 42 |
| Rutherford | 12 | 2 | 17 |
| Pearce | 8 | 2 | 10 |
| Kamdi | 5 | 2 | 7 |
| Robson | 5 | 2 | 6 |
| Crane | 6 | | 5 |
| Nilsen | 5 | | 5 |
| El Abd | 4 | | 4 |
| Charman | 3 | | 3 |

| | Scoring Games | Consec Sco Games | Total |
|---|---|---|---|
| Green | 3 | | 3 |
| Parsons | 2 | 2 | 3 |
| Tighe | 3 | | 3 |
| Beck | 2 | | 2 |
| White | 2 | | 2 |
| Field | 1 | | 1 |
| Prior | 1 | | 1 |
| Tuck | 1 | | 1 |
| Wollers | 1 | | 1 |
| Opponents | 2 | | 2 |

# BURGESS HILL TOWN

**Chairman:** Kevin Newell
**Secretary:** Tim Spencer (T) 07812 642 498 (E) timspencer57@hotmail.com
**Commercial Manager:** (T/E)
**Programme Editor:** John Rattle (T/E) john.rattle@hotmail.co.uk
**Ground Address:** Leylands Park, Maple Drive, Burgess Hill, West Sussex RH15 8DL
(T) 01444 254 832 **Manager:** Ian Chapman

## Club Factfile

**Founded:** 1882 **Nickname:** Hillians
**Previous Names:** None
**Previous Leagues:** Mid Sussex, Sussex County > 2003, Southern 2003-04

**Club Colours (change):** Green & black stripes (Yellow with blue trim)

**Ground Capacity:** 2,250 **Seats:** 307 **Covered:** Yes **Clubhouse:** Yes **Shop:** Yes

**Directions**
Turn east from A273 London Road into Leylands Road,
take 4th left sign posted Leyland Park.
Nearest station is Wivelsfield.

**Previous Grounds:** None

**Record Attendance:** 2,005 v AFC Wimbledon - Isthmian League Division 1 2004-05
**Record Victory:** Not known
**Record Defeat:** Not known
**Record Goalscorer:** Ashley Carr - 208
**Record Appearances:** Paul Williams - 499
**Additional Records:**

**Honours:**
Sussex County League x6 (Most recently 2001-02, 02-03). Isthmian Division One South 2014-15.
Sussex Senior Cup 1883-84, 84-85, 85-86.

### 10 YEAR RECORD

| 06-07 | 07-08 | 08-09 | 09-10 | 10-11 | 11-12 | 12-13 | 13-14 | 14-15 | 15-16 |
|---|---|---|---|---|---|---|---|---|---|
| Isth1S 14 | Isth1S 12 | Isth1S 19 | Isth1S 7 | Isth1S 7 | Isth1S 20 | Isth1S 8 | Isth1S 6 | Isth1S 1 | Isth P 21 |

# BURGESS HILL TOWN MATCH RESULTS 2015-16

| Date | Comp | H/A | Opponents | Att: | Result | | Goalscorers | Pos | No. |
|---|---|---|---|---|---|---|---|---|---|
| Aug 8 | IsthP | A | Needham Market | 313 | W | 2-1 | Keehan 31 (pen) P. Harding 47 | 4 | 1 |
| 11 | IsthP | H | VCD Athletic | 373 | W | 2-0 | L. Harding 44 Klrkwood 90 | 3 | 2 |
| 15 | IsthP | H | Grays Athletic | 458 | L | 1-2 | Smith 89 | 6 | 3 |
| 22 | IsthP | A | Enfield Town | 329 | L | 0-1 | | 10 | 4 |
| 26 | IsthP | H | Harrow Borough | 289 | L | 0-5 | | 13 | 5 |
| 29 | IsthP | A | Merstham | 162 | W | 2-1 | Kirkwood 6 P.Harding 8 | 9 | 6 |
| 31 | IsthP | H | Farnborough | 369 | W | 3-1 | L.Harding 17 Smith 69 Pearse 88 | 8 | 7 |
| Sept 6 | IsthP | A | Hampton & Richmond B | 382 | D | 1-1 | Smith 46 | 8 | 8 |
| 8 | IsthP | A | Harrow Borough | 161 | L | 0-1 | | 10 | 9 |
| **12** | **FAC1Q** | **A** | **Horsham YMCA** | **140** | **L** | **1-2** | **Perry 80** | | 10 |
| 19 | IsthP | H | Dulwich Hamlet | 507 | W | 3-2 | P Harding 30 Pearse 37 Pearson 85 | 8 | 11 |
| 23 | IsthP | H | Lewes | 638 | W | 2-1 | Saunders 32 35 | 7 | 12 |
| 26 | IsthP | A | Needham Market | 334 | D | 2-2 | Keehan 28 Perry 79 | 7 | 13 |
| 29 | IsthP | A | Staines Town | 175 | D | 2-2 | P.Harding 14 Johnson 80 | 7 | 14 |
| Oct 3 | IsthP | H | Wingate & Finchley | 357 | L | 0-1 | | 10 | 15 |
| 10 | IsthP | A | Leatherhead | 283 | L | 2-3 | Fisk 53 Smith 63 | 11 | 16 |
| 14 | IsthP | H | Staines Town | 337 | L | 0-2 | | 12 | 17 |
| 17 | IsthP | H | Metropolitan Police | 306 | W | 4-2 | P.Harding 23 Keehan 26 62 Smith 72 | 10 | 18 |
| 21 | IsthP | A | Lewes | 449 | W | 2-1 | Smith 11 L.Harding 76 | 9 | 19 |
| 27 | IsthP | A | VCD Athletic | 105 | D | 2-2 | Budd 45 Keehan 53 (pen) | | 20 |
| **31** | **FAT1Q** | **A** | **Hitchin Town** | **190** | **L** | **2-3** | **Smith 25 65** | | 21 |
| Nov 7 | IsthP | A | Grays Athletic | 148 | L | 0-2 | | 12 | 22 |
| 21 | IsthP | H | Billericay Town | 356 | D | 1-1 | Smith 50 | 12 | 23 |
| 28 | IsthP | A | Hendon | 117 | L | 0-1 | | 15 | 24 |
| Dec 6 | IsthP | A | Tonbridge Angels | 457 | W | 3-2 | Gargan 2 Fisk 75 Smith 78 | 14 | 25 |
| 12 | IsthP | H | Canvey Island | 357 | W | 3-2 | Keehan 27 (pen) 67 Smith 49 | 10 | 26 |
| 19 | IsthP | H | Merstham | 305 | W | 5-1 | GARGAN 4 ( 3 38 63 82) Keehan 34 (pen) | 9 | 27 |
| 26 | IsthP | A | Farnborough | 302 | L | 0-1 | | 12 | 28 |
| Jan 9 | IsthP | A | Leiston | 178 | D | 1-1 | P.Harding 84 | 15 | 29 |
| 16 | IsthP | H | Kingstonian | 369 | L | 1-3 | Fisk 23 | 15 | 30 |
| 19 | IsthP | A | East Thurrock United | 143 | L | 0-1 | | 15 | 31 |
| 23 | IsthP | A | Brentwood Town | 154 | D | 1-1 | Keehan 88 | 14 | 32 |
| 30 | IsthP | H | East Thurrock United | 412 | L | 0-2 | | 14 | 33 |
| Feb 3 | IsthP | H | Enfield Town | 302 | W | 1-0 | Kirkwood 11 | 13 | 34 |
| 6 | IsthP | A | Wingate & Finchley | 131 | L | 1-5 | Miles 90 | 13 | 35 |
| 20 | IsthP | A | Met Police | 116 | D | 1-1 | Smith 64 | 15 | 36 |
| 27 | IsthP | H | Brentwood Town | 506 | D | 1-1 | Fraser 66 | 15 | 37 |
| Mar 6 | IsthP | A | Kingstonian | 268 | L | 0-1 | | 15 | 38 |
| 12 | IsthP | H | Hampton & Richmond B | 412 | L | 1-2 | Keehan 23 | 17 | 39 |
| 19 | IsthP | A | Dulwich Hamlet | 1452 | D | 1-1 | Keehan 30 | 17 | 40 |
| 23 | IsthP | H | Leatherhead | 283 | L | 1-2 | Pearse 47 (pen) | 17 | 41 |
| 26 | IsthP | H | Leiston | 320 | D | 1-1 | L.Harding 20 | 17 | 42 |
| 28 | IsthP | A | Bognor RegisTown | 702 | L | 1-2 | L.Harding 73 | 17 | 43 |
| Apr 2 | IsthP | A | Billericay Town | 252 | D | 0-0 | | 18 | 44 |
| 6 | IsthP | H | Bognor Regis Town | 510 | L | 0-4 | | 18 | 45 |
| 16 | IsthP | A | Canvey Island | 216 | D | 3-3 | Doherty 35 P.Harding 39 Gayler 42 | 18 | 46 |
| 20 | IsthP | H | Hendon | 305 | L | 0-1 | | 18 | 47 |
| 23 | IsthP | H | Tonbridge Angels | 576 | D | 0-0 | | 21 | 48 |

| GOALSCORERS | Scoring Games | Consec Sco Games | Total | | Scoring Games | Consec Sco Games | Total |
|---|---|---|---|---|---|---|---|
| Smith | 11 | 2 | 12 | Budd | 1 | | 1 |
| Keehan | 10 | 2 | 11 | Doherty | 1 | | 1 |
| P.Harding | 7 | | 7 | Fraser | 1 | | 1 |
| Gargan | 2 | | 5 | Gaylor | 1 | | 1 |
| L.Harding | 5 | 2 | 5 | Johnson | 1 | | 1 |
| Fisk | 3 | | 3 | Miles | 1 | | 1 |
| Kirkwood | 3 | | 3 | Pearson | 1 | | 1 |
| Pearce | 3 | | 3 | | | | |
| Perry | 2 | | 2 | | | | |
| Saunders | 1 | | 2 | | | | |

# CANVEY ISLAND

**Chairman:** John Batch
**Secretary:** Gary Sutton **(T)** 07790 025 828 **(E)** g.sutton@sky.com
**Commercial Manager:** **(T/E)**
**Programme Editor:** Glen Eckett **(T/E)** gleneckett@gmail.com
**Ground Address:** The Frost Financial Stadium, Park Lane, Canvey Island, Essex SS8 7PX
**(T)** 01268 682 991 **Manager:** Danny Heale

## Club Factfile

**Founded:** 1926 **Nickname:** The Gulls
**Previous Names:** None
**Previous Leagues:** Southend & District, Thurrock & Thames Combination, Parthenon, Metropolitan, Greater London 1964-71, Essex Senior 1971-95, Isthmian 1995-2004, Conference 2004-06
**Club Colours (change):** Yellow and sky blue/sky blue/yellow (White with sky blue trim/white with sky blue trim/sky blue)

**Ground Capacity:** 4,100 **Seats:** 500 **Covered:** 827 **Clubhouse:** Yes **Shop:** Yes

**Directions**
A130 from A13 or A127 at Sadlers Farm roundabout.
One mile through Town Centre, first right past old bus garage.

**Previous Grounds:** None

**Record Attendance:** 3,553 v Aldershot Town - Isthmian League 2002-03
**Record Victory:** Not Known
**Record Defeat:** Not Known
**Record Goalscorer:** Andy Jones
**Record Appearances:** Steve Ward
**Additional Records:** Paid £5,000 to Northwich Victoria for Chris Duffy
Received £4,500 from Farnborough Town for Brian Horne
**Honours:**
Isthmian Division 1 1993-94, Premier Division 2003-04.
FA Trophy 2000-01. Essex Senior Cup 1998-99, 2000-01, 2001-02.

**10 YEAR RECORD**

| 06-07 | | 07-08 | | 08-09 | | 09-10 | | 10-11 | | 11-12 | | 12-13 | | 13-14 | | 14-15 | | 15-16 | |
|---|---|---|---|---|---|---|---|---|---|---|---|---|---|---|---|---|---|---|---|
| Isth1N | 6 | Isth1N | 5 | Isth P | 12 | Isth P | 16 | Isth P | 6 | Isth P | 8 | Isth P | 8 | Isth P | 13 | Isth P | 17 | Isth P | 14 |

# CANVEY ISLAND MATCH RESULTS 2015-16

| Date | Comp | H/A | Opponents | Att: | Result | Goalscorers | Pos | No. |
|---|---|---|---|---|---|---|---|---|
| Aug 8 | IsthP | A | Dulwich Hamlet | 877 | L 0-3 | | 23 | 1 |
| 11 | IsthP | H | Leiston | 247 | D 1-1 | Tuohy 84 | 17 | 2 |
| 15 | IsthP | H | Bognor Regis Town | 312 | D 1-1 | Tuohy 45 | 19 | 3 |
| 22 | IsthP | A | Leatherhead | 302 | D 4-4 | Curran 7 Tuohy 62 Agyakwa 83 Easterford 90 | 18 | 4 |
| 26 | IsthP | A | Grays Athletic | 289 | L 0-2 | | 19 | 5 |
| 29 | IsthP | H | Enfield Town | 326 | W 2-0 | Tuohy 6 18 | 18 | 6 |
| 31 | IsthP | A | Billericay Town | 471 | W 3-0 | Adeniji 13 Curran 18 90 | 12 | 7 |
| Sept 5 | IsthP | H | Hendon | 300 | W 3-2 | Tuohy 37 Halle 40 Chatting 71 | 10 | 8 |
| 8 | IsthP | H | Grays Athletic | 330 | L 0-3 | | 11 | 9 |
| **12** | **FAC1Q** | **A** | **Ipswich Wanderers** | **208** | **L 0-1** | | | 10 |
| 20 | IsthP | A | Kingstonian | 302 | L 1-2 | Tuohy 43 | 15 | 11 |
| 22 | IsthP | H | VCD Athletic | 192 | W 2-1 | Tuohy 26 60 | 11 | 12 |
| 26 | IsthP | A | Farnborough | 223 | W 6-2 | EYONG 3 (35 57 70) Halle 55 Tuohy 87 Lawson89 | 10 | 13 |
| 29 | IsthP | A | Wingate & Finchley | 119 | W 2-1 | Halle 70 Tuohy 89 | 5 | 14 |
| Oct 3 | IsthP | H | Brentwood Town | 310 | W 1-0 | Eyong 67 | 5 | 15 |
| 13 | IsthP | H | Wingate & Finchley | 250 | W 2-1 | Tuohy 27 70 | 3 | 16 |
| 17 | IsthP | H | Harrow Borough | 333 | W 1-0 | Halle 83 | 3 | 17 |
| 20 | IsthP | A | VCD Athletic | 106 | W 1-0 | Gordon 52 | 1 | 18 |
| 24 | IsthP | H | Dulwich Hamlet | 471 | L 1-2 | Poole 51 | 2 | 19 |
| 28 | IsthP | A | Leiston | 225 | D 1-1 | Poole 31 | | 20 |
| **31** | **FAT1Q** | **A** | **Needham Market** | **191** | **W 2-0** | **Stokes 15 Gilchrist 54** | | 21 |
| Nov 7 | IsthP | A | Bognor Regis Town | 335 | L 0-5 | | 5 | 22 |
| **14** | **FAT2Q** | **H** | **Metropolitan Police** | **187** | **L 0-2** | | | 23 |
| 21 | Isth P | A | Merstham | 165 | L 0-1 | | | 24 |
| 28 | Isth P | H | Leatherhead | 202 | W 3-1 | Chatting 9 Sheehan 17 Stokes 62 | 6 | 25 |
| Dec 5 | Isth P | H | Staines Town | 230 | L 2-3 | Sykes 74 Curran 79 | 9 | 26 |
| 12 | Isth P | A | Burgess Hill Town | 357 | L 2-3 | Chatting 19 Tuohy 90 | 9 | 27 |
| 19 | Isth P | A | Enfield Town | 386 | L 1-2 | Tuohy 27 | 12 | 28 |
| 26 | Isth P | H | Billericay Town | 621 | L 0-2 | | 13 | 29 |
| Jan 2 | Isth P | A | Neadham Market | 275 | W 3-2 | Tuohy 33 Miller-Rodney 70 Yiga 77 | 11 | 30 |
| 5 | Isth P | H | Metropolitan Police | 202 | L 0-3 | | 11 | 31 |
| 9 | Isth P | H | Tonbridge Angels | 361 | D 1-1 | Jones-Lewis 20 | 11 | 32 |
| 16 | Isth P | H | Hampton & Richmond B | 298 | L 0-4 | | 12 | 33 |
| 23 | Isth P | A | Lewes | 401 | L 1-3 | Dumas 44 | 13 | 34 |
| 26 | Isth P | H | East Thurrock United | 215 | L 0-4 | | 12 | 35 |
| 30 | Isth P | H | Farnborough | 221 | W 1-0 | Tuohy 80 | 12 | 36 |
| Feb 6 | Isth P | A | Brentwood Town | 148 | D 3-3 | Stokes 18 Gordon 34 (og) Sheehan 44 | 12 | 37 |
| 13 | Isth P | H | East Thurrock United | 308 | L 2-4 | Stokes 13 Tuohy 16 | 14 | 38 |
| 20 | Isth P | A | Harrow Borough | 136 | W 2-1 | Sheehan 9 Yiga 36 | 14 | 39 |
| 27 | Isth P | H | Lewes | 311 | W 5-2 | Halle 6 Curran 49 Tuohy 64 90 Akurang 87 | 11 | 40 |
| Mar 5 | Isth P | A | Hampton & Richmond B | 414 | L 0-5 | | 12 | 41 |
| 12 | Isth P | A | Hendon | 121 | D 2-2 | Akurang 45 80 | 11 | 42 |
| 19 | Isth P | H | Kingstonian | 259 | W 2-1 | Akurang 57 Johnson 61 | 11 | 43 |
| 26 | Isth P | A | Tonbridge Angels | 659 | L 0-2 | | 14 | 44 |
| Apr 2 | Isth P | H | Merstham | 221 | L 0-2 | | 15 | 45 |
| 5 | Isth P | H | Needham Market | 201 | L 1-2 | Tuohy 78 | 15 | 46 |
| 9 | Isth P | A | Met Police | 116 | W 1-0 | Charring 32 | 12 | 47 |
| 16 | Isth P | H | Burgess Hill Town | 216 | D 3-3 | Akurang 53 (pen) Tuohy 78 Chatting 80 | 13 | 48 |
| 23 | Isth P | A | Staines Town | 257 | D 2-2 | Tuohy 63 74 | 14 | 49 |

| GOALSCORERS | Scoring Games | Consec Sco Games | Total |
|---|---|---|---|
| *2014-15 Sands* | | | *11* |
| Tuohy | 19 | 3 | 24 |
| Akurang | 5 | 2 | 5 |
| Chatting | 5 | | 5 |
| Curran | 4 | | 5 |
| Halle | 5 | | 5 |
| Eyong | 4 | | 4 |
| Stokes | 3 | | 4 |
| Sheehan | 3 | | 3 |
| Poole | 2 | 2 | 2 |
| Yiga | 2 | | 2 |
| Adeniji | 1 | | 1 |
| Agyakwa | 1 | | 1 |

| | Scoring Games | Consec Sco Games | Total |
|---|---|---|---|
| Dumas | 1 | | 1 |
| Easterford | 1 | | 1 |
| Gilchrist | 1 | | 1 |
| Gordon | 1 | | 1 |
| Johnson | 1 | | 1 |
| Jones-Lewis | 1 | | 1 |
| Lawson | 1 | | 1 |
| Miller-Rodney | 1 | | 1 |
| Sykes | 1 | | 1 |
| Opponents | | | 1 |

# DULWICH HAMLET

**Chairman:** Liam Hickey
**Secretary:** Martin Eede **(T)** 07957 395 948 **(E)** eede.martin@gmail.com
**Commercial Manager:** **(T/E)**
**Programme Editor:** John Lawrence **(T/E)** John_lawrence@hotmail.co.uk
**Ground Address:** Champion Hill Stadium, Dog Kennell Hill, Edgar Kail Way SE22 8BD
**(T)** 0207 274 8707 **Manager:** Gavin Rose

2016-17 squad

## Club Factfile

**Founded:** 1893 **Nickname:** Hamlet
**Previous Names:** None
**Previous Leagues:** Camberwell 1894-97, Southern Suburban 1897-1900, 01-07, Dulwich 1900-01, Spartan 1907-08

**Club Colours (change):** Navy blue and pink/navy blue/navy blue (Red, white & black hoops/red/red)

**Ground Capacity:** 3,000 **Seats:** 500 **Covered:** 1,000 **Clubhouse:** Yes **Shop:** Yes

**Directions**
East Dulwich station, 200 yards.
Denmark Hill station, 10 minutes walk.
Herne Hill station then bus 37 stops near ground.
Buses 40 & 176 from Elephant & Castle, 185 from Victoria.

**Previous Grounds:** Woodwarde Rd 1893-95,College Farm 95-96,Sunray Ave 1896-02,Freeman's Gd,Champ Hill 02-12,Champ Hill (old grd)12-92

**Record Attendance:** 1,835 v Southport - FA Cup 1998-99
**Record Victory:** 13-0 v Walton-on-Thames, Surrey Senior Cup, 1936-37
**Record Defeat:** 1-10 v Hendon, Isthmian league, 1963-64
**Record Goalscorer:** Edgar Kail - 427 (1919-33)
**Record Appearances:** Reg Merritt - 576 (1950-66)
**Additional Records:** Received £35,000 from Charlton Athletic for Chris Dickson 2007

**Honours:**
FA Amateur Cup 1919-20, 31-32, 33-34, 36-37.
Isthmian League Premier Division x4, Division One 1977-78, Division One South 2012-13. London Senior Cup x5. Surrey Senior Cup x16.
London Challenge Cup 1998-99.

## 10 YEAR RECORD

| 06-07 | 07-08 | 08-09 | 09-10 | 10-11 | 11-12 | 12-13 | 13-14 | 14-15 | 15-16 |
|---|---|---|---|---|---|---|---|---|---|
| Isth1S 8 | Isth1S 6 | Isth1S 12 | Isth1S 12 | Isth1S 5 | Isth1S 3 | Isth1S 1 | Isth P 6 | Isth P 4 | Isth P 5 |

# DULWICH HAMLET MATCH RESULTS 2015-16

| Date | Comp | H/A | Opponents | Att: | Result | | Goalscorers | Pos | No. |
|---|---|---|---|---|---|---|---|---|---|
| Aug 8 | IsthP | H | Canvey Island | 877 | W | 3-0 | Pinnock 3 Scannell 40 90 | 1 | 1 |
| 11 | IsthP | A | Merstham | 321 | W | 2-0 | Willock 15 Scannell 90 | 1 | 2 |
| 15 | IsthP | A | Hendon | 268 | D | 1-1 | Carew 88 (pen) | 1 | 3 |
| 22 | IsthP | H | Staines Town | 1024 | L | 1-2 | Pinnock 45 | | 4 |
| 26 | IsthP | A | Leatherhead | 341 | L | 0-1 | | 8 | 5 |
| 29 | IsthP | H | Grays Athletic | 999 | D | 1-1 | Carew 19 | 10 | 6 |
| 31 | IsthP | A | Kingstonian | 442 | W | 3-0 | Erskine 9 68 Pinnock 70 | 9 | 7 |
| Sept 5 | IsthP | H | Billericay Town | 1547 | W | 1-0 | Murrell-Williamson 90 | 5 | 8 |
| 8 | IsthP | H | Leatherhead | 625 | W | 1-0 | Murrell-Wiliamson 31 | 5 | 9 |
| **12** | **FAC1Q** | **H** | **Hampton & Richmond B** | **404** | **W** | **1-0** | **Carew 88 (pen)** | | 10 |
| 19 | IsthP | A | Burgess Hill Town | 507 | L | 2-3 | Carew 36 Waldren 45 | 7 | 11 |
| 22 | IsthP | H | Hampton & Richmond B | 555 | D | 3-3 | Scannell 33 James 35 Willock 77 | 8 | 12 |
| **26** | **FAC2Q** | **A** | **Whitehawk** | **355** | **L** | **2-4** | **James 14 Carew 75 (pen)** | | 13 |
| 29 | IsthP | A | Met Police | 136 | W | 3-1 | Erskine 24 Carew 38 74 (pen) | 3 | 14 |
| Oct 3 | IsthP | H | VCD Athletic | 1961 | W | 5-2 | Erskine 3 31 Nelson 34 Murrell-Williamson 74 Fernandes 80 | | 15 |
| 10 | IsthP | A | Farnborough | 456 | W | 4-1 | Scannell 12 Waldren 28 Carew 51 (pen) Sweeney 89 | 2 | 16 |
| 13 | IsthP | H | Met Police | 726 | L | 1-2 | Sweeney 38 | 2 | 17 |
| 17 | IsthP | H | Brentwood Town | 1302 | W | 4-0 | Waldren 42 52 Willock 66 Sweeney 72 | 2 | 18 |
| 20 | IsthP | A | Hampton & Richmond B | 442 | L | 1-2 | Sweeney 30 | 4 | 19 |
| 24 | IsthP | A | Canvey Island | 471 | W | 2-1 | Sweeney 25 Erskine 37 | 1 | 20 |
| 27 | IsthP | H | Merstham | 869 | W | 4-0 | Murrell-Williamson 15 Willock 27 Clunis 45 Sweeney 50 | 1 | 21 |
| **31** | **FAT1Q** | | **Harrow Borough** | **165** | **W** | **3-0** | **Clunis 14 Scannell 56 (pen) McDonald 90** | | 22 |
| Nov 7 | IsthP | H | Hendon | 1423 | W | 4-2 | Pinnock 4 Clunis 36 Carew 56 (pen) McDonald 85 | 1 | 23 |
| **14** | **FAT2Q** | **H** | **VCD Athletic** | **795** | **W** | **2-0** | **McDonald 37 Nelson 85** | | 24 |
| 21 | IsthP | A | Bognor Regis Town | 770 | W | 3-2 | Clunis 38 Moss 49 Murrell-Williamson 67 | 1 | 25 |
| 24 | IsthP | A | Harrow Borough | 207 | L | 0-1 | | 1 | 26 |
| **28** | **FAT3Q** | **H** | **Margate** | **1479** | **W** | **2-1** | **Pinnock 75 Carew 90 (pen)** | | 27 |
| Dec 5 | IsthP | H | Needham Market | 1547 | L | 0-1 | | 1 | 28 |
| **12** | **FAT1** | **A** | **Bury Town** | **441** | **W** | **2-1** | **Clunis 38 Moss 58** | | 29 |
| 15 | IsthP | H | Leiston | 617 | D | 1-1 | Clunis 45 | 1 | 30 |
| 19 | IsthP | A | Grays Athletic | 254 | W | 2-1 | McDonald 55 Clunis 90 | 1 | 31 |
| 26 | IsthP | H | Kingstonian | 1713 | W | 5-1 | Waldren 22 Moss 30 71 Carew 39 Pinnock 48 | 1 | 32 |
| Jan 2 | IsthP | A | Tonbridge Angels | 1095 | D | 1-1 | Nelson 74 | | 33 |
| 9 | IsthP | H | Enfield Town | 2249 | W | 2-0 | Nelson 34 Murrell-Williamson 81 | 1 | 34 |
| **16** | **FAT2** | **H** | **Guiseley** | **1949** | **L** | **1-2** | **Nelson 43** | | 35 |
| 23 | IsthP | A | East Thurrock United | 311 | D | 2-2 | Moss 1 Clunis 75 | 2 | 36 |
| 30 | IsthP | H | Harrow Borough | 2012 | W | 4-0 | Clunis 39 77 Scannell 61 Erskine 82 | 1 | 37 |
| Feb 2 | IsthP | A | Staines Town | 260 | W | 3-1 | O'Caeull (og) 22 Carew 26 (pen) Moss 84 | 1 | 38 |
| 6 | IsthP | A | VCD Athletic | 257 | L | 2-3 | Moss 32 Clunis 45 | 2 | 39 |
| 10 | IsthP | A | Lewes | 424 | L | 1-3 | Waldren 62 | 2 | 40 |
| 13 | IsthP | H | Farnborough | 1390 | D | 2-2 | Clunis 19 Carew 45 | 3 | 41 |
| 27 | IsthP | H | East Thurrock United | 1607 | D | 2-2 | Clunis 90 Carew 90 (pen) | 4 | 42 |
| Mar 5 | IsthP | A | Wingate & Finchley | 331 | D | 1-1 | McDonald 63 | 4 | 43 |
| 12 | IsthP | A | Billericay Town | 424 | L | 1-4 | Carew 6 (pen) | 5 | 44 |
| 15 | IsthP | H | Wingate & Finchley | 584 | W | 2-1 | McDonald 18 Carew 22 | 4 | 45 |
| 19 | IsthP | H | Burgess Hill | 1452 | D | 1-1 | Moss 83 | 4 | 46 |
| 26 | IsthP | A | Enfield Town | 614 | D | 2-2 | Dixon 27 Akinyemi 57 | 5 | 47 |
| 28 | IsthP | H | Tonbridge Angels | 1434 | W | 2-1 | Akinyemi 3 10 | 5 | 48 |
| Apr 2 | IsthP | H | Bognor Regis Town | 1914 | W | 2-0 | Drage 42 Akinyemi 57 | 5 | 49 |
| 9 | IsthP | A | Leiston | 205 | D | 1-1 | James 60 | 6 | 50 |
| 13 | IsthP | A | Brentwood Town | 222 | W | 2-1 | Stokes 2 (og) Pinnock 48 | 5 | 51 |
| 16 | IsthP | H | Lewes | 2467 | W | 2-1 | Clunis 40 Pinnock 45 | 5 | 52 |
| 23 | IsthP | A | Needham Market | 502 | L | 1-2 | Akinyemi 63 | 5 | 53 |
| **26** | **PO SF** | **A** | **Bognor Regis** | **1402** | **W** | **1-0** | **Carew 90** | | 54 |
| **May 1** | **PO Final** | **A** | **East Thurrock United** | **1661** | **L** | **1-3** | **Hibbet 37** | | 55 |

| GOALSCORERS | Scoring Games | Consec Sco Games | Total |
|---|---|---|---|
| *2014-15 Carew and Vidal* | | | *12* |
| Carew | 16 | 2 | 17 |
| Clunis | 12 | 3 | 14 |
| Moss | 7 | 2 | 8 |
| Pinnock | 8 | 2 | 8 |
| Scannell | 6 | 2 | 7 |
| Erskine | 6 | 2 | 6 |
| McDonald | 6 | 3 | 6 |
| Murrell-Williamson | 6 | 2 | 6 |
| Sweeney | 6 | 6 | 6 |
| Waldren | 5 | | 6 |

| | Scoring Games | Consec Sco Games | Total |
|---|---|---|---|
| Akinyemi | 5 | | 5 |
| Nelson | 5 | 3 | 5 |
| Willock | 4 | | 4 |
| James | 3 | | 3 |
| Dixon | 1 | | 1 |
| Drage | 1 | | 1 |
| Erskine | 1 | | 1 |
| Fernandes | 1 | | 1 |
| Hibbet | 1 | | 1 |
| Opponents | | | 2 |

# ENFIELD TOWN

**Chairman:** Paul Reed

**Secretary:** Nigel Howard **(T)** 07969 831 140 **(E)** nigel.howard71@gmail.com

**Commercial Manager:** **(T/E)**

**Programme Editor:** Ken Brazier **(T/E)** ken.brazier@blueyonder.co.uk

**Ground Address:** Queen Elizabeth Stadium, Donkey Lane, Enfield EN1 3PL

**(T)** 07787 875 650 **Manager:** Bradley Quinton - 26/08/14

## Club Factfile

**Founded:** 2001 **Nickname:** ET's or Towners

**Previous Names:** Broke away from Enfield F.C. in 2001

**Previous Leagues:** Essex Senior League

**Club Colours (change):** White/blue/white (Yellow & blue/white/blue)

**Ground Capacity:** **Seats:** Yes **Covered:** Yes **Clubhouse:** **Shop:**

**Directions**

From the M25: Head towards London on the A10 from junction 25. Turn right into Carterhatch Lane at the Halfway House pub. Donkey Lane is first left after the pub.

From London/North Circular Road: Head north up the A10 and turn left to Carterhatch Lane at the Halfway House pub. Donkey Lane is first left after the pub.

**Previous Grounds:** Brimsdown Rovers FC 2001-2010

**Record Attendance:** 562 v Enfield - Middlesex Charity Cup 2002-03

**Record Victory:** 7-0 v Ilford (A) - 29/04/2003

**Record Defeat:** Not known

**Record Goalscorer:** Dan Clarke - 68

**Record Appearances:** Stuart Snowden - 147

**Additional Records:**

**Honours:**

Essex Senior League 2002-03, 04-05. Isthmian League Division 1 North Play-offs 2011-12.

### 10 YEAR RECORD

| 06-07 | 07-08 | 08-09 | 09-10 | 10-11 | 11-12 | 12-13 | 13-14 | 14-15 | 15-16 |
|---|---|---|---|---|---|---|---|---|---|
| Isth1N 3 | Isth1N 12 | Isth1N 12 | Isth1N 4 | Isth1N 6 | Isth1N 2 | Isth P 16 | Isth P 19 | Isth P 7 | Isth P 6 |

# ENFIELD TOWN MATCH RESULTS 2015-16

| Date | Comp | H/A | Opponents | Att: | Result | | Goalscorers | Pos | No. |
|---|---|---|---|---|---|---|---|---|---|
| Aug 8 | IsthP | H | Tonbridge Angels | 458 | L | 0-1 | | 22 | 1 |
| 10 | IsthP | A | Hendon | 245 | L | 0-1 | | 22 | 2 |
| 15 | IsthP | A | Billericay Town | 343 | L | 0-3 | | 24 | 3 |
| 22 | IsthP | H | Burgess Hill Town | 329 | W | 1-0 | Whitely 75 | 20 | 4 |
| 25 | IsthP | H | Leiston | 295 | L | 0-2 | | 20 | 5 |
| 29 | IsthP | A | Canvey Island | 320 | L | 0-2 | | 22 | 6 |
| 31 | IsthP | H | E.Thurrock Utd | 441 | D | 1-1 | Wynter 7 | 21 | 7 |
| Sept 5 | IsthP | A | Bognor Regis Town | 444 | D | 1-1 | Devyne 63 | 20 | 8 |
| 9 | IsthP | A | Leiston | 171 | L | 0-2 | | 21 | 9 |
| **12** | **FAC1Q** | **A** | **Billericay Town** | **333** | **D** | **1-1** | **Devyne 57** | | 10 |
| **15** | **FAC1Qr** | **H** | **Billericay Town** | **309** | **W** | **2-0** | **Campbell 51 Brislen-Hall 67** | | 11 |
| 19 | IsthP | H | Farnborough | 372 | W | 4-1 | Vilcu 3 Devyne 26 Ottaway 55 Kouassi 90 | 20 | 12 |
| 22 | IsthP | H | Wingate & Finchley | 331 | W | 2-0 | Vilcu 48 Devyne 73 | 16 | 13 |
| **26** | **FAC2Q** | **H** | **Ipswich Wanderers** | **342** | **W** | **1-0** | **Devyne 22** | | 14 |
| 29 | IsthP | A | Harrow Borough | 201 | W | 2-1 | Wynter 39 Bihmoutine 81 | 14 | 15 |
| Oct 3 | IsthP | H | Leatherhead | 367 | W | 4-0 | Campbell 3 Doyle 56 Wynter 67 Ottaway 80 | 14 | 16 |
| **10** | **FAC3Q** | **H** | **Hitchin Town** | **883** | **D** | **0-0** | | | 17 |
| **12** | **FAC3Qr** | **A** | **Hitchin Town** | **486** | **W** | **2-1** | **Ottaway 65 Vilcu 77** | | 18 |
| 17 | IsthP | H | Staines Town | 364 | W | 2-1 | Whitely 36 Bihmoutine 42 | 15 | 19 |
| **24** | **FAC4Q** | **A** | **Chesham United** | **759** | **L** | **1-2** | **Ottaway 90** | | 20 |
| 27 | IsthP | H | Hendon | 331 | W | 2-0 | Whitely 45 89 | 17 | 21 |
| **31** | **FAT1Q** | **H** | **Leighton Town** | **311** | **W** | **4-0** | **Devyne 8 Whitely 37 61 Wynter 58** | | 22 |
| Nov 2 | IsthP | A | Kingstonian | 271 | L | 0-1 | | 17 | 23 |
| 7 | IsthP | H | Billericay Town | 309 | D | 2-2 | Devyne 14 Whitely 26 | 16 | 24 |
| **14** | **FAT2Q** | **H** | **Thamesmead Town** | **270** | **L** | **0-2** | | | 25 |
| 21 | IsthP | A | Grays Athletic | 212 | L | 0-1 | | 17 | 26 |
| 28 | IsthP | H | Merstham | 284 | D | 2-2 | Muguo 17 Livings 49 (pen) | | 27 |
| Dec 5 | IsthP | H | Hampton & Richmond B | 292 | L | 2-3 | Campbell 34 Ottaway 43 | 17 | 28 |
| 12 | IsthP | A | Needham Market | 258 | W | 3-2 | Whitely 17 Joseph 54 LIvings 56 | 17 | 29 |
| 15 | IsthP | H | Harrow Borough | 216 | W | 3-0 | Ottaway 24 Kouassi 65 Devyne 80 | 16 | 30 |
| 19 | IsthP | H | Canvey Island | 396 | W | 2-1 | Campbell 38 45 | 14 | 31 |
| 22 | IsthP | A | Lewes | 377 | W | 2-0 | Ottaway 82 89 | 12 | 32 |
| 26 | IsthP | A | East Thurrock United | 238 | L | 0-1 | | 12 | 33 |
| 29 | IsthP | A | Wingate & Finchley | 405 | W | 2-1 | Devyne 57 Vilcu 90 | 10 | 34 |
| Jan 2 | IsthP | H | Brentwood Town | 352 | W | 2-1 | Devyne 38 Vilcu 90 | 6 | 35 |
| 9 | IsthP | A | Dulwich Hamlet | 2249 | L | 0-2 | | 9 | 36 |
| 16 | IsthP | H | Met Police | 323 | W | 2-0 | Devyne 17 Doyle 54 | 8 | 37 |
| 23 | IsthP | A | VCD Athletic | 154 | L | 2-3 | Joseph 42 77 | 9 | 38 |
| Feb 3 | IsthP | H | Burgess Hill Town | 302 | L | 0-1 | | 9 | 39 |
| 6 | IsthP | A | Leatherhead | 302 | W | 3-0 | Devyne 16 25 Whitely 42 | 9 | 40 |
| 13 | IsthP | H | Lewes | 348 | W | 2-1 | Whiteley 3 Doyle 90 | 8 | 41 |
| 20 | IsthP | A | Staines Town | 231 | W | 1-0 | Whitely 73 | 8 | 42 |
| 27 | IsthP | H | VCD Athletic | 351 | W | 3-0 | Whitely 21 58 Devyne 85 | 7 | 43 |
| Mar 5 | IsthP | A | Met Police | 110 | D | 2-2 | Devyne 32 Muguo 76 | 7 | 44 |
| 8 | IsthP | A | Tonbridge Angels | 307 | L | 1-3 | Whitely 34 | 7 | 45 |
| 19 | IsthP | A | Farnborough | 313 | D | 0-0 | | 9 | 46 |
| 22 | IsthP | H | Kingstonian | 338 | W | 4-0 | WHITELY 3 (17 38 46) Devyne 46 | 9 | 47 |
| 26 | IsthP | H | Dulwich Hamlet | 614 | D | 2-2 | Kirby 48 Whitely 81 | 9 | 48 |
| 28 | IsthP | A | Brentwood Town | 226 | W | 2-1 | Ottaway 37 Joseph 66 | 7 | 49 |
| 31 | IsthP | H | Bognor Regis Town | 406 | W | 2-1 | Whitely 32 Kirby 35 | 7 | 50 |
| Apr 2 | IsthP | H | Grays Athletic | 447 | W | 2-0 | Whiteley 6 `(pen) 90 (pen) | 6 | 51 |
| 9 | IsthP | A | Merstham | 465 | W | 4-0 | Whitely 2 66 Nehemie 59 (og) Ottaway 68 | 5 | 52 |
| 16 | IsthP | H | Needham Market | 519 | W | 3-0 | Devyne 36 Joseph 49 Quinton 90 | 6 | 53 |
| 29 | IsthP | A | Hampton & Richmond B | 2376 | D | 0-0 | | 6 | 54 |

| GOALSCORERS | Scoring Games | Consec Sco Games | Total |
|---|---|---|---|
| *2014-15 Whiteley* | | | *17* |
| Whitely | 17 | 4 | 23 |
| Devyne | 16 | 3 | 17 |
| Ottaway | 8 | | 10 |
| Camperll | 4 | | 5 |
| Joseph | 4 | | 5 |
| Vilcu | 5 | 2 | 5 |
| Wynter | 4 | | 4 |
| Doyle | 3 | | 3 |
| Bihmoutine | 2 | | 2 |
| Kirby | 2 | | 2 |
| Kouassi | 2 | | 2 |
| Livings | 2 | | 2 |
| Muguo | 2 | | 2 |
| Brislen-Hall | 1 | | 1 |
| Quinton | 1 | | 1 |
| Opposition | | | 1 |

# FOLKESTONE INVICTA

**Chairman:** Paul Morgan
**Secretary:** Richard Murrill **(T)** 07810 864 228 **(E)** richardmurrill@gmail.com
**Commercial Manager:** **(T/E)**
**Programme Editor:** Richard Murrill **(T/E)** richardmurrill@gmail.com
**Ground Address:** The Fullicks Stadium, Cheriton Road CT19 5JU
**(T)** 01303 257 461 **Manager:** Neil Cugley

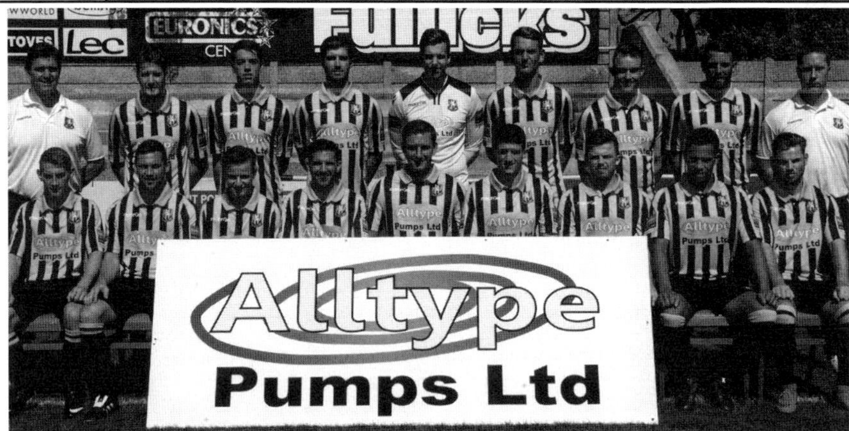


2015-16 Squad Back row:Jason Lillis (Coach),Phil Starkey,Callum Wraight, Matt Newman, Tim Roberts, Carl Rook, Jon Pilbeam, Josh Vincent, Roland Edge (coach)
Front row:Josh Stanford (now Faversham Town) Ronnie Dolan,Jordan Wright,Ian Draycott,Liam Friend (captain), Frankie Chappell, Chris Elliott, Nat Blanks, Ashley Miller.
Picture by Don Linkin

## Club Factfile

**Founded:** 1936 **Nickname:** The Seasiders
**Previous Names:** None
**Previous Leagues:** Kent 1990-98, Southern 1998-2004

**Club Colours (change):** Black & amber stripes/black/black (White & sky stripes/sky/sky)

**Ground Capacity:** 4,000 **Seats:** 900 **Covered:** Yes **Clubhouse:** Yes **Shop:** Yes

**Directions**
Leave the M20 motorway at junction 13, and head south onto the A20 (Cherry Garden Avenue). At the traffic lights, turn left onto the A2034 (Cheriton Road), pass the Harvey Grammar School and Stripes club - the ground is next left before Morrisons' supermarket; opposite the cemetery. Some car parking is available at Stripes.

**Previous Grounds:** South Road Hythe > 1991, County League matches on council pitches

**Record Attendance:** 7,881 v Margate - Kent Senior Cup 1958
**Record Victory:** 13-0 v Faversham Town - Kent League Division 1
**Record Defeat:** 1-7 v Crockenhill - Kent League Division 1
**Record Goalscorer:** Not Known
**Record Appearances:** Not Known
**Additional Records:**
**Honours:**
Isthmian League Division 1 South 2015-16.

### 10 YEAR RECORD

| 06-07 | | 07-08 | | 08-09 | | 09-10 | | 10-11 | | 11-12 | | 12-13 | | 13-14 | | 14-15 | | 15-16 | |
|---|---|---|---|---|---|---|---|---|---|---|---|---|---|---|---|---|---|---|---|
| Isth P | 18 | Isth P | 21 | Isth1S | 11 | Isth1S | 2 | Isth P | 22 | Isth1S | 4 | Isth1S | 5 | Isth1S | 2 | Isth1S | 2 | Isth1S | 1 |

# GRAYS ATHLETIC

**Chairman:** Steve Skinner
**Secretary:** Janet Packer **(T)** 07738 355 619 **(E)** graysathleticfc@hotmail.co.uk
**Commercial Manager:** **(T/E)**
**Programme Editor:** Glyn Jarvis **(T/E)** glyn.jarvis1@btinternet.com
**Ground Address:** Aveley FC, Mill Field, Mill Field Road, Aveley RM15 4SJ
**(T)** 07738 355 619 **Manager:** Jamie Stuart

## Club Factfile

**Founded:** 1890 **Nickname:** The Blues
**Previous Names:** None
**Previous Leagues:** Athenian 1912-14, 58-83, London 1914-24, 26-39, Kent 1924-26, Corinthian 1945-58, Isthmian 1958-2004, Conference 2004-10

**Club Colours (change):** All royal blue (All white)

**Ground Capacity:** 4,000 **Seats:** 400 **Covered:** 400 **Clubhouse:** Yes **Shop:** No

**Directions**
London - Southend A1306, turn into Sandy Lane at Aveley.

**Previous Grounds:** Recreation Ground Bridge Road. Rookery Hill (East Thurrock Utd). Rush Green Road.

**Record Attendance:** 9,500 v Chelmsford City - FA Cup 4th Qualifying Round 1959
**Record Victory:** 12-0 v Tooting & Mitcham United - London League 24/02/1923
**Record Defeat:** 0-12 v Enfield (A) - Athenian League 20/04/1963
**Record Goalscorer:** Harry Brand - 269 (1944-52)
**Record Appearances:** Phil Sammons - 673 (1982-97)
**Additional Records:**

**Honours:**
Conference South 2004-05. FA Trophy 2004-05, 05-06. Isthmian Division One North 2012-13.
Essex Senior Cup x8

### 10 YEAR RECORD

| 06-07 | 07-08 | 08-09 | 09-10 | 10-11 | 11-12 | 12-13 | 13-14 | 14-15 | 15-16 |
|---|---|---|---|---|---|---|---|---|---|
| Conf 19 | Conf 10 | Conf 19 | Conf 23 | Isth1N 10 | Isth1N 5 | Isth1N 1 | Isth P 14 | Isth P 6 | Isth P 15 |

# GRAYS ATHLETIC MATCH RESULTS 2015-16

| Date | Comp | H/A | Opponents | Att: | Result | | Goalscorers | Pos | No. |
|---|---|---|---|---|---|---|---|---|---|
| Aug 8 | IsthP | H | Hendon | 201 | D | 1-1 | Flegg 67 (og) | 10 | 1 |
| 11 | IsthP | A | Tonbridge Angels | 439 | W | 3-2 | Dumaka 26 48 Carlos 87 | 6 | 2 |
| 15 | IsthP | A | Burgess Hill Town | 458 | W | 2-1 | Dumaka 25 Fortnam-Tomlinson 59 | 4 | 3 |
| 22 | IsthP | H | Billericay Town | 263 | W | 2-0 | Fortnam-Tomlinson 45 Stevens 68 (pen) | 2 | 4 |
| 26 | IsthP | H | Canvey Island | 289 | W | 2-0 | Dumaka 74 Poole (og) 80 | 2 | 5 |
| 29 | IsthP | A | Dulwich Hamlet | 999 | D | 1-1 | Beaney 90 | 2 | 6 |
| 31 | IsthP | H | Brentwood Town | 205 | W | 4-0 | Leader 14 Dumaka 16 83 Agombar 32 | 1 | 7 |
| Sept 5 | IsthP | A | Leiston | 232 | W | 2-1 | Dumaka 7 89 | 1 | 8 |
| 8 | IsthP | A | Canvey Island | 330 | W | 3-0 | Carlos 35 Stevens 65 (pen) Dumaka 75 | 1 | 9 |
| **12** | **FAC1Q** | **H** | **Biggleswade United** | **182** | **W** | **5-0** | **Michael-Percil 16 Stadnyk (og) 77 Cronin 79 Carlos 80 89** | | 10 |
| 19 | IsthP | H | Bognor Regis Town | 207 | L | 0-2 | | 1 | 11 |
| 23 | IsthP | H | Staines Town | 173 | D | 1-1 | Cronin 90 | 2 | 12 |
| **26** | **FAC2Q** | **H** | **Hullbridge Sports** | **206** | **W** | **6-0** | **FORTNAM-TOMLINSON 3 (17 20 31) DUMAKA 3 (19 29 86)** | | 13 |
| 30 | IsthP | A | Leatherhhead | 272 | L | 0-3 | | 2 | 14 |
| Oct 3 | IsthP | H | Kingstonian | 191 | L | 1-3 | Michael-Percil 34 | 2 | 15 |
| **10** | **FAC3Q** | **A** | **Hanwell Town** | **311** | **W** | **2-1** | **Leader 17 Dumaka 89 (pen)** | | 16 |
| 14 | IsthP | H | Leatherhead | 172 | L | 0-2 | | 5 | 17 |
| 17 | IsthP | H | Lewes | 194 | W | 4-0 | Hutchings 2 Dumaka 27 34 Stevens 84 | 6 | 18 |
| **25** | **FAC4Q** | **H** | **Welling United** | **512** | **D** | **1-1** | **Addai 75** | | 19 |
| **27** | **FAC4Qr** | **A** | **Welling United** | **733** | **L** | **0-4** | | | 20 |
| **31** | **FAT1Q** | **H** | **Biggleswade Town** | **151** | **W** | **2-1** | **Fortnam-Tomlinson 7 Addai 40** | | 21 |
| Nov 3 | IsthP | A | Wingate & Finchley | 111 | L | 2-3 | Fortnam-Tomlinson 16 Michael-Percil 58 | 11 | 22 |
| 7 | IsthP | H | Burgess Hill Town | 148 | W | 2-0 | Fortnam-Tomlinson 30 Dumaka 70 | 9 | 23 |
| **14** | **FAT2Q** | **A** | **Waltham Abbey** | **146** | **W** | **2-0** | **Agombar 1 49** | | 24 |
| 21 | IsthP | H | Enfield Town | 211 | W | 1-0 | Fortnam-Tomlinson 16 | 10 | 25 |
| **28** | **FAT3Q** | **H** | **Corinthian Casuals** | **150** | **D** | **0-0** | | | 26 |
| **Dec 2** | **FAT3Qr** | **A** | **Corinthian Casuals** | **127** | **L** | **0-1** | | | 27 |
| 5 | IsthP | H | VCD Athletic | 111 | L | 0-1 | | 12 | 28 |
| 7 | IsthP | A | Hendon | 123 | D | 2-2 | Dumaka 3 38 | 12 | 29 |
| 12 | IsthP | A | Hampton & Richmond B | 404 | L | 1-3 | Fortnam-Tomlinson 90 | 12 | 30 |
| 15 | IsthP | A | Staines Town | 126 | W | 4-0 | FORTNAM-TOMLINSON 3 (23 60 79) Leader 40 | 9 | 31 |
| 19 | IsthP | H | Dulwich Hamlet | 254 | L | 1-2 | Fortnam-Tomlinson 67 (pen) | 11 | 32 |
| Jan 2 | IsthP | H | East Thurrock Utd | 255 | D | 0-0 | | 12 | 33 |
| 9 | IsthP | A | Merstham | 188 | D | 2-2 | Fortnam-Tomlinson 6 Beaney 53 | 14 | 34 |
| 16 | IsthP | H | Farnborough | 122 | W | 3-1 | Fortnam-Tomlinson 25 Carlos 71 Davidson 90 | 11 | 35 |
| 23 | IsthP | A | Met Police | 89 | W | 4-2 | Michael-Percil 22 Dumaka 35 47 Hutchings 66 | 10 | 36 |
| 30 | IsthP | H | Wingate & Finchley | 162 | D | 0-0 | | 9 | 37 |
| Feb 2 | IsthP | A | Billericay Town | 216 | D | 1-1 | Cronin 15 | 9 | 38 |
| 6 | IsthP | A | Kingstonian | 240 | L | 1-2 | Michael-Percil 9 | 10 | 39 |
| 9 | IsthP | A | Needham Market | 180 | D | 0-0 | | 10 | 40 |
| 13 | IsthP | H | Harrow Borough | 148 | W | 3-2 | Fortnam-Tomlinson 35 51 Dumaka 68 | 10 | 41 |
| 17 | IsthP | H | Tonbridge Angels | 221 | D | 1-1 | Hutchings 61 | 10 | 42 |
| 20 | IsthP | A | Lewes | 445 | D | 1-1 | Fortnam-Tomlinson 90 | 10 | 43 |
| 25 | IsthP | A | Brentwood Town | 122 | W | 2-1 | Beaney 82 (pen) 88 | 9 | 44 |
| 27 | IsthP | H | Met Police | 127 | D | 3-3 | Beaney 35 Carlos 56 Davidson 85 | 9 | 45 |
| Mar 5 | IsthP | A | Farnborough | 214 | L | 0-5 | | 9 | 46 |
| 8 | IsthP | A | Harrow Borough | 120 | L | 0-3 | | 9 | 47 |
| 12 | IsthP | H | Leiston | 144 | L | 0-2 | | 10 | 48 |
| 25 | IsthP | A | Bognor Regis Town | 451 | L | 0-3 | | 10 | 49 |
| 26 | IsthP | H | Merstham | 128 | L | 1-3 | Hutchings 76 | 10 | 50 |
| 28 | IsthP | A | East Thurrock Utd | 310 | L | 0-3 | | 11 | 51 |
| Apr 2 | IsthP | A | Enfield Town | 447 | L | 0-2 | | 12 | 52 |
| 9 | IsthP | H | Needham Market | 154 | L | 0-2 | | 14 | 53 |
| 16 | IsthP | H | Hampton & Richmond B | 255 | L | 0-3 | | 15 | 54 |
| 23 | IsthP | A | VCD Athletic | 110 | L | 2-4 | Papadimos 48 61 | 15 | 55 |

| GOALSCORERS | Scoring Games | Consec Sco Games | Total |
|---|---|---|---|
| ***2014-15 Ladapo*** | | | ***15*** |
| Dumaka | 13 | 3 | 21 |
| Fortnam-Tomlinson | 14 | | 19 |
| Carlos | 6 | | 6 |
| Beaney | 4 | | 5 |
| Michael-Percil | 5 | | 5 |
| Agombar | 2 | | 3 |
| Cronin | 3 | | 3 |
| Hutchings | 3 | | 3 |
| Leader | 3 | | 3 |
| Stevens | 3 | | 3 |
| Addai | 2 | | 2 |
| Davidson | 2 | | 2 |
| Papadimos | 1 | | 2 |
| Opponents | 3 | | 3 |

# HARLOW TOWN

**Chairman:** John Barnett
**Secretary:** Ray Dyer (T) 07841 667 098 (E) harlowtownfc@aol.com
**Commercial Manager:** (T/E)
**Programme Editor:** Mark Kettley (T/E) sundayonly1@aol.com
**Ground Address:** The Harlow Arena, off Elizabeth Way, The Pinnacles, Harlow CM19 5BE
(T) 01279 443 196 **Manager:** Danny Chapman

## Club Factfile

**Founded:** 1879 **Nickname:** Hawks
**Previous Names:** None
**Previous Leagues:** East Hertfordshire > 1932, Spartan 1932-39, 46-54, London 1954-61, Delphian 1961-63, Athenian 1963-73, Isthmian 1973-92, Inactive 1992-93, Southern 2004-06

**Club Colours (change):** All red with yellow trim (All yellow)

**Ground Capacity:** 3,500 **Seats:** 500 **Covered:** 500 **Clubhouse:** Yes **Shop:** Yes

**Directions**
Barrows Farm is situated on the western side of town just off of the Roydon Road (A1169) on the Pinnacles Industrial Estate.
If coming into Harlow from the M11 (North or South) exit at Junction 7 and follow the A414 until the first roundabout where you turn left onto the A1169. Follow the A1169 signed for Roydon until you see the ground ahead of you at the Roydon Road roundabout. Go straight over the roundabout and the entrance to the ground is on the left.
If coming into town from the west on the A414 turn right at the first roundabout (the old ground was straight ahead) signed Roydon A1169. Follow the A1169 for approx 1 mile and the entrance to the ground is on the right.

**Previous Grounds:** Marigolds 1919-22, Green Man Field 1922-60

**Record Attendance:** 9,723 v Leicester City - FA Cup 3rd Round replay 08/01/1980
**Record Victory:** 14-0 v Bishop's Stortford - 11/04/1925
**Record Defeat:** 0-11 v Ware (A) - Spartan Division 1 East 06/03/1948
**Record Goalscorer:** Dick Marshall scored 64 during 1928-29
**Record Appearances:** Norman Gladwin - 639 (1949-70)
**Additional Records:**

**Honours:**
Athenian League Division 1 1971-72. Isthmian League Division 1 1978-79, Division 2 North 1988-89, Division 1 North Play-offs 2015-16.
Essex Senior cup 1978-79

### 10 YEAR RECORD

| 06-07 | | 07-08 | | 08-09 | | 09-10 | | 10-11 | | 11-12 | | 12-13 | | 13-14 | | 14-15 | | 15-16 | |
|---|---|---|---|---|---|---|---|---|---|---|---|---|---|---|---|---|---|---|---|
| Isth1N | 2 | Isth P | 15 | Isth P | 20 | Isth1N | 22 | Isth1N | 4 | Isth1N | 7 | Isth1N | 21 | Isth1N | 4 | Isth1N | 2 | Isth1N | 3 |

# Top 50 - Twin Strikers

| | League | | | | | Total |
|---|---|---|---|---|---|---|
| **East Thurrock Utd** | **Isthmian Prem** | **Sam Higgins** | **44** | **Tom Wraight** | **22** | **66** |
| **Bognor Regis Town** | **Isthmian Prem** | **Jason Prior** | **42** | **Alfie Rutherford** | **17** | **59** |
| Grimsby Town | National League | Padraig Amond | 37 | Omar Bogle | 18 | 55 |
| AFC Fylde | National North | Danny Rowe | 34 | Dion Charles | 16 | 50 |
| **Tonbridge Angels** | **Isthmian Prem** | **Nathan Elder** | **27** | **Luke Blewden** | **22** | **49** |
| Stourbridge | N.P.L. Prem | Karl Hawley | 31 | Chris Lait | 16 | 47 |
| Ebbsfleet United | National South | Matt Godden | 30 | Danny Kedwell | 15 | 45 |
| Dover Athletic | National League | Stefan Payne | 23 | Rickie Miller | 21 | 44 |
| Whitehawk | National South | Danny Mills | 33 | Deering/ Robinson/Neilson | 11 | 44 |
| Ashton United | N.P.L. Prem | Martin Pilkington | 29 | Chris Baguley | 13 | 42 |
| Rushall Olympic | N.P.L. Prem | Luke Benbow | 22 | Alex Reid | 20 | 42 |
| Buxton | N.P.L. Prem | Liam Hardy | 24 | Brad Barraclough | 17 | 41 |
| North Ferriby United | National North | Tom Denton | 22 | Liam King | 19 | 41 |
| Blyth Spartans | N.P.L. Prem | Robbie Dale | 25 | Sean Reid | 15 | 40 |
| Cheltenham Town | National League | Danny Wright | 24 | Dan Holman | 16 | 40 |
| **Enfield Town** | **Isthmian Prem** | **Corey Whitely** | **23** | **Bobby Devyne** | **17** | **40** |
| **Grays Athletic** | **Isthmian Prem** | **Dumebi Dumaka** | **21** | **Bradley Fortnam-Tomlinson** | **19** | **40** |
| Hyde United | N.P.L. Prem | Scott Spencer | 23 | Ayrton Bevins | 17 | 40 |
| Cirencester Town | Southern Prem | Charlie Griffin | 26 | Zack Kotwica | 12 | 38 |
| Gosport Borough | National South | Justin Bennett | 29 | Dan Wooden | 9 | 38 |
| Macclesfield T | National League | Kristian Dennis | 30 | Danny Whitehead | 8 | 38 |
| Nantwich Town | N.P.L. Prem | Liam Shotton | 20 | Elliott Osborne | 18 | 38 |
| Salford City | N.P.L. Prem | James Poole | 19 | Danny Webber, | 19 | 38 |
| Maidenhead Utd | National South | Dave Tarpey | 21 | Ben Wright | 16 | 37 |
| Weston-s-Mare | National South | Scott Wilson | 23 | Dayle Grubb | 14 | 37 |
| Gateshead | National League | Ryan Bowman | 21 | Danny Johnson | 15 | 36 |
| **Staines Town** | **Isthmian Prem** | **Pat Cox** | **26** | **Luke Wanadio** | **10** | **36** |
| Chester | National Prem | Ross Hannah | 25 | John Rooney | 10 | 35 |
| Hungerford Town | Southern Prem | Nat Jarvis | 18 | Stefan Brown | 17 | 35 |
| Barwell | N.P.L. Prem | Brady Hickey | 17 | Jamie Towers | 17 | 34 |
| Hitchin Town | Southern Prem | Jonny McNamara | 18 | Rob Burns | 16 | 34 |
| Leamington | Southern Prem | Ben Mackey | 22 | Jack Edwards | 12 | 34 |
| Lincoln City | National League | Matt Rhead | 23 | Liam Hearn | 11 | 34 |
| **Merstham** | **Isthmian Prem** | **Charlie Penny** | **20** | **Fabio Saraiva** | **14** | **34** |
| Solihull Moors | National North | Akwasi Asante | 20 | Stefan Moore | 14 | 34 |
| Workington | N.P.L. Prem | Scott Allison | 21 | Connor Tinnion | 13 | 34 |
| Barrow | National League | Andy Cook | 23 | Jason Walker | 10 | 33 |
| Bishops Stortford | National South | Elliott Buchanan | 28 | Morgan Ferrier | 5 | 33 |
| Chesham United | Southern Prem | Dave Pearce | 17 | Ryan Blake | 16 | 33 |
| Darlington 1883 | N.P.L. Prem | Nathan Cartman | 19 | Lee Gaskell | 14 | 33 |
| Skelmersdale United | N.P.L. Prem | Chris Almond | 18 | Max Hazeldene | 15 | 33 |
| Sutton United | National South | Dan Fitchitt | 22 | Ross Stearn& TomBolarinwa | 11 | 33 |
| Boston United | National North | Dayle Southwell | 24 | Carl Piergianni | 8 | 32 |
| Chippenham Town | Southern Prem | Andy Sandell | 23 | Alan Griffin | 9 | 32 |
| Concord Rangers | National South | Steve Cawley | 19 | Ben Greenhalgh | 13 | 32 |
| Eastbourne Borough | National South | Nat Pinney | 23 | Jack Evans | 9 | 32 |
| Harrogate Town | National North | Brendon Daniels | 23 | Dom Knowles | 9 | 32 |
| Oxford City | National South | Bradley Bubb | 24 | Kynan Isaac | 8 | 32 |
| Poole Town | Southern Prem | Marvin Brooks | 17 | Luke Roberts | 15 | 32 |
| Chorley | National North | Darren Stephenson | 19 | Josh Hine | 12 | 31 |

# HARROW BOROUGH

**Chairman:** Peter Rogers
**Secretary:** Peter Rogers (T) 07956 185 685 (E) peter@harrowboro.co.uk
**Commercial Manager:** (T/E)
**Programme Editor:** Peter Rogers (T/E) 07956 185 685
**Ground Address:** Earlsmead, Carlyon Avenue, South Harrow HA2 8SS
(T) 0844 561 1347 **Manager:** Steve Baker - 25/01/15

## Club Factfile

**Founded:** 1933 **Nickname:** Boro
**Previous Names:** Roxonian 1933-38, Harrow Town 1938-66
**Previous Leagues:** Harrow & District 1933-34, Spartan 1934-40, 45-58, West Middlesex Combination 1940-41, Middlesex Senior 1941-45, Delphian 1956-63, Athenian 1963-75

**Club Colours (change):** All red (All blue)

**Ground Capacity:** 3,070 **Seats:** 350 **Covered:** 1,000 **Clubhouse:** Yes **Shop:** Yes

**Directions**
From the M25 junction 16, take the M40 East towards Uxbridge and London. Continue onto A40, passing Northolt Aerodrome on the left hand side. At the Target Roundabout junction (A312) turn left towards Northolt.
Just after passing Northolt Underground Station on the left hand side, turn left at the next set of traffic lights, onto Eastcote Lane, becoming Field End Road.
At next roundabout, turn right onto Eastcote Lane. At a small parade of shops, take the turning on the right into Carlyon Avenue. Earlsmead is the second turning on the right.

**Previous Grounds:** Northcult Road 1933-34.

**Record Attendance:** 3,000 v Wealdstone - FA Cup 1st Qualifying Road 1946
**Record Victory:** 13-0 v Handley Page (A) - 18/10/1941
**Record Defeat:** 0-8 on five occasions
**Record Goalscorer:** Dave Pearce - 153
**Record Appearances:** Les Currell - 582, Colin Payne - 557, Steve Emmanuel - 522
**Additional Records:**

**Honours:**
Isthmian League 1983-84.
Middlesex Senior Cup 1982-83, 92-93, 2014-15. Middlesex Premier Cup 1981-82.
Middlesex Senior Charity Cup 1979-80, 92-93, 2005-06, 06-07

### 10 YEAR RECORD

| 06-07 | 07-08 | 08-09 | 09-10 | 10-11 | 11-12 | 12-13 | 13-14 | 14-15 | 15-16 |
|---|---|---|---|---|---|---|---|---|---|
| Isth P 19 | Isth P 16 | Isth P 14 | Isth P 14 | Isth P 5 | Isth P 17 | Isth P 15 | Isth P 18 | Isth P 16 | Isth P 17 |

# HARROW BOROUGH MATCH RESULTS 2015-16

| Date | Comp | H/A | Opponents | Att: | Result | | Goalscorers | Pos | No. |
|---|---|---|---|---|---|---|---|---|---|
| Aug 8 | IsthP | H | Hampton & Richmond B | 189 | D | 1-1 | Charles-Smith 42 | 12 | 1 |
| 15 | IsthP | A | Lewes | 372 | D | 1-1 | Taylor 89 | 17 | 2 |
| 22 | IsthP | H | Brentwood Town | 132 | **W** | 1-0 | Charles-Smith 31 | 12 | 3 |
| 26 | IsthP | A | Burgess Hill Town | 289 | **W** | 5-0 | CHARLES-SMITH 3 (9 29 61) Taylor 43 Cascoe 74 | 6 | 4 |
| 29 | IsthP | H | Tonbridge Angels | 187 | D | 1-1 | Driver 69 | 7 | 5 |
| 31 | IsthP | A | Hendon | 251 | **W** | 1-0 | Charles-Smith 38 (pen) | 6 | 6 |
| Sept 5 | IsthP | H | Kingstonian | 217 | L | 1-3 | Cascoe 66 | 9 | 7 |
| 8 | IsthP | H | Burgess Hill Town | 161 | **W** | 1-0 | Driver 6 | 6 | 8 |
| **12** | **FAC1Q** | **A** | **Northwood** | **173** | **D** | **0-0** | | | 9 |
| **15** | **FAC1Qr** | **H** | **Northwood** | **156** | **L** | **0-1** | | | 10 |
| 19 | IsthP | A | Needham Market | 253 | **W** | 4-2 | Driver 11 Charles-Smith 47 83 McCall 51 | 6 | 11 |
| 22 | IsthP | A | Merstham | 117 | **W** | 1-0 | Charles-Smith 47 | 3 | 12 |
| 29 | IsthP | H | Enfield Town | 201 | L | 1-2 | French 40 | | 13 |
| Oct 3 | IsthP | A | Bognor Regis Town | 372 | L | 0-1 | | 9 | 14 |
| 17 | IsthP | A | Canvey Island | 333 | L | 0-1 | | 13 | 15 |
| 20 | IsthP | H | Merstham | 124 | L | 0-2 | | 14 | 16 |
| 24 | IsthP | A | Hampton & Richmond B | 344 | D | 2-2 | Driver 20 Taylor 81 | 15 | 17 |
| 27 | IsthP | H | Farnborough | 146 | **W** | 3-1 | Webb 4 McCall 26 42 | 14 | 18 |
| **31** | **FAT1Q** | **H** | **Dulwich Hamlet** | **185** | **L** | **0-3** | | | 19 |
| Nov 7 | IsthP | H | Lewes | 143 | **W** | 4-1 | Charles-Smith 23 75 Bryan 40 Webb 70 | 11 | 20 |
| 14 | IsthP | A | Billericay Town | 265 | L | 1-2 | Okenabirhie 87 | 11 | 21 |
| 21 | IsthP | H | VCD Athletic | 121 | L | 1-2 | Bruce 90 (og) | 14 | 22 |
| 24 | IsthP | H | Dulwich Hamlet | 207 | **W** | 1-0 | Webb 62 | 12 | 23 |
| 28 | IsthP | A | Wingate & Finchley | 135 | L | 1-3 | Taylor 13 | 12 | 24 |
| Dec 5 | IsthP | A | Leatherhead | 236 | **W** | 2-1 | Okenabirhie 49 Webb 84 | 11 | 25 |
| 7 | IsthP | A | Farnborough | 176 | L | 1-2 | Taylor 22 | 11 | 26 |
| 15 | IsthP | A | Enfield Town | 216 | L | 0-3 | | 13 | 27 |
| 19 | IsthP | A | Tonbridge Angels | 527 | D | 3-3 | Charles-Smith 45 (pen) Webb 50 Newman 58 | 13 | 28 |
| 26 | IsthP | H | Hendon | 264 | D | 5-5 | Drew 1 Driver 41 Charles-Smith 45 75 Okenabirhie 62 | 15 | 29 |
| Jan 23 | IsthP | H | Billericay Town | 161 | **W** | 2-1 | Driver 21 McCall 50 | 16 | 30 |
| 30 | IsthP | A | Dulwich Hamlet | 2021 | L | 0-4 | | 16 | 31 |
| Feb 2 | IsthP | H | East Thurrock United | 145 | L | 2-5 | Taylor 31 Driver 34 | 16 | 32 |
| 9 | IsthP | A | Metropolitan Police | 74 | L | 2-3 | McCall 89 90 | 17 | 33 |
| 13 | IsthP | A | Grays Athletic | 148 | L | 2-3 | Okenabirhie 28 Charles-Smith 80 | 17 | 34 |
| 20 | IsthP | H | Canvey Island | 138 | L | 1-2 | Charles-Smith 89 (pen) | 17 | 35 |
| Mar 1 | IsthP | A | Brentwood Town | 81 | L | 1-2 | Driver 90 | | 36 |
| 5 | IsthP | H | Leiston | 127 | D | 0-0 | | 19 | 37 |
| 8 | IsthP | H | Grays Athletic | 120 | **W** | 3-0 | Taylor 21 Okenabirhie 49 88 | 18 | 38 |
| 12 | IsthP | A | Kingstonian | 266 | L | 2-5 | Okenabirthie 88 Newman 90 | 18 | 39 |
| 16 | IsthP | A | Leiston | 130 | L | 0-2 | | 18 | 40 |
| 19 | IsthP | H | Needham Market | 135 | L | 0-2 | | 18 | 41 |
| 22 | IsthP | H | Bognor Regis Town | 169 | L | 1-2 | Charles-Smith 5 (pen) | 18 | 42 |
| 26 | IsthP | A | Staines Town | 221 | D | 1-1 | Cascoe 90 | 19 | 43 |
| Apr 2 | IsthP | A | VCD Athletic | 106 | **W** | 3-2 | Cascoe 4 Charles-Smith 37 86 | 19 | 44 |
| 5 | IsthP | H | Staines Town | 157 | **W** | 1-0 | McCall 45 | 16 | 45 |
| 9 | IsthP | H | Wingate & Finchley | 145 | **W** | 1-0 | Okenabirthie 68 | 16 | 46 |
| 13 | IsthP | H | Metropolitan Police | 125 | L | 0-3 | | 16 | 47 |
| 16 | IsthP | A | East Thurrock United | 279 | L | 0-2 | | 16 | 48 |
| 23 | IsthP | H | Leatherhead | 163 | D | 2-2 | Newman 24 Driver 86 | 17 | 49 |
| | | | | | | | | | 50 |

| GOALSCORERS | Scoring Games | Consec Sco Games | Total |
|---|---|---|---|
| ***2014-15 Charles-Smith*** | | | ***19*** |
| Charles-Smith | 13 | 2 | 19 |
| Driver | 9 | | 9 |
| Okenabirthie | 8 | | 8 |
| McCall | 5 | | 7 |
| Taylor | 7 | | 7 |
| Webb | 5 | | 5 |
| Cascoe | 3 | | 3 |
| Newman | 3 | | 3 |
| Bryan | 1 | | 1 |
| Cacoe | 1 | | 1 |
| Drew | 1 | | 1 |
| French | 1 | | 1 |
| Opponents | | | 1 |

# HAVANT AND WATERLOOVILLE

**Chairman:** Derek Pope
**Secretary:** Trevor Brock (T) 07768 271 143 (E) trevor.brock52@yahoo.com
**Commercial Manager:** Adrian Aymes (T/E) 07814 150 032
**Programme Editor:** Adrian Aymes (T/E) aaymes2125@aol.com
**Ground Address:** Westleigh Park, Martin Road, West Leigh, Havant PO7 5TH
**(T)** 02392 787 822 **Manager:** Lee Bradbury

## Club Factfile

**Founded:** 1998 **Nickname:** Hawks
**Previous Names:** Havant Town and Waterlooville merged in 1998
**Previous Leagues:** Southern 1998-2004

**Club Colours (change):** White/navy/white (All red)

**Ground Capacity:** 4,800 **Seats:** 562 **Covered:** 3,500 **Clubhouse:** Yes **Shop:** Yes

**Directions**
Ground is a mile and a half from Havant Town Centre. Take A27 to Havant then turn onto B2149 (Petersfield Road). Turn right at next junction after HERON pub into Bartons Road then take first right into Martin Road.

**Previous Grounds:** None

**Record Attendance:** 4,400 v Swansea City - FA Cup 3rd Round 05/01/2008
**Record Victory:** 9-0 v Moneyfields - Hampshire Senior Cup 23/10/2001
**Record Defeat:** 0-5 v Worcester City - Southern Premier 20/03/2004
**Record Goalscorer:** James Taylor - 138
**Record Appearances:** James Taylor - 297
**Additional Records:** Paid £5,000 to Bashley for John Wilson
Received £15,000 from Peterborough United for Gary McDonald
**Honours:**
Southern League Southern Division 1998-99. Russell Cotes Cup 2003-04.
Hampshire Senior Cup 2015-16.

**10 YEAR RECORD**

| 06-07 | 07-08 | 08-09 | 09-10 | 10-11 | 11-12 | 12-13 | 13-14 | 14-15 | 15-16 |
|---|---|---|---|---|---|---|---|---|---|
| Conf 4 | Conf S 7 | Conf S 15 | Conf S 6 | Conf S 9 | Conf S 19 | Conf S 10 | Conf S 6 | Conf S 5 | Nat S 20 |

# HAVANT & WATERLOOVILLE MATCH RESULTS 2015-16

| Date | Comp | H/A | Opponents | Att: | Result | Goalscorers | Pos | No. |
|---|---|---|---|---|---|---|---|---|
| Aug 8 | Nat South | A | Bishops Stortford | 353 | L 0-3 | | 22 | 1 |
| 11 | Nat South | H | Sutton United | 647 | L 0-2 | | 21 | 2 |
| 15 | Nat South | H | Margate | 613 | W 2-0 | Paterson 33 Strugnell 65 | 17 | 3 |
| 18 | Nat South | A | Hayes & Yeading | 194 | D 0-0 | | 16 | 4 |
| 22 | Nat South | H | Oxford City | 552 | W 2-1 | Clifton 31 Strugnell 84 | 13 | 5 |
| 29 | Nat South | A | Bath City | 769 | L 0-5 | | 15 | 6 |
| 31 | Nat South | H | Eastbourne Boro | 620 | W 4-0 | Clifton 13 Donnelly 29 (pen) 33 Paterson 60 | 12 | 7 |
| Sept 5 | Nat South | A | Chelmsford City | 736 | D 2-2 | Paterson 64 Stock 77 | 11 | 8 |
| 12 | Nat South | A | Maidstone United | 2054 | L 0-1 | | 14 | 9 |
| 15 | Nat South | H | Whiteleak | 539 | L 2-3 | Stock 38 Paterson 64 | 14 | 10 |
| 19 | Nat South | H | Ebbsfleet United | 751 | L 1-4 | Paterson 65 | 15 | 11 |
| **26** | **FAC2Q** | **A** | **Larkhall Athletic** | **210** | **D 1-1** | **Hayter 4** | | 12 |
| **29** | **FAC2Qr** | **H** | **Larkhall Athletic** | **197** | **W 4-2** | **Strugnell 36 Paterson 45 61 Donnelly 83** | | 13 |
| Oct 3 | Nat South | A | Truro City | 478 | L 0-3 | | 16 | 14 |
| **10** | **FAC3Q** | **A** | **Aveley** | **132** | **W 2-0** | **Morgan 30 Strugnell 82** | | 15 |
| 17 | Nat South | H | Wealdstone | 736 | L 1-2 | Hayter 89 | 19 | 16 |
| **24** | **FAC4Q** | **H** | **Cheltenham Town** | **622** | **D 3-3** | **Strugnell 52 Hayter 73 Paterson 76** | | 17 |
| **28** | **FAC4Qr** | **A** | **Cheltenham Town** | **1368** | **L 0-1** | | | 18 |
| 31 | Nat South | H | St Albans City | 557 | D 1-1 | Hayter 46 | 18 | 19 |
| Nov 7 | Nat South | A | Margate | 607 | L 1-4 | Cummings 81 | 19 | 20 |
| 10 | Nat South | A | Oxford City | 353 | W 3-1 | POKU 3 (4 8 52) | 18 | 21 |
| 14 | Nat South | H | Maidenhead United | 550 | W 3-1 | Poku 24 Ciardini 63 Donnelly 89 | 16 | 22 |
| 21 | Nat South | A | Sutton United | 979 | L 0-3 | | 15 | 23 |
| 24 | Nat South | A | Weston-s-Mare | 329 | L 2-3 | Donnelly 48 (pen) Hayter 89 | 18 | 24 |
| **28** | **FAT3Q** | **H** | **Basingstoke Town** | **277** | **W 2-1** | **Hayter 4 Swallow 80** | | 25 |
| Dec 5 | Nat South | A | Dartford | 738 | L 2-4 | Strugnell 49 Paterson 55 | 20 | 26 |
| **12** | **FAT1** | **H** | **Forest Green Rovers** | **266** | **W 2-0** | **Donnelly 68 (pen) Hayter 88** | | 27 |
| 19 | Nat South | H | Concord Rangers | 513 | W 2-1 | Donnelly 8 16 (pen) | 20 | 28 |
| 26 | Nat South | A | Gosport Borough | 1313 | L 1-2 | Donnelly 16 | 20 | 29 |
| Jan 9 | Nat South | A | Hemel Hempstead Town | 348 | L 0-2 | | 21 | 30 |
| **16** | **FAT2** | **H** | **Welling United** | **371** | **W 2-1** | **Hill 11 Mullings 64** | | 31 |
| 23 | Nat South | H | Basinstoke Town | 617 | W 1-0 | Paterson 87 | 20 | 32 |
| 30 | Nat South | A | Maidenhead United | 707 | D 2-2 | Donnelly 36 Swallow 67 | 20 | 33 |
| **Feb 6** | **FAT3Q** | **A** | **Grimsby Town** | **1613** | **L 0-3** | | | 34 |
| 9 | Nat South | H | Gosport Borough | 731 | L 1-3 | Swallow 21 | 20 | 35 |
| 16 | Nat South | H | Bishops Stortford | 410 | W 2-1 | Donnelly 28 69 | 20 | 36 |
| 20 | Nat South | A | Whitehawk | 308 | D 1-1 | Donnelly 89 | 20 | 37 |
| 23 | Nat South | H | Bath City | 424 | D 1-1 | Ciardini 12 | 20 | 38 |
| 27 | Nat South | H | Maidstone United | 835 | W 2-1 | Mullings 90 Hill 90 | 19 | 39 |
| Mar 1 | Nat South | A | Ebbsfleet United | 854 | D 2-2 | Medway 14 Hayter 74 | 19 | 40 |
| 5 | Nat South | H | Hemel Hempstead Town | 573 | L 1-2 | Hill 90 | 19 | 41 |
| 12 | Nat South | A | Basingstoke Town | 523 | D 1-1 | Swallow 45 | 19 | 42 |
| 19 | Nat South | H | Dartford | 661 | W 2-0 | Hayter 52 75 | 19 | 43 |
| 25 | Nat South | H | Hayes & Yeading | 747 | W 1-0 | Hayter 58 | 16 | 44 |
| 28 | Nat South | A | Eastbourne Boro | 614 | D 2-2 | Hayter 29 Hill 90 | 17 | 45 |
| Apr 2 | Nat South | A | Wealdstone | 646 | L 2-3 | Donnelly 60 Hayter 61 | 17 | 46 |
| 5 | Nat South | H | Chelmsford City | 588 | L 0-1 | | 17 | 47 |
| 16 | Nat South | A | St Albans City | 702 | L 0-6 | | 21 | 48 |
| 23 | Nat South | A | Concord Rangers | 435 | W 1-0 | Swallow 10 | 20 | 49 |
| 28 | Nat South | H | Truro City | 620 | D 0-0 | | 20 | 50 |
| 30 | Nat South | H | Weston-s-Mare | 885 | D 1-1 | Hayter 17 | 20 | 51 |

| GOALSCORERS | Scoring Games | Consec Sco Games | Total |
|---|---|---|---|
| *2014-15 Donnelly* | | | *17* |
| Donnelly | 11 | 3 | 14 |
| Hayter | 12 | 4 | 14 |
| Paterson | 9 | 2 | 10 |
| Strugnell | 6 | | 6 |
| Swallow | 5 | | 5 |
| Hill | 4 | | 4 |
| Poku | 2 | 2 | 4 |
| Ciardini | 2 | | 2 |
| Clifton | 2 | | 2 |
| Stock | 2 | | 2 |
| Mullings | 2 | | 2 |
| Cummings | 1 | | 1 |
| Medway | 1 | | 1 |
| Morgan | 1 | | 1 |

# HENDON

**Chairman:** Simon Lawrence
**Secretary:** Graham Etchell (T) 07973 698 552 (E) hendonfc@freenetname.co.uk
**Commercial Manager:** (T/E)
**Programme Editor:** Graham Etchell (T/E) hendonfc@freenetname.co.uk
**Ground Address:** Silver Jubilee Park, Townsend Lane, Kingsbury, London NW9 7NE
(T) 020 8205 1645 **Manager:** Gary McCann

## Club Factfile

**Founded:** 1908 **Nickname:** Dons or Greens
**Previous Names:** Christ Church Hampstead > 1908, Hampstead Town > 1933, Golders Green > 1946
**Previous Leagues:** Finchley & District 1908-11, Middlesex 1910-11, London 1911-14, Athenian 1914-63

**Club Colours (change):** Green/black/white (All royal blue)

**Ground Capacity:** 3,070 **Seats:** 350 **Covered:** 1,000 **Clubhouse:** Yes **Shop:**

**Directions**
From Staples Corner travel north along the A5, towards Edgware, through West Hendon, to the junction with Kingsbury Road (Red Lion public house on corner). Turn into Kingsbury Road and Townsend Lane is the 3rd turning on the left, at the top of the hill. The ground is in the bottom left hand corner of the Silver Jubilee Park.

**Previous Grounds:** Claremont Road. Vale Farm (Wembley FC). Earlsmead (Harrow Borough FC).

**Record Attendance:** 9,000 v Northampton Town - FA Cup 1st Round 1952
**Record Victory:** 13-1 v Wingate - Middlesex County Cup 02/02/1957
**Record Defeat:** 2-11 v Walthamstowe Avenue, Athenian League 09/11/1935
**Record Goalscorer:** Freddie Evans - 176 (1929-35)
**Record Appearances:** Bill Fisher - 787 - (1940-64)
**Additional Records:** Received £30,000 from Luton Town for Iain Dowie

**Honours:**
FA Amateur Cup 1959-60, 64-65, 71-72. Isthmian League 1964-65, 72-73. European Amateur Champions 1972-73.
Athenian League x3. London Senior Cup 1963-64, 68-69, 2014-15. Middlesex Senior Cup x14

### 10 YEAR RECORD

| 06-07 | 07-08 | 08-09 | 09-10 | 10-11 | 11-12 | 12-13 | 13-14 | 14-15 | 15-16 |
|---|---|---|---|---|---|---|---|---|---|
| Isth P 14 | Isth P 7 | Isth P 16 | Isth P 10 | Isth P 15 | Isth P 7 | Isth P 10 | Isth P 8 | Isth P 2 | Isth P 19 |

# HENDON MATCH RESULTS 2015-16

| Date | Comp | H/A | Opponents | Att: | Result | | Goalscorers | Pos | No. |
|---|---|---|---|---|---|---|---|---|---|
| Aug8 | IsthP | A | Grays Athletic | 201 | D | 1-1 | Morgan 8 | 13 | 1 |
| 10 | IsthP | H | Enfield Town | 245 | **W** | 1-0 | Morgan 22 (pen) | 7 | 2 |
| 15 | IsthP | H | Dulwich Hamlet | 268 | D | 1-1 | Shulton 65 | 9 | 3 |
| 22 | IsthP | A | Needham Market | 255 | **W** | 3-0 | L.Smith 15 Morgan 31 Shulton 72 | 4 | 4 |
| 24 | IsthP | H | East Thurrock United | 160 | L | 1-2 | Murphy 36 (pen) | 5 | 5 |
| 29 | IsthP | A | Leiston | 204 | L | 0-2 | | 12 | 6 |
| 31 | IsthP | H | Harrow Borough | 251 | L | 0-1 | | 12 | 7 |
| Sept5 | IsthP | A | Canvey Island | 300 | L | 2-3 | Morgan 15 Tingey 36 | 13 | 8 |
| 8 | IsthP | A | East Thurrock United | 143 | **W** | 4-2 | Morgan 4 Murphy 68 (pen) L.Smith 86 Da Costs 90 | 13 | 9 |
| **12** | **FAC1Q** | **A** | **AFC Sudbury** | **211** | **L** | **1-3** | **Morgan 15 (pen)** | | 10 |
| 19 | IsthP | H | Merstham | 133 | D | 2-2 | Morgan 56 (pen) 85 | 13 | 11 |
| 26 | IsthP | A | Leatherhead | 236 | **W** | 5-2 | L.Smith 2 69 Diedhou 33 82 Bettache 46 | 12 | 12 |
| 28 | IsthP | A | Kingstonian | 285 | L | 0-1 | | 14 | 13 |
| Oct3 | IsthP | H | Met Police | 116 | L | 0-2 | | 16 | 14 |
| 10 | IsthP | A | Hampton & Richmond B | 475 | L | 0-5 | | 19 | 15 |
| 12 | IsthP | H | Kingstonian | 183 | D | 1-1 | Short 74 | 18 | 16 |
| 17 | IsthP | H | VCD Athletic | 115 | **W** | 3-1 | L.Smith 3 Flegg 40 Capella 80 | 17 | 17 |
| 24 | IsthP | A | Merstham | 147 | L | 0-1 | | 18 | 18 |
| 27 | IsthP | A | EnfieldTown | 331 | L | 0-2 | | 18 | 19 |
| **Nov1** | **FAT1Q** | **H** | **AFC Sudbury** | **182** | **L** | **0-1** | | **19** | 20 |
| 7 | IsthP | A | Dulwich Hamlet | 1423 | L | 2-4 | Short 18 Drage 77 (og) | 19 | 21 |
| 14 | IsthP | H | Needham Market | 125 | L | 0-2 | | 19 | 22 |
| 21 | IsthP | A | Tonbridge Angels | 375 | L | 1-3 | Ibe 34 | | 23 |
| 28 | IsthP | H | Burgess Hill Town | 117 | **W** | 1-0 | Ibe 18 | 19 | 24 |
| 30 | IsthP | A | Farnborough | 198 | L | 0-1 | | 20 | 25 |
| Dec5 | IsthP | H | Bognor Regis Town | 144 | D | 1-1 | Robins 7 | 20 | 26 |
| 7 | IsthP | H | Grays Athletic | 123 | D | 2-2 | Cracknell 85 | 20 | 27 |
| 12 | IsthP | A | Billericay Town | 278 | L | 1-3 | Taggart 85 | 20 | 28 |
| 14 | IsthP | H | Farnborough | 136 | **W** | 3-0 | Short 25 Ehul 45 Stow 63 (og) | 18 | 29 |
| 19 | IsthP | H | Leiston | 119 | L | 2-4 | Pattie 68 Wallace 68 | 20 | 30 |
| 26 | IsthP | A | Harrow Borough | 264 | D | 5-5 | Casell 5 (og) Ibe 8 McCluskey 19 Robins 21 Wallace 59 | 19 | 31 |
| Jan2 | IsthP | H | Wingate & Finchley | 177 | **W** | 4-3 | Wallace 28 29 Ibe 64 82 | 19 | 32 |
| 23 | IsthP | A | Staines Town | 237 | **W** | 3-1 | Diedhiou 12 Ibe 66 Kirby 87 | 18 | 33 |
| Feb6 | IsthP | A | Met Police | 79 | L | 0-3 | | 18 | 34 |
| 13 | IsthP | H | Hampton & Richmond B | 218 | D | 1-1 | Diedhiou 27 | 18 | 35 |
| 20 | IsthP | A | VCD Athleric | 110 | **W** | 3-2 | Ibe 43 McCluskey 56 62 | 18 | 36 |
| 27 | IsthP | H | Staines Town | 202 | **W** | 2-0 | Taggart 2 55 | 17 | 37 |
| 29 | IsthP | H | Lewes | 147 | **W** | 2-0 | Robins 37 Maclaren 45 | 17 | 38 |
| Mar5 | IsthP | A | Lewes | 374 | D | 2-2 | Adams 12 58 | 15 | 39 |
| 12 | IsthP | H | Canvey Island | 121 | D | 2-2 | Diedhiou 21 Adams 82 (pen) | 16 | 40 |
| 26 | IsthP | H | Brentwood Town | 129 | D | 1-1 | Ibe 72 (pen) | 16 | 41 |
| 28 | IsthP | A | Wingate & Finchley | 340 | D | 1-1 | Diedhiou 21 | 17 | 42 |
| Apr2 | IsthP | H | Tonbridge Angels | 215 | L | 0-3 | | 17 | 43 |
| 5 | IsthP | A | Brentwood Town | 152 | L | 1-4 | Pattie 48 | 17 | 44 |
| 11 | IsthP | H | Leatherhead | 125 | L | 2-3 | McCluskey 32 53 | 17 | 45 |
| 18 | IsthP | H | Billericay Town | 135 | D | 1-1 | Seeby 44 | 16 | 46 |
| 20 | IsthP | A | Burgess Hill Town | 305 | **W** | 1-0 | McCluskey 83 | 16 | 47 |
| 23 | IsthP | A | Bognor Regis Town | 510 | L | 0-4 | | 19 | 48 |

| GOALSCORERS | Scoring Games | Consec Sco Games | Total | | Scoring Games | Consec Sco Games | Total |
|---|---|---|---|---|---|---|---|
| ***2014-15 Ibe*** | | | ***21*** | Taggart | 1 | | 2 |
| Ibe | 6 | 3 | 8 | Adams | 2 | | 2 |
| Morgan | 7 | 4 | 8 | Bettache | 1 | | 1 |
| Diedhiou | 5 | | 6 | Capella | 1 | | 1 |
| McCluskey | 5 | | 6 | Cracknell | 1 | | 1 |
| L.Smith | 4 | | 5 | Da Costa | 1 | | 1 |
| Wallace | 2 | | 4 | Ehul | 1 | | 1 |
| Adams | 3 | | 3 | Flegg | 1 | | 1 |
| Robins | 3 | | 3 | Kirby | 1 | | 1 |
| Short | 3 | | 3 | McLaren | 1 | | 1 |
| Murphy | 2 | | 2 | Seeby | 1 | | 1 |
| Pattie | 2 | | 2 | Tingey | 1 | | 1 |
| Shulton | 2 | | 2 | Opponents | | | 3 |

# KINGSTONIAN

**Chairman:** John Fenwick
**Secretary:** Philip WHatling **(T)** 07929 742 081 **(E)** secretary@kingstonian.com
**Commercial Manager:** **(T/E)**
**Programme Editor:** Robert Wooldridge **(T/E)** communications@kingstonian.com
**Ground Address:** Kingsmeadow Stadium, Kingston Road, Kingston KT1 3PB
**(T)** 0208 330 6869 **Manager:** Tommy Williams

Back Row (l-R): Ricky Sappleton, Peter Dean, Aaron Goode, Brendan Murphy-McVey, Harold Odametey, Malachi Hudson
Middle Row: Graham Harper, James Street, Sam Page, Tommy Williams, Rob Tolfrey, Pelayo Pico Gomez, Daniel Sweeney, Jeffrey Imudia, Keith Benjamin
Front Row: Dan Bennett, Richard Jolly, Ty Smith, Alan Inns, Filippo di Bonito, Patrik Ruzicka, Jake Kempton, George Wells, Micky Taylor.

## Club Factfile

**Founded:** 1885 **Nickname:** The K's
**Previous Names:** Kingston & Suburban YMCA 1885-87, Saxons 1887-90, Kingston Wanderers 1893-1904, Old Kingstonians 1908-19
**Previous Leagues:** Kingston & District, West Surrey, Southern Suburban, Athenian 1919-29, Isthmian 1929-98, Conference 1998-2001

**Club Colours (change):** Red and white hoops/black/red & black (Sky blue/blue/blue)

**Ground Capacity:** 4,262 **Seats:** 1,080 **Covered:** 2,538 **Clubhouse:** Yes **Shop:** Yes

**Directions**
Take Cambridge Road from Town Centre (A2043) to Malden Road.
From A3 turn off at New Malden and turn left onto A2043.
Ground is 1 mile on the left which is half a mile from Norbiton BR.

**Previous Grounds:** Several > 1921, Richmond Road 1921-89

**Record Attendance:** 4,582 v Chelsea - Freindly
**Record Victory:** 15-1 v Delft - 1951
**Record Defeat:** 0-11 v Ilford - Isthmian League 13/02/1937
**Record Goalscorer:** Johnnie Wing - 295 (1948-62)
**Record Appearances:** Micky Preston - 555 (1967-85)
**Additional Records:** Paid £18,000 to Rushden & Diamonds for David Leworthy 1997
Received £150,000 from West Ham United for Gavin Holligan 1999
**Honours:**
FA Amateur Cup 1932-33. Isthmian League 1933-34, 36-37, 97-98, Division 1 South 2008-09.
FAT Trophy 1998-99, 99-2000. Athenian League x2. London Senior Cup x3. Surrey Senior Cup x3.

### 10 YEAR RECORD

| 06-07 | 07-08 | 08-09 | 09-10 | 10-11 | 11-12 | 12-13 | 13-14 | 14-15 | 15-16 |
|---|---|---|---|---|---|---|---|---|---|
| Isth1S 13 | Isth1S 7 | Isth1S 1 | Isth P 5 | Isth P 7 | Isth P 11 | Isth P 11 | Isth P 2 | Isth P 11 | Isth P 7 |

# KINGSTONIAN MATCH RESULTS 2015-16

| Date | Comp | H/A | Opponents | Att: | Result | | Goalscorers | Pos | No. |
|---|---|---|---|---|---|---|---|---|---|
| Aug 8 | IsthP | A | Leiston | 175 | L | 1-2 | Gomez 21 | 20 | 1 |
| 10 | IsthP | H | Leatherhead | 333 | L | 0-3 | | 24 | 2 |
| 15 | IsthP | H | Met Police | 278 | **W** | 7-0 | BENNETT 3 (12 18 74) Dean 36 Gomez 70 Kempton 82 Smith 90 | 15 | 3 |
| 22 | IsthP | A | Wingate & Finchley | 272 | L | 1-2 | Bennett 80 | 16 | 4 |
| 24 | IsthP | H | VCD Athletic | 223 | **W** | 3-0 | Gomez 43 65 (pen) Smith 75 | 10 | 5 |
| 29 | IsthP | A | East Thurrock United | 171 | D | 2-2 | Bennett 40 Gomez 67 | 14 | 6 |
| 31 | IsthP | H | Dulwich Hamlet | 442 | L | 0-3 | | 15 | 7 |
| Sept5 | IsthP | A | Harrow Borough | 217 | **W** | 3-1 | Smith 5 Gomez 26 (pen) Kempton 74 | 12 | 8 |
| 8 | IsthP | A | VCD Athletic | 105 | **W** | 3-0 | Sappleton 60 70 Hudson 87 | 8 | 9 |
| **12** | **FAC1Q** | **H** | **Farnborough** | **282** | **D** | **1-1** | **Sappleton 11 (pen)** | | 10 |
| **14** | **FAC1Qr** | **A** | **Farnborough** | **199** | **W** | **3-2** | **Kempton 6 Smith 11 Bennett 40** | | 11 |
| 20 | IsthP | H | Canvey Island | 302 | **W** | 2-1 | Gomez 29 Sweeney 37 | 8 | 12 |
| 22 | IsthP | A | Bognor Regis Town | 351 | D | 0-0 | | 9 | 13 |
| **26** | **FAC2Q** | **A** | **Dunstable Town** | **173** | **L** | **0-2** | | | 14 |
| 28 | IsthP | H | Hendon | 285 | **W** | 1-0 | Murphy-McVey 86 | 9 | 15 |
| Oct 3 | IsthP | A | Grays Athletic | 191 | **W** | 3-1 | Bennett 30 Kempton 75 90 | 4 | 16 |
| 10 | IsthP | H | Billericay Town | 333 | D | 2-2 | Kempton 35 Goode 77 | 4 | 17 |
| 12 | IsthP | A | Hendon | 183 | D | 1-1 | Hudson 77 | 4 | 18 |
| 17 | IsthP | A | Tonbridge Angels | 545 | D | 1-1 | Kempton 29 | 8 | 19 |
| 24 | IsthP | H | Leiston | 264 | **W** | 1-0 | Page 43 | 6 | 20 |
| 28 | IsthP | A | Leatherhead | 354 | D | 0-0 | | | 21 |
| **31** | **FAT1Q** | **A** | **Leatherheead** | **260** | **W** | **5-2** | **Gomez 2 O'Leary 28 Dean 45 Oakley 49 Bennett 69** | | 22 |
| Nov 2 | IsthP | H | Enfield Town | 271 | W | 1-0 | Inns 68 | 4 | 23 |
| 7 | IsthP | A | Met Police | 345 | L | 1-2 | O'Leary 90 | 6 | 24 |
| **14** | **FAT2Q** | **A** | **Dorchester Town** | **312** | **D** | **2-2** | **Beccles 25 Gomez 28** | | 25 |
| **16** | **FAT2Qr** | **H** | **Dorchester Town** | **221** | **W** | **2-1** | **Bennett 14 30** | | 26 |
| 21 | IsthP | A | Lewes | 456 | **W** | 2-1 | Sappleton 87 90 | 4 | 27 |
| **28** | **FAT3Q** | **H** | **Truro City** | **316** | **L** | **0-3** | | | 28 |
| Dec 5 | IsthP | H | Merstham | 257 | **W** | 3-1 | Sappleton 15 Bennett 29 Gomez 40 | 3 | 29 |
| 12 | IsthP | A | Staines Town | 343 | **W** | 2-0 | Sappleton 34 Hudson 90 | 3 | 30 |
| 19 | IsthP | H | East Thurrock United | 272 | L | 1-4 | Gomez 20 | 5 | 31 |
| 26 | IsthP | A | Dulwich Hamlet | 1713 | L | 1-5 | Sappleton 11 | 6 | 32 |
| Jan 9 | IsthP | A | Hampton & Richmond B | 808 | L | 1-3 | Morgan 2 | 10 | 33 |
| 16 | IsthP | A | Burgess Hill Town | 369 | **W** | 3-1 | McCollin 3 31 Gomez 68 | 9 | 34 |
| 23 | IsthP | H | Needham Market | 273 | **W** | 4-2 | Hudson 56 60 McCollin 83 Bennett 90 | 8 | 35 |
| Feb 1 | IsthP | H | Wingate & Finchley | 262 | **W** | 2-1 | McCollin 4 10 | 6 | 36 |
| 6 | IsthP | H | Grays Athletic | 240 | **W** | 2-1 | Wells 18 McCollin 86 | 6 | 37 |
| 13 | IsthP | A | Billericay Town | 338 | D | 0-0 | | 7 | 38 |
| 20 | IsthP | H | Tonbridge Angels | 411 | L | 1-3 | McCollin 5 | 7 | 39 |
| 27 | IsthP | A | Needham Market | 195 | D | 0-0 | | 10 | 40 |
| Mar 6 | IsthP | H | Burgess Hill Town | 268 | **W** | 1-0 | Smith 68 | 8 | 41 |
| 12 | IsthP | H | Harrow Borough | 266 | **W** | 5-2 | Wells 1 Gomez 5 54 Smith 10 Beckles 77 | 6 | 42 |
| 14 | IsthP | H | Brentwood Town | 236 | **W** | 4-0 | Turner 19 81 McCollin 20 Gomez 43 (pen) | 4 | 43 |
| 19 | IsthP | A | Canvey Island | 259 | L | 1-2 | McCollin 49 | 5 | 44 |
| 22 | IsthP | A | Enfield Town | 338 | L | 0-4 | | 5 | 45 |
| 26 | IsthP | H | Hampton & Richmond B | 724 | **W** | 4-1 | Gomez 12 Inns 36 McCollin 65 Bennett 90 | 6 | 46 |
| Apr 2 | IsthP | H | Lewes | 251 | D | 2-2 | Bennett 24 Pinnock 59 | 7 | 47 |
| 4 | IsthP | H | Bognor Regis Town | 447 | **W** | 2-1 | McCollin 14 62 | 7 | 48 |
| 9 | IsthP | A | Brentwood Town | 133 | D | 0-0 | | 7 | 49 |
| 11 | IsthP | H | Farnborough | 291 | L | 1-2 | Bennett 73 | 7 | 50 |
| 17 | IsthP | H | Staines Town | 363 | L | 0-1 | | 7 | 51 |
| 19 | IsthP | A | Farnborough | 236 | L | 2-3 | Beckles 20 Bennett 90 | 7 | 52 |
| 23 | IsthP | A | Merstham | 266 | L | 1-3 | Beckles 90 | 7 | 53 |

| GOALSCORERS | Scoring Games | Consec Sco Games | Total |
|---|---|---|---|
| ***2014-15 Gomez*** | | | ***16*** |
| Gomez | 14 | 2 | 16 |
| Bennett | 13 | 2 | 16 |
| McCollin | 9 | | 12 |
| Sappleton | 7 | | 8 |
| Kempton | 6 | | 7 |
| Smith | 6 | | 6 |
| Hudson | 4 | | 5 |
| Beccles | 3 | | 3 |
| Dean | 2 | | 2 |
| O'Leary | 2 | | 2 |
| Inns | 2 | | 2 |
| Pinnock | 2 | | 2 |
| Turner | 2 | | 2 |
| Wells | 2 | | 2 |
| Goode | 1 | | 1 |
| Morgan | 1 | | 1 |
| Murphy-McVey | 1 | | 1 |
| Oakley | 1 | | 1 |
| Page | 1 | | 1 |
| Sweeney | 1 | | 1 |

# LEATHERHEAD

**Chairman:** TBC
**Secretary:** Jean Grant (T) 07815 187 460 (E) jeangrant65@hotmail.com
**Commercial Manager:** (T/E)
**Programme Editor:** TBC (T/E)
**Ground Address:** Fetcham Grove, Guildford Road, Leatherhead, Surrey KT22 9AS
(T) 01372 360 151 **Manager:** Mike Sandman

## Club Factfile

**Founded:** 1946 **Nickname:** The Tanners
**Previous Names:** None
**Previous Leagues:** Surrey Senior 1946-50, Metropolitan 1950-51, Delphian 1951-58, Corinthian 1958-63, Athenian 1963-72

**Club Colours (change):** Green/white/green (All red)

**Ground Capacity:** 3,400 **Seats:** 200 **Covered:** 45 **Clubhouse:** Yes **Shop:** Yes

**Directions**
M25 junction 9 to Leatherhead,
follow signs to Leisure Centre,
ground adjacent.
Half a mile from Leatherhead BR.

**Previous Grounds:** None

**Record Attendance:** 5,500 v Wimbledon - 1976
**Record Victory:** 13-1 v Leyland Motors - Surrey Senior League 1946-47
**Record Defeat:** 1-11 v Sutton United
**Record Goalscorer:** Steve Lunn scored 46 goals during 1996-97
**Record Appearances:** P Caswell - 200
**Additional Records:** Paid £1,500 to Croydon for B Salkeld
Received £1,500 from Croydon for B Salkeld

**Honours:**
Athenian League 1963-64.
Surrey Senior Cup 1968-69. Isthmian League cup 1977-78.

### 10 YEAR RECORD

| 06-07 | 07-08 | 08-09 | 09-10 | 10-11 | 11-12 | 12-13 | 13-14 | 14-15 | 15-16 |
|---|---|---|---|---|---|---|---|---|---|
| Isth1S 11 | Isth1S 17 | Isth1S 15 | Isth1S 5 | Isth1S 4 | Isth P 19 | Isth1S 6 | Isth1S 3 | Isth P 10 | Isth P 11 |

# LEATHERHEAD MATCH RESULTS 2015-16

| Date | Comp | H/A | Opponents | Att: | Result | | Goalscorers | Pos | No. |
|---|---|---|---|---|---|---|---|---|---|
| Aug 8 | IsthP | H | Lewes | 282 | W | 3-0 | Hughes-Mason 5 Karagiannis13 Nwokeji 90 | 2 | 1 |
| 10 | IsthP | A | Kingstonian | 333 | W | 3-0 | Karagiannis 5 17 Walsh 40 | 1 | 2 |
| 15 | IsthP | A | Staines Town | 293 | L | 0-1 | | 5 | 3 |
| 22 | IsthP | H | Canvey Island | 302 | D | 4-4 | Hughes-Mason 10 Karagiannis 23 40 Walsh 74 | 6 | 4 |
| 26 | IsthP | H | Dulwich Hamlet | 341 | W | 1-0 | Walsh 16 | 5 | 5 |
| 29 | IsthP | A | Brentwood Town | 102 | L | 1-4 | Hughes-Mason 90 | 5 | 6 |
| 31 | IsthP | H | Merstham | 275 | L | 0-2 | | 10 | 7 |
| Sept 5 | IsthP | A | East Thurrock United | 137 | D | 4-4 | Avery 53 Nnamani 61 Gallagher 73 Long 80 | 11 | 8 |
| 8 | IsthP | A | Dulwich Hamlet | 625 | L | 0-1 | | 13 | 9 |
| **12** | **FAC1Q** | **A** | **South Park** | **148** | **D** | **1-1** | **Hughes-Mason 84** | | 10 |
| 19 | IsthP | H | Wingate & Finchley | 240 | D | 0-0 | | 14 | 11 |
| **23** | **FAC1Qr** | **H** | **South Park** | **186** | **L** | **1-3** | **Burnett-Thomas 80** | | 12 |
| 26 | IsthP | H | Hendon | 236 | L | 2-5 | Karagiannis 26 49 | 16 | 13 |
| 30 | IsthP | H | Grays Athletic | 272 | W | 3-0 | Gallagher 13 28 Daly 64 | 16 | 14 |
| Oct 3 | IsthP | A | Enfield Town | 367 | L | 0-4 | | 17 | 15 |
| 10 | IsthP | H | Burgess Hill Town | 283 | W | 3-2 | KARAGIANNIS 3 (13 43 84 pen) | 15 | 16 |
| 14 | IsthP | A | Grays Athletic | 172 | W | 2-0 | Yuseff 51 Adeyinka 90 | 11 | 17 |
| 17 | IsthP | A | Billericay Town | 271 | L | 0-2 | | 14 | 18 |
| 21 | IsthP | H | Tonbridge Angels | 291 | L | 0-2 | | 15 | 19 |
| 24 | IsthP | A | Lewes | 360 | W | 4-3 | Hughes-Mason 10 KARAGIANNIS 3 (12 28 38) | 12 | 20 |
| 28 | IsthP | H | Kingstonian | 354 | D | 0-0 | | 15 | 21 |
| **31** | **FAT1Q** | **H** | **Kingstonian** | **260** | **L** | **1-5** | **Hughes-Mason 88 (pen)** | | 22 |
| Nov 21 | IsthP | A | Metropolitan Police | 143 | L | 0-1 | | 18 | 23 |
| 28 | IsthP | A | Canvey Island | 202 | L | 1-3 | Kinnear 27 | 18 | 24 |
| Dec 5 | IsthP | H | Harrow Borough | 236 | L | 1-2 | Hughes-Mason 9 | 18 | 25 |
| 12 | IsthP | A | Farnborough | 302 | W | 3-1 | Hughes-Mason 11 Dembele 61 Mahal 90 | 18 | 26 |
| 19 | IsthP | H | Brentwood Town | 145 | W | 1-0 | Kinnear 14 | 17 | 27 |
| 26 | IsthP | A | Merstham | 201 | W | 2-1 | Adeloye 69 Hughes-Mason 64 | 16 | 28 |
| Jan 6 | IsthP | H | Staines Town | 277 | W | 3-0 | Collin 2 (pen) Hughes-Mason 55 Bennett 83 (og) | 14 | 29 |
| 9 | IsthP | A | VCD Athletic | 113 | W | 1-0 | Freeman 10 | 12 | 30 |
| 16 | IsthP | A | Needham Market | 218 | L | 0-1 | | 13 | 31 |
| 23 | IsthP | H | Leiston | 264 | W | 3-2 | Collin 6 34 Hughes-Mason 23 | 12 | 32 |
| Feb 2 | IsthP | A | Tonbridge Angels | 335 | L | 0-4 | | 13 | 33 |
| 6 | IsthP | H | Enfield Town | 302 | L | 0-3 | | 14 | 34 |
| 10 | IsthP | H | Hampton & Richmond B | 367 | D | 2-2 | Collin 2 Hughes-Mason12 | 15 | 35 |
| 27 | IsthP | A | Leiston | 195 | L | 1-3 | Walsh 61 | 16 | 36 |
| Mar 5 | IsthP | H | Needham Market | 241 | D | 2-2 | Mahal 21 Collin 47 | 16 | 37 |
| 12 | IsthP | H | East Thurrock United | 251 | W | 2-1 | Collin 13 (pen) 80 | 15 | 38 |
| 16 | IsthP | H | Bognor Regis Town | 265 | L | 0-3 | | 15 | 39 |
| 19 | IsthP | A | Wingate & Finchley | 122 | D | 1-1 | Watt 43 | 15 | 40 |
| 23 | IsthP | A | Burgess Hill Town | 283 | W | 2-1 | Mahal 37 Walsh 38 | 14 | 41 |
| 26 | IsthP | H | VCD Athletic | 268 | W | 2-0 | Walsh 74 Mahal 90 | 13 | 42 |
| 28 | IsthP | A | Hampton & Richmond B | 707 | L | 0-2 | | 13 | 43 |
| Apr 2 | IsthP | H | Met Police | 225 | L | 1-3 | Bodkin 41 | 14 | 44 |
| 6 | IsthP | H | Billericay Town | 227 | W | 4-1 | Collin 19 Nnamani 32 Adeloye 81 Mahal 86 | 12 | 45 |
| 9 | IsthP | A | Bognor Regis Town | 421 | L | 0-5 | | 11 | 46 |
| 11 | IsthP | A | Hendon | 125 | W | 3-2 | Hughes-Mason 8 Collin 73 74 | 10 | 47 |
| 16 | IsthP | H | Farnborough | 317 | L | 0-1 | | 10 | 48 |
| 23 | IsthP | A | Harrow Borough | 163 | D | 2-2 | Adeloye 49 Mahal 61 | 11 | 49 |

| GOALSCORERS | Scoring Games | Consec Sco Games | Total | | Scoring Games | Consec Sco Games | Total |
|---|---|---|---|---|---|---|---|
| ***2014-15 Hughes-Mason*** | | | ***21*** | Avery | 1 | | 1 |
| Karagiannis | 6 | 2 | 13 | Bodkin | 1 | | 1 |
| Hughes-Mason | 12 | | 13 | Burnett-Thomas | 1 | | 1 |
| Collin | 7 | | 10 | Daly | 1 | | 1 |
| Mahal | 6 | | 6 | Dembele | 1 | | 1 |
| Walsh | 5 | 2 | 6 | Freeman | 1 | | 1 |
| Adeloye | 3 | | 3 | Long | 1 | | 1 |
| Gallagher | 3 | | 3 | Nwokeji | 1 | | 1 |
| Kinnear | 2 | | 2 | Watt | 1 | | 1 |
| Nnamani | 2 | | 2 | Yusseff | 1 | | 1 |
| Adeyinka | 1 | | 1 | Opponents | | | 1 |

# LEISTON

**Chairman:** Andrew Crisp
**Secretary:** David Rees **(T)** 07977 782 559 **(E)** gagrees@aol.com
**Commercial Manager:** **(T/E)**
**Programme Editor:** Jill Douglas **(T/E)** lhsjilldouglass@gmail.com
**Ground Address:** LTAA, Victory Road, Leiston IP16 4DQ
**(T)** 01728 830 308 **Manager:** Glenn Driver

2015-16 Squad

## Club Factfile

**Founded:** 1880 **Nickname:** The Blues
**Previous Names:** None
**Previous Leagues:** Suffolk & Ipswich, Eastern Counties > 2011.

**Club Colours (change):** All blue (All red)

**Ground Capacity:** 2,500 **Seats:** 124 **Covered:** 500 **Clubhouse:** **Shop:**

**Directions**
Take junction 28 off the M25, take the A12/A1023 exit to Chelmsford/Romford/Brentwood, keep left at the fork, follow signs for Chelmsford/A12 (E) and merge onto A12, at the roundabout, take the 3rd exit onto the A14 ramp, merge onto A14, at junction 58, exit toward A12, keep left at the fork, follow signs for Lowestoft/Woodbridge/A12 (N) and merge onto A12, go through 7 roundabouts, turn right onto A1094, turn left onto Snape Rd/B1069, continue to follow B1069, turn left onto Victory Rd, ground will be on the left.

**Previous Grounds:** Leiston Recreation Ground 1880-1918.

**Record Attendance:** **Att:** 271 v AFC Sudbury, 13.11.04.
**Record Victory:** Not known
**Record Defeat:** Not known
**Record Goalscorer:** Lee McGlone - 60 (League).
**Record Appearances:** Tim Sparkes - 154 (League).
**Additional Records:**

**Honours:**
Eastern Counties League Premier Division 2010-11. Isthmian League Division 1 North 2011-12.

**10 YEAR RECORD**

| 06-07 | | 07-08 | | 08-09 | | 09-10 | | 10-11 | | 11-12 | | 12-13 | | 13-14 | | 14-15 | | 15-16 | |
|---|---|---|---|---|---|---|---|---|---|---|---|---|---|---|---|---|---|---|---|
| ECP | 5 | ECP | 9 | ECP | 7 | ECP | 3 | ECP | 1 | Isth1N | 1 | Isth P | 12 | Isth P | 9 | Isth P | 9 | Isth P | 8 |

# LEISTON MATCH RESULTS 2015-16

| Date | Comp | H/A | Opponents | Att: | Result | | Goalscorers | Pos | No. |
|---|---|---|---|---|---|---|---|---|---|
| Aug 8 | IsthP | H | Kingstonian | 175 | W | 2-1 | Mills 40 Finch 50 | 5 | 1 |
| 11 | IsthP | A | Canvey Island | 247 | D | 1-1 | Ottley-Gooch 81 | 7 | 2 |
| 15 | IsthP | A | Merstham | 147 | W | 2-0 | Brothers 51 Francis 83 | 2 | 3 |
| 22 | IsthP | H | Lewes | 180 | W | 3-1 | Heath 18 Jefford 38 Francis 89 (pen) | 1 | 4 |
| 25 | IsthP | A | Enfield Town | 295 | W | 2-0 | Jefford 23 Ottley-Gooch 48 | 1 | 5 |
| 29 | IsthP | H | Hendon | 204 | W | 2-0 | Heath 25 Brothers 90 | 1 | 6 |
| 31 | IsthP | A | Needham Market | 411 | D | 2-2 | Finch 6 Clark 15 | 2 | 7 |
| Sept 5 | IsthP | H | Grays Athletic | 232 | L | 1-2 | Bullard 43 | 3 | 8 |
| 8 | IsthP | H | Enfield Town | 171 | W | 2-0 | Heath 18 Finch 22 | 3 | 9 |
| **12** | **FAC1Q** | **H** | **AFC Dunstable** | **161** | **W** | **1-0** | **Jefford 45** | | 10 |
| 19 | IsthP | A | Tonbridge Angels | 541 | W | 1-0 | Brothers 90 | 2 | 11 |
| 23 | IsthP | H | Brentwood Town | 152 | W | 2-0 | Jefford 47 Anderson 64 (og) | 1 | 12 |
| **26** | **FAC2Q** | **H** | **Tonbridge Angels** | **212** | **W** | **3-0** | **Jefford 18 Sands 46 73** | | 13 |
| 29 | IsthP | A | East Thurrock United | 163 | L | 0-4 | | 1 | 14 |
| Oct 3 | IsthP | H | Hampton & Richmond B | 197 | W | 3-1 | Heath 54 90 Francis 60 | 1 | 15 |
| **10** | **FAC3Q** | **H** | **Gloucester City** | **329** | **L** | **1-3** | **Boardley 81** | | 16 |
| 14 | IsthP | H | East Thurrock United | 147 | L | 0-3 | | 1 | 17 |
| 17 | IsthP | H | Farnborough | 129 | W | 4-2 | SANDS 3 ( 10 12 29 3pen) Finch 81 | | 18 |
| 24 | IsthP | A | Kingstonian | 284 | L | 0-1 | | 3 | 19 |
| 28 | IsthP | H | Canvey Island | 225 | D | 1-1 | Clark 2 | | 20 |
| **31** | **FAT1Q** | **A** | **Worthing** | **311** | **W** | **3-1** | **Jefford 53 Winter 67 Brothers 90** | | 21 |
| Nov 7 | IsthP | H | Merstham | 160 | W | 3-1 | Clark 20 Ottley-Gooch 42 Finch 76 | 2 | 22 |
| **14** | **FAT2Q** | **H** | **Corinthian Casuals** | **185** | **L** | **1-2** | **Francis 34 (pen)** | | 23 |
| 17 | IsthP | A | Wingate & Finchley | 131 | L | 0-1 | | 4 | 24 |
| 28 | IsthP | A | VCD Athletic | 82 | D | 0-0 | | 6 | 25 |
| Dec 5 | IsthP | H | Met Police | 138 | L | 1-2 | Dunbar 25 | | 26 |
| 12 | IsthP | A | Lewes | 394 | D | 1-1 | Francis 5 | 8 | 27 |
| 15 | IsthP | A | Dulwich Hamlet | 617 | D | 1-1 | Heath 9 | 7 | 28 |
| 19 | IsthP | A | Hendon | 119 | W | 4-2 | Heath 18 Finch 49 66 Francis 90 | 7 | 29 |
| 26 | IsthP | H | Needham Forest | 303 | W | 3-0 | Finch 18 Ottley-Gooch 20 Francis 42 | 5 | 30 |
| Jan 9 | IsthP | H | Burgess Hill Town | 178 | D | 1-1 | Jefford 50 | 5 | 31 |
| 23 | IsthP | A | Leatherhead | 284 | L | 2-3 | Trotter 61 Bullard 90 | 8 | 32 |
| 27 | IsthP | H | Staines Town | 134 | W | 3-1 | Bullard 53 72 Heath 73 | 6 | 33 |
| 30 | IsthP | H | VCD Athletic | 146 | W | 3-0 | Finch 9 29 Heath 40 | 5 | 34 |
| Feb 2 | IsthP | A | Bognor Regis Town | 372 | L | 0-3 | | 8 | 35 |
| 6 | IsthP | A | Hampton & Richmond B | 342 | L | 3-4 | Brothers 51 Broadley 90 Heath 90 | 8 | 36 |
| 9 | IsthP | A | Billericay Town | 164 | L | 1-4 | Ainsley 64 | 8 | 37 |
| 13 | IsthP | H | Wingate & Finchley | 152 | L | 0-1 | | 8 | 38 |
| 17 | IsthP | A | Brentwood Town | 98 | W | 2-0 | Clark 61 90 | 8 | 39 |
| 20 | IsthP | A | Farnborough | 164 | L | 0-3 | | 9 | 40 |
| 27 | IsthP | H | Leatherhead | 189 | W | 3-1 | Finch 20 29 (pen) Ainsley 90 (pen) | 8 | 41 |
| Mar 5 | IsthP | A | Harrow Borough | 127 | D | 0-0 | | 8 | 42 |
| 12 | IsthP | A | Grays Athletic | 144 | W | 2-0 | Heath 43 Taylor 87 | 7 | 43 |
| 16 | IsthP | H | Harrow Borough | 130 | W | 2-0 | Finch 33 Taylor 89 | 6 | 44 |
| 19 | IsthP | H | Tonbridge Angels | 197 | L | 1-2 | Finch 75 (pen) | 6 | 45 |
| 26 | IsthP | A | Burgess Hill Town | 320 | D | 1-1 | Clark 67 | 7 | 46 |
| 28 | IsthP | H | Billericay mTow | 201 | D | 1-1 | Jefford 43 | 8 | 47 |
| Apr 2 | IsthP | A | Staines Town | 181 | D | 2-2 | Jefford 10 Clark 61 | 8 | 48 |
| 9 | IsthP | H | Dulwich Hamlet | 205 | D | 1-1 | Finch 7 | 8 | 49 |
| 16 | IsthP | H | Bognor Regis Town | 285 | L | 0-2 | | 8 | 50 |
| 23 | IsthP | A | Met Police | 78 | W | 3-0 | Winter 15 Taylor 25 Heath 58 | 8 | 51 |

| GOALSCORERS | Scoring Games | Consec Sco Games | Total |
|---|---|---|---|
| ***2014-15 Heath*** | | | ***19*** |
| Finch | 11 | 2 | 15 |
| Heath | 11 | 2 | 12 |
| Jefford | 9 | | 9 |
| Clark | 6 | | 7 |
| Frances | 6 | | 7 |
| Brothers | 5 | | 5 |
| Sands | 3 | | 5 |
| Bullard | 3 | | 4 |
| Ottlry-Gooch | 4 | | 4 |

| | Scoring Games | Consec Sco Games | Total |
|---|---|---|---|
| Taylor | 3 | | 3 |
| Ainsley | 2 | | 2 |
| Boardley | 2 | | 2 |
| Winter | 2 | | 2 |
| Dunbar | 1 | | 1 |
| Mills | 1 | | 1 |
| Trotter | 1 | | 1 |
| Opponents | | | 1 |

# LOWESTOFT TOWN

**Chairman:** Gary Keyzor
**Secretary:** Terry Lynes **(T)** 0793 087 2947 **(E)** terrylynes@fsmail.net
**Commercial Manager:** Sam Hossack **(T/E)** 07842 007 189
**Programme Editor:** Terry Lynes **(T/E)** terrylynes@fsmail.net
**Ground Address:** Crown Meadow, Love Road, Lowestoft NR32 2PA
**(T)** 01502 573 818 / 567 280 **Manager:** Ady Gallagher

## Club Factfile

**Founded:** 1880 **Nickname:** The Trawler Boys or Blues
**Previous Names:** Original club merged with Kirkley in 1887 to form Lowestoft and became Lowestoft Town in 1890
**Previous Leagues:** North Suffolk 1897-35, Eastern Counties 1935-2009. Isthmian 2009-2014. Conference 2014-16.

**Club Colours (change):** All blue (All white)

**Ground Capacity:** 3,000 **Seats:** 466 **Covered:** 500 **Clubhouse:** Yes **Shop:** Yes

**Directions**
Head for Lowestoft town centre. After crossing Bascule Bridge and railway station turn right at traffic lights (sp A12 Yarmouth) into Katwyck Way. After 300 yards take 1st exit at roundabout into Raglan Street. At 'T' junction turn left into Love Road and ground is about 100 yards on right.

**Previous Grounds:** None

**Record Attendance:** 5,000 v Watford - FA Cup 1st Round 1967
**Record Victory:** Not Known
**Record Defeat:** Not Known
**Record Goalscorer:** Not Known
**Record Appearances:** Not Known
**Additional Records:**

**Honours:**
Eastern Counties League 1935-36 (shared), 37-38, 62-63, 64-65, 65-66, 66-67, 67-68, 69-70, 70-71, 77-78, 2005-06, 08-09.
Isthmian League Division 1 North 2009-10.
Suffolk Senior Cup 1902-03, 22-23, 25-26, 31-32, 35-36, 46-47, 47-48, 48-49, 55-56, Premier Cup 2014-15, 15-16.

### 10 YEAR RECORD

| 06-07 | | 07-08 | | 08-09 | | 09-10 | | 10-11 | | 11-12 | | 12-13 | | 13-14 | | 14-15 | | 15-16 | |
|---|---|---|---|---|---|---|---|---|---|---|---|---|---|---|---|---|---|---|---|
| ECP | 3 | ECP | 11 | ECP | 1 | Isth1N | 1 | Isth P | 4 | Isth P | 3 | Isth P | 2 | Isth P | 4 | Conf N | 16 | Nat N | 20 |

# LOWESTOFT TOWN MATCH RESULTS 2015-16

| Date | Comp | H/A | Opponents | Att: | Result | | Goalscorers | Pos | No. |
|---|---|---|---|---|---|---|---|---|---|
| Aug 8 | Nat North | H | AFC Telford United | 539 | W | 3-0 | Reed 69 77 Crow 70 | 1 | 1 |
| 11 | Nat North | A | Alfreton Town | 515 | W | 1-0 | Reed 63 | 2 | 2 |
| 15 | Nat North | A | Worcester City | 577 | L | 1-2 | Henderson 30 | 5 | 3 |
| 18 | Nat North | H | Nuneaton Town | 507 | L | 0-1 | | 7 | 4 |
| 22 | Nat North | A | AFC Fylde | 338 | L | 0-1 | | 12 | 5 |
| 29 | Nat North | H | Corby Town | 635 | D | 2-2 | Reed 13 Jarvis 86 | 11 | 6 |
| 31 | Nat North | A | North Ferriby United | 314 | D | 0-0 | | 13 | 7 |
| Sept 5 | Nat North | H | FC United | 1154 | L | 1-4 | Henderson 38 | 17 | 8 |
| 12 | Nat North | A | Stalybridge Celtic | 318 | L | 1-3 | Reed 69 | 18 | 9 |
| 15 | Nat North | A | Brackley Town | 208 | D | 2-2 | Reed 18 Henderson 82 | 17 | 10 |
| 19 | Nat North | H | Chorley | 588 | W | 2-0 | Jarvis 79 Eagle 90 | 15 | 11 |
| **26** | **FAC2Q** | **A** | **Bognor Regis Town** | **396** | **L** | **1-2** | **Crow 82** | | 12 |
| Oct 3 | Nat North | A | Hednesford Town | 378 | L | 1-2 | Reed 70 | 15 | 13 |
| 10 | Nat North | A | Curzon Ashton | 224 | L | 1-4 | Crow 71 | 17 | 14 |
| 17 | Nat North | H | Harrogate Town | 504 | L | 1-2 | Reed 38 | 19 | 15 |
| 24 | Nat North | H | Tamworth | 508 | L | 0-4 | | 20 | 16 |
| 31 | Nat North | A | Bradford PA | 279 | L | 0-3 | | 20 | 17 |
| Nov 7 | Nat North | H | Solihull Moors | 438 | D | 2-2 | Jarvis 25 Eagle 70 | 21 | 18 |
| 14 | Nat North | A | Gloucester City | 354 | W | 1-0 | Reed 34 | 21 | 19 |
| 21 | Nat North | H | Stockport County | 629 | D | 2-2 | Mason 75 Bammant 90 | 18 | 20 |
| **28** | **FAT3Q** | **H** | **St Albans City** | **420** | **W** | **4-0** | **Reed 40 Ainsley 42 (pen) Crow73 Woods-Garness 86** | | 21 |
| Dec 5 | Nat North | H | AlfretonTown | 487 | W | 1-0 | Reed 67 | 16 | 22 |
| 19 | Nat North | A | AFC Telford United | 1136 | L | 0-1 | | 19 | 23 |
| 26 | Nat North | H | Boston United | 696 | W | 3-0 | Jones 4 (og) Spillane 15 Reed 53 | 16 | 24 |
| 28 | Nat North | A | Corby Town | 616 | W | 5-3 | Reed 16 49 Ainsley 38 (pen) 90 (pen) Eagle 52 | 14 | 25 |
| Jan 2 | Nat North | A | Boston United | 1499 | L | 1-4 | Hodd 7 | 16 | 26 |
| **4** | **FAT1** | **A** | **Sutton United** | **454** | **L** | **1-3** | **Woods-Garness 42** | | 27 |
| 23 | Nat North | A | FC United | 3280 | L | 1-6 | Crow 73 | 18 | 28 |
| 30 | Nat North | H | Stalybridge Celtic | 570 | L | 0-2 | | 19 | 29 |
| Feb 16 | Nat North | H | AFC Fylde | 438 | W | 3-1 | Hannigan 5 (og) Spillane 59 Reed 80 (pen) | 18 | 30 |
| 20 | Nat North | H | Bradford PA | 627 | W | 3-0 | Reed 25 Jarvis 37 Spillane 51 | 17 | 31 |
| 23 | Nat North | H | Hednesford Town | 465 | D | 0-0 | | 17 | 32 |
| 27 | Nat North | A | Chorley Town | 913 | L | 0-2 | | 18 | 33 |
| Mar 5 | Nat North | H | Brackley Town | 506 | L | 1-2 | Spillane 35 | 20 | 34 |
| 12 | Nat North | A | Solihull Moors | 522 | L | 1-2 | Crow 63 | 20 | 35 |
| 19 | Nat North | H | Gainsborough Trinity | 530 | W | 1-0 | Jarvis 3 | 20 | 36 |
| 26 | Nat North | A | Nuneaton Town | 537 | L | 0-1 | | 20 | 37 |
| Apr 2 | Nat North | A | Stockport Co. | 2396 | W | 2-0 | Mason 38 Crow 79 | 20 | 38 |
| 5 | Nat North | A | Harrogate Town | 546 | L | 0-4 | | 20 | 39 |
| 9 | Nat North | H | Curzon Ashton | 477 | D | 0-0 | | 20 | 40 |
| 16 | Nat North | A | Gainsborough Trinity | 507 | D | 1-1 | Roma 79 (og) | 20 | 41 |
| 19 | Nat North | H | Worcester City | 508 | W | 2-1 | Crow 10 Deeks 80 | 19 | 42 |
| 23 | Nat North | A | Tamworth | 1418 | D | 1-1 | Smith 90 | 19 | 43 |
| 27 | Nat North | H | North Ferriby United | 549 | L | 0-3 | | 20 | 44 |
| 30 | Nat North | H | Gloucester City | 935 | D | 1-1 | Crow 24 | 20 | 45 |

| GOALSCORERS | Scoring Games | Consec Sco Games | Total |
|---|---|---|---|
| ***2014-15 Ainsley*** | | | ***14*** |
| Reed | 14 | 2 | 16 |
| Crow | 9 | | 9 |
| Jarvis | 4 | | 5 |
| Spillane | 4 | | 4 |
| Ainsley | 3 | | 3 |
| Eagle | 3 | | 3 |
| Henderson | 3 | | 3 |
| Mason | 2 | | 2 |
| Woods-Garness | 2 | | 2 |
| Bammant | 1 | | 1 |
| Deeks | 1 | | 1 |
| Hodd | 1 | | 1 |
| Smith | 1 | | 1 |

# MERSTHAM

**Chairman:** Chris Chapman

**Secretary:** Richard Baxter **(T)** 07720 290 027 **(E)** richardbaxter01@hotmail.com

**Commercial Manager:** **(T/E)**

**Programme Editor:** Kevin Austen **(T/E)** 07911 853 353

**Ground Address:** Moatside Stadium, Weldon Way, Merstham, Surrey RH1 3QB

**(T)** 01737 644 046 **Manager:** Hayden Bird

## Club Factfile

**Founded:** 1905 **Nickname:** Moatsiders

**Previous Names:** None

**Previous Leagues:** Redhill & District, Surrey Senior 1964-78, London Spartan 1978-84, Combined Counties 1984-2008

**Club Colours (change):** Yellow/black/black (All red)

**Ground Capacity:** 2,500 **Seats:** 174 **Covered:** 100 **Clubhouse:** Yes **Shop:** No

**Directions**

Leave Merstham village (A23) by School Hill,
take 5th right (Weldon Way).
Clubhouse and car park on the right.
Ten minutes walk from Merstham BR.

**Previous Grounds:** None

**Record Attendance:** 1,587 v AFC Wimbledon - Combined Counties League 09/11/2002

**Record Victory:** Not Known

**Record Defeat:** Not Known

**Record Goalscorer:** Not Known

**Record Appearances:** Not Known

**Additional Records:**

**Honours:**

Combined Counties League Premier Division 2007-08. Isthmian Div.1 South Play-off 2014-15.
Surrey Senior Cup 2015-16.

### 10 YEAR RECORD

| 06-07 | 07-08 | 08-09 | 09-10 | 10-11 | 11-12 | 12-13 | 13-14 | 14-15 | 15-16 |
|---|---|---|---|---|---|---|---|---|---|
| CCP 2 | CCP 1 | Isth1S 8 | Isth1S 16 | Isth1S 19 | Isth1S 9 | Isth1S 12 | Isth1S 7 | Isth1S 4 | Isth P 10 |

# MERSTHAM MATCH RESULTS 2015-16

| Date | Comp | H/A | Opponents | Att: | Result | | Goalscorers | Pos | No. |
|---|---|---|---|---|---|---|---|---|---|
| Aug 8 | IsthP | A | Bognor Regis Town | 420 | L | 3-4 | Hutchings 12 (pen) 39 Hall 85 | 18 | 1 |
| 11 | IsthP | H | Dulwich Hamlet | 321 | L | 0-2 | | 21 | 2 |
| 15 | IsthP | H | Leiston | 147 | L | 0-2 | | 23 | 3 |
| 22 | IsthP | A | Met Police | 85 | W | 3-2 | Hutchings 27 Cooper 49 Kavanagh 52 | 19 | 4 |
| 25 | IsthP | A | Billericay Town | 208 | D | 1-1 | Roberts 37 | 17 | 5 |
| 29 | IsthP | H | Burgess Hill Town | 162 | L | 1-2 | Hutchings 61 | 19 | 6 |
| 31 | IsthP | A | Leatherhead | 275 | W | 2-0 | Daly 32 Saraiva 63 | 16 | 7 |
| Sept 5 | IsthP | H | Needham Market | 136 | W | 2-0 | Kavanagh 76 Abnett 89 | 14 | 8 |
| 8 | IsthP | H | Billericay Town | 153 | L | 0-2 | | 16 | 9 |
| **12** | **FAC1Q** | **A** | **Bognor Regis Town** | **299** | **L** | **1-2** | **Rhule 84** | | 10 |
| 19 | IsthP | A | Hendon | 133 | D | 2-2 | Faulkes 72 Kavanagh 73 | 17 | 11 |
| 22 | IsthP | H | Harrow Borough | 117 | L | 0-1 | | 18 | 12 |
| 26 | IsthP | A | Hampton & Richmond B | 291 | L | 1-2 | Faulkes 34 | 17 | 13 |
| Oct 3 | IsthP | H | East Thurrock United | 503 | D | 2-2 | Kavanagh 33 Saraiva 60 | 20 | 14 |
| 6 | IsthP | A | Brentwood Town | 90 | W | 2-1 | Hutchings 23 Saraiva 35 (pen) | 16 | 15 |
| 10 | IsthP | A | VCD Athletic | 85 | W | 3-1 | Cooper 3 Penny 74 86 | 14 | 16 |
| 13 | IsthP | H | Hampton & Richmond B | 162 | L | 1-6 | Saraiva 76 | 16 | 17 |
| 17 | IsthP | H | Wingate & Finchley | 125 | L | 0-2 | | 19 | 18 |
| 20 | IsthP | A | Harrow Borough | 124 | W | 2-0 | Penny 65 Saraiva 75 (pen) | 16 | 19 |
| 24 | IsthP | H | Hendon | 147 | W | 1-0 | Penny 90 | 13 | 20 |
| 27 | IsthP | A | Dulwich Hamlet | 869 | L | 0-4 | | 16 | 21 |
| **31** | **FAT1Q** | **H** | **Harlow Town** | **123** | **D** | **0-0** | | | 22 |
| **Nov 3** | **FAT1Qr** | **A** | **Harlow Town** | **210** | **L** | **2-6** | **Abnett 45 Rhule 45** | | 23 |
| 7 | IsthP | A | Leiston | 160 | L | 1-3 | Cooper 77 | 17 | 24 |
| 21 | IsthP | H | Canvey Island | 165 | W | 1-0 | Page 85 | 15 | 25 |
| 24 | IsthP | H | Bognor Regis Town | 153 | W | 3-2 | Saraiva 23 Willock 82 Page 85 | 14 | 26 |
| 28 | IsthP | A | Enfield Town | 284 | D | 2-2 | Willock 55 Saraiva 77 | 14 | 27 |
| Dec 5 | IsthP | A | Kingstonian | 257 | L | 1-3 | Page 89 | 15 | 28 |
| 12 | IsthP | H | Tonbridge Angels | 197 | D | 2-2 | Penny 11 34 | 15 | 29 |
| 19 | IsthP | A | Burgess Hill Town | 305 | L | 1-5 | Penny 13 | 16 | 30 |
| 26 | IsthP | H | Leatherhead | 201 | L | 1-2 | Saraiva 74 | 17 | 31 |
| Jan 6 | IsthP | A | Lewes | 314 | L | 0-1 | | 18 | 32 |
| 9 | IsthP | H | Grays Athletic | 188 | D | 2-2 | Saraiva 8 Kavanagh 84 | 17 | 33 |
| 16 | IsthP | H | Staines Town | 172 | W | 5-1 | Henriques 15 Willock18 Kavanagh 57 Page 8 Samuels 84 | 17 | 34 |
| 23 | IsthP | A | Farnborough | 267 | W | 3-0 | Saraiva 55 89 Penny 79 | 17 | 35 |
| 30 | IsthP | H | Brentwood Town | 162 | L | 1-3 | Douglas 58 | 17 | 36 |
| Feb 6 | IsthP | A | East Thurrock United | 251 | W | 2-1 | Henriques 38 Penny 71 | 16 | 37 |
| 13 | IsthP | H | VCD Athletic | 145 | W | 6-1 | PENNY 4 ( 7 71 (pen) 80 90 (pen) ) Campbell 31 Saraiva 49 | 13 | 38 |
| 20 | IsthP | A | Wingate & Finchley | 121 | W | 3-1 | PENNY 3 ( 10 15 46 pen) | 12 | 39 |
| 27 | IsthP | H | Farnborough | 195 | D | 1-1 | Saraiva 25 | 13 | 40 |
| Mar 5 | IsthP | A | Staines Town | 146 | L | 0-2 | | 14 | 41 |
| 12 | IsthP | A | Needham Market | 231 | L | 0-1 | | 14 | 42 |
| 22 | IsthP | H | Met Police | 143 | W | 1-0 | Campbell 36 | 10 | 43 |
| 26 | IsthP | A | Grays Athletic | 128 | W | 3-1 | WILLOCK 3 ( 19 23 32) | 10 | 44 |
| 28 | IsthP | H | Lewes | 186 | D | 2-2 | Penny 74 (Pen) Willock 78 | 12 | 45 |
| Apr 2 | IsthP | A | Canvey Island | 221 | W | 2-0 | Samuels 42 Willock 46 | 10 | 46 |
| 9 | IsthP | H | Enfield Town | 465 | L | 0-4 | | 10 | 47 |
| 16 | IsthP | A | Tonbridge Angels | 609 | L | 2-3 | Penny 21 90 (pen) | 13 | 48 |
| 23 | IsthP | H | Kingstonian | 266 | W | 3-1 | Saraiva 21 Henriques 89 Penny 90 | 10 | 49 |

| GOALSCORERS | Scoring Games | Consec Sco Games | Total |
|---|---|---|---|
| Penny | 12 | 3 | 20 |
| Saraiva | 12 | 2 | 14 |
| Willock | 5 | 3 | 8 |
| Kavanagh | 6 | | 6 |
| Hutchings | 5 | | 5 |
| Page | 4 | | 4 |
| Cooper | 3 | | 3 |
| Henriques | 3 | | 3 |
| Abnett | 2 | | 2 |
| Campbell | 2 | | 2 |
| Faulkes | 2 | | 2 |
| Rhule | 2 | | 2 |
| Samuels | 2 | | 2 |
| Daly | 1 | | 1 |
| Douglas | 1 | | 1 |
| Hall | 1 | | 1 |
| Roberts | 1 | | 1 |

# METROPOLITAN POLICE

**Chairman:** Des Flanders
**Secretary:** Frank Thompson **(T)** 07747 764 349 **(E)** secretary@metpolicefc.co.uk
**Commercial Manager:** **(T/E)**
**Programme Editor:** Rich Nelson **(T/E)** rich@escapetosuomi.com
**Ground Address:** Imber Court, Ember Lane, East Molesey, Surrey KT8 0BT
**(T)** 0208 398 7358 **Manager:** Jim Cooper

## Club Factfile

**Founded:** 1919 **Nickname:** The Blues
**Previous Names:** None
**Previous Leagues:** Spartan 1928-60, Metropolitan 1960-71, Southern 1971-78

**Club Colours (change):** All blue (All red)

**Ground Capacity:** 3,000 **Seats:** 297 **Covered:** 1,800 **Clubhouse:** Yes **Shop:** No

**Directions**
From London A3 take A309 towards Scilly Isles roundabout then right into Hampton Court Way.
Left at first roundabout into Imber Court Road. Ground is in 300 yards.

**Previous Grounds:** None

**Record Attendance:** 4,500 v Kingstonian - FA Cup 1934
**Record Victory:** 10-1 v Tilbury - 1995
**Record Defeat:** 1-11 v Wimbledon - 1956
**Record Goalscorer:** Mario Russo
**Record Appearances:** Pat Robert
**Additional Records:**

**Honours:**
Spartan League x7.
Middlesex Senior Cup 1927-28, Surrey Senior Cup 1932-33, 2014-15. London Senior Cup 2009-10.
Isthmian League Division One South 2010-11.

### 10 YEAR RECORD

| 06-07 | 07-08 | 08-09 | 09-10 | 10-11 | 11-12 | 12-13 | 13-14 | 14-15 | 15-16 |
|---|---|---|---|---|---|---|---|---|---|
| Isth1S 6 | Isth1S 4 | Isth1S 4 | Isth1S 10 | Isth1S 1 | Isth P 12 | Isth P 6 | Isth P 17 | Isth P 5 | Isth P 12 |

# METROPOLITAN POLICE MATCH RESULTS 2015-16

| Date | Comp | H/A | Opponents | Att: | Result | Goalscorers | Pos | No. |
|---|---|---|---|---|---|---|---|---|
| Aug 8 | IsthP | H | Staines Town | 179 | D 0-0 | | 14 | 1 |
| 12 | IsthP | A | Lewes | 366 | W 2-1 | Collins 11 Pattison 76 | 10 | 2 |
| 15 | IsthP | A | Kingstonian | 278 | L 0-7 | | 14 | 3 |
| 22 | IsthP | H | Merstham | 85 | L 2-3 | Collins 38 54 | 15 | 4 |
| 25 | IsthP | H | Bognor Regis Town | 129 | W 1-0 | Case 52 | 11 | 5 |
| 29 | IsthP | A | Hampton & Richmond B | 298 | L 0-1 | | 15 | 6 |
| 31 | IsthP | H | Wingate & Finchley | 89 | L 1-3 | Yorke 86 | 17 | 7 |
| Sept 5 | IsthP | A | Farnborough | 314 | W 1-0 | Nurse 16 | 15 | 8 |
| 8 | IsthP | A | Bognor Regis Town | 301 | L 1-2 | Nurse 23 | 17 | 9 |
| **12** | **FAC1Q** | **H** | **Sittingbourne** | **86** | **D 0-0** | | | 10 |
| **15** | **FAC1Qr** | **A** | **Sittingbourne** | **141** | **L 0-1** | | | 11 |
| 19 | IsthP | H | VCD Athletic | 64 | D 1-1 | Collins 13 | 17 | 12 |
| 22 | IsthP | A | Billericay Town | 171 | L 0-6 | | 19 | 13 |
| 29 | IsthP | H | Dulwich Hamlet | 136 | L 1-3 | Barrett 61 | 21 | 14 |
| Oct 3 | IsthP | A | Hendon | 116 | W 2-0 | Roberts 66 Turner 81 | 19 | 15 |
| 10 | IsthP | H | Needham Market | 94 | W 1-0 | Barrett 70 | 17 | 16 |
| 13 | IsthP | A | Dulwich Hamlet | 726 | W 2-1 | Crook 45 Turner 86 | 13 | 17 |
| 17 | IsthP | A | Burgess Hill Town | 306 | L 2-4 | Collins 22 (pen) Onwuachu 83 | 16 | 18 |
| 20 | IsthP | H | Billericay Town | 83 | W 1-0 | Campbell 49 | 12 | 19 |
| 27 | IsthP | H | Lewes | 104 | D 0-0 | | 12 | 20 |
| **31** | **FAT1Q** | **A** | **AFC Hornchurch** | **110** | **W 3-2** | **Collins 22 Markus 51 Turner 81** | | 21 |
| Nov 7 | IsthP | H | Kingstonian | 345 | W 2-1 | Markus 42 Butler 76 | 14 | 22 |
| **14** | **FAT2Q** | **A** | **Canvey Island** | **187** | **W 2-0** | **Collins 89 90** | | 23 |
| 21 | IsthP | H | Leatherhead | 143 | W 1-0 | Campbell 68 | 11 | 24 |
| 24 | IsthP | H | Tonbridge Angels | 98 | L 0-3 | | 13 | 25 |
| **28** | **FAT3Q** | **H** | **Wealdstone** | **152** | **L 0-2** | | | 26 |
| Dec 5 | IsthP | A | Leiston | 138 | W 2-1 | L.Smith 14 Turner 83 | 13 | 27 |
| 12 | IsthP | H | Brentwood Town | 95 | D 0-0 | | 14 | 28 |
| 19 | IsthP | H | Hampton & Richmond B | 228 | L 0-3 | | 15 | 29 |
| 26 | IsthP | A | Wingate & Finchley | 124 | W 3-1 | Collins 25 Sutherland 39 Turner 78 | 14 | 30 |
| Jan 5 | IsthP | A | Canvey Island | 202 | L 3-0 | Bartley 54 Turner 59 L.Smith 71 | 14 | 31 |
| 16 | IsthP | A | Enfield Town | 323 | L 0-2 | | 14 | 32 |
| 23 | IsthP | H | Grays Athletic | 89 | L 2-4 | Turner 14 19 | 15 | 33 |
| Feb 6 | IsthP | H | Hendon | 79 | W 3-0 | L.SMITH 3 ( 12 40 76) | 15 | 34 |
| 9 | IsthP | H | Harrow Borough | 74 | W 3-2 | Hickey 1 Turner 3 Da Costa 8 | 12 | 35 |
| 13 | IsthP | A | Needham Market | 232 | D 1-1 | Crook 52 | 12 | 36 |
| 16 | IsthP | A | East Thurrock Utd | 155 | L 2-4 | L.Smith 44 Turner 58 (pen) | 12 | 37 |
| 20 | IsthP | H | Burgess Hill Town | 116 | D 1-1 | Salmon 24 | 13 | 38 |
| 27 | IsthP | A | Grays Athletic | 127 | D 3-3 | Turner 1 81 Collins 24 | 13 | 39 |
| Mar 1 | IsthP | A | Staines Town | 130 | L 1-3 | L.Smith 34 | 13 | 40 |
| 5 | IsthP | H | Enfield Town | 110 | D 2-2 | Salmon 61 Collins 73 | 13 | 41 |
| 12 | IsthP | H | Farnborough | 102 | L 1-2 | Collins 63 | 13 | 42 |
| 15 | IsthP | A | Tonbridge Angels | 343 | W 1-0 | L.Smith 27 | 11 | 43 |
| 19 | IsthP | A | VCD Athletic | 65 | D 3-3 | Sutherland 44 Collins 77 (pen) Taylor 84 | 12 | 44 |
| 22 | IsthP | A | Merstham | 143 | L 0-1 | | 11 | 45 |
| 26 | IsthP | H | East Thurrock United | 65 | L 0-3 | | 15 | 46 |
| Apr 2 | IsthP | A | Leatherhead | 225 | W 3-1 | L.Smith 3 G.Smith 62 Chislett 89 | 13 | 47 |
| 9 | IsthP | H | Canvey Island | 116 | L 0-1 | | 15 | 48 |
| 13 | IsthP | A | Harrow Borough | 125 | W 3-0 | L.Smith 9 Salmon 50 James 81 | 13 | 49 |
| 16 | IsthP | A | Brentwood Town | 122 | D 2-2 | L.Smith 35 (pen) Taylor 50 | 11 | 50 |
| 23 | IsthP | H | Leiston | 78 | L 0-3 | | 12 | 51 |

| GOALSCORERS | Scoring Games | Consec Sco Games | Total | | Scoring Games | Consec Sco Games | Total |
|---|---|---|---|---|---|---|---|
| ***2014-15 Collins*** | | | ***14*** | Bartley | 1 | | 1 |
| Collins | 11 | | 13 | Butler | 1 | | 1 |
| Turner | 10 | | 12 | Case | 1 | | 1 |
| L.Smith | 8 | | 11 | Chislett | 1 | | 1 |
| Salmon | 3 | | 3 | Da Costa | 1 | | 1 |
| Barrett | 2 | | 2 | Onwuachu | 1 | | 1 |
| Campbell | 2 | | 2 | HIckey | 1 | | 1 |
| Crook | 2 | | 2 | James | 1 | | 1 |
| Markus | 2 | | 2 | Pattison | 1 | | 1 |
| Nurse | 2 | | 2 | Roberts | 1 | | 1 |
| Sutherland | 2 | | 2 | G.Smith | 2 | | 2 |
| | | | | Taylor | 2 | | 2 |

# NEEDHAM MARKET

**Chairman:** Dr Keith Nunn
**Secretary:** Mark Easlea **(T)** 07795 456 502 **(E)** m.easlea@sky.com
**Commercial Manager:** **(T/E)**
**Programme Editor:** Darren Richardson **(T/E)** darrengrichardson@outlook.com
**Ground Address:** Bloomfields, Quinton Road, Needham Market IP6 8DA
**(T)** 01449 721 000 **Manager:** Mark Morsley

## Club Factfile

**Founded:** 1919 **Nickname:** The Marketmen
**Previous Names:** None
**Previous Leagues:** Suffolk & Ipswich Senior, Eastern Counties

**Club Colours (change):** All red with white trim (Blue with white trim)

**Ground Capacity:** 1,000 **Seats:** 250 **Covered:** 250 **Clubhouse:** Yes **Shop:** Yes

**Directions**
Quinton Road is off Barretts Lane which in turn is off Needham Market High Street.

**Previous Grounds:** Young's Meadow 1919. Crowley Park >1996.

**Record Attendance:** 750 v Ipswich Town - Suffolk Premier Cup 2007
**Record Victory:** 10-1 v I[swich Wanderers (A) , FA Cup Preliminary Round, 01/09/2007
**Record Defeat:** 2-6 v Lowestoft Town (A), FA Trophy First round Qualifier, 19/10/2010
**Record Goalscorer:** Craig Parker - 111 (2007-2011) Most goals in a season - Craig Parker 40 (2011-11).
**Record Appearances:** Rhys Barber - 334 (2006-2012)
**Additional Records:** Most goals scored in a season - 196 in 70 games (2007-08)

**Honours:**
Suffolk Senior Cup 1989-90, 2004-05. Suffolk & Ipswich Senior League 1995-96. East Anglian Cup 2006-07.
Eastern Counties Premier Division 2009-10. Isthmian Division One North 2014-15.

### 10 YEAR RECORD

| 06-07 | 07-08 | 08-09 | 09-10 | 10-11 | 11-12 | 12-13 | 13-14 | 14-15 | 15-16 |
|---|---|---|---|---|---|---|---|---|---|
| ECP 4 | ECP 2 | ECP 3 | ECP 1 | Isth1N 2 | Isth1N 4 | Isth1N 16 | Isth1N 5 | Isth1N 1 | Isth P 20 |

# NEEDHAM MARKET MATCH RESULTS 2015-16

| Date | Comp | H/A | Opponents | Att: | Result | | Goalscorers | Pos | No. |
|---|---|---|---|---|---|---|---|---|---|
| Aug 8 | IsthP | H | Burgess Hill Town | 313 | L | 1-2 | Ingram 52 | 21 | 1 |
| 11 | IsthP | A | Billericay Town | 248 | D | 1-1 | Hogg 86 | 15 | 2 |
| 15 | IsthP | A | Tonbridge Angels | 405 | D | 3-3 | Fenn 10 Newson 53 Izzet 76 (pen) | 18 | 3 |
| 22 | IsthP | H | Hendon | 255 | L | 0-3 | | 21 | 4 |
| 25 | IsthP | H | Wingate & Finchley | 201 | L | 1-3 | Hogg 34 | 21 | 5 |
| 29 | IsthP | A | VCD Athletic | 102 | D | 1-1 | Mills 69 | 21 | 6 |
| 31 | IsthP | H | Leiston | 411 | D | 2-2 | Mills 12 40 | 20 | 7 |
| Sept 5 | IsthP | A | Merstham | 136 | L | 0-2 | | 21 | 8 |
| 8 | IsthP | A | Wingate & Finchley | 138 | L | 0-6 | | 21 | 9 |
| **12** | **FAC1Q** | **H** | **Stanway Rovers** | **211** | **D** | **1-1** | **Newson 18** | | 10 |
| **15** | **FAC1Qr** | **A** | **Stanway Rovers** | **76** | **L** | **0-3** | | | 11 |
| 19 | IsthP | H | Harrow Borough | 253 | L | 2-4 | Izzet 53 Newson 68 | 22 | 12 |
| 26 | IsthP | A | Burgess Hill Town | 334 | D | 2-2 | Brothers 24 MIlls 87 | 23 | 13 |
| 29 | IsthP | A | Brentwood Town | 83 | L | 0-1 | | 21 | 14 |
| Oct 3 | IsthP | H | Lewes | 238 | W | 1-0 | Brothers 55 | 21 | 15 |
| 10 | IsthP | A | Met Police | 94 | L | 0-1 | | 21 | 16 |
| 17 | IsthP | H | Hampton & Richmond B | 230 | D | 1-1 | Fenn 84 | 21 | 17 |
| 27 | IsthP | H | Billericay Town | 255 | L | 1-3 | Mills 30 | 22 | 18 |
| **31** | **FAT1Q** | **H** | **Canvey Island** | **191** | **L** | **0-2** | | | 19 |
| Nov 3 | IsthP | H | East Thurrock United | 152 | L | 1-3 | Newson 88 | 22 | 20 |
| 7 | IsthP | H | Tonbridge Angels | 300 | W | 2-1 | Brothers 52 65 | 21 | 21 |
| 14 | IsthP | A | Hendon | 125 | W | 2-0 | Mills 22 Ingram 44 | | 22 |
| 17 | IsthP | A | East Thurrock United | 124 | W | 2-1 | Brothers 45 Miller 90 (og) | 10 | 23 |
| 21 | IsthP | A | Farnborough | 218 | D | 1-1 | Patrick 65 | 20 | 24 |
| 28 | IsthP | H | Brentwood Town | 248 | W | 4-0 | Davies 10 (pen) Ingram 36 Harrison 43 Mann 50 | | 25 |
| Dec 5 | IsthP | A | Dulwich Hamlet | 1547 | W | 1-0 | Davies 59 | 19 | 26 |
| 8 | IsthP | A | Staines Town | 143 | W | 2-0 | Mann 45 Brothers 82 | 19 | 27 |
| 12 | IsthP | H | Enfield Town | 258 | L | 2-3 | Ingram 52 Izzett 86 (pen) | 19 | 28 |
| 26 | IsthP | A | Leiston | 303 | L | 0-3 | | 20 | 29 |
| Jan 2 | IsthP | H | Canvey Island | 275 | L | 2-3 | Miller 15 Brothers 18 | 20 | 30 |
| 9 | IsthP | A | Bognor Regis Town | 492 | L | 1-2 | Brothers 39 | 20 | 31 |
| 16 | IsthP | H | Leatherhead | 216 | W | 1-0 | Coakley 29 | 20 | 32 |
| 19 | IsthP | H | VCD Athletic | 135 | L | 0-3 | | 20 | 33 |
| 23 | IsthP | A | Kingstonian | 272 | L | 2-4 | Davies 13 Ingram 55 | 20 | 34 |
| Feb 6 | IsthP | A | Lewes | 462 | D | 0-0 | | 19 | 35 |
| 9 | IsthP | H | Grays Athletic | 180 | D | 0-0 | | 19 | 36 |
| 13 | IsthP | H | Met Police | 232 | D | 1-1 | Patrick 73 | 19 | 37 |
| 20 | IsthP | A | Hampton & Richmond B | 436 | L | 0-5 | | 20 | 38 |
| 27 | IsthP | H | Kingstonian | 195 | D | 0-0 | | 19 | 39 |
| Mar 5 | IsthP | A | Leatherhead | 241 | D | 2-2 | Brothers 6 Miller 90 | 20 | 40 |
| 12 | IsthP | H | Merstham | 231 | W | 1-0 | Brothers 4 | 20 | 41 |
| 15 | IsthP | H | Staines Town | 154 | L | 0-1 | | 20 | 42 |
| 19 | IsthP | A | Harrow Borough | 135 | W | 2-0 | Mann 42 Coakley 83 | 20 | 43 |
| 26 | IsthP | H | Bognor Regis Town | 310 | L | 0-1 | | 20 | 44 |
| Apr 2 | IsthP | H | Farnborough | 225 | L | 0-2 | | 20 | 45 |
| 5 | IsthP | A | Canvey Island | 201 | W | 2-1 | Izzett 53 (pen) Brothers 55 | 20 | 46 |
| 9 | IsthP | A | Grays Athletic | 154 | W | 2-0 | Brothers 16 52 | 20 | 47 |
| 16 | IsthP | A | Enfield Town | 519 | L | 0-3 | | 20 | 48 |
| 23 | IsthP | H | Dulwich Hamlet | 502 | W | 2-1 | Ingram 36 60 | 20 | 49 |

| GOALSCORERS | Scoring Games | Consec Sco Games | Total | | Scoring Games | Consec Sco Games | Total |
|---|---|---|---|---|---|---|---|
| Brothers | 9 | | 10 | Coakley | 2 | | 2 |
| Ingram | 6 | | 7 | Miller | 2 | | 2 |
| Mills | 5 | | 6 | Patrick | 2 | | 2 |
| Izzett | 4 | | 4 | Harrison | 1 | | 1 |
| Newsom | 4 | | 4 | Opponents | 1 | | 1 |
| Davies | 3 | | 3 | | | | |
| Brothers | 2 | | 3 | | | | |
| Mann | 3 | | 3 | | | | |
| Fenn | 2 | | 2 | | | | |
| Hogg | 2 | | 2 | | | | |

# STAINES TOWN

**Chairman:** Matthew Boon
**Secretary:** Steven Parsons **(T)** 07850 794 315 **(E)** steve@stainestownfootballclub.co.uk
**Commercial Manager:** Roy Lewis **(T/E)** 07977 012 699
**Programme Editor:** Steve Parsons **(T/E)** steve@stainestownfootballclub.co.uk
**Ground Address:** Wheatsheaf Park, Wheatsheaf Lane, Staines TW18 2PD
**(T)** 01784 469 240 **Manager:** Johnson Hippolyte

## Club Factfile

**Founded:** 1892 **Nickname:** The Swans
**Previous Names:** Staines Albany & St Peters Institute merged in 1895. Staines 1905-18, Staines Lagonda 1918-25, Staines Vale (WWII)
**Previous Leagues:** Great Western Suburban, Hounslow & District 1919-20, Spartan 1924-35, 58-71, Middlesex Senior 1943-52, Parthenon 1952-53, Hellenic 1953-58, Athenian 1971-73, Isthmian 1973-2009, Conference 2009-15.

**Club Colours (change):** Yellow/blue/white

**Ground Capacity:** 3,000 **Seats:** 300 **Covered:** 850 **Clubhouse:** Yes **Shop:** Yes

**Directions**
Leave M25 at Junction 13. If coming from the North (anticlockwise), bear left onto A30 Staines By-Pass; if coming from the South (clockwise), go round the roundabout and back under M25 to join By-Pass. Follow A30 to Billet Bridge roundabout, which you treat like a roundabout, taking last exit, A308, London Road towards Town Centre. At 3rd traffic lights, under iron bridge, turn left into South Street, passing central bus station, as far as Thames Lodge (formerly Packhorse). Turn left here, into Laleham Road, B376, under rail bridge. After 1km, Wheatsheaf Lane is on the right, by the traffic island. Ground is less than 100 yds on left. Please park on the left.

**Previous Grounds:** Groundshared with Walton & Hersham and Egham Town whilst new Wheatsheaf stadium was built 2001-03.

**Record Attendance:** 2,750 v Banco di Roma - Barassi Cup 1975 (70,000 watched the second leg)
**Record Victory:** 14-0 v Croydon (A) - Isthmian Division 1 19/03/1994
**Record Defeat:** 1-18 - Wycombe Wanderers (A) - Great Western Suburban League 27/12/1909
**Record Goalscorer:** Alan Gregory - 122
**Record Appearances:** Dickie Watmore - 840
**Additional Records:**

**Honours:**
Spartan League 1959-60. Athenian League Division 2 1971-72, Division 1 1974-75, 88-89.
Middlesex Senior cup 1975-76, 76-77, 77-78, 88-89, 90-91, 94-95, 97-98, 2009-10, 12-13. Barassi Cup 1975-76.
Isthmian Full Members Cup 1994-95, Premier Division Play-off 2008-09.

### 10 YEAR RECORD

| 06-07 | 07-08 | 08-09 | 09-10 | 10-11 | 11-12 | 12-13 | 13-14 | 14-15 | 15-16 |
|---|---|---|---|---|---|---|---|---|---|
| Isth P 12 | Isth P 2 | Isth P 2 | Conf S 8 | Conf S 15 | Conf S 15 | Conf S 18 | Conf S 8 | Conf S 21 | Isth P 16 |

# STAINES TOWN MATCH RESULTS 2015-16

| Date | Comp | H/A | Opponents | Att: | Result | Goalscorers | Pos | No. |
|---|---|---|---|---|---|---|---|---|
| Aug 8 | IsthP | A | Met Police | 179 | D 0-0 | | 15 | 1 |
| 11 | IsthP | H | Bognor Regis Town | 313 | L 0-1 | | 16 | 2 |
| 15 | IsthP | H | Leatherhead | 293 | W 1-0 | Kalu 37 | 13 | 3 |
| 22 | IsthP | A | Dulwich Hamlet | 1024 | W 2-1 | Cox 16 (pen) 56 | 8 | 4 |
| 29 | IsthP | A | Wingate & Finchley | 245 | D 0-0 | | 13 | 5 |
| 31 | IsthP | H | Hampton & Richmond B | 402 | L 1-2 | Cox 71 | 14 | 6 |
| Sept 5 | IsthP | A | Brentwood Town | 136 | L 0-7 | | 18 | 7 |
| 7 | IsthP | A | Farnborough | 246 | W 3-2 | Wanadio 50 Hutchinson 82 Cox 88 | 14 | 8 |
| **12** | **FAC1Q** | **H** | **Faversham** | **188** | **D 2-2** | **Wanadio 42 Abdulla 55** | | 9 |
| **15** | **FAC1Q** | **A** | **Faversham** | **172** | **W 3-1** | **Cox 15 61 Bennett 54** | | 10 |
| 19 | IsthP | H | East Thurrock Utd | 209 | W 3-2 | Cox 14 (pen) M'Bengui 39 Wanadio 87 | 10 | 11 |
| 22 | IsthP | A | Grays Athletic | 173 | D 1-1 | Wanadio 25 | 12 | 12 |
| **26** | **FAC2Q** | **A** | **Stanway Rovers** | **195** | **W 1-0** | **Cox 45** | | 13 |
| 29 | IsthP | H | Burgess Hill Town | 175 | D 2-2 | Cox 56 Wanadio 78 | 13 | 14 |
| Oct 3 | IsthP | A | Billericay Town | 401 | W 3-2 | COX 3 (15 86 90) | 12 | 15 |
| **10** | **FAC3Q** | **A** | **East Thurrock Utd** | **263** | **W 6-3** | **COX 3 (12 pen 20 77) Hutchinson 22 Wanadio 29 55** | | 16 |
| 14 | IsthP | A | Burgess Hill Town | 337 | W 2-0 | Wanadio 66 Hutchinson 68 | 10 | 17 |
| 17 | IsthP | A | Enfield Town | 364 | L 1-2 | Hutchinson 62 | 12 | 18 |
| **24** | **FAC4Q** | **H** | **Gloucester City** | **417** | **W 2-1** | **Cox 26 (pen) 88** | | 19 |
| 27 | IsthP | A | Bognor Regis Town | 340 | L 0-3 | | 13 | 20 |
| **31** | **FAT1Q** | **A** | **VCD Athletic** | **102** | **L 1-2** | **Cox 64 (pen)** | | 21 |
| **Nov 7** | **FAC1** | **A** | **Leyton Orient** | **2287** | **L 1-6** | **Purse 23** | | 22 |
| 28 | IsthP | H | Lewes | 172 | W 3-0 | Kalu 28 Abdulla 32 Lodge 782 | 17 | 23 |
| Dec 1 | IsthP | H | Tonbridge Angels | 198 | D 1-1 | Abdulla 52 | 16 | 24 |
| 5 | IsthP | A | Canvey Island | 230 | W 3-2 | Brewer 4 Cox 54 (pen) Boakye 78 | 16 | 25 |
| 8 | IsthP | H | Needham Market | 143 | L 0-2 | | 16 | 26 |
| 12 | IsthP | H | Kingstonian | 343 | L 0-2 | | 16 | 27 |
| 15 | IsthP | H | Grays Athletic | 126 | L 0-4 | | 17 | 28 |
| 19 | IsthP | H | Wingate & Finchley | 179 | L 1-2 | Wanadio 66 | 18 | 29 |
| 26 | IsthP | A | Hampton & Richmond B | 646 | L 2-3 | Wanadio 65 Kalu 78 | 18 | 30 |
| 29 | IsthP | H | Farnborough | 239 | W 2-0 | Cox 14 41 | 16 | 31 |
| Jan 6 | IsthP | A | Leatherhead | 277 | L 0-3 | | 16 | 32 |
| 16 | IsthP | A | Merstham | 172 | L 1-5 | Cox 90 (pen) | 18 | 33 |
| 23 | IsthP | A | Hendon | 237 | L 1-3 | Boakye 30 | 19 | 34 |
| 26 | IsthP | A | Leiston | 134 | L 1-3 | M'Bengui 13 | 19 | 35 |
| Feb 2 | IsthP | H | Dulwich Hamlet | 260 | L 1-3 | Campbell 48 | 19 | 36 |
| 6 | IsthP | H | Billericay Town | 209 | L 0-1 | | 20 | 37 |
| 13 | IsthP | A | Tonbridge Angels | 385 | L 0-2 | | 20 | 38 |
| 16 | IsthP | H | VCD Athletic | 109 | W 1-0 | Cox 48 | 19 | 39 |
| 20 | IsthP | H | Enfield Town | 231 | L 0-1 | | 19 | 40 |
| 27 | IsthP | A | Hendon | 202 | L 0-2 | | 20 | 41 |
| Mar 1 | IsthP | H | Met Police | 130 | W 3-1 | Cox 6 Vanderhyde 66 Miller-Rodney 82 | 19 | 42 |
| 5 | IsthP | H | Merstham | 146 | W 2-0 | Brown 9 21 | 18 | 43 |
| 12 | IsthP | H | Brentwood Town | 131 | L 0-1 | | 19 | 44 |
| 15 | IsthP | A | Needham Market | 154 | W 1-0 | Hippolyte 83 | 18 | 45 |
| 19 | IsthP | A | East Thurrock United | 233 | D 0-0 | | 18 | 46 |
| 26 | IsthP | H | Harrow Borough | 221 | D 1-1 | Gondoh 53 | 18 | 47 |
| 28 | IsthP | A | VCD Athletic | 89 | W 3-0 | Brown 12 Hippolyte 46 Cox 63 | 16 | 48 |
| Apr 2 | IsthP | H | Leiston | 181 | D 2-2 | Hippolyte 7 Mitford 88 | 16 | 49 |
| 5 | IsthP | A | Harrow Borough | 157 | L 0-1 | | 17 | 50 |
| 9 | IsthP | A | Lewes | 422 | D 2-2 | Cox 76 Hippolyte 79 | 17 | 51 |
| 17 | IsthP | A | Kingstonian | 363 | W 1-0 | Brown 2 | 16 | 52 |
| 23 | IsthP | H | Canvey Island | 257 | D 2-2 | McKain 33 Boakye 71 | 16 | 53 |

| GOALSCORERS | Scoring Games | Consec Sco Games | Total |
|---|---|---|---|
| *2014-15 Theophanous* | | | *9* |
| Cox | 18 | 4 | 26 |
| Wanadio | 8 | | 10 |
| Brown | 3 | | 4 |
| Hutchinson | 4 | | 4 |
| Hipolytte | 4 | | 4 |
| Abdulla | 3 | | 3 |
| Boakye | 3 | | 3 |
| Kalu | 3 | | 3 |
| M'Bengui | 2 | | 2 |

| | Scoring Games | Consec Sco Games | Total |
|---|---|---|---|
| Bennett | 1 | | 1 |
| Brewer | 1 | | 1 |
| Campbell | 1 | | 1 |
| Gondoh | 1 | | 1 |
| Lodge | 1 | | 1 |
| McKain | 1 | | 1 |
| Miller-Rodney | 1 | | 1 |
| Mitford | 1 | | 1 |
| Purse | 1 | | 1 |
| Vanderhyde | 1 | | 1 |

# TONBRIDGE ANGELS

**Chairman:** Steve Churcher
**Secretary:** Charlie Cole (T) 07825 702 412 (E) chcole1063@aol.com
**Commercial Manager:** (T/E)
**Programme Editor:** Geoff Curtis (T/E) curtis.g10@ntlworld.com
**Ground Address:** Longmead Stadium, Darenth Avenue, Tonbridge, Kent TN10 3LW
(T) 01732 352 417 **Manager:** Steve McKimm

2015-16 Squad - Top Row L-R Melvin Slight (physio), Charlie Slocombe, Jack Brivio, Sonny Miles, Nathan Elder, Jerrome Sobers, Anthony Di Bernardo, Tom Parkinson, Tom Phipp, James Folkes, Laurence Ball, Luke Blewden, Chris Varney (kit manager)
Bottom Row L-R Jack Parter, Nick Wheeler, Charlie Webster, Justin Luchford (coach), Barry Moore (asst manager), Steve Churcher (chairman), Steve McKimm (manager), Kevin Shrimpton (goalkeeping coach), Lee Carey, Tommy Whitnell, Royce Greenidge

## Club Factfile

**Founded:** 1948 **Nickname:** Angels
**Previous Names:** Tonbridge Angels, Tonbridge F.C., Tonbridge A.F.C.
**Previous Leagues:** Southern 1948-80, 93-2004, Kent 1989-93, Isthmian 2004-11.

**Club Colours (change):** Blue with white trim/white (All red with white trim)

**Ground Capacity:** 2,500 **Seats:** 707 **Covered:** 1,500 **Clubhouse:** Yes **Shop:** Yes

**Directions**
From M25. Take A21 turning at Junction 5 to junction with A225/b245 (signposted Hildenborough). After passing Langley Hotel on left thake slightly hidden left turn into Dry Hill Park Road. Left again at mini roundabout into Shipbourne Road (A227) and then left again at next roundabout into Darenth Avenue' Longmead stadium can be found at the bottom of the hill at the far end of the car park.

**Previous Grounds:** The Angel 1948-80

**Record Attendance:** 8,236 v Aldershot - FA Cup 1951
**Record Victory:** 11-1 v Worthing - FA Cup 1951
**Record Defeat:** 2-11 v Folkstone - Kent Senior Cup 1949
**Record Goalscorer:** Jon Main scored 44 goals in one season including seven hat-tricks
**Record Appearances:** Mark Giham
**Additional Records:**

**Honours:**
Kent Senior Cup 1964-65, 74-75

### 10 YEAR RECORD

| 06-07 | 07-08 | 08-09 | 09-10 | 10-11 | 11-12 | 12-13 | 13-14 | 14-15 | 15-16 |
|---|---|---|---|---|---|---|---|---|---|
| Isth P 11 | Isth P 8 | Isth P 3 | Isth P 8 | Isth P 2 | Conf S 9 | Conf S 16 | Conf S 21 | Isth P 20 | Isth P 4 |

## TONBRIDGE ANGELS MATCH RESULTS 2015-16

| Date | Comp | H/A | Opponents | Att: | Result | | Goalscorers | Pos | No. |
|---|---|---|---|---|---|---|---|---|---|
| Aug 8 | IsthP | A | Enfield Town | 458 | **W** | 1-0 | Parkinson 88 | 7 | 1 |
| 11 | IsthP | H | Grays Athletic | 439 | L | 2-3 | Parkinson 4 Blewden 63 | 10 | 2 |
| 15 | IsthP | H | Needham Market | 405 | D | 3-3 | Blewden 16 Parkinson 25 Wheeler 85 | 11 | 3 |
| 22 | IsthP | A | Bognor Regis Town | 360 | **W** | 5-0 | Elder 10 BLEWDEN 3 (14 32 35) Whitnell 83 | 5 | 4 |
| 25 | IsthP | H | Brentwood Town | 431 | **W** | 4-0 | Phipp 62 Blewden 67 88 Whitnell 72 | 3 | 5 |
| 29 | IsthP | A | Harrow Borough | 187 | D | 1-1 | Phipp 6 | 4 | 6 |
| 31 | IsthP | H | VCD Athletic | 516 | **W** | 7-0 | Phipp 9 Wheeler 28 68 (p) Webster 37 Whitnell 37 Elder 80 Parkinson 88 | 4 | 7 |
| Sept 5 | IsthP | A | Wingate & Finchley | 229 | **W** | 1-0 | Whitnell 70 | 2 | 8 |
| 8 | IsthP | A | Brentwood Town | 171 | W | 1-0 | Ball 17 | 2 | 9 |
| **12** | **FAC1Q** | **H** | **Folkestone Invicta** | **574** | **D** | **1-1** | **Phipp 31 (pen)** | | 10 |
| **15** | **FAC1Q** | **A** | **Folkestone Invicta** | **365** | **W** | **2-1** | **Elder 69 75** | | 11 |
| 19 | IsthP | H | Leiston | 541 | L | 0-1 | | 3 | 12 |
| **26** | **FAC2Q** | **A** | **Leiston** | **212** | **L** | **1-3** | **Phipp 2** | | 13 |
| 30 | IsthP | A | Lewes | 460 | **W** | 1-0 | Blewden 43 | 3 | 14 |
| Oct 3 | IsthP | H | Farnborough | 501 | **W** | 2-0 | Blewden 12 55 | 2 | 15 |
| 17 | IsthP | H | Kingstonian | 545 | D | 1-1 | Elder 45 | 5 | 16 |
| 21 | IsthP | A | Leatherhead | 291 | **W** | 2-0 | Wheeler 4 Miles 45 | 6 | 17 |
| **31** | **FAT1Q** | **A** | **Phoenix Sports** | **244** | **D** | **1-1** | **Miles 56** | | 18 |
| **Nov 3** | **FAT1Qr** | **H** | **Phoenix Sports** | **339** | **W** | **2-0** | **Blewden 34 68** | | 19 |
| 7 | IsthP | A | Needham Market | 300 | L | 1-2 | Elder 38 | 8 | 20 |
| **14** | **FAT2Q** | **H** | **Cirencester Town** | **372** | **L** | **1-2** | **Elder 17** | | 21 |
| 17 | IsthP | H | Lewes | 278 | **W** | 1-0 | Elder 88 | 8 | 22 |
| 21 | IsthP | H | Hendon | 375 | **W** | 3-1 | Parkinson 32 Elder 42 Whitnell 63 | 3 | 23 |
| 24 | IsthP | A | Met Police | 98 | **W** | 3-0 | Fitzpatrick 7 Blewden 12 Riviere 51 | 2 | 24 |
| 28 | IsthP | A | Billericay Town | 375 | D | 1-1 | Parkinson 43 | 2 | 25 |
| Dec 1 | IsthP | A | Staines Town | 198 | D | 1-1 | Elder 62 | 2 | 26 |
| 5 | IsthP | H | Burgess Hill Town | 457 | L | 2-3 | Elder 19 54 | 2 | 27 |
| 12 | IsthP | A | Merstham | 197 | D | 2-2 | Thomas 56 Elder 58 | 2 | 28 |
| 19 | IsthP | H | Harrow Borough | 527 | D | 3-3 | Parkinson 40 Blewden 61 Allen 80 | 4 | 29 |
| 26 | IsthP | A | VCD Athletic | 267 | **W** | 3-0 | Elder 35 37 Blewden 60 | 3 | 30 |
| Jan 2 | IsthP | H | Dulwich Hamlet | 1095 | D | 1-1 | Elder 90 | 3 | 31 |
| 9 | IsthP | A | Canvey Islands | 361 | D | 1-1 | Parkinson 28 | 3 | 32 |
| 16 | IsthP | H | East Thurrock United | 553 | L | 1-2 | Elder 48 | 3 | 33 |
| 23 | IsthP | A | Hampton & Richmond B | 691 | D | 2-2 | Parkinson 71 Elder 90 | 5 | 34 |
| Feb 2 | IsthP | H | Leatherhead | 335 | **W** | 4-0 | Woods-Garness 21 Elder 79 Blewden 86 90 | 5 | 35 |
| 6 | IsthP | A | Farnborough | 242 | **W** | 2-1 | Allen 60 Parkinson 87 | 5 | 36 |
| 13 | IsthP | H | Staines Town | 385 | **W** | 2-0 | Whitnell 75 Wheeler 87 | 4 | 37 |
| 17 | IsthP | A | Grays Athletic | 221 | D | 1-1 | Parkinson 57 | 4 | 38 |
| 20 | IsthP | A | Kingstonian | 411 | **W** | 3-1 | Elder 70 Whitnell 75 Wheeler 90 | 3 | 39 |
| 23 | IsthP | H | Bognor Regis Town | 377 | L | 1-3 | Blewden 61 | 3 | 40 |
| 27 | IsthP | H | Hampton & Richmond B | 559 | **W** | 1-0 | Blewden 64 (pen) | 3 | 41 |
| Mar 5 | IsthP | A | East Thurrock United | 331 | L | 0-3 | | 3 | 42 |
| 8 | IsthP | H | Enfield Town | 307 | **W** | 3-1 | Miles 26 Blewden 50 64 | 3 | 43 |
| 12 | IsthP | H | Wingate & Finchley | 502 | **W** | 4-3 | Sobers 54 65 Elder 68 82 | 3 | 44 |
| 15 | IsthP | H | Met Police | 343 | L | 0-1 | | 3 | 45 |
| 19 | IsthP | A | Leiston | 197 | **W** | 2-1 | Blewdon 11(pen) Elder 32 | 3 | 46 |
| 26 | IsthP | H | Canvey Island | 659 | **W** | 2-0 | Miles 23 Sobers 40 | 3 | 47 |
| 28 | IsthP | A | Dulwich Hamlet | 1434 | L | 1-2 | Allen 70 | 3 | 48 |
| Apr 2 | IsthP | A | Hendon | 215 | **W** | 3-0 | Elder 47 Webster 47 Riviere 59 | 3 | 49 |
| 9 | IsthP | H | Billericay Town | 512 | D | 2-2 | Elder 62 Parkinson 64 | 4 | 50 |
| 16 | IsthP | H | Merstham | 609 | **W** | 3-2 | Elder 41 61 Wheeler 43 | 4 | 51 |
| 23 | IsthP | A | Burgess Hill Town | 576 | D | 0-0 | | 4 | 52 |

| GOALSCORERS | Scoring Games | Consec Sco Games | Total | | Scoring Games | Consec Sco Games | Total |
|---|---|---|---|---|---|---|---|
| ***2014-15 Medlock*** | | | ***18*** | Riviere | 2 | | 2 |
| Elder | 22 | 4 | 27 | Webster | 2 | | 2 |
| Blewden | 16 | 4 | 22 | Ball | 1 | | 1 |
| Parkinson | 12 | 3 | 12 | Fitzpatrick | 1 | | 1 |
| Wheeler | 7 | | 7 | Sobers | 1 | | 1 |
| Whitnall | 7 | 2 | 7 | Thomas | 1 | | 1 |
| Phipp | 5 | 3 | 5 | Woods-Garness | 1 | | 1 |
| Miles | 4 | | 4 | | | | |
| Sobers | 3 | | 3 | | | | |
| Allen | 2 | | 2 | | | | |

# WINGATE & FINCHLEY

**Chairman:** Aron Sharpe
**Secretary:** Tony Brooking **(T)** 07961 33 4523 **(E)** tony@wingatefinchley.com
**Commercial Manager:** N/A **(T/E)**
**Programme Editor:** Paul Lerman **(T/E)** paul@wingatefinchley.com
**Ground Address:** Maurice Rebak Stadium, Summers Lane, Finchley N12 0PD
**(T)** 0208 446 2217 **Manager:** Keith Rowland

## Club Factfile

**Founded:** 1991 **Nickname:** Blues
**Previous Names:** Wingate (founded 1946) and Finchley (founded late 1800s) merged in 1991
**Previous Leagues:** South Midlands 1991-95, Isthmian 1995-2004, Southern 2004-2006

**Club Colours (change):** Blue & white (Orange & black)

**Ground Capacity:** 8,500 **Seats:** 500 **Covered:** 500 **Clubhouse:** Yes **Shop:** No

**Directions**
The simplest way to get to The Harry Abrahams Stadium is to get on to the A406 North Circular Road.
If coming from the West (eg via M1), go past Henlys Corner (taking the left fork after the traffic lights) and then drive for about 1 mile. The exit to take is the one immediately after a BP garage. Take the slip road and then turn right at the lights onto the A1000.
If coming from the East (eg via A10, M11) take the A1000 turn off. At the end of the slip road turn left at the lights. Go straight over the next set of lights. Then after 100m pass through another set of lights, then at the next set of lights turn right into Summers Lane. The Abrahams Stadium is a few hundred metres down on the right hand side.

**Previous Grounds:** None

**Record Attendance:** 528 v Brentwood Town (Division One North Play-Off) 2010/11
**Record Victory:** 9-1 v Winslow (South Midlands League) 23/11/1991
**Record Defeat:** 0-9 v Edgware - Isthmian Division 2 15/01/2000
**Record Goalscorer:** Marc Morris 650 (including with Wingate FC) FA Record for one Club
**Record Appearances:** Marc Morris 720 (including with Wingate FC)FA Record for one Club
**Additional Records:**

**Honours:**
Isthmian League Cup 2010-11.
London Senior Cup 2010-11.

### 10 YEAR RECORD

| 06-07 | 07-08 | 08-09 | 09-10 | 10-11 | 11-12 | 12-13 | 13-14 | 14-15 | 15-16 |
|---|---|---|---|---|---|---|---|---|---|
| Isth1N 9 | Isth1N 18 | Isth1N 7 | Isth1N 3 | Isth1N 3 | Isth P 13 | Isth P 18 | Isth P 21 | Isth P 12 | Isth P 13 |

# WINGATE & FINCHLEY MATCH RESULTS 2015-16

| Date | Comp | H/A | Opponents | Att: | Result | | Goalscorers | Pos | No. |
|---|---|---|---|---|---|---|---|---|---|
| Aug 8 | IsthP | H | Brentwood Town | 104 | **W** | 2-1 | Healey 4 16 | 6 | 1 |
| 11 | IsthP | A | Hampton & Richmond B | 331 | **W** | 2-1 | Oliyide 60 Rifat 63 | 4 | 2 |
| 22 | IsthP | H | Kingstonian | 222 | **W** | 2-1 | Healey 25 46 | 3 | 3 |
| 25 | IsthP | A | Needham Market | 201 | **W** | 3-1 | Healey 12 Oliyide 20 Tejan-Sie 50 | 2 | 4 |
| 29 | IsthP | H | Staines Town | 245 | D | 0-0 | | 3 | 5 |
| 31 | IsthP | A | Met Police | 89 | **W** | 3-1 | Sogbanmu 7 Oliyide 12 Laney 78 | 3 | 6 |
| Sept 5 | IsthP | H | Tonbridge Angels | 229 | L | 0-1 | | 4 | 7 |
| 8 | IsthP | H | Needham Market | 138 | W | 6-0 | LANEY 3 ( 9 25 60) Healey 19 Hewitt 22 Weatherstone 78 | 3 | 8 |
| **12** | **FAC1Q** | **A** | **Long Buckby** | **96** | **W** | **4-0** | **Oliyide 6 Healey 10 78 Tejan-Sie 60** | | 9 |
| 19 | IsthP | A | Leatherhead | 24 | D | 0-0 | | 4 | 10 |
| 22 | IsthP | A | Enfield Town | 331 | L | 0-2 | | 4 | 11 |
| **26** | **FAC2Q** | **H** | **Concord Rovers** | **131** | **W** | **2-1** | **Tejan-Sie 18 Oliyide 87** | | 12 |
| 29 | IsthP | H | Canvey Island | 119 | L | 1-2 | Rifat 54 | 10 | 13 |
| Oct 3 | IsthP | A | Burgess Hill Town | 357 | **W** | 1-0 | Sogbanmu 68 | 8 | 14 |
| **10** | **FAC3Q** | **H** | **Weston-s-Mare** | **337** | **L** | **1-3** | **Oliyide 68 (pen)** | | 15 |
| 13 | IsthP | A | Canvey Island | 150 | L | 1-2 | Rifat 90 | 9 | 16 |
| 17 | IsthP | A | Merstham | 125 | **W** | 2-0 | Sogbanmu 27 Barney 74 | | 17 |
| 27 | IsthP | H | Hampton & Richmond B | 129 | L | 1-3 | Rifat 44 | 11 | 18 |
| **31** | **FAT1Q** | **H** | **Royston Town** | **103** | **L** | **0-2** | | | 19 |
| Nov 3 | IsthP | H | Grays Athletic | 111 | **W** | 3-2 | Barney 25 80 Laney 33 | 7 | 20 |
| 7 | IsthP | H | Farnborough | 138 | **W** | 4-3 | Laney 11 39 Barney 31 32 | | 21 |
| 14 | IsthP | A | Farnborough | 217 | L | 1-2 | Oliyide 72 | 8 | 22 |
| 17 | IsthP | H | Leiston | 131 | **W** | 1-0 | Bartram 20 | 6 | 23 |
| 21 | IsthP | A | E Thurrock United | 155 | D | 1-1 | Olliyidi 34 | 5 | 24 |
| 28 | IsthP | H | Harrow Borough | 135 | **W** | 3-1 | Healey 40 55 Bartram 52 | 3 | 25 |
| Dec 5 | IsthP | H | Billericay Town | 139 | L | 0-1 | | 4 | 26 |
| 12 | IsthP | A | VCD Athletic | 108 | L | 1-2 | Laney 6 | 6 | 27 |
| 19 | IsthP | A | Staines Town | 170 | **W** | 2-1 | Healey 51 Tejan-Sie 90 | 6 | 28 |
| 26 | IsthP | H | Met Police | 124 | L | 1-3 | Weatherstone 84 | 7 | 29 |
| 29 | IsthP | H | Enfield Town | 405 | L | 1-2 | Healey 37 | 7 | 30 |
| Jan 2 | IsthP | A | Hendon | 177 | L | 3-4 | Healey 28 Soloman 25 Brown 50 | 8 | 31 |
| 9 | IsthP | H | Lewes | 141 | D | 1-1 | Healey 84 (pen) | 8 | 32 |
| 23 | IsthP | H | Bognor Regis Town | 130 | L | 1-3 | Addai 51 | 11 | 33 |
| 30 | IsthP | A | Grays Athletic | 162 | D | 0-0 | | 11 | 34 |
| Feb 1 | IsthP | A | Kingstonian | 262 | L | 1-2 | Healey 6 | 11 | 35 |
| 6 | IsthP | H | Burgess Hill Town | 131 | **W** | 5-1 | Tejan-Sie 8 Healey 13 (pen) 52 Laney 31 Addai 63 | 11 | 36 |
| 13 | IsthP | A | Leiston | 152 | **W** | 1-0 | Olliyidi 88 | 11 | 37 |
| 20 | IsthP | H | Merstham | 121 | L | 1-3 | Douglas 7 (og) | 11 | 38 |
| Mar 5 | IsthP | H | Dulwich Hamlet | 331 | D | 1-1 | Fisher 54 (pen) | 11 | 39 |
| 12 | IsthP | A | Tonbridge A | 502 | L | 3-4 | Addai 16 Healey 29 51 | 12 | 40 |
| 15 | IsthP | A | Dulwich Hamlet | 584 | L | 1-2 | Pollock 49 | 13 | 41 |
| 19 | IsthP | H | Leatherhead | 122 | D | 1-1 | Healey 24 (pen) | 13 | 42 |
| 22 | IsthP | A | Brentwood Town | 107 | **W** | 1-0 | Fisher 41 | 12 | 43 |
| 26 | IsthP | A | Lewes | 560 | D | 0-0 | | 11 | 44 |
| 28 | IsthP | H | Hendon | 340 | D | 1-1 | Healey 1 | 10 | 45 |
| Apr 2 | IsthP | H | East Thurrock United | 149 | L | 1-3 | Fisher 31 | 11 | 46 |
| 9 | IsthP | A | Harrow Borough | 145 | L | 0-1 | | 13 | 47 |
| 13 | IsthP | A | Bognor & Regis | 391 | L | 0-6 | | 13 | 48 |
| 16 | IsthP | H | VCD Athletic | 132 | **W** | 2-0 | Healey 41 Hutchings 81 | 13 | 49 |
| 29 | IsthP | A | Billericay Town | 473 | L | 0-4 | | 13 | 50 |

| GOALSCORERS | Scoring Games | Consec Sco Games | Total | | Scoring Games | Consec Sco Games | Total |
|---|---|---|---|---|---|---|---|
| ***2014-15 Knight*** | | | ***30*** | Bartram | 2 | | 2 |
| Healey | 16 | 3 | 22 | Weatherstone | 2 | | 2 |
| Laney | 9 | 2 | 9 | Brown | 1 | | 1 |
| Olliyidi | 6 | | 9 | Hewitt | 1 | | 1 |
| Barney | 3 | | 5 | Hutchings | 1 | | 1 |
| Tejan-Sei | 4 | | 5 | Pollock | 1 | | 1 |
| Rifat | 4 | | 4 | Soloman | 1 | | 1 |
| Addai | 3 | | 3 | Opponents | | | 1 |
| Fisher | 3 | | 3 | | | | |
| Sogbanmu | 3 | | 3 | | | | |

# WORTHING

**Chairman:** George Dowell
**Secretary:** Steven Perkins (T) 07525 652004 (E) secretary@worthingfc.com
**Commercial Manager:** n/a (T/E)
**Programme Editor:** Paul Sengebusch (T/E) programme@worthingfc.com
**Ground Address:** Woodside Road, Worthing, West Sussex BN14 7HQ
**(T)** 01903 230 715 **Manager:** Jon Meeney & Gary Elphick

## Club Factfile

**Founded:** 1886 **Nickname:** Rebels
**Previous Names:** None
**Previous Leagues:** West Sussex 1896-1904, 1905-14, 19-20, Brighton Hove & District 1919-20, Sussex County 1920-40, Corinthian 1948-63, Athenian 1963-77
**Club Colours (change):** All red (All yellow)

**Ground Capacity:** 3,650 **Seats:** 500 **Covered:** 1,500 **Clubhouse:** Yes **Shop:**

**Directions**
A24 or A27 to Grove Lodge roundabout.
A24 (Town Centre exit) and right into South Farm Road.
Over five roundabouts take last on right (Pavilion Road) before level crossing.
Woodside Road on right, ground on left. 1/2 mile from BR.

**Previous Grounds:** None

**Record Attendance:** 3,600 v Wimbledon - FA Cup 14/11/1936
**Record Victory:** 25-0 v Littlehampton (H) - Sussex League 1911-12
**Record Defeat:** 0-14 v Southwick (A) - Sussex County League 1946-47
**Record Goalscorer:** Mick Edmonds - 276
**Record Appearances:** Mark Knee - 414
**Additional Records:** Received £7,500 from Woking for Tim Read 1990

**Honours:**
Sussex League 1920-21, 21-22, 26-27, 28-29, 30-31, 33-34, 38-39. Sussex League West 1945-46.
Isthmian League Division 2 1981-82, 92-93, Division 1 1982-83, Division 1 South Play-offs 2015-16.
Sussex Senior Cup x21.

**10 YEAR RECORD**

| 06-07 | 07-08 | 08-09 | 09-10 | 10-11 | 11-12 | 12-13 | 13-14 | 14-15 | 15-16 |
|---|---|---|---|---|---|---|---|---|---|
| Isth P 20 | Isth1S 5 | Isth1S 5 | Isth1S 3 | Isth1S 14 | Isth1S 7 | Isth1S 10 | Isth1S 15 | Isth1S 6 | Isth1S 3 |

# AFC HORNCHURCH

**Chairman:** Colin McBride
**Secretary:** Peter Butcher (T) 07918 645 109 (E) peter.butcher5@btinternet.com
**Commercial Manager:** Peter Butcher (T) 07918 645 109
**Programme Editor:** Peter Butcher (T) 07918 645 109
**Ground Address:** The Stadium, Bridge Avenue, Upminster, Essex RM14 2LX
(T) 01708 220 080 **Manager:** Jim McFarlane

**Founded:** 2005 **Nickname:** The Urchins
**Previous Names:** Formed in 2005 after Hornchurch F.C. folded
**Previous Leagues:** Essex Senior 2005-06. Isthmian 2006-12. Conference 2012-13.

**Club Colours (change):** Red and white (Blue & sky blue)

**Ground Capacity:** 3,500 **Seats:** 800 **Covered:** 1,400 **Clubhouse:** Yes **Shop:** Yes
**Previous Grounds:** None

**Record Attendance:** 3,500 v Tranmere Rovers - FA Cup 2nd Round 2003-04
**Record Victory:** Not known - If you know please email tw.publications@btinternet.com
**Record Defeat:** Not known - If you know please email tw.publications@btinternet.com
**Record Goalscorer:** Not known - If you know please email tw.publications@btinternet.com
**Record Appearances:** Not known - If you know please email tw.publications@btinternet.com
**Additional Records:** Won the Essex League with a record 64 points in 2005-06

**Senior Honours:**
Since reformation in 2005: Essex Senior League, League Cup and Memorial Trophy 2005-06.
Isthmian League Division 1 North 2006-07, Premier Division Play-offs 2011-12.
Essex Senior Cup 2012-13.

**10 YEAR RECORD**

| 06-07 | 07-08 | 08-09 | 09-10 | 10-11 | 11-12 | 12-13 | 13-14 | 14-15 | 15-16 |
|---|---|---|---|---|---|---|---|---|---|
| Isth1N 1 | Isth P 4 | Isth P 6 | Isth P 9 | Isth P 10 | Isth P 2 | Conf S 20 | Isth P 5 | Isth P 23 | Isth1N 5 |

# AVELEY

**Chairman:** Graham Gennings
**Secretary:** Craig Johnston (T) 07946 438 540 (E) craigjohnston@aveleyfc.freeserve.co.uk
**Commercial Manager:** (T)
**Programme Editor:** Craig Johnston (T) 07946 438 540
**Ground Address:** Mill Field, Mill Road, Aveley, Essex RM15 4SJ
(T) 01708 865 940 **Manager:** Justin Gardner

**Founded:** 1927 **Nickname:** The Millers
**Previous Names:** None
**Previous Leagues:** Thurrock Combination 1946-49, London 1949-57, Delphian 1957-63, Athenian 1963-73, Isthmian 1973-2004, Southern 2004-06
**Club Colours (change):** All blue (All red)

**Ground Capacity:** 4,000 **Seats:** 400 **Covered:** 400 **Clubhouse:** Yes **Shop:** No
**Previous Grounds:** None

**Record Attendance:** 3,741 v Slough Town - FA Amateur Cup 27/02/1971
**Record Victory:** 11-1 v Histon - 24/08/1963
**Record Defeat:** 0-8 v Orient, Essex Thameside Trophy
**Record Goalscorer:** Jotty Wilks - 214
**Record Appearances:** Ken Riley - 422
**Additional Records:**

**Senior Honours:**
Athenian League 1970-71. Isthmian League Division 1 North 2008-09.
Thameside Trophy 1980, 2005, 2007.

**10 YEAR RECORD**

| 06-07 | 07-08 | 08-09 | 09-10 | 10-11 | 11-12 | 12-13 | 13-14 | 14-15 | 15-16 |
|---|---|---|---|---|---|---|---|---|---|
| Isth1N 15 | Isth1N 11 | Isth1N 1 | Isth P 3 | Isth P 19 | Isth P 20 | Isth P 5 | Isth1N 13 | Isth1N 9 | Isth1N 12 |

# BOWERS & PITSEA

**Chairman:** Barry Hubbard
**Secretary:** Lee Stevens **(T)** 07910 626 727 **(E)** lee-stevens@sky.com
**Commercial Manager:** **(T)**
**Programme Editor:** Julia Marshall **(T)** jim@royds.com
**Ground Address:** Len Salmon Stadium, Crown Avenue, Pitsea, Basildon SS13 2BE
**(T)** 01268 581 977 **Manager:** Rob Small

**Founded:** 1946 **Nickname:**
**Previous Names:** Bowers United > 2004.
**Previous Leagues:** Thurrock & Thameside Combination. Olympian. Essex Senior >2016.

**Club Colours (change):** Red & white stripes/red/red (Sky blue/white/sky blue).

**Ground Capacity:** 2,000 **Seats:** 200 **Covered:** 1,000 **Clubhouse:** Yes **Shop:** Yes
**Previous Grounds:**

**Record Attendance:** **Att:** 1,800 v Billericay Town, FA Vase. **Most goals in a season:** David Hope - 50 1998-99.
**Record Victory:** 14-1 v Stansted, 2006-07
**Record Defeat:** 0-8 v Ford United, 1996-97
**Record Goalscorer:** Not known - If you know please email tw.publications@btinternet.com
**Record Appearances:** Not known - If you know please email tw.publications@btinternet.com
**Additional Records:** Essex Senior Champions 1980-81, 98-99.

**Senior Honours:**
Essex Senior 1980-81, 98-99, 2015-16.

**10 YEAR RECORD**

| 06-07 | 07-08 | 08-09 | 09-10 | 10-11 | 11-12 | 12-13 | 13-14 | 14-15 | 15-16 |
|---|---|---|---|---|---|---|---|---|---|
| ESen 4 | ESen 7 | ESen 11 | ESen 17 | ESen 14 | ESen 15 | ESen 19 | ESen 14 | ESen 2 | ESen 1 |

# BRENTWOOD TOWN

**Chairman:** Brian Hallett
**Secretary:** Ray Stevens **(T)** 07768 006 370 **(E)** r.w.stevens@btinternet.com
**Commercial Manager:** **(T)**
**Programme Editor:** Ken Hobbs **(T)** khobbs1057@aol.com
**Ground Address:** The Arena, Brentwood Centre, Doddinghurst Road, Brentwood CM15 9NN
**(T)** 07768 006 370 **Manager:** Tony Ilevoli

**Founded:** 1954 **Nickname:** Blues
**Previous Names:** Manor Athletic, Brentwood Athletic, Brentwood F.C.
**Previous Leagues:** Romford & District, South Essex Combination, London & Essex Border, Olympian, Essex Senior

**Club Colours (change):** Sky blue/white/white (All claret)

**Ground Capacity:** 1,000 **Seats:** 150 **Covered:** 250 **Clubhouse:** Yes **Shop:** No
**Previous Grounds:** King George's Playing Fields (Hartswood), Larkins Playing Fields 1957-93

**Record Attendance:** 472 v West Ham United - 27/07/2004
**Record Victory:** Not known - If you know please email tw.publications@btinternet.com
**Record Defeat:** Not known - If you know please email tw.publications@btinternet.com
**Record Goalscorer:** Not known - If you know please email tw.publications@btinternet.com
**Record Appearances:** Not known - If you know please email tw.publications@btinternet.com
**Additional Records:**

**Senior Honours:**
Essex Senior League 2000-01, 2006-07, League Cup 1975-76, 78-79, 90-91, 2006-07. Essex Olympian League Cup 1967-68.
Isthmian Div.1 North Play-off 2014-15.

**10 YEAR RECORD**

| 06-07 | 07-08 | 08-09 | 09-10 | 10-11 | 11-12 | 12-13 | 13-14 | 14-15 | 15-16 |
|---|---|---|---|---|---|---|---|---|---|
| ESen 1 | Isth1N 6 | Isth1N 3 | Isth1N 12 | Isth1N 5 | Isth1N 9 | Isth1N 9 | Isth1N 19 | Isth1N 4 | Isth P 22 |

# BRIGHTLINGSEA REGENT

**Chairman:** Terry Doherty
**Secretary:** Mark Gridley **(T)** 07528 933 106 **(E)** gridders43@pobox.com
**Commercial Manager:** **(T)**
**Programme Editor:** Mark Gridley **(T)** 07528 933 106
**Ground Address:** North Road, Brightlingsea, Essex CO7 0PL
**(T)** 01206 304 199 **Manager:** James Webster

**Founded:** 1928 **Nickname:** The Rs
**Previous Names:** Brightlingsea Athletic & Brightlingsea Town merged to form Brightlingsea United 1928-2005. Merged with Regent Park Rangers.
**Previous Leagues:** Essex Senior 1972-91. Eastern Counties 1990-02, 2011-14. Essex & Suffolk Border 2002-2011.

**Club Colours (change):** Red & black stripes/red/red (Pink & black/black with white trim/black with white trim)

**Ground Capacity:** **Seats:** **Covered:** **Clubhouse:** Yes **Shop:**
**Previous Grounds:** Bell Green (Bellfield Close). Recreation Ground (Regent Road) > 1920.

**Record Attendance:** 1,200 v Colchester United, friendly, 1988.
**Record Victory:** Not known - If you know please email tw.publications@btinternet.com
**Record Defeat:** Not known - If you know please email tw.publications@btinternet.com
**Record Goalscorer:** Not known - If you know please email tw.publications@btinternet.com
**Record Appearances:** Not known - If you know please email tw.publications@btinternet.com
**Additional Records:**

**Senior Honours:**
**League:** Essex Senior 1988-89, 89-90. Essex & Suffolk Border League 2010-11.

**10 YEAR RECORD**

| 06-07 | 07-08 | 08-09 | 09-10 | 10-11 | 11-12 | 12-13 | 13-14 | 14-15 | 15-16 |
|---|---|---|---|---|---|---|---|---|---|
| | | | | EsSuP 1 | EC1 5 | EC1 3 | ECP 2 | Isth1N 6 | Isth1N 8 |

# BURY TOWN

**Chairman:** Russell Ward
**Secretary:** Mrs Wendy Turner **(T)** 07795 661 959 **(E)** wturner@burytownfc.freeserve.co.uk
**Commercial Manager:** **(T)**
**Programme Editor:** Christopher Ward **(T)** cpward@burytownfc.co.uk
**Ground Address:** Ram Meadow, Cotton Lane, Bury St Edmunds IP33 1XP
**(T)** 01284 754 721 **Manager:** Ben Chenery

**Founded:** 1872 **Nickname:** The Blues
**Previous Names:** Bury St Edmunds 1872-1885, 1895-1908. Bury Town 1885-95. Bury United 1908-23.
**Previous Leagues:** Norfolk & Suffolk Border, Essex & Suffolk Border, Eastern Counties 1935-64, 76-87, 97-2006, Metropolitan 1964-71, Southern 1971-76, 87-97
**Club Colours (change):** All blue with white (orange/black/orange)

**Ground Capacity:** 3,500 **Seats:** 300 **Covered:** 1,500 **Clubhouse:** Yes **Shop:** Yes
**Previous Grounds:** Kings Road 1888-1978

**Record Attendance:** 2,500 v Enfield - FA Cup 1986
**Record Victory:** Not known - If you know please email tw.publications@btinternet.com
**Record Defeat:** Not known - If you know please email tw.publications@btinternet.com
**Record Goalscorer:** Doug Tooley
**Record Appearances:** Doug Tooley
**Additional Records:** Paid £1,500 to Chelmsford City for Mel Springett
Received £5,500 from Ipswich Town for Simon Milton
**Senior Honours:**
Eastern Counties League 1963-64.
Suffolk Premier Cup x10 Most recently 2012-13.
Southern League Division One Central 2009-10

**10 YEAR RECORD**

| 06-07 | 07-08 | 08-09 | 09-10 | 10-11 | 11-12 | 12-13 | 13-14 | 14-15 | 15-16 |
|---|---|---|---|---|---|---|---|---|---|
| Isth1N 17 | Isth1N 7 | SthC 7 | SthC 1 | Isth P 3 | Isth P 5 | Isth P 7 | Isth P 15 | Isth P 24 | Isth1N 13 |

# CHESHUNT

**Chairman:** Dean Williamson
**Secretary:** Nigel Griffiths **(T)** 07960 868 660 **(E)** clubsecretary@cheshuntfc.com
**Commercial Manager:** **(T)**
**Programme Editor:** Howard Bailey **(T)** programme@cheshuntfc.com
**Ground Address:** Cheshunt Stadium, Theobalds Lane, Cheshunt, Herts EN8 8RU
**(T)** 01992 625 793 **Manager:** Paul Wickenden

**Founded:** 1946 **Nickname:** Ambers
**Previous Names:**
**Previous Leagues:** London 1947-51, 56-59, Delphian 1952-55, Aetolian 1960-62, Spartan 1963-64, 88-93, Athenian 1965-76, Isthmian 1977-87, 94-2005, Southern 2006-08
**Club Colours (change):** Amber/black/black (Sky blue/white/sky blue)

**Ground Capacity:** 3,500 **Seats:** 424 **Covered:** 600 **Clubhouse:** Yes **Shop:** No
**Previous Grounds:** Gothic Sports Ground 1946-47. College Road 1947-50. Brookfield Lane 1950-52, 53-58.

**Record Attendance:** 5,000
**Record Victory:** v Bromley - FA Amateur Cup 2nd Round 28/01/1950
**Record Defeat:** 0-10 v Etonn Manor - London League 17/04/1956
**Record Goalscorer:** Eddie Sedgwick - 148 (1967-72, 1980)
**Record Appearances:** John Poole - 526 (1970-76, 79-83)
**Additional Records:** Received £10,000 from Peterborough United for Lloyd Opara

**Senior Honours:**
London League Premier Division 1950, Division 1 1948, 49. Athenian League Premier Division 1976, Division 1 1968.
Spartan League 1963. Isthmian League Division 2 2003.
London Charity Cup 1974. East Anglian Cup 1975. Herts Charity Cup 2006, 2008.

**10 YEAR RECORD**

| 06-07 | 07-08 | 08-09 | 09-10 | 10-11 | 11-12 | 12-13 | 13-14 | 14-15 | 15-16 |
|---|---|---|---|---|---|---|---|---|---|
| SthP 16 | SthP 22 | Isth1N 14 | Isth1N 15 | Isth1N 18 | Isth1N 18 | Isth1N 11 | Isth1N 15 | Isth1N 18 | Isth1N 6 |

# DEREHAM TOWN

**Chairman:** Ray Bales
**Secretary:** Ray Bales **(T)** 07769 644740 **(E)** ray.bayles@ntlworld.com
**Commercial Manager:** **(T)**
**Programme Editor:** Simon Barnes **(T)** football.barnesprint@btconnect.com
**Ground Address:** Aldiss Park, Norwich Road, Dereham, Norfolk NR20 3PX
**(T)** 01362 690 460 **Manager:** Matt Henman

**Founded:** 1884 **Nickname:** Magpies
**Previous Names:** Dereham and Dereham Hobbies.
**Previous Leagues:** Norwich District. Dereham & District. Norfolk & Suffolk. Anglian Comb. Eastern Counties > 2013.

**Club Colours (change):** White & black stripes/black/black. (Green/white/white)

**Ground Capacity:** 3,000 **Seats:** 50 **Covered:** 500 **Clubhouse:** Yes **Shop:** Yes
**Previous Grounds:** None

**Record Attendance:** **Att:** 3000 v Norwich City, Friendly, 07/2001.
**Record Victory:** Not known - If you know please email tw.publications@btinternet.com
**Record Defeat:** Not known - If you know please email tw.publications@btinternet.com
**Record Goalscorer:** Not known - If you know please email tw.publications@btinternet.com
**Record Appearances:** Not known - If you know please email tw.publications@btinternet.com
**Additional Records:**

**Senior Honours:**
Anglian Combination Division One 1989-90, Premier Division 97-98. Eastern Counties Premier Division 2012-13.
Norfolk Senior Cup 2005-06, 06-07, 15-16.

**10 YEAR RECORD**

| 06-07 | 07-08 | 08-09 | 09-10 | 10-11 | 11-12 | 12-13 | 13-14 | 14-15 | 15-16 |
|---|---|---|---|---|---|---|---|---|---|
| ECP 6 | ECP 4 | ECP 4 | ECP 10 | ECP 2 | ECP 10 | ECP 1 | Isth1N 7 | Isth1N 7 | Isth1N 9 |

# GREAT WAKERING ROVERS

**Chairman:** Tony Butcher
**Secretary:** Daniel Ellis (T) 07828 048 671 (E) secretary@gwrovers.com
**Commercial Manager:** (T)
**Programme Editor:** Daniel Ellis (T) secretary@gwrovers.com
**Ground Address:** Burroughs Park, Little Wakering Hall Lane, Great Wakering SS3 0HH
(T) 01702 217 812 **Manager:** Gary Ansell

**Founded:** 1919 **Nickname:** Rovers
**Previous Names:** Not known
**Previous Leagues:** Southend & Dist. 1919-81, Southend All. 1981-89, Essex Inter 1989-92, Essex Sen 1992-99, Isth. 1999-2004, Sthn 2004-05

**Club Colours (change):** Green and white stripes/green/green & white (Yellow/black/yellow & black hoops)

**Ground Capacity:** 2,500 **Seats:** 150 **Covered:** 300 **Clubhouse:** Yes **Shop:** No
**Previous Grounds:** Great Wakering Rec

**Record Attendance:** 1,150 v Southend United - Friendly 19/07/2006
**Record Victory:** 9-0 v Eton Manor - 27/12/1931
**Record Defeat:** 1-7 v Bowers United - Essex Senior League 01/04/1998
**Record Goalscorer:** Not known
**Record Appearances:** Not known - If you know please email tw.publications@btinternet.com
**Additional Records:**

**Senior Honours:**
Essex Senior League 1994-95, 2013-14. Isthmian League Division 3.

**10 YEAR RECORD**

| 06-07 | 07-08 | 08-09 | 09-10 | 10-11 | 11-12 | 12-13 | 13-14 | 14-15 | 15-16 |
|---|---|---|---|---|---|---|---|---|---|
| Isth1N 12 | Isth1N 13 | Isth1N 13 | Isth1N 9 | Isth1N 15 | Isth1N 22 | ESen 4 | ESen 1 | Isth1N 15 | Isth1N 18 |

# HARINGEY BOROUGH

**Chairman:** Aki Achillea
**Secretary:** John Bacon (T) 07979 050 190 (E) baconjw@hotmail.com
**Commercial Manager:** (T)
**Programme Editor:** Richard Brickell (T) botanybaykid@yahoo.co.uk
**Ground Address:** Coles Park, White Hart Lane, Tottenham, London N17 7JP
(T) 0208 889 1415 (Matchday) **Manager:** Tom Loizou

**Founded:** 1907 **Nickname:** Borough
**Previous Names:** Tufnell Park 1907-60. Edmonton. Wood Green Town.
**Previous Leagues:** London, Isthmian, Spartan, Delphian, Athenian, Spartan South Midlands > 2013. Essex Senior 2013-15.

**Club Colours (change):** Green

**Ground Capacity:** 2,500 **Seats:** 280 **Covered:** yes **Clubhouse:** Yes **Shop:** No
**Previous Grounds:**

**Record Attendance:** Att: 400
**Record Victory:** Not known - If you know please email tw.publications@btinternet.com
**Record Defeat:** Not known - If you know please email tw.publications@btinternet.com
**Record Goalscorer:** Not known - If you know please email tw.publications@btinternet.com
**Record Appearances:** Not known - If you know please email tw.publications@btinternet.com
**Additional Records:**

**Senior Honours:**
London Senior Cup 1912-13, 90-91, Athenian League 1913-14. Essex Senior 2014-15.

**10 YEAR RECORD**

| 06-07 | 07-08 | 08-09 | 09-10 | 10-11 | 11-12 | 12-13 | 13-14 | 14-15 | 15-16 |
|---|---|---|---|---|---|---|---|---|---|
| SSM P 21 | SSM1 2 | SSM P 18 | SSM P 15 | SSM P 8 | SSM P 5 | SSM P 9 | ESen 2 | ESen 1 | Isth1N 15 |

# HEYBRIDGE SWIFTS

**Chairman:** Gary White
**Secretary:** Chris Daines **(T)** 07973 342 283 **(E)** hsfcdaines@aol.com
**Commercial Manager:** **(T)**
**Programme Editor:** Chris Daines **(T)** hsfcdaines@aol.com
**Ground Address:** Scraley Road, Heybridge, Maldon, Essex CM9 8JA
**(T)** 01621 852 978 **Manager:** Jody Brown

**Founded:** 1880 **Nickname:** Swifts
**Previous Names:** Heybridge FC.
**Previous Leagues:** Essex & Suffolk Border, North Essex, South Essex, Essex Senior 1971-84

**Club Colours (change):** Black and white stripes/black/black (Red & black stripeswhite/white)

**Ground Capacity:** 3,000 **Seats:** 550 **Covered:** 1,200 **Clubhouse:** Yes **Shop:** Yes
**Previous Grounds:** One before Scraley Road.

**Record Attendance:** 2,477 v Woking - FA Trophy 1997
**Record Victory:** Not known - If you know please email tw.publications@btinternet.com
**Record Defeat:** Not known - If you know please email tw.publications@btinternet.com
**Record Goalscorer:** Julian Lamb - 115 (post War)
**Record Appearances:** Hec Askew - 500+. John Pollard - 496
**Additional Records:** Paid £1,000 for Dave Rainford and for Lee Kersey
Received £35,000 from Southend United for Simon Royce
**Senior Honours:**
Isthmian League Division 2 North 1989-90, Essex Senior League x3.
Essex Junior Cup 1931-32. East Anglian Cup 1993-94, 94-95.

**10 YEAR RECORD**

| 06-07 | 07-08 | 08-09 | 09-10 | 10-11 | 11-12 | 12-13 | 13-14 | 14-15 | 15-16 |
|---|---|---|---|---|---|---|---|---|---|
| Isth P 12 | Isth P 12 | Isth P 21 | Isth1N 6 | Isth1N 9 | Isth1N 16 | Isth1N 6 | Isth1N 3 | Isth1N 12 | Isth1N 20 |

# MALDON & TIPTREE

**Chairman:** Ed Garty
**Secretary:** Laura Hall **(T)** **(E)** club.secretary@maldontiptreefc.co.uk
**Commercial Manager:** **(T)**
**Programme Editor:** Andrew Drew **(T)** adam@threefivefour.co.uk
**Ground Address:** Wallace Binder Ground, Park Drive, Maldon CM9 5JQ
**(T)** 01621 853 762 **Manager:** Kevin Horlock

**Founded:** 2010 **Nickname:** The Hoops
**Previous Names:** Maldon Town (1975) and Tiptree United (1933) merged in 2010 to form today's club
**Previous Leagues:** None

**Club Colours (change):** Blue and red stripes/blue/blue (All orange)

**Ground Capacity:** 2,800 **Seats:** 155 **Covered:** 300 **Clubhouse:** Yes **Shop:**
**Previous Grounds:** None

**Record Attendance:** Not known
**Record Victory:** Not known - If you know please email tw.publications@btinternet.com
**Record Defeat:** Not known - If you know please email tw.publications@btinternet.com
**Record Goalscorer:** Not known
**Record Appearances:** Not known
**Additional Records:**
**Senior Honours:**
None

**10 YEAR RECORD**

| 06-07 | 07-08 | 08-09 | 09-10 | 10-11 | 11-12 | 12-13 | 13-14 | 14-15 | 15-16 |
|---|---|---|---|---|---|---|---|---|---|
| | | | | Isth1N 8 | Isth1N 11 | Isth1N 2 | Isth1N 9 | Isth1N 19 | Isth1N 7 |

# NORWICH UNITED

**Chairman:** John Hilditch
**Secretary:** Keith Cutmore **(T)** 07788 437 515 **(E)** secretary.nufc@hotmail.co.uk
**Commercial Manager:** **(T)**
**Programme Editor:** Barnes Print **(T)** simon@barnesprintltd.co.uk
**Ground Address:** Plantation Park, Blofield, Norwich NR13 4PL
**(T)** 01603 716 963 **Manager:** Steve Eastaugh

**Founded:** 1903 **Nickname:** Planters
**Previous Names:** Poringland & District > 1987
**Previous Leagues:** Norwich & District. Anglian Combination. Eastern Counties >2016.

**Club Colours (change):** Yellow & blue/blue/blue. (All grey)

**Ground Capacity:** 3,000 **Seats:** 100 **Covered:** 1,000 **Clubhouse:** Yes **Shop:** Yes
**Previous Grounds:**

**Record Attendance:** **Att:** 401 v Wroxham, Eastern Co. Lge, 1991-92. **Goalscorer:** M. Money. **Apps:** Tim Sayer.
**Record Victory:** Not known - If you know please email tw.publications@btinternet.com
**Record Defeat:** Not known - If you know please email tw.publications@btinternet.com
**Record Goalscorer:** Not known - If you know please email tw.publications@btinternet.com
**Record Appearances:** Not known - If you know please email tw.publications@btinternet.com
**Additional Records:**

**Senior Honours:**
Anglian Combination Premier Division 1988-99. Eastern Counties League Division One 1990-91, 01-02, Premier Division 2014-15, 15-16.
Anglian Combination Senior Cup 1983-84.

**10 YEAR RECORD**

| 06-07 | 07-08 | 08-09 | 09-10 | 10-11 | 11-12 | 12-13 | 13-14 | 14-15 | 15-16 |
|---|---|---|---|---|---|---|---|---|---|
| ECP 16 | ECP 15 | ECP 19 | ECP 15 | ECP 6 | ECP 9 | ECP 13 | ECP 6 | ECP 1 | ECP 1 |

# PHOENIX SPORTS

**Chairman:** Andrew Mortlock
**Secretary:** Alf Levy **(T)** 07795 182 927 **(E)** alf_levy@sky.com
**Commercial Manager:** **(T)**
**Programme Editor:** Jamie Brown **(T)** beeski5279@hotmail.co.uk
**Ground Address:** Phoenix Sports Ground, Mayplace Road East, Barnehurst, Kent DA8 3BJ
**(T)** 01322 526 159 **Manager:** Steve O'Boyle

**Founded:** 1935 **Nickname:**
**Previous Names:** St Johns Welling. Lakeside. Phoenix.
**Previous Leagues:** Spartan League. Kent County > 2011. Kent Invicta 2011-13.

**Club Colours (change):** Green/black/black (All red)

**Ground Capacity:** **Seats:** Yes **Covered:** Yes **Clubhouse:** Yes **Shop:**
**Previous Grounds:** Danson Park >1950.

**Record Attendance:** Not known - If you know please email tw.publications@btinternet.com
**Record Victory:** Not known - If you know please email tw.publications@btinternet.com
**Record Defeat:** Not known - If you know please email tw.publications@btinternet.com
**Record Goalscorer:** Not known - If you know please email tw.publications@btinternet.com
**Record Appearances:** Not known - If you know please email tw.publications@btinternet.com
**Additional Records:**

**Senior Honours:**
Kent County Division Two West 2004-05, Division One West 2007-08. Kent Invicta League 2012-13. Southern Counties East 2014-15.

**10 YEAR RECORD**

| 06-07 | 07-08 | 08-09 | 09-10 | 10-11 | 11-12 | 12-13 | 13-14 | 14-15 | 15-16 |
|---|---|---|---|---|---|---|---|---|---|
| KC1W 5 | KC1W 1 | KC P 8 | KC P 4 | KC P 5 | K_lv 2 | K_lv 1 | SCE 6 | SCE 1 | Isth1N 14 |

# ROMFORD

**Chairman:** Steve Gardener
**Secretary:** Colin Ewenson **(T)** 07973 717 074 **(E)** ewenson@aol.com
**Commercial Manager:** **(T)**
**Programme Editor:** Keith Preston **(T)** keithpreston72@yahoo.co.uk
**Ground Address:** Thurrock FC, South Way, Ship Lane, Aveley RM19 1YN
**(T)** 01708 865 492 **Manager:** Paul Martin

**Founded:** 1876 **Nickname:** Boro
**Previous Names:** Original club founded in 1876 folded during WW1, Reformed in 1929 folded again in 1978 and reformed in 1992
**Previous Leagues:** Athenian 1931-39, Isthmian 1945-59, 97-2002, Southern 1959-78, Essex Senior 1992-96, 2002-09

**Club Colours (change):** Yellow & blue

**Ground Capacity:** 4,500 **Seats:** 300 **Covered:** 1,000 **Clubhouse:** Yes **Shop:**
**Previous Grounds:** The Mill Field (Aveley FC).

**Record Attendance:** 820 v Leatherhead - Isthmian Division 2
**Record Victory:** Not known - If you know please email tw.publications@btinternet.com
**Record Defeat:** Not known - If you know please email tw.publications@btinternet.com
**Record Goalscorer:** Danny Benstock
**Record Appearances:** S Horne - 234
**Additional Records:**

**Senior Honours:**
Essex Senior League 1995-96, 2008-09. Isthmian League Division 2 1996-97.

**10 YEAR RECORD**

| 06-07 | 07-08 | 08-09 | 09-10 | 10-11 | 11-12 | 12-13 | 13-14 | 14-15 | 15-16 |
|---|---|---|---|---|---|---|---|---|---|
| ESen 2 | ESen 5 | ESen 1 | Isth1N 13 | Isth1N 12 | Isth1N 13 | Isth1N 8 | Isth1N 11 | Isth1N 20 | Isth1N 16 |

# SOHAM TOWN RANGERS

**Chairman:** Stuart Hamilton
**Secretary:** Simon Cullum **(T)** 07899 971 680 **(E)** strfc@live.co.uk
**Commercial Manager:** **(T)**
**Programme Editor:** Amy Doggett **(T)** Amy.Soham@gmail.com
**Ground Address:** Julius Martin Lane, Soham, Ely, Cambridgeshire CB7 5EQ
**(T)** 01353 720 732 **Manager:** Robbie Nightingale & David Theobald

**Founded:** 1947 **Nickname:** Town or Rangers
**Previous Names:** Soham Town and Soham Rangers merged in 1947
**Previous Leagues:** Peterborough & District, Eastern Counties 1963-2008, Southern 2008-11.

**Club Colours (change):** Green & white stripes/green/green & white (All blue with white trim)

**Ground Capacity:** 2,000 **Seats:** 250 **Covered:** 1,000 **Clubhouse:** Yes **Shop:** Yes
**Previous Grounds:**

**Record Attendance:** 3,000 v Pegasus - FA Amateur Cup 1963
**Record Victory:** Not known - If you know please email tw.publications@btinternet.com
**Record Defeat:** Not known - If you know please email tw.publications@btinternet.com
**Record Goalscorer:** Not known - If you know please email tw.publications@btinternet.com
**Record Appearances:** Not known - If you know please email tw.publications@btinternet.com
**Additional Records:**

**Senior Honours:**
Eastern Counties League Premier Division 2007-08

**10 YEAR RECORD**

| 06-07 | 07-08 | 08-09 | 09-10 | 10-11 | 11-12 | 12-13 | 13-14 | 14-15 | 15-16 |
|---|---|---|---|---|---|---|---|---|---|
| ECP | ECP 1 | SthC 15 | SthC 11 | SthC 17 | Isth1N 19 | Isth1N 7 | Isth1N 8 | Isth1N 11 | Isth1N 17 |

# THAMESMEAD TOWN

**Chairman:** Paul Bowden-Brown
**Secretary:** David Joy **(T)** 07990 612 495 **(E)** davejoyo@yahoo.co.uk
**Commercial Manager:** **(T)**
**Programme Editor:** Jamie Barwick **(T)** Jamie_barwick363@yahoo.co.uk
**Ground Address:** Bayliss Avenue, Thamesmead, London SE28 8NJ
**(T)** 0208 320 4470 **Manager:** Tommy Warrilow

**Founded:** 1970 **Nickname:** The Mead
**Previous Names:** None
**Previous Leagues:** Spartan 1987-91, Kent 1991-2008

**Club Colours (change):** All green (All light blue)

**Ground Capacity:** 400 **Seats:** 161 **Covered:** 125 **Clubhouse:** Yes **Shop:**
**Previous Grounds:** Crossways. Meridian Sports Ground > 1985.

**Record Attendance:** 400 v Wimbledon - Ground opening 1988
**Record Victory:** 9-0 v Kent Police - Kent League 19/04/1994
**Record Defeat:** Not known - If you know please email tw.publications@btinternet.com
**Record Goalscorer:** Delroy D'Oyley
**Record Appearances:** Not known - If you know please email tw.publications@btinternet.com
**Additional Records:**

**Senior Honours:**
Kent Senior Trophy 2004-05. Kent Premier 2007-08

**10 YEAR RECORD**

| 06-07 | 07-08 | 08-09 | 09-10 | 10-11 | 11-12 | 12-13 | 13-14 | 14-15 | 15-16 |
|---|---|---|---|---|---|---|---|---|---|
| Kent P 4 | Kent P 1 | Isth1N 18 | Isth1N 7 | Isth1N 17 | Isth1N 10 | Isth1N 3 | Isth P 22 | Isth1N 13 | Isth1N 10 |

# THURROCK

**Chairman:** Tommy South
**Secretary:** Val Pepperell **(T)** 07931 731 358 **(E)** thurrockmatchsec@live.co.uk
**Commercial Manager:** **(T)**
**Programme Editor:** Norman Posner **(T)** normpos@aol.com
**Ground Address:** South Way, Ship Lane, Grays, Essex RM19 1YN
**(T)** 01708 865 492 **Manager:** Mark Stimson

**Founded:** 1985 **Nickname:** Fleet
**Previous Names:** Purfleet > 2003
**Previous Leagues:** Essex Senior 1985-89, Isthmian 1989-2004

**Club Colours (change):** Yellow/green/green (All purple)

**Ground Capacity:** 4,500 **Seats:** 300 **Covered:** 1,000 **Clubhouse:** Yes **Shop:** Yes
**Previous Grounds:** None

**Record Attendance:** 2,572 v West Ham United - Friendly 1998
**Record Victory:** 10-0 v Stansted (H) - Essex Senior Lge 1986-87 and v East Ham United (A) - Essex Senior Lge 1987-88
**Record Defeat:** 0-6 v St Leonards Stamco (A) - FA Trophy 1996-97 and v Sutton United (H) - Isthmian League 1997-98
**Record Goalscorer:** George Georgiou - 106
**Record Appearances:** Jimmy McFarlane - 632
**Additional Records:**

**Senior Honours:**
Isthmian League Division 2 1991-92.
Essex Senior Cup 2003-04, 05-06.

**10 YEAR RECORD**

| 06-07 | 07-08 | 08-09 | 09-10 | 10-11 | 11-12 | 12-13 | 13-14 | 14-15 | 15-16 |
|---|---|---|---|---|---|---|---|---|---|
| Conf S 18 | Conf S 12 | Conf S 20 | Conf S 10 | Conf S 20 | Conf S 22 | Isth P 21 | Isth1N 6 | Isth1N 5 | Isth1N 2 |

# TILBURY

**Chairman:** Daniel Nash
**Secretary:** Anthony Mercer (T) 07718 881 593 (E) amercer67@googlemail.com
**Commercial Manager:** (T)
**Programme Editor:** Mark Kettlety (T) sundayonly1@aol.com
**Ground Address:** Chadfields, St Chads Road, Tilbury, Essex RM18 8NL
(T) 01375 843 093 **Manager:** Gary Henty - 10/14

**Founded:** 1895 **Nickname:** The Dockers
**Previous Names:**
**Previous Leagues:** Grays & District/South Essex, Kent 1927-31, London, South Essex Combination (Wartime), Corinthian 1950-57, Delphian 1962-63, Athenian 1963-73, Isthmian 1973-2004, Essex Senior 2004-05
**Club Colours (change):** Black & white stripes/black/red (Red & yellow stripes/red/yellow)

**Ground Capacity:** 4,000 **Seats:** 350 **Covered:** 1,000 **Clubhouse:** Yes **Shop:** No
**Previous Grounds:** A couple before moving in to Chafields in 1946-47.

**Record Attendance:** 5,500 v Gorleston - FA Cup 1949
**Record Victory:** Not known - If you know please email tw.publications@btinternet.com
**Record Defeat:** Not known - If you know please email tw.publications@btinternet.com
**Record Goalscorer:** Ross Livermore - 282 in 305 games
**Record Appearances:** Nicky Smith - 424 (1975-85)
**Additional Records:** Received £2,000 from Grays Athletic for Tony Macklin 1990 and from Dartford for Steve Connor 1985
**Senior Honours:**
Athenian League 1968-69. Isthmian League Division Two 1975-76.
Essex Senior Cup x4.

**10 YEAR RECORD**

| 06-07 | 07-08 | 08-09 | 09-10 | 10-11 | 11-12 | 12-13 | 13-14 | 14-15 | 15-16 |
|---|---|---|---|---|---|---|---|---|---|
| Isth1N 19 | Isth1N 20 | Isth1N 11 | Isth1N 11 | Isth1N 19 | Isth1N 3 | Isth1N 16 | Isth1N 16 | Isth1N 14 | Isth1N 11 |

# VCD ATHLETIC

**Chairman:** Gary Rump
**Secretary:** Chris Kew (T) 07877 520 729 (E) vcdathleticfc@gmail.com
**Commercial Manager:** (T)
**Programme Editor:** Chris Rixson (T) chris.rixson@yahoo.com
**Ground Address:** Oakwood, Old Road, Crayford DA1 4DN
(T) 01322 524 262 **Manager:** Keith McMahon

**Founded:** 1916 **Nickname:** The Vickers
**Previous Names:** Vickers (Erith). Vickers (Crayford) Now Vickers Crayford Dartford Athletic.
**Previous Leagues:** Dartford & District. Kent County. Isthmian

**Club Colours (change):** Green & white/white (Blue/black/black)

**Ground Capacity:** **Seats:** Yes **Covered:** Yes **Clubhouse:** Yes **Shop:** No
**Previous Grounds:** Groundshared with Thamesmead (5 seasons), Lordswood (2) and Greenwich Boro' (1) whilst waiting for planning at Oakwood.

**Record Attendance:** 13,500 Away v Maidstone, 1919.
**Record Victory:** Not known - If you know please email tw.publications@btinternet.com
**Record Defeat:** Not known - If you know please email tw.publications@btinternet.com
**Record Goalscorer:** Not known - If you know please email tw.publications@btinternet.com
**Record Appearances:** Not known - If you know please email tw.publications@btinternet.com
**Additional Records:**
**Senior Honours:**
Kent County League 1996-97. Kent League 2008-09. Isthmian Division One North 2013-14.
Kent Senior Trophy 2005-06, 08-09.

**10 YEAR RECORD**

| 06-07 | 07-08 | 08-09 | 09-10 | 10-11 | 11-12 | 12-13 | 13-14 | 14-15 | 15-16 |
|---|---|---|---|---|---|---|---|---|---|
| Kent P 2 | Kent P 2 | Kent P 1 | Isth1N 8 | Kent P 3 | Kent P 3 | Kent P 2 | Isth1N 1 | Isth P 18 | Isth P 24 |

# WALTHAM ABBEY

**Chairman:** John Martin
**Secretary:** David Hodges (T) 07742 364 447 (E) davehodges44@yahoo.co.uk
**Commercial Manager:** (T)
**Programme Editor:** Colin Reed (T) beerbelly44@yahoo.co.uk
**Ground Address:** Capershotts, Sewardstone Road, Waltham Abbey, Essex EN9 1NX
(T) 01992 711 287 **Manager:** Paul Joynes

**Founded:** 1944 **Nickname:** Abbotts
**Previous Names:** Abbey Sports amalgamated with Beechfield Sports in 1974 to form Beechfields. Club then renamed to Waltham Abbey in 1976
**Previous Leagues:** Spartan, Essex & Herts Border, Essex Senior

**Club Colours (change):** Green and white hoops/white/green (All blue)

**Ground Capacity:** 2,000 **Seats:** 300 **Covered:** 500 **Clubhouse:** Yes **Shop:** No
**Previous Grounds:** None

**Record Attendance:** Not known - If you know please email tw.publications@btinternet.com
**Record Victory:** Not known - If you know please email tw.publications@btinternet.com
**Record Defeat:** Not known - If you know please email tw.publications@btinternet.com
**Record Goalscorer:** Not known - If you know please email tw.publications@btinternet.com
**Record Appearances:** Not known - If you know please email tw.publications@btinternet.com
**Additional Records:**

**Senior Honours:**
London Spartan League Division 1 1977-78, Senior Division 1978-79.
London Senior Cup 1999. Essex Senior Cup 2004-05.

**10 YEAR RECORD**

| 06-07 | 07-08 | 08-09 | 09-10 | 10-11 | 11-12 | 12-13 | 13-14 | 14-15 | 15-16 |
|---|---|---|---|---|---|---|---|---|---|
| Isth1N 10 | Isth1N 14 | Isth1N 4 | Isth1N 21 | Isth1N 11 | Isth1N 14 | Isth1N 12 | Isth1N 18 | Isth1N 10 | Isth1N 21 |

# WARE

**Chairman:** Inanc Elitok
**Secretary:** Bill Spink (T) 07538 101 463 (E) spink405@btinternet.com
**Commercial Manager:** (T)
**Programme Editor:** Mark Kettlety (T) Sundayonly1@aol.com
**Ground Address:** Wodson Park, Wadesmill Road, Ware, Herts SG12 0UQ
(T) 01920 462 064 **Manager:** Ken Charlery

**Founded:** 1892 **Nickname:** Blues
**Previous Names:** None
**Previous Leagues:** East Herts, North Middlesex 1907-08, Herts County 1908-25, Spartan 1925-55, Delphian 1955-63, Athenian 1963-75, Isthmian 1975-2015. Southern 2015-16.

**Club Colours (change):** Blue with white stripes/blue/blue (Orange & white stripes/black/orange)

**Ground Capacity:** 3,300 **Seats:** 500 **Covered:** 312 **Clubhouse:** Yes **Shop:** Yes
**Previous Grounds:** Highfields, Canons Park, London Road, Presdales Lower Park 1921-26

**Record Attendance:** 3,800 v Hendon - FA Amateur Cup 1956-57
**Record Victory:** 10-1 v Wood Green Town
**Record Defeat:** 0-11 v Barnet
**Record Goalscorer:** George Dearman scored 98 goals during 1926-27
**Record Appearances:** Gary Riddle - 654
**Additional Records:**

**Senior Honours:**
Isthmian League Division 2 2005-06.
East Anglian Cup 1973-74. Herts Senior Cup x5.

**10 YEAR RECORD**

| 06-07 | 07-08 | 08-09 | 09-10 | 10-11 | 11-12 | 12-13 | 13-14 | 14-15 | 15-16 |
|---|---|---|---|---|---|---|---|---|---|
| Isth1N 7 | Isth1N 4 | Isth1N 9 | Isth1N 19 | Isth1N 14 | Isth1N 21 | Isth1N 19 | Isth1N 21 | Isth1N 10 | SthC 11 |

# WITHAM TOWN

**Chairman:** Mark Nicholls
**Secretary:** Kevin Carroll **(T)** 07743 827 505 **(E)** withamtownfcsecretary@gmail.com
**Commercial Manager:** **(T)**
**Programme Editor:** Jim Purtill **(T)** jim_purtill@yahoo.com
**Ground Address:** Village Glass Stadium, Spa Road, Witham CM8 1UN
**(T)** 01376 511 198 **Manager:** Adam Flint

**Founded:** 1947 **Nickname:** Town
**Previous Names:** None.
**Previous Leagues:** Mid. Essex. Essex & Suff. B. Essex Senior 1971-87. Isthmian 1987-2009

**Club Colours (change):** White/blue/green (All yellow).

**Ground Capacity:** 2,500 **Seats:** 157 **Covered:** 780 **Clubhouse:** Yes **Shop:** No
**Previous Grounds:** None

**Record Attendance:** **Att:** 800 v Billericay Town, Essex Senior Lge, May 1976.
**Record Victory:** Not known - If you know please email tw.publications@btinternet.com
**Record Defeat:** Not known - If you know please email tw.publications@btinternet.com
**Record Goalscorer:** Colin Mitchell.
**Record Appearances:** Keith Dent.
**Additional Records:**

**Senior Honours:**
Essex Senior League 1970-71, 85-86, 2011-12.

**10 YEAR RECORD**

| 06-07 | 07-08 | 08-09 | 09-10 | 10-11 | 11-12 | 12-13 | 13-14 | 14-15 | 15-16 |
|---|---|---|---|---|---|---|---|---|---|
| Isth1N 20 | Isth1N 20 | Isth1N 21 | ESen 2 | ESen 3 | ESen 1 | Isth1N 4 | Isth1N 2 | Isth P 22 | Isth1N 19 |

# WROXHAM

**Chairman:** Kevin Attree
**Secretary:** Chris Green **(T)** 07508 219 072 **(E)** secretary@wroxhamfc.com
**Commercial Manager:** **(T)**
**Programme Editor:** Barnes Print **(T)** football.barnesprint@btconnect.com
**Ground Address:** Trafford Park, Skinners Lane, Wroxham NR12 8SJ
**(T)** 01603 783 536 **Manager:** Damian Hilton

**Founded:** 1892 **Nickname:** Yachtsmen
**Previous Names:** None
**Previous Leagues:** East Norfolk. Norwich City. East Anglian. Norwich & Dist. Anglian Comb.

**Club Colours (change):** Blue & white/blue/blue (White with blue trim/white/blue)

**Ground Capacity:** 2,500 **Seats:** 50 **Covered:** 250 **Clubhouse:** Yes **Shop:** No
**Previous Grounds:** Norwich Road, The Avenue and Keys Hill. Moved in to Trafford Park around the time of WWII.

**Record Attendance:** **Att:** 1,011 v Wisbech Town, Eastern Co. Lge, 16.03.93.
**Record Victory:** Not known - If you know please email tw.publications@btinternet.com
**Record Defeat:** Not known - If you know please email tw.publications@btinternet.com
**Record Goalscorer:** Matthew Metcalf.
**Record Appearances:** Stu Larter.
**Additional Records:**

**Senior Honours:**
Anglian County League 1981-82, 82-83, 83-84, 84-85, 86-87.
Eastern Counties League Division One 1988-89, Prem 91-92, 92-93, 93-94, 96-97, 97-98, 98-99, 2006-07, 11-12.
Norfolk Senior Cup 1992-93, 95-96, 97-98, 99-00, 2003-04, 14-15.

**10 YEAR RECORD**

| 06-07 | 07-08 | 08-09 | 09-10 | 10-11 | 11-12 | 12-13 | 13-14 | 14-15 | 15-16 |
|---|---|---|---|---|---|---|---|---|---|
| ECP 1 | ECP 3 | ECP 5 | ECP 8 | ECP 3 | ECP 1 | Isth1N 14 | Isth1N 22 | Isth1N 8 | Isth1N 22 |

# CARSHALTON ATHLETIC

**Chairman:** Paul Dipre
**Secretary:** Chris Blanchard **(T)** 07583 817 519 **(E)** chrisblanchard@carshaltonathletic.co.uk
**Commercial Manager:** n/a **(T)**
**Programme Editor:** Chris Blanchard **(T)** 07583 817 519
**Ground Address:** War Memorial Sports Ground, Colston Avenue, Carshalton SM5 2PN
**(T)** 020 8642 2551 **Manager:** Peter Adeniyi

**Founded:** 1905 **Nickname:** Robins
**Previous Names:** None
**Previous Leagues:** Southern Suburban > 1911, Surrey Senior 1922-23, London 1923-46, Corinthian 1946-56, Athenian 1956-73, Isthmian 1973-2004, Conference 2004-06
**Club Colours (change):** All red

**Ground Capacity:** 8,000 **Seats:** 240 **Covered:** 4,500 **Clubhouse:** Yes **Shop:** Yes
**Previous Grounds:** None

**Record Attendance:** 7,800 v Wimbledon - London Senior Cup
**Record Victory:** 13-0 v Worthing - Isthmian League Cup 28/01/1991
**Record Defeat:** 0-11 v Southall - Athenian League March 1963
**Record Goalscorer:** Jimmy Bolton - 242
**Record Appearances:** Jon Warden - 504
**Additional Records:** Paid £15,000 to Enfield for Curtis Warmington
Received £30,000 from Crystal Palace for Ian Cox
**Senior Honours:**
Isthmian League Division 1 South 2002-03.
Surrey Senior Shield 1975-76. London Challenge Cup 1991-92. Surrey Senior Cup x3.

**10 YEAR RECORD**

| 06-07 | 07-08 | 08-09 | 09-10 | 10-11 | 11-12 | 12-13 | 13-14 | 14-15 | 15-16 |
|---|---|---|---|---|---|---|---|---|---|
| Isth P 13 | Isth P 18 | Isth P 4 | Isth P 17 | Isth P 13 | Isth P 16 | Isth P 20 | Isth P 23 | Isth1S 20 | Isth1S 10 |

# CHATHAM TOWN

**Chairman:** Jeff Talbot
**Secretary:** Henry Longhurst **(T)** 07967 465 554 **(E)** h.longhurst@sky.com
**Commercial Manager:** **(T)**
**Programme Editor:** TBA **(T)**
**Ground Address:** Maidstone Road Sports Ground, Maidstone Road, Chatham ME4 6LR
**(T)** 01634 812 194 **Manager:** Tony Beckingham

**Founded:** 1882 **Nickname:** Chats
**Previous Names:** Chatham FC 1882-1974, Medway FC 1974-79
**Previous Leagues:** Southern 1894-1900, 1920-21, 27-29, 83-88, 2001-, Kent 1894-96, 1901-1905, 29-59, 68-83, 88-2001, Aetolian 1959-64, Metropolitan 1964-68
**Club Colours (change):** Red with white sash/red with white sash/red (Blue with white sash/blue with white sash/blue)

**Ground Capacity:** 2,000 **Seats:** 600 **Covered:** 600 **Clubhouse:** Yes **Shop:** Yes
**Previous Grounds:** Great Lines, Chatham 1882-90

**Record Attendance:** 5,000 v Gillingham - 1980
**Record Victory:** Not known - If you know please email tw.publications@btinternet.com
**Record Defeat:** Not known - If you know please email tw.publications@btinternet.com
**Record Goalscorer:** Not known - If you know please email tw.publications@btinternet.com
**Record Appearances:** Not known - If you know please email tw.publications@btinternet.com
**Additional Records:** Received Transfer fee of £500. FA Cup Quarter finalists 1888/89.
**Senior Honours:**
Kent League 1894-95, 1903-04, 04-05, 71-72, 73-74, 75-76, 76-77, 79-80, 2000-01. Aetolian League 1963-64.
Kent Senior Cup 1885-86, 86-87, 87-88, 88-89, 94-95,1904-05, 10-11, 18-19. Kent Senior Shield 1919-20.

**10 YEAR RECORD**

| 06-07 | 07-08 | 08-09 | 09-10 | 10-11 | 11-12 | 12-13 | 13-14 | 14-15 | 15-16 |
|---|---|---|---|---|---|---|---|---|---|
| Isth1S 16 | Isth1S 18 | Isth1N 10 | Isth1S 17 | Isth1S 21 | Isth1N 15 | Isth1N 13 | Isth1N 12 | Isth1N 21 | Isth1S 19 |

# CHIPSTEAD

**Chairman:** Neil Turner
**Secretary:** Heather Armstrong **(T)** 07525 443 802 **(E)** heather.chipsteadfc@virginmedia.com
**Commercial Manager:** **(T)**
**Programme Editor:** Mark Budd **(T)** mgbudd70@yahoo.co.uk
**Ground Address:** High Road, Chipstead, Surrey CR5 3SF
**(T)** 01737 553 250 **Manager:** Anthony Williams

**Founded:** 1906 **Nickname:** Chips
**Previous Names:** None
**Previous Leagues:** Surrey Intermediate 1962-82, Surrey Premier 1982-86, Combined Counties 1986-2007

**Club Colours (change):** Green and white hoops/green/black (All red)

**Ground Capacity:** 2,000 **Seats:** 150 **Covered:** 200 **Clubhouse:** Yes **Shop:** Yes
**Previous Grounds:** None

**Record Attendance:** 1,170
**Record Victory:** Not known - If you know please email tw.publications@btinternet.com
**Record Defeat:** Not known - If you know please email tw.publications@btinternet.com
**Record Goalscorer:** Mick Nolan - 124
**Record Appearances:** Not known - If you know please email tw.publications@btinternet.com
**Additional Records:**

**Senior Honours:**
Combined Counties Premier 1989-90, 2006-07.

**10 YEAR RECORD**

| 06-07 | 07-08 | 08-09 | 09-10 | 10-11 | 11-12 | 12-13 | 13-14 | 14-15 | 15-16 |
|---|---|---|---|---|---|---|---|---|---|
| CCP 1 | Isth1S 15 | Isth1S 21 | Isth1S 19 | Isth1S 10 | Isth1S 12 | Isth1S 20 | Isth1S 13 | Isth1S 15 | Isth1S 21 |

# CORINTHIAN-CASUALS

**Chairman:** Brian Vandervilt
**Secretary:** Hanna Newton **(T)** 07535 648 642 **(E)** hanna.newton@icloud.com
**Commercial Manager:** **(T)**
**Programme Editor:** Stuart Tree **(T)** stuarttree@hotmail.co.uk
**Ground Address:** King George's Field, Queen Mary Close, Hook Rise South, KT6 7NA
**(T)** 0208 397 3368 **Manager:** James Bracken

**Founded:** 1939 **Nickname:** Casuals
**Previous Names:** Casuals and Corinthians merged in 1939
**Previous Leagues:** Isthmian 1939-84, Spartan 1984-96, Combined Counties 1996-97

**Club Colours (change):** Chocolate and pink halves/chocolate/chocolate (All blue)

**Ground Capacity:** 2,000 **Seats:** 161 **Covered:** 700 **Clubhouse:** Yes **Shop:** Yes
**Previous Grounds:** Kennington Oval, shared with Kingstonian and Dulwich Hamlet

**Record Attendance:** Not known - If you know please email tw.publications@btinternet.com
**Record Victory:** Not known - If you know please email tw.publications@btinternet.com
**Record Defeat:** Not known - If you know please email tw.publications@btinternet.com
**Record Goalscorer:** Cliff West - 219
**Record Appearances:** Simon Shergold - 526
**Additional Records:**

**Senior Honours:**
London Spartan League Senior Division 1985-86.
Surrey Senior Cup 2010-11.

**10 YEAR RECORD**

| 06-07 | 07-08 | 08-09 | 09-10 | 10-11 | 11-12 | 12-13 | 13-14 | 14-15 | 15-16 |
|---|---|---|---|---|---|---|---|---|---|
| Isth1S 22 | Isth1S 20 | Isth1S 20 | Isth1S 13 | Isth1S 20 | Isth1S 13 | Isth1S 14 | Isth1S 17 | Isth1S 13 | Isth1S 6 |

# CRAY WANDERERS

**Chairman:** Gary Hillman
**Secretary:** Mark Simpson **(T)** 07854 796 325 **(E)** marksimpson937@btinternet.com
**Commercial Manager:** **(T)**
**Programme Editor:** Phil Babbs **(T)** 07977 828 252
**Ground Address:** Bromley FC, Hayes Lane, Bromley, Kent BR2 9EF
**(T)** 020 8460 5291 **Manager:** Tony Russell - 04/05/2015

**Founded:** 1860 **Nickname:** Wanderers or Wands
**Previous Names:** Cray Old Boys (immediately after WW1); Sidcup & Footscray (start of WW2).
**Previous Leagues:** Kent 1894-1903, 1906-07, 1909-1914, 1934-38, 1978-2004; West Kent & South Suburban Leagues (before WW1); London 1920-1934, 1951-1959; Kent Amateur 1938-1939, 1946-1951; South London Alliance 1943-1946; Aetolian 1959-1964; Greater London 1964-1966; Metropolitan 1966-1971; Met. London 1971-1975: London Spartan 1975-1978.
**Club Colours (change):** Amber/black/amber (Pale blue & white stripes/white/pale blue)

**Ground Capacity:** 5,000 **Seats:** 1,300 **Covered:** 2,500 **Clubhouse:** Yes **Shop:** Yes
**Previous Grounds: Cont.** Northfield Farm (1950-51), Tothills (aka Fordcroft, 1951-1955), Grassmeade (1955-1973), Oxford Road (1973-1998).

**Record Attendance:** (Grassmeade) 2,160vLeytonstone – FA Am.C 3rd Rd, 1968-69; (Oxford R) 1,523vStamford – FAV QF 79-80; (Hayes L) 1,082vAFC Wim. – 04-05
**Record Victory:** 15-0 v Sevenoaks - 1894-95.
**Record Defeat:** 2-15 (H) and 0-14 (A) v Callenders Athletic - Kent Amateur League, 1947-48.
**Record Goalscorer:** Ken Collishaw 274 (1954-1965)
**Record Appearances:** John Dorey - 500 (1961-72).
**Additional Records:** Unbeaten for 28 Ryman League games in 2007-2008.

**Senior Honours:**
Kent League 1901-02, 80-81, 2002-03, 03-04 (League Cup 83-84, 2002-03); London League 1956-57, 57-58 (League Cup 54-55); Aetolian League 1962-63 (League Cup 63-64); Greater London League 1965-66 (League Cup 64-65, 65-66); Met. Lge Cup 1970-71; Met. London League & League Cup 1974-75; London Spartan League 1976-77, 77-78. Kent Amateur Cup 1930-31, 62-63, 63-64, 64-65. Kent Senior Trophy 1992-93, 2003-04.

**10 YEAR RECORD**

| 06-07 | 07-08 | 08-09 | 09-10 | 10-11 | 11-12 | 12-13 | 13-14 | 14-15 | 15-16 |
|---|---|---|---|---|---|---|---|---|---|
| Isth1S 12 | Isth1S 3 | Isth1S 2 | Isth P 15 | Isth P 9 | Isth P 9 | Isth P 17 | Isth P 24 | Isth1N 16 | Isth1N 4 |

# DORKING WANDERERS

**Chairman:** Marc White
**Secretary:** Martin Clarke **(T)** 07885 662 940 **(E)** m-clarke@blueyonder.co.uk
**Commercial Manager:** **(T)**
**Programme Editor:** Rob Cavallini **(T)** rob_cavallini@hotmail.com
**Ground Address:** West Humble Playing Fields, London Road, Dorking, Surrey RH5 6AD
**(T)** 07500 006 240 **Manager:** Marc White

**Founded:** 1999 **Nickname:** Wanderers
**Previous Names:** None
**Previous Leagues:** Crawley & District. Sussex County >2015.

**Club Colours (change):** Blue & black stripes/black/black (All red).

**Ground Capacity:** **Seats:** Yes **Covered:** Yes **Clubhouse:** Yes **Shop:**
**Previous Grounds:**

**Record Attendance:** Not known - If you know please email tw.publications@btinternet.com
**Record Victory:** Not known - If you know please email tw.publications@btinternet.com
**Record Defeat:** Not known - If you know please email tw.publications@btinternet.com
**Record Goalscorer:** Not known - If you know please email tw.publications@btinternet.com
**Record Appearances:** Not known - If you know please email tw.publications@btinternet.com
**Additional Records:**

**Senior Honours:**
Sussex County League Division Three 2010-11.

**10 YEAR RECORD**

| 06-07 | 07-08 | 08-09 | 09-10 | 10-11 | 11-12 | 12-13 | 13-14 | 14-15 | 15-16 |
|---|---|---|---|---|---|---|---|---|---|
| | | | | SxC3 1 | SxC2 3 | SxC1 20 | SxC1 8 | SxC1 2 | Isth1S 2 |

# EAST GRINSTEAD TOWN

**Chairman:** Richard Tramontin
**Secretary:** Brian McCorquodale **(T)** 07802 528 513 **(E)** brian.mcc@egtfc.co.uk
**Commercial Manager:** **(T)**
**Programme Editor:** Bruce Talbot **(T)** bruce.talbot@btinternet.com
**Ground Address:** The GAC Stadium, East Court, College Lane, East Grinstead RH19 3LS
**(T)** 01342 325 885 **Manager:** Mat Longhurst

**Founded:** 1890 **Nickname:** The Wasps
**Previous Names:** East Grinstead > 1997.
**Previous Leagues:** Mid Sussex, Sussex County, Souhern Amateur. Sussex County >2014.

**Club Colours (change):** Yellow & black/black/yellow & black (Blue & yellow/blue & yellow/blue)

**Ground Capacity:** 3,000 **Seats:** none **Covered:** 400 **Clubhouse:** Yes **Shop:** No
**Previous Grounds:** None

**Record Attendance: Att:** 2,006 v Lancing F A Am Cup, November 1947
**Record Victory:** Not known - If you know please email tw.publications@btinternet.com
**Record Defeat:** Not known - If you know please email tw.publications@btinternet.com
**Record Goalscorer:** Not known - If you know please email tw.publications@btinternet.com
**Record Appearances:** Guy Hill
**Additional Records:**
**Senior Honours:**
Sussex County League Division Two 2007-08.

**10 YEAR RECORD**

| 06-07 | | 07-08 | | 08-09 | | 09-10 | | 10-11 | | 11-12 | | 12-13 | | 13-14 | | 14-15 | | 15-16 | |
|---|---|---|---|---|---|---|---|---|---|---|---|---|---|---|---|---|---|---|---|
| SxC2 | 11 | SxC2 | 1 | SxC1 | 17 | SxC1 | 15 | SxC1 | 7 | SxC1 | 9 | SxC1 | 8 | SxC1 | 2 | Isth1S | 22 | Isth1S | 20 |

# FAVERSHAM TOWN

**Chairman:** Ray Leader
**Secretary:** Mrs Wendy Walker **(T)** 07789 638 367 **(E)** wendy-walker@hotmail.co.uk
**Commercial Manager:** **(T)**
**Programme Editor:** Paul Witcher **(T)** theoeviehae@yahoo.com
**Ground Address:** Shepherd Neame Stadium, Salters Lane, Faversham Kent ME13 8ND
**(T)** 01795 591 900 **Manager:** Ray Turner

**Founded:** 1884 **Nickname:** Lillywhites
**Previous Names:** Faversham Invicta, Faversham Services, Faversham Railway and Faversham Rangers pre War.
**Previous Leagues:** Metropolitan, Athenian, Kent

**Club Colours (change):** White/black/black (All yellow)

**Ground Capacity:** 2,000 **Seats:** 200 **Covered:** 1,800 **Clubhouse:** Yes **Shop:**
**Previous Grounds:** Moved in to Salters Lane in 1948.

**Record Attendance:** Not known - If you know please email tw.publications@btinternet.com
**Record Victory:** Not known - If you know please email tw.publications@btinternet.com
**Record Defeat:** Not known - If you know please email tw.publications@btinternet.com
**Record Goalscorer:** Not known - If you know please email tw.publications@btinternet.com
**Record Appearances:** Not known - If you know please email tw.publications@btinternet.com
**Additional Records:**
**Senior Honours:**
Kent League 1969-70, 70-71, 89-90, 2009-10.

**10 YEAR RECORD**

| 06-07 | | 07-08 | | 08-09 | | 09-10 | | 10-11 | | 11-12 | | 12-13 | | 13-14 | | 14-15 | | 15-16 | |
|---|---|---|---|---|---|---|---|---|---|---|---|---|---|---|---|---|---|---|---|
| Kent P | 12 | Kent P | 13 | Kent P | 4 | Kent P | 1 | Isth1S | 8 | Isth1S | 17 | Isth1S | 3 | Isth1S | 10 | Isth1S | 3 | Isth1S | 5 |

# GODALMING TOWN

**Chairman:** Kevin Young
**Secretary:** Jane Phillips (T) (E) j.phillips12@ntlworld.com
**Commercial Manager:** (T)
**Programme Editor:** Paul Grover (T) pauliegrover@gmail.com
**Ground Address:** Weycourt, Meadrow, Guildford, Surrey GU7 3JE
**(T)** 01483 417 520 **Manager:** Andy Hunt

**Founded:** 1950 **Nickname:** The G's
**Previous Names:** Godalming United 1950-71. Godalming & Farncombe 1971-79. Godalming Town 1979-92. Godalming & Guildford 1992-2005.
**Previous Leagues:** Combined Counties, Southern 2006-08, 12-16. Isthmian 2008-12.

**Club Colours (change):** Yellow/green/yellow (White/blue/white)

**Ground Capacity:** 3,000 **Seats:** 200 **Covered:** 400 **Clubhouse:** Yes **Shop:** Yes
**Previous Grounds:** Recreation Ground 1950-71. Brief spell at Broadwater Park whilst work was done on Weycourt.

**Record Attendance:** 1,305 v AFC Wimbledon - 2002
**Record Victory:** Not known - If you know please email tw.publications@btinternet.com
**Record Defeat:** Not known - If you know please email tw.publications@btinternet.com
**Record Goalscorer:** Not known - If you know please email tw.publications@btinternet.com
**Record Appearances:** Shaun Elliott - 360+
**Additional Records:**

**Senior Honours:**
Combined Counties League Premier Division 1983-84, 2005-06.
Surrey Senior Cup 2012-13.

**10 YEAR RECORD**

| 06-07 | 07-08 | 08-09 | 09-10 | 10-11 | 11-12 | 12-13 | 13-14 | 14-15 | 15-16 |
|---|---|---|---|---|---|---|---|---|---|
| Isth1S 22 | Sthsw 12 | Isth1S 9 | Isth1S 4 | Isth1S 17 | Isth1S 5 | SthC 3 | Sthsw 18 | SthC 8 | SthC 10 |

# GREENWICH BOROUGH

**Chairman:** Perry Skinner
**Secretary:** Jeff Duah-Kessie (T) (E) jeff@gbfc2013.com
**Commercial Manager:** (T)
**Programme Editor:** Jeff Duah-Kessie (T) jeff@gbfc2013.com
**Ground Address:** DGS Marine Stadium, Middle Park Avenue, Eltham SE9 5HP
**(T)** 07735 312 788 **Manager:** Gary Alexander

**Founded:** 1928 **Nickname:** Boro
**Previous Names:** Woolwich Borough Council Athletic 1928-65. London Borough of Greenwich 1965-84.
**Previous Leagues:** Woolwich & District 1928-29. Kent Amateur 1929-39, 46-48. South London Alliance 1948-76. London Spartan 1976-84. Kent/Southern Counties East 1984-2016.
**Club Colours (change):** Red & black/black/black. (Blue & black/black/black).

**Ground Capacity:** 4,097 **Seats:** 640 **Covered:** Yes **Clubhouse:** Yes **Shop:** Yes
**Previous Grounds:**

**Record Attendance:** **Att:** 2,000 v Charlton Athletic, turning on of floodlights, 1978.
**Record Victory:** Not known - If you know please email tw.publications@btinternet.com
**Record Defeat:** Not known - If you know please email tw.publications@btinternet.com
**Record Goalscorer:** Not known - If you know please email tw.publications@btinternet.com
**Record Appearances:** Not known - If you know please email tw.publications@btinternet.com
**Additional Records:** FA Cup: 4th Qualifying Round, 2014-15
FA Vase: 5th Round replay, 2007-08
**Senior Honours:**
Woolwich & District League 1928-29. South London Alliance Division Two 1954-55, Division One 1955-56, Premier Division 1960-61, 61-62, 62-63, 63-64, 64-65, 65-66, 73-74. London Spartan League 1979-80. Kent League 86-87, 87-88. Southern Counties East 2015-16.
Kent Senior Trophy 84-85..

**10 YEAR RECORD**

| 06-07 | 07-08 | 08-09 | 09-10 | 10-11 | 11-12 | 12-13 | 13-14 | 14-15 | 15-16 |
|---|---|---|---|---|---|---|---|---|---|
| Kent P 5 | Kent P 8 | Kent P 3 | Kent P 5 | Kent P 4 | Kent P 16 | Kent P 15 | SCE 9 | SCE 4 | SCE 1 |

# GUERNSEY

**Chairman:** Steve Dewsnip
**Secretary:** Mark Le Tissier **(T)** 07781 119 169 **(E)** mark.letissier@guernseyfc.com
**Commercial Manager:** **(T)**
**Programme Editor:** Nic Legg **(T)** Nic.legg@guernseyfc.com
**Ground Address:** Footes Lane Stadium, St Peter Port, Guernsey GY1 2UL
**(T)** 01481 747 279 **Manager:** Tony Vance

**Founded:** 2011 **Nickname:** Green Lions
**Previous Names:** None
**Previous Leagues:** Combined Counties 2011-13.

**Club Colours (change):** Green & white/white/green (Sky blue/sky blue/white)

**Ground Capacity:** 5,000 **Seats:** Yes **Covered:** Yes **Clubhouse:** Yes **Shop:**
**Previous Grounds:** None

**Record Attendance:** 4,290 v. Spennymoor Town, FA Vase semi-final first leg, 23/03/2013
**Record Victory:** 11-0 v Crawley Down Gatwick, Isthmian Division One South, 01/01/2014
**Record Defeat:** 2-6 v Horsham, Isthmian Division One South, 14/12/2013
**Record Goalscorer:** Ross Allen - 163 (Scored 57 in all comps during 2011-12)
**Record Appearances:** Dom Heaume - 136
**Additional Records:**
**Senior Honours:**
Combined Counties League Division One 2011-12, Premier Challenge Cup 2011-12.

**10 YEAR RECORD**

| 06-07 | 07-08 | 08-09 | 09-10 | 10-11 | 11-12 | 12-13 | 13-14 | 14-15 | 15-16 |
|---|---|---|---|---|---|---|---|---|---|
| | | | | | CC1 1 | CCP 2 | Isth1S 4 | Isth1S 10 | Isth1S 13 |

# HASTINGS UNITED

**Chairman:** Daivd Ormerod
**Secretary:** Tony Cosens **(T)** 07712 654 288 **(E)** richardcosens@btinternet.com
**Commercial Manager:** **(T)**
**Programme Editor:** Dan Willett **(T)** danwillet@hotmail.com
**Ground Address:** The Pilot Field, Elphinstone Road, Hastings TN34 2AX
**(T)** 01424 444 635 **Manager:** Darren Hare

**Founded:** 1894 **Nickname:** The Us
**Previous Names:** Hastings and St Leonards Amateurs, Hastings Town > 2002
**Previous Leagues:** South Eastern 1904-05, Southern 1905-10, Sussex County 1921-27, 52-85, Southern Amateur 1927-46, Corinthian 1946-48

**Club Colours (change):** Claret & blue (Yellow & black)

**Ground Capacity:** 4,050 **Seats:** 800 **Covered:** 1,750 **Clubhouse:** Yes **Shop:** Yes
**Previous Grounds:** Bulverhythe Recreation > 1976

**Record Attendance:** 4,888 v Nottingham Forest - Friendly 23/06/1996
**Record Victory:** Not known - If you know please email tw.publications@btinternet.com
**Record Defeat:** Not known - If you know please email tw.publications@btinternet.com
**Record Goalscorer:** Terry White scored 33 during 1999-2000
**Record Appearances:** Not known - If you know please email tw.publications@btinternet.com
**Additional Records:** Paid £8,000 to Ashford Town for Nicky Dent
Received £30,000 from Nottingham Forest for Paul Smith
**Senior Honours:**
Southern League Division 1 1991-92, 2001-01, League Cup 1994-95.

**10 YEAR RECORD**

| 06-07 | 07-08 | 08-09 | 09-10 | 10-11 | 11-12 | 12-13 | 13-14 | 14-15 | 15-16 |
|---|---|---|---|---|---|---|---|---|---|
| Isth1S 4 | Isth P 14 | Isth P 17 | Isth P 7 | Isth P 18 | Isth P 18 | Isth P 22 | Isth1S 5 | Isth1S 19 | Isth1S 7 |

# HERNE BAY

**Chairman:** Bill Dordoy
**Secretary:** John Bathurst **(T)** 07788 718 745 **(E)** johnbhbfc@aol.com
**Commercial Manager:** **(T)**
**Programme Editor:** John Bathurst **(T)** johnbhbfc@aol.com
**Ground Address:** Winch's Field, Stanley Gardens, Herne Bay CT6 5SG
**(T)** 01227 374 156 **Manager:** Sam Denly

**Founded:** 1886 **Nickname:** The Bay
**Previous Names:** None.
**Previous Leagues:** East Kent. Faversham & Dist. Cantebury & Dist. Kent Am. Athenian.

**Club Colours (change):** Blue & white/blue/blue (Yellow & black/yellow/yellow)

**Ground Capacity:** 3,000 **Seats:** 200 **Covered:** 1,500 **Clubhouse:** Yes **Shop:** Yes
**Previous Grounds:** Mitchell's Athletic Ground. Herne Bay Memorial Park.

**Record Attendance:** 2,303 v Margate, FA Cup 4th Qual. 1970-71.
**Record Victory:** 19-3 v Hythe Wanderers - Feb 1900.
**Record Defeat:** 0-11 v 7th Dragon Guards - Oct 1907.
**Record Goalscorer:**
**Record Appearances:**
**Additional Records:** Most League Victories in a Season: 34 - 1996-97.

**Senior Honours:**
Kent League 1991-92, 93-94, 96-97, 97-98, 2011-12, Premier Cup 1996-97, 2009-10, 2010-11.
Kent Senior Trophy 1978-79, 1996-97.

**10 YEAR RECORD**

| 06-07 | 07-08 | 08-09 | 09-10 | 10-11 | 11-12 | 12-13 | 13-14 | 14-15 | 15-16 |
|---|---|---|---|---|---|---|---|---|---|
| Kent P 9 | Kent P 6 | Kent P 6 | Kent P 2 | Kent P 2 | Kent P 1 | Isth1S 19 | Isth1S 18 | Isth1S 9 | Isth1S 8 |

# HORSHAM

**Chairman:** Kevin Borrett
**Secretary:** Jeff Barrett **(T)** 07712 888 980 **(E)** jeff.barrett@btinternet.com
**Commercial Manager:** **(T)**
**Programme Editor:** Jeff Barrett **(T)** jeff.barrett@btinternet.com
**Ground Address:** Horsham YMCA, Gorings Mead, Horsham RH13 5BP
**(T)** 01403 266 888 **Manager:** Dominic Di Paola

**Founded:** 1881 **Nickname:** Hornets
**Previous Names:**
**Previous Leagues:** West Sussex Senior, Sussex Co 1926-51, Metropolitan 1951-57, Corinthian 1957-63, Athenian 1963-73, Isthmian 1973-2015. Southern Combination 2015-16,

**Club Colours (change):** Orange/green/orange (All white)

**Ground Capacity:** 1,575 **Seats:** 150 **Covered:** 200 **Clubhouse:** Yes **Shop:**
**Previous Grounds:** Horsham Park, Hurst Park, Springfield Park

**Record Attendance:** 8,000 v Swindon - FA Cup 1st Round Novmber 1966
**Record Victory:** 16-1 v Southwick - Sussex County League 1945-46
**Record Defeat:** 1-11 v Worthing - Sussex Senior Cup 1913-14
**Record Goalscorer:** Mick Browning
**Record Appearances:** Mark Stepney
**Additional Records:**

**Senior Honours:**
Athenian League Division 1 1972-73. Southern Combination 2015-16.
Sussex Senior Cup x7

**10 YEAR RECORD**

| 06-07 | 07-08 | 08-09 | 09-10 | 10-11 | 11-12 | 12-13 | 13-14 | 14-15 | 15-16 |
|---|---|---|---|---|---|---|---|---|---|
| Isth1S 9 | Isth P 11 | Isth P 13 | Isth P 11 | Isth P 17 | Isth P 22 | Isth1S 15 | Isth1S 16 | Isth1S 24 | SCom 1 |

# HYTHE TOWN

**Chairman:** Paul Markland
**Secretary:** Martin Giles (T) 07908 763 101 (E) martinandsuegiles@gmail.com
**Commercial Manager:** (T)
**Programme Editor:** Andy Short (T) andyshort2@btinternet.com
**Ground Address:** Reachfields Stadium, Fort Road, Hythe CT21 6JS
(T) 01303 264 932 / 238 256 **Manager:** Clive Cook

**Founded:** 1910 **Nickname:** The Cannons
**Previous Names:** Hythe Town 1910-1992, Hythe United 1992-2001
**Previous Leagues:** Kent Amateur League, Kent League, Southern League, Kent County League, Kent League.

**Club Colours (change):** All red (All blue)

**Ground Capacity:** 3,000 **Seats:** 350 **Covered:** 2,400 **Clubhouse:** Yes **Shop:** No
**Previous Grounds:** South Road.

**Record Attendance:** 2,147 v Yeading, FA Vase Semi-Final, 1990.
**Record Victory:** 10-1 v Sporting Bengal, 2008-09
**Record Defeat:** 1-10 v Swanley Furness, 1997-98
**Record Goalscorer:** Dave Cook - 127
**Record Appearances:** John Walker - 354, Jason Brazier - 349, Lee Winfield - 344
**Additional Records:**
**Senior Honours:**
Kent League 1988-89, 2010-11.
Kent Senior Cup 2011-12.
Kent Senior Trophy 1990-91.

**10 YEAR RECORD**

| 06-07 | 07-08 | 08-09 | 09-10 | 10-11 | 11-12 | 12-13 | 13-14 | 14-15 | 15-16 |
|---|---|---|---|---|---|---|---|---|---|
| Kent P 6 | Kent P 4 | Kent P 2 | Kent P 3 | Kent P 1 | Isth1S 8 | Isth1S 4 | Isth1S 8 | Isth1S 16 | Isth1S 4 |

# LEWES

**Chairman:** Stuart Fuller
**Secretary:** Barry Collins (T) 07834 468 821 (E) barry@lewesfc.com
**Commercial Manager:** (T)
**Programme Editor:** TBC (T)
**Ground Address:** The Dripping Pan, Mountfield Road, Lewes, East Sussex BN7 2XD
(T) 01273 470 820 **Manager:** Darren Freeman

**Founded:** 1885 **Nickname:** Rooks
**Previous Names:** None
**Previous Leagues:** Mid Sussex 1886-1920, Sussex County 1920-65, Athenian 1965-77, Isthmian 1977-2004, Conference 2004-11.

**Club Colours (change):** Red and black stripes/black/black

**Ground Capacity:** 3,000 **Seats:** 400 **Covered:** 1,400 **Clubhouse:** Yes **Shop:** Yes
**Previous Grounds:** Played at Convent Field for two seasons before WWI

**Record Attendance:** 2,500 v Newhaven - Sussex County League 26/12/1947
**Record Victory:** Not known - If you know please email tw.publications@btinternet.com
**Record Defeat:** Not known - If you know please email tw.publications@btinternet.com
**Record Goalscorer:** 'Pip' Parris - 350
**Record Appearances:** Terry Parris - 662
**Additional Records:** Paid £2,000 for Matt Allen
Received £2,500 from Brighton & Hove Albion for Grant Horscroft
**Senior Honours:**
Mid Sussex League 1910-11, 13-14. Sussex County League 1964-65.
Sussex Senior Cup 1964-65, 70-71, 84-85, 2000-01, 05-06. Athenian League Division 2 1967-68, Division 1 1969-70.
Isthmian League Division 2 2001-02, Division 1 South 2003-04. Conference South 2007-08

**10 YEAR RECORD**

| 06-07 | 07-08 | 08-09 | 09-10 | 10-11 | 11-12 | 12-13 | 13-14 | 14-15 | 15-16 |
|---|---|---|---|---|---|---|---|---|---|
| Conf 9 | Conf S 1 | Conf 24 | Conf S 19 | Conf S 21 | Isth P 6 | Isth P 19 | Isth P 16 | Isth P 19 | Isth P 23 |

# MOLESEY

**Chairman:** Tracy Teague
**Secretary:** Tracy Teague **(T)** 07939 387 277 **(E)** teaguetracy90@gmail.com
**Commercial Manager:** **(T)**
**Programme Editor:** Anthony Scott **(T)** antscott@hotmail.com
**Ground Address:** 412 Walton Road, West Molesey KT8 2JG.
**(T)** 020 8979 4823 **Manager:** Peter Leilliott

**Founded:** 1953 **Nickname:** The Moles
**Previous Names:** None.
**Previous Leagues:** Surrey Senior. Spartan. Athethian. Isthmian. Combined Counties 2008-15.

**Club Colours (change):** White/black/black.

**Ground Capacity:** 4,000 **Seats:** 160 **Covered:** Yes **Clubhouse:** Yes **Shop:** Yes
**Previous Grounds:**

**Record Attendance:** 1,255 v Sutton United, Surrey Senior Cup sem-final 1966.
**Record Victory:** Not known - If you know please email tw.publications@btinternet.com
**Record Defeat:** Not known - If you know please email tw.publications@btinternet.com
**Record Goalscorer:** Michael Rose (139).
**Record Appearances:** Frank Hanley (453).
**Additional Records:** Surrey Senior League 1957-58.
**Senior Honours:**
Combined Counties Premier Division 2014-15.

**10 YEAR RECORD**

| 06-07 | 07-08 | 08-09 | 09-10 | 10-11 | 11-12 | 12-13 | 13-14 | 14-15 | 15-16 |
|---|---|---|---|---|---|---|---|---|---|
| Isth1S 15 | Isth1S 22 | CCP 11 | CCP 8 | CCP 3 | CCP 5 | CCP 10 | CCP 11 | CCP 1 | Isth1S 9 |

# RAMSGATE

**Chairman:** Phil Fennell
**Secretary:** Edward Lucas **(T)** 07710 859 034 **(E)** secretary@ramsgate-fc.co.uk
**Commercial Manager:** **(T)**
**Programme Editor:** Martin Able **(T)** media@ramsgate-fc.co.uk
**Ground Address:** Southwood Stadium, Prices Avenue, Ramsgate, Kent CT11 0AN
**(T)** 01843 591 662 **Manager:** Danny and Jim Ward

**Founded:** 1945 **Nickname:** Rams
**Previous Names:** Ramsgate Athletic > 1972
**Previous Leagues:** Kent 1949-59, 1976-2005, Southern 1959-76

**Club Colours (change):** All red (Yellow/black/black)

**Ground Capacity:** 5,000 **Seats:** 400 **Covered:** 600 **Clubhouse:** Yes **Shop:** Yes
**Previous Grounds:** None

**Record Attendance:** 5,200 v Margate - 1956-57
**Record Victory:** 11-0 & 12-1 v Canterbury City - Kent League 2000-01
**Record Defeat:** Not known - If you know please email tw.publications@btinternet.com
**Record Goalscorer:** Mick Willimson
**Record Appearances:** Not known - If you know please email tw.publications@btinternet.com
**Additional Records:**
**Senior Honours:**
Kent League Division 1 1949-50, 55-56, 56-57, Premier League 1998-99, 2004-05, Kent League Cup x6.
Isthmian League Division 1 2005-06, League Cup 2007-08.
Kent Senior Cup 1963-64, Kent Senior Trophy x3.

**10 YEAR RECORD**

| 06-07 | 07-08 | 08-09 | 09-10 | 10-11 | 11-12 | 12-13 | 13-14 | 14-15 | 15-16 |
|---|---|---|---|---|---|---|---|---|---|
| Isth P 8 | Isth P 5 | Isth P 22 | Isth1S 14 | Isth1S 9 | Isth1S 10 | Isth1S 7 | Isth1S 12 | Isth1S 21 | Isth1S 12 |

# SITTINGBOURNE

**Chairman:** Maurice Dunk
**Secretary:** John PItts (T) 07909 995 210 (E) sittingbournefc@outlook.com
**Commercial Manager:** (T)
**Programme Editor:** Peter Pitts (T) bournefc@hotmail.com
**Ground Address:** Woodstock Park, Broadoak Road, Sittingbourne ME9 8AG
(T) 01795 410 777 **Manager:** Nick Davis - 05/11/14

**Founded:** 1886 **Nickname:** Brickies
**Previous Names:** Sittingbourne United 1881-86
**Previous Leagues:** Kent 1894-1905, 1909-27, 30-39, 45-59, 68-91, South Eastern 1905-09, Southern 1927-30, 59-67

**Club Colours (change):** Red & black stripes/black/black & white

**Ground Capacity:** 3,000 **Seats:** 300 **Covered:** 600 **Clubhouse:** Yes **Shop:** Yes
**Previous Grounds:** Sittingbourne Rec. 1881-90, Gore Court 1890-92, The Bull Ground 1892-1990. Central Park 1990-2001

**Record Attendance:** 5,951 v Tottenham Hotspur - Friendly 26/01/1993
**Record Victory:** 15-0 v Orpington, Kent League 1922-23)
**Record Defeat:** 0-10 v Wimbledon, SL Cup 1965-66)
**Record Goalscorer:** Not known - If you know please email tw.publications@btinternet.com
**Record Appearances:** Not known - If you know please email tw.publications@btinternet.com
**Additional Records:** Paid £20,000 to Ashford Town for Lee McRobert 1993
Received £210,000 from Millwall for Neil Emblem and Michael Harle 1993
**Senior Honours:**
Southern League Southern Division 1992-93, 95-96. Kent League x7, League cup x4.
Kent Senior Cup 1901-02, 28-29, 29-30, 57-58.

**10 YEAR RECORD**

| 06-07 | 07-08 | 08-09 | 09-10 | 10-11 | 11-12 | 12-13 | 13-14 | 14-15 | 15-16 |
|---|---|---|---|---|---|---|---|---|---|
| Isth1S 10 | Isth1S 9 | Isth1S 6 | Isth1S 9 | Isth1S 11 | Isth1S 19 | Isth1S 9 | Isth1S 14 | Isth1S 12 | Isth1S 18 |

South Park F.C
Founded 1897

# SOUTH PARK

**Chairman:** Ricky Kidd
**Secretary:** Nick Thatcher (T) 07817 613 674 (E) spfc1897@hotmail.com
**Commercial Manager:** (T)
**Programme Editor:** Nick Thatcher (T) spfc1897@hotmail.com
**Ground Address:** King George's Field, Whitehall Lane, South Park RH2 8LG
(T) 01737 245 963 **Manager:** Malcolm Porter

**Founded:** 1897 **Nickname:** The Sparks
**Previous Names:** South Park & Reigate Town 2001-03.
**Previous Leagues:** Crawley & District > 2006. Combined Counties 2006-14.

**Club Colours (change):** All red (All blue with yellow trim)

**Ground Capacity:** 700 **Seats:** 100 **Covered:** Yes **Clubhouse:** Yes **Shop:** Yes
**Previous Grounds:** None

**Record Attendance:** Att: 643 v Metropolitan Police, 20/10/2012
**Record Victory:** Not known - If you know please email tw.publications@btinternet.com
**Record Defeat:** Not known - If you know please email tw.publications@btinternet.com
**Record Goalscorer:** Not known - If you know please email tw.publications@btinternet.com
**Record Appearances:** Not known - If you know please email tw.publications@btinternet.com
**Additional Records:**
**Senior Honours:**
**League:** Combined Counties Premier Division 2013-14.
**FA/County Cups:** Surrey Premier Cup 2010-11.

**10 YEAR RECORD**

| 06-07 | 07-08 | 08-09 | 09-10 | 10-11 | 11-12 | 12-13 | 13-14 | 14-15 | 15-16 |
|---|---|---|---|---|---|---|---|---|---|
| CC1 7 | CC1 12 | CC1 14 | CC1 6 | CC1 3 | CCP 8 | CCP 4 | CCP 1 | Isth1S 14 | Isth1S 11 |

# THREE BRIDGES

**Chairman:** Paul Faili
**Secretary:** Lorraine Bonner **(T)** **(E)** lorraine.bonner@lw.com
**Commercial Manager:** **(T)**
**Programme Editor:** Lorraine Bonner **(T)** lorraine.bonner@lw.com
**Ground Address:** Jubilee Walk, Three Bridges Road, Crawley, RH10 1LQ
**(T)** 01293 442 000 **Manager:** Paul Falli

**Founded:** 1901 **Nickname:** Bridges
**Previous Names:** Three Bridges Worth 1936-52, Three Bridges Utd 53-64
**Previous Leagues:** Mid Sussex, E Grinstead, Redhill & Dist 36-52

**Club Colours (change):** Amber & black stripes/black/black. (Blue & white stripes /blue/blue)

**Ground Capacity:** 3,500 **Seats:** 120 **Covered:** 600 **Clubhouse:** Yes **Shop:**
**Previous Grounds:** None

**Record Attendance:** 2,000 v Horsham 1948
**Record Victory:** Not known - If you know please email tw.publications@btinternet.com
**Record Defeat:** Not known - If you know please email tw.publications@btinternet.com
**Record Goalscorer:** Not known - If you know please email tw.publications@btinternet.com
**Record Appearances:** John Malthouse
**Additional Records:**
**Senior Honours:**
Sussex RUR Cup 1982-83. Sussex County League Division One 2011-12.

**10 YEAR RECORD**

| 06-07 | 07-08 | 08-09 | 09-10 | 10-11 | 11-12 | 12-13 | 13-14 | 14-15 | 15-16 |
|---|---|---|---|---|---|---|---|---|---|
| SxC1 12 | SxC1 6 | SxC1 5 | SxC1 7 | SxC1 5 | SxC1 1 | Isth1S 21 | Isth1S 19 | Isth1S 7 | Isth1S 14 |

# TOOTING & MITCHAM UNITED

**Chairman:** Steve Adkins
**Secretary:** Jackie Watkins **(T)** 07890 102 737 **(E)** jackie@tmunited.org
**Commercial Manager:** **(T)**
**Programme Editor:** David Penn **(T)** tmuprogramme@gmail.com
**Ground Address:** KNK Stadium, Imperial Fields, Bishopsford Road, Morden, Surrey SM4 6BF
**(T)** 0208 685 6193 **Manager:** Frank Wilson

**Founded:** 1932 **Nickname:** The Terrors
**Previous Names:** Tooting Town (Founded in 1887) and Mitcham Wanderers (1912) merged in 1932 to form Tooting & Mitcham FC.
**Previous Leagues:** London 1932-37, Athenian 1937-56

**Club Colours (change):** Black and white stripes/black/black (blue/white/blue)

**Ground Capacity:** 3,500 **Seats:** 600 **Covered:** 1,200 **Clubhouse:** Yes **Shop:** Yes
**Previous Grounds:** Sandy Lane, Mitcham

**Record Attendance:** 17,500 v Queens Park Rangers - FA Cup 2nd Round 1956-57 (At Sandy Lane)
**Record Victory:** 11-0 v Welton Rovers - FA Amateur Cup 1962-63
**Record Defeat:** 1-8 v Kingstonian - Surrey Senior Cup 1966-67
**Record Goalscorer:** Alan Ives - 92
**Record Appearances:** Danny Godwin - 470
**Additional Records:** Paid £9,000 to Enfield for David Flint
Received £10,000 from Luton Town for Herbie Smith
**Senior Honours:**
Athenian League 1949-50, 54-55. Isthmian League 1975-76, 59-60, Division 2 2000-01. Full Members Cup 1992-93. London Senior Cup 1942-43, 48-49, 58-59, 59-60, 2006-07, 07-08, 15-16. Surrey Senior cup 1937-38, 43-44, 44-45, 52-53, 59-60, 75-76, 76-77, 77-78, 2007-07. Surrey Senior Shield 1951-52, 60-61, 61-62, 65-66. South Thames Cup 1969-70.

**10 YEAR RECORD**

| 06-07 | 07-08 | 08-09 | 09-10 | 10-11 | 11-12 | 12-13 | 13-14 | 14-15 | 15-16 |
|---|---|---|---|---|---|---|---|---|---|
| Isth1S 2 | Isth1S 2 | Isth P 9 | Isth P 12 | Isth P 14 | Isth P 21 | Isth1S 16 | Isth1S 11 | Isth1S 11 | Isth1S 17 |

# WALTON CASUALS

**Chairman:** Tony Gale
**Secretary:** Gus Schofield (T) 07927 222 010 (E) g.schofield1@ntlworld.com
**Commercial Manager:** n/a (T)
**Programme Editor:** James Spiking (T) james@walton casuals.com
**Ground Address:** Whyteleafe FC, 15 Church Road, Whyteleafe, Surrey CR3 0AR
(T) 020 8660 5491 **Manager:** Anthony Gale

**Founded:** 1948 **Nickname:** The Stags
**Previous Names:**
**Previous Leagues:** Surrey Intermediate, Surrey Senior, Suburban, Surrey Premier, Combined Counties

**Club Colours (change):** Tangerine/black/tangerine (All light blue)

**Ground Capacity:** 2,000 **Seats:** 153 **Covered:** 403 **Clubhouse:** Yes **Shop:** Yes
**Previous Grounds:** Elm Grove Rec. 1948-69. Franklyn Road 1969-71. Stompond Lane 1971-72. Liberty Lane 1972-80.

**Record Attendance:** 1,748 v AFC Wimbledon - Combined Counties League 12/04/2004
**Record Victory:** Not known - If you know please email tw.publications@btinternet.com
**Record Defeat:** Not known - If you know please email tw.publications@btinternet.com
**Record Goalscorer:** Greg Ball - 77
**Record Appearances:** Craig Carley - 234
**Additional Records:**
**Senior Honours:**
Combined Counties League Premier Division 2004-05, League Cup 1999-2000.

**10 YEAR RECORD**

| 06-07 | 07-08 | 08-09 | 09-10 | 10-11 | 11-12 | 12-13 | 13-14 | 14-15 | 15-16 |
|---|---|---|---|---|---|---|---|---|---|
| Isth1S 17 | Isth1S 16 | Isth1S 17 | Isth1S 21 | Isth1S 12 | Isth1S 15 | Isth1S 22 | Isth1S 9 | Isth1S 18 | Isth1S 16 |

# WHYTELEAFE

**Chairman:** Mark Coote
**Secretary:** Chris Layton (T) 07718 457 875 (E) chris@theleafe.co.uk
**Commercial Manager:** (T)
**Programme Editor:** Chris Layton (T) chris@theleafe.co.uk
**Ground Address:** 15 Church Road, Whyteleafe, Surrey CR3 0AR
(T) 0208 660 5491 **Manager:** John Fowler

**Founded:** 1946 **Nickname:** Leafe
**Previous Names:** Not known - If you know please email tw.publications@btinternet.com
**Previous Leagues:** Caterham & Ed, Croydon, Thornton Heath & Dist, Surrey Interm. (East) 1954-58, Surrey Sen 58-75, Spartan 75-81, Athenian 81-84, Isthmian 84-2012
**Club Colours (change):** White with green slash (Red with black slash)

**Ground Capacity:** 5,000 **Seats:** 400 **Covered:** 600 **Clubhouse:** Yes **Shop:** Yes
**Previous Grounds:** Not known - If you know please email tw.publications@btinternet.com

**Record Attendance:** 2,210 v Chester City - FA Cup 1999-2000
**Record Victory:** Not known - If you know please email tw.publications@btinternet.com
**Record Defeat:** Not known - If you know please email tw.publications@btinternet.com
**Record Goalscorer:** Not known - If you know please email tw.publications@btinternet.com
**Record Appearances:** Not known - If you know please email tw.publications@btinternet.com
**Additional Records:** Paid £1,000 to Carshalton Athletic for Gary Bowyer
Received £25,000 for Steve Milton
**Senior Honours:**
Surrey Senior Cup 1968-69.
Southern Counties East (formerly Kent League) 2013-14.

**10 YEAR RECORD**

| 06-07 | 07-08 | 08-09 | 09-10 | 10-11 | 11-12 | 12-13 | 13-14 | 14-15 | 15-16 |
|---|---|---|---|---|---|---|---|---|---|
| Isth1S 20 | Isth1S 11 | Isth1S 18 | Isth1S 15 | Isth1S 16 | Isth1S 21 | Kent P 6 | SCE 1 | Isth1S 5 | Isth1S 15 |

# COMBINED COUNTIES LEAGUE

**Sponsored by:** Cherry Red Records
**Founded:** 1978

**Recent Champions - 2013:** Egham Town
**2014:** South Park **2015:** Molesey

| | PREMIER DIVISION | P | W | D | L | F | A | GD | Pts |
|---|---|---|---|---|---|---|---|---|---|
| 1 | Hartley Wintney | 42 | 34 | 4 | 4 | 126 | 39 | 87 | 106 |
| 2 | Ashford Town (Middx) | 42 | 31 | 3 | 8 | 112 | 51 | 61 | 96 |
| 3 | Camberley Town | 42 | 29 | 7 | 6 | 96 | 39 | 57 | 94 |
| 4 | Epsom & Ewell | 42 | 26 | 8 | 8 | 104 | 46 | 58 | 86 |
| 5 | Knaphill | 42 | 25 | 4 | 13 | 109 | 61 | 48 | 79 |
| 6 | Horley Town | 42 | 21 | 9 | 12 | 92 | 62 | 30 | 72 |
| 7 | Hanworth Villa | 42 | 21 | 4 | 17 | 76 | 71 | 5 | 67 |
| 8 | Colliers Wood United | 42 | 17 | 8 | 17 | 78 | 80 | -2 | 59 |
| 9 | Westfield | 42 | 16 | 11 | 15 | 63 | 68 | -5 | 59 |
| 10 | Farnham Town | 42 | 16 | 9 | 17 | 78 | 70 | 8 | 57 |
| 11 | Spelthorne Sports | 42 | 15 | 10 | 17 | 76 | 83 | -7 | 55 |
| 12 | Windsor | 42 | 15 | 10 | 17 | 71 | 79 | -8 | 55 |
| 13 | Bedfont Sports | 42 | 15 | 9 | 18 | 70 | 60 | 10 | 54 |
| 14 | Guildford City | 42 | 16 | 6 | 20 | 77 | 95 | -18 | 54 |
| 15 | Raynes Park Vale | 42 | 17 | 3 | 22 | 72 | 96 | -24 | 54 |
| 16 | AFC Hayes | 42 | 14 | 7 | 21 | 63 | 86 | -23 | 49 |
| 17 | Badshot Lea | 42 | 15 | 3 | 24 | 62 | 104 | -42 | 48 |
| 18 | Chertsey Town | 42 | 13 | 7 | 22 | 58 | 81 | -23 | 46 |
| 19 | Sutton Common Rovers | 42 | 13 | 6 | 23 | 66 | 85 | -19 | 45 |
| 20 | Redhill | 42 | 11 | 6 | 25 | 64 | 87 | -23 | 39 |
| 21 | Chessington & Hook United | 42 | 8 | 6 | 28 | 54 | 113 | -59 | 30 |
| 22 | Cove | 42 | 3 | 2 | 37 | 31 | 142 | -111 | 11 |

| | DIVISION ONE | P | W | D | L | F | A | GD | Pts |
|---|---|---|---|---|---|---|---|---|---|
| 1 | CB Hounslow United | 32 | 24 | 5 | 3 | 73 | 25 | 48 | 77 |
| 2 | Bedfont & Feltham | 32 | 24 | 2 | 6 | 95 | 41 | 54 | 74 |
| 3 | Abbey Rangers | 32 | 23 | 3 | 6 | 72 | 32 | 40 | 72 |
| 4 | Worcester Park | 32 | 18 | 5 | 9 | 79 | 40 | 39 | 59 |
| 5 | Eversley & California | 32 | 18 | 5 | 9 | 85 | 53 | 32 | 59 |
| 6 | Banstead Athletic | 32 | 17 | 6 | 9 | 74 | 47 | 27 | 57 |
| 7 | Cobham | 32 | 15 | 3 | 14 | 60 | 63 | -3 | 48 |
| 8 | Dorking | 32 | 15 | 1 | 16 | 64 | 61 | 3 | 46 |
| 9 | Staines Lammas | 32 | 14 | 3 | 15 | 61 | 54 | 7 | 45 |
| 10 | Ash United | 32 | 11 | 9 | 12 | 57 | 59 | -2 | 42 |
| 11 | Sandhurst Town | 32 | 9 | 8 | 15 | 57 | 89 | -32 | 35 |
| 12 | Frimley Green | 32 | 10 | 4 | 18 | 48 | 64 | -16 | 34 |
| 13 | Sheerwater | 32 | 10 | 3 | 19 | 55 | 70 | -15 | 33 |
| 14 | South Park Reserves | 32 | 8 | 6 | 18 | 53 | 85 | -32 | 30 |
| 15 | Dorking Wanderers Reserves | 32 | 5 | 8 | 19 | 32 | 66 | -34 | 23 |
| 16 | Farleigh Rovers | 32 | 7 | 2 | 23 | 43 | 100 | -57 | 23 |
| 17 | Epsom Athletic | 32 | 5 | 5 | 22 | 37 | 96 | -59 | 20 |

## PREMIER CHALLENGE CUP

**HOLDERS:** CAMBERLEY TOWN

**ROUND 1**

| | | | |
|---|---|---|---|
| Westfield | v | Farleigh Rovers | 3-1 |
| Redhill | v | Sandhurst Town | 5-2 |
| Sutton Common Rovers | v | Guildford City | 1-0 |
| Farnham Town | v | Ash United | 3-1 |
| Bedfont Sports | v | Abbey Rangers | 1-3 |
| Windsor | v | Colliers Wood United | 4-5 |
| Horley Town | v | Staines Lammas | 4-1 |

**ROUND 2**

| | | | |
|---|---|---|---|
| Cove | v | Cobham | 1-6 |
| Sheerwater | v | Frimley Green | 3-3, 7-8p |
| AFC Hayes | v | Raynes Park Vale | 0-1 |
| Westfield | v | CB Hounslow United | 1-0 |
| Dorking | v | Knaphill | 0-3 |
| Hanworth Villa | v | Chertsey Town | 1-2 aet |
| Redhill | v | Sutton Common Rovers | 3-0 |
| Farnham Town | v | Abbey Rangers | 3-2 |
| Camberley Town | v | Eversley & California | 4-2 |
| Badshot Lea | v | Spelthorne Sports | 2-4 |
| Bedfont & Feltham | v | Colliers Wood United | 1-5 |
| Dorking Wanderers Reserves | v | South Park Reserves | 2-1 |
| Hartley Wintney | v | Horley Town | 4-2 |
| Worcester Park | v | Chessington & Hook United | 1-5 |
| Banstead Athletic | v | Epsom & Ewell | 1-1, 6-7p |
| Ashford Town (Middx) | v | Epsom Athletic | 2-1 |

**ROUND 3**

| | | | |
|---|---|---|---|
| Cobham | v | Frimley Green | 3-0 |
| Raynes Park Vale | v | Westfield | 0-2 |
| Knaphill | v | Chertsey Town | 2-1 |
| Redhill | v | Farnham Town | 0-2 |
| Camberley Town | v | Spelthorne Sports | 5-1 |
| Colliers Wood United | v | Dorking Wanderers Reserves | 6-0 |
| Hartley Wintney | v | Chessington & Hook United | 0-1 |
| Epsom & Ewell | v | Ashford Town (Middx) | 0-3 |

**QUARTER FINALS**

| | | | |
|---|---|---|---|
| Cobham | v | Westfield | 2-0 |
| Knaphill | v | Farnham Town | 1-3 |
| Camberley Town | v | Colliers Wood United | 2-1 aet |
| Chessington & Hook United | v | Ashford Town (Middx) | 0-2 |

**SEMI FINALS**

| | | | |
|---|---|---|---|
| Ashford Town (Middx) | v | Camberley Town | 0-3 |
| Farnham Town | v | Cobham | 3-1 |

**FINAL**

| | | | |
|---|---|---|---|
| Camberley Town | v | Farnham Town | 1-3 |

## DIVISION ONE CHALLENGE CUP

**HOLDERS:** BEDFONT & FELTHAM

**ROUND 1**

| | | | |
|---|---|---|---|
| Banstead Athletic | v | Abbey Rangers | 3-1 |

**ROUND 2**

| | | | |
|---|---|---|---|
| Farleigh Rovers | v | Banstead Athletic | 2-2, 3-4p |
| Eversley & California | v | Worcester Park | 3-4 |
| Cobham | v | Sandhurst Town | 2-1 |
| Epsom Athletic | v | South Park Reserves | 3-2 |
| Frimley Green | v | Dorking | 1-5 |
| Sheerwater | v | Staines Lammas | 1-3 |
| Bedfont & Feltham | v | Dorking Wanderers Reserves | 3-0 |
| Ash United | v | CB Hounslow United | 0-2 |

**QUARTER FINALS**

| | | | |
|---|---|---|---|
| Banstead Athletic | v | Worcester Park | 0-1 |
| Cobham | v | Epsom Athletic | 6-1 |
| Dorking | v | Staines Lammas | 0-1 |
| Bedfont & Feltham | v | CB Hounslow United | 4-2 |

**SEMI FINALS**

| | | | |
|---|---|---|---|
| Worcester Park | v | Cobham | 2-0 |
| Staines Lammas | v | Bedfont & Feltham | 2-3 |

**FINAL**

| | | | |
|---|---|---|---|
| Bedfont & Feltham | v | Worcester Park | 0-1 |

## CLUB MOVEMENTS

**Premier Division - In:** Abbey Rangers (P), Bedfont & Feltham (P). CB Hounslow United (P). North Greenford United (R - Southern Div.1 Central). Walton & Hersham (R - Isthmian Div.1 South). **Out:** Ashford Town (Middx) (P - Southern Div.1 Central). Chessington & Hook United (R), Cove (R), Redhill (R).
**Division One - In:** AC London (S - Kent Invcta). Badshot (P - Aldershot & District). Chessington & Hook United (R), Cove (R), Redhill (R).
**Out:** Abbey Rangers (P), Bedfont & Feltham (P). CB Hounslow United (P). Dorking Wanderers Reserves (F). Sandhurst Town (S - Hellenic Div.1E).

| | PREMIER DIVISION | 1 | 2 | 3 | 4 | 5 | 6 | 7 | 8 | 9 | 10 | 11 | 12 | 13 | 14 | 15 | 16 | 17 | 18 | 19 | 20 | 21 | 22 |
|---|---|---|---|---|---|---|---|---|---|---|---|---|---|---|---|---|---|---|---|---|---|---|---|
| 1 | AFC Hayes | | 0-5 | 4-3 | 0-1 | 0-1 | 2-2 | 4-1 | 0-2 | 5-0 | 0-7 | 1-1 | 4-1 | 0-1 | 2-4 | 1-0 | 2-1 | 3-4 | 3-1 | 1-1 | 2-1 | 2-2 | 3-1 |
| 2 | Ashford Town (Middx) | 1-0 | | 4-0 | 3-2 | 1-0 | 2-1 | 7-1 | 1-1 | 3-1 | 2-3 | 2-1 | 4-1 | 4-1 | 1-1 | 3-3 | 6-4 | 4-2 | 4-1 | 2-1 | 2-0 | 0-1 | 2-1 |
| 3 | Badshot Lea | 2-1 | 0-4 | | 0-1 | 2-4 | 2-1 | 0-7 | 1-1 | 2-0 | 0-1 | 1-3 | 2-1 | 0-4 | 4-7 | 3-3 | 1-5 | 0-2 | 1-0 | 0-3 | 1-2 | 1-0 | 2-1 |
| 4 | Bedfont Sports | 2-3 | 0-1 | 0-1 | | 2-1 | 0-1 | 3-2 | 5-0 | 5-1 | 2-2 | 1-1 | 2-1 | 1-2 | 1-1 | 1-3 | 0-1 | 3-0 | 4-1 | 2-2 | 2-2 | 1-0 | 3-1 |
| 5 | Camberley Town | 3-0 | 2-1 | 2-0 | 2-0 | | 3-0 | 3-0 | 1-1 | 4-0 | 1-1 | 5-0 | 4-2 | 5-2 | 3-1 | 0-5 | 3-1 | 3-1 | 2-1 | 1-1 | 0-2 | 0-1 | 5-0 |
| 6 | Chertsey Town | 3-1 | 0-5 | 3-4 | 1-3 | 1-4 | | 3-0 | 0-1 | 3-1 | 3-5 | 4-1 | 0-0 | 0-3 | 1-0 | 0-2 | 1-4 | 1-0 | 5-1 | 1-2 | 0-0 | 1-1 | 4-2 |
| 7 | Chessington & Hook United | 2-1 | 0-2 | 0-3 | 2-1 | 0-0 | 2-0 | | 2-1 | 4-1 | 1-6 | 0-4 | 3-9 | 0-0 | 1-2 | 1-8 | 0-2 | 2-4 | 3-1 | 3-1 | 2-2 | 0-0 | 0-3 |
| 8 | Colliers Wood United | 5-1 | 1-2 | 1-2 | 1-1 | 1-4 | 4-1 | 2-1 | | 3-2 | 0-3 | 2-2 | 2-4 | 3-4 | 1-3 | 2-0 | 5-2 | 1-1 | 4-1 | 2-3 | 2-1 | 3-1 | 2-3 |
| 9 | Cove | 1-3 | 2-4 | 2-6 | 1-4 | 0-1 | 1-2 | 3-0 | 2-2 | | 0-7 | 1-6 | 2-0 | 0-3 | 0-7 | 0-4 | 0-5 | 0-1 | 0-5 | 3-3 | 1-0 | 0-2 | 0-2 |
| 10 | Epsom & Ewell | 1-1 | 0-1 | 4-1 | 1-0 | 2-3 | 0-1 | 1-0 | 3-1 | 1-0 | | 1-0 | 4-0 | 5-0 | 0-1 | 3-4 | 1-2 | 3-1 | 3-0 | 2-1 | 3-1 | 0-2 | 2-2 |
| 11 | Farnham Town | 1-0 | 1-2 | 1-2 | 2-5 | 1-1 | 1-3 | 1-1 | 1-2 | 4-0 | 1-2 | | 2-2 | 4-1 | 4-2 | 1-4 | 2-3 | 3-1 | 1-0 | 1-0 | 2-1 | 1-2 | 3-4 |
| 12 | Guildford City | 1-1 | 1-3 | 3-2 | 0-2 | 1-2 | 4-2 | 3-2 | 0-4 | 4-0 | 1-5 | 2-1 | | 0-0 | 2-5 | 1-1 | 3-2 | 5-3 | 5-2 | 2-4 | 0-1 | 1-3 | 2-1 |
| 13 | Hanworth Villa | 5-0 | 0-3 | 3-1 | 2-1 | 0-2 | 2-0 | 2-1 | 1-2 | 2-1 | 2-3 | 1-3 | 1-3 | | 1-3 | 0-0 | 1-0 | 5-0 | 0-4 | 2-0 | 3-0 | 2-2 | 6-0 |
| 14 | Hartley Wintney | 3-0 | 2-0 | 2-3 | 2-0 | 3-2 | 4-2 | 2-0 | 6-0 | 2-0 | 3-3 | 2-1 | 5-0 | 2-0 | | 2-2 | 2-1 | 10-0 | 5-0 | 4-1 | 2-1 | 4-0 | 1-0 |
| 15 | Horley Town | 3-1 | 3-2 | 0-3 | 2-1 | 1-3 | 0-0 | 1-0 | 2-1 | 3-0 | 2-2 | 1-1 | 0-3 | 0-2 | 0-1 | | 2-1 | 3-1 | 4-0 | 4-0 | 3-0 | 4-1 | 6-0 |
| 16 | Knaphill | 2-3 | 4-2 | 3-0 | 3-1 | 1-2 | 4-0 | 2-2 | 1-0 | 3-0 | 1-1 | 2-2 | 4-1 | 4-2 | 0-1 | 5-0 | | 3-2 | 2-1 | 6-1 | 4-1 | 4-1 | 2-2 |
| 17 | Raynes Park Vale | 4-1 | 3-2 | 4-1 | 1-0 | 1-7 | 2-0 | 3-2 | 3-3 | 3-1 | 0-3 | 0-2 | 2-0 | 1-2 | 1-2 | 2-3 | 0-1 | | 0-1 | 1-1 | 2-1 | 2-1 | 3-1 |
| 18 | Redhill | 0-0 | 0-4 | 6-0 | 2-2 | 0-1 | 3-1 | 6-0 | 3-0 | 3-0 | 0-1 | 0-1 | 0-1 | 3-2 | 0-5 | 3-2 | 1-2 | 1-3 | | 2-3 | 2-2 | 1-1 | 2-2 |
| 19 | Spelthorne Sports | 3-2 | 0-3 | 6-2 | 1-1 | 1-3 | 1-1 | 4-2 | 2-1 | 3-0 | 2-6 | 0-3 | 5-0 | 2-3 | 1-2 | 2-2 | 1-4 | 2-1 | 0-2 | | 5-2 | 2-0 | 2-0 |
| 20 | Sutton Common Rovers | 2-1 | 2-4 | 1-0 | 3-2 | 0-2 | 0-4 | 6-0 | 2-3 | 8-1 | 1-2 | 0-3 | 2-3 | 1-2 | 0-5 | 4-0 | 2-1 | 1-5 | 3-0 | 3-2 | | 2-1 | 1-1 |
| 21 | Westfield | 0-1 | 3-2 | 2-2 | 3-1 | 1-1 | 4-1 | 2-1 | 2-4 | 5-2 | 0-0 | 4-2 | 0-3 | 4-0 | 0-2 | 2-0 | 1-6 | 4-2 | 2-2 | 0-0 | 1-1 | | 0-4 |
| 22 | Windsor | 2-3 | 1-2 | 2-1 | 1-1 | 0-0 | 0-0 | 4-3 | 0-1 | 5-1 | 2-1 | 2-2 | 1-1 | 3-1 | 0-3 | 3-2 | 2-1 | 4-0 | 3-2 | 1-1 | 4-1 | 0-1 | |

| | DIVISION ONE | 1 | 2 | 3 | 4 | 5 | 6 | 7 | 8 | 9 | 10 | 11 | 12 | 13 | 14 | 15 | 16 | 17 |
|---|---|---|---|---|---|---|---|---|---|---|---|---|---|---|---|---|---|---|
| 1 | Abbey Rangers | | 3-1 | 1-0 | 2-1 | 0-2 | 2-3 | 6-0 | 1-0 | 2-0 | 2-0 | 2-1 | 3-1 | 8-1 | 2-1 | 3-0 | 2-1 | 1-0 |
| 2 | Ash United | 0-2 | | 1-5 | 1-2 | 2-1 | 3-1 | 2-3 | 2-1 | 2-2 | 3-0 | 1-2 | 2-1 | 2-2 | 1-1 | 2-5 | 0-0 | 4-1 |
| 3 | Banstead Athletic | 3-3 | 3-3 | | 4-1 | 0-4 | 2-0 | 4-2 | 0-1 | 5-1 | 0-2 | 5-2 | 6-2 | 1-1 | 3-0 | 4-1 | 5-1 | 1-2 |
| 4 | Bedfont & Feltham | 2-0 | 2-0 | 2-0 | | 0-0 | 3-1 | 5-2 | 5-1 | 7-0 | 4-1 | 1-0 | 3-0 | 7-0 | 2-1 | 10-2 | 1-4 | 1-1 |
| 5 | CB Hounslow United | 2-1 | 1-0 | 2-0 | 4-1 | | 2-2 | 3-2 | 2-0 | 2-0 | 3-1 | 3-0 | 1-0 | 4-0 | 1-0 | 3-3 | 6-0 | 2-1 |
| 6 | Cobham | 2-3 | 0-1 | 1-3 | 1-2 | 0-1 | | 1-4 | 3-0 | 4-0 | 0-2 | 3-1 | 3-2 | 3-2 | 0-2 | 3-2 | 1-0 | 3-3 |
| 7 | Dorking | 1-2 | 3-1 | 1-2 | 0-1 | 1-1 | 3-0 | | 2-0 | 4-2 | 0-2 | 4-1 | 3-0 | 5-1 | 3-4 | 3-5 | 2-1 | 4-3 |
| 8 | Dorking Wanderers Reserves | 1-3 | 1-1 | 0-3 | 1-2 | 0-1 | 3-3 | 1-0 | | 2-0 | 3-3 | 0-4 | 0-0 | 2-2 | 3-0 | 2-3 | 1-3 | 2-2 |
| 9 | Epsom Athletic | 1-2 | 5-1 | 0-0 | 1-8 | 0-3 | 0-4 | 1-0 | 1-3 | | 1-2 | 5-2 | 3-3 | 1-1 | 2-1 | 1-4 | 5-1 | 0-6 |
| 10 | Eversley & California | 0-3 | 1-2 | 2-0 | 2-3 | 2-2 | 6-2 | 2-0 | 5-3 | 6-0 | | 6-0 | 3-3 | 5-2 | 6-0 | 6-0 | 3-1 | 3-2 |
| 11 | Farleigh Rovers | 2-1 | 2-6 | 0-2 | 1-4 | 0-2 | 2-3 | 0-2 | 0-0 | 3-2 | 3-3 | | 2-0 | 0-2 | 0-3 | 5-3 | 1-0 | 0-4 |
| 12 | Frimley Green | 1-0 | 1-1 | 2-3 | 5-1 | 1-0 | 1-2 | 0-2 | 4-0 | 2-1 | 0-2 | 4-0 | | 4-1 | 2-3 | 2-0 | 1-3 | 2-1 |
| 13 | Sandhurst Town | 2-2 | 1-5 | 4-2 | 0-3 | 0-5 | 2-3 | 2-0 | 1-1 | 2-0 | 4-0 | 8-2 | 1-0 | | 4-2 | 1-1 | 2-6 | 0-3 |
| 14 | Sheerwater | 0-2 | 2-2 | 1-3 | 2-6 | 2-3 | 2-3 | 1-2 | 3-0 | 3-1 | 2-4 | 4-3 | 4-0 | 4-2 | | 1-4 | 5-0 | 0-1 |
| 15 | South Park Reserves | 1-5 | 3-2 | 2-2 | 0-2 | 1-3 | 2-3 | 3-4 | 1-0 | 0-0 | 2-2 | 5-4 | 0-1 | 0-2 | 0-0 | | 0-3 | 0-1 |
| 16 | Staines Lammas | 1-2 | 2-3 | 1-1 | 1-2 | 1-2 | 0-1 | 2-1 | 4-0 | 5-0 | 0-1 | 6-0 | 6-2 | 2-2 | 2-1 | 1-0 | | 1-0 |
| 17 | Worcester Park | 1-1 | 0-0 | 1-2 | 3-1 | 4-2 | 2-1 | 2-1 | 2-0 | 6-1 | 3-2 | 6-0 | 4-1 | 6-2 | 3-0 | 4-0 | 1-2 | |

## ABBEY RANGERS

Founded: 1976 Nickname:

**Secretary:** Graham Keable **(T)** 07711 042 588 **(E)** graham.keable@ntlworld.com
**Chairman:** Denis Healy **Manager:** Les Chatfield & Bob Thorpe **Prog Ed:** Clive Robertson
**Ground:** Addlestone Moor, Addlestone, KT15 2QH **(T)** 01932 422 962
**Capacity:** **Seats:** **Covered:** **Midweek Matchday:** Monday **Clubhouse:**

**Colours(change):** Black & white stripes/black/black
**Previous Names:**
**Previous Leagues:** Surrey Elite >2015
**Records:**
**Honours:**

**10 YEAR RECORD**

| 06-07 | 07-08 | 08-09 | 09-10 | 10-11 | 11-12 | 12-13 | 13-14 | 14-15 | 15-16 |
|---|---|---|---|---|---|---|---|---|---|
| | | | | | SuEl 10 | SuEl 7 | SuEl 3 | SuEl 4 | CC1 3 |

## AFC HAYES

Founded: 1976 Nickname: The Brook

**Secretary:** Barry Crump **(T)** 07966 468 029 **(E)** afchayesfootballsec@hotmail.co.uk
**Chairman:** Barry Stone **Manager:** Sean Berry **Prog Ed:** Graham White
**Ground:** Farm Park, Kingshill Avenue, Hayes UB4 8DD **(T)** 020 8845 0110
**Capacity:** 2,000 **Seats:** 150 **Covered:** 200 **Midweek Matchday:** Tuesday **Clubhouse:** Yes

**Colours(change):** Blue and white stripes/blue/blue
**Previous Names:** Brook House > 2007.
**Previous Leagues:** Spartan South Midlands, Isthmian, Conference, Southern 2007-15.
**Records:** Not known
**Honours:** Spartan South Midlands Premier South 1997-98, Premier Cup 1999-2000, Challenge Trophy 2003-04.
Isthmian Associate Members Trophy 2005-06. Middlesex Senior Cup 2008-09.

**10 YEAR RECORD**

| 06-07 | 07-08 | 08-09 | 09-10 | 10-11 | 11-12 | 12-13 | 13-14 | 14-15 | 15-16 |
|---|---|---|---|---|---|---|---|---|---|
| Conf S 20 | Sthsw 14 | Sthsw 9 | Sthsw 21 | SthC 19 | SthC 10 | SthC 15 | SthC 18 | SthC 22 | CCP 16 |

## BADSHOT LEA

Founded: 1907 Nickname: Baggies

**Secretary:** Mrs Nicky Staszkiewicz **(T)** 07921 466 858 **(E)** nstaszkiewicz@ashgatepublishing.com
**Chairman:** Mark Broad **Manager:** Ben Dillon **Prog Ed:** Peter Collison
**Ground:** Ash United, Shawfields Stadium, Youngs Drive off Shawfield Rd, Ash, GU12 6RE. **(T)** 01252 320 385
**Capacity:** 2,500 **Seats:** 152 **Covered:** 160 **Midweek Matchday:** Tuesday **Clubhouse:** Yes

**Colours(change):** All claret & sky blue
**Previous Names:**
**Previous Leagues:** Surrey Intermediate. Hellenic > 2008.
**Records:** **Att:** 276 v Bisley, 16.04.07.
**Honours:**

**10 YEAR RECORD**

| 06-07 | 07-08 | 08-09 | 09-10 | 10-11 | 11-12 | 12-13 | 13-14 | 14-15 | 15-16 |
|---|---|---|---|---|---|---|---|---|---|
| Hel1E 3 | Hel P 11 | CCP 7 | CCP 10 | CCP 6 | CCP 17 | CCP 7 | CCP 14 | CCP 8 | CCP 17 |

## BEDFONT & FELTHAM

Founded: 2012 Nickname: The Yellows

**Secretary:** Scott Savoy **(T)** 07539 219 924 **(E)** ssavoyffc@msn.com
**Chairman:** Brian Barry **Manager:** John Cook **Prog Ed:** Rob Healey
**Ground:** The Orchard, Hatton Road, Bedfont TW14 9QT **(T)** 020 8890 7264
**Capacity:** 1200 **Seats:** 100 **Covered:** 150 **Midweek Matchday:** Tuesday **Clubhouse:**

**Colours(change):** Yellow & blue/blue/blue
**Previous Names:** Bedfont FC and Feltham (1946) amalgamated in May 2012 but had to wait until 2013-14 before changing the name.
**Previous Leagues:**
**Records:**
**Honours:**

**10 YEAR RECORD**

| 06-07 | 07-08 | 08-09 | 09-10 | 10-11 | 11-12 | 12-13 | 13-14 | 14-15 | 15-16 |
|---|---|---|---|---|---|---|---|---|---|
| | | | | | | | CC1 5 | CC1 5 | CC1 2 |

## BEDFONT SPORTS

Founded: 2000 Nickname: The Eagles

**Secretary:** David Sturt **(T)** 07712 824 112 **(E)** dave.sturt2@blueyonder.co.uk
**Chairman:** David Reader **Manager:** Paul Johnson **Prog Ed:** Terry Reader
**Ground:** Bedfont Sports Club, Hatton Road, Bedfont TW14 8JA **(T)** 0208 831 9067
**Capacity:** 3,000 **Seats:** Yes **Covered:** 200 **Midweek Matchday:** Tuesday **Clubhouse:**

**Colours(change):** Red & black hoops/black/red & black hoops
**Previous Names:** Bedfont Sunday became Bedfont Sports in 2000 - Bedfont Eagles (1978) merged with the club shortly afterwards.
**Previous Leagues:** Middlesex County > 2009
**Records:**
**Honours:** Middlesex County Premier Cup 2009-10.

**10 YEAR RECORD**

| 06-07 | 07-08 | 08-09 | 09-10 | 10-11 | 11-12 | 12-13 | 13-14 | 14-15 | 15-16 |
|---|---|---|---|---|---|---|---|---|---|
| | | | CC1 9 | CC1 4 | CC1 2 | CCP 13 | CCP 17 | CCP 16 | CCP 13 |

## CAMBERLEY TOWN

Founded: 1895 Nickname: Reds or Town

**Secretary:** Ben Clifford **(T)** 07876 552 210 **(E)** benjaminclifford@sky.com
**Chairman:** Ronnie Wilson **Manager:** Dan Turkington
**Ground:** Krooner Park, Wilton Road, Camberley, Surrey GU15 2QW **(T)** 01276 65 392
**Capacity:** 1,976 **Seats:** 196 **Covered:** 300 **Midweek Matchday:** Tuesday **Clubhouse:** Yes **Shop:** Yes

**Colours(change):** Red and white stripes/red/red
**Previous Names:** None
**Previous Leagues:** Surrey Senior Lge. Spartan Lge. Athenian Lge. Isthmian Lge.
**Records:** **Att:** 2066 v Aldershot Town, Isthmian Div.2 25/08/90. **Apps:** Brian Ives.
**Honours:**

**10 YEAR RECORD**

| 06-07 | 07-08 | 08-09 | 09-10 | 10-11 | 11-12 | 12-13 | 13-14 | 14-15 | 15-16 |
|---|---|---|---|---|---|---|---|---|---|
| CCP 7 | CCP 3 | CCP 5 | CCP 3 | CCP 4 | CCP 6 | CCP 16 | CCP 2 | CCP 2 | CCP 3 |

## CB HOUNSLOW UNITED

Founded: 1989 Nickname:

**Secretary:** Frank James **(T)** 07958 718 930 **(E)** frank@bjmw.co.uk
**Chairman:** Frank James **Manager:** Barry Chapman **Prog Ed:** Frank James
**Ground:** Bedfont & Feltham FC, The Orchard, Hatton Road, Bedfont TW14 9QT **(T)** 0208 890 7264
**Capacity:** 1200 **Seats:** 100 **Covered:** Yes **Midweek Matchday:** Tuesday **Clubhouse:**

**Colours(change):** Green/black/green
**Previous Names:**
**Previous Leagues:** Middlesex County.
**Records:**
**Honours:** Combined Counties League Division One 2015-16.

**10 YEAR RECORD**

| 06-07 | 07-08 | 08-09 | 09-10 | 10-11 | 11-12 | 12-13 | 13-14 | 14-15 | 15-16 |
|---|---|---|---|---|---|---|---|---|---|
| CC1 12 | CC1 10 | CC1 10 | CC1 15 | CC1 14 | CC1 15 | CC1 8 | CC1 14 | CC1 7 | CC1 1 |

## CHERTSEY TOWN

Founded: 1890 Nickname: Curfews

**Secretary:** Chris Gay **(T)** 07713 473 313 **(E)** chrisegay@googlemail.com
**Chairman:** Steve Powers **Manager:** Kim Harris **Prog Ed:** Chris Gay
**Ground:** Alwyns Lane, Chertsey, Surrey KT16 9DW **(T)** 01932 561 774
**Capacity:** 3,000 **Seats:** 240 **Covered:** 760 **Midweek Matchday:** Tuesday **Clubhouse:** Yes **Shop:** Yes

**Colours(change):** Royal blue & white stripes/royal blue/royal blue
**Previous Names:** None
**Previous Leagues:** Metropolitan. Spartan. Athenian. Isthmian, Combined Counties 2006-11. Southern 2011-14.
**Records:** **Att:** 2150 v Aldershot Town, Isthmian Div.2 04/12/93. **Goals:** Alan Brown (54) 1962-63.
**Honours:** Surrey Senior Champions 1959, 61, 62. Isthmian League Cup 1994.

**10 YEAR RECORD**

| 06-07 | 07-08 | 08-09 | 09-10 | 10-11 | 11-12 | 12-13 | 13-14 | 14-15 | 15-16 |
|---|---|---|---|---|---|---|---|---|---|
| CCP 8 | CCP 8 | CCP 3 | CCP 2 | CCP 2 | SthC 17 | SthC 20 | SthC 21 | CCP 20 | CCP 18 |

## COLLIERS WOOD UNITED

Founded: 1874 | Nickname: The Woods

**Secretary:** Chris Clapham **(T)** 07812 181 601 **(E)** chrisclapham@blueyonder.co.uk
**Chairman:** Steve Turner **Manager:** Tony Hurrell **Prog Ed:** Chris Clapham
**Ground:** Wibandune Sports Gd, Lincoln Green, Wimbledon SW20 0AA **(T)** 0208 942 8062
**Capacity:** 2000 **Seats:** 102 **Covered:** 100 **Midweek Matchday:** Wednesday **Clubhouse:** Yes **Shop:** Yes

**Colours(change):** Royal blue/black/black
**Previous Names:** Vandyke Colliers United
**Previous Leagues:** Surrey County Senior
**Records:** **Att:** 151 v Guildford City 06/08/2010. **Win:** 9-1 v Bedfont 05/03/2008.
**Honours:**

**10 YEAR RECORD**

| 06-07 | 07-08 | 08-09 | 09-10 | 10-11 | 11-12 | 12-13 | 13-14 | 14-15 | 15-16 |
|---|---|---|---|---|---|---|---|---|---|
| CCP 13 | CCP 7 | CCP 14 | CCP 19 | CCP 11 | CCP 19 | CCP 18 | CCP 16 | CCP 11 | CCP 8 |

## EPSOM & EWELL

Founded: 1918 | Nickname: E's or Salts

**Secretary:** Peter Beddoe **(T)** 07767 078 132 **(E)** p.beddoe1@ntlworld.com
**Chairman:** Peter Beddoe **Manager:** Glyn Mandeville **Prog Ed:** Richard Lambert
**Ground:** Chipstead FC, High Road, Chipstead, Surrey CR5 3SF **(T)** 01737 553 250
**Capacity:** 2,000 **Seats:** 150 **Covered:** 200 **Midweek Matchday:** Tuesday **Clubhouse:** Yes

**Colours(change):** Royal blue & white hoops/royal blue/royal blue
**Previous Names:** Epsom T (previously Epsom FC) merged with Ewell & Stoneleigh in 1960
**Previous Leagues:** Corinthian. Athenian. Surrey Senior. Isthmian >2006.
**Records:** **Att:** 5000 v Kingstonian, FAC 2Q 15/10/49. **Goals:** Tommy Tuite - 391. **Apps:** Graham Morris - 658.
**Honours:**

**10 YEAR RECORD**

| 06-07 | 07-08 | 08-09 | 09-10 | 10-11 | 11-12 | 12-13 | 13-14 | 14-15 | 15-16 |
|---|---|---|---|---|---|---|---|---|---|
| CCP 17 | CCP 10 | CCP 4 | CCP 5 | CCP 10 | CCP 14 | CCP 5 | CCP 3 | CCP 7 | CCP 4 |

## FARNHAM TOWN

Founded: 1906 | Nickname: The Town

**Secretary:** Jane Warner **(T)** 07846 774 560 **(E)** janeannwarner@btinternet.com
**Chairman:** Ray Bridger **Manager:** Paul Tanner **Prog Ed:** Ben Williams
**Ground:** Memorial Ground, West Street, Farnham GU9 7DY **(T)** 01252 715 305
**Capacity:** 1,500 **Seats:** 50 **Covered:** **Midweek Matchday:** Tuesday **Clubhouse:** Yes

**Colours(change):** Claret & sky blue/white, claret & sky blue/sky blue
**Previous Names:**
**Previous Leagues:** Spartan 1973-75, London Spartan 1975-80, Combined Co. 1980-92, 93-2006, Isthmian 1992-93 (resigned pre-season).
**Records:**
**Honours:** Combined Counties League 1990-91, 91-92, Division 1 2006-07.

**10 YEAR RECORD**

| 06-07 | 07-08 | 08-09 | 09-10 | 10-11 | 11-12 | 12-13 | 13-14 | 14-15 | 15-16 |
|---|---|---|---|---|---|---|---|---|---|
| CC1 1 | CC1 5 | CC1 8 | CC1 11 | CC1 2 | CCP 12 | CCP 8 | CCP 15 | CCP 10 | CCP 10 |

## GUILDFORD CITY

Founded: 1996 | Nickname: The Sweeney

**Secretary:** Barry Underwood **(T)** 07757 730 304 **(E)** barry.underwood@guildfordcityfc.co.uk
**Chairman:** Mark Redhead **Manager:** Dean Thomas **Prog Ed:** Barry Underwood
**Ground:** Spectrum Leisure Centre, Parkway, Guildford GU1 1UP **(T)** 01483 443 322
**Capacity:** 1100 **Seats:** 269 **Covered:** Yes **Midweek Matchday:** Wednesday **Clubhouse:** Yes **Shop:** Yes

**Colours(change):** Red & white stripes/black/black
**Previous Names:** AFC Guildford 1996-2005. Guildford United 2005-06.
**Previous Leagues:** Surrey Senior. Combined Counties > 2012. Southern 2012-14.
**Records:** **Att:** 211 v Godalming & Guildford, 2004
**Honours:** Southern League 1937-38, 55-56, League cup 1962-63, 66-67.
Combined Counties Division One 2003-04, Premier Division 2010-11, 11-12

**10 YEAR RECORD**

| 06-07 | 07-08 | 08-09 | 09-10 | 10-11 | 11-12 | 12-13 | 13-14 | 14-15 | 15-16 |
|---|---|---|---|---|---|---|---|---|---|
| CCP 21 | CCP 2 | CCP 20 | CCP 7 | CCP 1 | CCP 1 | SthC 9 | Sthsw 22 | CCP 17 | CCP 14 |

## HANWORTH VILLA

Founded: 1976 Nickname: The Vilans

**Secretary:** Dave Brown **(T)** 07971 650 297 **(E)** david.h.brown@btconnect.com
**Chairman:** Gary Brunning **Manager:** Rufus Brevett **Prog Ed:** Gary Brunning
**Ground:** Rectory Meadows, Park Road, Hanworth TW13 6PN **(T)** 020 8831 9391
**Capacity:** 600 **Seats:** 100 **Covered:** Yes **Midweek Matchday:** Tuesday **Clubhouse:** Yes

**Colours(change):** Red & white/black/black
**Previous Names:**
**Previous Leagues:** Hounslow & District Lge. West Middlesex Lge. Middlesex County League.
**Records:**
**Honours:** West Middlesex Div. 1 & Div. 2 Champions. Middlesex County Champions 2002-03, 04-05.

**10 YEAR RECORD**

| 06-07 | 07-08 | 08-09 | 09-10 | 10-11 | 11-12 | 12-13 | 13-14 | 14-15 | 15-16 |
|---|---|---|---|---|---|---|---|---|---|
| CC1 6 | CC1 2 | CC1 2 | CCP 17 | CCP 5 | CCP 3 | CCP 9 | CCP 8 | CCP 19 | CCP 7 |

## HARTLEY WINTNEY

Founded: 1897 Nickname: The Row

**Secretary:** Elayne Duddridge **(T)** 07949 449 022 **(E)** mulley@ntlworld.com
**Chairman:** Luke Mullen **Manager:** Dan Brownlie & Anthony Millerick **Prog Ed:** Dan Brownlie
**Ground:** Memorial Playing Fields,Green Lane, Hartley Wintney RG27 8DL **(T)** 01252 843 586
**Capacity:** 2,000 **Seats:** 113 **Covered:** Yes **Midweek Matchday:** Tuesday **Clubhouse:** Yes **Shop:** Yes

**Colours(change):** All orange
**Previous Names:** None
**Previous Leagues:** Founder members of the Home Counties League (renamed Combined Counties League)
**Records:** 1,392 v AFC Wimbledon , 25/01/02.
**Honours:** Combined Counties League 1982-83, 2015-16.

**10 YEAR RECORD**

| 06-07 | 07-08 | 08-09 | 09-10 | 10-11 | 11-12 | 12-13 | 13-14 | 14-15 | 15-16 |
|---|---|---|---|---|---|---|---|---|---|
| CC1 16 | CC1 3 | CCP 21 | CC1 5 | CC1 7 | CC1 3 | CCP 19 | CCP 7 | CCP 9 | CCP 1 |

## HORLEY TOWN

Founded: 1896 Nickname: The Clarets

**Secretary:** Spencer Mitchell **(T)** 07802 962 499 **(E)** mitchandharri@yahoo.co.uk
**Chairman:** Mark Sale **Manager:** Anthony Jupp **Prog Ed:** Philippa Burbidge
**Ground:** The New Defence, Court Lodge Road, Horley RH6 8SP **(T)** 01293 822 000
**Capacity:** 1800 **Seats:** 101 **Covered:** Yes **Midweek Matchday:** Tuesday **Clubhouse:** Yes **Shop:** Yes

**Colours(change):** Claret & sky blue/sky blue/sky blue
**Previous Names:** Horley >1975
**Previous Leagues:** Surrey Senior, London Spartan, Athenian, Surrey County Senior, Crawley & District
**Records:** **Att:** 1,500 v AFC Wimbledon, 2003-04. **Goalscorer:** Alan Gates. **Win:** 12-1 v Egham. **Defeat:** 2-8 v Redhill 1956/57.
**Honours:**

**10 YEAR RECORD**

| 06-07 | 07-08 | 08-09 | 09-10 | 10-11 | 11-12 | 12-13 | 13-14 | 14-15 | 15-16 |
|---|---|---|---|---|---|---|---|---|---|
| CC1 2 | CCP 5 | CCP 12 | CCP 14 | CCP 16 | CCP 7 | CCP 12 | CCP 19 | CCP 12 | CCP 6 |

## KNAPHILL

Founded: 1924 Nickname: The Knappers

**Secretary:** Mike Clement **(T)** 07795 322 031 **(E)** knaphillfc.seniorsecretary@gmail.com
**Chairman:** David Freeman **Manager:** Keith Hills **Prog Ed:** David Freeman
**Ground:** Brookwood Country Park, Redding Way, Knaphill GU21 2AY **(T)** 01483 475 150
**Capacity:** 750 **Seats:** **Covered:** **Midweek Matchday:** Tuesday **Clubhouse:**

**Colours(change):** Red/black/red & black
**Previous Names:**
**Previous Leagues:** Surrey Intermediate > 2007
**Records:** **Att:** 323 v Guernsey. **Goalscorer:** Matt Baker - 24.
**Honours:** **Honours:** Woking & District League 1978-79. Surrey Intermediate League Division One 2005-06, Premier 06-07.

**10 YEAR RECORD**

| 06-07 | 07-08 | 08-09 | 09-10 | 10-11 | 11-12 | 12-13 | 13-14 | 14-15 | 15-16 |
|---|---|---|---|---|---|---|---|---|---|
| | CC1 7 | CC1 5 | CC1 3 | CC1 9 | CC1 12 | CC1 12 | CC1 3 | CCP 13 | CCP 5 |

## NORTH GREENFORD UNITED

Founded: 1944 Nickname: Blues

**Secretary:** Mrs Barbara Bivens (T) 07915 661 580 (E) barbarabivens@talktalk.net
**Chairman:** John Bivens **Manager:** Ricky Pither **Prog Ed:** Graham White
**Ground:** Berkeley Fields, Berkley Avenue, Greenford UB6 0NX (T) 0208 422 8923
**Capacity:** 2,000 **Seats:** 150 **Covered:** 100 **Midweek Matchday:** Tuesday **Clubhouse:** Yes

**Colours(change):** Royal blue & white/Royal blue/royal blue
**Previous Names:** None
**Previous Leagues:** London Spartan, Combined Counties 2002-10. Southern 2010-16.
**Records:** 985 v AFC Wimbledon
**Honours:** Combined Counties League Premier Division 2009-10

**10 YEAR RECORD**

| 06-07 | 07-08 | 08-09 | 09-10 | 10-11 | 11-12 | 12-13 | 13-14 | 14-15 | 15-16 |
|---|---|---|---|---|---|---|---|---|---|
| CCP 5 | CCP 6 | CCP 2 | CCP 1 | SthC 20 | SthC 18 | SthC 19 | SthC 20 | SthC 21 | SthC 22 |

## RAYNES PARK VALE

Founded: 1995 Nickname: The Vale

**Secretary:** Paul Armour (T) 07980 914 211 (E) paul.armour2@btinternet.com
**Chairman:** **Manager:** Gavin Bolger **Prog Ed:** Mike Hill
**Ground:** Prince George's Playing Field, Raynes Park SW20 9NB (T) 0208 540 8843
**Capacity:** 1500 **Seats:** 120 **Covered:** 100 **Midweek Matchday:** Tuesday **Clubhouse:** Yes

**Colours(change):** All blue
**Previous Names:** Raynes Park > 1995 until merger with Malden Vale.
**Previous Leagues:** Surrey County Premier Lge. Isthmian.
**Records:** **Att:** 1871 v AFC Wimbledon (At Carshalton Athletic).
**Honours:**

**10 YEAR RECORD**

| 06-07 | 07-08 | 08-09 | 09-10 | 10-11 | 11-12 | 12-13 | 13-14 | 14-15 | 15-16 |
|---|---|---|---|---|---|---|---|---|---|
| CCP 15 | CCP 19 | CCP 8 | CCP 18 | CCP 15 | CCP 9 | CCP 11 | CCP 10 | CCP 15 | CCP 15 |

## SPELTHORNE SPORTS

Founded: 1922 Nickname: Spelly

**Secretary:** Stephen Flatman (T) 07709 068 609 (E) flatty1@tiscali.co.uk
**Chairman:** Ian Croxford **Manager:** Steve Flatman **Prog Ed:** Yvonne Hunter
**Ground:** Spelthorne Sports Club, 296 Staines Rd West, Ashford Common, TW15 1RY (T) 01932 961 055
**Capacity:** **Seats:** Yes **Covered:** Yes **Midweek Matchday:** Tuesday **Clubhouse:** Yes

**Colours(change):** Navy & sky blue/navy blue/navy blue
**Previous Names:**
**Previous Leagues:** Surrey Intermediate (West) > 2009. Surrey Elite Intermediate 2009-11.
**Records:**
**Honours:** Surrey Elite Intermediate League 2010-11. Combined Counties Division One 2013-14.

**10 YEAR RECORD**

| 06-07 | 07-08 | 08-09 | 09-10 | 10-11 | 11-12 | 12-13 | 13-14 | 14-15 | 15-16 |
|---|---|---|---|---|---|---|---|---|---|
| | | | SuEI 5 | SuEI 1 | CC1 7 | CC1 6 | CC1 1 | CCP 6 | CCP 11 |

## SUTTON COMMON ROVERS

Founded: 1978 Nickname: Commoners

**Secretary:** Ken Reed (T) 07850 211 165 (E) scrfcsecretary@outlook.com
**Chairman:** Alan Salmon **Manager:** Darren Salmon **Prog Ed:** Gary Brigden
**Ground:** Sutton United FC, Gander Green Lane, Sutton. Surrey SM1 2EY (T) 020 8644 4440
**Capacity:** 500 **Seats:** No **Covered:** Yes **Midweek Matchday:** Monday **Clubhouse:** Yes **Shop:** Yes

**Colours(change):** All yellow
**Previous Names:** Inrad FC. Centre 21 FC . SCR Plough, SCR Grapes, SRC Litten Tree, SCR Kingfisher, Mole Valley SCR >2015.
**Previous Leagues:** South Eastern Combination.
**Records:**
**Honours:**

**10 YEAR RECORD**

| 06-07 | 07-08 | 08-09 | 09-10 | 10-11 | 11-12 | 12-13 | 13-14 | 14-15 | 15-16 |
|---|---|---|---|---|---|---|---|---|---|
| | | CC1 4 | CC1 1 | CCP 8 | CCP 21 | CC1 2 | CCP 18 | CCP 18 | CCP 19 |

## WALTON & HERSHAM

Founded: 1945 Nickname: Swans

**Secretary:** Grant Langley **(T)** 07969 068 731 **(E)** langley.grant@sky.com
**Chairman:** Alan Smith **Manager:** Simon Haughney
**Ground:** Sports Ground, Stompond Lane, Walton-on-Thames KT12 1HF **(T)** 01932 245 263
**Capacity:** 5,000 **Seats:** 400 **Covered:** 2,500 **Midweek Matchday:** Tuesday **Clubhouse:** Yes **Shop:** Yes

**Colours(change):** Red with white trim/red/red
**Previous Names:** Walton FC (Founded in 1895) amalgamated with Hersham FC in 1945.
**Previous Leagues:** Surrey Senior, Corinthian 1945-50, Athenian 1950-71. Isthmian 1971-2016.
**Records:** 10,000 v Crook Town - FA Amateur Cup 6th Round 1951-52
**Honours:** Athenian League 1968-69.
FA Amateur Cup 1972-73. Barassi Cup 1973-74.

**10 YEAR RECORD**

| 06-07 | 07-08 | 08-09 | 09-10 | 10-11 | 11-12 | 12-13 | 13-14 | 14-15 | 15-16 |
|---|---|---|---|---|---|---|---|---|---|
| Isth P 19 | Isth1S 10 | Isth1S 14 | Isth1S 8 | Isth1S 6 | Isth1S 11 | Isth1S 18 | Isth1S 21 | Isth1S 17 | Isth1S 22 |

## WESTFIELD

Founded: 1953 Nickname: The Field

**Secretary:** Michael Lawrence **(T)** 07780 684 416 **(E)** michaelgeorgelawrence@hotmail.com
**Chairman:** Stephen Perkins **Manager:** Dan Snare **Prog Ed:** Pat Kelly
**Ground:** Woking Park, off Elmbridge Lane, Kingfield, Woking GU22 9BA **(T)** 01483 771 106
**Capacity:** 1000 **Seats:** Yes **Covered:** Yes **Midweek Matchday:** Tuesday **Clubhouse:** Yes

**Colours(change):** Yellow/black/black
**Previous Names:** None
**Previous Leagues:** Surrey Senior
**Records:**
**Honours:** Surrey Senior League 1972-73, 73-74.

**10 YEAR RECORD**

| 06-07 | 07-08 | 08-09 | 09-10 | 10-11 | 11-12 | 12-13 | 13-14 | 14-15 | 15-16 |
|---|---|---|---|---|---|---|---|---|---|
| CC1 10 | CC1 4 | CC1 13 | CC1 16 | CC1 13 | CC1 8 | CC1 3 | CCP 4 | CCP 14 | CCP 9 |

## WINDSOR

Founded: 1892 Nickname: The Royalists

**Secretary:** Alan King **(T)** 07899 941 414 **(E)** windsorfcsecretary@aol.com
**Chairman:** Kevin Stott **Manager:** Mick Woodham **Prog Ed:** Matthew Stevens
**Ground:** Stag Meadow, St Leonards Road, Windsor, Berks SL4 3DR **(T)** 01753 860 656
**Capacity:** 3,085 **Seats:** 302 **Covered:** 650 **Midweek Matchday:** Tuesday **Clubhouse:** Yes **Shop:** Yes

**Colours(change):** All red, white & green
**Previous Names:** Windsor & Eton 1892-2011.
**Previous Leagues:** W.Berks, Gt Western, Suburban, Athenian 22-29,63-81, Spartan 29-32, Gt W.Comb. Corinthian 45-50, Met 50-60, Delphian 60-63, Isth 63-06, Sth06-11
**Records:** 8,500 - Charity Match
**Honours:** Athenian League 1979-80, 80-81. Isthmian League Division 1 1983-84. Southern League Division 1 South & West 2009-10.
Berks & Bucks Senior Cup x11. Senior Trophy 2014-15.

**10 YEAR RECORD**

| 06-07 | 07-08 | 08-09 | 09-10 | 10-11 | 11-12 | 12-13 | 13-14 | 14-15 | 15-16 |
|---|---|---|---|---|---|---|---|---|---|
| Sthsw 14 | Sthsw 8 | Sthsw 2 | Sthsw 1 | SthP Exp | CCP 2 | CCP 6 | CCP 6 | CCP 5 | CCP 12 |

# PREMIER DIVISION GROUND DIRECTIONS

**ABBEY RANGERS - Addlestone Moor, Surrey, KT15 2QH**
From Junction 11 M25. Exit A317 St. Peter's Way towards Chertsey, Addlestone and Weybridge. At roundabout take 2nd exit towards Addlestonemoor.

**AFC HAYES - Farm Park, Kingshill Avenue, Hayes UB4 8DD**
From the A40 McDonalds Target roundabout take A312 south towards Hayes. At White Hart roundabout take third exit into Yeading Lane. Turn right at first traffic lights into Kingshill Avenue. Ground approx one miles on the right-hand side.

**BADSHOT LEA - Ash United FC, Youngs Drive GU12 6RE - 01252 320 385**
FROM M3: Get off the M3 at J4, onto the A331: Take 3rd Exit off to Woking. Up to the roundabout turn left into Shawfields Road, follow road for about 500 yards, Football Ground is on the left, take next turning on your left into Youngs Drive where club is 50yards on. FROM M25: Get onto the A3 heading to Guildford/Portsmouth. Keep on this until you reach the A31(Hog's Back). Then go onto the A31 until you reach the exit for the A331 to Aldershot. Follow the signs for Aldershot, which will be the 1st exit off the A331.When you reach the roundabout take the exit for Woking, which will be the 3rd exit off. Up to the roundabout turn left into Shawfields Road, then as above.

**BEDFONT & FELTHAM - The Orchard, Hatten Road TW14 9QT - 0208 890 7264**
Hatton Road runs alongside the A30 at Heathrow. Ground is opposite the Duke of Wellington Public House.

**BEDFONT SPORTS - Bedfont Sports Club TW14 9QT - 020 8890 7264**
From Junction 13, M25 – Staines. At Crooked Billet roundabout turn right onto the A30 Signposted C. London, Hounslow. At Clockhouse Roundabout take the 2nd exit onto the A315 Signposted Bedfont. Turn left onto Hatton Road. Arrive on Hatton Road, Bedfont Sports Club.

**CB HOUNSLOW UNITED - See Bedfont & Feltham**

**CAMBERLEY TOWN - Krooner Park GU15 2QW - 01276 65392**
Exit M3 Motorway at Junction 4. At the end of the slip road take the right hand land signposted A331, immediately take the left hand lane signposted Frimley and Hospital (Red H Symbol) and this will lead you up onto the A325. Continue to the roundabout and turn left onto the B3411 (Frimley Road) Continue past Focus DIY store on Left and stay on B3411 for approx 1.5 miles. At the next Mini roundabout turn left into Wilton Road, proceed through industrial estate (past the Peugeot garage) and the entrance to the ground is right at the end.

**CHERTSEY TOWN - Alwyns Lane, Chertsey, Surrey KT16 9DW**
Leave M25 at junction 11, East on St. Peters Way (A317). Left at roundabout in Chertsey Road (A317). Left into Eastworth Road (A317). Straight on into Chilsey Green Road (A320), 3rd exit on roundabout (towards Staines) (A320). 1st right after car showrooms into St. Ann's Road (B375). Right at Coach & Horses in Grove Road (residential). Alwyns Lane is very narrow and not suitable for large motor coaches.

**COLLIERS WOOD UNITED - Wibbandune Sports Ground SW20 0AA - 0208 942 8062**
On A3 Southbound 1 mile from Robin Hood Gate.

**EPSOM & EWELL - Chipstead FC, High Road, Chipstead, Surrey CR5 3SF - 01737 553250**
From the Brighton Road north bound, go left into Church Lane and left into Hogcross Lane. High Road is on the right.

**FARNHAM TOWN - Memorial Ground, West St. GU9 7DY - 01252 715 305**
Follow A31 to Coxbridge roundabout (passing traffic lights at Hickleys corner. Farnham station to left.) At next roundabout take 3rd exit to Farnham town centre. At the mini roundabout take 2nd exit. The ground is to the left.

**GUILDFORD CITY - Spectrum Leisure Centre, Parkway, Guildford GU1 1UP**
From Guildford main line station, take no.100 shuttle bus to Spectrum. From London Road Station walk via Stoke Park. From A3, exit at Guildford – follow signs to leisure centre.

**HANWORTH VILLA - Rectory Meadows, Park Road TW13 6PN - 0208 831 9391**
From M25 and M3 once on the M3 towards London. This becomes the A316, take the A314 (Hounslow Rd) exit signposted Feltham & Hounslow. Turn left onto Hounslow Rd, at the second mini round about (Esso garage on the corner) turn left into Park Rd. Continue down Park Road past the Hanworth Naval Club on the right and Procter's Builders Merchants on the left. Follow the road around the 90 degree bend and continue to the end of the road past the Hanworth Village Hall. Once past the two houses next to the village hall turn left into Rectory Meadows.

**HARTLEY WINTNEY - Memorial Playing Fields RG27 8DL - 01252 843 586**
On entering Hartley Wintney via the A30 take the turn at the mini roundabout signposted A323 Fleet. Take the 1st right turn, Green Lane, which has St John's Church on the corner. Continue down Green Lane for about 800 metres and turn right into car park, which has a shared access with Greenfields School. Turn left at St John's Church if coming down the A323 from Fleet.

**HORLEY TOWN - The New Defence RH6 8RS - 07545 697 234**
From centre of town go North up Victoria where it meets the A23, straight across to Vicarage Lane, 2nd left into Court Lodge Road follow it through estate and we are behind adult education centre.

**KNAPHILL - Brookwood Country Park GU21 2AY - 01483 475 150**
From A3: A322 from Guildford through towards Worplesdon. At Fox Corner rounabaout, take 2bd exit onto Bagshot Road, A322 signposted Bagshot. Pat West Hill Golf Club, at traffice lights turn right onto Brookwood Lye Road, A324 signposted Woking. Turn left into Hermitage Road on A324, up to roundabout, take 1st exit onto Redding Way, then 1st left entering driveway towards car park and ground.

**NORTH GREENFORD UNITED - Berkeley Fields, Berkley Avenue, Greenford UB6 0NX - 0208 422 8923**
A40 going towards London. At the Greenford Flyover come down the slip road, keep in the left hand lane, turn left onto the Greenford Road (A4127). At the third set of traffic lights, turn right into Berkeley Av. Go to the bottom of the road. There is a large car park. We are on the right hand side.

**RAYNES PARK VALE - Prince Georges Fields SW20 9NB - 0208 540 8843**
Exit Raynes Park station into Grand Drive cross Bushey Road at the traffic lights continue up Grand Drive for 400 yards entrance on the left follow drive to clubhouse. From the A3. Onto Bushey Road towards South Wimbledon. Grand Drive on the right, ground in Grand Drive on the left hand side.

**SPELTHORNE SPORTS - 296 Staines Rd West, Ashford Common, TW15 1RY - 01932 783 625**
From M25 (J13) take the A30 exit to London (W)/Hounslow/Staines. At the roundabout, take the 1st exit onto Staines Bypass/A30 heading to London(W)/Hounslow/Staines/Kingston/A308. Turn left onto Staines Bypass/A308
Continue to follow A308. Go through 1 roundabout. Make a U-turn at Chertsey Rd. Ground will be on the left.

**SUTTON COMMON ROVERS - Sutton United FC, Borough Sports Ground, Gander Green Lane, Sutton, Surrey SM1 2EY**
Travel along the M25 to junction 8. Then north on the A217 for about 15-20 minutes. Ignoring signs for Sutton itself, stay on the A217 to the traffic lights by the Gander Inn (on the left), turn right into Gander Green Lane. The Borough Sports Ground is about 200 yards up this road on the left hand side, if you reach West Sutton station you have gone too far.

**WALTON & HERSHAM - Sports Ground, Stompond Lane, Walton-on-Thames KT12 1HF - 01932 245 263**
From Walton Bridge go over and along New Zealand Avenue, down one way street and up A244 Hersham Road. Ground is second on the right.

**WESTFIELD - Woking Park, off Elmbridge Lane GU22 7AA - 01483 771 106**
Follow signs to Woking Leisure Centre on the A247.

**WINDSOR - Stag Meadow, St Leonards Road, Windsor, Berks SL4 3DR - 01753 860 656**
Exit M4 at Junction 6, follow dual carriageway (signposted Windsor) to large roundabout at end, take third exit into Imperial Road, turn left at T-junction into St Leonards Road. Ground approx ½ mile on right opposite Stag & Hounds public house.

## AC LONDON

Founded: 2012 Nickname:

**Secretary:** Prince Choudary **(T)** 07579 59999 **(E)** princehaseebchoudary@gmail.com
**Chairman:** Prince Choudary **Manager:** Prince Choudary
**Ground:** Banstead Athletic FC, Merland Rise, Tadworth, Surrey KT20 5JG **(T)** **Capacity:** 4,000
**Colours(change):** Red &white/black/white (All navy blue)
**ADDITIONAL INFORMATION:**
**Previous League:** Kent Invicta 2015-16.

## ASH UNITED

Founded: 1911 Nickname: Green Army

**Secretary:** Paul Blair **(T)** 07795 612 664 **(E)** sec@ashunited.co.uk
**Chairman:** Kevin Josey **Manager:** Daniel Bishop **Prog Ed:** Paul Blair
**Ground:** Shawfields Stadium, Youngs Drive off Shawfield Road, Ash, GU12 6RE. **(T)** 01252 320 385 / 345 757 **Capacity:** 2500
**Colours(change):** All green & red.
**ADDITIONAL INFORMATION: Att:** 914 v AFC Wimbledon Combined Co 2002-03. **Goals:** Shaun Mitchell (216). **Apps:** Paul Bonner (582).
Aldershot Senior Cup 1998-99, 01-02.

## BAGSHOT

Founded: 1905 Nickname:

**Secretary:** Zane Wickens **(T)** 07810 007 389 **(E)** jwautomotiveuk@yahoo.co.uk
**Chairman:** John Wickens **Manager:** Brett Wickens
**Ground:** Fleet Spurs FC, Kennels Lane, Southwood, Farnborough, Hants GU14 0ST **(T)**
**Colours(change):** Yellow/blue/blue
**ADDITIONAL INFORMATION:**

## BALHAM

Founded: 2001 Nickname:

**Secretary:** Greg Cruttwell **(T)** 07763 581 523 **(E)** info@balhamblazers.org.uk
**Chairman:** Jennie Molyneux **Prog Ed:** Greg Cruttwell
**Ground:** Colliers Wood Utd, Wibandune Sports Gd, Lincoln Green, Wimbledon SW20 0AA **(T)** 020 8942 8062
**Colours(change):** White & black/black/black
**ADDITIONAL INFORMATION:**

## BANSTEAD ATHLETIC

Founded: 1944 Nickname: The A's

**Secretary:** Terry Molloy **(T)** 07958 436 483 **(E)** terrymolloy@leyfield.eclipse.co.uk
**Chairman:** Terry Molloy **Manager:** James Cameron **Prog Ed:** Bob Lockyar
**Ground:** Merland Rise, Tadworth, Surrey KT20 5JG **(T)** 01737 350 982 **Capacity:** 4000
**Colours(change):** Amber & black/black/black
**ADDITIONAL INFORMATION:**
**Previous Leagues:** London Spartan League. Athenian League. Isthmian > 2006.
**Honours:** London Spartan LC 1965-67. Athenian LC 190-82.
**Record Att:** 1400 v Leytonstone, FA Amateur Cup 1953. **Goals:** Harry Clark. **Apps:** Dennis Wall.

## CHESSINGTON & HOOK UNITED

Founded: 1921 Nickname: Chessey

**Secretary:** Steve Kent **(T)** 07774 491 009 **(E)** conquestexeccars@aol.com
**Chairman:** Graham Ellis **Manager:** Darren Woods **Prog Ed:** Eric Wicks
**Ground:** Chalky Lane, Chessington, Surrey KT9 2NF **(T)** 01372 602 263 **Capacity:** 3000
**Colours(change):** All blue
**ADDITIONAL INFORMATION:**

## COBHAM

Founded: 1892 Nickname: Hammers

**Secretary:** Barry Wilde **(T)** 07966 166 042 **(E)** barrywilde856@btinternet.com
**Chairman:** Dave Tippetts **Manager:** Barry Wilde **Prog Ed:** Sam Merison
**Ground:** Leg O'Mutton Field, Anvil Lane, Cobham KT11 1AA **(T)** 01932 866 386 **Capacity:** 2000
**Colours(change):** Red/black/black
**ADDITIONAL INFORMATION: Att:** 2000 - Charity game 1975.
**Honours:** Combined Counties League Cup 2001-02.

## COVE

Founded: 1897 Nickname:

**Secretary:** Graham Brown **(T)** 07713 250 093 **(E)** secretarycfc@aol.com
**Chairman:** Salvo di Prima **Manager:** Paul Duncan **Prog Ed:** Graham Brown
**Ground:** Oak Farm Fields, 7 Squirrels Lane, Farnborough GU14 8PB **(T)** 01252 543 615 **Capacity:** 2500
**Colours(change):** Yellow/black/yellow
**ADDITIONAL INFORMATION: Att:** 1798 v Aldershot Town, Isthmian Div.3 01/05/93.
Aldershot Senior Cup x6 Most recently 2012-13.

## DORKING

Founded: 1880 Nickname: The Chicks

**Secretary:** Ms. Hilary Baxter **(T)** 07817 672 817 **(E)** hilsb@live.co.uk
**Chairman:** Alan Gout **Manager:** Danny Fox **Prog Ed:** Lydia Rabbetts
**Ground:** Dorking Wand. FC West Humble Playing Fields, London Road, Dorking RH5 6AD **(T)**
**Colours(change):** Green & red stripes/white/red
**ADDITIONAL INFORMATION: Previous Names:** Guildford & Dorking (when club merged 1974). Dorking Town 1977-82.
**Previous Leagues:** Corinthian, Athenian, Isthmian > 2006.
**Record Att:** 4500 v Folkstone Town FAC 1955 & v Plymouth Argyle FAC 1993. **Goals:** Andy Bushell. **Apps:** Steve Lunn.

## EPSOM ATHLETIC

Founded: 1997 Nickname: The Blue Stallions

**Secretary:** Jamie Hazelgrave **(T)** 07769 330 335 **(E)** jbhazelgrave@gmail.com
**Chairman:** Paul Burstow **Manager:** Paul Burstow **Prog Ed:** Lewis Carpenter
**Ground:** Chessington & Hook United FC, Chalky Lane, Chessington, Surrey KT9 2NF **(T)** 01372 745 777 **Capacity:** 2,000
**Colours(change):** All navy blue with white trim
**ADDITIONAL INFORMATION:**
**Previous League:** Surrey Elite > 2012.
**Honours:** Surrey Elite 2011-12.

## EVERSLEY & CALIFORNIA

Founded: 2012 Nickname: The Boars

**Secretary:** Annette Borg **(T)** 07970 066 716 **(E)** secretary@eversley-californiafc.co.uk
**Chairman:** Ben Sharpe **Manager:** Phil Ruggles
**Ground:** ESA Sports Complex, Fox Lane, Eversley RG27 0NS **(T)** 0118 973 2400 **Capacity:** 300+
**Colours(change):** White & royal blue hoops/royal blue/royal blue
**ADDITIONAL INFORMATION:**
**Previous League:** Surrey Elite Intermediate.
**Honours:** Surrey Elite Intermediate 2008-09.

## FARLEIGH ROVERS

Founded: 1922 Nickname: The Foxes

**Secretary:** Peter Collard **(T)** 07545 444 820 **(E)** peter.collard@aquatots.com
**Chairman:** Mark Whittaker **Manager:** Matt Nash **Prog Ed:** Peter Collard
**Ground:** Parsonage Field, Harrow Road, Warlingham CR6 9EX **(T)** 01883 626 483 **Capacity:** 500
**Colours(change):** Red & black stripes/black/black
**ADDITIONAL INFORMATION:**
**Previous League:** Surrey County Premier.
**Honours:** Surrey County Premier 1982-83. Combined Counties Division One 2014-15.

## FRIMLEY GREEN

Founded: 1919 Nickname: The Green

**Secretary:** Mark O'Grady **(T)** 07812 026 390 **(E)** mogradyuk@yahoo.co.uk
**Chairman:** Matthew Flude **Manager:** Dan Huxley **Prog Ed:** Mark O'Grady
**Ground:** Frimley Green Rec. Ground, Frimley Green, Camberley GU16 6JY **(T)** 01252 835 089 **Capacity:** 2000
**Colours(change):** Blue with white trim/blue & white/blue
**ADDITIONAL INFORMATION: Record Att:** 1,152 v AFC Wimbledon 2002-03. **Win:** 6-1 v Farnham Town 21/12/02. **Defeat:** 1-7 v Walton Casuals
Combined Counties League Division One 2012-13.

## REDHILL

Founded: 1894 Nickname: Reds/Lobsters

**Secretary:** Kevin Sapsford **(T)** 07941 754 689 **(E)** ksapsford@hotmail.com
**Chairman:** Jerry O'Leary **Manager:** Perry Gough **Prog Ed:** Terry Austin
**Ground:** Kiln Brow, Three Arch Road, Redhill, Surrey RH1 5AE **(T)** 01737 762 129 **Capacity:** 2,000
**Colours(change):** Red & white stripes/red/red
**ADDITIONAL INFORMATION:** 8,000 v Hastings U FA Cup 1956
London League 1922-23. Athenian League 1924-25, 83-84.
Surrey Senior Cup 1928-29, 65-66.

## SHEERWATER

Founded: 1958 Nickname: Sheers

**Secretary:** Trevor Wenden **(T)** 07791 612 008 **(E)** trevor.wenden2@ntlworld.com
**Chairman:** **Manager:** Peter Ruggles **Prog Ed:** Trevor Wenden
**Ground:** Sheerwater Recreation Ground, Blackmore Crescent, Woking GU21 5NS **(T)** **Capacity:** 1,000
**Colours(change):** All royal blue
**ADDITIONAL INFORMATION:**
**Previous League:** Surrey County Premier.

## SOUTH PARK RESERVES

Founded: 1897 Nickname:

**Secretary:** Nick Thatcher **(T)** 07817 613 674 **(E)** spfc1897@hotmail.com
**Chairman:** Ricky Kidd **Manager:** Jason Stephens **Prog Ed:** Nick Thatcher
**Ground:** King George's Field, Whitehall Lane, South Park, Reigate, Surrey RH2 8LG **(T)** 01737 245 963
**Colours(change):** All red
**ADDITIONAL INFORMATION:**

## STAINES LAMMAS

Founded: 1926 Nickname:

**Secretary:** Bob Parry **(T)** 07771 947 757 **(E)** bobandtracey1@btopenworld.com
**Chairman:** Phil Ellery **Manager:** Adam Bessent **Prog Ed:** Bob Parry
**Ground:** The Lucan Pavilion, The Boradway, Laleham, Staines, Middlesex TW18 1RZ **(T)** 01784 465 204
**Colours(change):** All blue
**ADDITIONAL INFORMATION:**
**Record Att:** 107 v Hanworth Villa, January 2006. **Goalscorer:** Jay Coombs - 270+ **Win:** 19-1 v Cranleigh (Surrey Senior Lge) 19/03/03.
**Honours:** Combined Counties Division 1 2007-08, 08-09.

## WORCESTER PARK

Founded: 1921 Nickname: The Skinners

**Secretary:** Kristina Maitre **(T)** 07768 179 938 **(E)** kristinajayne@hotmail.co.uk
**Chairman:** Sam Glass **Manager:** Gary Taylor **Prog Ed:** Alan Pearce
**Ground:** Skinners Field, Green Lane, Worcester Park, Surrey KT4 8AJ **(T)** 0208 337 4995
**Colours(change):** All blue
**ADDITIONAL INFORMATION:**
**Previous League:** Surrey County Premier.
**Honours:** Surrey County Premier/Senior League 1999-2000, 2000-01. Combined Counties Division One 2010-11.

# DIVISION ONE GROUND DIRECTIONS

**AC LONDON - Banstead Athletic FC, Merland Rise KT20 5JG - 01737 350 982**
From M25 junction 8 follow signs to Banstead Sports Centre.

**ASH UNITED - Youngs Drive GU12 6RE - 01252 320 385**
FROM M3: Get off the M3 at J4, onto the A331: Take 3rd Exit off to Woking. Up to the roundabout turn left into Shawfields Road, follow road for about 500 yards, Football Ground is on the left, take next turning on your left into Youngs Drive where club is 50yards on. FROM M25: Get onto the A3 heading to Guildford/Portsmouth. Keep on this until you reach the A31(Hog's Back). Then go onto the A31 until you reach the exit for the A331 to Aldershot. Follow the signs for Aldershot, which will be the 1st exit off the A331.When you reach the roundabout take the exit for Woking, which will be the 3rd exit off. Up to the roundabout turn left into Shawfields Road, then as above.

**BAGSHOT - Kennels Lane Southwood Farnborough Hampshire, GU14 0ST**
From the M3 Junction 4A take the A327 towards Farnborough/Cove. Left at the roundabout, over the railway line, left at the next roundabout Kennels Lane is on the right opposite the Nokia building, entrance is 100 yards on the left. Postcode for Satellite Navigation systems GU14 0ST

**BALHAM - Colliers Wood United FC Wibbandune Sports Ground SW20 0AA - 0208 942 8062**
On A3 Southbound 1 mile from Robin Hood Gate.

**BANSTEAD ATHLETIC - Merland Rise KT20 5JG - 01737 350 982**
From M25 junction 8 follow signs to Banstead Sports Centre.

**CHESSINGTON & HOOK UNITED - Chalky Lane KT9 2NF - 01372 745 777**
Chalky Lane is off A243 (Opposite Chessington World of Adventures) which leads to Junction 9 on M25 or Hook Junction on the A3.

**COBHAM - Leg of Mutton Field - 07787 383 407**
From Cobham High Street, turn right into Downside Bridge Road and turn right into Leg of Mutton Field.

**COVE - Squirrel Lane GU14 8PB - 01252 543 615**
From M3 junction 4, follow signs for A325, then follow signs for Cove FC.

**DORKING - Dorking Wanderers FC, Westhumble Playing Fields, London Road, Dorking, Surrey RH5 6AD**
From the M25 go off at junction 9, take the A243 exit to A24/Leatherhead/Dorking. At the roundabout, take the 3rd exit onto A243. At the roundabout, take the 2nd exit onto Leatherhead By-Pass Rd/A243. At the roundabout, take the 2nd exit onto Leatherhead By-Pass Rd/A24. At the roundabout, take the 2nd exit and stay on Leatherhead By-Pass Rd/A24. At the roundabout, take the 1st exit onto Dorking Rd/A24. Continue to follow A24. At the roundabout, take the 2nd exit onto London Rd/A24. At the roundabout, take the 4th exit and stay on London Rd/A24.

**EPSOM ATHLETIC - Chessington & Hook United FC, Chalky Lane KT9 2NF - 01372 745 777**
Chalky Lane is off A243 (Opposite Chessington World of Adventures) which leads to Junction 9 on M25 or Hook Junction on the A3.

**EVERSLEY & CALIFORNIA - ESA Sports Complex, Fox Lane, Eversley RG27 0NS - 0118 973 2400**
Leave the M3 at junction 4a signposted Fleet/Farnborough. At the roundabout take the 2nd exit towards Yateley. At the roundabout take the 2nd exit towards Yateley. At the roundabout take the 2nd exit towards Yateley. At the roundabout take the 1st exit and proceed through Yateley on the Reading Road. At the roundabout take the 2nd exit and follow the road for about 1 mile. Turn right down the first turning for Fox Lane and then follow the road round to the right where the ground will be signposted.

**FARLEIGH ROVERS - Parsonage Field, Harrow Road CR6 9EX - 01883 626 483**
From M25 junction 6 left at lights up Godstone Hill (Caterham bypass) to roundabout. Take fourth turning off of roundabout. Up Succombs Hill then right into Westhall Rd. Right at the green then second left into Farleigh Rd. Left at mini round about continue still on Farleigh Road. Right at the Harrow Pub. This is Harrow Road. Right at the end of the houses and the ground is behind the houses.

**FRIMLEY GREEN - Frimley Green Recreation Groand GU16 6SY - 01252 835 089**
Exit M3 at junction 4 and follow the signs to Frimley High Street. At the mini roundabout in front of the White Hart public house turn into Church Road. At the top of the hill by the Church the road bends right and becomes Frimley Green Road. Follow the road for approx of a mile, go over the mini roundabout which is the entrance to Johnson's Wax factory, and the Recreation Ground is the second turning on the left, just past Henley Drive, which is on your right.

**RED HILL - Kiln Brow, Three Arch Road, Redhill, Surrey RH1 5AE**
On left hand side of A23 two and a half miles south of Redhill.

**SHEERWATER - Sheerwater Recreation Ground GU21 5QJ - 01932 348 192**
From M25(J11) take the A320 towards Woking, At Six Cross roundabout take the exit to Monument Road. At the lights turn left into Eve Road for Sheerwater Estate. First left is Blackmore Crescent, Entrance is Quarter of a mile on left.

**SOUTH PARK RESERVES - Whitehall Lane, South Park, Reigate, Surrey RH2 8LG - 01737 245 963**
From junction 8 of the M25, take A217 and follow signs to Gatwick. Follow through the one way system via Reigate town centre and continue on until traffic lights and crossroads by The Angel public house, turn right at these lights, into Prices Lane, and continue on road. After a sharp right bend into Sandcross Lane past Reigate Garden Centre. Take next left after school into Whitehall Lane.

**STAINES LAMMAS - The Lucan Pavilion, The Broadway, Laleham, Staines, Middlesex TW18 1RZ - 01784 465 204**
Leave M25 at junction 11 and take A317 towards Chertsey. At first roundabout keep left following A317. As the road straightens move into the right hand lane to the lights and straight on to the B387 Fordwater Road. Follow that road to the end and at the lights turn right onto Chertsey Bridge Road – B375. Go over Chertsey Bridge and continue to next roundabout and turn left onto Littleton Lane (Signed Laleham/Staines).Follow that road to the end and then turn left onto Shepperton Road B376.

**WORCESTER PARK- Skinners Field, Green Lane KT4 8AJ - 0208 337 4995**
From M25, come off at A3 turn off and head towards London, then come off at Worcester Park turn off, stay on this road until you pass station on your left and go under bridge, then take first left which is Green Lane, ground is 500 yards on the left.

# EAST MIDLANDS COUNTIES LEAGUE

**Sponsored by:** No sponsor
**Founded:** 2008

**Recent Champions: 2013:** Basford United
**2014:** Thurnby Nirvana **2015:** Bardon Hill

| | | P | W | D | L | F | A | GD | Pts |
|---|---|---|---|---|---|---|---|---|---|
| 1 | St Andrews | 36 | 28 | 2 | 6 | 115 | 29 | 86 | 86 |
| 2 | Radford | 36 | 25 | 4 | 7 | 105 | 41 | 64 | 79 |
| 3 | Ashby Ivanhoe | 36 | 24 | 5 | 7 | 86 | 33 | 53 | 77 |
| 4 | South Normanton Athletic | 36 | 24 | 5 | 7 | 84 | 34 | 50 | 77 |
| 5 | Aylestone Park | 36 | 21 | 5 | 10 | 84 | 54 | 30 | 68 |
| 6 | Anstey Nomads | 36 | 18 | 10 | 8 | 63 | 52 | 11 | 64 |
| 7 | Blaby & Whetstone Athletic | 36 | 18 | 5 | 13 | 85 | 57 | 28 | 59 |
| 8 | Holbrook Sports | 36 | 17 | 6 | 13 | 67 | 53 | 14 | 57 |
| 9 | Borrowash Victoria | 36 | 18 | 1 | 17 | 72 | 69 | 3 | 55 |
| 10 | Radcliffe Olympic | 36 | 16 | 6 | 14 | 70 | 56 | 14 | 54 |
| 11 | Graham Street Prims | 36 | 16 | 5 | 15 | 68 | 67 | 1 | 53 |
| 12 | Stapenhill | 36 | 12 | 6 | 18 | 51 | 64 | -13 | 42 |
| 13 | Barrow Town | 36 | 10 | 10 | 16 | 55 | 61 | -6 | 40 |
| 14 | Gedling Miners Welfare | 36 | 9 | 8 | 19 | 51 | 65 | -14 | 35 |
| 15 | Kimberley Miners Welfare | 36 | 9 | 6 | 21 | 43 | 83 | -40 | 33 |
| 16 | Holwell Sports | 36 | 8 | 7 | 21 | 52 | 97 | -45 | 31 |
| 17 | Ellistown & Ibstock United | 36 | 8 | 5 | 23 | 44 | 94 | -50 | 29 |
| 18 | Arnold Town (-3) | 36 | 7 | 4 | 25 | 48 | 118 | -70 | 22 |
| 19 | Greenwood Meadows (-1) | 36 | 3 | 2 | 31 | 25 | 141 | -116 | 10 |

Mickleover Royals withdrew - record expunged.

## LEAGUE CUP

**HOLDERS:** NORMANTON ATHLETIC

**ROUND 1**

| | | | |
|---|---|---|---|
| Graham Street Prims | v | Radford | 0-3 |
| Gedling Miners Welfare | v | St Andrews | 2-0 |
| Blaby & Whetstone Athletic | v | Holwell Sports | 3-1 |
| Borrowash Victoria | v | Ellistown & Ibstock United | 3-1 |

ROUND 2

| | | | |
|---|---|---|---|
| Mickleover Royals | v | Radford | AW |
| Blaby & Whetstone Athletic | v | Ashby Ivanhoe | 2-1 |
| Radcliffe Olympic | v | Gedling Miners Welfare | 5-0 |
| Anstey Nomads | v | Barrow Town | 3-1 |
| Greenwood Meadows | v | Kimberley Miners Welfare | 0-2 |
| Arnold Town | v | Aylestone Park | 2-2 |
| Aylestone Park | v | Arnold Town | 2-0 |
| Stapenhill | v | South Normanton Athletic | 0-4 |
| Holbrook Sports | v | Borrowash Victoria | 3-1 |

QUARTER FINALS

| | | | |
|---|---|---|---|
| Kimberley Miners Welfare | v | Radford | 0-4 |
| Blaby & Whetstone Athletic | v | Holbrook Sports | 2-0 |
| Radcliffe Olympic | v | Aylestone Park | 2-3 |
| South Normanton Athletic | v | Anstey Nomads | 9-2 |

SEMI FINALS

| | | | |
|---|---|---|---|
| Blaby & Whetstone Athletic | v | Aylestone Park | 2-3 |
| Radford | v | South Normanton Athletic | 0-3 |

FINAL

| | | | |
|---|---|---|---|
| Aylestone Park | v | South Normanton Athletic | 2-1 |

## CLUB MOVEMENTS

**In:** Belper United (P - Central Midlands South), Birstall United Social (P - Leicestershire Senior), Dunkirk (R - Midland League Prem.), West Bridgford (P - Notts Senior). **Out:** Mickleover Royals (F), St Andrews (P - Midlands League Prem.)

| | | 1 | 2 | 3 | 4 | 5 | 6 | 7 | 8 | 9 | 10 | 11 | 12 | 13 | 14 | 15 | 16 | 17 | 18 | 19 |
|---|---|---|---|---|---|---|---|---|---|---|---|---|---|---|---|---|---|---|---|---|
| 1 | Anstey Nomads | | 2-2 | 2-1 | 2-2 | 2-1 | 3-1 | 2-1 | 2-1 | 2-1 | 2-0 | 4-0 | 1-1 | 4-2 | 2-0 | 2-0 | 1-0 | 3-2 | 1-7 | 7-0 |
| 2 | Arnold Town | 1-2 | | 1-4 | 0-2 | 3-3 | 1-4 | 1-2 | 0-2 | 1-1 | 1-6 | 1-0 | 2-4 | 4-5 | 2-3 | 3-2 | 0-6 | 0-6 | 0-4 | 1-0 |
| 3 | Ashby Ivanhoe | 1-1 | 3-1 | | 2-1 | 3-0 | 5-0 | 3-1 | 5-0 | 2-0 | 1-3 | 7-1 | 3-1 | 4-1 | 2-0 | 4-0 | 4-1 | 2-3 | 0-3 | 1-0 |
| 4 | Aylestone Park | 5-1 | 6-0 | 2-1 | | 1-1 | 2-3 | 1-2 | 3-1 | 5-1 | 5-2 | 4-0 | 3-2 | 3-3 | 2-2 | 3-1 | 2-1 | 0-3 | 2-1 | 2-1 |
| 5 | Barrow Town | 2-2 | 1-2 | 2-2 | 5-1 | | 2-1 | 2-0 | 1-1 | 0-1 | 2-1 | 6-0 | 2-1 | 2-2 | 2-2 | 0-0 | 2-2 | 0-2 | 1-2 | 3-0 |
| 6 | Blaby & Whetstone Athletic | 1-1 | 6-3 | 1-3 | 3-1 | 2-1 | | 2-3 | 7-0 | 4-0 | 2-2 | 3-1 | 2-0 | 2-1 | 9-1 | 1-0 | 3-0 | 2-2 | 0-0 | 3-0 |
| 7 | Borrowash Victoria | 3-0 | 2-3 | 0-2 | 0-1 | 4-1 | 0-1 | | 4-3 | 1-0 | 2-3 | 5-0 | 0-1 | 1-2 | 3-0 | 5-3 | 3-0 | 4-3 | 1-8 | 1-2 |
| 8 | Ellistown & Ibstock United | 2-1 | 2-0 | 1-2 | 1-2 | 2-2 | 3-1 | 2-3 | | 3-2 | 0-1 | 3-0 | 1-4 | 1-3 | 1-1 | 0-1 | 0-4 | 1-6 | 1-9 | 2-3 |
| 9 | Gedling Miners Welfare | 0-0 | 4-1 | 0-0 | 1-4 | 3-1 | 1-1 | 1-2 | 1-2 | | 1-2 | 1-2 | 2-1 | 3-3 | 4-1 | 2-3 | 1-2 | 0-0 | 1-1 | 0-1 |
| 10 | Graham Street Prims | 0-0 | 6-1 | 1-2 | 0-1 | 0-2 | 2-1 | 3-1 | 1-0 | 0-0 | | 3-0 | 0-5 | 5-4 | 4-2 | 0-4 | 1-4 | 1-0 | 0-2 | 2-0 |
| 11 | Greenwood Meadows | 0-1 | 0-6 | 0-2 | 0-8 | 1-4 | 0-10 | 2-6 | 3-3 | 0-5 | 0-7 | | 0-2 | 0-2 | 0-2 | 1-3 | 2-5 | 0-9 | 0-4 | 2-3 |
| 12 | Holbrook Sports | 0-1 | 2-0 | 1-1 | 2-0 | 0-1 | 5-0 | 3-1 | 4-0 | 2-6 | 1-1 | 2-0 | | 5-1 | 3-2 | 0-2 | 0-4 | 0-2 | 1-4 | 2-2 |
| 13 | Holwell Sports | 2-0 | 1-1 | 0-3 | 0-5 | 1-0 | 1-2 | 2-4 | 4-1 | 0-2 | 0-5 | 2-1 | 2-3 | | 2-2 | 0-1 | 0-5 | 1-2 | 1-8 | 0-4 |
| 14 | Kimberley Miners Welfare | 1-1 | 2-0 | 0-6 | 1-2 | 2-1 | 2-1 | 0-4 | 0-1 | 2-1 | 3-0 | 1-4 | 1-3 | 3-0 | | 0-1 | 0-1 | 1-1 | 0-1 | 1-2 |
| 15 | Radcliffe Olympic | 4-4 | 4-3 | 0-1 | 0-2 | 1-0 | 1-2 | 0-1 | 5-1 | 2-3 | 6-2 | 2-2 | 0-2 | 0-0 | 4-1 | | 1-2 | 0-0 | 2-1 | 4-0 |
| 16 | Radford | 3-0 | 1-3 | 1-1 | 4-0 | 1-0 | 4-1 | 8-0 | 4-0 | 3-1 | 4-2 | 7-0 | 2-2 | 4-0 | 5-0 | 4-4 | | 1-0 | 2-1 | 3-1 |
| 17 | South Normanton Athletic | 2-0 | 6-0 | 2-1 | 3-0 | 4-0 | 2-1 | 1-0 | 2-1 | 3-1 | 2-2 | 1-0 | 0-1 | 2-0 | 2-1 | 2-1 | 2-4 | | 1-0 | 2-0 |
| 18 | St Andrews | 2-0 | 8-0 | 2-1 | 3-0 | 5-1 | 3-2 | 1-0 | 2-0 | 5-0 | 2-0 | 6-1 | 3-0 | 3-2 | 5-1 | 1-4 | 2-1 | 4-1 | | 0-1 |
| 19 | Stapenhill | 1-4 | 6-0 | 0-1 | 1-1 | 4-1 | 1-0 | 2-2 | 1-1 | 3-0 | 4-0 | 1-2 | 1-1 | 2-2 | 1-2 | 1-4 | 1-2 | 1-3 | 0-2 | |

## ANSTEY NOMADS

Founded: 1947 Nickname: Nomads

**Secretary:** Chris Hillebrandt **(T)** 0794 685 6430 **(E)** chille1055@hotmail.com
**Chairman:** Mike Prizeman **Manager:** Rob Harris **Prog Ed:** Helen Preston-Hayes
**Ground:** Davidson Homes Park, Cropston Road, Anstey, Leicester LE7 7BP **(T)** 0116 236 4868
**Colours(change):** Red & white

**ADDITIONAL INFORMATION: Previous Leagues:** Leicestershire Senior. Central Alliance. East Midlands Regional.
**Record Att:** 4,500 v Hayes, 2nd Round FA Amateur Cup.
**Senior Honours:** Leicestershire Senior League 1951-52, 53-54, 81-82, 82-83, 2008-09. Leicestershire Senior Cup 1994-95.

## ARNOLD TOWN

Founded: 1989 Nickname: Eagles

**Secretary:** Jevon Swinscoe **(T)** **(E)** graham@peckgraham.orangehome.co.uk
**Chairman:** Graham Peck **Manager:** David Marlow
**Ground:** Eagle Valley, Oxton Road, Arnold, Nottingham NG5 8PS **(T)** 0115 965 6000
**Colours(change):** All maroon.

**ADDITIONAL INFORMATION:**
**Previous Leagues:** Central Midland 1989-93. Northern Counites East 1993-2013.
**Record Att:** 3,390 v Bristol Rovers FAC 1-Dec 1967 **Goalscorer:** Peter Fletcher - 100. **App:** Pete Davey - 346. **Win:** 10-1 **Defeat:** 0-7
**Honours:** Northern Counties East 1985-86. Central Midlands 92-93. Northern Counties Div.1 93-94.

## ASHBY IVANHOE

Founded: 1948 Nickname:

**Secretary:** Martin Smith **(T)** **(E)** info@ashbyivanhoefc.com
**Chairman:** Stuart Bonser
**Ground:** NFU Sports Ground, Lower Packington Road, Ashby de la Zouch LE65 1TS **(T)** 07966 293 355
**Colours(change):** Blue/blue/red

**ADDITIONAL INFORMATION: Previous Leagues:** North Leicestershire League. Leicestershire Senior > 2014.
**Senior Honours:** Leicestershire Senior League Premier Division 2010-11.

## AYLESTONE PARK

Founded: 1968 Nickname:

**Secretary:** Steve Cramp **(T)** 07884 447 076 **(E)** apsec@hotmail.co.uk
**Chairman:** Bob Stretton MBE **Manager:** Richard Hill
**Ground:** Mary Linwood Recreation Ground, Saffron Lane, Leicester LE2 6TG **(T)** 0116 278 5485
**Colours(change):** All red

**ADDITIONAL INFORMATION:**
**Previous Name:** Aylestone Park Old Boys > 2007.
**Previous Leagues:** Leicestershire Senior 1992-2012.
**Honours:** Leicestershire Senior Cup 2012-13.

## BARROW TOWN

Founded: Late 1800s Nickname:

**Secretary:** Chris Newton **(T)** 07704 063 642 **(E)**
**Chairman:** Michael Bland **Manager:** Liam East
**Ground:** Riverside Park, Bridge Street, Quorn, Leicestershire LE12 8EN **(T)** 01509 620 650
**Colours(change):** Red & black

**ADDITIONAL INFORMATION:**
**Previous League:** Leicestershire Senior.
**Honours:** Leicester Senior League Division One 1992-93.

## BELPER UNITED

Founded: 1920 Nickname:

**Secretary:** **(T)** **(E)**
**Chairman:** Fraser Shaw
**Ground:** Borrowash Victoria FC, Anderson Electrical Arena, Spondon, Derby DE21 7PH **(T)**
**Colours(change):** Green & white

**ADDITIONAL INFORMATION:**
**Previous League:** Central Midlands >2016.
Original club folded in the late 1940's. In 1969 Milford Sports merged with Belper Park Rangers to form today's club.

## BIRSTALL UNITED SOCIAL

Founded: 1961 Nickname:

**Secretary:** **(T)** **(E)**
**Chairman:**
**Ground:** Meadow Lane, Birstall LE4 4FN **(T)** 0116 267 1230
**Colours(change):** White & black

**ADDITIONAL INFORMATION:**
**Previous Leagues:** Leicestershire Senior >2016.
**Honours:** Leicestershire Senior Division Two 1976-77, Premier 2015-16.

## BLABY & WHETSTONE ATHLETIC

Founded: Nickname:

**Secretary:** Javeed Virk **(T)** 0782 506 7853 **(E)** javvirk@hotmail.com
**Chairman:** Mark Jenkins
**Ground:** Warwick Road, Whetstome, Leicester LE8 6LW **(T)** 0116 286 4852
**Colours(change):** All navy
**ADDITIONAL INFORMATION:**
**Previous Lge:** Leicestershire Senior > 2011.

## BORROWASH VICTORIA

Founded: 1911 Nickname: The Vics

**Secretary:** Steven Parker **(T)** 07738 940 204 **(E)**
**Chairman:** Fraser Watson
**Ground:** Anderson Electrical Arena, Borrowash Road, Spondon, Derby DE21 7PH **(T)** 01332 669 688
**Colours(change):** Red & white stripes/black/black
**ADDITIONAL INFORMATION:**
**Previous League:** Central Midlands

## DUNKIRK

Founded: 1946 Nickname: The Boatmen

**Secretary:** Philip Allen **(T)** **(E)** philipallen1982@hotmail.co.uk
**Chairman:**
**Ground:** Ron Steel Spts Ground, Lenton Lane, Clifton Bridge, Nottingham NG7 2SA **(T)** 0115 985 0803 **Capacity:** 1,500
**Colours(change):** Red with white trim
**ADDITIONAL INFORMATION:**
**Previous Leagues:** Notts Amateur 1946-75, Notts All. 1975-95, Central Midlands 1995-2008, East Midlands Counties 2008-10. Mid All. 2010-14. Midland Football League 2014-16.

## ELLISTOWN & IBSTOCK UNITED

Founded: 2013 Nickname:

**Secretary:** Dave Hunt **(T)** **(E)**
**Chairman:** Andy Roach **Manager:** Darren Price
**Ground:** Terrace Road, Ellistown, Leicestershire LE67 1GD **(T)** 01530 230 152
**Colours(change):** Red & blue
**ADDITIONAL INFORMATION:**
Formed when Ellistown and Ibstock United merged in the summer of 2013.

## GEDLING MINERS WELFARE

Founded: 1919 Nickname:

**Secretary:** Norman Hay **(T)** 07748 138 732 **(E)** norman.hay@virginmedia.com
**Chairman:** Vic Hulme **Manager:** Graham Walker
**Ground:** Plains Social Club, Plains Road, Mapperley, Nottingham NG3 5RH **(T)** 0115 926 6300
**Colours(change):** Yellow & blue
**ADDITIONAL INFORMATION:**
**Previous League:** Central Midlands

## GRAHAM STREET PRIMS

Founded: 1904 Nickname: Prims

**Secretary:** Peter Davis **(T)** 07902 403 074 **(E)** j.davis16@sky.com
**Chairman:** John Lindsay
**Ground:** The Raygar, Arena, Baytree Cars Stadium, Borrowash Road, Spondon DE21 7PH **(T)** 07902 403 074
**Colours(change):** Red & white/black/black
**ADDITIONAL INFORMATION:**
**Previous League:** Central Midlands

## GREENWOOD MEADOWS

Founded: 1987 Nickname:

**Secretary:** **(T)** **(E)**
**Chairman:**
**Ground:** Lenton Lane Ground, Lenton Lane, Nr Clifton Bridge, Nottingham NG7 2SA **(T)** 07740 797 261 **Capacity:** 700
**Colours(change):** Green/black/green (Orange/white/orange)
**ADDITIONAL INFORMATION:**
**Previous League:** Central Midlands

## HOLBROOK SPORTS

Founded: 1996 Nickname:

**Secretary:** Amanda Bradley **(T)** **(E)**
**Chairman:** Howard Williams **Manager:** Paul Romney
**Ground:** Collum Joinery Ground, Shaw Lane, Holbrook, Derbyshire DE56 0TG **(T)** 01157794959/ 07854127010
**Colours(change):** All blue
**ADDITIONAL INFORMATION:**
**Previous League:** Central Midlands

## HOLWELL SPORTS

Founded: 1902 Nickname:

**Secretary:** **(T)** **(E)**
**Chairman:** Graham Lewin
**Ground:** Welby Road, Asfordby Hill, Melton Mowbray, Leicestershire LE14 3RD **(T)** 01664 561 407 **Capacity:** 1000
**Colours(change):** All Yellow & green
**ADDITIONAL INFORMATION: Previous Name:** Holwell Works 1902-1988.
**Previous League:** Leicestershire Senior > 2008
**Senior Honours:** Leicestershire Senior League Premier 1911-12, 87-88, 91-92, 92-93.

## KIMBERLEY MINERS WELFARE

Founded: 1926 Nickname:

**Secretary:** Danny Staley **(T)** **(E)**
**Chairman:** Neil Johnson **Manager:** Martin Lench & Ian Deakin
**Ground:** Kimberley MWFC, The Stag Ground, Kimberley, Nottingham NG16 2NB **(T)** 07572 863 155
**Colours(change):** Red & black/white/white
**ADDITIONAL INFORMATION:**
**Previous Leagues:** Spartan League. Notts Combination. Notts Amateur. Notts Alliance. Notts Intermediate. Nottinghamshire Senior > 2014.
**Honours:** Spartan League 1947-48, 64-65, 65-66. Notts Amateur League 1985-86. Notts Alliance Div.2 1994-95, Div.1 95-96.

## RADCLIFFE OLYMPIC

Founded: 1876 Nickname: Olympic

**Secretary:** Andrew Royce **(T)** **(E)**
**Chairman:** Rick Bright **Prog Ed:** Brendan Richardson
**Ground:** The Recreation Ground, Wharfe Lane, Radcliffe on Trent, Nottingham NG12 2AN **(T)** 07825 285 024
**Colours(change):** Blue & red/blue & red/blue (Red & black/black/red)
**ADDITIONAL INFORMATION:**
**League Honours:** Notts Alliance 1900-01, Div.2 31-32. Notts Realm Div.1 46-47. Midland Amateur Alliance Div.6 65-66, Div.4 66-67, Div.3 67-68. Central Alliance Premier 69-70. East Midlands Regional Div.1 70-71. Central Alliance Premier 80-81.
Notts Alliance Div.1 90-91, Div.3 2001-02, Senior 02-03, Central Midlands Premier 03-04, Supreme 08-09.

## RADFORD

Founded: 1964 Nickname:

**Secretary:** John Holt **(T)** 07508 384 276 **(E)** vote4holt@hotmail.co.uk
**Chairman:** Bob Thomas **Manager:** Glenn Russell **Prog Ed:** John Holt
**Ground:** Selhurst Street, Off Radford Road, Nottingham NG7 5EH **(T)** 0115 942 3250
**Colours(change):** All claret
**ADDITIONAL INFORMATION:**
**Previous Names:** Manlove & Allots 1964-71. Radford Olympic 1971-87.
**Previous Leagues:** Nottinghamshire Sunday 1964-78. East Midlands Regional 1978-83. Central Midlands 1983-2008.
**Honours:** East Midlands Regional League 1982-83. Central Midlands League Senior Cup 1983-84.

## SOUTH NORMANTON ATHLETIC

Founded: 1926 Nickname: The Shiners

**Secretary:** Stephen Harris **(T)** 07505 366 136 **(E)** manor2@ntlworld.com
**Chairman:** Phil Bailey
**Ground:** M J Robinson Structures Arena, Lees Lane South Normanton, Derby DE55 2AD **(T)** 07834 206 253
**Colours(change):** Blue & white
**ADDITIONAL INFORMATION: Previous Name:** South Normanton Miners Welfare > 1990.
**Previous League:** Alfreton & District Sunday Lge 1980-87, Mansfield Sunday Lge 1987-90, Central Midlands League 1990-03.
Northern Counties East 2003-08.
Club folded in 2008 and reformed in 2014.

## STAPENHILL

Founded: 1947 Nickname: The Swans

**Secretary:** John Holmes **(T)** 07805 411 307 **(E)**
**Chairman:** **Prog Ed:** John Holmes
**Ground:** Edge Hill, Maple Grove, Stapenhill DE15 9NN. **(T)** 01283 527 670
**Colours(change):** All red
**ADDITIONAL INFORMATION:**
**Previous Leagues:** Leicestershire Senior > 2007, 2008-13. Midland Combination. Midland Alliance 2007-08.
**League Honours:** Leicestershire Senior 1958–59, 59–60, 86–87, 88–89, 2006–07.

## WEST BRIDGFORD

Founded: 1990 Nickname:

**Secretary:** Adrian Clark **(T)** **(E)**

**Chairman:** Peter Stansbury **Manager:** Chris Marks & Stuart Robinson

**Ground:** Regatta Way, Gamston, West Bridgford, Nottingham NG2 5AT **(T)** 07791 633 221

**Colours(change):** Red & black

**ADDITIONAL INFORMATION:**

**Previous Leagues:** Nottinghamshire Senior >2016.

## GROUND DIRECTIONS

**ANSTEY NOMADS - Davidson Homes Park, Cropston Road, Anstey, Leicester LE7 7BP**
From A46 follow signs to Anstey and enter village by Leicester Road. Proceed to roundabout in centre of village and take 3rd exit. Pass Co-op store and car showroom and ground 100metres on right.

**ARNOLD TOWN - Eagle Valley, Oxton Road, Arnold, Nottingham NG5 8PS**
From South: From Nottingham, take the A60 Mansfield road. At the first traffic island half a mile north of Arnold, join the A614 towards Doncaster. After 200 yards, go through traffic lights and, after 300 yards, take the next turn right. The ground entrance is 200 yards on the right.
From North: A614 towards Nottingham. As you approach the first set of traffic lights, turn left 300 yards before the lights. The ground entrance is 200 yards on the right.
**From M1:** Leave at Junction 27. Head towards Hucknall/Nottingham. After one mile, turn right at the first set of traffic lights. One mile, turn first left at island and stay on this road for two miles until junction with A60. Turn right and, at the next island, turn left onto the A614 towards Doncaster. After 200 yards, go through traffic lights and, after 300 yards, take the next right turn. The ground entrance is 200 yards on the right.

**ASHBY IVANHOE - NFU Sports Ground, Lower Packington Road, Ashby de la Zouch LE65 1TS**
From A42 junction 12, follow signs for Ashby, pass golf club on the left, then pass car wash garage on right and take the second right onto Avenue Road. turn right at the end of the road onto Lower Packington Road, follow road around bends and the ground is on the right.

**AYLESTONE PARK - Mary Linwood Recreation Ground, Saffron Lane, Leicester LE2 6TG**
Leave the M1 at Junction 21. take Soar Valley Way (A563), over first set of traffic lights and turn right onto Saffron Lane at Southfields roundabout (B5366) Ground 400 metres on left. From Leicester City Centre, take Saffron Lane to Southfield Roundabout and ground 400 metres on left.

**BARROW TOWN - Riverside Park, Bridge Street, Quorn, Leicestershire LE12 8EN**
Leave A6 south of Loughborough near Quorn. From A6 take Barrow/Quorn exit and follow signs to Barrow. Ground 400 metres on right. **From Nottingham:** Take A60 and as you exit Hoton village follow signs for Prestwold and Barrow. On reaching Barrow go through village to roundabout at end of main street, turn right down hill and over river. Ground on left.

**BELPER UNITED - SEE BORROWASH VICTORIA FC, Anderson Electrical Arena, Spondon, Derby DE21 7PH**

**BIRSTALL UNITED SOCIAL - Meadow Lane, Birstall LE4 4FN - 0116 267 1230**

**BLABY & WHETSTONE ATHLETIC - Warwick Road, Whetstome, Leicester LE8 6LW**
From Junction of the M1 exit from roundabout onto A5460. At next roundabout take 4th exit onto B4114 for 1.3 miles then take first exit at next roundabout onto B582 Blaby Road. Having crossed railway bridge take 1st right onto Victoria Road. At the min roundabout take first exit onto High Street and at the next mini roundabout take 2nd exit onto Brook Street. At the next roundabout take 3rd exit onto Cambridge Road and immediately right by corner shop onto Warwick Road. Ground on right.

**BORROWASH VICTORIA - Anderson Electrical Arena, Borrowash Road, Spondon, Derby DE21 7PH**
From M1 Junction 25 travel towards Derby on A52. Take third turning left (directly under pedestrian footbridge) onto Borrowash Road. Past golf driving range on left and in approximately 400 metres turn left into the Asterdale Sports Centre.

**DUNKIRK - Ron Steel Spts Ground, Lenton Lane, Clifton Bridge, Nottingham NG7 2SA - 0115 985 0803**

**ELLISTOWN & IBSTOCK UNITED - Terrace Road, Ellistown, Leicestershire LE67 1GD**
From M1 Junction 22 take A511 towards Coalville. Go over first roundabout and in approximately 1 mile take left filter at second roundabout, signposted Ibstock. Take first left at next roundabout and follow road over bridge until T-junction. Turn right and ground 300 metres on left.

**GEDLING MINERS WELFARE - Plains Social Club, Plains Road, Mapperley, Nottingham NG3 5RH**
Situated on B684 in Mapperley. From Nottingham the ground is approached via Woodborough Road, From the north via A614 by Lime Lane Junction to Plains Road.

**GRAHAM STREET PRIMS - Asterdale Sports Centre, Borrowash Road, Spondon, Derbyshire DE21 7PH**
From M1 Junction 25 travel towards Derby on A52. Take third turning left (directly under pedestrian footbridge) onto Borrowash Road. Past golf driving range on left and in approximately 400 metres turn left into the Asterdale Sports Centre.

**GREENWOOD MEADOWS - Lenton Lane Ground, Lenton Lane, Nr Clifton Bridge, Nottingham NG7 2SA**
From M1 Junction 24 take A453 towards Nottingham. Go through Clifton and join A52 onto Clifton Bridge. Get in middle lane down slip road onto island under flyover signposted industrial estate. At island take immediate first left and immediate first left onto Lenton Lane. Ground 3rd turning on right.

**HOLBROOK SPORTS - Collum Joinery Ground, Shaw Lane, Holbrook, Derbyshire DE56 0TG**
Leave A38 at junction signposted Kilburn/Denby Pottery. From south turn left at end of slip road – from north turn right. Follow road through Kilburn to crossroads with traffic lights (Kilburn Toll Bar). Turn left and follow road under A38 to top of hill. Turn left (Hop Inn and Bulls Head). Follow road through Bargate and go over painted island. At Holbrook village look out for 'rural' petrol station (Venture Garage) and turn right shortly after into Shaw Lane. Ground 50 yards on Right.

**HOLWELL SPORTS - Welby Road, Asfordby Hill, Melton Mowbray, Leicestershire LE14 3RD**
From Derby. Take A52 to M1 J24 then A6 to Loughborough. At Zouch take left on A6006 to Asfordby And Asfordby Hill. At island take left turn and ground 300 metres on left. **From Nottingham** A52 to A6006, onto A46. Left onto A6006 and then as above. **From Leicester** – turn off A46 at Six Hills Hotel, left at t-junction, right at cross roads and then as above.

**KIMBERLEY MINERS WELFARE - The Stag Ground, Kimberley, Nottingham NG16 2NB**
Leave the M1 at Junction 26. Take A610 to Nottingham before you reach Nuthall Island. As Island take first exit signposted B600 Kimberley. Follow road for around 2 miles before you see Stag PH on the right hand side. Continue down road for a further 200 yards, entrance to ground between HAMA Medical Centre and Roots Emporium.

**RADCLIFFE OLYMPIC - The Recreation Ground, Wharfe Lane, Radcliffe on Trent, Nottingham NG12 2AN**
A1M- A1-A614-A6097 to the island on the A46. Go south towards Leicester, at next island turn tight on the A52 to Nottingham. At Radcliffe on Trent turn right at traffic lights, through the village to the church, turn right down Wharf Lane, ground is 250 yards on the left hand side, turn left down road before play area. **M1 from the south** to Junction 24 or from the north at Junction 26. Follow the Nottingham signs for A52. Radcliffe on Trent is approx. 5 miles outside of Nottingham, then turn left at the lights next to the RSPCA shelter and follow road to the church. Turn left down Wharf Street ground is 250 yards on the left hand side, turn left down road before play area.

**RADFORD - Selhurst Street, Off Radford Road, Nottingham NG7 5EH**
Directions to Radford FC from Junction 26 of M1
Leave the M1 at junction 26 (signposted Nottingham, Ilkeston), at roundabout take the 1st exit onto the A610 (signposted Nottingham) At roundabout take the 3rd exit onto the A610 (signposted Nottingham) Entering Nottingham. At next roundabout take the 2nd exit onto Nuthall Road - A610 (signposted Nottingham, Arnold), at traffic signals continue forward onto Nuthall Road - A610 (signposted City Centre) At traffic signals turn left onto Western Boulevard - A6514 (signposted Ring Road, Mansfield) Turn immediately right onto Wilkinson Street; go to top of street, past Tram Depot, follow tram line towards Nottingham At top of hill, (traffic lights turn right onto Radford Road – 4th turning on the right onto Selhurst Street -
Ground immediately on right (blue fencing).

**SOUTH NORMANTON ATHLETIC - M J Robinson Structures Arena, Lees Lane South Normanton, Derby DE55 2AD**
M1 Junction 28 take B6019 to Alfreton, turn right onto Market Street at the Shell petrol station, then take the 5th turning on the left onto Lees Lane opposite Ladbrooks. The ground is at the end of the lane.

**STAPENHILL - Edge Hill, Maple Grove, Stapenhill DE15 9NN**
**From North:** Exit A38 at Clay Mills and follow A5018 towards Burton. Follow A444 (Nuneaton). At Swan junction traffic lights turn right onto Stapenhill Road. At roundabout go straight over – 6th left onto Sycamore Road. Ground 500 yards on Maple Grove
**From South:** Follow A511 to Burton on Trent, at Swan junction traffic lights turn left onto Stapenhill Road. At roundabout go straight over – 6th left onto Sycamore Road. Ground 500 yards on Maple Grove.

**WEST BRIDGFORD - Regatta Way, Gamston, West Bridgford, Nottingham NG2 5AT - 07791 633 221**

# EASTERN COUNTIES LEAGUE

**Sponsored by:** Thurlow Nunn
**Founded:** 1935

**Recent Champions: 2013:** Dereham Town
**2014:** Hadleigh United **2015:** Norwich United

| PREMIER DIVISION | P | W | D | L | F | A | GD | Pts |
|---|---|---|---|---|---|---|---|---|
| 1 Norwich United | 38 | 32 | 2 | 4 | 90 | 30 | 60 | 98 |
| 2 Godmanchester Rovers | 38 | 30 | 4 | 4 | 130 | 38 | 92 | 94 |
| 3 Stanway Rovers | 38 | 28 | 6 | 4 | 102 | 38 | 64 | 90 |
| 4 Felixstowe & Walton United | 38 | 25 | 7 | 6 | 73 | 26 | 47 | 82 |
| 5 Kirkley & Pakefield | 38 | 22 | 7 | 9 | 78 | 44 | 34 | 73 |
| 6 Mildenhall Town | 38 | 18 | 10 | 10 | 76 | 42 | 34 | 64 |
| 7 Hadleigh United | 38 | 16 | 7 | 15 | 62 | 58 | 4 | 55 |
| 8 Saffron Walden Town | 38 | 17 | 3 | 18 | 50 | 48 | 2 | 54 |
| 9 Long Melford | 38 | 16 | 5 | 17 | 63 | 58 | 5 | 53 |
| 10 FC Clacton | 38 | 15 | 4 | 19 | 65 | 79 | -14 | 49 |
| 11 Brantham Athletic | 38 | 14 | 5 | 19 | 56 | 62 | -6 | 47 |
| 12 Haverhill Rovers | 38 | 11 | 8 | 19 | 40 | 73 | -33 | 41 |
| 13 Newmarket Town | 38 | 11 | 6 | 21 | 58 | 90 | -32 | 39 |
| 14 Walsham le Willows | 38 | 10 | 8 | 20 | 62 | 75 | -13 | 38 |
| 15 Ipswich Wanderers | 38 | 9 | 11 | 18 | 54 | 76 | -22 | 38 |
| 16 Gorleston | 38 | 10 | 7 | 21 | 43 | 79 | -36 | 37 |
| 17 Fakenham Town | 38 | 10 | 6 | 22 | 45 | 84 | -39 | 36 |
| 18 Swaffham Town | 38 | 9 | 8 | 21 | 55 | 92 | -37 | 35 |
| 19 Thetford Town | 38 | 9 | 6 | 23 | 57 | 98 | -41 | 33 |
| 20 Whitton United | 38 | 6 | 4 | 28 | 39 | 108 | -69 | 22 |

| DIVISION ONE | P | W | D | L | F | A | GD | Pts |
|---|---|---|---|---|---|---|---|---|
| 1 Wivenhoe Town | 36 | 28 | 5 | 3 | 101 | 34 | 67 | 89 |
| 2 Ely City | 36 | 28 | 2 | 6 | 87 | 38 | 49 | 86 |
| 3 Great Yarmouth Town | 36 | 26 | 2 | 8 | 98 | 37 | 61 | 80 |
| 4 Halstead Town | 36 | 24 | 3 | 9 | 78 | 49 | 29 | 75 |
| 5 Kings Lynn Town Res. | 36 | 21 | 7 | 8 | 85 | 42 | 43 | 70 |
| 6 Leiston Reserves | 36 | 19 | 2 | 15 | 86 | 69 | 17 | 59 |
| 7 Diss Town | 36 | 15 | 9 | 12 | 72 | 55 | 17 | 54 |
| 8 Haverhill Borough | 36 | 15 | 7 | 14 | 65 | 55 | 10 | 52 |
| 9 Woodbridge Town | 36 | 14 | 10 | 12 | 53 | 52 | 1 | 52 |
| 10 AFC Sudbury Reserves | 36 | 15 | 7 | 14 | 55 | 55 | 0 | 52 |
| 11 March Town United | 36 | 16 | 2 | 18 | 68 | 65 | 3 | 50 |
| 12 Braintree Town Reserves | 36 | 15 | 4 | 17 | 76 | 89 | -13 | 49 |
| 13 Debenham LC | 36 | 11 | 8 | 17 | 56 | 73 | -17 | 41 |
| 14 Stowmarket Town | 36 | 11 | 7 | 18 | 60 | 69 | -9 | 40 |
| 15 Cornard United | 36 | 9 | 5 | 22 | 42 | 73 | -31 | 32 |
| 16 Downham Town | 36 | 8 | 7 | 21 | 35 | 81 | -46 | 31 |
| 17 Dereham Town Reserves | 35 | 7 | 4 | 24 | 40 | 85 | -45 | 25 |
| 18 Team Bury | 35 | 5 | 5 | 25 | 32 | 90 | -58 | 20 |
| 19 Needham Market Res. | 36 | 5 | 2 | 29 | 42 | 120 | -78 | 17 |

| RESERVE DIVISION | P | W | D | L | F | A | GD | Pts |
|---|---|---|---|---|---|---|---|---|
| 1 Witham Town Res. | 34 | 24 | 4 | 6 | 111 | 39 | 72 | 76 |
| 2 Hadleigh United Res. | 34 | 24 | 3 | 7 | 101 | 49 | 52 | 75 |
| 3 Stanway Rovers Res. (-1) | 33 | 22 | 4 | 7 | 87 | 50 | 37 | 69 |
| 4 Woodbridge Town Res. | 32 | 17 | 7 | 8 | 70 | 55 | 15 | 58 |
| 5 Stowmarket Town Res. | 33 | 16 | 6 | 11 | 74 | 60 | 14 | 54 |
| 6 Brightlingsea Regent Res. | 33 | 14 | 8 | 11 | 71 | 56 | 15 | 50 |
| 7 Saffron Walden Town Res. | 34 | 14 | 6 | 14 | 61 | 58 | 3 | 48 |
| 8 Brantham Athletic Res. | 32 | 14 | 5 | 13 | 83 | 76 | 7 | 47 |
| 9 Felixstowe & Walton Utd Res. | 33 | 14 | 5 | 14 | 62 | 56 | 6 | 47 |
| 10 Walsham le Willows Res. | 33 | 12 | 6 | 15 | 70 | 66 | 4 | 42 |
| 11 Diss Town Res. | 33 | 12 | 5 | 16 | 55 | 73 | -18 | 41 |
| 12 Whitton United Res. (-1) | 33 | 11 | 8 | 14 | 69 | 74 | -5 | 40 |
| 13 Halstead Town Res. | 33 | 11 | 7 | 15 | 66 | 80 | -14 | 40 |
| 14 Lowestoft Town Res. | 32 | 11 | 6 | 15 | 61 | 77 | -16 | 39 |
| 15 Newmarket Town Res. | 34 | 11 | 3 | 20 | 52 | 90 | -38 | 36 |
| 16 Wivenhoe Town Res. | 33 | 10 | 2 | 21 | 72 | 96 | -24 | 32 |
| 17 Long Melford Res. (-1) | 32 | 8 | 5 | 19 | 65 | 93 | -28 | 28 |
| 18 Cornard United Res. | 31 | 4 | 4 | 23 | 36 | 118 | -82 | 16 |

## LEAGUE CUP

**HOLDERS:** NORWICH UNITED

**PRELIMINARY ROUND**

| | | | |
|---|---|---|---|
| Haverhill Borough | v | Long Melford | 0-2 |
| Cornard United | v | Godmanchester Rovers | 0-7 |
| Gorleston | v | Walsham le Willows | 4-2 |
| Wivenhoe Town | v | Hadleigh United | 2-1 |

ROUND 1

| | | | |
|---|---|---|---|
| Saffron Walden Town | v | Halstead Town | 1-0 |
| AFC Sudbury Reserves | v | Long Melford | 2-3 |
| Dereham Town Reserves | v | Mildenhall Town | 0-1 |
| Swaffham Town | v | King's Lynn Town Reserves | 2-3 |
| Thetford Town | v | Downham Town | 0-1 |
| Fakenham Town | v | Ely City | 2-1 |
| Haverhill Rovers | v | Newmarket Town | 1-2 |
| Braintree Town Reserves | v | Godmanchester Rovers | 2-4 |
| Felixstowe & Walton United | v | FC Clacton | 0-4 |
| Ipswich Wanderers | v | Whittton United | 5-0 |
| Norwich United | v | Team Bury | 9-1 |
| Needham Market Reserves | v | Leiston Reserves | 1-3 |
| Diss Town | v | Stowmarket Town | 1-3 |
| Kirkley & Pakefield | v | Gorleston | 1-0 |
| Wivenhoe Town | v | Woodbridge Town | 5-1 |
| Stanway Rovers | v | Brantham Athletic | 2-2, 5-6p |

ROUND 2

| | | | |
|---|---|---|---|
| Saffron Walden Town | v | Long Melford | 2-2, 3-5p |
| Mildenhall Town | v | King's Lynn Town Reserves | 4-1 |
| Downham Town | v | Fakenham Town | 2-2, 3-1p |
| Newmarket Town | v | Godmanchester Rovers | 0-4 |
| FC Clacton | v | Ipswich Wanderers | 1-1, 1-4p |
| Norwich United | v | Leiston Reserves | 3-1 |
| Stowmarket Town | v | Kirkley & Pakefield | 1-2 |
| Wivenhoe Town | v | Brantham Athletic | HW |

QUARTER FINALS

| | | | |
|---|---|---|---|
| Long Melford | v | Mildenhall Town | 0-1 |
| Downham Town | v | Godmanchester Rovers | 1-3 |
| Ipswich Wanderers | v | Norwich United | 1-4 |
| Kirkley & Pakefield | v | Wivenhoe Town | 5-0 |

SEMI FINALS

| | | | |
|---|---|---|---|
| Mildenhall Town | v | Godmanchester Rovers | 0-0, 6-5p |
| Norwich United | v | Kirkley & Pakefield | 0-0, 7-6p |

FINAL

| | | | |
|---|---|---|---|
| Mildenhall Town | v | Norwich United | 2-1 |

## DIVISION ONE LEAGUE CUP

**HOLDERS:** AFC SUDBURY RESERVES

**PRELIMINARY ROUND**

| | | | |
|---|---|---|---|
| AFC Sudbury Reserves | v | Leiston Reserves | 4-2 |
| Woodbridge Town | v | Cornard United | 1-2 |
| Dereham Town Reserves | v | Needham Market Reserves | 2-4 |

ROUND 1

| | | | |
|---|---|---|---|
| Wivenhoe Town | v | AFC Sudbury Reserves | 1-0 |
| March Town United | v | Team Bury | 2-1 |
| Debenham LC | v | Haverhill Borough | 1-3 |
| Cornard United | v | Braintree Town Reserves | 3-0 |
| Ely City | v | Needham Market Reserves | 5-0 |
| Stowmarket Town | v | King's Lynn Town Reserves | 1-0 |
| Diss Town | v | Halstead Town | 0-2 |
| Downham Town | v | Great Yarmouth Town | HW |

QUARTER FINALS

| | | | |
|---|---|---|---|
| Wivenhoe Town | v | March Town United | 0-0, 4-5p |
| Haverhill Borough | v | Cornard United | 3-2 |
| Ely City | v | Stowmarket Town | 0-1 |
| Halstead Town | v | Downham Town | 1-0 |

SEMI FINALS

| | | | |
|---|---|---|---|
| March Town United | v | Haverhill Borough | 0-3 |
| Stowmarket Town | v | Halstead Town | 2-1 |

FINAL

| | | | |
|---|---|---|---|
| Haverhill Borough | v | Stowmarket Town | 5-0 |

| | PREMIER DIVISION | 1 | 2 | 3 | 4 | 5 | 6 | 7 | 8 | 9 | 10 | 11 | 12 | 13 | 14 | 15 | 16 | 17 | 18 | 19 | 20 |
|---|---|---|---|---|---|---|---|---|---|---|---|---|---|---|---|---|---|---|---|---|---|
| 1 | Brantham Athletic | | 1-1 | 0-1 | 0-2 | 1-0 | 3-0 | 0-3 | 0-0 | 3-1 | 1-3 | 4-1 | 1-2 | 3-0 | 1-2 | 0-3 | 1-1 | 4-1 | 7-3 | 0-2 | 3-0 |
| 2 | Fakenham Town | 1-3 | | 1-5 | 0-2 | 1-6 | 0-3 | 3-0 | 2-0 | 1-1 | 0-1 | 3-1 | 3-3 | 3-6 | 0-2 | 1-1 | 2-6 | 0-1 | 1-0 | 2-0 | 2-1 |
| 3 | FC Clacton | 2-0 | 3-1 | | 1-2 | 1-4 | 4-0 | 0-3 | 0-2 | 2-2 | 2-2 | 2-0 | 0-4 | 0-1 | 2-4 | 3-0 | 2-4 | 4-1 | 3-0 | 1-1 | 4-3 |
| 4 | Felixstowe & Walton United | 3-2 | 2-0 | 3-0 | | 0-0 | 0-0 | 1-0 | 3-0 | 2-1 | 0-1 | 1-0 | 2-2 | 1-1 | 2-3 | 0-1 | 0-1 | 4-0 | 3-1 | 2-0 | 2-0 |
| 5 | Godmanchester Rovers | 4-2 | 5-0 | 2-4 | 3-2 | | 1-1 | 4-0 | 6-0 | 5-1 | 7-0 | 1-0 | 2-2 | 4-1 | 3-0 | 0-0 | 6-1 | 6-1 | 8-0 | 4-3 | 3-0 |
| 6 | Gorleston | 1-0 | 1-0 | 1-0 | 1-1 | 0-3 | | 1-2 | 2-1 | 0-3 | 1-1 | 1-2 | 2-5 | 1-2 | 0-2 | 3-0 | 0-4 | 3-0 | 1-3 | 1-3 | 4-2 |
| 7 | Hadleigh United | 5-0 | 2-2 | 1-0 | 0-4 | 2-3 | 4-2 | | 1-1 | 1-1 | 1-0 | 0-1 | 2-1 | 3-2 | 1-2 | 1-2 | 0-2 | 3-2 | 2-2 | 1-1 | 2-0 |
| 8 | Haverhill Rovers | 1-0 | 3-0 | 0-3 | 0-3 | 0-3 | 0-1 | 1-4 | | 1-1 | 0-1 | 0-3 | 0-1 | 1-2 | 0-1 | 1-0 | 3-1 | 1-1 | 0-4 | 2-1 | 1-1 |
| 9 | Ipswich Wanderers | 1-1 | 1-2 | 2-0 | 1-2 | 0-3 | 2-4 | 3-1 | 2-2 | | 1-2 | 0-3 | 2-1 | 4-1 | 2-6 | 1-0 | 1-2 | 1-1 | 0-1 | 2-2 | 3-1 |
| 10 | Kirkley & Pakefield | 2-0 | 0-0 | 4-1 | 1-1 | 5-0 | 1-0 | 2-1 | 2-2 | 3-1 | | 5-0 | 0-1 | 1-1 | 1-3 | 2-0 | 4-2 | 3-0 | 4-4 | 4-3 | 7-0 |
| 11 | Long Melford | 0-1 | 3-1 | 4-0 | 0-0 | 0-7 | 4-0 | 0-0 | 0-2 | 0-1 | 1-0 | | 0-2 | 6-1 | 1-2 | 0-3 | 1-2 | 2-2 | 4-1 | 3-0 | 5-1 |
| 12 | Mildenhall Town | 0-1 | 4-0 | 3-0 | 0-1 | 1-3 | 6-0 | 0-0 | 4-1 | 3-3 | 3-0 | 1-2 | | 3-1 | 0-2 | 1-0 | 1-1 | 2-1 | 4-0 | 1-1 | 4-0 |
| 13 | Newmarket Town | 1-4 | 3-4 | 0-2 | 1-3 | 1-5 | 1-1 | 2-1 | 2-3 | 3-1 | 1-0 | 0-3 | 2-1 | | 0-0 | 1-2 | 0-3 | 4-5 | 0-0 | 1-2 | 1-0 |
| 14 | Norwich United | 4-0 | 1-0 | 4-0 | 0-2 | 1-2 | 2-1 | 4-2 | 4-1 | 3-1 | 2-0 | 3-1 | 3-0 | 4-1 | | 2-0 | 0-0 | 3-1 | 4-0 | 1-0 | 3-0 |
| 15 | Saffron Walden Town | 0-1 | 4-1 | 4-0 | 2-3 | 1-2 | 3-2 | 0-3 | 0-1 | 3-0 | 0-2 | 0-2 | 2-1 | 0-2 | 1-2 | | 1-2 | 0-0 | 3-1 | 1-0 | 3-2 |
| 16 | Stanway Rovers | 2-1 | 1-0 | 6-0 | 0-1 | 3-2 | 3-2 | 2-0 | 6-1 | 6-0 | 3-0 | 4-1 | 1-1 | 2-2 | 1-0 | 2-1 | | 2-1 | 3-0 | 7-0 | 4-0 |
| 17 | Swaffham Town | 3-1 | 2-1 | 2-2 | 2-4 | 2-5 | 1-1 | 1-5 | 2-2 | 2-1 | 0-3 | 0-4 | 1-1 | 4-1 | 0-2 | 1-3 | 0-2 | | 3-1 | 1-2 | 7-0 |
| 18 | Thetford Town | 0-2 | 5-2 | 4-2 | 0-2 | 0-4 | 4-0 | 0-1 | 1-3 | 1-4 | 0-3 | 3-3 | 0-0 | 5-3 | 2-3 | 0-1 | 0-5 | 6-2 | | 3-2 | 0-0 |
| 19 | Walsham le Willows | 3-1 | 0-1 | 4-6 | 1-0 | 0-1 | 1-1 | 4-0 | 5-1 | 2-2 | 1-4 | 2-2 | 1-2 | 2-4 | 1-2 | 1-2 | 1-1 | 3-0 | 5-2 | | 0-2 |
| 20 | Whitton United | 3-3 | 1-3 | 0-3 | 0-7 | 1-3 | 5-0 | 2-4 | 0-2 | 0-0 | 0-4 | 2-0 | 1-5 | 3-2 | 0-4 | 1-3 | 2-4 | 0-1 | 1-0 | 4-2 | |

**CLUB MOVEMENTS**
**PREMIER DIVISION**
**In:** Ely City (P), Great Yarmouth Town (P), Wivehoe Town (P).
**Out:** Norwich United (P - Isthmian Div.1 North). Whitton United (R).
**DIVISION ONE**
**In:** Coggeshall Town (P - Essex & Suffolk Border), Framlingham Town (P - Suffolk & Ipswich). Holland (P - Essex & Suffolk Border), Whitton United (R), Wisbech St Mary (P - Cambridgeshire County).
**Out:** Ely City (P), Great Yarmouth Town (P), Wivehoe Town (P).

| | DIVISION ONE | 1 | 2 | 3 | 4 | 5 | 6 | 7 | 8 | 9 | 10 | 11 | 12 | 13 | 14 | 15 | 16 | 17 | 18 | 19 |
|---|---|---|---|---|---|---|---|---|---|---|---|---|---|---|---|---|---|---|---|---|
| 1 | AFC Sudbury Reserves | | 2-3 | 1-0 | 1-1 | 1-0 | 1-2 | 1-2 | 2-3 | 2-1 | 3-2 | 2-3 | 0-0 | 6-0 | 0-7 | 8-1 | 2-0 | 0-0 | 1-6 | 3-0 |
| 2 | Braintree Town Reserves | 2-0 | | 1-2 | 2-3 | 2-3 | 4-3 | 0-0 | 0-4 | 0-3 | 1-3 | 5-0 | 2-0 | 1-2 | 3-1 | 2-0 | 3-2 | 1-1 | 0-6 | 3-3 |
| 3 | Cornard United | 0-2 | 2-4 | | 1-3 | 1-4 | 1-3 | 0-1 | 0-3 | 3-2 | 0-4 | 2-0 | 1-3 | 0-3 | 0-1 | 2-1 | 0-0 | 3-3 | 0-4 | 0-0 |
| 4 | Debenham LC | 1-1 | 2-1 | 3-0 | | 1-2 | 0-7 | 5-0 | 0-3 | 0-3 | 1-3 | 1-1 | 1-0 | 1-6 | 3-0 | 0-3 | 2-2 | 4-0 | 2-4 | 1-1 |
| 5 | Dereham Town Reserves | 0-1 | 1-6 | 1-3 | 2-2 | | 0-2 | 0-1 | 1-5 | 0-3 | 1-3 | 0-4 | 1-2 | 1-2 | 2-1 | 3-3 | 1-2 | 4-1 | 0-5 | 1-2 |
| 6 | Diss Town | 0-1 | 9-2 | 1-1 | 5-1 | 3-0 | | 1-0 | 3-3 | 1-0 | 1-3 | 1-1 | 1-1 | 1-1 | 2-3 | 3-1 | 2-1 | 0-1 | 1-1 | 1-1 |
| 7 | Downham Town | 2-2 | 2-1 | 2-1 | 0-0 | 1-2 | 0-4 | | 2-2 | 2-3 | 2-3 | 0-3 | 2-2 | 0-5 | 1-4 | 1-1 | 0-1 | 2-2 | 0-3 | 3-1 |
| 8 | Ely City | 5-2 | 6-1 | 2-1 | 3-2 | 3-2 | 2-1 | 3-0 | | 0-1 | 1-0 | 1-0 | 1-3 | 4-1 | 1-0 | 4-0 | 2-1 | 2-1 | 2-0 | 1-0 |
| 9 | Great Yarmouth Town | 2-0 | 5-1 | 5-1 | 0-3 | 2-0 | 3-0 | 0-1 | 5-2 | | 1-1 | 4-1 | 3-1 | 6-1 | 5-2 | 9-0 | 3-2 | 1-0 | 0-0 | 2-0 |
| 10 | Halstead Town | 2-0 | 4-0 | 3-1 | 3-2 | 3-0 | 4-1 | 3-0 | 1-5 | 0-3 | | 2-2 | 1-0 | 1-1 | 1-0 | 1-0 | 3-2 | 5-2 | 2-3 | 2-1 |
| 11 | Haverhill Borough | 1-4 | 3-4 | 4-0 | 2-1 | 1-1 | 2-1 | 5-0 | 0-2 | 0-2 | 0-1 | | 1-1 | 4-0 | 1-5 | 1-0 | 3-0 | 5-0 | 2-3 | 0-1 |
| 12 | King's Lynn Town Reserves | 4-1 | 4-1 | 3-2 | 0-0 | 2-0 | 5-2 | 2-0 | 0-1 | 2-1 | 0-2 | 2-1 | | 3-1 | 2-1 | 7-1 | 2-2 | 6-0 | 4-0 | 4-0 |
| 13 | Leiston Reserves | 0-1 | 5-3 | 1-0 | 4-2 | 3-0 | 3-1 | 4-0 | 1-2 | 0-4 | 4-1 | 1-2 | 4-0 | | 2-4 | 5-2 | 7-0 | 5-0 | 0-5 | 1-2 |
| 14 | March Town United | 0-1 | 2-2 | 1-0 | 2-1 | 5-2 | 1-3 | 4-2 | 0-2 | 0-2 | 0-1 | 1-1 | 2-4 | 3-1 | | 3-2 | 3-1 | 2-0 | 1-3 | 1-2 |
| 15 | Needham Market Reserves | 1-2 | 0-3 | 0-3 | 1-5 | 0-4 | 0-1 | 5-1 | 0-2 | 2-6 | 0-3 | 3-4 | 1-10 | 1-4 | 1-2 | | 2-1 | 2-0 | 0-4 | 0-2 |
| 16 | Stowmarket Town | 0-0 | 2-3 | 0-3 | 2-0 | 7-0 | 1-1 | 1-4 | 4-1 | 0-1 | 5-1 | 2-3 | 2-0 | 0-3 | 4-0 | 4-1 | | 1-2 | 2-2 | 1-0 |
| 17 | Team Bury | 1-0 | 0-5 | 0-1 | 1-2 | - | 1-2 | 4-1 | 0-3 | 3-4 | 0-3 | 0-3 | 1-3 | 2-3 | 0-3 | 6-3 | 0-1 | | 0-4 | 0-0 |
| 18 | Wivenhoe Town | 2-0 | 2-3 | 2-2 | 5-0 | 1-0 | 3-0 | 2-0 | 1-0 | 4-3 | 2-1 | 1-0 | 2-2 | 2-1 | 4-1 | 2-1 | 6-1 | 3-0 | | 2-1 |
| 19 | Woodbridge Town | 1-1 | 2-1 | 2-5 | 2-0 | 1-1 | 2-2 | 1-0 | 2-1 | 2-0 | 4-2 | 1-1 | 0-1 | 4-1 | 3-2 | 2-3 | 3-3 | 3-0 | 1-2 | |

## BRANTHAM ATHLETIC

Founded: 1887 Nickname:

**Secretary:** Dan Allen **(T)** 07896 266 074 **(E)** branthamathfc@hotmail.co.uk
**Chairman:** Peter Crowhurst **Manager:** Paul Skingley - Jan 2015
**Ground:** Brantham Leisure Centre, New Village, Brantham CO11 1RZ **(T)** 01206 392 506
**Capacity:** 1,200 **Seats:** 200 **Covered:** 200 **Midweek Matchday:** Tuesday **Clubhouse:** Yes

**Colours(change):** All blue. (White/navy/navy)
**Previous Names:** Brantham & Stutton United 1996-98.
**Previous Leagues:** Eastern Counties. Suffolk & Ipswich.
**Records:** **Att:** 1,700 v VS Rugby, FA Vase 5R 1982-83.
**Honours:** Suffolk & Ipswich Senior League Champions 2007-08.

**10 YEAR RECORD**

| 06-07 | 07-08 | 08-09 | 09-10 | 10-11 | 11-12 | 12-13 | 13-14 | 14-15 | 15-16 |
|---|---|---|---|---|---|---|---|---|---|
| S&I S 4 | S&I S 1 | EC1 8 | EC1 3 | ECP 13 | ECP 3 | ECP 4 | ECP 11 | ECP 8 | ECP 11 |

## ELY CITY

Founded: 1885 Nickname: Robins

**Secretary:** Derek Oakey **(T)** 07720 542 882 **(E)** derek.oakey@tesco.net
**Chairman:** Robert Button **Manager:** Brady Stone - Feb 2014 **Prog Ed:** Barnes Print
**Ground:** Unwin Sports Ground, Downham Road, Ely CB6 2SH **(T)** 01353 662 035
**Capacity:** 1,500 **Seats:** 150 **Covered:** 350 **Midweek Matchday:** Tuesday **Clubhouse:** Yes **Shop:** Yes

**Colours(change):** All red. (All blue).
**Previous Names:** None.
**Previous Leagues:** Peterborough. Central Alliance.
**Records:** **Att:** 260 v Soham, Eastern Counties Div.1, 12.04.93.
**Honours:** Cambridgeshire Senior Cup 1947-48. Eastern Counties Division 1 1996-97.
Cambridgeshire Invitation Cup 2011-12, 12-13.

**10 YEAR RECORD**

| 06-07 | 07-08 | 08-09 | 09-10 | 10-11 | 11-12 | 12-13 | 13-14 | 14-15 | 15-16 |
|---|---|---|---|---|---|---|---|---|---|
| EC1 4 | EC1 2 | ECP 14 | ECP 9 | ECP 15 | ECP 2 | ECP 11 | ECP 17 | ECP 20 | EC1 2 |

## FAKENHAM TOWN

Founded: 1884 Nickname: Ghosts

**Secretary:** Paul Chivers **(T)** 01328 862 836 **(E)** chilvers.paul@yahoo.com
**Chairman:** William Clayton **Manager:** Neil Jarvis - May 2015 **Prog Ed:** Barnes Print
**Ground:** Clipbush Park, Clipbush Lane, Fakenham, Norfolk NR21 8SW **(T)**
**Capacity:** **Seats:** Yes **Covered:** Yes **Midweek Matchday:** Wednesday **Clubhouse:** Yes

**Colours(change):** Amber & black/black/black (White with blue trim/white/white)
**Previous Names:**
**Previous Leagues:**
**Records:** **Att:** 1,100 v Watford, official opening of new ground.
**Honours:** Norfolk Senior Cup 1970-71, 72-73, 73-74, 91-92, 93-94, 94-95.

**10 YEAR RECORD**

| 06-07 | 07-08 | 08-09 | 09-10 | 10-11 | 11-12 | 12-13 | 13-14 | 14-15 | 15-16 |
|---|---|---|---|---|---|---|---|---|---|
| EC1 10 | EC1 17 | EC1 20 | EC1 19 | EC1 14 | EC1 11 | EC1 5 | EC1 2 | ECP 13 | ECP 17 |

## FC CLACTON

Founded: 1892 Nickname: The Seasiders

**Secretary:** Danny Coyle **(T)** 07581 056 174 **(E)** fcclactonsecretary@gmail.com
**Chairman:** David Ballard **Manager:** David Coyle - October 2014 **Prog Ed:** Stephen Bugg
**Ground:** Rush Green Bowl, Rush Green Rd, Clacton-on-Sea CO16 7BQ **(T)** 07581 056 174
**Capacity:** 3,000 **Seats:** 200 **Covered:** Yes **Midweek Matchday:** Tuesday **Clubhouse:** Yes **Shop:** Yes

**Colours(change):** White & royal blue/royal blue/royal blue. (All red).
**Previous Names:** Clacton Town > 2007
**Previous Leagues:** Eastern Counties. Essex County. Southern League.
**Records:** **Att:** 3,505 v Romford, FA Cup 1952 at Old Road.
**Honours:** Eastern Counties Division 1 1994-95, 98-99.

**10 YEAR RECORD**

| 06-07 | 07-08 | 08-09 | 09-10 | 10-11 | 11-12 | 12-13 | 13-14 | 14-15 | 15-16 |
|---|---|---|---|---|---|---|---|---|---|
| ECP 21 | EC1 10 | EC1 7 | EC1 2 | ECP 16 | ECP 15 | ECP 20 | ECP 15 | ECP 16 | ECP 10 |

## FELIXSTOWE & WALTON UNITED Founded: 2000 Nickname: Seasiders

**Secretary:** Tony Barnes **(T)** 07584 010 933 **(E)** tgbarnes@live.co.uk
**Chairman:** Andy Wilding **Manager:** Kevin O'Donnell - Oct 2012 **Prog Ed:** Adam Whalley
**Ground:** Goldstar Ground, Dellwood Avenue, Felixstowe IP11 9HT **(T)** 01394 282 917
**Capacity:** 2,000 **Seats:** 200 **Covered:** 200 **Midweek Matchday:** Tuesday **Clubhouse:** Yes **Shop:** Yes

**Colours(change):** Red & white stripes/red/red. (Sky blue/sky blue/sky blue).
**Previous Names:** Felixstowe Port & Town and Walton United merged in July 2000.
**Previous Leagues:** None
**Records:**
**Honours:**

**10 YEAR RECORD**

| 06-07 | 07-08 | 08-09 | 09-10 | 10-11 | 11-12 | 12-13 | 13-14 | 14-15 | 15-16 |
|---|---|---|---|---|---|---|---|---|---|
| ECP 13 | ECP 8 | ECP 12 | ECP 7 | ECP 18 | ECP 18 | ECP 14 | ECP 3 | ECP 5 | ECP 4 |

## GODMANCHESTER ROVERS Founded: 1911 Nickname: Goody/Rovers

**Secretary:** Tracy Cosbey **(T)** 07837 193 514 **(E)** secretary@godmanchesterroversfc.co.uk
**Chairman:** Karl Hurst **Prog Ed:** Steve Bengree
**Ground:** The David Wilson Homes Ground, Godmanchester, Huntingdon PE29 2LQ **(T)**
**Capacity:** **Seats:** **Covered:** Yes **Midweek Matchday:** Wednesday **Clubhouse:** Yes

**Colours(change):** All blue (Red & white stripes/red/red)
**Previous Names:** None
**Previous Leagues:**
**Records:** **Att:** 138 v Cambridge City Reserves, Dec. 2003.
**Honours:** Eastern Counties League Division One 2011-12.
Huntingdonshire Senior Cup 2014-15.

**10 YEAR RECORD**

| 06-07 | 07-08 | 08-09 | 09-10 | 10-11 | 11-12 | 12-13 | 13-14 | 14-15 | 15-16 |
|---|---|---|---|---|---|---|---|---|---|
| EC1 17 | EC1 16 | EC1 10 | EC1 12 | EC1 9 | EC1 1 | ECP 5 | ECP 5 | ECP 2 | ECP 2 |

## GORLESTON Founded: 1887 Nickname: The Cards

**Secretary:** Colin Bray **(T)** 07918 186 645 **(E)** colin-bray@sky.com
**Chairman:** Alan Gordon **Manager:** Ricci Butler - May 2015 **Prog Ed:** Colin Bray
**Ground:** Emerald Park, Woodfarm Lane, Gorleston, Norfolk NR31 9AQ **(T)** 01493 602 802
**Capacity:** **Seats:** Yes **Covered:** Yes **Midweek Matchday:** Tuesday **Clubhouse:** Yes

**Colours(change):** All green (All sky blue)
**Previous Names:** None
**Previous Leagues:** Anglian Combination
**Records:** **Record Att:** 4,473 v Orient, FA Cup 1st Round, 29.11.51.
**Honours:** Norfolk & Suff. Lge (x 7). Norfolk Senior Cup x16 Most recently 2013-14.
Anglian Comb 1968-69. Eastern Counties 1952-53, 72-73, 79-80, 80-81. Division One 1995-96, 2010-11.

**10 YEAR RECORD**

| 06-07 | 07-08 | 08-09 | 09-10 | 10-11 | 11-12 | 12-13 | 13-14 | 14-15 | 15-16 |
|---|---|---|---|---|---|---|---|---|---|
| EC1 14 | EC1 8 | EC1 6 | EC1 4 | EC1 1 | ECP 12 | ECP 3 | ECP 4 | ECP 12 | ECP 16 |

## GREAT YARMOUTH TOWN Founded: 1897 Nickname:

**Secretary:** Paul Hubbard **(T)** 07791 696 900 **(E)** pmh03841@gmail.com
**Chairman:** Mike Guymer **Manager:** Martyn Sinclair & Adam Mason **Prog Ed:** Barnes Print Ltd
**Ground:** The Wellesley, Sandown Road, Great Yarmouth NR30 1EY **(T)** 07873 861 983
**Capacity:** 3,600 **Seats:** 500 **Covered:** 2,100 **Midweek Matchday:** Tuesday **Clubhouse:** Yes **Shop:** Yes

**Colours(change):** Yellow & black/black/yellow (White & black/black/white)
**Previous Names:** None
**Previous Leagues:** Norfolk & Suffolk >1935.
**Records:** **Att:** 8,944 v Crystal Palace FA Cup R1 52-53. **Goalscorer:** Gordon South - 298 (1927-47). **Apps:** Mark Vincent - 700 (84-05).
**Honours:** Norfolk & Suffolk League 1913-14, 26-27, 27-28. Eastern Counties League Champions 1968-69, Division 1 2009-10.
Norfolk Senior Cup (x13)

**10 YEAR RECORD**

| 06-07 | 07-08 | 08-09 | 09-10 | 10-11 | 11-12 | 12-13 | 13-14 | 14-15 | 15-16 |
|---|---|---|---|---|---|---|---|---|---|
| EC1 13 | EC1 11 | EC1 5 | EC1 1 | ECP 14 | ECP 21 | EC1 10 | EC1 8 | EC1 4 | EC1 3 |

## HADLEIGH UNITED

Founded: 1892 Nickname: Brettsiders

**Secretary:** Louise Hay **(T)** 07962 274 986 **(E)** louise.hay1@yahoo.co.uk
**Chairman:** Rolf Beggerow **Manager:** Ian Brown - Jan 2015 **Prog Ed:** Nick Barwick
**Ground:** The Millfield, Tinkers Lane, Duke St, Hadleigh IP7 5NF **(T)** 01473 822 165
**Capacity:** 3,000 **Seats:** 250 **Covered:** 500 **Midweek Matchday:** Tuesday **Clubhouse:** Yes

**Colours(change):** All navy blue (White/royal blue/royal blue)
**Previous Names:** None
**Previous Leagues:** Suffolk & Ipswich.
**Records:** **Att:** 518 v Halstead Town, FA Vase replay, 17.01.95.
**Honours:** Suffolk & Ipswich League Champions 1953-54, 56-57, 73-74, 76-77, 78-79.
Suffolk Senior Cup 1968-69, 71-72, 82-83, 2003-04. Eastern Counties League Champions 1993-94, 2013-14.

**10 YEAR RECORD**

| 06-07 | 07-08 | 08-09 | 09-10 | 10-11 | 11-12 | 12-13 | 13-14 | 14-15 | 15-16 |
|---|---|---|---|---|---|---|---|---|---|
| EC1 9 | EC1 5 | EC1 2 | ECP 18 | ECP 9 | ECP 11 | ECP 8 | ECP 1 | ECP 7 | ECP 7 |

## HAVERHILL ROVERS

Founded: 1886 Nickname: Rovers

**Secretary:** Peter Betts **(T)** 07539 229 114 **(E)** bettsyhaverhillrovers@hotmail.co.uk
**Chairman:** Steve Brown **Manager:** Mick Reardon
**Ground:** The New Croft, Chalkstone Way, Haverhill, Suffolk CB9 0BW **(T)** 01440 702 137
**Capacity:** 3,000 **Seats:** 200 **Covered:** 200 **Midweek Matchday:** Tuesday **Clubhouse:** Yes

**Colours(change):** Red/red/red & white (White/black/black & white).
**Previous Names:** None.
**Previous Leagues:** East Anglian. Essex & Suffolk Border.
**Records:** **Att:** 1,730 v Aldershot Town, FAC 4th Qualifying Round, 2006-07.
**Honours:** Essex & Suffolk Border League Champions 1947-48, 62-63, 63-64.
Eastern Counties League Cup 1964-65, League Champions 78-79. Suffolk Senior Cup 1995-96.

**10 YEAR RECORD**

| 06-07 | 07-08 | 08-09 | 09-10 | 10-11 | 11-12 | 12-13 | 13-14 | 14-15 | 15-16 |
|---|---|---|---|---|---|---|---|---|---|
| EC1 2 | ECP 10 | ECP 21 | ECP 12 | ECP 8 | ECP 14 | ECP 10 | ECP 7 | ECP 17 | ECP 12 |

## IPSWICH WANDERERS

Founded: 1983 Nickname: Wanderers

**Secretary:** Paul Crickmore **(T)** 07577 745 778 **(E)** iwfc@hotmail.co.uk
**Chairman:** Keith Lloyd **Manager:** Glenn Read - Oct 2011 **Prog Ed:** Joe Topple
**Ground:** SEH Sports Centre, Humber Doucy Lane, Ipswich IP4 3NR **(T)** 01473 720 691
**Capacity:** **Seats:** Yes **Covered:** Yes **Midweek Matchday:** Wednesday **Clubhouse:** Yes

**Colours(change):** All blue (All orange)
**Previous Names:** Loadwell Ipswich 1983-89
**Previous Leagues:**
**Records:** **Att:** 335 v Woodbridge, Eastern Counties League 1993-94.
**Honours:** Eastern Counties Div.1 Champions 1997-98, 04-05. Suffolk Senior Cup 2012-13.

**10 YEAR RECORD**

| 06-07 | 07-08 | 08-09 | 09-10 | 10-11 | 11-12 | 12-13 | 13-14 | 14-15 | 15-16 |
|---|---|---|---|---|---|---|---|---|---|
| ECP 10 | ECP 22 | EC1 17 | EC1 17 | EC1 10 | EC1 12 | EC1 4 | EC1 3 | ECP 9 | ECP 15 |

## KIRKLEY & PAKEFIELD

Founded: 1886 Nickname: The Kirks

**Secretary:** David Hackney **(T)** 01502 582 865 **(E)** davidra1945@hotmail.co.uk
**Chairman:** Robert Jenkerson **Manager:** Gaven Tipple - May 2015 **Prog Ed:** Colin Foreman
**Ground:** Walmer Road, Lowestoft NR33 7LE **(T)** 01502 513 549
**Capacity:** 2,000 **Seats:** 150 **Covered:** 150 **Midweek Matchday:** Tuesday **Clubhouse:** Yes **Shop:** Yes

**Colours(change):** Royal blue & white/royal blue/royal blue (All maroon).
**Previous Names:** Kirkley. Kirkley & Waveney 1929-33. Merged with Pakefield in 2007.
**Previous Leagues:** Norfolk & Suffolk. Anglian Combination.
**Records:** **Att:** 1,125 v Lowestoft Town. **Goalscorer:** Barry Dale - 241. **Apps:** Barry Dale - 495.
**Honours:** Suffolk Senior Cup 1900-01, 01-02, 24-25, 00-01, 01-02. Anglian Combination League 2001-02, 02-03.

**10 YEAR RECORD**

| 06-07 | 07-08 | 08-09 | 09-10 | 10-11 | 11-12 | 12-13 | 13-14 | 14-15 | 15-16 |
|---|---|---|---|---|---|---|---|---|---|
| ECP 7 | ECP 6 | ECP 6 | ECP 4 | ECP 12 | ECP 13 | ECP 12 | ECP 12 | ECP 4 | ECP 5 |

## LONG MELFORD

Founded: 1868 Nickname: The Villagers

**Secretary:** Richard Powell **(T)** 07897 751 298 **(E)** richard.j.powell@hotmail.co.uk
**Chairman:** Colin Woodhouse **Manager:** Jules Mumford - May 2012 **Prog Ed:** Andy Cussans
**Ground:** Stoneylands Stadium, New Road, Long Melford, Suffolk CO10 9JY **(T)** 01787 312 187
**Capacity:** **Seats:** Yes **Covered:** Yes **Midweek Matchday:** Tuesday **Clubhouse:** Yes

**Colours(change):** Black & white stripes/black/black (Yellow/blue/blue)
**Previous Names:**
**Previous Leagues:** Essex & Suffolk Border > 2003
**Records:**
**Honours:** Essex & Suffolk Border Champions x5. Suffolk Senior Cup x8.
Eastern Counties Division One 2014-15.

**10 YEAR RECORD**

| 06-07 | 07-08 | 08-09 | 09-10 | 10-11 | 11-12 | 12-13 | 13-14 | 14-15 | 15-16 |
|---|---|---|---|---|---|---|---|---|---|
| EC1 16 | EC1 19 | EC1 19 | EC1 16 | EC1 12 | EC1 9 | EC1 13 | EC1 11 | EC1 1 | ECP 9 |

## MILDENHALL TOWN

Founded: 1898 Nickname: The Hall

**Secretary:** Brian Hensby **(T)** 07932 043 261 **(E)** bhensby@talktalk.net
**Chairman:** Martin Tuck **Manager:** Dean Greygoose - Dec 2014 **Prog Ed:** Frank Marshall
**Ground:** Recreation Way, Mildenhall, Suffolk IP28 7HG **(T)** 01638 713 449
**Capacity:** 2,00 **Seats:** 50 **Covered:** 200 **Midweek Matchday:** Tuesday **Clubhouse:** Yes **Shop:** Yes

**Colours(change):** Amber/black/black. (Red & white/white/red).
**Previous Names:** None
**Previous Leagues:** Bury & District. Cambridgeshire. Cambridgeshire Premier.
**Records:** **Att:** 450 v Derby County, Friendly, July 2001.
**Honours:**

**10 YEAR RECORD**

| 06-07 | 07-08 | 08-09 | 09-10 | 10-11 | 11-12 | 12-13 | 13-14 | 14-15 | 15-16 |
|---|---|---|---|---|---|---|---|---|---|
| ECP 2 | ECP 5 | ECP 11 | ECP 6 | ECP 5 | ECP 7 | ECP 7 | ECP 10 | ECP 10 | ECP 6 |

## NEWMARKET TOWN

Founded: 1877 Nickname: The Jockeys

**Secretary:** Graham Edwards **(T)** 07757 635 887 **(E)** graham.edwards@ntlworld.com
**Chairman:** John Olive **Manager:** Kevin Grainger - Sept 2006 **Prog Ed:** Barnes Print Ltd
**Ground:** Town Ground, Cricket Field Road, Off Cheveley Rd, Newmarket CB8 8BT **(T)** 01638 663 637
**Capacity:** 2,750 **Seats:** 144 **Covered:** 250 **Midweek Matchday:** Tuesday **Clubhouse:** Yes **Shop:** Yes

**Colours(change):** Yellow/blue/blue (All red)
**Previous Names:** None
**Previous Leagues:** Bury Senior. Ipswich Senior. Essex & Suffolk B. United Counties.
**Records:** **Att:** 2,701 v Abbey United (now Cambridge Utd) FA Cup, 01.10.49.
**Honours:** Suffolk Senior Cup 1934-35, 93-94. Suffolk Premier Cup 1993-94, 94-95, 96-97.
Eastern Counties League Division 1 2008-09.

**10 YEAR RECORD**

| 06-07 | 07-08 | 08-09 | 09-10 | 10-11 | 11-12 | 12-13 | 13-14 | 14-15 | 15-16 |
|---|---|---|---|---|---|---|---|---|---|
| ECP 12 | ECP 21 | EC1 1 | ECP 16 | ECP 19 | ECP 20 | EC1 2 | ECP 9 | ECP 6 | ECP 13 |

## SAFFRON WALDEN TOWN

Founded: 1872 Nickname: The Bloods

**Secretary:** Rob Thurston **(T)** 07590 994 371 **(E)** swtfcsecretary@gmail.com
**Chairman:** Martin Johnson **Manager:** Stuart Wardley - May 2013 **Prog Ed:** Jim Duvall
**Ground:** The Meadow, 1 Catons Lane, Saffron Walden, Essex CB10 2DU **(T)** 01799 520 980
**Capacity:** **Seats:** Yes **Covered:** Yes **Midweek Matchday:** Tuesday **Clubhouse:** Yes

**Colours(change):** Red & black stripes/black/red (Blue & white stripes/blue/blue)
**Previous Names:** Saffron Walden > 1967
**Previous Leagues:** Essex Senior >2003. Eastern Counties 2004-11. Folded in 2011 reformed for 2012-13 season.
**Records:** **Goalscorer:** Alec Ramsey - 192. **Apps:** Les Page - 538.
**Honours:** Essex Senior League 1973-74, 99-00. Eastern Counties 1982-83. Essex Senior Challenge Trophy 1982-83, 83-84, 84-85.

**10 YEAR RECORD**

| 06-07 | 07-08 | 08-09 | 09-10 | 10-11 | 11-12 | 12-13 | 13-14 | 14-15 | 15-16 |
|---|---|---|---|---|---|---|---|---|---|
| EC1 12 | EC1 6 | EC1 7 | EC1 14 | EC1 6 | | EC1 6 | ECP 5 | EC1 3 | ECP 8 |

## STANWAY ROVERS

Founded: 1956 Nickname: Rovers

**Secretary:** Michael Pulford **(T)** 07736 045 007 **(E)** mpulford@colne.essex.sch.uk
**Chairman:** Roy Brett **Manager:** Angelo Harrop - Oct 2013 **Prog Ed:** Michael Pulford
**Ground:** Hawthorns, New Farm Road, Stanway, Colchester CO3 0PG **(T)** 01206 578 187
**Capacity:** 1,500 **Seats:** 100 **Covered:** 250 **Midweek Matchday:** Tuesday **Clubhouse:** Yes **Shop:** Yes

**Colours(change):** Amber & black/black/black. (White & red/red/red).
**Previous Names:** None.
**Previous Leagues:** Colchester & East Essex. Essex & Suffolk Border.
**Records:** **Att:** 365 v Coventry Sphinx – FA Vase 2007-08
**Honours:** Colchester & East Essex League Premier Division 1973-74.
Eastern Counties League Division One 2005-06, League Cup 2008-09, 11-12.

**10 YEAR RECORD**

| 06-07 | 07-08 | 08-09 | 09-10 | 10-11 | 11-12 | 12-13 | 13-14 | 14-15 | 15-16 |
|---|---|---|---|---|---|---|---|---|---|
| ECP 14 | ECP 7 | ECP 9 | ECP 5 | ECP 7 | ECP 5 | ECP 9 | ECP 13 | ECP 3 | ECP 3 |

## SWAFFHAM TOWN

Founded: 1892 Nickname: Pedlars

**Secretary:** Ray Ewart **(T)** 07990 526 744 **(E)** rayewart@aol.com
**Chairman:** Mick Simmons **Manager:** Paul Hunt - June 2010 **Prog Ed:** Andy Black
**Ground:** Shoemakers Lane, Swaffham, Norfolk PE37 7NT **(T)** 01760 722 700
**Capacity:** **Seats:** Yes **Covered:** Yes **Midweek Matchday:** Tuesday **Clubhouse:** Yes

**Colours(change):** Black & white stripes/black/black (All red)
**Previous Names:** None
**Previous Leagues:** Anglian Combination
**Records:** **Att:** 250 v Downham Town, Eastern Counties League Cup, 03.09.91.
**Honours:** Eastern Counties Division One 2000-01.

**10 YEAR RECORD**

| 06-07 | 07-08 | 08-09 | 09-10 | 10-11 | 11-12 | 12-13 | 13-14 | 14-15 | 15-16 |
|---|---|---|---|---|---|---|---|---|---|
| EC1 3 | ECP 20 | EC1 18 | EC1 14 | EC1 15 | EC1 13 | EC1 9 | EC1 7 | EC1 2 | ECP 18 |

## THETFORD TOWN

Founded: 1883 Nickname:

**Secretary:** Jackie Skipp **(T)** 07753 147 098 **(E)** jackieskipp@live.co.uk
**Chairman:** Nigel Armes **Manager:** David White - Oct 2015 **Prog Ed:** Barnes Print
**Ground:** Recreation Ground, Mundford Road, Thetford, Norfolk IP24 1NB **(T)** 01842 766 120
**Capacity:** **Seats:** Yes **Covered:** Yes **Midweek Matchday:** Tuesday **Clubhouse:** Yes

**Colours(change):** Claret & blue/claret/claret (All sky blue)
**Previous Names:** None
**Previous Leagues:** Norwich & District. Norfolk & Suffolk. Founder member of Eastern Counties League
**Records:** **Att:** 404 vs Attleborough Town Norfolk Senior Cup, 1997
**Honours:** Norfolk & Suffolk League 1954-55.
Norfolk Senior Cup 1947-48, 90-91.

**10 YEAR RECORD**

| 06-07 | 07-08 | 08-09 | 09-10 | 10-11 | 11-12 | 12-13 | 13-14 | 14-15 | 15-16 |
|---|---|---|---|---|---|---|---|---|---|
| EC1 11 | EC1 13 | EC1 16 | EC1 11 | EC1 5 | EC1 2 | ECP 19 | ECP 16 | ECP 14 | ECP 19 |

## WALSHAM-LE-WILLOWS

Founded: 1888 Nickname: The Willows

**Secretary:** Gordon Ross **(T)** 07742 111 892 **(E)** gordonaross2@gmail.com
**Chairman:** Keith Mills **Manager:** Paul Smith - July 2011 **Prog Ed:** Barnes Print
**Ground:** The Meadow, Summer Road, Walsham-le-Willows IP31 3AH **(T)** 01359 259 298
**Capacity:** **Seats:** 100 **Covered:** 100 **Midweek Matchday:** Wednesday **Clubhouse:** Yes

**Colours(change):** Yellow/red/yellow (Red/black/red & black)
**Previous Names:** None
**Previous Leagues:** Bury & District. Suffolk & Ipswich.
**Records:**
**Honours:** Suffolk & Ipswich Senior League Champions 2001-02, 02-03. Suffolk Senior Cup 2005-06.
Eastern Counties League Division 1 Champions 2006-07.

**10 YEAR RECORD**

| 06-07 | 07-08 | 08-09 | 09-10 | 10-11 | 11-12 | 12-13 | 13-14 | 14-15 | 15-16 |
|---|---|---|---|---|---|---|---|---|---|
| EC1 1 | ECP 16 | ECP 10 | ECP 13 | ECP 17 | ECP 17 | ECP 6 | ECP 8 | ECP 15 | ECP 14 |

## WIVENHOE TOWN

Founded: 1925 Nickname: The Dragons

**Secretary:** Lorraine Stevens **(T)** 07565 364 019 **(E)** lorraine.rogers@btopenworld.com
**Chairman:** Mo Osman **Manager:** Mo Osman **Prog Ed:** Richard Charnock
**Ground:** Maple Tree Cars Stadium, Broad Lane, Elmstead Road, Wivenhoe CO7 7HA **(T)**
**Capacity:** 2876 **Seats:** 161 **Covered:** 1300 **Midweek Matchday:** Wednesday **Clubhouse:** Yes **Shop:** Yes

**Colours(change):** Blue & white/blue/blue (Red & black/black/black)
**Previous Names:** Wivenhoe Rangers.
**Previous Leagues:** Brightlingsea & District, Colchester & East Essex. Essex & Suffolk Border, Essex Senior, Isthmian
**Records:** **Att:** 1,912 v Runcorn, FA Trophy, 1st Round, Feb. 1990. **Goalscorer:** (258 in 350 games). **Apps:** Keith Bain (538).
**Honours:** Isthmian Division 2 North 1987-88. Division 1 1989-90. Eastern Counties League Division One 2015-16.
Essex Senior Trophy 1987-88.

**10 YEAR RECORD**

| 06-07 | 07-08 | 08-09 | 09-10 | 10-11 | 11-12 | 12-13 | 13-14 | 14-15 | 15-16 |
|---|---|---|---|---|---|---|---|---|---|
| Isth1N 11 | Isth1N 22 | ECP 17 | ECP 20 | ECP 20 | ECP 19 | ECP 18 | ECP 19 | ECP 18 | EC1 1 |

## GROUND DIRECTIONS

**BRANTHAM ATHLETIC - Brantham Leisure Centre CO11 1RZ - 01206 392 506**
Turn off the A12 heading towards East Bergholt, stay on the B1070 through East Bergholt and go straight across the roundabout with the A137. Turn left immediately at the T-junction and follow this road around the sharp curve to the right and turn right immediately before the Village Hall. Follow this road around the sharp left hand turn and the Social Club and the car park are on the right.

**BRIGHTLINGSEA REGENT - North Road, Brightlingsea, Essex CO7 0PL - 01206 304 199**
Take exit 28 off M25, take slip road left for A12 toward Brentwood / Chelmsford / Romford, turn left onto slip road, merge onto A12, take slip road left for A120, take slip road left for A133, at roundabout, take 2nd exit, turn left onto B1029 / Great Bentley Road, turn right onto B1027 / Tenpenny Hill, and then immediately turn left onto B1029 / Brightlingsea Road, turn left to stay on B1029 / Ladysmith Avenue, bear left onto Spring Road, turn left onto North Road.

**CRC - The Trade Recruitment Stadium CB5 8LN - 01223 566 500**
Exit the A14 at the fourth junction (situated east of Cambridge), up the slip road to the roundabout (sign posted Stow-Cum-Quy). Turn right onto the A1303, and return westwards towards Cambridge. Go straight over the first roundabout, passing Marshall Airport to the left. Go straight over two sets of traffic lights to a roundabout. The Ground's floodlights can be seen from here and McDonald's is on the right.

**ELY CITY - Unwin Sports Ground CB6 2SH - 01353 662 035**
Follow signs for Kings Lynn/Downham Market as you approach Ely. Don't go into the city centre. After the Little Chef roundabout (junction of A10/A142) continue for approx half a mile until the next roundabout. Turn left for Little Downham (the B1411). There is also a sign for a Golf Course. The Golf Course is part of a Sports Complex which includes the football club. After turning left at the roundabout take another left after only about 50 metres into the Sports Complex entrance. The football club is at the end of the drive past the rugby club and tennis courts.

**FAKENHAM TOWN - Clipbush Pk, Clipbush Lane NR21 8SW - 01328 855 859**
Corner of A148 & Clipbush Lane.

**FC CLACTON - Rush Green Bowl CO16 7BQ - 01255 432 590**
Leave the A12 at junction 29, then at roundabout take the 1st exit, then merge onto the A120 (sign posted Clacton, Harwich). Branch left, then merge onto the A133 (sign posted Clacton). Continue along the A133 following signs to Clacton until St Johns Roundabout (tiled Welcome to Clacton sign) take the 4th exit onto St Johns Rd - B1027 (sign posted St Osyth) Entering Clacton On Sea B1027 (fire station on left). B1027 At second mini-roundabout turn left onto Cloes Lane (Budgens on right). Continue down Cloes Lane for about 1/2 mile, passing St.Clares School on your right, at traffic lights, turn right onto Rush Green Rd. Rush Green Bowl will then appear on the right after 1/4 mile.

**FELIXSTOWE & WALTON - Town Ground, Dellwood Ave IP11 9HT - 01394 282 917**
The A12 meets the A14 (Felixstowe to M1/M6 trunk road) at Copdock interchange, just to the South of Ipswich. For Felixstowe take the A14 heading east over the Orwell Bridge. Follow the A14, for approx. 14 miles until you come to a large roundabout with a large water tower on your right, take the 1st exit off the roundabout, which is straight on. Take the first exit at the next roundabout, straight ahead again. At the next roundabout take the fourth exit onto Beatrice Avenue, take the first left into Dellwood Avenue. The ground is 100 yards down on the left behind tall wooden fencing.

**GODMANCHESTER ROVERS - Bearscroft Lane PE29 2LQ - 07774 830 507**
From A14 turn off for Godmanchester. Take A1198 towards Wood Green Animal Shelter, Bearscroft Lane is half mile from A14 on the left.

**GORLESTON - Emerald Park, Woodfarm Lane NR31 9AQ - 01493 602 802**
On Magdalen Estate follow signs to Crematorium, turn left and follow road to ground.
**GREAT YARMOUTH TOWN - The Wellesley, Sandown Road NR30 1EY - 01493 656 099**
Just off Marine Parade 200 yards north of the Britannia Pier. Half a mile from the BR station.
**HADLEIGH UNITED - Millfield, Tinkers Lane IP7 5NG - 01473 822 165**
On reaching Hadleigh High Street turn into Duke Street (right next to Library), continue on for approximately 150 metres and take left turn into narrow lane immediately after going over small bridge, continue to end of the lane where you will find the entrance to club car park.
**HAVERHILL ROVERS - The New Croft, Chalkstone Way CB9 0LD - 01440 702 137**
Take the A143 in to Haverhill and, at the roundabout by Tesco, turn left and then right in the one in front of the store. Carry on over the next roundabout past Aldi on the left and past the Sports Centre, Cricket Club and garage on the left. Just after the Workspace Office Solutions building take a right towards the town centre (towards Parking (South). The drive way into Hamlet Croft is a small turning on the left just after Croft Lane (look for the sign for Tudor Close).
**IPSWICH WANDERERS - SEH Sports Centre IP4 3NR 01473 728 581**
**KIRKLEY & PAKEFIELD - K & P Community & Sports Club, Walmer Road, NR33 7LE - 01502 513 549.**
From A12 to Lowestoft town centre and go over roundabout at Teamways Garage and past Teamways Pub. Take next left into Walmer Road.
**LONG MELFORD - Stoneylands Stadium CO10 9JY - 01787 312 187**
Turn down St Catherine Road off Hall St (Bury-Sudbury road) and then turn left into New Road.
**MILDENHALL TOWN - Recreation Way, Mildenhall, Suffolk IP28 7HG - 01638 713449 (club)**
Next to swimming pool and car park a quarter of a mile from town centre.
**NEWMARKET TOWN - Town Ground, Cricket Field Road CB8 8BG - 01638 663 637 (club).**
Four hundred yards from Newmarket BR.Turn right into Green Road and right at cross roads into new Cheveley Rd. Ground is at top on left.
**SAFFRON WALDEN TOWN - Catons Lane CB10 2DU - 01799 522 789**
Into Castle Street off Saffron-W High St. Then left at T jct and 1st left by Victory Pub.
**STANWAY ROVERS - `Hawthorns', New Farm Road CO3 0PG - 01206 578 187**
Leave A12 at Jct 26 to A1124. Turn right(from London)or left from Ipswich onto Essex Yeomanry Way. A1124 towards Colchester 1st right into Villa Rd,then left into Chaple Rd, and left into New Farm Rd. Ground 400 yds on left.Nearest BR station is Colchester North. **SWAFFHAM TOWN - Shoemakers Lane PE37 7NT - 01760 722 700**
**THETFORD TOWN - Recreation Ground, Munford Road IP24 1NB - 01842 766 120**
**WIVENHOE TOWN - Broad Lane, Elmstead Road CO7 7HA - 01206 825 380**
The ground is situated off the B1027 to the north of Wivenhoe.

**DIVISION ONE**
**AFC SUDBURY RESERVES - The Mel Group Stadium, King's Marsh Brundon Lane, Sudbury CO10 7HN**
From Colchester, Bury St Edmunds and Ipswich: Enter Sudbury and follow signs for Halstead/Chelmsford. Go aross the river bridge and go under the old rail bridge, then turn right at the traffic lights (Kings Head) into Bulmer Road and the first right again into Brundon Lane. The road narrows before reaching ground on the right hand side.
**BRAINTREE TOWN RESERVES - The Amlin Stadium, Clockhouse Way, Cressing Rd, Braintree CM7 3RD**
Leave M11 at junction 8A (for Stansted Airport) and follow A120 towards Braintree and Colchester for 17 miles. At Gallows Corner roundabout (with WestDrive Kia on your right) take first exit into Cressing Road. Clockhouse Way and the entrance to the ground are three quarters of a mile on the left and are clearly sign-posted.
**COGGESHALL TOWN** - The Crops, West Street, Coggeshall CO6 1NS
From the M11 take junction 8, take the A120 exit to Stansted Airport/Colchester/B. Stortford. At the roundabout, take the 1st exit onto Thremhall Ave/A120. At Priory Wood Roundabout, take the 3rd exit onto the A120 ramp to Colchester. Continue onto A120.
At the roundabout, take the 2nd exit and stay on A120. At the roundabout, take the 3rd exit onto Coggeshall Rd/A120. Turn right onto West Street.
**CORNARD UNITED - Blackhouse Lane CO10 0NL - 07811 096 382**
Left off roundabout on A134 coming from Ipswich/Colchester into Sudbury, follow signs for Country Park - ground is immediately opposite along Blackhouse Lane.
**DEBENHAM LC - Debenham Leisure Centre IP14 6BL - 01728 861 101**
Approach Ipswich along the A14. Turn left at junction 51 onto the A140 signposted towards Norwich. After approx 4 miles turn right towards Mickfield and follow the road into Debenham turning left into Gracechurch Street. Debenham Leisure Centre is approx 1 mile on the right hand side.

**DEREHAM TOWN RESERVES - Aldiss Park, Norwich Road, Dereham, Norfolk NR20 3PX - 01362 690 460**

See Dereham Town - Isthmian Division One North.

**DISS TOWN - Brewers Green Lane IP22 4QP - 01379 651 223**

Off B1066 Diss -Thetford road near Roydon school. One and a half miles from Diss (BR).

**DOWNHAM TOWN - Memorial Field, Lynn Road PE38 9QE - 01366 388 424**

One and a quarter miles from Downham Market (BR) - continue to town clock, turn left and ground is three quarters of a mile down Lynn Road.

**FRAMLINGHAM TOWN - Framingham Sports Club, Badingham Road, Framlingham IP13 9HS**

Via the A14, take the A140 ramp to Diss/Norwich/B1078. At the roundabout, take the 1st exit onto A140, Follow A1120 and B1119 to your destination in Framlingham. Turn right onto Stowmarket Rd/A1120, Continue to follow A1120. Turn right onto B1119

Turn right onto College Rd/B1116. At the roundabout, take the 2nd exit onto Well Cl Square/B1116, Continue to follow B1116

Turn left onto Fore St/B1119, Continue to follow B1119. Slight left onto Badingham Rd/B1120

**HALSTEAD TOWN - Rosemary Lane CO9 1HR - 01787 472 082**

From A1311 Chelmsford to Braintree road follow signs to Halstead.

**HAVERHILL BOROUGH - Haverhill Rovers FC, The New Croft, Chalkestone Way, Haverhill CB9 0LD**

See Haverhill Rovers for directions.

**HOLLAND FC - Eastcliff Sports Ground, Dulwich Road, Holland-on-Sea CO15 5HP**

From Colchester, Get on A12 in Mile End from A134 and Via Urbis Romanae, Head south on Rotary Way. At the roundabout, take the 2nd exit and stay on Rotary Way. Turn left onto Westway/A134. At the roundabout, take the 5th exit and stay on Westway/A134. At the roundabout, take the 2nd exit and stay on Westway/A134. At Essex Hall Roundabout, take the 2nd exit onto A134. Turn left onto Turner Rd/A134. Continue to follow A134. Continue straight onto Via Urbis Romanae. At the roundabout, take the 2nd exit. At the roundabout, take the 3rd exit. At the roundabout, take the 2nd exit onto the A12 ramp to Ipswich/Felixstowe/A14/Harwich/A120. Take A120 and A133 to St John's Rd/B1027 in Clacton-on-Sea. Merge onto A12. Take the A120 ramp to Calchester North/A1232/Clacton Harwich. Keep right to continue on A120. At the roundabout, take the 1st exit onto Colchester Rd/A133. At the roundabout, take the 3rd exit onto A133. At the roundabout, take the 2nd exit and stay on A133. Go through 1 roundabout. Continue on B1027. Drive to Dulwich Rd in Holland-on-Sea.

**KING'S LYNN TOWN RESERVES -The Walks, Tennyson Road, King's Lynn PE30 5PB. - 01553 760 060**

See King's Lynn Town - Southern Premier Division.

**LEISTON RESERVES -The LTAA, Victory Road, Leiston, Suffolk IP16 4DQ -01728 830 308**

See Leiston - Isthmian Premier Division.

**MARCH TOWN UNITED - GER Sports Ground PE15 8HS - 01354 653 073**

5 mins from town centre, 10 mins from BR station.

**NEEDHAM MARKET RESERVES - Bloomfields, Quinton Road, Needham Market IP6 8DA.**

**STOWMARKET TOWN - Greens Meadow, Bury Road IP14 1JQ - 01449 612 533**

About 800 yards from Stowmarket station (BR).Turn right at lights and head out of town over roundabout into Bury Road, Ground is on the right.

**TEAM BURY - Ram Meadow, Cotton Lane IP33 1XP - 01284 754 721**

from the M11: Take junction 9 for the A11. Follow this road and make sure you get into the outside lane for the A14 signed Bury St Edmunds. Leave the A14 Junction 43, signposted to central Bury St Edmunds. Once clear of the exit roundabout, follow the signs to Town Centre. Take the first exit at the next roundabout (after 300 yards) into Northgate Street. At the second set of traffic lights (T - Junction), turn left into Mustow Street and first left into Cotton Lane, past the Hawkes garage and the Drive Car Showroom. Carry on down to the bottom of Cotton Lane and turn right in the council car park. The ground is at the far end of the car park, situated on the left hand side.

**WHITTON UNITED - King George V Playing Fields, Old Norwich Road, Ipswich IP1 6LE**

Located just off the busy A1156 Bury Road into Ipswich.

**WISBECH ST MARY - Wisbech St Mary Playing Fields, Beechings Close, Wisbech St Mary PE13 4SS**

**WOODBRIDGE TOWN - Notcutts Park, Fynn Road, Woodbridge IP12 4LS - 01394 385 308**

Get on A14 from A137, Follow A14 and A12 to Ipswich Rd/B1438, Continue on Ipswich Rd/B1438. Drive to Fynn Road in Woodbridge.

## AFC SUDBURY RESERVES
Founded: 1999 Nickname: AFC

**Secretary:** David Webb **(T)** 07885 327 510 **(E)** dave-afc@supanet.com
**Chairman:** Philip Turner **Manager:** Danny Laws - Jan 2015 **Prog Ed:** Darren Theobald
**Ground:** The Wardale Williams Stadium, Brundon Lane, Sudbury CO10 7HN **(T)** 01787 376 213
**Colours(change):** Yellow/blue/yellow (All red)
**ADDITIONAL INFORMATION:**

## BRAINTREE TOWN RESERVES
Founded: Nickname:

**Secretary:** Paul Tyler **(T)** 01376 327 544 **(E)** paulstyler@hotmail.co.uk
**Chairman:** Lee Harding **Manager:** Ross McPherson - Nov 2014
**Ground:** Stoneylands Stadium, New Road, Long Melford, Sudbury CO10 9JY **(T)** 01787 312 187
**Colours(change):** Orange/blue/orange (Sky blue & white stripes/white/sky blue)
**ADDITIONAL INFORMATION:**

## COGGESHALL TOWN
Founded: Nickname:

**Secretary:** Peter Smith **(T)** 07899 763 027 **(E)** secretary@coggeshalltownfc.co.uk
**Chairman:** Graeme Smith **Manager:** Graeme Smith
**Ground:** The Crops, West Street, Coggeshall CO6 1NS **(T)** 01376 562 843
**Colours(change):**
**ADDITIONAL INFORMATION:**
**Previous Leagues:** Essex & Suffolk Border >2016.
**League Honours:** Essex & Suffolk Border League Division One 2014-15, Premier Division 2015-16.

## CORNARD UNITED
Founded: 1964 Nickname: Ards

**Secretary:** Chris Lamb **(T)** 07851 367 326 **(E)** lambc@hotmail.co.uk
**Chairman:** Harvey Doherty **Manager:** Chris Tracey - Aug 2015 **Prog Ed:** Barnes Print
**Ground:** Blackhouse Lane, Great Cornard, Sudbury, Suffolk CO10 0NL **(T)**
**Colours(change):** All blue (Red & black)
**ADDITIONAL INFORMATION:**
**Record Att:** 400 v Colchester United 1997. **Goalscorer:** Andy Smiles. **Apps:** Keith Featherstone.
**Honours:** Essex & Suffolk Border League Champions 1988-89. Eastern Counties Division One 1989-90. Suffolk Senior Cup 89-90.

## DEBENHAM LC
Founded: 1991 Nickname: The Hornets

**Secretary:** Dan Snell **(T)** 07840 246 837 **(E)** snelly1992@hotmail.co.uk
**Chairman:** Pip Alden **Manager:** Stuart Reavell **Prog Ed:** Martyn Clarke
**Ground:** Debenham Leisure Centre, Gracechurch Street, Debenham IP14 6BL **(T)** 01728 861 101 **Capacity:** 1,000
**Colours(change):** Yellow/black/yellow & black. (All navy blue).
**ADDITIONAL INFORMATION:** **Record Att:** 1,026 vs AFC Wimbledon, FA Cup 2nd Qualifying Round, 29/092007.
**Record Goalscorer:** Lee Briggs. **Apps:** Steve Nelson.
**Previous Name:** Debenham Angels > 2005.
**Previous League:** Suffolk & Ipswich > 2005.

## DEREHAM TOWN RESERVES
Founded: Nickname:

**Secretary:** Kevin Woodgett **(T)** 07828 667 028 **(E)** kevinwoodgett@btinternet.com
**Chairman:** Ray Bayles **Manager:** Wayne Anderson - Mar 2015 **Prog Ed:** Barnes Print
**Ground:** Aldiss Park, Norwich Road, Dereham, Norfolk NR20 3PX **(T)** 01362 690 460
**Colours(change):** Black & white stripes/black/black (Green/white/white)
**ADDITIONAL INFORMATION:**

## DISS TOWN
Founded: 1888 Nickname: Tangerines

**Secretary:** Steve Flatman **(T)** 01379 641 406 **(E)** pam@dissfc.wanadoo.co.uk
**Chairman:** Richard Upson **Manager:** Ross Potter - Aug 2015 **Prog Ed:** Gary Enderby
**Ground:** Brewers Green Lane, Diss, Norfolk IP22 4QP **(T)** 01379 651 223
**Colours(change):** All tangerine (Sky blue/navy/sky blue)
**ADDITIONAL INFORMATION:** **Record Att:** 1,731 v Atherton LR, FA Vase Semi Final, 19.03.94.
**Honours:** Eastern Counties Division One 1991-92. FA Vase winners 1993-94.

## DOWNHAM TOWN

Founded: 1881 Nickname: Town

**Secretary:** George Dickson **(T)** 07545 181 242 **(E)** george.dickson@me.com
**Chairman:** Sandra Calvert **Manager:** Bob Warby - Jan 2015 **Prog Ed:** Barnes Print
**Ground:** Memorial Field, Lynn Road, Downham Market PE38 9AU **(T)**
**Colours(change):** Red/black/red (All blue)
**ADDITIONAL INFORMATION: Record Att:** 440 v Fakenham Town, 1999, Norfolk Senior Cup.
**Honours:** Peterborough Senior Cup 1961-62, 62-63, 66-67, 71-72, 86-87.
Peterborough League 1962-63, 73-74, 78-79, 86-87, 87-88. Norfolk Senior Cup 1963-64, 65-66.

## FRAMLINGHAM TOWN

Founded: 1887 Nickname: The Castlemen

**Secretary:** Fiona Whatling **(T)** 01728 724 038 **(E)** fionawhatling@tiscali.co.uk
**Chairman:** Dean Warner
**Ground:** Framingham Sports Club, Badingham Road, Framlingham IP13 9HS **(T)**
**Colours(change):** Green & white hoops/white/white
**ADDITIONAL INFORMATION:**
**Previous Leagues:** Framlingham League. Leiston League. Suffolk & Ipswich >2016.
**Honours:** Suffolk & Ipswich League, Division Two 1980-81, Senior Division 91-92.

## HALSTEAD TOWN

Founded: 1879 Nickname: Humbugs

**Secretary:** Steve Webber **(T)** 0753 945 154 **(E)** halsteadtownfc@aol.com
**Chairman:** Darren Mitchell **Manager:** Mark Benterman **Prog Ed:** Barnes Print
**Ground:** Rosemary Lane, Broton Industrial Estate, Halstead, Essex CO9 1HR **(T)** 01787 472 082
**Colours(change):** Black & white stripes/white/black (Red & white stripes/red/red)
**ADDITIONAL INFORMATION:**
**Record Att:** 4,000 v Walthamstowe Avenue, Essex Senior Cup 1949.
**Honours:** Eastern Counties Champions 1994-95, 95-96. Div.1 2002-03. Essex Senior Trophy 1994-95, 96-97.

## HAVERHILL BOROUGH

Founded: 2011 Nickname:

**Secretary:** Ben Cowling **(T)** 07904 685 010 **(E)** bencow_144@hotmail.com
**Chairman:** Ben Cowling **Manager:** Martin Westcott - Jan 2015
**Ground:** The New Croft, Chalkestone Way, Haverhill, Suffolk CB9 0BW **(T)** 01440 702 137 **Capacity:** 3,000
**Colours(change):** All royal blue (Grey/grey/red)
**ADDITIONAL INFORMATION:**
**Previous Names:** Haverhill Sports Association > 2013.
**Previous Leagues:** Essex & Suffolk Border > 2013.

## HOLLAND

Founded: 2006 Nickname:

**Secretary:** Darren Williams **(T)** **(E)**
**Chairman:** Mark Sorrell **Manager:** Rob Batten & Glenn Cowen
**Ground:** Eastcliff Sports Ground, Dulwich Road, Holland-on-Sea CO15 5HP **(T)** 07778 142 118
**Colours(change):** All Orange
**ADDITIONAL INFORMATION:**
**Previous Leagues:** Essex & Suffolk Border 2006-2016.

## KING'S LYNN RESERVES

Founded: Nickname:

**Secretary:** Norman Cesar **(T)** 07887 373 956 **(E)** ncesar1947@yahoo.co.uk
**Chairman:** Keith Chapman **Manager:** Robbie Back
**Ground:** The Walks Stadium, Tennyson Road, King's Lynn PE30 5PB. **(T)** 01553 760 060 **Capacity:** 8,200
**Colours(change):** Yellow/blue/yellow. (Turquoise/black/black).
**ADDITIONAL INFORMATION:**

## LEISTON RESERVES

Founded: Nickname:

**Secretary:** David Rees **(T)** 07977 782 559 **(E)** gagrees@aol.com
**Chairman:** Andy Crisp **Manager:** Glen Driver **Prog Ed:** Mark Barber
**Ground:** The LTAA, Victory Road, Leiston, Suffolk IP16 4DQ **(T)** 01728 830 308
**Colours(change):** All blue (All red)
**ADDITIONAL INFORMATION:**

## MARCH TOWN UNITED

Founded: 1885 Nickname: Hares

**Secretary:** Raymond Bennett **(T)** 01354 659 901 **(E)** r.bennett639@btinternet.com
**Chairman:** Phil White **Manager:** Chris Bartlett - May 2014 **Prog Ed:** Barnes Print
**Ground:** GER Sports Ground, Robin Goodfellow Lane, March, Cambs PE15 8HS **(T)** 01354 653 073
**Colours(change):** Amber & black/black/black (All blue)
**ADDITIONAL INFORMATION:**
**Record Att:** 7,500 v King's Lynn, FA Cup 1956.
**Honours:** United Counties League 1953-54. Eastern Counties 1987-88.

## NEEDHAM MARKET RESERVES

Founded: 1919 Nickname: The Marketmen

**Secretary:** Mark Easlea **(T)** 07795 456 502 **(E)** m.easlea@sky.com
**Chairman:** Dr Keith Nunn **Manager:** Kevin Horlock **Prog Ed:** Alex Moss
**Ground:** Bloomfields, Quinton Road, Needham Market IP6 8DA. **(T)** 01449 721 000 **Capacity:** 1,000
**Colours(change):** Red/red/red & white hoops (Blue & black stripes/black/blue)
**ADDITIONAL INFORMATION:**

## STOWMARKET TOWN

Founded: 1883 Nickname: Gold and Blacks

**Secretary:** Neil Sharp **(T)** 07747 774 030 **(E)** footballsecretary@stowmarkettownfc.co.uk
**Chairman:** Neil Sharp **Manager:** Rick Andrews - April 2013
**Ground:** Greens Meadow, Bury Road, Stowmarket, Suffolk IP14 1JQ **(T)** 01449 612 533
**Colours(change):** Old Gold & black/black/black (Claret/blue/claret)
**ADDITIONAL INFORMATION:**
**Previous League:** Essex & Suffolk Border. **Record Att:** 1,200 v Ipswich Town, friendly, July 1994.
**Honours:** Suffolk Senior Cup x10

## TEAM BURY

Founded: 2005 Nickname:

**Secretary:** Daniel Connor **(T)** 07931 309 282 **(E)** daniel.connor@wsc.ac.uk
**Chairman:** Kerry Heathcote **Manager:** Richard Archer - July 2015 **Prog Ed:** Ross Wilding
**Ground:** Bury Town FC, Ram Meadow, Cotton Lane, Bury St Edmunds IP33 1XP **(T)** 01284 754 721
**Colours(change):** All blue (All red)
**ADDITIONAL INFORMATION:**

## WHITTON UNITED

Founded: 1926 Nickname:

**Secretary:** Phil Pemberton **(T)** 07429 116 538 **(E)** pemby64@hotmail.com
**Chairman:** Mark Richards **Manager:** Paul Bugg - June 2012
**Ground:** King George V Playing Fields, Old Norwich Road, Ipswich IP1 6LE **(T)** 01473 464 030
**Colours(change):** Green and white stripes/green/green (All orange)
**ADDITIONAL INFORMATION: Att:** 528 v Ipswich Town, 29.11.95.
Suffolk & Ipswich League 1946-47, 47-48, 65-66, 67-68, 91-92, 92-93. Suffolk Senior Cup 1958-59, 62-63, 92-93.
Suffolk Premier Cup 2011-12. Eastern counties Division One 2013-14.

## WISBECH ST MARY

Founded: 1993 Nickname: The Saints

**Secretary:** **(T)** **(E)**
**Chairman:** **Manager:** Arran Duke
**Ground:** Wisbech St Mary Playing Fields, Beechings Close, Wisbech St Mary PE13 4SS **(T)** 07947 149 310
**Colours(change):** Purple with white trim/purple with white trim/purple
**ADDITIONAL INFORMATION:**
**Previous Leagues:** Cambridgeshire County >2016.

## WOODBRIDGE TOWN

Founded: 1885 Nickname: The Woodpeckers

**Secretary:** Terry Fryatt **(T)** 07803 073 558 **(E)** tfryatt6@btinternet.com
**Chairman:** John Beecroft **Manager:** Jamie Scales - July 2014
**Ground:** Notcutts Park, Fynn Road, Woodbridge IP12 4LS **(T)** 01394 385 308 **Capacity:** 3,000
**Colours(change):** Black & white stripes/black/black. (All red).
**ADDITIONAL INFORMATION: Att:** 3,000 v Arsenal, for the opening of the floodlights, 02.10.90.
Suffolk Senior Cup 1885, 77-78, 92-93, 93-94.
Ipswich & District Senior Champions 1912-13. Suffolk & Ipswich Senior 1988-89.

# ESSEX SENIOR LEAGUE

**Sponsored by:** No sponsor
**Founded:** 1971

**Recent Champions: 2013:** Burnham Ramblers
**2014:** Great Wakering Rovers **2015:** Haringey Borough

| | Premier Division | P | W | D | L | F | A | GD | Pts |
|---|---|---|---|---|---|---|---|---|---|
| 1 | Bowers & Pitsea | 40 | 31 | 3 | 6 | 118 | 34 | 84 | 96 |
| 2 | Basildon United | 40 | 30 | 4 | 6 | 109 | 45 | 64 | 94 |
| 3 | FC Romania | 40 | 27 | 8 | 5 | 114 | 43 | 71 | 89 |
| 4 | Barking | 40 | 23 | 10 | 7 | 101 | 50 | 51 | 79 |
| 5 | Ilford (-1) | 40 | 21 | 9 | 10 | 86 | 51 | 35 | 71 |
| 6 | Wadham Lodge | 40 | 19 | 10 | 11 | 85 | 56 | 29 | 67 |
| 7 | Clapton | 40 | 19 | 10 | 11 | 86 | 67 | 19 | 67 |
| 8 | London Bari | 40 | 17 | 12 | 11 | 60 | 52 | 8 | 63 |
| 9 | Stansted | 40 | 18 | 7 | 15 | 76 | 75 | 1 | 61 |
| 10 | Sawbridgeworth Town (-4) | 40 | 19 | 8 | 13 | 68 | 70 | -2 | 61 |
| 11 | Hullbridge Sports | 40 | 13 | 13 | 14 | 73 | 74 | -1 | 52 |
| 12 | Sporting Bengal United | 40 | 11 | 13 | 16 | 53 | 65 | -12 | 46 |
| 13 | Eton Manor | 40 | 13 | 6 | 21 | 73 | 96 | -23 | 45 |
| 14 | Burnham Ramblers | 40 | 12 | 8 | 20 | 62 | 87 | -25 | 44 |
| 15 | Greenhouse Sports | 40 | 13 | 4 | 23 | 58 | 94 | -36 | 43 |
| 16 | Southend Manor | 40 | 12 | 5 | 23 | 56 | 80 | -24 | 41 |
| 17 | Tower Hamlets | 40 | 10 | 6 | 24 | 49 | 90 | -41 | 36 |
| 18 | Takeley | 40 | 8 | 11 | 21 | 47 | 81 | -34 | 35 |
| 19 | Waltham Forest | 40 | 9 | 4 | 27 | 60 | 98 | -38 | 31 |
| 20 | Enfield 1893 | 40 | 9 | 4 | 27 | 70 | 125 | -55 | 31 |
| 21 | Newham | 40 | 4 | 9 | 27 | 40 | 111 | -71 | 21 |

## LEAGUE CHALLENGE CUP

**HOLDERS:** BOWERS & PITSEA

**ROUND 1**

| | | | |
|---|---|---|---|
| Barking | v | Waltham Forest | 3-0 |
| Basildon United | v | Newham | 4-2 |
| Ilford | v | London Bari | 2-1 |
| Sawbridgeworth Town | v | Hullbridge Sports | 2-0 |
| Takeley | v | Sporting Bengal United | 2-1 |

**ROUND 2**

| | | | |
|---|---|---|---|
| Stansted | v | Bowers & Pitsea | 0-1 |
| Southend Manor | v | FC Romania | 1-2 |
| Burnham Ramblers | v | Enfield 1893 | 2-1 |
| Clapton | v | Barking | 4-0 |
| Basildon United | v | Eton Manor | 2-1 |
| Ilford | v | Sawbridgeworth Town | 2-1 |
| Takeley | v | Greenhouse Sports | 2-0 |
| Tower Hamlets | v | Wadham Lodge | 3-5 |

**QUARTER FINALS**

| | | | |
|---|---|---|---|
| Bowers & Pitsea | v | FC Romania | 0-2 |
| Burnham Ramblers | v | Clapton | 3-2 |
| Basildon United | v | Ilford | 3-2 |
| Takeley | v | Wadham Lodge | 2-0 |

**SEMI FINALS**

| | | | |
|---|---|---|---|
| FC Romania | v | Burnham Ramblers | 3-2 |
| Basildon United | v | Takeley | 5-0 |

**FINAL**

| | | | |
|---|---|---|---|
| FC Romania | v | Basildon United | 0-3 |

**CLUB MOVEMENTS: In:** Barkingside (R - Isthmian D1N), Haringey & Waltham (NC from Greenhouse Sports), Redbridge (R - Isthmian), West Essex (P - Middlesex County). **Out:** Bowers & Pitsea (P - Isthmian D1N), Greenhouse Sports (NC to Haringey & Waltham), Newham (R - Essex Oly)

## GORDON BRASTED MEMORIAL CUP

**HOLDERS:** BARKING

**ROUND 1**

| | | | |
|---|---|---|---|
| Bowers & Pitsea | v | Eton Manor | 3-2 |
| Enfield 1893 | v | Takeley | 0-5 |
| Waltham Forest | v | Wadham Lodge | 1-1, 2-4p |
| Burnham Ramblers | v | London Bari | 3-2 |
| FC Romania | v | Barking | 2-2, 5-4p |

**ROUND 2**

| | | | |
|---|---|---|---|
| Bowers & Pitsea | v | Ilford | 4-1 |
| Clapton | v | Newham | 3-2 |
| Takeley | v | Wadham Lodge | 1-3 |
| Sawbridgeworth Town | v | Tower Hamlets | 2-1 |
| Greenhouse Sports | v | Stansted | 0-1 |
| Southend Manor | v | Sporting Bengal United | 3-3, 3-4p |
| Burnham Ramblers | v | Hullbridge Sports | 0-0, 5-6p |
| FC Romania | v | Basildon United | 3-3, 4-3p |

**QUARTER FINALS**

| | | | |
|---|---|---|---|
| Bowers & Pitsea | v | Clapton | AW |
| Wadham Lodge | v | Sawbridgeworth Town | 2-1 |
| Stansted | v | Sporting Bengal United | 2-1 |
| Hullbridge Sports | v | FC Romania | 2-1 |

**SEMI FINALS**

| | | | |
|---|---|---|---|
| Clapton | v | Wadham Lodge | 2-1 |
| Stansted | v | Hullbridge Sports | 2-1 |

**FINAL**

| | | | |
|---|---|---|---|
| Clapton | v | Stansted | 4-0 |

| | PREMIER DIVISION | 1 | 2 | 3 | 4 | 5 | 6 | 7 | 8 | 9 | 10 | 11 | 12 | 13 | 14 | 15 | 16 | 17 | 18 | 19 | 20 | 21 |
|---|---|---|---|---|---|---|---|---|---|---|---|---|---|---|---|---|---|---|---|---|---|---|
| 1 | Barking | | 1-0 | 1-0 | 3-2 | 3-1 | 5-1 | 3-0 | 1-3 | 3-0 | 1-1 | 2-2 | 0-0 | 4-1 | 0-1 | 3-2 | 4-0 | 3-4 | 4-1 | 8-0 | 1-0 | 4-2 |
| 2 | Basildon United | 1-1 | | 2-1 | 4-0 | 2-1 | 5-1 | 2-1 | 2-2 | 7-2 | 2-0 | 0-3 | 6-1 | 5-0 | 2-0 | 4-2 | 0-0 | 4-2 | 0-3 | 4-0 | 4-3 | 2-1 |
| 3 | Bowers & Pitsea | 3-1 | 1-2 | | 3-1 | 3-0 | 3-1 | 4-1 | 1-0 | 2-0 | 2-1 | 1-0 | 2-0 | 3-0 | 7-0 | 1-0 | 0-1 | 4-1 | 3-0 | 7-1 | 3-1 | 5-1 |
| 4 | Burnham Ramblers | 1-2 | 4-4 | 0-2 | | 0-2 | 3-2 | 2-0 | 1-3 | 2-0 | 1-1 | 1-4 | 3-0 | 2-2 | 0-0 | 1-2 | 3-1 | 0-4 | 2-1 | 1-1 | 4-1 | 1-4 |
| 5 | Clapton | 1-4 | 1-4 | 3-3 | 4-2 | | 3-0 | 3-2 | 0-4 | 3-2 | 3-2 | 3-3 | 1-0 | 1-1 | 1-2 | 1-0 | 1-1 | 2-2 | 1-0 | 2-0 | 2-0 | 4-1 |
| 6 | Enfield 1893 | 0-1 | 2-4 | 3-4 | 3-0 | 1-2 | | 1-5 | 2-5 | 2-1 | 2-2 | 3-2 | 0-5 | 3-2 | 0-4 | 0-1 | 2-2 | 2-2 | 8-2 | 2-1 | 0-1 | 1-6 |
| 7 | Eton Manor | 1-1 | 3-2 | 0-5 | 3-2 | 2-2 | 2-4 | | 1-3 | 4-1 | 1-7 | 2-4 | 2-4 | 5-1 | 1-2 | 2-3 | 3-0 | 0-3 | 3-0 | 4-3 | 1-1 | 3-2 |
| 8 | FC Romania | 4-3 | 0-2 | 2-2 | 8-2 | 2-0 | 4-3 | 6-3 | | 2-2 | 2-0 | 2-1 | 3-0 | 6-0 | 2-1 | 6-0 | 5-1 | 2-0 | 3-0 | 7-1 | 2-0 | 1-1 |
| 9 | Greenhouse Sports | 3-2 | 0-6 | 0-4 | 1-3 | 0-1 | 5-0 | 3-0 | 1-0 | | 0-6 | 1-3 | 2-1 | 1-3 | 2-3 | 4-2 | 3-2 | 2-1 | 1-1 | 2-1 | 0-2 | 3-1 |
| 10 | Hullbridge Sports | 3-3 | 0-1 | 0-9 | 1-3 | 4-4 | 6-2 | 2-2 | 1-1 | 2-0 | | 2-4 | 0-0 | 4-3 | 3-2 | 3-1 | 2-0 | 1-1 | 1-1 | 3-2 | 0-4 | 2-1 |
| 11 | Ilford | 1-1 | 2-3 | 2-0 | 2-4 | 0-0 | 5-2 | 4-0 | 0-1 | 2-2 | 0-1 | | 1-0 | 2-0 | 3-0 | 0-0 | 3-3 | 2-1 | 0-2 | 4-0 | 2-2 | 3-0 |
| 12 | London Bari | 2-2 | 1-2 | 1-4 | 3-0 | 1-1 | 2-1 | 0-0 | 2-1 | 3-2 | 2-2 | 1-1 | | 3-2 | 0-0 | 2-0 | 3-1 | 3-2 | 1-0 | 2-0 | 1-1 | 2-3 |
| 13 | Newham | 3-3 | 0-4 | 0-2 | 0-3 | 1-8 | 0-4 | 1-3 | 2-8 | 4-0 | 2-1 | 1-7 | 0-2 | | 1-2 | 0-4 | 1-1 | 1-2 | 0-2 | 0-1 | 1-1 | 0-0 |
| 14 | Sawbridgeworth Town | 0-3 | 0-5 | 0-3 | 2-1 | 3-3 | 4-1 | 2-1 | 0-3 | 1-1 | 2-0 | 0-1 | 1-1 | 2-2 | | 3-0 | 2-2 | 3-0 | 3-0 | 3-1 | 0-7 | 7-1 |
| 15 | Southend Manor | 1-0 | 0-1 | 0-7 | 3-0 | 1-5 | 4-0 | 1-3 | 0-1 | 7-0 | 1-4 | 2-0 | 1-3 | 0-0 | 0-1 | | 2-2 | 3-1 | 1-1 | 1-3 | 2-4 | 1-1 |
| 16 | Sporting Bengal United | 1-2 | 1-0 | 1-2 | 1-1 | 1-6 | 5-0 | 0-1 | 0-0 | 1-0 | 1-3 | 0-1 | 0-1 | 2-0 | 1-2 | 3-1 | | 1-1 | 1-1 | 3-1 | 2-1 | 3-1 |
| 17 | Stansted | 0-5 | 1-2 | 2-1 | 0-0 | 4-3 | 2-2 | 4-2 | 1-3 | 2-1 | 1-0 | 2-5 | 0-3 | 2-1 | 4-1 | 4-2 | 2-1 | | 5-0 | 0-1 | 1-1 | 4-2 |
| 18 | Takeley | 0-2 | 0-4 | 2-4 | 5-0 | 2-4 | 2-6 | 2-2 | 1-1 | 1-4 | 0-0 | 3-0 | 2-2 | 2-1 | 0-0 | 1-0 | 1-1 | 3-4 | | 2-0 | 0-2 | 2-3 |
| 19 | Tower Hamlets | 2-2 | 2-0 | 1-2 | 1-1 | 1-0 | 5-2 | 2-0 | 1-4 | 3-2 | 1-1 | 1-2 | 2-0 | 0-1 | 1-2 | 1-2 | 1-3 | 0-1 | 0-0 | | 2-2 | 1-3 |
| 20 | Wadham Lodge | 2-4 | 0-2 | 2-2 | 3-1 | 2-1 | 4-1 | 4-1 | 1-1 | 1-3 | 2-1 | 1-3 | 0-0 | 5-1 | 5-2 | 3-0 | 2-2 | 2-1 | 2-0 | 4-0 | | 3-1 |
| 21 | Waltham Forest | 0-5 | 2-3 | 0-3 | 1-4 | 1-2 | 4-0 | 0-3 | 3-1 | 0-1 | 4-0 | 1-2 | 1-2 | 1-1 | 1-5 | 1-3 | 0-1 | 1-2 | 2-1 | 1-4 | 1-3 | |

## BARKING

Founded: 1880 Nickname: The Blues

**Secretary:** Keith Whittington **(T)** 07904 090 959 **(E)** secretary@barking-fc.co.uk
**Chairman:** Rob O'Brien **Manager:** Glen Golby & Steve Willis **Prog Ed:** Derek Pedder
**Ground:** Mayesbrook Park, Lodge Avenue, Dagenham RM8 2JR **(T)** 0776 458 7112
**Capacity:** 2,500 **Seats:** 200 **Covered:** 600 **Midweek Matchday:** Tuesday **Clubhouse:** Yes **Shop:** Yes

**Colours(change):** All blue (All yellow)
**Previous Names:** Barking Rov. Barking Woodville. Barking Working Lads Institute, Barking Institute. Barking T. Barking & East Ham U.
**Previous Leagues:** South Essex, London, Athenian. Isthmian. Southern.
**Records:** **Att:** 1,972 v Aldershot, FA Cup 2nd Rnd, 1978. **Goalscorer:** Neville Fox - 241 (65-73). **Apps:** Bob Makin - 566.
**Honours:** Essex Senior Cup 1893-94, 95-96, 1919-20, 45-46, 62-63, 69-70, 89-90. London Senior Cup 1911-12, 20-21, 26-27, 78-79.

**10 YEAR RECORD**

| 06-07 | 07-08 | 08-09 | 09-10 | 10-11 | 11-12 | 12-13 | 13-14 | 14-15 | 15-16 |
|---|---|---|---|---|---|---|---|---|---|
| ESen 6 | ESen 9 | ESen 12 | ESen 8 | ESen 6 | ESen 7 | ESen 6 | ESen 12 | ESen 3 | ESen 4 |

## BARKINGSIDE

Founded: 1898 Nickname: The Side / Sky

**Secretary:** Jimmy Flanagan **(T)** 07956 894 194 **(E)** confclothing@aol.com
**Chairman:** Jimmy Flanagan **Manager:** Gus Gulfer
**Ground:** Cricketfield Stadium, 3 Cricklefield Place, Ilford IG1 1FY **(T)** 020 8552 3995
**Capacity:** 3,500 **Seats:** 216 **Covered:** Yes **Midweek Matchday:** Monday **Clubhouse:** Yes

**Colours(change):** Sky blue/navy blue/sky blue. (Yellow/yellow/navy)
**Previous Names:** None
**Previous Leagues:** London. Greater London. Met London. Spartan, South Midlands. Essex Senior > 2013. Isthmian 2013-16.
**Records:** **Att:** 957 v Arsenal Reserves, London League, 1957.
**Honours:** London Senior Cup 1996-97. Spartan South Midlands League Premier Division 1998-99. Essex Senior Cup 2008-09.

**10 YEAR RECORD**

| 06-07 | 07-08 | 08-09 | 09-10 | 10-11 | 11-12 | 12-13 | 13-14 | 14-15 | 15-16 |
|---|---|---|---|---|---|---|---|---|---|
| ESen 3 | ESen 3 | ESen 5 | ESen 9 | ESen 15 | ESen 8 | ESen 2 | Isth1N 20 | Isth1N 22 | Isth1N 23 |

## BASILDON UNITED

Founded: 1963 Nickname: The Bees

**Secretary:** Richard Mann **(T)** 07527 743 535 **(E)** ritchiemann@blueyonder.co.uk
**Chairman:** Dave Maxwell **Manager:** Aaron Bloxham **Prog Ed:** Richard Mann
**Ground:** The Longmans Motors Ltd Stadium, Gardiners Close, Basildon SS14 3AW **(T)** 01268 520 268
**Capacity:** 2,000 **Seats:** 400 **Covered:** 1,000 **Midweek Matchday:** Tuesday **Clubhouse:** Yes **Shop:** No

**Colours(change):** Yellow/black/yellow (Green/white/green)
**Previous Names:** Armada Sports.
**Previous Leagues:** Grays & Thurrock. Greater London. Essex Senior. Athenian. Isthmian.
**Records:** **Att:** 4,000 v West Ham, ground opening 11.08.70.
**Honours:** Isthmian League Division 2 Champions 1983-84.

**10 YEAR RECORD**

| 06-07 | 07-08 | 08-09 | 09-10 | 10-11 | 11-12 | 12-13 | 13-14 | 14-15 | 15-16 |
|---|---|---|---|---|---|---|---|---|---|
| ESen 10 | ESen 16 | ESen 8 | ESen 12 | ESen 12 | ESen 18 | ESen 13 | ESen 8 | ESen 12 | ESen 2 |

## BURNHAM RAMBLERS

Founded: 1900 Nickname: Ramblers

**Secretary:** Martin Leno **(T)** 07702 592 418 **(E)** martin.leno@btopenworld.com
**Chairman:** Martin Leno **Manager:** Lee Hughes **Prog Ed:** Martin Leno
**Ground:** Leslie Fields Stadium, Springfield Road CM0 8TE **(T)** 01621 784 383
**Capacity:** 2,000 **Seats:** 156 **Covered:** 300 **Midweek Matchday:** Tuesday **Clubhouse:** Yes **Shop:** No

**Colours(change):** Navy & sky blue stripes/navy/navy (All red).
**Previous Names:** None
**Previous Leagues:** North Essex. Mid-Essex. Olympian. South East Essex. Essex Senior > 2013. Isthmian 2013-15.
**Records:** **Att:** 1,500 v Arsenal, opening of stand.
**Honours:** Essex Senior League 2012-13.

**10 YEAR RECORD**

| 06-07 | 07-08 | 08-09 | 09-10 | 10-11 | 11-12 | 12-13 | 13-14 | 14-15 | 15-16 |
|---|---|---|---|---|---|---|---|---|---|
| ESen 5 | ESen 8 | ESen 7 | ESen 3 | ESen 7 | ESen 4 | ESen 1 | Isth1N 17 | Isth1N 24 | ESen 14 |

## CLAPTON

Founded: 1878 Nickname: Tons

**Secretary:** Shirley Doyle **(T)** 07983 588 883 **(E)** secretary@claptonfc.com
**Chairman:** John Murray-Smith **Manager:** Mike Walther
**Ground:** The Old Spotted Dog, Upton Lane, Forest Gate E7 9NP **(T)**
**Capacity:** 2,000 **Seats:** 100 **Covered:** 180 **Midweek Matchday:** Tuesday **Clubhouse:** Yes **Shop:** No

**Colours(change):** Red & white stripes/black/black (Blue & yellow stripes/blue & yellow/blue)
**Previous Names:** None
**Previous Leagues:** Southern (founder member). London. Isthmian (founder member).
**Records:** **Att:** 12,000 v Tottenham Hotspur, FA Cup, 1898-99. First English club to play on the continent, beating a Belgian XI in 1890.
**Honours:** Isthmian League Champions 1910-11, 22-23, Division 2 1982-83. Essex Senior Cup (x 4).

**10 YEAR RECORD**

| 06-07 | 07-08 | 08-09 | 09-10 | 10-11 | 11-12 | 12-13 | 13-14 | 14-15 | 15-16 |
|---|---|---|---|---|---|---|---|---|---|
| ESen 14 | ESen 11 | ESen 16 | ESen 16 | ESen 17 | ESen 17 | ESen 18 | ESen 10 | ESen 8 | ESen 7 |

## ENFIELD 1893 FC

Founded: 1893 Nickname:

**Secretary:** Mark Wiggs **(T)** 07957 647 820 **(E)** enfieldfc@ntlworld.com
**Chairman:** Steve Whittington **Manager:** Matt Hanning
**Ground:** The Harlow Arena, Elizabeth Way, Harlow, Essex CM19 5BE **(T)** 07957 647 820
**Capacity:** **Seats:** **Covered:** **Midweek Matchday:** Tuesday **Clubhouse:** Yes

**Colours(change):** White/royal blue/white (Green & black/green/green)
**Previous Names:** Enfield Spartans > 1900. Enfield > 2007.
**Previous Leagues:** Tottenham & District, North Middlesex, London, Athenian, Isthmian, Alliance, Southern
**Records:** **Att:** 10,000 v Spurs, floodlight opening at Southbury Rd., 10.10.62. **Goals:** Tommy Lawrence - 191 (1959-64). **Apps:** Andy Pape - 643 (85-92 93-99)
**Honours:** FA Trophy 1981-82, 87-88. Alliance League 1982-83, 85-86. FA Amateur Cup 1966-67, 69-70. Essex Senior League 2010-11.

**10 YEAR RECORD**

| 06-07 | 07-08 | 08-09 | 09-10 | 10-11 | 11-12 | 12-13 | 13-14 | 14-15 | 15-16 |
|---|---|---|---|---|---|---|---|---|---|
| Isth1N 13 | ESen 2 | ESen 2 | ESen 4 | ESen 1 | ESen 7 | ESen 9 | ESen 3 | ESen 16 | ESen 20 |

## ETON MANOR

Founded: 1901 Nickname: The Manor

**Secretary:** Enrique Nespereira **(T)** 07740 457 686 **(E)** nespereira@yahoo.co.uk
**Chairman:** Reg Curtis **Manager:** Tony Stavri **Prog Ed:** Reg Curtis
**Ground:** Broxbourne Borough FC, Goffs Lane, Cheshunt, Hertfordshire EN7 5QN **(T)** 07758 112 356
**Capacity:** 2,500 **Seats:** 200 **Covered:** 600 **Midweek Matchday:** Wednesday **Clubhouse:** Yes

**Colours(change):** Light blue/dark blue/dark blue (Red/white/red)
**Previous Names:** Wildernes Leyton.
**Previous Leagues:** London. Greater London. Metropolitan.
**Records:** **Att:** 600 v Leyton Orient, opening of floodlights. **Goalscorer:** Dave Sams.
**Honours:**

**10 YEAR RECORD**

| 06-07 | 07-08 | 08-09 | 09-10 | 10-11 | 11-12 | 12-13 | 13-14 | 14-15 | 15-16 |
|---|---|---|---|---|---|---|---|---|---|
| ESen 11 | ESen 4 | ESen 6 | ESen 15 | ESen 8 | ESen 14 | ESen 5 | ESen 11 | ESen 14 | ESen 13 |

## FC ROMANIA

Founded: 2006 Nickname:

**Secretary:** Terry Cecil **(T)** 07956 266 969 **(E)** terry.cecil@googlemail.com
**Chairman:** Ion Vintila **Manager:** Ion Vintila **Prog Ed:** Radu Brebene
**Ground:** Cheshunt FC, Theobalds Lane, Cheshunt, Herts EN8 8RU **(T)** 01992 625 793
**Capacity:** 3,500 **Seats:** 424 **Covered:** 600 **Midweek Matchday:** Wednesday **Clubhouse:** Yes

**Colours(change):** Yellow/red/blue/ (All sky blue)
**Previous Names:** None
**Previous Leagues:** Middlesex County 2006-13.
**Records:**
**Honours:**

**10 YEAR RECORD**

| 06-07 | 07-08 | 08-09 | 09-10 | 10-11 | 11-12 | 12-13 | 13-14 | 14-15 | 15-16 |
|---|---|---|---|---|---|---|---|---|---|
| | | | | | MidxP 2 | MidxP 2 | ESen 5 | ESen 6 | ESen 3 |

## HARINGEY & WALTHAM

Founded: 2000 Nickname:

**Secretary:** Tim Aleshe **(T)** 07956 491 958 **(E)** timbukk2@msn.com
**Chairman:** Trevor Duberry **Manager:** Dean Davis **Prog Ed:** Grant Duberry
**Ground:** TBA **(T)**
**Capacity:** **Seats:** **Covered:** **Midweek Matchday:** **Clubhouse:** **Shop:**

**Colours(change):** Purple & white/purple/purple (All tangerine)
**Previous Names:** Mauritius Sports merged with Walthamstow Ave & Pennant 2007. Mauritius Sports Ass. 09-11. Haringey & Waltham Dev. 11-13. Grhouse London 13-15
**Previous Leagues:** London Intermediate 2001-03. Middlesex County 2003-2007. **Previous Names Cont:** Greenhouse Sports 15-16.
**Records:**
**Honours:**

**10 YEAR RECORD**

| 06-07 | 07-08 | 08-09 | 09-10 | 10-11 | 11-12 | 12-13 | 13-14 | 14-15 | 15-16 |
|---|---|---|---|---|---|---|---|---|---|
| | ESen 13 | ESen 15 | ESen 18 | ESen 11 | ESen 12 | ESen 8 | ESen 18 | ESen 19 | ESen 15 |

## HULLBRIDGE SPORTS

Founded: 1945 Nickname:

**Secretary:** Mrs Beryl Petre **(T)** 07768 363 791 **(E)** beryl@petre1942.fsnet.co.uk
**Chairman:** TBA **Manager:** Rob Hodgson
**Ground:** Lower Road, Hullbridge, Hockley Essex SS5 6BJ **(T)** 01702 230 420
**Capacity:** 1,500 **Seats:** 60 **Covered:** 60 **Midweek Matchday:** Tuesday **Clubhouse:** Yes **Shop:** No

**Colours(change):**
**Previous Names:** None
**Previous Leagues:** Southend & District. Southend Alliance.
**Records:** **Att:** 800 v Blackburn Rovers, FA Youth Cup 1999-00.
**Honours:**

**10 YEAR RECORD**

| 06-07 | 07-08 | 08-09 | 09-10 | 10-11 | 11-12 | 12-13 | 13-14 | 14-15 | 15-16 |
|---|---|---|---|---|---|---|---|---|---|
| ESen 12 | ESen 14 | ESen 9 | ESen 11 | ESen 9 | ESen 11 | ESen 15 | ESen 9 | ESen 4 | ESen 11 |

## ILFORD

Founded: 1987 Nickname: The Foxes

**Secretary:** Marion Chilvers **(T)** 020 8591 5313 **(E)** rogerchilvers@aol.com
**Chairman:** Roger Chilvers **Manager:** Allen Fenn **Prog Ed:** Len Llewellyn
**Ground:** Cricklefield Stadium, 486 High Road, Ilford, Essex IG1 1FY **(T)** 020 8514 8352
**Capacity:** 3,500 **Seats:** 216 **Covered:** Yes **Midweek Matchday:** **Clubhouse:** Yes **Shop:** No

**Colours(change):** Blue and white hoops/royal blue/royal blue & white hoops (All red)
**Previous Names:** Reformed as Ilford in 1987 after the original club merged with Leytonstone in 1980.
**Previous Leagues:** Spartan 1987-94, Essex Senior 1996-2004, Isthmian 2004-05, 2006-13, Southern 2005-06.
**Records:** Not known
**Honours:** Isthmian League Division Two 2004-05.

**10 YEAR RECORD**

| 06-07 | 07-08 | 08-09 | 09-10 | 10-11 | 11-12 | 12-13 | 13-14 | 14-15 | 15-16 |
|---|---|---|---|---|---|---|---|---|---|
| Isth1N 21 | Isth1N 21 | Isth1N 17 | Isth1N 20 | Isth1N 20 | Isth1N 20 | Isth1N 22 | ESen 16 | ESen 10 | ESen 5 |

## LONDON BARI

Founded: 1995 Nickname:

**Secretary:** Emilia Tejuoso **(T)** 07570 806 966 **(E)** marketing@londonbarifc.co.uk
**Chairman:** Kashka Anthony Ray **Manager:** Christopher Davis-Emokpae **Prog Ed:** Jason Clarke
**Ground:** The Old Spotted Dog, Upton Lane, Forest Gate E7 9NP **(T)** 02076 840 793
**Capacity:** 2,000 **Seats:** 100 **Covered:** 180 **Midweek Matchday:** Tuesday **Clubhouse:** Yes

**Colours(change):** All red (All blue)
**Previous Names:** Bari FC.
**Previous Leagues:** South Essex 1995-98. Asian League. Essex Sunday Corinthian League > 2012.
**Records:**
**Honours:**

**10 YEAR RECORD**

| 06-07 | 07-08 | 08-09 | 09-10 | 10-11 | 11-12 | 12-13 | 13-14 | 14-15 | 15-16 |
|---|---|---|---|---|---|---|---|---|---|
| | | | | | EsxSC 1 | ESen 10 | ESen 20 | ESen 15 | ESen 8 |

## REDBRIDGE

Founded: 1958 Nickname: Motormen

**Secretary:** Bob Holloway **(T)** 07890 699 907 **(E)** r.holloway338@btinternet.com

**Chairman:** Jim Chapman **Manager:** Dave Ross & Ricky Eaton

**Ground:** Fords Sports and Social Club, Aldborough Road South, Ilford, IG3 3HG **(T)** 07890 699 907

**Capacity:** **Seats:** **Covered:** **Midweek Matchday:** Tuesday **Clubhouse:** Yes

**Colours(change):** All royal blue (All red)
**Previous Names:** Ford United 1958-2004
**Previous Leagues:** Aetolian 1959-64, Greater London 1964-71, Metropolitan 1971-74, Essex Senior 1974-97, Isthmian 1997-2004, 05-16.
**Records:** 58,000 v Bishop Auckland **Previous Leagues Cont:** Conference 2004-05
**Honours:** Aetolian League 1959-60, 61-62. Greater London League 1970-71. Essex Senior League 1991-92, 96-97.
Isthmian League Division 3 1998-99, Division 1 2001-02,

**10 YEAR RECORD**

| 06-07 | 07-08 | 08-09 | 09-10 | 10-11 | 11-12 | 12-13 | 13-14 | 14-15 | 15-16 |
|---|---|---|---|---|---|---|---|---|---|
| Isth1N 16 | Isth1N 3 | Isth1N 8 | Isth1N 18 | Isth1N 16 | Isth1N 6 | Isth1N 20 | Isth1N 14 | Isth1N 23 | Isth1N 24 |

## SAWBRIDGEWORTH TOWN

Founded: 1890 Nickname: Robins

**Secretary:** Richard Hogg **(T)** 07817 558 897 **(E)** rich.hogg@virgin.net

**Chairman:** Steve Day **Manager:** John Watters **Prog Ed:** Steve Tozer

**Ground:** Crofters End, West Road, Sawbridgeworth CM21 0DE **(T)** 01279 722 039

**Capacity:** 2,500 **Seats:** 175 **Covered:** 300 **Midweek Matchday:** Tuesday **Clubhouse:** Yes **Shop:** No

**Colours(change):** Red & black stripes/black/red & black (All blue)
**Previous Names:** Sawbridgeworth > 1976.
**Previous Leagues:** Stortford. Spartan. Herts County. Essex Olympian.
**Records:** **Att:** 610 v Bishops Stortford.
**Honours:**

**10 YEAR RECORD**

| 06-07 | 07-08 | 08-09 | 09-10 | 10-11 | 11-12 | 12-13 | 13-14 | 14-15 | 15-16 |
|---|---|---|---|---|---|---|---|---|---|
| ESen 8 | ESen 12 | ESen 13 | ESen 10 | ESen 16 | ESen 6 | ESen 14 | ESen 6 | ESen 5 | ESen 10 |

## SOUTHEND MANOR

Founded: 1955 Nickname: The Manor

**Secretary:** Steven Robinson **(T)** 07788 580 360 **(E)** southendmanor@btinternet.com

**Chairman:** Steven Robinson **Manager:** Stuart Marshall

**Ground:** The Arena, Southchurch Park, Northumberland Crescent, Southend SS1 2XB **(T)** 07788 580 360

**Capacity:** 2,000 **Seats:** 500 **Covered:** 700 **Midweek Matchday:** Tuesday **Clubhouse:** Yes **Shop:** No

**Colours(change):** Yellow/black/yellow & black (White & red/red/red)
**Previous Names:** None
**Previous Leagues:** Southend Borough Combination. Southend & District Alliance.
**Records:** **Att:** 1,521 v Southend United, opening floodlights, 22.07.91.
**Honours:** Essex Senior Division One 1987-88. Essex Senior League 1990-91.
Essex Senior League Cup 1987-88, 89-90, 2000-01. Essex Senior Trophy 1992-93.

**10 YEAR RECORD**

| 06-07 | 07-08 | 08-09 | 09-10 | 10-11 | 11-12 | 12-13 | 13-14 | 14-15 | 15-16 |
|---|---|---|---|---|---|---|---|---|---|
| ESen 9 | ESen 6 | ESen 4 | ESen 7 | ESen 5 | ESen 2 | ESen 7 | ESen 19 | ESen 18 | ESen 16 |

## SPORTING BENGAL UNITED

Founded: 1996 Nickname: Bengal Tigers

**Secretary:** Shakil Rahman **(T)** 07957 337 313 **(E)** shax101@hotmail.com

**Chairman:** Aroz Miah **Manager:** Imrul Gazi **Prog Ed:** Kamrul Islam

**Ground:** Mile End Stadium, Rhodeswell Rd, Off Burdett Rd E14 7TW **(T)** 020 8980 1885

**Capacity:** **Seats:** Yes **Covered:** **Midweek Matchday:** Wednesday **Clubhouse:**

**Colours(change):** All royal blue (Orange/black/black)
**Previous Names:** None.
**Previous Leagues:** Asian League. London Intermediate, Kent 2003-11.
**Records:** **Att:** 4,235 v Touring Phalco Mohammedan S.C.
**Honours:**

**10 YEAR RECORD**

| 06-07 | 07-08 | 08-09 | 09-10 | 10-11 | 11-12 | 12-13 | 13-14 | 14-15 | 15-16 |
|---|---|---|---|---|---|---|---|---|---|
| Kent P 17 | Kent P 17 | Kent P 17 | Kent P 15 | Kent P 15 | ESen 10 | ESen 11 | ESen 13 | ESen 20 | ESen 12 |

## STANSTED

Founded: 1902 Nickname: Blues

**Secretary:** Tom Williams **(T)** 07921 403 842 **(E)** tom.williams16@btopenworld.com
**Chairman:** Glyn Warwick **Manager:** Mark Ashford
**Ground:** Hargrave Park, Cambridge Road, Stansted CM24 8BX **(T)** 07921 403 842
**Capacity:** 2,000 **Seats:** 200 **Covered:** 400 **Midweek Matchday:** Tuesday **Clubhouse:** Yes **Shop:** No

**Colours(change):** All royal blue (White/grey/grey)
**Previous Names:** None.
**Previous Leagues:** Spartan. London. Herts County.
**Records:** **Att:** 828 v Whickham, FA Vase, 1983-84.
**Honours:**

**10 YEAR RECORD**

| 06-07 | 07-08 | 08-09 | 09-10 | 10-11 | 11-12 | 12-13 | 13-14 | 14-15 | 15-16 |
|---|---|---|---|---|---|---|---|---|---|
| ESen 16 | ESen 10 | ESen 10 | ESen 1 | ESen 2 | ESen 16 | ESen 17 | ESen 17 | ESen 7 | ESen 9 |

## TAKELEY

Founded: 1903 Nickname:

**Secretary:** Mick Rabey **(T)** 07831 845 466 **(E)** Takeleyfc@mail.com
**Chairman:** Pat Curran **Manager:** Marc Das **Prog Ed:** Dave Edwards
**Ground:** Station Road, Takeley, Bishop's Stortford CM22 6SQ **(T)** 01279 870 404
**Capacity:** **Seats:** Yes **Covered:** Yes **Midweek Matchday:** Tuesday **Clubhouse:** Yes

**Colours(change):** All royal blue (All red)
**Previous Names:** None.
**Previous Leagues:** Essex Intermediate/Olympian.
**Records:**
**Honours:** Essex Olympian League 2001-02.

**10 YEAR RECORD**

| 06-07 | 07-08 | 08-09 | 09-10 | 10-11 | 11-12 | 12-13 | 13-14 | 14-15 | 15-16 |
|---|---|---|---|---|---|---|---|---|---|
| EssxO 3 | EssxO 2 | ESen 3 | ESen 6 | ESen 13 | ESen 3 | ESen 3 | ESen 7 | ESen 11 | ESen 18 |

## TOWER HAMLETS

Founded: 2000 Nickname: Green Army

**Secretary:** Adam Richardson **(T)** 07535 858493 **(E)** thfcsecretary@hotmail.com
**Chairman:** Mohammed Nural Hoque **Manager:** Ade Abayomi
**Ground:** Mile End Stadium, Rhodeswell Rd, Poplar E14 7TW **(T)** 020 8980 1885
**Capacity:** 2,000 **Seats:** Yes **Covered:** Yes **Midweek Matchday:** Monday **Clubhouse:**

**Colours(change):** All green (Orange/black/black)
**Previous Names:** Bethnal Green United 2000-2013.
**Previous Leagues:** Middlesex 2000-09.
**Records:**
**Honours:**

**10 YEAR RECORD**

| 06-07 | 07-08 | 08-09 | 09-10 | 10-11 | 11-12 | 12-13 | 13-14 | 14-15 | 15-16 |
|---|---|---|---|---|---|---|---|---|---|
| | MidxP 8 | MidxP 1 | ESen 5 | ESen 4 | ESen 9 | ESen 12 | ESen 4 | ESen 17 | ESen 17 |

## WADHAM LODGE

Founded: 2008 Nickname:

**Secretary:** Sharon Fitch **(T)** 07903 061 692 **(E)** wadamlodge.fc@hotmail.com
**Chairman:** Martyn Fitch **Manager:** Neil Day **Prog Ed:** Anastasia Lazzair
**Ground:** Wadham Lodge Sports Ground, Kitchener Road, Walthamstow E17 4JP **(T)** 07903 061 692
**Capacity:** 3,500 **Seats:** 216 **Covered:** Yes **Midweek Matchday:** Wednesday **Clubhouse:** Yes

**Colours(change):**
**Previous Names:**
**Previous Leagues:** Essex Business House League 2008-09. Essex Olympian League 2009-15.
**Records:**
**Honours:** Essex Olympian League Division Three 2009-10, Division Two 2010-11.

**10 YEAR RECORD**

| 06-07 | 07-08 | 08-09 | 09-10 | 10-11 | 11-12 | 12-13 | 13-14 | 14-15 | 15-16 |
|---|---|---|---|---|---|---|---|---|---|
| | | | EsxO3 1 | EsxO2 1 | EsxO1 4 | EsxO1 2 | EsxOP 9 | EsxOP 4 | ESen 6 |

## WALTHAM FOREST

Founded: 1964 Nickname: The Stags

**Secretary:** Tony Brazier **(T)** 07715 640 171 **(E)** bjmapbr@ntlworld.com

**Chairman:** Turgut Esendagli **Manager:** Kern Kermal **Prog Ed:** Andy Perkins

**Ground:** Wadham Lodge, Kitchener Road, Walthamstow E17 4JP **(T)** 07715 640 171

**Capacity:** 3,500 **Seats:** 216 **Covered:** Yes **Midweek Matchday:** Wednesday **Clubhouse:** Yes

**Colours(change):** White/royal blue/royal blue (All yellow)

**Previous Names:** Pennant 1964-88. Walthamstow Pennant 1988-95. Merged with Leyton to form Leyton Pennant 1995-2003.

**Previous Leagues:** Isthmian 2003-04, 06-14. Southern 2004-06.

**Records:**

**Honours:** Essex Senior Cup 2005-06.

**10 YEAR RECORD**

| 06-07 | 07-08 | 08-09 | 09-10 | 10-11 | 11-12 | 12-13 | 13-14 | 14-15 | 15-16 |
|---|---|---|---|---|---|---|---|---|---|
| Isth1N 8 | Isth1N 19 | Isth1N 20 | Isth1N 16 | Isth1N 21 | Isth1N 17 | Isth1N 18 | Isth1N 23 | ESen 9 | ESen 19 |

## WEST ESSEX

Founded: 1989 Nickname:

**Secretary:** Dan Reading **(T)** 07956 557 438 **(E)** daniel.reading@marks-and-spencers.com

**Chairman:** Richard Kent **Manager:** Kwame Kwateng

**Ground:** Barking FC, Mayesbrook Park, Lodge Avenue, Dagenham RM8 2JR **(T)** 07956 557 438

**Capacity:** 2,500 **Seats:** 200 **Covered:** 600 **Midweek Matchday:** Tuesday **Clubhouse:** Yes

**Colours(change):** Red & black/red/black (Yellow & black/yellow/black)

**Previous Names:**

**Previous Leagues:** Middlesex County >2016

**Records:**

**Honours:** Middlesex County League Division One (Central & East) 2010-11, Premier Division 2015-16.

**10 YEAR RECORD**

| 06-07 | 07-08 | 08-09 | 09-10 | 10-11 | 11-12 | 12-13 | 13-14 | 14-15 | 15-16 |
|---|---|---|---|---|---|---|---|---|---|
| | | | | Midx1 1 | MidxP 11 | MidxP 10 | MidxP 9 | MidxP 7 | MidxP 1 |

| | Reserve Division | P | W | D | L | F | A | GD | Pts |
|---|---|---|---|---|---|---|---|---|---|
| 1 | Waltham Abbey Reserves | 22 | 19 | 1 | 2 | 59 | 29 | 30 | 58 |
| 2 | Redbridge Reserves | 22 | 17 | 0 | 5 | 63 | 39 | 24 | 51 |
| 3 | Thurrock Reserves | 22 | 15 | 4 | 3 | 74 | 27 | 47 | 49 |
| 4 | Heybridge Swifts Reserves | 22 | 11 | 3 | 8 | 62 | 40 | 22 | 36 |
| 5 | Grays Athletic Reserves | 22 | 10 | 5 | 7 | 67 | 49 | 18 | 35 |
| 6 | Hullbridge Sports Reserves | 22 | 9 | 3 | 10 | 43 | 48 | -5 | 30 |
| 7 | Sawbridgeworth Town Reserves | 22 | 8 | 4 | 10 | 43 | 47 | -4 | 28 |
| 8 | Southend Manor Reserves | 22 | 7 | 2 | 13 | 32 | 62 | -30 | 23 |
| 9 | Barking | 22 | 5 | 6 | 11 | 31 | 55 | -24 | 21 |
| 10 | Waltham Forest Reserves | 22 | 7 | 0 | 15 | 35 | 60 | -25 | 21 |
| 11 | Clapton Reserves | 22 | 3 | 4 | 15 | 36 | 59 | -23 | 13 |
| 12 | Takeley Reserves (-3) | 22 | 3 | 4 | 15 | 27 | 57 | -30 | 10 |

# HELLENIC LEAGUE

**Sponsored by:** Uhlsport
**Founded:** 1953
**Recent Champions: 2013:** Marlow
**2014:** Wantage Town **2015:** Flackwell Heath

| | PREMIER DIVISION | P | W | D | L | F | A | GD | Pts |
|---|---|---|---|---|---|---|---|---|---|
| 1 | Kidlington | 38 | 31 | 4 | 3 | 118 | 33 | 85 | 97 |
| 2 | Thatcham Town | 38 | 28 | 6 | 4 | 101 | 45 | 56 | 90 |
| 3 | Flackwell Heath | 38 | 26 | 4 | 8 | 98 | 50 | 48 | 82 |
| 4 | Ascot United | 38 | 23 | 7 | 8 | 75 | 42 | 33 | 76 |
| 5 | Brimscombe & Thrupp | 38 | 21 | 4 | 13 | 75 | 60 | 15 | 67 |
| 6 | Thame United | 38 | 19 | 7 | 12 | 58 | 46 | 12 | 64 |
| 7 | Highworth Town | 38 | 19 | 5 | 14 | 85 | 49 | 36 | 62 |
| 8 | Binfield | 38 | 19 | 5 | 14 | 79 | 63 | 16 | 62 |
| 9 | Oxford City Nomads | 38 | 18 | 5 | 15 | 65 | 64 | 1 | 59 |
| 10 | Longlevens AFC | 38 | 18 | 2 | 18 | 64 | 70 | -6 | 56 |
| 11 | Highmoor-Ibis | 38 | 16 | 5 | 17 | 57 | 60 | -3 | 53 |
| 12 | Lydney Town | 38 | 14 | 10 | 14 | 63 | 66 | -3 | 52 |
| 13 | Ardley United | 38 | 16 | 2 | 20 | 68 | 75 | -7 | 50 |
| 14 | Bracknell Town | 38 | 12 | 10 | 16 | 66 | 72 | -6 | 46 |
| 15 | Royal Wootton Bassett | 38 | 12 | 5 | 21 | 50 | 86 | -36 | 41 |
| 16 | Brackley Town Saints | 38 | 10 | 5 | 23 | 62 | 90 | -28 | 35 |
| 17 | Tuffley Rovers | 38 | 8 | 8 | 22 | 61 | 88 | -27 | 32 |
| 18 | Milton United | 38 | 6 | 9 | 23 | 45 | 95 | -50 | 27 |
| 19 | Abingdon United | 38 | 6 | 3 | 29 | 42 | 109 | -67 | 21 |
| 20 | Wokingham & Emmbrook | 38 | 3 | 4 | 31 | 37 | 106 | -69 | 13 |

| | DIVISION ONE EAST | P | W | D | L | F | A | GD | Pts |
|---|---|---|---|---|---|---|---|---|---|
| 1 | Penn & Tylers Green | 24 | 18 | 4 | 2 | 72 | 12 | 60 | 58 |
| 2 | Bicester Town | 24 | 18 | 3 | 3 | 67 | 31 | 36 | 57 |
| 3 | Henley Town | 24 | 14 | 4 | 6 | 63 | 37 | 26 | 46 |
| 4 | Headington Amateur's | 24 | 13 | 3 | 8 | 51 | 29 | 22 | 42 |
| 5 | Rayners Lane | 24 | 10 | 8 | 6 | 47 | 30 | 17 | 38 |
| 6 | Chinnor | 24 | 11 | 5 | 8 | 47 | 35 | 12 | 38 |
| 7 | Holyport | 24 | 10 | 4 | 10 | 44 | 43 | 1 | 34 |
| 8 | Finchampstead | 24 | 8 | 8 | 8 | 41 | 31 | 10 | 32 |
| 9 | Chalfont Wasps | 24 | 5 | 7 | 12 | 38 | 64 | -26 | 22 |
| 10 | Wantage Town Reserves | 24 | 6 | 4 | 14 | 30 | 58 | -28 | 22 |
| 11 | Didcot Town Reserves | 24 | 6 | 2 | 16 | 31 | 75 | -44 | 20 |
| 12 | Old Woodstock Town | 24 | 5 | 2 | 17 | 21 | 62 | -41 | 17 |
| 13 | Woodley United | 24 | 4 | 2 | 18 | 20 | 65 | -45 | 14 |

Reading Town withdrew - record expunged.

| | DIVISION ONE WEST | P | W | D | L | F | A | GD | Pts |
|---|---|---|---|---|---|---|---|---|---|
| 1 | Carterton | 26 | 21 | 3 | 2 | 74 | 23 | 51 | 66 |
| 2 | Cheltenham Saracens | 26 | 20 | 4 | 2 | 65 | 26 | 39 | 64 |
| 3 | Hook Norton | 26 | 18 | 3 | 5 | 66 | 28 | 38 | 57 |
| 4 | Fairford Town | 26 | 18 | 3 | 5 | 60 | 27 | 33 | 57 |
| 5 | Easington Sports | 26 | 13 | 5 | 8 | 63 | 41 | 22 | 44 |
| 6 | North Leigh | 26 | 10 | 2 | 14 | 52 | 62 | -10 | 32 |
| 7 | Purton | 26 | 7 | 9 | 10 | 43 | 44 | -1 | 30 |
| 8 | Shrivenham | 26 | 8 | 6 | 12 | 31 | 42 | -11 | 30 |
| 9 | Letcombe | 26 | 7 | 9 | 10 | 28 | 40 | -12 | 30 |
| 10 | Shortwood United Reserves (-1) | 26 | 8 | 5 | 13 | 47 | 62 | -15 | 28 |
| 11 | Cirencester Town Dev' | 26 | 7 | 6 | 13 | 48 | 53 | -5 | 27 |
| 12 | Clanfield 85' | 26 | 5 | 7 | 14 | 34 | 58 | -24 | 22 |
| 13 | New College Swindon | 26 | 4 | 2 | 20 | 25 | 68 | -43 | 14 |
| 14 | Tytherington Rocks | 26 | 3 | 2 | 21 | 22 | 84 | -62 | 11 |

## LEAGUE CHALLENGE CUP

**HOLDERS:** ARDLEY UNITED

**ROUND 1**

| | | | |
|---|---|---|---|
| Ardley United | v | Carterton | 1-2 |
| Ascot United | v | Wokingham & Emmbrook | 1-0 |
| Bracknell Town | v | Chinnor | 1-0 |
| Chalfont Wasps | v | Thatcham Town | 0-4 |
| Cheltenham Saracens | v | Longlevens AFC | 1-2 |
| Cirencester Town Development | v | Kidlington | 2-2, 4-2p |
| Fairford Town | v | Highworth Town | 3-3, 3-2p |
| Flackwell Heath | v | Didcot Town Reserves | 3-0 |
| Henley Town | v | Binfield | 1-2 |
| Hook Norton | v | Tytherington Rocks | 2-1 |
| New College Swindon | v | Purton | 5-3 |
| North Leigh United | v | Shrivenham | 2-0 |
| Old Woodstock Town | v | Highmoor-Ibis | 0-7 |
| Oxford City Nomads | v | Abingdon United | 4-0 |
| Penn & Tylers Green | v | Bicester Town | 2-0 |
| Rayners Lane | v | Stokenchurch | 2-1 |
| Reading Town | v | Holyport | AW |
| Wantage Town Reserves | v | Lydney Town | 1-8 |

**ROUND 2**

| | | | |
|---|---|---|---|
| Brackley Town Saints | v | Headington Amateurs | 5-2 |
| Bracknell Town | v | Royal-Wootton Bassett | 0-2 |
| Brimscombe & Thrupp | v | Woodley United | 6-0 |
| Cirencester Town Development | v | Letcombe | 1-0 |
| Finchampstead | v | Fairford Town | 2-1 |
| Flackwell Heath | v | Highmoor-Ibis | 3-2 |
| Longlevens | v | Clanfield | 4-1 |
| Milton United | v | Tuffley Rovers | 1-3 |
| Moreton Rangers | v | Binfield | 0-3 |
| New College Swindon | v | Lydney Town | 0-2 |
| North Leigh United | v | Thatcham Town | 0-5 |
| Penn & Tylers Green | v | Ascot United | 0-2 |
| Rayners Lane | v | Hook Norton | 0-4 |
| Holyport | v | Oxford City Nomads | 1-3 |
| Shortwood United Reserves | v | Carterton | 2-0 |
| Thame United | v | Easington Sports | 2-0 |

**ROUND 3**

| | | | |
|---|---|---|---|
| Finchampstead | v | Binfield | 1-3 |
| Ascot United | v | Thame United | 1-2 |
| Lydney Town | v | Oxford City Nomads | 2-1 |
| Thatcham Town | v | Shortwood United Reserves | 4-2 |
| Royal Wootton Bassett | v | Cirencester Town Development | 2-3 |
| Brimscombe & Thrupp | v | Tuffley Rovers | 4-2 |
| Longlevens AFC | v | Flackwell Heath | 2-4 aet |

**QUARTER FINALS**

| | | | |
|---|---|---|---|
| Brackley Town Saints | v | Thatcham Town | 4-4, 4-3p |
| Lydney Town | v | Thame United | 0-1 |
| Flackwell Heath | v | Binfield | 3-0 |
| Brimscombe & Thrupp | v | Cirencester Town Development | 7-1 |

**SEMI FINALS**

| | | | |
|---|---|---|---|
| Brackley Town Saints | v | Brimscombe & Thrupp | 2-0 |
| Thame United | v | Flackwell Heath | 3-3, 2-4p |

**FINAL**

| | | | |
|---|---|---|---|
| Brackley Town Saints | v | Flackwell Heath | 1-2 aet |

**CLUB MOVEMENTS**

**Premier Division - In:** Burnham (R - Southern D1S&W), Henley Town (P).
**Out:** Kidlington (P - Southern D1C).
**Division One East - In:** AFC Aldermaston (P - Thames Valley), Sandhurst (S - Combined Counties), Wokingham & Emmbrook (R).
**Division One West - In:** Abingdon United (R), Milton United (R), Woodstock Town formerley Old Woodstock Town (S - Div1E).

| PREMIER DIVISION | | 1 | 2 | 3 | 4 | 5 | 6 | 7 | 8 | 9 | 10 | 11 | 12 | 13 | 14 | 15 | 16 | 17 | 18 | 19 | 20 |
|---|---|---|---|---|---|---|---|---|---|---|---|---|---|---|---|---|---|---|---|---|---|
| 1 | Abingdon United | | 0-3 | 0-2 | 2-3 | 3-0 | 1-3 | 2-3 | 3-2 | 1-3 | 0-2 | 0-6 | 2-1 | 0-1 | 3-3 | 0-3 | 2-4 | 1-1 | 1-5 | 1-2 | 2-0 |
| 2 | Ardley United | 1-5 | | 1-3 | 1-0 | 3-1 | 6-4 | 0-1 | 0-6 | 7-1 | 0-4 | 0-3 | 0-2 | 2-1 | 3-1 | 0-1 | 7-1 | 2-3 | 0-0 | 2-1 | 5-0 |
| 3 | Ascot United | 3-0 | 1-0 | | 1-0 | 4-1 | 4-0 | 4-2 | 3-0 | 1-0 | 0-1 | 2-1 | 1-3 | 2-1 | 2-2 | 4-2 | 1-4 | 1-1 | 2-2 | 0-0 | 6-0 |
| 4 | Binfield | 4-0 | 1-1 | 4-0 | | 4-1 | 2-2 | 1-2 | 0-2 | 6-0 | 1-4 | 1-2 | 4-2 | 1-2 | 0-0 | 4-2 | 2-0 | 0-2 | 0-3 | 3-2 | 2-2 |
| 5 | Brackley Town Saints | 5-1 | 3-0 | 1-4 | 2-0 | | 0-1 | 7-2 | 2-5 | 2-4 | 2-5 | 2-2 | 3-1 | 1-2 | 4-1 | 0-1 | 1-1 | 1-1 | 0-2 | 3-2 | 3-1 |
| 6 | Bracknell Town | 3-1 | 0-1 | 0-1 | 2-3 | 2-1 | | 4-2 | 1-1 | 1-2 | 1-3 | 1-1 | 0-1 | 1-1 | 5-1 | 2-1 | 3-0 | 1-0 | 1-1 | 0-0 | 0-3 |
| 7 | Brimscombe & Thrupp | 1-1 | 1-2 | 1-1 | 5-1 | 1-2 | 2-1 | | 5-2 | 1-1 | 3-1 | 2-4 | 0-2 | 4-2 | 2-0 | 4-0 | 1-0 | 3-0 | 1-3 | 4-1 | 4-1 |
| 8 | Flackwell Heath | 2-0 | 3-1 | 2-0 | 2-1 | 4-0 | 3-2 | 4-0 | | 3-3 | 0-1 | 0-3 | 3-1 | 2-0 | 3-0 | 2-0 | 7-2 | 2-0 | 3-0 | 4-3 | 4-3 |
| 9 | Highmoor-Ibis | 6-0 | 2-1 | 0-1 | 1-4 | 3-0 | 1-2 | 1-2 | 0-2 | | 1-2 | 2-0 | 1-3 | 0-2 | 2-1 | 1-0 | 4-0 | 0-1 | 1-1 | 0-3 | 0-0 |
| 10 | Highworth Town | 4-0 | 0-2 | 2-2 | 2-3 | 2-1 | 2-2 | 3-0 | 1-2 | 0-2 | | 2-3 | 3-1 | 2-2 | 1-1 | 1-2 | 8-0 | 0-2 | 1-2 | 5-0 | 2-3 |
| 11 | Kidlington | 7-0 | 5-1 | 3-1 | 5-0 | 3-1 | 3-0 | 4-1 | 1-0 | 1-1 | 1-0 | | 4-1 | 4-2 | 9-2 | 8-1 | 6-2 | 1-0 | 2-1 | 3-3 | 1-0 |
| 12 | Longlevens AFC | 3-0 | 4-1 | 1-1 | 1-2 | 1-0 | 3-1 | 0-2 | 3-2 | 0-1 | 2-3 | 0-1 | | 3-0 | 1-4 | 1-1 | 3-2 | 1-2 | 2-3 | 2-1 | 3-2 |
| 13 | Lydney Town | 3-1 | 3-2 | 0-3 | 2-2 | 2-1 | 4-4 | 0-1 | 1-3 | 3-2 | 0-0 | 1-2 | 6-2 | | 0-0 | 3-2 | 3-2 | 2-2 | 1-3 | 1-1 | 3-0 |
| 14 | Milton United | 1-5 | 2-1 | 0-2 | 0-2 | 3-2 | 3-3 | 0-1 | 2-3 | 2-3 | 0-2 | 0-5 | 2-5 | 1-1 | | 0-2 | 2-2 | 0-1 | 1-4 | 0-3 | 5-0 |
| 15 | Oxford City Nomads | 2-1 | 4-0 | 2-3 | 0-4 | 1-1 | 2-0 | 0-3 | 2-2 | 3-1 | 3-2 | 2-0 | 4-0 | 1-0 | 5-0 | | 0-2 | 1-1 | 1-2 | 2-1 | 2-2 |
| 16 | Royal Wootton Bassett | 2-0 | 2-1 | 0-2 | 2-5 | 1-1 | 2-1 | 2-1 | 0-3 | 0-2 | 0-2 | 0-2 | 0-1 | 1-2 | 0-2 | 3-0 | | 2-0 | 0-1 | 2-2 | 2-1 |
| 17 | Thame United | 2-0 | 0-3 | 2-1 | 1-2 | 5-0 | 2-2 | 1-2 | 0-3 | 2-1 | 3-2 | 0-3 | 4-0 | 3-1 | 1-0 | 0-1 | 3-1 | | 0-0 | 1-0 | 5-1 |
| 18 | Thatcham Town | 6-2 | 3-1 | 2-1 | 2-0 | 7-2 | 6-2 | 0-0 | 3-2 | 2-0 | 2-0 | 0-2 | 3-1 | 4-3 | 5-0 | 3-2 | 1-2 | 3-2 | | 2-1 | 3-1 |
| 19 | Tuffley Rovers | 2-1 | 3-5 | 1-2 | 2-5 | 4-1 | 1-6 | 2-1 | 2-2 | 0-2 | 0-5 | 0-3 | 1-2 | 0-0 | 2-3 | 2-4 | 2-2 | 1-2 | 3-5 | | 4-0 |
| 20 | Wokingham & Emmbrook | 5-0 | 0-2 | 0-3 | 1-2 | 1-4 | 1-2 | 0-4 | 1-3 | 0-2 | 0-5 | 1-4 | 0-1 | 1-2 | 0-0 | 1-3 | 1-2 | 1-2 | 1-6 | 2-3 | |

| DIVISION ONE EAST | | 1 | 2 | 3 | 4 | 5 | 6 | 7 | 8 | 9 | 10 | 11 | 12 | 13 |
|---|---|---|---|---|---|---|---|---|---|---|---|---|---|---|
| 1 | Bicester Town | | 2-0 | 3-2 | 11-0 | 0-0 | 0-1 | 3-0 | 3-0 | 2-0 | 1-0 | 3-1 | 3-2 | 3-1 |
| 2 | Chalfont Wasps | 2-3 | | 0-2 | 7-3 | 1-1 | 1-5 | 1-3 | 1-5 | 1-0 | 0-2 | 3-6 | 4-4 | 4-2 |
| 3 | Chinnor | 1-1 | 2-2 | | 4-2 | 0-0 | 1-2 | 4-4 | 4-0 | 4-0 | 0-2 | 0-0 | 1-3 | 4-0 |
| 4 | Didcot Town Reserves | 1-5 | 2-2 | 1-4 | | 2-0 | 0-2 | 0-7 | 4-2 | 2-1 | 0-6 | 1-4 | 5-0 | 0-0 |
| 5 | Finchampstead | 2-3 | 6-0 | 3-2 | 3-0 | | 1-2 | 1-1 | 2-2 | 5-1 | 0-2 | 1-1 | 1-0 | 5-1 |
| 6 | Headington Amateur's | 2-3 | 2-3 | 3-4 | 2-0 | 2-2 | | 1-2 | 1-1 | 8-0 | 1-1 | 0-2 | 2-0 | 1-0 |
| 7 | Henley Town | 4-4 | 3-1 | 0-2 | 6-0 | 2-0 | 3-1 | | 2-2 | 0-1 | 1-3 | 2-1 | 0-1 | 3-1 |
| 8 | Holyport | 2-4 | 3-1 | 2-1 | 0-1 | 1-0 | 0-1 | 1-3 | | 4-0 | 1-0 | 2-0 | 2-1 | 6-0 |
| 9 | Old Woodstock Town | 0-2 | 5-0 | 1-0 | 0-4 | 2-2 | 1-4 | 1-5 | 3-1 | | 0-3 | 0-4 | 0-1 | 2-1 |
| 10 | Penn & Tylers Green | 5-0 | 0-0 | 5-0 | 3-1 | 4-0 | 2-0 | 5-1 | 3-1 | 4-0 | | 2-2 | 6-1 | 3-0 |
| 11 | Rayners Lane | 5-1 | 1-1 | 1-2 | 2-0 | 0-2 | 2-0 | 2-4 | 1-1 | 0-0 | 1-1 | | 4-1 | 3-0 |
| 12 | Wantage Town Reserves | 0-2 | 1-1 | 0-1 | 3-2 | 0-3 | 0-4 | 0-5 | 2-3 | 2-1 | 1-4 | 3-3 | | 3-0 |
| 13 | Woodley United | 0-5 | 1-2 | 0-2 | 1-0 | 2-1 | 0-4 | 1-2 | 5-2 | 3-2 | 0-6 | 0-1 | 1-1 | |

| DIVISION ONE WEST | | 1 | 2 | 3 | 4 | 5 | 6 | 7 | 8 | 9 | 10 | 11 | 12 | 13 | 14 |
|---|---|---|---|---|---|---|---|---|---|---|---|---|---|---|---|
| 1 | Carterton | | 3-1 | 1-0 | 4-0 | 4-1 | 1-1 | 3-0 | 1-0 | 5-0 | 2-0 | 2-0 | 4-0 | 2-1 | 4-1 |
| 2 | Cheltenham Saracens | 4-2 | | 1-0 | 4-3 | 0-0 | 1-2 | 1-0 | 4-1 | 4-0 | 3-2 | 1-1 | 2-0 | 4-0 | 5-1 |
| 3 | Cirencester Town Development | 0-7 | 2-3 | | 4-1 | 3-3 | 0-1 | 0-1 | 4-4 | 4-0 | 2-3 | 3-1 | 5-0 | 2-1 | 2-2 |
| 4 | Clanfield 85' | 1-3 | 0-3 | 2-2 | | 1-2 | 0-4 | 2-1 | 1-1 | 2-0 | 1-1 | 1-3 | 2-2 | 0-1 | 3-1 |
| 5 | Easington Sports | 0-5 | 2-3 | 3-0 | 4-3 | | 1-3 | 0-3 | 2-2 | 1-0 | 1-0 | 3-3 | 2-3 | 3-0 | 11-0 |
| 6 | Fairford Town | 1-3 | 1-1 | 2-0 | 3-0 | 0-1 | | 0-3 | 3-0 | 3-1 | 6-1 | 4-1 | 3-0 | 0-0 | 4-0 |
| 7 | Hook Norton | 1-2 | 3-4 | 2-2 | 4-1 | 2-1 | 5-0 | | 3-0 | 2-1 | 5-0 | 5-1 | 5-1 | 3-0 | 2-1 |
| 8 | Letcombe | 0-0 | 1-2 | 4-0 | 2-1 | 1-0 | 0-2 | 2-2 | | 2-0 | 1-3 | 2-1 | 0-0 | 1-0 | 1-0 |
| 9 | New College Swindon | 0-4 | 1-2 | 0-6 | 1-1 | 1-3 | 1-3 | 1-2 | 2-0 | | 2-1 | 0-1 | 0-4 | 3-4 | 5-1 |
| 10 | North Leigh | 1-1 | 1-6 | 2-1 | 1-4 | 0-4 | 5-1 | 1-2 | 4-1 | 6-2 | | 0-2 | 8-2 | 5-2 | 3-1 |
| 11 | Purton | 2-4 | 0-1 | 1-1 | 1-1 | 2-2 | 1-2 | 0-1 | 1-1 | 1-1 | 5-0 | | 1-1 | 1-0 | 1-2 |
| 12 | Shortwood United Reserves | 2-3 | 0-0 | 6-2 | 4-0 | 1-5 | 0-3 | 1-4 | 0-0 | 4-1 | 3-1 | 4-7 | | 1-0 | 8-2 |
| 13 | Shrivenham | 4-1 | 0-3 | 2-1 | 1-1 | 0-3 | 1-2 | 2-2 | 1-1 | 2-1 | 2-1 | 1-1 | 1-0 | | 5-0 |
| 14 | Tytherington Rocks | 2-3 | 0-2 | 0-2 | 1-2 | 1-5 | 0-6 | 1-3 | 3-0 | 0-1 | 0-2 | 1-4 | 1-0 | 0-0 | |

## ARDLEY UNITED

Founded: 1945 Nickname:

**Secretary:** Norman Stacey **(T)** 07711 009 198 **(E)** ardleyfc@gmail.com
**Chairman:** Norman Stacey **Manager:** Paul Davis **Prog Ed:** Peter Sawyer
**Ground:** The Playing Fields, Fritwell Road, Ardley OX27 7PA **(T)** 07711 009 198
**Capacity:** 1,000 **Seats:** 100 **Covered:** 200 **Midweek Matchday:** Tuesday **Clubhouse:** Yes **Shop:** No

**Colours(change):** All sky blue
**Previous Names:** None
**Previous Leagues:** Oxford Senior.
**Records:** **Att:** 670 v Oxford United July 2013.
**Honours:** Hellenic League Division One 1996-97, 97-98.

**10 YEAR RECORD**

| 06-07 | 07-08 | 08-09 | 09-10 | 10-11 | 11-12 | 12-13 | 13-14 | 14-15 | 15-16 |
|---|---|---|---|---|---|---|---|---|---|
| Hel P 4 | Hel P 13 | Hel P 5 | Hel P 7 | Hel P 3 | Hel P 3 | Hel P 5 | Hel P 2 | Hel P 8 | Hel P 13 |

## ASCOT UNITED

Founded: 1965 Nickname: Yellaman

**Secretary:** Mark Gittoes **(T)** 07798 701 995 **(E)** mark.gittoes@ascotunited.net
**Chairman:** Mike Harrison **Manager:** Jeff Lamb & Paul McGrotty **Prog Ed:** Neal Jeffs
**Ground:** Ascot Racecourse, Car Park 10, Winkfield Rd, Ascot SL5 7RA **(T)** 01344 291 107
**Capacity:** **Seats:** **Covered:** **Midweek Matchday:** Tuesday **Clubhouse:** Yes

**Colours(change):** Yellow & blue/blue/yellow
**Previous Names:** None.
**Previous Leagues:** Reading Senior.
**Records:** **Att:** 1,149 - 19/08/2011.
**Honours:**

**10 YEAR RECORD**

| 06-07 | 07-08 | 08-09 | 09-10 | 10-11 | 11-12 | 12-13 | 13-14 | 14-15 | 15-16 |
|---|---|---|---|---|---|---|---|---|---|
| ReadS 1 | Hel1E 4 | Hel1E 2 | Hel P 15 | Hel P 12 | Hel P 14 | Hel P 7 | Hel P 3 | Hel P 3 | Hel P 4 |

## BINFIELD

Founded: 1892 Nickname: Moles

**Secretary:** Rob Challis **(T)** 07515 336 989 **(E)** robchallis@binfieldfc.com
**Chairman:** Bob Bacon **Manager:** Roger Herridge **Prog Ed:** Colin Byers
**Ground:** Stubbs Lane off Hill Farm Lane, Binfield RG42 5NR **(T)** 01344 860 822
**Capacity:** **Seats:** yes **Covered:** yes **Midweek Matchday:** Monday **Clubhouse:** Yes

**Colours(change):** All red.
**Previous Names:** None.
**Previous Leagues:** Ascot & District. Great Western Combination. Reading & Dist. Chiltonian.
**Records:** **Att:** 1000+ Great Western Combination.
**Honours:** Hellenic League Division 1 East 2008-09.

**10 YEAR RECORD**

| 06-07 | 07-08 | 08-09 | 09-10 | 10-11 | 11-12 | 12-13 | 13-14 | 14-15 | 15-16 |
|---|---|---|---|---|---|---|---|---|---|
| Hel1E 11 | Hel1E 9 | Hel1E 1 | Hel P 8 | Hel P 2 | Hel P 8 | Hel P 3 | Hel P 5 | Hel P 6 | Hel P 8 |

## BRACKLEY TOWN SAINTS

Founded: 1890 Nickname: The Saints

**Secretary:** Matthew Wise **(T)** 07798 836 625 **(E)** matthewwise@banburylitho.co.uk
**Chairman:** Nick Johnson **Manager:** Nick Johnson **Prog Ed:** Steve Goodman
**Ground:** St James Park, Churchill Way, Brackley, Northamptonshire, NN13 8EJ **(T)** 01280 704 077
**Capacity:** 3,500 **Seats:** 300 **Covered:** 1,500 **Midweek Matchday:** Wednesday **Clubhouse:** Yes

**Colours(change):** Red & black/black/black
**Previous Names:** Brackley Town Development > 2015
**Previous Leagues:** None
**Records:**
**Honours:** None

**10 YEAR RECORD**

| 06-07 | 07-08 | 08-09 | 09-10 | 10-11 | 11-12 | 12-13 | 13-14 | 14-15 | 15-16 |
|---|---|---|---|---|---|---|---|---|---|
| | | | | | | | | Hel1E 2 | Hel P 16 |

## BRACKNELL TOWN

Founded: 1896 Nickname: The Robins

**Secretary:** Sophie McClurg **(T)** 07570 589 293 **(E)** sophie.mcclurg@bracknelltownfc.com
**Chairman:** Kayne Steinborn-Busse **Manager:** Mark Tallentire **Prog Ed:** Tom Canning
**Ground:** Larges Lane Bracknell RG12 9AN **(T)** 01344 412 305
**Capacity:** 2,500 **Seats:** 190 **Covered:** 400 **Midweek Matchday:** Tuesday **Clubhouse:** Yes **Shop:** Yes

**Colours(change):** All red
**Previous Names:** None
**Previous Leagues:** Great Western Comb., Surrey Senior 1963-70, London Spartan 1970-75, Isthmian 1984-2004, Southern 2004-10
**Records:** **Att:** 2,500 v Newquay - FA Amateur Cup 1971. **Goalscorer:** Justin Day. **Apps:** James Woodcock.
**Honours:**

**10 YEAR RECORD**

| 06-07 | 07-08 | 08-09 | 09-10 | 10-11 | 11-12 | 12-13 | 13-14 | 14-15 | 15-16 |
|---|---|---|---|---|---|---|---|---|---|
| Sthsw 19 | Sthsw 20 | Sthsw | Sthsw 22 | Hel P 16 | Hel P 21 | Hel1E 5 | Hel P 13 | Hel P 9 | Hel P 14 |

## BRIMSCOMBE & THRUPP

Founded: 1886 Nickname: Lilywhites

**Secretary:** Allan Boulton **(T)** 07850 471 331 **(E)** allanboulton1@sky.com
**Chairman:** Clive Baker **Manager:** Sam Prior **Prog Ed:** Robert Hill
**Ground:** 'The Meadow', London Road, Brimscombe Stroud, Gloucestershire GL5 2SH **(T)** 07833 231 464
**Capacity:** **Seats:** **Covered:** **Midweek Matchday:** Tuesday **Clubhouse:** Yes

**Colours(change):** All white
**Previous Names:** Brimscombe AFC 1886- late 1970s. Brimscombe and Thrupp merged.
**Previous Leagues:** Gloucestershire County
**Records:**
**Honours:** Gloucestershire County League 2010-11. Hellenic League Div.1 West 2012-13.

**10 YEAR RECORD**

| 06-07 | 07-08 | 08-09 | 09-10 | 10-11 | 11-12 | 12-13 | 13-14 | 14-15 | 15-16 |
|---|---|---|---|---|---|---|---|---|---|
| | | | GlCo 5 | GlCo 1 | Hel1W 4 | Hel1W 1 | Hel P 12 | Hel P 10 | Hel P 5 |

## BURNHAM

Founded: 1878 Nickname: The Blues

**Secretary:** Gary Reeves **(T)** 07919 415 141 **(E)** burnhamfcsec@aol.com
**Chairman:** Gary Reeves **Manager:** Dave Tuttle **Prog Ed:** AM Print & Copy
**Ground:** The Gore, Wymers Wood Road, Burnham, Slough SL1 8JG **(T)** 01628 668 654
**Capacity:** 2,500 **Seats:** Yes **Covered:** Yes **Midweek Matchday:** **Clubhouse:** Yes **Shop:** Yes

**Colours(change):** All blue
**Previous Names:** Burnham & Hillingdon 1985-87
**Previous Leagues:** Hellenic 1971-77, 95-99, Athenian 1977-84, London Spartan 1984-85, Southern 1985-95, 99-16.
**Records:** 2,380 v Halesowen Town - FA Vase 02/04/1983
**Honours:** Hellenic League 1975-76, 98-99, League Cup 1975-76, 98-99, Division 1 Cup 1971-72.
Southern League Division One Central 2012-13.

**10 YEAR RECORD**

| 06-07 | 07-08 | 08-09 | 09-10 | 10-11 | 11-12 | 12-13 | 13-14 | 14-15 | 15-16 |
|---|---|---|---|---|---|---|---|---|---|
| Sthsw 3 | Sthsw 10 | Sthsw 17 | SthM 3 | SthC 14 | SthC 15 | SthC 1 | SthP 20 | SthP 23 | Sthsw 21 |

## CARTERTON

Founded: 1922 Nickname:

**Secretary:** Nick Truman **(T)** 07837 521 332 **(E)** nicktruman@hotmail.com
**Chairman:** Tom Amer **Manager:** Ben Sadler **Prog Ed:** Tom Amer
**Ground:** Kilkenny Lane, Carterton, Oxfordshire OX18 1DY. **(T)** 07810 652 741
**Capacity:** 1,500 **Seats:** 75 **Covered:** 100 **Midweek Matchday:** Tuesday **Clubhouse:** Yes

**Colours(change):** All blue
**Previous Names:** Carterton FC > 1982. Carterton Town > 2004
**Previous Leagues:** Witney & District.
**Records:** **Att:** 650 v Swindon Town, July 2001. **Goalscorer:** Phil Rodney.
**Honours:** Hellenic League Division One West 2015-16

**10 YEAR RECORD**

| 06-07 | 07-08 | 08-09 | 09-10 | 10-11 | 11-12 | 12-13 | 13-14 | 14-15 | 15-16 |
|---|---|---|---|---|---|---|---|---|---|
| Hel P 12 | Hel P 18 | Hel P 12 | Hel P 17 | Hel P 19 | Hel1W 15 | Hel1W 5 | Hel1W 13 | Hel1W 10 | Hel1W 1 |

## FLACKWELL HEATH

Founded: 1907 Nickname: Heathens

**Secretary:** Jo Parsons **(T)** 07984 199 878 **(E)** joparsons19@sky.com
**Chairman:** Terry Glynn **Manager:** Paul Shone **Prog Ed:** Chris Parsons
**Ground:** Wilks Park, Magpie Lane, Heath End Rd, Flackwell Hth HP10 9EA **(T)** 01628 523 892 / 07932 952 538
**Capacity:** 2,000 **Seats:** 150 **Covered:** Yes **Midweek Matchday:** Tuesday **Clubhouse:** Yes

**Colours(change):** All red.
**Previous Names:** None.
**Previous Leagues:** Great Western Combination. Hellenic. Isthmian.
**Records:** **Att:** 1,500 v Oxford United, charity match, 1966. **Goalscorer:** Tony Wood. **Apps:** Lee Elliott.
**Honours:** Hellenic League Premier Division 2014-15. Berks & Bucks Senior Trophy 2015-16.

**10 YEAR RECORD**

| 06-07 | 07-08 | 08-09 | 09-10 | 10-11 | 11-12 | 12-13 | 13-14 | 14-15 | 15-16 |
|---|---|---|---|---|---|---|---|---|---|
| Isth1N 22 | Hel P 9 | Hel P 16 | Hel P 4 | Hel P 8 | Hel P 4 | Hel P 10 | Hel P 8 | Hel P 1 | Hel P 3 |

## HENLEY TOWN

Founded: 1871 Nickname: Red Kites

**Secretary:** Tony Kingston **(T)** 07712 139 592 **(E)** kingstontony6@gmail.com
**Chairman:** Kim Chapman **Manager:** Gerry McGinty **Prog Ed:** Grant Goddard
**Ground:** The Triangle Ground, Mill Lane, Henley RG9 4HB **(T)** 07758 376 369
**Capacity:** **Seats:** **Covered:** **Midweek Matchday:** Tuesday **Clubhouse:**

**Colours(change):** Red & black/red/red
**Previous Names:**
**Previous Leagues:**
**Records:** **Att:** 2000+ v Reading, 1922. **Goalscorer:** M. Turner.
**Honours:** Hellenic League Div.1 1963-64, 67-68, Div.1 East 2000-01. Chiltonian League Division 1 1987-88. Premier 1999-00.

**10 YEAR RECORD**

| 06-07 | 07-08 | 08-09 | 09-10 | 10-11 | 11-12 | 12-13 | 13-14 | 14-15 | 15-16 |
|---|---|---|---|---|---|---|---|---|---|
| Hel1E 16 | Hel1E 6 | Hel1E 7 | Hel1E 5 | Hel1E 2 | Hel P 7 | Hel1E 15 | Hel1E 7 | Hel1E 6 | Hel1E 3 |

## HIGHMOOR IBIS

Founded: 2001 Nickname: Mighty Moor

**Secretary:** Chris Gallimore **(T)** 07717 154 435 **(E)** chris.gallimore@sjpp.co.uk
**Chairman:** Martin Law **Manager:** Marcus Richardson **Prog Ed:** Martin Law
**Ground:** Scours Lane, Tilehurst, Reading RG30 6AY **(T)** 01189 453 999
**Capacity:** **Seats:** Yes **Covered:** Yes **Midweek Matchday:** Monday **Clubhouse:** Yes

**Colours(change):** All blue
**Previous Names:** Highmoor and Ibis merged to form today's club in 2001.
**Previous Leagues:** Reading > 2011.
**Records:**
**Honours:** Reading League Senior Division 2003-04, 10-11.

**10 YEAR RECORD**

| 06-07 | 07-08 | 08-09 | 09-10 | 10-11 | 11-12 | 12-13 | 13-14 | 14-15 | 15-16 |
|---|---|---|---|---|---|---|---|---|---|
| ReadS 2 | ReadS 6 | ReadS 2 | ReadS 4 | ReadS 1 | Hel1E 2 | Hel P 12 | Hel P 4 | Hel P 2 | Hel P 11 |

## HIGHWORTH TOWN

Founded: 1893 Nickname: Worthians

**Secretary:** Fraser Haines **(T)** 07939 032 451 **(E)** fraserhaines@btinternet.com
**Chairman:** Rohan Haines **Manager:** Jeff Roberts **Prog Ed:** Mike Markham
**Ground:** Elm Recreation Ground, Highworth SN6 7DD **(T)** 01793 766 263
**Capacity:** 2,000 **Seats:** 150 **Covered:** 250 **Midweek Matchday:** Wednesday **Clubhouse:** Yes **Shop:** No

**Colours(change):** Red/black/black
**Previous Names:** None.
**Previous Leagues:** Swindon & District. Wiltshire.
**Records:** **Att:** 2,000 v QPR, opening of floodlights. **Goalscorer:** Kevin Higgs. **Apps:** Rod Haines.
**Honours:** Hellenic League Champions 2004-05.
Wiltshire Senior Cup 2014-15.

**10 YEAR RECORD**

| 06-07 | 07-08 | 08-09 | 09-10 | 10-11 | 11-12 | 12-13 | 13-14 | 14-15 | 15-16 |
|---|---|---|---|---|---|---|---|---|---|
| Hel P 15 | Hel P 6 | Hel P 6 | Hel P 9 | Hel P 4 | Hel P 6 | Hel P 16 | Hel P 11 | Hel P 7 | Hel P 7 |

## LONGLEVENS AFC

Founded: 1954 Nickname: Levens

**Secretary:** Bill Davis **(T)** 07526 958 972 **(E)** bill1853@outlook.com
**Chairman:** Chris Bishop **Manager:** James French **Prog Ed:** Chris Bishop
**Ground:** Saw Mills End, Corinium Avenue, Gloucester GL4 3DG **(T)** 01452 530 388 (Clubhouse)
**Capacity:** **Seats:** **Covered:** **Midweek Matchday:** Tuesday **Clubhouse:** Yes

**Colours(change):** Red & black/black/red
**Previous Names:**
**Previous Leagues:** Gloucestershire Northern Senior > 2011. Gloucestershire County 2011-14.
**Records:**
**Honours:** Gloucestershire Northern League Division One 2008-09. Gloucestershire County 2012-13, 13-14.
Hellenic Division One West 2014-15.

**10 YEAR RECORD**

| 06-07 | 07-08 | 08-09 | 09-10 | 10-11 | 11-12 | 12-13 | 13-14 | 14-15 | 15-16 |
|---|---|---|---|---|---|---|---|---|---|
| GlN1 9 | GlN1 4 | GlN1 1 | GlN1 5 | GlN1 4 | GlCo 9 | GlCo 1 | GlCo 1 | Hel1W 1 | Hel P 10 |

## LYDNEY TOWN

Founded: 1911 Nickname: The Town

**Secretary:** Roger Sansom **(T)** 07887 842 125 **(E)** rogersansom@outlook.com
**Chairman:** Ashley Hancock **Manager:** Mark Lee **Prog Ed:** Roger Sansom
**Ground:** Lydney Recreation Ground, Swan Road, Lydney GL15 5RU **(T)** 01594 844 523
**Capacity:** **Seats:** **Covered:** **Midweek Matchday:** Tuesday **Clubhouse:**

**Colours(change):** Black & white/black/black
**Previous Names:** None
**Previous Leagues:** Hellenic 1980-84. Gloucestershire County 2005-06.
**Records:** **Att:** 375 v Ellwood, 05.11.05.
**Honours:** Gloucestershire County League 2005-06. Hellenic League Division 1 West 2006-07.

**10 YEAR RECORD**

| 06-07 | 07-08 | 08-09 | 09-10 | 10-11 | 11-12 | 12-13 | 13-14 | 14-15 | 15-16 |
|---|---|---|---|---|---|---|---|---|---|
| Hel1W 1 | Hel P 10 | Hel1W 8 | Hel1W 8 | Hel1W 5 | Hel1W 13 | Hel1W 10 | Hel1W 2 | Hel1W 3 | Hel P 12 |

## OXFORD CITY NOMADS

Founded: 1936 Nickname: The Nomads

**Secretary:** Sharon Smith **(T)** 07961 488 800 **(E)** sharon.smith23@talk21.com
**Chairman:** Richard Lawrence **Manager:** Craig Adey
**Ground:** Oxford City Stadium, Marsh Lane, Marston OX3 0NQ **(T)** 01865 744 493
**Capacity:** 3,000 **Seats:** 300 **Covered:** 400 **Midweek Matchday:** Tuesday **Clubhouse:** Yes **Shop:** Yes

**Colours(change):** All yellow
**Previous Names:** Quarry Nomads > 2005.
**Previous Leagues:** Chiltonian.
**Records:** **Att:** 334 v Headington Amateurs, 25.08.03.
**Honours:** Hellenic League Premier Division 2011-12.

**10 YEAR RECORD**

| 06-07 | 07-08 | 08-09 | 09-10 | 10-11 | 11-12 | 12-13 | 13-14 | 14-15 | 15-16 |
|---|---|---|---|---|---|---|---|---|---|
| Hel1E 12 | Hel1W 9 | Hel1W 3 | Hel P 10 | Hel P 17 | Hel P 1 | Hel P 4 | Hel P 9 | Hel P 13 | Hel P 9 |

## ROYAL WOOTTON BASSETT

Founded: 1882 Nickname: Bassett

**Secretary:** Ian Thomas **(T)** 07714 718 122 **(E)** ian.thomas@wbtfc.co.uk
**Chairman:** Andy Walduck **Manager:** Paul Braithwaite **Prog Ed:** Mark Smedley
**Ground:** Gerrard Buxton Sports Ground Malmesbury Rd Royal Wootton Bassett SN4 8DS **(T)** 01793 853 880
**Capacity:** 4,500 **Seats:** 550 **Covered:** 1,250 **Midweek Matchday:** Wednesday **Clubhouse:** Yes **Shop:** No

**Colours(change):** All blue
**Previous Names:** Wootton Bassett Town > 2015.
**Previous Leagues:** Wiltshire.
**Records:** **Record Att:** 2,103 v Swindon Town, July 1991. **Goalscorer:** Brian 'Tony' Ewing. **Apps:** Steve Thomas.
**Honours:**

**10 YEAR RECORD**

| 06-07 | 07-08 | 08-09 | 09-10 | 10-11 | 11-12 | 12-13 | 13-14 | 14-15 | 15-16 |
|---|---|---|---|---|---|---|---|---|---|
| Hel1W 11 | Hel1W 15 | Hel1W 4 | Hel1W 2 | Hel P 15 | Hel1W 5 | Hel1W 2 | Hel P 14 | Hel P 11 | Hel P 15 |

## THAME UNITED

Founded: 1883 Nickname: Red Kites

**Secretary:** Jake Collinge **(T)** 07753 502 955 **(E)** jake@jcpc.org.uk
**Chairman:** Jake Collinge **Manager:** Mark West **Prog Ed:** Jake Collinge
**Ground:** The ASM Stadium, Meadow View Pk, Tythrop Wa, Thame, Oxon, OX9 3RN **(T)** 01844 214 401
**Capacity:** 2,500 **Seats:** Yes **Covered:** Yes **Midweek Matchday:** Tuesday **Clubhouse:** Yes

**Colours(change):** Red & black/black/red.
**Previous Names:** Thame F.C.
**Previous Leagues:** Oxon Senior. Hellenic. South Midlands. Isthmian. Southern.
**Records:** **Att:** 1,382 v Oxford United Jan 2011. **Goalscorer:** Not known. **Apps:** Steve Mayhew.
**Honours:** Isthmian Division 2 1994-95.

**10 YEAR RECORD**

| 06-07 | 07-08 | 08-09 | 09-10 | 10-11 | 11-12 | 12-13 | 13-14 | 14-15 | 15-16 |
|---|---|---|---|---|---|---|---|---|---|
| Hel P 20 | Hel1E 10 | Hel1E 9 | Hel1E 1 | Hel P 10 | Hel P 9 | Hel P 9 | Hel P 10 | Hel P 5 | Hel P 6 |

## THATCHAM TOWN

Founded: 1895 Nickname: Kingfishers

**Secretary:** Ron Renton **(T)** 07561 149 558 **(E)** ron.renton@btinternet.com
**Chairman:** Eric Bailey **Manager:** Danny Robinson **Prog Ed:** Andy Morris
**Ground:** Waterside Park, Crookham Hill, Thatcham, Berks RG18 4QR **(T)** 01635 862 016
**Capacity:** 3,000 **Seats:** 300 **Covered:** 300 **Midweek Matchday:** Tuesday **Clubhouse:** Yes **Shop:** Yes

**Colours(change):** Blue and white/blue/blue
**Previous Names:** None
**Previous Leagues:** Hellenic 1974-82, Athenian 1982-84, London Spartan 1984-86, Wessex 1986-2006. Southern 2006-14.
**Records:** 1,400 v Aldershot - FA Vase
**Honours:** Hellenic League 1974-75. Wessex League 1995-96.

**10 YEAR RECORD**

| 06-07 | 07-08 | 08-09 | 09-10 | 10-11 | 11-12 | 12-13 | 13-14 | 14-15 | 15-16 |
|---|---|---|---|---|---|---|---|---|---|
| Sthsw 6 | Sthsw 15 | Sthsw 6 | Sthsw 12 | Sthsw 5 | Sthsw 8 | SthC 17 | Sthsw 19 | Hel P 12 | Hel P 2 |

## TUFFLEY ROVERS

Founded: 1929 Nickname: Rovers

**Secretary:** Neil Spiller **(T)** 07545 492 261 **(E)** admin@tuffleyroversfc.co.uk
**Chairman:** Neil Brinkworth **Manager:** Mark Prichett **Prog Ed:** Neil Spiller
**Ground:** Glevum Park Lower Tuffley Lane, Tuffley, Gloucester GL2 5DT **(T)** 07708 361 808
**Capacity:** 1,000 **Seats:** 100 **Covered:** yes **Midweek Matchday:** Tuesday **Clubhouse:** Yes

**Colours(change):** All claret
**Previous Names:** None
**Previous Leagues:** Gloucestershire County 1988-91, 2007-13. Hellenic 1991-06.
**Records:**
**Honours:** Gloucester County League 1990-91. Gloucestershire Northern League Division One 2006-07.

**10 YEAR RECORD**

| 06-07 | 07-08 | 08-09 | 09-10 | 10-11 | 11-12 | 12-13 | 13-14 | 14-15 | 15-16 |
|---|---|---|---|---|---|---|---|---|---|
| GlN1 1 | GlCo 4 | GlCo 11 | GlCo 3 | GlCo 6 | GlCo 3 | GlCo 2 | Hel1W 6 | Hel1W 2 | Hel P 17 |

## AFC ALDERMASTON
Founded: Nickname:

**Secretary:** Damion Bone **(T)** 07768 031 842 **(E)** damionbone@hotmail.com
**Chairman:** Martin Desay **Manager:** Kieran Jennings & Richard Desay **Prog Ed:** Martin Desay
**Ground:** Aldermaston Recreational Society, Aldermaston, Reading RG7 8UA **(T)** 01189 824 454
**Colours(change):** Red/red/black
**ADDITIONAL INFORMATION:**
**Previous Leagues:** Thames Valley (formerly Reading Senior) >2016

## BICESTER TOWN
Founded: 1876 Nickname: Foxhunters

**Secretary:** Roger Wise **(T)** 07814 676 319 **(E)** roger.wise10@gmail.com
**Chairman:** Tim Holloway **Manager:** Eddie Nix & John Prpa **Prog Ed:** Steve Marriott
**Ground:** Ardley United FC, The Playing Fields Fritwell Road Ardley OX27 7PA **(T)** 07711 009198
**Colours(change):** Red & black/black/red
**ADDITIONAL INFORMATION:** Original club folded in 2013.
**Honours:** Hellenic League 1960-61, 79-80, Division 1 1977-78.

## CHALFONT WASPS
Founded: 1922 Nickname: The Stingers

**Secretary:** Bob Cakebread **(T)** 07895 094 579 **(E)** robert.cakebread@btinternet.com
**Chairman:** Steve Waddington **Manager:** Gareth Williams & Paul Lindsay **Prog Ed:** Alan Yeomans
**Ground:** Crossleys, Bowstridge Lane Chalfont, St Giles HP8 4QN **(T)** 01494 875 050
**Colours(change):** Yellow and black/black/black
**ADDITIONAL INFORMATION: Record Att:** 82 v Didcot Town 17/12/2005.
**Honours:** Wycombe Combination Division One 1930-31, 60-61, Division Two 1948-49, Premier 1964-64. Hellenic League Division 1 East 2007-08.
Wycombe Senior Cup 2009-10.

## CHINNOR
Founded: 1971 Nickname:

**Secretary:** Daryl Ridgley **(T)** 07865 062 028 **(E)** daryl.ridgley@btopenworld.com
**Chairman:** Andy Bennett **Manager:** Ryan Davis & Craig Williams **Prog Ed:** Cathy Searl
**Ground:** Station Road, Chinnor, Oxon OX39 4PV **(T)** 01844 352 579
**Colours(change):** Yellow/black/yellow
**ADDITIONAL INFORMATION:**
**Previous League:** Oxfordshire Senior.
**Record Att:** 306 v Oxford Quarry Nomads, 29.08.2005.

## DIDCOT TOWN RESERVES
Founded: 1907 Nickname: Railwaymen

**Secretary:** Jacquelyn Chalk **(T)** 07535 313 940 **(E)** jacquelyn-dtfc@virginmedia.com
**Chairman:** John Bailey **Manager:** Chris Hurley **Prog Ed:** Jacquelyn Chalk
**Ground:** Draycott Engineering Loop Meadow Stadium, Bowmont Water, Didcot OX11 7GA **(T)** 01235 813 138 **Capacity:** 5,000
**Colours(change):** All red
**ADDITIONAL INFORMATION:**
**Previous League:** Hellenic Reserves.

## FINCHAMPSTEAD
Founded: 1952 Nickname: Finches

**Secretary:** Nick Markman **(T)** 07793 866 324 **(E)** finchsec@gmail.com
**Chairman:** Richard Laugharne **Manager:** Jon Laugharne **Prog Ed:** Richard Laugharne
**Ground:** The Memorial Ground, The Village, Finchampstead RG40 4JR **(T)** 0118 9732 890
**Colours(change):** Red & black/black/black
**ADDITIONAL INFORMATION:**
**Record Att:** 425 v Sandhurst, 1958-59.
**Honours:** Chiltonian League 1987-88. Reading Senior Challenge Cup 1986-87. Hellenic League Division 1 East 2001-02.

## HEADINGTON AMATEURS
Founded: 1949 Nickname: A's

**Secretary:** Donald Light **(T)** 07764 943 778 **(E)** donlight7@gmail.com
**Chairman:** Donald Light **Manager:** Stuart Bishop **Prog Ed:** Donald Light
**Ground:** Horspath Sports Ground, Oxford Rd, Horspath, Oxford OX4 2RR **(T)** 07764 943 778
**Colours(change):** All red
**ADDITIONAL INFORMATION:**
**Record Att:** 250 v Newport AFC, 1991. **Goalscorer:** Tony Penge. **Apps:** Kent Drackett.
**Honours:** Oxfordshire Senior League 1972-73, 73-74, 75-76, 76-77, Division 1 1968-69. Hellenic League Division One West 2010-11.

## HOLYPORT

Founded: 1934 Nickname: The Villagers

**Secretary:** Chris Hope **(T)** 07825 415 385 **(E)** christopher.pope@capita.co.uk
**Chairman:** Tony Andrews **Manager:** Barry Rake & Dan Wake **Prog Ed:** Richard Tyrell
**Ground:** Summerleaze Village SL6 8SP **(T)** 07515 789 415
**Colours(change):** Claret/green/claret
**ADDITIONAL INFORMATION: Att:** 218 v Eton Wick, 2006. **Goalscorer:** Jamie Handscomb - 78. **Apps:** Sam Jones - 216.
**Honours:** Norfolk Senior Cup 1999-2000. Hellenic League Division One East 2010-11.

## PENN & TYLERS GREEN

Founded: 1905 Nickname:

**Secretary:** Andrea Latta **(T)** 07904 538 868 **(E)** hsvlatta1955@yahoo.co.uk
**Chairman:** Tony Hurst **Manager:** Giovanni Sepede **Prog Ed:** James Keating
**Ground:** French School Meadows, Elm Road, Penn, Bucks HP10 8LF **(T)** 01494 815 346
**Colours(change):** Blue & white stripes/blue/blue
**ADDITIONAL INFORMATION:**
**Previous League:** Chiltonian (Founder member).
**Record Att:** 125 v Chalfont Wasps, August 2000.

## RAYNERS LANE

Founded: 1933 Nickname: The Lane

**Secretary:** Tony Pratt **(T)** 0208 422 6340 **(E)** richard.mitchell@tesco.net
**Chairman:** Martin Noblett **Manager:** Enda Hennessey **Prog Ed:** Richard Mitchell
**Ground:** Tithe Farm Social Club, Rayners Lane, South Harrow HA2 0XH **(T)** 0208 868 8724
**Colours(change):** Yellow/green/yellow
**ADDITIONAL INFORMATION:**
**Record Att:** 550 v Wealdstone 1983.
**Honours:** Hellenic League Division 1 1982-83, Division One West 2012-13.

## SANDHURST TOWN

Founded: 1910 Nickname: Fizzers

**Secretary:** Anne Brummer **(T)** 07760 881189 **(E)** anne83@me.com
**Chairman:** Tony Dean **Manager:** Steve Donnelly **Prog Ed:** Anne Brummer
**Ground:** Bottom Meadow, Memorial Ground, Yorktown Rd, GU47 9BJ **(T)** 01252 878 460 **Capacity:** 1000
**Colours(change):** Red/black/black.
**ADDITIONAL INFORMATION:**
**Previous Leagues:** Reading & District. East Berkshire. Aldershot Senior. Chiltonian.
**Record Att:** 2,449 v AFC Wimbledon, Combined Counties 17.08.2002.
**Honours:** Aldershot FA Senior Invitation Challenge Cup 2000-01, 05-06. Combined Counties Premier Challenge Cup 2010-11.

## WANTAGE TOWN RESERVES

Founded: Nickname: The Alfredians

**Secretary:** David Heggie **(T)** 07916 117 722 **(E)** daveheggie.wcfc@live.co.uk
**Chairman:** Tony Woodward **Manager:** Glyn Evans **Prog Ed:** Toni Cooper
**Ground:** Alfredian Park, Manor Road, Wantage OX12 8DW **(T)** 01235 764 781 **Capacity:** 1,500
**Colours(change):** Green & white/white/green
**ADDITIONAL INFORMATION:**

## WOKINGHAM & EMMBROOK

Founded: 2004 Nickname: Satsumas

**Secretary:** Bob Good **(T)** 07970 846 868 **(E)** secretary@wokinghamandemmbrookfcyouth.com
**Chairman:** Graham Tabor **Manager:** Clive McNelly **Prog Ed:** Clive McNelly
**Ground:** Lowther Road Wokingham RG41 1JB **(T)** 01189 780 209
**Colours(change):** Orange & black/black/black.
**ADDITIONAL INFORMATION: Att:** 305 v Binfield, 25.03.2005.
Reading Senior 2008-09, 11-12, 12-13. Hellenic Division One East 2014-15.

## WOODLEY UNITED

Founded: 1904 Nickname: Woods or United

**Secretary:** John Mailer **(T)** 07883 341 628 **(E)** john.mailer@hotmail.co.uk
**Chairman:** Mark Rozzler **Manager:** Michael Herbert **Prog Ed:** Mark Beaven
**Ground:** Scours Lane, Reading, Berkshire, RG30 6AY **(T)** 0118 9453 555
**Colours(change):** Sky blue/grey/sky blue
**ADDITIONAL INFORMATION: Previous Name:** Woodley Town > 2015 then merged with Woodley Hammers.
**Previous League:** Reading.
**Honours:** Reading Football League Senior Division 2008-09. Berkshire Trophy Centre Senior Cup 2008-09.

## ABINGDON UNITED

Founded: 1946 Nickname: The U's

**Secretary:** John Blackmore (T) 07747 615 691 (E) secretaryaufc@virginmedia.com
**Chairman:** Mrs Deborah Blackmore **Manager:** Steve Alman **Prog Ed:** Bill Fletcher
**Ground:** The Northcourt, Northcourt Road, Abingdon OX14 1PL (T) 01235 203 203 2,000
**Colours(change):** Yellow/blue/blue
**ADDITIONAL INFORMATION: Att:** 2,500 in 2007.
Hellenic League Division 1 1981-82, League Cup 1965-66. Berks & Bucks Senior Trophy x2.

## CHELTENHAM SARACENS

Founded: 1964 Nickname: Sara's

**Secretary:** Bob Attwood (T) 07778 502 539 (E) attwood_robert@sky.com
**Chairman:** Chris Hawkins **Manager:** Simon Goodwin & Michael Rhodes **Prog Ed:** Bob Attwood
**Ground:** Petersfield Park, Tewkesbury Road GL51 9DY (T) 01242 584 134
**Colours(change):** All royal blue
**ADDITIONAL INFORMATION: Att:** 327 v Harrow Hill 31/08/2003.
Glouscestershire Senior Cup 1991-92. Hellenic League Division 1 1999-2000.

## CIRENCESTER TOWN DEVELOPMENT

Founded: 2011 Nickname: Centurions

**Secretary:** Scott Griffin (T) 07968 338 106 (E) scott.griffin@cirentownfc.plus.com
**Chairman:** Steve Abbley **Manager:** Alan Lloyd **Prog Ed:** Mark O'Brien
**Ground:** Corinium Stadium, Kingshill Lane, Cirencester Glos GL7 1HS (T) 01285 654 543
**Colours(change):** Red & black/black/red.
**ADDITIONAL INFORMATION:**

## CLANFIELD

Founded: 1890 Nickname: Robins

**Secretary:** Mick Cross (T) 07758 808597 (E) jolimetz@ntlworld.com
**Chairman:** Mick Cross **Manager:** Peter Osborne **Prog Ed:** Trevor Cuss
**Ground:** Radcot Road, Clanfield OX18 2ST (T) 01367 810 314
**Colours(change):** All red
**ADDITIONAL INFORMATION:**
**Record Att:** 197 v Kidlington August 2002.
**Honours:** Hellenic League Division 1 1969-70.

## EASINGTON SPORTS

Founded: 1946 Nickname: The Clan

**Secretary:** Jamie Hunter (T) 07791 681 204 (E) jamiehunter@hotmail.co.uk
**Chairman:** Richard Meadows **Manager:** Ben Milner **Prog Ed:** Angie Clives
**Ground:** Addison Road, Banbury OX16 9DH (T) 01295 257 006
**Colours(change):** Red & white/red/red
**ADDITIONAL INFORMATION:**
**Record Att:** 258 v Hook Norton.
**Hnours:** Oxfordshire Senior League 1957-58, 58-59. Division 1 1965-66. Oxfordshire Senior Ben Turner Trophy 1970-71.

## FAIRFORD TOWN

Founded: 1891 Nickname: Town

**Secretary:** Bill Beach (T) 07919 940 909 (E) billnick54@hotmail.co.uk
**Chairman:** Mike Tanner **Manager:** Gareth Davies **Prog Ed:** Andrew Meaden
**Ground:** Cinder Lane, London Road, Fairford GL7 4AX (T) 01285 712 071 **Capacity:** 2,000
**Colours(change):** All red.
**ADDITIONAL INFORMATION: Att:** 1,525 v Coventry City, friendly, July 2000. **Goalscorer:** Pat Toomey.

## HOOK NORTON

Founded: 1898 Nickname: Hooky

**Secretary:** Colette Warner (T) 07890 649 170 (E) colwarner67@icloud.com
**Chairman:** Mike Barlow **Manager:** Joe Davies **Prog Ed:** Ali Reed
**Ground:** The Bourne, Hook Norton OX15 5PB (T) 01608 737 132
**Colours(change):** All navy blue
**ADDITIONAL INFORMATION:**
**Record Att:** 244 v Banbury United, 12/12/98.
**Honours:** Oxfordshire Senior League 1999-00, 00-01. Hellenic League Division 1 West 2001-02.

## LETCOMBE

Founded: 1910 Nickname: Brooksiders

**Secretary:** Des Williams **(T)** 07765 144 985 **(E)** deswilliams45@btinternet.com
**Chairman:** Dennis Stock **Manager:** David Richardson **Prog Ed:** Russell Stock
**Ground:** Bassett Road, Letcombe Regis OX12 9JU **(T)** 07765 144 985
**Colours(change):** All purple
**ADDITIONAL INFORMATION:**
**Record Att:** 203 v Old Woodstock Town, 29/08/04.
**Honours:** North Berkshire League Division One 1989-90. Chiltonian League Division One 1990-91.

## MILTON UNITED

Founded: 1909 Nickname: Miltonians

**Secretary:** Lee Chapple **(T)** 07845 961 276 **(E)** milton.united.fc@hotmail.co.uk
**Chairman:** Andy Burchette **Manager:** Marcus Brown **Prog Ed:** AM Print & Copy
**Ground:** Potash Lane, Milton Heights, OX13 6AG **(T)** 01235 832 999
**Colours(change):** Claret/sky blue/sky claret
**ADDITIONAL INFORMATION: Att:** 608 Carterton v Didcot Town, League Cup Final, 07.05.05. **Goalscorer:** Nigel Mott.
Hellenic League 1990-91. Division One East 2013-14.

## NEW COLLEGE SWINDON

Founded: 1984 Nickname: Blue College

**Secretary:** Matt Cosnett **(T)** 07846 204 174 **(E)** newcollegeswinfcsec@yahoo.co.uk
**Chairman:** Ian Howell **Manager:** Mark Teasdale **Prog Ed:** Matt Cosnett
**Ground:** Webbs Wood Stadium, South Marston, Swindon SN3 4BZ **(T)** 01793 824 828
**Colours(change):** All royal blue
**ADDITIONAL INFORMATION: Previous League:** Wiltshire > 2011.

## NORTH LEIGH RESERVES

Founded: 1908 Nickname: The Millers

**Secretary:** Keith Huxley **(T)** 07775 818 066 **(E)** huxley893@btinternet.com
**Chairman:** Peter King **Manager:** Paul Lewis & Malcolm McIntosh **Prog Ed:** Alan Blackwell
**Ground:** Eynsham Hall Park Sports Ground OX29 6SL. **(T)** 01993 880 157 **Capacity:** 2,000
**Colours(change):** Yellow & black/black/yellow
**ADDITIONAL INFORMATION:**
**Previous Leagues:** Hellenic Reserves.

## PURTON

Founded: 1923 Nickname: The Reds

**Secretary:** Alan Eastwood **(T)** 01793 729 844 **(E)** alan.eastwood83@ntlworld.com
**Chairman:** Alan Eastwood **Manager:** Justin Miller **Prog Ed:** Alan Eastwood
**Ground:** The Red House, Church Street, Purton SN5 4DY **(T)** 07774 086 421 (MD)
**Colours(change):** All red
**ADDITIONAL INFORMATION:**
**Honours:** Wiltshire League 1945-46, 46-47, 47-48. Wiltshire County League 1985-86. Hellenic League Division 1 1995-96, Division 1 West 2003-04. Wiltshire Senior Cup 1938-39, 48-49, 50-51, 54-55, 87-88, 88-89, 94-95.

## SHORTWOOD UNITED RESERVES

Founded: Nickname: The Wood

**Secretary:** Mark Webb **(T)** 07792 323 784 **(E)** squish.shortwoodfc@live.co.uk
**Chairman:** Peter Webb **Manager:** Paul Meredith **Prog Ed:** Paul Webb
**Ground:** Meadowbank, Shortwood, Nailsworth GL6 0SJ **(T)** 01453 833 936
**Colours(change):** Red & white/black/black
**ADDITIONAL INFORMATION:**
**Previous League:** Gloucestershire Northern Senior.
**Honours:** Gloucestershire Northern Senior League 2011-12. Hellenic Division 2 West 2012-13.

## SHRIVENHAM

Founded: 1900 Nickname: Shrivy

**Secretary:** James Dore **(T)** 07775 933 0761 **(E)** jdoreyboy@aol.com
**Chairman:** James Dore **Manager:** Michael McNally **Prog Ed:** Matt Hirst
**Ground:** The Recreation Ground, Barrington Park, Shrivenham SN6 8BJ **(T)** 07775 933 076
**Colours(change):** Blue & white/blue/blue.
**ADDITIONAL INFORMATION: Att:** 800 v Aston Villa, 21.05.2000.
Hellenic Division One West 2004-05.

## TYTHERINGTON ROCKS

Founded: 1896 | Nickname: The Rocks

**Secretary:** Ted Travell | **(T)** 01454 412 606 | **(E)** tramar1618@btinternet.com
**Chairman:** Ted Travell | **Manager:** Daniel Gillespie | **Prog Ed:** Mark Brown
**Ground:** Hardwicke Playing Field, Woodlands Road, Tytherington Glos GL12 8UJ | **(T)** 07837 555 776
**Colours(change):** Amber & black/black/black

**ADDITIONAL INFORMATION:**
**Previous League:** Gloucestershire County.
**Record Att:** 424 v Winterbourne United, 26/08/2007.

## WOODSTOCK TOWN

Founded: 1998 | Nickname:

**Secretary:** Ian Whelan | **(T)** 07827 894 869 | **(E)** ian.whelan@lucyelectric.com
**Chairman:** James Newton | **Manager:** Matt Pike | **Prog Ed:** AM Print & Copy
**Ground:** New Road, Woodstock OX20 1PD | **(T)** 07748 1522 246 | **Capacity:** 1,000
**Colours(change):** All red

**ADDITIONAL INFORMATION:** 258 v Kidlington, 27.08.01.
**Previous Leagues:** Oxfordshire Senior League 1998-99.
**Previous Names:** Old Woodstock Town 1998-2016.

| DIVISION TWO EAST | P | W | D | L | F | A | GD | Pts |
|---|---|---|---|---|---|---|---|---|
| 1 Penn & Tylers Green Reserves | 18 | 13 | 4 | 1 | 65 | 15 | 50 | 43 |
| 2 Thame United Reserves | 18 | 11 | 4 | 3 | 34 | 19 | 15 | 37 |
| 3 Sandhurst Town Reserves | 18 | 9 | 4 | 5 | 53 | 37 | 16 | 31 |
| 4 Flackwell Heath Reserves | 18 | 9 | 4 | 5 | 49 | 40 | 9 | 31 |
| 5 Ascot United Dev' | 18 | 8 | 2 | 8 | 35 | 33 | 2 | 26 |
| 6 Bracknell Town Dev' | 18 | 7 | 4 | 7 | 44 | 36 | 8 | 25 |
| 7 Stokenchurch | 18 | 5 | 3 | 10 | 35 | 49 | -14 | 18 |
| 8 Holyport Reserves | 18 | 4 | 5 | 9 | 22 | 37 | -15 | 17 |
| 9 Wokingham & Emmbrook Reserves | 18 | 4 | 4 | 10 | 35 | 61 | -26 | 16 |
| 10 Chinnor Reserves | 18 | 2 | 2 | 14 | 20 | 65 | -45 | 8. |

| DIVISION TWO WEST | P | W | D | L | F | A | GD | Pts |
|---|---|---|---|---|---|---|---|---|
| 1 Oxford City Nomads Dev' | 22 | 19 | 3 | 0 | 100 | 21 | 79 | 60 |
| 2 Kidlington Reserves | 22 | 14 | 2 | 6 | 70 | 35 | 35 | 44 |
| 3 Moreton Rangers | 22 | 13 | 5 | 4 | 57 | 29 | 28 | 44 |
| 4 Brimscombe & Thrupp Reserves | 22 | 10 | 8 | 4 | 52 | 31 | 21 | 38 |
| 5 Old Woodstock Town Reserves | 22 | 10 | 6 | 6 | 56 | 41 | 15 | 36 |
| 6 Fairford Town Reserves | 22 | 8 | 7 | 7 | 49 | 39 | 10 | 3[illegible] |
| 7 Highworth Town Reserves | 22 | 9 | 4 | 9 | 46 | 40 | 6 | 3[illegible] |
| 8 Purton Reserves | 22 | 8 | 5 | 9 | 58 | 63 | -5 | 2[illegible] |
| 9 Clanfield 85' Reserves | 22 | 5 | 3 | 14 | 39 | 65 | -26 | 1[illegible] |
| 10 Cheltenham Saracens Reserves | 22 | 5 | 2 | 15 | 27 | 66 | -39 | 1[illegible] |
| 11 Hook Norton Reserves | 22 | 4 | 1 | 17 | 23 | 93 | -70 | 1[illegible] |
| 12 Letcombe Reserves | 22 | 3 | 2 | 17 | 23 | 77 | -54 | 1[illegible] |

# GROUND DIRECTIONS

## PREMIER DIVISION

### ARDLEY UNITED - The Playing Fields OX27 7PA - 07711 009 198

From M40 travelling North. At the end of the slip road at junction 10 turn left onto B430. Take the first right and the ground is 10 yards on your right.
From M40 travelling South at the end of the slip road at junction 10 turn right, cross the motorway keeping in the right hand lane follow signs for B430. Take the first right and the ground is 10 yards on the right.
From the A34. Leave the A34 after the BP garage signed Middleton Stoney / Weston on the Green. Stay on this road some 10 miles to Ardley. After entering the village take the first left after passing the Fox and Hounds public house, and the ground is 10 yards on your right..

### ASCOT UNITED - Ascot Racecourse SL5 7RA - 07798 701 995

Directions to Racecourse – New postcode SL5 7LJ (If your sat nav does not have this postcode try SL5 7LN for A330 Winkfield Road) From Bracknell take A329 to Ascot. From Heatherwood Hospital roundabout take Ascot High Street. At first mini-roundabout go straight. At mini roundabout at end of High Street turn left along A330 Winkfield Road. Go under bridge and take first right signposted Car Park 7&8. Continue forwards past golf club, through gates and follow track to the end. Please arrive from Ascot High Street as some sat navs will direct you by a back road which ends in a locked gate and you will have to retrace your route.

**BINFIELD - Hill Farm Lane RG42 5NR - 01344 860 822**
From M4 Junction 10 take A329 signposted Wokingham & Binfield, at roundabout take 1st exit. Go through 1st set of traffic lights, turn left at 2nd set opposite Travel Lodge. Follow road through village over two mini-roundabouts, at 'T' junction with church in front of you turn right. Take left filter road after 150 yards into Stubbs Lane. Ground is on left at end of short lane.

**BRACKLEY TOWN SAINTS - St James Park, Churchill Way, Brackley, Northamptonshire, NN13 8EJ - 01280 704 077**
Take A43 from Northampton or Oxford, or A422 from Banbury to large roundabout south of town. Take exit marked Brackley (South) and follow towards the town (Tesco store on left). Pass the Locomotive public house and take first turning right, signposted Football Club, into Churchill Way - road leads into Club car park.

**BRACKNELL TOWN - Larges Lane Bracknell RG12 9AN - 01344 412 305**
Leave M4 at J10, take A329M signposted Wokingham & Bracknell. Follow road for 5 miles, over roundabout, pass Southern industrial estate (Waitrose etc.) on right to a 2nd roundabout with traffic lights; take 2nd exit and follow signposts for M3. At next roundabout take 1st exit. At next roundabout take 3rd exit, Church Road dual carriageway. This brings you to another roundabout with Bracknell & Wokingham college on right and Old Manor PH on left, take 5th exit for Ascot - A329. Go down hill on dual carriageway, London Road to next roundabout take 4th exit back up the dual carriageway, London Road, Larges Lane last left turn before reaching roundabout again. Ground 200 yards on right.

**BRIMSCOMBE & THRUPP - 'The Meadow', London Road, Brimscombe Stroud, Gloucestershire GL5 2SH - 07833 231 464**
9 miles north of Cirencester on A419. 2 miles south of Stroud on A419.

**BURHAM - The Gore, Wymers Wood Road, Burnham, Slough SL1 8JG - 01628 668 654**
Approx. 2 miles from M4 junction 7 and 5 miles from M40 junction 2. From M40 take A355 to A4 signposted Maidenhead. From M4 take A4 towards Maidenhead until you reach roundabout with Sainsbury Superstore on left. Turn right into Lent Rise Road and travel approx 11/2 miles over 2 double roundabouts. 100 yards after second double roundabout fork right into Wymers Wood Road. Ground entrance on right.

**CARTERTON - Kilkenny Lane OX18 1DY - 01993 842 410**
Leave A40 follow B4477 for Carterton continue along Monahan Way turning right at roundabout, at traffic lights turn right onto Upavon Way. At next set of lights turn right onto B4020 to Burford. Take 2nd right into Swinbrook Road carry onto Kilkenny Lane, a single-track road). Ground & car park 200 metres on left hand side.

**FLACKWELL HEATH - Wilks Park, Magpie Lane HP10 9EA - 01628 523 892**
Junction 4 of M40 Follow signs A404 (High Wycombe) Turn right at traffic lights halfway down Marlow Hill, signposted Flackwell Heath. Ground three (3) miles on left.

**HENLEY TOWN - The Triangle Ground RG9 4HB - 01491 411 083**
From Henley Town Centre take the A4155 towards Reading. Mill Lane is approximately one mile from the Town Centre on the left immediately before the Jet Garage. From M4 Junction 11 head towards Reading on the A33 inner distribution road then follow A4155 signed to Henley, turn right into Mill Lane after the Jet Garage. Ground & Car Park on the left over the Railway Bridge.

**HIGHMOOR - IBIS - Scours Lane Tilehurst Reading RG30 6AY - 01189 453 999**
Come off J12 of the M4 head along the A4 towards Reading, take a left onto Langley Hill and follow it all the way up onto Park Lane, continue onto School Road past the Tilehurst shops and then down onto Kentwood Hill. At the bottom of the hill take a right onto the Oxford Road towards Reading and just past the Waitrose Shop you need to take a left into an industrial estate and under the railway bridge and the ground will be in front of you to your right.

**HIGHWORTH TOWN - Elm Recreation Ground SN6 7DD - 01793 766 263**
From the A419 (Honda) roundabout travel in a North Easterly direction for 3.5 miles towards Highworth along the A361. Upon reaching Highworth, take the first exit at the Fox roundabout and immediately left into The Elms. After 100 yards, turn left into the Rec car park and the club is at the opposite end.

**KIDLINGTON - Yarnton Road OX5 1AT - 01865 841 526**
From Kidlington Roundabout take A4260 into Kidlington. After 3rd set of traffic lights take 2nd left into Yarnton Road. Ground 300 yards on left, just past Morton Avenue.

**LONGLEVENS AFC - Saw Mills End, Corinium Avenue, Gloucester GL4 3DG - 01452 530388 (Clubhouse)**
From South: From M5 Gloucester exit junction 11a, and bear left onto A417. At roundabout take 2nd exit continue on A417 for ½ mile. At next roundabout take 2nd exit (look for coroners court sign) for ½ mile then turn left on Sawmills End (Ibis Hotel). Ground is on the left just past hotel.
From North: From M5 Gloucester exit junction 11, at roundabout take third exit onto A40 for approx 2 miles. At roundabout take 2nd exit (A417) for 1 mile. At roundabout take 3rd exit (look for coroners court sign) for ½ mile then turn left on Sawmills End (Ibis Hotel). Ground is on the left just past hotel.

**LYDNEY TOWN - Lydney Recreation Ground GL15 5RU - 01594 844 523**
From Gloucester – take Lydney road off A48 down Highfield Hill and into the town centre. Take 1st left into Swan Road after 2nd set of pelican lights. From Chepstow – at by-pass roundabout take Lydney road. Go over railway crossing then take 2nd right into Swan Road.

**OXFORD CITY NOMADS - Oxford City Stadium OX3 0NQ - 01865 744 493**
From South: From Newbury travel along the A34 towards Oxford turn onto Ring Road heading towards London (East). Follow Ring Road over 5 roundabouts to the Green Road roundabout signposted London, M40 East. Go straight over towards Banbury. A fly-over is visible, turn left onto the slip road and follow road to Court Place Farm Stadium on left. From North: At the North Oxford roundabout, travel towards London M40 on the Eastern by-pass, turn off at the flyover, the ground is visible to the left as you go over bridge.

**ROYAL WOOTTON BASSETT - Gerrard Buxton Sports Ground Malmesbury Road Royal Wootton Bassett Wiltshire SN4 8DS - 01793 853 880**
On entering Royal Wootton Bassett from Jct 16 M4, take second exit off second roundabout near Prince of Wales Pub. The sports ground is about 400 yards on the right.

**THAME UNITED - The ASM Stadium, Meadow View Park, Tythrop Wa, Thame, Oxon, OX9 3RN 01844 214 401.** From the west: At the Oxford Road roundabout on the edge of Thame take the first left (sign posted Aylesbury) and follow the by-pass. At the next roundabout take the third exit on to Tythrop Way. The ground is 200 yards on the left.
From the east: Leave the M40 at Junction 6 and follow the signposts to Thame. On arriving in Thame, take the first right on to Wenman Road (B4012). Stay on the B4012 as it by-passes Thame, going straight over two roundabouts. The ground is on the right, directly off the by-pass, approximately half a mile after you pass Chinnor Rugby Club.

**THATCHAM TOWN - Waterside Park, Crookham Hill, Thatcham RG18 4QR - 01635 862 016**
From North, follow A34/A339 towards Newbury. Then follow A4 signposted Thatcham, continue on A4 through Thatcham until you come to a roundabout with a signpost to the Railway Station off to the right (Pipers Way). Continue to the station and go over the level crossing, ground is approximately 250m on left.
From West leave the M4 at junction 13 then follow the directions above. From the East, leave the M4 at junction 12 and follow A4 towards Newbury/Thatcham then follow directions above to the Railway station.

**TUFFLEY ROVERS - Glevum Park Lower Tuffley Lane, Tuffley, Gloucester GL2 5DT - 07708 361 808**
From the motorway junction 12 of the M5 motorway head towards Gloucester for a short distance on the B4008 down to a roundabout. At this roundabout take the second exit A38 towards Gloucester. After 1/2 mile you will reach another roundabout with a Holiday Inn on your right. Take the first exit continuing along the A38 on towards Gloucester until you reach a large traffic light junction at the end of the dual carriageway (approx 1.5 miles). At these lights continue straight over ignoring sign for Tuffley to the right. Once through this first set of lights keep to the right and keep in the right filter lane to the next lights. Turn right here and head towards City Centre and Historic Docks along the Old Bristol Road. Just after the newly shaped road straightens along the old road take the turning right in to Lower Tuffley Lane. Continue along Lower Tuffley Lane almost to the end and the entrance to the ground is on the left through a gateway directly after the commercial premises of Marshall Langston and opposite a large transport depot.

## DIVISION 1 EAST

**AFC ALDERMASTON - Aldermaston Recreational Society, Aldermaston, Reading RG7 8UA - 01189 824 454**
From A4 at Padworth, take A340 (Aldermaston/Tadley) to Calleva Park Roundabout. Take first left on A340, and then take next left at mini roundabout into AWE West Gate. Follow signs for Aldermaston Recreational Society. Car Park directly ahead. Enter ground through gate at end of car park. Ground is on right hand side.

**BICESTER TOWN - Ardley United FC, The Playing Fields OX27 7NZ - 07711 009 198**
From M40 travelling North. At the end of the slip road at junction 10 turn left onto B430. Take the first right and the ground is 10 yards on your right.
From M40 travelling South at the end of the slip road at junction 10 turn right, cross the motorway keeping in the right hand lane follow signs for B430. Take the first right and the ground is 10 yards on the right.
From the A34. Leave the A34 after the BP garage signed Middleton Stoney / Weston on the Green. Stay on this road some 10 miles to Ardley. After entering the village take the first left after passing the Fox and Hounds public house, and the ground is 10 yards on your right.

**CHALFONT WASPS - Crossleys Bowstridge Lane HP8 4QN - 01494 875 050**
A413 to Chalfont St Giles, follow signposts for village centre. Bowstridge Lane is 400 yards on left immediately after the shops. Crossleys is 400 yards along Bowstridge Lane on the right. Ground is directly ahead.

**CHINNOR - Station Road OX39 4PV - 01844 352 579**
Leave M40 at junction 6 and follow B4009 sign posted Princes Risborough. After 3 miles enter Chinnor and turn left at Crown PH roundabout. Ground is 400 yards on right.

**DIDCOT TOWN RESERVES - Loop Meadow Stadium OX11 7GA - 01235 813 138**
From A34 take A4130 towards Didcot, at first roundabout take first exit, at next roundabout take third exit, then straight across next two roundabouts, at 5th roundabout turn right into Avon Way, ground is on the left. Also footpath direct from Didcot Railway Station.

**FINCHAMPSTEAD - The Memorial Ground, The Village RG40 4JR - 0118 973 2890**
A321 from Wokingham, then fork right onto B3016. At the Greyhound Public House turn right onto the B3348. The ground is 200 yards on the right.

**HEADINGTON AM' - Horspath Sports Ground, Oxford Rd, Horspath, Oxford OX4 2RR - 07764 943 778**
A4142 (Oxford Ring Road - BMW Plant) turn into Horspath Road, follow road for 0.5 miles, ground is on left.

**HOLYPORT - Summerleaze Village SL6 8SP - 07702 369 708**
From the A4 Maidenhead take the B4447 towards Cookham after mile turn right into Ray Mill Road West, at the T-junction turn left into Blackamoor Lane. As road bends sharply you will see the entrance to the ground on left, signposted Holyport FC. Please observe speed limit down track to the ground.

**PENN & TYLERS GREEN - French School Meadows HP10 8LF - 01494 815 346**
From West - 'M40 to High Wycombe leave at J4. Follow A404 to Amersham, via Wycombe. Stay on A404 up the hill past railway station approx. 3 miles at Hazlemere Crossroads turn right onto the B474 signposted to Penn and Beaconsfield. Continue for approx. one mile go past three new houses on left, turn into Elm Road, the ground is on the left. From East -Leave M40 at Junction 2 and take the road signed Beaconsfield. From Beaconsfield follow the road through Penn towards Hazlemere, pass the pond on green and entrance to ground is on the right had side of road before the hill.

**RAYNERS LANE - Tithe Farm Social Club HA2 0XH - 0208 868 8724**
From A40 Polish War Memorial turn left into A4180 (West End Road), approx. 500 metres turn right into Station Approach, at traffic lights turn right into Victoria Road. At next roundabout continue straight on to traffic lights at junction with Alexandra Avenue (Matrix Bar & Restaurant on left). Continue straight on over traffic lights and take second turning on left into Rayners Lane. Ground is approximately half a mile on the left.

**SANDHURST TOWN - Bottom Meadow, Memorial Ground, Yorktown Rd, GU47 9BJ - 01252 878 460**
Coming from Camberley:
Once on the A321 (Yorktown Road), drive past the pitches and memorial park on your left, continue past the large car parks. Turn left in to a small car park opposite Park Road. There is a café (Pistachios in the Park), some skateboard ramps and a large barrier/gate. Drive through the gate and park on the grass area on the right-hand side. The Stadium itself is about 50 yards further down the track (it is visible in the corner).
Coming from Sandhurst Village:
Once on the A321 (Yorktown Road), driving away from the village shops, continue until you see a petrol station on your right. Continue for a further 50 yards where you need to turn right in to a small car park opposite Park Road. There is a café (Pistachios in the Park), some skateboard ramps and a large barrier/gate. Drive through the gate and park on the grass area on the right-hand side. The Stadium itself is about 50 yards further down the track (it is visible in the corner).

**WANTAGE TOWN RESERVES - Alfredian Park Manor Road, Wantage OX12 8DW - 01235 764 781**
Proceed to Market Square. Take road at southeast corner (Newbury Street signposted to Hungerford). Continue for approximately a quarter of a mile take right turning into the ground. Clearly marked "Wantage Town FC".

**WOKINGHAM & EMMB' - Emmbrook Sports & Social Club Lowther Rd, Wokingham. RG41 1JB 0118 9780 209**
From M4 - exit J10 – take right slip road signposted Reading (not Bracknell/Wokingham). After 100 yds exit to Winnersh Triangle /Earley . As you approach traffic lights go through both sets bearing right towards Earley/Winnersh /Wokingham . Continue to next set of traffic lights and keep left bearing left under Railway Bridge . Keep left and bear left at next set of traffic lights to Winnersh/Wokingham on A329 –Reading Road . Continue straight ahead to traffic lights – go straight ahead continuing on A329 –Reading Road passing Sainsbury's on your right . Continue through next lights, under bridge and past BP garage on the left . Once past the garage take next left into Old Forest Road . Go over the bridge to next turn on the right hand side into Lowther Road and immediately right into the Emmbrook Sports and Social Club.

**WOODLEY UNITED - Scours Lane, Reading, Berkshire, RG30 6AY - 0118 9453 555**
Come off J12 of the M4 head along the A4 towards Reading, take a left onto Langley Hill and follow it all the way up onto Park Lane, continue onto School Road past the Tilehurst shops and then down onto Kentwood Hill. At the bottom of the hill take a right onto the Oxford Road towards Reading and just past the Waitrose Shop you need to take a left into an industrial estate and under the railway bridge and the ground will be in front of you to your right.

## DIVISION 1 WEST

**ABINGDON UNITED - The Northcourt, Northcourt Road, Abingdon OX14 1PL - 01235 203 203**
From the north – Leave A34 at Abingdon north turning. Ground on right at first set of traffic lights.
From the south – Enter Town Centre, leave north on A4183 (Oxford Road).
Ground on left after one mile.

**CHELTENHAM SARACENS - PETERSFIELD PARK GL51 9DY - 01242 584 134**
Follow directions into Cheltenham following signs for railway station. At Station roundabout take Gloucester Road, in a Northerly direction for approx 2 miles. Turn left at lights past Tesco entrance onto Tewkesbury Rd, follow road past 'The Range' store over railway bridge. Take 1st left and then 1st left again, then left into service road into car park.

**CIRENCESTER TOWN DEV. - Corinium Stadium, Kingshill Lane, Cirencester Glos GL7 1HS - 01285 654 543**
Leave bypass at Burford Road roundabout. Aim for Stow, turn right at traffic lights, then right again at next junction, first left into Kingshill Lane. Ground 500 yards on right.

**CLANFIELD - Radcot Road OX18 2ST - 01367 810 314**
Situated on A4095 at southern end of village, 8 miles west of Witney and 4 miles east of Faringdon.

**EASINGTON SPORTS - Addison Road OX16 9DH - 01295 257 006**
From North/South M40- Leave M40 at J11, follow A422 to Banbury, 2nd r'about take A4260 to Adderbury. Go through three sets of traffic lights, at top of hill at T-junc' turn left. Take 3rd right into Addison Rd. From South West A361 – Entering Banbury take 1st right turning into Springfield Av after 'The Easington' PH. Follow road, take T-junc' right into Grange Rd, 1st right into Addison Rd. Ground on left at end of road.

**FAIRFORD TOWN - Cinder Lane London Road GL7 4AX - 01285 712 071**
Take A417 from Lechlade, turn left down Cinder Lane 150 yards after 40 mph sign. From Cirencester take Lechlade Road, turn right down Cinder Lane 400 yards after passing the Railway Inn.

**HOOK NORTON - The Bourne OX15 5PB - 01608 737 132**
From Oxford – A44 to junction with A361 turn right, take 1st left to a 'T' junction, turn right & enter village, after 30 MPH turn left then 1st right into 'The Bourne', take 1st left into ground.

**LETCOMBE - Bassett Road OX12 9JU - 07765 144 985**
Take the B4507 from Wantage (Sign posted White Horse). Turn left after half a mile to Letcombe Regis. Ground on Far side of Village, on the right hand side of road.

**MILTON UNITED - Potash Lane OX13 6AG - 01235 832 999**
Exit A34 at Milton, 10 miles south of Oxford & 12 miles north of junction 13 of M4. Take A4130 towards Wantage approximately 200 metres turn 1st left then right into Milton Hill. Ground 400 metres on the left.

**NEW COLLEGE SWINDON - Supermarine RFC Sports & Social Supermarine Road South Marston Swindon SN3 4BZ - 01793 824 828**
From M5 Junction 11a, take the A417 to Cirencester, then A419 Swindon. At the A361 junction by Honda Factory take road to Highworth. After one mile Club is on 4th roundabout.
From M4 Junction 15, take A419 towards Swindon Cirencester, take A361, then as above .
From A420 Swindon take A419 to Cirencester, near Honda factory take A361, then as above.

**NORTH LEIGH RESERVES - Eynsham Hall Park Sports Ground OX29 6SL - 07775 818 066**
Ground situated on A4095 Witney to Woodstock road, three miles east of Witney. Entrance 300 yards east of main park entrance.

**PURTON - The Red House SN5 4DY - 01793 770 262 MD**
Red House is near Village Hall Square; Purton is well signposted from all directions, situated on the B4041 Wootton Bassett to Cricklade Road, NW of Swindon.

**SHORTWOOD UNITED RESERVES - Meadowbank, Shortwood, Nailsworth GL6 0SJ 01453 833 936**
When entering Nailsworth from Stroud turn right at mini roundabout, when coming from Cirencester go straight over roundabout, and when from Bath turn left at mini roundabout.
Proceed up Spring Hill 30 yards turn left at Raffles Wine Warehouse, straight through town turn left at Brittannia Pub carry on for 1 mile until you come to Shortwood village you will see sign post on fork in the road keep to the left follow on for quarter of a mile ground opposite church.

**SHRIVENHAM - The Recreation Ground SN6 8BJ - 07775 933 076**
Shrivenham village is signposted off A420 Oxford to Swindon road, six miles east of Swindon, four miles west of Faringdon. Drive through village turn into Highworth Road, ground is on right, car park on left.

**TYTHERINGTON ROCKS - Hardwicke Playing Field GL12 8UJ - 07837 555 776**
From M5 Junction 14 take A38 for Bristol. Tytherington turn-off is approximately three (3) miles. Enter village, ground is signposted.

**WOODSTOCK TOWN - New Road, Woodstock OX20 1PD - 07748 152 243**
A44 from Oxford, turn right opposite The Crown into Hensington Road. After half a mile road bends to right, take 1st turning right into New Road. Ground on left.

# MIDLAND FOOTBALL LEAGUE

**Founded:** 2014 After the merger of the Midland Football Alliance (1994) and the Midland Football Combination (1927)

**Recent Champions: 2015:** Basford United

| | PREMIER DIVISION | P | W | D | L | F | A | GD | Pts |
|---|---|---|---|---|---|---|---|---|---|
| 1 | Hereford | 42 | 35 | 3 | 4 | 138 | 33 | 105 | 108 |
| 2 | Alvechurch | 42 | 32 | 5 | 5 | 99 | 30 | 69 | 101 |
| 3 | Sporting Khalsa | 42 | 25 | 8 | 9 | 90 | 49 | 41 | 83 |
| 4 | Shepshed Dynamo | 42 | 24 | 5 | 13 | 86 | 58 | 28 | 77 |
| 5 | Coleshill Town | 42 | 23 | 5 | 14 | 108 | 73 | 35 | 74 |
| 6 | Heanor Town | 42 | 22 | 7 | 13 | 99 | 77 | 22 | 73 |
| 7 | Walsall Wood | 42 | 21 | 7 | 14 | 76 | 66 | 10 | 70 |
| 8 | Lye Town | 42 | 22 | 3 | 17 | 86 | 58 | 28 | 69 |
| 9 | Highgate United (-3) | 42 | 19 | 10 | 13 | 75 | 60 | 15 | 64 |
| 10 | Stourport Swifts | 42 | 17 | 8 | 17 | 57 | 57 | 0 | 59 |
| 11 | Boldmere St Michaels | 42 | 18 | 5 | 19 | 70 | 81 | -11 | 59 |
| 12 | Rocester | 42 | 17 | 7 | 18 | 67 | 82 | -15 | 58 |
| 13 | AFC Wulfrunians | 42 | 16 | 9 | 17 | 70 | 74 | -4 | 57 |
| 14 | Loughborough University | 42 | 16 | 6 | 20 | 79 | 83 | -4 | 54 |
| 15 | Brocton | 42 | 15 | 8 | 19 | 75 | 88 | -13 | 53 |
| 16 | Westfields | 42 | 13 | 12 | 17 | 69 | 68 | 1 | 51 |
| 17 | Quorn | 42 | 12 | 9 | 21 | 71 | 78 | -7 | 45 |
| 18 | Long Eaton United | 42 | 12 | 9 | 21 | 63 | 85 | -22 | 45 |
| 19 | Coventry Sphinx | 42 | 12 | 3 | 27 | 68 | 98 | -30 | 39 |
| 20 | Dunkirk | 42 | 8 | 6 | 28 | 49 | 121 | -72 | 30 |
| 21 | Bardon Hill (-3) | 42 | 7 | 9 | 26 | 56 | 120 | -64 | 27 |
| 22 | Continental Star | 42 | 2 | 4 | 36 | 26 | 138 | -112 | 10 |

| | DIVISION TWO | P | W | D | L | F | A | GD | Pts |
|---|---|---|---|---|---|---|---|---|---|
| 1 | Alvis Sporting Club | 26 | 23 | 3 | 0 | 93 | 21 | 72 | 72 |
| 2 | Chelmsley Town | 26 | 20 | 3 | 3 | 71 | 27 | 44 | 63 |
| 3 | Droitwich Spa | 26 | 16 | 5 | 5 | 65 | 23 | 42 | 53 |
| 4 | Paget Rangers | 26 | 16 | 4 | 6 | 64 | 33 | 31 | 52 |
| 5 | Rostance Edwards | 26 | 15 | 2 | 9 | 44 | 34 | 10 | 47 |
| 6 | Sutton United | 26 | 11 | 1 | 14 | 50 | 54 | -4 | 34 |
| 7 | Coton Green | 26 | 7 | 7 | 12 | 33 | 54 | -21 | 28 |
| 8 | Hampton | 26 | 8 | 4 | 14 | 37 | 63 | -26 | 28 |
| 9 | Knowle | 26 | 6 | 9 | 11 | 36 | 49 | -13 | 27 |
| 10 | Barnt Green Spartak | 26 | 7 | 4 | 15 | 35 | 49 | -14 | 25 |
| 11 | Austrey Rangers | 26 | 5 | 9 | 12 | 36 | 53 | -17 | 24 |
| 12 | Feckenham | 26 | 6 | 6 | 14 | 47 | 74 | -27 | 24 |
| 13 | Fairfield Villa | 26 | 6 | 5 | 15 | 40 | 64 | -24 | 23 |
| 14 | Earlswood Town | 26 | 3 | 4 | 19 | 19 | 72 | -53 | 13 |

| | DIVISION THREE | P | W | D | L | F | A | GD | Pts |
|---|---|---|---|---|---|---|---|---|---|
| 1 | Leamington Hibernian | 28 | 21 | 3 | 4 | 88 | 38 | 50 | 66 |
| 2 | Redditch Borough | 28 | 20 | 2 | 6 | 90 | 34 | 56 | 62 |
| 3 | Smithswood Firs (-12) | 28 | 21 | 2 | 5 | 95 | 44 | 51 | 53 * |
| 4 | FC Stratford | 28 | 15 | 4 | 9 | 73 | 44 | 29 | 49 |
| 5 | Alcester Town | 28 | 16 | 0 | 12 | 74 | 53 | 21 | 48 |
| 6 | Barton United | 28 | 14 | 6 | 8 | 56 | 43 | 13 | 48 |
| 7 | Shipston Excelsior | 28 | 15 | 1 | 12 | 59 | 57 | 2 | 46 |
| 8 | Northfield Town | 28 | 14 | 4 | 10 | 62 | 61 | 1 | 46 |
| 9 | Inkberrow | 27 | 12 | 4 | 11 | 57 | 61 | -4 | 40 |
| 10 | Coventrians | 27 | 9 | 3 | 15 | 42 | 53 | -11 | 30 |
| 11 | Burntwood Town | 28 | 7 | 6 | 15 | 40 | 66 | -26 | 27 |
| 12 | Boldmere Sports & Social Falcons | 28 | 8 | 2 | 18 | 42 | 60 | -18 | 26 |
| 13 | Enville Athletic | 27 | 7 | 3 | 17 | 40 | 69 | -29 | 24 |
| 14 | Perrywood | 27 | 3 | 6 | 18 | 37 | 99 | -62 | 15 |
| 15 | AFC Solihull (-3) | 28 | 2 | 2 | 24 | 32 | 105 | -73 | 5 |

| | DIVISION ONE | P | W | D | L | F | A | GD | Pts |
|---|---|---|---|---|---|---|---|---|---|
| 1 | Coventry United | 38 | 33 | 1 | 4 | 123 | 33 | 90 | 100 |
| 2 | Bromsgrove Sporting | 38 | 29 | 4 | 5 | 102 | 41 | 61 | 91 |
| 3 | Nuneaton Griff | 38 | 27 | 5 | 6 | 119 | 41 | 78 | 86 |
| 4 | Leicester Road | 38 | 23 | 8 | 7 | 98 | 41 | 57 | 77 |
| 5 | Hinckley AFC | 38 | 23 | 6 | 9 | 116 | 53 | 63 | 75 |
| 6 | Pilkington XXX | 38 | 20 | 7 | 11 | 73 | 57 | 16 | 67 |
| 7 | Lichfield City | 38 | 19 | 7 | 12 | 87 | 60 | 27 | 64 |
| 8 | Heath Hayes | 38 | 20 | 4 | 14 | 57 | 43 | 14 | 64 |
| 9 | Littleton | 38 | 19 | 4 | 15 | 61 | 58 | 3 | 61 |
| 10 | Racing Club Warwick | 38 | 16 | 7 | 15 | 71 | 76 | -5 | 55 |
| 11 | Coventry Copsewood | 38 | 15 | 9 | 14 | 75 | 78 | -3 | 54 |
| 12 | Studley | 38 | 13 | 7 | 18 | 67 | 89 | -22 | 46 |
| 13 | Atherstone Town | 38 | 11 | 8 | 19 | 55 | 71 | -16 | 41 |
| 14 | Pershore Town | 38 | 11 | 5 | 22 | 51 | 69 | -18 | 38 |
| 15 | Cadbury Athletic | 38 | 10 | 4 | 24 | 48 | 69 | -21 | 34 |
| 16 | Heather St Johns | 38 | 10 | 3 | 25 | 56 | 115 | -59 | 33 |
| 17 | Bolehall Swifts | 38 | 9 | 3 | 26 | 65 | 103 | -38 | 30 |
| 18 | Stafford Town | 38 | 8 | 3 | 27 | 46 | 96 | -50 | 27 |
| 19 | Pelsall Villa | 38 | 7 | 6 | 25 | 46 | 122 | -76 | 27 |
| 20 | Southam United | 38 | 4 | 5 | 29 | 28 | 129 | -101 | 17 |

## LEAGUE CUP

**ROUND 1**

| | | | |
|---|---|---|---|
| Hinckley AFC | v | Coventry United | 4-0 |
| Loughborough University | v | Shepshed Dynamo | 1-6 |
| Brocton | v | Nuneaton Griff | 3-5 |
| Bromsgrove Sporting | v | Studley | 1-0 |
| Pershore Town | v | Hereford | 0-1 |
| Atherstone Town | v | Coventry Sphinx | 1-4 |
| Alvechurch | v | Boldmere St Michaels | 5-1 |
| Dunkirk | v | Long Eaton United | 3-2 |
| Stafford Town | v | Heanor Town | 3-4 |
| Sporting Khalsa | v | Heath Hayes | 2-1 |

**ROUND 2**

| | | | |
|---|---|---|---|
| Cadbury Athletic | v | Pilkington XXX | 2-0 |
| Southam United | v | Stourport Swifts | 0-1 |
| Hinckley AFC | v | Shepshed Dynamo | 1-2 |
| Nuneaton Griff | v | Bardon Hill | 1-0 |
| Highgate United | v | Bromsgrove Sporting | 5-3 |
| Racing Club Warick | v | Littleton | 1-5 |
| Hereford | v | Westfields | 4-1 |
| Coventry Sphinx | v | Alvechurch | 0-1 |
| Dunkirk | v | Heanor Town | 1-6 |
| Sporting Khalsa | v | Pelsall Villa | 3-0 |
| Coventry Copeswood | v | Heather St Johns | 3-0 |
| AFC Wulfrunians | v | Lye Town | 0-1 |
| Walsall Wood | v | Continental Star | 4-1 |
| Rocester | v | Lichfield City | 4-2 |
| Coleshill Town | v | Bolehall Swifts | 9-0 |
| Quorn | v | Leicester Road | 2-2, 4-3p |

**ROUND 3**

| | | | |
|---|---|---|---|
| Cadbury Athletic | v | Stourport Swifts | 0-1 |
| Shepshed Dynamo | v | Nuneaton Griff | 1-3 |
| Highgate United | v | Littleton | 1-0 |
| Hereford | v | Alvechurch | 3-1 |
| Heanor Town | v | Sporting Khalsa | 2-4 |
| Coventry Copeswood | v | Lye Town | 0-4 |
| Walsall Wood | v | Rocester | 6-1 |
| Coleshill Town | v | Quorn | 7-2 |

**QUARTER FINALS**

| | | | |
|---|---|---|---|
| Stourport Swifts | v | Nuneaton Griff | 1-0 |
| Highgate United | v | Hereford | 0-2 |
| Sporting Khalsa | v | Lye Town | 2-3 |
| Walsall Wood | v | Coleshill Town | 2-1 |

**SEMI FINALS**

| | | | |
|---|---|---|---|
| Stourport Swifts | v | Hereford | 0-1 |
| Hereford | v | Stourport Swifts | 3-0 |
| Lye Town | v | Walsall Wood | 2-2 |
| Walsall Wood | v | Lye Town | 0-0 |

**FINAL**

| | | | |
|---|---|---|---|
| Hereford | v | Walsall Wood | 3-1 |

## MIDLAND FOOTBALL LEAGUE - STEP 5/6/7

| PREMIER DIVISION | | 1 | 2 | 3 | 4 | 5 | 6 | 7 | 8 | 9 | 10 | 11 | 12 | 13 | 14 | 15 | 16 | 17 | 18 | 19 | 20 | 21 | 22 |
|---|---|---|---|---|---|---|---|---|---|---|---|---|---|---|---|---|---|---|---|---|---|---|---|
| 1 | AFC Wulfrunians | | 0-4 | 2-2 | 3-2 | 2-1 | 1-4 | 2-1 | 3-1 | 3-0 | 1-1 | 1-2 | 0-3 | 4-1 | 3-1 | 0-1 | 4-4 | 1-1 | 1-0 | 2-2 | 1-2 | 2-3 | 3-2 |
| 2 | Alvechurch | 0-3 | | 2-1 | 2-2 | 2-0 | 3-0 | 8-0 | 3-1 | 4-0 | 1-0 | 1-2 | 3-1 | 3-1 | 4-1 | 2-1 | 1-1 | 4-1 | 4-1 | 1-0 | 1-0 | 2-1 | 3-0 |
| 3 | Bardon Hill | 3-3 | 0-3 | | 0-2 | 1-3 | 2-2 | 3-1 | 1-5 | 2-2 | 3-5 | 0-2 | 1-4 | 1-1 | 0-7 | 1-0 | 2-1 | 0-1 | 0-3 | 0-2 | 0-3 | 2-4 | 0-4 |
| 4 | Boldmere St Michaels | 1-0 | 1-0 | 3-2 | | 2-3 | 1-6 | 5-0 | 2-1 | 3-2 | 1-2 | 0-3 | 0-2 | 2-1 | 0-2 | 2-1 | 2-1 | 1-3 | 1-2 | 0-0 | 3-0 | 2-2 | 2-1 |
| 5 | Brocton | 1-4 | 0-2 | 1-2 | 3-1 | | 0-3 | 2-1 | 4-2 | 2-4 | 5-5 | 0-4 | 3-1 | 1-2 | 3-4 | 0-5 | 2-2 | 3-0 | 1-2 | 1-4 | 3-2 | 1-1 | 1-1 |
| 6 | Coleshill Town | 2-1 | 2-0 | 3-2 | 1-1 | 0-2 | | 0-1 | 6-3 | 10-1 | 1-4 | 1-4 | 0-3 | 6-0 | 5-1 | 0-3 | 3-1 | 4-1 | 1-3 | 1-1 | 4-2 | 1-0 | 1-1 |
| 7 | Continental Star | 1-4 | 1-2 | 1-0 | 1-5 | 0-2 | 1-4 | | 1-1 | 1-4 | 0-3 | 1-5 | 0-1 | 0-2 | 0-0 | 0-4 | 0-0 | 0-2 | 1-3 | 2-4 | 1-2 | 1-2 | 0-7 |
| 8 | Coventry Sphinx | 2-3 | 0-3 | 2-3 | 3-0 | 0-3 | 2-3 | 5-2 | | 2-1 | 2-4 | 0-4 | 0-2 | 5-0 | 1-2 | 0-2 | 2-0 | 6-0 | 0-6 | 0-3 | 1-0 | 3-2 | 3-0 |
| 9 | Dunkirk | 0-1 | 1-4 | 3-3 | 0-1 | 2-1 | 0-7 | 3-0 | 1-0 | | 0-10 | 2-3 | 1-6 | 1-1 | 0-2 | 1-3 | 0-4 | 3-3 | 0-4 | 3-1 | 0-0 | 2-3 | 0-1 |
| 10 | Heanor Town | 0-0 | 0-4 | 1-0 | 7-2 | 2-2 | 1-0 | 7-0 | 4-1 | 3-0 | | 2-7 | 3-1 | 2-0 | 3-1 | 0-3 | 0-4 | 2-0 | 2-3 | 1-2 | 2-0 | 2-2 | 1-3 |
| 11 | Hereford | 1-1 | 1-1 | 7-0 | 2-1 | 4-1 | 4-5 | 6-0 | 6-1 | 4-1 | 8-0 | | 0-2 | 1-0 | 1-0 | 4-1 | 2-0 | 4-0 | 2-1 | 4-0 | 6-0 | 2-1 | 3-0 |
| 12 | Highgate United | 1-0 | 0-2 | 3-3 | 0-1 | 2-3 | 1-2 | 2-0 | 2-2 | 2-1 | 1-2 | 2-1 | | 4-3 | 1-0 | 3-2 | 4-0 | 1-2 | 1-1 | 1-1 | 1-1 | 2-1 | 0-2 |
| 13 | Long Eaton United | 5-1 | 0-2 | 1-4 | 3-3 | 2-4 | 4-3 | 6-1 | 2-0 | 2-0 | 1-2 | 0-4 | 1-1 | | 2-1 | 0-0 | 2-2 | 1-3 | 0-4 | 0-2 | 3-0 | 1-2 | 1-1 |
| 14 | Loughborough University | 5-1 | 2-1 | 7-2 | 4-1 | 1-2 | 3-1 | 6-1 | 3-2 | 4-3 | 2-2 | 0-5 | 3-3 | 0-4 | | 4-1 | 1-3 | 1-2 | 3-2 | 1-1 | 1-1 | 1-2 | 0-2 |
| 15 | Lye Town | 1-0 | 1-2 | 5-1 | 1-2 | 3-0 | 3-1 | 5-1 | 2-0 | 2-2 | 2-1 | 1-2 | 7-3 | 1-1 | 6-1 | | 1-0 | 0-1 | 1-2 | 1-0 | 0-4 | 2-3 | 1-2 |
| 16 | Quorn | 1-0 | 0-0 | 6-1 | 1-3 | 5-2 | 0-3 | 2-2 | 3-4 | 4-0 | 1-2 | 0-2 | 0-3 | 3-1 | 3-2 | 1-2 | | 2-4 | 1-4 | 2-3 | 1-1 | 1-2 | 2-1 |
| 17 | Rocester | 0-1 | 0-3 | 0-2 | 1-3 | 2-2 | 1-3 | 2-1 | 1-0 | 4-1 | 2-1 | 3-4 | 1-1 | 1-2 | 2-0 | 1-2 | 3-2 | | 1-0 | 4-2 | 0-2 | 5-0 | 4-4 |
| 18 | Shepshed Dynamo | 4-2 | 0-3 | 3-2 | 3-2 | 1-4 | 2-2 | 3-1 | 0-0 | 0-1 | 3-2 | 1-3 | 0-0 | 2-0 | 1-0 | 4-1 | 2-0 | 2-1 | | 1-3 | 2-0 | 0-3 | 2-2 |
| 19 | Sporting Khalsa | 2-3 | 2-3 | 6-1 | 2-1 | 2-2 | 5-2 | 3-0 | 4-1 | 4-0 | 1-3 | 0-3 | 5-2 | 2-1 | 2-0 | 1-0 | 1-1 | 4-0 | 2-1 | | 2-0 | 3-0 | 2-0 |
| 20 | Stourport Swifts | 3-1 | 2-2 | 4-1 | 3-0 | 1-0 | 0-1 | 3-0 | 1-2 | 1-0 | 1-2 | 2-0 | 1-0 | 3-1 | 0-2 | 2-3 | 0-3 | 2-2 | 1-2 | 0-0 | | 1-1 | 4-2 |
| 21 | Walsall Wood | 1-0 | 0-1 | 1-1 | 3-2 | 2-1 | 3-2 | 5-0 | 2-1 | 5-1 | 3-0 | 0-6 | 0-1 | 2-3 | 0-0 | 2-1 | 3-1 | 1-1 | 3-2 | 0-3 | 0-1 | | 4-0 |
| 22 | Westfields | 2-2 | 0-3 | 1-1 | 4-1 | 0-0 | 1-2 | 3-0 | 4-1 | 1-2 | 3-3 | 0-0 | 1-1 | 1-1 | 4-0 | 1-4 | 1-2 | 4-1 | 0-4 | 0-1 | 0-1 | 2-1 | |

| DIVISION ONE | | 1 | 2 | 3 | 4 | 5 | 6 | 7 | 8 | 9 | 10 | 11 | 12 | 13 | 14 | 15 | 16 | 17 | 18 | 19 | 20 |
|---|---|---|---|---|---|---|---|---|---|---|---|---|---|---|---|---|---|---|---|---|---|
| 1 | Atherstone Town | | 0-3 | 1-2 | 1-0 | 2-2 | 2-4 | 1-1 | 2-1 | 0-2 | 3-2 | 1-2 | 0-1 | 0-3 | 3-0 | 3-0 | 0-0 | 2-2 | 2-1 | 4-1 | 1-3 |
| 2 | Bolehall Swifts | 2-2 | | 2-6 | 0-5 | 2-3 | 1-5 | 1-3 | 3-1 | 0-5 | 1-4 | 4-0 | 0-2 | 3-7 | 4-2 | 0-4 | 1-8 | 3-3 | 11-0 | 1-0 | 0-3 |
| 3 | Bromsgrove Sporting | 3-1 | 4-1 | | 4-0 | 5-2 | 4-2 | 2-0 | 7-2 | 2-1 | 3-0 | 2-0 | 3-1 | 0-1 | 3-1 | 3-0 | 3-0 | 1-0 | 1-1 | 3-0 | 3-1 |
| 4 | Cadbury Athletic | 2-1 | 2-2 | 2-0 | | 1-1 | 2-1 | 0-3 | 0-2 | 0-1 | 1-2 | 1-3 | 0-2 | 2-3 | 1-3 | 1-1 | 1-3 | 4-2 | 4-0 | 2-3 | 0-2 |
| 5 | Coventry Copsewood | 0-2 | 0-3 | 1-4 | 2-1 | | 0-5 | 2-1 | 4-0 | 1-1 | 1-1 | 0-0 | 0-2 | 2-2 | 4-2 | 0-2 | 0-1 | 2-2 | 7-1 | 3-2 | 4-2 |
| 6 | Coventry United | 6-1 | 2-0 | 3-2 | 2-1 | 10-0 | | 2-0 | 6-2 | 2-2 | 0-3 | 2-1 | 3-0 | 3-2 | 11-0 | 1-0 | 3-0 | 3-1 | 3-1 | 2-1 | 1-0 |
| 7 | Heath Hayes | 2-1 | 3-1 | 1-2 | 0-1 | 2-0 | 2-1 | | 1-2 | 2-1 | 0-0 | 0-2 | 0-1 | 2-1 | 0-0 | 1-0 | 0-1 | 0-1 | 3-0 | 1-0 | 2-0 |
| 8 | Heather St Johns | 3-1 | 3-1 | 0-4 | 1-0 | 1-5 | 1-4 | 0-4 | | 2-3 | 0-2 | 3-4 | 2-2 | 0-3 | 3-2 | 1-0 | 0-5 | 2-5 | 5-0 | 1-0 | 0-2 |
| 9 | Hinckley AFC | 2-2 | 3-2 | 1-3 | 2-0 | 1-4 | 0-4 | 3-4 | 4-1 | | 3-2 | 2-0 | 1-1 | 1-1 | 3-3 | 3-1 | 4-1 | 0-1 | 4-0 | 9-0 | 8-2 |
| 10 | Leicester Road | 3-0 | 3-0 | 5-1 | 3-0 | 1-1 | 1-2 | 1-0 | 5-1 | 1-2 | | 2-0 | 4-2 | 4-0 | 2-2 | 5-0 | 2-2 | 7-3 | 5-0 | 1-1 | 5-0 |
| 11 | Lichfield City | 2-2 | 4-1 | 0-2 | 3-0 | 4-1 | 1-2 | 2-4 | 5-1 | 0-4 | 3-2 | | 2-2 | 0-3 | 1-1 | 1-1 | 5-1 | 3-2 | 3-1 | 3-1 | 5-1 |
| 12 | Littleton | 2-1 | 0-3 | 0-3 | 3-2 | 3-0 | 0-2 | 4-2 | 2-1 | 1-5 | 0-1 | 3-4 | | 1-4 | 3-0 | 4-1 | 0-1 | 1-0 | 2-0 | 2-1 | 1-4 |
| 13 | Nuneaton Griff | 1-1 | 1-0 | 4-0 | 2-0 | 4-0 | 0-1 | 2-0 | 10-0 | 3-0 | 2-2 | 2-1 | 4-3 | | 3-1 | 4-1 | 4-1 | 4-3 | 7-0 | 2-0 | 3-0 |
| 14 | Pelsall Villa | 2-1 | 2-1 | 2-2 | 2-6 | 2-1 | 0-3 | 3-4 | 4-2 | 0-2 | 1-2 | 0-8 | 0-0 | 0-7 | | 1-7 | 2-4 | 0-5 | 1-3 | 1-0 | 1-5 |
| 15 | Pershore Town | 0-2 | 4-1 | 0-1 | 2-2 | 0-1 | 1-5 | 0-1 | 3-1 | 1-4 | 1-3 | 0-1 | 0-1 | 3-2 | 3-0 | | 1-2 | 1-4 | 2-0 | 2-1 | 2- |
| 16 | Pilkington XXX | 2-3 | 1-0 | 0-5 | 2-0 | 1-3 | 0-2 | 0-1 | 2-2 | 3-2 | 1-1 | 2-2 | 1-0 | 2-1 | 5-1 | 3-1 | | 0-1 | 5-0 | 3-1 | 3-2 |
| 17 | Racing Club Warwick | 2-3 | 3-2 | 1-1 | 1-0 | 1-1 | 1-3 | 1-1 | 3-2 | 1-3 | 2-1 | 2-1 | 2-0 | 1-9 | 4-2 | 3-2 | 0-0 | | 0-1 | 3-1 | 0- |
| 18 | Southam United | 2-0 | 0-4 | 1-3 | 1-3 | 1-5 | 0-4 | 1-4 | 3-2 | 0-13 | 0-6 | 0-2 | 0-3 | 0-1 | 0-1 | 1-1 | 2-3 | 0-1 | | 2-2 | 4-4 |
| 19 | Stafford Town | 2-1 | 2-0 | 0-2 | 3-0 | 0-5 | 0-5 | 0-1 | 3-4 | 2-3 | 2-3 | 0-7 | 1-4 | 0-4 | 3-1 | 0-1 | 1-1 | 6-4 | 1-0 | | 1-3 |
| 20 | Studley | 3-2 | 3-1 | 3-3 | 0-1 | 3-7 | 0-3 | 3-1 | 1-1 | 0-8 | 0-1 | 2-2 | 0-2 | 3-3 | 3-0 | 2-2 | 0-3 | 3-0 | 1-1 | 2-4 | |

| DIVISION TWO | | 1 | 2 | 3 | 4 | 5 | 6 | 7 | 8 | 9 | 10 | 11 | 12 | 13 | 14 |
|---|---|---|---|---|---|---|---|---|---|---|---|---|---|---|---|
| 1 | Alvis Sporting Club | | 3-0 | 1-0 | 1-1 | 1-0 | 2-0 | 4-0 | 6-0 | 5-2 | 4-1 | 3-2 | 2-0 | 5-1 | 7-2 |
| 2 | Austrey Rangers | 1-1 | | 3-1 | 1-3 | 0-1 | 0-2 | 1-1 | 4-4 | 4-2 | 4-0 | 1-1 | 3-6 | 0-4 | 0-3 |
| 3 | Barnt Green Spartak | 1-3 | 1-2 | | 1-4 | 2-1 | 1-2 | 0-2 | 0-0 | 1-2 | 2-1 | 4-2 | 1-3 | 0-2 | 1-2 |
| 4 | Chelmsley Town | 0-4 | 5-1 | 2-1 | | 0-0 | 2-1 | 7-0 | 3-1 | 4-1 | 5-0 | 1-0 | 4-4 | 2-1 | 5- |
| 5 | Coton Green | 1-10 | 1-1 | 0-3 | 0-2 | | 2-2 | 2-0 | 1-3 | 1-1 | 1-5 | 6-0 | 2-1 | 2-2 | 3- |
| 6 | Droitwich Spa | 2-3 | 1-1 | 1-1 | 0-1 | 6-0 | | 9-1 | 2-0 | 4-1 | 6-1 | 2-0 | 2-1 | 3-0 | 3- |
| 7 | Earlswood Town | 2-7 | 0-0 | 2-3 | 0-4 | 1-0 | 0-4 | | 1-0 | 1-1 | 1-2 | 1-3 | 0-1 | 0-2 | 1- |
| 8 | Fairfield Villa | 0-0 | 1-4 | 2-1 | 1-2 | 4-1 | 0-3 | 3-2 | | 4-1 | 4-1 | 2-2 | 2-2 | 0-3 | 0- |
| 9 | Feckenham | 1-7 | 2-1 | 5-5 | 3-2 | 4-3 | 0-0 | 1-1 | 5-4 | | 1-1 | 6-1 | 1-5 | 1-2 | 2- |
| 10 | Hampton | 0-3 | 1-1 | 1-1 | 0-2 | 4-2 | 0-3 | 5-1 | 3-2 | 2-1 | | 1-1 | 2-4 | 0-3 | 2- |
| 11 | Knowle | 2-3 | 0-0 | 0-1 | 1-4 | 0-0 | 2-2 | 1-0 | 5-1 | 3-2 | 1-2 | | 1-1 | 0-0 | 2- |
| 12 | Paget Rangers | 0-1 | 4-0 | 4-1 | 0-3 | 1-1 | 2-0 | 1-0 | 2-0 | 4-1 | 5-0 | 1-3 | | 2-0 | 3- |
| 13 | Rostance Edwards | 0-3 | 2-1 | 1-0 | 3-1 | 0-1 | 1-3 | 3-0 | 2-1 | 2-0 | 2-1 | 3-1 | 1-4 | | 2- |
| 14 | Sutton United | 2-4 | 3-2 | 1-2 | 1-2 | 0-1 | 1-2 | 4-1 | 4-1 | 4-0 | 2-1 | 2-2 | 2-3 | 3-2 | |

**CLUB MOVEMENTS - Premier Division - In:** Coventry United (P), Shawbury United (P - West Midlands regional), St Andrews (P - East Midlands), Tividale (R - NPL D1S). **Out:** Bardon Hill (W - Leicestershire Senior), Continental Star (R - Div.2), Dunkirk (R - East Midlands),Hereford (P - Southern D1S&W).

## AFC WULFRUNIANS
Founded: 2005 Nickname:

**Secretary:** Ian Davies **(T)** 07989 953 738 **(E)** jaki.davies1512@btinternet.com
**Chairman:** David Pointon
**Ground:** Castlecroft Stadium, Castlecroft Road, Wolverhampton WV3 8NA **(T)** 01902 761410
**Capacity:** **Seats:** Yes **Covered:** Yes **Midweek Matchday:** **Clubhouse:** Yes

**Colours(change):** Red/black/red
**Previous Names:** None
**Previous Leagues:** West Midlands (Regional). Midland Alliance 2013-14.
**Records:**
**Honours:** West Midlands (Regional) League Division Two 2005-06, Premier Division 2008-09, 12-13.

**10 YEAR RECORD**

| 06-07 | 07-08 | 08-09 | 09-10 | 10-11 | 11-12 | 12-13 | 13-14 | 14-15 | 15-16 |
|---|---|---|---|---|---|---|---|---|---|
| WM1 2 | WMP 6 | WMP 1 | WMP 3 | WMP 3 | WMP 5 | WMP 1 | MidAl 8 | MFLP 7 | MFLP 13 |

## ALVECHURCH
Founded: 1929 Nickname: The Church

**Secretary:** Stephen Denny **(T)** 07710 012 733 **(E)** alvechurchfc@btinternet.com
**Chairman:** Richard Thorndike
**Ground:** Lye Meadow, Redditch Road, Alvechurch B48 7RS **(T)** 0121 445 2929
**Capacity:** 3,000 **Seats:** 100 **Covered:** 300 **Midweek Matchday:** Tuesday **Clubhouse:** Yes

**Colours(change):** Amber/black/black.
**Previous Names:** Alvechurch FC >1992. Re-formed in 1994.
**Previous Leagues:** Midland Combination. Midland Alliance > 2014.
**Records:**
**Honours:** Since 1994: Midland Combination Premier 2002-03.
Worcestershire Senior Urn 03-04, 04-05, 12-13, 15-16.

**10 YEAR RECORD**

| 06-07 | 07-08 | 08-09 | 09-10 | 10-11 | 11-12 | 12-13 | 13-14 | 14-15 | 15-16 |
|---|---|---|---|---|---|---|---|---|---|
| MidAl 10 | MidAl 14 | MidAl 10 | MidAl 7 | MidAl 20 | MidAl 13 | MidAl 11 | MidAl 13 | MFLP 15 | MFLP 2 |

## BOLDMERE ST. MICHAELS
Founded: 1883 Nickname: The Mikes

**Secretary:** Rob Paterson **(T)** 07528 177 046 **(E)** paterson_r3@sky.com
**Chairman:** Keith Fielding
**Ground:** Trevor Brown Memorial Ground, Church Road, Boldmere B73 5RY **(T)** 0121 373 4435
**Capacity:** 2,500 **Seats:** 230 **Covered:** 400 **Midweek Matchday:** Tuesday **Clubhouse:** Yes

**Colours(change):** White/black/black & white hoops
**Previous Names:** None.
**Previous Leagues:** West Midlands (Regional). Midland Combination. Midland Alliance > 2014.
**Records:**
**Honours:** AFA Senior Cup 1947-48. Midland Combination Premier 1985-86, 88-89, 89-90.

**10 YEAR RECORD**

| 06-07 | 07-08 | 08-09 | 09-10 | 10-11 | 11-12 | 12-13 | 13-14 | 14-15 | 15-16 |
|---|---|---|---|---|---|---|---|---|---|
| MidAl 7 | MidAl 4 | MidAl 4 | MidAl 6 | MidAl 3 | MidAl 12 | MidAl 9 | MidAl 2 | MFLP 9 | MFLP 11 |

## BROCTON
Founded: 1937 Nickname:

**Secretary:** Terry Homer **(T)** 07791 841 774 **(E)** terryhomer@yahoo.co.uk
**Chairman:** Brian Townsend
**Ground:** Silkmore Lane Sports Grd, Silkmore Lane, Stafford, Staffordshire ST17 4JH **(T)**
**Capacity:** **Seats:** 100 **Covered:** 100 **Midweek Matchday:** **Clubhouse:** Yes

**Colours(change):** Green & white/white/green
**Previous Names:** None
**Previous Leagues:** Rugeley & Dist 1946-48. Cannock Chase. Staffs Co. Staffs Sen./Mid Lge 1991-94/1994-2003. Midland Combination > 2014.
**Records:**
**Honours:** Midland Combination Premier 2013-14.

**10 YEAR RECORD**

| 06-07 | 07-08 | 08-09 | 09-10 | 10-11 | 11-12 | 12-13 | 13-14 | 14-15 | 15-16 |
|---|---|---|---|---|---|---|---|---|---|
| MCmP 15 | MCmP 9 | MCmP 16 | MCmP 7 | MCmP 8 | MCmP 6 | MCmP 5 | MCmP 1 | MFLP 13 | MFLP 15 |

## COLESHILL TOWN

Founded: 1894 Nickname:

**Secretary:** David Brown **(T)** 07799 075 828 **(E)** dave.brown@skanska.co.uk

**Chairman:** Paul Billing **Prog Ed:** David Brown

**Ground:** Pack Meadow, Packington Lane, Coleshill B46 3JQ **(T)** 01675 463 259

**Capacity:** **Seats:** **Covered:** **Midweek Matchday:** Tuesday **Clubhouse:** Yes

**Colours(change):** White/blue/red
**Previous Names:** None.
**Previous Leagues:** Midland Combination. Midland Alliance 2008-2014.
**Records:**
**Honours:** Midland Combination Division Two 1969-70. Premier 07-08.

**10 YEAR RECORD**

| 06-07 | 07-08 | 08-09 | 09-10 | 10-11 | 11-12 | 12-13 | 13-14 | 14-15 | 15-16 |
|---|---|---|---|---|---|---|---|---|---|
| MCmP 4 | MCmP 1 | MidAl 11 | MidAl 8 | MidAl 12 | MidAl 16 | MidAl 15 | MidAl 4 | MFLP 2 | MFLP 5 |

## COVENTRY SPHINX

Founded: 1946 Nickname: Sphinx

**Secretary:** Sharon Taylor **(T)** 07979 233 845 **(E)** sharon@coventrysphinx.co.uk

**Chairman:** Dannie Cahill

**Ground:** Sphinx Sports & Social Club, Sphinx Drive, Coventry CV3 1WA **(T)** 02476 451 361

**Capacity:** **Seats:** Yes **Covered:** Yes **Midweek Matchday:** Tuesday **Clubhouse:** Yes

**Colours(change):** Sky blue & white/navy/navy
**Previous Names:** Sphinx > 1995.
**Previous Leagues:** Midland Combination. Midland Alliance 2007-14.
**Records:**
**Honours:** Midland Combination Premier 2006-07.

**10 YEAR RECORD**

| 06-07 | 07-08 | 08-09 | 09-10 | 10-11 | 11-12 | 12-13 | 13-14 | 14-15 | 15-16 |
|---|---|---|---|---|---|---|---|---|---|
| MCmP 1 | MidAl 19 | MidAl 7 | MidAl 9 | MidAl 16 | MidAl 3 | MidAl 14 | MidAl 7 | MFLP 18 | MFLP 19 |

## COVENTRY UNITED

Founded: 2013 Nickname: Cov United

**Secretary:** Graham Wood **(T)** 07863 563 943 **(E)** graham.wood@coventryunited.co.uk

**Chairman:** Jason Kay **Manager:** Terry Anderson

**Ground:** Sphinx Sports & Social, Sphinx Drive, off Siddeley Drive, Coventry, CV3 1WD **(T)**

**Capacity:** **Seats:** Yes **Covered:** Yes **Midweek Matchday:** **Clubhouse:** Yes

**Colours(change):** Green & red
**Previous Names:** None
**Previous Leagues:** Midland Combination 2013-14.
**Records:**
**Honours:** Midland Football League Division Two 2014-15, Division One 2015-16.

**10 YEAR RECORD**

| 06-07 | 07-08 | 08-09 | 09-10 | 10-11 | 11-12 | 12-13 | 13-14 | 14-15 | 15-16 |
|---|---|---|---|---|---|---|---|---|---|
| | | | | | | | MCm2 2 | MFL2 1 | MFL1 1 |

## HEANOR TOWN

Founded: 1883 Nickname: The Lions

**Secretary:** Amanda Jones **(T)** 07581 015 868 **(E)** amanda.jones10@live.co.uk

**Chairman:** Geoff Clarence

**Ground:** The Town Ground, Mayfield Avenue, Heanor DE75 7EN **(T)** 01773 713 742

**Capacity:** 2,700 **Seats:** 100 **Covered:** 1,000 **Midweek Matchday:** Tuesday **Clubhouse:** Yes

**Colours(change):** White/black/white (Red/white/red)
**Previous Names:** None
**Previous Leagues:** Midland 1961-72. Central Midlands 1986-2008. East Midlands Counties 2008-12. Northern Counties East 2012-15.
**Records:**
**Honours:** East Midlands Counties 2011-12.

**10 YEAR RECORD**

| 06-07 | 07-08 | 08-09 | 09-10 | 10-11 | 11-12 | 12-13 | 13-14 | 14-15 | 15-16 |
|---|---|---|---|---|---|---|---|---|---|
| CM Su 14 | CM Su 11 | EMC 12 | EMC 7 | EMC 3 | EMC 1 | NCEP 11 | NCEP 8 | NCEP 6 | MFLP 6 |

## HIGHGATE UNITED

Founded: 1948 Nickname: Red or Gate

**Secretary:** Paul Davis **(T)** 07527 941 993 **(E)** jimmymerry777@gmail.com

**Chairman:** James Francis

**Ground:** The Coppice, Tythe Barn Lane, Shirley Solihull B90 1PH **(T)**

**Capacity:** **Seats:** **Covered:** **Midweek Matchday:** Tuesday **Clubhouse:**

**Colours(change):** All red
**Previous Names:** None.
**Previous Leagues:** Worcestershire/Midland Combination. Midland Alliance 2008-14.
**Records:** Not known
**Honours:** Midland Combination Premier 1972-73, 73-74, 74-75.
Midland Football League Division One 2014-15.

**10 YEAR RECORD**

| 06-07 | 07-08 | 08-09 | 09-10 | 10-11 | 11-12 | 12-13 | 13-14 | 14-15 | 15-16 |
|---|---|---|---|---|---|---|---|---|---|
| MCmP 3 | MCmP 2 | MidAl 13 | MidAl 18 | MidAl 18 | MidAl 20 | MidAl 19 | MidAl 3 | MFL1 1 | MFLP 9 |

## LONG EATON UNITED

Founded: 1956 Nickname: Blues

**Secretary:** Jim Fairley **(T)** 07971 416 444 **(E)** jim@longeatonutd.co.uk

**Chairman:** Jim Fairley

**Ground:** Grange Park, Station Rd, Long Eaton, Derbys NG10 2EG **(T)** 0115 973 5700

**Capacity:** 1,500 **Seats:** 450 **Covered:** 500 **Midweek Matchday:** Tuesday **Clubhouse:** Yes **Shop:** No

**Colours(change):** All blue
**Previous Names:**
**Previous Leagues:** Central Alliance 1956-61, Mid Co Football Lge 1961-82, NCE 1982-89, 2002-14. Central Midlands 1989-2002
**Records:** **Att:** 2,019 v Burton Albion FA Cup 1973
**Honours:** Derbyshire Senior Cup 1964-65, 75-76. Northern Counties East Div1S 1984-85. League Cup 2008-09.

**10 YEAR RECORD**

| 06-07 | 07-08 | 08-09 | 09-10 | 10-11 | 11-12 | 12-13 | 13-14 | 14-15 | 15-16 |
|---|---|---|---|---|---|---|---|---|---|
| NCEP 11 | NCEP 12 | NCEP 2 | NCEP 10 | NCEP 12 | NCEP 15 | NCEP 12 | NCEP 11 | MFLP 3 | MFLP 18 |

## LOUGHBOROUGH UNIVERSITY

Founded: 1920 Nickname:

**Secretary:** Margaret Folwell **(T)** 01509 226 127 (Office Hrs) **(E)** secretary@loughboroughfootball.co.uk

**Chairman:** Michael Skubala

**Ground:** Loughborough Uni Stadium, Holywell Sports Complex, Holywell Park LE11 3TU **(T)** 01509 228 774

**Capacity:** **Seats:** Yes **Covered:** Yes **Midweek Matchday:** **Clubhouse:** Yes

**Colours(change):** Purple/purple/grey
**Previous Names:** None
**Previous Leagues:** Leicestershire Senior. Midland Combination. Midland Alliance 2009-14.
**Records:**
**Honours:** Midland Combination 2008-09.

**10 YEAR RECORD**

| 06-07 | 07-08 | 08-09 | 09-10 | 10-11 | 11-12 | 12-13 | 13-14 | 14-15 | 15-16 |
|---|---|---|---|---|---|---|---|---|---|
| | MCmP 4 | MCmP 1 | MidAl 13 | MidAl 4 | MidAl 5 | MidAl 4 | MidAl 15 | MFLP 20 | MFLP 14 |

## LYE TOWN

Founded: 1930 Nickname:

**Secretary:** Paul Roberts **(T)** 07429 887 570 **(E)** dprobbo@gmail.com

**Chairman:** Brian Blakemore

**Ground:** Sports Ground, Stourbridge Road, Lye, Stourbridge, West Mids DY9 7DH **(T)** 01384 422 672

**Capacity:** **Seats:** **Covered:** **Midweek Matchday:** **Clubhouse:** Yes

**Colours(change):** Blue/blue/white
**Previous Names:**
**Previous Leagues:** Worcestershire Combination 1931-39. Birmingham & Dist/West Midlands (Regional) 1947-62/1962-2014.
**Records:**
**Honours:** West Midlands (Regional) 2013-14.
Worcestershire Senior Urn 2013-14.

**10 YEAR RECORD**

| 06-07 | 07-08 | 08-09 | 09-10 | 10-11 | 11-12 | 12-13 | 13-14 | 14-15 | 15-16 |
|---|---|---|---|---|---|---|---|---|---|
| WMP 8 | WMP 10 | WMP 11 | WMP 19 | WMP 11 | WMP 15 | WMP 2 | WMP 1 | MFLP 6 | MFLP 8 |

## QUORN

Founded: 1924 Nickname: Reds

**Secretary:** Reg Molloy **(T)** 07729 173 333 **(E)** k.molloy@ntlworld.com

**Chairman:** Stuart Turner

**Ground:** Farley Way Stadium, Farley Way, Quorn, Leicestershire LE12 8RB **(T)** 01509 620 232

**Capacity:** 1,550 **Seats:** 350 **Covered:** 250 **Midweek Matchday:** **Clubhouse:** Yes

**Colours(change):** All red

**Previous Names:** Quorn Methodists

**Previous Leagues:** Leicestershire Senior, Midland Alliance > 2007. NPL 2007-2012. United Counties 2012-13. Midland Alliance 2013-14.

**Records:** Not known

**Honours:** Leicestershire Senior Cup 1940, 1952, 1954.
Leicestershire Senior League 2000-01

**10 YEAR RECORD**

| 06-07 | 07-08 | 08-09 | 09-10 | 10-11 | 11-12 | 12-13 | 13-14 | 14-15 | 15-16 |
|---|---|---|---|---|---|---|---|---|---|
| MidAl 3 | NP 1 12 | NP1S 12 | NP1S 20 | NP1S 15 | NP1S 21 | UCL P 7 | MidAl 5 | MFLP 11 | MFLP 17 |

## ROCESTER

Founded: 1876 Nickname: Romans

**Secretary:** Barry Smith **(T)** 07770 762 825 **(E)** rocesterfc@btinternet.com

**Chairman:** Ian Cruddas **Prog Ed:** Barry Smith

**Ground:** Hillsfield, Mill Street, Rocester, Uttoxeter ST14 5JX **(T)** 01889 591 301

**Capacity:** 4,000 **Seats:** 230 **Covered:** 500 **Midweek Matchday:** Tuesday **Clubhouse:** Yes **Shop:** Yes

**Colours(change):** Amber & black stripes/black/black

**Previous Names:** None.

**Previous Leagues:** Staffs Sen. (Founder Member). W.Mids (Reg). Mid.All (FM) Southern. NPL. Midland Alliance 2005-14.

**Records:** **Apps:** Peter Swanwick 1962-82.

**Honours:** Staffordshire Senior 1985-86, 86-87. West Mids (Regional) Div.1 87-88. Midland Alliance 1998-99, 2003-04.

**10 YEAR RECORD**

| 06-07 | 07-08 | 08-09 | 09-10 | 10-11 | 11-12 | 12-13 | 13-14 | 14-15 | 15-16 |
|---|---|---|---|---|---|---|---|---|---|
| MidAl 12 | MidAl 5 | MidAl 20 | MidAl 16 | MidAl 14 | MidAl 6 | MidAl 13 | MidAl 20 | MFLP 12 | MFLP 12 |

## SHAWBURY UNITED

Founded: 1992 Nickname:

**Secretary:** Tracie Howells **(T)** 07950 740 089 **(E)** traciehowells72@yahoo.co.uk

**Chairman:** Chris Kirkup

**Ground:** Butler Sports Ground, Bowensfield, Wem, Shrewsbury SY4 5AP **(T)** 01939 233 287

**Capacity:** **Seats:** **Covered:** **Midweek Matchday:** **Clubhouse:**

**Colours(change):** Black & white/black/black

**Previous Names:**

**Previous Leagues:** West Midlands (Regional) >2016.

**Records:**

**Honours:** West Midlands (Regional) League Premier Division 2015-16.
Shropshire Challenge Cup 2012-13.

**10 YEAR RECORD**

| 06-07 | 07-08 | 08-09 | 09-10 | 10-11 | 11-12 | 12-13 | 13-14 | 14-15 | 15-16 |
|---|---|---|---|---|---|---|---|---|---|
| WMP 21 | WMP 2 | WMP 10 | WMP 21 | WMP 17 | WMP 10 | WMP 4 | WMP 4 | WMP 7 | WMP 1 |

## SHEPSHED DYNAMO

Founded: 1994 Nickname: Dynamo

**Secretary:** Danny Pole **(T)** 07866 500 187 **(E)** secretary@shepsheddynamo.co.uk

**Chairman:** Mick Sloan

**Ground:** The Dovecote, Butt Hole Lane, Shepshed, Leicestershire LE12 9BN **(T)** 01509 650 992

**Capacity:** 2,050 **Seats:** 570 **Covered:** 400 **Midweek Matchday:** **Clubhouse:** Yes **Shop:** Yes

**Colours(change):** Black and white stripes/black/black

**Previous Names:** Shepshed Albion/Charterhouse > 1994

**Previous Leagues:** Leics Sen 1907-16,19-27,46-50,51-81, Mid Co 81-82,N.C.E. 82-83,Sth 83-88,96-04,N.P.L.88-93,04-12,Mid Com 93-94,Mid All 94-95,13-14. UCL 12-13.

**Records:** 2,500 v Leicester City - Friendly 1996-97

**Honours:** Midland Counties League 1981-82, League Cup 81-82. Northern Counties East 1982-83, League Cup 82-83.
Midland Alliance 1995-96. Leicestershire Senior Cup x7

**10 YEAR RECORD**

| 06-07 | 07-08 | 08-09 | 09-10 | 10-11 | 11-12 | 12-13 | 13-14 | 14-15 | 15-16 |
|---|---|---|---|---|---|---|---|---|---|
| NP 1 20 | NP 1 15 | NP1S 8 | NP1S 17 | NP1S 21 | NP1S 22 | UCL P 9 | MidAl 16 | MFLP 16 | MFLP 4 |

## SPORTING KHALSA

Founded: 1991 Nickname:

**Secretary:** Manjit Gill **(T)** 07976 220 444 **(E)** manjit.gill@globeproperty.co.uk
**Chairman:** Rajinder Gill
**Ground:** Aspray Arena, Noose Lane, Willenhall WV13 3BB **(T)** 01902 219 208
**Capacity:** **Seats:** **Covered:** **Midweek Matchday:** **Clubhouse:**

**Colours(change):** Yellow & blue/blue/blue
**Previous Names:**
**Previous Leagues:** West Midlands (Regional) 1996-97, 2005-15.
**Records:**
**Honours:** West Midlands (Regional) Premier Division 2014-15.

**10 YEAR RECORD**

| 06-07 | 07-08 | 08-09 | 09-10 | 10-11 | 11-12 | 12-13 | 13-14 | 14-15 | 15-16 |
|---|---|---|---|---|---|---|---|---|---|
| WM1 15 | WM1 15 | WM1 17 | WM1 17 | WM1 3 | WMP 14 | WMP 11 | WMP 6 | WMP 1 | MFLP 3 |

## ST. ANDREWS

Founded: 1973 Nickname:

**Secretary:** Les Botting **(T)** 07793 500 937 **(E)** standrewsfc@btconnect.com
**Chairman:** Andy Ward **Prog Ed:** Les Botting
**Ground:** Canal Street, Aylestone, Leicester LE2 8LX **(T)** 0116 283 9298
**Capacity:** **Seats:** Yes **Covered:** Yes **Midweek Matchday:** **Clubhouse:** Yes

**Colours(change):** Black & white/black/black (Maroon/blue/maroon)
**Previous Names:**
**Previous Leagues:** Leicestershire City League 1973-85. Leicestershire Senior 1985-2008. East Midlands Counties 2008-16.
**Records:**
**Honours:** Leicestershire City Premier x4. Leicestershire Senior x3. East Midlands Counties League 2015-16.

**10 YEAR RECORD**

| 06-07 | 07-08 | 08-09 | 09-10 | 10-11 | 11-12 | 12-13 | 13-14 | 14-15 | 15-16 |
|---|---|---|---|---|---|---|---|---|---|
| LeicS | LeicS | EMC | EMC | EMC | EMC | EMC | EMC | EMC | EMC 1 |

## STOURPORT SWIFTS

Founded: 1882 Nickname: Swifts

**Secretary:** Graham Haighway **(T)** 07780 997 758 **(E)** ghaighway@hotmail.co.uk
**Chairman:** Chris Reynolds
**Ground:** Walshes Meadow, Harold Davis Drive, Stourport on Severn DY13 0AA **(T)** 01299 825 188
**Capacity:** 2,000 **Seats:** 250 **Covered:** 150 **Midweek Matchday:** **Clubhouse:** Yes **Shop:** Yes

**Colours(change):** Gold & black/black/black
**Previous Names:** None
**Previous Leagues:** Kidderminster/Worcestershire/West Midlands (Regional) > 1998, Midland Alliance 1998-2001, 12-14, Southern 2001-12.
**Records:** **Att:** 2,000
**Honours:** Midland Alliance 2000-01

**10 YEAR RECORD**

| 06-07 | 07-08 | 08-09 | 09-10 | 10-11 | 11-12 | 12-13 | 13-14 | 14-15 | 15-16 |
|---|---|---|---|---|---|---|---|---|---|
| SthM 22 | SthM 17 | SthM 16 | SthM 17 | Sthsw 17 | Sthsw 21 | MidAl 5 | MidAl 10 | MFLP 10 | MFLP 10 |

## TIVIDALE

Founded: 1953 Nickname:

**Secretary:** Leon Murray **(T)** 07939 234 813 **(E)** tividalefc@live.co.uk
**Chairman:** David Evans **Manager:** Phil Male & Ros Thorpe Caroline Wells
**Ground:** The Beeches, Packwood Road, Tividale, West Mids B69 1UL **(T)** 01384 211 743
**Capacity:** 3,000 **Seats:** Yes **Covered:** Yes **Midweek Matchday:** **Clubhouse:** Yes

**Colours(change):** All yellow (All navy blue)
**Previous Names:** Tividale Hall Youth Club 1953-56
**Previous Leagues:** Warwickshire & West Midlands Alliance 1956-66. West Midlands (Regional) 1966- 2011. Midland Alliance 2011-14.
**Records:** **Previous Lges Cont:** Northern Premier 2014-16.
**Honours:** Warwickshire & West Midlands Alliance Premier 1964-65. West Midlands (Regional) League Division One 1972-73, Premier Division 2010-11. Midland Alliance 2013-14.

**10 YEAR RECORD**

| 06-07 | 07-08 | 08-09 | 09-10 | 10-11 | 11-12 | 12-13 | 13-14 | 14-15 | 15-16 |
|---|---|---|---|---|---|---|---|---|---|
| WMP 2 | WMP 11 | WMP 13 | WMP 7 | WMP 1 | MidAl 4 | MidAl 8 | MidAl 1 | NP1S 8 | NP1S 22 |

## WALSALL WOOD

Founded: 1907 Nickname:

**Secretary:** George Evangelou (T) 07775 512 373 (E) gevangelou67@gmail.com

**Chairman:** Justin Hodgin

**Ground:** Oak Park, Lichfield Road, Walsall Wood, Walsall WS9 9NP (T)

**Capacity:** **Seats:** Yes **Covered:** Yes **Midweek Matchday:** **Clubhouse:** Yes

**Colours(change):** Red/red/white

**Previous Names:** Walsall Borough (formed when Walsall Wood & Walsall Sportsco merged) 1982-96.

**Previous Leagues:** Midland Combinataion 1986-92, 2006-13. Staffordshire Senior 1992-93. West Midlands 1993-2006. Mid Alliance 2013-14.

**Records:**

**Honours:** Worcestershire/Midland Combination 1951-52, 2012-13.

**10 YEAR RECORD**

| 06-07 | 07-08 | 08-09 | 09-10 | 10-11 | 11-12 | 12-13 | 13-14 | 14-15 | 15-16 |
|---|---|---|---|---|---|---|---|---|---|
| MidCo 12 | MidCo 11 | MidCo 7 | MidCo 6 | MidCo 9 | MidCo 14 | MidCo 1 | MidAl 6 | WMP 4 | MFLP 7 |

## WESTFIELDS

Founded: 1966 Nickname: The Fields

**Secretary:** Andrew Morris (T) 07860 410 548 (E) andrew@andrew-morris.co.uk

**Chairman:** John Morgan

**Ground:** Allpay Park, Widemarsh Common, Hereford HR4 9NA (T) 07860 410 548

**Capacity:** 2,000 **Seats:** 150 **Covered:** 150 **Midweek Matchday:** Tuesday **Clubhouse:** Yes **Shop:** Yes

**Colours(change):** All Maroon & sky blue/sky blue/sky blue & maroon

**Previous Names:** None.

**Previous Leagues:** Herefordshire Sunday. Worcester & Dist. West Midlands (Regional). Midland Alliance > 2014.

**Records:** **Att:** 590 v Hereford United, Hereford Senior Invitation Cup Final 2012. **Goalscorer:** Paul Burton. **Apps:** Jon Pugh.

**Honours:** Hereford Senior Cup 1985-86, 88-89, 91-92, 95-96, 01-02, 02-03, 04-05, 05-06, 07-08, 11-12, 12-13.
West Midlands (Regional) Premier 2002-03.

**10 YEAR RECORD**

| 06-07 | 07-08 | 08-09 | 09-10 | 10-11 | 11-12 | 12-13 | 13-14 | 14-15 | 15-16 |
|---|---|---|---|---|---|---|---|---|---|
| MidAl 16 | MidAl 11 | MidAl 17 | MidAl 5 | MidAl 6 | MidAl 2 | MidAl 2 | MidAl 12 | WMP 8 | MFLP 16 |

# GROUND DIRECTIONS - PREMIER DIVISION

**AFC WULFRUNIANS - Castlecroft Stadium, Castlecroft Road, Wolverhampton, WV3 8N - 01902-761 410**

Follow A454 (signposted Bridgnorth) and turn left at Mermaid Pub onto Windmill Lane. Turn right onto Castlecroft Avenue. Ground is straight across past Wightwick Cricket Ground.

**ALVECHURCH - Lye Meadow, Redditch Rd., Alvechurch, B48 7RS - 0121-445 2929**

M42 Junction 2. Take A441 towards Redditch. At first roundabout turn right onto A4120 signposted Alvechurch. Ground approx 1km on right. Car park entrance on right before ground.

**BOLDMERE ST. MICHAELS - The Trevor Brown Memorial Ground, Church Road, Boldmere, Sutton Coldfield B73 5RY - 0121-384 7531**

A38(M) from M6 junction 6 and A5127 from Birmingham to Yenton Traffic Lights. Left on A452 Chester Road, then 6th.right into Church Road.

From M6 junction 5 A452 Brownhills to Yenton Traffic Lights. Straight on then 6th right into Church Road.

**BROCTON - Ground: Silkmore Lane Sports Ground, Silkmore Lane , Stafford , Staffordshire , ST17 4JH**

From M6 J13 take A449 towards Stafford for 1.5 miles until reaching traffic lights by Esso petrol station. Turn right at lights into Rickescote Road, follow road round over railway bridge to mini island, at island bear left into Silkmore Lane. At next mini island take 4th exit for entrance to ground. From Lichfield/Rugeley. After passing Staffs Police HQ at Baswick go downhill past BMW garage and pub to large island, take 1st exit into Silkmore Lane, at next mini island take 2nd exit into ground entrance. Do not turn into Lancaster Road or Silkmore Crescent as directed by Sat Navs.

**COLESHILL TOWN - Pack Meadow, Packington Lane, Coleshill, B46 3JQ - 01675 463 259**
From M6 Junction 4 take A446 signposted Lichfield. Straight over 1st roundabout then immediately turn right across dual carriageway onto B4117 signposted Coleshill. After school on right, turn right into Packington Lane. Ground is ½ mile on left.

**COVENTRY SPHINX - Sphinx Drive, Off Siddeley Avenue, Coventry, CV3 1WA - 02476 451 361**
From M6. Leave M6 at Junction 3 and take A444 towards Coventry. Continue to Binley Road (6 roundabouts) and turn left on A428 Binley Road towards Binley. Pass a row of shops on left and Bulls Head public house on right. After the Bulls Head, turn 1st right into Biggin Hall Crescent. Then take the 5th left turn into Siddeley Avenue. Take 1st left into Sphinx Drive and the ground is at the end.
From M42 & A45. Follow A45 towards Coventry and take A4114 Coventry at Coventry Hill Hotel. At roundabout take 2nd exit to next roundabout and take 3rd exit onto Holyhead Road. After approx 2.5 miles you will come to Coventry Ring Road where you turn left and then get over to your right onto the ring road. Continue on Ring Road and leave at Junction 3 signposted M69 and Football Stadium. Follow signs for A428 Binley until you see Bulls Head public house on your right. Then follow the above instructions.

**COVENTRY UNITED - Sphinx Sports & Social, Sphinx Drive, off Siddeley Drive, Coventry, CV3 1WD**
See above

**HEANOR TOWN - The Town Ground, Mayfield Avenue, Heanor, Derbyshire, DE75 7EN**
From M1 take junction 26 and take A610 (Ripley) to the end of the dual carriageway and then take A608 to Heanor via Langley Mill. At traffic lights at the top of the hill take the left hand lane signposted Ilkeston. Take the 1st right at Mundy Street, take the 2nd left onto Godfrey Street. The ground is on the left where the road forks.
From the A608 Derby – Enter the town with Tesco on the left, turn right at the roundabout up to Heanor Town centre, turn right at the end of the market square. At the crossroads turn right onto Mundy Street, left onto Godfrey Street and the ground is on the left where the road forks.

**HEREFORD - Edgar Street, Hereford, HR4 9JU**
Edgar Street is part of the main A49 road running through the centre of Hereford. Coming from the M5, take junction 7 (Worcester South) and follow signs for A4103 Hereford. At Hereford follow the A4103 until it joins the A49. Follow the A49 to the ground on the left, turn left immediately after the ground into Blackfriars Street. Turn left into the Merton Meadow car park. The main Club entrance is ten yards after the turning on the left, the players entrance is midway down the main stand.

**HIGHGATE UNITED - The Coppice, Tythe Barn Lane, Shirley, Solihull, B90 1PH - 0121 744 4194**
From M42 Junction 4 take A34 towards Birmingham. Go to far end of Shirley Village and turn left into Haslucks Green Road. Take the left hand fork by the Colebrook pub and go past Shirley Station and the Drawbridge pub. At 'T' junction turn left and go over railway bridge. Turn left into Tythe Barn Lane and the ground is the 2nd entrance on the right approx 200 yards down the lane.
**LONG EATON UNITED - Grange Park, Station Road, Long Eaton, NG10 2EG. Tel: (0115) 973 5700.**
M1 Junc 25, take A52 towards Nottingham, to island by Bardills Garden Centre, right onto B6003. Approx 2 miles to end of road to T-junction. At traffic lights, turn right A453 and take 2nd left into Station Road. Entrance on left down un-named road opposite disused car park next to Grange School.

**LOUGHBOROUGH UNIVERSITY - Loughborough University Stadium, Holywell Sports Complex, Holywell Park, Loughborough, Leics, LE11 3TU - 01509 228 774**
From M42/A42 exit at Junction 13 and take the A512 towards Loughborough. After crossing Junction 23 of the M1 travel approx 3/4 mile to first traffic island. Turn right into University (LE11 3QF Red Building is on your right). Keep straight on at both small islands. Bear left into large spectator car park, entrance on left hand side. Please note that there is limited parking at Stadium for Officials/Team Coach/Cars.

**LYE TOWN - Sports Ground, Stourbridge Road, Lye, Stourbridge, West Mids DY9 7DH Tel: 01384-422672**
Situated on A458 Birmingham to Stourbridge RoadFrom M5 Junction 3, take road marked Kidderminster, as far as lights at the bottom of Hagley Hill. Turn right, then take the third turning off the first island. Carry straight on at the next island. Turn left at Lights/Crossroads, onto the A458. Ground approximately 400 yards on the left hand side.

**QUORN - Farley Way, Quorn, Leicestershire, LE12 8RB - 01509 620 232**
Exit Junction 21A of M1 Motorway onto A46. Proceed towards Loughborough on A6. Approx 2 miles from Loughborough turn left at island. After 200 yards turn left at traffic lights. Ground on left.

**ROCESTR - Hillsfield, Mill Street, Rocester, Uttoxeter, Staffordshire ST14 5JX - 01889 591 301**
From Uttoxeter take the B5030, signposted Ashbourne/Alton Towers After 3 miles turn right opposite the JCB factory over humpback bridge into Rocester village. Turn right at mini island into Mill Street, ground is 500 yards on the left immediately past the JCB Academy.

**SHAWBURY UNITED - Butler Sports Ground, Bowensfield, Wem, Shrewsbury. SY4 5AP Tel: 01939-233287**
From the A5 Shrewsbury by-pass, take the A49 heading towards Whitchurch. Go through the villages of Hadnall & Preston Brockhurst and then take a left turn at crossroads onto the B5063 sign posted Wem. At next junction turn right under Railway Bridge on to the B5476 into Mill Street. At next Junction by Church turn right into High Street, take the next left after pedestrian crossing into New Street and then next left by the Public House into Pyms Road. Take the 2nd left into Bowens Field and ground is 100 yards straight ahead.

**SHEPSHED DYNAMO - The Dovecote Stadium, Butthole lane, Shepshed, Leicestershire, LE12 9BN - 01509 650 992**
From Junction 23 of M1 motorway take the A512 towards Ashby. Turn right at first set of lights and after approx 1 mile take 2nd exit at mini roundabout (after petrol station). Carry on for half mile over speed humps. Butthole Lane is opposite the Black Swan Public House.

**SPORTING KHALSA - Aspray Arena, Noose Lane, Willenhall, WV13 3BB**
From M6 junction 10 take A454 towards Wolverhampton, after 1½ miles branch left, then at Keyway Island take the 2nd exit onto A454. Go through one roundabout and then at traffic lights make a U turn ar Neachells Road, turn left into Noose Lane

**ST. ANDREWS - Canal Street, Aylestone, Leicester LE2 8LX**
From the north to J21 of the M1. 1st left at roundabout and on to next roundabout. 2nd exit and follow A5460 towards Leicester. At 1st set of traffic lights turn right onto Braunstone Lane East. After approximately 1 mile turn left at T-junction and follow Aylestone Road towards Leicester. Take 3rd road on the left. Turn right at T-Junction and turn left at No Entry Signs over the canal bridge and left into ground.

**STOURPORT SWIFTS - Walshes Meadow, Harold Davies Drive, Stourport on Severn, Worcs, DY13 0AA - 01299 825 188**
Follw the one way system through Stourport Town Centre signposted 'Sports Centre'. Go over the river bridge and turn first left into Harold Davies Drive. Ground is at the rear of the Sports Centre.

**TIVIDALE - The Beeches, Packwood Road, Tividale, West Mids B69 1UL**
M5 Junction 2. Take A4123 towards Dudley. After approx 1.5 miles and after footbridge, take left up Trafalgar Road. Take 2nd right into Elm Terrace and then 1st left into Birch Crescent. Take 1st right into Packwood Road and ground is at end of road.

**WALSALL WOOD - Oak Park, Lichfield Road, Walsall Wood, Staffordshire, WS9 9NP- 07583 175 664**
From North- Leave M6 at Junction 12 and take A5 until big island just outside Brownhills (next island after 'The Turn' pub on left). Take A452 Chester Road North through Brownhills High Street to traffic lights at Shire Oak (Pub at junction on right hand side). Turn right onto A461 towards Walsall, go to next set of traffic lights, cross over and turn right immediately onto Oak Park Leisure Centre Car park (rear of Kentucky Fried Chicken). Proceed diagonally over car park and follow road round to ground entrance.
From South using M5/M6 motorways- M5 North past Junction 1 onto M6 North. Leave at Junction 9 (Wednesbury turn off) and take A4148 to Walsall. Proceed for about 2 miles over several islands until going down a hill alongside the Arboretum. At big island at bottom, turn right onto A461 for Lichfield. Take A461 for about 4 miles and go through Walsall Wood village (after Barons Court Hotel on right) up the hill after village, Oak Park is on the left opposite Fitness First. Turn left and go diagonally across Oak Park Leisure Centre car park. Follow road round to ground entrance.

**WESTFIELDS - 'Allpay park', Widemarsh Common, Grandstand Road., Hereford, HR4 9NA 07860 410 548**
On reaching the outskirts of Hereford from Worcester, continue along A4103, over roundabout signposted Holmer and Leisure Centre. Proceed for 1 mile to large roundabout by the "Starting Gate Inn" and turn left towards Hereford. Proceed for ½ mile, past Hereford Leisure Centre and at mini roundabout, turn right. Proceed 150 yards and bear left around the Common, in front of Cricket Pavilion and immediately turn right into the driveway for allpay.park.

## ATHERSTONE TOWN
Founded: 2004 Nickname: The Adders

**Secretary:** Graham Read **(T)** 07552 673 008 **(E)** grahamgdr777@aol.com
**Chairman:** Howard Kerry
**Ground:** Sheepy Road, Atherston, Warwickshire CV9 3AD **(T)** 01827 717 829
**Colours(change):** Red and white stripes/red/red
**ADDITIONAL INFORMATION:**
**Previous Leagues:** Midland Combination 2004-06, 2011-14. Midland Alliance 2006-08, 11-12. Southern 2008-11.
**Honours:** Midland Combination Division 1 2004-05, Premier Division 2005-06. Midland Alliance 2007-08.

## BOLEHILL SWIFTS
Founded: 1953 Nickname:

**Secretary:** Philip Crowley **(T)** 07702 786 722 **(E)** bolehallswifts.philcrowley@hotmail.co.uk
**Chairman:** Les Fitzpatrick
**Ground:** Rene Road, Bolehall, Tamworth, Staffordshire B77 3NN **(T)** 07702 786 722
**Colours(change):** Yellow/green/green
**ADDITIONAL INFORMATION: Previous Leagues:** Midland Combination > 2014.
**Honours:** Midland Combination Division 2 1984-85.

## BROMSGROVE SPORTING
Founded: 2009 Nickname: The Rouslers

**Secretary:** David Stephens **(T)** 07955 121 966 **(E)** dave@bromsgrovesporting.co.uk
**Chairman:** John Teece
**Ground:** The Victoria Ground, Birmingham Road, Bromsgrove, Worcs, B61 0DR **(T)** 01527 876949 **Capacity:** 4,893
**Colours(change):** Red & white stripes/royal blue/royal blue
**ADDITIONAL INFORMATION: Previous Leagues:** Midland Combination > 2014.

## CADBURY ATHLETIC
Founded: 1994 Nickname:

**Secretary:** Kevin Wilks **(T)** 07967 204 921 **(E)** cadburyathleticfc@hotmail.co.uk
**Chairman:** John Peckham
**Ground:** TSA Sports Ground, Eckersall Road, Kings Norton, Birmingham, B38 8SR **(T)** 0121 4584 570 **Capacity:** 1,500
**Colours(change):** Purple/purple/white
**ADDITIONAL INFORMATION:**

## CHELMSLEY TOWN
Founded: 1927 Nickname:

**Secretary:** **(T)** **(E)**
**Chairman:**
**Ground:** Coleshill FC Pack Meadow, Packington Lane, Coleshill, B46 3JQ **(T)** 07736 296 246 **Capacity:** 2,070
**Colours(change):** Sky blue & black
**ADDITIONAL INFORMATION:**
**Previous Names:** Christ Church 1927-69.
**Honours:** Midland Combination Division One 1987-88.

## COVENTRY COPSEWOOD
Founded: 1923 Nickname:

**Secretary:** David Wilson **(T)** 07884 585 440 **(E)** davide.wilson@hotmail.co.uk
**Chairman:** Robert Abercrombie
**Ground:** Copsewood Sports & Social Club, Allard Way, Binley, Coventry CV3 1JP **(T)** 07884 585 440 **Capacity:** 2,000
**Colours(change):** All blue
**ADDITIONAL INFORMATION: Previous Leagues:** Midland Combination > 2014.
**Previous Names:** G.P.T. Coventry > 2000, Coventry Marconi > 2005.
**Honours:** Midland Combination Challenge Cup 2006-07.

## HEATH HAYES
Founded: 1964 Nickname:

**Secretary:** Kathlyn Davies **(T)** 07969 203 063 **(E)** kathlyndavies@aol.com
**Chairman:** Craig Brotherton
**Ground:** Coppice Colliery Grd, Newlands Lane, Heath Hayes, Cannock, WS12 3HH **(T)** 07969 203 063 **Capacity:** 1,000
**Colours(change):** Blue & white/blue/white
**ADDITIONAL INFORMATION:**
Staffordshire County League Division 1 1977-78. West Midlands League Division 1 North 1998-99.
Midland Combination Premier Division 2009-10.

**CLUB MOVEMENTS**
**Division One - In:** Chelmsley Town (P), Uttoxeter Town (Staffordshire County).
**Out:** Coventry United (P), Pilkington XXX (W).

## HEATHER ST. JOHN'S

Founded: 1949 Nickname:

**Secretary:** Adrian Rock **(T)** 07952 633 331 **(E)** adrianrock@hotmail.co.uk
**Chairman:** Michael Brookes
**Ground:** St John's Park, Ravenstone Rd, Heather LE67 2QJ **(T)** 01530 263 986
**Colours(change):** All royal blue
**ADDITIONAL INFORMATION:**
Midland Combination 2010-11.

## HINCKLEY AFC

Founded: 2014 Nickname:

**Secretary:** Stephen Jelfs **(T)** 07720 299 313 **(E)** secretary@hinckleyafc.org.uk
**Chairman:**
**Ground:** St. John's Park, Ravenstone Road, Heather, Leicestershire, LE67 2QJ **(T)** 01530 263 986 **Capacity:** 1,500
**Colours(change):** Red & blue/blue/blue
**ADDITIONAL INFORMATION:**
**Honours:** Leicestershire Senior Cup 2015-16.

## LEICESTER ROAD

Founded: 2014 Nickname:

**Secretary:** Stuart Millidge **(T)** 07814 414 726 **(E)** stuchris@talktalk.net
**Chairman:** Ku Akeredulu
**Ground:** Leicester Road Stadium, Leicester Road, Hinckley, LE10 3DR **(T)**
**Colours(change):** Blue & red stripes/blue/blue
**ADDITIONAL INFORMATION:**

## LICHFIELD CITY

Founded: 1970 Nickname:

**Secretary:** Michael Tyler **(T)** 07756 521 301 **(E)** tylermick1954@hotmail.co.uk
**Chairman:** Darren Leaver
**Ground:** Brownsfield Park, Brownsfield Road, Lichfield, Staffs, WS13 6AY **(T)** 01543 258 338 **Capacity:** 1,500
**Colours(change):** Blue & white/blue/blue
**ADDITIONAL INFORMATION: Previous Leagues:** Midland Combination > 2014.

## LITTLETON

Founded: 1890 Nickname:

**Secretary:** Marion Brighton **(T)** 01386 832 906 **(E)** littletonfc@outlook.com
**Chairman:** Paul Harrison
**Ground:** 5 Acres, Pebworth Road, North Littleton, Evesham, Worcs, WR11 8QL **(T)** 07765 224 290 **Capacity:** 1,000
**Colours(change):** Red/red/white
**ADDITIONAL INFORMATION:**
**Previous Leagues:** Midland Combination > 2014.

## NUNEATON GRIFF

Founded: 1972 Nickname:

**Secretary:** Peter Kemp **(T)** 07944 457 250 **(E)** nuneatongriff@sky.com
**Chairman:** John Gore
**Ground:** The Pingles Stadium, Avenue Road, Nuneaton, Warwickshire CV11 4LX **(T)** 07944 457 250 **Capacity:** 1,500
**Colours(change):** Blue & white stripes/blue/blue
**ADDITIONAL INFORMATION: Previous Leagues:** Midland Combination > 2014.
**Honours:** Midland Combination Premier Division 1999-2000, 00-01.

## PELSALL VILLA

Founded: 1898 Nickname:

**Secretary:** Beth Wooley **(T)** 07855 049 239 **(E)** matchdaypvfc@gmail.com
**Chairman:** Mark Bentley
**Ground:** The Bush Ground, Walsall Road, Walsall, West Midlands WS3 4BP **(T)** 07982 143 343 **Capacity:** 2,000
**Colours(change):** Red/black/black
**ADDITIONAL INFORMATION: Previous Leagues:** Midland Combination > 2014.

## PERSHORE TOWN

Founded: 1988 Nickname:

**Secretary:** Cindy Webb **(T)** 07590 408 205 **(E)** cindywebb1@hotmail.co.uk
**Chairman:**
**Ground:** King George V Playing Field, King George's Way, Pershore WR10 1QU **(T)** 07841 377 788 1,000
**Colours(change):** Blue & white/blue/blue
**ADDITIONAL INFORMATION:**
**Previous Leagues:** Midland Alliance (Founder members). Midland Combination > 2014.
**Honours:** Midland Combination Division 2 1989-90, Premier 1993-94.

## RACING CLUB WARWICK

Founded: 1919 Nickname: Racers

**Secretary:** Pat Murphy **(T)** 07926 188 553 **(E)** pja.murphy@hotmail.co.uk
**Chairman:** Gary Vella
**Ground:** Townsend Meadow, Hampton Road, Warwick, Warwickshire CV34 6JP **(T)** 01926 495 786 **Capacity:** 1,300
**Colours(change):** Gold/black/black
**ADDITIONAL INFORMATION:** **Previous Leagues:** Midland Combination > 2014.
**Record Att:** 1,280 v Leamington FC, Midland All.26/12/2005. **Goalscorer:** Steve Edgington - 200. **Apps:** Steve Cooper - 600+
**Honours:** Midland Combination Premier Division 1987-88.

## SOUTHAM UNITED

Founded: 1905 Nickname:

**Secretary:** Charles Hill **(T)** 07449 761 688 **(E)** charles@southamunitedfc.com
**Chairman:** Charles Hill
**Ground:** Banbury Road, Southam, Warwickshire CV47 2BJ **(T)** 07802 949 781 **Capacity:** 1,000
**Colours(change):** Yellow/royal blue/royal blue
**ADDITIONAL INFORMATION:** **Previous Leagues:** Midland Combination > 2014.
**Honours:** Midland Combination Division 3 1980-81.

## STAFFORD TOWN

Founded: 1976 Nickname:

**Secretary:** David Howard **(T)** 07789 110 923 **(E)** staffordtown@hotmail.co.uk
**Chairman:** Gordon Evans
**Ground:** Evans Park, Riverway, Stafford ST16 3TH **(T)** 07789 110 923 **Capacity:** 2,500
**Colours(change):** All red
**ADDITIONAL INFORMATION:**
**Previous Leagues:** Midland Combination 1977-84, 2012-14. Staffordshire 1984-93. West Midlands (Regional) 1993-2012.
**Previous Names:** Stafford > 1981.

## STUDLEY

Founded: 1971 Nickname: Bees

**Secretary:** Bob Fletcher **(T)** 07745 310 077 **(E)** bobtheat@hotmail.co.uk
**Chairman:** Barry Cromwell
**Ground:** The Beehive, Abbeyfields Drive, Studley B80 7BE **(T)** 01527 853 817 **Capacity:** 1,500
**Colours(change):** Sky blue/navy/sky blue
**ADDITIONAL INFORMATION:** **Previous Names:** Studley BKL > 2002.
**Previous Leagues:** Redditch & Sth Warwicks Sunday Combination. Midland Combination 2013-14. Midland Alliance > 2013.
**Record Att:** 810 v Leamington 2003-04. Goalscorer: Brian Powell. Apps: Lee Adams - 523.
**Honours:** Midland Combination Div.1 1991-92. Worcestershire FA Senior Urn 00-01,01-02, 02-03.

## UTTOXETER TOWN

Founded: 1983 Nickname:

**Secretary:** Graham Shenton **(T)** 07984 582 252 **(E)** graham.shenton@vodafone.com
**Chairman:** Graham Shenton
**Ground:** Oldfields Sports Ground, Springfield Road, Uttoxeter, ST14 7JX **(T)** 01889 564 347 **Capacity:** 1,000
**Colours(change):** Yellow & navy (Blue & white)
**ADDITIONAL INFORMATION:** **Previous Leagues:** Staffordshire County Senior > 2014, 2015-16. Midland 2014-15.
**League Honours:** Staffordshire Senior Division One 2012-13.

# GROUND DIRECTIONS - DIVISION ONE

**ATHERSTONE TOWN - Sheepy Road, Atherston, Warwickshire CV9 3AD - 01827 717 829**
Take M42 towards Atherstone. Exit at Junction 10. Travel southbound on A5 towards Nuneaton for approximately 4 miles. At third roundabout take first exit to Holly Lane Industrial Estate. Over railway bridge (Aldi HQ on left). At the next roundabout turn right onto Rowlands Way. Ground is 300 yards on the right. Car park and street parking in Rowlands Way.

**BOLEHILL SWIFTS - Rene Road, Bolehall, Tamworth, Staffordshire B77 3NN**
Exit M42 at Junction 10, take A5 towards Tamworth, exit A5 at 2nd exit (Glascote & Amington Industrial Estate). Turn right onto Marlborough Way, at next island turn left (B5000), turn right into Argyle Street (opposite chip shop). At T-junction, turn left into Amington Road, drive over the canal bridge, and turn 2nd right into Leedham Avenue. Take right fork into Rene Road. Club is situated 150 yards on right immediately after school.

**BROMSGROVE SPORTING - The Victoria Ground, Birmingham Road, Bromsgrove, Worcs, B61 0DR**
From M5 J4 take A38 to Bromsgrove, after island at M42 J1, take 1st right at Traffic Lights (signposted Bromsgrove North). Ground is 1000 metres on right (opposite Tesco Garage). From M42 J1, follow above directions from islands.

**CADBURY ATHLETIC - TSA Sports Ground, Eckersall Road, Kings Norton, Birmingham, B38 8SR**
From Cotteridge A441 through and past Kings Norton Station, 150 yards turn right across dual carriageway at petrol station, approximately 300 yards there is a sharp bend, turn right. Ground is on right.

**CHELMSLEY TOWN - Coleshill FC Pack Meadow, Packington Lane, Coleshill, B46 3JQ**
From M6 Junction 4 take A446 signposted Lichfield. Straight over 1st roundabout then immediately turn right across dual carriageway onto B4117 signposted Coleshill. After school on right, turn right into Packington Lane. Ground is ½ mile on left.

**COVENTRY COPSEWOOD - Copsewood Sports & Social Club, Allard Way, Binley , Coventry , West Midlands , CV3 1HQ**
M6 South: Leave at junction 2 and follow A4600 signs for City Centre. Go over 3 roundabouts and past 1 set of traffic lights, on reaching the 2nd set of traffic lights with Coventry Oak pub on left, turn left down Hipswell Highway. Follow road for 1 mile and reach another set of lights (Fire Station is on left and Mill Pool pub is on right). Go over lights and the ground is 300 yards on the left. From M40: Follow A46 signs to Coventry and Leicester, stay on this road until very end, you then reach a roundabout with a flyover, go round the roundabout following M69 signs. This road takes you past Asda and you reach a set of traffic lights with a roundabout. Take 2nd left turn off the roundabout, again following M69 signs, This is Allard Way and takes you past Matalan on left, Go under railway bridge and ground is 400 yards on the right. A45 from Birmingham Direction: Follow A45 until reaching a slip road signposted A46, this slip road has the Festival Pub on left side of it. It is after a roundabout with big Peugeot car showroom on left. Go down slip road and take 2nd exit. , this is another slip road leading to A46, signposted B4114 Coventry. Follow road until reaching roundabout with a flyover, and then follow as M40 directions above.

**HEATH HAYES - Coppice Colliery Ground, Newlands Lane, Heath Hayes, Cannock, Staffordshire, WS12 3HH**
From M6 Junction 11 take the A4601 towards Cannock and at the 1st island turn right onto the A460 signposted Rugeley/Cannock Business Parks. At the double island (A5) go straight on still on A460 and over two islands. At the 3rd island, turn right onto A5190 signposted Lichfield. Pass Texaco garage on the right and take the next right turn into Newlands Lane. Entrance to the ground is 50 yards down the lane on the left under the barrier.

**HEATHER ST. JOHN'S - St. John's Park, Ravenstone Road, Heather LE67 2QJ - 01530 263 986**

Exit M42 at Junction 11. Take the road towards Measham, pass the Car Auctions and go over the traffic lights. At 2nd mini island take 2nd exit onto Leicester Road. After approximately 3 miles you will enter Heather. At T junction turn left. At mini island take 2nd exit onto Ravenstone Road and go up the hill. Ground is 200 metres on the left.

**HINCKLEY AFC - St. John's Park, Ravenstone Road, Heather, Leicestershire, LE67 2QJ - 01530 263986**

Exit M42 at Junction 11. Take the road towards Measham, pass the Car Auctions and go over the traffic lights. At 2nd mini island take 2nd exit onto Leicester Road. After approximately 3 miles you will enter Heather. At T junction turn left. At mini island take 2nd exit onto Ravenstone Road and go up the hill. Ground is 200 metres on the left.

**LEICESTER ROAD - Leicester Road Stadium, Leicester Road, Hinckley, LE10 3DR**

From North West: A5 Southbound at Dodwells roundabout (A5/A47) take 1st exit (Earl Shilton, A47 and Industrial Estates), straight over 3 roundabouts, straight over traffic lights, at next roundabout take the 3rd exit (B4668) towards Hinckley, the entrance is 200 yards on the right.
From M69, Junction 1: take A5 north (Tamworth/Nuneaton) then as above.

**LICHFIELD CITY - Brownsfield Park, Brownsfield Road , Lichfield , Staffordshire , WS13 6AY**

From M42 J10, follow A5 towards Brownhills, or J9 and follow A446 to Lichfield, then follow signs for A38 Lichfield/Derby. From Swinfen Roundabout take 3rd exit for A38 north and then take next off A38 onto A5192 (Cappers Lane). Follow A5192 through 2 islands onto Eastern Avenue. The Ground is on the right at the top of the hill next to Norgreen factory. From M6 J12, follow A5 towards Lichfield then A38 to Lichfield Derby, then follow instructions as above.

**LITTLETON - Five Acres, Pebworth Road, North Littleton , Evesham , Worcestershire , WR11 8QL**

Get on A46 and aim for Bidford-on-Avon, leave A46 at Bidford roundabout and follow signs for B439 (Bidford 0.5 miles). Come to roundabout in Bidford and take exit B4085 (Cleeve Prior), over a very narrow bridge controlled by traffic lights, straight over crossroads following sign to Honeybourne Broadway. Straight on for approx. 3 miles signpost right turn for the Littletons at crossroads, the ground is 1.25 miles on the right.

**NUNEATON GRIFF - The Pingles Stadium, Avenue Road , Nuneaton , Warwickshire , CV11 4LX**

From M5, M42 & M6: Take M6 south to junction 3 and leave by turning left onto A444 (Nuneaton). Stay on A444 through Bermuda Park, McDonalds and George Eliot Hospital roundabouts until reaching large roundabout with footbridge over road. Carry straight on (2nd exit) and downhill, taking right hand lane. At bottom of hill you reach Coton Arches Island, take 2nd exit (A4252 Avenue Road) and travel 1/2 mile to Cedar Tree Pub traffic lights, turn left into Stadium car park service road. It is unsuitable for coaches to turn around in. From A5: Travel south following signs for Nuneaton. After passing through Atherstone travel for 2 1/2 miles until junction with A444. At this junction (Royal Red Gate Pub) turn right at staggered junction and continue on A444 through Caldecote and Weddington into Nuneaton. Join one-way system at Graziers Arms by turning left and immediately take right hand lane for 300 yards and follow A444 for Coventry. At Third Island turn left on to dual carriageway (Coton Road) for 1/2 mile and turn left at Coton Arches island on to A4252 (Avenue Road) then as above.

**PELSALL VILLA - The Bush Ground, Walsall Road , Walsall , West Midlands , WS3 4BP**

Leave M6 at junction 7 sign-posted A34 Birmingham. Take A34 towards Walsall to 1st Island, turn right (marked Ring Road) across 3 islands. At large island at the bottom of the hill, take last exit marked Lichfield. Up hill and across next island to traffic lights, continue to next set of lights and turn left (B4154 Pelsall). Go over Railway Bridge to Old Bush Public House, the ground is next to the public house signposted Pelsall Cricket Club. From Birmingham East: Follow A452 from Spitfire Island then follow signs towards Brownhills. At the traffic lights at the Shire Oak P.H, turn left onto A461 (Walsall) and pass the entrance to Walsall Wood FC. At the traffic lights in Shelfield (The Spring Cottage PH) turn right (signposted Pelsall). At the next set of traffic lights turn left, the Bush is approx 400 yards on left. From: Coventry: Take A45 to Stonebridge Island, turn right onto A452 but then keep to the right following A446 (signposted Lichfield). Follow the A446 to Bassett's Pole Island. Take the 3rd exit onto A38 (Lichfield). Leave the A38 at sliproad for the A5 and take the 2nd exit at the island. Follow the A5 over next 2 islands and at Muckley Corner turn left (inside lane) to join A461. Go straight on at the traffic lights and follow directions as above.

**PERSHORE TOWN - King George V Playing Field, King George's Way , Pershore WR10 1QU**

M5 Junction 7, take B4080 (formerly A44) to Pershore. On entering the town turn left at 2nd set of traffic lights (signposted Leisure Centre). The ground is 300 yards on the left hand side.

**RACING CLUB WARWICK - Hampton Road , Warwick , Warwickshire , CV34 6JP**

M40 Junction 15, signposted Warwick. At roundabout with traffic lights take A429 to Warwick. Follow this road for 1/2 mile and you will come to houses on your left. Take the 2nd turn on the left into Shakespeare Avenue. Follow to T-junction. Turn right into Hampton Road. Entrance to ground is 50 yards on left.

**SOUTHAM UNITED - Banbury Road , Southam , Warwickshire , CV47 2BJ**

From Birmingham: M40 Junction 12, exit to A4451 to Southam. Approximately 6 1/2 miles to an island in Southam, turn right, at 2nd island turn right again, ground is 100 yards on right. From Coventry: take A423 Banbury Road; the ground is approximately 12 1/2 miles from Coventry

**STAFFORD TOWN - Evans Park, Riverway, Stafford ST16 3TH**

From M6 junction 13, take A449 towards Stafford for 1½ miles until reaching traffic lights by an Esso petrol station. Turn right at the lights into Rickerscote Road, follow the road round over railway bridge to a mini island. At the island bear left into Silkmore Lane, after approximately 600 yards take the 2nd exit at the mini island and carry on until a large island, take the 2nd exit towards Stafford town centre (A34 Lichfield Road). Go over the railway bridge with Alstrom factory on the left hand side. Straight on at 1st set of traffic lights, then bear left at next set of lights (A518 Uttoxeter) and follow road round with B&Q and Argos on your left hand side. At the roundabout (with KFC and Pizza Hut in front of you) take the 2nd exit (A518 Uttoxeter) and follow to traffic lights. Go straight over lights into Riverway, the ground entrance is approximately 80 yards on the right hand side. Follow the driveway behind the cricket pavilion to the stadium entrance.

**STUDLEY - The Beehive, Abbeyfields Drive, Studley, B80 7BF**

Leave M42 at junction 3 ( Redditch A435) and turn towards Redditch. Follow dual carriageway to the end. Stay on A435 and go straight on at island. Pass 'The Boot' public house and after 550 yards turn left into Abbeyfields Drive. The ground is on the right.

**UTTOXETER TOWN - Oldfields Sports Ground, Springfield Road, Uttoxeter, ST14 7JX**

Follow A50 into Uttoxeter. At Uttoxeter turn left onto A518 into the town, then straight over mini roundabout, left turn at next roundabout, and right turn at third roundabout onto A522 signposted Town Centre. Turn right into Bradley Street heading towards the town centre, then straight over at mini roundabout into Smithfield Road. Follow Smithfield Road, out of the town centre and turn right onto Springfield Road, signposted Windsor Park School, entrance to ground on left.

| Midland Football League Division Two | | |
|---|---|---|
| **ALVIS SPORTING CLUB** | Alvis Sports & Social Club, Green Lane, Coventry, CV3 6EA | 07904 496 954 |
| **BARNT GREEN SPARTEK** | The Coppice, Tythe Barn Lane, Shirley, Solihull B90 1PN | 07811 378 652 |
| **BLOXWICH TOWN** | Old Red Lion Ground, Somerfield Road, Walsall, WS3 2EH | 07917 857 642 |
| **CONTINENTAL STAR** | Rushall Olympic FC, Dales Lane, Rushall, Walsall, West Midlands WS4 1LJ | 01922 641 021 |
| **COTON GREEN** | New Mill Lane, Fazeley, Tamworth, B78 3RX | 07904 587 286 |
| **DROITWICH SPA** | King George Playing Fields, Briar Mill, Droitwich, WR9 0RZ | 07734 462 794 |
| **EARLSWOOD TOWN** | The Pavilions, Malthouse Lane, Earlswood, Solihull, B94 5DX | 07866 122 254 |
| **FAIRFIELD VILLA** | Recreation Ground, Stourbridge Road, Fairfield, Bromsgrove, Worcs, B61 9LZ | 07946 529 629 |
| **FECKENHAM** | Studley Sports & Social Club, Eldorado Close, Studley, Warwickshire, B80 7HP | 07703 020 499 |
| **HAMPTON** | Hampton Sports Club, Field Lane, Solihull, B91 2RT | 07786 915 274 |
| **KNOWLE** | The Robins Nest, Hampton Road, Knowle, Solihull, B93 0NX | 07738 822 916 |
| **LEAMINGTON HIBERNIAN** | Bishops Tachbrook Sports & S.C. The Meadow, Kingsley Rd, Leamington CV33 9RR | 07816 159 387 |
| **PAGET RANGERS** | Trevor Brown Memorial Ground, Church Road, Boldmere, Birmingham, B73 5RY | 07910 303 715 |
| **REDDITCH BOROUGH** | Redditch United FC, Valley Stadium, Bromsgrove Road, Redditch B97 4RN | |
| **SMITHSWOOD FIRS** | Mackadown Stadium, Mackadown Lane, Garretts Lane, Birmingham B33 0JJ | |
| **SUTTON UNITED** | Hollyfield Road, Sutton Coldfield, B75 7SE | 07836 763 811 |

**CLUB MOVEMENTS**
**Division Two - In:** Bloxwich Town (NC from Rostance Edwards), Continental Star (R - Prem), Leamington Hibernian (P), Redditch Borough (P), Smithswood Firs (P).
**Out:** Austrey Rangers (W), Chelmsley Town (P), Kenilworth Town (W).

# NORTH WEST COUNTIES LEAGUE

**Sponsored by:** Hallmark Security
**Founded:** 1982

**Recent Champions: 2013:** Padiham
**2014:** Norton United **2015:** Glossop North End

| PREMIER DIVISION | P | W | D | L | F | A | GD | Pts |
|---|---|---|---|---|---|---|---|---|
| 1 Colne | 42 | 31 | 7 | 4 | 105 | 41 | 64 | 100 |
| 2 Runcorn Linnets | 42 | 32 | 2 | 8 | 97 | 35 | 62 | 98 |
| 3 Atherton Collieries | 42 | 25 | 9 | 8 | 113 | 66 | 47 | 84 |
| 4 1874 Northwich | 42 | 24 | 6 | 12 | 89 | 62 | 27 | 78 |
| 5 West Didsbury & Chorlton | 42 | 21 | 5 | 16 | 81 | 65 | 16 | 68 |
| 6 Congleton Town | 42 | 19 | 10 | 13 | 79 | 65 | 14 | 67 |
| 7 Ashton Athletic | 42 | 17 | 10 | 15 | 73 | 68 | 5 | 61 |
| 8 Bootle | 42 | 17 | 10 | 15 | 75 | 75 | 0 | 61 |
| 9 Barnoldswick Town | 42 | 17 | 8 | 17 | 77 | 69 | 8 | 59 |
| 10 Abbey Hey | 42 | 16 | 11 | 15 | 67 | 66 | 1 | 59 |
| 11 Padiham | 42 | 16 | 9 | 17 | 84 | 90 | -6 | 57 |
| 12 Maine Road | 42 | 16 | 7 | 19 | 72 | 76 | -4 | 55 |
| 13 Runcorn Town | 42 | 15 | 7 | 20 | 70 | 76 | -6 | 52 |
| 14 Winsford United | 42 | 14 | 10 | 18 | 66 | 93 | -27 | 52 |
| 15 Cammell Laird 1907 | 42 | 14 | 8 | 20 | 71 | 83 | -12 | 50 |
| 16 Nelson | 42 | 13 | 9 | 20 | 69 | 70 | -1 | 48 |
| 17 AFC Liverpool | 42 | 11 | 15 | 16 | 86 | 92 | -6 | 48 |
| 18 AFC Darwen | 42 | 12 | 7 | 23 | 82 | 111 | -29 | 43 |
| 19 Squires Gate | 42 | 11 | 8 | 23 | 53 | 91 | -38 | 41 |
| 20 Alsager Town | 42 | 11 | 6 | 25 | 56 | 101 | -45 | 39 |
| 21 Silsden | 42 | 9 | 11 | 22 | 57 | 88 | -31 | 38 |
| 22 AFC Blackpool | 42 | 9 | 9 | 24 | 65 | 104 | -39 | 36. |

| DIVISION ONE | P | W | D | L | F | A | GD | Pts |
|---|---|---|---|---|---|---|---|---|
| 1 Hanley Town | 34 | 25 | 3 | 6 | 68 | 32 | 36 | 78 |
| 2 Irlam | 34 | 24 | 5 | 5 | 73 | 27 | 46 | 77 |
| 3 Barnton | 34 | 19 | 9 | 6 | 94 | 36 | 58 | 66 |
| 4 Stockport Town | 34 | 19 | 6 | 9 | 68 | 44 | 24 | 63 |
| 5 Bacup Borough | 34 | 17 | 6 | 11 | 81 | 54 | 27 | 57 |
| 6 Cheadle Town | 34 | 16 | 8 | 10 | 89 | 59 | 30 | 56 |
| 7 St Helens Town | 34 | 17 | 4 | 13 | 84 | 61 | 23 | 55 |
| 8 Holker Old Boys | 34 | 16 | 7 | 11 | 73 | 62 | 11 | 55 |
| 9 Litherland REMYCA | 34 | 16 | 6 | 12 | 63 | 51 | 12 | 54 |
| 10 Rochdale Town | 34 | 14 | 5 | 15 | 66 | 77 | -11 | 47 |
| 11 Ashton Town | 34 | 12 | 7 | 15 | 57 | 57 | 0 | 43 |
| 12 Daisy Hill | 34 | 12 | 6 | 16 | 56 | 72 | -16 | 42 |
| 13 Widnes | 34 | 10 | 5 | 19 | 67 | 77 | -10 | 35 |
| 14 Chadderton | 34 | 9 | 8 | 17 | 43 | 53 | -10 | 35 |
| 15 Northwich Manchester Villa | 34 | 10 | 4 | 20 | 48 | 77 | -29 | 34 |
| 16 Eccleshall | 34 | 9 | 5 | 20 | 53 | 77 | -24 | 32 |
| 17 Atherton LR | 34 | 4 | 6 | 24 | 32 | 103 | -71 | 18 |
| 18 Whitchurch Alport | 34 | 2 | 10 | 22 | 31 | 127 | -96 | 16 |

## LEAGUE CHALLENGE CUP FINAL

**HOLDERS:** ATHERTON COLLIERIES

**ROUND 1**

| | | | |
|---|---|---|---|
| Atherton LR | v | Daisy Hill | 1-2 |
| Barnton | v | Northwich Manchester Villa | 2-0 |
| Cheadle Town | v | Stockport Town | 1-2 |
| Eccleshall | v | Chadderton | 3-3, 4-3p |
| Hanley Town | v | St Helens Town | 4-1 |
| Irlam | v | Widnes | 2-1 |
| Litherland REMYCA | v | Holker Old Boys | 3-1 |
| Whitchurch Alport | v | Ashton Town | 1-5 |

ROUND 2

| | | | |
|---|---|---|---|
| Atherton Collieries | v | Litherland REMYCA | 2-0 |
| Rochdale Town | v | Colne | 1-2 |
| 1874 Northwich | v | Winsford United | 4-0 |
| Abbey Hey | v | Silsden | 0-1 |
| AFC Darwen | v | AFC Blackpool | 1-3 |
| AFC Liverpool | v | Padiham | 2-3 |
| Alsager Town | v | Stockport Town | 0-3 |
| Ashton Town | v | Runcorn Town | 1-2 |
| Barnoldswick Town | v | Ashton Athletic | 1-3 |
| Barnton | v | Bootle | 0-0, 4-3p |
| Daisy Hill | v | Cammell Laird 1907 | 0-4 |
| Hanley Town | v | Bacup Borough | 2-4 |
| Irlam | v | Runcorn Linnets | 2-0 |
| Maine Road | v | Squires Gate | 1-5 |
| Nelson | v | Congleton Town | 4-3 |
| West Didsbury & Chorlton | v | Eccleshall | 1-2 |

ROUND 3

| | | | |
|---|---|---|---|
| Eccleshall | v | Irlam | 2-0 |
| Nelson | v | Cammell Laird 1907 | 2-4 |
| Squires Gate | v | Colne | 2-5 |
| Stockport Town | v | Barnton | 1-3 |
| Padiham | v | Runcorn Town | 2-2, 4-5p |
| Silsden | v | AFC Blackpool | 0-1 |
| Ashton Athletic | v | 1874 Northwich | 2-2, 8-7p |
| Atherton Collieries | v | Bacup Borough | 5-1 |

QUARTER FINALS

| | | | |
|---|---|---|---|
| Barnton | v | Ashton Athletic | 3-1 |
| Cammell Laird 1907 | v | AFC Blackpool | 0-2 |
| Colne | v | Eccleshall | 0-3 |
| Runcorn Town | v | Atherton Collieries | 0-3 |

SEMI FINALS

| | | | |
|---|---|---|---|
| Colne | v | AFC Blackpool | 2-0 |
| Atherton Collieries | v | Barnton | 1-0 |

FINAL

| | | | |
|---|---|---|---|
| Atherton Collieries | v | Colne | 5-1 |

**CLUB MOVEMENTS - Premier Division - In:** Barnton (P), Hanley Town (P), Irlam (P), New Mills (R - Northern Premier). **Out:** AFC Blackpool (R), Alsager Town (R), Silsden (R), Colne (P - Northern Premier). **Division One - In:** AFC Blackpool (R), Alsager Town (R), Carlisle City (P - Northern Alliance), Charnock Richard (P - West Lancs), City of Liverpool (N), FC Oswestry Town (P - Mercian Regional Football League), Prestwich Heys (P - Manchester Lge) and Sandbach United (P - Cheshire) Silsden (R). **Out:** Barnton (P), Hanley Town (P), Irlam (P), Northwich Manchester Villa (Resigned), Rochdale Town (Removed due to ground grading now Manchester Lge).

## 1874 NORTHWICH

Founded: 2012 Nickname:

**Secretary:** Vicki England **(T)** **(E)**
**Chairman:** Paul Stockton **Manager:** Ian Street **Prog Ed:** Andy Dignum
**Ground:** Winsford United FC, Wharton Road, Winsford, Cheshire CW7 3AE **(T)** 07975 679 624
**Capacity:** 6,000 **Seats:** Seats **Covered:** Yes **Midweek Matchday:** Tuesday **Clubhouse:** Yes

**Colours(change):** Green/black/green & white (Claret/claret/sky blue)
**Previous Names:** None
**Previous Leagues:** None
**Records:** 563 v Runcorn Linnets, 23rd September 2014
**Honours:**

**10 YEAR RECORD**

| 06-07 | 07-08 | 08-09 | 09-10 | 10-11 | 11-12 | 12-13 | 13-14 | 14-15 | 15-16 |
|---|---|---|---|---|---|---|---|---|---|
| | | | | | | | NWC1 3 | NWCP 3 | NWCP 4 |

## ABBEY HEY

Founded: 1902 Nickname:

**Secretary:** Tony McAllister **(T)** 0161 231 7147 **(E)**
**Chairman:** James Whittaker **Manager:** Luke Gibson **Prog Ed:** Gordon Lester
**Ground:** The Abbey Stadium, Goredale Avenue, Gorton, Manchester M18 7HD **(T)** 0161 231 7147
**Capacity:** **Seats:** Yes **Covered:** Yes **Midweek Matchday:** Tuesday **Clubhouse:** Yes

**Colours(change):** Red/black/red (Blue/white/blue)
**Previous Names:**
**Previous Leagues:** Manchester Amateur, South East Lancashire, Manchester.
**Records:** 985 v FC United of Manchester, March 2006.
**Honours:** Manchester Amateur League 1964-65. South East Lancashire 1966-67, 68-69.
Manchester League Division One 1970-71, Premier 1981-82, 88-89, 88-89, 91-92, 93-94, 94-95.

**10 YEAR RECORD**

| 06-07 | 07-08 | 08-09 | 09-10 | 10-11 | 11-12 | 12-13 | 13-14 | 14-15 | 15-16 |
|---|---|---|---|---|---|---|---|---|---|
| NWC1 17 | NWC1 17 | NWCP 21 | NWCP 22 | NWC1 15 | NWC1 3 | NWC1 2 | NWCP 20 | NWCP 14 | NWCP 10 |

## AFC DARWEN

Founded: 2009 Nickname:

**Secretary:** Sarah Hindle **(T)** **(E)**
**Chairman:** Wayne Wild **Manager:** Scott Campbell **Prog Ed:** Steve Hart
**Ground:** Anchor Ground, Anchor Road, Darwen, Lancs, BB3 0BB **(T)** 01254 776 193
**Capacity:** **Seats:** Yes **Covered:** Yes **Midweek Matchday:** Wednesday **Clubhouse:** Yes

**Colours(change):** All red (All navy & yellow)
**Previous Names:**
**Previous Leagues:** West Lancashire 2009-10.
**Records:** **Att:** 842 v Hanley Town (Play off Final 2015)
**Honours:**

**10 YEAR RECORD**

| 06-07 | 07-08 | 08-09 | 09-10 | 10-11 | 11-12 | 12-13 | 13-14 | 14-15 | 15-16 |
|---|---|---|---|---|---|---|---|---|---|
| | | | WLaP 8 | NWC1 13 | NWC1 13 | NWC1 5 | NWC1 9 | NWC1 3 | NWCP 18 |

## AFC LIVERPOOL

Founded: 2008 Nickname: Reds

**Secretary:** Jamie Harper **(T)** **(E)**
**Chairman:** Chris Stirrup **Manager:** Kevin Dally **Prog Ed:** Paul Smith
**Ground:** The Marine Travel Arena (Marine FC), College Road, Crosby, Liverpool L23 3AS **(T)** 0151 924 1743 or 0151 286 9101
**Capacity:** 3,185 **Seats:** 400 **Covered:** 1,400 **Midweek Matchday:** Wednesday **Clubhouse:** Yes **Shop:** Yes

**Colours(change):** Red/red/red & white (All purple)
**Previous Names:** None
**Previous Leagues:** None
**Records:** **Att:** 604 v Wigan Robin Park 06/09/2008.
**Honours:** North West Counties Trophy 2008-09, 09-10.

**10 YEAR RECORD**

| 06-07 | 07-08 | 08-09 | 09-10 | 10-11 | 11-12 | 12-13 | 13-14 | 14-15 | 15-16 |
|---|---|---|---|---|---|---|---|---|---|
| | | NWC1 4 | NWC1 5 | NWC1 4 | NWCP 19 | NWCP 11 | NWCP 7 | NWCP 9 | NWCP 17 |

## ASHTON ATHLETIC

Founded: 1968 Nickname:

**Secretary:** J.S. (Taffy) Roberts **(T)** **(E)**
**Chairman:** Jimmy Whyte **Manager:** Jay Foulds, Ben Kay & Dougie Pitts **Prog Ed:** J.S. (Taffy) Roberts
**Ground:** Brocstedes Park, Downall Green, Ashton in Markerfield WN4 0NR **(T)** 01942 716 360
**Capacity:** 600 **Seats:** 100 **Covered:** 300 **Midweek Matchday:** Tuesday **Clubhouse:** Yes

**Colours(change):** Yellow/blue/yellow. (All maroon).
**Previous Names:** None.
**Previous Leagues:** Lancashire Combination, Manchester Amateur League
**Records:** **Att:** 202 v 1874 Northwich 14-02-2015. **Apps:** Steve Rothwell - 50+
**Honours:** Atherton Charity Cup 2006-07, 07-08, 08-09.
NWCFL Challenge Cup 2013-14.

**10 YEAR RECORD**

| 06-07 | 07-08 | 08-09 | 09-10 | 10-11 | 11-12 | 12-13 | 13-14 | 14-15 | 15-16 |
|---|---|---|---|---|---|---|---|---|---|
| NWC2 16 | NWC2 3 | NWCP 6 | NWCP 21 | NWCP 22 | NWCP 14 | NWCP 20 | NWCP 6 | NWCP 5 | NWCP 7 |

## ATHERTON COLLIERIES

Founded: 1916 Nickname: The Colts

**Secretary:** Emil Anderson **(T)** **(E)**
**Chairman:** Paul Gregory **Manager:** Michael Clegg **Prog Ed:** Joseph Gibbons
**Ground:** The Kensite Stadium, Alder Street, Atherton, Greater Manchester M46 9EY **(T)** 07968 548 056
**Capacity:** **Seats:** **Covered:** **Midweek Matchday:** Monday **Clubhouse:**

**Colours(change):** Black & white stripes/black/black (All yellow)
**Previous Names:**
**Previous Leagues:** Bolton Combination. Lancashire Combination. Cheshire County.
**Records:** **Att:** 3,300 in Lancashire Combination 1920's.
**Honours:** North West Counties League Division Three 1986-87, Division One 2014-15.

**10 YEAR RECORD**

| 06-07 | 07-08 | 08-09 | 09-10 | 10-11 | 11-12 | 12-13 | 13-14 | 14-15 | 15-16 |
|---|---|---|---|---|---|---|---|---|---|
| NWC1 7 | NWC1 15 | NWCP 22 | NWC1 6 | NWC1 5 | NWC1 4 | NWC1 4 | NWC1 5 | NWC1 1 | NWCP 3 |

## BARNOLDSWICK TOWN

Founded: 1972 Nickname:

**Secretary:** Lynn James **(T)** **(E)**
**Chairman:** Ian James **Manager:** Stewart Airdrie **Prog Ed:** Peter Naylor
**Ground:** Silentnight Stadium, West Close Road, Barnoldswick, Colne, BB18 5LJ **(T)** 07528 410 204
**Capacity:** **Seats:** Yes **Covered:** Yes **Midweek Matchday:** Tuesday **Clubhouse:** Yes

**Colours(change):** Yellow & Blue/blue/blue (All red)
**Previous Names:** Today's club formed after the merger of Barnoldswick United and Barnoldswick Park Rovers in 2003
**Previous Leagues:** Craven, East Lancashire, West Lancashire.
**Records:** **Att:** 334 v Spennymoor, FA Vase, 2011-12.
**Honours:** West Lancashire Division 1 1998-99

**10 YEAR RECORD**

| 06-07 | 07-08 | 08-09 | 09-10 | 10-11 | 11-12 | 12-13 | 13-14 | 14-15 | 15-16 |
|---|---|---|---|---|---|---|---|---|---|
| WLaP 13 | WLaP 10 | WLaP 6 | NWC1 2 | NWCP 7 | NWCP 4 | NWCP 9 | NWCP 16 | NWCP 19 | NWCP 9 |

## BARNTON

Founded: 1946 Nickname:

**Secretary:** Russell Stevenson **(T)** **(E)**
**Chairman:** Ian Ross **Manager:** Steve Lloyd **Prog Ed:** Russell Stevenson
**Ground:** Tonwfield, Townfield Lane, Barnton, Cheshire CW8 4LH **(T)** 07709 585 644
**Capacity:** **Seats:** **Covered:** **Midweek Matchday:** **Clubhouse:**

**Colours(change):** White & black stripes/white/white (All orange)
**Previous Names:**
**Previous Leagues:** Mid-Cheshire. Cheshire
**Records:** **Record Att:** 260 v Bramwell, 25/04/98.
**Honours:** Mid-Cheshire 1979-80, 82-83, 88-89, 96-97, 97-98, 98-99, 99-2000, 2000-01, 01-02, 02-03, 04-05. Cheshire Division Two 2012-13.
Cheshire Amateur Cup 1948-49, 68-69, 2001-02, 03-04. Cheshire Senior Cup 1980-81. Mid-Cheshire Challenge Cup 2013-14.

**10 YEAR RECORD**

| 06-07 | 07-08 | 08-09 | 09-10 | 10-11 | 11-12 | 12-13 | 13-14 | 14-15 | 15-16 |
|---|---|---|---|---|---|---|---|---|---|
| MidCh 9 | Ches1 11 | Ches1 16 | Ches2 10 | Ches2 13 | Ches2 13 | Ches2 1 | Ches1 5 | NWC1 7 | NWC1 3 |

## BOOTLE

Founded: 1954 Nickname:

**Secretary:** Joe Doran **(T)** 0151 531 0665 **(E)**
**Chairman:** Bobby Capstick **Manager:** Joe Doran **Prog Ed:** Dave Miley Junior
**Ground:** Delta Taxi Stadium, Vestey Rd, Off Bridle Road, Bootle L30 1NY **(T)** 0151 525 4796
**Capacity:** **Seats:** **Covered:** Yes **Midweek Matchday:** Tuesday **Clubhouse:** Yes

**Colours(change):** All blue (All yellow)
**Previous Names:** Langton Dock 1953 - 1973.
**Previous Leagues:** Liverpool Shipping. Lancashire Combination. Cheshire. Liverpool County Combination >2006.
**Records:** **Att:** 1,078 v Everton Reserves, Liverpool Senior Cup Feb 2010.
**Honours:** Liverpool County Combination 1964-65, 65-66, 67-68, 68-69, 69-70, 70-71, 71-72, 72-73, 73-74. Lancashire Comb. 1975-76, 76-77. Cheshire County Div.2 1978-79. North West Counties Div.1 2008-09. Liverpool County Senior Cup 2012-13.

**10 YEAR RECORD**

| 06-07 | 07-08 | 08-09 | 09-10 | 10-11 | 11-12 | 12-13 | 13-14 | 14-15 | 15-16 |
|---|---|---|---|---|---|---|---|---|---|
| NWC2 10 | NWC2 6 | NWC1 1 | NWCP 3 | NWCP 6 | NWCP 3 | NWCP 3 | NWCP 8 | NWCP 7 | NWCP 8 |

## CAMMELL LAIRD

Founded: 1907 Nickname: Lairds

**Secretary:** Anthony 'Toddy' Wood **(T)** 07931 761 429 **(E)** toddywood@hotmail.com
**Chairman:** Frank Games **Manager:** Neil Prince **Prog Ed:** Patrick Burke
**Ground:** NW Construction Stadium, St Peter's Road, Rock Ferry, Birkenhead CH42 1PY **(T)** 0151 645 3121
**Capacity:** 2,000 **Seats:** 150 **Covered:** Yes **Midweek Matchday:** Tuesday **Clubhouse:** Yes **Shop:** Yes

**Colours(change):** All blue (All yellow)
**Previous Names:** Kirklands 1922-44.
**Previous Leagues:** West Cheshire, North West Counties > 2006. NPL 2006-14 Resigned.
**Records:** **Att:** 1,700 v Harwich & Parkeston - FA Vase 5th Round 1990-91
**Honours:** North West Counties League Division 2, League Cup and Trophy 2004-05, Division 1 2005-06. West Cheshire League x19 (Most recently 2000-01). Cheshire Amateur Cup x11. Wirral Senior Cup.

**10 YEAR RECORD**

| 06-07 | 07-08 | 08-09 | 09-10 | 10-11 | 11-12 | 12-13 | 13-14 | 14-15 | 15-16 |
|---|---|---|---|---|---|---|---|---|---|
| NP 1 2 | NP1S 2 | NP P 18 | NP1S 16 | NP1N 19 | NP1N 22 | NP1N 2 | NP1N | NWC1 2 | NWCP 15 |

## CONGLETON TOWN

Founded: 1901 Nickname: Bears

**Secretary:** Ken Mead **(T)** 01260 278 152 **(E)**
**Chairman:** Steven Burgess **Manager:** Andy Alston **Prog Ed:** Ken Mead
**Ground:** Ivy Gardens, Booth Street, Crescent Road, Congleton, Cheshire CW12 4DG **(T)** 01260 274 460
**Capacity:** 5,000 **Seats:** 250 **Covered:** 1,200 **Midweek Matchday:** Tuesday **Clubhouse:** Yes **Shop:** Yes

**Colours(change):** Black & white/black/black. (Yellow/green/yellow).
**Previous Names:** Congleton Hornets
**Previous Leagues:** Crew & District, North Staffs, Macclesfield, Cheshire , Mid Cheshire, NW Co, NPL
**Records:** **Att:** 6,800 v Macclesfield, Cheshire Lge1953-54 **Goalscorer:** Mick Bidde 150+ **App:** Ray Clack 600+ Graham Harrison 600+
**Honours:** Crewe & District League 1901-02, 02-03, 03-04. North Staffs & District 1919-20. Macclesfield & District League 1939-40. Mid Cheshire League 1973-74, 75-76, 77-78. Cheshire Senior Cup 1920-21, 37-38.

**10 YEAR RECORD**

| 06-07 | 07-08 | 08-09 | 09-10 | 10-11 | 11-12 | 12-13 | 13-14 | 14-15 | 15-16 |
|---|---|---|---|---|---|---|---|---|---|
| NWC1 10 | NWC1 9 | NWCP 4 | NWCP 5 | NWCP 8 | NWCP 11 | NWCP 7 | NWCP 10 | NWCP 8 | NWCP 6 |

## HANLEY TOWN

Founded: 1966 Nickname:

**Secretary:** Ian Evans **(T)** **(E)**
**Chairman:** Paul Legge **Manager:** Dean Owen **Prog Ed:** Kelsey Stair
**Ground:** Abbey Lane, Bucknall, Stoke-on-Trent, Staffordshire ST2 8AJ **(T)** 07599 397 053
**Capacity:** **Seats:** **Covered:** **Midweek Matchday:** **Clubhouse:**

**Colours(change):** All blue (Red/white/red)
**Previous Names:**
**Previous Leagues:** Staffordshire County Senior.
**Records:** **Att:** 1,000 v Chasetown 1982.
**Honours:** Staffordshire County Senior League 2006-07, 11-12, 12-13. North West Counties League Division One 2015-16.

**10 YEAR RECORD**

| 06-07 | 07-08 | 08-09 | 09-10 | 10-11 | 11-12 | 12-13 | 13-14 | 14-15 | 15-16 |
|---|---|---|---|---|---|---|---|---|---|
| StfSP 1 | | | | StfSP 2 | StfSP 1 | StfSP 1 | NWC1 4 | NWC1 4 | NWC1 1 |

## IRLAM

Founded: 1969 Nickname:

**Secretary:** Warren Dodd **(T)** 07969 946 277 **(E)**

**Chairman:** Ron Parker **Manager:** Steve Nixon **Prog Ed:** Warren Dodd

**Ground:** Silver Street, Irlam, Manchester M44 6HR **(T)** 07969 946 277

**Capacity:** **Seats:** **Covered:** **Midweek Matchday:** **Clubhouse:**

**Colours(change):** All blue (Red/black/black)

**Previous Names:** Mitchell Shackleton.

**Previous Leagues:** Manchester Amateur. Manchester.

**Records:** **Att:** 1,600 v Hallam FA Vase.

**Honours:**

**10 YEAR RECORD**

| 06-07 | 07-08 | 08-09 | 09-10 | 10-11 | 11-12 | 12-13 | 13-14 | 14-15 | 15-16 |
|---|---|---|---|---|---|---|---|---|---|
| MancP 5 | MancP 8 | NWC1 8 | NWC1 10 | NWC1 9 | NWC1 10 | NWC1 14 | NWC1 10 | NWC1 14 | NWC1 2 |

## MAINE ROAD

Founded: 1955 Nickname: Blues

**Secretary:** Derek Barber **(T)** 0161 431 8243 **(E)**

**Chairman:** Ron Meredith **Manager:** Chris Hirst **Prog Ed:** Jeff Newman

**Ground:** Brantingham Road, Chorlton-cum-Hardy M21 0TT **(T)** 0161 861 0344

**Capacity:** 2,000 **Seats:** 200 **Covered:** 700 **Midweek Matchday:** Monday **Clubhouse:** Yes

**Colours(change):** All sky blue. (Red & black stripes/black/black).

**Previous Names:** City Supporters Rusholme 1955-late sixties.

**Previous Leagues:** Rusholme Sunday 1955-66, Manchester Amateur Sunday 1966-72 & Manchester 1972-87.

**Records:** **Att:** 3,125 v FC United Manchester, NWC Div.1, 04.11.06, at Stalybridge Celtic.

**Honours:** Manchester Premier League 1982-83, 83-84, 84-85, 85-86. North West Counties Division Two 1989-90, Challenge Cup 07-08.

**10 YEAR RECORD**

| 06-07 | 07-08 | 08-09 | 09-10 | 10-11 | 11-12 | 12-13 | 13-14 | 14-15 | 15-16 |
|---|---|---|---|---|---|---|---|---|---|
| NWC1 6 | NWC1 4 | NWCP 13 | NWCP 6 | NWCP 13 | NWCP 18 | NWCP 2 | NWCP 4 | NWCP 15 | NWCP 12 |

## NELSON

Founded: 1883 Nickname: Admirals

**Secretary:** Alan Pickering **(T)** **(E)**

**Chairman:** Fayyaz Ahmed **Manager:** Paul Fildes

**Ground:** Little Wembley, Lomeshaye Way, Nelson, Lancs BB9 7BN. **(T)** 01282 787 752

**Capacity:** 1500 **Seats:** 150 **Covered:** 200 **Midweek Matchday:** Tuesday **Clubhouse:** Yes **Shop:** Yes

**Colours(change):** All blue. (Orange/black/orange).

**Previous Names:** Reformed in 2011.

**Previous Leagues:** Since 1946: Lancs Comb 1946-82. NW Counties 1982-88, 92-2010. West Lancs 1988-92.

**Records:** **Att:** 14,143 v Bradford Park Avenue, Div.3 North, 10.04.26.

**Honours:** Football League Division Three North 1922-23.
North West Counties Division One 2013-14.

**10 YEAR RECORD**

| 06-07 | 07-08 | 08-09 | 09-10 | 10-11 | 11-12 | 12-13 | 13-14 | 14-15 | 15-16 |
|---|---|---|---|---|---|---|---|---|---|
| NWC1 20 | NWC1 20 | NWCP 17 | NWCP 17 | | NWC1 15 | NWC1 10 | NWC1 1 | NWCP 11 | NWCP 16 |

## NEW MILLS

Founded: pre1890 Nickname: The Millers

**Secretary:** Sue Hyde **(T)** 07795 115 708 **(E)** newmillsfs@yahoo.co.uk

**Chairman:** Raymond Coverley **Manager:** Garry Brown **Prog Ed:** James Lobley

**Ground:** Church Lane, New Mills, SK22 4NP **(T)** 01663 747 435

**Capacity:** 1,650 **Seats:** 120 **Covered:** 400 **Midweek Matchday:** Monday **Clubhouse:** Yes

**Colours(change):** Amber & black/black/black

**Previous Names:** New Mills St Georges until 1919

**Previous Leagues:** Manchester, North West Counties, Cheshire. Northern Premier 2011-16.

**Records:** **Att:** 4,500 v Hyde United, Manchester Junior Cup 09/09/1922

**Honours:** Manchester League Premier Division 1924, 26, 56, 63, 65, 66, 67, 68, 70, 71.
North West Counties Division Two 2007-08, Challenge Cup 2008-09, Premier Division 2010-11.

**10 YEAR RECORD**

| 06-07 | 07-08 | 08-09 | 09-10 | 10-11 | 11-12 | 12-13 | 13-14 | 14-15 | 15-16 |
|---|---|---|---|---|---|---|---|---|---|
| NWC2 | NWC2 1 | NWCP 2 | NWCP 2 | NWCP 1 | NP1S 9 | NP1N 3 | NP1N 16 | NP1N 21 | NP1N 22 |

## PADIHAM

Founded: 1878 Nickname: Caldersiders

**Secretary:** Alan Smith **(T)** 07775 717 698 **(E)** alansmithpadihamfc@yahoo.co.uk

**Chairman:** Frank Heys **Manager:** Steve Wilkes **Prog Ed:** Alan Smith

**Ground:** Arbories Memorial Sports Ground, Well Street, Padiham BB12 8LE **(T)** 01282 773 742

**Capacity:** 1,688 **Seats:** 159 **Covered:** Yes **Midweek Matchday:** Wednesday **Clubhouse:** Yes

**Colours(change):** All blue. (Red/blue/red).

**Previous Names:** None

**Previous Leagues:** Lancashire Comb. East Lancs Am. North East Lancs. West Lancs. North West Counties > 2013. NPL 2013-15.

**Records:** **Att:** 9,000 v Burnley, Dec.1884 (at Calderside Ground).

**Honours:** West Lancashire League Division Two 1971-72, 76-77, Division One 1999-00. North West Counties League 2012-13.

**10 YEAR RECORD**

| 06-07 | 07-08 | 08-09 | 09-10 | 10-11 | 11-12 | 12-13 | 13-14 | 14-15 | 15-16 |
|---|---|---|---|---|---|---|---|---|---|
| NWC2 3 | NWC2 12 | NWC1 2 | NWCP 10 | NWCP 4 | NWCP 15 | NWCP 1 | NP1N 19 | NP1N 22 | NWCP 11 |

## RUNCORN LINNETS

Founded: 2006 Nickname: Linnets

**Secretary:** Lynn Johnston **(T)** 01606 43008 **(E)**

**Chairman:** Derek Greenwood **Manager:** Joey Dunn **Prog Ed:** Jon Urquhart

**Ground:** Millbank Linnets Stadium, Murdishaw Ave, Runcorn, Cheshire WA7 6HP **(T)** 07050 801733 (Clubline)

**Capacity:** **Seats:** Yes **Covered:** Yes **Midweek Matchday:** Tuesday **Clubhouse:** Yes

**Colours(change):** Yellow & green/green/yellow & green (Blue & white/white/blue & white)

**Previous Names:** None

**Previous Leagues:** None.

**Records:** **Att:** 1,037 v Witton Albion, pre season friendly July 2010

**Honours:** NWCFL Challenge Cup 2012-13.

**10 YEAR RECORD**

| 06-07 | 07-08 | 08-09 | 09-10 | 10-11 | 11-12 | 12-13 | 13-14 | 14-15 | 15-16 |
|---|---|---|---|---|---|---|---|---|---|
| NWC2 2 | NWC1 12 | NWCP 11 | NWCP 11 | NWCP 12 | NWCP 5 | NWCP 6 | NWCP 2 | NWCP 2 | NWCP 2 |

## RUNCORN TOWN

Founded: 1967 Nickname:

**Secretary:** Linda Young **(T)** 01928 590 508 **(E)**

**Chairman:** Tony Riley **Manager:** Chris Herbert **Prog Ed:** Paul Watson

**Ground:** Pavilions Sports Complex, Sandy Lane, Weston Point, Runcorn WA7 4EX **(T)** 01928 590 508

**Capacity:** **Seats:** Yes **Covered:** Yes **Midweek Matchday:** Monday **Clubhouse:** Yes

**Colours(change):** All blue (All green)

**Previous Names:** Mond Rangers 1967-2005 (Amalgamated with ICI Weston 1974-75).

**Previous Leagues:** Runcorn Sunday 1967-73, Warrington & District 1973-84, West Cheshire 1984-10.

**Records:** **Att:** 803 v Runcorn Linnets, NWCFL Prem Div, December 2014

**Honours:** West Cheshire League Division Two 2006-07. Runcorn Senior Cup 2004-05, 05-06, 07-08.

**10 YEAR RECORD**

| 06-07 | 07-08 | 08-09 | 09-10 | 10-11 | 11-12 | 12-13 | 13-14 | 14-15 | 15-16 |
|---|---|---|---|---|---|---|---|---|---|
| WCh2 1 | WCh1 3 | WCh1 4 | WCh1 3 | NWC1 2 | NWCP 2 | NWCP 4 | NWCP 5 | NWCP 13 | NWCP 13 |

## SQUIRES GATE

Founded: 1948 Nickname:

**Secretary:** John Maguire **(T)** 01253 348 512 **(E)**

**Chairman:** Stuart Hopwood **Manager:** Daniel Penswick **Prog Ed:** Daniel Hayden

**Ground:** School Road, Marton, Blackpool, Lancs FY4 5DS **(T)** 01253 348 512

**Capacity:** 1,000 **Seats:** 100 **Covered:** Yes **Midweek Matchday:** Tuesday **Clubhouse:** Yes

**Colours(change):** All blue. (All red)

**Previous Names:** Squires Gate British Legion FC >1953.

**Previous Leagues:** Blackpool & District Amateur 1958-61. West Lancashire 1961-91.

**Records:** **Att:** 600 v Everton, friendly 1995.

**Honours:** Blackpool & District Amateur League Division One 1955-56, 56-57. West Lancashire League Division Two 1980-81.

**10 YEAR RECORD**

| 06-07 | 07-08 | 08-09 | 09-10 | 10-11 | 11-12 | 12-13 | 13-14 | 14-15 | 15-16 |
|---|---|---|---|---|---|---|---|---|---|
| NWC1 18 | NWC1 6 | NWCP 10 | NWCP 13 | NWCP 9 | NWCP 16 | NWCP 21 | NWCP 19 | NWCP 6 | NWCP 19 |

## WEST DIDSBURY & CHORLTON

Founded: 1908 Nickname: West

**Secretary:** Rob McKay (acting) **(T)** **(E)**

**Chairman:** Glyn Meacher **Manager:** Steve Settle **Prog Ed:** John Churchman

**Ground:** The Recreation Ground, End of Brookburn Road, Chorlton, Manchester M21 8FF **(T)** 07891 298 441

**Capacity:** **Seats:** Yes **Covered:** Yes **Midweek Matchday:** Tuesday **Clubhouse:** Yes

**Colours(change):** White & black/white/white (All blue)

**Previous Names:** Christ Church AFC 1908-1920. West Didsbury AFC 1920-2003.

**Previous Leagues:** Manchester Alliance pre 1920. Lancashire & Cheshire Amateur 1920-2006. Manchester 2006-2012.

**Records:** 460 v. FC United of Manchester July 2013

**Honours:** Manchester League Division One 2010-11. NWCL Division One Trophy 2012-13.

**10 YEAR RECORD**

| 06-07 | 07-08 | 08-09 | 09-10 | 10-11 | 11-12 | 12-13 | 13-14 | 14-15 | 15-16 |
|---|---|---|---|---|---|---|---|---|---|
| | | | | Manc1 1 | MancP 7 | NCE1 3 | NWCP 12 | NWCP 16 | NWCP 5 |

## WINSFORD UNITED

Founded: 1883 Nickname: Blues

**Secretary:** Robert Astles **(T)** 01606 558 447 **(E)**

**Chairman:** Mark Loveless **Manager:** Lee Duckworth **Prog Ed:** Robert Astles

**Ground:** The Barton Stadium, Kingsway, Winsford, Cheshire CW7 3AE **(T)** 01606 558 447

**Capacity:** 6,000 **Seats:** 250 **Covered:** 5,000 **Midweek Matchday:** Tuesday **Clubhouse:** Yes **Shop:** Yes

**Colours(change):** All blue (Yellow & black/black/black).

**Previous Names:** Over Wanderers 1883-1887

**Previous Leagues:** The Combination 1902-04. Cheshire County 1919-40, 47-82. Northern Premier League 1987-2001.

**Records:** **Att:** 8,000 v Witton Albion, 1947. **Goalscorer:** Graham Smith 66 **Apps:** Edward Harrop 400

**Honours:** Cheshire League 1920-21, 76-77. Cheshire Senior Cup 1958-59, 79-80, 92-93.
North West Counties League Division Two 2006-07.

**10 YEAR RECORD**

| 06-07 | 07-08 | 08-09 | 09-10 | 10-11 | 11-12 | 12-13 | 13-14 | 14-15 | 15-16 |
|---|---|---|---|---|---|---|---|---|---|
| NWC2 1 | NWC1 10 | NWCP 19 | NWCP 19 | NWCP 3 | NWCP 7 | NWCP 5 | NWCP 14 | NWCP 12 | NWCP 14 |

# GROUND DIRECTIONS - PREMIER DIVISION

**1874 NORTHWICH - The Barton Stadium, Kingsway, Winsford, Cheshire. CW7 3AE. 01606 558447**
From M6 junction 18, follow A54 through Middlewich for approx 3 miles, bear right at roundabout at Winsford Railway Station, follow road for approx 1 mile, turn right into Kingsway, ground is on the right.

**ABBEY HEY-The Abbey Stadium, Goredale Avenue, Gorton, Manchester M18 7HD. 0161 231 7147**
M60 to junction 24, take A57 to Manchester City Centre for approx 1 mile, at first set of major traffic lights (MacDonalds on right) pass through for approx 300yards, turn left immediatley before overhead railway bridge (A.H.F.C. sign) into Woodland Avenue. Take first right, pass under railway bridge, turn first left into Goredale Avenue.

**AFC DARWEN-Anchor Ground, Anchor Road, Darwen, Lancs, BB3 0BB. 07989-744584**
Leave M65 at Junction 4. At traffic lights turn left onto A666 (signposted Darwen). After approx ? mile turn left between Anchor Car Sales and the Anchor Pub. Bare right and ground 200 yards on left.

**AFC LIVERPOOL-The Marine Travel Arena (Marine FC), College Road, Crosby, Liverpool L23 3AS**
M57/M58 take the A5036 signposted Bootle & Docks, at the roundabout under the flyover turn right onto the A565 following signs for Crosby and Marine AFC. After passing Tesco Express on the right, turn left at the traffic lights (by Merchants Taylors School) into College Road, ground is approx ½ mile on the left..

**ASHTON ATHLETIC-Brocstedes Park, Downall Green, Ashton in Makerfield. WN4 0NR. 01942 716360**
M6 northbound to junction 25, follow the slip road to the island and turn right A49, proceed for approx 0.50 mile turning right into Soughers Lane. At the T junction turn right into Downall Green Road and go over the motorway bridge passing a church on your right. Turn 2nd right into Booths Brow Road and turn 2nd right again into Brocstedes Road which is a narrow street. After 200 yards turn right down a shale road into the car park and ground.
From The North: M6 southbound to junction 24, proceed on to the slip road keeping in the right hand lane, turn right go over the motorway bridge and immediately re-enter the M6 Northbound for approximately 100 yards. Leave at junction 25,Follow the slip road to the island and turn right A49, proceed for approx 0.50 mile turning right into Soughers Lane. At the T junction turn right into Downall Green Road and go over the motorway bridge passing a church on your right. Turn 2nd right into Booths Brow Road and turn 2nd right again into Brocstedes Road which is a narrow street. After 200 yards turn right down a shale road into the car park and ground.

**ATHERTON COLLIERIES-Alder Street, Atherton, Greater Manchester. M46 9EY. 07968 548056**
M61 to junction 5, follow sign for Westhoughton, turn left onto A6, turn right onto A579 (Newbrook Road/Bolton Road) into Atherton. At first set of traffic lights turn left into High Street, then second left into Alder Street to ground.

**BARNOLDSWICK TOWN-Silentnight Stadium, West Close Road, Barnoldswick, Colne, BB18 5EW. 01282 815817**
ravelling from Blackburn to Colne on M65 to end, straight on at roundabout onto Vivary Way onto North Valley Road. Through two sets of traffic lights to roundabout, turn left to Barnoldswick. Straight on till you come to roundabout in Kelbrook turn left to Barnoldswick.On entering Barnoldswick straight ahead at traffic lights, straight ahead at mini roundabout. Travel through built up area past Fosters Arms pub on left set back. Take first right onto Greenberfield Lane, travel 50 yards take middle single track (signposted) travel to bottom of track and bare right to car park at rear of ground.
Travelling from Barrow on A59 from Gisburn towards Skipton turn right at Barnoldswick signpost. Travel approx 2 miles taking 1st left onto

Greenberfield Lane, travel 50 yards take middle single track (signposted) travel to bottom of track bare right to car park at rear of ground. If using a SatNav use postcode BB18 5LJ.

**BARNTON - Tonwfield, Townfield Lane, Barnton, Cheshire CW8 4LH**

Turn off the A533 (Northwich to Runcorn) at the Beech Tree Inn (Barnton Village) into Beech Lane. Turn right at the 'T' junction with Townfield Lane - the ground is 200 yards on the left signed Memorial Hall. Note parking restrictions well signed.

**BOOTLE-Delta Taxi Stadium, Vestey Road, off Bridle Road, Bootle, L30 4UN. 0151 525 4796 or 07852 742790**

At Liverpool end of M57and M58 follow signs for Liverpool (A59 (S)), for 1 1/2 miles. At Aintree racecourse on left and Aintree Train Station on right ,turn right at lights into Park Lane. Turn left at second set of lights into Bridle Road. After 200 yards turn left at lights into Vestey Estate , ground 200 yards.

**CAMMELL LAIRD - NW Construction Stadium, St Peter's Road, Rock Ferry, Birkenhead CH42 1PY 0151 645 3121**

From Chester: M563/A41 towards Birkenhead, at New ferry signpost take the B5136 towards New ferry, approx 1 mile, turn right at traffic island into Proctor Road, ground at the bottom of Proctor Road. From Liverpool: Take the Birkenhead Tunnel, A41 for approx 1 mile, take the B5136 signposted New Ferry / Rock Ferry at big round-a-bout. Follow until the 2nd set of traffic lights, turn left, then first right into St Peters Road, ground at the bottom of the road on the left.

**COLNE-The XLCR Stadium, Harrison Drive, Colne, Lancashire. BB8 9SL. 01282 862545**

Follow M65 to end of motorway. Turn left and follow signs for Skipton and Keighley, continue to roundabout, take 1st left up Harrison Drive, across small roundabout, follow road to ground.

**CONGLETON TOWN-Booth Street, off Crescent Road, Congleton, Cheshire, CW12 4DG. 01260 274460**

On approach to Congleton from M6, past Waggon & Horses Pub, at 1st roundabout 2nd exit, past fire station, 2nd right into Booth Street. Ground at top of road.

**HANLEY TOWN - Abbey Lane, Bucknall, Stoke-on-Trent, Staffordshire ST2 8AJ.**

**IRLAM-Irlam Football Club, Silver Street, Irlam, Manchester M44 6HR. 07718 756402/07969 946277**

From Peel Green Roundabout (M60 Junction 11), take A57 to Irlam, and then B5320 into Lower Irlam. After passing Morsons Project, turn right into Silver Street, at Nags Head Pub. The ground is situated at the bottom of Silver Street on the right hand side.

**MAINE ROAD-Brantingham Road, Chorlton-cum-Hardy, Manchester. M21 0TT. 0161 861 0344**

M60 to junction 7, A56 towards Manchester. At traffic island follow signs for Manchester United, Lancs CC, turn right at next set of traffic lights signposted A5145 (Chorlton-cum-Hardy/Stockport), through next set of traffic lights. Take left fork at Y junction (traffic lights) onto A6010 Wilbraham Road) to Chorlton. Through traffic lights (ignore pedestrian lights) for approx 1 mile. Left at next traffic lights into Withington Road, rst left into Brantingham Road. Ground 300 yards on left. From North: M60 clockwise to junction 5 onto A5103 towards Manchester Centre for approx 2 miles, turn left at traffic lights (Wilbraham Road) A6010, then right at 2nd set of lights (Withington Road), first left into Brantingham Road. Ground 300 yards on left.

**NELSON-Little Wembley, Lomeshaye Way, Nelson, Lancs BB9 7BN.**

M65 to junction 13, take first exit towards Fence A6068, take second left towards nelson B6249, after ½ mile turn right (signposted Lomeshaye Village), ground 200 yards on the right.

**NEW MILLS - Church Lane, New Mills, SK22 4NP**

Via Buxton: Follow the A6 By-Pass, go straight through the roundabout, under railway bridge and about 1 mile further on turn right onto Marsh Lane (Past Furness Vale primary school), this road takes you straight to the ground. Coach drivers should proceed on the A6 a couple of miles urning right opposite the Swan.

rom Chesterfield, take the A619 then the A623 and after the hair pin bend at Sparrow pit, proceed down the A623 turning right onto the A6 By-Pass, Follow directions as above.

**PADIHAM -Arbories Memorial Sports Ground, Well Street, Padiham BB12 8LE. 01282 773 742**

M65 to Junction 8, then follow A6068 signposted Clitheroe and Padiham. At traffic lights at bottom of hill turn right into Dean Range/Blackburn Road towards Padiham. At next junction turn into Holland Street opposite church, then into Well St at the side of Hare & Hounds Pub to ground.

**RUNCORN LINNETS-Millbank Linnets Stadium, Murdishaw Ave, Runcorn, Cheshire. WA7 6HP. 07050 801733 (Clubline)**

rth East-M56 junction 12 take A557 Widnes/Northwich. At Roundabout take 1st Exit onto A557 heading Frodsham A56, go through 1 roundabout. Turn left at Chester Rd/A56, turn left at Chester Rd/A533. At the r'about, take the 2nd exit onto Murdishaw Ave. Destination on the Right. Head West on M56 towards Exit 11. At junction 11, take the A56 exit to Preston Brook/Daresbury. At the roundabout take the 1st exit onto Chester Rd/A56 heading to Preston Brook/Daresbury. Continue to follow Chester Rd, go through 2 roundabouts.At the roundabout take the 2nd exit onto Murdishaw Ave. Destination on the right.

**RUNCORN TOWN-Pavilions Sports Complex, Sandy Lane, Weston Point, Runcorn, Cheshire WA7 4EX. 01928 590 508**

M56 J12. Head towards Liverpool. Come off at 4th exit (Runcorn Docks), turn left at the top of slip road, left at T-Junction, then left into Pavilions. M62 J7. Head towards Runcorn. When crossing Runcorn Bridge, stay in the right hand lane. Follow road around and come off at second exit Runcorn Docks). Turn right at the top of slip road, left at T-Junction, then left into Pavilions.

**SQUIRES GATE-School Road, Marton, Blackpool, FY4 5DS. 01253 798583**

rom M55: At the end of the M55 (J4), continue along dual carriageway (A5230), and bear left at major roundabout, staying on A5230. At second affic lights, turn left onto B5261. After passing Shovels pub on left, turn left at lights, and first car park is on left after approx 50 yards. Parking is so available down the lane leading to the Club, on your left, after another 40 yards. If both these are full, parking is also available on the Shovels car park, or on the car park adjacent to the playing fields (turn right at the lights after passing the pub).

**WEST DIDSBURY & CHORLTON-The Recreation Ground, End of Brookburn Road, Chorlton, Manchester M21 8FF-07891 298441**

rom the M60 take junction 5 onto Princess Road towards city centre. Turn left at Christie Fields offices/Premier Inn onto Barlow Moor Road and ontinue past Chorlton Park to Chorlton bus station. Turn left into Beech Road, then 2nd left into Reynard Road and continue past the Chorltonville sign passing over 5 speed ramps as far as Brookburn Primary School. Turn left into Brookburn Road and continue to the end of the ul de sac, through the gateway and down the tarmac access which leads into the ground. From Stretford follow Edge Lane and turn right into St lements Road at church. Continue through Chorlton Green and pass graveyard on left and then Bowling Green PH. Go past school and turn immeately right and continue to end of Brookburn Road as above. There is car parking within the grounds of the club, but restricted access for coaches.

**WINSFORD UNITED-The Barton Stadium, Kingsway, Winsford, Cheshire. CW7 3AE. 01606 558447**

rom M6 junction 18, follow A54 through Middlewich for approx 3 miles, bear right at roundabout at Winsford Railway Station, follow road for pprox 1 mile, turn right into Kingsway, ground is on the right.

## AFC BLACKPOOL
Founded: 1947 Nickname: Mechs

**Secretary:** William Singleton **(T)** 01253 761 721 **(E)**
**Chairman:** Henry Baldwin **Manager:** Stuart Parker **Prog Ed:** William Singleton
**Ground:** Mechanics Ground, Jepson Way, Common Edge Road, Blackpool, FY4 5DY **(T)** 01253 761 721 **Capacity:** 2,000
**Colours(change):** Tangerine/Tangerine/white (White/navy blue/white)

**ADDITIONAL INFORMATION: Att:** 4,300 v FC United of Manchester, 18/02/2006 at Blackpool FC.
Lancashire County FA Shield 1957/58, 1960/61. West Lancashire League 1960/61, 61/62.
North West Counties League Division Three 1985/86, Division One 2010-11.

## ALSAGER TOWN
Founded: 1968 Nickname: The Bullets

**Secretary:** Chris Robinson **(T)** 07888 750 532 **(E)**
**Chairman:** Terry Greer **Manager:** Scott Dundas **Prog Ed:** John Shenton
**Ground:** The LAW Training Stadium, Woodland Court, Alsager ST7 2DP **(T)** 07888 750 532 **Capacity:** 3,000
**Colours(change):** White & black/white/white. (All red).

**ADDITIONAL INFORMATION: Att:** 606 v Whitley Bay - 14.11.2009. **Goalscorer:** Gareth Rowe. **Apps:** Wayne Brotherton.
Leek Cup 2001-02

## ASHTON TOWN
Founded: 1962 Nickname:

**Secretary:** Stephen Ochwat **(T)** **(E)**
**Chairman:** Mark Hayes **Manager:** John Brownrigg **Prog Ed:** Ian Promfrett
**Ground:** The Ashton Town Stadium, Edge Green St, Ashton-in-Makerfield, Wigan, WN4 8SL **(T)** 01942 724 448
**Colours(change):** Red & white/red/red (Orange/white/orange)

**ADDITIONAL INFORMATION:**
**Record Att:** 1,865 v FC United of Manchester 2007.
**Honours:** Warrington League Guardian Cup.

## ATHERTON L.R.
Founded: 1956 Nickname: The Panthers

**Secretary:** Ronnie Wilcox **(T)** **(E)**
**Chairman:** Jane Wilcock **Manager:** Adam Jones & Craig Jones **Prog Ed:** Howard Jones
**Ground:** Crilly Park, Spa Road, Atherton, Manchester M46 9JX **(T)** 01942883950/07921579532 **Capacity:** 3,000
**Colours(change):** Yellow/blue/yellow (Orange/black/black).

**ADDITIONAL INFORMATION: Record Att:** 2,300 v Aldershot Town F.A. Vase Q-Final replay 93-94. **Goalscorer:** Shaun Parker **App:** Jim Evans
**Honours:** North West Counties League 1992-93, 93-94. Champions Trophy 1992-93, 93-94.

## BACUP BOROUGH
Founded: 1875 Nickname: The Boro

**Secretary:** Wendy Ennis **(T)** **(E)**
**Chairman:** Frank Manning **Manager:** Brent Peters **Prog Ed:** Michael Carr
**Ground:** Brian Boys Stadium, Cowtoot Lane, Blackthorn, Bacup, OL13 8EE **(T)** 01706 878 655 **Capacity:** 3,000
**Colours(change):** White/black/black. (All yellow & blue).

**ADDITIONAL INFORMATION: Previous Name:** Bacup & Rossendale Borough >2015.
**Record Att:** 4,980 v Nelson 1947 **Goalscorer:** Jimmy Clarke
**Honours:** North West Counties League Division Two 2002-03, Challenge Cup 2003-04.

## CARLISLE CITY
Founded: 1975 Nickname:

**Secretary:** Martin Denovellis **(T)** **(E)**
**Chairman:** Brian Hall **Prog Ed:** Brian Hall
**Ground:** Gilford Park, Carlisle CA1 3AF **(T)** 01228 523 777
**Colours(change):** All sky blue (All navy blue)

**ADDITIONAL INFORMATION: Record Att:** 200 v. Northbank Carlisle 26th August 2015
**Previous League:** Northern Alliance >2016.

## CHADDERTON
Founded: 1946 Nickname: Chaddy

**Secretary:** David Shepherd **(T)** 0161 624 9733 **(E)**
**Chairman:** Bob Sopel **Manager:** Mark Howard **Prog Ed:** Bob Sopel
**Ground:** Andrew Street, Chadderton, Oldham, Greater Manchester OL9 0JT **(T)** 07506 104 005
**Colours(change):** All red & black (All orange & black)

**ADDITIONAL INFORMATION: Previous Leagues:** Oldham Amateur. Manchester Amateur. Manchester League. Lancashire Combination
**Record Att:** 2,352 v FC United of Manchester 2006.
**Honours:** Manchester Amateur League 1955-56, Division One 62-63. Manchester League Division Two 1964-65, Division One 66-67.
Gilgryst Cup 1969-70. Umbro International Cup 1999-00.

## CHARNOCK RICHARD

Founded: 1955 Nickname:

**Secretary:** David Rowland **(T)** **(E)**
**Chairman:** Shaun Tootell **Manager:** Andy Westwell **Prog Ed:** Josh Vosper
**Ground:** Mossie Park, Charter Lane, Charnock Richard, Chorley PR7 5LZ **(T)** 01257 792 558
**Colours(change):** Green & white/green/green (Yellow/blue/yellow)
**ADDITIONAL INFORMATION: Att:** 400 v Wigan Athletic on 20/7/14
**Previous Leagues:** Chorley Alliance. Preston & District. West Lancashire >2016
**Honours:** West Lancashire League Premier Division 1997-98, 2002-03, 08-09, 11-12, 12-13, 13-14, 14-15.
Northern Counties Senior Cup 2012-13

## CHEADLE TOWN

Founded: 1961 Nickname:

**Secretary:** Stuart Crawford **(T)** **(E)**
**Chairman:** Chris Davies **Manager:** Terry Hincks **Prog Ed:** Stuart Crawford
**Ground:** Park Road Stadium, Cheadle, Cheshire, SK8 2AN **(T)** 0161 428 2510
**Colours(change):** All green (Gold & blue/blue/blue).
**ADDITIONAL INFORMATION:**
**Record Att:** 3,377 v FC United of Manchester (At Stockport County). **Goalscorer:** Peter Tilley. **Apps:** John McArdle.
**Honours:** Manchester Division One 1979-80. Stockport Senior Cup 2012-13.

## CITY OF LIVERPOOL

Founded: 2015 Nickname:

**Secretary:** Peter Manning **(T)** **(E)** contact@colfc.co.uk
**Chairman:** Paul Manning **Manager:** Simon Burton **Prog Ed:** Martin Stewart
**Ground:** Delta Taxi Stadium, Vesty Road, off Bridle Road, Bootle, Liverpool L30 1NY **(T)** **Capacity:** 2,500
**Colours(change):** Purple/white/purple
**ADDITIONAL INFORMATION:**

## DAISY HILL

Founded: 1894 Nickname:

**Secretary:** Robert Naylor **(T)** 01942 818 544 **(E)**
**Chairman:** Graham Follows **Manager:** Craig & Marc Thomas, Brian Hart **Prog Ed:** Craig Thomas
**Ground:** New Sirs, St James Street, Westhoughton, Bolton, BL5 2EB **(T)** 01942 818 544
**Colours(change):** All blue (All red)
**ADDITIONAL INFORMATION:**
Reformed in 1952.
**Record Att:** 2,000 v Horwich RMI, Westhoughton Charity Cup Final 1979-80. **Goalscorer & Apps:** Alan Roscoe 300gls, 450app
**Honours:** Bolton Combination Premier Division 1962-63, 72-73, 75-76, 77-78.

## ECCLESHALL

Founded: 1971 Nickname:

**Secretary:** Jim Tunney **(T)** **(E)**
**Chairman:** Bob Lloyd (interim) **Manager:** Jim Leech **Prog Ed:** Richard Marsh
**Ground:** Pershall Park, Chester Road, Eccleshall, ST21 6NE **(T)** 01785 851 351 (MD)
**Colours(change):** Navy & sky blue/navy/navy (Red & white stripes/red/red)
**ADDITIONAL INFORMATION:**
**Record Att:** 2,011 v FC United of Manchester November 2005.
**Honours:** Staffordshire County League (North) 1982-83. Staffordshire Senior League 1989-90. Midland League 2001-02, 02-03.

## HOLKER OLD BOYS

Founded: 1936 Nickname: Cobs

**Secretary:** Maurice Watkin **(T)** **(E)**
**Chairman:** Richard John **Manager:** Scott Redhead **Prog Ed:** Dave Smith
**Ground:** Rakesmoor, Rakesmoor Lane, Hawcoat, Barrow-in-Furness, LA14 4QB **(T)** 01229 828 176
**Colours(change):** Green & white/green/green & white (Blue/white/white)
**ADDITIONAL INFORMATION:**
**Record Att:** 2,303 v FC United of Manchester FA Cup at Craven Park 2005-06. **Goalscorer:** Dave Conlin.
**Honours:** West Lancashire League 1986-87.

## FC OSWESTRY TOWN

Founded: 2013 Nickname:

**Secretary:** Andrew Burnett **(T)** **(E)**
**Chairman:** Ian Jones **Manager:** Dan Stevens **Prog Ed:** John Williams
**Ground:** The Venue, Burma Road, Oswestry, Shropshire SY11 4AS **(T)** 01691 684 840
**Colours(change):** All blue & white (All green & white)
**ADDITIONAL INFORMATION: Att:** 300 Shropshire County FA Cup 7th May 2016
**Previous League:** Shropshire County League: Mercian Premier League.

## LITHERLAND REMYCA
Founded: 1959 Nickname:

**Secretary:** Dave Evans **(T)** **(E)**
**Chairman:** Don Rimmer **Manager:** Phil Stafford **Prog Ed:** Gary Langley
**Ground:** Litherland Sports Park, Boundary Road, Litherland, Liverpool L21 7LA **(T)** 0151 288 6288
**Colours(change):** Red/black/red (Sky blue/navy blue/sky blue)

**ADDITIONAL INFORMATION: Previous Leagues:** I Zingari. Liverpool County. **Record Att:** 142 v Widnes 13-08-14
**League Honours:** Zingari Premier Division 1987-88, 93-94, 94-95, 95-96, Division Two 2005-06.
Liverpool County Division Two 2006-07. **FA/County Cups:** Lancashire Amateur Cup 1990-91.

## PRESTWICH HEYS
Founded: 1938 Nickname:

**Secretary:** **(T)** **(E)**
**Chairman:** Neil Gilmore **Prog Ed:** Stephen Howard
**Ground:** Adie Moran Park, Sandgate Road, Whitefield M45 6WG **(T)** 0161 7773 8888 (MD)
**Colours(change):** Red/white/red (Green/black/black)

**ADDITIONAL INFORMATION: Record Attendance:** 4,000 v. Highgate United, FA Amateur Cup 3rd Round 11th February 1967
**Honours:** Manchester League Premier Division 2015-16.

## SANDBACH UNITED
Founded: 2004 Nickname:

**Secretary:** John Clayton **(T)** **(E)**
**Chairman:** Paul Reel **Manager:** Andy Hockenhull **Prog Ed:** Gary Walker
**Ground:** Sandbach Community Football Centre, Hind Heath Road, Sandbach CW11 3LZ **(T)** 01270 768 389
**Colours(change):** Maroon & blue/blue/blue (White & blue/blue/blue)

**ADDITIONAL INFORMATION:**
**Previous Leagues:** Staffordshire County. Cheshire >2016.

## SILSDEN
Founded: 1904 Nickname:

**Secretary:** David Slater **(T)** **(E)**
**Chairman:** Sean McNulty **Manager:** James Gill **Prog Ed:** Peter Hanson
**Ground:** Keighley Road, Keighley Road, Silsden, BD20 0EH **(T)** 07939 151 829
**Colours(change):** All red (Blue & white/blue/blue).

**ADDITIONAL INFORMATION: Att:** 1,564 v FC United of Manchester- March 2007

## ST HELENS TOWN
Founded: 1946 Nickname: Town

**Secretary:** Jeff Voller **(T)** 0151 222 2963 **(E)**
**Chairman:** John McKiernan **Manager:** Nick Matthews & Alan Gillespie **Prog Ed:** Jeff Voller
**Ground:** Ruskin Drive Sportsground, Ruskin Drive, Dentons Green, St Helens WA10 6RP **(T)** 01942 716 360 **Capacity:** 600
**Colours(change):** Red & white stripes/white/red & white (All sky blue).

**ADDITIONAL INFORMATION: Att:** 8,500 v Manchester City 27/04/50. **Goalscorer:** S. Pennington. **App:** Alan Wellens
Lancashire Combination Division Two 1950-51, Premier 1971-72 . FA Vase 1986-87.

## STOCKPORT TOWN
Founded: 2014 Nickname:

**Secretary:** Rob Clare **(T)** **(E)**
**Chairman:** Seb Rowe **Manager:** Calum Sykes **Prog Ed:** Andy Calvert
**Ground:** Lambeth Grove, Woodley, Stockport SK6 1QX **(T)** 0161 494 3146
**Colours(change):** Red & white stripes/blue/red (Orange/black/orange)

**ADDITIONAL INFORMATION: Record Att:** 147

## WHITCHURCH ALPORT
Founded: 1946 Nickname:

**Secretary:** Peter Stokes **(T)** **(E)**
**Chairman:** Andrew Hough **Manager:** Luke Goddard and Carl Everall **Prog Ed:** Marc Haller
**Ground:** Yockings Park, Black Park Road, Whitchurch SY13 1PG **(T)**
**Colours(change):** All red (All blue)

**ADDITIONAL INFORMATION: Previous Leagues:** Cheshire. Mercian Regional League.
Shropshire County FA Challenge Premier Cup Winners: 1969/70, 1971/72, 1977/78, 1981/82, 1997/98, 2008/09
Shropshire County FA Challenge Cup Winners: 1950/51, 1953/54, 1957/58
Welsh FA Amateur Cup Winners: 1973/74

## WIDNES

Founded: 2003 Nickname: Vikings

**Secretary:** Bill Morley **(T)** **(E)**
**Chairman:** David Day **Manager:** Steve Hill **Prog Ed:** Bill Morley
**Ground:** Select Security Stadium, Lower House Lane, Widnes, Cheshire WA8 7DZ **(T)** 0151 510 6000
**Colours(change):** White/black/white (All blue)
**ADDITIONAL INFORMATION: Previous Names:** Formed as Dragons AFC in 2003. Widnes Dragons > 2012. Widnes Vikings 2012-14.
**Previous Leagues:** West Cheshire League.
**Record Att:** 345

# GROUND DIRECTIONS - DIVISION ONE

**AFC BLACKPOOL-Mechanics Ground, Jepson Way, Common Edge Road, Blackpool, Lancashire FY4 5DY. 01253 761721**
M6 to M55, exit at junction 4. At roundabout turn left along A583 to traffic lights, turn right into Whitehill Road, to traffic lights (2 miles). Go straight across the main road into Jepson Way, ground at top.

**ALSAGER TOWN-The Town Ground, Woodland Court, Alsager, Staffs, ST7 2DP 01270 882336**
M6 to Junction16, A500 towards Stoke, leave A500 at 2nd exit (A34 to Congleton) at 2nd set of traffic lights on A34 turn left for Alsager, turn right opposite Caradon/Twyfords Factory (500 Yards), into Moorhouse Ave, West Grove mile on right. No available parking within the ground.

**ASHTON TOWN-Edge Green Street, Ashton-in-Makerfield, Wigan, Greater Manchester. WN4 8SL. 01942 701483**
M6 to Junction 23, A49 to Ashton-in-Makerfield. Turn right at the traffic lights onto the A58 towards Bolton. After approx. three quarters of a mile, turn right into Golbourne Road. After 200 yards turn right into Edge Green Street. Ground at bottom of street.

**ATHERTON L.R.-Crilly Park, Spa Road, Atherton, Greater Manchester. M46 9XG. 01942 883950**
M61 to Junction 5, follow signs for Westhoughton, turn left onto A6, turn right at first lights into Newbrook Road, then turn right into Upton Road, passing Atherton Central Station. Turn left into Springfield Road and left again into Hillside Road into Spa Road and ground.

**BACUP BOROUGH-Brian Boys Stadium, Cowtoot Lane, Blackthorn, Bacup, Lancashire. OL13 8EE. 01706 878655**
From M62, take M66 onto A681, through Rawtenstall to Bacup Town Centre, turn left onto the A671 towards Burnley, after approx. 300 yards turn right immediately before the Irwell Inn climbing Cooper Street, turn right into Blackthorn Lane, then first left into Cowtoot Lane to ground.

**BARNTON - Tonwfield, Townfield Lane, Barnton, Cheshire CW8 4LH 07709 585 644**
Turn off the A533 (Northwich to Runcorn) at the Beech Tree Inn (Barnton Village) into Beech Lane. Turn right at the 'T' junction with Townfield Lane - the ground is 200 yards on the left signed Memorial Hall. Note parking restrictions well signed.

**CARLISLE CITY - Gilford Park, Carlisle CA1 3AF**
M6 to junction 42, follow the A6 towards Carlisle for approx 2 miles, turn left into Petteril Bank Road, by the Aldi Store. Follow this road for about mile and turn right into the ground. Access road just before the railway bridge.

**CHADDERTON-Andrew Street, Chadderton, Oldham, Greater Manchester OL9 0JT. 0161 624 9733**
M62 to junction 20, following A627(M) towards Manchester. Motorway becomes a dual carriageway, turn left at first major traffic lights (A699) Middleton Road, then second left into Burnley Street, Andrew Street at the end.

**CHARNOCK RICHARD - Mossie Park, Charter Lane, Charnock Richard, Chorley PR7 5LZ**
M6 to junction 28 (Leyland) at end of slip road turn right. Travel to the traffic lights and turn right onto the A49 towards Wigan, through Euxton and into Charnock Richard. Pass the Bowling Green Pub on the right, continue for ¾ mile and turn left into Church Lane. Turn first right into Charter lane, ground 500 yards on the right. M61 to junction 8 (Chorley) follow the signs for Southport on reaching the A49 follow signs for Wigan, through Charnock Richard directions then as above. PLEASE USE THE CLUB PARK. Do not park on the road.

**CHEADLE TOWN-Park Road Stadium, Cheadle, Cheshire, SK8 2AN. 0161 428 2510**
M60 to junction 2 (formerly M63 junction 11), follow A560 to Cheadle. Go through first main set of traffic lights and then first left after shops into Park Road. Ground at end of road.

**CITY OF LIVERPOOL - BOOTLE FC, Delta Taxi Stadium, Vesty Road, off Bridle Road, Bootle, Liverpool L30 1NY**
At Liverpool end of M57and M58 follow signs for Liverpool (A59 (S)), for 1 1/2 miles. At Aintree racecourse on left and Aintree Train Station on right ,turn right at lights into Park Lane. Turn left at second set of lights into Bridle Road. After 200 yards turn left at lights into Vestey Estate , ground 200 yards.

**DAISY HILL-New Sirs, St James Street, Westhoughton, Bolton, BL5 2EB. 01942 818 544.**
M61 to junction 5, A58 (Snydale Way/Park Road) for one and a half mile, left into Leigh Road (B5235) for 1 mile to Daisy Hill. Turn right into village 200 yards after mini roundabout, then left between church and school into St James Street. Ground 250 yards on left.

## NORTH WEST COUNTIES LEAGUE - STEP 5/6

**ECCLESHALL-Pershall Park, Chester Road, Eccleshall, ST21 6NE. 01785-851351 (Match Days Only)**

M6 to junction 14 then A5013 to Eccleshall, right at mini-roundabout and then left at next mini-roundabout into High Street B5026, ground 1 mile on right. M6 to junction 15, then A519 to Eccleshall right at mini-roundabout to High Street B5026, ground 1 mile on right.

**FC OSWESTRY TOWN - The Venue, Burma Road, Oswestry, Shropshire SY11 4AS**

From Chester take the A483 towards Wrexham / Oswestry. Once entering Oswestry at the 2nd round-a-bout turn left and left again to ground.

**HOLKER OLD BOYS-Rakesmoor, Rakesmoor Lane, Hawcoat, Barrow-in-Furness, Cumbria. LA14 4QB. 01229 828176**

M6 to junction 36. Take the A590 all the way to Barrow-in-Furness. At the borough boundary continue along the A590. After 1? miles you will pass the Kimberley Clark paper mill on your right. Immediately after passing the paper mill turn left into Bank Lane, signposted "Barrow Golf Club" on the left hand side of the A590 and "Hawcoat yard on the right hand side of the A590. Follow this road to the T- junction at the top of the hill outside the Golf Club. Turn left here into Rakesmoor Lane the ground is 200 yds. down the road on the right. *Please be advised that Rakesmoor Lane beyond the ground is a single-track road and as such is unsuitable for coaches. It is not possible to turn a coach into the ground when approaching from that direction.*

**ILITHERLAND REMYCA.- Litherland Sports Park, Boundary Road, Litherland, Liverpool L21 7LA. 0151 288 6288.**

End of M57/M58 ALONG Dunningsbridge Road towards Docks, Turn Right at Junction of Bootle Golf Course on the Right hand side into Boundary Road, 2nd turning on the left into sports park.

**PRESTWICH HEYS - Adie Moran Park, Sandgate Road, Whitefield M45 6WG**

M60 to junction 17 towards Whitefield, turn right into Clyde Avenue continue over traffic lights onto Thatch Leach Lane, turn right at the Frigate Public House, over motorway bridge, ground on the left.

**SANDBACH UNITED - Sandbach Community Football Centre, Hind Heath Road, Sandbach CW11 3LZ**

M6 to junction 17, take the A534 towards Sandbach, travel to traffic lights and go straight across, travel to round-a-bout, take the 2nd exit, travel to nest round-a-bout and take the 1st exit onto Crewe Road. Dtay on this roard for 1 mile and turn right at the traffic lights into Hind Heath Road ground approx ¾ mile on the right.

**SILSDEN-Keighley Road, Silsden, BD20 0EH**

A629 Skipton to Keighley road, take A6034, ground in on the left after the golf driving range.

**ST HELENS TOWN - Ruskin Drive Sportsground, Ruskin Drive, Dentons Green, St Helens WA10 6RP**

**STOCKPORT TOWN - Lambeth Grove, Woodley, Stockport SK6 1QX. 0161 494 3146**

Stockport Town Football Club is located at Stockport Sports Village, Lambeth Grove Woodley, SK6 1QX. The ground lies a short distance from the M60. To reach us from the motorway, you should leave at Junction 25, which is signposted for Bredbury. Follow signs from here for the A560 towards Bredbury and Sheffield. Just after passing the McDonalds Drive-Thru, take a left at the traffic lights and proceed down Stockport Road towards Woodley, passing both Morrisons and Homebase on your left before passing under the railway bridge at Bredbury Railway Station.

**WHITCHURCH ALPORT - Yockings Park, Black Park Road, Whitchurch SY13 1PG**

From the North either A41 or A49 into town. At main set of traffic lights turn first left (sign posted Whitchurch Alport FC) into Talbot Street, follow a long to Black Park Road, ground on the left. From the East A525 into Whitchurch, under the railway bridge and turn right into Queens Road, first left into Sainsbury Road then first right into Talbot Street than as above.

**WIDNES - Select Security Stadium, Lower House Lane, Widnes, Cheshire WA8 7DZ. 0151 510 6000**

From the M62 - Exit at Junction 7, take A568 dual carriageway towards Widnes (Following brown signs to Halton Stadium). Keep right after junction onto Ashley Way (A562). Take 2nd exit off roundabout (McDonald's on the right). Take 2nd exit off mini-roundabout into Lowerhouse Lane. From Runcorn & the South: Cross Widnes/Runcorn Bridge (A533). Follow signs to Widnes (A562). At roundabout take 3rd exit towards Widnes Town Centre. Take first left following brown signs to Halton Stadium(McDonald's on the right). Take 2nd exit off mini-roundabout into Lowerhouse Lane.

# NORTHERN COUNTIES EAST LEAGUE

**Sponsored by:** Toolstation
**Founded:** 1982

**Recent Champions: 2013:** Scarborough Town
**2014:** Brighouse Town **2015:** Shaw Lane Aquaforce

| PREMIER DIVISION | P | W | D | L | F | A | GD | Pts |
|---|---|---|---|---|---|---|---|---|
| Tadcaster Albion | 42 | 31 | 5 | 6 | 119 | 50 | 69 | 98 |
| Handsworth Parramore | 42 | 29 | 7 | 6 | 113 | 53 | 60 | 94 |
| Cleethorpes Town | 42 | 26 | 6 | 10 | 105 | 46 | 59 | 84 |
| Worksop Town | 42 | 26 | 5 | 11 | 118 | 60 | 58 | 83 |
| Bridlington Town | 42 | 25 | 4 | 13 | 83 | 54 | 29 | 79 |
| Pickering Town | 42 | 24 | 5 | 13 | 94 | 69 | 25 | 77 |
| Maltby Main | 42 | 20 | 8 | 14 | 85 | 77 | 8 | 68 |
| Staveley Miners Welfare | 42 | 20 | 6 | 16 | 86 | 72 | 14 | 66 |
| Rainworth Miners Welfare | 42 | 19 | 6 | 17 | 98 | 81 | 17 | 63 |
| Barton Town Old Boys | 42 | 18 | 8 | 16 | 75 | 60 | 15 | 62 |
| Albion Sports | 42 | 17 | 8 | 17 | 80 | 77 | 3 | 59 |
| Thackley | 42 | 17 | 8 | 17 | 80 | 84 | -4 | 59 |
| Clipstone | 42 | 15 | 10 | 17 | 85 | 70 | 15 | 55 |
| Liversedge | 42 | 13 | 9 | 20 | 61 | 93 | -32 | 48 |
| Retford United | 42 | 12 | 9 | 21 | 66 | 96 | -30 | 45 |
| Garforth Town | 42 | 12 | 7 | 23 | 64 | 89 | -25 | 43 |
| Parkgate | 42 | 12 | 6 | 24 | 55 | 90 | -35 | 42 |
| Athersley Recreation | 42 | 12 | 6 | 24 | 52 | 93 | -41 | 42 |
| Armthorpe Welfare | 42 | 10 | 10 | 22 | 55 | 92 | -37 | 40 |
| Pontefract Collieries | 42 | 11 | 6 | 25 | 60 | 110 | -50 | 39 |
| Brigg Town | 42 | 10 | 7 | 25 | 49 | 103 | -54 | 37 |
| Nostell Miners Welfare | 42 | 6 | 8 | 28 | 38 | 102 | -64 | 26 |

## LEAGUE CUP

**HOLDERS:** HANDSWORTH PARRAMORE

**ROUND 1**

| | | | |
|---|---|---|---|
| Glasshoughton Welfare | v | Lincoln Moorlands Railway | 4-3 aet |
| Hemsworth Miners Welfare | v | AFC Emley | 3-4 |
| Shirebrook Town | v | Dronfield Town | 1-0 |
| Teversal | v | Hull United | 1-0 |
| Yorkshire Amateur | v | Hall Road Rangers | 5-4 |
| Westella VIP | v | Selby Town | 0-1 |

**ROUND 2**

| | | | |
|---|---|---|---|
| Albion Sports | v | Nostell Miners Welfare | 5-0 |
| Winterton Rangers | v | Pontefract Collieries | 2-4 |
| AFC Emley | v | Liversedge | 3-3, 3-2p |
| Athersley Recreation | v | Penistone Church | 0-2 |
| Worsbrough Bridge Athletic | v | Brigg Town | 0-1 |
| Barton Town Old Boys | v | Rossington Main | 2-1 |

**ROUND 3**

| | | | |
|---|---|---|---|
| Clipstone | v | Grimsby Borough | 1-2 |
| Handsworth Parramore | v | Shirebrook Town | 5-1 |
| Retford United | v | Armthorpe Welfare | 3-5 |
| AFC Mansfield | v | Knaresborough Town | 1-2 |
| Bottsford Town | v | AFC Emley | 2-3 |
| Hallam | v | Selby Town | 1-2 aet |
| Worksop Town | v | Barton Town Old Boys | 0-2 |
| Glasshoughton Welfare | v | Pickering Town | 0-2 |

Pickering later removed for fielding ineligible player.

| | | | |
|---|---|---|---|
| Parkgate | v | Tadcaster Albion | 1-3 |
| Teversal | v | Albion Sports | 3-4 |
| Winterton Rangers | v | Cleethorpes Town | 0-4 |
| Bridlington Town | v | Brigg Town | 4-0 |
| Penistone Church | v | Maltby Main | 4-0 |
| Garforth Town | v | Staveley Miners Welfare | 1-2 |
| Yorkshire Amateur | v | Rainworth Miners Welfare | 2-3 |
| Thackley | v | Eccleshill United | 4-2 aet |

| PREMIER DIVISION | 1 | 2 | 3 | 4 | 5 | 6 | 7 | 8 | 9 | 10 | 11 | 12 | 13 | 14 | 15 | 16 | 17 | 18 | 19 | 20 | 21 | 22 |
|---|---|---|---|---|---|---|---|---|---|---|---|---|---|---|---|---|---|---|---|---|---|---|
| Albion Sports | | 4-1 | 3-1 | 3-5 | 1-5 | 2-1 | 4-1 | 0-0 | 1-0 | 0-1 | 5-1 | 1-3 | 2-1 | 1-0 | 2-5 | 4-3 | 2-3 | 3-1 | 0-0 | 0-2 | 1-3 | 1-1 |
| Armthorpe Welfare | 2-2 | | 0-1 | 1-5 | 0-2 | 1-0 | 1-1 | 1-6 | 3-1 | 0-2 | 5-1 | 2-5 | 2-1 | 2-3 | 2-3 | 3-0 | 2-2 | 1-1 | 0-4 | 2-2 | 2-0 | 0-4 |
| Athersley Recreation | 0-3 | 0-0 | | 1-1 | 1-2 | 0-3 | 1-2 | 2-0 | 5-0 | 0-2 | 3-1 | 0-2 | 2-0 | 0-3 | 1-4 | 2-1 | 4-1 | 1-2 | 0-4 | 0-5 | 2-2 | 0-6 |
| Barton Town Old Boys | 0-1 | 1-1 | 0-1 | | 2-0 | 1-0 | 0-3 | 0-2 | 4-0 | 0-1 | 2-4 | 2-2 | 3-0 | 3-0 | 1-1 | 2-0 | 0-0 | 2-1 | 1-1 | 4-3 | 3-1 | 2-2 |
| Bridlington Town | 2-1 | 1-0 | 4-0 | 0-1 | | 7-1 | 2-1 | 2-1 | 1-2 | 1-0 | 1-1 | 4-2 | 1-3 | 0-3 | 0-1 | 2-1 | 0-1 | 5-2 | 2-0 | 0-1 | 2-2 | 1-3 |
| Brigg Town | 3-3 | 2-2 | 1-1 | 2-1 | 0-4 | | 0-4 | 3-2 | 0-4 | 2-0 | 2-1 | 1-2 | 1-3 | 1-0 | 0-5 | 4-1 | 1-4 | 1-2 | 2-3 | 1-3 | 4-4 | 2-2 |
| Cleethorpes Town | 1-0 | 4-1 | 3-1 | 0-2 | 0-2 | 5-0 | | 3-3 | 1-2 | 1-1 | 3-0 | 5-1 | 0-1 | 4-0 | 2-3 | 4-0 | 3-1 | 5-1 | 3-2 | 1-0 | 1-0 | 3-0 |
| Clipstone | 1-1 | 2-3 | 2-3 | 0-2 | 0-1 | 2-0 | 2-3 | | 5-0 | 2-2 | 0-0 | 2-2 | 4-0 | 0-1 | 3-2 | 1-2 | 3-0 | 7-0 | 0-3 | 2-2 | 1-2 | 3-1 |
| Garforth Town | 0-2 | 2-2 | 2-0 | 0-2 | 3-3 | 2-0 | 0-1 | 2-2 | | 0-2 | 2-1 | 2-2 | 2-0 | 2-3 | 2-4 | 6-1 | 3-2 | 1-4 | 2-0 | 0-1 | 3-4 | 0-1 |
| Handsworth Parramore | 6-3 | 5-0 | 7-1 | 4-3 | 2-4 | 2-0 | 1-1 | 6-0 | 1-1 | | 0-0 | 1-0 | 5-0 | 4-3 | 3-0 | 2-1 | 2-1 | 3-1 | 2-4 | 1-4 | 3-3 | 5-0 |
| Liversedge | 2-1 | 4-0 | 2-0 | 4-3 | 1-4 | 1-2 | 1-0 | 4-1 | 1-6 | 1-1 | | 1-4 | 3-1 | 4-0 | 0-1 | 3-1 | 3-1 | 0-0 | 1-5 | 0-4 | 2-1 | 1-4 |
| Maltby Main | 2-1 | 2-1 | 1-0 | 1-0 | 2-1 | 0-0 | 2-5 | 3-3 | 0-1 | 1-2 | 2-2 | | 6-0 | 1-0 | 1-2 | 2-0 | 0-1 | 2-1 | 2-5 | 4-2 | 1-2 | 3-2 |
| Nostell Miners Welfare | 1-4 | 1-1 | 1-3 | 0-4 | 1-2 | 0-1 | 0-3 | 1-6 | 0-0 | 1-2 | 0-0 | 4-0 | | 1-1 | 2-1 | 2-2 | 2-4 | 2-0 | 1-2 | 0-5 | 1-4 | 1-4 |
| Parkgate | 0-3 | 0-1 | 1-4 | 2-3 | 2-1 | 3-0 | 2-1 | 1-3 | 2-1 | 1-3 | 2-2 | 0-2 | 1-1 | | 0-3 | 2-2 | 1-2 | 2-6 | 1-2 | 1-1 | 0-2 | 0-4 |
| Pickering Town | 1-0 | 2-0 | 1-1 | 2-1 | 2-3 | 4-1 | 0-3 | 3-2 | 5-1 | 2-3 | 2-1 | 3-3 | 5-2 | 3-2 | | 1-2 | 4-2 | 2-2 | 3-1 | 1-3 | 1-1 | 2-3 |
| Pontefract Collieries | 2-2 | 1-3 | 3-0 | 1-3 | 3-1 | 2-2 | 0-6 | 1-0 | 4-3 | 1-6 | 2-1 | 2-5 | 1-1 | 1-3 | 1-2 | | 3-1 | 2-5 | 4-6 | 0-1 | 2-5 | 1-7 |
| Rainworth Miners Welfare | 1-3 | 6-0 | 3-1 | 5-0 | 1-1 | 3-2 | 6-3 | 1-3 | 4-2 | 1-2 | 7-1 | 3-1 | 6-0 | 2-3 | 4-2 | 0-1 | | 2-2 | 2-2 | 1-3 | 1-0 | 1-3 |
| Retford United | 0-1 | 0-6 | 3-3 | 1-0 | 1-3 | 6-0 | 0-8 | 2-0 | 1-1 | 0-1 | 1-2 | 1-5 | 0-0 | 3-2 | 1-0 | 1-3 | 2-2 | | 2-1 | 0-1 | 1-2 | 2-2 |
| Staveley Miners Welfare | 4-1 | 3-0 | 0-1 | 2-2 | 0-2 | 0-2 | 0-3 | 2-2 | 2-1 | 2-6 | 3-1 | 2-2 | 2-1 | 4-0 | 0-1 | 0-1 | 0-2 | 2-1 | | 2-1 | 3-0 | 1-4 |
| Tadcaster Albion | 4-4 | 2-1 | 4-3 | 2-1 | 4-1 | 5-0 | 0-0 | 1-2 | 1-0 | 5-2 | 4-1 | 6-3 | 4-0 | 3-4 | 4-1 | 2-0 | 4-3 | 5-0 | 2-0 | | 4-0 | 4-1 |
| Thackley | 4-2 | 3-0 | 4-2 | 2-1 | 1-2 | 2-1 | 2-3 | 0-2 | 3-1 | 0-6 | 1-1 | 0-1 | 2-1 | 0-0 | 1-3 | 1-1 | 6-3 | 1-3 | 5-3 | 2-3 | | 1-2 |
| Worksop Town | 3-2 | 1-0 | 4-0 | 3-2 | 0-1 | 4-0 | 1-1 | 2-3 | 8-1 | 2-3 | 6-0 | 4-0 | 1-0 | 4-0 | 2-1 | 3-0 | 1-2 | 4-3 | 3-4 | 1-2 | 5-1 | |

## NORTHERN COUNTIES EAST LEAGUE - STEP 5/6

| | DIVISION ONE | P | W | D | L | F | A | GD | Pts |
|---|---|---|---|---|---|---|---|---|---|
| 1 | Hemsworth Miners Welfare | 40 | 31 | 5 | 4 | 128 | 49 | 79 | 98 |
| 2 | AFC Mansfield | 40 | 26 | 8 | 6 | 98 | 40 | 58 | 86 |
| 3 | Bottesford Town | 40 | 26 | 4 | 10 | 93 | 49 | 44 | 82 |
| 4 | AFC Emley | 40 | 22 | 11 | 7 | 132 | 50 | 82 | 77 |
| 5 | Penistone Church | 40 | 21 | 12 | 7 | 89 | 49 | 40 | 75 |
| 6 | Hallam | 40 | 20 | 12 | 8 | 87 | 43 | 44 | 72 |
| 7 | Shirebrook Town | 40 | 20 | 9 | 11 | 83 | 53 | 30 | 69 |
| 8 | Knaresborough Town | 40 | 19 | 7 | 14 | 82 | 60 | 22 | 64 |
| 9 | Hull United (-18) | 40 | 23 | 7 | 10 | 78 | 47 | 31 | 58 |
| 10 | Selby Town | 40 | 16 | 9 | 15 | 73 | 73 | 0 | 57 |
| 11 | Yorkshire Amateur | 40 | 17 | 5 | 18 | 90 | 101 | -11 | 56 |
| 12 | Westella VIP | 40 | 16 | 5 | 19 | 90 | 83 | 7 | 53 |
| 13 | Eccleshill United | 40 | 13 | 9 | 18 | 86 | 90 | -4 | 48 |
| 14 | Teversal | 40 | 11 | 12 | 17 | 62 | 90 | -28 | 45 |
| 15 | Dronfield Town | 40 | 12 | 7 | 21 | 67 | 88 | -21 | 43 |
| 16 | Glasshoughton Welfare | 40 | 10 | 7 | 23 | 62 | 101 | -39 | 37 |
| 17 | Hall Road Rangers | 40 | 7 | 11 | 22 | 60 | 106 | -46 | 32 |
| 18 | Winterton Rangers | 40 | 8 | 8 | 24 | 58 | 116 | -58 | 32 |
| 19 | Grimsby Borough | 40 | 8 | 8 | 24 | 64 | 132 | -68 | 32 |
| 20 | Rossington Main | 40 | 6 | 8 | 26 | 45 | 105 | -60 | 26 |
| 21 | Worsbrough Bridge Athletic | 40 | 3 | 6 | 31 | 32 | 134 | -102 | 15 |

Lincoln Moorlands Railway withdrew - record expunged.

League Cup continued

**ROUND 4**

| | | | |
|---|---|---|---|
| Armthorpe Welfare | v | Rainworth Miners Welfare | 1-4 |
| Grimsby Borough | v | Tadcaster Albion | 1-2 aet |
| Selby Town | v | Handsworth Parramore | 1-2 |
| AFC Emley | v | Knaresborough Town | 2-3 |
| Albion Sports | v | Barton Town Old Boys | 4-2 |
| Penistone Church | v | Bridlington Town | 0-2 |
| Thackley | v | Glasshoughton Welfare | 5-1 |
| Cleethorpes Town | v | Staveley Miners Welfare | 4-3 |

**QUARTER FINALS**

| | | | |
|---|---|---|---|
| Rainworth Miners Welfare | v | Albion Sports | 0-5 |
| Knaresborough Town | v | Tadcaster Albion | 1-3 |
| Handsworth Parramore | v | Cleethorpes Town | 3-5 aet |
| Thackley | v | Bridlington Town | 2-3 |

**SEMI FINALS**

| | | | |
|---|---|---|---|
| Bridlington Town | v | Cleethorpes Town | 0-1 |
| Tadcaster Albion | v | Albion Sports | 2-1 |

**FINAL**

| | | | |
|---|---|---|---|
| Cleethorpes Town | v | Tadcaster Albion | 3-2 |

### CLUB MOVEMENTS

**Premier Division - In:** AFC Mansfield (P), Bottesford Town (P), Harrogate Railway Athletic (R - NPL D1N), Hemsworth Miners Welfare (P).
**Out:** Brigg Town (R), Nostell Miners Welfare (R), Pontefract Collieries (R), Tadcaster Albion (P - NPL D1N).
**Division One - In:** Brigg Town (R), Campion (P - West Riding Amateur), Nostell Miners Welfare (R), Ollerton Town (P - Central Midlands League), Pontefract Collieries (R)
**Out:** AFC Mansfield (P), Bottesford Town (P), Hemsworth Miners Welfare (P), Hull United (R - Humber League due to ground grading issues).

| | DIVISION ONE | 1 | 2 | 3 | 4 | 5 | 6 | 7 | 8 | 9 | 10 | 11 | 12 | 13 | 14 | 15 | 16 | 17 | 18 | 19 | 20 | 21 |
|---|---|---|---|---|---|---|---|---|---|---|---|---|---|---|---|---|---|---|---|---|---|---|
| 1 | AFC Emley | | 3-5 | 2-3 | 4-0 | 1-1 | 5-0 | 13-0 | 4-1 | 1-1 | 3-0 | 2-2 | 2-0 | 2-0 | 5-0 | 3-3 | 2-2 | 4-0 | 6-3 | 10-0 | 5-0 | 4-0 |
| 2 | AFC Mansfield | 3-5 | | 2-0 | 2-0 | 2-0 | 3-1 | 6-0 | 5-0 | 0-0 | 0-1 | 1-0 | 1-1 | 1-2 | 1-1 | 3-1 | 1-1 | 2-1 | 1-1 | 8-0 | 9-0 | 3-1 |
| 3 | Bottesford Town | 4-2 | 0-2 | | 3-1 | 4-2 | 5-1 | 7-0 | 4-2 | 2-0 | 2-1 | 1-2 | 1-2 | 0-0 | 1-0 | 3-0 | 1-3 | 2-0 | 0-2 | 1-0 | 2-0 | 5-1 |
| 4 | Dronfield Town | 0-4 | 1-2 | 2-2 | | 2-4 | 2-1 | 4-0 | 2-3 | 1-1 | 1-2 | 9-0 | 0-3 | 2-3 | 2-2 | 4-1 | 1-1 | 1-1 | 1-5 | 2-0 | 2-0 | 1-2 |
| 5 | Eccleshill United | 1-4 | 1-3 | 1-3 | 4-2 | | 1-0 | 9-1 | 4-3 | 2-2 | 1-3 | 0-2 | 3-1 | 1-1 | 1-1 | 2-2 | 2-0 | 1-1 | 3-4 | 7-2 | 6-2 | 6-2 |
| 6 | Glasshoughton Welfare | 2-3 | 1-4 | 2-3 | 1-1 | 2-1 | | 3-0 | 1-1 | 2-4 | 1-2 | 1-2 | 0-5 | 3-3 | 5-0 | 0-3 | 1-4 | 2-3 | 2-1 | 1-3 | 5-1 | 3-3 |
| 7 | Grimsby Borough | 1-1 | 0-1 | 2-1 | 3-1 | 3-3 | 2-2 | | 6-3 | 0-5 | 2-3 | 1-2 | 1-3 | 2-3 | 2-2 | 1-3 | 2-4 | 5-3 | 2-2 | 5-0 | 3-1 | 1-4 |
| 8 | Hall Road Rangers | 1-4 | 1-1 | 1-6 | 1-2 | 5-5 | 1-2 | 4-0 | | 0-1 | 0-3 | 2-1 | 1-1 | 0-3 | 0-3 | 0-0 | 2-6 | 1-2 | 2-5 | 1-1 | 6-0 | 0-0 |
| 9 | Hallam | 2-2 | 3-1 | 2-3 | 4-1 | 0-1 | 2-3 | 2-2 | 5-0 | | 1-2 | 0-2 | 4-2 | 0-0 | 5-1 | 3-1 | 1-1 | 2-0 | 2-0 | 2-4 | 3-0 | 1-2 |
| 10 | Hemsworth Miners Welfare | 2-1 | 0-2 | 3-0 | 4-0 | 4-0 | 1-1 | 3-2 | 9-2 | 2-2 | | 1-1 | 6-1 | 3-3 | 4-0 | 5-2 | 2-1 | 6-0 | 5-2 | 5-2 | 8-1 | 6-1 |
| 11 | Hull United | 2-1 | 1-3 | 2-1 | 3-0 | 1-1 | 4-0 | 7-0 | 1-0 | 0-1 | 1-3 | | 0-0 | 1-2 | 3-0 | 0-3 | 2-0 | 2-2 | 4-2 | 2-1 | 5-0 | 4-1 |
| 12 | Knaresborough Town | 0-0 | 0-1 | 0-4 | 3-1 | 5-3 | 4-1 | 3-0 | 0-1 | 0-2 | 2-4 | 2-1 | | 0-0 | 5-0 | 2-1 | 2-3 | 3-0 | 2-1 | 3-4 | 2-1 | 2-2 |
| 13 | Penistone Church | 1-1 | 2-3 | 2-0 | 5-1 | 3-0 | 2-2 | 4-1 | 2-2 | 1-1 | 4-1 | 0-2 | 3-0 | | 3-0 | 4-5 | 1-2 | 5-1 | 4-2 | 1-0 | 6-1 | 2-0 |
| 14 | Rossington Main | 2-2 | 2-3 | 0-1 | 1-2 | 1-0 | 1-3 | 2-1 | 4-1 | 0-0 | 1-3 | 1-2 | 3-1 | 0-4 | | 1-2 | 0-4 | 0-5 | 2-5 | 1-3 | 0-2 | 0-2 |
| 15 | Selby Town | 1-0 | 2-2 | 2-2 | 2-4 | 1-0 | 4-0 | 5-2 | 1-0 | 0-0 | 2-4 | 1-3 | 0-5 | 1-1 | 3-1 | | 1-2 | 0-1 | 2-1 | 4-0 | 2-2 | 3-1 |
| 16 | Shirebrook Town | 1-2 | 0-0 | 0-1 | 3-0 | 0-2 | 5-1 | 0-2 | 4-1 | 1-2 | 2-2 | 2-0 | 1-1 | 3-0 | 6-3 | 3-1 | | 0-3 | 1-2 | 5-2 | 1-0 | 4-1 |
| 17 | Teversal | 0-5 | 1-0 | 2-5 | 1-1 | 2-0 | 0-2 | 2-2 | 3-3 | 0-5 | 0-1 | 0-5 | 2-0 | 2-2 | 2-0 | 1-1 | 2-2 | | 0-3 | 7-1 | 1-1 | 2-5 |
| 18 | Westella VIP | 4-3 | 0-3 | 0-1 | 1-3 | 5-2 | 4-0 | 4-0 | 2-3 | 1-4 | 1-2 | 1-1 | 0-3 | 1-2 | 1-1 | 3-0 | 0-2 | 3-3 | | 1-0 | 1-2 | 1-4 |
| 19 | Winterton Rangers | 1-1 | 4-1 | 1-1 | 3-4 | 5-0 | 1-2 | 1-3 | 1-1 | 0-4 | 0-4 | 1-1 | 1-5 | 0-1 | 3-3 | 0-4 | 0-0 | 3-1 | 2-3 | | 3-0 | 2-6 |
| 20 | Worsbrough Bridge Athletic | 0-7 | 0-3 | 1-6 | 0-2 | 2-3 | 2-1 | 1-1 | 1-1 | 1-5 | 0-4 | 0-3 | 1-2 | 0-3 | 1-2 | 0-2 | 1-2 | 2-3 | 1-7 | 1-1 | | 2-2 |
| 21 | Yorkshire Amateur | 1-3 | 2-4 | 1-2 | 3-1 | 3-2 | 5-1 | 5-3 | 1-3 | 1-3 | 1-4 | 0-1 | 0-6 | 2-1 | 6-3 | 4-1 | 3-1 | 2-2 | 2-5 | 4-2 | 4-1 | |

## AFC MANSFIELD

Founded: 2012 Nickname: The Bulls

**Secretary:** Andrew Saunders **(T)** 07973 491 739 **(E)** andrewasaunders@aol.com
**Chairman:** Andrew Saunders **Manager:** Rudy Funk **Prog Ed:** Peter Craggs
**Ground:** Forest Town Stadium, Clipstone Road West, Forest Town, Mansfield NG19 0EE **(T)** 07973 491 739
**Capacity:** **Seats:** **Covered:** **Midweek Matchday:** Wednesday **Clubhouse:** No

**Colours(change):** All red (Yellow/blue/blue)
**Previous Names:**
**Previous Leagues:** Central Midlands North 2012-14.
**Records:**
**Honours:** Central Midlands North 2013-14.

**10 YEAR RECORD**

| 06-07 | 07-08 | 08-09 | 09-10 | 10-11 | 11-12 | 12-13 | 13-14 | 14-15 | 15-16 |
|---|---|---|---|---|---|---|---|---|---|
| | | | | | | CMN 2 | CMN 1 | NCE1 7 | NCE1 2 |

## ALBION SPORTS

Founded: 1974 Nickname: Lions

**Secretary:** Jaj Singh **(T)** 07957 206 174 **(E)** singhalbionfc@hotmail.co.uk
**Chairman:** Kultar Singh **Manager:** Kulwinder Singh Sandhu **Prog Ed:** Peter Cusack
**Ground:** Throstle Nest, Newlands, Farsley, Leeds, LS28 5BE. **(T)** 0113 255 7292
**Capacity:** 3,500 **Seats:** 1,750 **Covered:** 1,750 **Midweek Matchday:** Wednesday **Clubhouse:** n/a

**Colours(change):** Yellow/royal blue/royal blue (All red)
**Previous Names:**
**Previous Leagues:** Bradford Amateur Sunday 1974-2007. West Riding County Amateur 2007-11.
**Records:**
**Honours:** Northern Counties East Division One 2012-13.

**10 YEAR RECORD**

| 06-07 | 07-08 | 08-09 | 09-10 | 10-11 | 11-12 | 12-13 | 13-14 | 14-15 | 15-16 |
|---|---|---|---|---|---|---|---|---|---|
| | | | | | NCE1 4 | NCE1 1 | NCEP 6 | NCEP 10 | NCEP 11 |

## ARMTHORPE WELFARE

Founded: 1926 Nickname: Wellie

**Secretary:** Craig Trewick **(T)** 07899 553 462 **(E)** armthorpe.welfare@hotmail.co.uk
**Chairman:** Steve Taylor **Manager:** Brian Johnston **Prog Ed:** Phil Wiffen
**Ground:** Welfare Ground, Church Street, Armthorpe, Doncaster DN3 3AG **(T)**
**Capacity:** 2,500 **Seats:** 250 **Covered:** 400 **Midweek Matchday:** Tuesday **Clubhouse:** No **Shop:** No

**Colours(change):** All royal blue (All red)
**Previous Names:**
**Previous Leagues:** Doncaster Senior 1976-83.
**Records:** **Att:** 2,000 v Doncaster R Charity Match 1985-86. **Goalscorer:** Martin Johnson. **App:** Gary Leighton. **Win:** 10-0. **Defeat:** 1-7
**Honours:** West Riding Challenge Cup 1981-82, 82-83. Northern Counties East Division 1 Central 1984-85.

**10 YEAR RECORD**

| 06-07 | 07-08 | 08-09 | 09-10 | 10-11 | 11-12 | 12-13 | 13-14 | 14-15 | 15-16 |
|---|---|---|---|---|---|---|---|---|---|
| NCEP 13 | NCEP 9 | NCEP 15 | NCEP 3 | NCEP 13 | NCEP 13 | NCEP 20 | NCEP 18 | NCEP 17 | NCEP 19 |

## ATHERSLEY RECREATION

Founded: 1979 Nickname: Penguins

**Secretary:** Peter Goodlad **(T)** 07910 121 070 **(E)** petegoodlad@yahoo.co.uk
**Chairman:** Michael Shepherd **Manager:** Sean Margison **Prog Ed:** Jamie Wallman
**Ground:** Sheerien Park, Ollerton Road, Athersley North, Barnsley, S71 3DP **(T)** 07910 121 070
**Capacity:** 2,000 **Seats:** 150 **Covered:** 420 **Midweek Matchday:** Wednesday **Clubhouse:** No **Shop:** Yes

**Colours(change):** White & black/black/black (All orange)
**Previous Names:**
**Previous Leagues:** Sheffield & Hallamshire County Senior 1997-2012.
**Records:**
**Honours:** Sheffield & Hallamshire County Senior Division Two 1997-98, Premier Division 1999-2000, 03-04, 04-05, 06-07, 08-09, 11-12

**10 YEAR RECORD**

| 06-07 | 07-08 | 08-09 | 09-10 | 10-11 | 11-12 | 12-13 | 13-14 | 14-15 | 15-16 |
|---|---|---|---|---|---|---|---|---|---|
| SHSP 1 | SHSP 2 | SHSP 1 | SHSP 2 | SHSP 2 | SHSP 1 | NCE1 2 | NCEP 10 | NCEP 13 | NCEP 18 |

## BARTON TOWN OLD BOYS

Founded: 1995 Nickname: Swans

**Secretary:** Peter Mitchell **(T)** 07927 623 932 **(E)** bartontown@gmail.com
**Chairman:** Mark Gregory **Manager:** Paul Foot **Prog Ed:** Trevor Richens
**Ground:** The Easy Buy Ground, Marsh Lane, Barton-on-Humber DN18 5JD **(T)** 01652 661 809
**Capacity:** 3,000 **Seats:** 240 **Covered:** 540 **Midweek Matchday:** Tuesday **Clubhouse:** Yes **Shop:** No

**Colours(change):** Sky blue/navy blue/sky blue (Orange/black/orange)
**Previous Names:**
**Previous Leagues:** Lincolnshire 1995-2000, Humber (Founder member) 2000-01, Central Midlands 2001-07.
**Records:**
**Honours:** Lincolnshire League 1996-97. Central Midlands League Supreme Division 2005-06.

**10 YEAR RECORD**

| 06-07 | 07-08 | 08-09 | 09-10 | 10-11 | 11-12 | 12-13 | 13-14 | 14-15 | 15-16 |
|---|---|---|---|---|---|---|---|---|---|
| CM Su 2 | NCE1 9 | NCE1 5 | NCE1 6 | NCE1 2 | NCEP 11 | NCEP 8 | NCEP 3 | NCEP 5 | NCEP 10 |

## BOTTESFORD TOWN

Founded: 1974 Nickname: The Poachers

**Secretary:** Andrew Allcock **(T)** 07837 838 630 **(E)** andrew.susworth@googlemail.com
**Chairman:** Tony Reeve **Manager:** John Corbett **Prog Ed:** Liz Gray
**Ground:** Birch Park, Ontario Road, Bottesford, Scunthorpe, DN17 2TQ **(T)** 01724 871 883
**Capacity:** 1,000 **Seats:** 90 **Covered:** 300 **Midweek Matchday:** Wednesday **Clubhouse:** Yes **Shop:** No

**Colours(change):** All blue & yellow (Green & black/black/black & green)
**Previous Names:**
**Previous Leagues:** Lincolnshire 1974-2000. Central Midlands 2000-07.
**Records:**
**Honours:** Lincolnshire League 1989-90, 90-91, 91-92. Central Midlands League Supreme Division 2006-07.

**10 YEAR RECORD**

| 06-07 | 07-08 | 08-09 | 09-10 | 10-11 | 11-12 | 12-13 | 13-14 | 14-15 | 15-16 |
|---|---|---|---|---|---|---|---|---|---|
| CM Su 1 | NCE1 3 | NCE1 6 | NCE1 9 | NCE1 17 | NCE1 16 | NCE1 15 | NCE1 3 | NCE1 8 | NCE1 3 |

## BRIDLINGTON TOWN

Founded: 1918 Nickname: Seasiders

**Secretary:** Gordon Gillott **(T)** 07786 879 895 **(E)** gavinbranton@yahoo.co.uk
**Chairman:** Peter Smurthwaite **Manager:** Gary Allanson **Prog Ed:** Dom Taylor & Gordon Gillott
**Ground:** Neil Hudgell Law Stadium, Queensgate, Bridlington YO16 7LN **(T)** 01262 606 879
**Capacity:** 3,000 **Seats:** 500 **Covered:** 500 **Midweek Matchday:** Tuesday **Clubhouse:** Yes **Shop:** Yes

**Colours(change):** All red (All white).
**Previous Names:** Original Bridlington Town folded in 1994. Greyhound FC changed to Bridlington Town.
**Previous Leagues:** Yorkshire 1924-39, 59-82, NCEL 1982-90, 99-2003, Northern Premier 1990-94, 2003-08
**Records:** **Att:** 1,006 v FC Utd of Manchester, NPLD1N, 03.11.07. **Goalscorer:** Neil Grimson. **Apps:** Neil Grimson - 200+ (1987-97).
**Honours:** FA Vase 1992-93. Yorkshire League 1974-75. Northern Counties East 1989-90, 2001-02, 09-10, NPL Division 1 1992-93.
ERCFA Senior Cup 19-20-21,21-22,22-23,30-31,52-53,56-57,60-61,64-65,66-67,69-70,71-72,88-89,92-93,2004-05,11-12,14-15, 15-16

**10 YEAR RECORD**

| 06-07 | 07-08 | 08-09 | 09-10 | 10-11 | 11-12 | 12-13 | 13-14 | 14-15 | 15-16 |
|---|---|---|---|---|---|---|---|---|---|
| NP 1 24 | NP1N 18 | NCEP 4 | NCEP 1 | NCEP 3 | NCEP 2 | NCEP 3 | NCEP 12 | NCEP 8 | NCEP 5 |

## CLEETHORPES TOWN

Founded: 1998 Nickname: The Owls

**Secretary:** Matthew Jones **(T)** 07415 068 996 **(E)** matt@cleethorpestownfc.co.uk
**Chairman:** David Patterson **Manager:** Marcus Newell **Prog Ed:** Craig Kendall
**Ground:** The Bradley Football Development Centre Bradley Road, Grimsby, DN37 0AG **(T)** 01472 325 300
**Capacity:** 1,000 **Seats:** 180 **Covered:** 200 **Midweek Matchday:** Wednesday **Clubhouse:** Yes

**Colours(change):** Blue & black/black/blue (Red & black/white/red)
**Previous Names:** LSS Lucarlys 1998-2008.
**Previous Leagues:** Lincolnshire 2003-05, 10-12. Central Midlands 2005-06. Humber Premier 2006-09.
**Records:**
**Honours:** Lincolnshire League 2011-12. Northern Counties East Division One 2013-14.

**10 YEAR RECORD**

| 06-07 | 07-08 | 08-09 | 09-10 | 10-11 | 11-12 | 12-13 | 13-14 | 14-15 | 15-16 |
|---|---|---|---|---|---|---|---|---|---|
| Humb 3 | Humb 10 | Humb 9 | Humb dnf | Lincs 3 | Lincs 1 | NCE1 4 | NCE1 1 | NCEP 4 | NCEP 3 |

## CLIPSTONE

Founded: 1928 Nickname: The Cobras

**Secretary:** Dave Paling **(T)** 07973 143 685 **(E)** sterlinghomes1@yahoo.co.uk
**Chairman:** Dave Paling **Manager:** Billy Fox **Prog Ed:** Nigel Splading
**Ground:** Worksop Van Hire Stad, Clipstone Rd East,Clipstone Village,Mansfield,NG21 9AB **(T)** 01623 627 262 / 07937 143 685
**Capacity:** 500 **Seats:** 60 **Covered:** 200 **Midweek Matchday:** Tuesday **Clubhouse:** Yes **Shop:** No

**Colours(change):** Black & white/black/black (All red)
**Previous Names:** Clipstone Welfare 1928-2013.
**Previous Leagues:** Notts Alliance 1991-94. Central Midlands 1994-2012.
**Records:**
**Honours:** Central Midlands League 1993-94, 96-97. Northern Counties East Division One 2014-15.

**10 YEAR RECORD**

| 06-07 | 07-08 | 08-09 | 09-10 | 10-11 | 11-12 | 12-13 | 13-14 | 14-15 | 15-16 |
|---|---|---|---|---|---|---|---|---|---|
| CM Su 5 | CM Su 20 | CM Su 9 | CM Su 10 | CM Su 9 | CMN 4 | NCE1 11 | NCE1 7 | NCE1 1 | NCEP 13 |

## GARFORTH TOWN

Founded: 1964 Nickname: The Miners

**Secretary:** Andrew Marsh **(T)** 07851 815 992 **(E)** secretary@garforthtown.net
**Chairman:** Brian Close **Manager:** Rob Hunter **Prog Ed:** Chris Mather
**Ground:** J S White & Co Community Stadium, Cedar Ridge, Garforth, Leeds LS25 2PF **(T)** 0113 287 7567
**Capacity:** 3,000 **Seats:** 278 **Covered:** 200 **Midweek Matchday:** Tuesday **Clubhouse:** Yes **Shop:** No

**Colours(change):** Yellow/blue/blue (Blue/yellow/yellow)
**Previous Names:** Garforth Miners 1964-85
**Previous Leagues:** Leeds Sunday Comb. 1972-76, West Yorkshire 1976-78, Yorkshire 1978-82, NCE 1982-2007. Northern Premier 2007-13.
**Records:** 2,428 v Chester, NPL Div.1 North, 29/04/2011
**Honours:** Northern Counties East Division 1 1997-98

**10 YEAR RECORD**

| 06-07 | 07-08 | 08-09 | 09-10 | 10-11 | 11-12 | 12-13 | 13-14 | 14-15 | 15-16 |
|---|---|---|---|---|---|---|---|---|---|
| NCEP 4 | NP1N 10 | NP1N 16 | NP1N 20 | NP1N 13 | NP1N 5 | NP1N 22 | NCEP 14 | NCEP 14 | NCEP 16 |

## HANDSWORTH PARRAMORE

Founded: 1936 Nickname: Amber Parras

**Secretary:** Max Ross **(T)** 07500 833 939 **(E)** maxross@blueyonder.co.uk
**Chairman:** Pete Whitehead **Manager:** Micky Godber **Prog Ed:** Ian Robinson
**Ground:** The Windsor Foodservice Stadium, Sandy Land, Worksop S80 1UJ **(T)** 01909 479 955
**Capacity:** 2,500 **Seats:** 200 **Covered:** 750 **Midweek Matchday:** Tuesday **Clubhouse:** Yes **Shop:** No

**Colours(change):** Amber & black/black/black (Red & black/red/red)
**Previous Names:** Parramore Sports > 2010. Sheffield Parramore 2010-2011. Worksop Parramore 2011-14.
**Previous Leagues:** Sheffield & Hallam County Senior 1985-2008. Central Midlands 2008-11
**Records:**
**Honours:** Central Midland League Supreme Division 2010-11.

**10 YEAR RECORD**

| 06-07 | 07-08 | 08-09 | 09-10 | 10-11 | 11-12 | 12-13 | 13-14 | 14-15 | 15-16 |
|---|---|---|---|---|---|---|---|---|---|
| SHS1 13 | SHS1 5 | CM P 4 | CM Su 8 | CM Su 1 | NCE1 3 | NCEP 7 | NCEP 4 | NCEP 7 | NCEP 2 |

## HARROGATE RAILWAY ATHLETIC

Founded: 1935 Nickname: The Rail

**Secretary:** Dave Shepherd **(T)** 07816 986 799 **(E)**
**Chairman:** Nigel Corner **Prog Ed:** Mark Doherty
**Ground:** Station View, Starbeck, Harrogate, North Yorkshire HG2 7JA **(T)** 01423 883 104
**Capacity:** 3,500 **Seats:** 300 **Covered:** 600 **Midweek Matchday:** Tuesday **Clubhouse:** Yes **Shop:** Yes

**Colours(change):** Red/green/red (All blue)
**Previous Names:** None
**Previous Leagues:** West Yorkshire, Harrogate & District, Yorkshire 1955-73, 80-82, Northern Counties East 1982-2006. Northern Premier 2006-16
**Records:** 3,500 v Bristol City - FA Cup 2nd Round 2002-03
**Honours:** Northern Counties East Division 2 North & League cup 1983-84, Division 1 1989-99.

**10 YEAR RECORD**

| 06-07 | 07-08 | 08-09 | 09-10 | 10-11 | 11-12 | 12-13 | 13-14 | 14-15 | 15-16 |
|---|---|---|---|---|---|---|---|---|---|
| NP 1 12 | NP1N 12 | NP1N 18 | NP1N 17 | NP1N 20 | NP1N 21 | NP1N 18 | NP1N 13 | NP1N 8 | NP1N 21 |

## HEMSWORTH MINERS WELFARE Founded: 1981 Nickname: Wells

**Secretary:** Derek Bucknall **(T)** **(E)** netsi1@sky.com
**Chairman:** Tony Benson **Manager:** Wayne Benn
**Ground:** MDC Sports Stadium, Wakefield Road, Fitzwilliam, Pontefract WF9 5AJ **(T)** 01977 614 997
**Capacity:** 2,000 **Seats:** 100 **Covered:** 100 **Midweek Matchday:** **Clubhouse:** Yes **Shop:** Yes

**Colours(change):** All blue (Volt/black/volt)
**Previous Names:**
**Previous Leagues:** West Riding County Amateur 1995-2008.
**Records:** **Att:** 505 v Kinsley Boys, 2007. **Goalscorer:** Paul Crapper - Total 375 - In a season 52. **Apps:** Paul Crapper - 809.
**Honours:** Northern Counties East Division One 2015-16.

**10 YEAR RECORD**

| 06-07 | 07-08 | 08-09 | 09-10 | 10-11 | 11-12 | 12-13 | 13-14 | 14-15 | 15-16 |
|---|---|---|---|---|---|---|---|---|---|
| | | NCE1 10 | NCE1 7 | NCE1 16 | NCE1 8 | NCE1 13 | NCE1 17 | NCE1 3 | NCE1 1 |

## LIVERSEDGE Founded: 1910 Nickname: Sedge

**Secretary:** Bryan Oakes **(T)** 07855 412 453 **(E)** bryan@bryanoakes.orangehome.co.uk
**Chairman:** Leigh Bromby **Manager:** Jonathan Rimmington **Prog Ed:** Peter Bell
**Ground:** Clayborn Ground, Quaker Lane, Hightown Road, Cleckheaton WF15 3RJ **(T)** 01274 862 108
**Capacity:** 2,000 **Seats:** 250 **Covered:** 750 **Midweek Matchday:** Tuesday **Clubhouse:** Yes **Shop:** Yes

**Colours(change):** Sky blue & navy/navy/navy (Red & black/black/black).
**Previous Names:**
**Previous Leagues:** Spen Valley, West Riding Co. Amateur 1922-72, Yorkshire 1972-82
**Records:** **Att:** 986 v Thackley **Goalscorer:** Denis Charlesworth **App:** Barry Palmer
**Honours:** Northern Counties East League Cup 2005-06.

**10 YEAR RECORD**

| 06-07 | 07-08 | 08-09 | 09-10 | 10-11 | 11-12 | 12-13 | 13-14 | 14-15 | 15-16 |
|---|---|---|---|---|---|---|---|---|---|
| NCEP 12 | NCEP 4 | NCEP 14 | NCEP 9 | NCEP 17 | NCEP 14 | NCEP 15 | NCEP 20 | NCEP 18 | NCEP 14 |

## MALTBY MAIN Founded: 1916 Nickname: Miners

**Secretary:** John Mills **(T)** 07795 693 683 **(E)** john_mills_@hotmail.co.uk
**Chairman:** Wilf Race **Manager:** Spencer Fearn & Mark Askwith **Prog Ed:** Nick Dunhill
**Ground:** Muglet Lane, Maltby, Rotherham S66 7JQ. **(T)** 07795 693 683
**Capacity:** 2,000 **Seats:** 150 **Covered:** 300 **Midweek Matchday:** Wednesday **Clubhouse:** No **Shop:** No

**Colours(change):** Red/black/black (All blue)
**Previous Names:** Maltby Miners Welfare 1970-96
**Previous Leagues:** Sheffield Co Senior. Yorkshire League 1973-82
**Records:** **Att:** 1,500 v Sheffield Weds (friendly) 1991-92
**Honours:** Sheffield & Hallamshire Senior Cup1977-78

**10 YEAR RECORD**

| 06-07 | 07-08 | 08-09 | 09-10 | 10-11 | 11-12 | 12-13 | 13-14 | 14-15 | 15-16 |
|---|---|---|---|---|---|---|---|---|---|
| NCEP 10 | NCEP 18 | NCEP 12 | NCEP 16 | NCEP 11 | NCEP 18 | NCEP 14 | NCEP 15 | NCEP 19 | NCEP 7 |

## PARKGATE Founded: 1969 Nickname: The Steelmen

**Secretary:** Bruce Bickerdike **(T)** 07831 664 710 **(E)** brucebickerdike@hotmail.co.uk
**Chairman:** Albert Dudill **Manager:** Steve Adams **Prog Ed:** Bruce Bickerdike
**Ground:** Roundwood Sports Complex, Green Lane, Rawmarsh, S62 6LA **(T)** 01709 826 600
**Capacity:** 1,000 **Seats:** 300 **Covered:** 300 **Midweek Matchday:** Tuesday **Clubhouse:** Yes **Shop:** No

**Colours(change):** All Red & White. (All blue).
**Previous Names:** BSC Parkgate (1982-86) RES Parkgate (pre 1994)
**Previous Leagues:** BIR County Senior. Yorkshire 1974-82.
**Records:** **Att:** v Worksop 1982
**Honours:** N.C.E. Division One 2006-07. Wilkinson Sword Trophy 2006-07.

**10 YEAR RECORD**

| 06-07 | 07-08 | 08-09 | 09-10 | 10-11 | 11-12 | 12-13 | 13-14 | 14-15 | 15-16 |
|---|---|---|---|---|---|---|---|---|---|
| NCE1 1 | NCEP 8 | NCEP 11 | NCEP 14 | NCEP 2 | NCEP 7 | NCEP 9 | NCEP 19 | NCEP 16 | NCEP 17 |

## PICKERING TOWN
Founded: 1888 Nickname: Pikes

**Secretary:** Stephen Chapman **(T)** 07733 056 664 **(E)** pickeringsec@aol.com
**Chairman:** Keith Usher **Manager:** Paul Marshall **Prog Ed:** Peter Dickinson
**Ground:** Recreation Club, off Mill Lane, Malton Road, Pickering YO18 7DB **(T)** 01751 473 317
**Capacity:** 2,000 **Seats:** 200 **Covered:** 500 **Midweek Matchday:** Tuesday **Clubhouse:** Yes **Shop:** Yes

**Colours(change):** All blue (All yellow).
**Previous Names:** None
**Previous Leagues:** Beckett, York & District, Scarborough & District, Yorkshire 1972-1982
**Records:** **Att:** 1,412 v Notts County (friendly) in August 1991
**Honours:** N.C.E. Div 2 1987-88. North Riding Cup 1990-91. Wilkinson Sword Trophy 2000-01. North Riding Senior Cup 2012-13.

**10 YEAR RECORD**

| 06-07 | 07-08 | 08-09 | 09-10 | 10-11 | 11-12 | 12-13 | 13-14 | 14-15 | 15-16 |
|---|---|---|---|---|---|---|---|---|---|
| NCEP 9 | NCEP 3 | NCEP 9 | NCEP 7 | NCEP 7 | NCEP 12 | NCEP 5 | NCEP 7 | NCEP 11 | NCEP 6 |

## RAINWORTH MINERS WELFARE
Founded: 1922 Nickname: The Wrens

**Secretary:** Les Lee **(T)** 07889 561 787 **(E)** leslielee7@ntlworld.com
**Chairman:** Les Lee **Manager:** Julian Watts **Prog Ed:** Paul Fryer
**Ground:** Welfare Ground, Kirklington Road, Rainworth, Mansfield NG21 0JY **(T)** 01623 792 495
**Capacity:** 2,201 **Seats:** 221 **Covered:** 350 **Midweek Matchday:** Tuesday **Clubhouse:** Yes

**Colours(change):** All White (All royal blue).
**Previous Names:** Rufford Colliery
**Previous Leagues:** Notts Alliance 1922-03, Central Midlands League 2003-07, Northern Counties East 2007-10. NPL 2010-15.
**Records:** 5,071 v Barton Rovers FA Vase SF 2nd Leg, 1982. (A record for a Vase match outside of the final)
**Honours:** Notts Senior Cup Winners 1981-82

**10 YEAR RECORD**

| 06-07 | 07-08 | 08-09 | 09-10 | 10-11 | 11-12 | 12-13 | 13-14 | 14-15 | 15-16 |
|---|---|---|---|---|---|---|---|---|---|
| CM Su 3 | NCE1 4 | NCE1 2 | NCEP 2 | NP1S 20 | NP1S 19 | NP1N 14 | NP1S 15 | NP1S 21 | NCEP 9 |

## RETFORD UNITED
Founded: 1987 Nickname: The Badgers

**Secretary:** Matt Wilson **(T)** 07980 824 469 **(E)** graham@gtaccounts.com
**Chairman:** Wayne Radford **Manager:** Darren Giovannetti **Prog Ed:** Matt Wilson
**Ground:** Cannon Park, Leverton Road, Retford, Notts DN22 6QF **(T)** 07980 824 469
**Capacity:** 2,000 **Seats:** 150 **Covered:** 200 **Midweek Matchday:** Tuesday **Clubhouse:** Yes **Shop:** Yes

**Colours(change):** Black and white/black/black (Yellow/royal blue/royal blue)
**Previous Names:**
**Previous Leagues:** Gainsborough & Dist, Nottinghamshire Alliance > 2001, Central Midlands 2001-04, Northern Counties East 2004-07
**Records:** 1,527 v Doncaster Rovers - Friendly July 2006. **Goalscorer:** Steve Hardy - 272 (1987-97). **Apps:** Andy Powell - 126 (1990-95)
**Honours:** Notts All. Div.1 2000-01. Central Mids Div.1 01-02, Supreme Division 03-04, Lge Cup 01-02, 03-04, Floodlit Cup 03-04. N.C.E. Prem. Division 06-07, 11-12, N.P.L. Div.1S 07-08, 08-09. Notts Sen. Cup 08-09.

**10 YEAR RECORD**

| 06-07 | 07-08 | 08-09 | 09-10 | 10-11 | 11-12 | 12-13 | 13-14 | 14-15 | 15-16 |
|---|---|---|---|---|---|---|---|---|---|
| NCEP 1 | NP1S 1 | NP1S 1 | NP P 6 | NP P 22 | NCEP 1 | NCEP 4 | NCEP 9 | NCEP 20 | NCEP 15 |

## STAVELEY MINERS WELFARE
Founded: 1989 Nickname: The Welfare

**Secretary:** Ele Reaney **(T)** 07530 055 849 **(E)** staveleyed@hotmail.co.uk
**Chairman:** Terry Damms **Manager:** Brett Marshall **Prog Ed:** Rich Williams
**Ground:** Inkersall Road, Staveley, Chesterfield, S43 3JL **(T)** 01246 471 441
**Capacity:** 5,000 **Seats:** 220 **Covered:** 400 **Midweek Matchday:** Wednesday **Clubhouse:** Yes **Shop:** Yes

**Colours(change):** Blue & white/white/white (All yellow)
**Previous Names:** None
**Previous Leagues:** Chesterfield & District Amateur 1989-91. County Senior 1991-93.
**Records:** 910 v Chesterfield, Friendly, 20/07/2011. **Goalscorer:** Ryan Damms - 102. **Apps:** Shane Turner.
**Honours:** County Senior League Division 3 1991-92, Division 2 1992-93. N.C.E. Division One 2010-11.

**10 YEAR RECORD**

| 06-07 | 07-08 | 08-09 | 09-10 | 10-11 | 11-12 | 12-13 | 13-14 | 14-15 | 15-16 |
|---|---|---|---|---|---|---|---|---|---|
| NCE1 6 | NCE1 8 | NCE1 4 | NCE1 4 | NCE1 1 | NCEP 5 | NCEP 13 | NCEP 17 | NCEP 9 | NCEP 8 |

## THACKLEY

Founded: 1930 Nickname: Dennyboys

**Secretary:** Stewart Willingham **(T)** 07961 669 405 **(E)** stuwillingham@hotmail.com
**Chairman:** Geoff Scott **Manager:** Chris Reape **Prog Ed:** Richard Paley
**Ground:** Dennyfield, Ainsbury Avenue, Thackley, Bradford BD10 0TL **(T)** 01274 615 571
**Capacity:** 3000 **Seats:** 300 **Covered:** 600 **Midweek Matchday:** Tuesday **Clubhouse:** Yes **Shop:** No

**Colours(change):** Red & white/white/red. (White/black/white).
**Previous Names:** Thackley Wesleyians 1930-39
**Previous Leagues:** Bradford Amateur, West Riding County Amateur, West Yorkshire, Yorkshire 1967-82
**Records:** **Att:** 1,500 v Leeds United 1983
**Honours:** West Riding County Cup 1963-64, 66-67, 73-74, 74-75. Bradford & District Senior Cup (x13).

**10 YEAR RECORD**

| 06-07 | 07-08 | 08-09 | 09-10 | 10-11 | 11-12 | 12-13 | 13-14 | 14-15 | 15-16 |
|---|---|---|---|---|---|---|---|---|---|
| NCEP 18 | NCEP 16 | NCEP 7 | NCEP 4 | NCEP 8 | NCEP 10 | NCEP 10 | NCEP 13 | NCEP 12 | NCEP 12 |

## WORKSOP TOWN

Founded: 1861 Nickname: Tigers

**Secretary:** Dan Stacey **(T)** 07962 346 514 **(E)** wtfcsecretary@gmail.com
**Chairman:** Kevin Keep **Manager:** Mark Shaw **Prog Ed:** Martin Golds
**Ground:** The Windsor Foodservice Stadium, off Sandy Lane, Worksop S80 1UJ **(T)** 07962 346 514
**Capacity:** 2,500 **Seats:** 200 **Covered:** 750 **Midweek Matchday:** Wednesday **Clubhouse:** Yes **Shop:** Yes

**Colours(change):** Amber with black/black/amber (White with black/white/white)
**Previous Names:** Not known
**Previous Leagues:** Central All.1947-49, 60-61, Midland Co. 1949-60, 61-68, 69-74, Northern Premier 1968-69, 74-2004, 2007-14, Conf. 2004-07
**Records:** 8,171 v Chesterfield - FA Cup 1925 (Central Avenue)
**Honours:** Sheffield Senior Cup 1923-24, 52-53, 54-55, 65-66, 69-70,72-73, 81-82, 84-85, 94-95, 96-97, 2002-03, 11-12.
Northern Premier League President's Cup 1985-86, 96-97, Chairman's Cup 2001-02.

**10 YEAR RECORD**

| 06-07 | 07-08 | 08-09 | 09-10 | 10-11 | 11-12 | 12-13 | 13-14 | 14-15 | 15-16 |
|---|---|---|---|---|---|---|---|---|---|
| Conf N 21 | NP P 9 | NP P 17 | NP P 18 | NP P 7 | NP P 15 | NP P 9 | NP P 4 | NCEP 2 | NCEP 4 |

# GROUND DIRECTIONS

**A.F.C. MANSFIELD - Forest Town Stadium, Clipstone Road West, Forest Town, Mansfield NG19 0EE. Tel: 07973 491 739**
The ground is situated approximately 3 miles to the north east of Mansfield town centre and sits on the B6030 Clipstone Road West. Pedestrian access can be gained via gates on Clipstone Road West with vehicle access via Main Avenue and then the 2nd right, turning into Second Avenue.

**ALBION SPORTS-Throstle Nest, Newlands, Farsley, Leeds, LS28 5BE. Tel: 0113 255 7292**
Come off the M606 at the roundabout. Take fourth exit onto Rooley Lane which is the A6177, continue to follow A6177 through two roundabouts then turn right onto Leeds Road A647. Continue to follow A647, go through roundabout. At next roundabout, take second exit onto Bradford Roa B6157. Follow for ½ mile before turning left onto New Street then turn right onto Newlands. Ground on left.

**ARMTHORPE WELFARE-Welfare Ground, Church Street, Armthorpe, Doncaster, DN3 3AG. Tel: (01302) 842795-Match days only**
From the north, turn left at main roundabout in the centre of Doncaster and straight across at next roundabout on to Wheatley Hall Road. Turn right on to Wentworth Road, go to top of hill towards the Hospital on to Armthorpe Road. From the south, take the M18 to J4 on to the A630. At 2nd roundabout, turn left and proceed to next roundabout, then turn right. Ground 400 yards on left behind Netto.

**ATHERSLEY RECREATION-Sheerien Park, Ollerton Road, Athersley North, Barnsley, S71 3DP. Tel: 07910 121070**
From North: M1 J38. Go down slip road, round roundabout and back under motorway. Take first left onto Haigh Lane, go to top of the hill and, at T-junction, turn right. At next T-junction, turn left onto Shaw Lane and go to bottom of hill. At T-junction of A61, turn right to Barnsley, go through first set of traffic lights and take first left onto Newstead Road. Follow to second roundabout and turn right onto Ollerton Road. Follow to second turn on left-do not take it but go past and entrance is between houses 123-125 Ollerton Road. Follow drive into ground.

**BARTON TOWN OLD BOYS-The Euronics Ground, Marsh Lane, Barton-on-Humber. Tel: (01652) 635838**
Approaching from the South on A15, Barton is the last exit before the Humber Bridge. Follow the A1077 into the town. Turn right at the mini roundabout at the bottom of the hill into Holydyke. Take second left onto George Street and then into King Street. Marsh Lane is opposite the junction of King Street and High Street. The ground is at the end of Marsh Lane, on the right, immediately after the cricket ground.

**BOTTESFORD TOWN-Birch Park, Ontario Road, Bottesford, Scunthorpe, DN17 2TQ. Tel: (01724) 871883**
Exit M180 via M181-Scunthorpe. At circle (Berkeley Hotel), turn right into Scotter Road. At circle (Asda) straight ahead, 2nd left into South Park road then on to Sunningdale Road, turn right into Goodwood Road, Birch Park at end (right turn). Please note that Goodwood Road is not suitable for large vehicles. Instead, take 2nd right off Sunningdale Road which is Quebec Road, then 2nd right which is Ontario Road down to th bottom and ground is on the left.

**BRIDLINGTON TOWN-Queensgate Stadium, Queensgate, Bridlington, East Yorkshire, YO16 7LN. Tel: (01262) 606879**
From South (Hull, Beeford, Barmston): Approach Bridlington on the A165, passing golf course on right and Broadacres Pub, Kingsmead Estate left. Straight through traffic lights to roundabout by B&Q. Turn right. At traffic lights turn left and over the railway bridge. At roundabout bear left and carry on heading north up Quay Road. After traffic lights turn right into Queensgate. Ground is 800 yards up the road on the right.
From South and West (Driffield, Hull, York): Approach Bridlington on A614. (This was formally the A166). Straight on at traffic lights (Hospital on right) and follow the road round the bend. At roundabout straight across to mini roundabout and bear right (second exit). Follow road around to right and to traffic lights. Straight on. At next traffic lights (just after Kwikfit) turn left into Queensgate. Ground is 800 yards up the road on the rig
From North (Scarborough): Approach Bridlington (Esso garage on right) at roundabout turn left then at mini roundabout second exit. Follow road around to right and to traffic lights. Straight on. At next traffic lights (just after Kwikfit) turn left into Queensgate. Ground is 800 yards up the road on the right.

**CLEETHORPES TOWN-The Bradley Football Development Centre, Bradley Road, Grimsby, DN37 0AG**
Head East along the M180/A180. Exit at the Great Coates Interchange. Travel back over motorway to first Roundabout. Take first exit and follow for two miles to Trawl Pub Roundabout. Take second exit, follow for two miles to Bradley Roundabout. Take second exit on to Bradley Road. The ground is approximately 500 yards on the left. **continued on page 382**

## AFC EMLEY

Founded: 2005 Nickname: Pewits

**Secretary:** Andrew Painten **(T)** 07931 353 515 **(E)** office@afcemley.co.uk
**Chairman:** Nigel Wakefield **Manager:** Darren Hepworth **Prog Ed:** Dan Brownhill
**Ground:** The Welfare Ground, Off Upper Lane, Emley, nr Huddersfield, HD8 9RE. **(T)** 01924 849 392 **Capacity:** 2,000
**Colours(change):** Claret & sky blue/sky blue/claret (Green/black/black)
**ADDITIONAL INFORMATION:**
**Previous League:** West Yorkshire 2005-06.

## BRIGG TOWN

Founded: 1864 Nickname: Zebras

**Secretary:** Tim Harris **(T)** 07446 294 837 **(E)** uksoccersafe@gmail.com
**Chairman:** Simon Harris **Manager:** Scott Hellewell & Paul Grimes **Prog Ed:** Tim Harris
**Ground:** The Hawthorns, Hawthorn Avenue, Brigg DN20 8PG **(T)** 01652 409 137 **Capacity:** 2,500
**Colours(change):** Black and white/black/red (Pink/navy/pink)
**ADDITIONAL INFORMATION:** 2,000 v Boston United - 1953
Midland Counties League 1977-78. FA Vase 1995-96, 2002-03. Northern Counties East Premier Division 2000-01.
Lincolnshire League x8, League Cup x5. Lincolnshire 'A' Senior Cup x4. Lincolnshire 'B' Senior Cup x5.

## CAMPION

Founded: 1963 Nickname:

**Secretary:** David Keegan **(T)** **(E)** campionafc@gmail.com
**Chairman:** Richard Holmes **Manager:** James Bicknell **Prog Ed:** Mark Palfreeman
**Ground:** Scotchman Road, Bradford, BD9 5DB. **(T)** 01274 491 919
**Colours(change):** Red & black/black/red (All royal blue)
**ADDITIONAL INFORMATION:**
**Previous Leagues:** Red Triangle 1975-81, 85-86. West Riding Amateur 1981-85, 86-2016.

## DRONFIELD TOWN

Founded: 1998 Nickname: None

**Secretary:** Darren Bradwell **(T)** 07906 682 960 **(E)** dronfieldtownfc@yahoo.co.uk
**Chairman:** Patrick Williams **Manager:** Craig Butler **Prog Ed:** Michael Payne
**Ground:** Stonelow Playing Fields, Stonelow Road, Dronfield, S18 2DA **(T)** **Capacity:** 500
**Colours(change):** Red & black/black with red/red & black (Yellow/blue/yellow)
**ADDITIONAL INFORMATION:**
**Previous Leagues:** Central Midlands > 2013.
**League honours:** Hope Valley B Division 2001-02, A Division 2002-03, Premiership 2003-04.
Midland Regional Alliance Division One 2005-06, Premier 2007-08. Central Midlands North 2012-13.

## ECCLESHILL UNITED

Founded: 1948 Nickname: The Eagles

**Secretary:** Adrian Benson **(T)** 07767 472 777 **(E)** adrian.benson@btinternet.com
**Chairman:** Adrian Benson **Manager:** Sean Regan **Prog Ed:** Paul Everett
**Ground:** Mitton Group Stadium, Kingsway, Wrose, Bradford, BD2 1PN **(T)** 01274 615 739 **Capacity:** 2,225
**Colours(change):** Blue & white/blue/blue (Red & white/red/red)
**ADDITIONAL INFORMATION:**
**Record Att:** 715 v Bradford City 1996-97. **Win:** 10-1. **Defeat:** 0-6.
**Honours:** Bradford Senior Cup 1985-86. Northern Counties East Division 1 1996-97.

## GLASSHOUGHTON WELFARE

Founded: 1964 Nickname: Welfare or Blues

**Secretary:** Frank MacLachlan **(T)** 07770 590 359 **(E)** frank.maclachlan@btinternet.com
**Chairman:** Jon Miles **Manager:** Darren Holmes **Prog Ed:** Garry Mollon
**Ground:** Glasshoughton Centre, Leeds Road, Glasshoughton, Castleford WF10 4PF **(T)** 01977 511 234 **Capacity:** 2,000
**Colours(change):** Royal blue & white/blue/blue (Green & white/white/white)
**ADDITIONAL INFORMATION: Att:** 350 v Ossett Albion, Presidents Cup 1998. **Win:** 8-1. **Defeat:** 0-8.
West Riding County Cup 1993-94.

## GRIMSBY BOROUGH

Founded: 2003 Nickname: The Wilderness Boys

**Secretary:** Nigel Fanthorpe **(T)** 07890 318 054 **(E)** nigelfanthorpe@hotmail.co.uk
**Chairman:** Tony Legget **Manager:** Daniel Barrett & Andy Liddle **Prog Ed:** Dan Sylvester
**Ground:** The Bradley Football Development Centre, Bradley Road, Grimsby, DN37 0AG **(T)** 07890 318 054 **Capacity:** 1,000
**Colours(change):** All red (White/black/white)
**ADDITIONAL INFORMATION:**
**Previous League:** Central Midlands 2004-08.
**FA/County Cups:** Lincolnshire Junior Cup 2007-08.

## HALL ROAD RANGERS

Founded: 1959 Nickname: Rangers

**Secretary:** Alan Chaplin **(T)** 07961 415 884 **(E)** alynn33@alynn33.karoo.co.uk
**Chairman:** Darren Sunley **Manager:** David Ricardo **Prog Ed:** Mike Harker
**Ground:** Hawroth Park, Dawson Drive, Hull HU6 7DY **(T)** 07815 629 497
**Colours(change):** Blue & white/blue & white/blue (Yellow & blue/yellow & blue/yellow)

**ADDITIONAL INFORMATION: App:**1,200 v Manchester City Aug 93 **Goalscorer:** G James **App:** G James
East Riding Senior Cup 1972-73, 93-94. N.C.E. Division Two 1990-91.

## HALLAM (SECOND OLDEST CLUB IN THE WORLD)

Founded: 1860 Nickname: Countrymen

**Secretary:** Kevin Scott **(T)** 07889 855 594 **(E)** kevinscottsport@yahoo.co.uk
**Chairman:** Steve Basford **Manager:** Ryan Hindley **Prog Ed:** Pete Wilding
**Ground:** Sandygate Road, Crosspool, Sheffield S10 5SE **(T)** 0114 230 9484 **Capacity:** 1,000
**Colours(change):** All blue (All yellow)

**ADDITIONAL INFORMATION: Att:** 2,000 v Hendon F.A. Amateur Cup. **Goalscorer:** A Stainrod 46. **App:** P. Ellis 500+. **Win:** 7-0 x2. **Defeat:** 0-7.
**Honours:** Northern Counties East League Cup 2003-04.
**Previous League:** Yorkshire 1952-82.

## KNARESBOROUGH TOWN

Founded: 1902 Nickname: None

**Secretary:** Clare Rudzinski **(T)** 07702 678 320 **(E)** knaresboroughtownafc@gmail.com
**Chairman:** Terry Hewlett **Manager:** Paul Stansfield **Prog Ed:** Daniel Rudzinski
**Ground:** Manse Lane, Knaresborough, HG5 8LF **(T)** 07702 678 320 **Capacity:** 1,000
**Colours(change):** Red/black/red (Yellow & black/black/yellow)

**ADDITIONAL INFORMATION:**
**Previous Leagues:** West Yorkshire 1971. Harrogate & District 1971-93. West Yorkshire 1993-2012.
**Honours:** West Yorkshire League Premier Division 2008-09.

## NOSTELL MINERS WELFARE

Founded: 1928 Nickname: The Welfare

**Secretary:** Granville Marshall **(T)** 01924 864 462 **(E)** nostwellmwfc@hotmail.com
**Chairman:** Simon Turfrey **Manager:** Graham Nicholas **Prog Ed:** Malcolm Lamb
**Ground:** The Welfare Ground, Crofton Co. Centre, Middle Lane, New Crofton WF4 1LB **(T)** 01924 866 010 **Capacity:** 1500
**Colours(change):** Yellow/black/black. (All blue).

**ADDITIONAL INFORMATION:**
West Yorkshire Premier Division 2004-05

## OLLERTON TOWN

Founded: 1988 Nickname: The Town

**Secretary:** Joanne Winter **(T)** **(E)**
**Chairman:** John Thomson **Manager:** Dave Winter **Prog Ed:** Liam Kent
**Ground:** The Lane, Walesby Lane, New Ollerton, Newark NG22 9UT **(T)** None
**Colours(change):** Red/black/red (All navy)

**ADDITIONAL INFORMATION:**
**Previous Names:** Ollerton & Bevercotes 1988-94.
**Previous League:** Notts Alliance 1991-2000. Central Midlands League 2000-16

## PENISTON CHURCH

Founded: 1906 Nickname: None

**Secretary:** David Hampshire **(T)** 07876 468 975 **(E)** davehampshire@talktalk.net
**Chairman:** Scott Fairbank **Manager:** Ian Richards **Prog Ed:** Andy Green
**Ground:** Church View Road, Penistone, Sheffield S36 6AT **(T)** 01226 370 095
**Colours(change):** Black & white/black/black (All light blue)

**ADDITIONAL INFORMATION:**
**Previous Leagues:** Sheffield & Hallamshire County Senior 1990-2014.

## PONTEFRACT COLLIERIES

Founded: 1958 Nickname: Colls

**Secretary:** Trevor Waddington **(T)** **(E)**
**Chairman:** TBC **Manager:** Craig Parry **Prog Ed:** Steve Hunt
**Ground:** Skinner Lane, Pontefract, WF8 4QE **(T)** 01977 600 818 **Capacity:** 1,200
**Colours(change):** Blue & white/blue & white/blue (Claret & sky blue/claret & sky blue/claret)

**ADDITIONAL INFORMATION: Att:** 1,000 v Hull City, floodlight opening 1987.
Northern Counties East League Division One 1983-84, 95-96.

## ROSSINGTON MAIN

Founded: 1919 Nickname: The Colliery

**Secretary:** Gerald Parsons **(T)** 07941 811 217 **(E)** g-parsons2@sky.com
**Chairman:** Carl Stokes **Manager:** Lee Holmes
**Ground:** Welfare Ground, Oxford Street, Rossington, Doncaster, DN11 0TE **(T)** 01302 865 524 (MD) **Capacity:** 2,000
**Colours(change):** All blue (All red)

**ADDITIONAL INFORMATION:**
**Record Att:** 1,243 v Doncaster Rovers 09/07/2013. **Goalscorer:** Lee Holmes - 115+. **Apps:** Dave Holvey - 250.
**League honours:** Central Midlands League Premier Division 1984-85.

## SELBY TOWN

Founded: 1919 Nickname: The Robins

**Secretary:** Thomas Arkley **(T)** 07830 218 657 **(E)** toonarkley@yahoo.co.uk
**Chairman:** Ralph Pearse **Manager:** Nigel Emery
**Ground:** The Fairfax Plant Hire Stadium, Richard Street, Scott Road, Selby YO8 4BN **(T)** 01757 210 900 **Capacity:** 5,000
**Colours(change):** All red (All blue).

**ADDITIONAL INFORMATION: Att:** 7,000 v Bradford PA FA Cup1st Round 1953-54
**League honours:** Yorkshire League 1934-35, 35-36, 52-53, 53-54. Northern Counties East Division One 1995-96.

## SHIREBROOK TOWN

Founded: 1985 Nickname: None

**Secretary:** Aimee Radford **(T)** 07983 809 608 **(E)** aimeeradford@yahoo.co.uk
**Chairman:** Dan Marsh **Manager:** Russ Eagle **Prog Ed:** Aimee Radford
**Ground:** Langwith Road, Shirebrook, Mansfield, NG20 8TF **(T)** 01623 742 535 **Capacity:** 2,000
**Colours(change):** Red/black/black (All white)

**ADDITIONAL INFORMATION:**
**Record Goalscorer:** Craig Charlesworth - 345. **Apps:** Martin Rowbottom - 384.
**League honours:** Central Midlands League Supreme Division 2000-01, 01-02. Northern Counties East Division One 2003-04.

## TEVERSAL

Founded: 1918 Nickname: Tevie Boys

**Secretary:** Kevin Newton **(T)** 07711 358 060 **(E)** kevin.newton@teversalfc.co.uk
**Chairman:** Peter Cockerill **Manager:** Dean Short **Prog Ed:** Kevin Newton
**Ground:** Teversal Grange Spts and So.Centre, Carnarvon St, Teversal, NG17 3HJ **(T)** 07711 358 060 **Capacity:** 2,000
**Colours(change):** Red/black/black (All royal blue)

**ADDITIONAL INFORMATION:**
**Previous Name:** Teversal Grange. **Previous League:** Central Midlands 2000-05.
**Honours:** Central Midlands League 2004-05.

## WESTELLA & WILLERBY

Founded: 1920 Nickname: None

**Secretary:** Rob Lester **(T)** 07970 632 755 **(E)** nobbylester@louiselester.karoo.co.uk
**Chairman:** Jeremy Alcock **Manager:** Leon Sewell **Prog Ed:** Phil Wood
**Ground:** The Euronics Ground, Marsh Lane, Barton-upon-Humber DN18 5JD **(T)** 01652 661 871
**Colours(change):** Black & white/black/black (Red/white/red)

**ADDITIONAL INFORMATION:**
**Previous League:** Central Midlands >2015.
**Previous Name:** Westella VIP >2016.

## WINTERTON RANGERS

Founded: 1930 Nickname: Rangers

**Secretary:** Graham Halliday **(T)** 07753 103 466 **(E)** ghtoon1892@gmail.com
**Chairman:** Wayne Turtle **Manager:** Lee Hastings **Prog Ed:** W. Turtle & M. Girdham
**Ground:** West Street, Winterton, Scunthorpe DN15 9QF. **(T)** 01724 732 628 **Capacity:** 3,000
**Colours(change):** All blue (All red)

**ADDITIONAL INFORMATION: Att:** 1,200 v Sheffield United, flood lights switch on, October 1978.
NCE Premier 2007-08.
Lincolnshire Senior Trophy 2015-16.

## WORSBROUGH BRIDGE ATHLETIC

Founded: 1923 Nickname: The Briggers

**Secretary:** Scott Aranyi **(T)** 07977 947 760 **(E)** cr.wyatt@btinternet.com
**Chairman:** Peter Schofield **Manager:** Ian shirt **Prog Ed:** Mark Booth
**Ground:** Park Road, Worsbrough Bridge, Barnsley S70 5LJ **(T)** 01226 284 452 **Capacity:** 2,000
**Colours(change):** Red/red/white (blue/blue/white)

**ADDITIONAL INFORMATION: Previous Leagues:** Barnsley 1952-61. County Senior 1962-70. Yorkshire 1971-82.
**Record Att:** 1,603 v Blyth Spatans, FA Amateur Cup 1971.
**League honours:** Barnsley League Division One 1952-53, 58-59, 59-60. County Senior League Division One 1965-66, 69-70.

## YORKSHIRE AMATEUR

Founded: 1918 Nickname: Ammers

**Secretary:** Simon Charlesworth **(T)** **(E)**
**Chairman:** Lincoln Richards **Manager:** Phil Harding & Lincoln Richards **Prog Ed:** David Packham
**Ground:** Bracken Edge, Roxholme Road, Leeds, LS8 4DZ (Sat. Nav. LS7 4JG) **(T)** 0113 289 2886 **Capacity:** 1,550
**Colours(change):** White/navy/red (All royal blue)

**ADDITIONAL INFORMATION: Previous Leagues:** Yorkshire 1920-24, 30-82.
**Record Att:** 4,000 v Wimbledon, FA Amateur Cup Quarter Final 1932.
**League honours:** Yorkshire League 1931-32, Division Two 1958-59, Division Three 1977-78.
**FA/County Cups:** West Riding Cup x3. Leeds & District Senior Cup.

**CLIPSTONE - The Lido Ground, Clipstone Road East, Clipstone Village, Mansfield, NG21 9AB. Tel: 01623 423730**
From M1 J29, take exit signposted A617 Mansfield. At next roundabout, take third exit continuing on the A617. Keep going straight on until you get to the Mansfield ring road with Riley's snooker hall on your right and a miner's statue on your left. Follow the road round underneath a pedestrian bridge and take the next left onto the A6191 (Ratcliffe Gate). After around half a mile, turn left onto the B6030 (Carter Lane). Follow the B6030 for about 3 miles, go straight on at a roundabout and the ground will be on your left.

**GARFORTH TOWN - Cedar Ridge, Garforth, Leeds LS25 2PF. Tel: 0113 287 7145**
From North: travel south on A1 and join M1. Turn off at 1st junc (47). From South: M1 to junc 47. From Leeds area: join M1 at junc 44 or 46 and turn off at junc 47. From West: M62 to junc 29, join M1 and off at junc 47. From junc 47: take turning signe 'Garforth' (A642). Approx. 200 yds turn left into housing estate opposite White House. (Cedar Ridge). Stadium at end of lane. From the South (alternative): A1, turn off on to A63 signposted 'Leeds' immediately after 'Boot & Shoe' Public House. At 1st roundabout turn right on to A656 and follow to next roundabout. Take 1st left on to A642 (Garforth) and follow from M1 junc 47.

**HANDSWORTH PARRAMORE-The Windsor Foodservice Stadium, Sandy Land, Worksop S80 1TJ. Tel: 01909 479 955**
From either the A1 or M1 J31, take the A57 towards Worksop. After approximately 7 miles, look out for the A60/Sandy Lane turnoff at the roundabout. Continue over two mini-roundabouts for ¾mile then turn left into the retail park and left again into the stadium car park.

**HARROGATE RAILWAY ATHLETIC - Station View, Starbeck, Harrogate, North Yorkshire HG2 7JA**
From All Areas I would suggest using the M1 A1 Link Road heading North. Once on the A1 North stay on it until Junction 47. Exit at Junction 47 and take the 1st Exit at the Roundabout A59 heading towards Knaresborough and Harrogate. At the next Roundabout take the 3rd exit A59 Knaresborough. Stay on the A59 through Knaresborough and on towards Harrogate, after approx 1 mile from Knaresborough you will enter Starbeck. Proceed through Starbeck over the Railway Crossing. Station View is the 1st Right after the Railway Crossing. The Ground is at the far end of Station View. If you are coming from Harrogate towards Knaresborough on the A59 turn left immediately prior to pelican crossing just before the Railway Crossing. The Ground is at the far end of Station View.

**HEMSWORTH MINERS WELFARE-Fitzwilliam Stadium, Wakefield Road, Fitzwilliam, Pontefract, WF9 5AJ. Tel: (01977) 614997**
From East/West: M62 to J32 towards Pontefract then follow A628 towards Hemsworth. At Ackworth roundabout (Stoneacre Suzuki Garage), take a right on to the A638 Wakefield Road. Travel half a mile to next roundabout then take first exit. Travel one mile to crossroads and turn left into Fitzwilliam. Pass a row of shops on your right and turn left after the bus shelter before an iron bridge. To ground. **From North**: A1 South to M62 then follow above directions. **From South:** A1(M) North to A638 Wakefield Road. Travel to Ackworth Roundabout (Stoneacre Suzuki Garage) and go straight across and follow the A638 to the next roundabout. Take first exit then to crossroads. Turn left into Fitzwilliam and pass row of shops on your right. Turn left after bus shelter before iron bridge and carry on to the ground. Alternative: M1 to J32 then take M18 to A1(M).

**LIVERSEDGE-Clayborn Ground, Quaker Lane, Hightown Road, Cleckheaton, WF15 8DF. Tel: (01274) 682108**
M62 J26, A638 into Cleckheaton, right at lights on corner of Memorial Park, through next lights and under railway bridge, first left (Hightown Rd) and Quaker Lane is approx 1/4 mile on left and leads to ground. From M1 J40, A638 thru Dewsbury and Heckmondwike to Cleckheaton, left at Memorial Park lights then as above. Buses 218 & 220 (Leeds-Huddersfield) pass top of Quaker Lane.

**MALTBY MAIN-Muglet Lane, Maltby, Rotherham, S66 7JQ. Tel: (07795) 693683**
Exit M18 at Junc 1 with A631. Two miles into Maltby, right at traffic lights at Queens Hotel corner on to B6427 Muglet Lane. Ground 3/4 mile on left.

**PARKGATE-Roundwood Sports Complex, Green Lane, Rawmarsh, Rotherham, S62 6LA. Tel: (01709) 826600**
From Rotherham A633 to Rawmarsh. From Doncaster A630 to Conisbrough, then A6023 through Swinton to Rawmarsh. Grd at Green Lane-right from Rotherham, left from Conisbrough at the Crown Inn. Ground 800yds on right.

**PICKERING TOWN-Recreation Club, off Mill Lane, Malton Rd, Pickering, YO18 7DB. Tel: (01751) 473317**
A169 from Malton. On entering Pickering, take 1st left past Police Station and BP garage into Mill Lane, ground 200 yds on right.

**RAINWORTH MINERS WELFARE - Welfare Ground, Kirklington Road, Rainworth, Mansfield NG21 0JY. Tel: 01623 792 495**
From M1 (Junction 29) – take A617. At Pleasley turn right onto the new Mansfield Bypass road which is still the A617 and follow to Rainworth. At roundabout with B6020 Rainworth is off to the right, but it is better to go straight over onto the new Rainworth Bypass and then right at the next roundabout (the ground can be seen on the way along the Bypass) At mini roundabout, turn right onto Kirklington Road and go down the hill for ¼ mile – ground and car park on the right. Alternatively you can reach the new A617 Bypass from the A38 via Junction 28 on the M1. From A614 at roundabout, take the A617 to Rainworth for 1 mile. Left at 1st roundabout into village. At mini roundabout right into Kirklington road – ¼ mile down hill as above.

**RETFORD UNITED - Cannon Park, Leverton Road, Retford, Notts DN22 6QF. Tel: (01777) 869 468 / 710 300**
Leave the A1 at Ranby and follow the A620 towards Retford. Go past Ranby prison and go straight on at the next 2 mini roundabouts. At the 3rd roundabout take the 3rd exit signposted Gainsborough. Passing Morrisons on the left, go through the traffic lights and move into the right hand lane. Turn right at the traffic lights. Turn left at the traffic lights by the Broken Wheel Public House into Leverton Road. Go past the Masons Arms Public House and go over 2 hump backed bridges. The ground is signposted and is on the right.

**STAVELEY MINERS WELFARE-Inkersall Road, Staveley, Chesterfield, S43 3JL. Tel: (01246) 471441**
M1 J30 follow A619 Chesterfield. Staveley is 3 miles from J30. Turn left at GK Garage in Staveley town centre into Inkersall Road. Ground is 200 yards on right at side of Speedwell Rooms.

**THACKLEY-Dennyfield, Ainsbury Avenue, Thackley, Bradford, BD10 0TL. Tel: (01274) 615571**
On main Leeds/Keighley A657 road, turn off at Thackley corner which is 2 miles from Shipley traffic lights and 1 mile from Greengates lights. Ainsbury Avenue bears to the right 200yds down the hill. Ground is 200yds along Ainsbury Avenue on the right.

**WORKSOP TOWN -The Windsor Foodservice Stadium, off Sandy Lane, Worksop S80 1UJ. Tel: (01909) 479 955**
From either the A1 or M1 J31, take the A57 towards Worksop. After approximately 7 miles, look out for the A60/Sandy Lane turnoff at the roundabout. Continue over two mini-roundabouts for ¾mile then turn left into the retail park and left again into the stadium car park.

**DIVISION ONE**

**A.F.C. EMLEY-The Welfare Ground, Off Upper Lane, Emley, nr Huddersfield, HD8 9RE. Tel: 01924 849392 or 07702 712287**
From M1 J38: Travel on road signposted to Huddersfield through the village of Bretton to the first roundabout. Take first exit off this roundabout signposted Denby Dale. After approximately one mile turn right at road signposted Emley. After 2 miles enter the village of Emley. Entrance to ground is opposite a white bollard in centre of road. (Narrow entrance).
From M1 J39: Travel on road signposted toward Denby Dale. Travel for approximately 3 miles up hill to first roundabout. Take 2nd exit and follow directions as above.

**BRIGG TOWN - The Hawthorns, Hawthorn Avenue, Brigg DN20 8PG Tel: 01652 409 137**
From M180 (Exit 4 - Scunthorpe East) A18 to Brigg. Leave Town via Wrawby Road, following signs for Airport and Grimsby. 100 metres after Sir John Nelthorpe Lower School, and immediately after bus stop/shelter, turn left into Recreation ground (signposted "Football Ground" ) and follow road into club car park.

**CAMPION - Scotchman Road, Bradford, BD9 5DB.**
Leave M62 at J26 to join M606. Stay until end and join A6177 Ring Road (East). Go past Asda supermarket and at first roundabout take first exit and join A650. Go past Leisure Exchange. Road becomes A6037. After approx ¾m turn left into Station Road. At junction, turn left and join A6177. At second set of lights, turn right into Manningham Lane, then turn left into Oak Lane at next lights. At second set of lights, turn right into Heaton Road. Take second left into Scotchman Road. Ground is approx 500m on right.

**DRONFIELD TOWN - Stonelow Playing Fields, Stonelow Road, Dronfield, S18 2DA**
From South: At M1 J29, 2nd exit A617 Chesterfield. At roundabout, take 4th exit (A61 Sheffield), then 2nd and 3rd exits at next roundabouts to stay on A61. Leave at first slip road signed Sheepbridge/Unstone. Right towards Unstone/Dronfield. Go across 1st mini roundabout, then right and immediate left at next mini roundabout onto Green Lane. Up hill, 2nd right onto Stonelow Road and 1st right onto Shireoaks. From North: At M1 J30, 3rd exit towards Renishaw. Through Renishaw and Eckington then right for Coal Aston. Left at first mini roundabout, keep on Green Lane, down steep hill and left onto Stonelow Road then take 1st right onto Shireoaks.

**ECCLESHILL UNITED-Kingsway, Wrose, Bradford, BD2 1PN. Tel: (01274) 615739**
M62 J26 onto M606, right onto Bradford Ring Road A6177, left on to A650 for Bradford at 2nd roundabout. A650 Bradford Inner Ring Road onto Canal Rd, branch right at Staples (Dixons Car showrooms on right), fork left after 30mph sign to junction with Wrose Road, across junction-continuation of Kings Rd, first left onto Kingsway. Ground is 200 yards on right.

**GLASSHOUGHTON WELFARE-The Glasshoughton Centre, Leeds Rd, Glasshoughton, Castleford, WF10 4PF. Tel: (01977) 511234**
Leave the M62 J32, signposted Castleford/Pontefract (A639). At the bottom of the slip road take the A656, taking carer to pick up the middle lane for Castleford. After approx. 1/4 mile, bear left at the first roundabout and, after a further 1/4 mile, left at the next roundabout on to Leeds Road. Ground is then 200 yards on the right.

**GRIMSBY BOROUGH-Grimsby Community Stadium, Bradley Road, Grimsby, DN37 0AG**
Head South East on the A180 to the Great Coates turn off come back over the A180 and follow for 1/2 mile to the roundabout, take first exit follow over one mini roundabout and through one set of traffic lights until you come to the Trawl Pub roundabout, take the second exit onto Littlecoates road and follow over one mini roundabout to the second roundabout and take the second exit onto Bradley Road. The ground is approx 800 yards on your left with car and coach parking facilities.

**HALL ROAD RANGERS- Haworth Park, Dawson Drive, Hull HU6 7AB. Tel: 07815 629 497**
From Humber Bridge roundabout A164 towards Beverley then turn right A1079 towards Hull. At second roundabout turn right going towards city centre. Go trhough two sets of lights tne turn left onto Emmott Road then left again on to Stanbury Road then left again onto Wadsworth Road/ Dawson Drive. After about 100 yards Haworth Park is on right.

**HALLAM-Sandygate, Sandygate Road, Crosspool, Sheffield, S10 5SE. Tel: (0114) 230 9484**
A57 Sheffield to Glossop Rd, left at Crosspool shopping area signed Lodge Moor on to Sandygate Rd. Ground half mile on left opposite Plough Inn. 51 bus from Crucible Theatre.

**KNARESBOROUGH TOWN-Manse Lane, Manse Lane, Knaresborough, HG5 8LF. Tel: 01423 548896**
From West/South Leeds Area: A658 or A61 towards Harrogate. Join A658 southern bypass towards York. At roundabout with B6164, turn left to Knaresborough. Turn left at second roundabout and travel over river bridge. Manse Lane is first on right alongside garage; From East Leeds Area: A58 or A1 to Wetherby. Join B6164 to Knaresborough then as above. From East on A59 from A1: Turn right at first roundabout. Manse Lane is first turn left after speed restriction sign.

**NOSTELL MINERS WELFARE-The Welfare Ground, Crofton Community Centre, Middle Lane, New Crofton, Wakefield, WF4 1LB. Tel: (01924) 866010**
M1 J39, head towards Wakefield (A638), Denby Dale road. Leave Wakefield on the A638 (Doncaster Rd), towards Wakefield Trinity Ground. Continue on this road for another 2 miles, you will pass the Red Beck Motel on your right. Go under the bridge and turn right opposite the Public house 'Crofton Arms'. Follow road through Crofton village (1 1/4 miles). Turn left at 'Slipper' public house, then right onto Middle Lane, follow road round to reach Crofton Community Centre.

**OLLERTON TOWN - The Lane, Walesby Lane, New Ollerton, Newark NG22 9UT**
From north and south on the A614, take the A6075 from the Ollerton roundabout towards Ollerton Village. At the next roundabout, leave at the first exit and immediately take a left (30m from roundabout) onto Walesby Lane. After approx 600m, just after the school, the ground is on the left.

**PENISTON CHURCH - Church View Road, Penistone, Sheffield S36 6AT. Tel: (01977) 600818**
From North: Leave M1 at J37, take 3rd exit A628 Manchester. After ½ mile take 2nd exit A628 Manchester. After approx 4 mile take 2nd exit A628 Manchester then at traffic lights turn left to Penistone Town Centre. On entering town centre after pelican crossing take 1st left Victoria Street then 2nd left. Ground is on your right. From South: Leave M1 at J35A at roundabout take 2nd exit A616 Manchester. At next roundabout take 2nd exit A616 Manchester then take 1st exit signed Penistone, Huddersfield A629. Follow this road through Wortley, Thurgoland and then take B6462 then travel under 3 railway bridges. Turn sharp left after 3rd bridge and follow road to the right onto Church View Road. Ground is approx 600 yards on left.

**PONTEFRACT COLLIERIES-Skinner Lane, Pontefract, WF8 4QE. Tel: (01977) 600818**
M62 jct32 (Xscape) towards Pontefract. Left at lights after roundabout for park entrance and retail park. Traffic through town should follow racecourse signs through lights to roundabout and back to lights.

**ROSSINGTON MAIN-Welfare Ground, Oxford Street, Rossington, Doncaster, DN11 0TE. Tel: (01302) 865524 (Matchdays only)**
Enter Rossington and go over the railway crossings. Passing the Welfare Club, Oxford Street is the next road on the right. The ground is at the bottom of Oxford Street.

**SELBY TOWN-Richard St, Scott Rd, Selby, YO8 4BN. Tel: (01757) 210900**
From Leeds, left at main traffic lights in Selby down Scott Rd, then 1st left into Richard St. From Doncaster, go straight across main traffic lights into Scott Rd then 1st left. From York, right at main traffic lights into Scott Rd and 1st left.

**SHIREBROOK TOWN-Shirebrook Staff Sports and Social Club, Langwith Road, Shirebrook, Mansfield, Notts, NG20 8TF. Tel: (01623) 742535**
Depart M1 at Junction 29, at roundabout take A617 towards Mansfield (for 3.5 miles), at next roundabout take 2nd Exit B6407 Common Lane towards Shirebrook (or 1.8 miles), go straight on at next roundabout (for 300 yards), at staggered crossroads turn right onto Main Street (for 1.1 miles), at T Junction turn right (for 100 yards), take the first road on your left (Langwith Road). The ground is 400 yards on the right.

**TEVERSAL-Teversal Grange Sports and Social Centre, Carnarvon Street, Teversal, Sutton-in-Ashfield, NG17 3HJ. Tel: (07773) 922539**
From North: Travel South on the M1 to junction 29 take the A6175 to Heath and Holmewood. Travel through Holmewood, and at the roundabout take the B6039 to Hardstaff and Tibshelf. At the T-junction in Tibshelf (pub on your left) turn left onto B6014 travelling over the motorway into Teversal. Follow the road round passing the Carnarvon Arms pub and under a bridge, take 2nd left onto Coppywood Close, travel to the top and following the road round with the ground at the top.
From South: From the M1 junction 28, take the A38 to Mansfield. Travel through a number of sets of traffic lights and after passing the Kings Mill Reservoir you will come to a major junction (King & Miller Pub and McDonalds on your left). Travel straight on taking the A6075 towards Mansfield Woodhouse, at the next set of traffic lights turn left onto the B6014 to Stanton Hill. You will come to a roundabout with a Kwik Save on your left, continue on the B6014 towards Tibshelf. Take the second right onto Coppywood Close, travel to the top and following the road round with the ground at the top.

**WESTELLA & WILLERBY - The Euronics Ground, Marsh Lane, Barton-upon-Humber DN18 5JD Tel: 01652 661 871**
On A15, Barton is last exit before Humber Bridge if coming from south or first exit if coming from north. Follow A1077 into town. Turn right at mini roundabout at bottom of hill into Holydyke. Take second left onto George Street and then into King Street. March Lane is opposite junction of King Street and High Street. The ground is at end of Marsh lane on right immediately after cricket ground.

**WINTERTON RANGERS-West Street, Winterton, Scunthorpe, DN15 9QF. Tel: (01724) 732628**
From Scunthorpe-Take A1077 Barton-on-Humber for 5 miles. On entering Winterton take 3rd right (Eastgate), 3rd left (Northlands Rd) and 1st right (West St). Ground 200 yards on left.

**WORSBOROUGH BRIDGE ATHLETIC-Park Road, Worsbrough Bridge, Barnsley, S70 5LJ. Tel: (01226) 284452**
On the A61, Barnsley-Sheffield road two miles south of Barnsley, 2 miles from M1 J36 opposite Blackburns Bridge.

**YORKSHIRE AMATEUR-Bracken Edge, Roxholme Road, Leeds, LS8 4DZ. Tel: (0113) 262 4093**
From South-M1 to Leeds, then A58 to Wetherby Road to Fforde Green Hotel, left at lights and proceed to Sycamore Avenue (on right). From East-A1 to Boot & Shoe Inn then to Shaftesbury Hotel, turn right into Harehills Lane, then to Sycamore Avenue.

# NORTHERN LEAGUE

**Sponsored by:** Ebac
**Founded:** 1889

**Recent Champions: 2013:** Darlington 1883
**2014:** Spennymoor Town **2015:** Marske United

| DIVISION ONE | P | W | D | L | F | A | GD | Pts |
|---|---|---|---|---|---|---|---|---|
| 1 Shildon | 42 | 31 | 3 | 8 | 135 | 37 | 98 | 96 |
| 2 Marske United | 42 | 26 | 3 | 13 | 86 | 60 | 26 | 81 |
| 3 Guisborough Town | 42 | 22 | 11 | 9 | 95 | 55 | 40 | 77 |
| 4 Morpeth Town | 42 | 24 | 5 | 13 | 89 | 64 | 25 | 77 |
| 5 North Shields | 42 | 21 | 9 | 12 | 77 | 48 | 29 | 72 |
| 6 Newton Aycliffe | 42 | 21 | 9 | 12 | 76 | 61 | 15 | 72 |
| 7 Consett | 42 | 21 | 8 | 13 | 92 | 76 | 16 | 71 |
| 8 Bishop Auckland | 42 | 20 | 7 | 15 | 80 | 79 | 1 | 67 |
| 9 Seaham Red Star | 42 | 18 | 11 | 13 | 90 | 85 | 5 | 65 |
| 10 Washington | 42 | 20 | 5 | 17 | 82 | 85 | -3 | 65 |
| 11 Dunston UTS | 42 | 18 | 8 | 16 | 78 | 64 | 14 | 62 |
| 12 Ashington | 42 | 18 | 6 | 18 | 85 | 76 | 9 | 60 |
| 13 Sunderland RCA | 42 | 15 | 9 | 18 | 73 | 89 | -16 | 54 |
| 14 Penrith | 42 | 14 | 10 | 18 | 67 | 75 | -8 | 52 |
| 15 Jarrow Roofing BCA | 42 | 15 | 6 | 21 | 90 | 102 | -12 | 51 |
| 16 Whitley Bay | 42 | 15 | 5 | 22 | 75 | 70 | 5 | 50 |
| 17 West Auckland Town | 42 | 15 | 5 | 22 | 56 | 84 | -28 | 50 |
| 18 Newcastle Benfield | 42 | 11 | 11 | 20 | 79 | 96 | -17 | 44 |
| 19 West Allotment Celtic | 42 | 11 | 7 | 24 | 50 | 105 | -55 | 40 |
| 20 Durham City | 42 | 9 | 9 | 24 | 59 | 95 | -36 | 36 |
| 21 Norton & Stockton Ancients | 42 | 8 | 8 | 26 | 67 | 120 | -53 | 32 |
| 22 Bedlington Terriers | 42 | 8 | 7 | 27 | 57 | 112 | -55 | 31 |

## CLUB MOVEMENTS

**Division One - In:** Chester-Le-Street (P), Ryhope CW (P), South Shields (P).
**Out:** Bedlington Terriers (R), Durham City (R), Norton & Stockton Ancients (R).

## LEAGUE CUP

**HOLDERS:** SHILDON

**ROUND 1**

| | | | |
|---|---|---|---|
| Chester-Le-Street | v | Northallerton Town | 2-0 |
| Darlington RA | v | Jarrow Roofing BCA | 1-2 |
| South Shields | v | Team Northumbria | 1-0 |
| Sunderland RCA | v | North Shields | 1-1, 4-3p |
| Tow Law Town | v | Whickham | 1-2 aet |
| Washington | v | Penrith | 0-2 |
| West Auckland Town | v | Hebburn Town | 2-1 |
| Bedlington Terriers | v | Alnwick Town | 6-0 |
| Morpeth Town | v | Bishop Auckland | 3-1 |
| Newcastle Benfield | v | Easington Colliery | 1-2 |
| Ryton & Crawcrook Albion | v | Seaham Red Star | 1-2 |
| West Allotment Celtic | v | Billingham Synthonia | 1-3 |

**ROUND 2**

| | | | |
|---|---|---|---|
| Ashington | v | Heaton Stannington | 2-0 |
| Durham City | v | Crook Town | 3-2 aet |
| Marske United | v | Whickham | 6-0 |
| South Shields | v | Chester-Le-Street | 2-1 |
| Thornaby | v | Birtley Town | 3-0 |
| Whitley Bay | v | Ryhope CW | 2-1 |
| Brandon United | v | Billingham Synthonia | 5-1 |
| Esh Winning | v | Billingham Town | 4-3aet |
| Guisborough Town | v | Jarrow Roofing BCA | 5-3 |
| Morpeth Town | v | Consett | 3-2 |
| Norton & Stockton Ancients | v | Dunston UTS | 0-1 |
| Shildon | v | Stokesley Sports Club | 11-0 |
| Willington | v | North Shields | 1-2 aet |
| Easington Colliery | v | Seaham Red Star | 0-2 |

Abandonded after 23 mins due to a waterlogged pitch

| | | | |
|---|---|---|---|
| Easington Colliery | v | Seaham Red Star | 3-1 |
| Penrith | v | Newton Aycliffe | 4-2 |
| Bedlington Terriers | v | West Auckland Town | 3-1 |

**ROUND 3**

| | | | |
|---|---|---|---|
| Durham City | v | Shildon | 0-3 |
| Marske United | v | Penrith | 2-0 |
| Thornaby | v | Esh Winning | 0-2 |
| Brandon United | v | Bedlington Terriers | 2-3 |
| Morpeth Town | v | Easington Colliery | 3-3, 4-5p |
| Guisborough Town | v | Ashington | 4-1 |
| Whitley Bay | v | Dunston UTS | 5-1 |
| South Shields | v | North Shields | 0-3 |

| | DIVISION ONE | 1 | 2 | 3 | 4 | 5 | 6 | 7 | 8 | 9 | 10 | 11 | 12 | 13 | 14 | 15 | 16 | 17 | 18 | 19 | 20 | 21 | 22 |
|---|---|---|---|---|---|---|---|---|---|---|---|---|---|---|---|---|---|---|---|---|---|---|---|
| 1 | Ashington | | 4-0 | 2-2 | 1-2 | 1-3 | 2-0 | 3-4 | 3-1 | 1-2 | 1-3 | 1-3 | 10-1 | 0-1 | 1-1 | 1-3 | 1-4 | 1-4 | 3-1 | 1-2 | 4-1 | 4-2 | 4- |
| 2 | Bedlington Terriers | 2-0 | | 2-2 | 2-4 | 0-8 | 2-1 | 1-3 | 1-2 | 4-4 | 1-2 | 2-2 | 1-3 | 0-3 | 5-3 | 2-3 | 1-3 | 1-6 | 2-2 | 0-2 | 1-3 | 0-1 | 2-1 |
| 3 | Bishop Auckland | 1-0 | 4-0 | | 6-2 | 2-1 | 1-1 | 3-2 | 4-2 | 0-2 | 3-2 | 2-1 | 0-2 | 1-0 | 3-0 | 3-0 | 2-1 | 0-4 | 4-1 | 2-0 | 2-2 | 3-1 | 1- |
| 4 | Consett | 0-5 | 2-0 | 5-1 | | 0-3 | 4-3 | 1-2 | 0-0 | 2-2 | 2-5 | 6-3 | 4-2 | 3-2 | 5-2 | 2-2 | 1-1 | 3-1 | 5-1 | 8-5 | 1-1 | 3-1 | 4- |
| 5 | Dunston UTS | 0-0 | 3-0 | 2-1 | 3-1 | | 2-0 | 1-1 | 0-1 | 3-0 | 1-4 | 4-2 | 1-1 | 0-0 | 4-1 | 2-3 | 3-1 | 0-1 | 4-0 | 0-1 | 0-2 | 3-1 | 1- |
| 6 | Durham City | 2-3 | 0-1 | 1-2 | 0-3 | 0-3 | | 1-0 | 5-1 | 1-2 | 0-4 | 3-3 | 0-5 | 1-1 | 5-5 | 4-1 | 3-4 | 1-3 | 1-0 | 3-2 | 4-1 | 0-2 | 2- |
| 7 | Guisborough Town | 2-0 | 5-2 | 0-2 | 2-1 | 1-1 | 6-0 | | 3-0 | 3-1 | 4-1 | 2-2 | 6-2 | 2-1 | 2-1 | 1-1 | 1-1 | 1-1 | 2-2 | 0-3 | 7-1 | 2-0 | 1- |
| 8 | Jarrow Roofing BCA | 0-3 | 1-2 | 2-2 | 3-2 | 5-2 | 5-1 | 3-4 | | 1-3 | 2-3 | 1-3 | 6-2 | 1-1 | 6-4 | 0-0 | 5-3 | 1-3 | 2-2 | 0-3 | 6-0 | 4-3 | 0- |
| 9 | Marske United | 1-2 | 3-0 | 4-3 | 2-1 | 1-1 | 0-3 | 0-2 | 2-1 | | 0-2 | 2-1 | 1-2 | 2-1 | 3-1 | 1-0 | 3-0 | 2-0 | 3-0 | 2-1 | 3-0 | 0-2 | 2- |
| 10 | Morpeth Town | 2-3 | 2-1 | 3-0 | 0-2 | 3-0 | 2-1 | 2-0 | 3-1 | 2-0 | | 2-1 | 0-2 | 0-2 | 6-0 | 4-2 | 2-2 | 0-4 | 0-0 | 3-0 | 3-1 | 1-3 | 3- |
| 11 | Newcastle Benfield | 0-3 | 1-1 | 1-3 | 1-1 | 4-1 | 0-0 | 1-1 | 3-4 | 1-4 | 2-2 | | 2-1 | 2-4 | 3-1 | 0-3 | 2-1 | 0-5 | 6-1 | 2-3 | 1-2 | 4-2 | 1- |
| 12 | Newton Aycliffe | 1-2 | 3-2 | 2-2 | 0-0 | 4-0 | 1-0 | 2-0 | 0-4 | 2-1 | 5-0 | 3-1 | | 0-1 | 4-1 | 1-1 | 1-2 | 3-0 | 1-1 | 2-2 | 0-0 | 0-0 | 1- |
| 13 | North Shields | 3-1 | 1-1 | 1-1 | 0-0 | 2-1 | 3-0 | 1-0 | 5-0 | 2-1 | 2-1 | 6-0 | 1-1 | | 2-2 | 5-1 | 2-2 | 1-0 | 1-2 | 2-3 | 1-2 | 2-0 | 1- |
| 14 | Norton & Stockton Ancients | 1-3 | 2-4 | 5-1 | 3-0 | 0-5 | 0-2 | 3-1 | 2-2 | 2-5 | 0-1 | 0-0 | 0-2 | 3-5 | | 3-0 | 2-0 | 1-4 | 3-2 | 3-3 | 0-1 | 1-2 | 4- |
| 15 | Penrith | 0-0 | 3-3 | 3-0 | 0-1 | 3-0 | 2-2 | 1-3 | 3-1 | 2-3 | 2-2 | 3-2 | 4-3 | 1-3 | 3-0 | | 1-1 | 0-3 | 0-2 | 3-2 | 1-0 | 2-3 | 0- |
| 16 | Seaham Red Star | 1-1 | 4-1 | 3-1 | 3-0 | 1-3 | 3-3 | 2-3 | 5-1 | 1-7 | 5-3 | 0-4 | 1-0 | 3-1 | 4-4 | 2-1 | | 2-2 | 6-4 | 2-2 | 2-2 | 3-1 | 2- |
| 17 | Shildon | 8-1 | 2-0 | 3-2 | 1-2 | 5-0 | 3-0 | 1-0 | 5-0 | 5-0 | 0-1 | 4-0 | 1-2 | 2-0 | 8-0 | 3-1 | 3-0 | | 3-0 | 7-1 | 5-0 | 4-0 | 2- |
| 18 | Sunderland RCA | 2-2 | 4-1 | 3-1 | 0-2 | 4-1 | 2-2 | 0-4 | 2-4 | 1-0 | 2-0 | 2-2 | 1-2 | 0-1 | 3-1 | 3-2 | 2-0 | 4-6 | | 4-2 | 0-0 | 1-2 | 2- |
| 19 | Washington | 3-1 | 3-0 | 1-4 | 1-0 | 2-1 | 2-1 | 0-0 | 4-2 | 2-3 | 2-2 | 3-5 | 2-0 | 2-4 | 3-0 | 3-1 | 1-3 | 4-2 | 1-2 | | 2-1 | 0-3 | 1- |
| 20 | West Allotment Celtic | 1-3 | 0-3 | 2-0 | 1-3 | 2-2 | 2-0 | 2-4 | 0-5 | 0-3 | 2-1 | 2-6 | 0-4 | 2-0 | 3-0 | 0-4 | 1-2 | 0-5 | 3-5 | 0-2 | | 1-3 | 3- |
| 21 | West Auckland Town | 2-1 | 4-2 | 0-3 | 2-1 | 0-0 | 1-2 | 2-7 | 0-2 | 1-4 | 0-2 | 1-1 | 0-2 | 0-2 | 1-1 | 0-1 | 1-2 | 0-4 | 2-1 | 2-1 | 2-2 | | 3- |
| 22 | Whitley Bay | 1-2 | 3-1 | 7-0 | 0-3 | 3-5 | 4-0 | 1-1 | 4-2 | 1-2 | 3-5 | 2-0 | 0-1 | 2-0 | 0-1 | 0-0 | 0-2 | 2-2 | 1-2 | 4-0 | 3-1 | 3-0 | |

| | DIVISION TWO | P | W | D | L | F | A | GD | Pts |
|---|---|---|---|---|---|---|---|---|---|
| 1 | South Shields | 42 | 35 | 2 | 5 | 122 | 31 | 91 | 107 |
| 2 | Ryhope CW | 42 | 30 | 4 | 8 | 121 | 65 | 56 | 94 |
| 3 | Chester-Le-Street | 42 | 28 | 6 | 8 | 106 | 44 | 62 | 90 |
| 4 | Team Northumbria | 42 | 26 | 11 | 5 | 101 | 41 | 60 | 89 |
| 5 | Billingham Synthonia | 42 | 25 | 8 | 9 | 81 | 37 | 44 | 83 |
| 6 | Easington Colliery | 42 | 22 | 10 | 10 | 106 | 59 | 47 | 76 |
| 7 | Thornaby | 42 | 23 | 6 | 13 | 93 | 65 | 28 | 75 |
| 8 | Northallerton Town | 42 | 21 | 10 | 11 | 81 | 48 | 33 | 73 |
| 9 | Heaton Stannington | 42 | 21 | 8 | 13 | 92 | 59 | 33 | 71 |
| 10 | Hebburn Town | 42 | 17 | 10 | 15 | 78 | 54 | 24 | 61 |
| 11 | Billingham Town | 42 | 18 | 7 | 17 | 80 | 67 | 13 | 61 |
| 12 | Whickham | 42 | 17 | 8 | 17 | 57 | 68 | -11 | 59 |
| 13 | Darlington RA | 42 | 18 | 4 | 20 | 86 | 89 | -3 | 58 |
| 14 | Tow Law Town | 42 | 14 | 11 | 17 | 75 | 82 | -7 | 53 |
| 15 | Brandon United | 42 | 14 | 4 | 24 | 77 | 98 | -21 | 46 |
| 16 | Ryton & Crawcrook Albion | 42 | 11 | 11 | 20 | 58 | 79 | -21 | 44 |
| 17 | Alnwick Town | 42 | 12 | 6 | 24 | 66 | 113 | -47 | 42 |
| 18 | Crook Town | 42 | 10 | 5 | 27 | 53 | 99 | -46 | 35 |
| 19 | Willington | 42 | 9 | 5 | 28 | 45 | 98 | -53 | 32 |
| 20 | Esh Winning | 42 | 7 | 6 | 29 | 46 | 127 | -81 | 27 |
| 21 | Birtley Town | 42 | 5 | 6 | 31 | 50 | 117 | -67 | 21 |
| 22 | Stokesley Sports Club | 42 | 4 | 2 | 36 | 33 | 167 | -134 | 14 |

### CLUB MOVEMENTS - Division Two

**In:** Bedlington Terriers (R), Blyth Town (P - Northern Alliance), Durham City (R), Norton & Stockton Ancients (R), Stockton Town (P - Wearside). **Out:** Birtley Town (R - Northern Alliance), Chester-Le-Street (P), Ryhope CW (P), South Shields (P), Stokesley Sports Club (R - Wearside).

### J.R. CLEATOR CUP
### (2015 League champions v League Cup winners)

| | | | |
|---|---|---|---|
| Marske United | v | Shildon | 0-2 |

**QUARTER FINALS**

| | | | |
|---|---|---|---|
| Esh Winning | v | Whitley Bay | 1-8 |
| Guisborough Town | v | Shildon | 3-2 |
| Marske United | v | Easington Colliery | 5-0 |
| Bedlington Terriers | v | North Shields | 0-3 |

**SEIM FINALS**

| | | | |
|---|---|---|---|
| Marske United | v | Whitley Bay | 3-1 |
| North Shields | v | Shildon | 2-2, 2-4p |

**FINAL**

| | | | |
|---|---|---|---|
| Marske United | v | Shildon | 1-1, 2-3p |

### ERNSET ARMSTRONG MEMORIAL CUP

**HOLDERS:** NORTON & STOCKTON ANCIENTS

**ROUND 1**

| | | | |
|---|---|---|---|
| Team Northumbria | v | Willington | 3-2 aet |
| Ryhope CW | v | Esh Winning | 4-1 |
| Birtley Town | v | Darlington RA | 0-2 |
| Brandon United | v | Ryton & Crawcrook Albion | 6-2 |
| Crook Town | v | Thornaby | 3-2 aet |
| Easington Colliery | v | Chester-Le-Street | 0-1 |

**ROUND 2**

| | | | |
|---|---|---|---|
| Chester-Le-Street | v | Alnwick Town | 6-1 |
| Ryhope CW | v | Crook Town | 4-2 aet |
| Billingham Synthonia | v | Stokesley Sports Club | 5-4 |
| Brandon United | v | Tow Law Town | 5-3 |
| Northallerton Town | v | Darlington RA | 1-1, 4-3p |
| Heaton Stannington | v | Whickham | 0-1 |
| Billingham Town | v | Team Northumbria | 1-0 |
| South Shields | v | Hebburn Town | 5-2 |

**QUARTER FINALS**

| | | | |
|---|---|---|---|
| Chester-Le-Street | v | Northallerton Town | 1-3 |
| Whickham | v | Ryhope CW | 0-1 |
| Billingham Synthonia | v | South Shields | 2-1 |
| Brandon United | v | Billingham Town | 1-0 |

**SEMI FINALS**

| | | | |
|---|---|---|---|
| Northallerton Town | v | Brandon United | 6-3 aet |
| Ryhope CW | v | Billingham Synthonia | 2-0 |

**FINAL**

| | | | |
|---|---|---|---|
| Northallerton Town | v | Ryhope CW | 2-0 |

| | DIVISION TWO | 1 | 2 | 3 | 4 | 5 | 6 | 7 | 8 | 9 | 10 | 11 | 12 | 13 | 14 | 15 | 16 | 17 | 18 | 19 | 20 | 21 | 22 |
|---|---|---|---|---|---|---|---|---|---|---|---|---|---|---|---|---|---|---|---|---|---|---|---|
| 1 | Alnwick Town | | 2-4 | 0-5 | 3-3 | 3-2 | 0-2 | 2-1 | 6-4 | 1-5 | 4-1 | 0-4 | 1-0 | 0-0 | 3-4 | 0-2 | 2-2 | 5-1 | 2-4 | 0-2 | 3-0 | 1-4 | 0-5 |
| 2 | Billingham Synthonia | 2-0 | | 2-2 | 5-0 | 1-2 | 0-0 | 3-2 | 0-1 | 2-0 | 2-0 | 1-1 | 2-0 | 2-2 | 2-2 | 2-0 | 1-0 | 7-0 | 0-2 | 0-0 | 2-0 | 2-0 | 3-0 |
| 3 | Billingham Town | 0-3 | 2-4 | | 1-0 | 4-2 | 1-3 | 4-1 | 1-4 | 1-1 | 1-1 | 2-4 | 1-1 | 0-2 | 1-1 | 1-0 | 1-3 | 3-1 | 1-2 | 2-1 | 5-2 | 1-0 | 7-1 |
| 4 | Birtley Town | 3-3 | 0-1 | 1-1 | | 3-1 | 3-4 | 0-2 | 0-4 | 2-2 | 3-1 | 1-6 | 0-0 | 1-2 | 1-2 | 1-2 | 1-3 | 9-0 | 0-9 | 0-4 | 0-2 | 0-1 | 2-4 |
| 5 | Brandon United | 6-0 | 2-1 | 0-3 | 3-2 | | 3-4 | 1-0 | 4-3 | 0-3 | 2-1 | 1-7 | 3-4 | 0-2 | 1-2 | 0-2 | 0-4 | 4-1 | 1-1 | 4-1 | 0-2 | 0-0 | 2-0 |
| 6 | Chester-Le-Street | 8-0 | 1-0 | 2-1 | 1-0 | 2-1 | | 5-1 | 2-0 | 3-2 | 7-0 | 2-1 | 1-2 | 6-2 | 2-2 | 6-0 | 0-3 | 5-1 | 0-0 | 6-0 | 1-2 | 1-0 | 3-0 |
| 7 | Crook Town | 1-2 | 0-1 | 2-3 | 5-1 | 0-4 | 1-4 | | 0-2 | 1-2 | 2-3 | 2-1 | 0-1 | 0-7 | 1-4 | 1-1 | 0-4 | 3-0 | 0-0 | 0-2 | 3-0 | 3-1 | 2-0 |
| 8 | Darlington RA | 2-0 | 1-3 | 0-2 | 4-1 | 2-4 | 2-1 | 1-0 | | 0-2 | 5-1 | 2-4 | 3-0 | 0-2 | 1-4 | 2-2 | 1-3 | 4-0 | 0-4 | 0-1 | 3-1 | 2-2 | 1-1 |
| 9 | Easington Colliery | 2-2 | 1-2 | 3-1 | 4-1 | 3-1 | 0-2 | 2-3 | 6-4 | | 3-0 | 1-1 | 5-1 | 0-0 | 4-0 | 2-2 | 0-1 | 4-1 | 2-2 | 3-2 | 7-0 | 0-2 | 4-3 |
| 10 | Esh Winning | 2-1 | 1-4 | 0-3 | 1-2 | 1-1 | 2-2 | 3-3 | 3-5 | 2-1 | | 0-3 | 1-5 | 1-1 | 1-6 | 1-3 | 0-4 | 2-1 | 0-4 | 0-1 | 2-5 | 2-3 | 2-4 |
| 11 | Heaton Stannington | 3-1 | 0-3 | 0-2 | 2-1 | 1-0 | 0-4 | 2-0 | 5-3 | 3-2 | 6-0 | | 2-2 | 0-0 | 1-2 | 4-0 | 3-2 | 3-1 | 2-3 | 1-1 | 1-1 | 3-2 | 2-0 |
| 12 | Hebburn Town | 3-0 | 1-3 | 1-1 | 3-0 | 1-2 | 1-2 | 4-0 | 2-0 | 0-0 | 3-0 | 0-1 | | 0-4 | 1-0 | 2-0 | 0-1 | 8-0 | 3-3 | 0-1 | 1-1 | 7-0 | 2-0 |
| 13 | Northallerton Town | 3-0 | 0-3 | 6-2 | 2-0 | 4-2 | 2-1 | 2-4 | 4-0 | 2-0 | 4-0 | 2-2 | 1-0 | | 0-1 | 0-1 | 0-1 | 8-2 | 1-3 | 1-2 | 3-0 | 2-2 | 2-1 |
| 14 | Ryhope CW | 7-1 | 2-1 | 3-0 | 3-2 | 3-2 | 2-3 | 5-1 | 3-2 | 2-4 | 5-1 | 3-1 | 3-0 | 3-0 | | 2-2 | 3-2 | 4-3 | 1-0 | 4-6 | 3-1 | 4-1 | 3-1 |
| 15 | Ryton & Crawcrook Albion | 1-2 | 1-1 | 0-3 | 4-0 | 4-4 | 0-1 | 1-1 | 1-3 | 1-7 | 1-1 | 3-1 | 0-3 | 0-1 | 1-5 | | 0-4 | 2-0 | 1-1 | 0-1 | 0-2 | 4-1 | 5-1 |
| 16 | South Shields | 4-1 | 3-0 | 3-2 | 2-0 | 3-1 | 2-0 | 5-0 | 6-0 | 1-2 | 4-2 | 2-1 | 2-0 | 2-3 | 2-0 | 4-0 | | 1-1 | 2-0 | 4-3 | 9-1 | 5-0 | 5-1 |
| 17 | Stokesley Sports Club | 0-6 | 0-4 | 0-6 | 3-0 | 2-1 | 0-3 | 1-1 | 0-3 | 2-4 | 0-3 | 0-5 | 2-4 | 2-0 | 0-6 | 0-6 | 0-3 | | 0-4 | 2-4 | 0-4 | 0-2 | 2-1 |
| 18 | Team Northumbria | 4-1 | 2-1 | 2-0 | 5-0 | 4-1 | 3-1 | 2-1 | 1-4 | 0-0 | 1-0 | 1-0 | 3-2 | 2-0 | 4-1 | 2-2 | 0-2 | 4-0 | | 1-1 | 1-0 | 1-0 | 6-0 |
| 19 | Thornaby | 1-0 | 1-1 | 2-1 | 6-1 | 5-6 | 1-3 | 3-1 | 3-4 | 2-3 | 9-0 | 1-0 | 2-2 | 1-3 | 2-1 | 2-1 | 0-1 | 9-1 | 1-1 | | 2-1 | 2-1 | 1-0 |
| 20 | Tow Law Town | 3-1 | 3-1 | 2-1 | 1-1 | 3-2 | 1-1 | 6-0 | 1-2 | 3-3 | 1-2 | 2-2 | 1-1 | 1-1 | 1-3 | 1-1 | 0-3 | 8-1 | 4-1 | 3-2 | | 2-3 | 0-0 |
| 21 | Whickham | 1-1 | 0-1 | 1-0 | 2-3 | 4-0 | 1-0 | 3-0 | 1-1 | 0-4 | 2-1 | 3-0 | 2-2 | 0-0 | 0-4 | 1-0 | 0-1 | 3-2 | 2-2 | 2-1 | 2-1 | | 2-1 |
| 22 | Willington | 2-3 | 0-1 | 0-1 | 3-1 | 2-1 | 1-1 | 1-4 | 2-1 | 0-3 | 0-1 | 0-3 | 0-5 | 0-0 | 2-3 | 2-1 | 1-4 | 1-0 | 1-6 | 0-1 | 2-2 | 1-0 | |

## ASHINGTON

Founded: 1883 Nickname: The Colliers

**Secretary:** Gavin Perry **(T)** 07870 737410 **(E)** gav@gavperry.co.uk
**Chairman:** Ian Lavery **Manager:** Steve Harmison - 08/02/15 **Prog Ed:** Ian Jobson
**Ground:** Woodhorn Lane, Ashington NE63 9FW **(T)** 01670 811 991
**Capacity:** **Seats:** **Covered:** **Midweek Matchday:** Tuesday **Clubhouse:** Yes **Shop:** Yes

**Colours(change):** Black & White stripes/black/black.
**Previous Names:** None
**Previous Leagues:** Northern Alliance, Football League, N. Eastern, Midland, Northern Counties, Wearside, N.P.L.
**Records:** **Att:** 13,199 v Rochdale FA Cup 2nd round 1950
**Honours:** Northern League Div.2 Champions 2000-01, 03-04.

**10 YEAR RECORD**

| 06-07 | 07-08 | 08-09 | 09-10 | 10-11 | 11-12 | 12-13 | 13-14 | 14-15 | 15-16 |
|---|---|---|---|---|---|---|---|---|---|
| NL 1 19 | NL 1 17 | NL 1 16 | NL 1 6 | NL 1 8 | NL 1 5 | NL 1 7 | NL 1 6 | NL 1 13 | NL 1 12 |

## BISHOP AUCKLAND

Founded: 1886 Nickname:

**Secretary:** David Strong **(T)** 07768763871 **(E)** david.strong@bishopafc.com
**Chairman:** Nick Postma **Prog Ed:** Nick Postma
**Ground:** Heritage Park, Bishop Auckland, Co. Durham DL14 9AE **(T)** 01388 604 605
**Capacity:** 2,004 **Seats:** 250 **Covered:** 722 **Midweek Matchday:** Tuesday **Clubhouse:** Yes **Shop:** No

**Colours(change):** Light & dark blue/blue/blue
**Previous Names:** Auckland Town 1889-1893
**Previous Leagues:** Northern Alliance 1890-91, Northern League 1893-1988, Northern Premier 1988-2006
**Records:** **Att:** 17,000 v Coventry City FA Cup 2nd round 1952 **App:** Bob Hardisty
**Honours:** (Post War) Northern League 1949-50, 50-51, 51-52, 53-54, 54-55, 55-56, 66-67, 84-85, 85-86 (18th Nth Lge title).
Durham Challenge Cup 2012-13.

**10 YEAR RECORD**

| 06-07 | 07-08 | 08-09 | 09-10 | 10-11 | 11-12 | 12-13 | 13-14 | 14-15 | 15-16 |
|---|---|---|---|---|---|---|---|---|---|
| NL 1 16 | NL 1 20 | NL 1 18 | NL 1 13 | NL 1 14 | NL 1 8 | NL 1 6 | NL 1 8 | NL 1 11 | NL 1 8 |

## CHESTER-LE-STREET TOWN

Founded: 1972 Nickname: Cestrians

**Secretary:** Lenny Lauchlan **(T)** 07807 419 872 **(E)** l.w.lauchlan@durham.ac.uk
**Chairman:** Joe Burlison **Prog Ed:** Keith Greener
**Ground:** Moor Park, Chester Moor, Chester-le-Street, Co.Durham DH2 3RW **(T)** 0191 388 7283
**Capacity:** **Seats:** **Covered:** **Midweek Matchday:** **Clubhouse:**

**Colours(change):** Blue & white hoops/white/white with blue trim
**Previous Names:**
**Previous Leagues:**
**Records:** **Previous Name:** Garden Farm 1972-78. **Previous League:** Wearside 1977-83.
**Honours:** **Record Att:** 893 v Fleetwood FA Vase 1985 **App:** Colin Wake 361.
**Honours:** Washington League 1975-6 Wearside League1980-81, Northern League Div 2 1983-84, 97-98.

**10 YEAR RECORD**

| 06-07 | 07-08 | 08-09 | 09-10 | 10-11 | 11-12 | 12-13 | 13-14 | 14-15 | 15-16 |
|---|---|---|---|---|---|---|---|---|---|
| | | | | | | | | | NL 2 3 |

## CONSETT

Founded: 1899 Nickname: Steelman

**Secretary:** David Pyke **(T)** 07889 419 268 **(E)** david_pyke@hotmail.co.uk
**Chairman:** Frank Bell **Prog Ed:** Gary Welford
**Ground:** Belle Vue Park, Ashdale Road, Consett, DH8 7BF **(T)** 01207 588 886
**Capacity:** 4,000 **Seats:** 400 **Covered:** 1000 **Midweek Matchday:** Tuesday **Clubhouse:** Yes **Shop:** No

**Colours(change):** All Red
**Previous Names:** None
**Previous Leagues:** N.All 1919-26, 35-37, N.E.C. 26-35, 37-58, 62-64, Midland 58-60, N.Co. 60-62, Wearside 64-70
**Records:** **Att:** 7000 v Sunderland Reserves, first match at Belle Vue 1950
**Honours:** Norh Eastern Lg 39-40 Div 2 26-27, Northern Counties Lg 61-62, Northern Leageu Div.2 1988-89, 05-06.

**10 YEAR RECORD**

| 06-07 | 07-08 | 08-09 | 09-10 | 10-11 | 11-12 | 12-13 | 13-14 | 14-15 | 15-16 |
|---|---|---|---|---|---|---|---|---|---|
| NL 1 4 | NL 1 2 | NL 1 2 | NL 1 10 | NL 1 2 | NL 1 15 | NL 1 9 | NL 1 11 | NL 1 9 | NL 1 7 |

## DUNSTON UTS
Founded: 1975 Nickname: The Fed

**Secretary:** Bill Montague **(T)** 07981 194 756 **(E)** w.montague@sky.com
**Chairman:** Malcolm James **Prog Ed:** Bill Montague
**Ground:** UTS Stadium, Wellington Rd, Dunston, Gateshead NE11 9JL **(T)** 0191 493 2935
**Capacity:** 2,000 **Seats:** 120 **Covered:** 400 **Midweek Matchday:** Wednesday **Clubhouse:** Yes **Shop:** No

**Colours(change):** All blue
**Previous Names:** Dunston Federation Brewery > 2007. Dunston Federation > 2009.
**Previous Leagues:** Northern Amateur & Wearside league
**Records:** **Att:** 1,550 v Sunderland Shipowners Cup Final 01.04.88 **Goalscorer:** Paul King **App:** Paul Dixon
**Honours:** Wearside League 1988-89, 89-90. Northern League Div.2 92-93. Div.1 2003-04, 04-05. FA Vase 2011-12.

**10 YEAR RECORD**

| 06-07 | 07-08 | 08-09 | 09-10 | 10-11 | 11-12 | 12-13 | 13-14 | 14-15 | 15-16 |
|---|---|---|---|---|---|---|---|---|---|
| NL 1 7 | NL 1 6 | NL 1 6 | NL 1 4 | NL 1 7 | NL 1 3 | NL 1 5 | NL 1 7 | NL 1 6 | NL 1 11 |

## GUISBOROUGH TOWN
Founded: 1973 Nickname: Priorymen

**Secretary:** Keith Smeltzer **(T)** 07811 850 388 **(E)** keithsmeltzer88@gmail.com
**Chairman:** Don Cowan **Prog Ed:** Danny Clark
**Ground:** King George V Ground, Howlbeck Road, Guisborough TS14 6LE **(T)** 01287 636 925
**Capacity:** **Seats:** Yes **Covered:** Yes **Midweek Matchday:** Wednesday **Clubhouse:** Yes

**Colours(change):** Red & white stripes/black/red
**Previous Names:** None
**Previous Leagues:** Northern Counties East 1982-85.
**Records:** **Att:** 3,112 v Hungerford FA Vase Semi-final. **Goalscorer:** Mark Davis 341. **Apps:** Mark Davis 587.
**Honours:** Northern Alliance 1979-80. Northern League Cup 1987-88. Nth Riding Sen Cup 1989-90, 90-91, 91-92, 92-93, 94-95

**10 YEAR RECORD**

| 06-07 | 07-08 | 08-09 | 09-10 | 10-11 | 11-12 | 12-13 | 13-14 | 14-15 | 15-16 |
|---|---|---|---|---|---|---|---|---|---|
| NL 2 9 | NL 2 12 | NL 2 7 | NL 2 5 | NL 2 2 | NL 1 16 | NL 1 11 | NL 1 4 | NL 1 3 | NL 1 3 |

## JARROW ROOFING BOLDON C.A.
Founded: 1987 Nickname: Roofing

**Secretary:** David Ramsey **(T)** 07791 707 363 **(E)** secretary@jarrowroofingfc.co.uk
**Chairman:** Richard McLoughlin **Prog Ed:** James Petherick
**Ground:** Boldon CA Sports Ground, New Road, Boldon Colliery NE35 9AL **(T)** 07714 525 549
**Capacity:** 3,500 **Seats:** 150 **Covered:** 800 **Midweek Matchday:** Tuesday **Clubhouse:** Yes

**Colours(change):** Blue and yellow/blue/blue
**Previous Names:**
**Previous Leagues:** S. Tyneside Senior 1987-88, Tyneside Am. 1988-91, Wearside 1991-96
**Records:** **Att:** 500 v South Shields **Goalscorer:** Mick Hales **App:** Paul Chow
**Honours:**

**10 YEAR RECORD**

| 06-07 | 07-08 | 08-09 | 09-10 | 10-11 | 11-12 | 12-13 | 13-14 | 14-15 | 15-16 |
|---|---|---|---|---|---|---|---|---|---|
| NL 1 15 | NL 1 22 | NL 2 16 | NL 2 3 | NL 1 19 | NL 1 20 | NL 2 4 | NL 2 3 | NL 1 7 | NL 1 15 |

## MARSKE UNITED
Founded: 1956 Nickname: The Seasiders

**Secretary:** Mark Hathaway **(T)** 07772 686 794 **(E)** admin@marskeunitedfc.com
**Chairman:** Peter Collinson **Prog Ed:** Martin Jobling
**Ground:** GER Stad., Mount Pleasant Avenue, Marske by the Sea, Redcar TS11 7BW **(T)** 07772 686 794
**Capacity:** **Seats:** Yes **Covered:** Yes **Midweek Matchday:** Tuesday **Clubhouse:** Yes

**Colours(change):** All blue
**Previous Names:** None
**Previous Leagues:** Wearside 1985-97.
**Records:** **Defeat:** 3-9. **Goalscorer:** Chris Morgan 169. **Apps:** Mike Kinnair 583.
**Honours:** Teesside League 1980-81, 84-85. Wearside League 1995-96. North Riding Senior Cup 1994-95.
North Riding County Cup 1980-81, 85-86. Northern League Division One 2014-15.

**10 YEAR RECORD**

| 06-07 | 07-08 | 08-09 | 09-10 | 10-11 | 11-12 | 12-13 | 13-14 | 14-15 | 15-16 |
|---|---|---|---|---|---|---|---|---|---|
| NL 2 5 | NL 2 8 | NL 2 5 | NL 2 4 | NL 2 3 | NL 1 18 | NL 1 19 | NL 1 16 | NL 1 1 | NL 1 2 |

## MORPETH TOWN

Founded: 1909 Nickname: Highwaymen

**Secretary:** David McMeekan **(T)** 07425 135 301 **(E)** drmcmeekan@yahoo.co.uk

**Chairman:** Ken Beattie **Prog Ed:** David McMeekan

**Ground:** Craik Park, Morpeth Common, Morpeth, Northumberland, NE61 2YX **(T)** 07425 135 301

**Capacity:** **Seats:** Yes **Covered:** Yes **Midweek Matchday:** Wednesday **Clubhouse:** Yes

**Colours(change):** Amber & black/black/amber & black

**Previous Names:** None

**Previous Leagues:** Northern Alliance > 1994.

**Records:**

**Honours:** Northern Alliance 1983-84, 93-94, Northern League Division 2 1995-96. Northumberland Senior Cup 2006-07.

**10 YEAR RECORD**

| 06-07 | | 07-08 | | 08-09 | | 09-10 | | 10-11 | | 11-12 | | 12-13 | | 13-14 | | 14-15 | | 15-16 | |
|---|---|---|---|---|---|---|---|---|---|---|---|---|---|---|---|---|---|---|---|
| NL 1 | 10 | NL 1 | 8 | NL 1 | 12 | NL 1 | 21 | NL 2 | 20 | NL 2 | 4 | NL 2 | 3 | NL 1 | 17 | NL 1 | 8 | NL 1 | 4 |

## NEWCASTLE BENFIELD

Founded: 1988 Nickname: The Lions

**Secretary:** Gary Thompson **(T)** 07525 275 641 **(E)** gctwnphg@gmail.com

**Chairman:** James Rowe **Prog Ed:** Ian Cusack

**Ground:** Sam Smiths Park, Benfield Road, Walkergate NE6 4NU **(T)** 07525 275 641

**Capacity:** 2,000 **Seats:** 150 **Covered:** 250 **Midweek Matchday:** Wednesday **Clubhouse:** Yes **Shop:** No

**Colours(change):** Blue & white/blue/blue

**Previous Names:** Heaton Corner House. Newcastle Benfield Saints.

**Previous Leagues:** Northern Alliance 1988-2003

**Records:**

**Honours:** Northern Alliance Div 2 Champions 1989-90, Div 1 1994-95, 2002-03.
Northern League Cup 2006-07. Northern League Champions 2008-09.

**10 YEAR RECORD**

| 06-07 | | 07-08 | | 08-09 | | 09-10 | | 10-11 | | 11-12 | | 12-13 | | 13-14 | | 14-15 | | 15-16 | |
|---|---|---|---|---|---|---|---|---|---|---|---|---|---|---|---|---|---|---|---|
| NL 1 | 5 | NL 1 | 4 | NL 1 | 1 | NL 1 | 5 | NL 1 | 4 | NL 1 | 12 | NL 1 | 21 | NL 1 | 14 | NL 1 | 10 | NL 1 | 18 |

## NEWTON AYCLIFFE

Founded: 1965 Nickname: Aycliffe

**Secretary:** Stephen Cunliffe **(T)** 07872 985 501 **(E)** stecunliffe@aol.com

**Chairman:** Alan Oliver **Prog Ed:** Stephen Cunliffe

**Ground:** Moore Lane Park, Moore Lane, Newton Aycliffe, Co. Durham DL5 5AG **(T)** 01325 312 768

**Capacity:** **Seats:** Yes **Covered:** Yes **Midweek Matchday:** Wednesday **Clubhouse:** Yes

**Colours(change):** All blue

**Previous Names:** None

**Previous Leagues:** Wearside 1984-94, 2008-09. Durham Alliance > 2008.

**Records:** **Att:** 520 v Teesside Athletic (Sunderland Shipwoners Final) 2008-09.

**Honours:** Darlington & District Division 'A' 2004-05. Durham Alliance League 2007-08. Wearside League 2008-09.
Northern League Division Two 2010-11. Durham County Challenge Cup 2015-16.

**10 YEAR RECORD**

| 06-07 | | 07-08 | | 08-09 | | 09-10 | | 10-11 | | 11-12 | | 12-13 | | 13-14 | | 14-15 | | 15-16 | |
|---|---|---|---|---|---|---|---|---|---|---|---|---|---|---|---|---|---|---|---|
| | | DuAl | 1 | Wear | 1 | NL 2 | 9 | NL 2 | 1 | NL 1 | 9 | NL 1 | 17 | NL 1 | 18 | NL 1 | 18 | NL 1 | 6 |

## NORTH SHIELDS

Founded: 1992 Nickname: Robins

**Secretary:** Sean Redford **(T)** 07929 336 645 **(E)** sean_061@yahoo.co.uk

**Chairman:** Alan Matthews **Prog Ed:** Craig Dobson

**Ground:** Daren Persson Staduim, Ralph Gardner Park, West Percy Rd, Chirton, North **(T)** 07759 766 732

**Capacity:** **Seats:** **Covered:** **Midweek Matchday:** **Clubhouse:**

**Colours(change):** All red

**Previous Names:** Preston Colliery > 1928, North Shields Athletic 1995-99.

**Previous Leagues:** Wearside.

**Records:**

**Honours:** FA Amateur Cup 1968-69, N.C.E. Prem Div 91-92, Lge Cup 90-91. Wearside League 1998-99, 01-02, 03-04.
Northern League Division Two 2013-14. Northumberland Senior Cup 2015-16.

**10 YEAR RECORD**

| 06-07 | | 07-08 | | 08-09 | | 09-10 | | 10-11 | | 11-12 | | 12-13 | | 13-14 | | 14-15 | | 15-16 | |
|---|---|---|---|---|---|---|---|---|---|---|---|---|---|---|---|---|---|---|---|
| NL 2 | 18 | NL 2 | 17 | NL 2 | 15 | NL 2 | 6 | NL 2 | 4 | NL 2 | 8 | NL 2 | 8 | NL 2 | 1 | NL 1 | 4 | NL 1 | 5 |

## PENRITH

Founded: 1894 Nickname: Blues

**Secretary:** TBC **(T)** **(E)**
**Chairman:** Brian Williams **Prog Ed:** Brian Kirkbride
**Ground:** The Stadium, Frenchfield Park, Frenchfield, Penrith CA11 8UA **(T)** 01768 865 990
**Capacity:** 4,000 **Seats:** 200 **Covered:** 1,000 **Midweek Matchday:** Tuesday **Clubhouse:** Yes **Shop:** No

**Colours(change):** White/blue/blue
**Previous Names:** Penrith FC. Penrith Town.
**Previous Leagues:** Carlisle & Dist. Northern 1942-82. NWC 1982-87, 90-97. NPL 1987-90.
**Records:** 2,100 v Chester 1981
**Honours:** Northern League Division 2 Champions 2002-03, 07-08.

**10 YEAR RECORD**

| 06-07 | 07-08 | 08-09 | 09-10 | 10-11 | 11-12 | 12-13 | 13-14 | 14-15 | 15-16 |
|---|---|---|---|---|---|---|---|---|---|
| NL 2 7 | NL 2 1 | NL 1 7 | NL 1 14 | NL 1 17 | NL 1 19 | NL 1 13 | NL 1 13 | NL 1 14 | NL 1 14 |

## RYHOPE COLLIERY WELFARE

Founded: Nickname:

**Secretary:** Dougie Benison **(T)** 07901 545 760 **(E)** dougie.benison@btinternet.com
**Chairman:** Darren Norton **Prog Ed:** Dougie Benison
**Ground:** Ryhope Recreation Park, Ryhope Street, Ryhope, Sunderland SR2 0AB **(T)**
**Capacity:** **Seats:** **Covered:** **Midweek Matchday:** **Clubhouse:**

**Colours(change):** Red & white/red/red
**Previous Names:**
**Previous Leagues:**
**Records:** **Previous Names:** Vaux Ryhope 1988-92.
**Honours:** **Previous League:** Wearside > 2012, 2013-14. Northern League 2012-13.
**League honours:** Wearside League 1927-28, 61-62, 62-63, 63-64, 65-66, 2010-11, 11-12.

**10 YEAR RECORD**

| 06-07 | 07-08 | 08-09 | 09-10 | 10-11 | 11-12 | 12-13 | 13-14 | 14-15 | 15-16 |
|---|---|---|---|---|---|---|---|---|---|
| | | | | Wear 1 | Wear 1 | NL 2 2 | Wear 2 | NL 2 6 | NL 2 2 |

## SEAHAM RED STAR

Founded: 1973 Nickname: The Star

**Secretary:** Dave Copeland **(T)** 07834 473 001 **(E)** davidcopelandc@aol.com
**Chairman:** Des Johnson **Prog Ed:** Dave Copeland
**Ground:** Seaham Town Park, Stockton Road, Seaham. Co.Durham SR7 0HY **(T)**
**Capacity:** **Seats:** **Covered:** **Midweek Matchday:** **Clubhouse:**

**Colours(change):** Red & white stripes/red/red with white turnover
**Previous Names:** Seaham Colliery Welfare Red Star 1978-87.
**Previous Leagues:** Wearside 1979-83.
**Records:** **Att:** 1,500 v Guisborough. **App:** Michael Whitfield.
**Honours:** Durham Challenge Cup 1979-80, Wearside League & League Cup 1981-82, Northern League Cup 1992-93.
Northern League Division Two 2014-15.

**10 YEAR RECORD**

| 06-07 | 07-08 | 08-09 | 09-10 | 10-11 | 11-12 | 12-13 | 13-14 | 14-15 | 15-16 |
|---|---|---|---|---|---|---|---|---|---|
| NL 2 2 | NL 1 14 | NL 1 21 | NL 2 12 | NL 2 17 | NL 2 20 | NL 2 10 | NL 2 4 | NL 2 1 | NL 1 9 |

## SHILDON

Founded: 1890 Nickname: Railwaymen

**Secretary:** Gareth Howe **(T)** 07976 822 453 **(E)** gareth.howe3@btopenworld.com
**Chairman:** David Dent **Prog Ed:** Martyn Tweddle
**Ground:** Dean Street, Shildon, Co. Durham DL4 1HA **(T)** 01388 773 877
**Capacity:** 4,000 **Seats:** 480 **Covered:** 1000 **Midweek Matchday:** Wednesday **Clubhouse:** Yes **Shop:** No

**Colours(change):** All red
**Previous Names:** Shildon Athletic > 1923.
**Previous Leagues:** Auckland & Dist 1892-86, Wear Valley 1896-97, Northern 1903-07, North Eastern 1907-32
**Records:** **Att:** 11,000 v Ferryhill Athletic, Durham Senior Cup 1922 **Goalscorer:** Jack Downing 61 (1936-7) **App:** Bryan Dale
**Honours:** Durham Amateur Cup 1901-02, 02-03, Durham Challenge Cup 1907-08, 25-26, 71-72,
Northern League Champions 1933-34, 34-35, 35-36,36-37, 39-40, 2015-16, Division Two 2001-02.

**10 YEAR RECORD**

| 06-07 | 07-08 | 08-09 | 09-10 | 10-11 | 11-12 | 12-13 | 13-14 | 14-15 | 15-16 |
|---|---|---|---|---|---|---|---|---|---|
| NL 1 9 | NL 1 5 | NL 1 8 | NL 1 2 | NL 1 5 | NL 1 10 | NL 1 8 | NL 1 3 | NL 1 2 | NL 1 1 |

## SOUTH SHIELDS

Founded: 1974 Nickname: Mariners

**Secretary:** Philip Reay **(T)** 07506 641 815 **(E)** philip.reay@southshieldsfc.co.uk
**Chairman:** Geoff Thompson **Prog Ed:** Daniel Prince
**Ground:** Mariners Park, Shaftesbury Avenue, Jarrow, Tyne & Wear NE32 3UP **(T)** 0191 4547800
**Capacity:** **Seats:** **Covered:** **Midweek Matchday:** Tuesday **Clubhouse:**

**Colours(change):** Claret & blue/white/white
**Previous Names:** South Shields Mariners.
**Previous Leagues:** Northern Alliance 1974-76, Wearside 1976-95.
**Records:** **Att:**1,500 v Spennymoor, Durham Challenge Cup Final 1994-95.
**Honours:** Northern Alliance 1974-75, 75-76, Wearside League 1976-77, 92-93, 94-95. Northern Division Two 2015-16. Monkwearmouth Charity Cup 1986-87.

**10 YEAR RECORD**

| 06-07 | 07-08 | 08-09 | 09-10 | 10-11 | 11-12 | 12-13 | 13-14 | 14-15 | 15-16 |
|---|---|---|---|---|---|---|---|---|---|
| NL 2 4 | NL 2 2 | NL 1 19 | NL 1 11 | NL 1 11 | NL 1 13 | NL 1 23 | NL 2 17 | NL 2 15 | NL 2 1 |

## SUNDERLAND RYHOPE C.A.

Founded: 1961 Nickname:

**Secretary:** Rob Jones **(T)** 07932 951 842 **(E)** Robert-jones10@live.co.uk
**Chairman:** Graham Defty **Prog Ed:** Colin Wilson
**Ground:** Meadow Park, Beachbrooke, Stockton Rd, Ryhope, Sunderland SR2 0NZ **(T)** 07932 951 842
**Capacity:** 2,000 **Seats:** 150 **Covered:** 200 **Midweek Matchday:** Wednesday **Clubhouse:** Yes

**Colours(change):** Red & white/black/red
**Previous Names:** Ryhope Community Ass. FC
**Previous Leagues:** S.C. Vaux: Tyne & Wear, NorthEastern Am a Ryhope CA N Alliance.>82
**Records:** Not Known
**Honours:** Northern Alliance League Cup 1981.

**10 YEAR RECORD**

| 06-07 | 07-08 | 08-09 | 09-10 | 10-11 | 11-12 | 12-13 | 13-14 | 14-15 | 15-16 |
|---|---|---|---|---|---|---|---|---|---|
| NL 2 19 | NL 2 4 | NL 2 4 | NL 2 2 | NL 1 13 | NL 1 4 | NL 1 22 | NL 1 19 | NL 1 16 | NL 1 13 |

## WASHINGTON

Founded: 1947 Nickname: Mechanics

**Secretary:** Barry Spendley **(T)** 07810 536 964 **(E)** barry.spendley@outlook.com
**Chairman:** Derek Armstrong **Prog Ed:** Bob Goodwin
**Ground:** Nissan Sports Complex, Washington Road Sunderland SR5 3NS **(T)** 0191 415 2354
**Capacity:** **Seats:** Yes **Covered:** Yes **Midweek Matchday:** Tuesday **Clubhouse:** Yes

**Colours(change):** All red
**Previous Names:** Washington Mechanics, Washington Ikeda Hoover.
**Previous Leagues:** Gateshead & District, Washington Amateur, Northern Alliance: 1967-68, Wearside: 1968-88
**Records:** **Att:** 3,800 v Bradford Park Avenue FA Cup 1970.
**Honours:** Washington Amateur: 1956-57,57-58, 58-59,59-60,61-62,62-63, League Cup: 1955-56, 58-59, 60-61, 64-65.

**10 YEAR RECORD**

| 06-07 | 07-08 | 08-09 | 09-10 | 10-11 | 11-12 | 12-13 | 13-14 | 14-15 | 15-16 |
|---|---|---|---|---|---|---|---|---|---|
| NL 2 3 | NL 1 21 | NL 2 7 | NL 2 18 | NL 2 16 | NL 2 14 | NL 2 12 | NL 2 9 | NL 2 2 | NL 1 10 |

## WEST ALLOTMENT CELTIC

Founded: 1928 Nickname:

**Secretary:** Ted Ilderton **(T)** 07795 246 245 **(E)** tedilderton@gmail.com
**Chairman:** Jim Wilson **Prog Ed:** Craig Dobson
**Ground:** Whitley Park, Whitley Road, Benton NE12 9FA **(T)** 07795 246 245
**Capacity:** **Seats:** **Covered:** **Midweek Matchday:** Monday **Clubhouse:**

**Colours(change):** Green & white hoops/green/green
**Previous Names:**
**Previous Leagues:** Tynemouth & District. Northern Amateur. Northern Alliance.
**Records:** **Att:** 510 v Cray Wanderers FA Vase 2004
**Honours:** Northern Am. 1956-57, 57-58, 58-59, 59-60, 81-82, 82-83, Div 2: 38-39. Northern Alliance: 1986-87, 90-91, 91-92, 97-98, 98-99, 99-2000, 01-02, 03-04. Northern League Div 2 2004-05

**10 YEAR RECORD**

| 06-07 | 07-08 | 08-09 | 09-10 | 10-11 | 11-12 | 12-13 | 13-14 | 14-15 | 15-16 |
|---|---|---|---|---|---|---|---|---|---|
| NL 1 18 | NL 1 13 | NL 1 9 | NL 1 15 | NL 1 20 | NL 2 7 | NL 2 7 | NL 2 2 | NL 1 19 | NL 1 19 |

## WEST AUCKLAND TOWN

Founded: 1893 Nickname: West

**Secretary:** Wayne Jones **(T)** 07951 292 036 **(E)** waynenoj25@hotmal.co.uk

**Chairman:** Jim Palfreyman **Prog Ed:** Jim Palfreyman

**Ground:** Darlington Road, West Auckland, Co. Durham DL14 9AQ **(T)** 07951 292 036

**Capacity:** 3,000 **Seats:** 250 **Covered:** 250 **Midweek Matchday:** Tuesday **Clubhouse:** Yes **Shop:** No

**Colours(change):** Yellow/black/yellow

**Previous Names:** Auckland St Helens. St Helens. West Auckland.

**Previous Leagues:** Auck&D.,Wear Val,Sth D'ham All.Mid D'ham, Nth Lge 1919-20.Palantine 20-24.Sth D'ham 27-28.Gaunless Val 33-34

**Records:** Att: 6,000 v Dulwich Hamlet FA Amateur Cup 1958-59

**Honours:** Sir Thomas Lipton Trophy 1909, 1911, Northern League 1959-60, 60-61. Div 2 1990-91. League Cup 1958-59, 62-63, Durham Challenge Cup 1964-65

**10 YEAR RECORD**

| 06-07 | 07-08 | 08-09 | 09-10 | 10-11 | 11-12 | 12-13 | 13-14 | 14-15 | 15-16 |
|---|---|---|---|---|---|---|---|---|---|
| NL 1 6 | NL 1 16 | NL 1 20 | NL 1 16 | NL 1 6 | NL 1 2 | NL 1 4 | NL 1 5 | NL 1 5 | NL 1 17 |

## WHITLEY BAY

Founded: 1897 Nickname: The Bay

**Secretary:** Derek Breakwell **(T)** 07889 888 187 **(E)** dbreakwell@hotmail.co.uk

**Chairman:** Paul McIlduff **Prog Ed:** Peter Fox

**Ground:** Hillheads Park, Rink Way, Whitley Bay, NE25 8HR **(T)** 0191 291 3637

**Capacity:** 4,500 **Seats:** 450 **Covered:** 650 **Midweek Matchday:** Tuesday **Clubhouse:** Yes **Shop:** Yes

**Colours(change):** Blue & white stripes/blue/blue

**Previous Names:** Whitley Bay Athletic 1950-58

**Previous Leagues:** Tyneside 1909-10, Northern All. 1950-55, N. Eastern 1955-58, Northern 1958-88 N.P.L. 1988-00

**Records:** 7,301 v Hendon, FA Amateur Cup 1965.

**Honours:** Northern Alliance 1952-53, 53-54. Northern League 1964-65, 65-66, 06-07. NPL Div 1 1990-91, FA Vase 2001-02, 08-09, 09-10, 10-11.

**10 YEAR RECORD**

| 06-07 | 07-08 | 08-09 | 09-10 | 10-11 | 11-12 | 12-13 | 13-14 | 14-15 | 15-16 |
|---|---|---|---|---|---|---|---|---|---|
| NL 1 1 | NL 1 3 | NL 1 3 | NL 1 3 | NL 1 3 | NL 1 6 | NL 1 3 | NL 1 10 | NL 1 15 | NL 1 16 |

## ALNWICK TOWN
Founded: 1879 Nickname:

**Secretary:** Cyril Cox **(T)** 0191 236 6456 **(E)** uk2usa@hotmail.co.uk
**Chairman:** Tommy McKie **Prog Ed:** Michael Cook
**Ground:** St. Jame's Park, Weavers Way, Alnwick, Northumberland NE66 1BG **(T)** 01665 603 162
**Colours(change):** Black & white stripes/black/black
**ADDITIONAL INFORMATION: Previous Names:** Alnwick Utd Services 1879-1900, Alnwick Utd Juniors 1900-1936.
**Previous Lge:** Northern Alliance 1935-82, 2007-11. Northern League 1982-2007.
**League honours:** Nothern Alliance title 9 times.

## BEDLINGTON TERRIERS COMM.
Founded: 1949 Nickname: Terriers

**Secretary:** Robin Ramsey **(T)** 07980 622 112 **(E)** robin.ramsey@hotmail.com
**Chairman:** Ronan Liddane **Prog Ed:** Terry Browne
**Ground:** Doctor Pit Welfare Park, Park Road, Bedlington NE22 5AT **(T)** 07935 840 277 3,000
**Colours(change):** All red.
**ADDITIONAL INFORMATION: Att:** 2,400 v Colchester United FA Cup 1st round **Goalscorer:** John Milner
Northern Lge Div 1: 97-98, 98-99, 99-00, 2000-01, 01-02. Northumberland Senior Cup 1996-97, 97-98, 2001-02,03-04.

## BILLINGHAM SYNTHONIA
Founded: 1923 Nickname: Synners

**Secretary:** Graham Craggs **(T)** 07702 530 335 **(E)** graham.craggs@gb.abb.com
**Chairman:** David Hillerby **Prog Ed:** Graeme Goodman
**Ground:** The Stadium, Central Ave, Billingham, Cleveland TS23 1LR **(T)** 01642 532 348 **Capacity:** 1,970
**Colours(change):** Green & white quarters/white/white
**ADDITIONAL INFORMATION: Att:** 4,200 v Bishop Auckland 1958 **Goalscorer:** Tony Hetherington **App:** Andy Harbron
Northern Lge 1956-57, 88-89, 89-90, 95-96. Div.2 86-87.

## BILLINGHAM TOWN
Founded: 1967 Nickname: Billy Town

**Secretary:** Peter Martin **(T)** 07873 794 768 **(E)** peterwlmartin@hotmail.com
**Chairman:** Peter Martin **Prog Ed:** Peter Martin
**Ground:** Bedford Terrace, Billingham, Cleveland TS23 4AE **(T)** 07873 794 768 **Capacity:** 3,000
**Colours(change):** Blue/black/blue
**ADDITIONAL INFORMATION: Att:** 1,500 v Man City FA Youth Cup 1985 **Goalscorer:** Paul Rowntree 396 **App:** Paul Rowntree 505
Durham Cup 1976-77, 77-78, 2003-04

## BLYTH TOWN
Founded: Nickname:

**Secretary:** Barry William Elliott **(T)** 07710 715045 **(E)** barry.elliott8@btinternet.com
**Chairman:** Barry William Elliott **Prog Ed:** Chrissie Pringle
**Ground:** Off Sandringham Aveneue, South Newsham, Blyth NE24 3PS **(T)** 07710 715045
**Colours(change):** All white
**ADDITIONAL INFORMATION:**
Northern Alliance League Premier Division 2015-16.

## BRANDON UNITED
Founded: 1968 Nickname: United

**Secretary:** Barry Ross **(T)** 07555 586 305 **(E)** kayowe48@gmail.com
**Chairman:** David Bussey **Prog Ed:** Dean Johnson
**Ground:** Welfare Park, Rear Commercial Street, Brandon DH7 7PL **(T)** 07555 586 305
**Colours(change):** All red
**ADDITIONAL INFORMATION: Previous League:** Wearside 1981-83. **Record Att:** 2,500 F.A. Sunday Cup Seim-final.
**Record: Goalscorer:** Tommy Holden. **Apps:** Derek Charlton 1977-86. **Honours:** F.A. Sunday Cup 1975-76.
Northern Alliance Division 2 1977-78, 78-79. Northern League 2002-03, Division 2 1984-85, 99-2000.

## CROOK TOWN
Founded: 1889 Nickname: Black & Ambers

**Secretary:** Jonathon Hughes **(T)** 07801 013253 **(E)** crooktownafc2015@yahoo.co.uk
**Chairman:** Vince Kirkup **Prog Ed:** Jonathon Hughes
**Ground:** The Sir Tom Cowie Millfield, West Road, Crook, Co.Durham DL15 9PW **(T)** 01388 762 959
**Colours(change):** Amber/black/black
**ADDITIONAL INFORMATION:**
FA Amateur Cup 1900-01, 53-54, 58-59, 61-62, 63-64. Northern League x5 Div.2 2012-13, League Cup x3.
Durham Challenge Cup x4. Durham Benefit Bowl x6. Ernest Armstrong Memorial Trophy 1997.

## DARLINGTON R.A.

Founded: 1993 Nickname:

**Secretary:** Alan Hamilton **(T)** 07872 324 808 **(E)** nobbydarlo@ntlworld.com
**Chairman:** Doug Hawman **Prog Ed:** Alan Hamilton
**Ground:** Brinkburn Road, Darlington, Co. Durham DL3 9LF **(T)** 01325 468 125
**Colours(change):** All red
**ADDITIONAL INFORMATION:**
**Previous League:** Darlington & District 1993-99.
**Honours:** Auckland & District League 2000-01. Wearside League 2004-05.

## DURHAM CITY

Founded: 1949 Nickname: City

**Secretary:** Fred Usher **(T)** 07901804087 **(E)** fredusher@sky.com
**Chairman:** Olivier Bernard
**Ground:** Belle View Staduim, Delves Lane, Consett, Co. Durham DH8 7BF **(T)** 01207 588 886
**Colours(change):** Yellow/blue/blue
**ADDITIONAL INFORMATION:** 2,750 v Whitley Bay - FA Vase Semi-final 2001-02
Northern League 1994-95, 2007-08. Northern Premier League Division 1 North 2008-09, Chairman's Cup 2008-09.

## EASINGTON COLLIERY

Founded: 1913 Nickname:

**Secretary:** Billy Banks **(T)** 07967 286 559 **(E)** pa@finishingtouchesteesside.co.uk
**Chairman:** Paul Adamson Andy Collage **Prog Ed:** John Hunter
**Ground:** Memorial Avenue, Seaside Lane, Easington Colliery SR8 3PL **(T)**
**Colours(change):** Green & white/green/green
**ADDITIONAL INFORMATION:**
**Previous Names:** Easington Colliery Welfare 1913-64, 1973-80. Amalgamated with Easington Rangers in 1980 to form todays club.
**Previous Leagues:** Wearside: 1913-37, 39-64, 73-88, 2007-10, 2012-15 , Northern League: 1985-2005, 2011-12, Northern Alliance: 2005-07.

## ESH WINNING

Founded: 1885 Nickname: Stags

**Secretary:** Matthew Burdess **(T)** 07432 648 072 **(E)** matthewburdess1995@hotmail.co.uk
**Chairman:** Charles Ryan **Prog Ed:** Matthew Burdess
**Ground:** West Terrace, Waterhouse, Durham DH7 9BQ **(T)** 07432 648 072 **Capacity:** 3,500
**Colours(change):** Yellow/green/green
**ADDITIONAL INFORMATION:**
**Record Att:** 5,000 v Newcastle Utd Res. 1910 & Bishop Auckland 1921 **Goalscorer:** Alan Dodsworth 250+ **App:** Neil McLeary - 194.
**League honours:** Northern League Champions 1912-13.

## HEATON STANNINGTON

Founded: 1910 Nickname: The Stan

**Secretary:** Ken Rodger **(T)** 07587 690295 **(E)** kenneth@krodger.fsnet.co.uk
**Chairman:** Bill Pitt **Prog Ed:** Kevin Mochrie
**Ground:** Grounsell Park, Newton Road, High Heaton, Newcastle upon Tyne NE7 7HP **(T)** 0191 281 9230
**Colours(change):** Black & white stripes/black/black
**ADDITIONAL INFORMATION:**
**Previous Leagues:** Northern Alliance >2013.
**Honours:** Northern Alliance 2011-12, 12-13.

## HEBBURN TOWN

Founded: 1912 Nickname: Hornets

**Secretary:** David Patterson **(T)** 07979 033185 **(E)** davepatter@yahoo.co.uk
**Chairman:** Bill Laffey **Prog Ed:** Richard Bainbridge
**Ground:** Hebburn Sports & Social, Victoria Rd West, Hebburn, Tyne & Wear NE31 1UN **(T)** 0191 483 5101
**Colours(change):** Yellow & black stripes/black/black
**ADDITIONAL INFORMATION: Att:** 503 v Darwen FA Cup Prelim replay 07/09/1991, **Win:** 10-1. **Defeat:** 3-10.
Tyneside League 1938-39, Northern Combination 1943-44, Wearside League 1966-67.

## NORTHALLERTON TOWN

Founded: 1994 Nickname: Town

**Secretary:** Lesley Clark **(T)** 07891 595 267 **(E)** lesleyclark05@yahoo.co.uk
**Chairman:** Les Hood **Prog Ed:** Andrew Pattinson
**Ground:** The Calvert Stadium, Ainderby Road, Northallerton DL7 8HA **(T)** 01609 778 337
**Colours(change):** Black & white stripes/black/black & white
**ADDITIONAL INFORMATION: Previous Name:** Northallerton FC 1994. **Previous League:** Harrogate & District.
**Record Att:** 695 v Farnborough Town FA Trophy 3rd Round 20/02/1993.
**Honours:** Northern League Division 2 1996-97, League Cup 1993-94.

## NORTON & STOCKTON ANCIENTS
Founded: 1959 Nickname: Ancients

**Secretary:** Michael Mulligan **(T)** 07850 622 544 **(E)** m.mulligan@nasafc.co.uk
**Chairman:** Michael Mulligan **Prog Ed:** Michael Mulligan
**Ground:** Norton (Teesside) Sports Complex, Station Rd, Norton TS20 1PE **(T)** 01642 530 203 **Capacity:** 2,000
**Colours(change):** Amber/black/black
**ADDITIONAL INFORMATION: Att:** 1,430 v Middlesbrough, Friendly 1988.
Northern League Cup 1982-83.

## RYTON & CRAWCROOK ALBION
Founded: 1970 Nickname:

**Secretary:** Stevie Carter **(T)** 07939 573 108 **(E)** racafc@outlook.com
**Chairman:** Richard Hands **Prog Ed:** Chris Holt
**Ground:** Kingsley Park, Stannerford Road, Crawcrook NE40 3SN **(T)** 0191 413 4448 **Capacity:** 2,000
**Colours(change):** Blue & black stripes/black/blue
**ADDITIONAL INFORMATION: Att:** 1,100 v Newcastle United 1998
Northern Alliance Division 1 Champions 1996-97.

## STOCKTON TOWN
Founded: Nickname:

**Secretary:** Rob Sexton **(T)** 07505 900 815 **(E)** 1962.rvs@gmail.com
**Chairman:** Martin Hillerby **Prog Ed:** Paul Beards
**Ground:** Bishopton Road West, Stockton-on-Tees TS19 0QD **(T)** 01642 604 915
**Colours(change):** Yellow/blue/yellow
**ADDITIONAL INFORMATION:**
Wearside League 2015-16.

## TEAM NORTHUMBRIA
Founded: 1999 Nickname:

**Secretary:** Tom Robinson **(T)** 07772 598192 **(E)** thomas.robinson@northumbria.ac.uk
**Chairman:** Tony Stokle
**Ground:** Coach Lane, Benton, Newcastle upon Tyne NE7 7XA **(T)** 0191 215 6575
**Colours(change):** All red
**ADDITIONAL INFORMATION:**
Northern Alliance Premier 2005-06. Northern League Division Two 2011-12.

## THORNABY
Founded: 1980 Nickname:

**Secretary:** Trevor Wing **(T)** 07860 780 446 **(E)** trevor.wing10@btinternet.com
**Chairman:** Laurence Lyons **Prog Ed:** Trevor Wing
**Ground:** Teesdale Park, Acklam Road, Thornaby, Stockton on Tees TS17 7JU **(T)** 01642 672 896
**Colours(change):** All blue
**ADDITIONAL INFORMATION: Previous Names:** Stockton Cricket Club 1965-1980, Stockton 1980-99 and Thornaby-on-Tees 1999-2000
**Previous League:** Wearside 1981-85. **Records Att:** 3,000 v Middlesbrough friendly Aug 1986 **App:** Michael Watson
**Honours:** North Riding County Cup, 1985-86, Northern Lge Div 2 1987-88, 91-92

## TOW LAW TOWN
Founded: 1890 Nickname: Lawyers

**Secretary:** Steve Moralee **(T)** 07810 238 731 **(E)** stephen.moralee@btinternet.com
**Chairman:** Kevin McCormick (Interim) **Prog Ed:** John Dixon
**Ground:** Ironworks Ground, Tow Law, Bishop Auckland DL13 4EQ **(T)** 01388 731 443 **Capacity:** 6,000
**Colours(change):** Black & white stripes/black/black
**ADDITIONAL INFORMATION:** 5,500 v Mansfield Town FA Cup 1967.
Northern League Champions 1923-24, 24-25, 94-95. League Cup 73-74.

## WHICKHAM
Founded: 1944 Nickname:

**Secretary:** Lynn Ready **(T)** 07775 620 859 **(E)** whickhamfcsecretary@hotmail.co.uk
**Chairman:** Paul Taylor **Prog Ed:** Ross Gregory
**Ground:** Glebe Sports Club, Rectory Lane, Whickham NE11 9NQ **(T)** 0191 4200 186
**Colours(change):** Black & white stripes/black/black
**ADDITIONAL INFORMATION: Record Att:** 3,165 v Windsor & Eton FA Vase SF 1981.
**Honours:** FA Vase 1980-81, Wearside Lge 77-78, 87-88, Sunderland Shipowners Cup 77-78, 80-81,
Northern Comb 69-70, 72-73, 73-74 Lge Cup 60-61, 73-74

## WILLINGTON

Founded: 1906 Nickname:

**Secretary:** Geoff Siddle **(T)** 07949 919 865 **(E)** siddle403@btinternet.com
**Chairman:** Robert Nichols **Manager:** Robert Lee **Prog Ed:** Geoff Siddle
**Ground:** Hall Lane, Willington, Co. Durham DL15 0QG **(T)** 01388 745 912 **Capacity:** 7,000
**Colours(change):** Blue & white/blue/blue

**ADDITIONAL INFORMATION:**
**Previous Leagues:** Northern League. Wearside > 2013.
**Records (Lge/Cup post 1939): Goalscorer:** Brett Cummings - 150, 1992-08. Apps: Brett Cummings - 407, 1992-08.
**Honours:** Northern League 1913-14, 25-26, 29-30. FA Amateur Cup 1949-50.

# GROUND DIRECTIONS

**ALNWICK TOWN-** M1, at exit 32, take slip road left for M18 toward The North / Doncaster / Hull, at exit 2, take slip road left for A1(M) toward the North, keep straight onto A1 / Doncaster by Pass, keep straight onto A1(M), take slip road for A1(M) / Aberford by Pass, road name changes to A1 / Leeming Lane, keep straight onto A1(M), keep left onto A1, take slip road left for A1068 toward Alnwick / Alnmouth, at roundabout, take 1st exit onto Willowburn Avenue, turn left, and then immediately turn left onto St James Estate, ground is on the right.

**ASHINGTON-**Leave the A1 at the junction with the A19 north of Newcastle. Go along the A19 eastwards untio the next roundabout . Here take the second left (A189) signposted to Bedlington and Ashington. Continue along A189 until reach Woodhorn roundabout, turn left onto A197. Turn left at first roundabout. Just before the hospital car park entrance, turn right. Ground is on left.

**BEDLINGTON TERRIERS-**From the A1:- Take the Seaton Burn turn off and at the roundabout take the second turn off (A1088).
At the next roundabout, take the first turnoff to pass Aesica on the left. Straight over at the next roundabout.
You will go down a dip, over a bridge and back up the other side, do not turn off, continue on the same road until you come into Bedlington. At the top of the bank there is a roundabout outside the Red Lion pub, go straight over. Down the hill there is another roundabout at the Netto shop, take the second turnoff (turning right). Follow the road past the Police station and Law courts and the road bends sharply to the left. Continue around the corner, take the second right. The ground is at the top of the street.

**BILLINGHAM SYNTHONIA-**Leave A19 onto A1027 sign posted towards Billingham. Continue straight ahead over a couple of roundabouts, and you will be on Central Avenue. The ground is on left opposite an empty office block.

**BILLINGHAM TOWN-**Leave A19 on A1027 signed Billingham. Turn left at third roundabout, into Cowpen Lane. Go over a railway bridge, then first left into Warwick Crescent, then first left again into Bedford Terrace (follow one-way signs) to the ground.

**BISHOP AUCKLAND-NORTH:** From junction 60 of the A1 follow the A689 to Bishop Auckland. Go straight across the next 2 roundabouts. At the 3rd roundabout turn left onto the A688 and straight across the next 2 roundabouts. At the following roundabout turn left at Aldi and then go straight across at the next roundabout. The stadium is 200 yards on your right. **SOUTH:** From junction 58 from the A1, take the A68 towards Bishop Auckland. At the West Auckland by-pass, turn right at the roundabout. Go straight across at the next roundabout and the stadium is located 500 yards on your left.

**BLYTH TOWN -** From A1 North & South. Exit A1 at junction for A19/Tyne Tunnel/Cramlington. At the roundabout take 3rd exit staying on A19
At next roundabout (Moor Farm) take 2nd exit onto A189. After 2.2 miles take the exit to A192 Seaton Delaval/Cramlington. At roundabout take 3rd exit onto A1061 Blyth. At next roundabout take 2nd exit A1061 Blyth. At next roundabout take 2nd exit A1061 Town Centre/South Beach
Go over the railway line and turn left at the traffic lights. South Newsham Pavilion is on your left.

**BRANDON UNITED-**Leave A1 on A690, go through Durham and continue on A690. Once at 'Langley Moor' (you go under a railway bridge), turn right at the "Lord Boyne" pub. After 100 yards take the next left. Go up the road for approx half a mile, and turn right at the newsagents. Take the next left, and Brandon's ground is up a small track.

**CHESTER LE STREET-**Leave A1M at junction 63 and take the A167 towards Chester Le Street and Durtham. Keep going along this road for a couple of miles. You will go under a railway bridge, and as the road begins to climb, you will see the Chester Moor pub on your left. Turn into the pub and the ground is accessed along a track at the rear of the pub car park.

**CONSETT-**Take the A692 from the east into Consett. On the edge of the town, the A692 takes a left at a roundabout. Continue along the A692 for approx 100 yards, before turning right into Leadgate Road. Go along here for approx .25 mile, and turn right into Ashdale Road. There is a road sign for the Leisure Centre pointing into Ashdale Road. The ground is approx 200 yards along Ashdale Road on your right.

**CROOK TOWN-**Leave the A1 at Junction 62, and take the A690 towards Durham. Keep on this road through Durham, Meadowfield, Willington and Helmington Row. When you arrive in Crook town centre keep going straight ahead, as the A690 becomes the A689. The ground is situated on this road on your right, approximately 300 yards from the town centre.

**DARLINGTON RAILWAY ATHLETIC-**Leave A1(M) at junction 58 and follow the A68 into Darlington. Continue along the road until you see the Brown Trout public house on your right. Turn left at this point into Brinkburn Road, and the ground is 100 yards along on the left.

**DUNSTON U.T.S.-**From south take Dunston/Whickham exit off A1M. Turn right at top of slip road into Dunston Road and head down the bank. As the road veers left, the road becomes Wellington Road, and the ground is situated on your left.

**DURHAM CITY-**Leave the A1M at J62 (signed Durham City) At the top of the slip road turn left. After about 1/2 mile bear left (signed Belmont + Dragonville). At the top of the slip road turn left.
At traffic lights turn left then take the 2nd left, the stadium is on your right.

**EASINGTON COLLIERY -**Welfare Park, Easington Colliery SR8 3JJ.

**ESH WINNING-**Leave the A1 at Junction 62, and take the A690 towards Durham. Keep on this road through Durham. Once you start to head down a bank on the A690, you will come to a roundabout. Take the right turn onto the B6302, which will be signposted towards Ushaw Moor. Keep on this road though Ushaw Moor (there is a staggered crossroads to negotiate), and carry on the B6302 into Esh Winning. Keep on going as the ground is not in Esh Winning, but the next village along, Waterhouses. When the road takes a sharp left you will see a track continuing straight ahead. The ground is along this track.

**GUISBOROUGH TOWN-**Turn off the A19 into the A174, then come off at the second junction, turning right onto the A172. Follow this round until roundabout with A1043, take left exit to join the A1043. Take right at next roundabout to join the A171. At second roundabout turn right into Middlesbrough Road (will be signposted towards Guisborough) then take left turning at traffic lights into Park Lane. Take first left into Howlbeck Road, and the ground is at the end of the road.

**HEATON STANNINGTON -** Grounsell Park, Newton Road, High Heaton, Newcastle upon Tyne NE7 7HP. Tel: 0191 281 9230

**HEBBURN TOWN-**Leave A1M on A194(M) (junction 65) and follow signs for Tyne Tunnel. Continue until fourth roundabout and turn left on to B1306 (Hebburn, Mill Lane). Right at traffic lights into Victoria Road. Ground 200 yards long this road on the left.

**JARROW ROOFING-**From south take A19 and follow signs for Tyne Tunnel. Turn right at junction marked Boldon Colliery (Testo Roundabout) on to the A184. Turn left at the next r'about, into the B1293, and head towards Asda. At second r'about, turn right at end of retail park. At the r'about at the entrance to Asda, take the "10 to" exit, and you will pass a large brick building on you right, known as The Shack. Turn right into the car park after this building, and at the far end of the car park there is a small lane that leads off left. Roofers ground is at the end of this track.

**MARSKE UNITED** -Leave A19 and join Parkway (A174) to Marske until Quarry Lane r'about. Take exit (A1085) into Marske. Take the next right after you pass under a railway, into Meadow Rd. Take the next left into Southfield Rd and the entrance is on your left shortly before a T-junc.

**MORPETH TOWN**-From south. Turn off the A1 onto A197, sign posted Morpeth. Turn left at sign pointing Belsay (B6524). Take right turn just before bridge under the A1. Ground is signposted and up a small track is on the right.

**NEWCASTLE BENFIELD**-Take the A1058 from either the Tyne Tunnel or central Newcastle. Turn off this road at the junction with Benfield Road. Turn south at this junction, and the Crosslings building will be on your left. Ground is around 400 metres on left, by taking the first turning after passing railway bridge. The ground is 100 yards along this road.

**NEWTON AYCLIFFE**-From North, leave the A1at junction 60, and travel west along the A689 towards Bishop Auckland. At the roundabout, turn left to join A167. Travel along here for a couple of miles, and at first traffic lights and turn right onto B6443 (Central Avenue). At first roundabout (Tesco's) turn left into Shafto Way then 3rd left into Gunn Way then right into Moore Lane.

**NORTH SHIELDS**-Continue north on the A19 after Tyne Tunnel. Take right exit at roundabout onto the A1058. At next roundabout take third exit at Billy Mill, signed to North Shields. At roundabout with A193, turn right, then take second left into Silkey's Lane. Ground is 100 yards on left.

**NORTHALLERTON TOWN**-Leave A1 at Leeming Bar (A684) and follow signs to Northallerton. Approaching the town take the left turn B1333, signed Romanby. Ground is on left after 50 yards in Romanby.

**NORTON & STOCKTON ANCIENTS** -Leave A19 at Stockton/Norton turn off (A1027) and follow signs to Norton. At the roundabout at the top of the bank take a right turn onto the B1274. Take the next right into Station Road. Ground entrance is on left of road in a large sports complex, the entrance to which is just before the railway crossing. The ground a 200 yards along this track.

**PENRITH**-Turn off M6 at junction 40 then onto dual carriageway to Appleby and Scotch Corner. Take the A686 (signposted Alston), for approximately half a mile. Then take a right turn (opposite Carleton Road), and follow the track running parallel with the A66. Turn left into the sports complex and follow the road to the far end.

**RYHOPE CW** - From the A1 exit onto A168 toward A19/Thirsk/Teesside. Continue onto A19. Take the A1018 ramp to Sunderland. At the roundabout, take the 2nd exit onto Stockton Rd/A1018. Continue to follow Stockton Road. Go through 2 roundabouts. Slight left onto Ryhope Street S/B1286. Ground will be on the left.

**RYTON & CRAWCROOK ALBION**-Leave the A1 at the south side of the River Tyne (A694). At the roundabout take the A695 (sign posted Blaydon). At Blaydon take the B6317 through Ryton to reach Crawcrook. Turn right at the traffic lights (sign posted Ryton/Clara Vale). Kingsley Park is situated approximately 500 meters on the right.

**SEAHAM RED STAR**-Leave A19 on B1404 slip road. Follow signs to Seaham/Ryhope. Turn right at traffic lights on to the B1285. Then left at Red Star social club approximately 200 yards after the traffic lights. There is a car park at the next roundabout behid their social club The ground is a short walk at the top of the park.

**SHILDON**-Leave A1M at junction 58. Follow A68 signed Bishop Auckland, turn right at roundabout onto A6072. At Shildon turn right at second roundabout (onto B6282) , then left into Byerley Rd (still the B6282). Right at Timothy Hackworth pub into Main St., then at the top of the bank, left into Dean Street.

**SOUTH SHIELDS- Filtrona Park, Shaftesbury Ave, South Shields, Tyne & Wear, NE32 3UP**
By Metro the ground is close to Bede Metro Station.

**STOCKTON TOWN** - Directions from A19: Take the A1027 (towards Stockton/Norton). Take 2nd Exit at first roundabout and 2nd Exit at the second roundabout. At lights (near Sainsburys) turn right onto Bishopton Road West.
Directions from A66: Take the A135 (Yarm Rd) towards Stockton, at 2nd set of lights turn left onto A1027 (Hartburn Lane). Travel along past Park (on right) and as road bears left, get into filter to turn right to follow A1027. At roundabout take 2nd exit, at 2nd set of lights (near Sainsburys) turn left onto Bishopton Road West. Stockton Town FC is on the left next door to the 6th Form College (Access via the college car park).

**SUNDERLAND R.C.A.**-From the A19, leave at the junction with the A690, but on that roundabout take the B1286 through Doxford Park. Continue along this road for some time (there are number of roundabouts), but there are signposts to Ryhope along this road. You will eventually come to a T-junction at the end of the B1286, and turn right onto the A1018. After 200 yards you will come to another roundabout, here take a right turn. Then take the next right into a new housing estate. There is a board at the entrance pointing you to Meadow Park, the home of R.C.A. The ground is at the far end of the estate.

**TEAM NORTHUMBRIA**-Take the A1058 from either the A19 or central Newcastle. Turn off this road at the junction with Benfield Road. Turn north at large Crosslings warehouse into Red Hall Drive, this then becomes Coach Lane. The ground is on the right just past Newcastle University halls of residence.

**THORNABY**-Turn off A19 onto A1130 and head towards Thornaby. Continue along Acklam Road for about half a mile. Ground is signposted from the main road- on the right up a track between houses after half a mile.

**TOW LAW TOWN**-Leave the A1 at junction 58 and turn on to A68. Follow signs for Tow Law/Corbridge. Ground is at far end of Tow Law on the left side. The ground is situated on Ironworks Road, which is the first left after a sharp left hand bend on the A68 in Tow Law.

**WASHINGTON**-Leave the A19 on slip road marked "Nissan Offices" as you pass Sunderland travelling north. This is the A1290. Continue to follow "Nissan Offices" signs. Left at traffic lights, then right at roundabout into complex. Ground is at far end of the plant.

**WEST ALLOTMENT CELTIC**-Continue on the A19 north after Tyne Tunnel until A191 exit. Take left exit marked Gosforth & Newcastle. A191 for three miles. The ground, The Blue Flames Sports Ground is on left.

**WEST AUCKLAND TOWN**-Leave A1 at junction 58 on to the A68. Follow signs to W. Auckland/Corbridge. On entering village, ground is behind factory on left side. Ground is up a track on the left side of road next to Oakley Grange Farm.

**WHICKHAM**-From A1M take the A692 junction, and travel in the direction signed to Consett. At top of the back the road forks left towards Consett, but you should take the right fork along the B6317 to Whickham. Follow this road for 1.5 miles, left turn into Rectory Lane (B6316). Take first right into Holme Avenue, and then first left. The ground is at top of lane. More car parking can be found further along Rectory Lane, take the next right. Walk past the cricket pitch to access the football club.

**WHITLEY BAY**-Leave the A19 on the A191, and turn eastwards towards Whitely Bay. Continue along New York Road (A191) which then becomes Rake Lane (A191). Pass hospital on right & then into Shields Rd. and Hillheads Rd (both A191). Ground is to the right, floodlights can be seen from miles away! It is next to an ice rink.

**WILLINGTON** - Hall Lane, Willington, Co. Durham DL15 0QG. Tel: 01388 745 912

# SOUTH WEST PENINSULA LEAGUE

**Sponsored by:** Carlsberg

**Founded:** 2007

**Recent Champions: 2013:** Bodmin Town

**2014:** Plymouth Parkway **2015:** St Austell

| PREMIER DIVISION | P | W | D | L | F | A | GD | Pts |
|---|---|---|---|---|---|---|---|---|
| 1 Bodmin Town | 38 | 27 | 8 | 3 | 130 | 43 | +87 | |
| 2 St Austell | 38 | 26 | 4 | 8 | 104 | 54 | +50 | |
| 3 Tavistock | 38 | 24 | 5 | 9 | 104 | 42 | +62 | |
| 4 Plymouth Parkway | 38 | 22 | 9 | 7 | 95 | 43 | +52 | |
| 5 Godolphin Atlantic | 38 | 18 | 7 | 13 | 71 | 61 | +10 | |
| 6 Saltash United | 38 | 18 | 5 | 15 | 66 | 59 | +7 | |
| 7 Witheridge | 38 | 17 | 8 | 13 | 68 | 77 | -9 | |
| 8 Torpoint Athletic | 38 | 16 | 7 | 15 | 60 | 61 | -1 | |
| 9 Ivybridge Town | 38 | 16 | 6 | 16 | 74 | 68 | +6 | |
| 10 Helston Athletic | 38 | 14 | 10 | 14 | 64 | 68 | -4 | |
| 11 Falmouth Town | 38 | 14 | 8 | 16 | 57 | 64 | -7 | |
| 12 Exmouth Town | 38 | 15 | 4 | 19 | 67 | 83 | -16 | |
| 13 Cullompton Rangers | 38 | 12 | 10 | 16 | 64 | 71 | -7 | |
| 14 Launceston | 38 | 9 | 17 | 12 | 51 | 58 | -7 | |
| 15 Camelford | 38 | 10 | 11 | 17 | 51 | 80 | -29 | |
| 16 Callington Town | 38 | 9 | 12 | 17 | 55 | 77 | -22 | |
| 17 St Blazey | 38 | 11 | 5 | 22 | 58 | 99 | -41 | |
| 18 Newquay | 38 | 11 | 4 | 23 | 52 | 98 | -46 | |
| 19 Stoke Gabriel | 38 | 9 | 7 | 22 | 58 | 68 | -10 | |
| 20 Elburton Villa | 38 | 6 | 5 | 27 | 40 | 115 | -75 | |

### CLUB MOVEMENTS

**Premier Division - In:** Tiverton Town Reserves (P). Plymouth Argyle Reserves (P).
**Out:** Elburton Villa (R - D1W). Stoke Gabriel (R - D1E).
**Division One East- In:** Stoke Gabriel (R). Torridgeside (P - North Devon)
**Out:** Okehampton Argyle (R - Devon & Exeter). Tiverton Town Reserves (P).
**Division One West - In:** Elburton Villa (R). Plymouth Majon (P - Plymouth & West).
**Out:** Plymouth Argyle Reserves (P).

| DIVISION ONE EAST | P | W | D | L | F | A | GD | Pts |
|---|---|---|---|---|---|---|---|---|
| 1 Tiverton Town Reserves (P) | 34 | 28 | 5 | 1 | 101 | 26 | 75 | 89 |
| 2 Teignmouth (+3) | 34 | 19 | 9 | 5 | 74 | 34 | 40 | 69 |
| 3 University of Exeter | 34 | 21 | 6 | 7 | 75 | 46 | 29 | 69 |
| 4 St Martins | 34 | 19 | 9 | 6 | 74 | 42 | 32 | 66 |
| 5 Galmpton United | 34 | 16 | 5 | 11 | 66 | 59 | 7 | 53 |
| 6 Alphington | 34 | 16 | 4 | 14 | 65 | 57 | 8 | 52 |
| 7 Newton Abbot Spurs | 34 | 15 | 5 | 14 | 69 | 62 | 7 | 50 |
| 8 Axminster Town | 34 | 14 | 7 | 13 | 72 | 61 | 11 | 49 |
| 9 Brixham | 34 | 15 | 3 | 16 | 80 | 66 | 14 | 48 |
| 10 Appledore | 34 | 13 | 7 | 12 | 69 | 57 | 12 | 46 |
| 11 Budleigh Salterton | 34 | 12 | 9 | 13 | 60 | 55 | 5 | 45 |
| 12 Sidmouth Town | 34 | 14 | 3 | 17 | 69 | 73 | –4 | 45 |
| 13 Exwick Villa | 34 | 13 | 5 | 16 | 51 | 77 | –26 | 44 |
| 14 Crediton United | 34 | 11 | 5 | 18 | 56 | 74 | –18 | 38 |
| 15 Liverton United | 34 | 9 | 7 | 18 | 55 | 79 | –24 | 34 |
| 16 Bovey Tracey | 34 | 9 | 4 | 21 | 60 | 88 | –28 | 31 |
| 17 Totnes & Dartington | 34 | 9 | 3 | 22 | 52 | 105 | –53 | 30 |
| 18 Okehampton Argyle (-3) | 34 | 0 | 4 | 29 | 42 | 129 | –87 | 1 |

| DIVISION ONE WEST | P | W | D | L | F | A | GD | Pts |
|---|---|---|---|---|---|---|---|---|
| 1 Mousehole | 32 | 30 | 1 | 1 | 131 | 17 | 114 | 92 |
| 2 Plymouth Argyle Reserves | 32 | 26 | 3 | 3 | 98 | 25 | 73 | 81 |
| 3 Sticker | 32 | 24 | 2 | 6 | 92 | 38 | 54 | 74 |
| 4 Penryn Athletic | 32 | 19 | 4 | 9 | 97 | 36 | 61 | 61 |
| 5 Plymstock United | 32 | 17 | 6 | 9 | 59 | 48 | 11 | 57 |
| 6 St Dennis | 32 | 18 | 1 | 13 | 92 | 84 | 8 | 55 |
| 7 Liskeard Athletic | 32 | 16 | 5 | 11 | 91 | 63 | 28 | 53 |
| 8 Bude Town | 32 | 16 | 5 | 11 | 84 | 60 | 24 | 53 |
| 9 Wendron United | 32 | 11 | 8 | 13 | 56 | 75 | –19 | 41 |
| 10 Penzance | 32 | 12 | 5 | 15 | 58 | 82 | –24 | 41 |
| 11 Holsworthy | 32 | 12 | 3 | 17 | 56 | 64 | –8 | 39 |
| 12 Illogan RBL | 32 | 8 | 5 | 19 | 56 | 98 | –42 | 29 |
| 13 Millbrook | 32 | 6 | 5 | 21 | 49 | 99 | –50 | 23 |
| 14 Wadebridge Town | 32 | 4 | 10 | 18 | 40 | 94 | –54 | 22 |
| 15 Dobwalls | 32 | 6 | 2 | 24 | 35 | 83 | –48 | 20 |
| 16 Porthleven | 32 | 5 | 5 | 22 | 35 | 92 | –57 | 20 |
| 17 Vospers Oak Villa | 32 | 4 | 6 | 22 | 47 | 118 | –71 | 18 |

## WALTER C PARSON CUP (Formerly Throgmorton)

**HOLDERS:** GODOLPHIN ATLANTIC

**ROUND 1**

| | | | |
|---|---|---|---|
| Alphington | v | Crediton United | 0-2 |
| Axminster Town | v | Appledore | 2-4 |
| Elburton Villa | v | Cullompton Rangers | 2-4 |
| Falmouth Town | v | Penryn Athletic | 2-1 |
| Galmpton United | v | St Martins | 2-2, AWp |
| Holsworthy | v | Bovey Tracey | 2-1 |
| Launceston | v | Callington Town | 1-2 |
| Liskeard Athletic | v | Totnes & Dartington | 6-3 |
| Liverton United | v | Plymstock United | 1-1, AWp |
| Millbrook | v | Okehampton Argyle | HW |
| Mousehole | v | Illogan RBL | 6-0 |
| Newton Abbot Spurs | v | Bude Town | 6-2 |
| Newquay | v | St Dennis | 3-1 |
| Penzance | v | Dobwells | 2-3 |
| Plymouth Argyle | v | Brixham | 1-3 |
| Porthleven | v | Helston Athletic | 0-1 |
| Stoke Gabriel | v | Exwick Villa | 2-2, AWp |
| Tavistock | v | Torpoint Athletic | 2-1 |
| Teignmouth | v | Wadebridge Town | 6-0 |
| Tiverton Town | v | Budleigh Salterton | 4-0 |
| University of Exeter | v | Sidmouth Town | 5-1 |
| Vospers Oak Villa | v | Camelford | 0-4 |
| Wendon United | v | Sticker | 3-1 |

**ROUND 2**

| | | | |
|---|---|---|---|
| Appledore | v | Exwick Villa | 8-1 |
| Bodmin Town | v | St Martins | 3-0 |
| Callington Town | v | Tavistock | 0-3 |
| Camelford | v | Newton Abbot Spurs | 0-2 |
| Crediton United | v | Witheridge | 2-4 |
| Cullompton Rangers | v | Exmouth Town | 1-0 |
| Dobwalls | v | St Blazey | 2-3 |
| Godolphin Atlantic | v | Plymstock United | 5-2 |
| Helston Athletic | v | Falmouth Town | 3-1 |
| Holsworthy | v | Teignmouth | 0-2 |
| Liskeard Athletic | v | Brixham | 1-0 |
| Millbrook | v | Ivybridge Town | 0-8 |
| Mousehole | v | Newquay | 3-1 |
| Saltash United | v | Plymouth Parkway | 4-3 |
| St Austell | v | Wendron United | 8-2 |
| Tiverton Town | v | University of Exeter | 1-2 |

**ROUND 3**

| | | | |
|---|---|---|---|
| Bodmin Town | v | Witheridge | 1-0 |
| Cullompton Rangers | v | Saltash United | 1-3 |
| Ivybridge Town | v | St Blazey | 3-2 |
| Liskeard Athletic | v | Godolphin Atlantic | 0-7 |
| Mousehole | v | Appledore | 4-0 |
| Tavistock | v | Newton Abbot Spurs | 4-1 |
| Teignmouth | v | Helston Athletic | 3-4 |
| University of Exeter | v | St Austell | 2-3 |

**QUARTER FINALS**

| | | | |
|---|---|---|---|
| Helston Athletic | v | Bodmin Town | 0-2 |
| Ivybridge Town | v | Godolphin Atlantic | |
| Mousehole | v | Tavistock | 4-2 |
| Saltash United | v | St Austell | 1-3 |

**SEMI FINALS**

| | | | |
|---|---|---|---|
| Bodmin Town | v | Mousehole | 3-2 |
| Godolphin Atlantic | v | St Austell | 2-1 |

**FINAL**

| | | | |
|---|---|---|---|
| Bodmin Town | v | Godolphin Atlantic | 4-1 aet |

## BODMIN TOWN
Founded: 1896 Nickname:

**Secretary:** Nick Giles **(T)** **(E)** nickgiles@live.co.uk
**Chairman:** James Chapman **Manager:** Darren Gilbert
**Ground:** Priory Park, Bodmin, Cornwall PL31 2AE **(T)** 01208 78165
**Colours(change):** Yellow & black (All white)
**ADDITIONAL INFORMATION:**
**Previous League:** South Western.
**Honours:** South Western League 1990-91, 93-94, 2005-06.
South West Peninsula Premier Division 2007-08, 08-09, 11-12, 12-13, 15-16. Cornwall Senior Cup 2011-12, 12-13, 15-16.

## CALLINGTON
Founded: 1989 Nickname: The Pasty Men

**Secretary:** Nick Smith **(T)** **(E)** womble1954@me.com
**Chairman:** Andrew Long **Manager:** Steve Matters
**Ground:** Ginsters Marshfield Parc PL17 7DR **(T)** 01579 382 647
**Colours(change):** Red & black (Yellow & blue)
**ADDITIONAL INFORMATION:**
**Previous League:** South Western.
**League honours:** South West Peninsula Division One West 2013-14.

## CAMELFORD
Founded: 1893 Nickname: Camels

**Secretary:** Hilary Kent **(T)** **(E)** hilarykent@camelfordfc.fsnet.co.uk
**Chairman:** Ollie Rowe **Manager:** Reg Hambly
**Ground:** Trefew Park, PL32 9TS **(T)**
**Colours(change):** White & blue (Blue & white)
**ADDITIONAL INFORMATION:**
**Honours:** South West Peninsula Division One West 2010-11.

## CULLOMPTON RANGERS
Founded: 1945 Nickname: The Cully

**Secretary:** Alan Slark **(T)** **(E)** alanslark1@tiscali.co.uk
**Chairman:** Brian Horner **Manager:** Hedley Steele
**Ground:** Speeds Meadow, Cullompton EX15 1DW **(T)** 01884 33090
**Colours(change):** Red & black (Blue & white)
**ADDITIONAL INFORMATION:**
**Previous League:** Devon County 1992-2007.

## EXMOUTH TOWN
Founded: 1933 Nickname: The Town

**Secretary:** Brian Barnden **(T)** **(E)** brian7645@btinternet.com
**Chairman:** Bob Chamberlain **Manager:** Richard Pears
**Ground:** King George V, Exmouth EX8 3EE **(T)** 01395 263 348
**Colours(change):** All royal blue (All red)
**ADDITIONAL INFORMATION:**
**Previous League:** Devon & Exeter League > 2007.
**Honours:** South West Peninsula Division 1 East 2012-13.

## FALMOUTH TOWN
Founded: 1949 Nickname: The Ambers

**Secretary:** Wayne Pascoe **(T)** **(E)** pascoerichard@hotmail.com
**Chairman:** Graham Medlin **Manager:** Gary Pascoe & Andrew Westgarth
**Ground:** Bickland Park, Bickland Water Road, Falmouth TR11 4PB **(T)** 01326 375 156
**Colours(change):** Amber & black (All blue)
**ADDITIONAL INFORMATION:**
**Honours:** South Western League 1961-62, 65-66, 67-68, 70-71, 71-72, 72-73, 73-74, 85-86, 86-87, 88-89, 89-90, 91-92, 96-97, 99 -2000. Western League 1974-75, 75-76, 76-77, 77-78. Cornwall Combination 1983-84.

## GODOLPHIN ATLANTIC AFC
Founded: 1980 Nickname: G Army

**Secretary:** Margaret Ashwood **(T)** **(E)** godolphin.arms@btconnect.com
**Chairman:** Tania Semmens **Manager:** Jamie Lowry
**Ground:** Godolphin Way, Cornwall TR7 3BU **(T)**
**Colours(change):** Sky blue & white (Maroon & black)
**ADDITIONAL INFORMATION:**
**Previous League:** East Cornwall Premier > 2008.
**Honours:** South West Peninsula Div.1 West 2012-13.

## HELSTON ATHLETIC

Founded: 1896 Nickname: The Blues

**Secretary:** Paul Hendy **(T)** **(E)** paul.m.hendy@btinternet.com
**Chairman:** Paul Hendy **Manager:** Steve 'Sid' Taylor
**Ground:** Kellaway Park, Helston TR13 8PJ **(T)** 01326 573742 (Clubhouse)
**Colours(change):** All blue (All white)
**ADDITIONAL INFORMATION:**
**Honours:** South West Peninsula Div.1 West 2014-15.

## IVYBRIDGE TOWN

Founded: 1925 Nickname: The Ivys

**Secretary:** Paul Cocks **(T)** **(E)** secretary@ivybridgefc.com
**Chairman:** Dave Graddon **Manager:** Nicky Marker
**Ground:** Erme Valley, Ermington Road, Ivybridge PL21 9ES **(T)** 01752 896 686
**Colours(change):** Green & black (Yellow & blue)
**ADDITIONAL INFORMATION:**
**Previous League:** Devon County.
**Honours:** Devon County League 2005-06.

## LAUNCESTON

Founded: 1891 Nickname: The Clarets

**Secretary:** Keith Ellacott **(T)** **(E)** launcestonfc@aol.com
**Chairman:** Alan Bradley
**Ground:** Pennygillam Ind. Est., Launceston PL15 7ED **(T)** 01566 773 279
**Colours(change):** All claret (Sky blue & black)
**ADDITIONAL INFORMATION:**
**Previous League:** South Western.
**Honours:** South Western League 1995-96.

## NEWQUAY

Founded: 1890 Nickname: The Peppermints

**Secretary:** John Moore **(T)** **(E)** bubbamoore68@sky.com
**Chairman:** Don Pratt **Manager:** Tony MacKellar
**Ground:** Mount Wise TR7 2BU **(T)** 01637 872 935
**Colours(change):** Red & white (Blue & yellow)
**ADDITIONAL INFORMATION:**
**League honours:** South West Peninsula Division One West 2011-12.

## PLYMOUTH ARGYLE RESERVES

Founded: 1886 Nickname: The Pilgrims

**Secretary:** Glyn Carpenter **(T)** **(E)** chippycarps@gmail.com
**Chairman:** James Brent **Manager:** Kevin Nancekivell
**Ground:** Coach Road TQ12 1EJ **(T)**
**Colours(change):** Green & white (All yellow)
**ADDITIONAL INFORMATION:**

## PLYMOUTH PARKWAY AFC

Founded: 1988 Nickname: The Parkway

**Secretary:** Genny Turner **(T)** **(E)** gennyt@sky.com
**Chairman:** Mark Russell **Manager:** Kevin Hendy & Darren Stewart
**Ground:** Bolitho Park, St Peters Road, Manadon, Plymouth PL5 3JH **(T)**
**Colours(change):** Yellow & blue (Red & blue)
**ADDITIONAL INFORMATION:**
**Previous Name:** Ex-Air Flyers Plymouth.
**Previous League:** South Western 1998-2007.
**League honours:** South West Peninsula Premier Division 2013-14. **Cups:** Throgmorton Cup 2010-11, 2013-14.

## SALTASH UNITED

Founded: 1945 Nickname: The Ashes

**Secretary:** Steve Ladlow **(T)** **(E)** steve.ladlow57@gmail.com
**Chairman:** Bill Wakeham **Manager:** Matt Cusack
**Ground:** Kimberley Stadium, Callington Road, Saltash PL12 6DX **(T)** 01752 845 746
**Colours(change):** Red & white stripes & black (Blue & black)
**ADDITIONAL INFORMATION:**
**Previous League:** South Western 2006-07.
**Honours:** South Western League 1953-54, 75-76. Western League Division 1 1976-77, Premier 1984-85, 86-87, 88-89.

## ST. AUSTELL

Founded: 1890 Nickname: The Lily Whites

**Secretary:** Neil Powell **(T)** **(E)** neilpowell9@aol.com
**Chairman:** James Hutchings **Manager:** Jason Chapman & Dan Nancarrow
**Ground:** Poltair Park, Trevarthian Road, St Austell PL25 4LR **(T)** 01726 66099
**Colours(change):** All white (Yellow & blue)
**ADDITIONAL INFORMATION:**
**Previous League:** South Western 1951-2007.

## ST. BLAZEY

Founded: 1896 Nickname: The Green & Blacks

**Secretary:** George Allen **(T)** **(E)** geoallen.spurs1@btinternet.com
**Chairman:** Martin Richards **Manager:** Alan Carey
**Ground:** Blaise Park, Station Road, St Blazey PL24 2ND **(T)** 01725 814 110 **Capacity:** 3,000
**Colours(change):** Green & black (Blue & white)
**ADDITIONAL INFORMATION:**
**Previous League:** South Western 1951-2007.
**League honours:** South Western Lge 1954-55, 57-58, 62-63, 63-64, 80-81, 82-83, 98-99, 2000-01, 01-02, 02-03, 03-04, 04-05, 06-07.

## TAVISTOCK

Founded: 1888 Nickname: The Lambs

**Secretary:** Shaun Greening **(T)** **(E)** secretary@tavistockfc.com
**Chairman:** Chris Fenner **Manager:** Stuart Henderson
**Ground:** Langsford Park, Red & Black Club, Crowndale Road, Tavistock PL19 8JR **(T)** 01822 614 447
**Colours(change):** White with red & black (All blue)
**ADDITIONAL INFORMATION:**
**Previous League:** South Western 1968-2007.
**Honours:** South West Peninsula League Division One East 2014-15.

## TIVERTON RESERVES

Founded: 1913 Nickname: Tivvy

**Secretary:** Celia Graham **(T)** **(E)** celiagraham@talktalk.net
**Chairman:** Peter Buxton **Manager:** Warren Patmore
**Ground:** Ladysmead EX16 6SG **(T)** 01884 252 397
**Colours(change):** All yellow (All white)
**ADDITIONAL INFORMATION:**
**Honours:** South West Peninsula League Division One East 2015-16.

## TORPOINT ATHLETIC

Founded: 1887 Nickname: The Point

**Secretary:** Robbie Morris **(T)** **(E)** robbietafc81@live.co.uk
**Chairman:** Paul Whitworth **Manager:** Dan Cole
**Ground:** The Mill, Mill Lane, Carbeile Road, Torpoint PL11 2RE **(T)** 01752 812 889
**Colours(change):** Yellow & black (All blue)
**ADDITIONAL INFORMATION:**
**Previous League:** South Western 1962-2007.
**Honours:** South Western League 1964-65, 66-67.

## WITHERIDGE

Founded: 1920 Nickname: The Withy

**Secretary:** Chris Cole **(T)** **(E)** chriscole128@hotmail.com
**Chairman:** Andre Pike **Manager:** Peter Buckingham
**Ground:** Edge Down Park, Fore Street, Witheridge EX16 8AH **(T)** 01884 861 511
**Colours(change):** All blue (Orange & blue)
**ADDITIONAL INFORMATION:**
**Previous League:** Devon County 2006-07.

# GROUND DIRECTIONS-PREMIER DIVISION

**BODMIN TOWN-Priory Park, Bodmin, Cornwall PL31 2AE. Tel: 01208 781 65.**
Situated in Priory Park through main car park. Use football car park on Saturdays.

**CALLINGTON - Ginsters Marshfield Parc PL17 7DR. Tel: 01579 382 647.**
Ground is in the grounds of Callington Community College which is a quarter of a mile from the town centre.

**CAMELFORD-Trefrew Park PL32 9TS.**
From the South drive into Camelford up Victoria Road for 300 yards, turn left into Oakwood Rise. Follow road around for approximately 300 yards. Entrance is on the right up the lane. From the North as you enter Camelford turn right into Oakwood Rise then as above.

**CULLOMPTON RANGERS-Speeds Meadow, Cullompton EX15 1DW. Tel: 01884 33090.**
Leave M5 at junction 28, left at Town Centre, at Meadow Lane turn left past Sports Centre, at end of road turn right, then in 100 yards turn left into ground at end of lane.

**EXMOUTH TOWN -King George V, Exmouth EX8 3EE. Tel: 01395 263348.**
From Junction 30 of M5 take te A376 to Exmouth, on entering the town the ground is on your right, before the railway station.

**FALMOUTH TOWN-Bickland Park, Bickland Water Road, Falmouth TR11 4PB. Tel: 01326 375 156.**
Take Penryn by-pass from Asda roundabout. Leave by-pass at Hillhead roundabout, take first right and follow industrial estate signs. Ground 1/2 mile on the left.

**GODOLPHIN ATLENTIC -Godlphin Way TR7 3BU.**
Off Henver Road turn into Godolphin Way and ground is then first entrance on the left.

**HELSTON - Kellaway Park, Helston TR13 8PJ Tel: 01326 573 742.**
From Redruth, go across 5 roundabouts, final one by Tesco, then turn first left.

**IVYBRIDGE TOWN-Erme Valley, Ermington Road, Ivybridge. Tel: 01752 896 686.**
From Plymouth-leave A38 at Ivybridge and follow signs towards Ermington. Ground is immediately next to South Devon Tennis Centre. From Exeter-leave A38 at Ivybridge. Ground is in front of you at the end of the slip road.

**LAUNCESTON-Pennygillam, Pennygillam Ind. Est., Launceston PL15 7ED. Tel: 01566 773 279.**
Leave A30 onto Pennygillam roundabout, turn into Pennygillam Industrial Estate. Ground is 400 yards on the left.

**NEWQUAY AFC-Mount Wise TR7 2BU**
From link road turn right onto Mount Wise, just past traffic lights turn Right into Clevedon Road.

**PLYMOUTH ARGYLE RESERVES - Coach Road TQ12 1EJ**
Ground is located at the Devon County FA Head-Quarters in Newton Abbot.

**PLYMOUTH PARKWAY-Bolitho Park, St Peters Road, Manadon, Plymouth PL5 3OZ.**
From Cornwall/Exeter exit at the Manadon/Tavistock junction off the Plymouth Parkway (A38), off roundabout into St Peters Road. Entrance is one mile on the right.

**SALTASH UNITED-Ground: Kimberley Stadium, Callington Road, Saltash PL12 6DX. Tel: 01752 845 746.**
At the top of Town Centre fork right at mini-roundabout. Ground is situated 400m ahead on the left-hand side next to Leisure Centre and Police Station.

**ST AUSTELL-Poltair Park, Trevarthian Road, St Austell PL25 4LR Tel: 07966 130 158**
Near Poltair School and St Austell Brewery (5 minutes from St Austell Rail Station).

**ST BLAZEY-Blaise Park, Station Road, St Blazey PL24 2ND. Tel: 01725 814 110.**
A390 from Lostwithiel to St Austell. At village of St Blazey turn left at traffic lights by Church/Cornish Arms pub into Station Road. Ground is 200 yards on the left.

**LISKEARD ATHLETIC-Lux Park Sport Association, Coldstyle Road, Lux Park, Liskeard PL14 2HZ. Tel: 01579 342 665.**
From the Parade (middle of town) turn left at the monument, then first right following signs for Leisure Centre at Lux Park.

**STOKE GABRIEL - G J Churchward Memorial TQ9 6RR. Tel: 01803 782 913.**
At Tweenaway Cross turn Right, after quarter of a mile turn Left at the Parkers Arms Inn. After approx 1 mile ground entrance is signposted on your right, before the village itself.

**TAVISTOCK - G J Churchward Memorial TQ9 6RR. Tel: 01803 782 913.**
Take signs for Tavistock College and Sports Centre, go past the College and the ground entrance is a further 100 meters on your left hand side.

**TIVERTON RESERVES - Ladysmead EX16 6SG**
Exit the M5 at Junction 27, Head towards Tiverton on the A361 dual carriageway travelling for about seven miles. Ignore the first junction for A396 Tiverton and Bickleigh (Gornhay Cross) and keep going (this is important) a little further until you reach a large roundabout. Turn left at the roundabout take first exit (A3126) for the Town Centre and Castle, continue along that road for about 400 yds crossing a new roundabout, passing college, and and Tiverton Rugby Club until you meet a mini roundabout. Go straight across the mini roundabout & you will see Ladysmead.

**TORPOINT ATHLETIC-The Mill, Mill Lane, Carbeile Road, Torpoint PL11 2NA. Tel: 01752 812 889.**
Take turning at Carbeile Inn onto Carbeille Road and first turning on the right into Mill Lane.

**WITHERIDGE-Edge Down Park, Fore Street, Witheridge EX16 8AH. Tel: 01884 861 511.**
B3137 Tiverton to Witheridge, on entering the village football pitch is on the right-hand side before the Fire Station and School.

| South West Peninsula Division One East | | |
|---|---|---|
| **ALPHINGTON** | The Chronicles, Church Road, Alphington, Exeter EX2 8SW | 01392 279 556 |
| **APPLEDORE** | Marshford, Churchill Way, Appledore EX39 1PA | 01237 475 015 |
| **AXMINSTER TOWN** | Tiger Way EX13 5HN | |
| **BOVEY TRACEY** | Mill Marsh Park, Ashburton Rd, Bovey TQ13 9FF | 01626 833 896 |
| **BRIXHAM AFC** | Wall Park Road TQ5 9UE | |
| **BUDLEIGH SALTERTON** | Greenway Lane, Budleigh Salterton EX9 6SG | 01395 443 850 |
| **CREDITON UNITED** | Lords Meadow, Commercial Road, Crediton EX17 1ER | 01363 774 671 |
| **EXWICK VILLA** | College Sports Hub, Exwick, Exeter EX4 2BQ | |
| **GALMPTON UNITED AFC** | War Memorial Playing Field, Greenway Road, Galmpton, Brixham TQ5 0LN | |
| **LIVERTON UNITED** | Halford, Liverton TQ12 6JF | |
| **NEWTON ABBOT SPURS** | Recreation Ground, Marsh Road, Newton Abbot TQ12 2AR | 01626 365 343 |
| **SIDMOUTH TOWN** | Manstone Recreation Ground, Manstone Lane, Sidmouth EX10 9TF | 01395 577 087 |
| **ST. MARTINS AFC** | Minster Park, Exminster EX6 8AT | |
| **STOKE GABRIEL** | G J Churchward Memorial TQ9 6RR | 01803 782 913 |
| **TEIGNMOUTH** | Coombe Valley, Coombe Lane, Teignmouth TQ14 9EX | 01626 776 688 |
| **TORRIDGESIDE** | Donnacroft, Torrington EX38 7HT | |
| **TOTNES & DARTINGTON SC** | Foxhole Sports Ground, Dartington TQ9 6EB | |
| **UNIVERSITY OF EXETER** | University Sports Ground, Topsham Road, Topsham EX3 0LY | 01392 879 542 |

| South West Peninsula Division One West | | |
|---|---|---|
| **BUDE TOWN** | Broadclose Park EX23 8DR | |
| **DOBWALLS** | Lantoom Park, Duloe Road, Dobwalls PL14 4LU | 07721 689 380 |
| **ELBURTON VILLA** | Haye Road, Elburton, Plymouth PL9 8HS | 01752 480 025 |
| **HOLSWORTHY AFC** | Upcott Field, North Road, Holsworthy EX22 6HF | 01409 254 295 |
| **ILLOGAN RBL** | Oxland Parc TR16 4DG | 01209 216 488 |
| **LISKEARD ATHLETIC** | Lux Park PL14 3HZ | 01579 342 665 |
| **MILLBROOK AFC** | Jenkins Park PL10 1EN | 01752 822 113 |
| **MOUSEHOLE** | Trungle Parc, Paul, Penzance TR19 6UG | 01736 731 518 |
| **PENRYN ATHLETIC** | Kernick, Kernick Road, Penryn TR10 9EW | 01326 375 182 |
| **PENZANCE** | Penlee Park, Alexandra Place, Penzance TR18 4NE | 01736 361 964 |
| **PLYMOUTH MAJON** | Derriford Road PL6 8BH | |
| **PLYMSTOCK UNITED** | Dean Cross, Dean Cross Road, Plymstock PL9 7AZ | 01752 406 776 |
| **PORTHLEVEN** | Gala Parc, Mill Lane, Porthleven TR13 9LQ | 01326 569 655 |
| **ST. DENNIS** | Boscawen Park, St Dennis PL26 8DW | 01726 822 635 |
| **STICKER** | Burngullow Park PL26 7EN | 01726 71003 |
| **VOSPERS OAK VILLA** | Weston Mill, Ferndale Road, Weston Mill, Plymouth PL2 2EL | 01752 363 352 |
| **WADEBRIDGE TOWN** | Bodieve Park, Bodieve Road, Wadebridge PL27 6EA | 01208 812 537 |
| **WENDRON UNITED** | Underlane TR13 0EH | 01209 860 946 |

# SOUTHERN COMBINATION FOOTBALL LEAGUE

**Sponsored by:** Macron Store

**Founded:** 1920 (As Sussex County League >2015)

**Recent Champions: 2013:** Peacehaven & Telscombe **2014:** East Preston **2015:** Littlehampton Town

| DIVISION ONE | P | W | D | L | F | A | GD | Pts |
|---|---|---|---|---|---|---|---|---|
| 1 Horsham | 38 | 31 | 4 | 3 | 131 | 22 | 109 | 97 |
| 2 Eastbourne Town | 38 | 27 | 5 | 6 | 107 | 42 | 65 | 86 |
| 3 Newhaven | 38 | 25 | 3 | 10 | 120 | 39 | 81 | 78 |
| 4 Lancing | 38 | 24 | 5 | 9 | 98 | 46 | 52 | 77 |
| 5 Chichester City | 38 | 23 | 5 | 10 | 99 | 46 | 53 | 74 |
| 6 Pagham | 38 | 23 | 4 | 11 | 94 | 49 | 45 | 73 |
| 7 Horsham YMCA | 38 | 22 | 5 | 11 | 105 | 62 | 43 | 71 |
| 8 Loxwood | 38 | 22 | 5 | 11 | 95 | 60 | 35 | 71 |
| 9 Broadbridge Heath | 38 | 19 | 6 | 13 | 75 | 57 | 18 | 63 |
| 10 Eastbourne United Association | 38 | 19 | 6 | 13 | 81 | 72 | 9 | 63 |
| 11 Littlehampton Town | 38 | 19 | 3 | 16 | 103 | 76 | 27 | 60 |
| 12 Arundel | 38 | 16 | 8 | 14 | 88 | 68 | 20 | 56 |
| 13 Hassocks (-1) | 38 | 13 | 9 | 16 | 59 | 66 | -7 | 47 |
| 14 Worthing United | 38 | 12 | 6 | 20 | 68 | 83 | -15 | 42 |
| 15 AFC Uckfield Town | 38 | 8 | 9 | 21 | 62 | 91 | -29 | 33 |
| 16 Wick & Barnham United | 38 | 10 | 2 | 26 | 55 | 105 | -50 | 32 |
| 17 Shoreham | 38 | 8 | 5 | 25 | 53 | 94 | -41 | 29 |
| 18 Hailsham Town | 38 | 4 | 6 | 28 | 47 | 149 | -102 | 18 |
| 19 East Preston (R) | 38 | 3 | 3 | 32 | 35 | 144 | -109 | 12 |
| 20 St Francis Rangers (R) | 38 | 1 | 3 | 34 | 10 | 214 | -204 | 6 |

### CLUB MOVEMENTS

**Premier Division - In:** Crawley Down Gatwick (P). Haywards Heath Town (P).

**Out:** East Preston (R). Horsham (P - Isthmian Div.1 South). St Francis Rangers (R).

**Division One - In:** AFC Varndeanians (P). Billinghurst (P).

**Out:** Crawley Down Gatwick (P). Haywards Heath Town (P).

## LEAGUE CUP

**HOLDERS:** NEWHAVEN

**ROUND 1**

| | | | |
|---|---|---|---|
| Steyning Town | v | Storrington | 2-1 |
| Langney Wanderers | v | Saltdean United | 4-0 |
| Southwick | v | Midhurst & Easebourne | 9-0 |
| Haywards Heath Town | v | Little Common | 0-2 |
| Sidlesham | v | Oakwood | 1-4 |

**ROUND 2**

| | | | |
|---|---|---|---|
| Mile Oak | v | Arundel | 2-5 |
| Ringmer | v | AFC Uckfield Town | 2-7 |
| Newhaven | v | St Francis Rangers | 7-4 |
| Steyning Town | v | Wick & Barnham United | 2-1 |
| Langney Wanderers | v | Eastbourne United | 1-2 |
| Chichester City | v | Loxwood | 2-3 aet |
| Eastbourne Town | v | Shoreham | 3-1 |
| Horsham | v | Pagham | 2-1 |
| Broadbridge Heath | v | East Preston | 8-1 |
| Selsey | v | Southwick | 2-0 |
| Little Common | v | Bexhill United | 3-2 |
| Oakwood | v | Littlehampton Town | 3-1 |
| Hailsham Town | v | Seaford Town | 6-0 |
| Worthing United | v | Lancing | 2-2, 5-6p |
| Horsham YMCA | v | Crawley Down Gatwick | 5-3 aet |
| Tie awarded to Crawley D.G. after Horsham YMCA played an ineligible player. | | | |
| Hassocks | v | Lingfield | 5-1 |

**ROUND 3**

| | | | |
|---|---|---|---|
| Arundel | v | AFC Uckfield Town | 1-3 |
| Newhaven | v | Steyning Town | 2-1 |
| Eastbourne United | v | Loxwood | 0-1 |
| Eastbourne Town | v | Horsham | 0-1 |
| Broadbridge Heath | v | Selsey | 3-0 |
| Little Common | v | Oakwood | 4-3 aet |
| Hailsham Town | v | Lancing | 1-4 |
| Crawley Down Gatwick | v | Hassocks | 2-3 |

**QUARTER FINALS**

| | | | |
|---|---|---|---|
| AFC Uckfield Town | v | Newhaven | 1-4 aet |
| Loxwood | v | Horsham | 1-2 |
| Broadbridge Heath | v | Little Common | 2-1 |
| Broadbridge played an ineligable player - tie awarded to Little Common | | | |
| Lancing | v | Hassocks | 4-0 |

**SEMI FINALS**

| | | | |
|---|---|---|---|
| Newhaven | v | Horsham | 2-1 |
| Little Common | v | Lancing | 0-1 |

**FINAL**

| | | | |
|---|---|---|---|
| Newhaven | v | Lancing | 1-2 |

| DIVISION ONE | P | W | D | L | F | A | GD | Pts |
|---|---|---|---|---|---|---|---|---|
| 1 Haywards Heath Town | 32 | 30 | 0 | 2 | 123 | 23 | 100 | 90 |
| 2 Crawley Down Gatwick | 32 | 24 | 2 | 6 | 88 | 50 | 38 | 74 |
| 3 Oakwood | 32 | 19 | 3 | 10 | 89 | 64 | 25 | 60 |
| 4 Storrington | 32 | 18 | 4 | 10 | 68 | 45 | 23 | 58 |
| 5 Southwick | 32 | 17 | 5 | 10 | 75 | 54 | 21 | 56 |
| 6 Mile Oak | 32 | 17 | 4 | 11 | 61 | 52 | 9 | 55 |
| 7 Little Common | 32 | 16 | 2 | 14 | 75 | 61 | 14 | 50 |
| 8 Lingfield | 32 | 15 | 3 | 14 | 76 | 66 | 10 | 48 |
| 9 Langney Wanderers | 32 | 14 | 5 | 13 | 73 | 55 | 18 | 47 |
| 10 Steyning Town | 32 | 14 | 3 | 15 | 56 | 63 | -7 | 45 |
| 11 Sidlesham | 32 | 14 | 1 | 17 | 54 | 72 | -18 | 43 |
| 12 Ringmer | 32 | 10 | 7 | 15 | 47 | 68 | -21 | 37 |
| 13 Selsey | 32 | 9 | 4 | 19 | 53 | 88 | -35 | 31 |
| 14 Bexhill United | 32 | 8 | 5 | 19 | 48 | 74 | -26 | 29 |
| 15 Midhurst & Easebourne | 32 | 7 | 7 | 18 | 37 | 64 | -27 | 28 |
| 16 Seaford Town | 32 | 5 | 4 | 23 | 22 | 67 | -45 | 19 |
| 17 Saltdean United | 32 | 2 | 7 | 23 | 30 | 109 | -79 | 13 |

| DIVISION THREE | P | W | D | L | F | A | GD | Pts |
|---|---|---|---|---|---|---|---|---|
| 1 AFC Varndeanians | 30 | 22 | 4 | 4 | 91 | 26 | 65 | 70 |
| 2 Roffey | 30 | 20 | 4 | 6 | 101 | 37 | 64 | 64 |
| 3 Cowfold | 30 | 19 | 6 | 5 | 81 | 34 | 47 | 63 |
| 4 Rottingdean Village | 30 | 19 | 6 | 5 | 71 | 32 | 39 | 63 |
| 5 Billingshurst | 30 | 19 | 5 | 6 | 73 | 35 | 38 | 62 |
| 6 Bosham | 30 | 18 | 5 | 7 | 70 | 27 | 43 | 59 |
| 7 Upper Beeding | 30 | 14 | 10 | 6 | 70 | 39 | 31 | 52 |
| 8 Montpelier Villa | 30 | 15 | 2 | 13 | 70 | 61 | 9 | 47 |
| 9 Rustington | 30 | 11 | 7 | 12 | 68 | 64 | 4 | 40 |
| 10 Westfield | 30 | 11 | 5 | 14 | 58 | 69 | -11 | 38 |
| 11 Ferring | 30 | 9 | 4 | 17 | 54 | 77 | -23 | 31 |
| 12 Clymping | 30 | 7 | 4 | 19 | 57 | 96 | -39 | 25 |
| 13 Alfold | 30 | 5 | 8 | 17 | 41 | 75 | -34 | 23 |
| 14 Ifield Galaxy | 30 | 7 | 1 | 22 | 41 | 108 | -67 | 22 |
| 15 AFC Roffey Club | 30 | 3 | 4 | 23 | 34 | 95 | -61 | 13 |
| 16 Hurstpierpoint | 30 | 2 | 3 | 25 | 24 | 129 | -105 | 9 |

### CLUB MOVEMENTS

**Division Three - In:** Jarvis Brook (P - Mid Sussex), Lancing United (P - West Sussex), Sidlesham (R), Worthing Town Leisure (P - Brighton, Worthing & District).

**Out:** AFC Varndeanians (P), Billingshurst (P), Hurstpierpoint (R - Mid Sussex), Ifield Galaxy (W).

## AFC UCKFIELD TOWN
Founded: 1988 Nickname: The Oaks

**Secretary:** ustin Farrow **(T)** 07906 853 082 **(E)** justin.farrow@pacficlifere.com
**Chairman:** Tom Parker
**Ground:** The Oaks, Old Eastbourne Road, Uckfield TN22 5QL **(T)** 01825 890 905
**Capacity:** **Seats:** **Covered:** **Midweek Matchday:** **Clubhouse:** Yes

**Colours(change):** Red & black/black/black (All blue)
**Previous Names:** Wealden 1988-2010. AFC Uckfield & Uckfield Town merged in 2014.
**Previous Leagues:**
**Records:**
**Honours:** Sussex County League Division 2 League Cup 2004-05, Division Two 2010-11.

**10 YEAR RECORD**

| 06-07 | | 07-08 | | 08-09 | | 09-10 | | 10-11 | | 11-12 | | 12-13 | | 13-14 | | 14-15 | | 15-16 | |
|---|---|---|---|---|---|---|---|---|---|---|---|---|---|---|---|---|---|---|---|
| SxC2 | 4 | SxC2 | 9 | SxC2 | 15 | SxC2 | 8 | SxC2 | 1 | SxC1 | 8 | SxC1 | 21 | SxC2 | 10 | SxC2 | 2 | SCP | 15 |

## ARUNDEL
Founded: 1889 Nickname: Mulletts

**Secretary:** Kathy Wilson **(T)** 07778 783 294 **(E)** kathymwilson@btinternet.com
**Chairman:** Bob Marchant **Prog Ed:** Kathy Wilson
**Ground:** Mill Road, Arundel, W. Sussex BN18 9QQ **(T)** 01903 882 548
**Capacity:** 2,200 **Seats:** 100 **Covered:** 200 **Midweek Matchday:** Tuesday **Clubhouse:** Yes **Shop:** No

**Colours(change):** Red & white/white/red (All Blue)
**Previous Names:**
**Previous Leagues:** West Sussex
**Records:** **Att:** 2,200 v Chichester (League) 1967-68 **Goalscorer:** Paul J Bennett **App:** 537 Paul Bennett (Goalkeeper)
**Honours:** Sussex County Champions 1957-58, 58-59, 86-87.

**10 YEAR RECORD**

| 06-07 | | 07-08 | | 08-09 | | 09-10 | | 10-11 | | 11-12 | | 12-13 | | 13-14 | | 14-15 | | 15-16 | |
|---|---|---|---|---|---|---|---|---|---|---|---|---|---|---|---|---|---|---|---|
| SxC1 | 3 | SxC1 | 3 | SxC1 | 2 | SxC1 | 12 | SxC1 | 9 | SxC1 | 17 | SxC1 | 14 | SxC1 | 12 | SxC1 | 10 | SCP | 12 |

## BROADBRIDGE HEATH
Founded: 1919 Nickname:

**Secretary:** Andrew Crisp **(T)** 07501 057 654 **(E)** crispandy@hotmail.com
**Chairman:** Keith Soane
**Ground:** Broadbridge Leisure Centre, Wickhurst Lane Broadbridge Heath Horsham RH12 **(T)** 01403 211 311
**Capacity:** **Seats:** **Covered:** **Midweek Matchday:** **Clubhouse:**

**Colours(change):** Blue & white/blue & white/blue (White/red/red)
**Previous Names:** None
**Previous Leagues:** Horsham & District >1971. West Sussex 1971-79. Southern Counties Combination 1979-83.
**Records:**
**Honours:**

**10 YEAR RECORD**

| 06-07 | | 07-08 | | 08-09 | | 09-10 | | 10-11 | | 11-12 | | 12-13 | | 13-14 | | 14-15 | | 15-16 | |
|---|---|---|---|---|---|---|---|---|---|---|---|---|---|---|---|---|---|---|---|
| SxC2 | 17 | SxC2 | 17 | SxC2 | 9 | SxC2 | 14 | SxC2 | 6 | SxC2 | 5 | SxC2 | 6 | SxC2 | 2 | SxC1 | 9 | SCP | 9 |

## CHICHESTER CITY
Founded: 2000 Nickname: Chi

**Secretary:** Mark Warren **(T)** 07774 942 643 **(E)** mark@chichestercityfc.co.uk
**Chairman:** Brent Williams
**Ground:** Oaklands Park, Chichester, W Sussex PO19 6AR **(T)** 01243 533 368
**Capacity:** 2,000 **Seats:** none **Covered:** 200 **Midweek Matchday:** Tuesday **Clubhouse:** Yes **Shop:** Yes

**Colours(change):** White & green/green/white (Orange & black/orange/orange)
**Previous Names:** Chichester FC (pre 1948), Chichester City 1948-2000. Merged with Portfield in 2000, Chicester City Utd 2000-08
**Previous Leagues:**
**Records:**
**Honours:** Sussex County Division One 2003-04.

**10 YEAR RECORD**

| 06-07 | | 07-08 | | 08-09 | | 09-10 | | 10-11 | | 11-12 | | 12-13 | | 13-14 | | 14-15 | | 15-16 | |
|---|---|---|---|---|---|---|---|---|---|---|---|---|---|---|---|---|---|---|---|
| SxC1 | 11 | SxC1 | 16 | SxC1 | 7 | SxC1 | 3 | SxC1 | 14 | SxC1 | 20 | SxC1 | 19 | SxC1 | 11 | SxC1 | 14 | SCP | 5 |

## CRAWLEY DOWN GATWICK

Founded: 1993 Nickname: The Anvils

**Secretary:** Mick Martin **(T)** 07973 620 759 **(E)** martinmd@btinternet.com
**Chairman:** Donal Barrett
**Ground:** The Haven Centre, Hophurst Lane, Crawley Down RH10 4LJ **(T)** 01342 717 140
**Capacity:** 1,000 **Seats:** **Covered:** 50 **Midweek Matchday:** **Clubhouse:** Yes

**Colours(change):** All Red (All green)
**Previous Names:** Crawley Down United > 1993. Crawley Down Village > 1999. Crawley Down > 2012.
**Previous Leagues:** Mid Sussex, Sussex County > 2011. Isthmian 2011-14.
**Records:** 404 v East Grinstead Town 96
**Honours:** Sussex County Division One 2010-11.

**10 YEAR RECORD**

| 06-07 | 07-08 | 08-09 | 09-10 | 10-11 | 11-12 | 12-13 | 13-14 | 14-15 | 15-16 |
|---|---|---|---|---|---|---|---|---|---|
| SxC2 16 | SxC2 6 | SxC2 3 | SxC1 8 | SxC1 1 | Isth1S 16 | Isth1S 13 | Isth1S 23 | SxC1 19 | SC1 2 |

## EASTBOURNE TOWN

Founded: 1881 Nickname: Town

**Secretary:** Mark Potter **(T)** 07720 846 857 **(E)** eastbournetownfc@live.co.uk
**Chairman:** Tony Guarino
**Ground:** The Saffrons, Compton Place Road, Eastbourne BN21 1EA **(T)** 01323 724 328
**Capacity:** 3,000 **Seats:** 200 **Covered:** Yes **Midweek Matchday:** **Clubhouse:** Yes **Shop:** No

**Colours(change):** Yellow/blue/blue (Red/blue/red)
**Previous Names:** Devonshire Park 1881-89
**Previous Leagues:** Southern Amateur 1907-46, Corinthian 1960-63, Athenian 1963-76, Sussex County 1976-2007. Isthmian 2007-14.
**Records:** 7,378 v Hastings United - 1953
**Honours:** Sussex County League 1976-77.
Sussex Senior Cup x12. Sussex RUR Charity Cup x4 Most recently 2014-15. AFA Senior Cup x2.

**10 YEAR RECORD**

| 06-07 | 07-08 | 08-09 | 09-10 | 10-11 | 11-12 | 12-13 | 13-14 | 14-15 | 15-16 |
|---|---|---|---|---|---|---|---|---|---|
| SxC1 1 | Isth1S 19 | Isth1S 13 | Isth1S 22 | Isth1S 18 | Isth1S 14 | Isth1S 11 | Isth1S 24 | SxC1 4 | SCP 2 |

## EASTBOURNE UNITED ASSOCIATION

Founded: 1894 Nickname: The U's

**Secretary:** Dean Allchin **(T)** 07949 588 497 **(E)** deanallchin@hotmail.co.uk
**Chairman:** Brian Cordingley
**Ground:** The Oval, Channel View Road, Eastbourne, BN22 7LN **(T)** 01323 726 989
**Capacity:** 3,000 **Seats:** 160 **Covered:** 160 **Midweek Matchday:** Tuesday **Clubhouse:** Yes **Shop:** Yes

**Colours(change):** White/black/white (Light blue/white/light blue).
**Previous Names:** Eastbourne Old Comrades, Eastbourne United (merged with Shinewater Assoc in 2000)
**Previous Leagues:** Metropolitan 1956-64, Athenian 64-77, Isthmian 77-92
**Records:** **Att:** 11,000 at Lynchmore
**Honours:** Sussex County Division Two 2013-14.

**10 YEAR RECORD**

| 06-07 | 07-08 | 08-09 | 09-10 | 10-11 | 11-12 | 12-13 | 13-14 | 14-15 | 15-16 |
|---|---|---|---|---|---|---|---|---|---|
| SxC1 7 | SxC1 11 | SxC1 1 | SxC1 6 | SxC1 20 | SxC2 6 | SxC2 4 | SxC2 1 | SxC1 12 | SCP 10 |

## HAILSHAM TOWN

Founded: 1885 Nickname: The Stringers

**Secretary:** Stuart Fairway **(T)** 07831 223 874 **(E)** stuartfairway1984@googlemail.com
**Chairman:** Derek York
**Ground:** The Beaconfield, Western Road, Hailsham BN27 3JF **(T)** 01323 840 446
**Capacity:** 2,000 **Seats:** none **Covered:** 100 **Midweek Matchday:** Tuesday **Clubhouse:** Yes

**Colours(change):** Yellow & green/green/green (All light blue)
**Previous Names:** Hailsham.
**Previous Leagues:** East Sussex, Southern Combination
**Records:** **Att:** 1350 v Hungerford T. FA Vase Feb 89 **Goalscorer:** Howard Stephens 51 **App:** Phil Comber 713
**Honours:**

**10 YEAR RECORD**

| 06-07 | 07-08 | 08-09 | 09-10 | 10-11 | 11-12 | 12-13 | 13-14 | 14-15 | 15-16 |
|---|---|---|---|---|---|---|---|---|---|
| SxC1 6 | SxC1 13 | SxC1 15 | SxC1 19 | SxC1 16 | SxC2 2 | SxC1 12 | SxC1 16 | SxC1 17 | SCP 18 |

## HASSOCKS

Founded: 1902 Nickname: The Robins

**Secretary:** Sarah Dalgleish **(T)** 07919 926 863 **(E)** markd.sarahw@btinternet.com
**Chairman:** Roger Hobbs
**Ground:** The Beacon, Brighton Road, Hassocks BN6 9NA **(T)** 01273 846 040
**Capacity:** 1,800 **Seats:** 270 **Covered:** 100 **Midweek Matchday:** Tuesday **Clubhouse:** Yes **Shop:** No

**Colours(change):** All Red. (All green)
**Previous Names:**
**Previous Leagues:** Mid Sussex, Brighton & Hove & Dist and Southern Counties Comb
**Records:** **Att:** 610 v Burgess Hill Town **Goalscorer:** Pat Harding 43
**Honours:**

**10 YEAR RECORD**

| 06-07 | 07-08 | 08-09 | 09-10 | 10-11 | 11-12 | 12-13 | 13-14 | 14-15 | 15-16 |
|---|---|---|---|---|---|---|---|---|---|
| SxC1 5 | SxC1 7 | SxC1 16 | SxC1 14 | SxC1 6 | SxC1 4 | SxC1 7 | SxC1 6 | SxC1 15 | SCP 13 |

## HAYWARDS HEATH TOWN

Founded: 1888 Nickname:

**Secretary:** Mark Russ **(T)** 07796 677 661 **(E)** marussy@mac.com
**Chairman:** Mick Cottingham
**Ground:** Hanbury Park Stadium, Haywards Heath RH16 4GL **(T)** 01444 412 837
**Capacity:** **Seats:** **Covered:** **Midweek Matchday:** **Clubhouse:**

**Colours(change):** All blue (All red)
**Previous Names:**
**Previous Leagues:**
**Records:**
**Honours:** Sussex County League 1949-50, 69-70. Sussex Senior Cup 1957-58.
Southern Combination League (formerly Sussex County) Division One 2015-16.

**10 YEAR RECORD**

| 06-07 | 07-08 | 08-09 | 09-10 | 10-11 | 11-12 | 12-13 | 13-14 | 14-15 | 15-16 |
|---|---|---|---|---|---|---|---|---|---|
| SxC3 6 | SxC3 3 | SxC3 3 | SxC3 3 | SxC3 8 | SxC3 15 | SxC3 2 | SxC2 5 | SxC2 9 | SC1 1 |

## HORSHAM YMCA

Founded: 1898 Nickname: YM's

**Secretary:** Andy Flack **(T)** 07775 857 392 **(E)** andy.flack@horsham.gov.uk
**Chairman:** Ron Moulding
**Ground:** Gorings Mead, Horsham, West Sussex RH13 5BP **(T)** 01403 252 689
**Capacity:** 1,575 **Seats:** 150 **Covered:** 200 **Midweek Matchday:** **Clubhouse:** Yes **Shop:** No

**Colours(change):** White/black/red (All red)
**Previous Names:**
**Previous Leagues:** Horsham & District, Brighton & Hove, Mid Sussex, Sussex County > 2006, Isthmian 2006-11.
**Records:** 950 v Chelmsford City - FA Cup 2000
**Honours:** Sussex League 2004-05, 05-06.
John O'Hara Cup 2001-02.

**10 YEAR RECORD**

| 06-07 | 07-08 | 08-09 | 09-10 | 10-11 | 11-12 | 12-13 | 13-14 | 14-15 | 15-16 |
|---|---|---|---|---|---|---|---|---|---|
| Isth1S 9 | Isth1S 21 | SxC1 3 | Isth1S 11 | Isth1S 22 | SxC1 16 | SxC1 10 | SxC1 4 | SxC1 5 | SCP 7 |

## LANCING

Founded: 1941 Nickname:

**Secretary:** John Rea **(T)** 07598 301 296 **(E)** john.rea62@yahoo.com
**Chairman:** Martin Gander
**Ground:** Culver Road, Lancing, West Sussex BN15 9AX **(T)** 01903 767 285
**Capacity:** **Seats:** **Covered:** **Midweek Matchday:** **Clubhouse:** Yes

**Colours(change):** Yellow/blue/yellow (White/black/black)
**Previous Names:** Lancing Athletic
**Previous Leagues:** Brighton & Hove & District.
**Records:**
**Honours:** Brighton League 1946-47, 47-48.

**10 YEAR RECORD**

| 06-07 | 07-08 | 08-09 | 09-10 | 10-11 | 11-12 | 12-13 | 13-14 | 14-15 | 15-16 |
|---|---|---|---|---|---|---|---|---|---|
| SxC2 14 | SxC2 12 | SxC2 9 | SxC2 11 | SxC2 2 | SxC1 2 | SxC1 13 | SxC1 18 | SxC1 8 | SCP 4 |

## LITTLEHAMPTON TOWN

Founded: 1896 Nickname: Golds

**Secretary:** Paul Cox **(T)** 07771 623 224 **(E)** paulcox280458@yahoo.co.uk

**Chairman:** Robert McAlees

**Ground:** St Flora Sportsfield, St Flora's Road, Littlehampton BN17 6BD **(T)** 01903 716 390

**Capacity:** **Seats:** **Covered:** **Midweek Matchday:** **Clubhouse:**

**Colours(change):** Gold/black/black (White/white/red)

**Previous Names:** Littlehampton 1896-1938.

**Previous Leagues:** None

**Records:** Lost in the FAC Prelim v Tunbridge W. 15-16 on pens after 40 kicks had been taken - At the time a European record and one short of the World record.

**Honours:** Sussex County Division Two 2003-04, 12-13, Division One 2014-15.

**10 YEAR RECORD**

| 06-07 | 07-08 | 08-09 | 09-10 | 10-11 | 11-12 | 12-13 | 13-14 | 14-15 | 15-16 |
|---|---|---|---|---|---|---|---|---|---|
| SxC1 20 | SxC2 8 | SxC2 14 | SxC2 12 | SxC2 11 | SxC2 4 | SxC2 1 | SxC1 3 | SxC1 1 | SCP 11 |

## LOXWOOD

Founded: 1920 Nickname: Magpies

**Secretary:** John Bellamy **(T)** 07917 135 212 **(E)** bellas.john@btinternet.com

**Chairman:** Barry Hunter

**Ground:** Loxwood Sports Ass., Plaistow Road, Loxwood RH14 0RQ **(T)** 07791 766 857

**Capacity:** **Seats:** **Covered:** **Midweek Matchday:** **Clubhouse:**

**Colours(change):** Black & white/black/white (All red)

**Previous Names:**

**Previous Leagues:** West Sussex > 2006.

**Records:**

**Honours:** Sussex County League Division Three 2007-08.

**10 YEAR RECORD**

| 06-07 | 07-08 | 08-09 | 09-10 | 10-11 | 11-12 | 12-13 | 13-14 | 14-15 | 15-16 |
|---|---|---|---|---|---|---|---|---|---|
| SxC3 7 | SxC3 1 | SxC2 10 | SxC2 5 | SxC2 6 | SxC2 5 | SxC2 9 | SxC2 3 | SxC1 6 | SCP 8 |

## NEWHAVEN

Founded: 1887 Nickname:

**Secretary:** Martin Garry **(T)** 07768 508 011 **(E)** martin.garry@premierfoods.co.uk

**Chairman:** Martin Garry

**Ground:** The Trafalgar Ground, Fort Road Newhaven East Sussex BN9 9DA **(T)** 01273 513 940

**Capacity:** **Seats:** Yes **Covered:** Yes **Midweek Matchday:** **Clubhouse:** Yes

**Colours(change):** All red & yellow (All blue)

**Previous Names:** None

**Previous Leagues:** None

**Records:**

**Honours:** Sussex County League Division One 1953-54, 73-74, Division Two 1971-72, 90-91, Division Three 2011-12.

**10 YEAR RECORD**

| 06-07 | 07-08 | 08-09 | 09-10 | 10-11 | 11-12 | 12-13 | 13-14 | 14-15 | 15-16 |
|---|---|---|---|---|---|---|---|---|---|
| SxC3 9 | SxC3 5 | SxC3 4 | SxC3 9 | SxC3 7 | SxC3 1 | SxC2 2 | SxC1 13 | SxC1 7 | SCP 3 |

## PAGHAM

Founded: 1903 Nickname: The Lions

**Secretary:** Tony Shea **(T)** 07889 862 970 **(E)** bigteeshea@googlemail.com

**Chairman:** Tony Shea

**Ground:** Nyetimber Lane, Pagham, West Sussex PO21 3JY **(T)** 01243 266 112

**Capacity:** 2,000 **Seats:** 200 **Covered:** 200 **Midweek Matchday:** **Clubhouse:** Yes **Shop:** No

**Colours(change):** White/black/black (Green/green/red)

**Previous Names:** None

**Previous Leagues:** Chichester 1903-50, West Sussex 50-69

**Records:** **Att:** 1,200 v Bognor 1971 **Goalscorer:** Dick De Luca **App:** Graham Peach

**Honours:** Sussex County Division Two 1978-79, 86-87, 2006-07. Division One 80-81, 87-88, 88-89.

**10 YEAR RECORD**

| 06-07 | 07-08 | 08-09 | 09-10 | 10-11 | 11-12 | 12-13 | 13-14 | 14-15 | 15-16 |
|---|---|---|---|---|---|---|---|---|---|
| SxC2 1 | SxC1 9 | SxC1 11 | SxC1 17 | SxC1 4 | SxC1 6 | SxC1 5 | SxC1 7 | SxC1 3 | SCP 6 |

## PEACEHAVEN & TELSCOMBE

Founded: 1923 Nickname:

**Secretary:** Derek Earley **(T)** 07717 178 483 **(E)** derek@peacehavenfc.com
**Chairman:** Sue Norwood Tony Coade - 17/12/14 Antony Scott
**Ground:** The Sports Park, Piddinghoe Ave, Peacehaven, BN10 8RJ **(T)** 01273 582 471
**Capacity:** **Seats:** Yes **Covered:** Yes **Midweek Matchday:** **Clubhouse:** Yes

**Colours(change):** Black & white
**Previous Names:** Formed when Peacehaven Rangers and Telscombe Tye merged.
**Previous Leagues:** Sussex County > 2013. Isthmian 2013-16.
**Records:** Not known
**Honours:** Sussex County Division One 1978-79, 81-82, 82-83, 91-92, 92-93, 94-95, 95-96, 2012-13, Division Three 2005-06, Division Two 2008-09.

**10 YEAR RECORD**

| 06-07 | 07-08 | 08-09 | 09-10 | 10-11 | 11-12 | 12-13 | 13-14 | 14-15 | 15-16 |
|---|---|---|---|---|---|---|---|---|---|
| SxC2 5 | SxC2 4 | SxC2 1 | SxC1 2 | SxC1 3 | SxC1 5 | SxC1 1 | Isth1S 1 | Isth P 21 | Isth1S 24 |

## SHOREHAM

Founded: 1892 Nickname: Musselmen

**Secretary:** Clive Harman **(T)** 07761 054 431 **(E)** clive.harman.1966@btinternet.com
**Chairman:** Stuart Slaney
**Ground:** Middle Road, Shoreham-by-Sea, West Sussex, BN43 6LT **(T)** 01273 454 261
**Capacity:** 1,500 **Seats:** 150 **Covered:** 700 **Midweek Matchday:** **Clubhouse:** Yes **Shop:** No

**Colours(change):** All blue (All red).
**Previous Names:** None.
**Previous Leagues:** West Sussex.
**Records:** **Att:** 1,342 v Wimbledon
**Honours:** Sussex County Division One 1951-52, 52-53, 77-78. Division Two 61-62, 76-77, 93-94. John O'Hara League Cup 2007-08.

**10 YEAR RECORD**

| 06-07 | 07-08 | 08-09 | 09-10 | 10-11 | 11-12 | 12-13 | 13-14 | 14-15 | 15-16 |
|---|---|---|---|---|---|---|---|---|---|
| SxC1 13 | SxC1 12 | SxC1 6 | SxC1 9 | SxC1 18 | SxC1 18 | SxC1 17 | SxC1 14 | SxC1 16 | SCP 17 |

## WICK

Founded: 2013 Nickname:

**Secretary:** Marc Hilton **(T)** 07771 810 757 **(E)** wickfootballclub@outlook.com
**Chairman:** Linda Hallett
**Ground:** Crabtree Park, Coomes Way, Wick, Littlehampton, W Sussex BN17 7LS **(T)** 01903 713 535
**Capacity:** 1,000 **Seats:** 100 **Covered:** Yes **Midweek Matchday:** **Clubhouse:** Yes

**Colours(change):** Red & blue/red/red (Yellow/black/black).
**Previous Names:** Wick merged with Barnham to form today's club in June 2013.
**Previous Leagues:** West Sussex
**Records:**
**Honours:**

**10 YEAR RECORD**

| 06-07 | 07-08 | 08-09 | 09-10 | 10-11 | 11-12 | 12-13 | 13-14 | 14-15 | 15-16 |
|---|---|---|---|---|---|---|---|---|---|
| SxC1 16 | SxC1 5 | SxC1 4 | SxC1 4 | SxC1 15 | SxC1 14 | SxC1 16 | SxC2 6 | SxC2 3 | SCP 16 |

## WORTHING UNITED

Founded: 1952 Nickname:

**Secretary:** Mark Sanderson **(T)** 07968 856 183 **(E)** helsnmark@aol.com
**Chairman:** Steve Taylor
**Ground:** The Robert Albon Memorial Ground, Lyons Way BN14 9JF **(T)** 01903 234 466
**Capacity:** **Seats:** Yes **Covered:** Yes **Midweek Matchday:** **Clubhouse:** Yes

**Colours(change):** Sky blue & white/blue/sky blue (Red & black/black/red)
**Previous Names:** Wigmore Athletic 1952-88. Amalgamated with Southdown to form Worthing United in 1988.
**Previous Leagues:**
**Records:**
**Honours:** Sussex County Division Two 1973-74, 2014-15, Division Three 1989-90.

**10 YEAR RECORD**

| 06-07 | 07-08 | 08-09 | 09-10 | 10-11 | 11-12 | 12-13 | 13-14 | 14-15 | 15-16 |
|---|---|---|---|---|---|---|---|---|---|
| SxC1 18 | SxC1 17 | SxC1 20 | SxC2 2 | SxC2 3 | SxC1 14 | SxC1 22 | SxC1 20 | SxC2 1 | SCP 14 |

## AFC VARNDEANIANS
Founded: 1929 Nickname:

**Secretary:** Norman Wright **(T)** 07523 889 878 **(E)** norman.wright233@ntlworld.com
**Chairman:** Dave Bridges
**Ground:** Withdean Stadium, Tongdean Lane, Brighton BN1 5JD **(T)**
**Colours(change):** red & black/black/black (Yellow/green/yellow)
**ADDITIONAL INFORMATION:**
Mid Sussex & Brighton League Premier Division x7.
Southern Combination League (formerly Sussex County) Division Two 2015-16.

## BEXHILL UNITED
Founded: 2002 Nickname: The Pirates

**Secretary:** Simon Dunne **(T)** 07983 134 245 **(E)** simon_dunne@hotmail.co.uk
**Chairman:** Bill Harrison
**Ground:** The Polegrove, Brockley Road, Bexhill on Sea TN39 3EX **(T)** 07791 368 049
**Colours(change):** White & black/black/black (Sky blue/white/sky blue)
**ADDITIONAL INFORMATION:**

## BILLINGSHURST
Founded: 1891 Nickname: Hurst

**Secretary:** Jan Tilley **(T)** 07834 786 750 **(E)** kevtilley@btinternet.com
**Chairman:** Kevin Tilley
**Ground:** Jubilee Fields, Newbridge Road, Billingshurst, West Sussex. RH14 9HZ **(T)** 01403 786 445
**Colours(change):** Red & black/black/black (All sky blue)
**ADDITIONAL INFORMATION:**

## EAST PRESTON
Founded: 1966 Nickname:

**Secretary:** Keith Freeman **(T)** 07986 596 913 **(E)** keweia@btinternet.com
**Chairman:** Terry Doyle
**Ground:** Roundstone Recreation Ground, Lashmar Road, East Preston BN16 1ES **(T)** 01903 776 026
**Colours(change):** Black & white/black/black & white (All red)
**ADDITIONAL INFORMATION:**
Sussex County League Division Three 1983-84, Division Two 1997-98, 2011-12, Division One 2013-14.

## LANGNEY WANDERERS
Founded: 2010 Nickname:

**Secretary:** Tracey Saunders **(T)** 07711 811 017 **(E)** saunderstracey@sky.com
**Chairman:** Stephen Saunders
**Ground:** Shinewater Lane Playing Field, off Lavender Close, Milfoil Drive in north Langney, **(T)**
**Colours(change):** Blue & black/black/black (Black & pink/black/pink)
**ADDITIONAL INFORMATION:**

## LINGFIELD
Founded: 1893 Nickname: The Lingers

**Secretary:** John Tovey **(T)** 07778 879 144 **(E)** john.tovey@virginmedia.co.uk
**Chairman:** Bill Blenkin
**Ground:** Sports Pavillion, Godstone Road, Lingfield, Surrey RH7 6BT **(T)** 01342 834 269 **Capacity:** 1,000+
**Colours(change):** Red & Yellow/red/red. (Blue & white/blue/blue)
**ADDITIONAL INFORMATION:**

## LITTLE COMMON
Founded: 1966 Nickname: The Green Lane Boys

**Secretary:** Daniel Eldridge **(T)** 07759 125 252 **(E)** danieleldridge11@btinternet.com
**Chairman:** Daniel Eldridge
**Ground:** Little Common Recreation Ground, Green Lane, Bexhill on Sea TN39 4PH **(T)** 01424 845 861
**Colours(change):** Claret & blue/claret/claret (Yellow & black/black/black)
**ADDITIONAL INFORMATION:**
**Previous Name:** Albion United > 1986. **Previous League:** East Sussex 1994-2005.
**Honours:** East Sussex League 1975-76, 76-77, 2004-05.

## MIDHURST & EASEBOURNE

Founded: 1946 Nickname: The Stags

**Secretary:** Chris Shoesmith **(T)** 07790 379 643 **(E)** chris@contractcandles.com
**Chairman:** Darren Chiverton
**Ground:** Rotherfield, Dodsley Lane, Easebourne, Midhurst GU29 9BE **(T)** 01730 816 557
**Colours(change):** Blue/black/blue (Orange/blue/orange)
**ADDITIONAL INFORMATION:**
**Previous League:** West Sussex 1999-2002.
**Honours:** Sussex County League Division 2 Cup 1988-89, Division 3 Cup 2002-03.

## MILE OAK

Founded: 1960 Nickname: The Oak

**Secretary:** Chris Tew **(T)** 07733 323 453 **(E)** chris_tew@lineone.net
**Chairman:** Phil Brotherton
**Ground:** Mile Oak Recreation Ground, Chalky Road, Portslade BN41 2YU **(T)** 01273 423 854
**Colours(change):** Orange & black/black/black (All green)
**ADDITIONAL INFORMATION:**
**Previous League:** Brighton & Hove District.
**Honours:** Brighton & Hove District 1980-81. Sussex County League Division 2.

## OAKWOOD

Founded: 1962 Nickname: The Oaks

**Secretary:** Madeleine Williams **(T)** 07873 875 994 **(E)** peteandmad@blueyonder.co.uk
**Chairman:** Stuart Lovegrove
**Ground:** Tinsley Lane, Three Bridges, Crawley RH10 8AJ **(T)** 01293 515 742
**Colours(change):** Red & black/black/black (Blue & white/white/white)
**ADDITIONAL INFORMATION:**
**Previous League:** Southern Counties Combination 1980-84.
**Honours:** Sussex County Division 2 Cup 1989-90.

## RINGMER

Founded: 1906 Nickname: Blues

**Secretary:** Derek McDougall **(T)** 07842 169 264 **(E)** mcdougall64@btinternet.com
**Chairman:** Derek McDougall
**Ground:** Caburn Ground, Anchor Field, Ringmer BN8 5QN **(T)** 01273 812 738 **Capacity:** 1,000
**Colours(change):** Light blue & blue/blue/light blue. (Yellow/yellow/red).
**ADDITIONAL INFORMATION:** 1,350 v Southwick, Sussex County League, 1970-71.
Sussex County Division Two 1968-69. Division One 1970-71. Sussex Senior Cup 1972-73.

## SALTDEAN UNITED

Founded: 1966 Nickname: The Tigers

**Secretary:** Kevin Radcliffe **(T)** 07717 501 045 **(E)** secretary@saltdeanunitedfc.co.uk
**Chairman:** Robert Thomas
**Ground:** Hill Park, Coombe Vale Saltdean Brighton East Sussex BN2 8HJ **(T)** 01273 309 898
**Colours(change):** Red & black/black/black (Yellow & blue/blue/yellow)
**ADDITIONAL INFORMATION:**
**Previous Leagues:** Brighton > 1984.

## SEAFORD TOWN

Founded: 1888 Nickname: The Badgers

**Secretary:** John Smith **(T)** 07940 511 504 **(E)** johnsmithn@btinternet.com
**Chairman:** Bob Thomsett
**Ground:** The Crouch, Bramber Road, Seaford BN25 1AG **(T)** 01323 892 221
**Colours(change):** All red (All yellow)
**ADDITIONAL INFORMATION:**
**Honours:** Sussex County League Division Two 2005-06.

## SELSEY

Founded: 1903 Nickname: Blues

**Secretary:** Paul Senior **(T)** 07871 060 549 **(E)** selseyfootballclub@yahoo.com
**Chairman:** David Lee
**Ground:** The Bunn Leisure Stadium, High Street, Selsey, Chichester, PO20 0QH **(T)** 01243 603 420 **Capacity:** 1,000
**Colours(change):** All blue (All yellow).
**ADDITIONAL INFORMATION: Att:** 750-800 v Chichester or Portfield 1950's
Sussex County Division Two 1963-64, 75-76.

## SOUTHWICK

Founded: 1882 Nickname: The Wickers

**Secretary:** Jackie Royston (T) 07958 656 530 (E) jackieroyston@gmail.com
**Chairman:** Alan Petken
**Ground:** Old Barn Way, Southwick BN42 4NT (T) 01273 701 010
**Colours(change):** Red & black/black/black (Yellow & black/yellow/yellow)
**ADDITIONAL INFORMATION:**
**Previous League:** Isthmian 1985-92.
**Honours:** Sussex County League Division 1 x6, Division Three 2014-15. Sussex Senior Cup x10.

## ST. FRANCIS RANGERS

Founded: 2002 Nickname: Saints/Rangers

**Secretary:** John Goss (T) 07748 785 240 (E) j.goss@yahoo.co.uk
**Chairman:** Doug Benjamin **Prog Ed:** John Goss
**Ground:** Colwell Ground, Princess Royal Hospital, Lewes Rd, Haywards Hth RH16 4EX (T) 01444 474 021 **Capacity:** 1,000
**Colours(change):** Black & white/black/black (Yellow/white/yellow)
**ADDITIONAL INFORMATION:**

## STEYNING TOWN

Founded: 1892 Nickname: The Barrowmen

**Secretary:** Daniel Fuller-Smith (T) 07889 367 956 (E) daniel@fuller-smith.co.uk
**Chairman:** Richard Woodbridge
**Ground:** The Shooting Field, Steyning, West Sussex BN44 3RQ (T) 01903 814 601
**Colours(change):** Red & white/red/red (All blue)
**ADDITIONAL INFORMATION:**
**Honours:** Sussex County League Division 2 1977-78, Division 1 1984-85, 85-86, League Cup 1978-79, 83-84, 85-86.

## STORRINGTON

Founded: 1920 Nickname: The Swans

**Secretary:** Keith Dalmon (T) 07889 367 956 (E) keithdalmon@btinternet.com
**Chairman:** Nigel Dyer
**Ground:** Recreation Ground, Pulborough Road, Storrington RH20 4HJ (T) 01903 745 860
**Colours(change):** All blue (Maroon/white/maroon)
**ADDITIONAL INFORMATION:**
**Honours:** Sussex County League Division 2 Cup 1979, Division 3 Cup 1998, Division 3 2005.
Vernon Wentworth Cup 1998, 2003.

# GROUND DIRECTIONS - PREMIER & DIVISION ONE

**AFC UCKFIELD TOWN - The Oaks, Old Eastbourne Road, Uckfield, East Sussex TN22 5QL-07847 662 337**
Next to Rajdutt Restaurant on Old Eastbourne Road, south of Uckfield town centre.

**ARUNDEL - Mill Road, Arundel, West Sussex BN18 9QQ-01903 882 548**
On A27 from Worthing over railway bridge to roundabout. Second exit into Queen St to Town Centre. Cross Bridge over river, and turn right at miniroundabout. Enter pay and display car par on right. Ground entrance is located at the far left hand corner of the car park.

**BROADBRIDGE HEATH - Wickhurst Lane, Broadbridge Heath, Horsham RH12 3YS-01403 211 311**
Alongside A24, Horsham north/south bypass. From the A24 Horsham Bypass, at the large roundabout/underpass take the Broadbridge Heath Bypass towards Guildford and then at the first roundabout turn left into Wickhurst Lane.

**CHICHESTER CITY - Oaklands Park, Oaklands Way, Chichester PO19 6AR-07845 105 822**
Half a mile north of the city centre, adjacent to festival theatre. Turn into Northgate car park and entrance to the ground is next to the Chichester Rackets Club.

**CRAWLEY DOWN GATWICK -The Haven Sportsfield, Hophurst Lane, Crawley Down RH10 4LJ - 01342 717 140**
From B2028 South, turn right into Vicarage Road, pass the War Memorial (left side), Haven Centre is 200 Metres on your left. From 2028 North, turn left into Sandy Lane at the end of the road, turn left into Hophurst Lane (War Memorial on your right side), Haven Centre 200 Metres on your left. From A22 Felbridge, turn left at Felbridge traffic lights (A264), after 200 Metres fork left into Crawley Down Road (changes to Hophurst Hill and then Hopshurst Lane). Haven Centre on your right side.

**EASTBOURNE TOWN - The Saffrons, Compton Place Road, Eastbourne BN21 1EA - 01323 724 328**
From the A2270 into the Town Centre when you come to a mini roundabout by the railway station turn into Grove Road (opposite Eastbourne Railway Station). Past the Town all straight over then 2nd left into Compton Place Road.

**EASTBOURNE UNITED AFC-The Oval, Channel View Ropad, Eastbourne, East Sussex BN22 7LN-011323 726989**
From A27 Polegate bypass follow new A22 (Golden Jubilee Way) and cross roundabout into Highfield Link. At next roundabout take slip road left into Lottbridge Drive. At second roundabout take third exit into Seaside. 400 yards turn left opposite 'Co-op' into Channel View Road. Oval is second turning left.

**HAILSHAM TOWN-The Beaconsfield, Western Road, Hailsham, East Sussex BN27 3DN-01323 840446**

Turn off A22 at Diplocks Way roundabout. Ground on left (alleyway signposted opposite SETYRES WEALDEN) just before end of Diplocks Way.

**HASSOCKS-The Beacon, Brighton Rd., Hassocks BN6 9NA-01273 846040**

Off A273 Pyecombe Road to Burgess Hill. Ground is 300 yards south of Stonepound crossroads (B2116) to Hurstpeirpoint or Hassocks.

**HAYWARDS HEATH TOWN - Hanbury Park Stadium, Haywards Heath RH16 3PX-01444 412 837.**

A272 to Haywards Heath Town Centre. At Sussex roundabout, north on B2708 (Hazelgrove Road) take first right into New England Road. Fourth right Allen Road leads to ground. Allen Road is the only vehicular and pedestrian access to the ground.

**HORSHAM YMCA - Gorings Mead, Horsham, West Sussex RH13 5BP-01403 252 689**

Travel north on the A23, turning off onto the A272 at Bolney. Continue on the A272 to Cowfold then follow the A281 to Horsham. On entering the outskirts of the town, follow the A281 (Brighton Road) a short distance and Gorings Mead is a turning on the left. The entrance to the ground is at the bottom of Gorings Mead.

**LANCING - Culver Road, Lancing, West Sussex BN15 9AX. -01903 767 285.**

A27 to Manor Roundabout, south down Grinstead Lane, second right. Left at mini-roundabout, next turning right Culver Road. From railway 3rd turning on left (heading north) past Merry Monk public house.

**LITTLEHAMPTON TOWN - The Sportsfield, St Flora's Road, Littlehampton BN17 6BD-01903 716 390**

Leave A259 at Waterford Business Park and turn into Horsham Road. After Shell Garage turn left into St. Floras Road. Ground is at the end of road on the left.

**LOXWOOD - Loxwood Sports Association, Plaistow Road, Loxwood RH14 0SX-01404 753 185**

Leave A272 between Billinghurst and Wisborough Green and join the B2133 for 3.4 miles. On entering Loxwood Village take 1st left into Plaistow Road, ground situated 100 yards on the left.

**NEWHAVEN - Fort Road Recreation Ground, Newhaven, East Sussex BN9 9EE. -01273 513 940.**

From A259, follow the one way system around the town of Newhaven. Turn left into South Road (pass the Police Station) which becomes Fort Road. The ground is visible on the right just past a small parade of shops and before the approach road to Newhaven Fort. Postcode for Sat-nav users: BN9 9DA

**PAGHAM - Nyetimber Lane, Pagham, West Sussex PO21 3JY-01243 266 112**

A27 to junction of A259 on the Chichester Bypass. Exit to Pagham (Vinnetrow Road). At the Bear Inn (right hand side) turn left into Nyetimber Lane. The ground is 200 metres on right.

**SHOREHAM - Middle Road, Shoreham-by-Sea, West Sussex BN43 6LT-01273 454 261**

A27 to Shoreham. At Southlands Hospital turn left down Hammy Lane. Ground at bottom of Lane.

**WICK - Crabtree Park, Coomes Way, Wick, Littlehampton, West Sussex BN17 7LS Tel No: 01903 713 535**

A27 to Crossbush. A284 towards Littlehampton. After one mile over level crossing left into Coomes Way next to Locomotive pub. Ground at end.

**WORTHING UNITED - The Robert Albion Memorial Ground, Lyons Way, Worthing BN14 9JF. 01903 234 466.**

From the West past Hill Barn roundabout to second set of traffic lights, turn left into Lyons Way. From East first set of traffic lights at end of Sompting bypass, turn right into Lyons Way.

## DIVISION ONE

**AFC VARNDEANIANS - Withdean Stadium, Tongdean Lane, Brighton BN1 5JD - 07523 889 878**

Heading south on the A23, turn right opposite Withdean Park into Togdean Lane, and go under railway bridge.

**BEXHILL UNITED - The Polegrove, Brockley Road, Bexhill-on-Sea, East Sussex TN39 3EX-07815 425 682.**

From west take A259, at Little Common roundabout take fourth exit into Cooden Sea Road, Turn Left at Cooden Beech Hotel into Cooden Drive. About 1½ miles further, turn right for Brockley Road. Ground at bottom on the right hand side

**BILLINGSHURST - Jubilee Fields, Newbridge Road, Billingshurst, West Sussex. RH14 9HZ - 01403 786 445**

Follow A272 towards Petworth/Midhurst. When leaving the by-pass roundabout appr 50yds further on turn right to Jubilee Fields. (entrance to recycling tip) Follow Road Round.

**EAST PRESTON - Roundstone Recreation Ground, Lashmar Road, East Preston, West Sussex BN16 1ES - 01903 776026**

From Worthing proceed west for six miles on A259 to The Roundstone PH. From the roundabout, take the first exit, signposted East Preston. Turn left over the railway crossing. Turn left soon afterwards, and then first right into Roundstone Drive. Turn left into Lashmar Road and the approach road to the ground is on the right.

**LANGNEY WANDERERS - Shinewater Lane Playing Field, off Lavender Close, Milfoil Drive in north Langney, Eastbourne, East Sussex BN23 8DQ.**

A22 from Boship Roundabout : exit roundabout A22 , 1.3 miles 2nd exit onto A22, 0.7 miles 2nd exit onto A22 1.6 miles turn left onto Polegate bypass , 1.8 miles at roundabout 2nd exit onto Golden Jubilee Way A22, 0.1 miles 2nd exit Golden Jubilee Way Eastbourne, 0.6 miles 1st exit at roundabout onto Willingdon Drove , 0.6 miles turn left onto Milfoil Drive, 157 yards Shinewater Lane on your right.

**LINGFIELD - Sports Pavillion, Godstone Road, Lingfield, Surrey RH7 6BT - 01342 834 269**

A22 (London to Eastbourne Road) 4 miles north of East Grinstead, to Mormon Temple roundabout, take exit Lingfield (B2028) Newchapel Road for 1½ miles. Turn left at mini-roundabout. Ground ½ mile on left.

**LITTLE COMMON - Little Common Spts Pavilion, Little Common Rec., Green Lane, Bexhill-on-Sea, TN39 4PH-01424 845 861.**
From the west take the A259, at Little Common roundabout take second exit into Peartree Lane and then left into Little Common Recreation Ground car park.

**MIDHURST & EASEBOURNE - Rotherfield, Dodsley Lane, Easebourne, Midhurst, W. Sussex GU29 9BE-01730 816 557.**
Ground one mile out of Midhurst on London Road (A286) opposite Texaco Garage. Ample car parking.

**MILE OAK - Mile Oak Recreation Ground, Chalky Road, Portslade-01273 423 854.**
From A27 (Brighton Bypass) leave at A293 exit. Right at first roundabout. Ground 1 mile on right. Parking in the Sports Centre opposite the ground (park) entrance.

**OAKWOOD - Tinsley Lane, Three Bridges, Crawley RH10 8AJ - 01293 515 742.**
From the South on M23, take junction 10 exit left onto A2011, next roundabout take fourth exit right, next roundabout second exit, take first right into Tinsley Lane. Ground entrance 100 metres on left.

**RINGMER - Caburn Ground, Anchor Field, Ringmer-01273 812 738**
From Lewes road turn right into Springett Avenue, opposite Ringmer village

**SALTDEAN UNITED - Hill Park, Coombe Vale, Saltdean, Brighton BN2 8HJ-01273 309 898.**
From Brighton Pier proceed east along coast road to Rottingdean. Straight through Rottingdean lights then after ¼ mile turn left at Saltdean Lido. Proceed inland for approx. ½ mile then bear left down bridleway to Clubhouse.

**SEAFORD TOWN - The Crouch, Bramber Road, Seaford BN25 1AG-01323 892 221.**
A259 to Seaford. At mini roundabout by station, turn left (coming from Newhaven) or RIGHT (from Eastbourne). At end of Church Street, across junction, then left at end. After 500m turn left up Ashurst Road Bramber Road is at the top.

**SELSEY - High Street Ground, Selsey, Chichester, West Sussex-01243 603420**
Entering Selsey go straight over roundabout and straight over to mini-roundabout to traffic lights. Turn sharp right at lights, through supermarket car park to ground.

**SOUTHWICK - Old Barn Way, off Manor Hall Way, Southwick, Brighton BN42 4NT-01273 701 010**
A27 from Brighton take first left after Southwick sign to Leisure Centre. Ground adjacent. Five minutes walk from Fishergate or Southwick stations.

**ST FRANCIS RANGERS - Colwell Ground, The Princess Royal Hospital, Lewes Road, Haywards Heath, RH16 4EX Tel No: 01444 474 021 and social club 01444 441 881**
Enter through the main Hospital at mini-roundabout bear right and follow one way system. On reaching Sports Complex sign- straight ahead pass bowling green, tennis courts and swimming pool. Turn left through gate down unmade path to ground and parking.

**STEYNING TOWN - The Shooting Field, Steyning, W. Sussex BN44 3RP. -01903 812 228.**
Entering Steyning from the west. Take 1st left in the High St (Tanyard Lane) Follow into Shooting Field estate, ground is 4th turn on the left. Entering Steyning from the east. From the High St., turn right into Church St.. Turn left by Church into Shooting Field estate. NB Coaches MUST park in Church Street Car Park.

**STORRINGTON - Recreation Ground, Pulborough Road, Storrington RH20 4HJ-01903 745 860.**
Turn west on A283 (off A24). Ground opposite pond to west of village centre.

| Southern Combination Division Two | | |
|---|---|---|
| AFC ROFFEY CLUB | Spooners Road (off Crawley Road), Horsham, West Sussex, RH12 4DY | 01403 210 223 |
| ALFOLD | Recreation Ground, Dunsfold Road, Alfold, Surrey GU6 8JB | 07836 553 594 |
| BOSHAM | Recreation Ground, Walton Lane, Bosham, West Sussex PO10 8QF | 01243 681 279 |
| CLYMPING | Clymping Village Hall, Clymping, Littlehampton BN17 5GW | 07951 196 784 |
| COWFOLD | The Sports Ground, Bolney Road, Cowfold, West Sussex RH13 8AA | 07742 281 989 |
| FERRING | The Glebelands, Ferring, West Sussex BN12 5JL | 01903 243 618 |
| JARVIS BROOK | Limekiln Playing Fields, Palesgate Lane, Crowborough TN6 3HG | 07968 561 226 |
| LANCING UNITED | Croshaw Recreation Ground, Boundstone Lane, Lancing, West Sussex BN15 9LH | 07827 356 118 |
| MONTPELLIER VILLA | Falmer Sports Complex, University of Sussex, Pavillion Rd, Brighton BN1 9PJ | 07988 692 283 |
| ROFFEY | Bartholomew Way, Horsham RH12 5JL | 07763 973 101 |
| ROTTINGDEAN VILLAGE | Rottingdean Sports Centre, Falmer Road, Rottingdean BN2 7DA | 01273 306 436 |
| RUSTINGTON | Recreation Ground, Jubilee Avenue, Rustington BN16 3NB | 07966 217 603 |
| SIDLESHAM | Recreation Ground, Selsey Road Sidlesham Nr Chichester PO20 7RD | 07887 981 267 |
| UPPER BEEDING | Memorial Playing Fields, High Street, Upper Beeding BN44 3WN | 07710 900 629 |
| WESTFIELD | The Parish Field, Main Road, Westfield TN35 4SB | 07928 176 658 |
| WORTHING TOWN LEISURE | Palatine Park, Palatine Road, Worthing, Sussex BN12 6JN | 07710 768 744 |

# SOUTHERN COUNTIES EAST LEAGUE

**Sponsored by:** None
**Founded:** As the Kent League in 1966
**Recent Champions: 2013:** Erith & Belvedere
**2014:** Whyteleafe **2015:** Phoenix Sports

| PREMIER DIVISION | P | W | D | L | F | A | GD | Pts |
|---|---|---|---|---|---|---|---|---|
| 1 Greenwich Borough | 36 | 26 | 7 | 3 | 121 | 50 | 71 | 85 |
| 2 Hollands & Blair | 36 | 22 | 7 | 7 | 108 | 40 | 68 | 73 |
| 3 Ashford United (-1) | 36 | 23 | 7 | 6 | 95 | 46 | 49 | 66 |
| 4 Lordswood | 36 | 15 | 14 | 7 | 62 | 44 | 18 | 59 |
| 5 Sevenoaks Town | 36 | 16 | 10 | 10 | 61 | 50 | 11 | 58 |
| 6 Corinthian | 36 | 15 | 11 | 10 | 73 | 61 | 12 | 56 |
| 7 Crowborough Athletic | 36 | 14 | 9 | 13 | 65 | 77 | -12 | 51 |
| 8 Canterbury City | 36 | 15 | 5 | 16 | 64 | 59 | 5 | 50 |
| 9 Deal Town | 36 | 15 | 5 | 16 | 76 | 73 | 3 | 50 |
| 10 Cray Valley PM | 36 | 14 | 8 | 14 | 57 | 58 | -1 | 50 |
| 11 AFC Croydon Athletic | 36 | 13 | 7 | 16 | 58 | 64 | -6 | 46 |
| 12 Beckenham Town | 36 | 11 | 11 | 14 | 68 | 93 | -25 | 44 |
| 13 Erith Town | 36 | 12 | 7 | 17 | 53 | 73 | -20 | 43 |
| 14 Tunbridge Wells | 36 | 11 | 6 | 19 | 57 | 61 | -4 | 39 |
| 15 Rochester United | 36 | 10 | 9 | 17 | 43 | 77 | -34 | 39 |
| 16 Erith & Belvedere | 36 | 10 | 8 | 18 | 54 | 66 | -12 | 38 |
| 17 Fisher | 36 | 10 | 7 | 19 | 40 | 79 | -39 | 37 |
| 18 Croydon | 36 | 9 | 8 | 19 | 46 | 61 | -15 | 35 |
| 19 Holmesdale | 36 | 4 | 8 | 24 | 45 | 114 | -69 | 20 |

### CLUB MOVEMENTS

**Premier Division - In:** Bearsted (P), Sheppey United (P), Whitstable Town (R - Isthmian Div.1 South).
**Out:** Greenwich Borough (P), Holmesdale (R)

## LEAGUE CUP

**HOLDERS:** GREENWICH BOROUGH

**ROUND 1**

| | | | |
|---|---|---|---|
| Lordswood | v | Rochester United | 2-1 |
| Beckenham Town | v | Holmesdale | 2-0 |
| Cray Valley PM | v | Tunbridge Wells | 2-2, HW on pens |

**ROUND 2**

| | | | |
|---|---|---|---|
| AFC Croydon Athletic | v | Croydon | 0-3 |
| Canterbury City | v | Greenwich Borough | 1-1, 5-6p |
| Crowborough Athletic | v | Hollands & Blair | 2-4 |
| Lordswood | v | Ashford United | 3-4 |
| Corinthian | v | Beckenham Town | 4-2 |
| Erith & Belvedere | v | Fisher | 3-2 |
| Cray Valley PM | v | Erith Town | 2-0 |
| Deal Town | v | Sevenoaks Town | 4-2 |

**QUARTER FINALS**

| | | | |
|---|---|---|---|
| Croydon | v | Greenwich Borough | 1-0 |
| Hollands & Blair | v | Ashford United | 4-0 |
| Corinthian | v | Erith & Belvedere | 0-1 |
| Cray Valley PM | v | Deal Town | 1-0 |

**SEMI FINALS**

| | | | |
|---|---|---|---|
| Croydon | v | Hollands & Blair | 0-5 |
| Hollands & Blair | v | Croydon | 2-0 |
| | | | |
| Erith & Belvedere | v | Cray Valley PM | 1-2 |
| Cray Valley PM | v | Erith & Belvedere | 1-4 |

**FINAL**

| | | | |
|---|---|---|---|
| Hollands & Blair | v | Erith & Belvedere | 2-0 |

| PREMIER DIVISION | 1 | 2 | 3 | 4 | 5 | 6 | 7 | 8 | 9 | 10 | 11 | 12 | 13 | 14 | 15 | 16 | 17 | 18 | 19 |
|---|---|---|---|---|---|---|---|---|---|---|---|---|---|---|---|---|---|---|---|
| 1 AFC Croydon Athletic | | 1-2 | 2-6 | 0-1 | 1-2 | 3-4 | 4-1 | 2-1 | 0-0 | 3-0 | 2-0 | 3-0 | 0-6 | 0-4 | 5-1 | 1-2 | 0-1 | 0-1 | 3- |
| 2 Ashford United | 3-4 | | 6-1 | 2-0 | 1-1 | 1-0 | 6-1 | 2-0 | 5-3 | 4-2 | 1-2 | 2-1 | 0-2 | 2-0 | 2-1 | 1-1 | 4-0 | 1-1 | 2- |
| 3 Beckenham Town | 3-3 | 3-3 | | 5-2 | 1-1 | 1-2 | 1-1 | 1-2 | 2-1 | 1-0 | 1-1 | 3-1 | 4-4 | 0-4 | 1-5 | 0-2 | 1-3 | 2-2 | 2- |
| 4 Canterbury City | 0-1 | 0-2 | 6-1 | | 3-1 | 0-1 | 3-1 | 1-0 | 2-1 | 2-0 | 0-6 | 1-2 | 3-4 | 2-3 | 6-0 | 1-2 | 1-2 | 2-3 | 2- |
| 5 Corinthian | 5-3 | 1-2 | 2-2 | 1-1 | | 2-1 | 3-0 | 3-2 | 2-3 | 5-0 | 3-1 | 1-0 | 0-2 | 3-2 | 2-2 | 2-2 | 1-2 | 1-2 | 1- |
| 6 Cray Valley PM | 1-1 | 0-5 | 2-2 | 1-3 | 3-1 | | 4-5 | 2-0 | 2-3 | 1-0 | 2-0 | 1-2 | 1-1 | 2-1 | 5-3 | 3-0 | 0-0 | 4-1 | 0- |
| 7 Crowborough Athletic | 1-0 | 1-1 | 3-5 | 0-4 | 2-2 | 4-3 | | 1-0 | 2-2 | 1-1 | 3-0 | 2-2 | 2-4 | 0-6 | 6-1 | 2-1 | 4-2 | 3-1 | 1- |
| 8 Croydon | 1-2 | 0-4 | 7-1 | 0-1 | 2-2 | 0-0 | 1-3 | | 2-1 | 2-2 | 3-1 | 0-2 | 2-2 | 1-1 | 1-2 | 1-2 | 2-3 | 0-4 | 1- |
| 9 Deal Town | 2-0 | 2-6 | 1-3 | 0-3 | 1-6 | 2-1 | 1-2 | 1-2 | | 3-0 | 7-0 | 4-1 | 4-3 | 0-3 | 5-0 | 4-4 | 4-1 | 2-2 | 4- |
| 10 Erith & Belvedere | 0-2 | 2-2 | 2-0 | 3-2 | 2-3 | 1-3 | 2-0 | 1-2 | 1-0 | | 2-1 | 7-0 | 4-0 | 3-1 | 5-0 | 2-2 | 0-1 | 1-3 | 2- |
| 11 Erith Town | 1-1 | 0-2 | 3-2 | 3-3 | 3-2 | 0-0 | 3-2 | 3-0 | 1-3 | 1-1 | | 0-2 | 1-7 | 1-0 | 2-1 | 1-1 | 3-1 | 0-1 | 2- |
| 12 Fisher | 1-1 | 1-4 | 0-1 | 1-1 | 0-3 | 2-0 | 2-2 | 1-0 | 1-3 | 1-1 | 0-5 | | 2-5 | 3-6 | 1-0 | 1-0 | 1-1 | 0-3 | 0- |
| 13 Greenwich Borough | 2-0 | 4-2 | 2-2 | 4-0 | 4-0 | 3-1 | 5-1 | 4-3 | 4-1 | 2-0 | 3-2 | 4-0 | | 4-4 | 7-0 | 1-3 | 5-0 | 4-0 | 1- |
| 14 Hollands & Blair | 1-0 | 0-1 | 6-1 | 4-1 | 3-1 | 3-0 | 1-0 | 1-1 | 3-0 | 6-0 | 4-0 | 6-1 | 0-0 | | 7-0 | 3-3 | 7-2 | 1-1 | 3- |
| 15 Holmesdale | 5-2 | 2-3 | 2-4 | 0-0 | 1-2 | 1-3 | 0-2 | 1-1 | 2-2 | 1-0 | 1-1 | 1-4 | 4-7 | 0-6 | | 0-0 | 1-1 | 0-2 | 2- |
| 16 Lordswood | 2-2 | 3-0 | 3-2 | 1-1 | 2-2 | 1-1 | 2-1 | 1-2 | 1-0 | 4-1 | 5-0 | 0-0 | 0-1 | 1-3 | 4-0 | | 0-0 | 0-1 | 3- |
| 17 Rochester United | 1-1 | 0-7 | 1-1 | 0-2 | 1-1 | 1-2 | 1-2 | 1-3 | 1-4 | 3-1 | 2-1 | 1-2 | 1-4 | 3-3 | 2-0 | 0-1 | | 1-2 | 0- |
| 18 Sevenoaks Town | 0-1 | 3-3 | 7-1 | 3-2 | 2-3 | 3-1 | 2-2 | 0-0 | 1-2 | 0-3 | 1-3 | 1-0 | 1-2 | 1-2 | 2-2 | 0-0 | 1-1 | | 2- |
| 19 Tunbridge Wells | 1-4 | 2-1 | 0-1 | 1-2 | 1-2 | 2-0 | 0-1 | 2-1 | 3-0 | 2-2 | 3-1 | 3-2 | 1-4 | 2-0 | 4-3 | 2-3 | 1-2 | 0-1 | |

**At the end of the 2015-16 season the**
## KENT INVICTA LEAGUE (formed in 2011)
**merged with the Southern Counties East League, becoming Division One**

| | DIVISION ONE | P | W | D | L | F | A | GD | Pts |
|---|---|---|---|---|---|---|---|---|---|
| 1 | Bearsted | 38 | 29 | 4 | 5 | 91 | 33 | 58 | 91 |
| 2 | Sheppey United | 38 | 27 | 6 | 5 | 107 | 36 | 71 | 87 |
| 3 | Glebe | 38 | 26 | 4 | 8 | 107 | 45 | 62 | 82 |
| 4 | Sutton Athletic | 38 | 25 | 4 | 9 | 114 | 53 | 61 | 79 |
| 5 | Bridon Ropes | 38 | 21 | 7 | 10 | 73 | 49 | 24 | 70 |
| 6 | APM Contrast | 38 | 20 | 9 | 9 | 86 | 44 | 42 | 69 |
| 7 | Gravesham Borough | 38 | 21 | 5 | 12 | 118 | 66 | 52 | 68 |
| 8 | Lydd Town | 38 | 21 | 5 | 12 | 90 | 48 | 42 | 68 |
| 9 | Seven Acre & Sidcup | 38 | 20 | 5 | 13 | 91 | 72 | 19 | 65 |
| 10 | AC London (-6) | 38 | 15 | 12 | 11 | 77 | 59 | 18 | 51 |
| 11 | FC Elmstead | 38 | 14 | 8 | 16 | 73 | 74 | -1 | 50 |
| 12 | Meridian VP | 38 | 14 | 7 | 17 | 71 | 92 | -21 | 49 |
| 13 | Forest Hill Park | 38 | 13 | 7 | 18 | 46 | 69 | -23 | 46 |
| 14 | Phoenix Sports Reserves | 38 | 12 | 5 | 21 | 46 | 80 | -34 | 41 |
| 15 | Crockenhill | 38 | 11 | 7 | 20 | 57 | 90 | -33 | 40 |
| 16 | Orpington | 38 | 10 | 6 | 22 | 44 | 68 | -24 | 36 |
| 17 | Kent Football United | 38 | 6 | 6 | 26 | 47 | 119 | -72 | 24 |
| 18 | Eltham Palace | 38 | 6 | 3 | 29 | 36 | 132 | -96 | 21 |
| 19 | Rusthall | 38 | 4 | 8 | 26 | 40 | 97 | -57 | 20 |
| 20 | Lewisham Borough | 38 | 2 | 8 | 28 | 29 | 117 | -88 | 14 |

### CLUB MOVEMENTS
**Division One - In:** Holmesdale (R). K Sports (NC from APM Contrast), Snodland Town (P - Kent County), Sporting Club Thamesmead (NC from Seven Acre & Sidcup).
**Out:** AC London (S - Combined Counties), Bearsted (P), Sheppey United (P),

### CHALLENGE CUP

**HOLDERS:** HOLLANDS & BLAIR

**ROUND 1**

| | | | |
|---|---|---|---|
| Bearsted | v | Kent Football United | 4-2 |
| Meridian VP | v | Sutton Athletic | 1-4 |
| Seven Acre & Sidcup | v | Lewisham Borough | 4-1 |
| Rusthall | v | Lydd Town | 2-5 |

**ROUND 2**

| | | | |
|---|---|---|---|
| Bridon Ropes | v | FC Elmstead | 3-1 |
| Gravesham Borough | v | Sheppey United | 1-0 |
| Eltham Palace | v | Bearsted | 1-4 |
| Forest Hill Park | v | Sutton Athletic | 2-3 |
| Orpington | v | Phoenix Sports Reserves | 1-0 |
| Crockenhill | v | Glebe | 1-4 |
| APM Contrast | v | Seven Acre Sidcup | 1-0 |
| AC London | v | Lydd Town | 4-2 |

**QUARTER FINALS**

| | | | |
|---|---|---|---|
| Bridon Ropes | v | Gravesham Borough | 2-1 |
| Bearsted | v | Sutton Athletic | 0-1 |
| Orpington | v | Glebe | 0-7 |
| APM Contrast | v | AC London | 1-0 |

**SEMI FINALS**

| | | | |
|---|---|---|---|
| Bridon Ropes | v | Sutton Athletic | 1-1 |
| Sutton Athletic | v | Bridon Ropes | 3-2 |
| Glebe | v | APM Contrast | 3-1 |

**FINAL**

| | | | |
|---|---|---|---|
| Glebe | v | Sutton Athletic | 2-1 |

| | DIVISION ONE | 1 | 2 | 3 | 4 | 5 | 6 | 7 | 8 | 9 | 10 | 11 | 12 | 13 | 14 | 15 | 16 | 17 | 18 | 19 | 20 |
|---|---|---|---|---|---|---|---|---|---|---|---|---|---|---|---|---|---|---|---|---|---|
| 1 | AC London | | 2-1 | 0-3 | 4-1 | 1-1 | 4-1 | 1-3 | 2-0 | 1-2 | 1-4 | 6-4 | 3-0 | 2-2 | 1-1 | 1-0 | 2-1 | 7-1 | 1-1 | 1-1 | 3-3 |
| 2 | APM Contrast | 1-1 | | 2-3 | 2-1 | 5-0 | 2-0 | 1-1 | 4-1 | 1-2 | 3-1 | 5-1 | 6-0 | 1-0 | 0-0 | 4-0 | 3-0 | 2-0 | 0-2 | 1-1 | 1-0 |
| 3 | Bearsted | 1-0 | 0-2 | | 2-1 | 8-1 | 7-0 | 4-2 | 2-0 | 0-2 | 3-1 | 6-0 | 3-1 | 1-0 | 4-3 | 2-0 | 3-0 | 2-0 | 4-0 | 0-0 | 4-3 |
| 4 | Bridon Ropes | 2-1 | 1-1 | 3-0 | | 1-1 | 5-0 | 5-2 | 2-1 | 0-0 | 5-1 | 1-0 | 1-0 | 1-2 | 1-2 | 2-1 | 3-1 | 2-0 | 0-1 | 2-0 | 1-3 |
| 5 | Crockenhill | 1-1 | 0-4 | 1-2 | 1-2 | | 4-0 | 3-2 | 5-3 | 1-3 | 2-0 | 2-0 | 3-1 | 1-4 | 1-2 | 0-2 | 4-1 | 0-0 | 1-2 | 1-2 | 0-4 |
| 6 | Eltham Palace | 1-3 | 1-5 | 0-1 | 2-3 | 0-2 | | 1-3 | 1-2 | 2-11 | 3-2 | 3-3 | 3-0 | 1-1 | 1-3 | 2-1 | 0-1 | 1-0 | 2-3 | 0-4 | 0-6 |
| 7 | FC Elmstead | 0-0 | 0-3 | 0-2 | 1-3 | 2-1 | 6-1 | | 4-0 | 1-1 | 3-3 | 1-0 | 2-1 | 1-3 | 4-2 | 2-2 | 1-4 | 1-1 | 1-3 | 1-5 | 5-0 |
| 8 | Forest Hill Park | 1-1 | 0-0 | 0-2 | 0-2 | 3-2 | 1-1 | 2-1 | | 2-3 | 1-1 | 3-2 | 2-0 | 1-0 | 4-2 | 0-1 | 2-1 | 1-0 | 1-0 | 0-4 | 1-2 |
| 9 | Glebe | 1-3 | 1-2 | 1-3 | 1-1 | 1-2 | 7-0 | 4-0 | 3-1 | | 3-0 | 3-2 | 9-1 | 2-1 | 5-3 | 1-0 | 1-2 | 3-0 | 2-3 | 2-2 | 2-0 |
| 10 | Gravesham Borough | 5-1 | 2-2 | 4-1 | 0-3 | 2-0 | 13-0 | 1-3 | 1-0 | 4-1 | | 2-2 | 5-1 | 1-6 | 5-1 | 6-0 | 7-2 | 3-0 | 4-3 | 1-3 | 5-1 |
| 11 | Kent Football United | 0-2 | 1-0 | 0-0 | 0-6 | 4-4 | 3-2 | 0-8 | 1-3 | 0-3 | 1-2 | | 1-1 | 3-2 | 2-3 | 3-1 | 3-1 | 0-3 | 3-7 | 0-2 | 0-6 |
| 12 | Lewisham Borough | 1-1 | 1-3 | 0-5 | 1-2 | 1-3 | 6-1 | 1-0 | 1-1 | 0-6 | 1-9 | 0-2 | | 0-5 | 0-1 | 1-1 | 0-1 | 1-1 | 0-1 | 0-2 | 1-1 |
| 13 | Lydd Town | 3-2 | 3-2 | 4-0 | 1-2 | 4-0 | 3-0 | 0-0 | 4-1 | 0-1 | 3-1 | 8-1 | 3-1 | | 3-1 | 1-0 | 3-0 | 3-3 | 2-2 | 1-2 | 2-3 |
| 14 | Meridian VP | 1-7 | 3-3 | 0-2 | 1-1 | 2-0 | 3-0 | 3-4 | 2-2 | 0-4 | 1-1 | 3-1 | 2-2 | 1-2 | | 3-0 | 2-0 | 4-1 | 2-1 | 1-4 | 1-3 |
| 15 | Orpington | 0-3 | 3-3 | 0-0 | 1-3 | 0-1 | 4-0 | 1-3 | 2-3 | 0-1 | 2-3 | 2-0 | 2-1 | 0-5 | 2-0 | | 2-0 | 5-1 | 0-2 | 1-1 | 2-3 |
| 16 | Phoenix Sports Reserves | 0-2 | 0-2 | 0-0 | 3-3 | 1-1 | 1-0 | 2-1 | 0-1 | 1-2 | 0-6 | 3-1 | 2-2 | 2-1 | 2-1 | 1-2 | | 3-1 | 3-2 | 2-3 | 1-1 |
| 17 | Rusthall | 2-2 | 3-4 | 0-1 | 1-1 | 4-4 | 1-2 | 1-2 | 2-1 | 0-3 | 0-5 | 1-1 | 4-1 | 1-2 | 2-5 | 0-1 | 1-2 | | 1-0 | 0-4 | 1-6 |
| 18 | Seven Acre & Sidcup | 5-4 | 4-2 | 2-6 | 3-0 | 7-1 | 4-2 | 0-0 | 0-0 | 1-5 | 1-3 | 6-1 | 5-0 | 3-1 | 2-4 | 2-2 | 2-1 | 4-2 | | 1-2 | 4-1 |
| 19 | Sheppey United | 3-0 | 2-1 | 0-2 | 2-0 | 5-1 | 4-1 | 5-1 | 2-1 | 3-1 | 1-4 | 6-0 | 7-0 | 1-2 | 8-0 | 3-1 | 3-1 | 2-0 | 5-1 | | 3-4 |
| 20 | Sutton Athletic | 1-0 | 3-2 | 0-2 | 6-0 | 4-1 | 0-1 | 4-1 | 6-0 | 2-4 | 2-0 | 2-1 | 8-0 | 3-0 | 7-2 | 1-0 | 6-0 | 6-1 | 3-1 | 0-0 | |

## AFC CROYDON ATHLETIC

Founded: 2012 Nickname: The Rams

**Secretary:** Peter Smith **(T)** 07907 588 496 **(E)** secretary@afccroydonathletic.co.uk

**Chairman:** Paul Smith **Manager:** Kevin Raynor **Prog Ed:** Peter Smith

**Ground:** Mayfield Stadium, off Mayfield Road, Thornton Heath CR7 6DN **(T)**

**Capacity:** **Seats:** 163 **Covered:** 660 **Midweek Matchday:** Wednesday **Clubhouse:** Yes Yes

**Colours(change):** All maroon (Yellow/dark blue/yellow)

**Previous Names:** Norwood FC and Wandsworth FC amalgamated in 1986 to form Wandsworth & Norwood > 1990

**Previous Leagues:** Wandsworth Parthenon 1960-64, Surrey Senior 1964-77, London Spartan 1977-79. Isthmian > 2012. Co.Co 2012-15.

**Records:** **Record Att:** 1,372 v AFC Wimbledon 2004-05

**Honours:** **Previous Names:** Norwood FC and Wandsworth FC amalgamated in 1986 to form Wandsworth & Norwood > 1990. Croydon Athletic 1990-2012.

**10 YEAR RECORD**

| 06-07 | 07-08 | 08-09 | 09-10 | 10-11 | 11-12 | 12-13 | 13-14 | 14-15 | 15-16 |
|---|---|---|---|---|---|---|---|---|---|
| Isth1S 19 | Isth1S 13 | Isth1S 10 | Isth1S 1 | Isth P 21 | Isth1S dnf | | | CC1 2 | SCE 11 |

## ASHFORD UNITED

Founded: 1930 Nickname: The Nuts&Bolts

**Secretary:** Denise Peach **(T)** 07886 731 501 **(E)** aufootballclub@yahoo.com

**Chairman:** Derek Pestridge **Manager:** Danny Lye **Prog Ed:** Dave Read

**Ground:** The Homelands, Ashford Road TN26 1NJ **(T)** 01233 611 838

**Capacity:** **Seats:** Yes **Covered:** Yes **Midweek Matchday:** Tuesday **Clubhouse:** Yes

**Colours(change):** Green & white (Yellow & green)

**Previous Names:** Ashford Town 1930-2010.

**Previous Leagues:** Kent Invicta >2013

**Records:** **Att:** @ Homelands - 3,363 v Fulham, FAC 1st Rnd 1994. **Goalscorer:** Dave Arter - 192. **Apps:** Peter McRobert - 765.

**Honours:** Kent League 1948-49. Kent Senior Cup 1958-59, 62-63, 92-93, 95-96.

**10 YEAR RECORD**

| 06-07 | 07-08 | 08-09 | 09-10 | 10-11 | 11-12 | 12-13 | 13-14 | 14-15 | 15-16 |
|---|---|---|---|---|---|---|---|---|---|
| Isth1S 18 | Isth1S 8 | Isth1S 7 | Isth1S 20 | | K_Iv 5 | K_Iv 3 | SCE 2 | SCE 2 | SCE 3 |

## BEARSTED

Founded: 1895 Nickname:

**Secretary:** Roy Benton **(T)** 07849 809 875 **(E)** benton951@aol.com

**Chairman:** Duncan Andrews **Manager:** Kevin Stevens **Prog Ed:** Duncan Andrews

**Ground:** Otham Sports Club, Honey Lane, Otham, Maidstone ME15 8RG **(T)** 07860 360 280

**Capacity:** **Seats:** **Covered:** **Midweek Matchday:** Tuesday **Clubhouse:**

**Colours(change):** White/blue/blue (All yellow)

**Previous Names:**

**Previous Leagues:** Kent County >2011

**Records:**

**Honours:** Kent Invicta League 2015-16.

**10 YEAR RECORD**

| 06-07 | 07-08 | 08-09 | 09-10 | 10-11 | 11-12 | 12-13 | 13-14 | 14-15 | 15-16 |
|---|---|---|---|---|---|---|---|---|---|
| KC P 6 | KC P 8 | KC P 6 | KC P 8 | KC P 8 | K_Iv 7 | K_Iv 4 | K_Iv 6 | K_Iv 2 | K_Iv 1 |

## BECKENHAM TOWN

Founded: 1887 Nickname: Reds

**Secretary:** Peter Palmer **(T)** 07774 728 758 **(E)** peterpalmer3@sky.com

**Chairman:** Jason Huntley **Manager:** Jason Huntley **Prog Ed:** Peter Palmer

**Ground:** Eden Park Avenue, Beckenham Kent BR3 3JL **(T)** 07774 728 758

**Capacity:** 4,000 **Seats:** 120 **Covered:** 120 **Midweek Matchday:** Tuesday **Clubhouse:** Yes **Shop:** Yes

**Colours(change):** All red (All blue).

**Previous Names:** Stanhope Rovers.

**Previous Leagues:** South East London Amateur. Metropolitan. London Spartan.

**Records:** **Att:** 720 v Berkhamsted, FA Cup 1994-95. **Goalscorer:** Ricky Bennett. **Apps:** Lee Fabian - 985.

**Honours:**

**10 YEAR RECORD**

| 06-07 | 07-08 | 08-09 | 09-10 | 10-11 | 11-12 | 12-13 | 13-14 | 14-15 | 15-16 |
|---|---|---|---|---|---|---|---|---|---|
| Kent P 11 | Kent P 3 | Kent P 15 | Kent P 4 | Kent P 10 | Kent P 6 | Kent P 11 | SCE 8 | SCE 9 | SCE 12 |

## CANTERBURY CITY

Founded: 1904 Nickname:

**Secretary:** Martyn Sexton **(T)** 07738 933 683 **(E)** mjsexton@btinternet.com
**Chairman:** Tim Clark **Manager:** Ben Smith **Prog Ed:** Martyn Sexton
**Ground:** Ashford United FC, Homelands, Ashford Rd., Kingsnorth TN26 1NJ **(T)**
**Capacity:** 3,000 **Seats:** 200 **Covered:** 1,500 **Midweek Matchday:** Wednesday **Clubhouse:** Yes **Shop:** Yes

**Colours(change):** Burgundy/burgundy/white (All green)
**Previous Names:**
**Previous Leagues:** Kent 1947-59, 94-01, Metropolitan 1959-60, Southern 1960-61, 94, Kent County 2007-11.
**Records:**
**Honours:** Kent County League Division One East 2007-08, 08-09.

**10 YEAR RECORD**

| 06-07 | 07-08 | 08-09 | 09-10 | 10-11 | 11-12 | 12-13 | 13-14 | 14-15 | 15-16 |
|---|---|---|---|---|---|---|---|---|---|
| | KC1E 1 | KC1E 1 | KC P 5 | KC P 2 | Kent P 9 | Kent P 9 | SCE 12 | SCE 12 | SCE 8 |

## CORINTHIAN

Founded: 1972 Nickname:

**Secretary:** Sue Billings **(T)** 07734 855 554 **(E)** corinthians@billingsgroup.com
**Chairman:** R J Billings **Manager:** Michael Golding
**Ground:** Gay Dawn Farm, Valley Road, Longfield DA3 8LY **(T)** 01474 573 118
**Capacity:** **Seats:** **Covered:** **Midweek Matchday:** Tuesday **Clubhouse:** Yes

**Colours(change):** Green & white hoops/white/white (Yellow/green/green)
**Previous Names:** Welling United Reserves > 2009.
**Previous Leagues:** Southern 1985-91.
**Records:**
**Honours:**

**10 YEAR RECORD**

| 06-07 | 07-08 | 08-09 | 09-10 | 10-11 | 11-12 | 12-13 | 13-14 | 14-15 | 15-16 |
|---|---|---|---|---|---|---|---|---|---|
| | | Kent 2 6 | Kent P 14 | Kent P 12 | Kent P 7 | Kent P 4 | SCE 5 | SCE 6 | SCE 6 |

## CRAY VALLEY PAPER MILLS

Founded: 1919 Nickname: Millers

**Secretary:** Dave Wilson **(T)** 07715 961 886 **(E)** wilson433@ntlworld.com
**Chairman:** Frank May **Prog Ed:** Dave Wilson
**Ground:** Badgers Sports, Middle Park Avenue, Eltham SE9 5HT **(T)**
**Capacity:** **Seats:** **Covered:** **Midweek Matchday:** Tuesday **Clubhouse:**

**Colours(change):** Green/black/black (All sky blue).
**Previous Names:** None
**Previous Leagues:** Spartan 1991-97, Spartan South Midlands 1997-98, London Intermediate 1998-01, Kent County 2001-11.
**Records:**
**Honours:** Kent County League Premier Division 2004-05.

**10 YEAR RECORD**

| 06-07 | 07-08 | 08-09 | 09-10 | 10-11 | 11-12 | 12-13 | 13-14 | 14-15 | 15-16 |
|---|---|---|---|---|---|---|---|---|---|
| KC P 7 | KC P 9 | KC P 5 | KC P 6 | KC P 3 | Kent P 11 | Kent P 8 | SCE 7 | SCE 7 | SCE 10 |

## CROWBOROUGH ATHLETIC

Founded: 1894 Nickname: The Crows

**Secretary:** Eric Gillett **(T)** 07879 434467 **(E)** emgillett@hotmail.co.uk
**Chairman:** Tony Bowen **Manager:** Sean Muggeridge **Prog Ed:** Malcolm Boyes
**Ground:** Crowborough Co. Stadium, Alderbrook Rec, Fermor Road, TN6 3DJ **(T)** 07879 434 467
**Capacity:** 2,000 **Seats:** **Covered:** 150 **Midweek Matchday:** Tuesday **Clubhouse:**

**Colours(change):** Navy blue/sky blue/navy blue (All red).
**Previous Names:**
**Previous Leagues:** Sussex County 1974-2008. Isthmian 2008-09. Sussex County 2009-14.
**Records:**
**Honours:** Sussex County Division One 2007-08. League Cup 2006-07.

**10 YEAR RECORD**

| 06-07 | 07-08 | 08-09 | 09-10 | 10-11 | 11-12 | 12-13 | 13-14 | 14-15 | 15-16 |
|---|---|---|---|---|---|---|---|---|---|
| SxC1 4 | SxC1 1 | Isth1S 22 | SxC1 18 | SxC1 12 | SxC1 13 | SxC1 15 | SxC1 5 | SCE 10 | SCE 7 |

## CROYDON

Founded: 1953 Nickname: The Trams

**Secretary:** Andy Hillburn (Fixture) **(T)** 020 8657 1825 **(E)** andy.hillburn@landregistry.gsi.gov.uk
**Chairman:** Dickson Gill **Manager:** Dickson Gill **Prog Ed:** Simon Hawkins
**Ground:** Croydon Sports Arena, Albert Road, South Norwood SE25 4QL **(T)** 02086 545 524 (CH - 0208 654 8555)
**Capacity:** 8,000 **Seats:** 500 **Covered:** 1,000 **Midweek Matchday:** Wednesday **Clubhouse:** Yes **Shop:** Yes

**Colours(change):** Sky & navy blue/sky & navy/sky (Yellow & purple/yellow & purple/yellow)
**Previous Names:** Croydon Amateurs 1953-73.
**Previous Leagues:** Surrey Senior 1953-63. Spartan 1963-64. Athenian 1964-74. Isthmian1974- 2006. Kent 2006-09. Combined Counties 2009-14.
**Records:** **Att:**1,600 v Dorking,Surrey Sen Lge Charity Final 05/54. **G'scorer:**Fred Morris - 147 (59-64). **Apps:**Alec Jackson - 452(77-88)
**Honours:** Surrey Senior League Cup 1960-61, 62-63. Surrey Senior Charity Cup 1962-63. Spartan Lg 1963-64. Athenian Div.2 1965-66. Surrey Senior Cup 1981-82. Isthmian League Division One 1999-00. London Senior Cup 2001-02. Kent Lge Charity Shield 09.

**10 YEAR RECORD**

| 06-07 | 07-08 | 08-09 | 09-10 | 10-11 | 11-12 | 12-13 | 13-14 | 14-15 | 15-16 |
|---|---|---|---|---|---|---|---|---|---|
| Kent P 3 | Kent P 12 | Kent P 9 | CCP 16 | CCP 20 | CCP 16 | CCP 14 | CCP 13 | SCE 18 | SCE 18 |

## DEAL TOWN

Founded: 1908 Nickname: Town

**Secretary:** Natalie Benville **(T)** 07854 051 628 **(E)** secretary@dealtownfc.co.uk
**Chairman:** Robert Marriott **Manager:** Derek Hares **Prog Ed:** Colin Adams
**Ground:** Charles Sports Ground, St Leonards Road, Deal CT14 9BB **(T)** 01304 375 623
**Capacity:** 2,500 **Seats:** 180 **Covered:** 180 **Midweek Matchday:** Tuesday **Clubhouse:** Yes **Shop:** Yes

**Colours(change):** Black & white/black/white (All red).
**Previous Names:** Deal Cinque Ports FC > 1920
**Previous Leagues:** Thanet. East Kent. Kent. Aetolian. Southern. Greater London.
**Records:** **Att:** 2,495 v Newcastle Town, FA Vase S-F, 26.03.2000.
**Honours:**

**10 YEAR RECORD**

| 06-07 | 07-08 | 08-09 | 09-10 | 10-11 | 11-12 | 12-13 | 13-14 | 14-15 | 15-16 |
|---|---|---|---|---|---|---|---|---|---|
| Kent P 8 | Kent P 9 | Kent P 12 | Kent P 9 | Kent P 11 | Kent P 15 | Kent P 12 | SCE 13 | SCE 13 | SCE 9 |

## ERITH & BELVEDERE

Founded: 1922 Nickname: Deres

**Secretary:** Adam Peters **(T)** 07984 090 805 **(E)** clubsec_erithandbelvederefc@live.com
**Chairman:** John McFadden **Manager:** John Wilfort **Prog Ed:** Brian Spurrell / Martin Tarrant
**Ground:** Welling FC, Park View Road, Welling, DA16 1SY **(T)** 07984 090 805
**Capacity:** 4,000 **Seats:** 1,070 **Covered:** 1,000 **Midweek Matchday:** Tuesday **Clubhouse:** Yes **Shop:** Yes

**Colours(change):** Blue & white quarters/blue/blue. (Red & white quarters/red/red)
**Previous Names:** Belvedere & District FC (Formed 1918 restructured 1922)
**Previous Leagues:** Kent. London. Corinthian. Athenian. Southern. Kent League 2005-13. Isthmian 2013-14.
**Records:** 5,573 v Crook C.W., FA Amateur Cup 19/02/1949
**Honours:** Kent League 1981-82, 2012-13. London Senior Cup 1944-45.

**10 YEAR RECORD**

| 06-07 | 07-08 | 08-09 | 09-10 | 10-11 | 11-12 | 12-13 | 13-14 | 14-15 | 15-16 |
|---|---|---|---|---|---|---|---|---|---|
| Kent P 7 | Kent P 7 | Kent P 8 | Kent P 12 | Kent P 5 | Kent P 2 | Kent P 1 | Isth1N 24 | SCE 3 | SCE 16 |

## ERITH TOWN

Founded: 1959 Nickname: The Dockers

**Secretary:** Paul Carter **(T)** 07863 347 587 **(E)** paul_carter40@yahoo.co.uk
**Chairman:** Ian Birrell **Manager:** Ricky Bennett & Ian Jenkins **Prog Ed:** Ian Birrell
**Ground:** Oakwood, Old Road, Crayford Kent DA1 4DN **(T)**
**Capacity:** **Seats:** **Covered:** **Midweek Matchday:** Wednesday **Clubhouse:**

**Colours(change):** Red & black stripe/black/black. (Yellow & black stripe/white/white).
**Previous Names:** Woolwich Town 1959-89 and 1990-97.
**Previous Leagues:** London Metropolitan Sunday. London Spartan.
**Records:** **Att:** 325 v Charlton Athletic, friendly. **Goalscorer:** Dean Bowey.
**Honours:**

**10 YEAR RECORD**

| 06-07 | 07-08 | 08-09 | 09-10 | 10-11 | 11-12 | 12-13 | 13-14 | 14-15 | 15-16 |
|---|---|---|---|---|---|---|---|---|---|
| Kent P 14 | Kent P 5 | Kent P 7 | Kent P 12 | Kent P 8 | Kent P 4 | Kent P 3 | SCE 3 | SCE 19 | SCE 13 |

## FISHER

Founded: 1908 Nickname: The Fish

**Secretary:** Ian Murphy **(T)** 07854 172 490 **(E)** ian@fisherfc.co.uk
**Chairman:** Ben Westmancott **Manager:** Billy Walton **Prog Ed:** Jevon Hall
**Ground:** St Pauls Sports Ground, Salter Road, Rotherhithe, London SE16 **(T)**
**Capacity:** **Seats:** **Covered:** **Midweek Matchday:** Tuesday **Clubhouse:**

**Colours(change):** Black & white stripe/black/black. (Orange/orange/black).
**Previous Names:** Fisher Athletic. Reformed as Fisher F.C. in 2009.
**Previous Leagues:** Parthenon, Kent Amateur, London Spartan, Southern, Isthmian, Conference.
**Records:** **Att:** 4,283 v Barnet Conference 04/05/1991. **Goalscorer:** Paul Shinners - 205. **Apps:** Dennis Sharp - 720.
**Honours:** Southern League Southern Division 1982-83, Premier 86-87, Eastern 2004-05. Kent Senior Cup 1983-84. Isthmian League Cup 2005-06.

**10 YEAR RECORD**

| 06-07 | 07-08 | 08-09 | 09-10 | 10-11 | 11-12 | 12-13 | 13-14 | 14-15 | 15-16 |
|---|---|---|---|---|---|---|---|---|---|
| Conf S 10 | Conf S 4 | Conf S 22 | Kent P 13 | Kent P 16 | Kent P 10 | Kent P 14 | SCE 14 | SCE 16 | SCE 17 |

## HOLLANDS & BLAIR

Founded: 1970 Nickname: Blair

**Secretary:** Laurence Plummer **(T)** 07540 841 799 **(E)** laurence.plummer@btinternet.com
**Chairman:** Barry Peirce **Manager:** Bryan Greenfield **Prog Ed:** Richard Day
**Ground:** Star Meadow Sports Club, Darland Avenue, Gillingham, Kent ME7 3AN **(T)** 01634 573839
**Capacity:** **Seats:** Yes **Covered:** Yes **Midweek Matchday:** Wednesday **Clubhouse:** Yes

**Colours(change):** All red (Yellow & blue/blue/blue)
**Previous Names:** Hollands & Blair United 1970-74
**Previous Leagues:** Rochester & District 1970-2004. Kent County 2004-11
**Records:** **Att:** 232 v Sutton Athletic KIC Shield November 2014. **Goalscorer:** Ben Christy - 155. **Apps:** Mick Moran - 399.
**Honours:** Kent County Division One East 2005-06, Premier 2008-9, 10-11. Kent Invicta 2013-14, 14-15.

**10 YEAR RECORD**

| 06-07 | 07-08 | 08-09 | 09-10 | 10-11 | 11-12 | 12-13 | 13-14 | 14-15 | 15-16 |
|---|---|---|---|---|---|---|---|---|---|
| KC P 8 | KC P 5 | KC P 1 | KC P 2 | KC P 1 | K_Iv 3 | K_Iv 2 | K_Iv 1 | K_Iv 1 | SCE 2 |

## LORDSWOOD

Founded: 1968 Nickname: Lords

**Secretary:** Steve Lewis **(T)** 07968 429 941 **(E)** slew1953@hotmail.co.uk
**Chairman:** Ron Constantine **Manager:** James Collins **Prog Ed:** Paul Caulfield
**Ground:** Martyn Grove, Northdane Way, Walderslade, ME5 8YE **(T)** 01634 669 138
**Capacity:** 600 **Seats:** 123 **Covered:** 123 **Midweek Matchday:** Tuesday **Clubhouse:** Yes **Shop:** No

**Colours(change):** Orange/black/orange (Grey/grey/blue).
**Previous Names:** None.
**Previous Leagues:** Rochester & Dist. Kent County.
**Records:**
**Honours:**

**10 YEAR RECORD**

| 06-07 | 07-08 | 08-09 | 09-10 | 10-11 | 11-12 | 12-13 | 13-14 | 14-15 | 15-16 |
|---|---|---|---|---|---|---|---|---|---|
| Kent P 13 | Kent P 16 | Kent P 16 | Kent P 16 | Kent P 13 | Kent P 12 | Kent P 5 | SCE 11 | SCE 15 | SCE 4 |

## ROCHESTER UNITED

Founded: 1982 Nickname:

**Secretary:** Tony Wheeler **(T)** 07775 735 543 **(E)** tony.wheelerrufc@yahoo.co.uk
**Chairman:** Paul Porter **Manager:** Matt Hume
**Ground:** Rochester United Sports Ground, Rede Court Road, Strood, Kent ME2 3TU **(T)** 01634 710577
**Capacity:** **Seats:** **Covered:** **Midweek Matchday:** Wednesday **Clubhouse:**

**Colours(change):** Red/black/black (Grey/grey/red)
**Previous Names:** Templars. Bly Spartans.
**Previous Leagues:** Kent County > 2011. Founder Members of Kent Invicta 2011-12.
**Records:**
**Honours:** Kent County League Division One West 2007-08. Kent Invicta League 2011-12.

**10 YEAR RECORD**

| 06-07 | 07-08 | 08-09 | 09-10 | 10-11 | 11-12 | 12-13 | 13-14 | 14-15 | 15-16 |
|---|---|---|---|---|---|---|---|---|---|
| KC1W 2 | KC1W 1 | KC P 10 | KC P 12 | KC P 15 | K_Iv 1 | Kent P 13 | SCE 15 | SCE 20 | SCE 15 |

## SEVENOAKS TOWN

Founded: 1883 Nickname: Town

**Secretary:** Sam Lansdale **(T)** 07809 403 688 **(E)** samlansdale@gmail.com
**Chairman:** Paul Lansdale **Manager:** Micky Collins **Prog Ed:** Ian Murphy
**Ground:** Greatness Park, Seal Road, Sevenoaks TN14 5BL **(T)** 01732 741 987
**Capacity:** 2,000 **Seats:** 110 **Covered:** 200 **Midweek Matchday:** Wednesday **Clubhouse:**

**Colours(change):** Blue & black/black/black (Green & white/green/green).
**Previous Names:** None.
**Previous Leagues:** Sevenoaks League. Kent Amateur/County.
**Records:**
**Honours:**

**10 YEAR RECORD**

| 06-07 | 07-08 | 08-09 | 09-10 | 10-11 | 11-12 | 12-13 | 13-14 | 14-15 | 15-16 |
|---|---|---|---|---|---|---|---|---|---|
| Kent P 10 | Kent P 11 | Kent P 14 | Kent P 6 | Kent P 7 | Kent P 14 | Kent P 17 | SCE 16 | SCE 8 | SCE 5 |

## SHEPPEY UNITED

Founded: 1890 Nickname:

**Secretary:** Jonathon Longhurst **(T)** 07713 065 099 **(E)** jonl@bond-group.co.uk
**Chairman:** Matt Smith **Manager:** Ernie Batten **Prog Ed:** Mike Wood
**Ground:** Tiger Stadium, Holm Park, Queenborough Road ME12 3DB **(T)** 01795 669 547
**Capacity:** **Seats:** **Covered:** **Midweek Matchday:** Tuesday **Clubhouse:**

**Colours(change):** Red & white stripes/black/black (Yellow/royal blue/royal blue)
**Previous Names:** AFC Sheppy 2007-2010. Sheppey & Sheerness United after merger 2013-14.
**Previous Leagues:** Kent County > 2014.
**Records:**
**Honours:** Kent Senior Trophy 2015-16.

**10 YEAR RECORD**

| 06-07 | 07-08 | 08-09 | 09-10 | 10-11 | 11-12 | 12-13 | 13-14 | 14-15 | 15-16 |
|---|---|---|---|---|---|---|---|---|---|
| KC1E 9 | KC1E 2 | KC1E 2 | KC1E 11 | KC1E 11 | KC1E 4 | KC P Exp | KC P 2 | K_lv 5 | K_lv 2 |

## TUNBRIDGE WELLS

Founded: 1886 Nickname: The Wells

**Secretary:** Phill Allcorn **(T)** 07900 243 508 **(E)** secretary@twfcexec.com
**Chairman:** Clive Maynard **Manager:** Jason Bourne **Prog Ed:** Bob Lucas
**Ground:** Culverden Stadium, Culverden Down, Tunbridge Wells TN4 9SG **(T)** 01892 520 517
**Capacity:** 3,750 **Seats:** 250 **Covered:** 1,000 **Midweek Matchday:** Tuesday **Clubhouse:** Yes **Shop:** No

**Colours(change):** All red (White/black/white)
**Previous Names:** None.
**Previous Leagues:** Isthminan. London Spartan.
**Records:** **Att:** 1,754 v Hadleigh United, FA Vase SF 1st Leg 2012-13. **Goalscorer:** John Wingate - 151. **Apps:** Tony Atkins - 410.
**Honours:** Kent Senior Trophy 2012-13.

**10 YEAR RECORD**

| 06-07 | 07-08 | 08-09 | 09-10 | 10-11 | 11-12 | 12-13 | 13-14 | 14-15 | 15-16 |
|---|---|---|---|---|---|---|---|---|---|
| Kent P 15 | Kent P 10 | Kent P 10 | Kent P 7 | Kent P 6 | Kent P 5 | Kent P 7 | SCE 4 | SCE 5 | SCE 14 |

## WHITSTABLE TOWN

Founded: 1886 Nickname: Oystermen or Natives

**Secretary:** Hellen Sprawling **(T)** 07590 116 735 **(E)** secretary@whitstabletownfc.co.uk
**Chairman:** Joe Brownett **Manager:** Scott Porter **Prog Ed:** Andy Short
**Ground:** The Belmont Ground, Belmont Road, Belmont, Whitstable CT5 1QP **(T)** 01227 266 012
**Capacity:** 2,000 **Seats:** 500 **Covered:** 1,000 **Midweek Matchday:** Tuesday **Clubhouse:** Yes Yes

**Colours(change):** Red & white sash/white/red & white (All yellow)
**Previous Names:**
**Previous Leagues:** East Kent 1897-1909, Kent 1909-59, Aetolian 1959-60, Kent Amateur 1960-62, 63-64, South East Anglian 1962-63,
**Records:** 2,500 v Gravesend & Northfleet - FA Cup 19/10/1987. **Previous Lges:** Greater London 1964-67, Kent 1967-2007. Isthmian 2007-16.
**Honours:** Kent Amateur Cup 1928-29.
Kent League 2006-07, League Trophy 2006-07.

**10 YEAR RECORD**

| 06-07 | 07-08 | 08-09 | 09-10 | 10-11 | 11-12 | 12-13 | 13-14 | 14-15 | 15-16 |
|---|---|---|---|---|---|---|---|---|---|
| Kent P 10 | Isth1S 14 | Isth1S 16 | Isth1S 18 | Isth1S 15 | Isth1S 18 | Isth1S 17 | Isth1S 20 | Isth1S 8 | Isth1S 23 |

## BRIDON ROPES
Founded: 1935 Nickname: The Ropes

**Secretary:** Clive Smith **(T)** 07795 966 110 **(E)** cburtonsmith@gmail.com
**Chairman:** Richard Clements **Manager:** Mark Murison **Prog Ed:** Clive Smith
**Ground:** Meridian Sports & Social Club, Charlton Park Lane, Charlton, London SE7 8QS **(T)** 0208 856 1923
**Colours(change):** All blue (All red)
**ADDITIONAL INFORMATION:**
**Previous Lge:** Kent County > 2011.

## CROCKENHILL
Founded: 1946 Nickname: The Crocks

**Secretary:** Steve Cullen **(T)** 07702 886 966 **(E)** steve.cullen@virgin.net
**Chairman:** Steve Cullen **Manager:** Kevin Dalrymple **Prog Ed:** Alan Curnick
**Ground:** Wested Meadow Ground, Eynesford Road, Crockenhill, Kent BR8 8EJ **(T)** 01322 666 067
**Colours(change):** Red & white hoops/black/black (Yellow/blue/blue)
**ADDITIONAL INFORMATION:**
**Previous Lge:** Kent County > 2011.

## ELTHAM PALACE
Founded: 1961 Nickname: Palace

**Secretary:** George Lush **(T)** 07861 885 590 **(E)** georgelush@hotmail.co.uk
**Chairman:** Ian Rooney **Prog Ed:** George Lush
**Ground:** Foxbury Avenue, Chislehurst, Bromley BR7 6HA **(T)**
**Colours(change):** Blue/white/blue (All orange)
**ADDITIONAL INFORMATION:**

## FC ELMSTEAD
Founded: 1958 Nickname: The Cocks

**Secretary:** Tony Aliband **(T)** 07825 889 120 **(E)** fcelmstead@gmail.com
**Chairman:** Tony Aliband **Manager:** Fabio Rossi **Prog Ed:** Fabio Rossi
**Ground:** Holmesdale FC, Oakley Rown, Bromley, Kent BR2 8HQ **(T)**
**Colours(change):** Blue/red/red (Yellow & blue stripes/blue/blue)
**ADDITIONAL INFORMATION:**
**Previous League:** Kent County > 2015

## FOREST HILL PARK
Founded: 1992 Nickname:

**Secretary:** Clayton Walters **(T)** 07774 294 236 **(E)** info@fhpfc.co.uk
**Chairman:** John Simpson **Manager:** Canturk Yanpur **Prog Ed:** Canturk Yanpur
**Ground:** Ladywell Arena, Silvermere Road, Catford, London SE6 4QX **(T)** 0208 314 1986
**Colours(change):** All blue (White or red/blue/blue)
**ADDITIONAL INFORMATION:**
**Previous League:** Kent County >2015
**League Titles:** South London Alliance Division One 2005-06. Kent County Division Two West 2009-10.

## GLEBE
Founded: 2013 Nickname:

**Secretary:** Peter Dale **(T)** 07877 766 794 **(E)** peter@epc-4-less.co.uk
**Chairman:** Rocky McMillan **Manager:** Adam Woodward **Prog Ed:** Peter Dale
**Ground:** Foxbury Avenue, Chislehurst, Bromley BR7 6SD **(T)**
**Colours(change):** Red & black/black/red (Sky blue/navy/sky blue)
**ADDITIONAL INFORMATION:**
London Senior Trophy 2015-16.

## GRAVESHAM BOROUGH
Founded: 1927 Nickname: Boro

**Secretary:** Sam Searle **(T)** 07859 057 799 **(E)** graveshamboroughfc@aol.co.uk
**Chairman:** Scott Williamson **Manager:** Kevin Hake **Prog Ed:** Sam Searle
**Ground:** Chatham Town FC, Maidstone Road, Chatham, Kent ME4 6LR **(T)**
**Colours(change):** All red (Yellow/black/yellow)
**ADDITIONAL INFORMATION:**
**Previous Name:** Beauwater Thames. Fleet Leisure > 2014.
**Previous League:** Kent County > 2013.

## HOLMESDALE

Founded: 1956 Nickname: The Dalers

**Secretary:** Ross Mitchell **(T)** 07875 730 862 **(E)** mitchell1982@sky.com
**Chairman:** Mark Harris **Manager:** Simon Copely **Prog Ed:** Mark Harris
**Ground:** Holmesdale Sp.& Soc.Club, 68 Oakley Rd, Bromley BR2 8HQ **(T)** 020 8462 4440
**Colours(change):** Green & yellow/green/yellow. (All blue).
**ADDITIONAL INFORMATION: Goals:** M Barnett - 410 (in 429 apps).

## K SPORTS

Founded: 1919 Nickname: The Paperboys

**Secretary:** Karen Grieves **(T)** 07947 797 886 **(E)** karengrieves@aol.com
**Chairman:** Philip Hudson **Manager:** Kris Browning
**Ground:** Cobdown Sports & Social Club, Station Road, Ditton, Aylesford, Kent ME20 6AU **(T)**
**Colours(change):** Black & white/black/black & white (All gold)
**ADDITIONAL INFORMATION: Previous Names:** Reeds International 1974-90. APM 1990-2009. APM Contrast 2009-16.
**Previous League:** Kent County >2015.

## KENT FOOTBALL UNITED

Founded: 2010 Nickname:

**Secretary:** Sam McNeil **(T)** 07860 654 558 **(E)** kentelitefc@hotmail.co.uk
**Chairman:** Roy McNeil **Manager:** Ennio Gonnella **Prog Ed:** Sam McNeil
**Ground:** Holm Park, Queenborough Road, Sheerness ME12 3DB **(T)** 07860 654 558
**Colours(change):** All blue (Yellow/black/yellow)
**ADDITIONAL INFORMATION:**

## LEWISHAM BOROUGH

Founded: 2003 Nickname: The Boro

**Secretary:** Ray Simpson **(T)** 07958 946 236 **(E)** raymondsimpson40@yahoo.com
**Chairman:** Ray Simpson **Manager:** Ray Simpson **Prog Ed:** Juliet Walker
**Ground:** Ladywell Arena, Silvermere Road, Catford, London SE6 4QX **(T)**
**Colours(change):** Blue & white/blue/blue (All red)
**ADDITIONAL INFORMATION:**
**Previous Lge:** Kent county > 2011.

## LYDD TOWN

Founded: 1885 Nickname:

**Secretary:** Bruce Marchant **(T)** 07899 738 108 **(E)** brucemarchant@hotmail.com
**Chairman:** Pat Lindsey **Manager:** Liam Smith **Prog Ed:** Bruce Marchant
**Ground:** The Lindsey Field, Dengemarsh Road, Lydd, Kent TN29 9JH **(T)** 01797 321 904
**Colours(change):** Green/green/red (Yellow & blue/yellow/yellow)
**ADDITIONAL INFORMATION:**
**Previous Lge:** Kent County > 2011.

## MERIDIAN VP

Founded: 1995 Nickname:

**Secretary:** Mike Rumin **(T)** 07874 624 638 **(E)** mrumin@gmail.com
**Chairman:** Dwinder Tamna **Manager:** Richard Dimmock **Prog Ed:** Mike Rumin
**Ground:** Meridian Sports & Social Club, 110 Charlton Park Lane, London SE7 8QS **(T)** 0208 856 1923
**Colours(change):** All blue (All red)
**ADDITIONAL INFORMATION:**
**Previous Lge:** Kent County > 2011.
**Previous Name:** Meridan 1995-2013.

## ORPINGTON

Founded: 1939 Nickname: The O's

**Secretary:** Phil Alder **(T)** 07752 396 423 **(E)** Philip.alder@defra.gsi.gov.uk
**Chairman:** Steve Hall **Manager:** Marc Bentz **Prog Ed:** Phil Alder
**Ground:** Green Court Road, Crockenhill, Kent BR8 8HF **(T)** 07940 355 595
**Colours(change):** Amber/black/black (All blue)
**ADDITIONAL INFORMATION:**
**Previous Lge:** Kent County > 2011.

## PHOENIX SPORTS RESERVES

Founded: 1935 Nickname:

**Secretary:** Alf Levy **(T)** 07795 182 927 **(E)** alf-levy@sky.com
**Chairman:** Andy Mortlock **Manager:** Ben Kotey **Prog Ed:** Alf Levy
**Ground:** Phoenix Sports Ground, Mayplace Road East, Barnehurst, Kent DA7 6JT **(T)** 01322 526 159
**Colours(change):** Green/black/black (All Red or all green)
**ADDITIONAL INFORMATION:**
**Previous Names:** St Johns Welling. Lakeside. Phoenix.

## RUSTHALL

Founded: 1890 Nickname: The Rustics

**Secretary:** Katie Whitmore **(T)** 07801 296 553 **(E)** katiewhitmore13@hotmail.com
**Chairman:** Joe Croker **Manager:** Steven Sands **Prog Ed:** Richard Smith
**Ground:** Jockey Farm, Nellington Road, Rusthall, Tunbridge Wells, Kent TN4 8SH **(T)** 07865 396 299
**Colours(change):** Green & white stripes/green/green (Red & white stripes/red/red)
**ADDITIONAL INFORMATION:**
**Previous Lge:** Kent County > 2011.

## SNODLAND TOWN

Founded: 2012 Nickname:

**Secretary:** Terry Reeves **(T)** 07894 488 451 **(E)** terry.reeves55@virginmedia.com
**Chairman:** Mel Rayfield **Manager:** Gavin Gillies **Prog Ed:** Alan Totham
**Ground:** Potyns Field, Paddlesworth Road, Snodland ME6 5DP **(T)** 07894 488 451
**Colours(change):** Blue & yellow/blue/blue (Navy & red/navy/navy
**ADDITIONAL INFORMATION:**
**Previous Leagues:** Kent County >2016

## SPORTING CLUB THAMESMEAD

Founded: 1900 Nickname:

**Secretary:** Lee Hill **(T)** 07834 583 395 **(E)** lhsasfc@gmail.com
**Chairman:** Sam Taylor **Manager:** Lee Hill **Prog Ed:** Sam Taylor
**Ground:** Sporting Club Thamesmead, Bayliss Avenue, Thamesmead, London SE28 8NJ **(T)** 0208 320 4488
**Colours(change):** Red & black/black/black (Green & yellow/green/green)
**ADDITIONAL INFORMATION:**
**Previous Lge:** Kent County > 2011.

## SUTTON ATHLETIC

Founded: 1898 Nickname:

**Secretary:** Guy Eldridge **(T)** 07778 053 433 **(E)** guy.eldridge@btconnect.com
**Chairman:** John Ball **Manager:** Ben Young **Prog Ed:** John Ball
**Ground:** London Hire Stadium, Lower Road, Hextable, Kent BR8 7RZ **(T)** 01322 665 377
**Colours(change):** Green & white/green/green (Black & white stripe/black/white)
**ADDITIONAL INFORMATION:**
**Previous Names:** Sutton United > 2012.
**Previous League:** Kent County > 2011.

# SPARTAN SOUTH MIDLANDS LEAGUE

**Sponsored by:** Molten

**Founded:** 1998

**Recent Champions: 2013:** Dunstable Town
**2014:** Hanwell Town **2015:** Kings Langley

| PREMIER DIVISION | P | W | D | L | F | A | GD | Pts |
|---|---|---|---|---|---|---|---|---|
| 1 AFC Dunstable | 42 | 32 | 6 | 4 | 118 | 33 | 85 | 102 |
| 2 London Colney | 42 | 27 | 8 | 7 | 93 | 37 | 56 | 89 |
| 3 Hoddesdon Town | 42 | 27 | 8 | 7 | 82 | 36 | 46 | 89 |
| 4 Welwyn Garden City | 42 | 22 | 8 | 12 | 88 | 49 | 39 | 74 |
| 5 Berkhamsted | 42 | 22 | 8 | 12 | 93 | 63 | 30 | 74 |
| 6 Hadley | 42 | 22 | 5 | 15 | 82 | 55 | 27 | 71 |
| 7 Holmer Green | 42 | 22 | 4 | 16 | 86 | 82 | 4 | 70 |
| 8 Hertford Town | 42 | 20 | 8 | 14 | 112 | 82 | 30 | 68 |
| 9 Cockfosters | 42 | 18 | 13 | 11 | 82 | 62 | 20 | 67 |
| 10 Biggleswade United | 42 | 20 | 7 | 15 | 64 | 54 | 10 | 67 |
| 11 Wembley | 42 | 19 | 6 | 17 | 77 | 61 | 16 | 63 |
| 12 Tring Athletic | 42 | 17 | 12 | 13 | 66 | 56 | 10 | 63 |
| 13 London Tigers | 42 | 17 | 9 | 16 | 64 | 75 | -11 | 60 |
| 14 Sun Sports | 42 | 16 | 7 | 19 | 76 | 83 | -7 | 55 |
| 15 Stotfold | 42 | 14 | 9 | 19 | 68 | 83 | -15 | 51 |
| 16 FC Broxbourne Borough | 42 | 11 | 8 | 23 | 58 | 96 | -38 | 41 |
| 17 Oxhey Jets | 42 | 11 | 3 | 28 | 59 | 128 | -69 | 36 |
| 18 Leverstock Green | 42 | 9 | 8 | 25 | 76 | 107 | -31 | 35 |
| 19 St Margaretsbury | 42 | 8 | 9 | 25 | 56 | 96 | -40 | 33 |
| 20 Colney Heath | 42 | 9 | 6 | 27 | 38 | 87 | -49 | 33 |
| 21 Harefield United | 42 | 9 | 4 | 29 | 42 | 106 | -64 | 31 |
| 22 Bedford (-3) | 42 | 9 | 6 | 27 | 58 | 107 | -49 | 30 |

## PREMIER DIVISION CUP

**HOLDERS:** BERKHAMSTED

**ROUND 1**

| | | | |
|---|---|---|---|
| Colney Heath | v | Berkhamsted | 1-5 |
| Biggleswade United | v | Harefield United | 6-0 |
| FC Broxbourne Borough | v | Wembley | 1-0 |
| Welwyn Garden City | v | Stotfold | 3-2 |
| Cockfosters | v | AFC Dunstable | 1-1, 5-4p |
| Tring Athletic | v | Leverstock Green | 0-1 |

**ROUND 2**

| | | | |
|---|---|---|---|
| St Margaretsbury | v | London Tigers | 2-4 |
| Hadley | v | Berkhamsted | 4-1 |
| Biggleswade United | v | Sun Sports | 2-4 |
| FC Broxbourne Borough | v | Welwyn Garden City | 3-8 |
| Hoddesdon Town | v | Cockfosters | 2-1 |
| Leverstock Green | v | Bedford | 2-4 |
| Oxhey Jets | v | Holmer Green | 3-2 |
| London Colney | v | Hertford Town | 6-3 |

**QUARTER FINALS**

| | | | |
|---|---|---|---|
| London Tigers | v | Hadley | 3-5 |
| Sun Sports | v | Welwyn Garden City | 1-4 |
| Hoddesdon Town | v | Bedford | 3-1 |
| Oxhey Jets | v | London Colney | 0-7 |

**SEMI FINALS**

| | | | |
|---|---|---|---|
| Hadley | v | Welwyn Garden City | 0-3 |
| Hoddesdon Town | v | London Colney | 0-0, 3-1p |

**FINAL**

| | | | |
|---|---|---|---|
| Welwyn Garden City | v | Hoddesdon Town | 0-1 |

## CLUB MOVEMENTS

**Premier Division - In:** Crawley Green (P), Edgware Town (P), Leighton Town (R - Southern Div.1 Central).
**Out:** AFC Dunstable (P), Bedford (R), Harefield United (R).

**Division One - In:** Bedford (R), Biggleswade FC (N), Hadley Wood & Wingate (P - Herts Senior County), Harefield United (R), Kensington Borough (P) (NC from AFC Hillgate).
**Out:** Crawley Green (P), Edgware Town (P), New Bradwell St Peter (R), Woodford Town (W).

**Division Two - In:** New Bradwell St Peter (R), Enfield Borough (N), MK Galacticos (P - North Bucks Intermediate), St Neots Town Reserves (N), Thame Rangers (N - Youth team connected to Thame United), Tring Town AFC (N), Unite MK (NC from Wolverton Town).
**Out:** AFC Hillgate (P) (NC to Kensington Borough), Kent Athletic (F).

| PREMIER DIVISION | 1 | 2 | 3 | 4 | 5 | 6 | 7 | 8 | 9 | 10 | 11 | 12 | 13 | 14 | 15 | 16 | 17 | 18 | 19 | 20 | 21 | 22 |
|---|---|---|---|---|---|---|---|---|---|---|---|---|---|---|---|---|---|---|---|---|---|---|
| 1 AFC Dunstable | | 3-2 | 6-1 | 2-0 | 1-1 | 2-1 | 8-0 | 1-1 | 2-1 | 4-1 | 0-1 | 2-0 | 4-2 | 0-1 | 4-1 | 5-1 | 4-2 | 4-0 | 3-0 | 2-0 | 1-1 | 4-2 |
| 2 Bedford | 1-4 | | 1-0 | 1-0 | 0-0 | 2-0 | 2-2 | 0-1 | 1-2 | 2-4 | 1-2 | 5-4 | 1-1 | 2-1 | 1-3 | 3-2 | 2-2 | 0-2 | 1-2 | 0-2 | 0-4 | 1-3 |
| 3 Berkhamsted | 2-1 | 7-1 | | 0-4 | 2-2 | 3-0 | 1-1 | 3-1 | 4-1 | 2-1 | 2-2 | 2-2 | 3-2 | 1-3 | 3-0 | 8-2 | 4-1 | 0-0 | 2-1 | 4-0 | 2-0 | 4-1 |
| 4 Biggleswade United | 1-0 | 3-0 | 0-0 | | 1-0 | 2-2 | 2-0 | 1-4 | 5-1 | 0-2 | 0-1 | 1-0 | 4-0 | 0-1 | 1-1 | 0-1 | 2-1 | 3-2 | 2-1 | 0-1 | 1-5 | 1-0 |
| 5 Cockfosters | 1-3 | 4-1 | 0-3 | 2-2 | | 3-0 | 2-1 | 1-2 | 1-1 | 3-3 | 0-3 | 2-3 | 2-2 | 0-0 | 5-0 | 4-1 | 2-2 | 2-1 | 3-1 | 3-2 | 2-0 | 2-0 |
| 6 Colney Heath | 1-1 | 2-0 | 0-3 | 2-1 | 0-2 | | 2-6 | 0-2 | 1-2 | 1-0 | 0-1 | 1-3 | 0-0 | 0-3 | 1-0 | 1-2 | 1-2 | 3-2 | 2-3 | 1-1 | 0-1 | 3-1 |
| 7 FC Broxbourne Borough | 0-1 | 3-3 | 6-2 | 1-2 | 0-4 | 1-2 | | 0-6 | 1-5 | 3-2 | 2-1 | 1-2 | 3-2 | 0-3 | 1-0 | 1-2 | 3-0 | 1-1 | 1-2 | 2-2 | 0-2 | 2-0 |
| 8 Hadley | 0-2 | 3-2 | 1-2 | 0-1 | 1-3 | 5-0 | 1-0 | | 3-0 | 5-1 | 2-4 | 2-0 | 0-1 | 0-0 | 0-1 | 2-2 | 4-2 | 0-3 | 1-0 | 3-1 | 4-0 | 0-2 |
| 9 Harefield United | 1-4 | 2-1 | 0-2 | 0-4 | 0-2 | 3-2 | 3-0 | 0-3 | | 1-9 | 0-2 | 0-5 | 0-1 | 0-4 | 1-4 | 3-2 | 0-1 | 1-1 | 0-3 | 0-2 | 0-3 | 1-2 |
| 10 Hertford Town | 1-3 | 5-2 | 2-5 | 1-1 | 5-1 | 3-1 | 3-3 | 3-0 | 2-2 | | 3-1 | 7-2 | 3-2 | 2-2 | 3-2 | 6-2 | 6-1 | 4-0 | 2-1 | 3-0 | 2-5 | 2-3 |
| 11 Hoddesdon Town | 1-1 | 3-2 | 2-0 | 2-3 | 2-2 | 2-2 | 1-0 | 3-0 | 3-1 | 1-1 | | 3-0 | 3-0 | 1-0 | 2-1 | 6-0 | 2-0 | 2-1 | 3-0 | 1-1 | 0-1 | 2-0 |
| 12 Holmer Green | 0-7 | 3-1 | 2-1 | 1-3 | 2-1 | 1-0 | 3-1 | 3-0 | 2-0 | 3-1 | 0-0 | | 3-2 | 1-3 | 2-2 | 4-0 | 2-1 | 3-4 | 4-1 | 2-3 | 5-3 | 1-1 |
| 13 Leverstock Green | 2-5 | 4-5 | 3-2 | 5-0 | 0-6 | 8-1 | 2-1 | 1-4 | 1-1 | 3-1 | 3-0 | 0-1 | | 2-7 | 1-3 | 5-2 | 3-5 | 3-5 | 0-1 | 0-0 | 0-2 | 3-4 |
| 14 London Colney | 0-0 | 3-2 | 1-0 | 0-0 | 2-2 | 1-0 | 8-0 | 4-0 | 1-3 | 2-1 | 1-1 | 5-1 | 2-1 | | 0-2 | 5-1 | 2-0 | 1-0 | 5-1 | 0-4 | 2-1 | 3-1 |
| 15 London Tigers | 1-3 | 2-0 | 0-3 | 2-0 | 0-2 | 3-0 | 1-1 | 1-1 | 3-0 | 2-0 | 0-3 | 1-0 | 2-2 | 2-0 | | 2-2 | 1-0 | 1-3 | 2-2 | 2-0 | 0-6 | 0-4 |
| 16 Oxhey Jets | 1-3 | 1-2 | 1-5 | 3-2 | 1-4 | 5-1 | 3-1 | 0-4 | 3-2 | 1-3 | 0-3 | 1-4 | 3-0 | 1-5 | 4-2 | | 2-4 | 0-1 | 2-4 | 1-0 | 2-5 | 0-1 |
| 17 St Margaretsbury | 0-1 | 0-2 | 2-0 | 2-2 | 2-2 | 0-1 | 1-2 | 0-2 | 2-1 | 1-5 | 1-2 | 0-2 | 4-4 | 1-4 | 2-4 | 1-1 | | 2-5 | 4-4 | 0-1 | 1-0 | 0-2 |
| 18 Stotfold | 0-5 | 4-1 | 1-2 | 2-3 | 3-1 | 2-1 | 0-0 | 0-5 | 0-1 | 1-2 | 1-5 | 4-1 | 3-3 | 1-0 | 0-1 | 0-1 | 0-3 | | 4-4 | 0-3 | 0-4 | 3-1 |
| 19 Sun Sports | 0-3 | 4-1 | 3-1 | 1-3 | 4-0 | 0-0 | 5-2 | 2-3 | 2-0 | 0-3 | 0-3 | 2-4 | 4-1 | 1-2 | 3-3 | 2-0 | 5-0 | 1-3 | | 1-1 | 1-3 | 1-0 |
| 20 Tring Athletic | 0-5 | 3-1 | 4-0 | 1-3 | 1-1 | 1-2 | 0-1 | 2-2 | 2-1 | 5-1 | 2-0 | 5-1 | 2-1 | 0-0 | 3-3 | 4-0 | 1-0 | 1-1 | 1-1 | | 1-2 | 2-1 |
| 21 Welwyn Garden City | 0-1 | 1-1 | 1-1 | 1-0 | 3-0 | 1-0 | 3-4 | 1-3 | 7-1 | 2-2 | 0-1 | 3-1 | 3-0 | 1-4 | 0-1 | 2-0 | 1-1 | 2-2 | 5-1 | 0-0 | | 2-0 |
| 22 Wembley | 1-3 | 6-1 | 1-1 | 2-0 | 1-2 | 3-0 | 1-0 | 2-1 | 3-0 | 1-1 | 2-1 | 0-3 | 2-0 | 0-2 | 6-2 | 8-0 | 2-2 | 2-2 | 0-1 | 4-1 | 1-1 | |

| DIVISION ONE | P | W | D | L | F | A | GD | Pts |
|---|---|---|---|---|---|---|---|---|
| 1 Edgware Town | 38 | 30 | 6 | 2 | 130 | 45 | 85 | 96 |
| 2 Crawley Green | 38 | 27 | 5 | 6 | 83 | 41 | 42 | 86 |
| 3 Baldock Town | 38 | 26 | 4 | 8 | 93 | 41 | 52 | 82 |
| 4 Harpenden Town | 38 | 22 | 5 | 11 | 87 | 50 | 37 | 71 |
| 5 Chesham United Reserves (-3) | 38 | 21 | 5 | 12 | 77 | 55 | 22 | 65 |
| 6 Wodson Park | 38 | 19 | 5 | 14 | 79 | 59 | 20 | 62 |
| 7 Risborough Rangers | 38 | 18 | 8 | 12 | 68 | 60 | 8 | 62 |
| 8 Buckingham Athletic | 38 | 16 | 10 | 12 | 57 | 44 | 13 | 58 |
| 9 New Bradwell St Peter | 38 | 17 | 7 | 14 | 62 | 66 | -4 | 58 |
| 10 Codicote | 38 | 17 | 3 | 18 | 61 | 73 | -12 | 54 |
| 11 Broadfields United | 38 | 14 | 7 | 17 | 74 | 81 | -7 | 49 |
| 12 Southall | 38 | 13 | 8 | 17 | 68 | 77 | -9 | 47 |
| 13 Woodford Town | 38 | 13 | 5 | 20 | 71 | 67 | 4 | 44 |
| 14 Ampthill Town | 38 | 14 | 2 | 22 | 60 | 77 | -17 | 44 |
| 15 Brimsdown (-1) | 38 | 12 | 7 | 19 | 62 | 93 | -31 | 42 |
| 16 Hillingdon Borough | 38 | 11 | 6 | 21 | 56 | 83 | -27 | 39 |
| 17 Hatfield Town | 38 | 10 | 7 | 21 | 49 | 70 | -21 | 37 |
| 18 Langford | 38 | 9 | 9 | 20 | 62 | 97 | -35 | 36 |
| 19 Winslow United | 38 | 9 | 7 | 22 | 51 | 82 | -31 | 34 |
| 20 Arlesey Town Reserves | 38 | 2 | 4 | 32 | 31 | 120 | -89 | 10 |

## DIVISION ONE CUP

**HOLDERS:** WELWYN GARDEN CITY

**ROUND 1**

| | | | |
|---|---|---|---|
| Brimsdown | v | Ampthill Town | 1-2 |
| Arlesey Town Reserves | v | Langford | 2-1 |
| Baldock Town | v | Wodson Park | 2-2, 4-2p |
| Hatfield Town | v | Edgware Town | 1-4 |

**ROUND 2**

| | | | |
|---|---|---|---|
| Winslow United | v | Crawley Green | 1-2 |
| Harpenden Town | v | Chesham United Reserves | 3-1 |
| Risborough Rangers | v | Hillingdon Borough | 1-2 |
| Ampthill Town | v | Broadfields United | 1-2 |
| New Bradwell St Peter | v | Arlesey Town Reserves | 2-3 |
| Codicote | v | Woodford Town | 1-4 |
| Baldock Town | v | Southall | 1-1, 7-6p |
| Edgware Town | v | Buckingham Athletic | 4-0 |

**QUARTER FINALS**

| | | | |
|---|---|---|---|
| Crawley Green | v | Harpenden Town | 1-1, 5-4p |
| Hillingdon Borough | v | Broadfields United | 1-3 |
| Arlesey Town Reserves | v | Woodford Town | 2-3 |
| Baldock Town | v | Edgware Town | 2-3 |

**SEMI FINALS**

| | | | |
|---|---|---|---|
| Crawley Green | v | Broadfields United | 3-0 |
| Woodford Town | v | Edgware Town | 1-3 |

**FINAL**

| | | | |
|---|---|---|---|
| Crawley Green | v | Edgware Town | 2-1 |

## CHALLENGE TROPHY

**HOLDERS:** KINGS LANGLEY

**ROUND 1**

| | | | |
|---|---|---|---|
| Amersham Town | v | Broadfields United | 0-5 |
| Hoddesdon Town | v | Baldock Town | 5-0 |
| New Bradwell St Peter | v | Kent Athletic | 3-1 |
| Hadley | v | Oxhey Jets | 3-2 |
| Cockfosters | v | Wodson Park | 0-0, 5-4p |
| AFC Dunstable | v | Wembley | 4-1 |
| Crawley Green | v | Welwyn Garden City | 2-3 |
| Risborough Rangers | v | Clean Slate | 5-1 |
| Edgware Town | v | Colney Heath | 3-0 |
| Brimsdown | v | Mursley United | 1-1, 3-4p |
| Hatfield Town | v | Totternhoe | 3-1 |
| Langford | v | Winslow United | 1-1, 5-3p |
| Aston Clinton | v | Holmer Green | 3-4 |
| Buckingham Athletic | v | FC Broxbourne Borough | 1-3 |
| Wolverton Town | v | London Tigers | 1-4 |
| St Albans City Reserves | v | Bedford | 5-0 |
| Stony Stratford Town | v | Old Bradwell United | 1-2 |
| Chesham United Reserves | v | AFC Hillgate | 5-1 |
| Leverstock Green | v | Sun Sports | 2-3 |
| Harpenden Town | v | Biggleswade United | 0-4 |
| Stotfold | v | London Colney | 1-2 |
| Berkhamsted | v | Aylesbury United Reserves | 4-2 |
| Ampthill Town | v | Tring Corinthians | 2-2, 6-5p |
| Southall | v | Grendon Rangers | 5-1 |
| Tring Athletic | v | St Margaretsbury | 4-1 |
| Hertford Town | v | Hale Leys United | 4-1 |
| Hillingdon Borough | v | Loughton Manor | 2-1 |
| Pitstone & Ivinghoe | v | Woodford Town | 2-3 |

**ROUND 2**

| | | | |
|---|---|---|---|
| Codicote | v | Broadfields United | 5-1 |
| Harefield United | v | Hoddesdon Town | 1-2 |
| New Bradwell St Peter | v | Hadley | 0-3 |
| Cockfosters | v | AFC Dunstable | 0-2 |
| Welwyn Garden City | v | Risborough Rangers | 3-2 |
| Edgware Town | v | Mursley United | 9-2 |
| Hatfield Town | v | Langford | 1-2 |
| Holmer Green | v | FC Broxbourne Borough | 0-3 |
| London Tigers | v | Arlesey Town Reserves | 7-1 |
| St Albans City Reserves | v | The 61FC (Luton) | 12-1 |
| Old Bradwell United | v | Chesham United Reserves | 0-3 |
| Sun Sports | v | Biggleswade United | 1-2 |
| London Colney | v | Berkhamsted | 1-2 |

| DIVISION ONE | 1 | 2 | 3 | 4 | 5 | 6 | 7 | 8 | 9 | 10 | 11 | 12 | 13 | 14 | 15 | 16 | 17 | 18 | 19 | 20 |
|---|---|---|---|---|---|---|---|---|---|---|---|---|---|---|---|---|---|---|---|---|
| 1 Ampthill Town | | 6-1 | 1-3 | 1-2 | 2-3 | 1-2 | 1-0 | 1-1 | 1-2 | 1-4 | 1-2 | 4-1 | 5-1 | 4-2 | 0-2 | 3-0 | 2-5 | 4-0 | 0-0 | 3-2 |
| 2 Arlesey Town Reserves | 2-3 | | 0-7 | 1-2 | 1-3 | 2-2 | 0-10 | 2-3 | 0-1 | 2-3 | 2-4 | 0-0 | 0-3 | 1-2 | 0-1 | 0-2 | 2-2 | 0-1 | 0-7 | 1-3 |
| 3 Baldock Town | 3-0 | 2-2 | | 2-1 | 2-3 | 0-2 | 2-0 | 1-2 | 5-1 | 2-3 | 3-0 | 5-0 | 1-5 | 2-0 | 4-0 | 3-1 | 7-1 | 1-0 | 2-0 | 2-1 |
| 4 Brimsdown | 3-1 | 4-1 | 4-2 | | 2-2 | 0-3 | 0-2 | 1-2 | 1-4 | 2-2 | 2-0 | 2-2 | 1-1 | 2-3 | 0-1 | 1-2 | 0-0 | 3-2 | 2-1 | 1-1 |
| 5 Broadfields United | 4-0 | 5-0 | 2-3 | 0-3 | | 2-2 | 2-3 | 3-1 | 1-1 | 1-3 | 1-6 | 1-2 | 2-2 | 1-2 | 4-0 | 1-2 | 3-2 | 2-0 | 4-4 | 2-1 |
| 6 Buckingham Athletic | 3-0 | 5-1 | 2-2 | 1-0 | 3-3 | | 1-1 | 0-2 | 1-1 | 2-2 | 3-2 | 1-0 | 3-1 | 0-1 | 3-2 | 2-0 | 0-2 | 3-0 | 1-2 | 0-2 |
| 7 Chesham United Reserves | 2-1 | 3-0 | 2-3 | 2-1 | 0-1 | 0-1 | | 2-1 | 2-0 | 0-2 | 2-1 | 1-1 | 2-4 | 3-0 | 2-2 | 5-1 | 2-1 | 2-3 | 2-1 | 4-0 |
| 8 Codicote | 1-2 | 2-0 | 0-2 | 1-2 | 2-1 | 1-0 | 5-3 | | 0-1 | 0-5 | 0-6 | 3-2 | 1-2 | 3-1 | 3-1 | 1-1 | 3-2 | 0-1 | 3-1 | 1-1 |
| 9 Crawley Green | 3-2 | 3-0 | 0-0 | 8-0 | 3-1 | 2-1 | 3-0 | 2-1 | | 2-2 | 0-2 | 2-1 | 3-1 | 4-0 | 2-0 | 2-1 | 4-0 | 2-0 | 4-1 | 3-1 |
| 10 Edgware Town | 5-1 | 3-1 | 1-1 | 9-2 | 3-3 | 0-1 | 4-0 | 5-1 | 3-1 | | 3-1 | 3-1 | 5-0 | 2-0 | 3-1 | 4-1 | 2-1 | 12-3 | 2-1 | 3-2 |
| 11 Harpenden Town | 6-0 | 4-2 | 0-4 | 2-3 | 3-1 | 2-0 | 2-3 | 3-0 | 2-1 | 2-2 | | 3-1 | 3-0 | 1-2 | 1-0 | 1-1 | 6-2 | 2-0 | 1-1 | 0-1 |
| 12 Hatfield Town | 2-0 | 5-0 | 0-3 | 5-1 | 3-2 | 0-0 | 1-2 | 0-3 | 0-3 | 0-1 | 1-0 | | 3-1 | 1-1 | 0-2 | 2-4 | 2-0 | 2-2 | 2-4 | 1-2 |
| 13 Hillingdon Borough | 0-1 | 1-2 | 1-4 | 1-4 | 2-1 | 0-0 | 0-2 | 0-1 | 1-4 | 2-7 | 1-1 | 2-1 | | 4-1 | 0-0 | 4-2 | 1-3 | 5-4 | 0-2 | 0-2 |
| 14 Langford | 0-3 | 1-0 | 0-1 | 4-3 | 1-2 | 1-3 | 3-3 | 4-5 | 0-0 | 0-8 | 1-3 | 1-2 | 2-2 | | 3-3 | 2-2 | 4-4 | 3-4 | 3-4 | 3-1 |
| 15 New Bradwell St Peter | 3-2 | 1-2 | 2-1 | 6-1 | 3-0 | 3-2 | 1-2 | 2-1 | 1-2 | 2-1 | 1-5 | 2-0 | 3-1 | 3-2 | | 1-1 | 2-1 | 1-1 | 1-0 | 4-3 |
| 16 Risborough Rangers | 4-1 | 5-0 | 2-0 | 4-2 | 3-2 | 1-0 | 2-2 | H-W | 6-0 | 0-1 | 1-2 | 3-2 | 3-0 | 1-1 | 1-0 | | 2-2 | 3-2 | 2-1 | 2-1 |
| 17 Southall | H-W | 4-1 | 0-3 | 1-1 | 3-4 | 2-0 | 0-1 | 5-0 | 1-2 | 0-3 | 2-2 | 3-0 | 1-0 | 5-1 | 2-2 | 3-2 | | 1-0 | 1-0 | 2-5 |
| 18 Winslow United | 1-2 | 3-1 | 2-3 | 4-1 | 0-1 | 0-3 | 1-2 | 3-2 | 1-3 | 1-2 | 0-1 | 1-1 | 0-4 | 1-1 | 1-1 | 3-0 | 1-1 | | 1-1 | 1-0 |
| 19 Wodson Park | 2-0 | 2-1 | 0-1 | 4-2 | 3-0 | 2-0 | 2-1 | 2-0 | 0-1 | 2-3 | 2-4 | 1-0 | 2-3 | 3-2 | 5-2 | 3-0 | 3-1 | 3-1 | | 2-2 |
| 20 Woodford Town | A-W | 2-0 | 0-1 | 5-0 | 5-0 | 1-1 | 1-2 | 3-5 | 1-3 | 2-4 | 0-1 | 1-2 | 1-0 | 3-4 | 4-0 | 0-0 | 4-2 | 3-2 | 4-5 | |

## CHALLENGE TROPHY continued...

| | | | |
|---|---|---|---|
| Ampthill Town | v | Southall | 2-0 |
| Tring Athletic | v | Hertford Town | 3-5 |
| Hillingdon Borough | v | Woodford Town | 1-2 |

ROUND 3

| | | | |
|---|---|---|---|
| Codicote | v | Hoddesdon Town | 1-0 |
| Hadley | v | AFC Dunstable | 0-3 |
| Welwyn Garden City | v | Edgware Town | 4-2 |
| Langford | v | FC Broxbourne Borough | 2-2, 2-4p |
| London Tigers | v | St Albans City Reserves | HW |
| Chesham United Reserves | v | Biggleswade United | 0-0, 4-3p |
| Berkhamsted | v | Ampthill Town | 10-1 |
| Hertford Town | v | Woodford Town | 4-2 |

**QUARTER FINALS**

| | | | |
|---|---|---|---|
| Codicote | v | AFC Dunstable | 3-2 |
| Welwyn Garden City | v | FC Broxbourne Borough | 3-3, 5-4p |
| London Tigers | v | Chesham United Reserves | 2-3 |
| Berkhamsted | v | Hertford Town | 4-0 |

**SEMI FINALS**

| | | | |
|---|---|---|---|
| Codicote | v | Welwyn Garden City | 1-3 |
| Chesham United Reserves | v | Berkhamsted | 0-3 |

**FINAL**

| | | | |
|---|---|---|---|
| Welwyn Garden City | v | Berkhamsted | 4-3 |

| | DIVISION TWO | P | W | D | L | F | A | GD | Pts |
|---|---|---|---|---|---|---|---|---|---|
| 1 | Kent Athletic | 30 | 27 | 1 | 2 | 138 | 37 | 101 | 82 |
| 2 | Hale Leys United | 30 | 24 | 4 | 2 | 124 | 34 | 90 | 76 |
| 3 | Old Bradwell United | 30 | 24 | 1 | 5 | 79 | 36 | 43 | 73 |
| 4 | Pitstone & Ivinghoe | 30 | 18 | 4 | 8 | 98 | 66 | 32 | 58 |
| 5 | AFC Hillgate | 30 | 17 | 2 | 11 | 68 | 47 | 21 | 53 |
| 6 | Loughton Manor | 30 | 14 | 5 | 11 | 62 | 56 | 6 | 47 |
| 7 | Aston Clinton | 30 | 13 | 5 | 12 | 65 | 61 | 4 | 44 |
| 8 | Totternhoe | 30 | 12 | 6 | 12 | 65 | 64 | 1 | 42 |
| 9 | Tring Corinthians | 30 | 10 | 5 | 15 | 52 | 50 | 2 | 35 |
| 10 | Stony Stratford Town (-3) | 30 | 11 | 4 | 15 | 60 | 64 | -4 | 34 |
| 11 | Mursley United | 30 | 10 | 3 | 17 | 47 | 83 | -36 | 33 |
| 12 | Amersham Town | 30 | 9 | 4 | 17 | 57 | 81 | -24 | 31 |
| 13 | Unite MK FC | 30 | 8 | 6 | 16 | 49 | 79 | -30 | 30 |
| 14 | Grendon Rangers | 30 | 4 | 5 | 21 | 33 | 102 | -69 | 17 |
| 15 | Clean Slate | 30 | 4 | 3 | 23 | 45 | 121 | -76 | 15 |
| 16 | The 61FC (Luton) | 30 | 2 | 8 | 20 | 30 | 91 | -61 | 14 |

Aylesbury United Reserves withdrew - record expunged.
St. Albans City Reserves withdrew - record expunged.
Wolverton Town withdrew - record expunged.

## DIVISION TWO CUP

**HOLDERS:** HALE LEYS UNITED

**ROUND 1**

| | | | |
|---|---|---|---|
| The 61FC (Luton) | v | Pitstone & Ivinghoe | 1-3 |
| Kent Athletic | v | Mursley United | 5-0 |

**ROUND 2**

| | | | |
|---|---|---|---|
| Totternhoe | v | St Albans City Reserves | 3-2 |
| Loughton Manor | v | Amersham Town | 2-0 |
| Wolverton Town | v | Clean Slate | 5-1 |
| AFC Hillgate | v | Pitstone & Ivinghoe | 3-2 |
| Hale Leys United | v | Kent Athletic | 7-0 |
| Grendon Rangers | v | Stony Stratford Town | 0-5 |
| Old Bradwell United | v | Aston Clinton | 2-3 |
| Aylesbury United Reserves | v | Tring Corinthians | 0-12 |

**QUARTER FINALS**

| | | | |
|---|---|---|---|
| Totternhoe | v | Loughton Manor | 2-0 |
| Wolverton Town | v | AFC Hillgate | 0-3 |
| Hale Leys United | v | Stony Stratford Town | 3-3, 4-3p |
| Aston Clinton | v | Tring Corinthians | 4-1 |

**SEMI FINALS**

| | | | |
|---|---|---|---|
| Totternhoe | v | AFC Hillgate | 3-0 |
| Hale Leys United | v | Aston Clinton | 5-0 |

**FINAL**

| | | | |
|---|---|---|---|
| Totternhoe | v | Hale Leys United | 2-3 |

| | DIVISION TWO | 1 | 2 | 3 | 4 | 5 | 6 | 7 | 8 | 9 | 10 | 11 | 12 | 13 | 14 | 15 | 16 |
|---|---|---|---|---|---|---|---|---|---|---|---|---|---|---|---|---|---|
| 1 | AFC Hillgate | | 3-1 | 3-1 | 8-0 | 2-0 | 1-2 | 3-2 | 2-1 | 6-0 | 2-3 | 2-4 | 0-2 | 3-1 | 2-2 | 2-1 | 3-0 |
| 2 | Amersham Town | 0-3 | | 2-3 | 7-3 | 6-0 | 2-8 | 1-5 | 1-1 | 0-2 | 0-2 | 1-2 | 3-2 | 3-0 | 2-3 | 4-0 | 2-3 |
| 3 | Aston Clinton | 0-3 | 1-3 | | 3-2 | 5-1 | 1-1 | 1-7 | 1-2 | 3-2 | 3-2 | 2-2 | 3-2 | 5-0 | 4-0 | 0-5 | 5-0 |
| 4 | Clean Slate | 1-2 | 2-4 | 0-3 | | 3-1 | 0-6 | 2-7 | 0-4 | 1-2 | 1-7 | 2-7 | 2-4 | 2-0 | 0-0 | 1-5 | 4-2 |
| 5 | Grendon Rangers | 1-6 | 3-1 | 0-2 | 1-1 | | 0-1 | 0-5 | 1-4 | 2-1 | 3-4 | 0-7 | 1-1 | 5-4 | 0-2 | 2-1 | 1-5 |
| 6 | Hale Leys United | 5-1 | 9-0 | 3-3 | 8-0 | 10-2 | | 1-2 | 4-1 | 6-0 | 4-0 | 6-1 | 2-1 | 9-0 | 2-1 | 4-2 | 4-1 |
| 7 | Kent Athletic | 5-1 | 5-0 | 2-1 | 8-0 | 6-1 | 4-2 | | 5-3 | 4-2 | 2-0 | 6-0 | 5-1 | 6-2 | 9-0 | 3-1 | 3-0 |
| 8 | Loughton Manor | 3-1 | 3-3 | 2-0 | 4-4 | 5-0 | 0-1 | 2-6 | | 3-1 | 0-3 | 1-6 | 2-0 | 5-2 | 2-1 | 2-1 | 1-1 |
| 9 | Mursley United | 2-1 | 1-2 | 3-1 | 3-4 | 3-1 | 1-7 | 1-6 | 3-2 | | 1-3 | 2-6 | 3-2 | 1-0 | 2-1 | 3-2 | 1-1 |
| 10 | Old Bradwell United | 2-1 | 5-1 | 1-0 | 4-2 | 4-1 | 1-2 | 2-1 | 4-0 | 0-0 | | H-W | 2-0 | 5-0 | 4-1 | 2-0 | 3-1 |
| 11 | Pitstone & Ivinghoe | 4-1 | 3-2 | 2-5 | 2-1 | 2-2 | 1-4 | 0-1 | 1-2 | 5-2 | 7-2 | | 4-2 | 5-0 | 4-5 | 3-2 | 1- |
| 12 | Stony Stratford Town | 0-1 | 3-0 | 2-2 | 7-1 | 2-1 | 3-4 | 1-6 | 1-0 | 3-0 | 0-4 | 1-3 | | 4-1 | 1-1 | 3-1 | 7-0 |
| 13 | The 61FC (Luton) | 1-1 | 1-2 | 1-1 | 1-0 | 1-1 | 0-0 | 1-6 | 0-4 | 2-1 | 1-2 | 4-6 | 2-2 | | 1-4 | 0-0 | 3-4 |
| 14 | Totternhoe | 2-0 | 2-1 | 4-1 | 7-4 | 5-0 | 2-3 | 2-2 | 0-0 | 6-2 | 0-1 | 3-4 | 6-0 | 0-0 | | 1-3 | 1-3 |
| 15 | Tring Corinthians | 0-1 | 1-1 | 2-4 | 2-1 | 2-1 | 2-2 | 1-2 | 2-0 | 1-1 | 2-3 | 1-3 | 2-0 | 1-1 | 5-0 | | 1-0 |
| 16 | Unite MK FC | 1-3 | 2-2 | 2-1 | 2-1 | 1-1 | 1-4 | 5-7 | 1-3 | 2-1 | 0-4 | 3-3 | 2-3 | 3-0 | 2-3 | 0-3 | |

## BERKHAMSTED

Founded: 2009 Nickname: Comrades

**Secretary:** Keith Hicks **(T)** 07767 430 087 **(E)** keith55hicks@gmail.com
**Chairman:** Steve Davis **Manager:** Tommy Garratt **Prog Ed:** Grant Hastie
**Ground:** Broadwater, Lower Kings Road, Berkhamsted HP4 2AL **(T)** 01442 865 977
**Capacity:** 2,500 **Seats:** 170 **Covered:** 350 **Midweek Matchday:** **Clubhouse:** Yes **Shop:** Yes

**Colours(change):** White/black/black (White/black/black)
**Previous Names:** None
**Previous Leagues:** None
**Records:**
**Honours:** Spartan South Midlands League Division 1 2009-10, 10-11.

**10 YEAR RECORD**

| 06-07 | 07-08 | 08-09 | 09-10 | 10-11 | 11-12 | 12-13 | 13-14 | 14-15 | 15-16 |
|---|---|---|---|---|---|---|---|---|---|
| | | | SSM1 1 | SSM1 1 | SSM P 7 | SSM P 11 | SSM P 5 | SSM P 6 | SSM P 5 |

## BIGGLESWADE UNITED

Founded: 1929 Nickname:

**Secretary:** Tracey James **(T)** 07714 661 827 **(E)** tracey.james58@btinternet.com
**Chairman:** Chris Lewis **Manager:** Cristian Colas **Prog Ed:** Tracey James
**Ground:** Second Meadow, Fairfield Rd, Biggleswade, Beds SG18 0BS **(T)** 07714 661 827
**Capacity:** 2,000 **Seats:** 30 **Covered:** 130 **Midweek Matchday:** Wednesday **Clubhouse:** Yes **Shop:** No

**Colours(change):** Red/navy/red (Royal blue/blue/blue)
**Previous Names:** None
**Previous Leagues:** Beds & District and Midland. Herts County.
**Records:** **Att:** 250 v Biggleswade Town
**Honours:** Spartan South Midlands Division One 1996-97, Premier Division 2008-09. Hunts FA Premier Cup 1998-99.
Beds Senior Trophy 2003-04. Beds Senior Cup 2001-02.

**10 YEAR RECORD**

| 06-07 | 07-08 | 08-09 | 09-10 | 10-11 | 11-12 | 12-13 | 13-14 | 14-15 | 15-16 |
|---|---|---|---|---|---|---|---|---|---|
| SSM P 14 | SSM P 18 | SSM P 1 | SSM P 20 | SSM P 20 | SSM P 19 | SSM P 18 | SSM P 17 | SSM P 13 | SSM P 10 |

## COCKFOSTERS

Founded: 1921 Nickname: Fosters

**Secretary:** Graham Bint **(T)** 07729 709 926 **(E)** graham.bint@btinternet.com
**Chairman:** Roy Syrett **Manager:** Dean Barker - 18/05/15 **Prog Ed:** Alan Simmons
**Ground:** Cockfosters Sports Ground, Chalk Lane, Cockfosters, Herts EN4 9JG **(T)** 0208 449 5833
**Capacity:** **Seats:** Yes **Covered:** Yes **Midweek Matchday:** **Clubhouse:**

**Colours(change):** All red (All blue)
**Previous Names:** Cockfosters Athletic 1921-68.
**Previous Leagues:** Barnet 1921-30s. Wood Green 1930s-46. Northern Suburban Int. 1946-66. Hertfordshire County 1966-1991. Spartan 1991-97.
**Records:** 408 v Saffron Walden.
**Honours:** London Interim Cup 1970-71, 89. Herts Sen Co Lge 1978-79, 80-81, 83-84. Aubrey Cup 1978-79, 84-85.
Herts Interm Cup 1978-79.

**10 YEAR RECORD**

| 06-07 | 07-08 | 08-09 | 09-10 | 10-11 | 11-12 | 12-13 | 13-14 | 14-15 | 15-16 |
|---|---|---|---|---|---|---|---|---|---|
| SSM1 2 | SSM1 17 | SSM1 19 | SSM1 11 | SSM1 15 | SSM1 9 | SSM1 2 | SSM P 8 | SSM P 18 | SSM P 9 |

## COLNEY HEATH

Founded: 1907 Nickname: Magpies

**Secretary:** Dean Penny **(T)** 07920 289 069 **(E)** deanpenny@btinternet.com
**Chairman:** Martin Marlborough **Manager:** Micky Nathan **Prog Ed:** Martin Marlborough
**Ground:** The Recreation Ground, High St, Colney Heath, St Albans AL4 0NP **(T)** 01727 824 325
**Capacity:** **Seats:** **Covered:** **Midweek Matchday:** **Clubhouse:** Yes

**Colours(change):** Black & white stripes/black/black (All blue)
**Previous Names:** None
**Previous Leagues:** Herts Senior County League 1953-2000
**Records:**
**Honours:** Herts County League Div 2 Champions 1953-54 Div 1 A 55-56, Prem 58-99, 99-00, Div 1 88-89,
Spartan South Midlands Div 1 2005-06 , SSML Cup 05-06

**10 YEAR RECORD**

| 06-07 | 07-08 | 08-09 | 09-10 | 10-11 | 11-12 | 12-13 | 13-14 | 14-15 | 15-16 |
|---|---|---|---|---|---|---|---|---|---|
| SSM P 16 | SSM P 15 | SSM P 12 | SSM P 5 | SSM P 5 | SSM P 8 | SSM P 13 | SSM P 3 | SSM P 14 | SSM P 20 |

## CRAWLEY GREEN

Founded: 1989 Nickname:

**Secretary:** Eddie Downey **(T)** 07956 107 477 **(E)** eddie.downey@hotmail.com
**Chairman:** Alan Clark **Manager:** Mark Smith **Prog Ed:** Alan Clark
**Ground:** Barton Rovers FC, Sharpenhoe Road, Barton Le Cay, Beds MK45 4SD **(T)** 01582 882 398
**Capacity:** **Seats:** **Covered:** **Midweek Matchday:** **Clubhouse:** Yes

**Colours(change):** All maroon (Sky blue/navy blue/navy blue)
**Previous Names:** None
**Previous Leagues:** None
**Records:**
**Honours:**

**10 YEAR RECORD**

| 06-07 | 07-08 | 08-09 | 09-10 | 10-11 | 11-12 | 12-13 | 13-14 | 14-15 | 15-16 |
|---|---|---|---|---|---|---|---|---|---|
| SSM2 3 | SSM2 2 | SSM1 16 | SSM1 8 | SSM1 4 | SSM1 6 | SSM1 4 | SSM1 5 | SSM1 7 | SSM1 2 |

## EDGWARE TOWN

Founded: 1939 Nickname: The Wares

**Secretary:** Daren Bloor **(T)** 07773 312 110 **(E)** secretary@edgwaretown.co.uk
**Chairman:** Antony Manzi **Manager:** Fabio Valenti **Prog Ed:** Antony Manzi
**Ground:** Silver Jubilee Park, Townsend Lane, London NW9 7NE **(T)** 0208 205 1645
**Capacity:** **Seats:** **Covered:** **Midweek Matchday:** **Clubhouse:**

**Colours(change):** All green (Red & black/black/black)
**Previous Names:** Edgware 1972-87. Original Edgware Town folded in 2008 and re-formed in 2014.
**Previous Leagues:** Corinthian 1946-63. Athenian 1963-84. Spartan 1984-90, 2006-07. Isthmian 1990-2006, 2007-08.
**Records:**
**Honours:** Spartan South Midlands League 1987-88, 89-90, 2006-07, Division One 2015-16.

**10 YEAR RECORD**

| 06-07 | 07-08 | 08-09 | 09-10 | 10-11 | 11-12 | 12-13 | 13-14 | 14-15 | 15-16 |
|---|---|---|---|---|---|---|---|---|---|
| SSM P 1 | Isth1N 8 | | | | | | | SSM1 9 | SSM1 1 |

## FC BROXBOURNE BOROUGH

Founded: 1959 Nickname:

**Secretary:** Graham Dodd **(T)** 07973 701 515 **(E)** graham@leterboxconsultancy.co.uk
**Chairman:** John Murphy **Manager:** Terry Gritton **Prog Ed:** Graham Dodd
**Ground:** Broxbourne Borougn V & E Club, Goffs Lane, Cheshunt, Herts EN7 5QN **(T)** 01992 624 281
**Capacity:** 500 **Seats:** 300 **Covered:** yes **Midweek Matchday:** Tuesday **Clubhouse:** Yes **Shop:** No

**Colours(change):** All Blue. (All yellow)
**Previous Names:** Somerset Ambury V & E > 2002, Broxbourne Borough V & E 2002-12
**Previous Leagues:** Herts Senior
**Records:** **Record Att:** 120 **Goalscorer:** Wayne Morris **App:** Brian Boehmer
**Honours:**

**10 YEAR RECORD**

| 06-07 | 07-08 | 08-09 | 09-10 | 10-11 | 11-12 | 12-13 | 13-14 | 14-15 | 15-16 |
|---|---|---|---|---|---|---|---|---|---|
| SSM P 8 | SSM P 12 | SSM P 4 | SSM P 9 | SSM P 10 | SSM P 13 | SSM2 3 | SSM1 6 | SSM1 2 | SSM P 16 |

## HADLEY

Founded: 1882 Nickname:

**Secretary:** Bob Henderson **(T)** 07748 267 295 **(E)** gensecretary@hadleyfc.com
**Chairman:** Guy Slee **Manager:** Micky Hazard **Prog Ed:** Guy Slee
**Ground:** Hadley Sports Ground, Brickfield Lane, Arkley, Barnet EN3 3LD **(T)** 07905 446 331
**Capacity:** 2,000 **Seats:** 150 **Covered:** 250 **Midweek Matchday:** **Clubhouse:** Yes **Shop:** Yes

**Colours(change):** Red/black/black (Black & white stripes/white/white)
**Previous Names:** None
**Previous Leagues:** Barnet & Dist. 1922-57, Nth Suburban 57-70, Mid Herts 70-77, Herts Sen. 77-85, 99-2007, Sth Olym. 85-99, W Herts 2007-08.
**Records:**
**Honours:** Hertfordshire Senior County League Division 3 1977-78, Division 1 2001-02, Premier 2003-04, 04-05.
West Hertfordshire League 2007-08. Aubrey Cup 2005-06.

**10 YEAR RECORD**

| 06-07 | 07-08 | 08-09 | 09-10 | 10-11 | 11-12 | 12-13 | 13-14 | 14-15 | 15-16 |
|---|---|---|---|---|---|---|---|---|---|
| HertP 2 | WHert 1 | SSM2 2 | SSM1 2 | SSM P 14 | SSM P 15 | SSM P 12 | SSM P 13 | SSM P 9 | SSM P 6 |

## HERTFORD TOWN

Founded: 1908 Nickname: The Blues

**Secretary:** Peter Sinclair **(T)** 07748 195 237 **(E)** pdsinx@hotmail.com
**Chairman:** Peter Sinclair **Manager:** Gavin Kelsey **Prog Ed:** Ken Williams
**Ground:** Hertingfordbury Park, West Street, Hertford, SG13 8EZ **(T)** 01992 583 716
**Capacity:** 6,500 **Seats:** 200 **Covered:** 1,500 **Midweek Matchday:** Tuesday **Clubhouse:** Yes **Shop:** Yes

**Colours(change):** Blue/blue/blue & white hoops (All yellow)
**Previous Names:** None
**Previous Leagues:** Herts Co. Spartan. Delphian 59-63. Athenian 63-72. Eastern Co 72-73.
**Records:** **Att:** 5,000 v Kingstonian FA Am Cup 2nd Round 55-56 **App:** Robbie Burns
**Honours:** Herts Senior Cup 66-67 East Anglian Cup 62-63, 69-70

**10 YEAR RECORD**

| 06-07 | 07-08 | 08-09 | 09-10 | 10-11 | 11-12 | 12-13 | 13-14 | 14-15 | 15-16 |
|---|---|---|---|---|---|---|---|---|---|
| SSM P 3 | SSM P 4 | SSM P 10 | SSM P 16 | SSM P 9 | SSM P 16 | SSM P 17 | SSM P 16 | SSM P 11 | SSM P 8 |

## HODDESDON TOWN

Founded: 1879 Nickname: Lilywhites

**Secretary:** Jane Sinden **(T)** 01767 247 526 **(E)** janedsinden@fsmail.net
**Chairman:** Roger Merton **Manager:** Paul Halsey **Prog Ed:** Jane Sinden
**Ground:** Wodson Park, Wadesmill Road, Ware, Herts SG12 0UQ **(T)** 01920 462 064
**Capacity:** **Seats:** **Covered:** **Midweek Matchday:** **Clubhouse:**

**Colours(change):** White/black/red (All blue)
**Previous Names:** None
**Previous Leagues:** Hertfordshire County 1920-25. Spartan 1963-75. London Spartan 1975-77. Athenian 1977-84.
**Records:**
**Honours:** **(FA Comps & League):** FA Vase 1974-75 (1st Winners).
Spartan League Champions 1970-71, Division 1 1935-36, Division 2 'B' 1927-28

**10 YEAR RECORD**

| 06-07 | 07-08 | 08-09 | 09-10 | 10-11 | 11-12 | 12-13 | 13-14 | 14-15 | 15-16 |
|---|---|---|---|---|---|---|---|---|---|
| SSM1 5 | SSM1 3 | SSM1 5 | SSM1 4 | SSM1 9 | SSM1 3 | SSM1 3 | SSM P 6 | SSM P 19 | SSM P 3 |

## HOLMER GREEN

Founded: 1908 Nickname:

**Secretary:** Matt Brades **(T)** 07801 216 632 **(E)** bradesm@dnb.com
**Chairman:** Rob Shed **Manager:** Rob Shed **Prog Ed:** John Anderson
**Ground:** Airedale Park, Watchet Lane, Holmer Green, Bucks HP15 6UF **(T)** 01494 711 485
**Capacity:** 1,000 **Seats:** 25 **Covered:** yes **Midweek Matchday:** Tuesday **Clubhouse:** Yes

**Colours(change):** Green & white hoops/green/green
**Previous Names:** None
**Previous Leagues:** Chesham 1908-38, Wycombe Combination 1984-95, Chiltonian 1995-98.
**Records:**
**Honours:** Spartan South Midlands Senior 1995-96, 98-99, Division 1 2009-10.

**10 YEAR RECORD**

| 06-07 | 07-08 | 08-09 | 09-10 | 10-11 | 11-12 | 12-13 | 13-14 | 14-15 | 15-16 |
|---|---|---|---|---|---|---|---|---|---|
| SSM P 19 | SSM P 20 | SSM P 20 | SSM1 1 | SSM P 17 | SSM P 20 | SSM P 22 | SSM P 12 | SSM P 20 | SSM P 7 |

## LEIGHTON TOWN

Founded: 1885 Nickname: Reds

**Secretary:** Sheelah McGregor **(T)** 07967 398 429 **(E)** sheelahm@hotmail.com
**Chairman:** Iain McGregor **Manager:** Paul Burgess **Prog Ed:** James D'Arcy
**Ground:** Lake Street, Leighton Buzzard, Beds LU7 1RX **(T)** 01525 373 311
**Capacity:** 2,800 **Seats:** 155 **Covered:** 300 **Midweek Matchday:** **Clubhouse:** Yes

**Colours(change):** Red & white stripes/red/red (All sky blue)
**Previous Names:** Leighton United 1922-63
**Previous Leagues:** Leighton & District, South Midlands 1922-24, 26-29, 46-54, 55-56, 76-92, Spartan 1922-53, 67-74,
**Records:** 1,522 v Aldershot Town - Isthmian League Division 3 30/01/1993. **Previous Lges:** United Counties 1974-76, Isthmian. Southern >2016.
**Honours:** South Midlands League 1966-67, 91-92. Isthmian League Division 2 2003-04.
Bedfordshire Senior Cup 1926-27, 67-68, 69-70, 92-93.

**10 YEAR RECORD**

| 06-07 | 07-08 | 08-09 | 09-10 | 10-11 | 11-12 | 12-13 | 13-14 | 14-15 | 15-16 |
|---|---|---|---|---|---|---|---|---|---|
| SthM 18 | SthM 9 | SthM 8 | SthM 10 | SthC 7 | SthC 13 | SthC 21 | SthC 19 | SthC 18 | SthC 21 |

## LEVERSTOCK GREEN

Founded: 1895 Nickname: The Green

**Secretary:** Brian Barter **(T)** 07982 072 783 **(E)** b.barter@btopenworld.com
**Chairman:** Brian Barter **Manager:** Paul Hunt **Prog Ed:** Brian Barter
**Ground:** Pancake Lane, Leverstock Green, Hemel Hempstead, Herts HP2 4NQ **(T)** 01442 246 280
**Capacity:** 1,500 **Seats:** 50 **Covered:** 100 **Midweek Matchday:** Tuesday **Clubhouse:** Yes **Shop:** No

**Colours(change):** White/green/green (Orange/black/orange)
**Previous Names:** None
**Previous Leagues:** West Herts (pre 1950) & Herts County 50-91
**Records:** **Att:** 1,000 **App:** Jonnie Wallace
**Honours:** South Midlands Senior Division 1996-97.

**10 YEAR RECORD**

| 06-07 | 07-08 | 08-09 | 09-10 | 10-11 | 11-12 | 12-13 | 13-14 | 14-15 | 15-16 |
|---|---|---|---|---|---|---|---|---|---|
| SSM P 5 | SSM P 7 | SSM P 6 | SSM P 10 | SSM P 4 | SSM P 11 | SSM P 15 | SSM P 20 | SSM P 15 | SSM P 18 |

## LONDON COLNEY

Founded: 1907 Nickname: Blueboys

**Secretary:** Dave Brock **(T)** 07508 035 835 **(E)** davebrock42@hotmail.com
**Chairman:** Tony Clafton **Manager:** Joe Sweeney **Prog Ed:** Johnny Armitt
**Ground:** Cotlandswick Playing Fields, London Colney, Herts AL2 1DW **(T)** 01727 822 132
**Capacity:** **Seats:** Yes **Covered:** Yes **Midweek Matchday:** **Clubhouse:** Yes

**Colours(change):** All royal blue (All red)
**Previous Names:**
**Previous Leagues:** Herts Senior 1955-93.
**Records:** 300 v St Albans City Hertfordshire Senior Cup 1998-99.
**Honours:** Herts Senior League 1956-57, 59-60, 86-87, 88-89. 89-90.
South Midlands Senior Division 1994-95. Spartan South Midlands Premier Division 2001-02, Division One 2011-12.

**10 YEAR RECORD**

| 06-07 | 07-08 | 08-09 | 09-10 | 10-11 | 11-12 | 12-13 | 13-14 | 14-15 | 15-16 |
|---|---|---|---|---|---|---|---|---|---|
| SSM P 10 | SSM P 22 | SSM1 9 | SSM1 3 | SSM1 5 | SSM1 1 | SSM P 7 | SSM P 7 | SSM P 2 | SSM P 2 |

## LONDON TIGERS

Founded: 2006 Nickname: Tigers

**Secretary:** Mick Wilkins **(T)** 07802 212 787 **(E)** wilki1@aol.com
**Chairman:** Mesba Ahmed **Manager:** Miguel De'Souza **Prog Ed:** Zilu Miah
**Ground:** Avenue Park, Western Avenue, Perivale, Greenford UB6 8GA **(T)** 020 7289 3395 (10am-6pm)
**Capacity:** **Seats:** **Covered:** **Midweek Matchday:** **Clubhouse:**

**Colours(change):** Orange/black/black (Yellow & black stripes/black/black)
**Previous Names:** Kingsbury Town and London Tigers merged in 2006. Kingsbury London Tigers 2006-11.
**Previous Leagues:** None
**Records:**
**Honours:**

**10 YEAR RECORD**

| 06-07 | 07-08 | 08-09 | 09-10 | 10-11 | 11-12 | 12-13 | 13-14 | 14-15 | 15-16 |
|---|---|---|---|---|---|---|---|---|---|
| SSM P 13 | SSM P 14 | SSM P 5 | SSM P 8 | SSM P 12 | SSM P 14 | SSM P 20 | SSM P 15 | SSM P 17 | SSM P 13 |

## OXHEY JETS

Founded: 1972 Nickname: Jets

**Secretary:** David Fuller **(T)** 07786 627 659 **(E)** d.g.fuller@ntlworld.com
**Chairman:** Phil Andrews **Manager:** Bob Wyatt **Prog Ed:** David Fuller
**Ground:** Boundary Stadium, Altham Way, South Oxhey, Watford WD19 6FW **(T)** 020 8421 6277
**Capacity:** 1,000 **Seats:** 150 **Covered:** 100 **Midweek Matchday:** Wednesday **Clubhouse:** Yes **Shop:** No

**Colours(change):** All royal blue (All green)
**Previous Names:** None
**Previous Leagues:** Herts Senior County
**Records:** **Att:** 376 v Hendon, FA Cup 2011-12 **Goalscorer:** Gary Page - 335 **App:** Eddie O'Connor - 825
**Honours:** Herts Senior County Premier 2000-01, 01-02, 02-03. Herts Senior Aubery Cup 2001-02, 02-03. Herts Senior Centenary Trophy 2001-02, 04-05. West Herts St Mary's Cup 2003-04, 11-12, 13-14. SSML Div 1 Champions 2004-2005. Herts FA Charity Shield 2009-10, 10-11, 12-13.

**10 YEAR RECORD**

| 06-07 | 07-08 | 08-09 | 09-10 | 10-11 | 11-12 | 12-13 | 13-14 | 14-15 | 15-16 |
|---|---|---|---|---|---|---|---|---|---|
| SSM P 7 | SSM P 19 | SSM P 13 | SSM P 11 | SSM P 19 | SSM P 17 | SSM P 3 | SSM P 18 | SSM P 12 | SSM P 17 |

## ST MARGARETSBURY

Founded: 1894 Nickname: Athletic

**Secretary:** Phil Hayward **(T)** 07721 415 579 **(E)** smfc@niche-direct.com
**Chairman:** Gary Stock **Manager:** John Barker **Prog Ed:** Gary Stock
**Ground:** Recreation Ground, Station Road, St Margarets SG12 8EH **(T)** 01920 870 473
**Capacity:** 1,000 **Seats:** 60 **Covered:** 60 **Midweek Matchday:** Tuesday **Clubhouse:** Yes **Shop:** No

**Colours(change):** Red & black hoops/black/red & black hoops (Yellow & black stripes/yellow/black)
**Previous Names:** Stanstead Abbots > 1962
**Previous Leagues:** East Herts, Hertford & District, Waltham & District, 47-48 Herts Co. 48-92
**Records:** **Att:** 450 v Stafford Rangers FA Cup 2001-02
**Honours:** Spartan League 1995-96 Herts Senior Centenary Trophy 1992-93, Herts Charity Shield 1997-98

**10 YEAR RECORD**

| 06-07 | 07-08 | 08-09 | 09-10 | 10-11 | 11-12 | 12-13 | 13-14 | 14-15 | 15-16 |
|---|---|---|---|---|---|---|---|---|---|
| SSM P 15 | SSM P 11 | SSM P 14 | SSM P 14 | SSM P 18 | SSM P 12 | SSM P 4 | SSM P 4 | SSM P 8 | SSM P 19 |

## STOTFOLD

Founded: 1946 Nickname: The Eagles

**Secretary:** Julie Longhurst **(T)** 07752 430 493 **(E)** julie.longhurst46@virginmedia.com
**Chairman:** Phil Pateman **Manager:** Ron Bates **Prog Ed:** Phil Pateman
**Ground:** Roker Park, The Green, Stotfold, Hitchin, Herts SG5 4AN **(T)** 01462 730 765
**Capacity:** 5,000 **Seats:** 300 **Covered:** 300 **Midweek Matchday:** Tuesday **Clubhouse:** Yes

**Colours(change):** Amber/black/black. (Green & white stripes/green/green).
**Previous Names:** None
**Previous Leagues:** Biggleswade & Dist, Norths Herts & South Midlands, United Counties > 2010
**Records:** **Att:**1,000 **Goalscorer:** Roy Boon **Apps:** Roy Boon & Dave Chellew
**Honours:** S. Midlands League 1980-81. Bedfordshire Senior Cup 1964-65, 93-94. Bedfordshire Premier Cup 1981-82, 98-99. United Counties League 2007-08.

**10 YEAR RECORD**

| 06-07 | 07-08 | 08-09 | 09-10 | 10-11 | 11-12 | 12-13 | 13-14 | 14-15 | 15-16 |
|---|---|---|---|---|---|---|---|---|---|
| UCL P 19 | UCL P 1 | UCL P 2 | UCL P 7 | SSM P 13 | SSM P 9 | SSM P 14 | SSM P 19 | SSM P 16 | SSM P 15 |

## SUN SPORTS

Founded: 1898 Nickname:

**Secretary:** Chris Manning **(T)** 07798 927 818 **(E)** seniorfootball@sunpostal.co.uk
**Chairman:** James Kempster **Manager:** Tim O'Sullivan **Prog Ed:** Chris Manning
**Ground:** Sun Postal Sports Club, Bellmountwood Avenue, Watford, Herts WD17 3BN **(T)** 01923 227 453
**Capacity:** **Seats:** **Covered:** **Midweek Matchday:** **Clubhouse:** Yes

**Colours(change):** Yellow/royal blue/royal blue (All red)
**Previous Names:** Sun Engraving FC 1898-1935. Sun Sports 1935-95. Sun Postal Sports 1995-2014.
**Previous Leagues:** Watford & District. Hertfordshire Senior County 1935-2003.
**Records:**
**Honours:** Spartan South Midlands Division One 2013-14.

**10 YEAR RECORD**

| 06-07 | 07-08 | 08-09 | 09-10 | 10-11 | 11-12 | 12-13 | 13-14 | 14-15 | 15-16 |
|---|---|---|---|---|---|---|---|---|---|
| SSM1 13 | SSM1 17 | SSM1 20 | SSM1 14 | SSM1 11 | SSM1 22 | SSM1 17 | SSM1 1 | SSM P 5 | SSM P 14 |

## TRING ATHLETIC

Founded: 1958 Nickname: Athletic

**Secretary:** Bob Winter **(T)** 07979 816 528 **(E)** robert.winter2007@ntlworld.com
**Chairman:** Mick Eldridge **Manager:** Ian Richardson **Prog Ed:** Barry Simmons
**Ground:** Grass Roots Stadium, Pendley Sports Centre, Cow Lane, Tring HP23 5NT **(T)** 01442 891 144
**Capacity:** 1,233 **Seats:** 150 **Covered:** 100+ **Midweek Matchday:** Tuesday **Clubhouse:** Yes **Shop:** Yes

**Colours(change):** Red/black/black (Yellow/green/green)
**Previous Names:** None
**Previous Leagues:** West Herts 58-88
**Records:** **Goalscorer:** Andy Humphreys - 209 **App:** Mark Boniface - 642
**Honours:** Spartan South Midlands Senior Division 1999-00

**10 YEAR RECORD**

| 06-07 | 07-08 | 08-09 | 09-10 | 10-11 | 11-12 | 12-13 | 13-14 | 14-15 | 15-16 |
|---|---|---|---|---|---|---|---|---|---|
| SSM P 11 | SSM P 10 | SSM P 8 | SSM P 3 | SSM P 2 | SSM P 6 | SSM P 22 | SSM P 10 | SSM P 10 | SSM P 12 |

## WELWYN GARDEN CITY

Founded: 1921 Nickname: Citizens

**Secretary:** Karen Browne **(T)** 07807 338 854 **(E)** kazzie.browne@gmail.com
**Chairman:** Ollie Croft **Manager:** Adam Fisher **Prog Ed:** Karen Browne
**Ground:** Herns Lane, Welwyn Garden City, Herts AL7 1TA **(T)** 01707 329 358
**Capacity:** **Seats:** **Covered:** **Midweek Matchday:** **Clubhouse:**

**Colours(change):** Claret/claret/sky blue (Orange/black/orange)
**Previous Names:**
**Previous Leagues:** Metropolitan & Greater London.
**Records:**
**Honours:** South Midlands League 1973-74, Division 1 1981-82, 2014-15.

**10 YEAR RECORD**

| 06-07 | 07-08 | 08-09 | 09-10 | 10-11 | 11-12 | 12-13 | 13-14 | 14-15 | 15-16 |
|---|---|---|---|---|---|---|---|---|---|
| SSM P 4 | SSM P 16 | SSM P 9 | SSM P 22 | SSM1 17 | SSM1 17 | SSM1 13 | SSM1 4 | SSM1 1 | SSM P 4 |

## WEMBLEY

Founded: 1946 Nickname: The Lions

**Secretary:** Mrs Jean Gumm **(T)** 07876 125 784 **(E)** wembleyfc@aol.com
**Chairman:** Brian Gumm **Manager:** Ian Bates **Prog Ed:** Richard Markiewicz
**Ground:** Vale Farm, Watford Road, Sudbury, Wembley HA0 3HG. **(T)** 0208 904 8169
**Capacity:** 2450 **Seats:** 350 **Covered:** 950 **Midweek Matchday:** Tuesday **Clubhouse:** Yes **Shop:** No

**Colours(change):** Red & white/red/red (All blue)
**Previous Names:** None
**Previous Leagues:** Middlesex Lge. Spartan. Delphian. Corinthian. Athenian. Isthmian.
**Records:** **Att:** 2654 v Wealdstone, FA Amateur Cup 1952-53. **Goals:** Bill Handraham (105). **Apps:** Spud Murphy (505).
**Honours:**

**10 YEAR RECORD**

| 06-07 | 07-08 | 08-09 | 09-10 | 10-11 | 11-12 | 12-13 | 13-14 | 14-15 | 15-16 |
|---|---|---|---|---|---|---|---|---|---|
| CCP 3 | CCP 14 | CCP 17 | CCP 15 | CCP 14 | CCP 10 | CCP 15 | CCP 9 | SSM P 7 | SSM P 11 |

# DIVISION ONE

## AMPTHILL TOWN

Founded: 1881 Nickname:

**Secretary:** Eric Turner **(T)** 07887 872 632 **(E)** ericturner789@btinternet.com
**Chairman:** Lee Roberts **Manager:** Gary Maidment **Prog Ed:** Eric Turner
**Ground:** Ampthill Park, Woburn Street, Ampthill MK45 2HX **(T)** 01525 404 440
**Colours(change):** Yellow/blue/blue (Orange/black/black)
**ADDITIONAL INFORMATION:**
Bedfordshire Senior Trophy 2011-12, 15-16.

## ARLESEY TOWN RESERVES

Founded: Nickname:

**Secretary:** Chris Sterry **(T)** 07540 201 473 **(E)** chris.sterry@ntlworld.com
**Chairman:** John Morrell **Manager:** James Tizard **Prog Ed:** Steve Hazelwood
**Ground:** New Lamb Meadow, Hitchen Road, Arlesey, Beds. SG15 6RS **(T)** 01462 734 504
**Colours(change):** Light & dark blue/dark blue/dark blue (All yellow)
**ADDITIONAL INFORMATION:**
**Previous League:** Bedfordshire County >2013.

## BALDOCK TOWN

Founded: Nickname:

**Secretary:** Lee Rusbridge **(T)** 07981 789 037 **(E)** baldocktownfc@gmail.com
**Chairman:** Graham Kingham **Manager:** Luke Gregson **Prog Ed:** Lynn Parker
**Ground:** Stotfold FC, Roker Park, The Green SG5 4AN **(T)** 01462 730 765
**Colours(change):** All red (All navy blue)
**ADDITIONAL INFORMATION:**
**Previous League:** Hertfordshire Senior County > 2013.

## BEDFORD

Founded: 1957 Nickname:

**Secretary:** Paolo Riccio **(T)** 07983 396 750 **(E)** paoloriccio@btinternet.com
**Chairman:** Lui La Mura **Manager:** Mark Nervais **Prog Ed:** Paolo Riccio
**Ground:** McMullen Park, Meadow Lane, Cardington, Bedford, MK44 3SB **(T)** 07831 594 444
**Colours(change):** Black & white stripes/black/black (All maroon)
**ADDITIONAL INFORMATION: Att:** (at Fairhill) 1,500 v Bedford Town-South Mids Div 1 1992 **Apps:** Simon Fordham - 418
Bedfordshire Senior Trophy 2012-13.

## BIGGLESWADE FC

Founded: Nickname:

**Secretary:** Emma Tyrrell **(T)** 07720 656 580 **(E)** emma-tyrrell@02.co.uk
**Chairman:** Jeremy Reynolds **Manager:** David Northfield **Prog Ed:** Jeremy Reynolds
**Ground:** Biggleswade Town FC, Langford Road, Biggleswade SG18 9JT **(T)** 01767 318 202
**Colours(change):** Green & white/green/green (Yellow/blue/blue)
**ADDITIONAL INFORMATION:**

## BRIMSDOWN

Founded: Nickname:

**Secretary:** Gulay Nil Ermiya **(T)** 07984 409 955 **(E)** gulayermiya1996@googlemail.com
**Chairman:** Alp Ermiya **Manager:** Serkan Poyraz
**Ground:** Haringey Borough FC, Coles Park, White Hart Lane, Tottenham, London N17 7JP **(T)** 0208 889 1415
**Colours(change):** Yellow & navy stripes/navy/navy (Blue & white stripes/white/white)
**ADDITIONAL INFORMATION:**

## BROADFIELDS UNITED

Founded: Nickname:

**Secretary:** Chris Webster **(T)** 07944 370 116 **(E)** websterlocke@aol.com
**Chairman:** Dave Bugden **Manager:** Ryan Duffy **Prog Ed:** Conor Duffy
**Ground:** Harefield United FC, Breakspear Road North, Harefield, Middlesex UB9 6NE **(T)** 01895 823 474
**Colours(change):** All royal blue (All yellow)
**ADDITIONAL INFORMATION:**
**Previous League:** Middlesex >2015

## BUCKINGHAM ATHELTIC

Founded: Nickname:

**Secretary:** Colin Howkins **(T)** 07751 659 769 **(E)** colin@thehowkins.co.uk
**Chairman:** Tony Checkley **Manager:** Mark Carter **Prog Ed:** Tony Checkley
**Ground:** Stratford Fields, Stratford Road, Buckingham MK18 1NY **(T)** 01280 816 945 (MD)
**Colours(change):** Sky blue/navy blue/navy blue (All orange)
**ADDITIONAL INFORMATION:**

## CHESHAM UNITED RESERVES

Founded: Nickname:

**Secretary:** Alan Lagden **(T)** 01494 782 022 **(E)** a.lagden@sky.com
**Chairman:** Brian McCarthy **Manager:** Emanuel Asare **Prog Ed:** Steve Doman
**Ground:** The Meadow, Amy Lane, Chesham, Bucks HP5 1NE **(T)** 01494 783 964
**Colours(change):** All claret (Yellow/black/yellow)
**ADDITIONAL INFORMATION:**

## CODICOTE

Founded: 1913 Nickname:

**Secretary:** Ian Moody **(T)** 07980 920 674 **(E)** codicote.fc@hotmail.co.uk
**Chairman:** James Bundy **Manager:** Steve Young **Prog Ed:** James Bundy
**Ground:** John Clenebts Memorial Ground, Bury Lane, Codicote SG4 8XY **(T)** 01438 821 072
**Colours(change):** Red/black/black (White/black/white)
**ADDITIONAL INFORMATION:**
**Previous Leagues:** Hertfordshire County 1913-27, 1993-2012. North Hertfordshire 1927-93.
**Honours:** North Herts League Division One 1929-30, 1974-75, Division Two 1968-69, Premier Division 1977-78.
Herts Senior County League 2011-12.

## HADLEY WOOD & WINGATE

Founded: Nickname:

**Secretary:** Stephen Jennings **(T)** 07834 206 063 **(E)** mark@wingatefinchley.com
**Chairman:** Keith Garber **Manager:** Frankie Webb **Prog Ed:** Mark Felstein
**Ground:** The Abrahams Stadium, Summers Lane, London N12 0PD **(T)** 0208 446 2217
**Colours(change):** Blue/navy/navy (Orange/black/black)
**ADDITIONAL INFORMATION:**
**Previous Leagues:** Herts Senior County >2016

## HAREFIELD UNITED

Founded: 1868 Nickname: Hares

**Secretary:** Ray Green **(T)** 07834 771212 **(E)** rayigreen1@btinternet.com
**Chairman:** Gary South **Manager:** Jason Shaw **Prog Ed:** Ray Green
**Ground:** Preston Park, Breakespeare Road North, Harefield, UB9 6NE **(T)** 01895 823 474 **Capacity:** 1,200
**Colours(change):** Red & black/red/red (White & black/black/black)
**ADDITIONAL INFORMATION: Att:** 430 v Bashley FA Vase
Middlesex Premier Cup 1985-86

## HARPENDEN TOWN

Founded: 1891 Nickname: Town

**Secretary:** Stephen Hartnup **(T)** 07796 955 197 **(E)** stephen@hartnup.com
**Chairman:** Roman Motyczak **Manager:** Danny Plumb **Prog Ed:** Ray Collins
**Ground:** Rothamstead Park, Amenbury Lane, Harpenden AL5 2EF **(T)** 07734700226/07702604771
**Colours(change):** Yellow/royal blue/royal blue (All red)
**ADDITIONAL INFORMATION:**
**Previous Name:** Harpenden FC 1891-1908. **Previous League:** Hertfordshire County.
**Honours:** South Midlands League x2. Hertfordshire Junior Cup x5.

## HATFIELD TOWN

Founded: 1886 Nickname: Blueboys

**Secretary:** Joanne Maloney **(T)** 07725 071 014 **(E)** secretary@hatfieldtownfc.co.uk
**Chairman:** Chris Maloney **Manager:** Kev Pearman **Prog Ed:** Tom Bailey
**Ground:** Gosling Sport Park, Stanborough Rd, Welwyn Garden City, Herts AL8 6XE **(T)** 01707 384 300 **Capacity:** 1,500
**Colours(change):** All royal blue (Orange/black/black).
**ADDITIONAL INFORMATION:**
Herts Senior Champions 2007-08

## HILLINGDON BOROUGH

Founded: 19190 Nickname: Boro

**Secretary:** Nicki Gill **(T)** 07734 472 137 **(E)** accounts@middlesexstadium.com
**Chairman:** Davinder Dhand **Manager:** Ian Crane **Prog Ed:** Bart Accardo
**Ground:** Middlesex Stadium, Breakspear Rd, Ruislip HA4 7SB **(T)** 01895 639 544 **Capacity:** 1,500
**Colours(change):** White/royal blue/royal blue (All blue)
**ADDITIONAL INFORMATION:**
South Midlands Cup 1996-97.

## KENSINGTON BOROUGH

Founded: Nickname:

**Secretary:** Ahmed Bhairien **(T)** 07814 517 086 **(E)** a.bhairien_kenboro@hotmail.com
**Chairman:** Adrian Maloney **Manager:** Mohammed Bakkali **Prog Ed:** Ahmed Bhairien
**Ground:** Amersham Town FC, Spratleys Meadow, School Lane, Amersham HP7 0EL **(T)** 0207 289 3395
**Colours(change):** All green (Yellow/black/black)
**ADDITIONAL INFORMATION:**

## LANGFORD

Founded: 1908 Nickname: Reds

**Secretary:** Ian Chessum **(T)** 07749 102 060 **(E)** ianchessum@hotmail.com
**Chairman:** Ian Chessum **Manager:** Phil Childs **Prog Ed:** Ian Chessum
**Ground:** Forde Park, Langford Road, Henlow, Beds SG16 6AF **(T)** 01462 816 106 **Capacity:** 2,000
**Colours(change):** Red & white stripes/red/red (All blue).
**ADDITIONAL INFORMATION: Record Att:** 450 v QPR 75th Anniversary 1985

## RISBOROUGH RANGERS

Founded: Nickname:

**Secretary:** Nick Bishop **(T)** 07855 958 236 **(E)** nick@lloydlatchford.co.uk
**Chairman:** Richard Woodward **Manager:** Jamie Rayner **Prog Ed:** Richard Woodward
**Ground:** " Windsors" Horsenden Lane, Princes Risborough. Bucks HP27 9NE **(T)** 07849 843632 (MD only)
**Colours(change):** All red (White/black/white)

**ADDITIONAL INFORMATION:**
Berks & Bucks Intermediate Cup 2015-16.

## SOUTHALL

Founded: 1871 Nickname:

**Secretary:** Sumeet Kainth **(T)** 07727 154 351 **(E)** sskainth@hotmail.co.uk
**Chairman:** Charanjit Singh Gill **Manager:** Paul Palmer **Prog Ed:** Gurmail Dhaliwal
**Ground:** Hanwell Town FC, Perivale Lane, Perivale, Greenford, Middlesex UB6 8TL **(T)** 0208 998 1701
**Colours(change):** Red & white/black/black (Dark blue/dark blue/black)

**ADDITIONAL INFORMATION:**
**Previous Names:** Southall Athletic.

## WINSLOW UNITED

Founded: 1891 Nickname:

**Secretary:** Gareth Robins **(T)** 07825 450 259 **(E)** garethrobins75@gmail.com
**Chairman:** Andy Setterfield **Manager:** John Mulholland **Prog Ed:** Gareth Robins
**Ground:** The Recreation Ground, Elmfields Gate, Winslow, Bucks MK18 3JG **(T)** 01296 713 057
**Colours(change):** Yellow/blue/yellow (Green & black stripes/black/black)

**ADDITIONAL INFORMATION:**

## WODSON PARK

Founded: 1997 Nickname:

**Secretary:** Lee Cook **(T)** 07717 458 446 **(E)** lee.cook@wodsonmail.co.uk
**Chairman:** Lee Cook **Manager:** Kristian Munt **Prog Ed:** Lee Cook
**Ground:** Woodson Park Sports Centre, Wadesmill Road, Herts SG12 0UQ **(T)** 01920 487 091
**Colours(change):** Sky & navy blue /navy blue/navy blue (All red)

**ADDITIONAL INFORMATION:**

# GROUND DIRECTIONS-PREMIER & DIVISION ONE

**AMERSHAM TOWN - Spratleys Meadow, School Lane, Amersham, Bucks HP7 No telephone**
From London, take the A413 towards Aylesbury. At the first roundabout in Amersham where the A413 turns left, keep straight on. Then carry on straight over the next four roundabouts to Amersham Old Town. At the western end of the Old Town turn right into right into Mill Lane. At the top of Mill Lane turn left into School Lane. Ground is 100 yards on the left.

**AMPTHILL TOWN - Ampthill Park, Woburn Street, Ampthill Tel: 01525 404440.**
From the South, leave M1 at junction 12 Toddington. Turn right as signposted until you meet the junction with the Ampthill bypass. Go straight across until you meet a mini-roundabout at the town centre. Turn left into Woburn Street. The ground is about half a mile on the right, just past a lay-by. From the North, leave the M1 at J13 and turn left. At first set of traffic lights, turn right onto A507 Ridgmont bypass. Continue until you see the right-hand turning signposted for Ampthill. Ground is about a mile on the left, opposite the rugby ground.

**ARLESEY TOWN RESERVES - New Lamb Meadow, Hitchen Road, Arlesey, Beds. SG15 6RS Tel 01462 734 504**
From junction 10 on the A1(M) follow the A507 towards Shefford. At the 3rd roundabout turn left signposted Arlesey station. Follow the road for 1.5 miles through village, ground is on the left.
From M1 North, junction 13 follow A507 to Clophill. Continue straight over roundabout through Shefford & Henlow to roundabout signposted Arlesey station, then as above.
From M1 junction 10, take A1081 Airport Way onto A505 Hitchin Road towards Hitchen. Turn left onto A600 Bedford Road past Hitchin Town FC, turn right at 2nd roundabout to Ickleford. Go through village and bear left to Arlesey, ground is on the right.

**BALDOCK TOWN - Stotfold FC, roker Park, The Green SG5 4AN. Tel 01462 730 765**
At A1 junction 10, take the A507 to Stotfold and right into town. Proceed along High Street and at traffic lights turn right (from Hitchin – straight over traffic lights) towards Astwick Turn right at the Crown pub into The Green. The ground is set back from The Green on the left.

**BEDFORD FC - McMullen Park, Meadow Lane, Cardington, Bedford, MK44 3SB. Tel 01234 831024**
From the M1 Junction 13: take the A421 on to the Bedford Bypass, take the third exit onto the A603, the ground is 250 yards on the left.
From the A1 at Sandy: take A603 to Bedford. The ground is on the right just before you reach the Bedford Bypass.

**BERKHAMSTED - Broadwater, Lower Kings Road, Berkhamsted HP4 2AL Tel 01442 865977**
Exit A41 onto A416. Go straight over the town centre traffic lights into Lower Kings Road. Go over the canal bridge and take first left into Broadwater. Follow the road to the left, going parallel to the canal. The ground is on the right hand side, sandwiched between the canal and the railway.

## SPARTAN SOUTH MIDLANDS LEAGUE - STEP 5/6/7

**BIGGLESWADE FC - Langford Road, Biggleswade SG18 9JT Tel 01767 318 202**
From the south – up the A1, past the first roundabout (Homebase) signposted Biggleswade. At next roundabout (Sainsburys) turn right onto A6001. As you approach the Town Centre, go straight over the mini roundabout following signs for Langford (Teal Road). At traffic lights, turn right (still heading towards Langford). Continue along Hitchin Street over two mini roundabouts and as you pass under the A1, the ground entrance is 200 yards on the right. From the north – exit A1 at the Sainsburys roundabout and follow instructions as above.

**BIGGLESWADE UNITED - Second Meadow, Fairfield Road, Biggleswade SG18 0BS Tel 01767 316270**
From A1 south take second roundabout (Sainsbury's NOT Homebase). Cross the river bridge and then take second left into Sun Street then take first left into Fairfield Road and travel to the very end and into lane. From A1 north, take first roundabout (Sainsbury's) and follow previous instructions.

**BRIMSDOWN - Haringey Borough FC, Coles Park, White Hart Lane, Tottenham, London N17 7JP Tel 0208 889 1415**
At junction 25 of the M25 or from the A406 (North Circular Road) turn south onto the A10 (Great Cambridge Road) towards Central London. At the junction of the A10 and White Hart Lane turn right (use slip road at traffic lights) into White Hart Lane and the ground is about 500 yards on the left, some 150 yards after a petrol station. PUBLIC TRANSPORT: Bus W3 from Finsbury Park station to Northumberland Park station via Alexandra Palace station and Wood Green underground station passes ground. In other direction W3 can be boarded at White Hart Lane station).

**BROADFIELDS UNITED - Harefield United FC, Breakspear Road North, Harefield, Middlesex, UB9 6NE Tel: 01895 823474.**
From the M25 at Junction 16 turn left. At the roundabout turn right towards Denham and at the next roundabout turn left then right at the end of the road. Turn left by the Pub and follow the road over the canal and into the village. Go straight across the roundabout into Breakspear Road and the ground is approximately 800 metres on the right.

**BROXBOURNE BOROUGH - Broxbourne Borough V & E Club, Goffs Lane, Cheshunt, Herts EN7 5QN Tel 01992 624 281**
From M25 junction 25, take A10 north towards Cheshunt. At first roundabout take first exit onto B198 (Cuffey & Goffs Oak) At the second roundabout take third exit into Goffs Lane. Ground is on the immediate right.

**BUCKINGHAM ATHLETIC - Stratford Fields, Stratford Road, Buckingham MK18 1NY Tel: 01280 816945 (match days & opening hours only)**
From Oxford, Aylesbury or Bletchley: take the Buckingham ring road to the roundabout where the A422 from Stony Stratford/Deanshanger meet-turn left, towards town centre. The ground is situated on the left behind fir trees at the bottom of the hill where 30mph begins (opposite a recently-built block of luxury apartments). From Milton Keynes: Up A5 then (A422) to Buckingham-straight across roundabout towards the town centre-ground location as above. From M1: come off at junction 13 and follow A421 straight through, turning right where it meets the Buckingham ring road – then follow as above, turning left at the next-but-one roundabout.

**CHESHAM UNITED RESERVES - The Meadow, Amy Lane, Chesham, Bucks HP5 1NE Tel 01494 783964**
Take J20 off the M25 to the A41 Aylesbury/Hemel follow this road for about 7 miles, your turn off is after the Service Station, the turn off is for Berkhamsted/Chesham, take the right hand lane in the slip road to the A416 to Chesham. Follow this road through Ashley Green (being careful of the speed trap) past the college on your left, when you get to the bottom of the hill take a left turn at the mini roundabout. Follow the road for about 1.5 miles, go straight over the next two roundabouts, then get in to the left lane to take the first exit from the next roundabout, you will pass a pub called the Red Lion on your right shortly after this. Follow the road to a mini roundabout; take the right exit going past two petrol stations either side of the road. Ground is on the third exit off the next roundabout. See club website for other routes.

**COCKFOSTERS - Cockfosters Sports Ground, Chalk Lane, Cockfosters, Herts EN4 9JG Tel: 020 8449 5833**
Leaving the M25 motorway at junction 24 (Potters Bar), take the A111 signposted to Cockfosters. The ground is situated approximately 2 miles from the motorway on the right immediately before Cockfosters Underground Station. VEHICLE DRIVERS PLEASE BE AWARE THAT THE YELLOW LINES & PARKING RESTRICTIONS IN CHALK LANE ARE STRICTLY ENFORCED UP TO 6.30PM INCLUDING SATURDAYS

**CODICOTE - John Clenebts Memorial Ground, Bury Lane, Codicote SG4 8XY Tel 01438 821 072**
From A1 (M) junction 6, take the A1000 turn off at Welwyn then to Codicote via B656. At Codicote turn right after the Bell Public house into Bury Lane. The ground entrance is on the left opposite the church.

**COLNEY HEATH - The Recreation Ground, High Street, Colney Heath, St Albans, Herts AL4 0NS Tel 01727 826188**
From the A1, leave at junction 3 and follow A414 St. Albans. At long roundabout take the left into the village and ground is just past the school on left after 400 yards.

From the M25, leave at junction 22 and follow B556 Colney Heath. On entering the village turn left at Queens Head PH (roundabout) and follow High Street for ½ mile. The ground is on the right just before the school.

From M1 going south; leave at junction 7. At Park Street roundabout follow A414 Hatfield. Continue on A414 past London Colney. Enter Colney Heath coming round the long roundabout and into village. The ground is past the school on the left after 400 yards.

**CRAWLEY GREEN - Barton Rovers FC, Sharpenhoe Road, Barton Le Cay, Beds MK45 4SD Tel 01582 882398**
From M1 J12, turn right from South turn left from North, onto the A5120. After approximately 1.5 miles, take the second turning on the right signposted Harlington and Barton. Follow the road through Sharpenhoe to Barton. At mini-roundabout turn right and after about 400 yards, turn right into the ground. Ground entrance is in Luton Road.

**EDGWARE TOWN - Silver Jubilee Park, Townsend Lane, London NW9 7NE Tel: 0208 205 1645**
From Edgware tube station, turn left onto Station Road and then left onto Edgware Road. Go South for about two miles on Edgware Road, turn right onto Kingsbury Road. Turn first left onto Townsend Lane down to the bottom of the hill and then turn left into the park through the park barriers..

**HADLEY - Hadley Sports Ground, Brickfield Lane, Arkley, Barnet EN3 3LD Tel 07905 446 331**
From M25, exit junction 23 (South Mimms) go south on the A1 to Stirling Corner roundabout. Take the left exit onto Barnet Road and continue until the first set of traffic lights. Go straight over and then take the immediate first left opposite the Gate Oublic House into Brickfield Lane. The ground is approximately 75 yards on the left.

**HADLEY WOOD & WINGATE - The Abrahams Stadium, Summers Lane, London N12 0PD Tel 0208 446 2217**
From the A406 North Circular Road, take the North Finchley exit and join the A1000. Go past the leisure centre on the right and continue to the next set of traffic lights. Enter the right hand filler road and turn into Summers Lane. The ground is approximately 200 yards on the right

**HAREFIELD UNITED - Preston Park, Breakspear Road North, Harefield, Middlesex, UB9 6NE Tel: 01895 823474.**
From the M25 at Junction 16 turn left. At the roundabout turn right towards Denham and at the next roundabout turn left then right at the end of the road. Turn left by the Pub and follow the road over the canal and into the village. Go straight across the roundabout into Breakspear Road and the ground is approximately 800 metres on the right.

**HARPENDEN TOWN - Rothamstead Park, Amenbury Lane, Harpenden AL5 2EF Tel: 07968 120032**
Approaching Harpenden from St. Albans, turn left into Leyton Road at mini-roundabout by the Silver Cup and Fire Station. Coming from Luton, go through the town and as you leave (just past The George) turn right into Leyton Road. Turn left in Amenbury Lane and then left into car park after 300 yards. Entrance to the Club is up the pathway, diagonally across the car park in the far corner from the entrance. This is a pay-and-display car park up to 6.30pm.

**HATFIELD TOWN - Gosling Sports Park, Stanborough Road, Welwyn Garden City, Herts AL8 6XE Tel 01707 384300**
From A1 (M) junction 4, take A414 towards Hertford/Welwyn Garden City. At the roundabout take the 1st exit onto the A6129, heading to Stanborough/Wheathampstead. At the next roundabout take the 2nd exit onto the A6129 Stanborough Road. At the next roundabout take the 3rd exit into Gosling Sports Park.

**HERTFORD TOWN - Hertingfordbury Park, West Street, Hertford, Herts SG13 8EZ Tel 01992 583716**
From the A1 follow the A414 to Hertford until you see Gates Ford Dealership on the right. At next roundabout double back and immediately past Gates (now on your left) turn left into West Street. This is a narrow road and when it bears left, turn right and go down the hill and over a bridge to the ground. From the A10 follow the A414 until you see Gates.

**HILLINGDON BOROUGH - Middlesex Stadium, Breakspear Road, Ruislip, Middlesex HA4 7SB Tel 01895 639544**
From M40/A40 eastbound, leave the A40 at the Swakeleys roundabout, exit is sign-posted Ickenham & Ruislip and take the B467. At the second mini-roundabout turn left into Breakspear Road South. After approx 1 mile, turn right into Breakspear Road by the Breakspear Arms PH. The ground is a further 1/2 mile on the left-hand side.

**HODDESDON TOWN - Wodson Park, Wadesmill Road, Ware, Herts SG12 0UQ Tel 01920 462 064**
A10 off junction A602 and B1001 turn right at roundabout after 300 yards and follow Ware sign, past Rank factory. Turn left at main road onto A1170 (Wadesmill Road) Stadium is on the right after 3/4 mile.

**HOLMER GREEN - Airedale Park, Watchet Lane, Holmer Green, Bucks HP15 6UF Tel 01494 711485**
From Amersham on A404 High Wycombe Road. After approx 2 miles turn right into Sheepcote Dell Road. Continue until end of road at Bat & Ball pub. Turn right, then immediately left. Continue approx 1/2 mile until double mini-roundabouts. Turn left in front of the Mandarin Duck restaurant into Airedale Park 150 yards on the right

**KENSINGTON BOROUGH - Amersham Town FC, Spratleys Meadow, School Lane, Amersham HP7 0EL Tel: 07507 261 534**
From London take the A413 towards Aylesbury. At first roundabout in Amersham, where A413 turns left, keep straight on and over the next four roundabouts to Amersham Old Town. At the Western end of the Old Town turn right into Mill Lane. At the top of Mill Lane turn left into School Lane and the ground is 100 yards on the left.

**KINGS LANGLEY - Gaywood Park, Hempstead Road, Kings Langley Herts WD4 8BS Tel: 07976 692801**
From M25 leave at junction 20. Take A4251 to Kings Langley. Go through the village. The ground is approximately 1/2 mile on the right.

**LANGFORD - Forde Park, Langford Road, Henlow, Beds SG16 6AG Tel: 01462 816106.**
From West along A57 to Henlow then north on A6001. Ground at north end of Henlow. From North and East, leave A1 at Langford water tower then into Langford. Turn left at Boot Restaurant. Follow A6001 round to the left. Club is 1/2 mile away.

**LEVERSTOCK GREEN - Pancake Lane, Leverstock Green, Hemel Hempstead, Herts Tel: 01442 246280.**
From M1 at Junction 8, Follow A414 to second roundabout turn left along Leverstock Green Way. Pancake Lane is on the left 300 yards past the Leather Bottle Public House. Ground is 300 yards on left. All visitors are requested to park inside the ground.

**LONDON COLNEY - Cotlandswick Playing Fields, London Colney, Herts AL2 1DW Tel: 01727 822132.**
From M25 J22, follow the A1081 signposted to St Albans. At London Colney roundabout take A414, signposted Hemel Hempstead/Watford. There is a hidden turn into the ground after approximately 500 metres (just after lay-by) signposted Sports Ground and London Colney FC. Follow the ground around between the Rugby and Irish clubs to ground entrance.

**LONDON LIONS - Hemel Hemstead FC, Vauxhall Road, Hemel Hempstead, HP2 4HW Tel 01442 259 777**
From M1 motorway exit at junction 8 onto the A414 towards Hemel Hempstead.After the second roundabout, get into the outside lane and turn right onto Leverstock Green Road. At mini roundabout, turn left into Vauxhall Road, at next mini roundabout, take the second exit into the ground.

**LONDON TIGERS - Avenue Park, Western Avenue, Perivale, Greenford, Middlesex UB6 8GA Tel 020 7289 3395 (10am-6pm) – out of hours please call 07949 189191**
Exit junction 16 of the M25 onto the A40 (M) towards London. After you pass the Target roundabout there will be a sharp left turn at the 100yard marker for the Greenford slip road from the A40 into Avenue Park, just past the overhead footbridge. If coming from Central London or Hangar Lane, drive up to the Target roundabout and do a U-turn onto the eastbound carriageway and turn left into Avenue Park after the footbridge. The nearest Tube station is Greenford on the Central Line, which is a 10-minute walk.

**NEW BRADWELL ST PETER - Recreation Ground, Bradwell Road, Bradville, Milton Keynes MK13 7AD Tel: 01908 313 835.**
From M1 J14 go towards Newport Pagnell, turn left at first roundabout into H3 (A422 Monks Way). Go six roundabouts then turn right into V6 (Grafton Street). At first roundabout drive all the way around and then take the first left. At first mini-roundabout, turn left. Go 1/2 mile and straight across next mini-roundabout. Ground is then immediately on the left.

**OXHEY JETS - Boundary Stadium, Altham Way (off Little Oxhey Lane), South Oxhey, Watford WD19 6FW Tel: 020 8421 6277**
From Bushey + Oxhey Station, take Pinner Road (A4008) and continue along Oxhey Lane towards Harrow. At the traffic lights turn right into Little Oxhey Lane. Altham Way is on left just after crossing a narrow railway bridge. Please park in the large swimming pool car park marked “Jets overflow parking” to avoid either blocking in cars, or being blocked in.

**RISBOROUGH RANGERS - ” Windsors” Horsenden Lane, Princes Risborough. Bucks HP27 9NE Tel 07849 843632 (MD only)**
On entering Prices Risborough from Aylesbury, turn left at first roundabout. At the second roundabout turn right. Go pass Esso petrol station on left hand side. After approximately 400 yards take the right fork. Take second turn on left (Picts Lane). At junction turn right over the railway bridge and then immediately right again. Ground is approximately 200 yards on the right hand side.

**SOUTHALL - Hanwell Town FC, Perivale Lane, Perivale, Greenford, Middlesex UB6 8TL Tel 020 8998 1701**
From West, junction 16 M25 and follow A40 (M) towards London. Go over the Greenford flyover and get into the nearside lane signposted Ealing & Perivale. Exit and turn right across the A40. The ground is immediately on the left. Turn left into Perivale Lane and the entrance is 500 yards on the left. Nearest railway station is Perivale (London Underground – Central Line).

**ST. MARGARETSBURY - Recreation Ground, Station Road, St. Margarets, Herts SG12 8EH Tel: 01920 870473**
A10 to Cambridge. Exit at A414 Harlow & Chelmsford. Proceed 400 yards to Amwell roundabout and take 3rd exit (B181) to Stanstead Abbotts. Ground is 1/2 mile on the right-hand side.

## SPARTAN SOUTH MIDLANDS LEAGUE - STEP 5/6/7

**STONY STRATFORD TOWN - Ostlers Lane, Stony Stratford, Milton Keynes MK11 1AR Tel: 07914 012709**
From Dunstable on the A5 heading north: On approaching Bletchley continue on the main A5 trunk road signposted to Towcester & Hinckley. Continue to the very end of dual carriageway, where you will meet a main roundabout. This is where the main A5 intersects with the A508 to Northampton. At this roundabout take first exit, this is the old (single carriageway) A5. Follow the main road, straight through the traffic lights, over the river bridge and take the second turning right into Ostlers Lane. The ground is approx 200yds on the right.
From Buckingham on the A422: Continue on the A422, straight on at the first roundabout (pedestrian footbridge overhead). Continue on until you meet the next roundabout and take the last exit (the old single carriageway A5). Then proceed as above.

**STOTFOLD - Roker Park, The Green, Stotfold, Hitchin, Herts SG5 4AN Tel 01462 730765**
At A1 junction 10, take the A507 to Stotfold and right into town. Proceed along High Street and at traffic lights turn right (from Hitchin – straight over traffic lights) towards Astwick Turn right at the Crown pub into The Green. The ground is set back from The Green on the left.

**SUN SPORTS - Sun Postal Sports Club, Bellmountwood Avenue, Watford, Herts WD17 3BM Tel: 01923 227453**
From Watford town centre take the A411 (Hempstead Road) away from the Town Hall towards Hemel Hempstead. At 2nd set of traffic lights turn left into Langley Way. At the next roundabout, where there is a parade of shops on the left and the "Essex Arms" on the right, take the third exit into Cassiobury Drive. Then take the first turn left into Bellmountwood Avenue then at the left hand bend turn right into the Club entrance.

**TRING ATHLETIC - The Grass Roots Stadium, Pendley Sports Centre, Cow Lane, Tring, Herts HP23 5NT. Tel: 01442 891144**
From M25 take A41 to Aylesbury. At roundabout at junction take last exit sign-posted Berkhamsted. Turn next left into Cow Lane. Stadium is on the right at end of Cow Lane.

**WELWYN GARDEN CITY - Herns Way, Welwyn Garden City, Herts AL7 1TA Tel: 01707 329358**
Best Route to the Ground: From A1 (M) follow Welwyn Garden City signpost A1000. Take second exit off one-way system, sign-posted Panshanger. Ground is 400 yards on left.

**WEMBLEY - Vale Farm, Watford Road HA0 3AG - 0208 904 8169**
From Sudbury Town Station 400 yards along Watford Road.

**WINSLOW UNITED - The Recreation Ground, Elmfields Gate, Winslow, Bucks MK18 3JG Tel 01296 713057**
Best Route to the Ground: A413 from Aylesbury to Winslow, turn right from High Street into Elmfields Gate. Ground is100 yards on left. A421 Milton Keynes to Buckingham, turn left through Great Horwood to Winslow. Turn left from High Street into Elmfields Gate. PLEASE PARK IN PUBLIC CAR PARK OPPOSITE GROUND IF POSSIBLE.

**WODSON PARK - Woodson Park Sports Centre, Wadesmill Road, Herts SG12 0UQ Tel 01920 487 091**
From the South: leave the M25 at junction 25 and take the A10 north past Cheshunt and Hoddesdon. After crossing the Lea Valley with Ware below and to your right, leave the A10 at the junction for the A1170 (signposted for Wadesmill and Thundridge). The slip road comes off the A10 onto a roundabout Turn left (first exit) onto Wadesmill Road (A1170) and come back over the A10 to a second roundabout. Go straight over and take the first turn on the left into Wodson Park Sports Centre. The football ground is on the far left of the car park. From the North: Leave the A10 at the Ware North turn off (A1170) The slip road takes you to a roundabout. Turn right (3rd exit) into Wadesmill Road and take the first left into Wodson Park Sports Centre.

**WOODFORD TOWN - Goldsdown Stadium, Goldsdown Road, Enfield Middlesex EN3 7RP Tel: 0208 804 5491**
M25 junction 25, then head south on the A10. Turn left at the second set of traffic lights into Caterhatch Lane. At the end of the road, turn right at the roundabout into Hertford Road. At the next mini roundabout turn left into Green Street. At the next mini roundabout turn left into Goldsdown Road and the ground is directly ahead.

| Spartan South Midlands Division Two | | |
|---|---|---|
| **AMERSHAM TOWN** | Spratleys Meadow, School Lane, Amersham, Bucks HP7 0EL | 07816 193 10 |
| **ASTON CLINTON** | Aston Clinton Park, London Road, Aston Clinton HP22 5HL | 07890 624 39 |
| **CLEAN SLATE** | The Downs Barn Pavilion, Pannier Place, Downs Barn, Milton Keynes MK14 7QP | 01908 617 49 |
| **ENFIELD BOROUGH** | Donkey Lane, Enfield EN1 3PL | 07761 814 84 |
| **GRENDON RANGERS** | The Village Hall, Main Street, Grendon Underwood, Aylesbury, Bucks. HP18 0SP | 07979 470 73 |
| **HALE LEYS UNITED** | Fairford Leys Pitch, Andrews Way, Aylesbury, Bucks. HP17 8QQ | 07731 444 65 |
| **LOUGHTON MANOR** | Loughton Sports & Social Club, Linceslade Grove, Loughton, Milton Keynes MK5 8DJ | 07775 643 83 |
| **MK GALACTICOS** | North Furzton Sports Ground, Lynmouth Crescent, Milton Keynes MK4 1HD | 07739 471 36 |
| **MURSLEY UNITED** | The Playing Field, Station Road, Mursley MK17 0SA | 07512 663 64 |
| **NEW BRADWELL ST PETER** | Recreation Ground, Bradwell Road, Bradville, Milton Keynes MK13 7AD | 01908 313 83 |
| **OLD BRADWELL UNITED** | Stony Stratford FC, Ostlers Lane, Milton Keynes MK11 1AR | 07914 012 70 |
| **PITSTONE AND IVINGHOE** | Pitstone Pavilion & Sports Hall, Marsworth Road, Pitstone LU7 9AP | 07732 309 52 |
| **ST. NEOTS TOWN RESERVES** | St. Neots Town FC, Kester Way, St. Neots PE19 6SN | 01480 470 01 |
| **STONY STRATFORD TOWN** | Ostlers Lane, Stony Stratford, Milton Keynes MK11 1AR | 07914 012 70 |
| **THAME RANGERS** | Meadow View Park, Thame, Oxon OX9 3RN | 01844 214 40 |
| **THE 61 FC (LUTON)** | Kingsway Ground, Beverley Road, Luton LU4 8EU | 07749 531 49 |
| **TOTTERNHOE** | Tptternhoe Recreation Ground, Dunstable Road, Totternhoe, Beds LU6 1QP | 01582 606 73 |
| **TRING CORINTHIANS** | Icknield Way, Tring, Herts HP23 5HJ | 07886 528 21 |
| **TRING TOWN AFC** | Miswell Lane Pavilion, Miswell Lane, Tring HP23 4EX | 07720 535 35 |
| **UNITE MK** | MK Irish Club, Manor Fields, Watling Street, Bletchley, Milton Keynes MK2 2HX | 01908 375 97 |

# UNITED COUNTIES LEAGUE

**Sponsored by:** ChromaSport & Trophies
**Founded:** 1895
**Recent Champions: 2013:** Holbeach United
**2014:** Spalding United **2015:** AFC Rushden & Dia.

| | PREMIER DIVISION | P | W | D | L | F | A | GD | Pts |
|---|---|---|---|---|---|---|---|---|---|
| 1 | AFC Kempston Rovers | 42 | 28 | 13 | 1 | 111 | 31 | 80 | 97 |
| 2 | Leicester Nirvana | 42 | 31 | 4 | 7 | 129 | 51 | 78 | 97 |
| 3 | Newport Pagnell Town | 42 | 26 | 5 | 11 | 94 | 54 | 40 | 83 |
| 4 | Holbeach United | 42 | 21 | 7 | 14 | 94 | 63 | 31 | 70 |
| 5 | Cogenhoe United | 42 | 20 | 9 | 13 | 70 | 67 | 3 | 69 |
| 6 | Eynesbury Rovers | 42 | 20 | 8 | 14 | 64 | 48 | 16 | 68 |
| 7 | Sleaford Town | 42 | 21 | 5 | 16 | 83 | 69 | 14 | 68 |
| 8 | Wisbech Town | 42 | 19 | 9 | 14 | 82 | 68 | 14 | 66 |
| 9 | Kirby Muxloe (-3) | 42 | 19 | 8 | 15 | 63 | 58 | 5 | 62 |
| 10 | Deeping Rangers | 42 | 16 | 12 | 14 | 81 | 64 | 17 | 60 |
| 11 | Harborough Town | 42 | 18 | 6 | 18 | 57 | 59 | -2 | 60 |
| 12 | Yaxley (-6) | 42 | 19 | 7 | 16 | 93 | 79 | 14 | 58 |
| 13 | Northampton Spencer | 42 | 16 | 9 | 17 | 74 | 81 | -7 | 57 |
| 14 | Rothwell Corinthians | 42 | 17 | 5 | 20 | 60 | 67 | -7 | 56 |
| 15 | Desborough Town | 42 | 16 | 7 | 19 | 64 | 79 | -15 | 55 |
| 16 | Boston Town | 42 | 14 | 6 | 22 | 76 | 92 | -16 | 48 |
| 17 | Peterborough Northern Star | 42 | 13 | 8 | 21 | 70 | 84 | -14 | 47 |
| 18 | Harrowby United | 42 | 13 | 8 | 21 | 70 | 102 | -32 | 47 |
| 19 | Northampton Sileby Rangers (-6) | 42 | 12 | 10 | 20 | 78 | 94 | -16 | 40 |
| 20 | Wellingborough Town | 42 | 11 | 7 | 24 | 57 | 90 | -33 | 40 |
| 21 | Oadby Town | 42 | 9 | 7 | 26 | 66 | 89 | -23 | 34 |
| 22 | Huntingdon Town | 42 | 2 | 2 | 38 | 26 | 173 | -147 | 8 |

## CLUB MOVEMENTS

**Premier Division - In:** Northampton ON Checks (P), Peterborough Sports (P).
**Out:** AFC Kempston Rovers (P - Southern D1 Central), Northampton Spencer (F).
**Division One - In:** Daventry Town (Resigned from Northern Premier Div.1 South), Melton Town - formerly Melton Mowbray (P - Leicestershire Senior), Whittlesey Athletic (P - Peterborough & District).
**Out:** Northampton ON Checks (P), Peterborough Sports (P).

## LEAGUE CUP

**HOLDERS:** AFC RUSHDEN & DIAMONDS

**PRELIMINARY ROUND**

| | | | |
|---|---|---|---|
| Desborough Town | v | Deeping Rangers | 3-2 |
| Oadby Town | v | Irchester United | 4-1 |
| Peterborough Sports | v | Burton Park Wanderers | 4-0 |
| Kirby Muxloe | v | Sleaford Town | 4-2 |
| Holbeach United | v | Bugbrooke St Michaels | 4-1 |
| Wellingborough Town | v | Long Buckby | 2-0 |
| Boston Town | v | Stewarts & Lloyds | 4-3 |
| Raunds Town | v | Yaxley | 0-2 |
| Leicester Nirvana | v | Newport Pagnell Town | 2-1 |
| Rothwell Corinthians | v | Oakham United | 2-3 |

**ROUND 1**

| | | | |
|---|---|---|---|
| Desborough Town | v | Cogenhoe United | 0-2 |
| Harrowby United | v | Wellingborough Whitworth | 6-2 |
| St Neots Town Saints | v | Eynesbury Rovers | 0-8 |
| AFC Kempston Rovers | v | Northampton Spencer | 4-2 |
| Rushden & Higham United | v | Buckingham Town | 3-2 |
| Lutterworth Athletic | v | Oadby Town | 0-1 |
| Thrapston Town | v | Peterborough Sports | 1-2 |
| Peterborough Northern Star | v | Huntingdon Town | 4-0 |
| Kirby Muxloe | v | Woodford United | 3-2 |
| Holbeach United | v | Blackstones | 4-0 |
| Long Buckby | v | Northampton Sileby Rangers | 2-4 |
| Boston Town | v | Potton United | 4-2 |
| Northampton ON Chenecks | v | Wisbech Town | 2-3 |
| Yaxley | v | Leicester Nirvana | 1-2 |
| Bourne Town | v | Oakham United | 3-3, 1-3p |
| Harborough Town | v | Olney Town | 2-3 |

| | PREMIER DIVISION | 1 | 2 | 3 | 4 | 5 | 6 | 7 | 8 | 9 | 10 | 11 | 12 | 13 | 14 | 15 | 16 | 17 | 18 | 19 | 20 | 21 | 22 |
|---|---|---|---|---|---|---|---|---|---|---|---|---|---|---|---|---|---|---|---|---|---|---|---|
| 1 | AFC Kempston Rovers | | 7-0 | 3-1 | 2-1 | 3-0 | 3-0 | 0-0 | 3-2 | 1-1 | 9-0 | 5-0 | 2-0 | 2-0 | 3-1 | 1-1 | 1-1 | 4-0 | 2-1 | 1-0 | 1-0 | 2-1 | 3-0 |
| 2 | Boston Town | 0-2 | | 1-3 | 0-2 | 1-3 | 2-2 | 1-0 | 5-1 | 0-1 | 6-1 | 1-1 | 2-3 | 3-2 | 2-2 | 2-3 | 4-2 | 1-3 | 0-1 | 3-3 | 2-1 | 1-1 | 4-0 |
| 3 | Cogenhoe United | 3-3 | 5-0 | | 2-1 | 2-1 | 0-0 | 2-0 | 1-4 | 1-5 | 3-0 | 0-0 | 4-3 | 1-4 | 2-1 | 3-1 | 2-4 | 0-0 | 0-1 | 1-0 | 1-1 | 3-1 | 2-1 |
| 4 | Deeping Rangers | 1-1 | 1-3 | 3-0 | | 0-0 | 0-2 | 0-0 | 7-3 | 1-3 | 7-2 | 0-1 | 3-2 | 1-0 | 1-1 | 5-1 | 1-0 | 4-2 | 1-1 | 1-1 | 5-1 | 2-2 | 4-2 |
| 5 | Desborough Town | 0-2 | 4-3 | 2-0 | 0-1 | | 2-2 | 2-4 | 6-1 | 1-0 | 4-0 | 1-3 | 2-4 | 0-2 | 2-1 | 0-4 | 3-2 | 1-0 | 0-1 | 2-1 | 3-0 | 1-1 | 3-2 |
| 6 | Eynesbury Rovers | 2-1 | 0-1 | 0-0 | 4-2 | 1-0 | | 4-0 | 2-0 | 0-0 | 6-0 | 1-0 | 1-2 | 0-3 | 1-3 | 0-1 | 2-1 | 0-1 | 2-1 | 1-2 | 2-1 | 1-0 | 1-2 |
| 7 | Harborough Town | 1-6 | 1-1 | 3-0 | 1-0 | 2-0 | 0-3 | | 2-0 | 0-1 | 4-1 | 0-1 | 1-2 | 0-1 | 1-0 | 4-0 | 3-1 | 3-2 | 2-1 | 2-0 | 1-2 | 1-5 | 1-3 |
| 8 | Harrowby United | 0-2 | 5-2 | 1-1 | 3-0 | 1-1 | 2-2 | 0-2 | | 0-3 | 3-0 | 1-0 | 1-6 | 1-4 | 6-0 | 3-0 | 1-3 | 3-2 | 0-2 | 3-1 | 3-0 | 1-1 | 1-3 |
| 9 | Holbeach United | 3-3 | 1-2 | 4-2 | 3-1 | 3-1 | 1-3 | 5-0 | 2-0 | | 3-1 | 4-0 | 1-2 | 1-2 | 4-0 | 2-2 | 3-2 | 4-2 | 1-2 | 2-0 | 5-0 | 5-3 | 0-1 |
| 10 | Huntingdon Town | 0-7 | 1-4 | 1-2 | 0-3 | 2-4 | 1-1 | 0-3 | 0-0 | 1-5 | | 1-2 | 1-8 | 2-3 | 0-5 | 0-5 | 0-4 | 0-1 | 1-3 | 0-3 | 1-0 | 1-6 | 0-3 |
| 11 | Kirby Muxloe | 1-2 | 1-0 | 1-4 | 0-0 | 8-0 | 2-1 | 2-1 | 5-0 | 3-2 | 3-0 | | 0-3 | 0-2 | 4-2 | 1-1 | 0-0 | 0-0 | 3-1 | 3-0 | 0-0 | 0-3 | 0-2 |
| 12 | Leicester Nirvana | 2-2 | 3-0 | 5-1 | 1-1 | 6-1 | 0-2 | 2-0 | 5-0 | 7-0 | 2-1 | 1-0 | | 5-1 | 4-0 | 2-2 | 0-0 | 4-2 | 3-2 | 2-3 | 4-1 | 1-2 | 4-0 |
| 13 | Newport Pagnell Town | 1-1 | 4-3 | 1-1 | 1-0 | 4-2 | 2-1 | 1-2 | 7-1 | 3-1 | 8-0 | 1-0 | 2-4 | | 2-2 | 7-0 | 2-1 | 3-2 | 2-0 | 2-0 | 2-2 | 0-1 | 2-1 |
| 14 | Northampton Sileby Rangers | 0-4 | 4-1 | 2-3 | 4-4 | 1-1 | 1-1 | 1-1 | 4-4 | 1-1 | 7-2 | 2-2 | 3-4 | 0-1 | | 1-2 | 2-1 | 3-2 | 3-1 | 3-2 | 1-2 | 3-1 | 1-3 |
| 15 | Northampton Spencer | 1-1 | 2-1 | 0-1 | 3-2 | 1-4 | 2-3 | 0-1 | 1-1 | 3-2 | 7-0 | 1-2 | 0-3 | 0-0 | 0-1 | | 2-0 | 2-1 | 1-3 | 4-2 | 1-2 | 1-2 | 1-4 |
| 16 | Oadby Town | 0-4 | 1-3 | 1-3 | 3-1 | 1-2 | 1-2 | 2-3 | 1-2 | 2-3 | 4-0 | 0-2 | 1-5 | 0-1 | 3-1 | 1-0 | | 2-2 | 1-2 | 2-1 | 1-1 | 2-4 | 2-3 |
| 17 | Peterborough Northern Star | 1-1 | 2-3 | 1-2 | 4-1 | 2-2 | 2-3 | 1-0 | 4-5 | 0-0 | 2-1 | 2-1 | 1-4 | 2-1 | 4-3 | 2-3 | 4-3 | | 0-1 | 3-1 | 1-1 | 2-4 | 3-0 |
| 18 | Rothwell Corinthians | 1-3 | 1-3 | 1-1 | 1-4 | 2-1 | 3-0 | 2-1 | 5-1 | 2-1 | 3-0 | 1-3 | 1-3 | 0-2 | 3-4 | 1-1 | 1-1 | 1-0 | | 1-3 | 1-3 | 2-3 | 1-0 |
| 19 | Sleaford Town | 0-3 | 3-1 | 4-2 | 0-3 | 1-0 | 2-1 | 0-0 | 2-1 | 2-2 | 7-2 | 4-1 | 1-0 | 3-2 | 1-0 | 4-6 | 1-2 | 3-1 | 1-0 | | 4-0 | 3-3 | 4-0 |
| 20 | Wellingborough Town | 1-2 | 3-1 | 0-3 | 1-1 | 0-1 | 1-0 | 0-3 | 3-2 | 2-1 | 8-0 | 2-3 | 2-3 | 3-4 | 3-2 | 1-2 | 1-1 | 0-1 | 2-0 | 1-5 | | 0-3 | 0-2 |
| 21 | Wisbech Town | 2-2 | 3-2 | 1-0 | 1-3 | 1-1 | 0-1 | 1-1 | 0-1 | 2-1 | 0-1 | 3-0 | 0-2 | 3-2 | 1-2 | 1-2 | 5-3 | 4-1 | 2-0 | 1-3 | 3-2 | | 1-1 |
| 22 | Yaxley | 1-1 | 3-1 | 1-2 | 2-2 | 3-0 | 0-3 | 3-2 | 2-2 | 2-4 | 5-1 | 3-4 | 1-3 | 2-0 | 4-0 | 4-4 | 6-3 | 2-2 | 2-2 | 1-2 | 8-3 | 5-0 | |

## UNITED COUNTIES LEAGUE - STEP 5/6

| | DIVISION ONE | P | W | D | L | F | A | GD | Pts |
|---|---|---|---|---|---|---|---|---|---|
| 1 | Peterborough Sports | 36 | 33 | 0 | 3 | 140 | 24 | 116 | 99 |
| 2 | Northampton ON Chenecks | 36 | 24 | 6 | 6 | 89 | 40 | 49 | 78 |
| 3 | Stewarts & Lloyds Corby | 36 | 22 | 6 | 8 | 72 | 40 | 32 | 72 |
| 4 | Olney Town (-3) | 36 | 19 | 5 | 12 | 89 | 73 | 16 | 59 |
| 5 | Bourne Town | 36 | 16 | 10 | 10 | 70 | 63 | 7 | 58 |
| 6 | Long Buckby AFC | 36 | 17 | 6 | 13 | 70 | 51 | 19 | 57 |
| 7 | Potton United | 36 | 18 | 3 | 15 | 61 | 52 | 9 | 57 |
| 8 | Raunds Town | 36 | 15 | 10 | 11 | 69 | 69 | 0 | 55 |
| 9 | Thrapston Town | 36 | 13 | 10 | 13 | 70 | 62 | 8 | 49 |
| 10 | Blackstones (-3) | 36 | 14 | 9 | 13 | 64 | 70 | -6 | 48 |
| 11 | Lutterworth Athletic | 36 | 14 | 6 | 16 | 69 | 79 | -10 | 48 |
| 12 | Oakham United | 36 | 12 | 11 | 13 | 65 | 71 | -6 | 47 |
| 13 | Rushden and Higham United | 36 | 13 | 8 | 15 | 67 | 75 | -8 | 47 |
| 14 | Woodford United | 36 | 12 | 5 | 19 | 63 | 86 | -23 | 41 |
| 15 | Wellingborough Whitworth | 36 | 10 | 8 | 18 | 63 | 84 | -21 | 38 |
| 16 | Irchester United | 36 | 10 | 7 | 19 | 58 | 86 | -28 | 37 |
| 17 | Buckingham Town | 36 | 7 | 9 | 20 | 51 | 81 | -30 | 30 |
| 18 | Bugbrooke St Michaels | 36 | 5 | 8 | 23 | 38 | 86 | -48 | 23 |
| 19 | Burton Park Wanderers | 36 | 3 | 3 | 30 | 30 | 106 | -76 | 12 |

St Neots Town Saints withdrew - record expunged.

| | DIVISION ONE | 1 | 2 | 3 | 4 | 5 | 6 | 7 | 8 | 9 | 10 | 11 | 12 | 13 | 14 | 15 | 16 | 17 | 18 | 19 |
|---|---|---|---|---|---|---|---|---|---|---|---|---|---|---|---|---|---|---|---|---|
| 1 | Blackstones | | 2-2 | 1-1 | 3-1 | 1-0 | 4-2 | 0-2 | 0-3 | 3-3 | 3-3 | 6-1 | 0-9 | 2-2 | 0-0 | 1-1 | 3-2 | 2-4 | 0-0 | 4-1 |
| 2 | Bourne Town | 1-0 | | 3-0 | 3-0 | 6-1 | 4-2 | 2-0 | 2-3 | 1-0 | 5-0 | 3-2 | 1-4 | 0-3 | 0-3 | 2-1 | 2-2 | 2-2 | 3-3 | 1-1 |
| 3 | Buckingham Town | 1-1 | 4-2 | | 1-1 | 0-0 | 1-0 | 2-4 | 3-3 | 1-1 | 1-1 | 1-2 | 1-3 | 2-4 | 2-4 | 2-3 | 1-3 | 2-3 | 1-1 | 0-1 |
| 4 | Bugbrooke St Michaels | 1-2 | 1-2 | 0-1 | | 2-1 | 2-3 | 0-2 | 1-1 | 0-3 | 1-3 | 0-2 | 1-6 | 2-1 | 0-0 | 2-3 | 0-2 | 2-2 | 1-1 | 2-0 |
| 5 | Burton Park Wanderers | 2-3 | 0-2 | 1-2 | 2-1 | | 3-1 | 0-2 | 1-2 | 0-5 | 2-3 | 0-3 | 0-1 | 1-6 | 1-3 | 0-1 | 0-3 | 0-3 | 1-2 | 0-6 |
| 6 | Irchester United | 0-2 | 1-2 | 1-0 | 3-3 | 3-2 | | 2-2 | 2-2 | 0-2 | 5-2 | 1-0 | 1-7 | 0-3 | 2-0 | 3-4 | 3-1 | 4-1 | 2-2 | 2-3 |
| 7 | Long Buckby AFC | 1-2 | 1-1 | 1-1 | 2-1 | 4-0 | 3-0 | | 6-0 | 2-3 | 3-1 | 1-1 | 3-0 | 1-0 | 4-0 | 4-1 | 0-1 | 1-1 | 1-3 | 1-2 |
| 8 | Lutterworth Athletic | 1-2 | 4-2 | 2-1 | 1-3 | 3-0 | 2-1 | 1-1 | | 1-4 | 3-3 | 2-3 | 0-1 | 2-1 | 3-1 | 5-3 | 3-5 | 2-1 | 3-0 | 2-3 |
| 9 | Northampton ON Chenecks | 3-1 | 3-2 | 6-2 | 4-0 | 3-2 | 2-1 | 2-1 | 2-0 | | 1-2 | 4-3 | 2-0 | 2-0 | 2-2 | 4-0 | 2-1 | 3-0 | 1-1 | 0-1 |
| 10 | Oakham United | 2-0 | 2-2 | 5-2 | 3-3 | 4-1 | 2-2 | 2-0 | 2-1 | 2-2 | | 1-2 | 1-5 | 1-0 | 2-2 | 3-1 | 0-2 | 2-2 | 1-2 | 2-3 |
| 11 | Olney Town | 0-2 | 0-1 | 5-4 | 5-0 | 6-0 | 6-2 | 5-3 | 3-2 | 3-2 | 2-1 | | 0-7 | 2-3 | 0-2 | 5-3 | 1-0 | 4-4 | 4-3 | 3-3 |
| 12 | Peterborough Sports | 2-1 | 5-0 | 7-0 | 6-1 | 5-2 | 9-0 | 5-0 | 5-1 | 2-1 | 2-0 | 2-0 | | 2-0 | 5-1 | 3-0 | 1-0 | 1-0 | 5-1 | 7-0 |
| 13 | Potton United | 2-1 | 0-1 | 2-0 | 0-1 | 0-1 | 1-0 | 0-3 | 1-0 | 2-1 | 2-1 | 2-1 | 0-4 | | 2-2 | 0-4 | 2-1 | 4-0 | 2-0 | 0-1 |
| 14 | Raunds Town | 3-2 | 5-2 | 1-3 | 3-3 | 3-0 | 4-3 | 1-5 | 1-1 | 0-0 | 4-0 | 1-5 | 1-2 | 5-4 | | 4-3 | 1-1 | 1-2 | 2-0 | 3-2 |
| 15 | Rushden and Higham United | 1-2 | 2-2 | 3-2 | 4-1 | 1-1 | 1-3 | 0-1 | 2-1 | 0-3 | 2-0 | 1-1 | 0-3 | 2-2 | 0-0 | | 1-2 | 3-2 | 2-2 | 3-2 |
| 16 | Stewarts & Lloyds Corby | 3-0 | 3-3 | 1-0 | 2-0 | 4-2 | 3-1 | 4-0 | 3-1 | 1-2 | 1-1 | 1-1 | 2-1 | 1-0 | 1-2 | 3-1 | | 0-0 | 1-0 | 3-1 |
| 17 | Thrapston Town | 4-1 | 2-1 | 1-2 | 3-1 | 0-0 | 1-1 | 3-1 | 6-0 | 0-2 | 1-3 | 2-4 | 1-2 | 1-2 | 3-1 | 1-1 | 0-3 | | 3-0 | 1-1 |
| 18 | Wellingborough Whitworth | 4-3 | 1-2 | 3-4 | 2-0 | 7-2 | 0-0 | 2-1 | 1-3 | 1-6 | 0-3 | 0-3 | 1-5 | 3-4 | 4-2 | 1-3 | 2-3 | 2-5 | | 4-1 |
| 19 | Woodford United | 2-4 | 0-0 | 1-0 | 4-0 | 5-1 | 0-1 | 2-3 | 3-5 | 2-3 | 1-1 | 3-1 | 1-6 | 1-4 | 0-1 | 2-6 | 2-3 | 1-5 | 1-4 | |

### LEAGUE CUP continued...

**ROUND 2**

| | | | |
|---|---|---|---|
| Cogenhoe United | v | Harrowby United | 2-0 |
| Eynesbury Rovers | v | AFC Kempston Rovers | 1-0 |
| Rushden & Higham United | v | Oadby Town | 1-7 |
| Peterborough Sports | v | Peterborough Northern Star | 3-0 |
| Kirby Muxloe | v | Holbeach United | 1-2 |
| Northampton Sileby Rangers | v | Boston Town | 3-5 |
| Wisbech Town | v | Leicester Nirvana | 0-0, 5-4p |
| Oakham United | v | Olney Town | 1-4 |

QUARTER FINALS

| | | | |
|---|---|---|---|
| Cogenhoe United | v | Eynesbury Rovers | 1-0 |
| Oadby Town | v | Peterborough Sports | 0-2 |
| Holbeach United | v | Boston Town | 1-0 |
| Wisbech Town | v | Olney Town | 4-2 |

SEMI FINALS

| | | | |
|---|---|---|---|
| Cogenhoe United | v | Peterborough Sports | 0-2 |
| Holbeach United | v | Wisbech Town | 2-0 |

FINAL

| | | | |
|---|---|---|---|
| Peterborough Sports | v | Holbeach United | 0-0, 6-5p |

## BOSTON TOWN

Founded: 1964 Nickname: Poachers

**Secretary:** Edward Graves **(T)** 07963 418 434 **(E)** btfcsec@hotmail.co.uk
**Chairman:** Mick Vines **Manager:** Nathan Colins **Prog Ed:** Eddie Graves
**Ground:** DWB Stadium, Tattershall Road, Boston, Lincs PE21 9LR **(T)** 01205 365 470
**Capacity:** 6,000 **Seats:** 450 **Covered:** 950 **Midweek Matchday:** Tuesday **Clubhouse:** Yes

**Colours(change):** All blue
**Previous Names:** Boston > 1994
**Previous Leagues:** Lincs, Central Alliance, Eastern co, Midland N. Co. E, C. Mids
**Records:** **Att:** 2,700 v Boston United FA Cup 1970. **Goalscorer:** Gary Bull 57 during 2006-07 season.
**Honours:** Midland League 1974-75, 78-79, 80-81. Central Midlands 88-89. United Counties League 1994-95, 2000-01.

**10 YEAR RECORD**

| 06-07 | 07-08 | 08-09 | 09-10 | 10-11 | 11-12 | 12-13 | 13-14 | 14-15 | 15-16 |
|---|---|---|---|---|---|---|---|---|---|
| UCL P 2 | UCL P 6 | UCL P 5 | UCL P 5 | UCL P 7 | UCL P 14 | UCL P 10 | UCL P 14 | UCL P 12 | UCL P 16 |

## COGENHOE UNITED

Founded: 1958 Nickname: Cooks

**Secretary:** Jon Wright **(T)** 07793 465 478 **(E)** cogenhoeunited@outlook.com
**Chairman:** Derek Wright **Prog Ed:** Brian Kempster
**Ground:** Compton Park, Brafield Road, Cogenhoe NN7 1ND **(T)** 01604 890 521
**Capacity:** 5,000 **Seats:** 100 **Covered:** 200 **Midweek Matchday:** Tuesday **Clubhouse:** Yes **Shop:** No

**Colours(change):** All blue
**Previous Names:**
**Previous Leagues:** Central Northants Comb, prem 67-84
**Records:** **Att:** 1,000 Charity game 90 **Goalscorer & Appearances:** Tony Smith
**Honours:** United Counties League 2004-05. Buckingham Charity Cup 2010-11.

**10 YEAR RECORD**

| 06-07 | 07-08 | 08-09 | 09-10 | 10-11 | 11-12 | 12-13 | 13-14 | 14-15 | 15-16 |
|---|---|---|---|---|---|---|---|---|---|
| UCL P 5 | UCL P 9 | UCL P 9 | UCL P 8 | UCL P 15 | UCL P 12 | UCL P 8 | UCL P 5 | UCL P 5 | UCL P 5 |

## DEEPING RANGERS

Founded: 1964 Nickname: Rangers

**Secretary:** Austin Goldsmith **(T)** 07852 977 095 **(E)** drfcsecretary@gmail.com
**Chairman:** Paul Smith **Manager:** Michael Goode **Prog Ed:** Lee Holmes
**Ground:** The Haydon Whitham Stadium, Outgang Road, Market Deeping PE6 8LQ **(T)** 01778 344 701
**Capacity:** 1,000 **Seats:** 180 **Covered:** 250 **Midweek Matchday:** Tuesday **Clubhouse:** Yes

**Colours(change):** Claret & blue stripes/claret/claret.
**Previous Names:** None
**Previous Leagues:** Peterborough & District 1966 - 1999.
**Records:**
**Honours:** Lincs Sen Cup, B Cup, Peterborough FA Cup (3). UCL Premier Champions 2006-07

**10 YEAR RECORD**

| 06-07 | 07-08 | 08-09 | 09-10 | 10-11 | 11-12 | 12-13 | 13-14 | 14-15 | 15-16 |
|---|---|---|---|---|---|---|---|---|---|
| UCL P 1 | UCL P 7 | UCL P 4 | UCL P 4 | UCL P 14 | UCL P 4 | UCL P 5 | UCL P 4 | UCL P 9 | UCL P 10 |

## DESBOROUGH TOWN

Founded: 1896 Nickname: Ar Tam

**Secretary:** John Lee **(T)** 07645 806 652 **(E)** johnlee@froggerycottage85.fsnet.co.uk
**Chairman:** Ernie Parsons **Manager:** Chris Bradshaw **Prog Ed:** John Lee
**Ground:** Waterworks Field, Braybrooke Rd, Desborough NN14 2LJ **(T)** 01536 761 350
**Capacity:** 8,000 **Seats:** 250 **Covered:** 500 **Midweek Matchday:** Tuesday **Clubhouse:** Yes

**Colours(change):** All royal blue
**Previous Names:** None
**Previous Leagues:** None
**Records:** **Att:** 8,000 v Kettering Town
**Honours:** N'hants/Utd Co. Champs 1900-01, 01-02, 06-07, 20-21, 23-24, 24-25, 27-28, 48-49, 66-67. Lge C 77-78, 00-01, 07-08. N'hants Sen C 1910-11, 13-14, 28-29, 51-52. Northants Senior Cup 1910-11, 13-14, 28-29, 51-52.

**10 YEAR RECORD**

| 06-07 | 07-08 | 08-09 | 09-10 | 10-11 | 11-12 | 12-13 | 13-14 | 14-15 | 15-16 |
|---|---|---|---|---|---|---|---|---|---|
| UCL P 14 | UCL P 3 | UCL P 11 | UCL P 18 | UCL P 19 | UCL P 16 | UCL P 11 | UCL P 10 | UCL P 14 | UCL P 15 |

## EYNESBURY ROVERS

Founded: 1897 Nickname: Rovers

**Secretary:** Catherine Watts **(T)** 07787 567 338 **(E)** erfcsecretary@gmail.com
**Chairman:** Matt Plumb **Manager:** Mark Ducket **Prog Ed:** Graham Mills
**Ground:** Alfred Hall Memorial Ground, Hall Road, Eynesbury, St Neots PE19 2SF **(T)** 07938 511 581uc
**Capacity:** **Seats:** **Covered:** **Midweek Matchday:** **Clubhouse:** Yes

**Colours(change):** Royal & white stripes/royal/royal
**Previous Names:** None
**Previous Leagues:** United Counties 1946-52. Eastern Counties 1952-63.
**Records:** **Att:** 5,000 v Fulham 1953 (Stanley Matthews guested for Eynesbury).
**Honours:** United Counties Division 1 1976-77.
Huntingdonshire Senior Cup x11. Huntingdonshire Premier Cup 1950-51, 90-91, 95-96.

**10 YEAR RECORD**

| 06-07 | 07-08 | 08-09 | 09-10 | 10-11 | 11-12 | 12-13 | 13-14 | 14-15 | 15-16 |
|---|---|---|---|---|---|---|---|---|---|
| UCL 1 10 | UCL 1 13 | UCL 1 7 | UCL 1 3 | UCL 1 6 | UCL 1 6 | UCL 1 3 | UCL 1 2 | UCL P 11 | UCL P 6 |

## HARBOROUGH TOWN

Founded: 1976 Nickname:

**Secretary:** Pauline Winston **(T)** 07446 415 329 **(E)** p.winston2402@btinternet.com
**Chairman:** Peter Dougan **Manager:** Nick Pollard **Prog Ed:** Gary Wainwright
**Ground:** Bowden's Park, Northampton Road, Market Harborough, Leics. LE16 9HF **(T)** 01858 467 339
**Capacity:** **Seats:** Yes **Covered:** Yes **Midweek Matchday:** Tuesday **Clubhouse:** Yes

**Colours(change):** Yellow/black/yellow
**Previous Names:**
**Previous Leagues:** Northants Combination
**Records:**
**Honours:** Northants Combination 2009-10.

**10 YEAR RECORD**

| 06-07 | 07-08 | 08-09 | 09-10 | 10-11 | 11-12 | 12-13 | 13-14 | 14-15 | 15-16 |
|---|---|---|---|---|---|---|---|---|---|
| | | | NhCo 1 | UCL 1 17 | UCL 1 2 | UCL P 19 | UCL P 17 | UCL P 20 | UCL P 11 |

## HARROWBY UNITED

Founded: 1949 Nickname: The Arrows

**Secretary:** Michael Atter **(T)** 07742 077 474 **(E)** mjproperty@fsmail.net
**Chairman:** Michael Atter **Manager:** Nick Anderson
**Ground:** Dickens Road, Grantham NG31 9RB **(T)** 01476 401 201
**Capacity:** **Seats:** **Covered:** **Midweek Matchday:** **Clubhouse:**

**Colours(change):** TBC
**Previous Names:** Harrowby United 1949-2009. Grantham Rangers 2009-2010. Reformed as Harrowby United in 2012.
**Previous Leagues:** Grantham 1949-66, 2006-07. Central Alliance. East Midlands Regional. UCL 1990-06. Lincolnshire 2007-08. C.Mids 2007-10.
**Records:**
**Honours:** United Counties Division One 1991-92.
Lincolnshire Junior Cup 2011-12.

**10 YEAR RECORD**

| 06-07 | 07-08 | 08-09 | 09-10 | 10-11 | 11-12 | 12-13 | 13-14 | 14-15 | 15-16 |
|---|---|---|---|---|---|---|---|---|---|
| | Lincs 16 | CM Su 17 | CM Su 18 | | | UCL 1 6 | UCL 1 3 | UCL P 17 | UCL P 18 |

## HOLBEACH UNITED

Founded: 1929 Nickname: Tigers

**Secretary:** James McMartin **(T)** 07747 165 701 **(E)** jamesmcmartin3@btinternet.com
**Chairman:** Dave Dougill **Manager:** Tom Roberts
**Ground:** Carters Park, Park Road, Holbeach, Lincs PE12 7EE **(T)** 01406 424 761
**Capacity:** 4,000 **Seats:** 200 **Covered:** 450 **Midweek Matchday:** Tuesday **Clubhouse:** Yes **Shop:** No

**Colours(change):** Yellow & black stripes/black/yellow (Blue & white stripes/blue/blue)
**Previous Names:**
**Previous Leagues:** Peterborough U Co L 46-55, Eastern 55-62, Midland Co 62-63
**Records:** **Att:** 4,094 v Wisbech 1954
**Honours:** United Counties League 1989-90, 02-03, 12-13. Lincs Sen A Cup (4), Senior Cup B 57-58
Lincolnshire Senior Trophy 2011-12, 12-13.

**10 YEAR RECORD**

| 06-07 | 07-08 | 08-09 | 09-10 | 10-11 | 11-12 | 12-13 | 13-14 | 14-15 | 15-16 |
|---|---|---|---|---|---|---|---|---|---|
| UCL P 11 | UCL P 11 | UCL P 16 | UCL P 16 | UCL P 17 | UCL P 6 | UCL P 1 | UCL P 11 | UCL P 6 | UCL P 4 |

## HUNTINGDON TOWN

Founded: 1995 Nickname:

**Secretary:** Russell Yezek **(T)** 07974 664 818 **(E)** russell.yezek@ntlworld.com

**Chairman:** Doug Mcilwain **Manager:** Bob Warby **Prog Ed:** Doug Mcilwain

**Ground:** Jubilee Park, Kings Ripton Road,, Huntingdon, Cambridgeshire PE28 2NR **(T)** 07974 664 818

**Capacity:** **Seats:** **Covered:** **Midweek Matchday:** **Clubhouse:**

**Colours(change):** Red & black stripes/black/red (All blue)

**Previous Names:**

**Previous Leagues:** Cambridgeshire.

**Records:**

**Honours:** Cambridgeshire Div.1B 1999-2000. Hunts. Junior Cup 1999-00, 2000-01, 01-02. Hunts Scott Gatty Cup 2001-02. United Counties League Division One 2011-12.

**10 YEAR RECORD**

| 06-07 | 07-08 | 08-09 | 09-10 | 10-11 | 11-12 | 12-13 | 13-14 | 14-15 | 15-16 |
|---|---|---|---|---|---|---|---|---|---|
| UCL 1 14 | UCL 1 4 | UCL 1 14 | UCL 1 8 | UCL 1 5 | UCL 1 1 | UCL P 4 | UCL P 2 | UCL P 16 | UCL P 22 |

## KIRBY MUXLOE

Founded: 1910 Nickname:

**Secretary:** Sean Anderson **(T)** 07813 255 298 **(E)** seckmfc@gmail.com

**Chairman:** Les Warren **Manager:** John Love **Prog Ed:** Sean Anderson

**Ground:** Kirby Muxloe Sports Club, Ratby Lane LE9 2AQ **(T)** 0116 239 2301

**Capacity:** **Seats:** **Covered:** Yes **Midweek Matchday:** Tuesday **Clubhouse:** Yes

**Colours(change):** Yellow & blue stripes/blue/blue

**Previous Names:**

**Previous Leagues:** Leicester Mutual. Leicester City. Leics Senior. East Mid Counties 2008-09. Midland All 2009-14. Midland Football 2014-15.

**Records:**

**Honours:** Leicestershire Co. Cup 2006-07. Leicestershire Senior Champions 2007-08. East Midlands Counties Champions 2008-09.

**10 YEAR RECORD**

| 06-07 | 07-08 | 08-09 | 09-10 | 10-11 | 11-12 | 12-13 | 13-14 | 14-15 | 15-16 |
|---|---|---|---|---|---|---|---|---|---|
| LeicS 2 | LeicS 1 | EMC 1 | MidAl 10 | MidAl 9 | MidAl 11 | MidAl 12 | MidAl 14 | MFLP 5 | UCL P 9 |

## LEICESTER NIRVANA

Founded: 2008 Nickname:

**Secretary:** Zak Hajat **(T)** 07811 843 136 **(E)** nirvanafc@hotmail.co.uk

**Chairman:** Kirk Master **Manager:** Damion Quailey & Hannah Dingley **Prog Ed:** Ian Payshorn

**Ground:** Gleneagles Avenue, Leicester LE5 7LU **(T)** 01162 660 009

**Capacity:** **Seats:** **Covered:** Yes **Midweek Matchday:** **Clubhouse:**

**Colours(change):** Red & black stripes/black/black (Blue & black stripes/blue/blue)

**Previous Names:** Thurnby Rangers and Leicester Nirvana merged to form today's club in 2008. Thurnby Nirvana 2008-15.

**Previous Leagues:** Leicestershire Senior >2010 East Midland Counties 2010-14

**Records:**

**Honours:** Leicestershire Senior Premier Division 2004-05. East Midland Counties 2013-14. Leicestershire Challenge Cup 2015-16.

**10 YEAR RECORD**

| 06-07 | 07-08 | 08-09 | 09-10 | 10-11 | 11-12 | 12-13 | 13-14 | 14-15 | 15-16 |
|---|---|---|---|---|---|---|---|---|---|
| LeicS 5 | LeicS 18 | LeicS 6 | LeicS 3 | EMC 9 | EMC 7 | EMC 3 | EMC 1 | UCL P 2 | UCL P 2 |

## NEWPORT PAGNELL TOWN

Founded: 1963 Nickname: Swans

**Secretary:** Steve Handley (Fixture) **(T)** 07867 528 475 **(E)** julieandsteveh1@gmail.com

**Chairman:** TBC **Manager:** Darren Lynch **Prog Ed:** Ben Sharpe

**Ground:** Willen Road, Newport Pagnell MK16 0DF **(T)** 01908 611 993

**Capacity:** 2,000 **Seats:** 100 **Covered:** 100 **Midweek Matchday:** Tuesday **Clubhouse:** Yes **Shop:** No

**Colours(change):** White & green stripes/white/white

**Previous Names:** Newport Pagnell Wanderers > 1972.

**Previous Leagues:** North Bucks 1963-71. South Midlands 1971-73.

**Records:**

**Honours:** United Counties League Div.1 1981-82, 2001-02. Bucks & Berks Intermediate Cup 2001-02. Berks & Bucks Senior Trophy 2009-10, 10-11.

**10 YEAR RECORD**

| 06-07 | 07-08 | 08-09 | 09-10 | 10-11 | 11-12 | 12-13 | 13-14 | 14-15 | 15-16 |
|---|---|---|---|---|---|---|---|---|---|
| UCL P 7 | UCL P 15 | UCL P 3 | UCL P 6 | UCL P 3 | UCL P 5 | UCL P 6 | UCL P 16 | UCL P 10 | UCL P 3 |

## NORTHAMPTON O.N. CHENECKS

Founded: 1946 Nickname: The Chens

**Secretary:** Bryan Lewis **(T)** 07920 108 300 **(E)** cytringan@tesco.net
**Chairman:** Eddie Slinn **Manager:** Graham Cottle **Prog Ed:** Gina Cottle
**Ground:** Old Northamptonians Sports Ground, Billing Road, Northampton NN1 5RT **(T)** 01604 634 045
**Capacity:** **Seats:** **Covered:** **Midweek Matchday:** **Clubhouse:**

**Colours(change):** White/navy/navy
**Previous Names:** Chenecks FC 1946-60. ON (Old Northamptonians) Chenecks 1960-
**Previous Leagues:** Northampton Minor 1946-50. Northampton Town 1950-69.
**Records:**
**Honours:** United Counties League Division One 1977-78, 79-80. Northants Junior Cup 2009-10, 13-14, 14-15.

**10 YEAR RECORD**

| 06-07 | 07-08 | 08-09 | 09-10 | 10-11 | 11-12 | 12-13 | 13-14 | 14-15 | 15-16 |
|---|---|---|---|---|---|---|---|---|---|
| UCL 1 15 | UCL 1 6 | UCL 1 4 | UCL 1 4 | UCL 1 14 | UCL 1 12 | UCL 1 11 | UCL 1 6 | UCL 1 6 | UCL 1 2 |

## NORTHAMPTON SILEBY RANGERS

Founded: 1968 Nickname: Sileby

**Secretary:** Dave King **(T)** 07783 150 082 **(E)** daveron51@yahoo.com
**Chairman:** Robert Clarke **Manager:** Lee Duffy **Prog Ed:** Dave Battams
**Ground:** Fernie Fields Sports Ground, Moulton, Northampton NN3 6FR **(T)** 01604 670 366
**Capacity:** **Seats:** Yes **Covered:** Yes **Midweek Matchday:** Wednesday **Clubhouse:** Yes

**Colours(change):** Red/black/red
**Previous Names:** Northampton Vanaid > 2000.
**Previous Leagues:** Northampton League > 1993.
**Records:** Att: 78.
**Honours:** Northampton Town League 1988-89 89-90. UCL Div 1 1993-94, 2002-03, 04-05, 12-13.

**10 YEAR RECORD**

| 06-07 | 07-08 | 08-09 | 09-10 | 10-11 | 11-12 | 12-13 | 13-14 | 14-15 | 15-16 |
|---|---|---|---|---|---|---|---|---|---|
| UCL 1 12 | UCL 1 12 | UCL 1 3 | UCL 1 9 | UCL 1 9 | UCL 1 16 | UCL 1 1 | UCL P 15 | UCL P 18 | UCL P 19 |

## OADBY TOWN

Founded: 1937 Nickname: The Poachers

**Secretary:** Kevin Zupp **(T)** 07580 004 110 **(E)** zuppy101@hotmail.co.uk
**Chairman:** Alan Lathwell **Manager:** Dave Clay & Graham Chambers **Prog Ed:** Kevin Zupp
**Ground:** Freeway Park, Wigston Road, Oadby LE2 5QG **(T)** 01162 715 728
**Capacity:** 5,000 **Seats:** 224 **Covered:** 224 **Midweek Matchday:** Tuesday **Clubhouse:** Yes **Shop:** Yes

**Colours(change):** All red
**Previous Names:** Oadby Imperial > 1951.
**Previous Leagues:** Leicestershire Senior. Midland Alliance > 2011. East Midlands Counties 2011-12.
**Records:**
**Honours:** Leicestershire Senior Div.2 1951-52. Prem 63-64, 67-68, 68-69, 72-73, 94-95, 96-97, 97-98, 98-99. Midland Alliance 99-00. United Counties Division One 2013-14.

**10 YEAR RECORD**

| 06-07 | 07-08 | 08-09 | 09-10 | 10-11 | 11-12 | 12-13 | 13-14 | 14-15 | 15-16 |
|---|---|---|---|---|---|---|---|---|---|
| MidAl 11 | MidAl 17 | MidAl 19 | MidAl 14 | MidAl 22 | EMC 3 | UCL 1 4 | UCL 1 1 | UCL P 13 | UCL P 21 |

## PETERBOROUGH NORTHERN STAR

Founded: 1900 Nickname:

**Secretary:** Amanda Knighton **(T)** 07541 296 270 **(E)** clubsecretary@pnsfc.co.uk
**Chairman:** Tony Zirpolo **Manager:** Raff Mazzarella **Prog Ed:** Tim Symonds
**Ground:** Branch Bros Stadium, Chestnut Avenue, Peterborough, Cambs PE1 4PE **(T)** 01733 552 416
**Capacity:** 1,500 **Seats:** none **Covered:** yes **Midweek Matchday:** Wednesday **Clubhouse:** Yes

**Colours(change):** Black & white stripes/black/black
**Previous Names:** Eye Utd >2005
**Previous Leagues:** Peterborough Lge >2003
**Records:**
**Honours:** Peterborough League 2002-03. Hinchingbrooke Cup 2009-10. United Counties League Division One 2008-09. UCL Knock-out Cup 2010-11.

**10 YEAR RECORD**

| 06-07 | 07-08 | 08-09 | 09-10 | 10-11 | 11-12 | 12-13 | 13-14 | 14-15 | 15-16 |
|---|---|---|---|---|---|---|---|---|---|
| UCL 1 5 | UCL 1 2 | UCL 1 1 | UCL 1 2 | UCL P 6 | UCL P 7 | UCL P 13 | UCL P 9 | UCL P 7 | UCL P 17 |

## PETERBOROUGH SPORTS

Founded: 1908 Nickname: The Turbines

**Secretary:** John Robinson **(T)** 07894 445 991 **(E)** jrobo1510@gmail.com
**Chairman:** Stephen Cooper **Manager:** James Dean **Prog Ed:** Stephen Cooper
**Ground:** 651 Lincoln Road, Peterborough PE1 3HA **(T)** 01733 567 835
**Capacity:** **Seats:** **Covered:** **Midweek Matchday:** **Clubhouse:**

**Colours(change):** All blue
**Previous Names:** Brotherhoods Engineering Works 1908-99. Bearings Direct during 1999-2001.
**Previous Leagues:** Northants League (former UCL) 1919-23. Peterborough & District 1923-2013.
**Records:**
**Honours:** Northants League 1919-20, United Counties League 1919-20, Division One 2015-16.
Peterborough & District League Division Three 1925-26, Division Three South 1980-81, Premier 2006-07. Northants Junior Cup 2006-07.

**10 YEAR RECORD**

| 06-07 | 07-08 | 08-09 | 09-10 | 10-11 | 11-12 | 12-13 | 13-14 | 14-15 | 15-16 |
|---|---|---|---|---|---|---|---|---|---|
| P&D P 1 | | | | | | P&D P 3 | UCL 1 16 | UCL 1 5 | UCL 1 1 |

## ROTHWELL CORINTHIANS

Founded: 1934 Nickname: Corinthians

**Secretary:** David Rhinds **(T)** 07955 100 795 **(E)** corinthsofficial@gmail.com
**Chairman:** Mark Budworth **Manager:** Shaun Sparrow **Prog Ed:** David Rhinds
**Ground:** Sergeants Lawn, Desborough Road, Rothwell NN14 6JR **(T)** 01536 711 706
**Capacity:** **Seats:** 50 **Covered:** 200 **Midweek Matchday:** **Clubhouse:** Yes

**Colours(change):** Red & black stripes/black/black
**Previous Names:** None
**Previous Leagues:** Kettering & District Amateur/East Midlands Alliance 1934 - 1995.
**Records:**
**Honours:**

**10 YEAR RECORD**

| 06-07 | 07-08 | 08-09 | 09-10 | 10-11 | 11-12 | 12-13 | 13-14 | 14-15 | 15-16 |
|---|---|---|---|---|---|---|---|---|---|
| UCL 1 7 | UCL 1 3 | UCL P 21 | UCL P 21 | UCL P 21 | UCL 1 8 | UCL 1 17 | UCL 1 15 | UCL 1 2 | UCL P 14 |

## SLEAFORD TOWN

Founded: 1968 Nickname: Town

**Secretary:** Ms Jenny O'Rourke **(T)** 07777 604 325 **(E)** jennyorourke@btinternet.com
**Chairman:** Susan Jones **Manager:** Paul Ward **Prog Ed:** Jamie Shaw
**Ground:** Eslaforde Park, Boston Road, Sleaford, Lincs NG34 9GH **(T)** 01529 415 951
**Capacity:** **Seats:** 88 **Covered:** 88 **Midweek Matchday:** Tuesday **Clubhouse:** Yes

**Colours(change):** Green/black/green
**Previous Names:**
**Previous Leagues:** Lincolnshire
**Records:**
**Honours:** United Counties League Division One 2005-06.

**10 YEAR RECORD**

| 06-07 | 07-08 | 08-09 | 09-10 | 10-11 | 11-12 | 12-13 | 13-14 | 14-15 | 15-16 |
|---|---|---|---|---|---|---|---|---|---|
| UCL 1 2 | UCL P 14 | UCL P 15 | UCL P 9 | UCL P 18 | UCL P 19 | UCL P 18 | UCL P 13 | UCL P 19 | UCL P 7 |

## WELLINGBOROUGH TOWN

Founded: 2004 Nickname: Doughboys

**Secretary:** Mick Walden **(T)** 07817 841 752 **(E)** mwalden@dsl.pipex.com
**Chairman:** Mark Darnell **Manager:** Jon Mitchell & Stuart Goosey **Prog Ed:** Neil Morris
**Ground:** The Dog & Duck, London Road, Wellingborough NN8 2DP **(T)** 01933 441 388
**Capacity:** **Seats:** Yes **Covered:** Yes **Midweek Matchday:** Tuesday **Clubhouse:** Yes

**Colours(change):** Yellow & blue/blue/blue
**Previous Names:** Original team (Formed 1867) folded in 2002 reforming in 2004
**Previous Leagues:** Metropolitan. Southern.
**Records:**
**Honours:** United Counties League 1964-65.

**10 YEAR RECORD**

| 06-07 | 07-08 | 08-09 | 09-10 | 10-11 | 11-12 | 12-13 | 13-14 | 14-15 | 15-16 |
|---|---|---|---|---|---|---|---|---|---|
| UCL P 3 | UCL P 10 | UCL P 18 | UCL P 11 | UCL P 5 | UCL P 8 | UCL P 15 | UCL P 8 | UCL P 15 | UCL P 20 |

## WISBECH TOWN

Founded: 1920 Nickname: Fenmen

**Secretary:** Gavin Clarey **(T)** 07919 100 060 **(E)** gav@wisbechtownfc.co.uk
**Chairman:** P A Brenchley **Manager:** Paul Creasy **Prog Ed:** Spencer Larham
**Ground:** The Elgoods Fenland Stadium, Lynn Road, Wisbech PE14 7AL **(T)** 01945 581 511
**Capacity:** **Seats:** 118 **Covered:** Yes **Midweek Matchday:** Tuesday **Clubhouse:** Yes

**Colours(change):** All red
**Previous Names:** None
**Previous Leagues:** Peterborough 1920-35. UCL 1935-50. EC 1950-52, 70-97, 2003-13. Midland 1952-58. Southern 1958-70, 97-2002.
**Records:** **Att:** 8,044 v Peterborough Utd, Midland Lge 25/08/1957 **Goalscorer:** Bert Titmarsh - 246 (1931-37) **Apps:** Jamie Brighty - 731
**Honours:** United Counties League Champions 1946-47, 47-48. Southern League Division 1 1961-62.
Eastern Counties League 1971-72, 76-77, 90-91, League Cup 2010-11. East Anglian Cup 1987-88.

**10 YEAR RECORD**

| 06-07 | 07-08 | 08-09 | 09-10 | 10-11 | 11-12 | 12-13 | 13-14 | 14-15 | 15-16 |
|---|---|---|---|---|---|---|---|---|---|
| ECP 11 | ECP 12 | ECP 16 | ECP 11 | ECP 4 | ECP 4 | ECP 2 | UCL P 7 | UCL P 3 | UCL P 8 |

## YAXLEY

Founded: 1900 Nickname: The Cuckoos

**Secretary:** Ms Samantha Dunkley **(T)** 07539 890 145 **(E)** buzzing945@hotmail.com
**Chairman:** Gary Warman **Manager:** Brett Whaley **Prog Ed:** Jeff Lenton
**Ground:** In2itive Park, Leading Drove, Holme Road, Yaxley, Peterborough PE7 3NA **(T)** 01733 244 928
**Capacity:** 1,000 **Seats:** 150 **Covered:** yes **Midweek Matchday:** Tuesday **Clubhouse:** Yes **Shop:** Yes

**Colours(change):** All blue
**Previous Names:** Yaxley Rovers.
**Previous Leagues:** Peterborough & Dist., Hunts & West Anglia
**Records:** **Goalscorer:** Ricky Hailstone 16
**Honours:** United Counties League Division One 1996-97. Hunts Senior Cup (7), UCL Cup 2005-2006

**10 YEAR RECORD**

| 06-07 | 07-08 | 08-09 | 09-10 | 10-11 | 11-12 | 12-13 | 13-14 | 14-15 | 15-16 |
|---|---|---|---|---|---|---|---|---|---|
| UCL P 15 | UCL P 16 | UCL P 14 | UCL P 19 | UCL P 16 | UCL P 18 | UCL P 12 | UCL P 6 | UCL P 4 | UCL P 12 |

## BLACKSTONES
Founded: 1920 Nickname: Stones

**Secretary:** Ian MacGillivray **(T)** 07749 620 825 **(E)** imacgilli@aol.com
**Chairman:** Gary Peace **Prog Ed:** Ian MacGillivray
**Ground:** Lincoln Road, Stamford, Lincs PE9 1SH **(T)** 01780 757 835 **Capacity:** 1,000
**Colours(change):** Black & green stripes/black/black
**ADDITIONAL INFORMATION: Record Att:** 700 v Glinton
**Honours:** Lincolnshire Senior Cup A 1992-93, 2003-04. Lincolnshire Senior Trophy 2010-11.

## BOURNE TOWN
Founded: 1883 Nickname: Wakes

**Secretary:** Tony Hull **(T)** 07709 785 273 **(E)** tonyhull2@hotmail.com
**Chairman:** Darren Munton & Steve Elger **Manager:** Jimmy McDonnell **Prog Ed:** Tony Hull
**Ground:** Abbey Lawn, Abbey Road, Bourne, Lincs PE10 9EN **(T)** 07598 815 357
**Colours(change):** Claret & sky blue stripes/claret/claret (All red)
**ADDITIONAL INFORMATION:**
**Record Att:** FA Trophy 1970 **Goalscorer:** David Scotney.
U.C.L. Champions 1968-69, 69-70, 71-72, 90-91. Lincolnshire Senior A Cup 1971-72, 2005-06.

## BUCKINGHAM TOWN
Founded: 1883 Nickname: Robins

**Secretary:** Vince Hyde **(T)** 07787 256 899 **(E)** buckinghamtownfc@hotmail.com
**Chairman:** Vince Hyde **Manager:** Gary Ollard
**Ground:** Irish Centre, Manor Fields, Bletchley, Milton Keynes MK2 2HX **(T)** 01908 375 978
**Colours(change):** All red
**ADDITIONAL INFORMATION:**
Paid: £7,000 to Wealdstone for Steve Jenkins 1992 Received: £1,000 from Kettering Town for Terry Shrieves.
**Honours:** Southern League Southern Division 1990-91. U.C.L. 1983-84, 85-86. Berks & Bucks Senior Cup 1983-84.

## BUGBROOKE ST MICHAELS
Founded: 1929 Nickname: Badgers

**Secretary:** Graham Connew **(T)** 07799 492 280 **(E)** graybags05@btinternet.com
**Chairman:** Kevin Gardner **Manager:** Mitch Austin **Prog Ed:** Peter Louch
**Ground:** Birds Close, Gayton Road, Bugbrooke NN7 3PH **(T)** 01604 830 707
**Colours(change):** White/black/black (Yellow & blue stripes/blue/blue)
**ADDITIONAL INFORMATION:**
**Record Att:** 1,156. **Golascorer:** Vince Thomas. **Apps:** Jimmy Nord.
**Honours:** Northants Junior Cup 1989-90, 2011-12, Central Northants Comb. x6. U.C.L. Division 1 Champions 1998-99.

## BURTON PARK WANDERERS
Founded: 1961 Nickname: The Wanderers

**Secretary:** Dave Borrett **(T)** 07794 959 915 **(E)** daveborrett66@gmail.com
**Chairman:** Mark Patrick **Manager:** Luke Smith **Prog Ed:** Michaela Wills
**Ground:** Burton Park, Polwell Lane, Burton Latimer, Northants NN15 5PS **(T)** 07980 013 506
**Colours(change):** Blue & black stripes/black/black
**ADDITIONAL INFORMATION:**
**Record Att:** 253 v Rothwell, May 1989.

## DAVENTRY TOWN
Founded: 1886 Nickname: The Town

**Secretary:** Brian Porter **(T)** 07903 859107 **(E)** club.secretary@dtfc.co.uk
**Chairman:** Iain Humphrey **Manager:** Arron Parkinson & Andy Marks **Prog Ed:** Brian Porter
**Ground:** Communications Park, Browns Road, Daventry, Northants NN11 4NS **(T)** 01327 311 239 **Capacity:** 2,000
**Colours(change):** Purple/white/purple (Black & white stripes/black/black)
**ADDITIONAL INFORMATION:** 850 v Utrecht (Holland) - 1989
**Previous Leagues:** Northampton Town (pre-1987), Central Northways Comb 1987-89, United Counties 1989-2010. Southern 2010-15. Northern Premier 2015-16.
**Honours:** United Counties League Division 1 1989-90, 90-91, 2000-01, 2007-08, Premier Division 2009-10.

## IRCHESTER UNITED
Founded: 1883 Nickname: The Romans

**Secretary:** Glynn Cotter **(T)** 07802 728 736 **(E)** glynn.cotter@btinternet.com
**Chairman:** Geoff Cotter **Manager:** Steve Sargent & Matty Freeman **Prog Ed:** David Cockings
**Ground:** Alfred Street, Irchester NN29 7DR **(T)** 01933 312 877 **Capacity:** 1,000
**Colours(change):** Red/white/red
**ADDITIONAL INFORMATION:**
Northants Lge Div 2 1930-31, 31-32, Rushden & District Lge (9), Northants Jnr Cup 1929-30, 33-34, 48-49, 75-76.
United Counties League Division 1 2009-10.

## LONG BUCKBY AFC
Founded: 1937 Nickname: Bucks

**Secretary:** Dave Austin **(T)** 07710 723 477 **(E)** lbafc.dja@gmail.com
**Chairman:** Dave Austin **Prog Ed:** Dave Austin
**Ground:** Station Road, Long Buckby NN6 7QA **(T)** 07749 393 045 **Capacity:** 1,000
**Colours(change):** All claret
**ADDITIONAL INFORMATION: Att:** 750 v Kettering Town
United Counties League Div.2 1970-71, 71-72, Premier Division 2011-12. Northants Senior Cup 2008-09. Munsell Cup 2009.

## LUTTERWORTH ATHLETIC
Founded: 1983 Nickname:

**Secretary:** Darren Jones **(T)** 07836 214 178 **(E)** djones20335783@aol.com
**Chairman:** Mick English **Manager:** Mick English **Prog Ed:** Darren Jones
**Ground:** Weston Arena, Hall Park, Hall Lane, Bitteswell, Lutterworth LE17 4LN **(T)** 01455 554 046
**Colours(change):** Green & white hoops/white/white
**ADDITIONAL INFORMATION:**
**Previous League:** Leicestershire Senior > 2012. East Midlands Counties 2012-13.

## MELTON TOWN
Founded: Nickname:

**Secretary:** Carol Lewis **(T)** 07754 472 283 **(E)** secretarymeltonmowbrayfc@hotmail.com
**Chairman:** Sam Ellis **Manager:** Tony Thorpe
**Ground:** King Edward VII, Burton Road, Melton Mowbray LE13 1DR **(T)** 01664 480 576
**Colours(change):** Red/black/black (All red)
**ADDITIONAL INFORMATION:**
**Previous Names:** Melton Mowbray >2016.
**Previous Leagues:** Leicestershire Senior >2016.

## OAKHAM UNITED
Founded: 1940s Nickname: Imps

**Secretary:** Craig Shuttleworth **(T)** 07817 578 896 **(E)** secretary@oakhamunited.co.uk
**Chairman:** Alistair Forbes **Manager:** W Oldacker, A Baily & S Hayes **Prog Ed:** Craig Shuttleworth
**Ground:** Main Road, Barleythorpe, Oakham, Rutland, LE15 7EE **(T)** 01572 757 484
**Colours(change):** Yellow/green/yellow
**ADDITIONAL INFORMATION: Previous Names:** In the 60s Oakham Imperial merged with Oakham Town to form today's club.
**Previous League:** Peterborough & District >2015
**League Honours:** Peterborough & District Premier Division 2014-15.

## OLNEY TOWN
Founded: 1903 Nickname: The Nurserymen

**Secretary:** Andrew Baldwin **(T)** 07932 141 623 **(E)** andew@abaldwin.go-plus.net
**Chairman:** Paul Tough **Manager:** Neil Griffiths **Prog Ed:** Paul Tough
**Ground:** Recreation Ground, East Street, Olney, Bucks MK46 4DW **(T)** 01234 712 227
**Colours(change):** All green
**ADDITIONAL INFORMATION:**
**Previous League:** Rushden & District.
**Honours:** U.C.L. Div 1 1972-73. Berks & Bucks Intermediate Cup 1992-93.

## POTTON UNITED
Founded: 1943 Nickname: Royals

**Secretary:** Mrs Bev Strong **(T)** 07703 442 565 **(E)** bev.strong@tiscali.co.uk
**Chairman:** Alan Riley **Manager:** Darren Staniforth **Prog Ed:** Mrs Bev Strong
**Ground:** The Hollow, Bigglewade Road, Potton, Beds SG19 2LU **(T)** 01767 261 100
**Colours(change):** All blue
**ADDITIONAL INFORMATION:**
**Record Att:** 470 v Hastings Town, FA Vase 1989.
**Honours:** U.C.L. 1986-87, 88-89, Div.1 2003-04. Beds Senior Cup x5. Huntingdonshire Premier Cup x4. E.Anglian Cup 1996-97

## RAUNDS TOWN
Founded: 1946 Nickname: Shopmates

**Secretary:** David Jones **(T)** 07763 492 184 **(E)** david.jones180@ntlworld.com
**Chairman:** Mrs Lesley Jones **Manager:** James Le Masseur **Prog Ed:** Carl Mallet
**Ground:** Kiln Park, London Road, Raunds, Northants NN9 6EQ **(T)** 01933 623 351 **Capacity:** 3,000
**Colours(change):** Red & black stripes/black/black
**ADDITIONAL INFORMATION: Record Att:** 1500 v Crystal Palace 1991 **Goalscorer:** Shaun Keeble. **App:** Martin Lewis - 355
**Honours:** Northants Senior Cup 1990-91.

## RUSHDEN & HIGHAM UNITED

Founded: Formed: 2007 Nickname:

**Secretary:** Scott Freeman **(T)** 07771 727 265 **(E)** rhufcsec@yahoo.co.uk
**Chairman:** John O'Connor **Prog Ed:** Jayne Rogers
**Ground:** Hayden Road, Rushden, Northants NN10 0HX **(T)** 01933 410 036
**Colours(change):** Orange/orange/black
**ADDITIONAL INFORMATION:**
Club was formed after the merger of Rushden Rangers and Higham Town.

## STEWARTS & LLOYDS CORBY

Founded: 1935 Nickname: The Foundrymen

**Secretary:** John Davies **(T)** 07588 018 397 **(E)** foundrychairman@hotmail.co.uk
**Chairman:** John Davies **Prog Ed:** Billy Gerrard
**Ground:** Recreation Ground, Occupation Road, Corby NN17 1EH **(T)** 01536 401 497 **Capacity:** 1,500
**Colours(change):** Red & black stripes/black/red
**ADDITIONAL INFORMATION: Record Goalscorer:** Joey Martin 46
United Counties League Division One 1973-74, 74-75, Premier 85-86, 08-09.

## THRAPSTON TOWN

Founded: 1960 Nickname: Venturas

**Secretary:** Kevin O'Brien **(T)** 07894 534 093 **(E)** kvnob@aol.com
**Chairman:** Gary Petts **Manager:** Ian Walker **Prog Ed:** Kevin O'Brien
**Ground:** Chancery Lane, Thrapston, Northants NN14 4JL **(T)** 01832 732 470 **Capacity:** 1,000
**Colours(change):** Blue & white stripes/blue/white
**ADDITIONAL INFORMATION:**
**Honours:** Kettering Amateur League 1970-71, 72-73, 73-74, 77-78. Northants Junior Cup 1987-88, 98-99, 03-04.

## WELLINGBOROUGH WHITWORTH

Founded: 1973 Nickname: Flourmen

**Secretary:** Julian Souster **(T)** 07825 632 545 **(E)** whitworthfc@yahoo.co.uk
**Chairman:** Martin Goodes **Prog Ed:** Julian Souster
**Ground:** Victoria Mill Ground, London Road, Wellingborough, Northants NN8 2DP **(T)** 07825 632 545
**Colours(change):** Red & black stripes/black/red
**ADDITIONAL INFORMATION:**
**Previous Name:** Whitworths. **Previous League:** East Midlands Alliance > 1985.
**Honours:** Rushden & District League 1976-77. Northants Junior Cup 1996. U.C.L. Division One 2006-07.

## WHITTLESEY ATHLETIC

Founded: Nickname:

**Secretary:** Gail Archer **(T)** 07941 631 681 **(E)** gail_archer@hotmail.com
**Chairman:** Wayne Gale **Manager:** Andy Lodge **Prog Ed:** Gail Archer
**Ground:** Feldale Field, Drybread Road, Whittlesey, PE7 1YP **(T)** 07941 631 681
**Colours(change):** Blue & black stripes/blue/blue
**ADDITIONAL INFORMATION:**
**Previous Leagues:** Peterborough & District > 2016

## WOODFORD UNITED

Founded: 1946 Nickname: Reds

**Secretary:** Andrew Worrall **(T)** 07500 067 734 **(E)** andy.worrall@engel.at
**Chairman:** Mrs Yvonne Worrall **Manager:** Joe Featherstone **Prog Ed:** Andrew Worrall
**Ground:** Byfield Road, Woodford Halse, Daventry, Northants NN11 3QR **(T)** 01327 263 734 **Capacity:** 3,000
**Colours(change):** All red
**ADDITIONAL INFORMATION:** 1,500 v Stockport County
United Counties League Division 2 1973-74, Premier Division 2005-06.

# GROUND DIRECTIONS

**BLACKSTONES FC -** From Stamford Centre take A6121 towards Bourne. Turn left into Lincoln Road. Ground on the right hand side. Go into town on A16 from Spalding. Turn left at roundabout into Liquor Pond Street becoming Queen Street over railway crossing along Sleaford Road. Turn right into Carlton Road then right at crossroads into Fydell Street. Over railway crossing and river take 2nd left (sharp turn) into Tattershall Road. Continue over railway crossing, ground on left.

**BOSTON TOWN -** Go into town on A16 from Spalding. Turn left at roundabout into Liquor Pond Street becoming Queen Street over railway crossing along Sleaford Road. Turn right into Carlton Road then right at crossroads into Fydell Street. Over railway crossing and river take 2nd left (sharp turn) into Tattershall Road. Continue over railway crossing, ground on left.

**BOURNE TOWN -** From Town Centre turn east on A151 towards Spalding into Abbey Road. Ground approximately half a mile on right.

**BUCKINGHAM TOWN -** Take A413 out of Buckingham and continue on that road until entering Winslow. As you enter Winslow there is a garage on the right hand side. Take the 1st turn right past the garage (Avenue Road) and then the 1st turn right again into Park Road. Entrance at end of road through the blue gates. Bear left into the car park..

**BUGBROOKE ST MICHAELS -** At M1 Junction 16 take A45 to Northampton. At first roundabout follow signs to Bugbrooke. Go straight through village, ground entrance immediately past last house on the left.

**BURTON PARK WANDERERS -** From A14 take J10 towards Burton Latimer, at Alpro roundabout turn right, then straight over roundabout next to Versalift then right at Morrisions. Follow the round around the top of Morrisions continue until you are past the small Alumasc building on the left. Entrance to ground is next left.

**COGENHOE UNITED -** From A45 Northampton Ring Road turn as indicated to Billing/Cogenhoe. Go over River Nene and up hill ignoring first turning on left to Cogenhoe. Take next left and ground is on right hand side.

**DEEPING RANGERS -** From Town Centre head north on B1524 towards Bourne. Turn right onto Towngate East at Towngate Tavern Pub. Go straight over mini roundabout onto Outgang Road. Ground 1/4 mile on left. From A16 by pass at roundabout with the A15 Bourne Road turn towards Deeping then left into Northfields Road, then left into Towngate/Outgang Road. Ground 1/4 mile on left.

**DESBOROUGH TOWN -** Take exit 3 marked Desborough off the A14 and follow bypass for 2 miles. At roundabout turn right and ground is 200 yards on the left hand side.

**EYNESBURY ROVERS -** From the A1 take the A428 towards Cambridge. Turn left at the Tesco roundabout and continue on Barford Road for half a mile going straight on at 4 roundabouts. Turn left into Hardwick Road and left into Hall Road. Ground at end of road

**HARBOROUGH TOWN -** Half a mile south of Market Harborough on the A508. 4 miles north of the A14 junction 2 towards Market Harborough turn left towards Leisure Centre, but keep left passed inflatable dome on the right, then through large car park, club house straight in front, with parking area.

**HARROWBY UNITED -** From A1 take B6403, go past roundabout, to Ancaster and take road for Harrowby. Follow the road into Grantham, ground on right opposite Tesco Express.

**HOLBEACH UNITED -** Approaching Town Centre traffic lights from Spalding Direction take Second Left, or from Kings Lynn direction take sharp right, into Park Road. Ground is 300 yards on the left.

**HUNTINGDON TOWN -** At the A1 Brampton Hut roundabout, follow signs for A14 East until reaching the Spittals Interchange roundabout, Follow the A141 towards St Ives/March and go over 3 roundabouts. Take next left turn at traffic lights towards Kings Ripton and the ground is on the left.

**IRCHESTER UNITED -** From A509 Wellingborough/Newport Pagnell Road turn into Gidsy Lane to Irchester. Turn left into Wollaston Road B659. Alfred Street is on left hand side with the ground at the end.

**KIRBY MUXLOE -** From M1 leave at JCTT 21A and follow the signposts for Kirby Muxloe. As you enter the village, at the roundabout take 2nd exit onto Ratby Lane. At mini Roundabout take 2nd exit and the ground is 200 yards on the right hand side. From A47 at Traffic lights turn right onto Colchester Road A563 Continue on A563 for approximately 6 miles turning onto A5630 Anstey Lane. After approximately 2 miles turn left on A46 towards M1 just before next left and then follow directions to Kirby Muxtoe, as you enter the village, at the roundabout take 2nd exit onto Ratby Lane. At mini roundabout take 2nd exit and the ground is 200 yards on the right hand side.

**LEICESTER NIRVANA -** From M1—Exit at Jct 22 (A50/A511 to Leicester/Coalville. Follow A50 to Leicester, until you reach signs for A563 (Glenfirth Way). After Sainsbury's, turn right then immediately left in to Gleneagles Avenue. Entrance is at the bottom of the cul de sac.

**LONG BUCKBY AFC -** From the Village Centre turn into Station Road. Ground on left hand side. Parking is available in South Close adjacent to the Rugby Club (do NOT park "half on half off" the pavement outside the ground)

**LUTTERWORTH ATHLETIC -** Exit the M1 at junction 20 and take the first exit at the roundabout. Then take the third exit at the next roundabout and head into Lutterworth. Continue on through Lutterworth, and when you have eft the town continue for half a mile before taking the first left. The ground is immediately on your left.

**MELTON TOWN -** From Town centre follow signs for A1/Oakham. 1/2 mile up Burton Road ground is on the left.

**NEWPORT PAGNELL TOWN -** From the A422 Newport Pagnell by pass turn into Marsh End Road, then first right into Willen Road.

**NORTHAMPTON ON CHENECKS -** Leave A45 at exit marked Bedford A428 and Town Centre. Take exit into Rushmere Road marked Abington, Kingsthorpe and County Cricket. At first set of lights turn left into Billing Road, sports ground 250 yards on the right.

**NORTHAMPTON SILEBY RANGERS -** Approach from A43 (Kettering): From large roundabout with traffic lights, take the A5076 Talavera Way exit, signpostedto Market Harborough, Moulton Park and Kingsthorpe. The entrance to the ground is about a quarter of a mile on the left. Approach from A45: Take exit to A43 Ring Road / Kettering / Corby. Go straight over 1 roundabout to large roundabout with traffic lights. Then follow directions above.

**OADBY TOWN -** A14 Desborough, A6 towards Market Harborough. Follow A6 towards Leicester. Enter Oadby, go past Sainsbury's (traffic lights), next set of lights turn left. Signpost Oadby Town Centre, follow road over mini roundabout (St Peters Church in foreground) bear left towards Wigston. Follow road over roundabout, through the next lights, ground on the left.

**OAKHAM UNITED -** Oakham United Football Club is located on the main road running through the village of Barleythorpe (B640). The B640 links the town centre to the A606 Oakham bypass.

**OLNEY TOWN -** From the North enter via A509 Warrington Road then turn left into Midland Road and immediately right into East Street. Ground on left hand side after Fire Station. From Milton Keynes: Follow the A509 into Olney, over river bridge, 200 metres past the Swan Bistro and public house and take the first turning right onto the market square immediately before the traffic lights), follow road to the right onto a one way system into East Street. Follow East Street for 500 metres, the ootball Club is on the right hand side, car park entrance being the immediately following right turn.

**PETERBOROUGH NORTHERN STAR -** From A1 turn on to A1139 Fletton Parkway. Follow signs for A47 Wisbech. Exit at Junction 7 (near Perkins Engines Site). At top of slip road turn left into Eastfield Road. At Traffic lights turn right into Newark Avenue and then first right in to Eastern Avenue. Take 2nd left in to Chestnut Avenue and the club is on the right behind steel Palisade Fencing

**PETERBOROUGH SPORTS -** From the North - Come in on the A15 Southbound and cross the large A47 Roundabout just past Morrison's on your right. ***Take the left hand slip road at a set of traffic lights after approximately 400 yards and turn right at the T-Junction after 50 yards. The entrance to the ground is approx 400 yards down on your left in front of a church and before a zebra crossing where there is a sign to the health centre. If journeying from the East take the turning from the A47 signposted City Centre and follow instructions from *** above. If journeying from the South or West come in via the A47 and take the exit signposted City Centre. You go straight on at this roundabout (back up alongside A47) and then take the 3rd (right) at the large roundabout with the A15 and follow instructions from *** above.

**POTTON UNITED -** From Sandy, take B1042 into Potton. Head towards Potton Town Centre and take right turn towards Biggleswade (B1040). The ground is on left hand side at foot of hill

**RAUNDS TOWN -** From North, East or West, take A14 J13 and follow A45 signs to Raunds. Turn left at roundabout by BP garage. From South follow A45 towards Thrapston. Turn right at roundabout by BP garage. Ground on left.

**ROTHWELL CORINTHIANS -** A14 to Rothwell. Take B669 towards Desborough. Ground on right at rear of cricket field opposite last houses on the left. Parking on verge or in adjacent field if gate open. Access to ground via footpath.

**RUSHDEN AND HIGHAM UNITED -** From A6/A45 (Chowns Mill Roundabout) take Higham / Rushden bypass at 3rd roundabout, take the 3rd exit onto Newton Road, then immediately right after Newton Road School into Cromwell road this then leads into Hayden Road. Ground is approx. 100 yards on left hand side. From Bedford (A6) take Rushden / Higham Bypass and at the 1st roundabout take the 1st exit onto Newton Road, then turn immediately right after Newton Road School into Cromwell road this the leads into Hayden Road. Ground is approx. 100 yards on the left hand side.

**SLEAFORD TOWN -** 15 Sleaford By-pass, roundabout to A17 Holdingham Roundabout third exit towards Boston on A17 Take second exit of A17 towards Sleaford ground is 1 mile on right hand side before you enter Sleaford

**SPALDING UNITED -** Follow signs to Spalding Town Centre. From the north drive south down Pinchbeck Road towards Spalding. At traffic lights turn right into Kings Road. At the next set of lights turn left into Winfrey Avenue. The Ground is on the left. From the south follow signs to The Railway station and Bus Stations. The Ground is opposite the Bus Station on Winfrey Avenue. There is parking outside the ground in a pay and display car park.

**STEWARTS & LLOYDS CORBY -** From the Oundle/Weldon Road turn at roundabout into A6086 Lloyds Road and continue to roundabout. Take second exit going over railway line along Rockingham Road. Continue over speed bumps then turn left into Occupation Road and first right into Cannock Road. Ground is beyond the British Steel Club and Rugby pitch.

**THRAPSTON TOWN -** Exit A14 at A605 roundabout, travel towards Peterborough till 1st roundabout (approx 700 metres).Take first exit into Thrapston. AT traffic lights turn into Oundle Road adjacent to Masons Arms Pub. Turn left into Devere Road and ground at bottom of hill.

**WELLINGBOROUGH TOWN -** Leave A.45 at Wellingborough turn-off, pass Tesco's Store on left-hand side, up to roundabout. Take first exit to town centre. Ground is 300 yards on right-hand side. Entry just past the Dog & Duck public house adjacent to entry to Whitworths ground.

**WELLINGBOROUGH WHITWORTH -** Leave A45 by pass and go past Tescos etc. Turn left at roundabout then turn right immediately after Dog and Duck pub and go through 2nd gate down to the ground .

**WHITTLESEY ATHLETIC -** Approx 200/300 metres from Strawbear Pub, field gate access is next to house number 112 Drybread Road.

**WISBECH TOWN -** From A1 follow signs for Wisbech (A47). At the outskirts of Wisbech, take 2nd exit off roundabout, signposted A47. After 1.5 miles, go straight over at the next roundabout. At next roundabout (another 3.1 miles on, Total Garage on right) take first exit (signposted B198 West Walton/Walsoken). Cross over next roundabout (which is new, so not marked on some maps and sat navs) and follow road for just over a mile. The entrance to the stadium is on the right via the right turn lane.

**WOODFORD UNITED -** A361 Daventry to Banbury Road. Turn left in Byfield. Follow road to Woodford Halse. Ground on left just past industrial estate.

**YAXLEY -** Leave A1 at Norman Cross and travel towards Peterborough. Turn off A15 at traffic lights. Bear immediately right and go past cemetery. At bottom of hill turn right into Main Street then left into Holme Road. After short distance go over small bridge and turn left between a bungalow and house into Leading Drove. Ground on left hand side.

# WESSEX LEAGUE

**Sponsored by:** Sydenhams

**Founded:** 1986

**Recent Champions: 2013:** Blackfield & Langley

**2014:** Sholing **2015:** Petersfield Town

| | PREMIER DIVISION | P | W | D | L | F | A | GD | Pts |
|---|---|---|---|---|---|---|---|---|---|
| 1 | Salisbury | 40 | 34 | 3 | 3 | 126 | 29 | 97 | 105 |
| 2 | Sholing | 40 | 26 | 7 | 7 | 80 | 38 | 42 | 85 |
| 3 | Blackfield & Langley | 40 | 26 | 5 | 9 | 92 | 45 | 47 | 83 |
| 4 | Andover Town | 40 | 25 | 7 | 8 | 97 | 58 | 39 | 82 |
| 5 | Horndean | 40 | 22 | 7 | 11 | 87 | 56 | 31 | 73 |
| 6 | AFC Portchester | 40 | 20 | 11 | 9 | 86 | 41 | 45 | 71 |
| 7 | Team Solent | 40 | 21 | 4 | 15 | 78 | 71 | 7 | 67 |
| 8 | Moneyfields | 40 | 19 | 8 | 13 | 71 | 61 | 10 | 65 |
| 9 | Bemerton Heath Harlequins | 40 | 18 | 9 | 13 | 87 | 64 | 23 | 63 |
| 10 | Newport (IoW) | 40 | 18 | 3 | 19 | 65 | 66 | -1 | 57 |
| 11 | Cowes Sports | 40 | 15 | 10 | 15 | 67 | 76 | -9 | 55 |
| 12 | Fareham Town | 40 | 14 | 9 | 17 | 64 | 71 | -7 | 51 |
| 13 | Lymington Town | 40 | 14 | 9 | 17 | 51 | 65 | -14 | 51 |
| 14 | Brockenhurst | 40 | 11 | 11 | 18 | 71 | 87 | -16 | 44 |
| 15 | Whitchurch United | 40 | 12 | 8 | 20 | 66 | 82 | -16 | 44 |
| 16 | Hamworthy United | 40 | 12 | 5 | 23 | 58 | 86 | -28 | 41 |
| 17 | Verwood Town | 40 | 10 | 10 | 20 | 47 | 74 | -27 | 40 |
| 18 | Bournemouth | 40 | 10 | 7 | 23 | 56 | 100 | -44 | 37 |
| 19 | Fawley | 40 | 6 | 13 | 21 | 53 | 85 | -32 | 31 |
| 20 | Alresford Town | 40 | 5 | 5 | 30 | 44 | 127 | -83 | 20 |
| 21 | Folland Sports | 40 | 5 | 3 | 32 | 48 | 112 | -64 | 18 |

| | DIVISION ONE | P | W | D | L | F | A | GD | Pts |
|---|---|---|---|---|---|---|---|---|---|
| 1 | Portland United | 34 | 27 | 3 | 4 | 97 | 25 | 72 | 84 |
| 2 | Amesbury Town | 34 | 24 | 5 | 5 | 89 | 36 | 53 | 77 |
| 3 | Tadley Calleva | 34 | 22 | 6 | 6 | 98 | 41 | 57 | 72 |
| 4 | United Services Portsmouth (-3) | 34 | 20 | 4 | 10 | 71 | 49 | 22 | 61 |
| 5 | Laverstock & Ford | 34 | 17 | 7 | 10 | 68 | 51 | 17 | 58 |
| 6 | Christchurch | 34 | 16 | 8 | 10 | 75 | 49 | 26 | 56 |
| 7 | Alton | 34 | 16 | 4 | 14 | 70 | 64 | 6 | 52 |
| 8 | AFC Stoneham | 34 | 14 | 9 | 11 | 75 | 56 | 19 | 51 |
| 9 | Romsey Town | 34 | 16 | 2 | 16 | 50 | 54 | -4 | 50 |
| 10 | Downton | 34 | 13 | 7 | 14 | 52 | 54 | -2 | 46 |
| 11 | Hythe & Dibden | 34 | 13 | 6 | 15 | 55 | 68 | -13 | 45 |
| 12 | Fleet Spurs | 34 | 12 | 8 | 14 | 70 | 82 | -12 | 44 |
| 13 | Ringwood Town | 34 | 12 | 5 | 17 | 73 | 64 | 9 | 41 |
| 14 | New Milton Town | 34 | 10 | 8 | 16 | 46 | 65 | -19 | 38 |
| 15 | Totton & Eling | 34 | 9 | 4 | 21 | 67 | 72 | -5 | 31 |
| 16 | Andover New Street | 34 | 8 | 4 | 22 | 30 | 111 | -81 | 28 |
| 17 | Pewsey Vale | 34 | 6 | 2 | 26 | 33 | 97 | -64 | 20 |
| 18 | East Cowes Victoria | 34 | 4 | 2 | 28 | 36 | 117 | -81 | 14 |

## CLUB MOVEMENTS

**Premier Division - In:** Amesbury Town (P), Bashley (R - Southern Div.1 S&W) Portland United (P).
**Out:** Folland, Sports (R), Salisbury (P - Southern Division One South & West).

**Division One - In:** Baffins Milton Rovers (P - Hampshire League), Folland (R), Hamble Club (P - Hampshire League), Shaftesbury (P - Dorset Premier), Weymouth Reserves (P - Dorset Premier).
**Out:** Amesbury Town (P), Portland United (P).

| | PREMIER DIVISION | 1 | 2 | 3 | 4 | 5 | 6 | 7 | 8 | 9 | 10 | 11 | 12 | 13 | 14 | 15 | 16 | 17 | 18 | 19 | 20 | 21 |
|---|---|---|---|---|---|---|---|---|---|---|---|---|---|---|---|---|---|---|---|---|---|---|
| 1 | AFC Portchester | | 1-1 | 1-1 | 2-2 | 2-2 | 2-0 | 2-2 | 5-1 | 0-0 | 1-0 | 4-0 | 2-0 | 3-0 | 2-0 | 5-1 | 5-1 | 4-1 | 1-0 | 6-0 | 3-1 | 1-1 |
| 2 | Alresford Town | 0-5 | | 1-3 | 1-6 | 2-5 | 3-6 | 0-1 | 1-2 | 2-1 | 3-2 | 3-0 | 1-2 | 2-1 | 1-3 | 0-2 | 1-6 | 1-4 | 1-7 | 3-3 | 2-3 | 0-2 |
| 3 | Andover Town | 2-2 | 6-1 | | 4-1 | 3-2 | 2-1 | 2-2 | 3-3 | 5-0 | 4-1 | 3-0 | 2-1 | 2-3 | 3-1 | 1-2 | 4-0 | 0-2 | 3-2 | 2-0 | 3-1 | 4-1 |
| 4 | Bemerton Heath Harlequins | 2-0 | 8-1 | 2-1 | | 1-5 | 2-0 | 7-3 | 1-5 | 1-2 | 5-1 | 0-0 | 3-1 | 1-3 | 1-1 | 3-0 | 0-4 | 1-3 | 1-1 | 2-2 | 4-1 | 1-0 |
| 5 | Blackfield & Langley | 1-1 | 3-2 | 0-0 | 4-2 | | 4-0 | 3-0 | 2-0 | 2-0 | 2-1 | 5-0 | 2-1 | 2-1 | 3-0 | 0-1 | 2-0 | 0-1 | 1-1 | 2-1 | 2-2 | 2-0 |
| 6 | Bournemouth | 1-1 | 1-3 | 1-2 | 1-4 | 1-4 | | 2-1 | 1-3 | 1-0 | 3-0 | 0-2 | 1-0 | 0-1 | 0-1 | 2-2 | 0-3 | 0-2 | 1-2 | 0-0 | 2-1 | 5-0 |
| 7 | Brockenhurst | 3-3 | 6-1 | 2-2 | 0-3 | 0-2 | 4-2 | | 5-2 | 1-1 | 3-1 | 1-4 | 3-3 | 0-1 | 1-1 | 1-1 | 4-1 | 0-0 | 2-3 | 2-0 | 0-1 | 2-4 |
| 8 | Cowes Sports | 1-0 | 0-0 | 0-2 | 1-1 | 1-4 | 4-1 | 4-2 | | 3-1 | 1-2 | 3-0 | 1-4 | 3-5 | 1-1 | 1-0 | 0-1 | 0-6 | 1-1 | 4-0 | 1-0 | 2-2 |
| 9 | Fareham Town | 1-2 | 4-1 | 1-3 | 2-2 | 2-1 | 3-1 | 2-2 | 5-0 | | 1-1 | 3-0 | 3-0 | 1-5 | 2-0 | 0-0 | 0-1 | 2-3 | 0-2 | 0-2 | 6-0 | 1-1 |
| 10 | Fawley | 1-4 | 1-1 | 1-1 | 3-2 | 0-3 | 0-0 | 3-3 | 1-2 | 2-3 | | 4-3 | 1-1 | 1-1 | 1-1 | 1-2 | 3-2 | 2-4 | 0-2 | 1-1 | 0-0 | 2-2 |
| 11 | Folland Sports | 1-4 | 2-2 | 1-2 | 1-3 | 0-4 | 0-3 | 1-3 | 2-3 | 1-2 | 2-5 | | 1-2 | 0-5 | 1-2 | 2-3 | 1-2 | 1-6 | 1-2 | 2-4 | 3-2 | 0-2 |
| 12 | Hamworthy United | 0-3 | 2-1 | 0-6 | 1-3 | 1-2 | 2-4 | 7-1 | 2-0 | 2-2 | 4-2 | 3-2 | | 2-3 | 1-3 | 2-1 | 1-3 | 0-2 | 1-2 | 0-2 | 0-1 | 2-1 |
| 13 | Horndean | 3-2 | 2-0 | 4-1 | 2-2 | 3-2 | 6-1 | 1-2 | 1-1 | 4-0 | 1-1 | 3-0 | 6-2 | | 3-1 | 2-2 | 1-0 | 0-3 | 0-0 | 2-0 | 2-1 | 2-0 |
| 14 | Lymington Town | 1-5 | 2-0 | 0-3 | 0-4 | 2-0 | 1-2 | 1-0 | 0-0 | 1-1 | 3-3 | 1-3 | 2-0 | 3-1 | | 0-1 | 3-2 | 1-2 | 4-2 | 1-2 | 1-1 | 2-2 |
| 15 | Moneyfields | 1-0 | 2-0 | 1-2 | 1-0 | 0-2 | 5-2 | 5-2 | 2-3 | 1-0 | 4-1 | 3-2 | 0-1 | 2-0 | 2-3 | | 2-2 | 1-6 | 2-0 | 1-4 | 0-0 | 2-2 |
| 16 | Newport (IoW) | 2-0 | 4-0 | 2-3 | 1-0 | 3-1 | 2-2 | 1-0 | 3-2 | 2-3 | 2-1 | 2-4 | 1-2 | 1-1 | 1-0 | 0-3 | | 0-3 | 0-1 | 0-1 | 1-2 | 6-2 |
| 17 | Salisbury | 2-0 | 6-0 | 6-0 | 3-1 | 1-2 | 9-1 | 3-0 | 1-0 | 6-0 | 2-0 | 4-2 | 5-1 | 4-3 | 1-0 | 2-2 | 1-0 | | 1-0 | 2-0 | 5-0 | 1-2 |
| 18 | Sholing | 3-0 | 1-0 | 3-0 | 1-0 | 1-0 | 1-1 | 4-3 | 4-0 | 2-1 | 2-1 | 1-0 | 2-0 | 2-0 | 5-0 | 2-3 | 4-1 | 1-1 | | 3-1 | 3-2 | 2-1 |
| 19 | Team Solent | 1-0 | 4-1 | 2-3 | 0-1 | 3-2 | 9-1 | 0-2 | 0-4 | 3-5 | 2-1 | 3-2 | 3-1 | 3-1 | 1-2 | 3-2 | 3-0 | 0-6 | 2-1 | | 2-0 | 7-2 |
| 20 | Verwood Town | 0-2 | 1-0 | 1-2 | 1-1 | 2-3 | 2-2 | 0-2 | 2-2 | 4-0 | 0-1 | 1-1 | 3-3 | 3-2 | 1-0 | 0-5 | 0-1 | 1-2 | 1-1 | 0-2 | | 3-2 |
| 21 | Whitchurch United | 1-0 | 7-1 | 3-2 | 1-3 | 3-4 | 7-3 | 3-0 | 2-2 | 1-3 | 2-0 | 4-0 | 0-0 | 0-2 | 0-2 | 2-1 | 0-1 | 0-4 | 0-3 | 1-2 | 0-2 | |

## LEAGUE CUP

**HOLDERS:** AFC PORCHESTER

### ROUND 1

| | | | |
|---|---|---|---|
| Blackfield & Langley | v | Team Solent | 0-1 |
| Hamworthy United | v | United Services Portsmouth | 0-2 |
| AFC Porchester | v | Fareham Town | 2-3 |
| Bournemouth | v | Moneyfields | 1-1, 4-5p |
| Sholing | v | Folland Sports | 2-0 |
| Alresford Town | v | East Cowes Victoria | 8-1 |
| Pewsey Vale | v | Brockenhurst | 2-2, 3-5p |

### ROUND 2

| | | | |
|---|---|---|---|
| Team Solent | v | United Services Portsmouth | 7-0 |
| Fareham Town | v | Alton Town | 2-4 |
| Amesbury Town | v | Christchurch | 1-0 (aet) |
| Salisbury | v | Fleet Spurs | 5-2 |
| Moneyfields | v | Tadley Calleva | 3-2 (aet) |
| Portland United | v | Horndean | 2-1 (aet) |
| Bemerton Heath Harlequins | v | Downton | 2-0 |
| Andover New Street | v | Andover Town | 0-9 |
| Whitchurch United | v | Newport (IOW) | 2-4 |
| AFC Stoneham | v | Ringwood Town | 0-2 |
| Sholing | v | Laverstock & Ford | 5-0 |
| Verwood Town | v | Lymington Town | 3-0 |
| Romsey Town | v | Hythe & Dibden | 3-1 |
| Totton & Eling | v | Fawley | 3-0 |
| New Milton Town | v | Cowes Sports | 1-4 |
| Alresford Town | v | Brockenhurst | 0-3 |

### ROUND 3

| | | | |
|---|---|---|---|
| Team Solent | v | Alton Town | 4-0 |
| Amesbury Town | v | Salisbury | 2-4 |
| Moneyfields | v | Portland United | 1-2 |
| Bemerton Heath Harlequins | v | Andover Town | 2-0 |
| Newport (IOW) | v | Ringwood Town | 4-0 |
| Sholing | v | Verwood Town | 3-0 |
| Romsey Town | v | Totton & Eling | 2-2, 4-5p |
| Cowes Sports | v | Brockenhurst | 3-4 (aet) |

### QUARTER FINALS

| | | | |
|---|---|---|---|
| Team Solent | v | Salisbury | 3-1 |
| Portland United | v | Bemerton Heath Harlequins | 2-1 |
| Newport (IOW) | v | Sholing | 3-2 (aet) |
| Totton & Eling | v | Brockenhurst | 0-3 |

### SEMI FINALS

| | | | |
|---|---|---|---|
| Team Solent | v | Portland United | 2-1 (aet) |
| Newport (IOW) | v | Brockenhurst | 2-0 |

### FINAL

| | | | |
|---|---|---|---|
| Team Solent | v | Newport (IOW) | 1-0 |

| | DIVISION ONE | 1 | 2 | 3 | 4 | 5 | 6 | 7 | 8 | 9 | 10 | 11 | 12 | 13 | 14 | 15 | 16 | 17 | 18 |
|---|---|---|---|---|---|---|---|---|---|---|---|---|---|---|---|---|---|---|---|
| 1 | AFC Stoneham | | 1-1 | 0-1 | 4-0 | 5-0 | 2-1 | 5-1 | 2-2 | 4-1 | 1-1 | 3-1 | 4-0 | 1-1 | 1-2 | 2-0 | 0-4 | 0-2 | 1-2 |
| 2 | Alton | 4-0 | | 4-1 | 5-1 | 2-4 | 2-2 | 4-0 | 0-2 | 1-0 | 3-2 | 2-0 | 2-1 | 1-4 | 4-0 | 0-3 | 1-2 | 4-2 | 6-3 |
| 3 | Amesbury Town | 3-3 | 4-0 | | 8-0 | 3-0 | 2-0 | 4-1 | 2-2 | 3-1 | 2-0 | 2-0 | 5-0 | 3-1 | 3-2 | 4-1 | 2-2 | 1-0 | 2-1 |
| 4 | Andover New Street | 1-5 | 1-1 | 0-5 | | 1-4 | 1-0 | 5-1 | 3-2 | 3-1 | 1-1 | 0-1 | 1-1 | 0-5 | 1-0 | 2-3 | 2-4 | 0-7 | 0-5 |
| 5 | Christchurch | 4-1 | 6-0 | 1-3 | 5-0 | | 0-3 | 4-0 | 1-1 | 0-0 | 2-2 | 5-0 | 4-1 | 0-1 | 1-0 | 0-1 | 2-2 | 2-1 | 6-0 |
| 6 | Downton | 1-6 | 2-2 | 1-0 | 0-1 | 0-6 | | 1-0 | 0-0 | 3-1 | 1-2 | 2-2 | 4-0 | 0-5 | 2-2 | 2-1 | 3-2 | 6-0 | 2-0 |
| 7 | East Cowes Victoria | 5-6 | 2-0 | 0-3 | 0-1 | 3-3 | 1-4 | | 2-2 | 4-1 | 0-2 | 0-6 | 2-3 | 0-2 | 3-0 | 1-2 | 1-4 | 4-3 | 0-2 |
| 8 | Fleet Spurs | 2-1 | 3-7 | 0-2 | 8-0 | 0-2 | 0-3 | 3-0 | | 0-2 | 7-4 | 4-2 | 3-1 | 1-6 | 1-7 | 5-1 | 4-2 | 2-2 | 0-5 |
| 9 | Hythe & Dibden | 1-3 | 3-1 | 0-4 | 3-1 | 2-2 | 1-1 | 3-1 | 5-1 | | 3-0 | 2-0 | 3-4 | 0-6 | 3-2 | 2-1 | 2-3 | 2-1 | 0-1 |
| 10 | Laverstock & Ford | 1-1 | 3-1 | 1-1 | 5-0 | 4-1 | 1-0 | 4-0 | 2-0 | 2-3 | | 1-1 | 3-0 | 2-0 | 4-1 | 2-1 | 1-0 | 3-0 | 2-0 |
| 11 | New Milton Town | 0-5 | 1-2 | 2-0 | 1-1 | 3-1 | 2-0 | 2-0 | 1-1 | 1-1 | 3-2 | | 3-0 | 0-2 | 0-2 | 2-3 | 1-1 | 0-4 | 2-3 |
| 12 | Pewsey Vale | 0-2 | 0-1 | 0-2 | 3-0 | 1-3 | 1-4 | 2-0 | 1-2 | 2-3 | 0-0 | 0-3 | | 1-0 | 0-3 | 1-3 | 1-3 | 4-2 | 1-3 |
| 13 | Portland United | 3-2 | 3-1 | 3-1 | 5-1 | 2-0 | 5-0 | 8-0 | 4-2 | 3-1 | 2-1 | 6-0 | 1-0 | | 1-0 | 1-0 | 0-0 | 2-0 | 2-0 |
| 14 | Ringwood Town | 5-1 | 0-2 | 2-1 | 7-0 | 2-2 | 1-2 | 8-2 | 3-2 | 1-1 | 2-4 | 2-4 | 6-2 | 2-2 | | 2-0 | 1-3 | 2-4 | 1-1 |
| 15 | Romsey Town | 1-1 | 2-1 | 1-3 | 1-2 | 0-2 | 1-0 | 4-1 | 1-1 | 2-0 | 1-3 | 2-1 | 4-1 | 2-1 | 1-0 | | 1-3 | 3-1 | 0-3 |
| 16 | Tadley Calleva | 3-0 | 2-1 | 3-3 | 4-0 | 4-0 | 1-0 | 5-0 | 5-1 | 5-0 | 3-0 | 1-1 | 9-0 | 2-4 | 4-2 | 3-1 | | 4-0 | 1-2 |
| 17 | Totton & Eling | 0-0 | 1-3 | 2-3 | 4-0 | 0-0 | 3-2 | 6-1 | 2-4 | 1-3 | 5-1 | 0-0 | 9-1 | 1-2 | 0-2 | 0-2 | 0-3 | | 3-4 |
| 18 | United Services Portsmouth | 2-2 | 3-1 | 2-3 | 2-0 | 1-2 | 0-0 | 5-0 | 1-2 | 1-1 | 5-2 | 5-0 | H-W | 0-4 | 2-1 | 1-0 | 4-1 | 2-1 | |

## AFC PORTCHESTER

Founded: 1971 Nickname: Portchy/Royals

**Secretary:** Andy Girling **(T)** 07824 332 229 **(E)** secretary@afcportchester.co.uk
**Chairman:** Paul Kelly
**Ground:** Wicor Recreation Ground Cranleigh Road Portchester Hampshire PO16 9DP **(T)** 01329 233 833 (Clubhouse)
**Capacity:** **Seats:** Yes **Covered:** Yes **Midweek Matchday:** Tuesday **Clubhouse:** Yes

**Colours(change):** Tangerine/black/tangerine (All sky blue)
**Previous Names:** Loyds Sports 1971-73. Colourvison Rangers 1973-76. Wilcor Mill 1976-2003.
**Previous Leagues:** City of Portsmouth Sunday. Portsmouth & District >1998. Hampshire 1998-2004.
**Records:**
**Honours:** Hampshire League Division One 2001-02.

**10 YEAR RECORD**

| 06-07 | 07-08 | 08-09 | 09-10 | 10-11 | 11-12 | 12-13 | 13-14 | 14-15 | 15-16 |
|---|---|---|---|---|---|---|---|---|---|
| Wex2 4 | Wex1 14 | Wex1 19 | Wex1 6 | Wex1 3 | Wex1 2 | WexP 15 | WexP 8 | WexP 3 | WexP 6 |

## ALRESFORD TOWN

Founded: 1898 Nickname: The Magpies

**Secretary:** Keith Curtis **(T)** 07703 346 672 **(E)** secretary.alresfordtownfc@gmail.com
**Chairman:** Trevor Ingram **Prog Ed:** Gregory Boughton
**Ground:** Arlebury Park, The Avenue, Alresford, Hants SO24 9EP **(T)** 01962 735 100 or 07703 346 672
**Capacity:** **Seats:** Yes **Covered:** Yes **Midweek Matchday:** Tuesday **Clubhouse:** Yes

**Colours(change):** Black & white stripes/black/black. (All yellow)
**Previous Names:**
**Previous Leagues:** Winchester League, North Hants league, Hampshire League
**Records:**
**Honours:** Winchester League Division Two & One
Hampshire Senior Cup 2012-13.

**10 YEAR RECORD**

| 06-07 | 07-08 | 08-09 | 09-10 | 10-11 | 11-12 | 12-13 | 13-14 | 14-15 | 15-16 |
|---|---|---|---|---|---|---|---|---|---|
| Wex1 2 | WexP 21 | WexP 18 | WexP 17 | WexP 15 | WexP 15 | WexP 2 | WexP 2 | WexP 16 | WexP 20 |

## AMESBURY TOWN

Founded: 1904 Nickname: Blues

**Secretary:** Chris Green **(T)** 07581 245 510 **(E)** amesburytownfc@gmail.com
**Chairman:** Stephen Pearce **Prog Ed:** Mark Hilton
**Ground:** Bonnymead Park Recreation Road Amesbury SP4 7BB **(T)** 01980 623 489
**Capacity:** **Seats:** **Covered:** Yes **Midweek Matchday:** Wednesday **Clubhouse:** Yes

**Colours(change):** Blue & white/blue/blue & white (Black & yellow/black/black & yellow)
**Previous Names:** Amesbury FC 1904-1984.
**Previous Leagues:** Western 1994-97. Hampshire 1998-2004.
**Records:** **Att:** 625 - 1997.
**Honours:**

**10 YEAR RECORD**

| 06-07 | 07-08 | 08-09 | 09-10 | 10-11 | 11-12 | 12-13 | 13-14 | 14-15 | 15-16 |
|---|---|---|---|---|---|---|---|---|---|
| Wex1 18 | Wex1 11 | Wex1 12 | Wex1 11 | Wex1 13 | Wex1 14 | Wex1 14 | Wex1 10 | Wex1 4 | Wex1 2 |

## ANDOVER TOWN

Founded: 2013 Nickname:

**Secretary:** Chris Robins **(T)** 07737 320 807 **(E)** andovertownfc@sparsholt.ac.uk
**Chairman:** Stuart Barlow
**Ground:** Portway Stadium, West Portway, Portway Industrial Estate, Andover AP10 3LF **(T)**
**Capacity:** **Seats:** Yes **Covered:** Yes **Midweek Matchday:** Tuesday **Clubhouse:** Yes

**Colours(change):** All blue (All white)
**Previous Names:** None
**Previous Leagues:** None
**Records:**
**Honours:** None

**10 YEAR RECORD**

| 06-07 | 07-08 | 08-09 | 09-10 | 10-11 | 11-12 | 12-13 | 13-14 | 14-15 | 15-16 |
|---|---|---|---|---|---|---|---|---|---|
| | | | | | | | Wex1 2 | WexP 12 | WexP 4 |

## BASHLEY

Founded: 1947 Nickname: The Bash

**Secretary:** Mike Cranidge **(T)** 07591 187 663 **(E)** footballsecretary@bashleyfc.org.uk
**Chairman:** Laurence Flanagan
**Ground:** Bashley Road Ground, Bashley Road, New Milton, Hampshire BH25 5RY **(T)** 01425 620 280
**Capacity:** 4,250 **Seats:** 250 **Covered:** 1,200 **Midweek Matchday:** Tuesday **Clubhouse:** Yes **Shop:** Yes

**Colours(change):** Gold/black/black (White/blue/blue)
**Previous Names:** None
**Previous Leagues:** Bournemouth 1953-83, Hampshire 1983-86, Wessex 1986-89, Southern 1989-2004, 06-16. Isthmian 2004-06
**Records:** 3,500 v Emley - FA Vase Semi-final 1st Leg 1987-88
**Honours:** Wessex League 1986-87, 87-88, 88-89. Southern League Southern Division 1989-90, Division 1 South & West 2006-07.

**10 YEAR RECORD**

| 06-07 | 07-08 | 08-09 | 09-10 | 10-11 | 11-12 | 12-13 | 13-14 | 14-15 | 15-16 |
|---|---|---|---|---|---|---|---|---|---|
| Sthsw 1 | SthP 5 | SthP 14 | SthP 7 | SthP 11 | SthP 13 | SthP 17 | SthP 23 | Sthsw 22 | Sthsw 22 |

## BEMERTON HEATH HARLEQUINS

Founded: 1989 Nickname: Quins

**Secretary:** Andy Hardwick **(T)** 07561 164 068 **(E)** sec.bhhfc@hotmail.co.uk
**Chairman:** Steve Slade
**Ground:** The Clubhouse, Western Way, Bemerton Heath Salisbury SP2 9DT **(T)** 01722 331 925
**Capacity:** 2,100 **Seats:** 250 **Covered:** 350 **Midweek Matchday:** Tuesday **Clubhouse:** Yes **Shop:** No

**Colours(change):** Black & white/black/black & white (All orange)
**Previous Names:** Bemerton Athletic, Moon FC & Bemerton Boys merged in 1989
**Previous Leagues:** Salisbury & Wilts Comb, Salisbury & Andover Sunday
**Records:** **Att:**1,118 v Aldershot Town **App:** Keith Richardson
**Honours:** Wiltshire Senior Cup 1992-93. Wessex League Cup 2009-10.

**10 YEAR RECORD**

| 06-07 | 07-08 | 08-09 | 09-10 | 10-11 | 11-12 | 12-13 | 13-14 | 14-15 | 15-16 |
|---|---|---|---|---|---|---|---|---|---|
| WexP 11 | WexP 13 | WexP 12 | WexP 3 | WexP 2 | WexP 2 | WexP 5 | WexP 7 | WexP 13 | WexP 9 |

## BLACKFIELD & LANGLEY

Founded: 1935 Nickname: Watersiders

**Secretary:** Claire Sinclair **(T)** 07990 518 710 **(E)** bandlfc@hotmail.com
**Chairman:** Owen Lightfoot
**Ground:** Gang Warily Rec., Newlands Rd, Southampton SO45 1GA **(T)** 02380 893 603
**Capacity:** 2,500 **Seats:** 180 **Covered:** Yes **Midweek Matchday:** Tuesday **Clubhouse:** Yes

**Colours(change):** Green & white/white/green & white (All maroon).
**Previous Names:**
**Previous Leagues:** Southampton Senior. Hampshire.
**Records:** **Att:** 240
**Honours:** Hampshire League 1987-88, Division Two 1984-85, Southampton Senior Cup (4).
Wessex League Premier Division 2012-13.

**10 YEAR RECORD**

| 06-07 | 07-08 | 08-09 | 09-10 | 10-11 | 11-12 | 12-13 | 13-14 | 14-15 | 15-16 |
|---|---|---|---|---|---|---|---|---|---|
| Wex1 16 | Wex1 10 | Wex1 2 | WexP 8 | WexP 14 | WexP 16 | WexP 1 | WexP 6 | WexP 5 | WexP 3 |

## BOURNEMOUTH

Founded: 1875 Nickname: Poppies

**Secretary:** Patricia Painter **(T)** 07894 948 267 **(E)** bournemouthpoppiesfc@gmail.com
**Chairman:** Bob Corbin
**Ground:** Victoria Park, Namu Road, Winton, Bournemouth BH9 2RA **(T)** 01202 515 123
**Capacity:** 3,000 **Seats:** 205 **Covered:** 205 **Midweek Matchday:** Tuesday **Clubhouse:** Yes **Shop:** Yes

**Colours(change):** All Red (Yellow & blue/blue/blue)
**Previous Names:** Bournemouth Rovers, Bournemouth Wanderers, Bournemouth Dean Park
**Previous Leagues:** Hampshire
**Records:** Goalscorer (since 1990) Darren McBride 95 (111+26 games) Apps (since 1990) Mark Dancer 358 (318+40 games)
**Honours:** Wessex League Cup Winners 2010-11.

**10 YEAR RECORD**

| 06-07 | 07-08 | 08-09 | 09-10 | 10-11 | 11-12 | 12-13 | 13-14 | 14-15 | 15-16 |
|---|---|---|---|---|---|---|---|---|---|
| WexP 5 | WexP 5 | WexP 15 | WexP 4 | WexP 5 | WexP 9 | WexP 13 | WexP 15 | WexP 18 | WexP 18 |

## BROCKENHURST

Founded: 1898 | Nickname: The Badgers

**Secretary:** Ruth Mundy **(T)** 07508 898 779 **(E)** info@brockenhurstfc.co.uk

**Chairman:**

**Ground:** Grigg Lane, Brockenhurst, Hants SO42 7RE **(T)** 01590 623 544

**Capacity:** 2,000 **Seats:** 200 **Covered:** 300 **Midweek Matchday:** Tuesday **Clubhouse:** Yes

**Colours(change):** Blue & white/blue/blue. (All green).
**Previous Names:**
**Previous Leagues:** Hampshire
**Records:** **Att:** 1,104 v St Albans City
**Honours:** Hampshire League 1975-76. Wessex League Division One 2012-13.

**10 YEAR RECORD**

| 06-07 | 07-08 | 08-09 | 09-10 | 10-11 | 11-12 | 12-13 | 13-14 | 14-15 | 15-16 |
|---|---|---|---|---|---|---|---|---|---|
| WexP 13 | WexP 6 | WexP 5 | WexP 13 | | | Wex1 1 | WexP 11 | WexP 14 | WexP 14 |

## COWES SPORTS

Founded: 1881 | Nickname: Yachtsmen

**Secretary:** Bill Murray **(T)** 01983 245 720 **(E)** secretary.cowessportsfc@outlook.com

**Chairman:** Ian Lee

**Ground:** Westwood Park Reynolds Close off Park Rd Cowes Isle of Wight PO31 7NT **(T)** 01983 718 277

**Capacity:** **Seats:** Yes **Covered:** Yes **Midweek Matchday:** Tuesday **Clubhouse:** Yes

**Colours(change):** Blue & White/black/blue (Purple/white/red)
**Previous Names:**
**Previous Leagues:** Hampshire 1980-94
**Records:**
**Honours:** Hampshire League 1993-94.

**10 YEAR RECORD**

| 06-07 | 07-08 | 08-09 | 09-10 | 10-11 | 11-12 | 12-13 | 13-14 | 14-15 | 15-16 |
|---|---|---|---|---|---|---|---|---|---|
| WexP 9 | WexP 9 | WexP 13 | WexP 22 | Wex1 8 | Wex1 6 | Wex1 4 | Wex1 3 | Wex1 2 | WexP 11 |

## FAREHAM TOWN

Founded: 1946 | Nickname: Creeksiders

**Secretary:** Paul Procter **(T)** 07445 805 122 **(E)** farehamtnfc@gmail.com

**Chairman:** Nick Ralls

**Ground:** Cams Alders, Palmerston Drive, Fareham, Hants PO14 1RH **(T)** 07445 805 122

**Capacity:** 2,000 **Seats:** 450 **Covered:** 500 **Midweek Matchday:** Tuesday **Clubhouse:** Yes **Shop:** Yes

**Colours(change):** Red & black/red/black/ (All blue)
**Previous Names:** None
**Previous Leagues:** Portsmouth, Hampshire & Southern
**Records:** **Att:** 2,015 v Spurs (friendly 1985)
**Honours:** Hampshire Senior Cup 1957, 1963, 1968, 1993. Hampshire League Champions.

**10 YEAR RECORD**

| 06-07 | 07-08 | 08-09 | 09-10 | 10-11 | 11-12 | 12-13 | 13-14 | 14-15 | 15-16 |
|---|---|---|---|---|---|---|---|---|---|
| WexP 8 | WexP 8 | WexP 10 | WexP 6 | WexP 8 | WexP 12 | WexP 9 | WexP 10 | WexP 19 | WexP 12 |

## FAWLEY

Founded: 1923 | Nickname: Oilers

**Secretary:** Kevin Mitchell **(T)** 07836 259 682 **(E)** kevin.mitchell@wienerberger.com

**Chairman:** Kevin Mitchell **Prog Ed:** Kevin Mitchell

**Ground:** Waterside Spts & Soc. club, 179 Long Lane, Holbury, Soto, SO45 2PA **(T)** 02380 893 750 (Club)

**Capacity:** **Seats:** **Covered:** Yes **Midweek Matchday:** Wednesday **Clubhouse:** Yes

**Colours(change):** All blue (All red)
**Previous Names:** Esso Fawley > 2002
**Previous Leagues:** Hampshire Premier > 2004.
**Records:**
**Honours:**

**10 YEAR RECORD**

| 06-07 | 07-08 | 08-09 | 09-10 | 10-11 | 11-12 | 12-13 | 13-14 | 14-15 | 15-16 |
|---|---|---|---|---|---|---|---|---|---|
| Wex1 5 | Wex1 6 | Wex1 9 | Wex1 2 | WexP 20 | WexP 19 | WexP 17 | WexP 20 | WexP 17 | WexP 19 |

## HAMWORTHY UNITED

Founded: 1926 | Nickname: The Hammers

**Secretary:** Kevin Keats **(T)** 07540 142276 **(E)** hamworthyutdsecretary@gmail.com

**Chairman:** Steve Harvey

**Ground:** The County Ground, Blandford Close, Hamworthy, Poole BH15 4BF **(T)** 01202 674 974

**Capacity:** 2,000 **Seats:** **Covered:** Yes **Midweek Matchday:** Tuesday **Clubhouse:** Yes **Shop:** No

**Colours(change):** Maroon & sky blue/sky blue/maroon (All yellow)

**Previous Names:** Hamworthy St. Michael merged with Trinidad Old Boys 1926

**Previous Leagues:** Dorset Premier

**Records:**

**Honours:** Dorset Premier League 2002-03, 03-04.

**10 YEAR RECORD**

| 06-07 | 07-08 | 08-09 | 09-10 | 10-11 | 11-12 | 12-13 | 13-14 | 14-15 | 15-16 |
|---|---|---|---|---|---|---|---|---|---|
| WexP 15 | WexP 10 | WexP 8 | WexP 16 | WexP 9 | WexP 7 | WexP 10 | WexP 12 | WexP 10 | WexP 16 |

## HORNDEAN

Founded: 1887 | Nickname: Deans

**Secretary:** Mandy Winter **(T)** 07900 384588 **(E)** horndeanfc1887@gmail.com

**Chairman:** David Sagar

**Ground:** Five Heads Park Five Heads Road Horndean Hampshire PO8 9NZ **(T)** 02392 591 363

**Capacity:** **Seats:** Yes **Covered:** Yes **Midweek Matchday:** Wednesday **Clubhouse:** Yes

**Colours(change):** All red (All yellow)

**Previous Names:**

**Previous Leagues:** Hampshire 1972-86, 1995-2004. Wessex 1986-95

**Records:** **Att:** 1,560 v Waterlooville, Victory Cup, April 1971. **Goalscorer:** Frank Bryson 348 (including 83 during the 1931-32 season)

**Honours:**

**10 YEAR RECORD**

| 06-07 | 07-08 | 08-09 | 09-10 | 10-11 | 11-12 | 12-13 | 13-14 | 14-15 | 15-16 |
|---|---|---|---|---|---|---|---|---|---|
| WexP 16 | WexP 11 | WexP 22 | Wex1 12 | Wex1 2 | WexP 17 | WexP 11 | WexP 17 | WexP 11 | WexP 5 |

## LYMINGTON TOWN

Founded: 1876 | Nickname: Town

**Secretary:** Barry Torah **(T)** 07849 646 234 **(E)** Secretary.lymingtontownfc@yahoo.com

**Chairman:** George Shaw **Prog Ed:** Barry Torah

**Ground:** The Sports Ground, Southampton Road, Lymington SO41 9ZG **(T)**

**Capacity:** 3,000 **Seats:** 200 **Covered:** 300 **Midweek Matchday:** Tuesday **Clubhouse:** Yes

**Colours(change):** Red/black/red (Yellow/blue/blue)

**Previous Names:** None

**Previous Leagues:** Hampshire.

**Records:**

**Honours:** Wessex League Cup 2006-07.

**10 YEAR RECORD**

| 06-07 | 07-08 | 08-09 | 09-10 | 10-11 | 11-12 | 12-13 | 13-14 | 14-15 | 15-16 |
|---|---|---|---|---|---|---|---|---|---|
| WexP 12 | WexP 20 | WexP 18 | WexP 20 | WexP 11 | WexP 14 | WexP 19 | WexP 14 | WexP 9 | WexP 13 |

## MONEYFIELDS

Founded: 1987 | Nickname: Moneys

**Secretary:** Peter Larkin **(T)** 07913 721 047 **(E)** secretary@moneyfieldsfc.co.uk

**Chairman:** Mick Marsh

**Ground:** Moneyfields Sports Ground, Moneyfield Ave, Copnor, P'mouth PO3 6LA **(T)** 02392 665 260

**Capacity:** 1,500 **Seats:** 150 **Covered:** 150 **Midweek Matchday:** Tuesday **Clubhouse:** Yes **Shop:** Yes

**Colours(change):** Yellow/navy/navy (All white).

**Previous Names:** Portsmouth Civil Service

**Previous Leagues:** Portsmouth. Hampshire.

**Records:** **Att:** 250 v Fareham, WexD1 05-06 **Goalscorer:** Lee Mould 86 **App:** Matt Lafferty - 229 **Win:** 9-0v Blackfield & Langley 01-02.

**Honours:** Portsmouth Premier Champions 1990-91, 91-92. Senior Cup 1990-91.
Hampshire Division Three 1991-92, Division Two 1992-93, Division One 1996-97.

**10 YEAR RECORD**

| 06-07 | 07-08 | 08-09 | 09-10 | 10-11 | 11-12 | 12-13 | 13-14 | 14-15 | 15-16 |
|---|---|---|---|---|---|---|---|---|---|
| WexP 7 | WexP 7 | WexP 3 | WexP 12 | WexP 7 | WexP 4 | WexP 4 | WexP 9 | WexP 4 | WexP 8 |

## NEWPORT (I.O.W.)

Founded: 1888 Nickname: The Port

**Secretary:** Lisa Woodward **(T)** 07917 043 152 **(E)** secretary.newport.iwfc@gmail.com
**Chairman:** David Hayles
**Ground:** St George's Park, St George's Way, Newport PO30 2QH **(T)** 01983 525 027
**Capacity:** 5,000 **Seats:** 300 **Covered:** 1,000 **Midweek Matchday:** Tuesday **Clubhouse:** Yes **Shop:** Yes

**Colours(change):** Yellow/blue/yellow. (Red/white/red)
**Previous Names:**
**Previous Leagues:** I.O.W. 1896-28. Hants 28-86. Wessex 86-90.
**Records:** **Att:** 2,270 v Portsmouth (friendly) 07.07.2001. **Goalscorer:** Roy Grilfillan - 220 1951-57. **Apps:** Jeff Austin - 540 1969-87.
**Honours:** Southern League Eastern Division 2000-01. Hants Senior Cup (x8). I.O.W. Cup (34)

**10 YEAR RECORD**

| 06-07 | 07-08 | 08-09 | 09-10 | 10-11 | 11-12 | 12-13 | 13-14 | 14-15 | 15-16 |
|---|---|---|---|---|---|---|---|---|---|
| SthS 20 | SthS 22 | WexP 6 | WexP 9 | WexP 10 | WexP 13 | WexP 6 | WexP 4 | WexP 7 | WexP 10 |

## PORTLAND UNITED

Founded: 1921 Nickname: Blues

**Secretary:** Randle Gates **(T)** 07928 341 060 **(E)** secretary.portlandutdfc@aol.com
**Chairman:** Robin Satherlay
**Ground:** New Grove Corner, Grove Road, Portland DT5 1DP **(T)** 01305 861 489
**Capacity:** **Seats:** **Covered:** **Midweek Matchday:** Tuesday **Clubhouse:** Yes

**Colours(change):** All royal blue (White/black/black)
**Previous Names:**
**Previous Leagues:** Western 1925-70. Dorset Combination 1970-76, 77-2001, Dorset Premier 2006-07. Wessex 2001-02.
**Records:**
**Honours:** Western League Division Two 1930-31, 31-32. Dorset Combination 1998-99, 99-2000, Dorset Premier 2007-08, 08-09, 12-13, 13-14. Wessex League Division One 2015-16.

**10 YEAR RECORD**

| 06-07 | 07-08 | 08-09 | 09-10 | 10-11 | 11-12 | 12-13 | 13-14 | 14-15 | 15-16 |
|---|---|---|---|---|---|---|---|---|---|
| Dor P 3 | Dor P 1 | Dor P 1 | Dor P 8 | Dor P 4 | Dor P 3 | Dor P 1 | Dor P 1 | Dor P 2 | Wex1 1 |

## SHOLING

Founded: 1884 Nickname: The Boatmen

**Secretary:** Greg Dickson **(T)** 07496 804 555 **(E)** secretary.sholingfc@gmail.com
**Chairman:** Gerry Roberts
**Ground:** The Universal Stadium, Portsmouth Road, Sholing, SO19 9PW **(T)** 02380 403 829
**Capacity:** **Seats:** Yes **Covered:** Yes **Midweek Matchday:** Tuesday **Clubhouse:** Yes

**Colours(change):** Red & white/white/red & white (Blue & white/blue/white)
**Previous Names:** Woolston Works, Thornycrofts (Woolston) 1918-52, Vospers 1960-2003, Vosper Thorneycroft FC/VTFC 2003-10
**Previous Leagues:** Hampshire 1991-2004, Wessex 2004-09, 2013-14. Southern 2009-13, 2014-15.
**Records:** **Att:** 150
**Honours:** Hampshire Premier Division 2000-01, 03-04. FA Vase 2013-14.
Wessex Premier 2013-14.

**10 YEAR RECORD**

| 06-07 | 07-08 | 08-09 | 09-10 | 10-11 | 11-12 | 12-13 | 13-14 | 14-15 | 15-16 |
|---|---|---|---|---|---|---|---|---|---|
| WexP 3 | WexP 2 | WexP 2 | Sthsw 4 | Sthsw 2 | Sthsw 4 | Sthsw 7 | WexP 1 | Sthsw 17 | WexP 2 |

## TEAM SOLENT

Founded: 2007 Nickname: The Sparks

**Secretary:** Liam Dell **(T)** 07881 014 588 **(E)** secretary.teamsolent@solent.ac.uk
**Chairman:** Bill Moore
**Ground:** Test Park, Lower Broomhill Road, Southampton SO16 9BP **(T)**
**Capacity:** **Seats:** Yes **Covered:** Yes **Midweek Matchday:** Monday **Clubhouse:** Yes

**Colours(change):** All red (All white).
**Previous Names:** None
**Previous Leagues:** Hampshire Premier 2007-11.
**Records:**
**Honours:** Wessex Division One 2014-15.

**10 YEAR RECORD**

| 06-07 | 07-08 | 08-09 | 09-10 | 10-11 | 11-12 | 12-13 | 13-14 | 14-15 | 15-16 |
|---|---|---|---|---|---|---|---|---|---|
| | HantP 7 | HantP 3 | HantP 2 | HantP 2 | Wex1 3 | Wex1 3 | Wex1 6 | Wex1 1 | WexP 7 |

## VERWOOD TOWN

Founded: 1920 Nickname: The Potters

**Secretary:** Nigel Watts **(T)** 07517 077 566 **(E)** secretary@vtfc.co.uk

**Chairman:** Steve Jefferis

**Ground:** Potterne Park Potterne Way Verwood Dorset BH21 6RS **(T)** 01202 814 007

**Capacity:** **Seats:** Yes **Covered:** Yes **Midweek Matchday:** Wednesday **Clubhouse:** Yes

**Colours(change):** Red & black/red/black (Royal blue & black stripes/royal blue/royal blue)

**Previous Names:**

**Previous Leagues:** Hampshire

**Records:**

**Honours:** Wessex League Division One 2011-12.

**10 YEAR RECORD**

| 06-07 | 07-08 | 08-09 | 09-10 | 10-11 | 11-12 | 12-13 | 13-14 | 14-15 | 15-16 |
|---|---|---|---|---|---|---|---|---|---|
| Wex1 6 | Wex1 4 | Wex1 13 | Wex1 7 | Wex1 9 | Wex1 1 | WexP 14 | WexP 19 | WexP 15 | WexP 17 |

## WHITCHURCH UNITED

Founded: 1903 Nickname: Jamboys

**Secretary:** Cara Lewis **(T)** 07788 535 359 **(E)** secretary.wufc@gmail.com

**Chairman:** Brian Jackman **Prog Ed:** John Rutledge

**Ground:** Longmeadow Winchester Road Whitchurch Hampshire RG28 7RB **(T)** 01256 892 493

**Capacity:** **Seats:** Yes **Covered:** Yes **Midweek Matchday:** Wednesday **Clubhouse:** Yes

**Colours(change):** Red & white stripes/red/red (All blue)

**Previous Names:** Formed in 1903 after the amalgamation of Whitchurch Rovers and Whitchurch Albion.

**Previous Leagues:** Hampshire >1992, 1994-95. Wessex 1992-94.

**Records:**

**Honours:** Hampshire League Division Two 1989-90.

**10 YEAR RECORD**

| 06-07 | 07-08 | 08-09 | 09-10 | 10-11 | 11-12 | 12-13 | 13-14 | 14-15 | 15-16 |
|---|---|---|---|---|---|---|---|---|---|
| Wex2 12 | Wex1 17 | Wex1 6 | Wex1 10 | Wex1 7 | Wex1 8 | Wex1 2 | WexP 13 | WexP 6 | WexP 15 |

## AFC STONEHAM
Founded: 1919 Nickname:

**Secretary:** Geoff Smith (T) 07765 046 429 (E) secretary@afcstoneham.co.uk
**Chairman:** Mark Stupple
**Ground:** The Elliots Arena, Jubilee Park, Chestnut Avenue, Eastleigh SO50 9PF (T) 07765 046 429
**Colours(change):** All purple (Pink/black/black)
**ADDITIONAL INFORMATION:**
**Previous League:** Hampshire Premier League >2015.

## ALTON TOWN
Founded: 1947 Nickname: The Brewers

**Secretary:** Wayne Dickson (T) 07709 715 322 (E) secretary.altontownfc@hotmail.com
**Chairman:** Jim McKell
**Ground:** Alton (Bass) Sports Ground, Anstey Road, Alton, Hants GU34 2RL (T) **Capacity:** 2,000
**Colours(change):** White/black/black (Purple/white/white)
**ADDITIONAL INFORMATION:**
Hants Senior Cup 1958, 1969, 1972 & 1978. Hampshire Champions 2001-02.
**Previous League:** Combined Counties 2013-15.

## ANDOVER NEW STREET
Founded: 1895 Nickname: The Street

**Secretary:** Kerry Tobin (T) 07976 630 218 (E) andovernewstreetfc@hotmail.co.uk
**Chairman:** Martin Tobin
**Ground:** Foxcotte Park Charlton Andover Hampshire SP11 0TA (T) 01264 358 358
**Colours(change):** Green & black/black/black (Yellow & black/yellow/yellow)
**ADDITIONAL INFORMATION:**
**Record Att:** 240.
**Honours:** Trophyman Cup 2003-04.

## BAFFINS MILTON ROVERS
Founded: Nickname:

**Secretary:** Yvonne Fradgley-Smith (T) 07980 403 336 (E) baffinsmiltonrovers@hotmail.co.uk
**Chairman:** Lynne Stagg
**Ground:** Langstone Harbour Sports Ground, Eastern Road, Portsmouth PO3 5LY (T)
**Colours(change):** Gold/black/black (Yellow/navy/navy)
**ADDITIONAL INFORMATION:**
Hampshire Premier League Premier Division 2015-16.

## CHRISTCHURCH
Founded: 1885 Nickname: The Church

**Secretary:** Sian Corbin (T) 07766 913 571 (E) secretary@christchurchfc.co.uk
**Chairman:** Fiona Clements
**Ground:** Hurn Bridge S.C, Avon Causeway, Christchurch BH23 6DY (T) 01202 473 792 **Capacity:** 1,200
**Colours(change):** All Blue (All yellow)
**ADDITIONAL INFORMATION: App:** John Haynes
Hants Jnr Cup (3), Hants Intermediate Cup 86-87, Bournemouth Senior Cup (5)

## DOWNTON
Founded: 1905 Nickname: The Robins

**Secretary:** Brian Ford (T) 07422 520 818 (E) info@downtonfc.com
**Chairman:** Colin Stainer
**Ground:** Brian Whitehead Sports Ground Wick Lane Downton Wiltshire SP5 3NF (T) 01725 512 162
**Colours(change):** All red (Yellow/blue/blue)
**ADDITIONAL INFORMATION: Att:** 55 v AFC Bournemouth - Friendly.
Wiltshire Senior Cup 1979-80, 80-81. Wiltshire Junior Cup 1949-50. Wessex League Cup 1995-96.
Wessex League Division One 2010-11.

## EAST COWES VICTORIA ATHLETIC
Founded: 1885 Nickname: The Vics

**Secretary:** Darren Dyer (T) 07725 128 701 (E) ecvafc@outlook.com
**Chairman:** Paul Phelps **Prog Ed:** Darren Dyer
**Ground:** Beatrice Avenue Whippingham East Cowes Isle of Wight PO32 6PA (T) 01983 297 165
**Colours(change):** Red & white/black/black (Orange/black/orange)
**ADDITIONAL INFORMATION:**

## FLEET SPURS

Founded: 1948 Nickname: Spurs

**Secretary:** Gemma Applegarth **(T)** 07808 732 011 **(E)** wessex@fleetspurs.co.uk
**Chairman:** Bryan Sheppard **Prog Ed:** Bryan Sheppard
**Ground:** Kennels Lane Southwood Farnborough Hampshire, GU14 0ST **(T)**
**Colours(change):** Blue with red trim/blue/blue (Green/red/green )
**ADDITIONAL INFORMATION:**

## FOLLAND SPORTS

Founded: 1938 Nickname: Planemakers

**Secretary:** Adrian Harris **(T)** 07774 962 813 **(E)** follandsportsfc@hotmail.co.uk
**Chairman:** Adrian Strammell **Prog Ed:** Adrian Harris
**Ground:** Folland Park, Kings Ave, Hamble, Southampton SO31 4NF **(T)** 02380 452 173 **Capacity:** 1,000
**Colours(change):** All red (All blue)
**ADDITIONAL INFORMATION:**
Southampton Senior Cup 1984-85, 86-87, 91-92. Wessex League Division 1 2009-10.

## HAMBLE CLUB

Founded: 1969 Nickname: The Monks

**Secretary:** Colin Williams **(T)** 07977 324 923 **(E)** secretary.hambleclubfc@gmail.com
**Chairman:** Mike Clarke
**Ground:** Hamble Community Facility, Hamble Lane SO31 4TS **(T)** 07977 324 923
**Colours(change):** All yellow (All red)
**ADDITIONAL INFORMATION:**
**Previous Leagues:** Hampshire >2016

## HYTHE & DIBDEN

Founded: 1902 Nickname:

**Secretary:** Scott Johnston **(T)** 07825 550 624 **(E)** hythedibdenfc@aol.com
**Chairman:** Dave Cox **Prog Ed:** Scott Johnston
**Ground:** Clayfields, Claypit Lane, Dibden SO45 5TN **(T)** 07825 550 624
**Colours(change):** Green/white/green (All blue)
**ADDITIONAL INFORMATION:**

## LAVERSTOCK & FORD

Founded: 1956 Nickname: The Stock

**Secretary:** Matthew McMahon **(T)** 07795 665 731 **(E)** sec.laverstockandfordfc@gmail.com
**Chairman:** John Pike
**Ground:** The Dell, Church Road, Laverstock, Salisbury, Wilts SP1 1QX **(T)** 01722 327 401
**Colours(change):** Green & white hoops/green/green (Yellow/blue/white)
**ADDITIONAL INFORMATION:**

## NEW MILTON TOWN

Founded: 1998 Nickname: The Linnets

**Secretary:** Scott McFarlane **(T)** 07875 660 695 **(E)** enquiries@newmiltontownfc.com
**Chairman:** John Breaker
**Ground:** Fawcetts Fields, Christchurch Road, New Milton BH25 6QB **(T)** 01425 628 191 **Capacity:** 3,000
**Colours(change):** Maroon & blue stripes/blue/blue (White/black/white)
**ADDITIONAL INFORMATION:**
**Honours:** Wessex League 1998-99, 04-05.

## PEWSEY VALE

Founded: 1948 Nickname: Vale

**Secretary:** **(T)** 07720 351 937 (Chairman) **(E)** pewseyvalefc@hotmail.co.uk
**Chairman:** Lewis Taylor
**Ground:** Recreation Ground, Kings Corne,r Ball Road, Pewsey SN9 5BS **(T)** 01672 5629 090
**Colours(change):** White/navy/navy (All yellow)
**ADDITIONAL INFORMATION:**
**Previous League:** Wiltshire.

## RINGWOOD TOWN

Founded: 1879 Nickname:

**Secretary:** Aubrey Hodder **(T)** 07754 460 501 **(E)** ringwoodtownfc@live.co.uk
**Chairman:** Phil King **Prog Ed:** Phil King
**Ground:** The Canotec Stadium, Long Lane, Ringwood, Hampshire BH24 3BX **(T)** 01425 473 448
**Colours(change):** Red with white trim/red/red (Orange/black/orange)
**ADDITIONAL INFORMATION:**

## ROMSEY TOWN

Founded: 1886 Nickname: Town

**Secretary:** Clare Crossland **(T)** 07864 877 274 **(E)** romseytownfc@gmail.com
**Chairman:** Ken Jacobs
**Ground:** The Bypass Ground, South Front, Romsey SO51 8GJ **(T)** 01794 516 691
**Colours(change):** Red & black/black/black (Yellow/royal blue/royal blue)
**ADDITIONAL INFORMATION:**
Wessex League Champions 1989-90.

## SHAFTESBURY TOWN

Founded: 1888 Nickname:

**Secretary:** Phil Tobin **(T)** 07917 652438 **(E)** secretary@shaftesburyfc.co.uk
**Chairman:** Steven Coffen
**Ground:** Cockrams, Coppice Street, Shaftesbury SP7 8PF **(T)** 07917 652 438
**Colours(change):** Red & white/black/black (All blue)
**ADDITIONAL INFORMATION:**
Dorset Premier League Premier Division 2015-16.

## TADLEY CALLEVA

Founded: 1989 Nickname:

**Secretary:** Tom Walton **(T)** 07516 544 151 **(E)** secretary.tadleycalleva@gmail.com
**Chairman:** Sandy Russell
**Ground:** Barlows Park Silchester Road Tadley Hampshire RG26 3PX **(T)** 07787 501 028
**Colours(change):** All yellow (All white)
**ADDITIONAL INFORMATION:**

## TOTTON & ELING

Founded: 1925 Nickname: The Millers

**Secretary:** Rox Lomax **(T)** 02380 861 590 **(E)** tandemillers2@gmail.com
**Chairman:** Andy Tipp
**Ground:** Millers Park,Little Tesrwood Farm Salisbury Road Totton SO40 2RW **(T)** 7545 182 379
**Colours(change):** Red & black/black/red & black (Blue/blueyellow)
**ADDITIONAL INFORMATION:** 2,763 v AFC Wimbledon, FA Vase (game switched to AFC Wimbedon).
Hampshire Champions 1987-88, 88-89. Wessex Division 1 2008-09.

## UNITED SERVICES PORTSMOUTH

Founded: 1962 Nickname: The Navy

**Secretary:** Bob Brady **(T)** 07887 541 782 **(E)** usportsmouthfc@hotmail.co.uk
**Chairman:** Richard Stephenson Lt. RN **Prog Ed:** Charlie Read
**Ground:** Victory Stadium HMS Temeraire Burnaby Road Portsmouth PO1 2HB **(T)** 02392 573 041 (Gr'sman)
**Colours(change):** Royal blue & red stripes/royal blue/royal blue (All white)
**ADDITIONAL INFORMATION:**
**Previous Name:** Portsmouth Royal Navy 1962-2005.
**Honours:** Hampshire League Division Two 1967-68, 77-78, 80-81. Portsmouth Senior Cup 2011-12.

## WEYMOUTH RESERVES

Founded: 1896 Nickname: The Terras

**Secretary:** Ray Pearce **(T)** 07801 697 474 **(E)** wfcresec@btopenworld.com
**Chairman:** Chris Pugsley
**Ground:** Bob Lucas Stadium, Radipole Lane, Weymouth DT4 9XJ **(T)** 01305 785 558
**Colours(change):** Claret/white/sky blue (All yellow)
**ADDITIONAL INFORMATION:**

# GROUND DIRECTIONS

**AFC PORTCHESTER - Wicor Recreation Ground Cranleigh Road Portchester Hampshire PO16 9DP 07798 734678 (M)**
Leave the M27 at Junction 11 and follow the signs to Portchester into Portchester Road. Carry on for approx 1 mile at the large roundabout, take the 3rd exit into Cornaway Lane and at the 'T' junction turn right in Cranleigh Road and follow the road to the end. Postcode for Satellite Navigation systems PO16 9DP

**AFC STONEHAM - Jubilee Park, Chestnut Avenue, Eastleigh SO50 9PF**

**ALRESFORD TOWN FC - Arlebury Park The Avenue Alresford Hampshire SO24 9EP 01962 735 100**
Alresford is situated on the A31 between Winchester and Alton. Arlebury Park is on the main avenue into Alresford opposite Perins School.
Postcode for Satellite Navigation systems SO24 9EP

**ALTON TOWN - Alton (Bass) Sports Ground, Anstey Road, Alton, Hants GU34 2RL**
Leave the A31 at the B3004 signposted to Alton. Follow the road round to the left passing Anstey Park on the right, the ground is then immediately on the left – opposite the turning into Anstey Lane. Postcode for Satellite Navigation systems GU34 2RL

**AMESBURY TOWN FC - Bonnymead Park Recreation Road Amesbury SP4 7BB 01980 623489**
From Salisbury take A345 to Amesbury, turn left just past the bus station and proceed through the one way system, when road splits with Friar Tuck Café and Lloyds Bank on left turn left and follow road over the river bridge and when road bears sharp right turn left into Recreation Road.
From A303 at Countess Roundabout go into Amesbury, straight over traffic lights, at mini-roundabout turn right into one way system and follow directions as above.
Postcode for Satellite Navigation systems SP4 7BB

**ANDOVER NEW STREET FC - Foxcotte Park Charlton Andover Hampshire SP11 0HS 01264 358358 Weekends from Midday, Evenings from 1900 hrs**
From Basingstoke follow the A303 to Weyhill roundabout. At roundabout turn right and 2nd roundabout turn left on to A342. Approx 1/2 mile turn right into Short Lane, continue into Harroway Lane to the 'T' junction at the top. Turn right into Foxcotte Lane and continue for about 3/4 mile then turn left, this still Foxcotte Lane, to the top some 3/4 mile to the roundabout straight across into Foxcotte Park. Postcode for Satellite Navigation systems SP11 0TA.

**ANDOVER TOWN - Portway Stadium,Portway Industrial Estate, Andover AP10 3LF**
Leave A303 at Junction for A342 . If from the East cross back over A303. At large roundabout take A342 across the face of the Premier Hotel. First right into the Portway Industrial Estate then follow the one way system and after the road swings right at the bottom of the hill the ground is on the left.

**BAFFINS MILTON ROVERS - The Kendall Stadium PO3 5LY**
Travelling towards Portsmouth on the M27 continue onto A27. Take the A2030 (s) exit toward Portsmouth(E)/Southsea. At the roundabout, take the 4th exit onto Eastern Road/A2030. Turn left at Anchorage Road. Destination will be on the left.
Travelling towards Portsmouth on the A3(M) merge onto A27. Take the A2030 exit toward Portsmouth(E)/Central Southsea. At the roundabout, take the 2nd exit onto Eastern Road/A2030. Turn left at Anchorage Road. Destination will be on the left.

**BEMERTON HEATH HARLEQUINS FC - The Clubhouse Western Way Bemerton Heath Salisbury Wiltshire SP2 9DT 01722 331925 (Club) 331218 (Office)**
Turn off the A36 Salisbury to Bristol road at Skew Bridge (right turn if coming out of Salisbury), 1st left into Pembroke Road for 1/2 mile, 2nd left along Western Way – Ground is 1/4 mile at the end of the road. 40 minutes walk fro Salisbury railway station. Bus service 51 or 52 from the city centre.
Postcode for Satellite Navigation systems SP2 9DP

**BLACKFIELD & LANGLEY FC - Gang Warily Community and Recreation Centre Newlands Road Fawley Southampton SO45 1GA 02380 893 603**
Leave M27 at Junction 2 signposted A326 to Fawley. Head South along A326 through several roundabouts. Pass the Holbury P/H on your right at roundabout take the right fork signposted Lepe and Fawley.At the 1st set of traffic lights turn left then turn left into the ground, approx 200 yards. There is a sign at the traffic lights indicating Blackfield & Langley FC. Postcode for Satellite Navigation systems SO45 1GA

**BOURNEMOUTH FC - Victoria Park Namu Road Winton Bournemouth Dorset BH9 2RA 01202 515 123**
From the North and East – A338 from Ringwood. Take the 3rd exit signed A3060 Wimborne, going under the road you've just left. Stay on this road passing Castlepoint Shopping Centre (on your right), then the Broadway Hotel on your right, keep straight ahead passing the Horse & Jockey on your left, keep to the nearside lane. At roundabout take the 1st exit marked A347, pass Redhill Common on your right and the fire station on your left: continue on the A347 turning left at the filter with the pub – The Ensbury Park Hotel – immediately in front of you. 1st left into Victoria Avenue, and then third right into Namu Road, turning right at the end into the lane for the ground entrance.
From the West – A35 from Poole. Take the A3049 Dorset Way passing Tower Park (which is hidden from view) on your right, at the next roundabout take the second exit, and then the first exit at the next roundabout, taking up a position in the outside lane. At the next roundabout (with a pub called the Miller and Carter Steakhouse on your right) take the third exit, Wallisdown Road A3049. Go through the shopping area of Wallisdown across two roundabouts and at the third one take the first exit, you will see the ground on your right as you approach the pelican crossing. Turn right into Victoria Avenue, then third right into Namu Road, turning right at the end into the lane for the ground entrance. Postcode for Satellite Navigation systems BH9 2RA

**BROCKENHURST FC - Grigg Lane Brockenhurst Hampshire SO42 7RE 01590 623544**
Leave the M27 at Junction 1 and take the A337 to Lyndhurst. From Lyndhurst take the A337 signposted Brockenhurst, turn right at Careys Manor Hotel into Grigg Lane. Ground situated 200 yards on the right. Postcode for Satellite Navigation systems SO42 7RE

**CHRISTCHURCH FC - Hurn Bridge Sports Club Avon Causeway Hurn Christchurc Dorset BH23 6DY 01202 473 792**
A338 from Ringwood turn off at sign for Bournemouth International Airport (Hurn) on left. At T junction turn right, continue through traffic lights, at the small roundabout in Hurn turn right away from the Airport, exit signed Sopley and 100 yards on the right is Hurn Bridge Sports Ground. Postcode for Sat. Nav. systems BH23 6DY

**COWES SPORTS FC - Westwood Park Reynolds Close off Park Road Cowes Isle of Wight PO31 7NT 01983 293 793**
Turn left out of the Cowes pontoon, 1st right up Park Road approx 1/2 mile take the 4th right into Reynolds Close. Postcode for Sat. Nav. systems PO31 7NT

**DOWNTON FC - Brian Whitehead Sports Ground Wick Lane Downton Wiltshire SP5 3NF 01725 512 162**
The ground is situated 6 miles south of Salisbury on the A338 to Bournemouth. In the village – sign to the Leisure Centre (to west) – this is Wick Lane – football pitch and Club approx 1/4 mile on the left. Postcode for Satellite Navigation systems SP5 3NF

**EAST COWES VICTORIA FC - Beatrice Avenue Whippingham East Cowes Isle of Wight PO32 6PA 01983 297 165**

From East Cowes ferry terminal follow Well Road into York Avenue until reaching Prince of Wells PH, turn at the next right into Crossways Road then turn left into Beatrice Avenue, from Fishbourne follow signs to East Cowes and Whippingham Church, ground is 200 yards from the church on Beatrice Avenue.
Postcode for Satellite Navigation systems PO32 6PA

**FAREHAM TOWN FC - Cams Alders Football Stadium Cams Alders Palmerston Drive Fareham Hampshire PO14 1BJ 07930 853 235 (Club)**

Leave the M27 at Junction 11. Follow signs A32 Fareham – Gosport. Pass under the viaduct with Fareham Creek on your left, straight over at the roundabout then fork right – B3385 sign posted Lee-on-Solent. Over the railway bridge, Newgate Lane and turn immediately first right into Palmerston Business Park, follow the road to the ground. Postcode for Satellite Navigation systems PO14 1BJ

**FAWLEY AFC - Waterside Sports and Social Club 179-182 Long Lane Holbury Southampton Hampshire SO45 2PA 02380 893750 (Club) 896621 (Office)**

Leave the M27 at Junction 2 and follow the A326 to Fawley/Beaulieu. Head south for approx 7 miles. The Club is situated on the right hand side 2/3 mile after crossing the Hardley roundabout. The Club is positioned directly behind the service road on the right hand side. Postcode for Satellite Navigation systems SO45 2PA

**FLEET SPURS FC - Kennels Lane Southwood Farnborough Hampshire, GU14 0ST**

From the M3 Junction 4A take the A327 towards Farnborough/Cove. Left at the roundabout, over the railway line, left at the next roundabout Kennels Lane is on the right opposite the Nokia building, entrance is 100 yards on the left. Postcode for Satellite Navigation systems GU14 0ST

**FOLLAND SPORTS - Folland Park Kings Avenue Hamble-Le-Rice Southampton Hampshire SO31 4NF 02380 452 173**

Leave the M27 at Junction 8 and take the turning for Southampton East At the Windhover roundabout take the exit for Hamble (B3397) Hamble Lane, proceed for 3 miles. Upon entering Hamble the ground is on the right via Kings Avenue, opposite the Harrier P/H. Postcode for Satellite Navigation systems SO31 4NF

**HAMBLE CLUB - Hamble Community Facility SO31 4TS 07977 324 923**

Travelling on the M27 leave at junction 8, take the A3024 exit to Southampton (E)/Hamble. At the roundabout, take the 3rd exit onto A3024. At the roundabout, take the 2nd exit onto Hamble Lane/A3025. At the roundabout, take the 2nd exit and stay on Hamble Lane/A3025. At the roundabout, take the 2nd exit and stay on Hamble Lane/A3025. Continue straight onto Hamble Lane/B3397. At the roundabout, take the 1st exit and stay on Hamble Lane/B3397. Turn right for Hamble Club.

**HAMWORTHY UNITED FC - The County Ground Blandford Close Hamworthy Poole Dorset BH15 4BF 01202 674 974**

From M27 to Cadnam – follow A31 to Ringwood – A347/A348 Ferndown - Bearcross – follow on this road until you pass the Mountbatten Arms on your left – turn right at next roundabout onto the A3049 and follow the signs to Dorchester and Poole. Continue on this dual carriageway over the flyover to the next roundabout – straight across and take the 2nd exit left off the dual carriageway to Upton / Hamworthy – go straight across 2 mini roundabouts and continue to Hamworthy passing the Co-op store on your left – then turn left at the 2nd set of traffic lights into Blandford Close. Postcode for Satellite Navigation systems BH15 4BF

**HORNDEAN FC - Five Heads Park Five Heads Road Horndean Hampshire PO8 9NZ 02392 591 363**

Leave A3(M) at Junction 2 and follow signs to Cowplain. Take the slip road passing Morrisons store on the right crossing over the mini roundabout then continue to the set of traffic lights ensuring you are in the right hand lane signed Horndean. Turn right at these traffic lights and continue on for approximately 400 yards until you reach the Colonial Bar on your left, next junction on your left after the Colonial Bar is Five Heads Road, turn left into Five Heads Road and the ground is approx 1/4 mile along this road. Postcode for Satellite Navigation systems PO8 9NZ

**HYTHE & DIBDEN FC - Clayfield, Claypit Lane, Dibden SO45 5TN 07769 951 982**

Postcode for Satellite Navigation systems SO45 5TN

**LAVERSTOCK & FORD FC - The Dell Church Road Laverstock Salisbury Wiltshire SP1 1QX 01722 327 401**

From Southampton – At the end of the carriageway from Southampton (A36) turn right at traffic lights for the Park & Ride by the Tesco store. Turn left at the traffic lights over the narrow bridge then take the next turning into Manor Farm Road. Take the next turning right into Laverstock Road, (do not turn left under the railway bridge). Keep left into Laverstock village, past the Church and the Club is situated on the left hand side directly opposite the Chinese takeaway and shop.
From Bournemouth – Follow the A36 to Southampton past Salisbury College and straight across the Tesco roundabout take left at traffic lights into the Park & Ride (take the corner slowly, the road goes back on itself) then follow directions as above. Postcode for Satellite Navigation systems SP1 1QX

**LYMINGTON TOWN FC - The Sports Ground Southampton Road Lymington Hampshire SO41 9ZG 01590 671 305 (Club)**

From the North & East – Leave the M27 at Junction 1 (Cadnam/New Forest) and proceed via Lyndhurst then Brockenhurst on the A337. On the outskirts of Lymingto proceed through main set of traffic lights with Royal Quarter Housing Development and the Police Station on your right hand side. Continue for just another 250 metres and turn left immediately into St Thomas's Park with he ground in front of you.
Alternatively, turn left at the traffic lights into Avenue Road then first right, Oberland Court, with the Lymington Bowling Club facing you.
If travelling from the direction of Christchurch & New Milton using the A337 pass the White Hart P/H on the outskirts of Pennington and proceed down and up Stanford Hill. Passing the Waitrose Supermarket on your left hand side, the ground is situated immediately on your right hand side sign posted St Thomas Park.
Postcode for Satellite Navigation systems SO41 9ZG

**MONEYFIELDS FC - Moneyfields Sports Ground Moneyfield Avenue Copnor Portsmouth Hampshire PO3 6LA 02392 665 260 (Club) 07766 250 812 (M)**

Leave the A27 from the West and East at the Southsea turn off (A2030). Head down the Eastern Road and turn right into Tangiers Road at the fourth set of traffic lights – continue along this road until you pass the school and shops on your left and take the next right into Folkestone Road carrying on through to Martins Road and the Moneyfields Sports & Social Club is directly in front of you. Postcode for Satellite Navigation systems PO3 6LA

**NEW MILTON TOWN FC - Fawcett Fields Christchurch Road New Milton Hampshire BH25 6QB 01425 628 191**

Leave the M27 at Junction 2 and follow the signs to Lyndhurst. Carry on this road over four roundabouts and take the next slip road.At the traffic lights turn right to Lyndhurst. Go around the one way system and follow the signs to Christchurch (A35). After 10 miles at the Cat and Fiddle Public House turn left and continue towarc the Chewton Glen Hotel. First exit at roundabout A337 to New Milton.The ground is one mile on the left. Postcode for Sat. Nav. systems BH25 6QB

**NEWPORT (IOW) FC - St Georges Park St Georges Way Newport Isle of Wight PO30 2QH 01983 525 027 (Club)**

From the Fishbourne Car Ferry Terminal take the A3054 towards Newport. At the large roundabout in the town centre take the A3020 towards Sandown, under the footbridge then 1st exit off the next roundabout. The ground is 200 yards on the left. Postcode for Satellite Navigation systems PO30 2QH

**PEWSEY VALE FC - Recreation Ground Kings Corner Ball Road Pewsey 01672 562 900**

From Pewsey's King Alfred statue, take the B3087 Burbage Road for 100 yards and then turn right into the Co-op car park, park in top right hand corner next to the bowls and tennis club and then walk through to the ground. Postcode for Satellite Navigation systems SN9 5BS

**PORTLAND UNITED - New Grove Corner, Grove Road, Portland DT5 1DP 01305 861 489**

**RINGWOOD TOWN FC - The Canotec Stadium Long Lane Ringwood Hampshire BH24 3BX 01425 473 448**

Travel to Ringwood via the A31 (M27). From Ringwood town centre travel 1 mile on the B3347 towards Christchurch. At the Texaco petrol station turn into Moortown Lane and after 200 yards turn right into Long Lane. The ground is situated 250 yards on your left. Postcode for Satellite Navigation systems BH24 3BX

**ROMSEY TOWN FC - The Bypass Ground South Front Romsey Hampshire SO51 8GJ**

The ground is situated on the south of the town on the A27/A3090 roundabout (Romsey by pass), adjacent to the Romsey Rapids and Broadlands Estate.
Postcode for Satellite Navigation systems SO51 8GJ

**SHAFTESBURY TOWN - Cockrams, Coppice Street, Shaftesbury SP7 8PF 07917 652438**

Travelling South on the A350 into Shaftesbury, at the roundabout, take the 2nd exit onto Little Content Lane/A30/A350. Continue to follow A30/A350. Go through one roundabout. Turn right onto Coppice Street. Destination will be on the right. Travelling North on the A350 into Shaftesbury, at the roundabout, take the 2nd exit onto Christy's Lane/A30/A350. Turn left onto Coppice Street. Destination will be on the right.

**SHOLING - Silverlake Arena, Portsmouth Road, Sholing, SO19 9PW**

Leave the M27 at J8 and follow the signs towards Hamble. As you drive up dual carriageway (remain in the L/H lane), you come to Windover roundabout. Take the second exit towards Hamble. Take the R/H lane and carry on straight across the small roundabout. After 200 yards bear right across a second small roundabout (2nd exit). After about 100 yards turn right into Portsmouth Road. Follow straight on for about half mile. VT ground is on right opposite a lorry entrance.

**TADLEY CALLEVA FC - Barlows Park Silchester Road Tadley Hampshire RG26 3PX**

From M3 Basingstoke Junction 6 take the A340 to Tadley, travel through Tadley and at the main traffic lights turn right into Silchester Road, proceed for 0.5 mile then turn left into the car park. Postcode for Satellite Navigation systems RG26 3PX

**TEAM SOLENT - Test Park, Lower Broomhill Road, Southampton SO16 9QZ**

Leave the M27 at junction 3 for M271. Take the first slip road off the M271 and then first exit off the roundabout on to Lower Broomhill Road. Carry on to the next roundabout and take the last exit, (coming back on yourself) into Redbridge lane and the entrance to Test Park is approx. 500m on right.
From City centre take the Millbrook road to the M271, first slip road off on to roundabout, 3rd exit on to Lower Broomhill Way and then as above.
Postcode for Satellite Navigation systems SO16 9QZ

**TOTTON & ELING FC - Millers Park,Little Tesrwood Farm Salisbury Road Totton SO40 2RW 07445 523 103**

Leave M27 at Junction.2 and take A326 exit signposted Totton/Fawley. Almost immediately leave A326 onto slip road signposted Totton Town Centre which will meet the A36 (Salisbury Road). Turn left on to A36 and proceed for approx. three quarters of a mile and the ground entrance is on the left just before the Calmore Roundabout.

**UNITED SERVICES PORTSMOUTH FC - Victory Stadium HMS Temeraire Burnaby Road Portsmouth Hampshire PO1 2HB**
**02392 724235 (Clubhouse) 02392 725315 (Office)**

Leave the M27 at Junction 12 and join the M275 to Portsmouth. Follow the signs to Gunwharf, turn right at the traffic lights into Park Road then left at the next set of lights into Burnaby Road and the entrance is at the end of this road on the right.via HMS Temeraire.
NB Car parking in HMS Temeraire is for Senior Club and Match Officials only on the production of a current Sydenhams League (Wessex) pass. Free car parking for players and supporters is at the Portsmouth University Nuffield car park opposite the Registry Public House – follow Anglesea Road and signs for Southsea/Ferry Terminals, go under railway bridge past lights, keeping US Rogby Stadium on your right into Hampshire Terrace and keeping right, LOOP back into Anglesey Road, go through pedestrian lights and then immediately left into the car park. From car park turn right past pedestrian lights into Cambridge Road, then right into Burnaby Road. Postcode for Satellite Navigation systems PO1 2HB

**VERWOOD TOWN FC - POTTERNE PARK POTTERNE WAY VERWOOD DORSET BH21 6RS 01202 814 007**

Turn off the A31 at Verwood/Matchams junctions just West of Ringwood Town centre exit (immediately after garage if coming from the East) to join the B3081. Follow the B3081 through the forest for approximately 4 miles coming into Verwood itself. At the second set of traffic lights turn left into Black Hill. At the roundabout take the 1st exit left into Newtown Road. At the end of Newtown Road turn left and then 1st left into Potterne Way. Note: Along Black Hill on the left you will pass Bradfords Building Merchants and the entrance to the Verwood Sports & Social Club where post match refreshments are made available.
Postcode for Satellite Navigation systems BH21 6RS

**WEYMOUTH RESERVES - Bob Lucas Stadium, Radipole Lane, Weymouth DT4 9XJ 01305 785 558**

Approach Weymouth from Dorchester on the A354.
Turn right at first roundabout onto Weymouth Way, continue to the next roundabout then turn right (signposted Football Ground).
At the next roundabout take third exit into the ground.

**WHITCHURCH UNITED FC - Longmeadow Winchester Road Whitchurch Hampshire RG28 7RB 01256 892 493**

From the South – take the A34 (North), 2 miles north of Bullington Cross take the Whitchurch exit. Head for Whitchurch Town Centre. The ground is 500 yards on your right. Postcode for Satellite Navigation systems RG28 7RB

# WEST MIDLANDS (REGIONAL) LEAGUE

**Sponsored by:** None

**Founded:** 1889

**Recent Champions: 2013:** AFC Wulfrunians

**2014:** Lye Town **2015:** Sporting Khalsa

| PREMIER DIVISION | P | W | D | L | F | A | GD | Pts |
|---|---|---|---|---|---|---|---|---|
| 1 Shawbury United | 42 | 29 | 7 | 6 | 140 | 46 | 94 | 94 |
| 2 A.F.C. Bridgnorth | 42 | 29 | 6 | 7 | 123 | 43 | 80 | 93 |
| 3 Malvern Town | 42 | 25 | 3 | 14 | 114 | 72 | 42 | 78 |
| 4 Wolverhampton Sporting Community | 42 | 23 | 8 | 11 | 130 | 69 | 61 | 77 |
| 5 Haughmond | 42 | 22 | 10 | 10 | 111 | 69 | 42 | 76 |
| 6 Wolverhampton Casuals | 42 | 22 | 8 | 12 | 111 | 81 | 30 | 74 |
| 7 Dudley Sports | 42 | 21 | 11 | 10 | 82 | 63 | 19 | 74 |
| 8 Cradley Town | 42 | 20 | 10 | 12 | 89 | 63 | 26 | 70 |
| 9 Pegasus Juniors | 42 | 21 | 3 | 18 | 87 | 77 | 10 | 66 |
| 10 Ellesmere Rangers | 42 | 19 | 8 | 15 | 92 | 72 | 20 | 65 |
| 11 Wellington | 42 | 16 | 13 | 13 | 86 | 67 | 19 | 61 |
| 12 Smethwick Rangers | 42 | 18 | 7 | 17 | 89 | 99 | –10 | 61 |
| 13 Dudley Town | 42 | 17 | 10 | 15 | 66 | 82 | –16 | 61 |
| 14 Stone Old Alleynians | 42 | 18 | 4 | 20 | 74 | 85 | –11 | 58 |
| 15 Black Country Rangers | 42 | 15 | 11 | 16 | 73 | 65 | 8 | 56 |
| 16 Bewdley Town | 42 | 16 | 8 | 18 | 72 | 78 | –6 | 56 |
| 17 Gornal Athletic | 42 | 12 | 5 | 25 | 67 | 94 | –27 | 41 |
| 18 Willenhall Town | 42 | 10 | 7 | 25 | 63 | 110 | –47 | 37 |
| 19 Wellington Amateurs | 42 | 9 | 7 | 26 | 46 | 115 | –69 | 34 |
| 20 Bilston Town | 42 | 8 | 9 | 25 | 50 | 105 | –55 | 33 |
| 21 Bromyard Town | 42 | 9 | 5 | 28 | 66 | 134 | –68 | 32 |
| 22 Tipton Town | 42 | 0 | 6 | 36 | 26 | 168 | –142 | 6 |

**CLUB MOVEMENTS**

**Premier Division - In:** Shifnal Town (P).
**Out:** Bromyard Town (R). Shawbury United (P - Midland League). Tipton Town (R)
**Division One - In:** Bromyard Town (R), Newport Town (P). Old Wulfrunians (P), Tipton Town (R).
**Out:** AFC Ludlow (F), Shifnal Town (P). Trysull (F).
**Division Two - In:** Allscott (N - Mercian Reg Lge), Bewdley Town Reserves (N), West Bromwich United (N).
**Out:** Red Star Alma (S - Staffs County Senior League), Powick Rangers (W), Bilbrook (W), Tividale Res (W), Wren's Nest Res (W).

| DIVISION ONE | P | W | D | L | F | A | GD | Pts |
|---|---|---|---|---|---|---|---|---|
| 1 Shifnal Town | 32 | 25 | 3 | 4 | 81 | 34 | 47 | 78 |
| 2 Hereford Lads Club | 32 | 21 | 4 | 7 | 77 | 37 | 40 | 67 |
| 3 AFC Ludlow | 32 | 20 | 4 | 8 | 87 | 44 | 43 | 64 |
| 4 Wednesfield | 32 | 18 | 8 | 6 | 70 | 37 | 33 | 62 |
| 5 Darlaston Town (1874) | 32 | 15 | 9 | 8 | 84 | 52 | 32 | 54 |
| 6 St Martins | 32 | 17 | 2 | 13 | 82 | 69 | 13 | 53 |
| 7 Kington Town | 32 | 15 | 5 | 12 | 72 | 64 | 8 | 50 |
| 8 Trysull | 32 | 15 | 3 | 14 | 58 | 49 | 9 | 48 |
| 9 Wem Town | 32 | 14 | 4 | 14 | 74 | 71 | 3 | 46 |
| 10 Wrens Nest | 32 | 11 | 6 | 15 | 54 | 83 | -29 | 39 |
| 11 F C Stafford | 32 | 9 | 8 | 15 | 50 | 69 | -19 | 35 |
| 12 Worcester Raiders | 32 | 9 | 6 | 17 | 71 | 86 | -15 | 33 |
| 13 Shenstone Pathfinders | 32 | 10 | 2 | 20 | 45 | 75 | -30 | 32 |
| 14 Team Dudley | 32 | 8 | 6 | 18 | 56 | 78 | -22 | 30 |
| 15 Penncroft | 32 | 7 | 9 | 16 | 49 | 76 | -27 | 30 |
| 16 Bustleholme | 32 | 8 | 5 | 19 | 50 | 90 | -40 | 29 |
| 17 Wyrley | 32 | 5 | 6 | 21 | 44 | 90 | -46 | 21 |

Bartestree withdrew - record expunged.

| DIVISION TWO | P | W | D | L | F | A | GD | Pts |
|---|---|---|---|---|---|---|---|---|
| 1 Newport Town | 28 | 24 | 2 | 2 | 113 | 40 | 73 | 74 |
| 2 Old Wulfrunians | 27 | 17 | 3 | 7 | 69 | 30 | 39 | 54 |
| 3 Warstone Wanderers | 28 | 14 | 6 | 8 | 89 | 69 | 20 | 48 |
| 4 W'Ton United | 28 | 14 | 5 | 9 | 60 | 63 | -3 | 47 |
| 5 Red Star Alma | 28 | 12 | 8 | 8 | 69 | 56 | 13 | 44 |
| 6 Telford Juniors | 28 | 10 | 10 | 8 | 60 | 45 | 15 | 40 |
| 7 Bilbrook F C | 27 | 12 | 4 | 11 | 56 | 62 | -6 | 40 |
| 8 Powick Rangers | 26 | 10 | 8 | 8 | 53 | 40 | 13 | 38 |
| 9 Gornal Colts | 28 | 9 | 5 | 14 | 69 | 86 | -17 | 32 |
| 10 Malvern Town u21 | 27 | 8 | 7 | 12 | 53 | 60 | -7 | 31 |
| 11 Wonder Vaults | 28 | 9 | 4 | 15 | 56 | 68 | -12 | 31 |
| 12 Tipton Youth AFC | 27 | 8 | 3 | 16 | 68 | 79 | -11 | 27 |
| 13 Sikh Hunters (-3) | 27 | 7 | 5 | 15 | 52 | 101 | -49 | 23 |
| 14 Tividale Reserves | 21 | 5 | 4 | 12 | 43 | 60 | -17 | 19 |
| 15 Wrens Nest Res | 28 | 4 | 6 | 18 | 37 | 88 | -51 | 18 |

| PREMIER DIVISION | 1 | 2 | 3 | 4 | 5 | 6 | 7 | 8 | 9 | 10 | 11 | 12 | 13 | 14 | 15 | 16 | 17 | 18 | 19 | 20 | 21 | 22 |
|---|---|---|---|---|---|---|---|---|---|---|---|---|---|---|---|---|---|---|---|---|---|---|
| 1 A.F.C. Bridgnorth | | 0–2 | 4–2 | 10–1 | 0–0 | 1–0 | 3–3 | 1–0 | 1–0 | 3–1 | 2–0 | 1–0 | 7–1 | 0–0 | 2–2 | 3–2 | 3–1 | 1–0 | 5–0 | 6–1 | 5–1 | 2–[illegible] |
| 2 Bewdley Town | 0–4 | | 3–0 | 1–1 | 0–0 | 2–1 | 0–2 | 1–0 | 2–2 | 1–2 | 2–2 | 1–4 | 3–2 | 2–3 | 1–4 | 1–2 | 4–1 | 2–2 | 3–1 | 1–4 | 2–3 | 3–[illegible] |
| 3 Bilston Town | 0–5 | 0–6 | | 2–2 | 0–0 | 3–0 | 3–2 | 2–2 | 0–2 | 0–3 | 4–1 | 1–2 | 1–4 | 2–4 | 0–1 | 2–1 | 2–1 | 0–0 | 1–1 | 1–2 | 1–4 | 1–[illegible] |
| 4 Black Country Rangers | 1–4 | 2–0 | 5–0 | | 5–1 | 1–1 | 0–4 | 1–3 | 0–1 | 4–0 | 0–1 | 0–2 | 1–0 | 0–1 | 2–1 | 0–0 | 5–1 | 1–2 | 0–1 | 2–3 | 4–2 | 1–[illegible] |
| 5 Bromyard Town | 0–6 | 0–2 | 6–3 | 3–4 | | 3–3 | 1–2 | 3–2 | 1–6 | 3–1 | 0–5 | 3–6 | 1–7 | 0–2 | 2–4 | 0–1 | 5–3 | 1–5 | 4–0 | 1–2 | 0–4 | 0–[illegible] |
| 6 Cradley Town | 1–2 | 4–1 | 2–2 | 0–3 | 4–0 | | 5–1 | 2–2 | 3–0 | 2–2 | 1–1 | 1–2 | 4–0 | 1–0 | 0–2 | 3–4 | 3–0 | 3–2 | 7–1 | 2–1 | 3–2 | 3–[illegible] |
| 7 Dudley Sports | 3–1 | 0–0 | 4–1 | 0–2 | 5–4 | 0–0 | | 1–0 | 1–2 | 2–2 | 3–1 | 2–1 | 2–0 | 2–1 | 5–1 | 3–4 | 5–0 | 1–1 | 2–1 | 4–5 | 0–3 | 0–[illegible] |
| 8 Dudley Town | 0–4 | 1–4 | 2–1 | 2–2 | 2–1 | 3–2 | 1–1 | | 1–0 | 2–1 | 1–2 | 3–3 | 2–1 | 0–3 | 1–2 | 1–1 | 3–0 | 0–2 | 3–0 | 2–1 | 2–2 | 0–[illegible] |
| 9 Ellesmere Rangers | 0–4 | 1–4 | 8–0 | 4–1 | 0–0 | 1–1 | 2–2 | 2–3 | | 2–2 | 0–3 | 1–4 | 1–3 | 1–2 | 2–1 | 5–0 | 11–1 | 3–3 | 4–1 | 1–0 | 3–2 | 2–[illegible] |
| 10 Gornal Athletic | 1–0 | 0–1 | 1–3 | 3–1 | 4–0 | 1–2 | 0–3 | 2–1 | 1–2 | | 2–4 | 2–3 | 0–1 | 2–4 | 3–3 | 1–4 | 5–1 | 2–2 | 5–3 | 4–1 | 3–1 | 0–[illegible] |
| 11 Haughmond | 1–3 | 1–1 | 1–1 | 3–3 | 1–2 | 3–1 | 0–0 | 8–1 | 2–0 | 3–0 | | 1–3 | 4–2 | 0–2 | 5–0 | 5–1 | 6–0 | 2–2 | 1–1 | 1–0 | 2–5 | 5–[illegible] |
| 12 Malvern Town | 4–2 | 4–1 | 1–0 | 1–1 | 5–2 | 0–4 | 0–1 | 6–3 | 3–0 | 5–0 | 0–3 | | 1–2 | 0–1 | 6–0 | 4–3 | 6–0 | 2–1 | 2–0 | 2–1 | 3–4 | 1–[illegible] |
| 13 Pegasus Juniors | 3–0 | 1–1 | 4–2 | 0–4 | 8–1 | 1–2 | 3–1 | 1–2 | 2–1 | 2–1 | 1–2 | 2–1 | | 1–0 | 2–0 | 1–0 | 5–2 | 1–4 | 2–1 | 6–1 | 2–2 | 4–[illegible] |
| 14 Shawbury United | 1–1 | 5–0 | 3–0 | 0–0 | 3–4 | 7–0 | 6–0 | 2–2 | 5–1 | 3–1 | 4–4 | 5–2 | 1–2 | | 11–1 | 5–3 | 8–0 | 2–0 | 5–0 | 3–2 | 5–0 | 6–[illegible] |
| 15 Smethwick Rangers | 3–1 | 3–2 | 0–0 | 0–5 | 4–2 | 1–2 | 0–1 | 1–3 | 2–4 | 3–1 | 3–4 | 3–1 | 4–2 | 2–2 | | 0–1 | 6–0 | 3–1 | 2–0 | 3–1 | 3–3 | 2–[illegible] |
| 16 Stone Old Alleynians | 1–4 | 1–3 | 2–1 | 1–0 | 0–1 | 1–2 | 1–2 | 3–0 | 1–2 | 2–1 | 2–4 | 4–5 | 3–0 | 1–2 | 3–2 | | 4–2 | 2–1 | 3–1 | 2–1 | 0–1 | 0–[illegible] |
| 17 Tipton Town | 0–6 | 0–2 | 0–3 | 0–0 | 0–3 | 0–5 | 0–0 | 0–1 | 0–3 | 0–2 | 0–5 | 0–4 | 0–3 | 1–7 | 1–3 | 1–1 | | 3–6 | 1–3 | 1–1 | 0–0 | 0–[illegible] |
| 18 Wellington | 3–3 | 2–1 | 1–0 | 0–3 | 2–1 | 1–1 | 2–2 | 1–2 | 1–1 | 2–1 | 4–1 | 2–3 | 3–0 | 2–3 | 3–0 | 4–1 | 1–1 | | 1–2 | 4–1 | 3–2 | 2–[illegible] |
| 19 Wellington Amateurs | 0–2 | 1–3 | 3–0 | 1–2 | 0–0 | 1–4 | 0–4 | 1–1 | 3–2 | 0–4 | 0–6 | 2–8 | 2–1 | 0–4 | 3–3 | 1–1 | 2–1 | 1–5 | | 1–0 | 0–4 | 0–[illegible] |
| 20 Willenhall Town | 0–7 | 1–2 | 1–4 | 2–2 | 3–1 | 1–1 | 0–2 | 2–2 | 0–2 | 2–0 | 2–2 | 2–0 | 0–0 | 3–7 | 2–6 | 0–2 | 4–3 | 3–2 | 0–3 | | 2–4 | 3–[illegible] |
| 21 Wolverhampton Casuals | 3–0 | 4–1 | 2–1 | 5–0 | 5–2 | 2–3 | 2–3 | 1–2 | 1–3 | 7–0 | 0–3 | 2–1 | 3–2 | 2–1 | 2–2 | 3–2 | 7–0 | 0–0 | 5–2 | 3–2 | | 3–[illegible] |
| 22 Wolverhampton Sporting Community | 0–4 | 3–0 | 8–0 | 3–0 | 4–3 | 1–0 | 1–1 | 0–2 | 3–4 | 4–0 | 6–2 | 4–3 | 4–2 | 1–1 | 6–3 | 2–3 | 10–0 | 3–1 | 4–0 | 5–0 | 2–2 | |

### AFC BRIDGNORTH

Founded: 2013 Nickname:

**Secretary:** Steve Groome **(T)** 07748 302 650 **(E)** steve_groome2003@yahoo.co.uk
**Chairman:** Stan Parkes
**Ground:** Crown Meadow, Innage Lane, Bridgnorth WV16 4HS **(T)** 07748 302 650
**Colours(change):**
**ADDITIONAL INFORMATION:**

### BEWDLEY TOWN

Founded: 1978 Nickname:

**Secretary:** Steve Godfrey **(T)** 07739 626 169 **(E)** stevegodfrey09@gmail.com
**Chairman:** Geoff Edwards
**Ground:** Ribbesford Meadows, Ribbesford, Bewdley, Worcs DY12 2TJ **(T)** 07739 626 169
**Colours(change):**
**ADDITIONAL INFORMATION:**
**Honours:** Worcestershire Senior Urn 2011-12.

### BILSTON TOWN COMMUNITY

Founded: 2007 Nickname:

**Secretary:** Paul lloyd **(T)** 07949 315 489 **(E)** paulelloyd@hotmail.co.uk
**Chairman:** Graham Hodson
**Ground:** Queen Street Stadium, Queen Street, Bilston WV14 7EX **(T)** 07725 816 043
**Colours(change):**
**ADDITIONAL INFORMATION:**

### BLACK COUNTRY RANGERS

Founded: 1996 Nickname:

**Secretary:** Andy Harris **(T)** 07891 128 896 **(E)** bcrfc@outlook.com
**Chairman:** Paul Garner
**Ground:** Cradley Town F C, Beeches View Avenue, Cradley, Halesowen B63 2HB **(T)** 07891 128 896
**Colours(change):**
**ADDITIONAL INFORMATION:**
**Honours:** West Midlands (Regional) Division One 2010-11.

### CRADLEY TOWN

Founded: 1948 Nickname:

**Secretary:** David Attwood **(T)** 07708 659 636 **(E)** d.attwood@sky.com
**Chairman:** Trevor Thomas
**Ground:** The Beeches, Beeches View Avenue, Cradley, Halesowen B63 2HB **(T)** 07708 659 636
**Colours(change):**
**ADDITIONAL INFORMATION:**

### DUDLEY SPORTS

Founded: 1978 Nickname:

**Secretary:** John Lewis **(T)** 07737 099 385 **(E)** kath-john.lewis@blueyonder.co.uk
**Chairman:** Kathryn Conroy
**Ground:** Hillcrest Avenue, Brierley Hill, West Mids DY5 3QH **(T)** 01384 349 413
**Colours(change):**
**ADDITIONAL INFORMATION:**

### DUDLEY TOWN

Founded: 1893 Nickname:

**Secretary:** David Ferrier **(T)** 07986 549 675 **(E)** davef.dtfc@blueyonder.co.uk
**Chairman:** Stephen Austin
**Ground:** The Dell Stadium, Bryce Road, Brierley Hill, West Mids DY5 4NE **(T)** 07986 549 675
**Colours(change):**
**ADDITIONAL INFORMATION:**

## ELLESMERE RANGERS
Founded: 1969 Nickname: The Rangers

**Secretary:** John Edge **(T)** 07947 864 357 **(E)** john.edge2@homecall.co.uk
**Chairman:** Neil Williams
**Ground:** Beech Grove, Ellesmere, Shropshire SY12 0BT **(T)** 07947 864 357 **Capacity:** 1250
**Colours(change):**
**ADDITIONAL INFORMATION:**
**Previous Leagues:** West Midlands > 20120. Midland Alliance 2010-2013.
**Honours:** West Midlands League Premier Division 2009-10.

## GORNAL ATHLETIC
Founded: 1945 Nickname:

**Secretary:** Kevin Williams **(T)** 07762 585 149 **(E)** k.williams880@btinternet.com
**Chairman:** John Sheppard
**Ground:** Garden Walk Stadium, Garden Walk, Lower Gornal, Dudley DY3 2NR **(T)** 07762 585 149
**Colours(change):**
**ADDITIONAL INFORMATION:**
West Midlands (Regional) Division One South 2003-04, Premier Division 2011-12.

## HAUGHMOND
Founded: 1980 Nickname:

**Secretary:** Stuart Williams **(T)** 07785 531 754 **(E)** stuartlwilliams@btinternet.com
**Chairman:** William Gough
**Ground:** Sundorne Sports Village, Sundorne Road, Shrewsbury. SY1 4RQ **(T)** 07785 531 754
**Colours(change):**
**ADDITIONAL INFORMATION:**

## MALVERN TOWN
Founded: 1947 Nickname:

**Secretary:** Margaret Scott **(T)** 07944 110 402 **(E)** marg@malverntown.co.uk
**Chairman:** Christopher Pinder
**Ground:** HD anywhere Community Stadium, Lamgland Avenue, Malvern WR14 2EQ **(T)** 07944 110 402 **Capacity:** 2,500
**Colours(change):**
**ADDITIONAL INFORMATION: Records: Att:** 1,221 v Worcester City FA Cup. **Goals:** Graham Buffery. **Apps:** Nick Clayton.
**Honours:** Worcestershire Senior Urn x8 Most recently 2014-15. Midland Combination Division One 1955-56.

## PEGASUS JUNIORS
Founded: 1955 Nickname: The Redmen

**Secretary:** Nik Marsh **(T)** 07816 121 248 **(E)** nikmarsh1982@gmail.com
**Chairman:** Chris Wells
**Ground:** Old School Lane, Hereford HR1 1EX **(T)** 07816 121 248 **Capacity:** 1,000
**Colours(change):**
**ADDITIONAL INFORMATION: Att:** 1,400 v Newport AFC, 1989-90.
**Honours:** Worcestershire Senior Urn 85-86. Hellenic Div.1 Champions 84-85, 98-99.
**Previous Lge:** Hellenic > 2011.

## SHIFNAL TOWN
Founded: 1964 Nickname:

**Secretary:** Ron Finney **(T)** 07986 563 156 **(E)** eve.ronfinney@hotmail.co.uk
**Chairman:** Peter Bradley
**Ground:** Phoenix Park, Coppice Green Lane, Shifnal, Shrops TF11 8PD **(T)** 07986 563 156
**Colours(change):**
**ADDITIONAL INFORMATION:**
**Honours:** West Midlands (Regional) League Premier Division 2006-07, Division One 2015-16.

## SMETHWICK RANGERS
Founded: 1977 Nickname:

**Secretary:** TBC **(T)** **(E)**
**Chairman:** TBC
**Ground:** Hillcrest Avenue, Brierley Hill, West Mids. DY5 3QH **(T)** 01384 826 420
**Colours(change):**
**ADDITIONAL INFORMATION:**
**Previous Name:** AFC Smethwick.
**Honours:** West Midlands Division One 2012-13.

## STONE OLD ALLEYNIANS

Founded: 1962 Nickname:

**Secretary:** Philip Johnson **(T)** 07813 553 087 **(E)** phil@onthepitch.freeserve.co.uk
**Chairman:** Dave Mardling
**Ground:** Wellbeing Park, Yarnfield Lane, Yarnfield ST15 0NF **(T)** 07813 553 087
**Colours(change):**
**ADDITIONAL INFORMATION:**

## WELLINGTON

Founded: 1968 Nickname:

**Secretary:** Michael Perkins **(T)** 07842 186 643 **(E)** perkins@haworth13.freeserve.co.uk
**Chairman:** Phillip Smith
**Ground:** Wellington Playing Field, Wellington, Hereford HR4 8AZ **(T)** 07842 186 643 (MD)
**Colours(change):**
**ADDITIONAL INFORMATION:**

## WELLINGTON AMATEURS

Founded: 1950 Nickname:

**Secretary:** Ben Coates **(T)** 07738 715 038 **(E)** bcoates9@icloud.com
**Chairman:** Dave Gregory
**Ground:** Wickes Stadium, School grove, Oakengates, telford, Shrops TF2 6BQ **(T)** 07738 715 038
**Colours(change):**
**ADDITIONAL INFORMATION:**

## WILLENHALL TOWN

Founded: 1953 Nickname: The Lockmen

**Secretary:** Simon Hall **(T)** 07901 560 691 **(E)** chairperson@wtfcofficial.co.uk
**Chairman:** Simon Hall
**Ground:** Queen Street Stadium, Queen Street, Bilston, Wolverhampton. WV14 7EX **(T)** 07901 560 691
**Colours(change):**
**ADDITIONAL INFORMATION:**
**Previous Leagues:** Staffs Co, West Mids 1975-78, 1991-94, Southern 1982-91, 2005-08, Midland All. 1994-2004, 2010-12, N.P.L 2004-05, 2008-10.
**Honours:** Staffs County Premier 1974-75. West Mids Division 1 1975-76, Premier 77-78. Southern League Midland Division 1983-84.

## WOLVERHAMPTON CASUALS

Founded: 1899 Nickname:

**Secretary:** Michael Green **(T)** 07870 737 229 **(E)** mickgreen7@hotmail.com
**Chairman:** Garath Deacon
**Ground:** Brinsford Stadium, Brinsford Lane, Wolverhampton WV10 7PR **(T)** 07870 737 229
**Colours(change):**
**ADDITIONAL INFORMATION:**

## WOLVERHAMPTON SPORTING COMMUNITY

Founded: 2001 Nickname:

**Secretary:** Mark Hobson **(T)** 07966 505 425 **(E)** wolvessporting@yahoo.co.uk
**Chairman:** John Quarry
**Ground:** Pride Park, Hazel Lane, Great Wyrley, Staffs WS6 6AA **(T)** 07966 505 425
**Colours(change):**
**ADDITIONAL INFORMATION:**
**Previous Name:** Heath Town Rangers 2001-10.

## PREMIER LEAGUE CUP

**ROUND 1**

| | | | |
|---|---|---|---|
| Dudley Sports | v | Haughmond | 2-5 (aet) |
| Bromyard Town | v | Bewdley Town | 5-0 |
| Bilston Town Community | v | Shawbury United | 2-1 |
| Pegasus Juniors | v | Black Country Rangers | 4-3 |
| Ellesmere Rangers | v | Malvern Town | HW |
| Gornal Athletic | v | Wellington | 3-2 |

**ROUND 2**

| | | | |
|---|---|---|---|
| Haughmond | v | Cradley Town | 1-2 |
| Wellington Amateurs | v | Wolverhampton Casuals | 0-4 |
| Bromyard Town | v | Wolverhampton Sporting C | 1-2 |
| Bilston Town Community | v | Pegasus Juniors | 3-4 |
| Smethwick Rangers | v | Tipton Town | 2-1 |
| Dudley Town | v | Stone Old Alleynians | 2-3 (aet) |

| | | | |
|---|---|---|---|
| Ellesmere Rangers | v | Willenhall Town | 4-1 |
| AFC Bridgnorth | v | Gornal Athletic | 2-1 |
| **QUARTER FINALS** | | | |
| Cradley Town | v | Wolverhampton C. | 1-0 (aet) |
| Wolverhampton Sporting C | v | Pegasus Juniors | 2-0 |
| Smethwick Rangers | v | Stone Old Alleynians | 3-0 |
| Ellesmere Rangers | v | AFC Bridgnorth | 1-2 |
| **SEMI FINALS** | | | |
| Cradley Town | v | Wolverhampton Sporting C | 3-4 (aet) |
| Smethwick Rangers | v | AFC Bridgnorth | 3-0 |
| **FINAL** | | | |
| Wolverhampton Sporting C | v | Smethwick Rangers | 0-1 |
| **Division One League Cup Final** | | | |
| Worcester Raiders | v | Kington Town | 3-2 |
| **Divison Two League Cup Final** | | | |
| Bilbrook | v | Newport Town | 3-2 |

## West Midlands (Regional) Division One

| | | |
|---|---|---|
| **BROMYARD TOWN** | Delahay Meadow, Stourport Road, Bromyard HR7 4NT | 07885 849 948 |
| **BUSTLEHOLME** | Tipton Town F C, Wednesbury Oak Road, Tipton, West Mid. DY4 0BS | 07805 829 354 |
| **DARLASTON TOWN** | Bentley Leisure Pavilion, Bentley Road North, Bentley, Walsall. WS2 0EA | 0759 3281 513 |
| **FC STAFFORD** | Wolgarstone Sports Centre, Cannock Road, Stafford ST19 5RX | 07788 809 143 |
| **HEREFORD LADS CLUB** | Hereford Lads Club, Widemarsh Common, Hereford HR4 9NA | 07837 665 745 |
| **KINGTON TOWN** | Mill Street, Kington, Herefordshire. HR5 3AL | 07900 310 020 |
| **NEWPORT TOWN** | Shuker Playing Fields, Shuker Close, Newport,Shropshire TF10 7SG | 07961 017 524 |
| **OLD WULFRUNIANS** | Memorial Ground, Castlecroft Road, Wolverhampton WV3 8NA | 07875 688 730 |
| **PENNCROFT** | Aldersley Leisure Village, Aldersley Road, Wolverhampton WV6 9NW | 07964 725 516 |
| **SHENSTONE PATHFINDER** | Shenston Pavilion Club, Birmingham Road, Shenstone WS14 0LR | 07917 372 398 |
| **ST MARTINS** | The Venue, Burma Road, Parkhall, Oswestry, Shrops. SY11 4AS | 07903 756 790 |
| **TEAM DUDLEY** | The Dell Stadium, Bryce Road, Brierley Hill DY5 4NE | 07921 571 359 |
| **TIPTON TOWN** | Tipton Sports Academy, Wednesbury Oak Road, Tipton DY4 0BS | 07535 975 142 |
| **WEDNESFIELD** | Cottage Ground, Amos Lane, Wednesfield WV11 1ND | 07807 868 763 |
| **WEM TOWN** | Butler Sports Centre, Bowens Field, Wem SY4 5AP | 07790 426 152 |
| **WORCESTER RAIDERS** | Claines Lane, Worcestershire WR3 7SS | 07532 266 897 |
| **WRENS NEST** | The Beeches, Packwood Road, Tividale B69 1UL | 07963 935 601 |
| **WYRLEY** | Long Lane, Essington, Wolverhampton. WS6 6AT | 07899 960 806 |

# GROUND DIRECTIONS - PREMIER DIVISION

**AFC BRIDGNORTH - Crown Meadow, Innage Lane, Bridgnorth. WV16 4HL Tel: 01746 763 001**

Follow signs for Shrewsbury A458 over River Bridge on bypass. At next island turn right (Town Centre). At ?T? Junction turn right, first left into Victoria Road. Turn right at crossroads by Woodberry Down. Follow road round to right. Club is on the right 300 yards from crossroads.

**BEWDLEY TOWN - Ribbesford Meadows, Ribbesford, Bewdley, Worcs. DY12 2TJ Tel: 07739-626169**

From Kidderminster follow signs to Bewdley on A456 past West Midlands Safari Park and follow signs to Town Centre at next Island. Go over River Bridge into Town and turn left at side of Church (High Street). Stay on this road for 1 ½ miles. Entrance to ground is on left.

**BILSTON TOWN COMMUNITY - Queen Street, Bilston WV14 7EX Tel: 07949 315 489**

From M6 Junction 10 take A454 to Wolverhampton then pick up A563 to Bilston. Turn left at 2nd roundabout and left at mini roundabout by the ambulance station. under the by-pass bridge and first left into Queens Street. Ground is 500 yards on left

**BLACK COUNTRY RANGERS - see Cradley Town F C. Tel: 07746-231195/01384-569658**

**CRADLEY TOWN - The Beeches, Beeches View Avenue, Cradley, Halesowen, West Mids. B63 2HB Tel: 07799-363467** From M5 Junction 3 take A456 Manor Way (SP Kidderminster). Straight on at first island, turn right (second exit) at second island into Hagley Road (B4183). Pass Foxhunt Inn on left and turn third (careful some might say second!!) left into Rosemary Road. Straight on into Lansdowne Road/Dunstall Road and turn left at T-junction into HuntingtreeRoad/Lutley Mill Road. Left again at next T-junction into Stourbridge Road (A458) and immediately left again into Beecher Road East. First left into Abbey Road and after 250 yards swing right up along Meres Road. Take first left into Hedgefield Grove go straight to the end where the ground entrance is almost opposite in Beeches View Avenue between house numbers 48 and 50.

**DUDLEY SPORTS - Hillcrest Avenue, Brierley Hill, West Mids. DY5 3QH Tel: 01384-826420**

The Ground is situated in Brierley Hill, just off A461. It can be approached from Stourbridge off the Ring Road to Amblecote, turning right at third set of traffic lights or from Dudley passing through Brierley Hill Town centre. A – Z ref, 4H, page 67.

**DUDLEY TOWN - The Dell Stadium, Bryce Road, Brierley Hill, West Mids. DY5 4NE Tel: 01384-812943**

From M5 Junction 4 follow signs for Stourbridge. From the Ring Road, take A491 sign posted Wolverhampton.

At the second set of lights, turn right onto Brettle Lane A461. After approx 6 miles you will approach Brierley Hill High Street. Turn left at lights onto bank Street. You will see Civic hall and Police Station. Carry on over small bridge and at next set of traffic lights you will see Bryce Road and Stadium is on your left. A-Z Birmingham 5F 93 A-Z West Midlands 5B 88

**ELLESMERE RANGERS - Beech Grove, Ellesmere, Shropshire, SY12 0BT - 07947 864 357**

Follow A5 Wellington and take A495 to Ellesmere. On Approaching Ellesmere, straight over at roundabout, then turn left into housing estate opposite Lakelands School. At crossroads, turn left and the 1st right down the lane to Beech Grove Playing Fields.

**GORNAL ATHLETIC - Lower Gornal, Dudley, West Midlands DY3 2NR Tel: 07762 585 149**

From Dudley, take A459 to Sedgley, past the Fire Station. Turn left at the Green Dragon Public House, on the B4175 (Jews Lane). Follow the road until you come to the Old Bull's Head Pub, turn left into Redhall Road. Take the second left to Garden Walk.

From Wolverhampton, use A449 past Wombourne. Turn left at Himley House lights. (B4176) Over next set of major traffic lights at Bull Street. Second left into Central Drive. Left into Bank Road. Follow road round to the Ground.

**HAUGHMOND - Shrewsbury Sports Village, Sundorne Road, Shrewsbury. SY1 4RQ Tel: 07785 531 754**

M54 - Continue on M54, this then merges to the A5. At first roundabout, take second exit signed A49. Continue to next mini-roundabout, take first exit. Go straight over next mini-roundabout - Sundorne Road. Next mini-roundabout, take first exit. This is the Sports Village.

**MALVERN TOWN - Langland Stadium, Langland Avenue, Malvern. WR14 2QE Tel: 01684-574068**

Leave M5 at Junction 7 and turn towards Worcester. Turn left at next roundabout onto A4440 towards Malvern. Straight over next two roundabouts and take left slip road onto A449 at next roundabout. When approaching Malvern, turn left onto B4208 signposted Welland. Straight over three roundabouts and then take the third left into Orford Way. Take the third left into Langland Avenue. Ground is 300 yards on left.

**PEGASUS JUNIORS - Old School Lane, Hereford. HR1 1EX Tel: 07980-465995**

Approach City on A4103 from Worcester. At roundabout on outskirts take 2nd exit (A4103) over railway bridge, traffic light controlled. Take 2nd turning on left into Old School Lane. Ground entrance 150 metres on left. Approach City on A49 from Leominster. On City outskirts take 1st exit at roundabout – Roman Road. First turning on right is Old School Lane. Ground entrance 150 metres on left.

**SHIFNAL TOWN - Phoenix Park, Coppice Green Lane, Shifnal, Shrops TF11 8PD Tel: 07986 563 156**

Via the M6 get on to the M54 and follow signs for Wales/Telford/Wolverhampton/Shrewsbury/A5. At junction 3, take the A41 exit to Whitchurch/Weston. Continue on Newport Road/A41. Turn left and continue onto Stanton Road. Turn right onto Curriers Lane. Turn right onto High Street/B4379. Continue to follow B4379. Turn right onto Drayton Road. Turn right onto Cornwallis Drive.

**SMETHWICK RANGERS - Hillcrest Avenue, Brierley Hill, West Mids. DY5 3QH Tel: 01384-826420**

The Ground is situated in Brierley Hill, just off A461. It can be approached from Stourbridge off the Ring Road to Amblecote, turning right at third set of traffic lights or from Dudley passing through Brierley Hill Town centre. A – Z ref, 4H, page 67.

**STONE OLD ALLEYNIANS - Wellbeing Park, Yarnfield Lane, Yarnfield, Nr Stone, Staffs. ST15 0NF Tel: 01785 761 891**

From the South Junction 14 (M6), take A34 towards Stone. Carry on A34 until you see Wayfarer Public House on left. Immediately after Pub, turn left towards Yarnfield. Follow road and once over the motorway bridge, continue for ½ mile. Ground is on left.

**WELLINGTON - Wellington Playing Field, Wellington, Hereford. HR4 8AZ**

The Ground is situated in Wellington, behind School and opposite the Church. Wellington is 8 miles South of Leominster or 6 miles North of Hereford on the A49. At the Hereford end of the dual carriageway take the turn for Wellington.

**WELLINGTON AMATEURS - Wickes Stadium, School Grove, Oakengates, Telford, Shrops. TF2 6BQ**

From M54 take Junction 5. At roundabout take first left onto Rampart Way. At traffic lights take the first left onto A442 (Eastern Primary). Leave A442 at next junction. At roundabout (Greyhound Interchange), take the second exit onto B5061 (Holyhead Road). Just after red brick Church on right, turn right onto Vicar Street. Take the next left into School Grove. Continue to the end of the street and proceed up the slope onto the Car Park.

**WILLENHALL TOWN - Queen Street Stadium, Queen Street, Bilston, Wolverhampton WV14 7EX**

From M6 Junction 10, take A454 to Wolverhampton, then pick up A563 to Bilston. Turn left at second roundabout and left at mini roundabout by the Ambulance station, under the by-pass bridge. First left into Queen Street. Ground in 500 yards on left.

**WOLVERHAMPTON CASUALS - Brinsford Stadium, Brinsford Lane, Wolverhampton. WV10 7PR Tel: 01902-783214**

Turn onto M54 off M6 Northbound. Take Junction 2 and turn right onto A449 to Stafford. Go to next island and come back on yourself towards M54. Brinsford Lane is approximately ½ mile from island on left. Ground is 200 yards on left in Brinsford Lane.

**WOLVERHAMPTON SPORTING C. - Wednesfield F C, Cottage Ground, Amos Lane, Wednesfield WV11 1ND Tel: 01902-735506**

Going south, leave M6 at Junction 11 onto A460 towards Wolverhampton. After approx. 3 miles turn left at the Millhouse Public House into Pear Tree Lane. Continue on across mini-island into Knowle Lane. At Red Lion Public House continue across mini-island into Long Knowle Lane. Continue across mini-island into Amos Lane. Ground is about ½ mile along on left hand side.

Going north, leave M6 at Junction 10A onto M54. Leave M54 at Junction 1 onto A460 towards Wolverhampton. Turn left at Millhouse Public House and continue as above.

# WESTERN LEAGUE

**Sponsored by:** Toolstation
**Founded:** 1892
**Recent Champions: 2013:** Bishop Sutton
**2014:** Larkhall Athletic **2015:** Melksham Town

| PREMIER DIVISION | P | W | D | L | F | A | GD | Pts |
|---|---|---|---|---|---|---|---|---|
| 1 Odd Down (Bath) (-3) | 38 | 28 | 4 | 6 | 98 | 45 | 53 | 85 |
| 2 Barnstaple Town | 38 | 27 | 4 | 7 | 78 | 33 | 45 | 85 |
| 3 Bristol Manor Farm | 38 | 25 | 5 | 8 | 109 | 44 | 65 | 80 |
| 4 Buckland Athletic | 38 | 24 | 6 | 8 | 91 | 34 | 57 | 78 |
| 5 Melksham Town | 38 | 22 | 7 | 9 | 65 | 38 | 27 | 73 |
| 6 Willand Rovers | 38 | 21 | 7 | 10 | 72 | 52 | 20 | 70 |
| 7 Street | 38 | 20 | 5 | 13 | 82 | 63 | 19 | 65 |
| 8 Bradford Town | 38 | 19 | 5 | 14 | 91 | 58 | 33 | 62 |
| 9 Gillingham Town | 38 | 16 | 8 | 14 | 75 | 65 | 10 | 56 |
| 10 Shepton Mallet (-9) | 38 | 18 | 7 | 13 | 61 | 52 | 9 | 52 |
| 11 Brislington | 38 | 14 | 5 | 19 | 44 | 64 | -20 | 47 |
| 12 Cadbury Heath | 38 | 11 | 10 | 17 | 66 | 77 | -11 | 43 |
| 13 Sherborne Town | 38 | 10 | 10 | 18 | 50 | 70 | -20 | 40 |
| 14 Bitton | 38 | 11 | 6 | 21 | 55 | 73 | -18 | 39 |
| 15 Cribbs | 38 | 10 | 7 | 21 | 55 | 72 | -17 | 37 |
| 16 Bridport | 38 | 10 | 6 | 22 | 51 | 90 | -39 | 36 |
| 17 Hallen | 38 | 11 | 3 | 24 | 49 | 94 | -45 | 36 |
| 18 Longwell Green Sports (-1) | 38 | 10 | 7 | 21 | 45 | 90 | -45 | 36 |
| 19 Clevedon Town | 38 | 6 | 6 | 26 | 33 | 100 | -67 | 24 |
| 20 Welton Rovers | 38 | 4 | 8 | 26 | 42 | 98 | -56 | 20 |

Winterbourne United withdrew - record expunged.

| DIVISION ONE | P | W | D | L | F | A | GD | Pts |
|---|---|---|---|---|---|---|---|---|
| 1 Chipping Sodbury Town | 40 | 23 | 7 | 10 | 84 | 52 | 32 | 76 |
| 2 Wells City | 40 | 23 | 7 | 10 | 91 | 61 | 30 | 76 |
| 3 Chard Town | 40 | 22 | 8 | 10 | 70 | 49 | 21 | 74 |
| 4 Oldland Abbotonians | 40 | 22 | 6 | 12 | 81 | 54 | 27 | 72 |
| 5 Cheddar | 40 | 21 | 9 | 10 | 81 | 57 | 24 | 72 |
| 6 Portishead Town | 40 | 20 | 10 | 10 | 83 | 52 | 31 | 70 |
| 7 Hengrove Athletic | 40 | 21 | 7 | 12 | 57 | 37 | 20 | 70 |
| 8 Ashton & Backwell United (-3) | 40 | 20 | 9 | 11 | 86 | 56 | 30 | 66 |
| 9 Keynsham Town | 40 | 20 | 6 | 14 | 84 | 65 | 19 | 66 |
| 10 Corsham Town | 40 | 17 | 9 | 14 | 81 | 61 | 20 | 60 |
| 11 Almondsbury UWE | 40 | 16 | 8 | 16 | 75 | 56 | 19 | 56 |
| 12 Wellington | 40 | 15 | 10 | 15 | 71 | 56 | 15 | 55 |
| 13 Radstock Town | 40 | 16 | 6 | 18 | 67 | 71 | -4 | 54 |
| 14 Chippenham Park | 40 | 14 | 11 | 15 | 51 | 52 | -1 | 53 |
| 15 Calne Town | 40 | 15 | 7 | 18 | 60 | 76 | -16 | 52 |
| 16 Wincanton Town | 40 | 13 | 7 | 20 | 75 | 90 | -15 | 46 |
| 17 Warminster Town | 40 | 13 | 7 | 20 | 52 | 75 | -23 | 46 |
| 18 Roman Glass St George | 40 | 11 | 7 | 22 | 71 | 95 | -24 | 40 |
| 19 Devizes Town | 40 | 11 | 5 | 24 | 55 | 107 | -52 | 38 |
| 20 Westbury United | 40 | 8 | 6 | 26 | 50 | 98 | -48 | 30 |
| 21 Bishop Sutton | 40 | 2 | 2 | 36 | 29 | 134 | -105 | 8 |

## CLUB MOVEMENTS

**Premier Division - In:** Chipping Sodbury Town (P), Wells City (P).

**Out:** Barnstaple Town (P - Southern Div.1 S&W), Welton Rovers (R).

## CLUB MOVEMENTS

**Division One - In:** Bishops Lydeard (P - Somerset County), Welton Rovers (R)

**Out:** Chipping Sodbury Town (P), Wells City (P).

| PREMIER DIVISION | 1 | 2 | 3 | 4 | 5 | 6 | 7 | 8 | 9 | 10 | 11 | 12 | 13 | 14 | 15 | 16 | 17 | 18 | 19 | 20 |
|---|---|---|---|---|---|---|---|---|---|---|---|---|---|---|---|---|---|---|---|---|
| 1 Barnstaple Town | | 2-0 | 2-1 | 4-1 | 2-0 | 2-0 | 2-1 | 3-1 | 4-0 | 3-1 | 2-1 | 1-0 | 2-0 | 1-4 | 1-2 | 2-2 | 2-0 | 0-1 | 2-0 | 2-0 |
| 2 Bitton | 0-1 | | 2-3 | 4-1 | 1-2 | 0-2 | 0-1 | 2-0 | 5-0 | 3-2 | 1-4 | 0-1 | 0-2 | 1-2 | 2-4 | 1-0 | 1-1 | 3-3 | 9-1 | 0-1 |
| 3 Bradford Town | 2-3 | 3-0 | | 1-3 | 4-1 | 4-0 | 0-2 | 5-1 | 1-1 | 4-0 | 1-4 | 5-1 | 6-0 | 0-1 | 2-2 | 1-2 | 3-0 | 4-2 | 4-2 | 1-4 |
| 4 Bridport | 0-2 | 2-0 | 3-1 | | 1-3 | 0-4 | 1-0 | 2-1 | 1-1 | 1-4 | 2-1 | 4-3 | 0-3 | 1-0 | 2-3 | 0-3 | 1-4 | 0-3 | 2-2 | 0-2 |
| 5 Brislington | 2-3 | 2-1 | 0-0 | 1-1 | | 1-1 | 0-2 | 1-0 | 1-0 | 2-1 | 1-2 | 2-1 | 1-0 | 0-3 | 0-2 | 1-3 | 2-0 | 1-3 | 1-0 | 0-1 |
| 6 Bristol Manor Farm | 2-2 | 6-0 | 5-0 | 5-4 | 2-3 | | 2-2 | 1-3 | 2-1 | 3-1 | 1-1 | 4-0 | 6-0 | 0-0 | 1-0 | 3-2 | 5-0 | 6-0 | 3-2 | 0-1 |
| 7 Buckland Athletic | 1-0 | 4-0 | 2-0 | 2-1 | 2-1 | 4-3 | | 3-1 | 5-0 | 6-1 | 5-0 | 1-0 | 0-2 | 0-2 | 1-2 | 1-0 | 5-0 | 1-2 | 4-1 | 1-1 |
| 8 Cadbury Heath | 4-2 | 0-0 | 1-2 | 3-2 | 4-1 | 1-5 | 2-4 | | 1-1 | 0-0 | 1-2 | 0-2 | 4-4 | 1-1 | 2-2 | 2-2 | 3-2 | 3-1 | 1-0 | 6-2 |
| 9 Clevedon Town | 0-2 | 2-4 | 0-4 | 2-4 | 1-2 | 0-4 | 0-6 | 0-3 | | 0-1 | 1-4 | 2-1 | 2-1 | 1-4 | 0-5 | 0-1 | 1-2 | 2-3 | 1-0 | 1-4 |
| 10 Cribbs | 1-2 | 1-2 | 0-1 | 7-0 | 0-1 | 1-4 | 2-1 | 5-2 | 0-1 | | 1-4 | 2-2 | 2-3 | 0-3 | 0-2 | 2-2 | 1-0 | 2-5 | 4-0 | 1-1 |
| 11 Gillingham Town | 0-2 | 7-0 | 2-6 | 5-2 | 2-0 | 1-3 | 0-6 | 3-1 | 1-1 | 3-1 | | 0-1 | 4-0 | 1-1 | 0-2 | 0-1 | 0-0 | 2-0 | 2-2 | 1-1 |
| 12 Hallen | 0-2 | 1-1 | 2-1 | 2-1 | 3-2 | 0-6 | 1-3 | 1-3 | 5-1 | 2-1 | 2-5 | | 3-0 | 0-1 | 0-4 | 4-3 | 2-1 | 0-3 | 1-3 | 1-3 |
| 13 Longwell Green Sports | 2-0 | 0-3 | 1-1 | 1-1 | 1-1 | 1-4 | 0-4 | 2-0 | 1-1 | 1-2 | 1-1 | 2-1 | | 0-3 | 2-4 | 0-5 | 0-6 | 0-3 | 1-0 | 0-3 |
| 14 Melksham Town | 0-2 | 2-2 | 1-3 | 0-2 | 2-1 | 0-3 | 0-4 | 3-3 | 2-0 | 1-0 | 2-1 | 6-0 | 4-2 | | 4-0 | 0-1 | 2-1 | 1-2 | 2-1 | 2-0 |
| 15 Odd Down (Bath) | 1-1 | 0-2 | 0-4 | 2-0 | 1-0 | 2-1 | 0-0 | 4-0 | 6-1 | 2-0 | 1-3 | 7-1 | 5-3 | 1-0 | | 2-1 | 4-0 | 3-2 | 4-0 | 2-1 |
| 16 Shepton Mallet | 0-2 | 4-1 | 1-0 | 2-0 | 2-2 | 1-0 | 2-0 | 1-1 | 4-3 | 0-0 | 1-2 | 4-1 | 0-2 | 0-1 | 1-4 | | 1-0 | 0-5 | 3-2 | 0-2 |
| 17 Sherborne Town | 1-1 | 1-1 | 3-1 | 2-2 | 4-1 | 1-2 | 1-3 | 0-0 | 1-2 | 2-2 | 2-1 | 2-0 | 2-1 | 0-0 | 3-5 | 3-4 | | 2-1 | 1-0 | 0-4 |
| 18 Street | 2-1 | 1-2 | 2-5 | 3-2 | 3-0 | 2-4 | 2-2 | 2-1 | 4-1 | 1-1 | 5-1 | 5-3 | 0-0 | 0-1 | 1-3 | 0-0 | 4-0 | | 2-1 | 1-2 |
| 19 Welton Rovers | 0-7 | 1-0 | 0-5 | 1-1 | 2-3 | 0-2 | 2-2 | 2-5 | 1-1 | 1-3 | 1-1 | 1-1 | 1-5 | 1-2 | 1-4 | 2-0 | 1-1 | 1-2 | | 3-5 |
| 20 Willand Rovers | 0-4 | 3-1 | 2-2 | 3-0 | 3-1 | 1-4 | 0-0 | 2-1 | 0-1 | 1-2 | 4-3 | 2-0 | 5-1 | 2-2 | 2-1 | 0-2 | 1-1 | 2-1 | 1-3 | |

| | DIVISION ONE | 1 | 2 | 3 | 4 | 5 | 6 | 7 | 8 | 9 | 10 | 11 | 12 | 13 | 14 | 15 | 16 | 17 | 18 | 19 | 20 | 21 |
|---|---|---|---|---|---|---|---|---|---|---|---|---|---|---|---|---|---|---|---|---|---|---|
| 1 | Almondsbury UWE | | 1-3 | 2-0 | 3-0 | 3-3 | 1-1 | 6-1 | 0-1 | 1-1 | 3-2 | 1-1 | 1-0 | 0-3 | 1-2 | 1-0 | 4-0 | 4-1 | 2-3 | 1-4 | 5-0 | 4-0 |
| 2 | Ashton & Backwell United | 1-1 | | 5-0 | 4-2 | 1-2 | 1-3 | 0-2 | 2-1 | 2-1 | 2-2 | 0-1 | 2-0 | 3-4 | 2-1 | 1-1 | 3-1 | 1-2 | 1-0 | 2-2 | 5-0 | 6-3 |
| 3 | Bishop Sutton | 2-5 | 1-4 | | 0-2 | 1-2 | 1-3 | 1-4 | 0-3 | 0-3 | 1-3 | 0-2 | 2-4 | 0-6 | 2-2 | 1-6 | 1-0 | 0-2 | 0-8 | 1-2 | 2-1 | 1-6 |
| 4 | Calne Town | 2-1 | 2-2 | 2-1 | | 1-1 | 2-1 | 1-0 | 0-6 | 1-0 | 1-1 | 2-2 | 2-1 | 3-3 | 4-2 | 4-0 | 2-0 | 1-3 | 0-1 | 1-5 | 1-2 | 0-1 |
| 5 | Chard Town | 1-0 | 0-3 | 3-1 | 2-1 | | 0-2 | 0-0 | 2-3 | 3-1 | 3-0 | 1-0 | 0-2 | 0-3 | 1-1 | 0-0 | 2-1 | 2-0 | 3-0 | 1-2 | 2-0 | 3-0 |
| 6 | Cheddar | 1-0 | 1-1 | 3-0 | 6-1 | 1-2 | | 2-2 | 3-0 | 2-2 | 5-1 | 0-0 | 2-3 | 0-2 | 1-0 | 1-3 | 4-0 | 2-0 | 1-1 | 3-3 | 4-2 | 2-2 |
| 7 | Chippenham Park | 1-3 | 1-1 | 1-0 | 4-1 | 2-2 | 0-2 | | 0-1 | 2-2 | 0-2 | 0-1 | 0-0 | 0-1 | 3-1 | 2-0 | 2-3 | 0-2 | 2-1 | 4-2 | 4-0 | 2-1 |
| 8 | Chipping Sodbury Town | 2-1 | 3-1 | 8-1 | 1-2 | 1-1 | 2-0 | 4-0 | | 4-2 | 2-1 | 2-0 | 2-2 | 1-1 | 2-2 | 2-1 | 3-1 | 3-1 | 1-0 | 0-2 | 1-1 | 3-3 |
| 9 | Corsham Town | 1-1 | 2-3 | 1-0 | 1-2 | 1-2 | 4-1 | 0-1 | 1-1 | | 5-1 | 1-1 | 5-1 | 3-2 | 1-1 | 7-1 | 2-2 | 1-1 | 4-2 | 1-0 | 4-0 | 3-0 |
| 10 | Devizes Town | 1-0 | 0-3 | 4-1 | 4-2 | 0-3 | 1-2 | 1-0 | 0-3 | 1-2 | | 2-1 | 1-0 | 0-2 | 0-7 | 2-5 | 0-3 | 2-1 | 3-0 | 1-4 | 1-2 | 3-3 |
| 11 | Hengrove Athletic | 2-0 | 0-3 | 1-0 | 0-1 | 2-1 | 1-2 | 4-0 | 1-0 | 2-1 | 1-0 | | 2-0 | 0-2 | 1-1 | 4-3 | 4-1 | 1-2 | 0-0 | 3-1 | 7-0 | 2-0 |
| 12 | Keynsham Town | 3-2 | 4-1 | 8-1 | 2-1 | 6-1 | 4-2 | 2-2 | 1-4 | 3-2 | 5-2 | 2-0 | | 2-1 | 4-0 | 3-2 | 3-2 | 1-0 | 0-0 | 3-3 | 2-2 | 2-0 |
| 13 | Oldland Abbotonians | 3-1 | 3-4 | 0-0 | 1-3 | 0-2 | 0-2 | 2-1 | 3-0 | 2-3 | 6-1 | 0-2 | 2-0 | | 2-3 | 3-0 | 3-2 | 1-1 | 3-2 | 2-0 | 3-2 | 3-1 |
| 14 | Portishead Town | 2-1 | 1-1 | 1-0 | 3-1 | 1-0 | 1-2 | 0-0 | 3-1 | 2-1 | 2-1 | 0-1 | 3-2 | 1-3 | | 1-2 | 6-1 | 2-3 | 0-0 | 3-0 | 1-1 | 4-1 |
| 15 | Radstock Town | 0-3 | 2-1 | 2-0 | 2-1 | 0-3 | 1-2 | 0-0 | 2-4 | 0-1 | 3-1 | 0-0 | 2-1 | 2-0 | 2-2 | | 2-1 | 3-1 | 1-2 | 0-3 | 2-0 | 1-1 |
| 16 | Roman Glass St George | 2-4 | 2-2 | 6-2 | 2-1 | 2-2 | 1-2 | 0-3 | 1-0 | 0-1 | 7-3 | 1-0 | 2-4 | 2-2 | 1-2 | 2-6 | | 2-1 | 3-4 | 3-1 | 3-1 | 2-3 |
| 17 | Warminster Town | 1-2 | 2-1 | 3-2 | 1-1 | 1-2 | 2-3 | 0-2 | 0-1 | 1-0 | 2-2 | 2-1 | 1-0 | 0-1 | 0-4 | 2-1 | 2-2 | | 1-1 | 0-3 | 3-1 | 0-3 |
| 18 | Wellington | 1-1 | 0-2 | 3-1 | 1-0 | 2-5 | 1-2 | 0-0 | 2-0 | 3-0 | 7-0 | 0-1 | 3-1 | 1-1 | 1-2 | 3-1 | 4-4 | 3-3 | | 1-3 | 3-0 | 4-0 |
| 19 | Wells City | 2-0 | 0-2 | 5-1 | 4-2 | 2-1 | 4-2 | 2-1 | 3-0 | 4-1 | 2-2 | 1-2 | 2-0 | 3-0 | 0-4 | 1-4 | 1-1 | 4-2 | 2-1 | | 2-1 | 4-1 |
| 20 | Westbury United | 0-3 | 0-3 | 3-1 | 1-1 | 1-2 | 2-2 | 0-1 | 2-4 | 1-3 | 2-3 | 1-3 | 2-3 | 2-0 | 2-4 | 1-2 | 2-0 | 5-1 | 2-1 | 1-1 | | 3-1 |
| 21 | Wincanton Town | 2-2 | 2-1 | 5-0 | 1-3 | 1-4 | 3-1 | 1-1 | 3-4 | 4-6 | 4-0 | 3-0 | 1-0 | 1-2 | 0-5 | 3-2 | 1-2 | 4-1 | 0-1 | 2-2 | 4-1 | |

## LES PHILLIPS CUP

**HOLDERS:** WILLAND ROVERS

**PRELIMINARY ROUND**

| | | | |
|---|---|---|---|
| Odd Down (Bath) | v | Oldland Abbotonians | 1-2 |
| Shepton Mallet | v | Radstock Town | 1-0 |
| Bradford Town | v | Brislington | 3-2 (aet) |
| Corsham Town | v | Cheddar | 0-3 |
| Almondsbury UWE | v | Ashton & Backwell United | 1-0 |
| Longwell Green Sports | v | Chipping Sodbury Town | 2-0 |
| Wellington | v | Sherborne Town | 0-1 |
| Chard Town | v | Calne Town | 1-0 |
| Keynsham Town | v | Chippenham Park | 1-0 |
| Bridport | v | Bishop Sutton | 3-2 |

**ROUND 1**

| | | | |
|---|---|---|---|
| Winterbourne United | v | Street | 5-1 |
| Bradford Town | v | Devizes Town | 5-0 |
| Clevedon Town | v | Willand Rovers | 0-4 |
| Welton Rovers | v | Gillingham Town | 1-2 |
| Bitton | v | Hallen | 0-1 |
| Oldland Abbotonians | v | Buckland Athletic | 0-3 |
| Bristol Manor Farm | v | Wells City | 5-1 |
| Shepton Mallet | v | Bridport | 3-1 |
| Warminster Town | v | Cheddar | 1-4 |
| Cribbs | v | Portishead Town | 2-1 |
| Westbury United | v | Almondsbury UWE | 1-3 |
| Melksham Town | v | Longwell Green Sports | 2-0 |
| Sherborne Town | v | Cadbury Heath | 1-2 (aet) |
| Hengrove Athletic | v | Chard Town | 4-2 (aet) |
| Wincanton Town | v | Keynsham Town | 0-3 |
| Barnstaple Town | v | Roman Glass St George | 6-0 |

**ROUND 2**

| | | | |
|---|---|---|---|
| Winterbourne United | v | Bradford Town | AW |
| Willand Rovers | v | Gillingham Town | 2-1 |
| Hallen | v | Buckland Athletic | 0-4 |
| Bristol Manor Farm | v | Shepton Mallet | 4-3 |
| Cheddar | v | Cribbs | 0-4 |
| Almondsbury UWE | v | Melksham Town | 2-3 |
| Cadbury Heath | v | Hengrove Athletic | 1-2 |
| Keynsham Town | v | Barnstaple Town | 1-1, 7-6p |

**QUARTER FINALS**

| | | | |
|---|---|---|---|
| Bradford Town | v | Willand Rovers | 1-2 |
| Buckland Athletic | v | Bristol Manor Farm | 1-0 |
| Cribbs | v | Melksham Town | 1-4 (aet) |
| Hengrove Athletic | v | Keynsham Town | 1-0 |

**SEMI FINALS**

| | | | |
|---|---|---|---|
| Willand Rovers | v | Buckland Athletic | 1-0 |
| Melksham Town | v | Hengrove Athletic | 1-2 (aet) |

**FINAL**

| | | | |
|---|---|---|---|
| Willand Rovers | v | Hengrove Athletic | 1-2 |

## BITTON

Founded: 1922 Nickname: The Ton

**Secretary:** Rebecca Jones **(T)** 07966 590 633 **(E)** rebecca@johndeanbuilding.co.uk
**Chairman:** John Langdon **Manager:** Daniel Langdon
**Ground:** Rapid Solicitors Ground, Bath Road, Bitton, Bristol BS30 6HX. **(T)** 01179 323 222
**Capacity:** 1,000 **Seats:** 48 **Covered:** 200 **Midweek Matchday:** Tuesday **Clubhouse:** Yes

**Colours(change):** Red & white/black/black (Yellow/green/yellow)
**Previous Names:**
**Previous Leagues:** Avon Premier Combination, Gloucestershire County
**Records:** **Goalscorer:** A. Cole
**Honours:** Somerset Senior Cup 1992-93. Les Phillips Cup 2007-08. Western League Premier Division 2008-09.

**10 YEAR RECORD**

| 06-07 | 07-08 | 08-09 | 09-10 | 10-11 | 11-12 | 12-13 | 13-14 | 14-15 | 15-16 |
|---|---|---|---|---|---|---|---|---|---|
| WestP 8 | WestP 7 | WestP 1 | WestP 8 | WestP 2 | WestP 2 | WestP 7 | WestP 6 | WestP 7 | WestP 14 |

## BRADFORD TOWN

Founded: 1992 Nickname:

**Secretary:** Nikki Akers **(T)** 07866 693 167 **(E)** bradfordtownfc@gmail.com
**Chairman:** Mark Hodkinson **Manager:** Danny Greaves
**Ground:** Bradford Sports & Social Club, Trowbridge Rd, Bradford on Avon BA15 1EE **(T)** 07801 499 168
**Capacity:** **Seats:** **Covered:** **Midweek Matchday:** Wednesday **Clubhouse:** Yes

**Colours(change):** All blue (All red)
**Previous Names:**
**Previous Leagues:** Wiltshire Senior > 2005.
**Records:**
**Honours:** Western League Division One 2013-14.

**10 YEAR RECORD**

| 06-07 | 07-08 | 08-09 | 09-10 | 10-11 | 11-12 | 12-13 | 13-14 | 14-15 | 15-16 |
|---|---|---|---|---|---|---|---|---|---|
| West1 17 | West1 13 | West1 3 | West1 4 | West1 6 | West1 5 | West1 3 | West1 1 | WestP 8 | WestP 8 |

## BRIDPORT

Founded: 1885 Nickname: Bees

**Secretary:** Chris Tozer **(T)** 07500 064 317 **(E)** sevie@tiscali.co.uk
**Chairman:** Adrian Scadding **Manager:** Adam Scadding
**Ground:** St Mary's Field, Bridport, Dorset DT6 5LN **(T)** 01308 423 834
**Capacity:** **Seats:** **Covered:** **Midweek Matchday:** Tuesday **Clubhouse:** Yes

**Colours(change):** Red/black/black (All yellow)
**Previous Names:**
**Previous Leagues:** Dorset Combination 1984-89.
**Records:** **Att:** 1,150 v Exeter City 1981.
**Honours:** Dorset Senior Cup x8. Dorset Senior Amateur Cup x6.

**10 YEAR RECORD**

| 06-07 | 07-08 | 08-09 | 09-10 | 10-11 | 11-12 | 12-13 | 13-14 | 14-15 | 15-16 |
|---|---|---|---|---|---|---|---|---|---|
| West1 11 | West1 18 | West1 13 | West1 10 | West1 3 | WestP 14 | WestP 14 | WestP 12 | WestP 14 | WestP 16 |

## BRISLINGTON

Founded: 1956 Nickname: Bris

**Secretary:** Angela Hazel **(T)** 07724 829090 **(E)** brislingtonsecretary@gmail.com
**Chairman:** Steve Jenkins **Manager:** Lee Perks
**Ground:** Ironmould Lane, Brislington, Bristol BS4 4TZ **(T)** 01179 774 030
**Capacity:** 2,000 **Seats:** 144 **Covered:** 1,500 **Midweek Matchday:** Tuesday **Clubhouse:** Yes **Shop:** No

**Colours(change):** Red & black/black/black. (All royal blue)
**Previous Names:**
**Previous Leagues:** Somerset Senior until 1991
**Records:**
**Honours:** Somerset Senior League 1988-89. Somerset Premier Cup 1992-93. Western League Division One 1994-95.

**10 YEAR RECORD**

| 06-07 | 07-08 | 08-09 | 09-10 | 10-11 | 11-12 | 12-13 | 13-14 | 14-15 | 15-16 |
|---|---|---|---|---|---|---|---|---|---|
| WestP 17 | WestP 13 | WestP 10 | WestP 9 | WestP 15 | WestP 7 | WestP 2 | WestP 10 | WestP 10 | WestP 11 |

## BRISTOL MANOR FARM

Founded: 1964 Nickname: The Farm

**Secretary:** Richard Lloyd **(T)** 07840 888 735 **(E)** nonskittler@msn.com
**Chairman:** Geoff Sellek **Manager:** Lee Lashenko
**Ground:** The Creek, Portway, Sea Mills, Bristol BS9 2HS **(T)** 0117 968 3571
**Capacity:** 2,000 **Seats:** 98 **Covered:** 350 **Midweek Matchday:** Tuesday **Clubhouse:** Yes **Shop:** No

**Colours(change):** Red/black/black (Yellow/blue/yellow)
**Previous Names:**
**Previous Leagues:** Bristol Suburban 64-69, Somerset Senior 69-77
**Records:** **Att;** 500 v Portway **App:** M. Baird
**Honours:** Western League Division One 1982-83.
Gloucestershire Challenge Trophy 1987-88, 2015-16. Gloucestershire Amateur Cup 1989-90.

**10 YEAR RECORD**

| 06-07 | 07-08 | 08-09 | 09-10 | 10-11 | 11-12 | 12-13 | 13-14 | 14-15 | 15-16 |
|---|---|---|---|---|---|---|---|---|---|
| WestP 12 | WestP 16 | WestP 5 | WestP 7 | WestP 7 | WestP 8 | WestP 18 | WestP 2 | WestP 4 | WestP 3 |

## BUCKLAND ATHLETIC

Founded: 1977 Nickname: The Bucks

**Secretary:** Christine Holmes **(T)** 07856 525 730 **(E)** phardingham@virginmedia.com
**Chairman:** Roy Holmes **Manager:** Ellis Laight
**Ground:** Homers Heath, South Quarry, Kingskerswell Road, Newton Abbot TQ12 5JU **(T)** 01626 361 020
**Capacity:** **Seats:** Yes **Covered:** Yes **Midweek Matchday:** Wednesday **Clubhouse:** Yes

**Colours(change):** Yellow with black trim/yellow/yellow (All navy blue)
**Previous Names:**
**Previous Leagues:** Devon County League 2000-07. South West Pininsula.
**Records:**
**Honours:** South West Peninsula League Premier Division 2009-10, 10-11. Throgmorton Cup 2009-10.

**10 YEAR RECORD**

| 06-07 | 07-08 | 08-09 | 09-10 | 10-11 | 11-12 | 12-13 | 13-14 | 14-15 | 15-16 |
|---|---|---|---|---|---|---|---|---|---|
| Devon 13 | SWPP 14 | SWPP 3 | SWPP 1 | SWPP 1 | SWPP 2 | WestP 10 | WestP 11 | WestP 2 | WestP 4 |

## CADBURY HEATH

Founded: Nickname:

**Secretary:** Martin Painter **(T)** 07971 399 268 **(E)** martinbristol1955@hotmail.com
**Chairman:** Steve Plenty **Manager:** Andy Black
**Ground:** Springfield, Cadbury Heath Road, Bristol BS30 8BX **(T)** 07971 399 268
**Capacity:** **Seats:** **Covered:** **Midweek Matchday:** Wednesday **Clubhouse:** Yes

**Colours(change):** Red & white/red/red (Yellow/blue/blue)
**Previous Names:**
**Previous Leagues:** Gloucestershire County 1968-75, 80-2000. Midland Combination 1975-77.
**Records:**
**Honours:** Gloucestershire County League 1998-99. Western League Division One 2011-12.

**10 YEAR RECORD**

| 06-07 | 07-08 | 08-09 | 09-10 | 10-11 | 11-12 | 12-13 | 13-14 | 14-15 | 15-16 |
|---|---|---|---|---|---|---|---|---|---|
| West1 9 | West1 5 | West1 4 | West1 11 | West1 4 | West1 1 | WestP 4 | WestP 13 | WestP 11 | WestP 12 |

## CHIPPING SODBURY TOWN

Founded: 1885 Nickname:

**Secretary:** Justin Carpenter **(T)** 07980 967 738 **(E)** justincarpenter@outlook.com
**Chairman:** Mike Fox **Manager:** Karl Reese
**Ground:** The Ridings, Wickwar Road, Chipping Sodbury, Bristol BS37 6BQ **(T)** 07980 967 738
**Capacity:** **Seats:** **Covered:** **Midweek Matchday:** Tuesday **Clubhouse:**

**Colours(change):** Black & white stripes/black/black (Red & white/white/white)
**Previous Names:**
**Previous Leagues:** Gloucester County >2015.
**Records:**
**Honours:** Western League Division One 2015-16.

**10 YEAR RECORD**

| 06-07 | 07-08 | 08-09 | 09-10 | 10-11 | 11-12 | 12-13 | 13-14 | 14-15 | 15-16 |
|---|---|---|---|---|---|---|---|---|---|
| | | GlCo 17 | GlCo 8 | GlCo 3 | GlCo 18 | GlCo 15 | GlCo 11 | GlCo 3 | West1 1 |

## CLEVEDON TOWN
Founded: 1880 Nickname: Seasiders

**Secretary:** Brian Rose **(T)** 07768 100 632 **(E)** brian.rose@blueyonder.co.uk
**Chairman:** Mark Lewis **Manager:** Micky Bell
**Ground:** Hand Stadium, Davis Lane, Clevedon BS21 6TG **(T)**
**Capacity:** 3,500 **Seats:** 300 **Covered:** 1,600 **Midweek Matchday:** Wednesday **Clubhouse:** Yes **Shop:** Yes

**Colours(change):** Blue with white stripes/blue/blue (Yellow & black/blue/yellow)
**Previous Names:** Clevedon FC and Ashtonians merged in 1974
**Previous Leagues:** Weston & District, Somerset Senior, Bristol Charity, Bristol & District, Bristol Suburban, Western 1974-93, Sthern 1993-2015.
**Records:** 2,300 v Billingham Synthonia - FA Amateur Cup 1952-53
**Honours:** Somerset Senior Cup 1901-02, 04-05, 28-29, 2000-01, 01-02. Somerset Premier Cup x4.
Southern League Western Division 1992-93, 2005-06, Midland Division 1998-99.

**10 YEAR RECORD**

| 06-07 | 07-08 | 08-09 | 09-10 | 10-11 | 11-12 | 12-13 | 13-14 | 14-15 | 15-16 |
|---|---|---|---|---|---|---|---|---|---|
| SthP 18 | SthP 11 | SthP 18 | SthP 21 | Sthsw 20 | Sthsw 20 | Sthsw 15 | Sthsw 17 | Sthsw 18 | WestP 19 |

## CRIBBS
Founded: 1958 Nickname:

**Secretary:** Simon Hartley **(T)** 07970 744 063 **(E)** welshwizard1973@aol.com
**Chairman:** Dave Nelson **Manager:** Tony Beecham
**Ground:** The Lawns, Station Road, Henbury, Bristol BS10 7TB **(T)** 0117 950 2303
**Capacity:** **Seats:** **Covered:** **Midweek Matchday:** Tuesday **Clubhouse:**

**Colours(change):** All blue (Red/red/white)
**Previous Names:** AXA>211. Cribbs Friends Life 2011-13
**Previous Leagues:** Gloucestershire County > 2012.
**Records:**
**Honours:** Gloucester County League 2011-12.

**10 YEAR RECORD**

| 06-07 | 07-08 | 08-09 | 09-10 | 10-11 | 11-12 | 12-13 | 13-14 | 14-15 | 15-16 |
|---|---|---|---|---|---|---|---|---|---|
| GlCo 11 | GlCo 5 | GlCo 6 | GlCo 11 | GlCo 2 | GlCo 1 | West1 8 | West1 5 | West1 3 | WestP 5 |

## GILLINGHAM TOWN
Founded: 1879 Nickname:

**Secretary:** Matthew Baker **(T)** 07725 623 195 **(E)** matt@yellowboxsolutions.co.uk
**Chairman:** Pat Fricker **Manager:** Neil Waddleton
**Ground:** Hardings Lane, Gillingham, Dorset SP8 4HX **(T)** 01747 823 673
**Capacity:** **Seats:** **Covered:** **Midweek Matchday:** Tuesday **Clubhouse:** Yes

**Colours(change):** All tangerine (Sky blue/navy/navy)
**Previous Names:**
**Previous Leagues:** Dorset Premier 1970-2008.
**Records:**
**Honours:**

**10 YEAR RECORD**

| 06-07 | 07-08 | 08-09 | 09-10 | 10-11 | 11-12 | 12-13 | 13-14 | 14-15 | 15-16 |
|---|---|---|---|---|---|---|---|---|---|
| Dor P 9 | Dor P 2 | Dor P 12 | Dor P 3 | Dor P 7 | West1 3 | WestP 3 | WestP 3 | WestP 15 | WestP 9 |

## HALLEN
Founded: 1949 Nickname:

**Secretary:** Richard Stokes **(T)** 07791 492 640 **(E)** sinbad88@hotmail.co.uk
**Chairman:** Lee Fairman **Manager:** Tom Collett
**Ground:** Hallen Centre, Moorhouse Lane, Hallen Bristol BS10 7RU **(T)** 01179 505 559
**Capacity:** 2,000 **Seats:** 200 **Covered:** 200 **Midweek Matchday:** Tuesday **Clubhouse:** Yes

**Colours(change):** Navy & royal blue/black/royal blue (All yellow)
**Previous Names:** Lawrence Weston Ath, Lawrence Weston Hallen
**Previous Leagues:** Gloucestershire County, Hellenic
**Records:** **Att:** 803 v Bristol Rovers 1997
**Honours:** Gloucestershire Co. Lge 1988-89, 92-93. Western Division One 2003-04.

**10 YEAR RECORD**

| 06-07 | 07-08 | 08-09 | 09-10 | 10-11 | 11-12 | 12-13 | 13-14 | 14-15 | 15-16 |
|---|---|---|---|---|---|---|---|---|---|
| WestP 9 | WestP 15 | WestP 9 | WestP 12 | WestP 16 | WestP 4 | WestP 9 | WestP 15 | WestP 17 | WestP 17 |

## LONGWELL GREEN SPORTS

Founded: 1966 Nickname: The Green

**Secretary:** David Heal **(T)** 07954 466 599 **(E)** daveheal04@gmail.com
**Chairman:** John Gibbs **Manager:** Ali Biggs
**Ground:** Longwell Green Com. Centre, Shellards Road BS30 9AD **(T)** 01179 323 722
**Capacity:** 1,000 **Seats:** Yes **Covered:** 100 **Midweek Matchday:** Tuesday **Clubhouse:** Yes **Shop:** Yes

**Colours(change):** Blue & white/black/black (Yellow/blue/blue)
**Previous Names:** None
**Previous Leagues:** Gloucestershire County.
**Records:** **Att:** 500 v Mangotsfield 2005
**Honours:**

**10 YEAR RECORD**

| 06-07 | 07-08 | 08-09 | 09-10 | 10-11 | 11-12 | 12-13 | 13-14 | 14-15 | 15-16 |
|---|---|---|---|---|---|---|---|---|---|
| West1 8 | West1 8 | West1 2 | WestP 11 | WestP 17 | WestP 13 | WestP 15 | WestP 14 | WestP 16 | WestP 18 |

## MELKSHAM TOWN

Founded: 1876 Nickname: Town

**Secretary:** Mark Jeffery **(T)** 07739 905 575 **(E)** markmtfc@virginmedia.com
**Chairman:** Dave Wiltshire **Manager:** Darren Perrin
**Ground:** Eastern Way, Melksham, Wiltshire, SN12 7GU **(T)**
**Capacity:** **Seats:** Yes **Covered:** Yes **Midweek Matchday:** Monday **Clubhouse:** Yes

**Colours(change):** Yellow/black/black (All red)
**Previous Names:** Melksham > 1951.
**Previous Leagues:**
**Records:** **Att:** 2,821 v Trowbridge Town, FA Cup 1957-58.
**Honours:** Western League Division 1 1979-80, 96-97, Premier Division 2014-15.
Wiltshire Shield x6. Wiltshire Senior Cup x6 Most recently 2015-16.

**10 YEAR RECORD**

| 06-07 | 07-08 | 08-09 | 09-10 | 10-11 | 11-12 | 12-13 | 13-14 | 14-15 | 15-16 |
|---|---|---|---|---|---|---|---|---|---|
| WestP 5 | WestP 11 | WestP 11 | WestP 19 | WestP 8 | West1 2 | WestP 13 | WestP 7 | WestP 1 | WestP 5 |

## ODD DOWN (BATH)

Founded: 1901 Nickname: The Down

**Secretary:** Lorraine Brown **(T)** 07734 924 435 **(E)** lorainebrown@btinternet.com
**Chairman:** Dave Loxton **Manager:** Ray Johnston
**Ground:** Lew Hill Memorial Ground, Combe Hay Lane, Odd Down BA2 8PA **(T)** 01225 832 491
**Capacity:** 1,000 **Seats:** 160 **Covered:** 250 **Midweek Matchday:** Tuesday **Clubhouse:** Yes **Shop:** No

**Colours(change):** Blue & white/blue/white (Yellow & blue/blue/yellow)
**Previous Names:**
**Previous Leagues:** Wilts Premier, Bath & District & Somerset Senior
**Records:** **App:** Steve Fuller 475 **Goalscorer:** Joe Matano 104
**Honours:** Western League Premier Division 2015-16.

**10 YEAR RECORD**

| 06-07 | 07-08 | 08-09 | 09-10 | 10-11 | 11-12 | 12-13 | 13-14 | 14-15 | 15-16 |
|---|---|---|---|---|---|---|---|---|---|
| WestP 11 | WestP 21 | West1 19 | West1 2 | WestP 8 | WestP 9 | WestP 8 | WestP 4 | WestP 5 | WestP 1 |

## SHEPTON MALLET

Founded: 1986 Nickname:

**Secretary:** Gary Banfield **(T)** 07762 880 705 **(E)** gkrkb@tiscali.co.uk
**Chairman:** John Hugill **Manager:** Rob Cousins
**Ground:** Playing Fields, Old Wells Road, West Shepton, Shepton Mallet BA4 5XN **(T)** 01749 344 609
**Capacity:** 2,500 **Seats:** 120 **Covered:** Yes **Midweek Matchday:** Tuesday **Clubhouse:** Yes

**Colours(change):** Black & white/black/black & white (Navy & yellow/navy/navy)
**Previous Names:**
**Previous Leagues:** Somerset Senior.
**Records:** **Att:** 274 v Chippenham Town FA Cup 2000-01.
**Honours:** Somerset Senior League 2000-01.
Somerset Senior Cup 1997-98.

**10 YEAR RECORD**

| 06-07 | 07-08 | 08-09 | 09-10 | 10-11 | 11-12 | 12-13 | 13-14 | 14-15 | 15-16 |
|---|---|---|---|---|---|---|---|---|---|
| West1 20 | West1 11 | West1 17 | West1 17 | West1 14 | West1 16 | West1 7 | West1 2 | WestP 9 | WestP 10 |

## SHERBORNE TOWN

Founded: 1894 Nickname:

**Secretary:** Colin Goodland **(T)** 07929 090 612 **(E)** colingoodland@live.co.uk
**Chairman:** John Bowers **Manager:** Gerry Pearson
**Ground:** Raleigh Grove, Terrace Playing Field, Sherborne DT9 5NS **(T)** 01935 816 110
**Capacity:** **Seats:** Yes **Covered:** Yes **Midweek Matchday:** Wednesday **Clubhouse:** Yes

**Colours(change):** Black & white/black/white (Green/white/black).
**Previous Names:**
**Previous Leagues:** Dorset Premier
**Records:** **Att:** 1,000 v Eastleigh, Andy Shephard Memorial match 27.07.03.
**Honours:** Dorset Premier League 1981-82, Dorset Senior Cup 2003-04.
Western League Division One 2012-13.

**10 YEAR RECORD**

| 06-07 | 07-08 | 08-09 | 09-10 | 10-11 | 11-12 | 12-13 | 13-14 | 14-15 | 15-16 |
|---|---|---|---|---|---|---|---|---|---|
| West1 4 | West1 2 | WestP 12 | WestP 18 | WestP 14 | WestP 17 | West1 1 | WestP 9 | WestP 12 | WestP 13 |

## STREET

Founded: 1880 Nickname: The Cobblers

**Secretary:** James Vickery **(T)** 07792 866 367 **(E)** streetfootballclub@outlook.com
**Chairman:** Ian Badman **Manager:** Richard Fey
**Ground:** The Tannery Ground, Middlebrooks, Street BA16 0TA **(T)** 01458 445 987
**Capacity:** 2,000 **Seats:** 120 **Covered:** 25 **Midweek Matchday:** Tuesday **Clubhouse:** Yes

**Colours(change):** Green/white/green (All red)
**Previous Names:** None
**Previous Leagues:** Somerset Senior.
**Records:** **Att;** 4,300 v Yeovil Town FA Cup 47
**Honours:** Somerset Senior League 1996-97.

**10 YEAR RECORD**

| 06-07 | 07-08 | 08-09 | 09-10 | 10-11 | 11-12 | 12-13 | 13-14 | 14-15 | 15-16 |
|---|---|---|---|---|---|---|---|---|---|
| WLaP 19 | WestP 18 | WestP 13 | WestP 6 | WestP 13 | WestP 10 | WestP 6 | WestP 5 | WestP 13 | WestP 7 |

## WELLS CITY

Founded: 1890 Nickname:

**Secretary:** David Green **(T)** 07584 045 238 **(E)** daveg55@hotmail.co.uk
**Chairman:** Steve Loxton **Manager:** Mark Read
**Ground:** Athletic Ground, Rowdens Road, Wells, Somerset BA5 1TU **(T)** 01749 679 971
**Capacity:** **Seats:** **Covered:** **Midweek Matchday:** Tuesday **Clubhouse:**

**Colours(change):** All blue (All yellow)
**Previous Names:**
**Previous Leagues:** Somerset County.
**Records:**
**Honours:** Western League Division One 2009-10.
Somerset Premier Cup 2015-16.

**10 YEAR RECORD**

| 06-07 | 07-08 | 08-09 | 09-10 | 10-11 | 11-12 | 12-13 | 13-14 | 14-15 | 15-16 |
|---|---|---|---|---|---|---|---|---|---|
| SomP 5 | SomP 2 | West1 10 | West1 1 | WestP 9 | WestP 12 | WestP 19 | West1 6 | West1 19 | West1 2 |

## WILLAND ROVERS

Founded: 1946 Nickname: Rovers

**Secretary:** Dom Clark **(T)** 07546 561 212 **(E)** domclarkwillandrovers@gmail.com
**Chairman:** Mike Mitchell **Manager:** Russel Jee
**Ground:** Silver Street, Willand, Collumpton, Devon EX15 2RG **(T)** 01884 33885
**Capacity:** 2,000 **Seats:** 75 **Covered:** 150 **Midweek Matchday:** Wednesday **Clubhouse:** Yes

**Colours(change):** White/blue/blue (Yellow/blue/yellow)
**Previous Names:** None.
**Previous Leagues:** Devon County.
**Records:** **Att:** 650 v Newton Abbot 1992-3 **Goalscorer:** Paul Foreman
**Honours:** Devon County League 1998-99, 00-01, Western League Division One 2004-05, Les Phillips Cup 2006-07.

**10 YEAR RECORD**

| 06-07 | 07-08 | 08-09 | 09-10 | 10-11 | 11-12 | 12-13 | 13-14 | 14-15 | 15-16 |
|---|---|---|---|---|---|---|---|---|---|
| WestP 6 | WestP 3 | WestP 3 | WestP 2 | WestP 4 | WestP 5 | WestP 11 | WestP 8 | WestP 6 | WestP 6 |

# PREMIER DIVISION GROUND DIRECTIONS

**BITTON - Recreation Ground, Bath Road, Bitton, Bristol BS30 6HX 0117 932 3222 -** From M4 leave at Junction 18. Take A46 towards Bath, at first roundabout take A420 for Wick / Bridgeyate. On approach to Bridgeyate turn left at mini-roundabout onto A4175 and follow for 2.2 miles, then turn left for Bath on A431. The ground is 100 yards on the right.

From Bath take A431, go through Kelston and Bitton village. Ground is on the left. From Chippenham take A420 to Bristol and turn left at mini-roundabout onto A4175 and follow as above.

**BRADFORD TOWN - Bradford Sports & Social Club, Trowbridge Road, Bradford on Avon, Wiltshire BA15 1EW 01225 866 649 -** From Bath or Melksham on entering Bradford on Avon follow the signs for A363 to Trowbridge. The ground is after a mini roundabout and behind a stone wall on the right hand side. From Trowbridge, follow A363 to Bradford-on-Avon. The ground is just past shop on right, behind stone wall on left.

**BRIDPORT - St Marys Field, Bridport, Dorset DT6 5LN 01308 423 834 -** Follow Bridport by-pass in any direction to the Crown Inn roundabout. Take exit to town centre, at first set of traffic lights (Morrisons) turn left. Ground is 200 yards on the right.

**BRISLINGTON - Ironmould Lane, Brislington, Bristol BS4 4TZ 0117 977 4030 -** On A4 Bristol to Bath road, about 500 yards on Bath side of Park & Ride. Opposite the Wyevale Garden Centre.

**BRISTOL MANOR FARM - The Creek, Portway, Sea Mills, Bristol BS9 2HS 0117 968 3571 -** Leaving M5 at Junction 18, take A4 marked Bristol. U-turn on dual carriageway by Bristol and West Sports Ground and then ground is half-mile on left hand side

**BUCKLAND ATHLETIC - Homers Heath, Kingskerwell Road, Newton Abbot TQ12 5JU - 01626 361020 - From Plymouth :** Take the exit off the A38 marked Newton Abbot. Travel for approx 5 miles until you come to a roundabout. Turn left and head downhill towards another Roundabout. Turn right & drive for approx 800 yards. Go straight across the B&Q R/bout. Travel along the avenue, and at the top end of this road, turn left and head towards the train Station. Go past the station, go over the railway and get into the right hand lane. At the 2nd set of traffic lights turn right. Go under the railway and follow this road to the next mini roundabout. Go straight across. Go up the hill and down the other side. The ground is situated on the right hand side, opposite Combined linen services. **From Exeter:** Take the A380 signposted Torquay and travel along this road until you reach Penn Inn roundabout. Take the right hand lane and follow the road around which takes you into the left lane and towards the town centre. Take the 1st left and you are now on the main road towards Decoy. The same directions then apply as above. Coaches will not be able to go through the tunnel at Decoy. Please phone for these directions.

**CADBURY HEATH - Springfield, Cadbury Heath Road, Bristol BS30 8BX 0117 967 5731 (social club) -** M5-M4-M32 Exit 1 follow signs for ring road, exit roundabout for Cadbury Heath left, 100m mini roundabout straight across, 400m mini roundabout turn right into Tower Road North, 150m turn right into Cadbury Heath Road, ground 50m on right via Cadbury Heath Social Club car park.

**CHIPPING SODBURY TOWN - The Ridings, Wickwar Road, Chipping Sodbury, BS37 6GA -** Travelling north and south M5 – Exit at junction 14, B4509 follow signs to WickWar, at roundabout take third exit onto B4058, turn left onto B4509, at "T" junction turn right onto Wickwar High Street B4060. At mini roundabout continue forward onto Sodbury Road. Road merges into the Wickwar Road, continue on this road for two miles. Ground is on the left hand side. Travelling east and west M4 – Exit at junction 18, A46 Bath Road, follow signs to Yate. At traffic lights bear left onto A432 Badminton Road, stay on this road for three miles. At roundabout take third exit Wickwar Road. Ground is on the right hand side

**CORSHAM TOWN - Southbank, Lacock Road, Corsham, Wiltshire SN13 9HS 01249 715609 -** A4 into Corsham, at Hare and Hounds Roundabout take the Melksham Road B3353 until the War Memorial, then Lacock Road. Ground a half a mile on the right side.

**CRIBBS - The Lawns, Station Road, Henbury, Bristol BS10 7TB - 0117 950 2303 -** From M5 J17 follow signs to Bristol West & Clifton on the A4018 dual carriageway cross two roundabouts, at 3rd roundabout take fourth exit and follow signs to M5, take 1st turning left after car dealers, ground straight ahead.

**GILLINGHAM TOWN - Hardings Lane, Gillingham, Dorset SP8 4HX 01747 823 673 -** Proceed to middle of town to the High Street. Hardings Lane is a turning off of the High Street, at the Shaftesbury or Southern end of the High Street.

**HALLEN - Hallen Centre, Moorhouse Lane, Hallen, Bristol BS10 7RU 0117 950 5559 -** From Junction 17 M5 follow A4018 towards Bristol. At third roundabout turn right into Crow Lane. Proceed to T junction - turn right and right again at mini roundabout by Henbury Lodge Hotel. At next mini roundabout turn left into Avonmouth Way. Continue for 1.5 miles into Hallen village. At crossroads turn left into Moorhouse Lane

**ILFRACOMBE TOWN - Marlborough Park, Ilfracombe, Devon EX34 8PD 01271 865 939 -** Take A361 for Ilfracombe and in town take first right after traffic lights. Follow Marlborough Road to top and ground is on the left.

**LONGWELL GREEN SPORTS - Longwell Green Community Centre, Shellards Road, Longwell Green BS30 9DW 0117 932 3722 -** Leave Junction 1 M32 follow signs for Ring Road (A4174). At Kingsfield roundabout turn into Marsham Way. At first set of traffic lights turn left into Woodward Drive. Continue to min roundabout and turn right into Parkway Road and continue to Shellards Road. Ground is situated to the rear of the Community Centre.

**MELKSHAM TOWN - Eastern Way, Melksham, Wiltshire, SN12 7GU -** From north continue on A350 past Asda following signs to Bowerhill. At big roundabout "The Spa" take first exit signposted Calne (A3102). At next roundabout take second exit (A3102 Calne) and continue one mile until reaching roundabout, second left, ground 800 yards on the right..

**ODD DOWN - Lew Hill, Memorial Ground, Combe Hay Lane, Odd Down, Bath BA2 8AP 01225 832 491 -** Situated behind Odd Down Park & Ride on main A367 Bath to Exeter road.

**SHEPTON MALLET - Playing Fields, Old Wells Road, West Shepton, Shepton Mallet BA4 5XN - 01749 344 609 -** From the town take B3136 (Glastonbury Road) for approximately 1/2 mile. Turn right at junction of Old Wells Road near King William Public House. Approximately 300 yards up the Old Wells Road turn left into the playing fields.

**SHERBORNE TOWN - Raleigh Grove, The Terrace Playing Field, Sherborne, Dorset DT9 5NS 01935 816 110 -** From Yeovil take A30 - marked Sherborne. On entering town turn right at traffic lights, over next traffic lights and at the next junction turn right. Go over bridge, take second left marked 'Terrace Pling Fields'. Turn into car park, football club car park is situated in the far right-hand corner.

**STREET - The Tannery Field, Middlebrooks, Street, Somerset BA16 0TA 01458 445 987 -** Ground is signposted from both ends of A39 and B3151.

**WELLS CITY - Athletic Ground, Rowdens Road, Wells, Somerset BA5 1TU 01749 679 971 -** From North & Southwest - Follow A39 to Strawberry Way to roundabout, follow A371 East Somerset Way and take right turn into Rowdens Road. Ground is on left. From East - Follow A371 from Shepton Mallet. After approximately 5 miles on East Somerset Way take left turn into Rowdens Road. Ground is on left.

**WILLAND ROVERS - Silver Street, Willand, Cullompton, Devon EX15 2RG 01884 33885 -** Leave M5 Junction 27 and take first left at roundabout. Follow signs to Willand. After passing Halfway House pub on right, go straight over mini-roundabout (signposted to Cullompton) ground is 400 metres on left hand side.

## ALMONDSBURY U.W.E.

Founded: Nickname:

**Secretary:** Douglas Coles **(T)** 07748 655 399 **(E)** doug2004.coles@blueyonder.co.uk
**Chairman:** Mike Blessing **Manager:** John Black
**Ground:** The Field, Almondsbury, Bristol BS32 4AA **(T)** 01454 612 240
**Colours(change):** Green & white/green/green (Yellow & blue/yellow/blue)
**ADDITIONAL INFORMATION:**

## ASHTON & BACKWELL UNITED

Founded: 2010 Nickname:

**Secretary:** Miss Charlie Cole **(T)** 07866 024 499 **(E)** ashtonbackwellsecretary@gmail.com
**Chairman:** Jim Biggins **Manager:** Richard Coombes
**Ground:** The Lancer Scott Stadium, West Town Road, Backwell. BS48 3HQ **(T)** 01275 461 273
**Colours(change):** Maroon & navy/navy/navy (Yellow & royal blue/royal blue/yellow)
**ADDITIONAL INFORMATION:**
**Previous Names:** Formed when Backwell United merged with the Senior and Youth section of Ashton Boys FC.

## BISHOP SUTTON

Founded: 1977 Nickname: Bishops

**Secretary:** Malcolm Hunt **(T)** 07799 623 901 **(E)** bishopsuttonafcsecretary@hotmail.co.uk
**Chairman:** Colin Merrick **Manager:** Colin Merrick
**Ground:** Lakeview, Wick Road, Bishops Sutton, Bristol BS39 5XN. **(T)** 07532 126 483 **Capacity:** 1,500
**Colours(change):** All blue (All yellow)
**ADDITIONAL INFORMATION: Att:** 400 v Bristol City
Somerset Junior Cup 1980-81. Western League Division One 1997-98, Premier Division 2012-13.

## BISHOPS LYDEARD

Founded: Nickname:

**Secretary:** Gary Brown **(T)** 07956 682 367 **(E)** doggybrown@msn.com
**Chairman:** Gary Brown **Manager:** Brett Andrews
**Ground:** Cottlestone Road, Bishops Lydeard, Taunton, TA4 3BA **(T)** 07956 682 367
**Colours(change):** Red & black stripes/black/black (Yellow/blue/blue)
**ADDITIONAL INFORMATION:**
Somerset County League Premier Division 2015-16.

## CALNE TOWN

Founded: 1886 Nickname: Lilywhites

**Secretary:** Wayne McLaughlin **(T)** 07795 833 702 **(E)** wmm498@msn.com
**Chairman:** Simon Gardner **Manager:** Neurin Jones
**Ground:** Bremhill View, Calne, Wiltshire SN11 9EE **(T)** 07795 833 702
**Colours(change):** Black & white/black/black (All blue)
**ADDITIONAL INFORMATION:**
**Record Att:** 1,100 v Swindon, friendly 1987. **Goalscorer:** Robbie Lardner. **Apps:** Gary Swallow - 259.
**Honours:** Wiltshire Senior Cup x4 Most recently 2011-12.

## CHARD TOWN

Founded: Nickname: The Robins

**Secretary:** Gavin Churhill **(T)** 07813 714 815 **(E)** chardtownfcsecretary@outlook.com
**Chairman:** Lyndsey Gage
**Ground:** Denning Sports Field, Zembard Lane, Chard, Somerset TA20 1JL **(T)** 01460 61402
**Colours(change):** Red/red/white (Dark blue/dark blue/white)
**ADDITIONAL INFORMATION:**
**Honours:** Somerset Senior League 1949-50, 53-54, 59-60, 67-68, 69-70. Somerset Senior Cup 1952-53, 66-67.
South West Counties Cup 1988-89.

## CHEDDAR

Founded: 1892 Nickname: The Cheesemen

**Secretary:** Alan Cooper **(T)** 07845 870 8121 **(E)** alancooper7@sky.com
**Chairman:** Simon Brooks **Manager:** Jared Greenhalgh
**Ground:** Bowdens Park, Draycott Road, Cheddar BS27 3RL **(T)** 01934 707 271
**Colours(change):** Yellow & black/black/yellow (All blue)
**ADDITIONAL INFORMATION:**
**Previous Leagues:** Cheddar Valley. Weston Super Mare & District. Somerset Senior > 2012.
**Honours:** Cheddar Valley League 1910-11. Somerset Senior League Premier Division 2011-12.

## CHIPPENHAM PARK

Founded: | Nickname:

**Secretary:** Tim Smith | **(T)** 07528 796 837 | **(E)** tim.smith@bristol.ac.uk
**Chairman:** Damien Coulter | **Manager:** Dave Ferris
**Ground:** Hardenhuish Park, Bristol Road, Chippenham SN14 6LR | **(T)** 01249 650 400
**Colours(change):** All blue (All green)
**ADDITIONAL INFORMATION:**
**Previous League:** Wiltshire > 2013.

## CORSHAM TOWN

Founded: 1884 | Nickname:

**Secretary:** Richard Taylor | **(T)** 07944 183 973 | **(E)** richtaylor_ctfc@hotmail.com
**Chairman:** Tim Parker | **Manager:** Nigel Tripp
**Ground:** Southbank Ground, Lacock Road, Corsham SN13 9HS | **(T)** 07963 030 652 | **Capacity:** 1,500
**Colours(change):** Red & white/red/red (Yellow/blue/yellow)
**ADDITIONAL INFORMATION: Att:** 550 v Newport Co. FA Cup **App:** Craig Chaplin
Wiltshire Senior Cup 1975-76, 96-97, 04-05. Western Premier Division 2006-07.

## DEVIZES TOWN

Founded: 1885 | Nickname:

**Secretary:** Neil Fautley | **(T)** 07891 341 344 | **(E)** neil@hallmarkflooring.co.uk
**Chairman:** Shaun Moffat | **Manager:** Darren Walters
**Ground:** Nursteed Road, Devizes, Wiltshire SN10 3DX | **(T)** 01380 722 817
**Colours(change):** Red & white stripes/black/black (All blue)
**ADDITIONAL INFORMATION:**
**Honours:** Western League Division One 1999-2000. Wiltshire Senior Cup x14.

## HENGROVE ATHLETIC

Founded: 1948 | Nickname: The Grove

**Secretary:** Graham Whitaker | **(T)** 07970 848 285 | **(E)** grahamwhitaker1@btinternet.com
**Chairman:** Mike Greatbanks | **Manager:** Jamie Hillman
**Ground:** Norton Lane, Whitchurch, Bristol BS14 9TB | **(T)** 07434 173 074
**Colours(change):** All green (All maroon)
**ADDITIONAL INFORMATION:**
Somerset County League Premier Division 2005-06. Somerset Senior Cup 1979-80.

## KEYNSHAM TOWN

Founded: 1895 | Nickname: K's

**Secretary:** Julian French | **(T)** 07814 609 853 | **(E)** julian.french@friendslifeservices.co.uk
**Chairman:** Malcolm Trainer | **Manager:** Chris King
**Ground:** AJN Stadium, Bristol Road, Keynsham BS31 2BE | **(T)** 0117 986 5878
**Colours(change):** Amber/black/Amber (All maroon)
**ADDITIONAL INFORMATION:**
**Previous League:** Somerset Senior.
**Honours:** Somerset Senior Cup 1951-52, 57-58, 2002-03.

## MALMESBURY VICTORIA

Founded: 1896 | Nickname: The Vics

**Secretary:** Brendon Rice | **(T)** 07825 172 500 | **(E)** brendon@innov.co.uk
**Chairman:** Phil Exton | **Manager:** Kevin Bridgeman
**Ground:** Flying Monk Ground, Gloucester Road, SN16 0AJ | **(T)** 01666 822 141
**Colours(change):** Black & white stripes/black/red (Red & white/red/black)
**ADDITIONAL INFORMATION: Previous Leagues:** Hellenic > 2014. Wiltshire 2014-16.
**Record Att:** 310 - August 2009
**Honours:** Wiltshire League 1999-00, 2014-15. Wiltshire Senior Cup 01-02.

## OLDLAND ABBOTONIANS

Founded: 1910 | Nickname: The O's

**Secretary:** Martin McConachie | **(T)** 07432 614 494 | **(E)** secretary@oldlandfootball.com
**Chairman:** Robert Clarke | **Manager:** Dale Dempsey
**Ground:** Aitchison Playing Field, Castle Road, Oldland Common, Bristol BS30 9SZ | **(T)** 01179 328 263
**Colours(change):** Blue & white/blue/blue (All yellow)
**ADDITIONAL INFORMATION:**
**Previous League:** Somerset County.
**Honours:** Les Phillips Cup 2008-09.

## PORTISHEAD TOWN

Founded: 1910 Nickname: Posset

**Secretary:** Jean Harrison **(T)** 07969 045 310 **(E)** jemaha11@talktalk.net
**Chairman:** Mark Stallard **Manager:** Alan Tyers
**Ground:** Bristol Road, Portishead, Bristol BS20 6QG **(T)** 01275 817 600
**Colours(change):** White/black/black (All red)
**ADDITIONAL INFORMATION:**
**Previous League:** Somerset County.
**Honours:** Somerset County League 2004-05.

## RADSTOCK TOWN

Founded: 1895 Nickname:

**Secretary:** Debbie Smith **(T)** 07828 665 636 **(E)** rtfcsecretary@outlook.com
**Chairman:** Simon Wilkinson **Manager:** Shane Smith
**Ground:** Southfields Recreation Ground, Southfields, Radstock BA3 2NZ **(T)** 01761 435 004 **Capacity:** 1,250
**Colours(change):** Red/black/red (All blue)
**ADDITIONAL INFORMATION:**

## ROMAN GLASS ST GEORGE

Founded: Nickname:

**Secretary:** Emily Baldwin **(T)** 07708 277 592 **(E)** emilyjaynebaldwin@outlook.com
**Chairman:** Roger Hudd **Manager:** Andy Gurney
**Ground:** Oaklands Park, Gloucester Road, Alomndsbury BS32 4AG **(T)** 01454 612 220
**Colours(change):** White/black/black (All red)
**ADDITIONAL INFORMATION:**
**Previous League:** Gloucestershire County.
**Honours:** Gloucestershire County League 2006-07.

## WARMINSTER TOWN

Founded: 1878 Nickname:

**Secretary:** Chris Robbins **(T)** 07734 025 196 **(E)** Chrisjrobbins1@virginmedia.com
**Chairman:** Pete Russell **Manager:** Mark Breffit
**Ground:** Weymouth Street, Warminster BA12 9NS **(T)** 01985 217 828
**Colours(change):** Red & black/black/red & black (Light blue/dark blue/light blue)
**ADDITIONAL INFORMATION:**
**Previous Leagues:** Wiltshire County > 1930, 1945-83, 2002-06. Western League 1930-39, 83-2002. Wessex 2006-12.

## WELLINGTON

Founded: 1892 Nickname: Wellie

**Secretary:** David Derrick **(T)** 07519 843 737 **(E)** david230275@googlemail.com
**Chairman:** Mike Hall **Manager:** Clive Jones
**Ground:** Wellington Playing Field, North Street, Wellington TA21 8LY **(T)** 01823 664 810 **Capacity:** 3,000
**Colours(change):** Tangerine/black/tangerine (Claret/blue/claret)
**ADDITIONAL INFORMATION: Record Goalscorer:** Ken Jones

## WELTON ROVERS

Founded: 1887 Nickname: Rovers

**Secretary:** Malcolm Price **(T)** 07970 791 644 **(E)** malcolm@weltonr.plus.com
**Chairman:** Ryan Grubb **Manager:** Clive Scott
**Ground:** West Clewes, North Road, Midsomer Norton, Bath BA3 2QD **(T)** 02762 412 097 **Capacity:** 2,400
**Colours(change):** Green & white/green/green (Yellow/blue/yellow).
**ADDITIONAL INFORMATION: Att:** 2,000 v Bromley FA Am Cup 1963 **Goalscorer:** Ian Henderson 51
Somerset Senior Cup (10). Somerset Premier Cup 2009-10.

## WESTBURY UNITED

Founded: 1921 Nickname: White Horsemen

**Secretary:** Martin Pearce **(T)** 07535 631 052 **(E)** secretary@westburyunited.co.uk
**Chairman:** Matt Bright **Manager:** James Goddard
**Ground:** Meadow Lane, Westbury, Wiltshire BA13 3QA **(T)** 01373 823 409
**Colours(change):** Green & white stripes/green/green (All dark blue)
**ADDITIONAL INFORMATION:**
**Record Att:** 4,000 v Llanelli FA Cup 1st Round 1937 & v Walthamstow Avenue FA Cup 1937.
**Honours:** Wiltshire League 1934-35, 37-38, 38-39, 49-50, 50-51, 55-56. Western League Div.1 1991-92. Wilts Senior Cup x4.

## WINCANTON TOWN

Founded: 1890 Nickname: Winky

**Secretary:** James Stewart (T) 07534 902 360 (E) j.stewart2012@hotmail.co.uk
**Chairman:** Andy Stewart **Manager:** Chris Wise & Andrew Mitchell
**Ground:** Wincanton Sports Ground, Moor Lane, Wincanton. BA9 9RA (T) 01963 31815
**Colours(change):** Yellow & black/black/black (All green)
**ADDITIONAL INFORMATION:**
**Previous League:** Dorset Premier >2013.

# DIVISION ONE GROUND DIRECTIONS

**ALMONDSBURY UWE - The Field, Almondsbury, Bristol BS34 4AA 01454 612 240 -** Exit M5 at Junction 16. Arriving from the south take the left exit lane. Turn left at lights and ground is 150m on right hand side. Arriving from east take right hand lane on slip road. Take 3rd exit and ground is 150m on right hand side.

**ASHTON & BACKWELL UNITED - Backwell Recreation Ground, West Town Road, Backwell. BS48 3HQ - 07916 120 382 -** Off the main A370 in Backwell, travelling from Bristol the entrance is on the right, apprximately 500 metres after the crossroads. Travelling from Weston Super Mare the entrance to the ground is on the left approximately 500 metrs past the New Inn Pub and Restaurant.

**BISHOP SUTTON - Lakeview, Wick Road, Bishop Sutton BS39 5XN 01275 333097 -** On main A368 Bath to Weston-Super-Mare road at rear of Butchers Arms Public House.

**BISHOPS LYDEARD - Cottlestone Road, Bishops Lydeard, Taunton, TA4 3BA - 07956 682 367**
Exit M5 at Junction 25, take A358 towards Minehead. Once past Marine Camp. Go straight over roundabout and take first right turn into Bishops Lydeard. At T Junction turn right and Head through village past the Co-Op. Continue for 1.5 Miles and club is on right hand side.

**CALNE TOWN - Bremhill View, Calne, Wiltshire SN11 9EE** - Take A4 to Calne from Chippenham, on approaching Calne turn left at the first roundabout on to A3102 Calne bypass. At the next roundabout turn right, next left and then right and right again.

**CHARD TOWN - Dening Sports Field, Zembard Lane, Chard, Somerset TA20 1JL 01460 61402 -** From A30 High Street, follow Swimming Pool/Sports Centre signs via Helliers road. Turn right into Crimchard, turn left into Zembard Lane. Ground is on right hand side.

**CHEDDAR - Bowdens Park, Draycott Road, Cheddar BS27 3RL - 01934 707 271 -** FROM WELLS: Take the A371 (Weston Super Mare) through Draycott and Bowdens Park is on your left about half a mile past Cheddar Garden Centre (if you get to the church you've gone too far). FROM WESTON: Head towards Wells on the A371 and go through the village of Cheddar. The church is on your right as you come out of the village and Bowdens Park is 200 yards past the church on your right hand side.

**CHIPPENHAM PARK - Hardenhuish Park, Bristol Road, Chippenham. SN14 6LR 01249 650 400 -** Exit 17 from M4. Follow A350 towards Chippenham for three miles to first roundabout, take second exit (A350); follow road to third roundabout (junction with A420). Turn left and follow signs to town centre. Ground is 1km on left hand side adjacent to pedestrian controlled traffic lights. Car/Coach park located adjacent to traffic lights.

**DEVIZES TOWN - Nursteed Road, Devizes, Wiltshire SN10 3DX 01380 722 817 -** Leave Devizes on A342 for Andover. Ground is on the right hand side opposite Eastleigh Road.

**HENGROVE ATHLETIC - Norton Lane, Whitchurch, Bristol BS14 0BT 01275 832 894 -** Take A37 from Bristol through Whitchurch village past Maes Knoll pub, over hump bridge taking next turning on right, which is Norton Lane. Ground is immediately after Garden Centre.

**KEYNSHAM TOWN - Crown Field, Bristol Road, Keynsham BS31 2DZ 0117 986 5876 -** On A4175 off the Bristol to Bath A4. On left immediately after 30mph sign.

**MALMESBURY VICTORIA - Flying Monk Ground, Gloucester Road, Malmesbury, SN16 9JS 01666 822141 -** At M4 Junction 14, take A429 to Cirencester, at priory roundabout take Second exit. At Wychurch roundabout take second exit, after 500 yards at roundabout take first exit B4014, after ½ mileat roundabout take first exit towards town centre. At bottom of hill club is behind the Co-Op. Entrance is via lane opposite the bus stop. Enter with caution as the lane is narrow and used by the general public.

**OLDLAND ABBOTONIANS - Aitchison Playing Field, Castle Road, Oldland Common, Bristol BS30 9PP 0117 932 8263 -** Exit M4 at Jct19 to M32. Exit M32 at Jct 1after 400 yds and take 1st exit from roundabout for A4174. Straight over traffic lights to next roundabout continuing on A4174. Go over five roundabouts for approximately 4.8 miles. At next roundabout take 1st exit to Deanery Road (A420) and continue for 0.9 miles to Griffin Public house and turn right into Bath Road (A4175) . Continue for 1.3 miles to Oldland Common High Street and look for Dolphin Public House. Turning for Castle Street is next left between Chinese Chip Shop and Post Office. Ground is at the end of Castle Road.

**PORTISHEAD - Bristol Road, Portishead, Bristol BS20 6QG 01275 817 600 -** Leave M5 at Junction 19 and take road to Portishead. At outskirts of town take 1st exit from small roundabout signposted Clevedon and Police H.Q. Ground is 150 yds along road on left by bus stop.

**RADSTOCK TOWN - Southfields Recreation Ground, Southfields, Radstock BA3 2NZ 01761 435 004 -** The town of Radstock is situated 15 miles south east of Bristol and 8 miles southwest of Bath on the A367. At the double roundabout in Radstock town centre take the A362 towards Frome. The ground is on the right hand bend, third turning. Turn right into Southfield, ground is 200 yards ahead.

**ROMAN GLASS ST GEORGE - Oaklands Park, Gloucester Road, Almondsbury BS32 4AG 07708 277592 -** Exit M5 at Junction 16. Arriving from the south take the left exit lane. Turn left at lights and ground is 100m on left hand side. Arriving from east take right hand lane on slip road. Take 3rd exit nd ground is 100m on left hand side.

**WARMINSTER TOWN - Weymouth Street, Warminster, BA12 9NS - 01454 612220 -** A36 from Salisbury, head for town centre, turn left at traffic lights in the town centre signposted A350 Shaftesbury. Club is situated approx. 400 yards on left hand side at top of Weymouth Street.

**WELLINGTON - The Playing Field, North Street, Wellington, Somerset TA21 8NA 01749 679 971 -** Leave the M5 motorway at Junction 26 and follow directions to Wellington. At town centre traffic lights take turning into North Street. Take the next left adjacent to the Fire Station and signposted 'Car Park'. The ground is in the corner of the car park.

**WELTON ROVERS - West Clewes, North Road, Midsomer Norton BA3 2QD 01761 412 097 -** The ground is on the main A362 in Midsomer Norton.

**WESTBURY UNITED - Meadow Lane, Westbury, Wiltshire BA13 3AF 01373 823 409 -** From town centre proceed along Station Road towards rail station. At double mini roundabout turn right. Ground is 300 metres on left hand side opposite Fire Station.

**WINCANTON TOWN - Wincanton Sports Ground, Moor Lane, Wincanton. BA9 9EJ - 01963 31815 -** Travelling to Wincanton on the A357 via Sturminster Newton turn right at the roundabout after passing under the A303 into Laurence Hill and follow the road across three further roundabouts into Southgate Road. Traffic from the A303 will also enter Southgate Road when following the signs to the town. At the junction turn right in the direction of Buckhorn Weston going under the A303 again before entering Moor Lane. Wincanton Sports Centre is on the left.

# ANGLIAN COMBINATION

**Sponsored by:** Almary Green
**Founded:** 1964
**Recent Champions:**
**2013:** Acle United
**2014:** Acle United **2015:** Acle United
**angliancombination.org.uk**

| PREMIER DIVISION | P | W | D | L | F | A | GD | Pts |
|---|---|---|---|---|---|---|---|---|
| 1 Acle United | 30 | 21 | 5 | 4 | 76 | 25 | 51 | 68 |
| 2 Spixworth | 30 | 19 | 5 | 6 | 77 | 41 | 36 | 62 |
| 3 Harleston Town | 30 | 18 | 5 | 7 | 59 | 48 | 11 | 59 |
| 4 Norwich CEYMS | 30 | 14 | 7 | 9 | 77 | 53 | 24 | 49 |
| 5 St Andrews | 30 | 14 | 7 | 9 | 50 | 48 | 2 | 49 |
| 6 Blofield United | 30 | 14 | 4 | 12 | 77 | 64 | 13 | 46 |
| 7 Kirkley & Pakefield Reserves | 30 | 13 | 1 | 16 | 60 | 68 | -8 | 40 |
| 8 Mulbarton Wanderers | 30 | 11 | 5 | 14 | 46 | 48 | -2 | 38 |
| 9 Wroxham Reserves | 30 | 10 | 6 | 14 | 50 | 65 | -15 | 36 |
| 10 Long Stratton | 30 | 11 | 3 | 16 | 39 | 61 | -22 | 36 |
| 11 Cromer Town (-1) | 30 | 10 | 6 | 14 | 32 | 49 | -17 | 35 |
| 12 Caister | 30 | 10 | 4 | 16 | 54 | 60 | -6 | 34 |
| 13 Mattishall | 30 | 9 | 7 | 14 | 38 | 60 | -22 | 34 |
| 14 Reepham Town | 30 | 9 | 6 | 15 | 49 | 59 | -10 | 33 |
| 15 Dersingham Rovers | 30 | 9 | 3 | 18 | 43 | 54 | -11 | 30 |
| 16 Scole United | 30 | 8 | 6 | 16 | 45 | 69 | -24 | 30 |

| DIVISION ONE | P | W | D | L | F | A | GD | Pts |
|---|---|---|---|---|---|---|---|---|
| 1 Waveney | 30 | 23 | 4 | 3 | 88 | 29 | 59 | 73 |
| 2 Stalham Town | 30 | 22 | 1 | 7 | 96 | 45 | 51 | 67 |
| 3 Beccles Town | 30 | 19 | 6 | 5 | 85 | 45 | 40 | 63 |
| 4 Aylsham | 30 | 16 | 7 | 7 | 76 | 62 | 14 | 55 |
| 5 Bungay Town | 30 | 15 | 5 | 10 | 72 | 53 | 19 | 50 |
| 6 Sheringham | 30 | 15 | 5 | 10 | 70 | 64 | 6 | 50 |
| 7 North Walsham Town | 30 | 14 | 5 | 11 | 85 | 69 | 16 | 47 |
| 8 Bradenham Wanderers | 30 | 13 | 6 | 11 | 72 | 53 | 19 | 45 |
| 9 Hellesdon | 30 | 13 | 5 | 12 | 70 | 61 | 9 | 44 |
| 10 Loddon United | 30 | 12 | 7 | 11 | 70 | 65 | 5 | 43 |
| 11 Wymondham Town | 30 | 12 | 4 | 14 | 58 | 66 | -8 | 40 |
| 12 Holt United | 30 | 7 | 5 | 18 | 37 | 77 | -40 | 26 |
| 13 Foulsham (-1) | 30 | 6 | 4 | 20 | 56 | 97 | -41 | 21 |
| 14 Hindringham | 30 | 4 | 8 | 18 | 44 | 80 | -36 | 20 |
| 15 Poringland Wanderers | 30 | 3 | 8 | 19 | 40 | 76 | -36 | 17 |
| 16 Hempnall | 30 | 3 | 6 | 21 | 34 | 111 | -77 | 15 |

## DON FROST CUP

(Premier Division champions v Mummery Cup holders)

Acle United v Spixworth 1-3

## MUMMERY CUP
### (Premier and Division One Clubs)

**HOLDERS:** SPIXWORTH

**ROUND 1**

| | | | |
|---|---|---|---|
| Dersingham Rovers | v | Wroxham Reserves | 1-3 |
| Aylsham | v | Bungay Town | 4-1 |
| Mulbarton Wanderers | v | Kirkley & Pakefield Reserves | 1-0 |
| Holt United | v | North Walsham Town | 2-4 |
| Foulsham | v | Sheringham | 1-0 |
| Scole United | v | Harleston Town | 3-2 |
| Cromer Town | v | Caister | 1-3 |
| Long Stratton | v | Hellesdon | 2-1 |
| Spixworth | v | Waveney | 3-1 |
| Reepham Town | v | Mattishall | 1-3 |
| Stalham Town | v | St Andrews | 2-3 |
| Hindringham | v | Norwich CEYMS | 0-2 |
| Wymondham Town | v | Loddon United | 2-2, 3-2p |
| Bradenham Wanderers | v | Blofield United | 1-2 |
| Poringland Wanderers | v | Acle United | 1-3 |
| Beccles Town | v | Hempnall | 7-0 |

**ROUND 2**

| | | | |
|---|---|---|---|
| Wroxham Reserves | v | Aylsham | 3-0 |
| Mulbarton Wanderers | v | North Walsham Town | 7-1 |
| Foulsham | v | Scole United | 1-2 |
| Caister | v | Long Stratton | 2-1 |
| Spixworth | v | Mattishall | 2-1 |
| St Andrews | v | Norwich CEYMS | 4-1 |
| Wymondham Town | v | Blofield United | 1-10 |
| Acle United | v | Beccles Town | 3-2 |

**QUARTER FINALS**

| | | | |
|---|---|---|---|
| Wroxham Reserves | v | Mulbarton Wanderers | 6-1 |
| Scole United | v | Caister | 0-3 |
| Spixworth | v | St Andrews | 4-2 |
| Blofield United | v | Acle United | 3-3, 2-4p |

**SEMI FINALS**

| | | | |
|---|---|---|---|
| Wroxham Reserves | v | Caister | 0-1 |
| Spixworth | v | Acle United | 3-1 |

**FINAL**

Caister v Spixworth 0-1

## CYRIL BALLYN TROPHY
### (Division Two, Three, Four, Five and Six first teams and external league reserve sides)

**FINAL** **HOLDERS:** BUNGAY TOWN

East Harling v Mundford 0-1

## CS MORLEY CUP
### (Anglian Combination reserve teams)

**FINAL** **HOLDERS:** HINGHAM ATHLETIC

Gorleston Reserves v Gayton United 4-0

| PREMIER DIVISION | 1 | 2 | 3 | 4 | 5 | 6 | 7 | 8 | 9 | 10 | 11 | 12 | 13 | 14 | 15 | 16 |
|---|---|---|---|---|---|---|---|---|---|---|---|---|---|---|---|---|
| 1 Acle United | | 2-0 | 3-2 | 7-0 | 0-3 | 0-1 | 5-0 | 5-0 | 3-0 | 3-1 | 6-0 | 3-0 | 3-2 | 1-1 | 1-0 | 1-1 |
| 2 Blofield United | 2-4 | | 3-1 | 1-2 | 3-1 | 1-3 | 5-1 | 3-0 | 1-0 | 1-5 | 3-3 | 1-4 | 7-1 | 0-5 | 2-3 | 4-3 |
| 3 Caister | 1-2 | 3-1 | | 1-2 | 1-0 | 1-2 | 3-5 | 0-2 | 3-3 | 3-1 | 5-3 | 3-0 | 6-1 | 1-4 | 0-2 | 2-2 |
| 4 Cromer Town | 1-2 | 1-2 | 0-2 | | 1-0 | 1-1 | 0-0 | 2-3 | 1-3 | 0-2 | 2-1 | 2-1 | 0-2 | 2-6 | 0-0 | 1-1 |
| 5 Dersingham Rovers | 0-3 | 1-1 | 2-2 | 1-2 | | 1-2 | 5-1 | 3-0 | 2-3 | 2-4 | 2-1 | 0-1 | 1-3 | 1-3 | 3-0 | 3-1 |
| 6 Harleston Town | 0-6 | 2-1 | 3-0 | 0-1 | 3-1 | | 2-1 | 3-2 | 1-1 | 2-3 | 3-2 | 3-4 | 2-1 | 0-0 | 1-2 | 3-0 |
| 7 Kirkley & Pakefield Reserves | 0-3 | 3-1 | 5-0 | 1-2 | 4-1 | 1-3 | | 5-1 | 4-1 | 3-2 | 0-5 | 2-1 | 2-1 | 2-4 | 3-2 | 3-0 |
| 8 Long Stratton | 3-2 | 1-4 | 1-0 | HW | 0-2 | 1-2 | 2-3 | | 2-0 | 0-0 | 0-3 | 0-1 | 1-0 | 1-2 | 2-3 | 4-3 |
| 9 Mattishall | 1-1 | 2-5 | 1-0 | 0-3 | 0-3 | 2-2 | 3-2 | 1-1 | | 3-2 | 1-5 | 1-1 | 3-1 | 2-1 | 0-3 | 2-4 |
| 10 Mulbarton Wanderers | 0-1 | 0-1 | 1-1 | 1-2 | 1-0 | 0-3 | 1-0 | 2-0 | 3-0 | | 0-2 | 2-1 | 1-2 | 1-3 | 1-1 | 3-0 |
| 11 Norwich CEYMS | 3-2 | 2-2 | 0-3 | 1-1 | 6-0 | 0-1 | 3-1 | 1-2 | 1-1 | 3-0 | | 4-4 | 1-4 | 4-2 | 3-0 | 7-1 |
| 12 Reepham Town | 0-0 | 1-2 | 1-3 | 2-1 | 2-2 | 0-1 | 0-2 | 3-2 | 0-3 | 3-3 | 1-3 | | 3-0 | 2-5 | 1-2 | 6-1 |
| 13 Scole United | 1-2 | 1-6 | 2-4 | 1-1 | 1-0 | 3-3 | 2-0 | 4-1 | 0-1 | 1-4 | 4-4 | 3-2 | | 0-0 | 2-2 | 1-2 |
| 14 Spixworth | 0-2 | 5-4 | 1-0 | 2-1 | 3-0 | 8-3 | 3-2 | 2-2 | 1-0 | 4-1 | 0-2 | 2-3 | 4-0 | | 2-0 | 2-1 |
| 15 St Andrews | 1-1 | 1-7 | 3-2 | 3-0 | 2-1 | 1-2 | 5-3 | 0-2 | 2-0 | 2-0 | 2-2 | 2-0 | 1-1 | 1-1 | | 4-3 |
| 16 Wroxham Reserves | 1-2 | 3-3 | 4-1 | 2-0 | 0-2 | 3-2 | 2-1 | 2-3 | 2-0 | 1-1 | 0-2 | 1-1 | 2-0 | 2-1 | 2-0 | |

## Anglian Combination Premier Division

|  |  |  |
|---|---|---|
| ACLE UNITED | Bridewell Lane, Acle, Norwich NR13 3RA | 01493 752 989 |
| BLOFIELD UNITED | Old Yarmouth Road, Blofield, Norwich NR13 4LE | 07748 863 203 |
| CAISTER | Caister Playing Fields, off Allendale Road, Caister-on-Sea NR30 5ES | 07852 212 210 |
| CROMER TOWN | Cabbell Park, Mill Road, Cromer NR27 0AD | 07940 092131 |
| HARLESTON TOWN | Harleston Recreation Ground, Wilderness Lane, Harleston IP20 9DD | 07887 781 603 |
| KIRKLEY & PAKEFIELD RESERVES | Kirkley & Pakefield Comm. Centre, Walmer Road, Lowestoft NR33 7LE | 01502 513 549 |
| LONG STRATTON | Long Stratton Playing Field, Long Stratton, Manor Road NR15 2XR | 07806 792 840 |
| MATTISHALL | Mattishall Playing Fields, South Green, Mattishall, Norwich NR20 3JY | 01362 850 246 |
| MULBARTON WANDERERS | Mulberry Park #1, Mulbarton, Norfolk NR14 8AE | 07738 668 407 |
| NORWICH CEYMS | Hilltops Sports Centre, Main Road, Swardeston, Norwich NR14 8DU | 01508 578 826 |
| REEPHAM TOWN | Stimpsons Piece, Station Road, Reepham NR10 4LJ | 07887 442 470 |
| SPIXWORTH | Spixworth Village Hall, Crostick Lane, Spixworth, Norwich NR10 3NQ | 01603 898 092 |
| ST ANDREWS | Thorpe Recreation Ground, Laundry Lane, Thorpe St Andrew, Norwich NR7 0XQ | 01603 300 316 |
| STALHAM TOWN | Rivers Park Stalham #1 Stepping Stone Lane, Stalham, Norfolk NR12 9ER | 07818 418 677 |
| WAVENEY | Barnards Meadow, Barnards Way, Lowestoft, Suffolk NR32 2HF | 07772 766 243 |
| WROXHAM RESERVES | Trafford Park, Skinners Lane, Wroxham NR12 8SJ | 01603 783 538 |

| VISION TWO | P | W | D | L | F | A | GD | Pts |
|---|---|---|---|---|---|---|---|---|
| Mundford | 30 | 22 | 6 | 2 | 110 | 32 | 78 | 72 |
| Attleborough Town | 30 | 22 | 5 | 3 | 98 | 32 | 66 | 71 |
| East Harling | 30 | 19 | 3 | 8 | 84 | 41 | 43 | 60 |
| Wells Town | 30 | 18 | 3 | 9 | 74 | 43 | 31 | 57 |
| UEA | 30 | 16 | 5 | 9 | 73 | 55 | 18 | 53 |
| Yelverton | 30 | 14 | 6 | 10 | 60 | 54 | 6 | 48 |
| Acle United Reserves | 30 | 14 | 4 | 12 | 61 | 52 | 9 | 46 |
| Easton | 30 | 12 | 8 | 10 | 101 | 80 | 21 | 44 |
| Hoveton Wherrymen (-2) | 30 | 13 | 2 | 15 | 55 | 62 | -7 | 39 |
| Caister Reserves (-1) | 30 | 12 | 2 | 16 | 67 | 77 | -10 | 37 |
| Sprowston Athletic (-1) | 30 | 10 | 5 | 15 | 51 | 71 | -20 | 34 |
| Martham | 30 | 8 | 4 | 18 | 62 | 117 | -55 | 28 |
| Thetford Rovers | 30 | 7 | 6 | 17 | 54 | 88 | -34 | 27 |
| Blofield United Res. (-1) | 30 | 8 | 3 | 19 | 48 | 81 | -33 | 26 |
| Horsford United | 30 | 6 | 4 | 20 | 40 | 104 | -64 | 22 |
| Norwich CEYMS Res. (-1) | 30 | 2 | 8 | 20 | 47 | 96 | -49 | 13 |

| VISION THREE | P | W | D | L | F | A | GD | Pts |
|---|---|---|---|---|---|---|---|---|
| Watton United | 30 | 24 | 3 | 3 | 91 | 24 | 67 | 75 |
| Mattishall Reserves | 30 | 24 | 1 | 5 | 134 | 52 | 82 | 73 |
| Redgate Rangers | 30 | 23 | 3 | 4 | 99 | 30 | 69 | 72 |
| Hemsby | 30 | 19 | 1 | 10 | 87 | 60 | 27 | 58 |
| Brandon Town | 30 | 17 | 4 | 9 | 78 | 59 | 19 | 55 |
| Freethorpe | 30 | 15 | 4 | 11 | 72 | 52 | 20 | 49 |
| Sprowston Wanderers (-2) | 30 | 16 | 3 | 11 | 58 | 54 | 4 | 49 |
| Buxton | 30 | 13 | 6 | 11 | 59 | 57 | 2 | 45 |
| South Walsham | 30 | 11 | 6 | 13 | 62 | 63 | -1 | 39 |
| Beccles Caxton | 30 | 12 | 3 | 15 | 72 | 84 | -12 | 39 |
| Swaffham Town Reserves | 30 | 9 | 6 | 15 | 59 | 88 | -29 | 33 |
| Fakenham Town Res. (-3) | 30 | 9 | 6 | 15 | 47 | 53 | -6 | 30 |
| Loddon United Res. (-1) | 30 | 8 | 3 | 19 | 52 | 96 | -44 | 26 |
| Long Stratton Res. (-1) | 30 | 6 | 4 | 20 | 43 | 81 | -38 | 21 |
| Costessey Sports | 30 | 7 | 0 | 23 | 44 | 125 | -81 | 21 |
| Downham Town Res. (-4) | 30 | 0 | 1 | 29 | 23 | 102 | -79 | -3 |

### CLUB MOVEMENTS

**VE NORTH: In:** Castle Acre Swifts (Central & South Norfolk / 1), Gayton United Reserves (North West Norfolk Div 1), acham (North West Norfolk Div 1), Narborough (Central & uth Norfolk Div 1). **Out:** Costessey Sports Reserfes (W), ımstead Rangers (W).
**'E SOUTH: In:** Belton (Great Yarmouth & District), verton reserves (Norwich & District Div 1).

| DIVISION FOUR | P | W | D | L | F | A | GD | Pts |
|---|---|---|---|---|---|---|---|---|
| 1 Sheringham Reserves (-1) | 26 | 20 | 3 | 3 | 113 | 25 | 88 | 62 |
| 2 Gayton United | 26 | 19 | 4 | 3 | 118 | 36 | 82 | 61 |
| 3 Earsham | 26 | 18 | 4 | 4 | 87 | 38 | 49 | 58 |
| 4 Dersingham Rovers Res. | 26 | 16 | 4 | 6 | 82 | 39 | 43 | 52 |
| 5 Hingham Athletic | 26 | 15 | 3 | 8 | 68 | 46 | 22 | 48 |
| 6 Stalham Town Res. (-2) | 26 | 15 | 1 | 10 | 50 | 39 | 11 | 44 |
| 7 Bungay Town Reserves | 26 | 13 | 3 | 10 | 60 | 57 | 3 | 42 |
| 8 St Andrews Reserves | 26 | 11 | 4 | 11 | 60 | 45 | 15 | 37 |
| 9 Feltwell United | 26 | 11 | 4 | 11 | 56 | 56 | 0 | 37 |
| 10 Reepham Town Reserves | 26 | 8 | 3 | 15 | 40 | 73 | -33 | 27 |
| 11 North Walsham Town Res. (-3) | 26 | 6 | 2 | 18 | 31 | 87 | -56 | 17 |
| 12 Thorpe Village (-1) | 26 | 4 | 4 | 18 | 37 | 106 | -69 | 15 |
| 13 Wymondham Town Res. (-3) | 26 | 3 | 1 | 22 | 21 | 80 | -59 | 7 |
| 14 Horsford United Res. (-4) | 26 | 2 | 2 | 22 | 27 | 123 | -96 | 4 |

Redgrave Rangers withdrew - record expunged.
Sprowston Athletic Reserves withdrew - record expunged.

| DIVISION FIVE NORTH | P | W | D | L | F | A | GD | Pts |
|---|---|---|---|---|---|---|---|---|
| 1 Bradenham Wanderers Res. | 28 | 24 | 2 | 2 | 98 | 20 | 78 | 74 |
| 2 UEA Reserves | 28 | 23 | 3 | 2 | 119 | 32 | 87 | 72 |
| 3 Hellesdon Reserves | 28 | 20 | 3 | 5 | 105 | 44 | 61 | 63 |
| 4 Aylsham Reserves | 28 | 17 | 4 | 7 | 83 | 29 | 54 | 55 |
| 5 Necton | 28 | 16 | 4 | 8 | 82 | 57 | 25 | 52 |
| 6 Cromer Town Res. (-2) | 28 | 13 | 5 | 10 | 74 | 47 | 27 | 42 |
| 7 Plumstead Rangers | 28 | 13 | 3 | 12 | 61 | 65 | -4 | 42 |
| 8 Wells Town Reserves (-3) | 28 | 13 | 5 | 10 | 74 | 46 | 28 | 41 |
| 9 Hindringham Res. (-1) | 28 | 11 | 6 | 11 | 68 | 71 | -3 | 38 |
| 10 South Walsham Res. (-1) | 28 | 10 | 1 | 17 | 47 | 75 | -28 | 30 |
| 11 Easton Reserves | 28 | 8 | 2 | 18 | 48 | 81 | -33 | 26 |
| 12 Mundford Reserves (-2) | 28 | 7 | 1 | 20 | 34 | 89 | -55 | 20 |
| 13 Spixworth Reserves (-6) | 28 | 7 | 2 | 19 | 45 | 63 | -18 | 17 |
| 14 Costessey Sports Res. (-3) | 28 | 4 | 1 | 23 | 34 | 164 | -130 | 10 |
| 15 Martham Reserves (-4) | 28 | 3 | 0 | 25 | 35 | 124 | -89 | 5 |

Foulsham Reserves withdrew - record expunged.

| DIVISION FIVE SOUTH | P | W | D | L | F | A | GD | Pts |
|---|---|---|---|---|---|---|---|---|
| 1 Gorleston Reserves | 28 | 28 | 0 | 0 | 125 | 13 | 112 | 84 |
| 2 Waveney Reserves (-1) | 28 | 21 | 2 | 5 | 77 | 24 | 53 | 64 |
| 3 Harleston Town Reserves | 28 | 18 | 5 | 5 | 93 | 39 | 54 | 59 |
| 4 Beccles Town Reserves | 28 | 17 | 6 | 5 | 91 | 42 | 49 | 57 |
| 5 Gt Yarmouth Town Res. (-1) | 28 | 17 | 2 | 9 | 110 | 41 | 69 | 52 |
| 6 Scole United Res. (-1) | 28 | 16 | 3 | 9 | 115 | 53 | 62 | 50 |
| 7 Attleborough Town Res. | 28 | 15 | 4 | 9 | 94 | 59 | 35 | 49 |
| 8 Thetford Town Res. (-2) | 28 | 16 | 1 | 11 | 94 | 67 | 27 | 47 |
| 9 Mulbarton Wanderers Res. (-1) | 28 | 13 | 5 | 10 | 90 | 57 | 33 | 43 |
| 10 Thetford Rovers Res. (-1) | 28 | 11 | 0 | 17 | 41 | 88 | -47 | 32 |
| 11 East Harling Res. (-1) | 28 | 6 | 1 | 21 | 54 | 117 | -63 | 18 |
| 12 Poringland Wanderers Res. (-4) | 28 | 5 | 3 | 20 | 30 | 95 | -65 | 14 |
| 13 Newton Flotman (-1) | 28 | 5 | 0 | 23 | 39 | 136 | -97 | 14 |
| 14 Hempnall Reserves (-1) | 28 | 2 | 2 | 24 | 24 | 155 | -131 | 7 |
| 15 Freethorpe Reserves (-4) | 28 | 2 | 2 | 24 | 22 | 113 | -91 | 4 |

Corton Seltic withdrew - record expunged.

# BEDFORDSHIRE COUNTY LEAGUE

**Sponsored by:** No sponsor
**Founded:** 1904
**Recent Champions:**
**2013:** Caldecote
**2014:** AFC Oakley M&DH
**2015:** Renhold United
**bedfordshirefootballleague.co.uk**

| PREMIER DIVISION | P | W | D | L | F | A | GD | Pts |
|---|---|---|---|---|---|---|---|---|
| 1 AFC Oakley M&DH | 30 | 22 | 4 | 4 | 99 | 45 | 54 | 70 |
| 2 Renhold United | 30 | 21 | 3 | 6 | 78 | 49 | 29 | 66 |
| 3 Wilstead | 30 | 20 | 2 | 8 | 107 | 55 | 52 | 62 |
| 4 AFC Kempston Town & Bedford Col. | 30 | 19 | 1 | 10 | 86 | 51 | 35 | 58 |
| 5 Flitwick Town | 30 | 17 | 5 | 8 | 61 | 37 | 24 | 56 |
| 6 Marston Shelton Rovers | 30 | 16 | 4 | 10 | 66 | 52 | 14 | 52 |
| 7 Cranfield United | 30 | 16 | 2 | 12 | 77 | 63 | 14 | 50 |
| 8 Ampthill Town Reserves | 30 | 13 | 8 | 9 | 72 | 63 | 9 | 47 |
| 9 Shefford Town & Campton | 30 | 14 | 4 | 12 | 70 | 66 | 4 | 46 |
| 10 Ickwell & Old Warden | 30 | 14 | 4 | 12 | 70 | 53 | 17 | 45 |
| 11 Sharnbrook | 30 | 10 | 5 | 15 | 59 | 61 | -2 | 34 |
| 12 Sandy | 30 | 10 | 2 | 18 | 38 | 76 | -38 | 32 |
| 13 Caldecote | 30 | 7 | 5 | 18 | 38 | 73 | -35 | 26 |
| 14 Pavenham (-2) | 30 | 7 | 6 | 17 | 44 | 70 | -26 | 25 |
| 15 Elstow Abbey (-1) | 30 | 2 | 1 | 27 | 25 | 126 | -101 | 6 |
| 16 Eastcotts AFC (-12) | 30 | 4 | 0 | 26 | 24 | 74 | -50 | 0 |

**In:** Kempston Rovers Development (N), Stevington (P)

**Out:** Eastcotts AFC (W), Elstow Abbey (R), Pavenham (W).

## BRITANNIA CUP

**HOLDERS:** AFC KEMPSTON TOWN & BEDFORD COLLEGE

**ROUND 1**

| | | | |
|---|---|---|---|
| Pavenham | v | Sharnbrook | 1-5 |
| Shefford Town & Campton | v | AFC Kempston Town & B.C. | 6-0 |
| Ickwell & Old Warden | v | Marston Shelton Rovers | 3-4 aet |
| Eastcotts AFC | v | AFC Oakley M&DH | 2-3 |
| Flitwick Town | v | Wilstead | 1-0 |
| Cranfield United | v | Sandy | 3-0 |
| Caldecote | v | Elstow Abbey | 3-1 |
| Ampthill Town Reserves | v | Renhold United | 2-2, 4-3p |

**QUARTER FINALS**

| | | | |
|---|---|---|---|
| Sharnbrook | v | Shefford Town & Campton | 5-2 |
| Marston Shelton Rovers | v | AFC Oakley M&DH | 1-7 |
| Flitwick Town | v | Cranfield United | 2-5 |
| Caldecote | v | Ampthill Town Reserves | 1-2 |

**SEMI FINALS**

| | | | |
|---|---|---|---|
| Sharnbrook | v | AFC Oakley M&DH | 4-5 |
| Cranfield United | v | Ampthill Town Reserves | 1-4 |

**FINAL**

| | | | |
|---|---|---|---|
| AFC Oakley M&DH | v | Ampthill Town Reserves | 2-0 |

| DIVISION ONE | P | W | D | L | F | A | GD | Pts |
|---|---|---|---|---|---|---|---|---|
| 1 Sundon Park Rangers | 24 | 15 | 7 | 2 | 71 | 40 | 31 | 52 |
| 2 Stevington (-4) | 24 | 17 | 4 | 3 | 59 | 31 | 28 | 51 |
| 3 Queens Park Crescents | 24 | 12 | 4 | 8 | 50 | 36 | 14 | 40 |
| 4 AFC Kempston Tn & Bedford Coll Res. | 24 | 11 | 6 | 7 | 65 | 50 | 15 | 39 |
| 5 Meltis Albion | 24 | 11 | 6 | 7 | 58 | 54 | 4 | 39 |
| 6 Henlow | 24 | 11 | 1 | 12 | 54 | 43 | 11 | 34 |
| 7 Potton Town (-4) | 24 | 12 | 2 | 10 | 51 | 47 | 4 | 34 |
| 8 Westoning (-1) | 24 | 10 | 1 | 13 | 52 | 50 | 2 | 30 |
| 9 Shefford Town & Campton Res. (-1) | 24 | 7 | 7 | 10 | 34 | 47 | -13 | 2 |
| 10 Ickleford (-3) | 24 | 8 | 4 | 12 | 27 | 44 | -17 | 2 |
| 11 Riseley Sports | 24 | 6 | 6 | 12 | 52 | 61 | -9 | 2 |
| 12 Houghton Athletic (-3) | 24 | 5 | 2 | 17 | 46 | 78 | -32 | 1 |
| 13 AFC Oakley M&DH Res. (-7) | 24 | 4 | 4 | 16 | 20 | 58 | -38 | |

| PREMIER DIVISION | 1 | 2 | 3 | 4 | 5 | 6 | 7 | 8 | 9 | 10 | 11 | 12 | 13 | 14 | 15 | 16 |
|---|---|---|---|---|---|---|---|---|---|---|---|---|---|---|---|---|
| 1 AFC Kempston Town & Bedford College | | 1-2 | 2-3 | 5-1 | 3-0 | 3-2 | 5-0 | 2-1 | 2-1 | 0-1 | 3-0 | 4-1 | 2-0 | 2-4 | 3-2 | 4- |
| 2 AFC Oakley M&DH | 1-2 | | 2-2 | 4-1 | 3-2 | 9-3 | 5-1 | 2-0 | 3-0 | 5-0 | 5-0 | 2-1 | 5-1" | 4-4 | 2-3 | 4- |
| 3 Ampthill Town Reserves | 4-1 | 1-2 | | 2-1 | 4-4 | 5-0 | 6-0 | 0-0 | 1-1 | 2-4 | 2-0 | 0-3 | 5-0 | 1-1 | 1-5 | 2 |
| 4 Caldecote | 1-7 | 0-1 | 1-4 | | 0-4 | 2-0 | 3-0 | 1-1 | 0-2 | 0-3 | 0-2 | 1-3 | 1-1 | 2-1 | 2-2 | 1 |
| 5 Cranfield United | 1-1 | 2-4 | 1-3 | 2-3 | | 6-2 | 5-0 | 0-4 | 2-1 | 3-1 | 6-1 | 5-1 | 7-1 | 2-0 | 4-2 | 3 |
| 6 Eastcotts AFC | 2-4 | 0-6 | 0-1 | 1-3 | 3-2 | | A-W | A-W | 3-1 | 1-3 | 1-0 | 1-5 | A-W | 0-3 | 0-3 | 1 |
| 7 Elstow Abbey | 0-8 | 2-6 | 1-2 | 2-5 | 1-3 | A-W | | 0-2 | 2-2 | 1-2 | 1-4 | 3-4 | 0-2 | 3-1 | 0-7 | 1 |
| 8 Flitwick Town | 0-2 | 2-3 | 1-0 | 3-2 | 2-1 | 3-0 | 5-0 | | 2-0 | 3-3 | 3-1 | 3-3 | 4-2 | 2-1 | 1-2 | 3 |
| 9 Ickwell & Old Warden | 5-1 | 1-4 | 7-0 | 0-2 | 2-3 | 2-0 | 10-0 | 1-3 | | 2-1 | 4-2 | 2-2 | 1-1 | 1-3 | A-W | 3 |
| 10 Marston Shelton Rovers | 4-2 | 4-2 | 3-3 | 1-1 | 2-3 | H-W | 2-1 | 1-3 | 2-3 | | 3-1 | 2-0 | 3-0 | 2-3 | 8-1 | 1 |
| 11 Pavenham | 1-5 | 1-1 | 2-2 | 3-1 | 0-1 | H-W | 6-1 | 1-1 | 2-4 | 2-1 | | 0-3 | 2-1 | 1-1 | 1-1 | 2 |
| 12 Renhold United | 2-1 | 5-1 | 5-2 | 3-2 | 4-1 | H-W | 1-0 | 1-2 | 3-1 | 1-1 | 2-1 | | 2-0 | 4-2 | 4-3 | 0 |
| 13 Sandy | 0-6 | 0-2 | 2-5 | 1-0 | 0-4 | 3-0 | 3-2 | 1-5 | 2-3 | 0-3 | 3-1 | 1-5 | | H-W | 4-0 | 1 |
| 14 Sharnbrook | 1-2 | 1-1 | 1-4 | 4-0 | 5-0 | H-W | 7-1 | 1-0 | 0-1 | 0-2 | 4-4 | 3-5 | 2-3 | | 5-3 | 1 |
| 15 Shefford Town & Campton | 3-2 | 1-3 | 4-3 | 1-1 | 4-0 | 3-2 | 4-0 | 2-1 | 1-3 | 2-3 | 3-2 | 1-2 | 0-3 | 4-0 | | 2 |
| 16 Wilstead | 6-1 | 3-5 | 7-2 | 7-0 | 4-0 | 3-2 | 11-2 | 2-1 | 4-6 | 4-0 | 4-1 | 2-3 | 3-2 | 5-0 | 4-1 | |

## Bedfordshire County Premier Division

| | | |
|---|---|---|
| **AFC KEMPSTON & BEDFORD COL.** | McMullen Park, Meadow Lane, Cardington, Bedford, MK44 3SB | |
| **AFC OAKLEY SPORTS M&DH** | Oakley Village Sports Centre, Oakley, Bedford MK43 7RU | |
| **AMPTHILL TOWN RESERVES** | Club Pavilion Woburn Rd Bedford Bedfordshire MK40 1EG | |
| **CALDECOTE** | The Playing Fields, Harvey Close, Upper Caldecote SG18 9BQ | |
| **CRANFIELD UNITED** | Crawley Road, Cranfield, Bedfordshire MK43 0AA | 01234 751 444 |
| **FLITWICK TOWN** | Flitwick Community Football Centre, Ampthill Road, Flitwick MK45 1BA | |
| **ICKWELL & OLD WARDEN** | Ickwell Green, Ickwell, Bedfordshire SG18 9EE | |
| **KEMPSTON ROVERS DEV.** | Hillgrounds Stadium, Hillgrounds Road, Kemspton, Bedfordshire MK42 8SZ | 01234 852 346 |
| **MARSTON SHELTON ROVERS** | Bedford Road, Marston Moretaine, Bedford MK43 0LE | |
| **RENHOLD UNITED** | Renhold Playing Fields, Renhold, Bedford MK41 0LR | |
| **SANDY** | Bedford Road, Sandy SG19 1EL | |
| **SHARNBROOK** | Playing Fields, Lodge Road, Sharnbrook MK44 1JP | |
| **SHEFFORD TOWN & CAMPTON** | Campton Playing Field, Rectory Road, Campton, Bedfordshire SG17 5PF | |
| **STEVINGTON** | Pavenham Playing Field, Pavenham, Bedfordshire MK43 7PE | |
| **WILSTEAD** | Jubilee Playing Fields, Bedford Road, Wilstead MK45 3HE | |
| **WOOTTON BLUE CROSS** | Weston Park, Bedford Road., Wootton MK43 9JT | |

| IVISION TWO | P | W | D | L | F | A | GD | Pts |
|---|---|---|---|---|---|---|---|---|
| Clapham Sports | 20 | 16 | 0 | 4 | 93 | 35 | 58 | 48 |
| Cople & Bedford SA | 20 | 15 | 3 | 2 | 67 | 24 | 43 | 48 |
| Cranfield United Reserves | 20 | 13 | 3 | 4 | 47 | 24 | 23 | 42 |
| Flitwick Town Reserves | 20 | 10 | 5 | 5 | 49 | 28 | 21 | 35 |
| Atletico Europa | 20 | 9 | 4 | 7 | 44 | 40 | 4 | 31 |
| Kempston Hammers Sports (-1) | 20 | 8 | 5 | 7 | 54 | 39 | 15 | 28 |
| Lea Sports PSG | 20 | 8 | 2 | 10 | 51 | 57 | -6 | 26 |
| Bedford United (-1) | 20 | 6 | 4 | 10 | 32 | 55 | -23 | 21 |
| Wootton Village | 20 | 2 | 5 | 13 | 31 | 69 | -38 | 11 |
| Marston Shelton Rovers Res. (-4) | 20 | 4 | 2 | 14 | 37 | 74 | -37 | 10 |
| Kempston Athletic | 20 | 2 | 1 | 17 | 31 | 91 | -60 | 7 |

Elstow Abbey Reserves withdrew - record expunged.

ıt: Bedford United (W), Kempston Athletic (R),

ırston Shelton Rovers Reserves (R), Wootton Village (R)

| | DIVISION THREE | P | W | D | L | F | A | GD | Pts |
|---|---|---|---|---|---|---|---|---|---|
| 1 | Wixams | 22 | 20 | 1 | 1 | 91 | 20 | 71 | 61 |
| 2 | Sundon Park Rovers | 22 | 14 | 3 | 5 | 52 | 30 | 22 | 45 |
| 3 | Wilstead Reserves | 22 | 13 | 3 | 6 | 73 | 47 | 26 | 42 |
| 4 | Caldecote Reserves | 22 | 12 | 2 | 8 | 61 | 51 | 10 | 38 |
| 5 | Renhold United Res. (-1) | 22 | 10 | 5 | 7 | 49 | 41 | 8 | 34 |
| 6 | White Eagles (-1) | 22 | 10 | 3 | 9 | 56 | 51 | 5 | 32 |
| 7 | AFC Dunton (-5) | 22 | 9 | 6 | 7 | 52 | 50 | 2 | 28 |
| 8 | Dinamo Flitwick (-6) | 22 | 9 | 2 | 11 | 58 | 76 | -18 | 23 |
| 9 | Shefford Town & Campton 'A' (-4) | 22 | 6 | 3 | 13 | 31 | 57 | -26 | 17 |
| 10 | Meltis Albion Res. (-1) | 22 | 5 | 1 | 16 | 33 | 63 | -30 | 15 |
| 11 | Sandy Reserves | 22 | 3 | 3 | 16 | 22 | 59 | -37 | 12 |
| 12 | Clifton (-4) | 22 | 4 | 2 | 16 | 42 | 75 | -33 | 10 |

| | DIVISION FOUR | P | W | D | L | F | A | GD | Pts |
|---|---|---|---|---|---|---|---|---|---|
| 1 | Mid Beds Tigers | 18 | 15 | 2 | 1 | 98 | 18 | 80 | 47 |
| 2 | Caldecote 'A' | 18 | 12 | 3 | 3 | 60 | 42 | 18 | 39 |
| 3 | Bedford Albion | 18 | 12 | 1 | 5 | 61 | 46 | 15 | 37 |
| 4 | Stevington Reserves | 18 | 11 | 0 | 7 | 58 | 38 | 20 | 33 |
| 5 | Polonia Bedford (-1) | 18 | 11 | 0 | 7 | 46 | 32 | 14 | 32 |
| 6 | AFC Kempston T&Bedford Coll 'A' (-1) | 18 | 8 | 1 | 9 | 70 | 63 | 7 | 24 |
| 7 | Flitwick Town 'A' | 18 | 6 | 3 | 9 | 41 | 60 | -19 | 21 |
| 8 | Westoning Reserves (-3) | 18 | 4 | 1 | 13 | 46 | 57 | -11 | 10 |
| 9 | Henlow Reserves | 18 | 3 | 1 | 14 | 36 | 78 | -42 | 10 |
| 10 | Lidlington United Sports (-1) | 18 | 2 | 0 | 16 | 25 | 107 | -82 | 5 |

Staughton withdrew - record expunged.

**Out:** Bedford Albion (P), Mid Beds Tigers (W), Polonia Bedford (W).

## CENTENARY CUP

**INAL** **HOLDERS:** MELTIS ALBION

Jueens Park Crescents v Ickleford 1-0

## JUBILEE CUP

**FINAL** **HOLDERS:** STEVINGTON

Flitwick Town Reserves v Cranfield United Res. 1-1, 2-3p

## WATSON SHIELD

**FINAL**

BYSL Ampthill Town v Renhold United Reserves 0-4

# CAMBRIDGESHIRE COUNTY LEAGUE

**Sponsored by:** Kershaw Mechanical Services Ltd
**Founded:** 1891
**Recent Champions:**
**2013:** Great Shelford
**2014:** Over Sports **2015:** Great Shelford

| PREMIER DIVISION | P | W | D | L | F | A | GD | Pts |
|---|---|---|---|---|---|---|---|---|
| 1 Great Shelford | 34 | 25 | 2 | 7 | 79 | 40 | 39 | 77 |
| 2 Hardwick | 34 | 21 | 6 | 7 | 105 | 59 | 46 | 69 |
| 3 Fulbourn Institute | 34 | 18 | 8 | 8 | 84 | 44 | 40 | 62 |
| 4 Eaton Socon | 34 | 18 | 8 | 8 | 70 | 42 | 28 | 62 |
| 5 Wisbech St Mary | 34 | 17 | 10 | 7 | 77 | 40 | 37 | 61 |
| 6 Lakenheath | 34 | 18 | 5 | 11 | 89 | 53 | 36 | 59 |
| 7 Brampton | 34 | 18 | 3 | 13 | 70 | 60 | 10 | 57 |
| 8 West Wratting | 34 | 17 | 5 | 12 | 97 | 53 | 44 | 56 |
| 9 Linton Granta | 34 | 14 | 3 | 17 | 79 | 69 | 10 | 45 |
| 10 Cherry Hinton | 34 | 14 | 3 | 17 | 57 | 84 | -27 | 45 |
| 11 Foxton | 34 | 13 | 4 | 17 | 72 | 75 | -3 | 43 |
| 12 Gamlingay United | 34 | 12 | 6 | 16 | 67 | 87 | -20 | 42 |
| 13 Cambridge City Reserves | 34 | 11 | 5 | 18 | 63 | 87 | -24 | 38 |
| 14 Fowlmere | 34 | 10 | 7 | 17 | 55 | 85 | -30 | 37 |
| 15 Over Sports | 34 | 10 | 5 | 19 | 48 | 71 | -23 | 35 |
| 16 Sawston United | 34 | 10 | 5 | 19 | 51 | 85 | -34 | 35 |
| 17 Hemingfords United | 34 | 6 | 7 | 21 | 58 | 98 | -40 | 25 |
| 18 Cottenham United | 34 | 8 | 0 | 26 | 36 | 125 | -89 | 24 |

**Out:** Wisbech St. Mary (P - United Counties).

## PREMIER DIVISION CUP

**HOLDERS:** GREAT SHELFORD

**ROUND 1**

| | | | |
|---|---|---|---|
| Wisbech St Mary | v | Fowlmere | 1-5 |
| Fulbourn Institute | v | Hemingfords United | 4-0 |

**ROUND 2**

| | | | |
|---|---|---|---|
| Over Sports | v | Foxton | 3-1 |
| Brampton | v | Linton Granta | 5-3 |
| Great Shelford | v | Sawston United | 4-0 |
| Fowlmere | v | Cottenham United | 4-1 |
| Fulbourn Institute | v | Cambridge City Reserves | 1-2 |
| Eaton Socon | v | Hardwick | 0-5 |
| Cherry Hinton | v | Gamlingay United | 1-4 |
| West Wratting | v | Lakenheath | 4-1 |

**QUARTER FINALS**

| | | | |
|---|---|---|---|
| Over Sports | v | Brampton | 2-3 |
| Great Shelford | v | Fowlmere | 4-1 |
| Cambridge City Reserves | v | Hardwick | 1-5 |
| Gamlingay United | v | West Wratting | 3-1 |

**SEMI FINALS**

| | | | |
|---|---|---|---|
| Brampton | v | Great Shelford | 0-2 |
| Hardwick | v | Gamlingay United | AW |

**FINAL**

| | | | |
|---|---|---|---|
| Great Shelford | v | Gamlingay United | 0-2 |

| PREMIER DIVISION | 1 | 2 | 3 | 4 | 5 | 6 | 7 | 8 | 9 | 10 | 11 | 12 | 13 | 14 | 15 | 16 | 17 | 18 |
|---|---|---|---|---|---|---|---|---|---|---|---|---|---|---|---|---|---|---|
| 1 Brampton | | 4-1 | 5-2 | 5-0 | 1-0 | 2-4 | 3-2 | 0-2 | 3-2 | 0-3 | 0-3 | 4-0 | 2-0 | 3-0 | 2-2 | 7-0 | 2-1 | 2- |
| 2 Cambridge City Reserves | 1-2 | | 0-1 | 4-0 | 1-3 | 3-2 | 3-2 | 2-2 | 2-6 | 3-5 | 0-0 | 6-2 | 0-0 | 4-1 | 2-3 | 6-1 | 2-1 | 0- |
| 3 Cherry Hinton | 0-0 | 5-2 | | 3-0 | 1-1 | 2-4 | 2-3 | 2-2 | 3-0 | 1-0 | 4-3 | 4-6 | 2-4 | 0-2 | 2-1 | 3-1 | 1-5 | 2- |
| 4 Cottenham United | 2-1 | 1-0 | 0-3 | | 1-4 | 0-2 | 4-2 | 0-4 | 1-7 | 1-3 | 0-5 | 3-2 | 1-3 | 0-2 | 2-1 | 3-5 | 1-3 | 1- |
| 5 Eaton Socon | 2-1 | 1-1 | 4-0 | 1-2 | | 2-0 | 1-3 | 0-2 | 0-2 | 3-2 | 1-1 | 0-0 | 5-2 | 7-1 | 3-0 | 3-0 | 2-1 | 1- |
| 6 Fowlmere | 1-3 | 1-4 | 2-0 | 4-2 | 0-1 | | 3-1 | 0-9 | 5-3 | 1-2 | 2-3 | 1-4 | 1-5 | 3-2 | 1-4 | 1-1 | 0-0 | 0- |
| 7 Foxton | 0-1 | 5-2 | 5-1 | 8-2 | 0-3 | 2-2 | | 3-4 | 4-0 | 2-0 | 3-4 | 3-0 | 0-6 | 2-6 | 2-1 | 1-2 | 3-1 | 1- |
| 8 Fulbourn Institute | 1-2 | 0-1 | 6-2 | 1-0 | 2-2 | 1-1 | 1-2 | | 2-3 | 0-1 | 1-2 | 2-1 | 5-0 | 4-2 | 3-3 | 3-3 | 2-0 | 2- |
| 9 Gamlingay United | 4-0 | 1-0 | 5-2 | 4-0 | 2-3 | 2-1 | 3-3 | 1-2 | | 0-3 | 1-6 | 0-1 | 1-1 | 2-2 | 2-2 | 1-5 | 4-2 | 1- |
| 10 Great Shelford | 1-0 | 3-0 | 4-1 | 4-0 | 2-0 | 4-0 | 3-2 | 2-1 | 1-0 | | 2-2 | 3-1 | 0-4 | 3-2 | 2-1 | 2-0 | 1-4 | 4- |
| 11 Hardwick | 4-0 | 8-1 | 3-0 | 4-2 | 5-2 | 2-2 | 3-1 | 0-1 | 8-0 | 0-1 | | 9-2 | 2-1 | 4-3 | 2-1 | 3-1 | 6-3 | 2- |
| 12 Hemingfords United | 4-4 | 7-0 | 1-2 | 3-1 | 1-3 | 0-4 | 1-1 | 1-3 | 3-3 | 1-2 | 3-3 | | 0-5 | 1-5 | 3-1 | 2-2 | 3-6 | 2- |
| 13 Lakenheath | 3-2 | 0-2 | 0-1 | 10-1 | 1-3 | 2-1 | 0-3 | 2-2 | 5-3 | 4-0 | 2-3 | 5-0 | | 2-2 | 6-1 | 3-1 | 2-1 | 1- |
| 14 Linton Granta | 3-1 | 5-2 | 1-3 | 10-1 | 0-0 | 3-4 | 2-0 | 0-2 | 0-1 | 4-2 | 7-0 | 3-1 | 2-3 | | 2-3 | 1-2 | 1-2 | 2- |
| 15 Over Sports | 0-2 | 3-1 | 0-1 | 0-1 | 3-2 | 0-0 | 1-0 | 1-5 | 0-2 | 0-1 | 4-1 | 2-1 | 1-0 | 0-2 | | 0-3 | 4-3 | 1- |
| 16 Sawston United | 3-4 | 0-5 | 0-1 | 3-1 | 2-4 | 1-1 | 1-2 | 0-5 | 2-1 | 0-5 | 3-1 | 3-1 | 1-2 | 0-1 | 3-0 | | 0-3 | 1 |
| 17 West Wratting | 3-1 | 5-0 | 3-0 | 12-2 | 1-1 | 7-0 | 3-1 | 4-2 | 11-0 | 1-1 | 1-2 | 1-0 | 0-4 | 3-0 | 4-3 | 1-1 | | 1- |
| 18 Wisbech St Mary | 5-1 | 2-2 | 6-0 | 2-0 | 0-2 | 6-1 | 5-0 | 0-0 | 3-0 | 0-7 | 2-1 | 0-0 | 3-1 | 4-0 | 4-1 | 3-0 | H-W | |

## Cambridgeshire County Premier Division

|  |  |
|---|---|
| **BRAMPTON** | Thrapston Road Playing Fields, Brampton, Huntingdon PE28 4TB |
| **CAMBRIDGE CITY RESERVES** | Cottenham Village College, High Street, Cottenham, Cambridge CB24 8UA |
| **CHATTERIS TOWN** | West Street, Chatteris, Cambridgeshire PE16 6HW |
| **CHERRY HINTON** | Recreation Ground, High Street, Cherry Hinton Cambridge CB1 9HZ |
| **EATON SOCON** | River Road, Eaton Ford, St Neots PE19 3AU |
| **FOWLMERE** | Fowlmere Village Hall #1, Chrishall Road, Fowlmere, Royston SG8 7RE |
| **FOXTON** | Hardman Road, off High Street, Foxton CB22 6RP |
| **FULBOURN INSTITUTE** | Fulbourn Recreation, Home End, Fulbourn CB21 5HS |
| **GAMLINGAY UNITED** | Gamlingay Community Centre, Stocks Lane, Gamlingay, Cambridgeshire SG19 3JR |
| **GREAT SHELFORD** | Recreation Ground, Woollards Lane, Great Shelford CB2 5LZ |
| **HARDWICK** | Egremont Road, Hardwick, Cambridge CB3 7XR |
| **HEMINGFORDS UNITED** | Peace Memorial Playing Field #1, Manor Road, Hemingford Grey PE28 9BX |
| **LAKENHEATH** | The Pit, Wings Road, Lakenheath IP27 9HN |
| **LINTON GRANTA** | Recreation Ground, Meadow Lane, Linton, Cambridge CB21 6HX |
| **OUTWELL SWIFTS** | Outwell Playing Field The Nest, Wisbech Road, Outwell, Wisbechech PE14 8PA |
| **OVER SPORTS** | Over Recreation Ground, The Doles, Over, Cambridge CB4 5NW |
| **SAWSTON UNITED** | Spicers Sports Ground, New Road, Sawston CB22 4BW |
| **WEST WRATTING** | Recreation Ground, Bull Lane, West Wratting CB21 5NJ |

## WILLIAM COCKELL CUP

**FINAL** **HOLDERS:** FULBOURN INSTITUTE RESERVES

Chatteris Town v Milton 3-0

## PERCY OLDHAM CUP

**FINAL** **HOLDERS:** GODMANCHESTER ROVERS RESERVES

Comberton United v Needingworth United 5-3

| SENIOR DIVISION A | | P | W | D | L | F | A | GD | Pts |
|---|---|---|---|---|---|---|---|---|---|
| | Outwell Swifts | 28 | 24 | 1 | 3 | 76 | 26 | 50 | 73 |
| | Chatteris Town | 28 | 21 | 3 | 4 | 95 | 27 | 68 | 66 |
| | Milton | 28 | 15 | 4 | 9 | 86 | 56 | 30 | 49 |
| | Soham United | 28 | 15 | 3 | 10 | 66 | 41 | 25 | 48 |
| | Barrington | 28 | 13 | 3 | 12 | 62 | 68 | -6 | 42 |
| | Cambridge University Press | 28 | 12 | 5 | 11 | 63 | 65 | -2 | 41 |
| | Somersham Town | 28 | 11 | 5 | 12 | 55 | 57 | -2 | 38 |
| | Royston Town A | 28 | 11 | 5 | 12 | 47 | 60 | -13 | 38 |
| | Fulbourn Institute Res. | 28 | 10 | 6 | 12 | 43 | 56 | -13 | 36 |
| 0 | Soham Town Rangers Res. | 28 | 10 | 5 | 13 | 53 | 60 | -7 | 35 |
| 1 | Hundon | 28 | 10 | 4 | 14 | 45 | 77 | -32 | 34 |
| 2 | Girton United | 28 | 9 | 6 | 13 | 58 | 70 | -12 | 33 |
| 3 | Ely City Reserves | 28 | 7 | 7 | 14 | 50 | 64 | -14 | 28 |
| 4 | Paxton United | 28 | 6 | 4 | 18 | 48 | 77 | -29 | 22 |
| 5 | Orwell | 28 | 4 | 3 | 21 | 41 | 84 | -43 | 15 |

: Great Paxton (NC from Paxton United)

| ENIOR DIVISION B | | P | W | D | L | F | A | GD | Pts |
|---|---|---|---|---|---|---|---|---|---|
| | Burwell Swifts | 30 | 23 | 4 | 3 | 109 | 31 | 78 | 73 |
| | Comberton United | 30 | 23 | 4 | 3 | 99 | 38 | 61 | 73 |
| | Bar Hill | 30 | 20 | 4 | 6 | 99 | 34 | 65 | 64 |
| | Godmanchester Rovers Res. | 30 | 20 | 3 | 7 | 95 | 46 | 49 | 63 |
| | Witchford 96 | 30 | 16 | 3 | 11 | 61 | 53 | 8 | 51 |
| | Needingworth United | 30 | 14 | 5 | 11 | 58 | 56 | 2 | 47 |
| | Bluntisham Rangers | 30 | 12 | 5 | 13 | 52 | 76 | -24 | 41 |
| | Sawston Rovers | 30 | 12 | 3 | 15 | 60 | 70 | -10 | 39 |
| | Whittlesford United | 30 | 11 | 6 | 13 | 54 | 69 | -15 | 39 |
| | West Wratting Reserves | 30 | 11 | 4 | 15 | 51 | 66 | -15 | 37 |
| | Ashdon Villa | 30 | 10 | 3 | 17 | 60 | 80 | -20 | 33 |
| 2 | Lakenheath Reserves | 30 | 8 | 8 | 14 | 51 | 79 | -28 | 32 |
| 3 | Wimblington | 30 | 8 | 5 | 17 | 48 | 77 | -29 | 29 |
| 4 | Cambridge University Press Res | 30 | 7 | 2 | 21 | 42 | 87 | -45 | 23 |
| 5 | Hardwick Reserves | 30 | 6 | 4 | 20 | 35 | 70 | -35 | 22 |
| 6 | Hemingfords United Res. | 30 | 5 | 5 | 20 | 37 | 79 | -42 | 20 |

ut: Hemingfords United Reserves (R - D1B). Wimblington (R - D2B)

| DIVISION ONE A | | P | W | D | L | F | A | GD | Pts |
|---|---|---|---|---|---|---|---|---|---|
| 1 | Red Lodge | 22 | 17 | 3 | 2 | 61 | 30 | 31 | 54 |
| 2 | Haverhill Borough Res. | 22 | 17 | 2 | 3 | 75 | 23 | 52 | 53 |
| 3 | Histon Hornets Sports | 22 | 15 | 2 | 5 | 70 | 34 | 36 | 47 |
| 4 | Cherry Hinton Reserves | 22 | 12 | 1 | 9 | 67 | 46 | 21 | 37 |
| 5 | Duxford United | 22 | 9 | 6 | 7 | 43 | 47 | -4 | 33 |
| 6 | Sawston United Reserves | 22 | 10 | 2 | 10 | 64 | 56 | 8 | 32 |
| 7 | Great Chishill | 22 | 7 | 4 | 11 | 44 | 60 | -16 | 25 |
| 8 | Exning United | 22 | 6 | 5 | 11 | 60 | 74 | -14 | 23 |
| 9 | Linton Granta Reserves | 22 | 6 | 5 | 11 | 39 | 59 | -20 | 23 |
| 10 | Debden | 22 | 4 | 5 | 13 | 40 | 69 | -29 | 17 |
| 11 | Balsham | 22 | 4 | 4 | 14 | 30 | 59 | -29 | 16 |
| 12 | Saffron Rangers | 22 | 3 | 5 | 14 | 36 | 72 | -36 | 14 |

**In:** Milton Reserves (S - D1B), Over Sports Reserves (S - D1B).

**Out:** Saffron Rangers (W).

| DIVISION ONE B | | P | W | D | L | F | A | GD | Pts |
|---|---|---|---|---|---|---|---|---|---|
| 1 | Wisbech St Mary Res. | 26 | 23 | 0 | 3 | 67 | 19 | 48 | 69 |
| 2 | Buckden | 26 | 20 | 2 | 4 | 96 | 31 | 65 | 62 |
| 3 | Fordham | 26 | 16 | 3 | 7 | 54 | 31 | 23 | 51 |
| 4 | Eaton Socon Reserves | 26 | 15 | 3 | 8 | 74 | 36 | 38 | 48 |
| 5 | March Town United Res. | 26 | 15 | 0 | 11 | 52 | 42 | 10 | 45 |
| 6 | Alconbury | 26 | 13 | 4 | 9 | 66 | 47 | 19 | 43 |
| 7 | Littleport Town | 26 | 14 | 1 | 11 | 45 | 37 | 8 | 43 |
| 8 | Chatteris Town Reserves | 26 | 9 | 4 | 13 | 33 | 59 | -26 | 31 |
| 9 | Huntingdon United | 26 | 6 | 7 | 13 | 61 | 59 | 2 | 25 |
| 10 | St Ives Rangers | 26 | 7 | 4 | 15 | 51 | 77 | -26 | 25 |
| 11 | Swavesey Institute | 26 | 8 | 1 | 17 | 52 | 86 | -34 | 25 |
| 12 | Manea United (-3) | 26 | 8 | 2 | 16 | 47 | 78 | -31 | 23 |
| 13 | Over Sports Res. (-3) | 26 | 7 | 2 | 17 | 38 | 60 | -22 | 20 |
| 14 | Milton Reserves | 26 | 3 | 3 | 20 | 43 | 117 | -74 | 12 |

## CAMBRIDGESHIRE COUNTY LEAGUE - STEP 7

| DIVISION TWO A | P | W | D | L | F | A | GD | Pts |
|---|---|---|---|---|---|---|---|---|
| 1 Steeple Bumpstead | 26 | 22 | 2 | 2 | 103 | 28 | 75 | 68 |
| 2 Steeple Morden | 26 | 20 | 5 | 1 | 73 | 27 | 46 | 65 |
| 3 Cambourne Rovers | 26 | 16 | 5 | 5 | 66 | 33 | 33 | 53 |
| 4 Thaxted Rangers | 26 | 15 | 6 | 5 | 76 | 44 | 32 | 51 |
| 5 Saffron Crocus | 26 | 12 | 3 | 11 | 66 | 46 | 20 | 39 |
| 6 Papworth | 26 | 11 | 2 | 13 | 61 | 54 | 7 | 35 |
| 7 City Life (-3) | 26 | 11 | 4 | 11 | 47 | 54 | -7 | 34 |
| 8 Fowlmere Reserves (-3) | 26 | 11 | 3 | 12 | 53 | 61 | -8 | 33 |
| 9 Gamlingay United Res. | 26 | 7 | 6 | 13 | 31 | 69 | -38 | 27 |
| 10 Abington United | 26 | 7 | 5 | 14 | 30 | 64 | -34 | 26 |
| 11 Eynesbury Rovers A (-3) | 26 | 8 | 2 | 16 | 55 | 66 | -11 | 23 |
| 12 Litlington Athletic | 26 | 5 | 5 | 16 | 57 | 91 | -34 | 20 |
| 13 Meldreth (-3) | 26 | 6 | 3 | 17 | 32 | 69 | -37 | 18 |
| 14 Paxton United Res. (-3) | 26 | 4 | 3 | 19 | 24 | 68 | -44 | 12 |

| DIVISION TWO B | P | W | D | L | F | A | GD | Pts |
|---|---|---|---|---|---|---|---|---|
| 1 Houghton & Wyton | 26 | 20 | 2 | 4 | 91 | 23 | 68 | 62 |
| 2 Fenstanton | 26 | 18 | 4 | 4 | 80 | 38 | 42 | 58 |
| 3 March Rangers | 26 | 16 | 2 | 8 | 72 | 58 | 14 | 50 |
| 4 Ely Crusaders | 26 | 14 | 4 | 8 | 79 | 48 | 31 | 46 |
| 5 Isleham United | 26 | 13 | 6 | 7 | 68 | 44 | 24 | 45 |
| 6 Little Downham Swifts | 26 | 13 | 3 | 10 | 87 | 55 | 32 | 42 |
| 7 Bar Hill Reserves | 26 | 12 | 6 | 8 | 62 | 44 | 18 | 42 |
| 8 Brampton Reserves | 26 | 12 | 1 | 13 | 49 | 49 | 0 | 37 |
| 9 Mildenhall United | 26 | 11 | 2 | 13 | 52 | 71 | -19 | 35 |
| 10 Soham United Reserves | 26 | 8 | 4 | 14 | 48 | 72 | -24 | 28 |
| 11 Wisbech St Mary A | 26 | 8 | 4 | 14 | 44 | 70 | -26 | 28 |
| 12 Mepal Sports | 26 | 6 | 9 | 11 | 52 | 71 | -19 | 27 |
| 13 Cottenham United Res. | 26 | 4 | 3 | 19 | 27 | 81 | -54 | 15 |
| 14 Bluntisham Rangers Res. (-3) | 26 | 1 | 2 | 23 | 29 | 116 | -87 | 2 |

**In:** Wimblington (R - S2B)

| DIVISION THREE A | P | W | D | L | F | A | GD | Pts |
|---|---|---|---|---|---|---|---|---|
| 1 Bassingbourn | 24 | 21 | 1 | 2 | 75 | 23 | 52 | 64 |
| 2 Clare Town | 24 | 19 | 0 | 5 | 94 | 39 | 55 | 57 |
| 3 Whittlesford United Res. | 24 | 17 | 2 | 5 | 101 | 40 | 61 | 53 |
| 4 Offord United | 24 | 15 | 2 | 7 | 56 | 40 | 16 | 47 |
| 5 Eaton Socon A | 24 | 14 | 2 | 8 | 71 | 53 | 18 | 44 |
| 6 Melbourn (-3) | 24 | 14 | 2 | 8 | 65 | 37 | 28 | 41 |
| 7 Linton Granta A | 24 | 8 | 1 | 15 | 54 | 77 | -23 | 25 |
| 8 Hundon Reserves | 24 | 7 | 4 | 13 | 30 | 63 | -33 | 25 |
| 9 Hardwick A (-3) | 24 | 9 | 0 | 15 | 44 | 76 | -32 | 24 |
| 10 Foxton Reserves (-3) | 24 | 7 | 3 | 14 | 41 | 52 | -11 | 21 |
| 11 Duxford United Reserves | 24 | 6 | 3 | 15 | 51 | 66 | -15 | 21 |
| 12 Girton United Reserves | 24 | 5 | 4 | 15 | 42 | 71 | -29 | 19 |
| 13 Wilbraham (-12) | 24 | 2 | 0 | 22 | 12 | 99 | -87 | -6 |

**Out:** Wilbaham (W).

| DIVISION THREE B | P | W | D | L | F | A | GD | Pts |
|---|---|---|---|---|---|---|---|---|
| 1 AFC Barley Mow | 24 | 20 | 2 | 2 | 109 | 30 | 79 | 62 |
| 2 Upwell Town | 24 | 18 | 1 | 5 | 79 | 33 | 46 | 55 |
| 3 The Eagle | 24 | 15 | 4 | 5 | 72 | 50 | 22 | 49 |
| 4 West Row Gunners (-3) | 24 | 12 | 4 | 8 | 66 | 46 | 20 | 37 |
| 5 Chatteris Fen Tigers | 24 | 11 | 1 | 12 | 62 | 72 | -10 | 34 |
| 6 Earith United | 24 | 9 | 4 | 11 | 65 | 57 | 8 | 31 |
| 7 Burwell Swifts Res. (-3) | 24 | 11 | 1 | 12 | 47 | 49 | -2 | 31 |
| 8 Alconbury Reserves | 24 | 9 | 0 | 15 | 54 | 67 | -13 | 27 |
| 9 Wisbech St Mary B | 24 | 8 | 3 | 13 | 42 | 59 | -17 | 27 |
| 10 Benwick Athletic | 24 | 8 | 3 | 13 | 33 | 68 | -35 | 27 |
| 11 Lakenheath Casuals | 24 | 8 | 1 | 15 | 44 | 69 | -25 | 25 |
| 12 Waterbeach Colts Old Boys | 24 | 7 | 2 | 15 | 34 | 60 | -26 | 23 |
| 13 Wimblington Res. (-3) | 24 | 6 | 2 | 16 | 41 | 88 | -47 | 17 |

**In:** Offord United (S - D3A)

| DIVISION FOUR A | P | W | D | L | F | A | GD | Pts |
|---|---|---|---|---|---|---|---|---|
| 1 Mott MacDonald | 22 | 20 | 0 | 2 | 63 | 20 | 43 | 60 |
| 2 Cherry Hinton A (-3) | 22 | 13 | 4 | 5 | 60 | 33 | 27 | 40 |
| 3 Kedington United | 22 | 12 | 4 | 6 | 63 | 49 | 14 | 40 |
| 4 Sawston Rovers Res. | 22 | 12 | 4 | 6 | 61 | 47 | 14 | 40 |
| 5 Cambridge Ambassadors | 22 | 11 | 3 | 8 | 64 | 42 | 22 | 36 |
| 6 Saffron Dynamos | 22 | 9 | 4 | 9 | 48 | 34 | 14 | 31 |
| 7 Finchingfield (-3) | 22 | 10 | 2 | 10 | 34 | 39 | -5 | 29 |
| 8 Papworth Reserves | 22 | 7 | 4 | 11 | 42 | 55 | -13 | 25 |
| 9 Buckden Reserves | 22 | 7 | 3 | 12 | 38 | 47 | -9 | 24 |
| 10 Milton A | 22 | 5 | 6 | 11 | 38 | 61 | -23 | 21 |
| 11 Guilden Morden | 22 | 2 | 5 | 15 | 24 | 56 | -32 | 11 |
| 12 Sawston United "A" (-3) | 22 | 3 | 3 | 16 | 21 | 73 | -52 | 9 |

**In:** Comberton United Reserves (N),
**Out:** Finchingfield (W).

| DIVISION FOUR B | P | W | D | L | F | A | GD | Pts |
|---|---|---|---|---|---|---|---|---|
| 1 Tuddenham 08 | 18 | 15 | 1 | 2 | 72 | 23 | 49 | 4 |
| 2 Doddington United | 18 | 14 | 1 | 3 | 65 | 23 | 42 | 4 |
| 3 Wisbech St Mary C | 18 | 14 | 1 | 3 | 68 | 27 | 41 | 4 |
| 4 Fordham Reserves | 18 | 7 | 3 | 8 | 27 | 29 | -2 | 2 |
| 5 Isleham United Reserves | 18 | 7 | 2 | 9 | 32 | 34 | -2 | 2 |
| 6 Witchford 96 Reserves | 18 | 7 | 1 | 10 | 42 | 47 | -5 | 2 |
| 7 March Rangers Reserves | 18 | 5 | 2 | 11 | 24 | 50 | -26 | 1 |
| 8 Hemingfords United A | 18 | 5 | 2 | 11 | 39 | 72 | -33 | 1 |
| 9 Chatteris Town A | 18 | 5 | 1 | 12 | 43 | 56 | -13 | 1 |
| 10 Coldham United | 18 | 3 | 2 | 13 | 24 | 75 | -51 | 1 |

**In:** Upwell Twon Reserves (P).

| DIVISION FIVE A | P | W | D | L | F | A | GD | Pts |
|---|---|---|---|---|---|---|---|---|
| 1 Wickhambrook | 22 | 18 | 1 | 3 | 74 | 22 | 52 | 55 |
| 2 Haverhill Rovers A | 22 | 15 | 2 | 5 | 65 | 28 | 37 | 47 |
| 3 Suffolk Punch Haverhill | 21 | 13 | 3 | 5 | 78 | 32 | 46 | 42 |
| 4 Steeple Morden Res. | 22 | 11 | 3 | 8 | 54 | 41 | 13 | 36 |
| 5 Harston 2015 | 22 | 10 | 3 | 9 | 34 | 49 | -15 | 33 |
| 6 Saffron Crocus Res. | 22 | 10 | 0 | 12 | 49 | 65 | -16 | 30 |
| 7 Fulbourn Institute "A" | 22 | 8 | 4 | 10 | 70 | 46 | 24 | 28 |
| 8 Clare Town Reserves | 22 | 7 | 7 | 8 | 42 | 43 | -1 | 28 |
| 9 Barrington Reserves | 21 | 7 | 6 | 8 | 53 | 35 | 18 | 27 |
| 10 Thaxted Rangers Res. | 22 | 6 | 6 | 10 | 55 | 74 | -19 | 24 |
| 11 Histon Hornets Sports Res. | 22 | 7 | 3 | 12 | 41 | 80 | -39 | 24 |
| 12 Haslingfield (-3) | 22 | 0 | 0 | 22 | 19 | 119 | -100 | -3 |

**In:** Barton Mills (S - D5B), Bassingbourn Reserves (N), Bottisham Sports (N), Cottenham United "A" (S - D5B), Lakenheath Casuals Reserves (S - D5B), Steeple Morden "A" (N).
**Out:** Haslingfield (W),

| DIVISION FIVE B | P | W | D | L | F | A | GD | Pts |
|---|---|---|---|---|---|---|---|---|
| 1 Guyhirn | 22 | 17 | 3 | 2 | 100 | 31 | 69 | 5 |
| 2 Ely Crusaders Reserves | 22 | 17 | 2 | 3 | 86 | 34 | 52 | 5 |
| 3 Burwell Tigers | 22 | 14 | 4 | 4 | 89 | 22 | 67 | 4 |
| 4 Marchester United | 22 | 13 | 3 | 6 | 68 | 42 | 26 | 4 |
| 5 Needingworth United Res. | 22 | 12 | 5 | 5 | 90 | 40 | 50 | 4 |
| 6 Wicken Athletic | 22 | 8 | 8 | 6 | 65 | 65 | 0 | 3 |
| 7 Upwell Town Reserves | 22 | 9 | 3 | 10 | 51 | 51 | 0 | 3 |
| 8 Cottenham United "A" | 22 | 7 | 3 | 12 | 47 | 70 | -23 | 2 |
| 9 Lakenheath Casuals Res. (-3) | 22 | 5 | 3 | 14 | 35 | 92 | -57 | 1 |
| 10 Benwick Athletic Reserves | 22 | 4 | 2 | 16 | 40 | 89 | -49 | 1 |
| 11 Barton Mills | 22 | 4 | 1 | 17 | 42 | 105 | -63 | 1 |
| 12 Chatteris Town B | 22 | 3 | 1 | 18 | 26 | 98 | -72 | 1 |

**In:** AFC Christchurch (N), Colham United Reserves (N), Fenstanton Reserves (N), Houghton & Wyton Reserves (N), Huntingdon United Reserves (N), March Town United "A" (N), Outwell Swifts Reserves (N), Upwell Town "A" (N).

# CENTRAL MIDLANDS LEAGUE

**Sponsored by:** Abacus Lighting **Founded:** 1971
**Recent Champions: 2013:** (N) Dronfield Town (S) Sutton Town AFC
**2014:** (N) AFC Mansfield (S) Clifton All Whites **2015:** Bilsthorpe (N) Mickleover Royals (S)

| | NORTH DIVISION | P | W | D | L | F | A | GD | Pts |
|---|---|---|---|---|---|---|---|---|---|
| 1 | Glapwell | 28 | 23 | 1 | 4 | 148 | 38 | 110 | 70 |
| 2 | Ollerton Town | 28 | 21 | 1 | 6 | 94 | 33 | 61 | 64 |
| 3 | Phoenix (-3) | 28 | 20 | 3 | 5 | 82 | 43 | 39 | 60 |
| 4 | Appleby Frodingham | 28 | 18 | 4 | 6 | 96 | 33 | 63 | 58 |
| 5 | Harworth Colliery Institute | 28 | 17 | 4 | 7 | 86 | 37 | 49 | 55 |
| 6 | Askern | 28 | 16 | 2 | 10 | 89 | 53 | 36 | 50 |
| 7 | Retford | 28 | 14 | 3 | 11 | 63 | 42 | 21 | 45 |
| 8 | Dronfield Town Reserves | 28 | 12 | 7 | 9 | 69 | 58 | 11 | 43 |
| 9 | Brodsworth Welfare | 28 | 12 | 2 | 14 | 64 | 61 | 3 | 38 |
| 10 | Thorne Colliery | 28 | 9 | 5 | 14 | 51 | 66 | -15 | 32 |
| 11 | Easington United | 28 | 7 | 6 | 15 | 48 | 71 | -23 | 27 |
| 12 | Bilsthorpe | 28 | 7 | 3 | 18 | 33 | 61 | -28 | 24 |
| 13 | Newark Town | 28 | 6 | 3 | 19 | 55 | 96 | -41 | 21 |
| 14 | Dinnington Town | 28 | 3 | 3 | 22 | 31 | 122 | -91 | 12 |
| 15 | Welbeck Welfare (-2) | 28 | 1 | 1 | 26 | 23 | 218 | -195 | 2 |

Bentley Colliery, Easington United & Thoresby CW withdrew - records expunged.

| | SOUTH DIVISION | P | W | D | L | F | A | GD | Pts |
|---|---|---|---|---|---|---|---|---|---|
| 1 | Selston | 34 | 26 | 5 | 3 | 121 | 45 | 76 | 83 |
| 2 | Belper United | 34 | 23 | 4 | 7 | 94 | 35 | 59 | 73 |
| 3 | Hucknall Town | 34 | 23 | 2 | 9 | 97 | 33 | 64 | 71 |
| 4 | Pinxton | 34 | 22 | 3 | 9 | 96 | 52 | 44 | 69 |
| 5 | Sherwood Colliery | 34 | 19 | 5 | 10 | 88 | 64 | 24 | 62 |
| 6 | Blidworth Welfare | 34 | 18 | 7 | 9 | 85 | 60 | 25 | 61 |
| 7 | Hucknall Rolls Leisure | 34 | 17 | 6 | 11 | 80 | 46 | 34 | 57 |
| 8 | Swanwick Pentrich Road | 34 | 16 | 9 | 9 | 82 | 58 | 24 | 57 |
| 9 | Matlock Town Reserves | 34 | 14 | 7 | 13 | 68 | 66 | 2 | 49 |
| 10 | Eastwood Community | 34 | 13 | 7 | 14 | 83 | 74 | 9 | 46 |
| 11 | Linby Colliery | 34 | 13 | 5 | 16 | 63 | 62 | 1 | 44 |
| 12 | Clay Cross Town | 34 | 13 | 5 | 16 | 64 | 74 | -10 | 44 |
| 13 | Collingham | 34 | 13 | 3 | 18 | 60 | 87 | -27 | 42 |
| 14 | Bulwell | 34 | 12 | 5 | 17 | 80 | 102 | -22 | 41 |
| 15 | Mickleover RBL | 34 | 8 | 3 | 23 | 64 | 109 | -45 | 27 |
| 16 | Holbrook St Michaels | 34 | 6 | 5 | 23 | 40 | 118 | -78 | 23 |
| 17 | Keyworth United (-2) | 34 | 4 | 3 | 27 | 43 | 112 | -69 | 13 |
| 18 | Southwell City | 34 | 2 | 4 | 28 | 26 | 137 | -111 | 10 |

## LEAGUE CHALLENGE CUP

**HOLDERS:** HUCKNALL TOWN

**ROUND 1**

| | | | |
|---|---|---|---|
| Keyworth United | v | Clay Cross Town | 3-2 |
| Collingham | v | Brodsworth Welfare | 3-1 |
| Dronfield Town Reserves | v | Pinxton | 0-3 |
| Matlock Town Reserves | v | Eastwood Community | 1-0 |

**ROUND 2**

| | | | |
|---|---|---|---|
| Ollerton Town | v | Thoresby CW | HW |
| Selston | v | Holbrook St Michaels | 4-2 |
| Bilsthorpe | - | Bye | |
| Belper United | v | Welbeck Welfare | 7-1 |
| Keyworth United | v | Newark Town | 4-0 |
| Swanwick Pentrich Road | v | Easington United | 3-0 |
| Blidworth Welfare | v | Glapwell | 2-1 |
| Phoenix | v | Thorne Colliery | 8-5 |
| Linby Colliery | v | Collingham | 2-0 |
| Mickleover RBL | v | Pinxton | 1-4 |
| Appleby Frodingham | v | Dinnington Town | 7-2 |
| Matlock Town Reserves | v | Askern | 1-2 |
| Southwell City | v | Sherwood Colliery | 2-6 |
| Hucknall Rolls Leisure | v | Hucknall Town | 3-2 |
| Bulwell | v | Retford | 3-0 |
| Harworth C.I. | v | Bentley Colliery | 1-1, 9-8p |

**ROUND 3**

| | | | |
|---|---|---|---|
| Ollerton Town | v | Selston | 1-0 |
| Bilsthorpe | v | Belper United | 0-2 |

| | DIVISION NORTH | 1 | 2 | 3 | 4 | 5 | 6 | 7 | 8 | 9 | 10 | 11 | 12 | 13 | 14 | 15 |
|---|---|---|---|---|---|---|---|---|---|---|---|---|---|---|---|---|
| 1 | Appleby Frodingham | | 0-0 | 3-1 | 4-3 | 9-2 | 3-0 | 4-0 | 0-4 | 0-0 | 3-0 | 2-1 | 1-1 | 3-1 | 6-0 | 23-0 |
| 2 | Askern | 1-4 | | 0-1 | 4-1 | 6-0 | 5-3 | 2-1 | 7-0 | 2-5 | 6-0 | 5-1 | 1-1 | 3-1 | 3-1 | 13-0 |
| 3 | Bilsthorpe | 2-3 | 2-0 | | 0-2 | 2-2 | 0-3 | 2-1 | 1-4 | 0-1 | 1-1 | 0-5 | 1-2 | 1-4 | 5-0 | 6-0 |
| 4 | Brodsworth Welfare | 1-1 | 3-1 | 3-0 | | 7-2 | 2-3 | 2-0 | 1-5 | 1-0 | 3-0 | 0-3 | 1-2 | 4-3 | 1-3 | 5-1 |
| 5 | Dinnington Town | 0-3 | 1-7 | 0-2 | 0-5 | | 2-3 | 1-1 | 1-9 | 0-6 | 3-3 | 0-6 | 0-2 | 0-2 | 3-1 | 4-0 |
| 6 | Dronfield Town Reserves | 4-0 | 4-1 | 4-0 | 5-2 | 3-0 | | 3-3 | 1-3 | 1-4 | 3-2 | 2-3 | 1-4 | 2-1 | 3-3 | 10-0 |
| 7 | Easington Utd | 0-2 | 1-2 | 0-0 | 2-2 | 7-1 | 1-1 | | 0-3 | 2-6 | 3-0 | 1-4 | 3-2 | 0-4 | 3-2 | 5-2 |
| 8 | Glapwell | 2-0 | 5-3 | 5-1 | 5-1 | 10-0 | 6-0 | 8-1 | | 8-3 | 7-2 | 5-1 | 1-4 | 2-4 | 12-0 | 23-1 |
| 9 | Harworth Colliery Institute | 6-2 | 0-1 | 5-0 | 2-1 | 7-2 | 0-0 | 2-0 | 0-3 | | 4-0 | 1-2 | 1-2 | 3-0 | 2-1 | 10-2 |
| 10 | Newark Town | 0-3 | 3-5 | 2-1 | 4-1 | 5-3 | 1-2 | 4-4 | 1-3 | 2-7 | | 0-5 | 1-3 | 3-4 | 3-2 | 9-1 |
| 11 | Ollerton Town | 2-1 | 5-1 | 3-0 | 1-0 | 2-1 | 4-2 | 4-2 | 1-3 | 1-1 | 4-0 | | 3-1 | 2-0 | 3-0 | 12-0 |
| 12 | Phoenix | H-W | 5-3 | 1-0 | 5-0 | 8-0 | 3-1 | 5-1 | 3-2 | 0-4 | 8-1 | 3-2 | | 4-4 | 1-5 | 6-2 |
| 13 | Retford | 2-3 | 4-0 | 1-0 | 4-1 | 0-1 | 1-1 | 2-0 | 1-3 | 2-0 | 2-1 | 1-0 | 0-1 | | 1-4 | 5-0 |
| 14 | Thorne Colliery | 0-1 | 0-2 | 6-1 | 1-4 | 3-1 | 1-1 | 1-4 | 0-0 | 1-1 | 2-1 | 1-2 | 3-0 | 0-0 | | 6-1 |
| 15 | Welbeck Welfare | 0-12 | 1-5 | 0-3 | 0-7 | 3-1 | 3-3 | 0-2 | 0-7 | 1-5 | 3-6 | 0-12 | 1-5 | 0-9 | 1-4 | |

| | DIVISION SOUTH | 1 | 2 | 3 | 4 | 5 | 6 | 7 | 8 | 9 | 10 | 11 | 12 | 13 | 14 | 15 | 16 | 17 | 18 |
|---|---|---|---|---|---|---|---|---|---|---|---|---|---|---|---|---|---|---|---|
| 1 | Belper Utd | | 0-1 | 11-1 | 3-1 | 0-2 | 2-2 | 1-2 | 3-0 | 2-1 | 3-1 | 3-1 | 3-1 | 6-0 | 0-3 | 0-1 | 1-1 | 7-0 | 3-0 |
| 2 | Blidworth Welfare | 0-0 | | 3-2 | 2-5 | 0-2 | 1-4 | 8-1 | 1-0 | 1-2 | 6-0 | 2-0 | 2-2 | 3-1 | 3-4 | 1-1 | 5-1 | 3-0 | 2-2 |
| 3 | Bulwell | 0-1 | 1-2 | | 1-3 | 3-3 | 3-3 | 5-1 | 0-1 | 5-4 | 6-4 | 1-8 | 1-2 | 6-2 | 4-2 | 1-7 | 5-0 | 3-0 | 2-2 |
| 4 | Clay Cross Town | 0-3 | 6-2 | 0-2 | | 1-3 | 0-4 | 5-0 | 1-1 | 3-2 | 3-2 | 0-3 | 2-1 | 0-4 | 0-5 | 0-5 | 1-2 | 2-4 | 0-2 |
| 5 | Collingham | 0-3 | 2-5 | 3-3 | 3-1 | | 3-2 | 1-0 | 1-0 | 1-3 | 3-2 | 2-0 | 1-4 | 7-2 | 0-7 | 1-4 | 2-4 | 4-0 | 2-5 |
| 6 | Eastwood Community | 2-4 | 1-3 | 4-2 | 3-3 | 1-0 | | 1-3 | 1-3 | 1-4 | 4-0 | 1-0 | 0-2 | 4-1 | 4-0 | 1-1 | 4-4 | 10-0 | 3-3 |
| 7 | Holbrook St Michaels | 1-4 | 2-3 | 1-4 | 1-2 | 3-1 | 1-6 | | 0-4 | 1-5 | 3-2 | 1-3 | 2-3 | 3-1 | 0-5 | 0-5 | 2-2 | 2-0 | 0-5 |
| 8 | Hucknall Rolls Leisure | 3-3 | 1-1 | 2-3 | 5-0 | 3-0 | 3-1 | 8-0 | | 1-0 | 6-0 | 3-1 | 2-4 | 4-0 | 4-1 | 2-2 | 0-1 | 4-0 | 1-2 |
| 9 | Hucknall Town | 4-1 | 1-1 | 4-1 | 1-1 | 3-0 | 3-0 | 7-1 | 2-0 | | 2-0 | 4-0 | 4-1 | 2-0 | 1-2 | 1-2 | 4-0 | 7-0 | 0-2 |
| 10 | Keyworth United | 0-3 | 2-6 | 4-2 | 1-4 | 1-2 | 0-3 | 0-0 | 0-1 | 1-5 | | 2-0 | 2-6 | 1-4 | 1-2 | 2-3 | 0-6 | 2-0 | 1-5 |
| 11 | Linby Colliery | 1-4 | 1-2 | 1-2 | 0-6 | 3-0 | 3-1 | 3-0 | 2-0 | 1-4 | 2-0 | | 3-0 | 2-1 | 0-3 | 2-2 | 2-2 | 6-0 | 1-1 |
| 12 | Matlock Town Reserves | 1-2 | 1-1 | 2-4 | 1-2 | 1-1 | 2-2 | 0-0 | 5-2 | 0-5 | 5-1 | 1-1 | | 0-1 | 0-3 | 5-4 | 2-2 | 3-0 | 2-1 |
| 13 | Mickleover RBL | 0-5 | 2-4 | 3-1 | 1-1 | 4-2 | 8-1 | 1-1 | 2-3 | 0-4 | 3-4 | 2-4 | 1-5 | | 2-7 | 0-4 | 1-2 | 7-1 | 2-2 |
| 14 | Pinxton | 1-3 | 3-0 | 4-1 | 1-1 | 3-0 | 3-1 | 5-0 | 2-2 | 1-4 | 2-0 | 2-1 | 3-1 | 4-0 | | 0-5 | 0-1 | 5-1 | 1-3 |
| 15 | Selston | 3-1 | 2-0 | 3-2 | 3-1 | 3-2 | 4-1 | 6-0 | 1-4 | 1-0 | 5-2 | 4-1 | 6-0 | 8-3 | 5-1 | | 1-3 | 3-1 | 2-1 |
| 16 | Sherwood Colliery | 1-3 | 1-4 | 8-0 | 3-2 | 7-1 | 4-1 | 4-2 | 2-1 | 1-2 | 3-1 | 3-1 | 0-2 | 3-1 | 0-4 | 2-3 | | 5-0 | 1-4 |
| 17 | Southwell City | 0-5 | 4-7 | 1-1 | 0-4 | 0-4 | 0-4 | 3-3 | 3-5 | 1-0 | 2-2 | 0-3 | 0-3 | 0-3 | 3-3 | 0-8 | 1-4 | | 0-2 |
| 18 | Swanwick Pentrich Road | 0-1 | 3-0 | 3-2 | 0-3 | 6-1 | 1-2 | 5-3 | 1-1 | 0-2 | 2-2 | 3-3 | 2-0 | 5-1 | 1-4 | 4-4 | 1-5 | 3-1 | |

## LEAGUE CHALLENGE CUP

| | | | |
|---|---|---|---|
| Keyworth United | v | Swanwick Pentrich Road | 0-1 |
| Blidworth Welfare | v | Phoenix | 4-1 |
| Linby Colliery | v | Pinxton | 1-3 |
| Appleby Frodingham | v | Askern | 4-2 |
| Sherwood Colliery | v | Hucknall Rolls Leisure | 1-2 |
| Bulwell | v | Harworth CI | 4-3 |

**QUARTER FINALS**

| | | | |
|---|---|---|---|
| Ollerton Town | v | Belper United | 3-0 |
| Swanwick Pentrich Road | v | Blidworth Welfare | 1-1, 2-4p |
| Pinxton | v | Appleby Frodingham | 1-5 |
| Hucknall Rolls Leisure | v | Bulwell | 4-1 |

**SEMI FINALS**

| | | | |
|---|---|---|---|
| Ollerton Town | v | Blidworth Welfare | 2-4 |
| Appleby Frodingham | v | Hucknall Rolls Leisure | 0-1 |

**FINAL**

| | | | |
|---|---|---|---|
| Blidworth Welfare | v | Hucknall Rolls Leisure | 1-2 |

## Central Midlands Division North

| | | |
|---|---|---|
| AFC BENTLEY | Bentley MW, 105 The Avenue, Bentley, Doncaster, Sth Yorks DN5 0PN | 01302 874 420 |
| APPLEBY FRODINGHAM | Brumby Hall Sports Ground, Ashby Road, Scunthorpe, DN16 1AA | 01724 402134 |
| ASKERN | Welfare Sports Ground, Manor Way, Doncaster Road, Askern, DN6 0AJ | |
| BILSTHORPE | Bilsthorpe Sports Ground, Eakring Road, Bilsthorpe, Newark NG22 8QW | 07986 284762 |
| CLAY CROSS TOWN | The 'I WANT PET FOODS' Ground, Clay Cross, Chesterfield, Derbyshire S45 9QF | 07542 715 705 |
| COLLINGHAM | Collingham FC, Station Road, Collingham, Newark, Notts NG23 7RA | 01636 892 303 |
| DINNINGTON TOWN | Phoenix Park, 131 Laughton Road, Dinnington, Nr Sheffield S25 2PP | 07854 722 465 |
| DRONFIELD TOWN RESERVES | Gosforth Fields, Bubnell Road, Dronfield Woodhouse S18 8QY | |
| FC BOLSOVER | Bolsover Sports and Social Club | |
| HARWORTH COLLIERY INSTITUTE | Recreation Ground, Scrooby Road, Bircotes, Doncaster DN11 8JT | 01302 750614 |
| NEWARK TOWN | Collingham FC, Station Road, Collingham NG23 7RA | 01636 892303 |
| PHOENIX SPORTS & SOCIAL | Phoenix Sports Complex, Bawtry Road, Brinsworth, Rotherham S60 5PA | 01709 363 788 |
| RETFORD | | |
| THORNE COLLIERY | Moorends Welfare, Grange Road, Moorends, Thorne, Doncaster DN8 4LU | 07855 545221 |
| TIDESWELL UNITED | | |
| WELBECK LIONS | Elkesley Road, Meden Vale, Mansfield, Nottinghamshire NG20 9P | |

**CLUB MOVEMENTS**

**NORTH In: In:** AFC Bentley (NC from Brodsworth Welfare), Clay Cross Town (S - South), Collingham (S - South), FC Bolsover (N), Tideswell United, Welbeck Lions (NC from Welbeck Welfare)
**Out:** Brodsworth Welfare (NC to AFC Bentley), Glapwell (F), Ollerton Town (P - NCE), Welbeck Welfare (NC to Welbeck Lions).

**SOUTH In:** South Normanton (N), Teversal Reserves (N).
**Out:** Belper United (P - East Midlands Counties), Bulwell (W), Clay Cross Town (S - North), Collingham (S - North), Hucknall Rolls Leisure (W)

## Central Midlands Division South

| | | |
|---|---|---|
| BLIDWORTH WELFARE | Blidworth Welfare Miners SC, Mansfield Road, Blidworth, Mansfield NG21 0LR | 01623 793 361 |
| EASTWOOD COMMUNITY | Corination Park, Chewton Street, Eastwood NG16 3HB | |
| HOLBROOK ST MICHAELS | Holbrook Park, Mackney Road, Holbrook, Belper, Derbyshire DE56 0T | |
| HUCKNALL TOWN AFC | Watnall Road, Hucknall, Nottingham, Nottinghamshire NG15 6E | |
| KEYWORTH UNITED | | |
| LINBY COLLIERY WELFARE | Linby Colliery Welfare Ground, Church Lane, Linby, Nottinghamshire NG15 8A | |
| MATLOCK TOWN RESERVES | The Autoworld Arena, Causeway Lane, Matlock, Derbyshire DE4 3AR | |
| MICKLEOVER RBL | Mickleover RBL, Poppyfields Drive, Mickleover, Derby DE3 9GQ | 01332 513 548 |
| PINXTON | Van Elle Welfare Arena, Wharf Road, Pinxton NG16 6LG | 01773 810 650 |
| SELSTON | | |
| SHERWOOD COLLIERY | Debdale Lane, Mansfield Woodhouse, Mansfield, Nottinghamshire NG19 7N | 01623 631 747 |
| SOUTH NORMANTON | M J Robinson Structures Arena, Lees Lane, South Normanton, Derbyshire DE55 2AD | 07834 206 253 |
| SOUTHWELL CITY | War Memorial Recreation Ground, Bishop's Drive, Southwell NG25 0JP | 01636 814 386 |
| SWANWICK PENTRICH ROAD | Highfield Road, Swanwick, Alfreton, Derbyshire DE55 1BW | |
| TEVERSAL RESERVES | Teversal Grange Spts and So.Centre, Carnarvon St, Teversal, NG17 3HJ | |

# CHESHIRE LEAGUE

**Sponsored by:** Hallmark Security
**Founded:** 1919
**Recent Champions:**
**2013:** Knutsford
**2014:** Garswood United
**2015:** Linotype Cheadle HN

| PREMIER DIVISION | | P | W | D | L | F | A | GD | Pts |
|---|---|---|---|---|---|---|---|---|---|
| 1 | Knutsford | 30 | 20 | 5 | 5 | 68 | 29 | 39 | 65 |
| 2 | Linotype Cheadle HN | 30 | 20 | 1 | 9 | 77 | 40 | 37 | 61 |
| 3 | Whaley Bridge | 30 | 16 | 5 | 9 | 67 | 45 | 22 | 53 |
| 4 | Sandbach United | 30 | 16 | 4 | 10 | 69 | 44 | 25 | 52 |
| 5 | Greenalls Padgate St Oswalds | 30 | 14 | 6 | 10 | 59 | 54 | 5 | 48 |
| 6 | Congleton Vale | 30 | 14 | 5 | 11 | 55 | 44 | 11 | 47 |
| 7 | Crewe | 30 | 14 | 2 | 14 | 54 | 57 | -3 | 44 |
| 8 | Gamesley | 30 | 12 | 5 | 13 | 64 | 68 | -4 | 41 |
| 9 | Rudheath Social | 30 | 13 | 2 | 15 | 44 | 54 | -10 | 41 |
| 10 | Poynton | 30 | 12 | 3 | 15 | 63 | 58 | 5 | 39 |
| 11 | Eagle Sports | 30 | 12 | 3 | 15 | 47 | 50 | -3 | 39 |
| 12 | Malpas | 30 | 10 | 8 | 12 | 57 | 73 | -16 | 38 |
| 13 | Garswood United | 30 | 9 | 7 | 14 | 47 | 48 | -1 | 34 |
| 14 | Rylands | 30 | 9 | 6 | 15 | 36 | 55 | -19 | 33 |
| 15 | Denton Town FC | 30 | 9 | 4 | 17 | 62 | 98 | -36 | 31 |
| 16 | Styal | 30 | 5 | 4 | 21 | 38 | 90 | -52 | 19 |

**Out:** Gamesley (W), Sandbach United (P - NWC)

| DIVISION ONE | | P | W | D | L | F | A | GD | Pts |
|---|---|---|---|---|---|---|---|---|---|
| 1 | Wythenshawe Town | 20 | 14 | 3 | 3 | 65 | 18 | 47 | 45 |
| 2 | Altrincham FC Reserves | 20 | 13 | 4 | 3 | 55 | 25 | 30 | 43 |
| 3 | Billinge FC | 20 | 12 | 4 | 4 | 65 | 34 | 31 | 40 |
| 4 | Middlewich Town | 20 | 10 | 3 | 7 | 53 | 38 | 15 | 33 |
| 5 | Golborne Sports | 20 | 8 | 5 | 7 | 48 | 47 | 1 | 29 |
| 6 | Pilkington | 20 | 9 | 2 | 9 | 34 | 65 | -31 | 29 |
| 7 | Daten | 20 | 7 | 3 | 10 | 39 | 49 | -10 | 24 |
| 8 | Grappenhall Sports FC | 20 | 5 | 5 | 10 | 33 | 65 | -32 | 20 |
| 9 | Egerton | 20 | 5 | 2 | 13 | 38 | 56 | -18 | 17 |
| 10 | Tarporley Victoria | 20 | 4 | 5 | 11 | 26 | 46 | -20 | 17 |
| 11 | Maine Road Reserves | 20 | 4 | 2 | 14 | 25 | 38 | -13 | 14 |

## DIVISION ONE CUP

**HOLDERS:** GAMESLEY

**ROUND 1**

| | | | |
|---|---|---|---|
| Greenalls Padgate St Oswa | v | Crewe | 1-1, 4-3p |
| Styal | v | Linotype Cheadle HN | 0-4 |
| Knutsford | v | Congleton Vale | 1-0 |
| Poynton | v | Eagle Sports | 2-2, 5-4p |
| Denton Town | v | Garswood United | 2-1 |
| Rylands | v | Gamesley | 5-1 |
| Malpas | v | Whaley Bridge | 0-2 |
| Sandbach United | v | Rudheath Social | 3-1 |

**QUARTER FINALS**

| | | | |
|---|---|---|---|
| Greenalls Padgate St Oswa | v | Linotype Cheadle HN | 1-0 |
| Knutsford | v | Poynton | 3-0 |
| Denton Town | v | Rylands | 2-3 |
| Whaley Bridge | v | Sandbach United | 2-0 |

**SEMI FINALS**

| | | | |
|---|---|---|---|
| Greenalls Padgate St Oswa | v | Knutsford | 0-4 |
| Rylands | v | Whaley Bridge | 1-2 |

**FINAL**

| | | | |
|---|---|---|---|
| Knutsford | v | Whaley Bridge | 1-1, 8-9p |

## MEMORIAL CUP

**FINAL** **HOLDERS:** EAGLE SPORTS

| | | | |
|---|---|---|---|
| Linotype Cheadle LN | v | Gamesley | 3-2 |

## DIVISION ONE & TWO CHALLENGE CUP

**FINAL** **HOLDERS:** WYTHENSHAW TOWN

| | | | |
|---|---|---|---|
| Altrincham FC Reserves | v | Golborne Sports | TBC |

| DIVISION TWO | | P | W | D | L | F | A | GD | Pts |
|---|---|---|---|---|---|---|---|---|---|
| 1 | AFC Macclesfield | 22 | 20 | 1 | 1 | 88 | 23 | 65 | 61 |
| 2 | Halebank FC | 22 | 14 | 4 | 4 | 99 | 44 | 55 | 46 |
| 3 | Warrington Town Reserve | 22 | 15 | 1 | 6 | 90 | 39 | 51 | 46 |
| 4 | FC St Helens | 22 | 14 | 3 | 5 | 55 | 44 | 11 | 45 |
| 5 | Lostock Gralam | 22 | 12 | 5 | 5 | 49 | 45 | 4 | 41 |
| 6 | Mersey Valley FC | 22 | 12 | 1 | 9 | 76 | 50 | 26 | 37 |
| 7 | West Didsbury & Chorlton Res. | 22 | 7 | 2 | 13 | 44 | 54 | -10 | 23 |
| 8 | Cheadle Town FC Res. | 22 | 6 | 5 | 11 | 39 | 59 | -20 | 23 |
| 9 | Cuddington FC | 22 | 7 | 0 | 15 | 45 | 76 | -31 | 21 |
| 10 | Unicorn Athletic | 22 | 5 | 2 | 15 | 45 | 99 | -54 | 17 |
| 11 | Moore United FC | 22 | 2 | 6 | 14 | 33 | 70 | -37 | 12 |
| 12 | Litherland Remyca | 22 | 3 | 0 | 19 | 31 | 91 | -60 | 9 |

**In:** AFC Denton (N), Barnton Reserves (N), Broadheath Central (Altrincham & District), Deva Christleton (Chester & Wirral), Ford Motors (West Cheshire), Orford (Warrington & District), Sandbach United Reserves (Reserve Div.1), Windle Labour (Warrington & District), Winstanley Warriors (Wigan & District). **Out:** Litherland Remyca Reserves (W)

| | PREMIER DIVISION | 1 | 2 | 3 | 4 | 5 | 6 | 7 | 8 | 9 | 10 | 11 | 12 | 13 | 14 | 15 | 16 |
|---|---|---|---|---|---|---|---|---|---|---|---|---|---|---|---|---|---|
| 1 | Congleton Vale | | 3-1 | 3-5 | 1-1 | 0-2 | 2-2 | 1-2 | 0-2 | 1-3 | 1-2 | 2-0 | 4-1 | 3-0 | 1-1 | 3-0 | 0-2 |
| 2 | Crewe | 3-5 | | 3-1 | 1-2 | 3-2 | 3-1 | 5-2 | 2-0 | 2-1 | 0-1 | 1-5 | 2-1 | 2-0 | 1-2 | 2-3 | 3-2 |
| 3 | Denton Town | 1-2 | 4-1 | | 5-4 | 1-6 | 1-4 | 6-2 | 1-2 | 1-5 | 2-2 | 3-6 | 1-2 | 4-2 | 1-0 | 2-1 | 1-4 |
| 4 | Eagle Sports | 2-3 | 2-1 | 6-0 | | H-W | 1-2 | 1-2 | 0-3 | 0-2 | 4-1 | 3-3 | 1-0 | 0-1 | 2-4 | 3-1 | 2-1 |
| 5 | Gamesley | 3-2 | H-W | 2-5 | 3-0 | | 3-3 | 1-3 | 3-4 | 4-0 | 4-2 | 2-0 | 1-0 | 1-2 | 4-0 | 2-2 | 5-3 |
| 6 | Garswood United | 0-2 | 2-3 | 0-0 | 0-1 | 4-3 | | 4-2 | 1-1 | 0-2 | 1-2 | 1-3 | 2-2 | 1-2 | 0-1 | 1-1 | 1-1 |
| 7 | Greenalls Padgate St Oswalds | 3-2 | 3-3 | 3-1 | 1-0 | 1-1 | 1-3 | | 0-1 | 2-0 | 2-4 | 3-3 | 0-1 | 2-0 | 2-2 | 0-0 | 3-2 |
| 8 | Knutsford | 1-0 | 5-0 | 5-0 | 1-0 | 4-0 | 1-0 | 1-0 | | 4-1 | 2-2 | 3-1 | 0-3 | 2-2 | 1-0 | 5-1 | 1-2 |
| 9 | Linotype Cheadle HN | 1-2 | 2-1 | 5-0 | 3-2 | 5-1 | 3-2 | 2-1 | 3-1 | | 3-0 | 3-1 | 0-1 | 4-0 | 2-5 | 4-1 | 2-0 |
| 10 | Malpas | 2-4 | 2-2 | 6-6 | 3-1 | 3-3 | 0-4 | 1-1 | 1-3 | 2-0 | | 4-3 | 4-1 | 2-2 | 3-4 | 2-5 | 1-5 |
| 11 | Poynton | 0-2 | 0-1 | 5-2 | 1-3 | 3-0 | 1-0 | 0-3 | 2-4 | 1-5 | 0-0 | | 4-2 | 2-0 | 4-1 | 4-0 | 3-4 |
| 12 | Rudheath Social | 2-1 | 1-2 | 3-0 | 0-0 | 2-4 | 3-2 | 2-4 | 1-0 | 1-5 | 0-1 | 2-1 | | 0-3 | 1-0 | 4-2 | 3-2 |
| 13 | Rylands | 0-0 | 0-1 | 2-2 | 1-2 | 2-0 | 1-2 | 2-0 | 1-1 | 0-5 | 2-0 | 1-4 | 0-1 | | 1-1 | 3-1 | 1-2 |
| 14 | Sandbach United | 0-2 | 1-3 | 3-0 | 4-1 | 6-0 | 1-0 | 1-2 | 1-3 | 2-1 | 1-2 | 2-1 | 4-2 | 7-1 | | 2-1 | 2-1 |
| 15 | Styal | 0-1 | 2-1 | 2-4 | 1-3 | 3-3 | 0-2 | 2-6 | 0-6 | 0-3 | 5-1 | 0-2 | 2-1 | 2-4 | 0-10 | | 0-6 |
| 16 | Whaley Bridge | 2-2 | 2-1 | 7-2 | 1-0 | 5-1 | 1-2 | 2-3 | 1-1 | 2-2 | 2-1 | 1-0 | 2-1 | 1-0 | 1-1 | H-W | |

| Cheshire League Premier Division | | |
|---|---|---|
| ALTRINCHAM RESERVES | Egerton Youth Club FC, Egerton Youth Club, Mereheath Lane, Knutsford WA16 6SL | |
| CONGLETON VALE | Congleton High School, Box Lane, Congleton, Cheshire CW12 4NS | |
| CREWE | Cumberland Arena, Thomas Street, Crewe CW1 2BD | |
| DENTON TOWN | Whittles Park, Heather Lea, Denton M34 6EJ | |
| EAGLE SPORTS | Eagle Sports Club, Thornton Road, Great Sankey, Warrington WA5 2SZ | |
| GARSWOOD UNITED | The Wooders, Simms Garswood Road, Garswood, Ashton-in-Makerfield WN4 0XH | |
| GREENALLS PADGATE ST OS'WLD | Carlsberg Tetley Social Club, Long Lane, Warrington WA2 8PU | |
| KNUTSFORD | Manchester Road, Knutsford WA16 0NT | |
| LINOTYPE & CHEADLE HN | The Heath, Norbreck Avenue, Cheadle, Stockport SK8 2ET | |
| MALPAS | Malpas & District Sports Club, Wrexham Road, Malpas, Cheshire SY14 7EJ | |
| POYNTON | Poynton Sports Club, London Road North, Poynton, Cheshire SK12 1AG | |
| RUDHEATH SOCIAL | Lostock Gralam FC, Park Stad, Manchester Rd, Lostock Gralam, Northwich CW9 7PJ | |
| RYLANDS | Rylands Recreation Club, Gorsey Lane, Warrington WA2 7RZ | |
| STYAL | Altrincham Road, Styal, Wilmslow SK9 4JE | |
| WHALEY BRIDGE | Horwich Park, Park Road, Whaley Bridge, High Peak SK23 7DJ | |
| WYTHENSHAWE TOWN | Ericstan Park, Timpson Road, Wythenshawe M23 9LL | 0161 998 5076 |

# DORSET PREMIER LEAGUE

**Sponsored by:** BeSpoke Teamwear
**Founded:** 1957
**Recent Champions: 2013:** Portland United
**2014:** Portland United **2015:** Hamorthy Recreation

| | | P | W | D | L | F | A | GD | Pts |
|---|---|---|---|---|---|---|---|---|---|
| 1 | Shaftesbury Town | 32 | 28 | 1 | 3 | 112 | 26 | 86 | 85 |
| 2 | Hamworthy Recreation | 32 | 23 | 4 | 5 | 95 | 43 | 52 | 73 |
| 3 | Weymouth Reserves | 32 | 20 | 7 | 5 | 83 | 34 | 49 | 67 |
| 4 | Merley Cobham Sports | 32 | 20 | 3 | 9 | 77 | 45 | 32 | 63 |
| 5 | Balti Sports | 32 | 16 | 8 | 8 | 93 | 59 | 34 | 56 |
| 6 | Sherborne Town Reserves | 32 | 14 | 9 | 9 | 68 | 43 | 25 | 51 |
| 7 | Parley Sports | 32 | 15 | 5 | 12 | 78 | 58 | 20 | 50 |
| 8 | Swanage Town & Herston | 32 | 15 | 4 | 13 | 72 | 69 | 3 | 49 |
| 9 | Holt United | 32 | 14 | 5 | 13 | 73 | 77 | -4 | 47 |
| 10 | Hamworthy United Res. (-3) | 32 | 13 | 5 | 14 | 60 | 70 | -10 | 41 |
| 11 | Westland Sports | 32 | 10 | 8 | 14 | 54 | 60 | -6 | 38 |
| 12 | Bridport Reserves | 32 | 10 | 7 | 15 | 49 | 65 | -16 | 37 |
| 13 | Mere Town | 32 | 8 | 7 | 17 | 55 | 72 | -17 | 31 |
| 14 | Blandford United | 32 | 7 | 6 | 19 | 41 | 71 | -30 | 27 |
| 15 | Wareham Rangers | 32 | 7 | 5 | 20 | 49 | 85 | -36 | 26 |
| 16 | South Cheriton United (-3) | 32 | 6 | 6 | 20 | 45 | 93 | -48 | 21 |
| 17 | Cranborne | 32 | 1 | 0 | 31 | 28 | 162 | -134 | 3 |

**In:** Dorchester Sports (P - Dorset Senior), Gillingham Town Reserves (P - Dorset Senior), Sturminster Newton (P - Dorset Senior).
**Out:** Shaftesbury Town (P- Wessex), South Cheriton (W), Weymouth Reserves (P - Wessex).

## LEAGUE CUP

**HOLDERS:** HAMWORTHY RECREATION

**PRELIMINARY ROUND**

| | | | |
|---|---|---|---|
| Holt Utd | v | Weymouth Reserves | 0-1 |
| Wareham Rangers | v | Shaftesbury Town | 2-3 |

**ROUND 1**

| | | | |
|---|---|---|---|
| Blandford United | v | Swanage Town & Herston | 2-5 |
| Bridport Reserves | v | Weymouth Reserves | 2-0 |
| Cranborne | - | BYE | |
| Hamworthy Recreation | v | Parley Sports | 3-1 |
| Hamworthy United Res. | v | Mere Town | 1-3 |
| South Cheriton | v | Merley Cobham Sports | 0-2 |
| Shaftesbury Town | v | Balti Sports | 5-1 |
| Westland Sports | v | Sherborne Town | |

**QUARTER FINALS**

| | | | |
|---|---|---|---|
| Hamworthy Recreation | v | Mere Town | 3-0 |
| Merley Cobham Sports | v | Swanage Town & Herston | 2-1 |
| Shaftesbury Town | v | Bridport Reserves | 3-1 |
| Cranborne | v | Sherborne Town Reserves | 0-5 |

**SEMI FINALS**

| | | | |
|---|---|---|---|
| Hamworthy Recreation | v | Merley Cobham Sports | 1-2 |
| Shaftesbury Town | v | Sherborne Town Reserves | AW |

**FINAL**

| | | | |
|---|---|---|---|
| Merley Cobham Sports | v | Sherborne Town Reserves | 2-1 |

| | PREMIER DIVISION | 1 | 2 | 3 | 4 | 5 | 6 | 7 | 8 | 9 | 10 | 11 | 12 | 13 | 14 | 15 | 16 | 17 |
|---|---|---|---|---|---|---|---|---|---|---|---|---|---|---|---|---|---|---|
| 1 | Balti Sports | | 4-1 | 2-3 | 10-1 | 2-3 | 5-0 | 2-2 | 3-1 | 3-2 | 0-2 | 3-1 | 3-3 | 4-0 | 4-0 | 5-2 | 3-1 | 1-1 |
| 2 | Blandford United | 3-3 | | 3-1 | 3-1 | 2-5 | 2-1 | 1-3 | 2-2 | 1-2 | 0-2 | 1-4 | 0-4 | 1-2 | 2-0 | 2-1 | 1-1 | 1-2 |
| 3 | Bridport Reserves | 0-1 | 1-0 | | 6-0 | 0-7 | 2-2 | 4-4 | 1-1 | 0-1 | 5-1 | 0-2 | 1-1 | 0-3 | 2-2 | 4-1 | 3-2 | 0-1 |
| 4 | Cranborne | 2-4 | 2-4 | 0-4 | | 0-6 | 0-4 | 2-3 | 4-2 | 1-5 | 2-4 | 0-11 | 0-4 | 0-4 | 1-5 | 0-6 | 0-3 | 2-6 |
| 5 | Hamworthy Recreation | 5-1 | 3-0 | 5-0 | 5-3 | | 3-1 | 2-1 | 3-2 | 4-1 | 2-2 | 1-2 | 5-1 | 4-0 | 3-1 | 3-2 | 3-3 | 1-4 |
| 6 | Hamworthy United Reserves | 0-2 | 1-0 | 2-0 | 3-1 | 2-1 | | 4-5 | 2-2 | 2-3 | 3-1 | 1-0 | 0-0 | 0-3 | 4-1 | 5-2 | 1-1 | 0-3 |
| 7 | Holt United | 3-3 | 3-1 | 3-2 | 4-2 | 0-4 | 3-2 | | 3-1 | 0-3 | 2-1 | 1-1 | 0-1 | 7-0 | 2-3 | 2-0 | 2-3 | 0-2 |
| 8 | Mere Town | 1-1 | 2-3 | 1-0 | 5-1 | 2-3 | 2-4 | 1-2 | | 1-5 | 4-1 | 0-4 | 1-1 | 5-3 | 2-3 | 2-1 | 2-1 | 0-3 |
| 9 | Merley Cobham Sports | 0-5 | 3-0 | 1-1 | 3-0 | 1-2 | 3-1 | 4-1 | 4-2 | | 2-2 | 1-3 | 2-0 | 3-0 | 3-1 | 5-0 | 3-1 | 1-3 |
| 10 | Parley Sports | 2-0 | 1-0 | 4-0 | 5-1 | 2-4 | 3-0 | 7-2 | 1-2 | 1-2 | | 1-2 | 1-4 | 6-1 | 2-2 | 5-1 | 1-1 | 3-1 |
| 11 | Shaftesbury Town | 7-1 | 2-1 | 4-0 | 8-0 | 2-1 | 6-0 | 7-0 | 1-0 | 3-0 | 2-1 | | 2-1 | 8-0 | 2-5 | 3-1 | 5-1 | 3-1 |
| 12 | Sherborne Town Reserves | 3-3 | 5-0 | 2-1 | 3-1 | 1-2 | 1-3 | 4-1 | 2-0 | 2-2 | 1-2 | 1-2 | | 2-2 | 4-0 | 3-0 | 2-0 | 0-3 |
| 13 | South Cheriton United | 3-7 | 1-1 | 1-3 | 4-0 | 3-0 | 1-1 | 3-3 | 0-1 | 0-5 | 2-5 | 0-1 | 0-4 | | 0-4 | 2-3 | 0-2 | 2-2 |
| 14 | Swanage Town & Herston | 2-2 | 5-2 | 6-0 | 6-1 | 0-1 | 3-4 | 1-4 | 3-2 | 1-0 | 0-3 | 1-6 | 2-2 | 4-0 | | 2-0 | 2-1 | 1-4 |
| 15 | Wareham Rangers FC | 2-6 | 0-0 | 0-0 | 6-0 | 1-1 | 2-6 | 1-4 | 3-3 | 2-1 | 4-2 | 0-3 | 1-5 | 3-2 | 1-2 | | 1-1 | 0-1 |
| 16 | Westland Sports | 2-0 | 3-2 | 1-3 | 4-0 | 1-3 | 4-0 | 2-1 | 1-1 | 1-3 | 3-1 | 2-3 | 2-0 | 3-3 | 1-4 | 0-2 | | 2-2 |
| 17 | Weymouth Reserves | 1-0 | 1-1 | 1-2 | 12-0 | 0-0 | 5-1 | 3-2 | 3-2 | 1-3 | 3-3 | 0-2 | 1-1 | 1-0 | 4-0 | 5-0 | 3-0 | |

## Dorset Premier League

| | | |
|---|---|---|
| **BALTI SPORTS** | Weymouth Collage, Cranford Avenue, Weymouth, Dorset DT4 7LA | |
| **BLANDFORD UNITED** | Blandford Recreation Ground, Park Road, Blandford Forum DT11 7BX | |
| **BRIDPORT RESERVES** | St Marys Field, Skilling Hill Road, Bridport DT6 5LA | 01308 423 834 |
| **CRANBORNE** | Mick Loader Recreation Ground, Penny's Lane, Cranborne, Wimborne BH21 5QE | 01725 517 440 |
| **DORCHESTER SPORTS** | The Avenue Stadium, Weymouth Avenue, Dorchester, Dorset DT1 2RY | 01305 262 451 |
| **GILLINGHAM TOWN RESERVES** | Hardings Lane, Gillingham, Dorset SP8 4HX | 01747 823 673 |
| **HAMWORTHY RECREATION** | Hamworthy Rec. Club, Magna Road, Canford Magna, Wimborne BH21 3AE | 01202 881 922 |
| **HAMWORTHY UNITED RESERVES** | The County Ground, Blandford Close, Hamworthy, Poole BH15 4BF | 01202 674 974 |
| **HOLT UNITED** | Petersham Lane | |
| **MERE TOWN** | Mere Recreation Ground | |
| **MERLEY COBHAM SPORTS** | Cobham Sports & Social Club, Merley House Lane, Wimborne BH21 3AA | 01202 885 773 |
| **PARLEY SPORTS** | Parley Sports Club, Christchurch Road, West Parley BH22 8SQ | 01202 573 345 |
| **SHERBORNE TOWN RESERVES** | Raleigh Grove, The Terrace Playing Fields, Sherborne DT9 5NS | 01935 816 110 |
| **STURMINSTER NEWTON** | Barnetts Field, Honeymead Lane, Sturminster Newton, Dorset DT10 1EW | 01258 471 406 |
| **SWANAGE TOWN & HERSTON** | Day's Park, off De Moulham Road, Swanage BH19 2JW | 01929 424 673 |
| **WAREHAM RANGERS** | Purbeck Sports Centre, Worgret Road, Wareham, Dorset BH20 4PH | 01929 556 454 |
| **WESTLAND SPORTS** | Alvington Development Centre, Alvington Lane, Yeovil, BA22 8UX | 07977 102799 |

# ESSEX & SUFFOLK BORDER LEAGUE

**Sponsored by:** Kent Blaxill Building Products
**Founded:** 1911
**Recent Champions: 2013:** Gas Recreation. **2014:** Gas Recreation. **2015:** West Bergholt.

| PREMIER DIVISION | P | W | D | L | F | A | GD | Pts |
|---|---|---|---|---|---|---|---|---|
| 1 Coggeshall Town | 26 | 23 | 0 | 3 | 81 | 21 | 60 | 69 |
| 2 Gas Recreation | 26 | 19 | 5 | 2 | 120 | 29 | 91 | 62 |
| 3 Holland FC | 26 | 18 | 5 | 3 | 81 | 29 | 52 | 59 |
| 4 Little Oakley | 26 | 16 | 5 | 5 | 69 | 27 | 42 | 53 |
| 5 West Bergholt | 26 | 16 | 5 | 5 | 76 | 35 | 41 | 53 |
| 6 Alresford Colne Rangers | 26 | 17 | 0 | 9 | 71 | 33 | 38 | 51 |
| 7 University of Essex | 26 | 14 | 2 | 10 | 82 | 53 | 29 | 44 |
| 8 Tollesbury (-3) | 26 | 9 | 4 | 13 | 49 | 66 | -17 | 30 |
| 9 Harwich & Parkeston (+2) | 26 | 6 | 6 | 14 | 38 | 60 | -22 | 26 |
| 10 Hatfield Peverel | 26 | 7 | 2 | 17 | 42 | 68 | -26 | 23 |
| 11 Earls Colne | 26 | 5 | 3 | 18 | 31 | 119 | -88 | 18 |
| 12 Barnston AFC | 26 | 5 | 2 | 19 | 35 | 96 | -61 | 17 |
| 13 White Notley (+1) | 26 | 3 | 3 | 20 | 29 | 94 | -65 | 13 |
| 14 Lawford Lads | 26 | 1 | 4 | 21 | 19 | 93 | -74 | 7 |

Tiptree Jobserve withdrew - record expunged.

| DIVISION ONE | P | W | D | L | F | A | GD | Pts |
|---|---|---|---|---|---|---|---|---|
| 1 Wormingford Wanderers | 30 | 25 | 2 | 3 | 104 | 31 | 73 | 77 |
| 2 Weeley Athletic | 30 | 22 | 4 | 4 | 85 | 27 | 58 | 70 |
| 3 Cinque Port | 30 | 19 | 5 | 6 | 102 | 39 | 63 | 62 |
| 4 Little Oakley Reserves | 30 | 19 | 5 | 6 | 71 | 32 | 39 | 62 |
| 5 Hedinghams United | 30 | 15 | 3 | 12 | 69 | 59 | 10 | 48 |
| 6 Dedham Old Boys | 30 | 14 | 5 | 11 | 67 | 52 | 15 | 47 |
| 7 Coggeshall Town Res. | 30 | 13 | 3 | 14 | 72 | 66 | 6 | 42 |
| 8 Holland FC Reserves | 30 | 12 | 3 | 15 | 59 | 63 | -4 | 39 |
| 9 Kelvedon Social (+2) | 30 | 10 | 6 | 14 | 61 | 64 | -3 | 38 |
| 10 Gas Recreation Res. | 30 | 10 | 6 | 14 | 82 | 82 | 0 | 36 |
| 11 Boxted Lodgers | 30 | 10 | 5 | 15 | 73 | 64 | 9 | 35 |
| 12 West Bergholt Reserves | 30 | 10 | 5 | 15 | 81 | 75 | 6 | 35 |
| 13 University of Essex Res. (-1) | 30 | 10 | 5 | 15 | 52 | 74 | -22 | 34 |
| 14 Alresford Colne Rangers Res. | 30 | 7 | 10 | 13 | 34 | 59 | -25 | 31 |

| DIVISION TWO | P | W | D | L | F | A | GD | Pts |
|---|---|---|---|---|---|---|---|---|
| 1 Cressing United | 28 | 26 | 1 | 1 | 122 | 25 | 97 | 79 |
| 2 Tiptree Jobserve Res. | 28 | 19 | 4 | 5 | 114 | 39 | 75 | 61 |
| 3 FC Clacton Reserves | 28 | 19 | 2 | 7 | 138 | 38 | 100 | 59 |
| 4 Little Oakley A | 28 | 16 | 7 | 5 | 63 | 48 | 15 | 55 |
| 5 Brightlingsea Regent A | 28 | 16 | 3 | 8 | 78 | 46 | 32 | 51 |
| 6 Tiptree Park | 28 | 14 | 6 | 8 | 73 | 45 | 28 | 48 |
| 7 Great Bentley | 28 | 14 | 6 | 7 | 78 | 63 | 15 | 48 |
| 8 Colchester Athletic | 28 | 15 | 2 | 11 | 76 | 65 | 11 | 47 |
| 9 Kelvedon Social Res. | 28 | 9 | 2 | 17 | 56 | 94 | -38 | 29 |
| 10 Team Brantham | 28 | 7 | 7 | 14 | 52 | 81 | -29 | 28 |
| 11 Earls Colne Reserves | 28 | 9 | 1 | 18 | 40 | 80 | -40 | 28 |
| 12 Hatfield Peverel Res. | 28 | 8 | 1 | 19 | 54 | 79 | -25 | 25 |
| 13 Lawford Lads Reserves | 28 | 5 | 4 | 19 | 39 | 89 | -50 | 19 |
| 14 Boxted Lodgers Res. | 8 | 5 | 2 | 21 | 45 | 86 | -41 | 17 |
| 15 Bradfield Rovers Res. | 28 | 3 | 0 | 25 | 31 | 181 | -150 | 9 |

**CLUB MOVEMENTS**

**PREMIER DIVISION - In:** Brantham Athletic Reserves (Eastern Counties Res.Div.), Cinque Port (P), Coggeshall Town Reserves (P), Holland FC Reserves (P), Ipswich Wanderers Reserves (Sussex & Ipswich), Weeley Athletic (P).
**Out:** Coggeshall Town (P - Eastern Counties),
Holland FC (P - Eastern Counties), Lawford Lads (R).

**DIVISION ONE - In:** Cressing United (P), FC Clacton Reserves (P), Lawford Lads (R), Tiptree Jobserve (P).
**Out:** Bradfield Rovers (R), Cinque Port (P),
Coggeshall Town Reserves (P), Holland FC Reserves (P),
Mersea Island (R), Weeley Athletic (P)..

**DIVISION TWO - In:** Bradfield Rovers (R), Mersea Island (R),
**Out:** Cressing United (P), FC Clacton Reserves (P),
Tiptree Jobserve (P).

**DIVISION THREE - new for 2016-17**
Barnston AFC Reserves (New)
Belle Vue Social (P- Colchester & East Essex Prem.)
Bradfield Rovers FC Reserves (R)
Bures United (Colchester & East Essex Prem.)
Colne Engaine (Colchester & East Essex D2)
Connaught Red Star (P - Colchester & East Essex Prem.)
Dedham Old Boys FC Reserves (New)
Dunmow United FC (N)
Flitch United FC (P- Mid Essex League D1)
Holland FC 'A' (N).
Tiptree Heath FC (N)
Weeley Athletic Reserves (P - Colchester & East Essex D2)

| PREMIER DIVISION | 1 | 2 | 3 | 4 | 5 | 6 | 7 | 8 | 9 | 10 | 11 | 12 | 13 | 14 | 15 |
|---|---|---|---|---|---|---|---|---|---|---|---|---|---|---|---|
| 1 Alresford Colne Rangers | | 5-2 | 2-1 | 3-2 | 1-3 | 2-2 | 2-2 | 0-4 | 5-1 | 0-2 | 6-0 | 4-0 | 7-1 | 0-3 | 2-4 |
| 2 Barnston AFC | 1-0 | | 5-0 | 2-7 | 1-1 | 1-3 | 1-3 | AW | 2-2 | 0-5 | 0-1 | 2-4 | 1-0 | 2-2 | 1-1 |
| 3 Boxted Lodgers | 1-3 | 1-6 | | 0-3 | 2-5 | 2-4 | AW | 0-1 | 1-2 | 1-1 | 1-0 | 1-2 | 0-5 | 1-4 | 1-4 |
| 4 Coggeshall Town | 1-0 | 2-0 | 1-0 | | 1-0 | 4-1 | 2-2 | 1-1 | 5-1 | 0-2 | 1-0 | 3-0 | 0-2 | 2-0 | 1-1 |
| 5 Dedham Old Boys | 3-0 | 2-2 | 4-0 | 6-4 | | 2-1 | 3-4 | 0-3 | 7-0 | 0-4 | 3-3 | 0-2 | 4-1 | 0-4 | 2-2 |
| 6 Earls Colne | 7-4 | 1-2 | 3-1 | 0-6 | 1-4 | | 2-4 | 1-3 | 4-1 | 1-4 | 1-3 | 1-1 | 0-3 | 1-10 | 3-5 |
| 7 Gas Recreation | 4-2 | 4-1 | 12-0 | AW | 3-1 | 11-0 | | 3-0 | 10-2 | 2-1 | 10-0 | 3-3 | 3-0 | 1-2 | 5-0 |
| 8 Holland FC | 11-1 | 1-1 | 6-2 | 1-1 | 1-1 | 5-0 | 2-1 | | 9-0 | 4-2 | 9-0 | 4-2 | 0-2 | 3-4 | 1-1 |
| 9 Lawford Lads | 0-2 | 0-5 | 0-0 | 0-5 | 1-3 | 1-1 | 0-6 | 1-7 | | 0-2 | 1-6 | 2-5 | 1-7 | AW | 0-1 |
| 10 Little Oakley | 3-1 | 3-1 | 5-0 | 3-0 | 6-1 | 8-1 | 2-1 | 1-2 | 2-0 | | 2-1 | 6-2 | 1-5 | 1-4 | 3-0 |
| 11 Tiptree Jobserve | 0-0 | 0-3 | 3-1 | 1-3 | 1-1 | 2-0 | 0-3 | 2-3 | HW | 1-4 | | 1-3 | 1-2 | 0-7 | 0-6 |
| 12 Tollesbury | 2-2 | 5-0 | 3-0 | 0-0 | 3-2 | 5-2 | 3-1 | 2-4 | HW. | 1-1 | 2-1 | | 2-3 | 1-5 | 2-2 |
| 13 University of Essex | 0-0 | 0-4 | 4-0 | 4-0 | 4-0 | 5-0 | 2-1 | 3-0 | 2-0 | 0-2 | 3-3 | 0-0 | | 0-1 | 3-1 |
| 14 West Bergholt | 4-0 | 5-1 | 14-1 | 4-2 | 6-1 | 5-0 | 1-5 | 1-0 | 6-0 | 1-0 | 7-0 | 8-0 | 4-0 | | 2-1 |
| 15 White Notley | 4-2 | 1-2 | 6-1 | 3-2 | 3-2 | 9-0 | 1-4 | 1-3 | 4-0 | 0-1 | 1-2 | 2-0 | 4-0 | 0-1 | |

## LEAGUE CUP

**HOLDERS:** LITTLE OAKLEY

**PRELIMINARY ROUND**

| | | | |
|---|---|---|---|
| Hedinghams United | v | Mersea Island | 4-1 |
| Weeley Athletic | v | Barnston AFC | 6-1 |
| West Bergholt | v | Bradfield Rovers | 5-0 |
| Kelvedon Social | v | Dedham Old Boys | 0-2 |
| Tollesbury | v | Holland FC | 0-4 |
| Hatfield Peverel | v | Great Bentley | 2-0 |
| Tiptree Park | v | Little Oakley | 0-7 |
| Coggeshall Town | v | Wormingford Wanderers | 2-1 |
| Gas Recreation | v | Tiptree Jobserve | AW |
| White Notley | v | Harwich & Parkeston | 3-3 |
| Cressing United | v | Cinque Port | 0-2 |
| University of Essex | v | FC Clacton Reserves | 4-1 |
| Lawford Lads | v | Team Brantham | 3-0 |
| Brightlingsea Regent A | v | Boxted Lodgers | 0-1 |
| Colchester Athletic | v | Alresford Colne Rangers | 1-7 |

**ROUND 1**

| | | | |
|---|---|---|---|
| Hatfield Peverel | v | Dedham Old Boys | 1-2 |
| Little Oakley | v | Earls Colne | 6-1 |
| University of Essex | v | Weeley Athletic | 0-3 |
| Boxted Lodgers | v | Gas Recreation | HW |
| Holland | v | Lawford Lads | 6-0 |
| Alresford Colne Rangers | v | Coggeshall Town | 0-1 |
| Hedinghams United | v | Cinque Port | 2-0 |
| Harwich & Parkeston | v | West Bergholt | 3-2 |

**QUARTER FINAL**

| | | | |
|---|---|---|---|
| Harwich & Parkeston | v | Weeley Athletic | 0-4 |
| Dedham Old Boys | v | Holland FC | 0-4 |
| Little Oakley | v | Coggeshall Town | 0-2 |
| Hedinghams United | v | Boxted Lodgers | 2-1 |

**SEMI FINAL**

| | | | |
|---|---|---|---|
| Hedinghams United | v | Coggeshall Town | 1-2 |
| Holland FC | v | Weeley Athletic | 5-1 |

**FINAL**

| | | | |
|---|---|---|---|
| Coggeshall Town | v | Holland FC | 0-0, 4-2p |

## Essex & Suffolk Border League Premier Division

| | | |
|---|---|---|
| ALRESFORD COLNE RANGERS | Ford Lane, Alresford, Colchester CO7 8AU | 07896 54 122 |
| BARNSTON | High Easter Road Barnston CM6 1LZ | 07813 200 189 |
| BRANTHAM ATHLETIC RES. | | |
| CINQUE PORT | | |
| COGGESHALL TOWN RESERVES | | |
| EARLS COLNE | Green Farm Meadow, Halstead Road, Earls Colne, Colchester CO6 2NG | 01787 223 584 |
| GAS RECREATION | Bromley Road, Colchester CO4 3JE | 01206 860 383 |
| HARWICH & PARKESTON | Royal Oak, Main Road, Dovercourt, Harwich CO12 4AA | 01255 503 643 |
| HATFIELD PEVEREL | The Keith Bigden Memorial Ground, Wickham Bishops Rd, Hatfield Peverel CM3 2JL | |
| HOLLAND RESERVES | | |
| IPSWICH WANDERERS RES. | | |
| LITTLE OAKLEY | War Memorial Club Ground, Harwich Road, Little Oakley, Harwich CO12 5ED | 01255 880 370 |
| TOLLESBURY | EShrub End Community and Sports Centre, Boadicea Way, Colchester | 01621 869 358 |
| UNIVERSITY OF ESSEX | University Essex Sports Centre, Wivenhoe Park, Colchester CO4 3SQ | 01206 873 250 |
| WEELEY | | |
| WEST BERGHOLT | Lorkin Daniel Field, Lexden Road, West Bergholt, Colchester CO6 3BW | 01206 241 525 |
| WHITE NOTLEY | Oak Farm, Faulkbourne, Witham CM8 1SF | 01376 519864 |

# ESSEX OLYMPIAN LEAGUE

**Sponsored by:** ProKit UK
**Founded:** 1966
**Recent Champions:**
**2013:** Frenford Senior
**2014:** Southminster St. Leonards
**2015:** Harold Wood Athletic

| PREMIER DIVISION | P | W | D | L | F | A | GD | Pts |
|---|---|---|---|---|---|---|---|---|
| 1 Kelvedon Hatch | 26 | 17 | 4 | 5 | 56 | 29 | 27 | 55 |
| 2 Manford Way (-3) | 26 | 17 | 4 | 5 | 70 | 39 | 31 | 52 |
| 3 Harold Wood Athletic | 26 | 16 | 2 | 8 | 57 | 35 | 22 | 50 |
| 4 Springfield | 26 | 16 | 2 | 8 | 53 | 41 | 12 | 50 |
| 5 White Ensign | 26 | 15 | 3 | 8 | 63 | 43 | 20 | 48 |
| 6 Bishops Stortford Swifts | 26 | 13 | 3 | 10 | 59 | 51 | 8 | 42 |
| 7 Frenford Senior | 26 | 12 | 3 | 11 | 41 | 36 | 5 | 39 |
| 8 Hannakins Farm | 26 | 10 | 5 | 11 | 45 | 49 | -4 | 35 |
| 9 Rayleigh Town | 26 | 9 | 6 | 11 | 43 | 40 | 3 | 33 |
| 10 Buckhurst Hill (-3) | 26 | 8 | 6 | 12 | 43 | 56 | -13 | 27 |
| 11 May & Baker E.C. | 26 | 6 | 9 | 11 | 41 | 58 | -17 | 27 |
| 12 Harold Hill | 26 | 7 | 2 | 17 | 32 | 53 | -21 | 23 |
| 13 Newham United | 26 | 7 | 1 | 18 | 45 | 78 | -33 | 22 |
| 14 Newbury Forest | 26 | 2 | 4 | 20 | 36 | 76 | -40 | 10 |

## SENIOR CUP

**HOLDERS:** KELVDON HATCH

**ROUND 1**

| | | | |
|---|---|---|---|
| Roydon | v | Old Chelmsfordians | 1-4 |
| East Londoners | v | Snaresbrook | 3-2 |
| Canning Town | v | Great Baddow | 1-4 |
| FC Hamlets | v | Leigh Ramblers | 1-2 aet |
| Basildon Town | v | Catholic United | 0-4 |
| Rochford Town | v | Debden Sports | 3-1 |
| Old Barkabbeyans | v | Upminster | 4-0 |
| Hutton | v | Sungate | 6-1 |
| LOASS DTB | v | Shenfield AFC | 0-3 |
| Galleywood | v | Old Southendian | 1-3 |
| Broomfield | v | Leytonstone United | 6-2 |
| Stambridge United | v | Ongar Town | 0-2 |
| Dagenham United | v | Westhamians | 4-3 |
| Toby | v | Ramsden Scotia | 7-1 |
| Runwell Sports | v | Benfleet | 5-1 |
| Herongate Athletic | v | Southend Sports | 5-2 |
| Epping | v | Ryan | 0-4 |

**ROUND 2**

| | | | |
|---|---|---|---|
| Hannakins Farm | v | Old Chelmsfordians | 5-4 aet |
| Bishops Stortford Swifts | v | East Londoners | 5-1 |
| Great Baddow | v | Kelvedon Hatch | 2-4 aet |

| PREMIER DIVISION | 1 | 2 | 3 | 4 | 5 | 6 | 7 | 8 | 9 | 10 | 11 | 12 | 13 | 14 |
|---|---|---|---|---|---|---|---|---|---|---|---|---|---|---|
| 1 Bishops Stortford Swifts | | 5-2 | 1-4 | 2-6 | 3-0 | 2-2 | 3-1 | 2-2 | 3-1 | 7-2 | 2-3 | 0-1 | 3-2 | 1-2 |
| 2 Buckhurst Hill | 2-1 | | 0-2 | 3-1 | 0-1 | 0-2 | 3-4 | 1-5 | 0-2 | 4-4 | 3-0 | 0-0 | 0-2 | 5-5 |
| 3 Frenford Senior | 0-1 | 0-0 | | 3-0 | 4-3 | 3-1 | 0-2 | 1-3 | 1-0 | 2-1 | 4-2 | 1-2 | 0-3 | 0-2 |
| 4 Hannakins Farm | 0-1 | 3-0 | 3-4 | | 0-1 | 1-2 | 1-1 | 3-2 | 0-3 | 2-0 | 5-3 | 1-1 | 3-2 | 3-1 |
| 5 Harold Hill | 2-3 | 1-2 | 3-3 | 3-5 | | 2-0 | 0-2 | 1-3 | 1-0 | 2-1 | 0-3 | 1-0 | 0-1 | 1-3 |
| 6 Harold Wood Athletic | 3-2 | 6-0 | 1-0 | 5-0 | 2-1 | | 2-0 | 1-3 | 0-1 | 3-0 | 2-4 | 1-0 | 1-2 | 4-2 |
| 7 Kelvedon Hatch | 2-0 | 1-1 | 2-1 | 1-0 | 2-0 | 3-0 | | 2-3 | 3-3 | 1-0 | 4-0 | 3-0 | 1-1 | 1-2 |
| 8 Manford Way | 3-1 | 3-2 | 0-2 | 1-1 | 1-0 | 0-2 | 2-3 | | 5-1 | 4-1 | 3-2 | 1-1 | 3-1 | 3-2 |
| 9 May & Baker E.C. | 2-2 | 2-2 | 2-1 | 2-2 | 3-3 | 1-1 | 1-3 | 1-7 | | 2-2 | 1-2 | 2-2 | 2-3 | 3-5 |
| 10 Newbury Forest | 2-5 | 1-2 | 0-0 | 2-3 | 0-3 | 0-4 | 0-4 | 1-2 | 2-2 | | 5-1 | 1-4 | 2-3 | 1-3 |
| 11 Newham United | 2-4 | 1-4 | 1-3 | 1-1 | 2-0 | 4-3 | 1-5 | 1-5 | 1-2 | 1-3 | | 2-5 | 1-2 | 3-2 |
| 12 Rayleigh Town | 1-2 | 0-2 | 1-0 | 0-1 | 4-0 | 3-4 | 1-3 | 2-3 | 2-1 | 5-1 | 3-1 | | 1-1 | 2-4 |
| 13 Springfield | 3-1 | 0-3 | 2-1 | 4-0 | 5-3 | 0-3 | 1-2 | 4-3 | 0-1 | 3-1 | 4-1 | 2-0 | | 0-4 |
| 14 White Ensign | 1-2 | 4-2 | 0-1 | 1-0 | 1-0 | 1-2 | 3-0 | 0-0 | 5-0 | 4-3 | 3-2 | 2-2 | 1-2 | |

## Essex Olympian League Premier Division

| | | |
|---|---|---|
| **BISHOP'S STORTFORD SWIFTS** | Silver Leys, Hadham Road (A1250), Bishop's Stortford CM23 2QE | 07500 901 621 |
| **BUCKHURST HILL** | Roding Lane, Buckhurst Hill IG9 6BJ | |
| **CANNING TOWN** | Newham Leisure Centre, 281 Prince Regents Lane, London E13 8SD | 020 7511 4477 |
| **FRENFORD SENIOR** | Frenford Clubs, The Drive, Ilford, Essex, IG1 3PS | 020 8518 0992 |
| **HANNAKINS FARM** | Hannakins Farm Community Centre, Rosebay Avenue, Billericay CM12 0SY | 01277 630 851 |
| **HAROLD HILL** | Henderson Sports & Social Club, Kenilworth Avenue, Harold Park, RM3 9NW | 01708 343 019 |
| **HAROLD WOOD ATHLETIC** | Harold Wood Recreation Park, Harold View, Harold Wood RM3 0LX | 01708 375 698 |
| **KELVEDON HATCH** | New Hall, School Road, Kelvedon Hatch, Brentwood CM15 0DH | 07950 807 419 |
| **LEIGH RAMBLERS** | Belfairs Park, Eastwood Road North, Leigh on Sea, Essex SS9 4LR | 01702 421 077 |
| **MANFORD WAY** | London Marathon Sports Ground, Forest Road, Hainault IG6 3HJ | 0208 500 3486 |
| **MAY & BAKER CLUB** | May & Baker Spts/Soc. Club, Dagenham Road, Dagenham RM7 0QX | 0208 919 2156 / 3156 |
| **RAYLEIGH TOWN** | Rayleigh Town Sports/Soc. Club, London Road, Rayleigh SS6 9DT | 01268 784 001 |
| **SPRINGFIELD** | Springfield Hall Park, Arun Close, Springfield CM1 7QE | 01245 492 441 |
| **WHITE ENSIGN** | Borough Football Combination Hq, Eastwoodbury Lane, Southend on Sea SS2 6UD | 01702 520 482 |

## SENIOR CHALLENGE CUP (Premier Champions v Senior Cup Holders)

**FINAL**

| | | | |
|---|---|---|---|
| Southminster St Leonards | v | Rayleigh Town | 1-0 |

| DIVISION ONE | | P | W | D | L | F | A | GD | Pts |
|---|---|---|---|---|---|---|---|---|---|
| 1 | Canning Town | 22 | 16 | 2 | 4 | 54 | 27 | 27 | 50 |
| 2 | Leigh Ramblers | 22 | 15 | 4 | 3 | 61 | 27 | 34 | 49 |
| 3 | Snaresbrook | 22 | 13 | 4 | 5 | 54 | 47 | 7 | 43 |
| 4 | Runwell Sports (-3) | 22 | 12 | 4 | 6 | 53 | 34 | 19 | 37 |
| 5 | Basildon Town | 22 | 12 | 0 | 10 | 42 | 34 | 8 | 36 |
| 6 | Old Chelmsfordians | 22 | 10 | 2 | 10 | 44 | 49 | -5 | 32 |
| 7 | Hutton | 22 | 8 | 5 | 9 | 39 | 43 | -4 | 29 |
| 8 | Shenfield A.F.C. (-3) | 22 | 10 | 1 | 11 | 49 | 44 | 5 | 28 |
| 9 | Old Southendian | 22 | 8 | 3 | 11 | 44 | 50 | -6 | 27 |
| 10 | Galleywood | 22 | 6 | 4 | 12 | 31 | 40 | -9 | 22 |
| 11 | Ongar Town (-3) | 22 | 2 | 4 | 16 | 20 | 63 | -43 | 7 |
| 12 | Toby (-3) | 22 | 2 | 3 | 17 | 20 | 53 | -33 | 6 |

| DIVISION TWO | | P | W | D | L | F | A | GD | Pts |
|---|---|---|---|---|---|---|---|---|---|
| 1 | Catholic United | 22 | 17 | 2 | 3 | 76 | 31 | 45 | 53 |
| 2 | Great Baddow | 22 | 14 | 5 | 3 | 64 | 29 | 35 | 47 |
| 3 | FC Hamlets | 22 | 12 | 5 | 5 | 52 | 24 | 28 | 41 |
| 4 | Ramsden Scotia | 22 | 12 | 4 | 6 | 52 | 37 | 15 | 40 |
| 5 | Rochford Town | 22 | 12 | 3 | 7 | 59 | 40 | 19 | 39 |
| 6 | Herongate Athletic | 22 | 11 | 5 | 6 | 53 | 42 | 11 | 38 |
| 7 | Ryan F.C. | 22 | 9 | 3 | 10 | 60 | 56 | 4 | 30 |
| 8 | East Londoners | 22 | 7 | 4 | 11 | 43 | 56 | -13 | 25 |
| 9 | Old Barkabbeyans (-3) | 22 | 7 | 1 | 14 | 47 | 59 | -12 | 19 |
| 10 | Lakeside | 22 | 4 | 3 | 15 | 44 | 82 | -38 | 15 |
| 11 | Roydon | 22 | 4 | 2 | 16 | 35 | 73 | -38 | 14 |
| 12 | Westhamians (-6) | 22 | 4 | 1 | 17 | 26 | 82 | -56 | 7 |

| DIVISION THREE | | P | W | D | L | F | A | GD | Pts |
|---|---|---|---|---|---|---|---|---|---|
| 1 | Benfleet | 22 | 16 | 2 | 4 | 67 | 27 | 40 | 50 |
| 2 | Sungate | 22 | 14 | 3 | 5 | 60 | 42 | 18 | 45 |
| 3 | Upminster | 22 | 13 | 2 | 7 | 51 | 47 | 4 | 41 |
| 4 | Broomfield | 22 | 11 | 4 | 7 | 56 | 36 | 20 | 37 |
| 5 | Harold Wood Athletic Res. | 22 | 10 | 4 | 8 | 46 | 41 | 5 | 34 |
| 6 | Frenford Senior Res. | 22 | 10 | 3 | 9 | 43 | 41 | 2 | 33 |
| 7 | Debden Sports | 22 | 9 | 3 | 10 | 30 | 43 | -13 | 30 |
| 8 | Hutton Reserves | 22 | 7 | 3 | 12 | 35 | 45 | -10 | 24 |
| 9 | May & Baker E.C. Res. | 22 | 6 | 6 | 10 | 34 | 44 | -10 | 24 |
| 10 | Leytonstone United | 22 | 5 | 6 | 11 | 41 | 63 | -22 | 21 |
| 11 | Epping (-6) | 22 | 5 | 4 | 13 | 41 | 54 | -13 | 13 |
| 12 | Southend Sports (-6) | 22 | 5 | 2 | 15 | 39 | 60 | -21 | 11 |

| DIVISION FOUR | | P | W | D | L | F | A | GD | Pts |
|---|---|---|---|---|---|---|---|---|---|
| 1 | Old Chelmsfordians Res. | 24 | 19 | 2 | 3 | 61 | 24 | 37 | 59 |
| 2 | Rayleigh Town Res. | 24 | 17 | 3 | 4 | 83 | 17 | 66 | 54 |
| 3 | White Ensign Res. (-3) | 24 | 13 | 3 | 8 | 68 | 53 | 15 | 39 |
| 4 | Newham United Res. (-9) | 24 | 13 | 3 | 8 | 61 | 42 | 19 | 33 |
| 5 | Kelvedon Hatch Res. | 24 | 8 | 8 | 8 | 36 | 42 | -6 | 32 |
| 6 | Leigh Ramblers Res. | 24 | 10 | 2 | 12 | 42 | 62 | -20 | 32 |
| 7 | Toby Reserves (-3) | 24 | 10 | 4 | 10 | 63 | 61 | 2 | 31 |
| 8 | Canning Town Res. | 24 | 8 | 2 | 14 | 49 | 67 | -18 | 29 |
| 9 | Old Southendian Res. (-3) | 24 | 8 | 4 | 12 | 46 | 52 | -6 | 25 |
| 10 | Manford Way Reserves | 24 | 7 | 3 | 14 | 47 | 73 | -26 | 24 |
| 11 | Runwell Sports Res. | 24 | 6 | 5 | 13 | 36 | 60 | -24 | 23 |
| 12 | Catholic United Res. (-3) | 24 | 7 | 3 | 14 | 60 | 74 | -14 | 21 |
| 13 | Old Barkabbeyans Res. (-9) | 24 | 8 | 2 | 14 | 50 | 75 | -25 | 17 |

## SENIOR CUP continued...

| | | | |
|---|---|---|---|
| Lakeside | v | Harold Wood Athletic | 0-3 |
| Leigh Ramblers | v | Catholic United | 2-4 |
| Rochford Town | v | Old Barkabbeyans | 2-1 |
| Harold Hill | v | Hutton | 1-1, 6-7p |
| Newbury Forest | v | May & Baker E.C. | 2-0 |
| Shenfield AFC | v | Frenford Senior | 2-3 |
| Springfield | v | Manford Way | 0-1 |
| Old Southendian | v | Broomfield | 5-1 |
| Newham United | v | White Ensign | 2-4 |
| Buckhurst Hill | v | Rayleigh Town | 3-0 |
| Ongar Town | v | Dagenham United | 5-2 |
| Toby | v | Runwell Sports | 2-2, 5-4p |
| Herongate Athletic | v | Ryan | 3-6 aet |

**ROUND 3**

| | | | |
|---|---|---|---|
| Hannakins Farm | v | Bishops Stortford Swifts | 1-4 |
| Kelvedon Hatch | v | Harold Wood Athletic | 2-0 |
| Catholic United | v | Rochford Town | 5-3 |
| Hutton | v | Newbury Forest | 6-3 |
| Frenford Senior | v | Manford Way | 0-2 |
| Old Southendian | v | White Ensign | 0-7 |
| Buckhurst Hill | v | Ongar Town | 3-2 |
| Toby | v | Ryan | 5-3 |

**QUARTER FINALS**

| | | | |
|---|---|---|---|
| Toby | v | Bishops Stortford Swifts | 1-4 aet |
| Buckhurst Hill | v | Kelvedon Hatch | 2-2, 2-4p |
| White Ensign | v | Catholic United | 4-0 |
| Manford Way | v | Hutton | 3-1 |

**SEMI FINALS**

| | | | |
|---|---|---|---|
| Bishops Stortford Swifts | v | Kelvedon Hatch | 1-2 |
| White Ensign | v | Manford Way | 1-3 |

**FINAL**

| | | | |
|---|---|---|---|
| Kelvedon Hatch | v | Manford Way | 1-0 |

| RESERVES DIVISION TWO | | P | W | D | L | F | A | GD | Pts |
|---|---|---|---|---|---|---|---|---|---|
| 1 | Galleywood Reserves | 20 | 16 | 3 | 1 | 68 | 19 | 49 | 51 |
| 2 | Harold Hill Reserves | 20 | 15 | 2 | 3 | 80 | 30 | 50 | 47 |
| 3 | Sungate Reserves | 20 | 14 | 3 | 3 | 59 | 20 | 39 | 45 |
| 4 | Basildon Town Reserves | 20 | 10 | 3 | 7 | 47 | 50 | -3 | 33 |
| 5 | Dagenham United | 20 | 9 | 2 | 9 | 36 | 50 | -14 | 29 |
| 6 | Shenfield A.F.C. Res. (-6) | 20 | 9 | 3 | 8 | 52 | 36 | 16 | 24 |
| 7 | Springfield Res. (-6) | 20 | 9 | 3 | 8 | 47 | 41 | 6 | 24 |
| 8 | Herongate Athletic Res. | 20 | 7 | 1 | 12 | 47 | 58 | -11 | 22 |
| 9 | Upminster Res. (-21) | 20 | 7 | 1 | 12 | 43 | 41 | 2 | 1 |
| 10 | Benfleet Reserves (-10) | 20 | 1 | 1 | 18 | 17 | 99 | -82 | -6 |
| 11 | Leytonstone United Res. (-21) | 20 | 2 | 0 | 18 | 21 | 73 | -52 | -15 |

### CLUB MOVEMENTS

**Division One:**

**In** London APSA formerly Newham (R - Essex Senior).

**Division Three:**

**In:** Brentwood Town Reserves (N), Shoebury Town (Southend Borough & District).

**Division Five:**

**In:** Bishops Stortford Swifts Reserves (N), Newbury Forest Reserves (N), Southend Sports Reserves (N - Southend Borough & District).

**Out:** Leytonstone United Reserves (W), Upminster Reserves (W).

# GLOUCESTERSHIRE COUNTY LEAGUE

**Sponsored by:** Marcliff
**Founded:** 1968
**Recent Champions:**
**2013:** Longlevens. **2014:** Longlevens
**2015:** Cheltenham Civil Service

| | | P | W | D | L | F | A | GD | Pts |
|---|---|---|---|---|---|---|---|---|---|
| 1 | AEK Boco | 32 | 25 | 4 | 3 | 74 | 25 | 49 | 79 |
| 2 | Henbury | 32 | 21 | 3 | 8 | 95 | 43 | 52 | 66 |
| 3 | Frampton United | 32 | 19 | 8 | 5 | 76 | 30 | 46 | 65 |
| 4 | Thornbury Town | 32 | 20 | 5 | 7 | 64 | 29 | 35 | 65 |
| 5 | Rockleaze Rangers | 32 | 17 | 4 | 11 | 65 | 49 | 16 | 55 |
| 6 | Broadwell Amateurs | 32 | 17 | 3 | 12 | 65 | 46 | 19 | 54 |
| 7 | Bishops Cleeve Res. (+3) | 32 | 16 | 5 | 11 | 70 | 56 | 14 | 53 |
| 8 | Patchway Town | 32 | 16 | 5 | 11 | 52 | 48 | 4 | 53 |
| 9 | Gala Wilton (-3) | 32 | 16 | 3 | 13 | 74 | 56 | 18 | 48 |
| 10 | Bristol Telephones (-3) | 32 | 14 | 7 | 11 | 74 | 49 | 25 | 46 |
| 11 | Hardwicke | 32 | 14 | 3 | 15 | 69 | 59 | 10 | 45 |
| 12 | Ellwood | 32 | 8 | 5 | 19 | 43 | 83 | -40 | 29 |
| 13 | Kingswood | 32 | 8 | 2 | 22 | 45 | 109 | -64 | 26 |
| 14 | Hanham Athletic (-1) | 32 | 6 | 8 | 18 | 37 | 66 | -29 | 25 |
| 15 | Yate Town Reserves | 32 | 4 | 7 | 21 | 42 | 86 | -44 | 19 |
| 16 | Cheltenham Civil Service | 32 | 4 | 7 | 21 | 32 | 82 | -50 | 19 |
| 17 | Southmead CS Athletic (-3) | 32 | 6 | 3 | 23 | 37 | 98 | -61 | 18 |

## LES JAMES LEAGUE CUP

**HOLDERS:** THORNBURY TOWN

**PRELIMINARY ROUND**

| | | | |
|---|---|---|---|
| Gala Wilton | v | Broadwell Amateurs | 2-0 |
| Rockleaze Rangers | v | Kings Stanley | HW |

**FIRST ROUND**

| | | | |
|---|---|---|---|
| AEK Boco | v | Hardwicke | 1-4 |
| *(Tie abandoned after 77mins - Hardwick awarded the game)* | | | |
| Bishops Cleeve Reserves | v | Southmead CS Athletic | 3-1 |
| Bristol Telephones | v | Hanham Athletic | 3-1 |
| Frampton United | v | Thornbury Town | 0-3 |
| Henbury | v | Ellwood | 2-0 |
| Patchway Town | v | Kingswood | 2-1 |
| Cheltenham Civil Service | v | Rockleaze Rangers | 1-2 |
| Gala Wilton | v | Yate Town Reserves | 4-0 |

**SECOND ROUND**

| | | | |
|---|---|---|---|
| Bristol Telephones | v | Hardwicke | 1-2 |
| Gala Wilton | v | Bishops Cleeve Rangers | 3-2 |
| *(Gala were disqualified for fielding an ineligible player)* | | | |
| Patchway Town | v | Rockleaze Rangers | 2-2, 3-4p |
| Thornbury Town | v | Henbury | 2-1 |

**SEMI FINALS**

| | | | |
|---|---|---|---|
| Hardwicke | v | Thornbury Town | 1-0 |
| Rockleaze Rangers | v | Bishops Cleeve Res. | 0-0, 4-2p |

**FINAL**

| | | | |
|---|---|---|---|
| Hardwicke | v | Rockleaze Rangers | 1-0 |
| (At Tytherington Rocks Football Club) | | | Attendance 151 |

| | | 1 | 2 | 3 | 4 | 5 | 6 | 7 | 8 | 9 | 10 | 11 | 12 | 13 | 14 | 15 | 16 | 17 |
|---|---|---|---|---|---|---|---|---|---|---|---|---|---|---|---|---|---|---|
| 1 | AEK Boco | | 2-1 | 0-3 | 3-1 | 0-0 | 4-1 | 1-1 | 1-0 | 3-0 | 1-0 | 4-2 | 4-1 | 3-1 | 4-1 | 3-2 | 0-0 | 1-0 |
| 2 | Bishops Cleeve Reserves | 1-2 | | H-W | 2-3 | 1-1 | 4-1 | 3-3 | 0-3 | 3-0 | 2-0 | 1-0 | 2-1 | 2-3 | 7-0 | 4-0 | 2-1 | 6-0 |
| 3 | Bristol Telephones | 0-1 | 3-1 | | 0-1 | 3-0 | 8-1 | 3-1 | 5-3 | 3-3 | 3-1 | 1-3 | 2-2 | 0-1 | 1-2 | 5-1 | 3-3 | 1-3 |
| 4 | Broadwell Amateurs | 2-0 | 1-2 | 2-1 | | 5-1 | 2-0 | 2-4 | 3-1 | 2-1 | 3-0 | 1-2 | 4-0 | 0-2 | 1-2 | 7-0 | 2-1 | 4-1 |
| 5 | Cheltenham Civil Service | 1-4 | 0-1 | 0-0 | 1-3 | | 1-2 | 0-4 | 2-1 | 1-2 | 3-2 | 0-4 | 1-4 | 2-3 | 2-3 | 1-1 | 0-0 | 1-1 |
| 6 | Ellwood | 0-3 | 2-1 | 0-1 | 0-1 | 4-0 | | 0-6 | 1-1 | 5-0 | 2-1 | 2-1 | 3-4 | 2-2 | 0-4 | 3-1 | 1-2 | 3-3 |
| 7 | Frampton United | 0-2 | 6-1 | 2-0 | 2-0 | 2-0 | 0-0 | | 1-1 | 2-0 | 4-0 | 4-1 | 6-0 | 4-1 | 1-3 | 4-0 | 0-0 | 2-1 |
| 8 | Gala Wilton | 1-3 | 2-4 | 2-4 | 2-0 | 4-1 | 6-0 | 2-0 | | 4-1 | 4-1 | 5-1 | 5-1 | 0-1 | 3-0 | 6-0 | 1-3 | 4-4 |
| 9 | Hanham Athletic | 0-0 | 2-2 | 1-1 | 2-2 | 1-1 | 1-0 | 0-3 | 1-2 | | 4-1 | 1-3 | 1-2 | 0-1 | 0-1 | 1-0 | 0-1 | 0-0 |
| 10 | Hardwicke | 0-4 | 4-2 | 4-2 | 1-1 | 4-2 | 4-1 | 1-2 | 3-0 | 6-2 | | 0-2 | 7-0 | 2-1 | 1-1 | 4-1 | 0-2 | 1-0 |
| 11 | Henbury | 2-3 | 0-2 | 1-1 | 3-1 | 4-1 | 3-0 | 2-3 | 7-1 | 4-1 | 3-2 | | 8-0 | 2-1 | 2-1 | 2-2 | 5-0 | 2-1 |
| 12 | Kingswood | 0-4 | 3-3 | 0-7 | 4-2 | 1-4 | 2-4 | 0-4 | 3-2 | 2-3 | 1-3 | 2-8 | | 2-1 | 0-4 | 2-0 | 0-1 | 0-3 |
| 13 | Patchway Town | 2-1 | 1-1 | 1-3 | 0-2 | 4-1 | 2-1 | 1-1 | 0-1 | 3-2 | 2-1 | 1-1 | 2-0 | | 2-2 | 1-0 | 2-1 | 3-1 |
| 14 | Rockleaze Rangers | 0-1 | 0-1 | 2-5 | 2-0 | 6-0 | 4-1 | 1-1 | 2-0 | 1-1 | 1-3 | 0-3 | 3-1 | 4-2 | | 3-0 | 1-2 | 5-2 |
| 15 | Southmead CS Athletic | 1-3 | 5-3 | 1-1 | 1-4 | 0-2 | 5-3 | 1-2 | 1-2 | 3-2 | 1-7 | 0-6 | 3-2 | 2-1 | 1-4 | | 0-1 | 2-0 |
| 16 | Thornbury Town | 0-2 | 5-0 | 4-1 | 3-1 | 5-1 | 6-0 | 2-0 | 1-2 | 1-0 | 1-1 | 1-3 | 4-1 | 3-0 | 1-0 | 5-0 | | 2-0 |
| 17 | Yate Town Reserves | 1-7 | 2-5 | 2-3 | 2-2 | 3-1 | 0-0 | 1-1 | 1-3 | 3-4 | 1-4 | 0-5 | 1-4 | 1-4 | 0-2 | 4-2 | 0-2 | |

**LES JAMES LEAGUE CUP WINNERS 2015-16 - HARDWICKE FOOTBALL CLUB Back Row (L to R)** Tony Chivers (Assistant Manager), Richard Mansell, Lee Chivers (Manager) Will Higgins, Andrew Price Will Matthews, Dan Chivers, Jay Hunt, Pat Vernall, Shane Thorp, Kenneth Edwards, Lewis Tonks. **Front Row (behind the board):** Rob Hine, Steve Bick, Nick Jones, Craig Harris, Jamie Reid, Tobie Webb.

**LEAGUE CHAMPIONS 2015-16 - AEK BOCO FOOTBALL CLUB**
**Back Row (L to R):** Mark Thomas (Assistant Manager) John Lester ( Assistant Manager), Joe Pople (Keeper), Dan Brister behind him , Rich Sperring (capt), Jason Thatcher, Joes Reeves with Ben Menear behind him, Liam Crewe, Liam Powell, Jordan Scott, Austin Shopland, Liam Jenkins. Paddy (physio). **Front Row:** Bradley Wheadon, Jack Winter, Charlie Stevens, Callum Ball, Leon Maloney Gary Lancaster (Manager)

| Gloucestershire County League | | |
|---|---|---|
| **AEK BOCO** | True Clarity Pavilion, Greenbank Road, Hanham, Bristol BS15 3RZ | 0117 9477331 |
| **BISHOPS CLEEVE RESERVES** | Kayte Lane, Southam, Cheltenham GL52 3PD | 01242 676166 |
| **BRISTOL TELEPHONES** | BTRA Sports Ground, Stockwood Lane, Stockwood, Bristol BS14 8SJ | 01275 891 776 |
| **BROADWELL AMATEURS** | The Hawthorns, Broadwell, Gloucestershire GL16 7BE | |
| **CHELTENHAM CIVIL SERVICE** | Civil Service Sports Ground, Tewkesbury Road, Uckington, Cheltenham GL51 9SL | 01242 680 424 |
| **FRAMPTON UNITED** | The Bell Field, Bridge Road, Frampton on Severn, Gloucestershire GL2 7HA | 07817 486933 |
| **GALA WILTON** | The Gala Club, Fairmile Gardens, Tewkesbury Road, Longford, Glou GL2 9EB | 01452 524 447 |
| **HANHAM ATHLETIC** | The Playing Fields Pavilion, 16 Vicarage Road, Hanham, Bristol BS15 3AH | 0117 9678291 |
| **HARDWICKE AFC** | Hardwicke Playing Field, Green Lane, GL2 4QA | |
| **HENBURY** | Arnell Drive Playing Field, Lorain Walk, Henbury, Bristol BS10 7AS | 0117 959 0475 |
| **KINGSWOOD** | Kingswood PF, Wickwar Road, Kingswood, Wotton-under-Edge GL12 8RF | 07971 682091 |
| **LEBEQ UNITED** | Oaklands Park Almondsbury Bristol | |
| **LITTLE STOKE** | Little Stoke Playing Fields | |
| **PATCHWAY TOWN** | Scott Park, Coniston Road, Patchway, Bristol BS34 5JR | 0117 949 3952 |
| **ROCKLEAZE RANGERS** | Coombe Dingle Sport Complex, Coombe Dingle, Bristol BS9 2BJ | 0117 962 6718 |
| **SOUTHMEAD CS ATHLETIC** | Pen Park Sports Pavillion, Jarratts Road, Bristol BS10 6WF | 0117 9508362 |
| **STONEHOUSE TOWN** | Oldends Lane, Stonehouse, Glos GL10 2DG | |
| **THORNBURY TOWN** | Mundy Playing Fields, Kington Lane, Thornbury BS35 1NA | 01454 413645 |

**CLUB MOVEMENTS**
**New teams elected in:** Lebeq United, Little Stoke and Stonehouse Town.
**Teams resigning:** Ellwood, Kings Stanley and Yate Town Reserves.

# HAMPSHIRE PREMIER LEAGUE

**Sponsored by:** Puma Engineering
**Founded:** 2007
**Recent Champions:**
**2013:** Locks Heath
**2014:** Baffins Milton Rovers
**2015:** Hamble Club

| SENIOR DIVISION | P | W | D | L | F | A | GD | Pts |
|---|---|---|---|---|---|---|---|---|
| 1 Baffins Milton Rovers | 34 | 31 | 1 | 2 | 107 | 26 | 81 | 94 |
| 2 Otterbourne | 34 | 30 | 0 | 4 | 132 | 22 | 110 | 90 |
| 3 Hamble Club | 34 | 27 | 4 | 3 | 122 | 25 | 97 | 85 |
| 4 Liss Athletic | 34 | 23 | 4 | 7 | 92 | 51 | 41 | 73 |
| 5 Bush Hill | 34 | 22 | 5 | 7 | 86 | 44 | 42 | 71 |
| 6 Winchester Castle | 34 | 15 | 3 | 16 | 52 | 59 | -7 | 48 |
| 7 QK Southampton | 34 | 14 | 6 | 14 | 55 | 65 | -10 | 48 |
| 8 Infinity | 34 | 14 | 6 | 14 | 54 | 81 | -27 | 48 |
| 9 Liphook United | 34 | 11 | 9 | 14 | 46 | 65 | -19 | 42 |
| 10 Fleetlands | 34 | 12 | 6 | 16 | 71 | 102 | -31 | 42 |
| 11 Clanfield | 34 | 11 | 7 | 16 | 55 | 65 | -10 | 40 |
| 12 Locks Heath | 34 | 12 | 4 | 18 | 58 | 74 | -16 | 40 |
| 13 Paulsgrove | 34 | 11 | 3 | 20 | 61 | 80 | -19 | 36 |
| 14 Overton United | 34 | 8 | 7 | 19 | 54 | 88 | -34 | 31 |
| 15 Headley United | 34 | 9 | 2 | 23 | 52 | 91 | -39 | 29 |
| 16 Hedge End Rangers | 34 | 7 | 6 | 21 | 34 | 77 | -43 | 27 |
| 17 Stockbridge | 34 | 6 | 1 | 27 | 44 | 98 | -54 | 19 |
| 18 Colden Common | 34 | 4 | 4 | 26 | 36 | 98 | -62 | 16 |

**Out:** Baffins Milton Rovers (P - Wessex), Hamble Club (P - Wessex), Otterbourne (F).

| DIVISION ONE | P | W | D | L | F | A | GD | Pts |
|---|---|---|---|---|---|---|---|---|
| 1 Andover Lions | 18 | 15 | 0 | 3 | 47 | 14 | 33 | 45 |
| 2 Hayling United | 18 | 14 | 1 | 3 | 59 | 19 | 40 | 43 |
| 3 Four Marks | 18 | 11 | 3 | 4 | 50 | 30 | 20 | 36 |
| 4 Broughton | 18 | 9 | 4 | 5 | 48 | 43 | 5 | 31 |
| 5 Upham | 18 | 10 | 0 | 8 | 43 | 38 | 5 | 30 |
| 6 Netley Central Sports | 18 | 7 | 2 | 9 | 32 | 39 | -7 | 23 |
| 7 Sway | 18 | 6 | 1 | 11 | 27 | 35 | -8 | 19 |
| 8 Lyndhurst | 18 | 4 | 2 | 12 | 29 | 58 | -29 | 14 |
| 9 AFC Petersfield (-1) | 18 | 3 | 5 | 10 | 18 | 45 | -27 | 13 |
| 10 Michelmersh & Timsbury | 18 | 1 | 2 | 15 | 12 | 44 | -32 | 5 |

**In:** South Wonston Swifts (Andover & District)
**Out:** Broughton (W)

## SENIOR CUP

**HOLDERS: AFC STONEHAM**

**ROUND 1**

| | | | |
|---|---|---|---|
| Liphook United | v | Netley Central Sports | 2-1 |
| Hamble Club | v | Sway | 5-1 |
| Hedge End Rangers | v | Bush Hill | 3-5 |
| Four Marks | v | Hayling United | 3-1 |
| Andover Lions | v | Lynhurst | 15-1 |
| Paulsgrove | v | Colden Common | 4-0 |
| Burridge | v | Fleetlands | 7-3 |
| Stocksbridge | v | Overton United | 1-4 |
| Winchester Castle | v | QK Southampton | HW |
| Otterbourne | v | Locks Heath | 3-0 |
| Liss Athletic | v | Broughton | 6-2 |
| Baffins Milton Rovers | v | Upham | 3-1 |
| AFC Petersfield | v | Headley United | 0-0, 0-2p |

**ROUND 2**

| | | | |
|---|---|---|---|
| Liphook United | v | Hamble Club | 1-2 |
| Bush Hill | v | Four Marks | 9-6 aet |
| Andover Lions | v | Paulsgrove | 1-2 aet |
| Burridge | v | Overton United | 6-0 |
| Michelmersh & Timsbury | v | Winchester Castle | 0-3 |
| Otterbourne | v | Liss Athletic | 2-4 |
| Baffins Milton Rovers | v | Clanfield | 2-1 aet |
| Infinity | v | Headley United | 3-1 |

**QUARTER FINALS**

| | | | |
|---|---|---|---|
| Hamble Club | v | Bush Hill | 3-2 aet |
| Paulsgrove | v | Burridge | 2-1 |
| Winchester Castle | v | Liss Athletic | 1-4 |
| Baffins Milton Rovers | v | Infinity | 5-0 |

**SEMI FINALS**

| | | | |
|---|---|---|---|
| Hamble Club | v | Paulsgrove | 4-1 |
| Liss Athletic | v | Baffins Milton Rovers | 3-3, 7-6p |

**FINAL**

| | | | |
|---|---|---|---|
| Hamble Club | v | Liss Athletic | 2-0 |

| SENIOR DIVISION | 1 | 2 | 3 | 4 | 5 | 6 | 7 | 8 | 9 | 10 | 11 | 12 | 13 | 14 | 15 | 16 | 17 | 18 |
|---|---|---|---|---|---|---|---|---|---|---|---|---|---|---|---|---|---|---|
| 1 Baffins Milton Rovers | | 3-1 | 6-0 | 1-0 | 4-1 | 2-1 | H-W | 1-0 | 6-1 | 3-0 | 4-1 | 7-0 | 2-1 | 4-0 | 3-2 | 8-3 | H-W | 3-1 |
| 2 Bush Hill | 1-0 | | 3-3 | 4-1 | 5-3 | 1-1 | 3-0 | 6-1 | 2-0 | 3-2 | 2-4 | 2-3 | 1-0 | 4-0 | 2-0 | 2-0 | 4-1 | 1-1 |
| 3 Clanfield | 0-2 | 1-2 | | 1-0 | 2-2 | 0-0 | 3-1 | 1-1 | 0-1 | 2-0 | 1-5 | 5-3 | 0-2 | 0-2 | 1-3 | 2-1 | 2-1 | 1-0 |
| 4 Colden Common | 2-5 | 1-6 | 2-2 | | 3-3 | 0-5 | 0-1 | 4-2 | 0-3 | 0-2 | 1-6 | 0-1 | 2-3 | 3-2 | 3-0 | A-W | 4-1 | 0-4 |
| 5 Fleetlands | 1-4 | 3-0 | 1-1 | 3-0 | | 0-8 | 3-2 | 5-3 | 1-1 | 1-2 | 2-3 | 5-0 | 0-17 | 4-4 | 3-1 | 2-1 | 2-4 | 0-2 |
| 6 Hamble Club | 3-1 | 3-1 | 1-1 | 7-0 | 3-1 | | 7-0 | 2-0 | H-W | 4-2 | 3-1 | 4-1 | 1-2 | 6-0 | 6-2 | 3-2 | H-W | 6-2 |
| 7 Headley United | 2-3 | 3-4 | 3-0 | 1-1 | 5-2 | 1-4 | | 1-2 | 4-1 | 2-4 | 0-2 | 0-3 | 0-3 | 0-3 | 5-4 | 2-0 | 3-2 | 0-4 |
| 8 Hedge End Rangers | 0-4 | 1-3 | 1-3 | 1-0 | 1-1 | 0-1 | 0-2 | | 1-2 | 0-2 | 1-2 | 2-0 | 0-7 | 1-2 | 2-2 | 1-3 | 2-1 | 0-2 |
| 9 Infinity | 1-7 | 1-5 | 2-1 | 2-2 | 3-2 | 1-10 | 2-1 | 1-2 | | 1-0 | 2-6 | 0-5 | 0-3 | 4-1 | H-W | 0-0 | H-W | 2-1 |
| 10 Liphook United | 1-1 | 1-1 | 1-0 | H-W | 1-3 | 0-4 | 1-1 | 0-2 | 2-2 | | 1-1 | 2-1 | 0-5 | 1-1 | 2-2 | 3-1 | 2-0 | 4-2 |
| 11 Liss Athletic | 1-3 | 2-2 | 4-2 | 6-2 | 1-0 | 0-3 | 2-0 | 5-0 | 1-1 | 4-2 | | 2-0 | 1-0 | 2-1 | 1-5 | 2-1 | H-W | 3-1 |
| 12 Locks Heath | 0-4 | 1-3 | 1-4 | 6-1 | 2-5 | 0-0 | 4-1 | 1-3 | 2-3 | 3-1 | 1-3 | | 0-1 | 2-2 | 3-1 | 2-2 | 2-2 | 2-0 |
| 13 Otterbourne | 1-2 | H-W | 2-1 | 6-1 | 8-0 | 3-2 | 11-1 | 6-0 | H-W | 4-0 | H-W | 2-0 | | 2-0 | 6-0 | 5-1 | 4-1 | 6-1 |
| 14 Overton United | 0-4 | 1-4 | 1-3 | 2-1 | 0-3 | 0-3 | 3-5 | 2-2 | 4-6 | 2-2 | 3-3 | 2-3 | 2-5 | | 4-1 | 1-3 | 2-0 | 3-2 |
| 15 Paulsgrove | 0-3 | 0-3 | 4-1 | 3-0 | 5-1 | 0-4 | 2-1 | 2-0 | 5-1 | 3-3 | 3-4 | 0-2 | 0-3 | 0-3 | | 1-2 | 3-2 | 2-0 |
| 16 QK Southampton | 1-4 | 2-1 | 3-0 | 4-1 | 1-2 | 1-7 | 2-1 | 0-0 | 3-3 | 4-1 | 3-2 | 3-0 | 1-3 | 1-1 | 2-1 | | H-W | 2-2 |
| 17 Stockbridge | A-W | 1-2 | 1-10 | 3-1 | 3-5 | 0-6 | 4-2 | 3-2 | 1-6 | A-W | 0-10 | 2-4 | 2-8 | 2-0 | 3-2 | 1-2 | | 1-4 |
| 18 Winchester Castle | 0-3 | 0-2 | 3-1 | 2-0 | 2-1 | 0-4 | 2-1 | 0-0 | 3-1 | 2-1 | 1-2 | H-W | 0-3 | 2-0 | 1-2 | 1-0 | 4-2 | |

| Hampshire Premier League | | |
|---|---|---|
| ANDOVER LIONS | Charlton Leisure Centre, West Portway Industrial Estate, Andover SP10 3LF | |
| BUSH HILL | Mansel Park, Evenlode Road, Millbrook, Southampton SO16 9LT | |
| CLANFIELD | Peel Park, Chalton Lane, Clanfield, Waterlooville PO8 0RJ | 07765 238 231 |
| FLEETLANDS | DARA Fleetlands, Lederle Lane, Gosport PO13 0AA | 01329 239 723 |
| HAYLING UNITED | Hayling College, Church Road, Hayling Island, Hampshire PO11 0NU | |
| HEADLEY UNITED | Headley Playing Fields, Mill Lane, Headley, Bordon, GU35 0PD | |
| HEDGE END RANGERS | Norman Rodaway Rec Grd, Heathouse Lane, Hedge End, Southampton SO30 0LE | |
| INFINITY | Knowle Village Community Hall, Knowle Avenue, Knowle, Fareham PO17 5LG | |
| LIPHOOK UNITED | Recreation Ground, London Road, Liphook GU30 7AN | |
| LISS ATHLETIC | Newman Collard Playing Fields Liss GU33 7LH | 01730 894 022 |
| LOCKS HEATH | Locksheath Rec, 419 Warsash Rd, Titchfield Common, Fareham PO14 4JX | |
| OVERTON UNITED | Overton Recreation Centre, Bridge Street, Overton RG25 3HD | 01256 770 561 |
| PAULSGROVE | Paulsgrove Social Club, Marsden Road, Paulsgrove, Portsmouth PO6 4JB | 02392 324 102 |
| QK SOUTHAMPTON | Lordshill Recreation Ground, Redbridge Lane, Lordshill, Southampton SO16 0XN | |
| STOCKBRIDGE | Stockbridge Recreation Ground, High Street, Stockbridge SO20 6EU | |
| WINCHESTER CASTLE | Hants Co. Council Spts Grd, Petersfield Rd (A31),Chilcombe, Winchester SO23 8ZB | |

# HERTS SENIOR COUNTY LEAGUE

**Sponsored by:** HertSavers Credit Union
**Founded:** 1898 reformed 1935
**Recent Champions:**
**2013:** Metropolitan Police Bushey
**2014:** Bedmond Sports & S.C.
**2015:** Belstone

| PREMIER DIVISION | | P | W | D | L | F | A | GD | Pts |
|---|---|---|---|---|---|---|---|---|---|
| 1 | Standon and Puckeridge | 32 | 26 | 3 | 3 | 101 | 31 | 70 | 81 |
| 2 | Belstone | 32 | 19 | 4 | 9 | 86 | 63 | 23 | 61 |
| 3 | Letchworth Garden City Eagles | 32 | 18 | 5 | 9 | 80 | 55 | 25 | 59 |
| 4 | Hadley Wood & Wingate | 32 | 17 | 5 | 10 | 91 | 59 | 32 | 56 |
| 5 | London Lions | 32 | 16 | 6 | 10 | 94 | 57 | 37 | 54 |
| 6 | Sandridge Rovers | 32 | 16 | 3 | 13 | 54 | 41 | 13 | 51 |
| 7 | Bovingdon | 32 | 14 | 9 | 9 | 65 | 56 | 9 | 51 |
| 8 | Cuffley | 32 | 12 | 9 | 11 | 55 | 63 | -8 | 45 |
| 9 | Buntingford Town | 32 | 12 | 7 | 13 | 63 | 65 | -2 | 43 |
| 10 | Ware Sports | 32 | 12 | 7 | 13 | 55 | 67 | -12 | 43 |
| 11 | Bushey Sports Club | 32 | 11 | 7 | 14 | 58 | 59 | -1 | 40 |
| 12 | Sarratt | 32 | 10 | 6 | 16 | 60 | 76 | -16 | 36 |
| 13 | Chipperfield Corinthians | 32 | 10 | 6 | 16 | 59 | 82 | -23 | 36 |
| 14 | Evergreen | 32 | 9 | 7 | 16 | 46 | 74 | -28 | 34 |
| 15 | Wormley Rovers | 32 | 9 | 6 | 17 | 62 | 96 | -34 | 33 |
| 16 | Hatfield Social | 32 | 6 | 4 | 22 | 50 | 95 | -45 | 22 |
| 17 | Hinton | 32 | 4 | 8 | 20 | 35 | 75 | -40 | 20 |
| | Old Parmiterians withdrew - record expunged | | | | | | | | |
| | | | 0 | | | | | | |

| DIVISION ONE | | P | W | D | L | F | A | GD | Pts |
|---|---|---|---|---|---|---|---|---|---|
| 1 | Bedmond Sports and Social Club | 26 | 21 | 4 | 1 | 91 | 23 | 68 | 67 |
| 2 | Knebworth | 26 | 19 | 4 | 3 | 67 | 34 | 33 | 61 |
| 3 | Bengeo Trinity | 26 | 15 | 7 | 4 | 65 | 34 | 31 | 52 |
| 4 | Harefield United U21 | 26 | 13 | 5 | 8 | 75 | 55 | 20 | 44 |
| 5 | FC Lemsford | 26 | 11 | 9 | 6 | 40 | 28 | 12 | 42 |
| 6 | Croxley Green FC | 26 | 11 | 5 | 10 | 66 | 60 | 6 | 38 |
| 7 | Broadfields | 26 | 11 | 2 | 13 | 49 | 55 | -6 | 35 |
| 8 | Ickleford | 26 | 8 | 10 | 8 | 39 | 42 | -3 | 34 |
| 9 | Lings Elite | 26 | 9 | 6 | 11 | 41 | 52 | -11 | 33 |
| 10 | AFC Hatfield | 26 | 9 | 5 | 12 | 54 | 69 | -15 | 32 |
| 11 | Lemsford | 26 | 6 | 7 | 13 | 30 | 66 | -36 | 25 |
| 12 | Hampstead Heath | 26 | 5 | 3 | 18 | 39 | 66 | -27 | 18 |
| 13 | Hertford Town U21 | 26 | 4 | 5 | 17 | 34 | 56 | -22 | 17 |
| 14 | Hatfield Town Reserves | 26 | 3 | 2 | 21 | 28 | 78 | -50 | 11 |
| | Brache Sparta withdrew - record expunged | | | | | | | | |
| | Colney Heath Reserves withdrew - record expunged | | | | | | | | |

## AUBERY CUP

**HOLDERS:** HSTFIELD SOCIAL

**ROUND 1**

| | | | |
|---|---|---|---|
| Brache Sparta 2015 | v | Lings Elite | AW |
| FC Lemsford | v | AFC Hatfield | 3-1 |
| Bushey Sports Club | v | Hertford Town U21 | 4-3 |
| Bedmond Sports and Social Club | v | Letchworth Garden City Eagles | 4-2 |

**Round 2**

| | | | |
|---|---|---|---|
| Harefield United U21 | v | Bushey Rangers | HW |
| Sarratt | v | Chipperfield Corinthians | |
| Kimpton Rovers | v | Bovingdon | AW |
| Hinton | v | Sandridge Rovers | 5-5, 4-2p |
| Hatfield Social | v | Ickleford | 2-2, 8-9p |
| Lemsford | v | Old Parmiterians | 4-4, 3-4p |
| Belstone | v | Colney Heath Reserves | HW |
| Knebworth | v | Hatfield Town Reserves | 7-0 |
| Bedmond Sports and Social Club | v | Broadfields | 7-2 |
| Evergreen | v | Bengeo Trinity | 4-5 |
| Bushey Sports Club | v | Ware Sports | 2-4 |
| Hampstead Heath | v | Wormley Rovers | 2-2, 3-5p |
| FC Lemsford | v | Lings Elite | 5-2 |
| Standon and Puckeridge | v | Cuffley | HW |
| Hadley Wood & Wingate | v | London Lions | 3-1 |
| Croxley Green FC | v | Buntingford Town | 2-4 |

**Round 3**

| | | | |
|---|---|---|---|
| Hinton | v | Ware Sports | 0-6 |
| Buntingford Town | v | Bovingdon | 0-2 |
| Buntingford Town | v | Bovingdon | AW |
| Harefield United U21 | v | Standon and Puckeridge | 2-2, 4-3p |
| *(Match awarded to Standon and Puckeridge)* | | | |
| Wormley Rovers | v | Knebworth | 2-1 |
| Bengeo Trinity | v | FC Lemsford | 2-1 |
| Hadley Wood & Wingate | v | Old Parmiterians | 7-0 |
| Ickleford | v | Belstone | 0-6 |
| Bedmond Sports and Social Club | v | Sarratt | 2-0 |

**Quarter Final**

| | | | |
|---|---|---|---|
| Bovingdon | v | Bedmond Sports and Social Club | 0-4 |
| Ware Sports | v | Hadley Wood & Wingate | 1-2 |
| Wormley Rovers | v | Belstone | 1-5 |
| Standon and Puckeridge | v | Bengeo Trinity | 4-0 |

**Semi Final**

| | | | |
|---|---|---|---|
| Bedmond Sports and Social Club | v | Hadley Wood & Wingate | 2-0 |
| Belstone | v | Standon and Puckeridge | 3-1 |

**Final**

| | | | |
|---|---|---|---|
| Belstone | v | Bedmond Sports and Social Club | 3-0 |

| | PREMIER DIVISION | 1 | 2 | 3 | 4 | 5 | 6 | 7 | 8 | 9 | 10 | 11 | 12 | 13 | 14 | 15 | 16 | 17 |
|---|---|---|---|---|---|---|---|---|---|---|---|---|---|---|---|---|---|---|
| 1 | Belstone | | 0-3 | 2-2 | 4-0 | 4-1 | 3-3 | 4-0 | 4-3 | 4-2 | 2-1 | 2-1 | 6-4 | 1-3 | 6-2 | 0-5 | 5-2 | 4-3 |
| 2 | Bovingdon | 1-3 | | 2-2 | 2-1 | 6-0 | 2-1 | 1-1 | 1-2 | 1-2 | 2-2 | 1-2 | 2-2 | 1-1 | 2-0 | 0-2 | 0-1 | 3-2 |
| 3 | Buntingford Town | 2-1 | 4-1 | | 1-2 | 5-1 | 1-1 | 3-2 | 2-0 | 8-3 | 2-1 | 3-0 | 3-1 | 0-3 | 0-4 | AW | 1-1 | 1-3 |
| 4 | Bushey Sports Club | 3-4 | 0-0 | 7-1 | | 0-2 | 1-1 | 2-2 | 2-2 | 4-0 | 4-0 | 0-3 | 0-4 | 3-0 | 1-0 | 2-4 | 6-0 | 3-1 |
| 5 | Chipperfield Corinthians | 1-3 | 1-2 | 2-1 | 2-3 | | 0-2 | 3-1 | 5-3 | 3-2 | 3-3 | 1-2 | 0-3 | 1-1 | 2-2 | 1-4 | 1-2 | 1-2 |
| 6 | Cuffley | 5-3 | 1-1 | 4-3 | 0-0 | 2-3 | | 2-3 | 3-2 | 0-4 | 2-1 | 3-6 | 1-0 | 2-0 | 1-1 | 2-1 | 2-5 | 2-2 |
| 7 | Evergreen | 1-6 | 1-2 | 2-1 | 0-0 | 1-6 | 0-1 | | 2-0 | 1-1 | 2-2 | 5-3 | 1-2 | 0-3 | 4-2 | 0-2 | 1-0 | 4-2 |
| 8 | Hadley Wood & Wingate | 1-1 | 3-5 | 3-3 | 2-0 | 1-2 | 4-0 | 2-2 | | 7-1 | 3-0 | 2-1 | 3-3 | 3-1 | 5-1 | 4-2 | 7-4 | 5-1 |
| 9 | Hatfield Social | 1-2 | 1-3 | 3-3 | 3-1 | 2-0 | 1-3 | 2-3 | 1-2 | | 1-3 | 2-4 | 2-6 | 0-3 | 4-3 | 3-3 | 2-1 | 1-2 |
| 10 | Hinton | 0-0 | 1-3 | 2-1 | 3-2 | 2-2 | 0-2 | 1-3 | 1-5 | 0-0 | | 1-2 | 0-1 | 0-1 | 0-1 | 2-3 | 2-1 | 1-4 |
| 11 | Letchworth Garden City Eagles | HW | 2-3 | 1-1 | 6-1 | 4-3 | 2-1 | 5-1 | 1-3 | 2-0 | 9-1 | | 2-1 | 3-2 | 2-3 | 0-4 | 3-0 | 1-1 |
| 12 | London Lions | 4-1 | 5-5 | 1-2 | 2-2 | 9-2 | 5-0 | 5-0 | 2-4 | 5-0 | 5-0 | 2-2 | | 2-1 | 3-1 | 0-3 | 5-2 | 3-2 |
| 13 | Sandridge Rovers | 3-1 | 0-1 | 3-0 | 0-2 | 1-2 | 1-0 | 2-0 | HW | 2-1 | 0-0 | 1-2 | 3-1 | | 1-2 | 0-2 | 3-1 | 5-0 |
| 14 | Sarratt | 0-2 | 2-6 | 1-2 | 1-2 | 4-2 | 3-3 | 2-0 | 0-2 | 6-1 | 1-1 | 3-1 | 0-4 | 2-4 | | 2-5 | 1-1 | 4-2 |
| 15 | Standon and Puckeridge | 5-3 | 7-0 | 3-0 | 3-1 | 1-1 | 3-1 | 2-0 | 2-1 | 5-1 | 3-2 | 0-0 | 1-0 | 4-0 | 5-2 | | 4-0 | 7-0 |
| 16 | Ware Sports | 0-1 | 2-1 | 4-2 | 2-1 | 2-2 | 1-3 | 2-0 | 2-4 | 2-1 | 2-1 | 2-2 | 2-2 | 4-0 | 1-1 | 2-0 | | 1-1 |
| 17 | Wormley Rovers | 1-4 | 2-2 | 1-3 | 4-2 | 2-3 | 1-1 | 3-3 | 4-3 | 3-2 | 3-1 | 2-6 | 4-2 | 0-6 | 1-3 | 1-6 | 2-3 | |

| RESERVE NORTH & EAST | P | W | D | L | F | A | GD | Pts |
|---|---|---|---|---|---|---|---|---|
| 1 Buntingford Town Res. | 14 | 12 | 1 | 1 | 33 | 14 | 19 | 37 |
| 2 Cuffley Reserves | 14 | 9 | 3 | 2 | 38 | 17 | 21 | 30 |
| 3 Nirankari Hitchin* (-6) | 14 | 11 | 0 | 3 | 46 | 16 | 30 | 27 |
| 4 Knebworth Reserves | 14 | 6 | 1 | 7 | 24 | 29 | -5 | 19 |
| 5 Letchworth Garden City Eagles Res. | 14 | 6 | 1 | 7 | 34 | 42 | -8 | 19 |
| 6 Sandridge Rovers Res. | 14 | 4 | 1 | 9 | 33 | 37 | -4 | 13 |
| 7 Lemsford Reserves | 14 | 2 | 2 | 10 | 20 | 43 | -23 | 8 |
| 8 Wormley Rovers Res. | 14 | 1 | 1 | 12 | 15 | 45 | -30 | 4 |

Tottenhall withdrew - record expunged.

Welwyn Pegasus withdrew - record expunged.

| RESERVE SOUTH & WEST | P | W | D | L | F | A | GD | Pts |
|---|---|---|---|---|---|---|---|---|
| 1 "Hadley ""A""" | 16 | 14 | 1 | 1 | 75 | 11 | 64 | 43 |
| 2 Sarratt Res | 16 | 11 | 1 | 4 | 63 | 23 | 40 | 34 |
| 3 Lings Elite U21 | 16 | 10 | 3 | 3 | 57 | 39 | 18 | 33 |
| 4 Bovingdon Reserves | 16 | 9 | 1 | 6 | 41 | 33 | 8 | 28 |
| 5 Bushey Sports Club Res. | 16 | 6 | 5 | 5 | 39 | 29 | 10 | 23 |
| 6 Evergreen Reserves | 16 | 6 | 4 | 6 | 38 | 37 | 1 | 22 |
| 7 Berkhamsted Raiders | 16 | 4 | 0 | 12 | 31 | 54 | -23 | 12 |
| 8 Chipperfield Corinthians Res. | 16 | 2 | 3 | 11 | 27 | 56 | -29 | 9 |
| 9 Bushey Rangers Reserves | 16 | 1 | 0 | 15 | 12 | 101 | -89 | 3 |

Old Parmiterians Reserves withdrew - record expunged.

## Herts Senior County League Premier Division

|  |  |  |
|---|---|---|
| BEDMOND SPORTS & SOCIAL | Toms Lane Recreation Ground, Toms Lane, Bedmond, Abbots Langley WD5 0RB | 01923 267 991 |
| BELSTONE | The Medburn Ground, Watling Street, Radlett WD6 3AB | 020 8207 2395 |
| BOVINGDON | Green Lane, Bovingdon, Hemel Hempstead HP3 0LA | 01442 832 628 |
| BUNTINGFORD TOWN | The Bury Sainsbury Distribution Centre, London Road, Buntingford SG9 9HZ | 01763 271 522 |
| BUSHEY SPORTS CLUB | Met Police Sports Club, Aldenham Road, Bushey, Watford WD2 3TR | 01923 243 947 |
| CHIPPERFIELD CORINTHIANS | Queens Street, Chipperfield, Kings Langley WD4 9BT | 01923 269 554 |
| CUFFLEY | King George's Playing Fields, Northaw Road East, Cuffley EN6 4LU | 07815 174 434 |
| EVERGREEN | Southway, Abbots Langley, WATFORD, Hertfordshire WD4 8PN | |
| KNEBWORTH | Knebworth Recreation Ground, Watton Road, Knebworth, Hertfordshire SG3 6AH | |
| LETCHWORTH G. C. EAGLES | Pixmore Playing Fields, Ledgers Lane, Baldock Road, Letchworth SG6 2EN | 07855 337 175 |
| LONDON LIONS | Hemel Hemstead FC, Vauxhall Road, Hemel Hempstead, HP2 4HW | 01442 259 777 |
| SANDRIDGE ROVERS | Spencer Recreation Ground, Sandridge, St Albans AL4 9DD | 01727 835 506 |
| SARRATT | King George V Playing Fields, George V Way, Sarratt WD3 6AU | 07711 618 028 |
| STANDON & PUCKERIDGE | Station Road, Standon, Ware SG11 1QT | 01920 823 460 |
| WARE SPORTS | Wodson Park Sports Centre, Wadesmill Road, WARE, Hertfordshire SG12 0RB | |
| WORMLEY ROVERS | Wormley Sports Club, Church Lane, Wormley EN10 7QF | 01992 460 650 |

**CLUB MOVEMENTS**
**Premier Division**
**Out:** Hadley Wood & Wingate (Spartan South Midlands)

**Division One**
**In:** Baldock Town Reserves (SSML Reserve Division), Oaklands College (N), Stevenage Borough (N).
**Out:** Croxley Green (F).

# HUMBER PREMIER LEAGUE

**Sponsored by:** No sponsor
**Founded:** 2000
**Recent Champions:**
**2013:** Beverley Town
**2014:** Beverley Town
**2015:** Sculcoates Amateurs

| PREMIER DIVISION | P | W | D | L | F | A | GD | Pts |
|---|---|---|---|---|---|---|---|---|
| 1 Wawne United | 30 | 22 | 2 | 6 | 101 | 55 | 46 | 68 |
| 2 Crown FC | 30 | 20 | 3 | 7 | 75 | 40 | 35 | 63 |
| 3 Pocklington Town | 30 | 16 | 8 | 6 | 65 | 39 | 26 | 56 |
| 4 Sculcoates Amateurs | 30 | 16 | 7 | 7 | 75 | 37 | 38 | 55 |
| 5 Reckitts AFC | 30 | 15 | 7 | 8 | 77 | 50 | 27 | 52 |
| 6 East Riding Rangers | 30 | 14 | 10 | 6 | 60 | 39 | 21 | 52 |
| 7 Chalk Lane | 30 | 15 | 7 | 8 | 52 | 40 | 12 | 52 |
| 8 Goole United | 30 | 12 | 4 | 14 | 67 | 67 | 0 | 40 |
| 9 Hessle Rangers | 30 | 11 | 4 | 15 | 55 | 77 | -22 | 37 |
| 10 Beverley Town | 30 | 10 | 6 | 14 | 58 | 57 | 1 | 36 |
| 11 South Cave | 30 | 10 | 5 | 15 | 55 | 71 | -16 | 35 |
| 12 Bridlington Sports Club | 30 | 9 | 5 | 16 | 64 | 76 | -12 | 32 |
| 13 Hedon Rangers | 30 | 8 | 2 | 20 | 46 | 87 | -41 | 26 |
| 14 AFC Rovers | 30 | 8 | 2 | 20 | 42 | 90 | -48 | 26 |
| 15 Driffield Evening Institute | 30 | 6 | 7 | 17 | 58 | 73 | -15 | 25 |
| 16 Hornsea Town | 30 | 7 | 3 | 20 | 53 | 105 | -52 | 24 |

| DIVISION ONE | P | W | D | L | F | A | GD | Pts |
|---|---|---|---|---|---|---|---|---|
| 1 North Ferriby Athletic | 22 | 18 | 0 | 4 | 70 | 22 | 48 | 54 |
| 2 Hunters FC | 22 | 15 | 3 | 4 | 91 | 47 | 44 | 48 |
| 3 Walkington | 22 | 13 | 6 | 3 | 67 | 36 | 31 | 45 |
| 4 Long Riston | 22 | 10 | 3 | 9 | 37 | 44 | -7 | 33 |
| 5 Park Athletic | 22 | 10 | 1 | 11 | 52 | 54 | -2 | 31 |
| 6 Hessle United FC | 22 | 9 | 4 | 9 | 50 | 54 | -4 | 31 |
| 7 Hull United AFC Res. | 22 | 8 | 5 | 9 | 33 | 44 | -11 | 29 |
| 8 AFC Northfield | 22 | 6 | 7 | 9 | 52 | 59 | -7 | 25 |
| 9 Westella & Willerby | 22 | 6 | 5 | 11 | 33 | 56 | -23 | 23 |
| 10 Brandesburton | 22 | 6 | 3 | 13 | 49 | 73 | -24 | 21 |
| 11 Howden AFC | 22 | 6 | 1 | 15 | 46 | 64 | -18 | 19 |
| 12 Hall Road Rangers Res. | 22 | 5 | 2 | 15 | 32 | 59 | -27 | 17 |

**In:** Bridlington Town Reserves (East Riding County), East Yorkshire Carnegie (N), LIV Supplies AFC (N)
**Out:** Long Riston, Park Athletic (F)

## LEAGUE CUP

**HOLDERS:** HULL UNITED AFC

**ROUND 1**

| | | | |
|---|---|---|---|
| Hessle Rangers | v | Sculcoates Amateurs | 2-5 aet |
| Reckitts AFC | v | Hull United AFC Reserves | 1-3 |
| AFC Rovers | v | Bridlington Sports Club | 1-4 |
| Beverley Town | v | Hessle United | 0-4 |
| Hornsea Town | v | South Cave | 0-1 |
| North Ferriby Athletic | v | Goole United | 0-1 |
| Hunters FC | v | Brandesburton | 4-3 |
| AFC Northfield | v | Driffield JFC | HW |
| Howden AFC | v | East Riding Rangers | 2-4 |
| Walkington | v | Little Weighton | 3-1 |
| Crown FC | v | Chalk Lane | 3-2 aet |
| Park Athletic | v | Driffield Evening Institute | 6-3 |
| Westella & Willerby | v | Pocklington Town | 3-5 |
| Hedon Rangers | v | Hall Road Rangers Reserves | 3-0 |

**ROUND 2**

| | | | |
|---|---|---|---|
| Sculcoates Amateurs | v | Hull United AFC Reserves | 2-1 |
| Bridlington Sports Club | v | Hessle United | 5-2 |
| South Cave | v | Goole United | 3-1 |
| Hunters FC | v | Wawne United | 2-4 |
| AFC Northfield | v | East Riding Rangers | 3-0 |
| Walkington | v | Crown FC | 1-0 |
| Park Athletic | v | Pocklington Town | 0-2 |
| Long Riston | v | Hedon Rangers | 2-5 aet |

**QUARTER FINALS**

| | | | |
|---|---|---|---|
| Sculcoates Amateurs | v | Bridlington Sports Club | 1-2 |
| South Cave | v | Wawne United | 0-2 |
| AFC Northfield | v | Walkington | 2-3 |
| Pocklington Town | v | Hedon Rangers | 1-0 |

**SEMI FINALS**

| | | | |
|---|---|---|---|
| Bridlington Sports Club | v | Wawne United | 1-2 |
| Walkington | v | Pocklington Town | 1-0 |

**FINAL**

| | | | |
|---|---|---|---|
| Wawne United | v | Walkington | 3-4 |

| PREMIER DIVISION | 1 | 2 | 3 | 4 | 5 | 6 | 7 | 8 | 9 | 10 | 11 | 12 | 13 | 14 | 15 | 16 |
|---|---|---|---|---|---|---|---|---|---|---|---|---|---|---|---|---|
| 1 AFC Rovers | | 1-6 | 2-4 | 2-2 | 0-2 | 1-6 | 1-0 | 3-9 | 2-3 | 3-0 | 3-1 | 1-1 | 1-6 | 1-6 | 1-4 | 2-4 |
| 2 Beverley Town | 4-1 | | 1-2 | 0-1 | 0-1 | 4-3 | 1-1 | 0-2 | 4-2 | 0-2 | 4-0 | 1-1 | 2-2 | 1-3 | 6-2 | 1-3 |
| 3 Bridlington Sports Club | 1-4 | 1-1 | | 0-1 | 1-3 | 0-1 | 4-4 | 3-2 | 3-1 | 4-1 | 6-2 | 2-3 | 1-5 | 2-3 | 2-0 | 2-4 |
| 4 Chalk Lane | 1-0 | 2-0 | 4-0 | | 0-2 | 1-1 | 1-0 | 3-0 | 1-2 | 1-1 | 2-4 | 1-0 | 2-1 | 1-4 | 4-0 | 3-2 |
| 5 Crown FC | 4-0 | 1-2 | 4-0 | 0-0 | | 5-1 | 4-1 | 1-1 | 1-0 | 2-1 | 5-0 | 3-0 | 1-2 | 1-0 | 1-2 | 6-2 |
| 6 Driffield Evening Institute | 3-4 | 0-4 | 3-3 | 2-2 | 2-3 | | 1-4 | 7-2 | 3-3 | 2-3 | 2-2 | 2-2 | 1-2 | 1-1 | 2-3 | 0-4 |
| 7 East Riding Rangers | 0-1 | 3-1 | 4-0 | 1-1 | 2-0 | 3-2 | | 0-0 | 5-3 | 1-1 | 2-1 | 0-0 | 4-3 | 2-1 | 0-3 | 5-1 |
| 8 Goole United | 5-0 | 1-1 | 1-6 | 3-1 | 3-1 | 1-0 | 1-0 | | 1-2 | 1-2 | 5-1 | 3-5 | 2-1 | 1-1 | 5-2 | 0-3 |
| 9 Hedon Rangers | 2-1 | 3-1 | 1-1 | 1-4 | 1-4 | 0-3 | 1-3 | 1-4 | | 4-1 | 3-4 | 0-8 | 0-3 | 1-4 | 2-4 | 3-4 |
| 10 Hessle Rangers | 2-3 | 5-4 | 3-1 | 4-3 | 4-4 | 0-4 | 0-5 | 4-2 | 1-2 | | 2-4 | 2-2 | 2-3 | 1-2 | 4-1 | 1-5 |
| 11 Hornsea Town | 2-0 | 4-3 | 1-5 | 0-2 | 1-5 | 0-2 | 4-4 | 1-7 | 2-0 | 3-1 | | 1-4 | 1-1 | 3-9 | 2-4 | 3-7 |
| 12 Pocklington Town | 3-1 | 1-3 | 3-1 | 1-0 | 0-2 | 3-0 | 0-2 | 2-1 | 2-0 | 4-1 | 4-1 | | 1-1 | 3-2 | 2-0 | 2-3 |
| 13 Reckitts AFC | 3-2 | 1-2 | 3-2 | 3-4 | 7-3 | 3-0 | 1-1 | 4-1 | 3-0 | 1-2 | 4-1 | 1-1 | | 2-2 | 4-3 | 1-2 |
| 14 Sculcoates Amateurs | 2-0 | 2-0 | 3-3 | 0-1 | 1-3 | 3-0 | 0-0 | 5-0 | 5-0 | 4-0 | 4-1 | 1-2 | 0-0 | | 4-3 | 0-2 |
| 15 South Cave | 0-1 | 0-0 | 4-3 | 2-2 | 1-2 | 3-2 | 1-1 | 3-0 | 1-4 | 1-2 | 2-1 | 1-1 | 2-3 | 1-2 | | 2-2 |
| 16 Wawne United | 4-0 | 6-1 | 4-1 | 4-1 | 5-1 | 4-2 | 1-2 | 4-3 | 4-1 | 1-2 | 3-2 | 2-4 | 4-3 | 1-1 | 6-0 | |

# KENT COUNTY LEAGUE

**Sponsored by:** NRG
**Founded:** 1922
**Recent Champions:**
**2013:** Hildenborough Athletic
**2014:** Metrogas
**2015:** Metrogas

| PREMIER DIVISION | P | W | D | L | F | A | GD | Pts |
|---|---|---|---|---|---|---|---|---|
| 1 Faversham Strike Force Seniors | 28 | 19 | 5 | 4 | 77 | 38 | 39 | 62 |
| 2 Kennington | 28 | 17 | 5 | 6 | 60 | 31 | 29 | 56 |
| 3 Snodland Town | 28 | 17 | 4 | 7 | 71 | 43 | 28 | 55 |
| 4 Stansfeld (Oxford & Bermondsey) (-1) | 28 | 16 | 6 | 6 | 73 | 37 | 36 | 53 |
| 5 Bexley | 28 | 17 | 1 | 10 | 55 | 39 | 16 | 52 |
| 6 Erith 147 Sports | 28 | 13 | 6 | 9 | 47 | 38 | 9 | 45 |
| 7 Staplehurst Monarchs United | 28 | 10 | 6 | 12 | 45 | 59 | -14 | 36 |
| 8 Greenways | 28 | 10 | 4 | 14 | 35 | 50 | -15 | 34 |
| 9 Fleetdown United (-1) | 28 | 10 | 4 | 14 | 41 | 40 | 1 | 33 |
| 10 Metrogas (-1) | 27 | 10 | 4 | 13 | 40 | 50 | -10 | 33 |
| 11 Borden Village (-1) | 27 | 9 | 7 | 11 | 46 | 58 | -12 | 33 |
| 12 Guru Nanak | 28 | 8 | 4 | 16 | 40 | 51 | -11 | 28 |
| 13 Hildenborough Athletic (-1) | 28 | 8 | 3 | 17 | 35 | 72 | -37 | 26 |
| 14 Halstead United | 28 | 6 | 3 | 19 | 23 | 55 | -32 | 21 |
| 15 Tudor Sports (-1) | 28 | 4 | 8 | 16 | 33 | 60 | -27 | 19 |

| DIVISION ONE EAST | P | W | D | L | F | A | GD | Pts |
|---|---|---|---|---|---|---|---|---|
| 1 Lydd Town Reserves | 20 | 16 | 0 | 4 | 66 | 42 | 24 | 48 |
| 2 New Romney | 20 | 14 | 4 | 2 | 54 | 23 | 31 | 46 |
| 3 East Kent College | 20 | 12 | 4 | 4 | 53 | 34 | 19 | 40 |
| 4 Hawkinge Town | 20 | 10 | 2 | 8 | 42 | 45 | -3 | 32 |
| 5 Hollands & Blair Res. | 20 | 8 | 7 | 5 | 52 | 44 | 8 | 31 |
| 6 Ide Hill (-1) | 20 | 9 | 1 | 10 | 43 | 44 | -1 | 27 |
| 7 Sutton Athletic Res. (-1) | 20 | 7 | 5 | 8 | 39 | 35 | 4 | 25 |
| 8 Deal Community Sports | 20 | 6 | 2 | 12 | 48 | 46 | 2 | 20 |
| 9 APM Contrast Res. (-3) | 20 | 6 | 4 | 10 | 30 | 41 | -11 | 19 |
| 10 Bearsted Reserves (-1) | 20 | 5 | 4 | 11 | 27 | 41 | -14 | 18 |
| 11 Bredhurst Juniors (-1) | 20 | 0 | 1 | 19 | 11 | 70 | -59 | 0 |

| DIVISION ONE WEST | P | W | D | L | F | A | GD | Pts |
|---|---|---|---|---|---|---|---|---|
| 1 Farnborough OB Guild | 20 | 17 | 1 | 2 | 59 | 21 | 38 | 52 |
| 2 Peckham Town | 20 | 16 | 1 | 3 | 82 | 26 | 56 | 49 |
| 3 Stansfeld (Ox & B) Res. | 20 | 15 | 1 | 4 | 55 | 28 | 27 | 46 |
| 4 Otford United | 20 | 14 | 1 | 5 | 63 | 26 | 37 | 43 |
| 5 Long Lane | 20 | 10 | 3 | 7 | 45 | 28 | 17 | 33 |
| 6 Halls AFC | 20 | 7 | 5 | 8 | 35 | 31 | 4 | 26 |
| 7 Chipstead | 20 | 6 | 3 | 11 | 42 | 50 | -8 | 21 |
| 8 AFC Mottingham | 20 | 6 | 2 | 12 | 27 | 51 | -24 | 20 |
| 9 Bexlians (-1) | 20 | 5 | 2 | 13 | 34 | 62 | -28 | 16 |
| 10 Oaks & Junior Red Seniors (-1) | 20 | 2 | 2 | 16 | 18 | 68 | -50 | 7 |
| 11 Belvedere | 20 | 1 | 1 | 18 | 19 | 88 | -69 | 4 |

## BILL MANKLOW INTER REGIONAL CHALLENGE CUP

**HOLDERS: STANSFEILD O&B**

**ROUND 1**

| | | | |
|---|---|---|---|
| Bredhurst Juniors | v | Lydd Town Reserves | 3-4 |
| Farnborough OBG | v | Belvedere | 1-0 aet |
| Bexlians | v | Borden Village | 2-5 |
| Peckham Town | v | Stansfeld O&B | 3-1 |
| Metrogas | v | Staplehurst Monarchs United | 2-1 |
| New Romney | v | Long Lane | 1-3 |

**ROUND 2**

| | | | |
|---|---|---|---|
| Bexley | v | Hollands & Blair Reserves | 1-2 |
| Park Regis | v | Tudor Sports | AW |
| APM Contrast Reserves | v | Lydd Town Reserves | 2-3 aet |
| Hildenborough Athletic | v | Farnborough OBG | 1-3 |
| Borden Village | v | Ide Hill | 4-1 |
| Peckham Town | v | Sutton Athletic Reserves | 3-2 |
| Metrogas | v | Halls AFC | 3-2 aet |
| East Kent College | v | Bearsted Reserves | 5-0 |
| Snodland Town | v | Fleetdown United | 3-2 |
| Kennington | v | Blackheath United | 6-1 |
| AFC Mottingham | v | Erith 147 Sports | 1-4 |
| Guru Nanak | v | Otford United | 5-2 aet |
| Chipstead | v | Long Lane | 6-3 aet |
| Halstead United | v | Hawkinge Town | 1-3 |
| Faversham Strike Force | v | Deal Community Sports | 8-3 |
| Greenways | v | Oaks & Junior Red Seniors | 4-1 |

**ROUND 3**

| | | | |
|---|---|---|---|
| Hollands & Blair Reserves | v | Tudor Sports | 2-4 |
| Lydd Town Reserves | v | Farnborough OBG | 2-1 |
| Borden Village | v | Peckham Town | 2-4 |
| Metrogas | v | East Kent College | 2-3 aet |
| Snodland Town | v | Kennington | 3-1 |
| Erith 147 Sports | v | Guru Nanak | 3-2 |
| Chipstead | v | Hawkinge Town | 2-2, 4-1p |
| Faversham Strike Force | v | Greenways | 3-2 |

**QUARTER FINALS**

| | | | |
|---|---|---|---|
| Tudor Sports | v | Lydd Town Reserves | 2-3 aet |
| Peckham Town | v | East Kent College | 3-4 aet |
| Snodland Town | v | Erith 147 Sports | 2-4 |
| Chipstead | v | Faversham Strike Force | 2-4 |

**SEMI FINALS**

| | | | |
|---|---|---|---|
| Lydd Town Reserves | v | East Kent College | 2-3 |
| Erith 147 Sports | v | Fav | 1-2 |

**FINAL**

| | | | |
|---|---|---|---|
| East Kent College | v | Faversham Strike Force | 5-1 |

| PREMIER DIVISION | 1 | 2 | 3 | 4 | 5 | 6 | 7 | 8 | 9 | 10 | 11 | 12 | 13 | 14 | 15 |
|---|---|---|---|---|---|---|---|---|---|---|---|---|---|---|---|
| 1 Bexley | | 2-1 | 1-3 | 2-5 | 1-0 | 0-2 | 1-4 | 2-0 | 3-0 | 2-1 | 2-0 | 0-1 | 0-1 | 3-0 | 2-2 |
| 2 Borden Village | 3-1 | | 2-0 | 1-0 | 0-0 | 1-2 | 7-3 | 3-1 | 3-1 | 0-5 | P-P | 1-7 | 2-9 | 2-1 | 3-4 |
| 3 Erith 147 Sports | 0-2 | 1-1 | | 2-2 | 0-2 | 2-1 | 2-0 | 2-0 | 3-0 | 2-1 | 2-2 | 6-0 | 1-4 | 3-0 | 4-2 |
| 4 Faversham Strike Force Seniors | 2-1 | 1-1 | 7-2 | | 3-2 | 5-0 | 1-0 | 3-2 | 7-1 | 3-1 | 2-1 | 2-3 | 1-1 | 2-2 | 1-1 |
| 5 Fleetdown United | 4-3 | 0-0 | 0-2 | 2-3 | | 1-2 | 2-5 | 1-0 | 3-0 | 0-2 | 0-1 | 0-1 | 0-2 | 2-3 | 4-1 |
| 6 Greenways | 0-2 | 4-2 | 0-2 | 2-5 | 2-3 | | 0-1 | 1-0 | 1-0 | 1-3 | 0-0 | 3-2 | 1-1 | 3-0 | 2-2 |
| 7 Guru Nanak | 1-2 | 0-0 | 2-1 | 1-2 | 0-3 | 3-0 | | 1-2 | 3-0 | 1-1 | 3-1 | 2-3 | 2-3 | 0-1 | 4-2 |
| 8 Halstead United | 0-1 | 0-2 | 0-0 | 1-2 | 0-2 | 3-0 | 3-2 | | 0-0 | 2-3 | 2-1 | 1-6 | 0-5 | 1-0 | 0-2 |
| 9 Hildenborough Athletic | 1-6 | 2-1 | 3-2 | 0-4 | 2-0 | 2-1 | 2-0 | 3-2 | | 1-3 | 4-2 | 1-2 | 4-4 | 2-2 | 1-2 |
| 10 Kennington | 3-1 | 4-3 | 1-2 | 1-0 | 2-0 | 1-3 | 2-0 | 3-0 | 2-3 | | 2-0 | 2-1 | 0-0 | 2-0 | 1-0 |
| 11 Metrogas | 1-2 | 3-1 | 0-0 | 0-2 | 2-0 | 1-0 | 3-0 | 5-1 | 4-1 | 0-6 | | 3-5 | 0-2 | 2-2 | 3-2 |
| 12 Snodland Town | 0-1 | 1-1 | 3-1 | 4-1 | 1-4 | 1-0 | 0-0 | 3-0 | 4-1 | 1-1 | 1-4 | | 0-2 | 6-4 | 5-0 |
| 13 Stansfeld (Oxford & Bermondsey) | 3-4 | 2-3 | 0-0 | 2-5 | 0-4 | 4-0 | 1-0 | 1-1 | 5-0 | 1-3 | 3-0 | 1-3 | | 8-2 | 4-1 |
| 14 Staplehurst Monarchs United | 0-6 | 3-1 | 2-1 | 1-2 | 1-1 | 2-2 | 4-0 | 1-0 | 1-0 | 2-2 | 5-0 | 0-6 | 0-2 | | 1-0 |
| 15 Tudor Sports | 1-2 | 1-1 | 0-1 | 1-4 | 1-1 | 1-2 | 2-2 | 0-1 | 2-0 | 2-2 | 0-1 | 1-1 | 0-2 | 0-5 | |

## Kent County League Premier Division

| | | |
|---|---|---|
| BEXLEY | STC Sports Ground, Ivor Grove, New Eltham, London SE9 2AJ | 0208 858 2057 |
| BORDEN VILLAGE | Borden Playstool, Wises Lane, Borden, Sittingbourne Kent ME9 8LP | 07921 912 209 |
| ERITH '147 SPORTS | Oxford Road, Sidcup, Kent DA14 6LW | 0208 300 2987 |
| FARNBOROUGH OBG | Farnborough Sports Club, Farrow Field, Off High Street, Farnborough, Kent BR6 7BA | 01689 862 949 |
| FAVERSHAM STRIKE FORCE | Sittingbourne Community College, (3G Pitch), Swanstree Avenue, Kent ME10 4NL | 01795 425 825 |
| FLEETDOWN UNITED | Heath Lane Open Space, Heath Lane (Lower), Dartford DA1 2QH | 01322 273 848 |
| GREENWAYS | Old Southfields, Nursery Mews, Off Cedar Avenue, Gravesend DA12 5JT | 07805 406 003 |
| GURU NANAK | Guru Nanak Sports Ground, Khalsa Avenue (Off Trinity Road), Gravesend DA12 1LU | 07956 514 264 |
| HILDENBOROUGH ATHLETIC | Racecourse Sports Ground, The Slade, Tonbridge TN9 1DS (SatNav: TN9 1HR) | 07595 386 657 |
| KENNINGTON | The Julie Rose Stadium, Willesborough Road, Kennington, Ashford, Kent TN24 9QX | 01233 613 131 |
| LYDD TOWN RESERVES | The Lindsey Field, Dengemarsh Road, Lydd, Kent TN29 9JH | 01797 321 904 |
| METROGAS | Marathon Playing Fields, Forty Foot Way, Avery Hill Road, New Eltham SE9 2EX | 020 8859 1579 |
| PECKHAM TOWN | Pynners Close, Dulwich Common, London SE21 7HA | |
| PUNJAB UNITED | Elite Venue, Hawkins Avenue, Dunkirk Close, Gravesend, Kent DA12 5ND | 01474 323 817 |
| STANSFELD O & B CLUB | Marathon Playing Fields, Forty Foot Way, Avery Hill Road, New Eltham SE9 2EX | 020 8859 1579 |
| STAPLEHURST & MONARCHS UTD | Jubilee Sports Ground, Headcorn Road, Staplehurst TN12 0DS | 01580 892 292 |

**CLUBS RENAMED FOR 2016/17:** K Sports Reserves formerly APM Contrast Reserves; AFC Morzinga formerly Oaks & Junior Reds Seniors; Sporting Club Thamesmead Reserves formerly Seven Acre & Sidcup Reserves

**LUB MOVEMENTS**
**remier Division**
**ut:** Snodland Town (P – Southern Counties East Div 1);
alstead United (R); Tudor Sports (R)
**:** Punjab United (FA); Lydd Town Reserves (P); Farnborough OBG (P);
eckham Town (P)
**ivision One East**
**ut:** Lydd Town Reserves (P)
**:** Kings Hill (P); Rolvenden (P); South Darenth (P)
**ivision One West**
**ut:** Farnborough OBG (P); Peckham Town (P); Belvedere (R)
**ivision One Wes In:** Halstead United (R); Tudor Sports (R); Lewisham
thletic (P); Club Langley (P); Orpington Reserves (P); Old Roan (P)
**ivision Two East**
**ut:** Kings Hill (P); Rolvenden (P); South Darenth (P)
**:** Willesborough Athletic (P); Cuxton 91 (P): West Farleigh (P); Snodland Town Reserves (P); Aylesford (P)

**Division Two West**
**Out:** Lewisham Athletic (P); Club Langley (P); Orpington Reserves (P); Old Roan (P); Metrogas Reserves (R)
**In:** Belvedere (R); South East Athletic (P); Welling Park (P); Nomads (P); Old Roan Reserves (P)
**Division Three East**
**Out:** Willesborough Athletic (P); Cuxton 91 (P): West Farleigh (P); Snodland Town Reserves (P); Aylesford (P)
**In:** Rochester City; Wateringbury; AEI Sports; Burgess Hodgson; Larkfield & New Hythe Reserves; Willesborough Athletic Reserves; Tonbridge Invicta; Rusthall Reserves
**Division Three West**
**Out:** South East Athletic (P); Welling Park (P); Nomads (P); Old Roan Reserves (P)
**In:** Metrogas Reserves (R); AFC Bexley; Welling Town; HF Sports Paulista; Sydenham Sports; Drummond Athletic

| VISION TWO EAST | P | W | D | L | F | A | GD | Pts |
|---|---|---|---|---|---|---|---|---|
| Kings Hill | 20 | 16 | 1 | 3 | 67 | 26 | 41 | 49 |
| Rolvenden | 20 | 15 | 2 | 3 | 62 | 21 | 41 | 47 |
| South Darenth (-1) | 19 | 13 | 2 | 4 | 52 | 22 | 30 | 40 |
| Larkfield & New Hythe Wanderers | 20 | 11 | 3 | 6 | 42 | 25 | 17 | 36 |
| Deal Town Reserves | 20 | 10 | 4 | 6 | 47 | 27 | 20 | 34 |
| Sheppey United Res. | 20 | 9 | 3 | 8 | 29 | 28 | 1 | 30 |
| New Romney Res. (-3) | 19 | 7 | 1 | 11 | 40 | 48 | -8 | 19 |
| Ashford United Res. | 20 | 6 | 0 | 14 | 41 | 59 | -18 | 18 |
| East Kent College Res. (-1) | 20 | 4 | 3 | 13 | 29 | 56 | -27 | 14 |
| Sittingbourne Community (-1) | 20 | 5 | 0 | 15 | 33 | 82 | -49 | 14 |
| Kennington Reserves | 20 | 3 | 1 | 16 | 35 | 83 | -48 | 10 |

| | DIVISION TWO WEST | P | W | D | L | F | A | GD | Pts |
|---|---|---|---|---|---|---|---|---|---|
| 1 | Lewisham Athletic | 21 | 16 | 5 | 0 | 74 | 23 | 51 | 53 |
| 2 | Club Langley (+3) | 22 | 14 | 1 | 7 | 45 | 29 | 16 | 46 |
| 3 | Orpington Reserves | 22 | 12 | 6 | 4 | 42 | 29 | 13 | 42 |
| 4 | Old Roan (-3) | 21 | 10 | 7 | 4 | 48 | 38 | 10 | 34 |
| 5 | Fleetdown United Res. | 22 | 10 | 3 | 9 | 41 | 39 | 2 | 33 |
| 6 | Johnson & Phillips | 22 | 9 | 3 | 10 | 48 | 44 | 4 | 30 |
| 7 | Crayford Arrows | 20 | 7 | 3 | 10 | 42 | 46 | -4 | 24 |
| 8 | Dulwich Village | 22 | 5 | 6 | 11 | 33 | 46 | -13 | 21 |
| 9 | FC Elmstead Reserves | 22 | 5 | 6 | 11 | 35 | 58 | -23 | 20 |
| 10 | Metrogas Reserves (-6) | 20 | 8 | 1 | 11 | 41 | 59 | -18 | 19 |
| 11 | Old Bromleians | 20 | 5 | 3 | 12 | 36 | 51 | -15 | 18 |
| 12 | Long Lane Reserves | 22 | 2 | 6 | 14 | 30 | 53 | -23 | 12 |

### LES LECKIE CUP

INAL — HOLDERS: LYDD TOWN RESERVES
olvenden v Larkfield & New Hythe Wanderers 2-3

### BARRY BUNDOCK WEST KENT SHIELD

FINAL — HOLDERS: LEWISHAM ATHLETIC
Fleetdown United Res. v Lewisham Athletic 1-2

| VISION THREE EAST | P | W | D | L | F | A | GD | Pts |
|---|---|---|---|---|---|---|---|---|
| Willesborough Athletic | 20 | 14 | 2 | 4 | 83 | 24 | 59 | 44 |
| Cuxton 91 | 20 | 12 | 4 | 4 | 100 | 32 | 68 | 40 |
| West Farleigh | 20 | 10 | 5 | 5 | 56 | 34 | 22 | 35 |
| Snodland Town Res. (-1) | 20 | 10 | 4 | 6 | 43 | 43 | 0 | 33 |
| Yalding & Laddingford | 20 | 9 | 5 | 6 | 50 | 40 | 10 | 32 |
| Aylesford (-1) | 20 | 10 | 3 | 7 | 47 | 38 | 9 | 32 |
| Little Sharsted | 20 | 9 | 1 | 10 | 65 | 75 | -10 | 28 |
| University of Kent (-1) | 20 | 7 | 6 | 7 | 63 | 49 | 14 | 26 |
| Staplehurst Monarchs United Res. | 20 | 5 | 5 | 10 | 32 | 48 | -16 | 20 |
| Guru Nanak Reserves | 20 | 4 | 2 | 14 | 44 | 74 | -30 | 14 |
| Tankerton (-3) | 20 | 1 | 1 | 18 | 15 | 141 | -126 | 1 |

| | DIVISION THREE WEST | P | W | D | L | F | A | GD | PTS |
|---|---|---|---|---|---|---|---|---|---|
| 1 | South East Athletic | 24 | 18 | 5 | 1 | 66 | 23 | 43 | 59 |
| 2 | Welling Park | 24 | 16 | 3 | 5 | 80 | 37 | 43 | 51 |
| 3 | Nomads | 24 | 15 | 5 | 4 | 71 | 24 | 47 | 50 |
| 4 | Old Roan Reserves (-1) | 24 | 16 | 2 | 6 | 66 | 28 | 38 | 49 |
| 5 | Parkwood Rangers | 24 | 12 | 2 | 10 | 57 | 57 | 0 | 38 |
| 6 | Bexley Reserves | 24 | 11 | 3 | 10 | 57 | 48 | 9 | 36 |
| 7 | Peckham Town Reserves | 24 | 9 | 6 | 9 | 43 | 45 | -2 | 33 |
| 8 | Meridian VP Reserves | 24 | 8 | 6 | 10 | 63 | 62 | 1 | 30 |
| 9 | Bridon Ropes Reserves | 24 | 7 | 5 | 12 | 54 | 65 | -11 | 26 |
| 10 | Hildenborough Athletic Res. (-1) | 24 | 7 | 4 | 13 | 49 | 69 | -20 | 24 |
| 11 | Seven Acre & Sidcup Res. | 24 | 4 | 4 | 16 | 39 | 101 | -62 | 16 |
| 12 | Farnborough OB Guild Res. (-1) | 24 | 4 | 4 | 16 | 36 | 74 | -38 | 15 |
| 13 | Halls AFC Reserves | 24 | 3 | 3 | 18 | 29 | 77 | -48 | 12 |

# SEASON 2015-2016

Faversham Strike Force Seniors FC
Premier Division Champions

Kennington FC
Premier Division Runners-Up

Farnborough Old Boys Guild FC
Division One West Champions

Willesborough Athletic FC
Division Three East Champions

Willesborough Athletic FC
Division Three West Champions

East Kent College FC
'Bill Manklow' Inter-Regional Challenge Cup Winners

Lewisham Athletic FC
'Barry Bundock' West Kent Challenge Shield Winners

Daniel Hanshaw - Cuxton 91 FC
Leading Goal Scorer

Tony Woods - Referee of the Year

Larkfield & New Hythe Wanderers FC
Eastern Section 'Les Leckie' Cup Winners

Daniel Conneally - South East Athletic FC
Aford Awards Manager of the Year

Daniel Hollis - South East Athletic FC
Secretary of the Year

LEAGUE CONTACT
Philip Smith - Marketing & Communications Officer
Telephone: 07939 046182
Email: philip.smith@kentcountyfootballleague.co.uk

# LEICESTERSHIRE SENIOR LEAGUE

**Sponsored by:** Everards Brewery
**Founded:** 1919
**Recent Champions:**
**2013:** Rothley Imperial
**2014:** Allexton & New Parks
**2015:** Sileby Town

| PREMIER DIVISION | P | W | D | L | F | A | GD | Pts |
|---|---|---|---|---|---|---|---|---|
| 1 Birstall United | 32 | 26 | 2 | 4 | 93 | 26 | 67 | 80 |
| 2 Sileby Town | 32 | 24 | 6 | 2 | 106 | 31 | 75 | 78 |
| 3 Melton Mowbray (-3) | 32 | 23 | 4 | 5 | 114 | 43 | 71 | 70 |
| 4 Blaby & Whetstone Athletic Res. | 31 | 21 | 2 | 8 | 84 | 41 | 43 | 65 |
| 5 Ingles | 32 | 20 | 4 | 8 | 81 | 39 | 42 | 64 |
| 6 Barlestone St Giles | 31 | 14 | 4 | 13 | 60 | 54 | 6 | 46 |
| 7 Saffron Dynamo (-3) | 31 | 13 | 8 | 10 | 58 | 61 | -3 | 44 |
| 8 GNG (-3) | 32 | 13 | 7 | 12 | 64 | 73 | -9 | 43 |
| 9 Earl Shilton Albion | 31 | 13 | 3 | 15 | 55 | 75 | -20 | 42 |
| 10 Cottesmore Amateurs | 32 | 10 | 8 | 14 | 54 | 64 | -10 | 38 |
| 11 Ashby Ivanhoe Reserves | 32 | 9 | 2 | 21 | 52 | 79 | -27 | 29 |
| 12 Kirby Muxloe Res. (-3) | 32 | 9 | 5 | 18 | 45 | 90 | -45 | 29 |
| 13 Allexton & New Parks (-3) | 32 | 9 | 4 | 19 | 62 | 101 | -39 | 28 |
| 14 Friar Lane & Epworth (-3) | 32 | 8 | 6 | 18 | 68 | 83 | -15 | 27 |
| 15 Lutterworth Athletic Res.(-4) | 32 | 9 | 4 | 19 | 59 | 92 | -33 | 27 |
| 16 Rothley Imperial (-3) | 28 | 7 | 2 | 19 | 50 | 77 | -27 | 20 |
| 17 Desford | 32 | 4 | 1 | 27 | 38 | 114 | -76 | 13 |

Caterpillar withdrew - record expunged.
Dunton & Broughton Rangers - withdrew - record expunged.

| CHAMPIONSHIP DIV. ONE | P | W | D | L | F | A | GD | Pts |
|---|---|---|---|---|---|---|---|---|
| 1 Shelthorpe Dynamo | 30 | 24 | 4 | 2 | 113 | 35 | 78 | 76 |
| 2 NKF Burbage | 30 | 23 | 2 | 5 | 101 | 31 | 70 | 71 |
| 3 Lutterworth Town | 30 | 20 | 1 | 9 | 107 | 35 | 72 | 61 |
| 4 Coalville Town Dev. (-3) | 30 | 19 | 3 | 8 | 64 | 43 | 21 | 57 |
| 5 Ibstock United | 30 | 18 | 2 | 10 | 84 | 52 | 32 | 56 |
| 6 Highfield Rangers | 30 | 16 | 1 | 13 | 86 | 62 | 24 | 49 |
| 7 Quorn Reserves | 30 | 15 | 1 | 14 | 77 | 65 | 12 | 46 |
| 8 Aylestone Park OB Res. | 30 | 13 | 4 | 13 | 78 | 62 | 16 | 43 |
| 9 Barrow Town Res. (-6) | 30 | 14 | 3 | 13 | 59 | 58 | 1 | 39 |
| 10 Borrowash Victoria Res. (-3) | 30 | 13 | 3 | 14 | 69 | 77 | -8 | 39 |
| 11 FC Khalsa GTB (-3) | 30 | 11 | 2 | 17 | 43 | 92 | -49 | 32 |
| 12 Hathern (-6) | 30 | 11 | 3 | 16 | 71 | 77 | -6 | 30 |
| 13 Ratby Sports | 30 | 7 | 5 | 18 | 50 | 94 | -44 | 26 |
| 14 Anstey Town | 30 | 7 | 4 | 19 | 52 | 93 | -41 | 25 |
| 15 Leicester Road Res. (-6) | 30 | 5 | 3 | 22 | 47 | 85 | -38 | 12 |
| 16 Holwell Sports Res. (-21) | 30 | 2 | 3 | 25 | 28 | 168 | -140 | -12 |

| DIVISION ONE | P | W | D | L | F | A | GD | Pts |
|---|---|---|---|---|---|---|---|---|
| 1 Friar Lane & Epworth Res. | 22 | 19 | 1 | 2 | 99 | 26 | 73 | 58 |
| 2 Ingles Reserves | 22 | 14 | 3 | 5 | 54 | 22 | 32 | 45 |
| 3 Earl Shilton Albion Res. | 22 | 12 | 4 | 6 | 48 | 37 | 11 | 40 |
| 4 Sileby Town Reserves | 21 | 11 | 4 | 6 | 62 | 37 | 25 | 37 |
| 5 Birstall United Reserves | 21 | 10 | 4 | 7 | 40 | 36 | 4 | 34 |
| 6 Lutterworth Town Res. | 19 | 9 | 4 | 6 | 58 | 31 | 27 | 31 |
| 7 Hathern Reserves | 21 | 7 | 4 | 10 | 42 | 52 | -10 | 25 |
| 8 GNG Reserves | 22 | 6 | 5 | 11 | 43 | 61 | -18 | 23 |
| 9 Desford Reserves | 22 | 5 | 5 | 12 | 41 | 63 | -22 | 20 |
| 10 Melton Mowbray Res. | 21 | 5 | 5 | 11 | 41 | 72 | -31 | 20 |
| 11 Barlestone St Giles Res. (-4) | 21 | 4 | 4 | 13 | 31 | 76 | -45 | 12 |
| 12 Cottesmore Amateurs Res. | 22 | 2 | 5 | 15 | 22 | 68 | -46 | 11 |

## BEACON BITTER CUP

**HOLDERS:** FRIAR LANE & EPWORTH

**PRELIMINARY ROUND**

| | | | |
|---|---|---|---|
| Lutterworth Athletic Reserves | v | Barlestone St Giles | 2-2, 1-3p |
| Ingles | v | Dunton & Broughton Ranger | HW |
| Ashby Ivanhoe Reserves | v | Kirby Muxloe Reserves | 3-0 |
| St Andrews Reserves | v | Desford | AW |
| Coalville Town Dev. | v | Oadby Town Reserves | 4-2 |
| Quorn Reserves | v | Borrowash Victoria Reserves | 2-3 |

**ROUND 1**

| | | | |
|---|---|---|---|
| Birstall United | v | Barlestone St Giles | 4-0 |
| Saffron Dynamo | v | Ingles | 1-9 |
| Melton Mowbray | v | GNG | 5-1 |
| Friar Lane & Epworth | v | Cottesmore Amateurs | 1-0 |
| Blaby & Whetstone Athletic | v | Ashby Ivanhoe Reserves | 3-2 |
| Rothley Imperial | v | Desford | 2-1 |
| FC Khalsa GTB | v | Barrow Town Reserves | 1-2 |
| Asfordby Amateurs | v | Holwell Sports Reserves | AW |
| Caterpillar | v | Earl Shilton Albion | AW |
| Sileby Town | v | Allexton & New Parks | 3-0 |
| Shelthorpe Dynamo | v | Ibstock United | 0-2 |
| Leicester Road Reserves | v | Aylestone Park OB Reserves | 3-0 |
| NKF Burbage | v | Ratby Sports | 4-0 |
| Lutterworth Town | v | Highfield Rangers | 6-0 |
| Anstey Town | v | Coalville Town Dev. | 2-3 |
| Borrowash Victoria Reserves | v | Hathern | 1-1, 5-4p |

**ROUND 2**

| | | | |
|---|---|---|---|
| Birstall United | v | Ingles | 2-0 |
| Melton Mowbray | v | Friar Lane & Epworth | 0-4 |
| Blaby & Whetstone Athletic | v | Rothley Imperial | 3-1 |
| Barrow Town Reserves | v | Holwell Sports Reserves | HW |
| Earl Shilton Albion | v | Sileby Town | 3-2 |
| Ibstock United | v | Leicester Road Reserves | 3-2 |
| NKF Burbage | v | Lutterworth Town | 2-4 |
| Coalville Town Dev. | v | Borrowash Victoria Reserves | 4-1 |

**QUARTER FINALS**

| | | | |
|---|---|---|---|
| Birstall United | v | Friar Lane & Epworth | 9-0 |
| Blaby & Whetstone Athletic | v | Barrow Town Reserves | 1-1, 4-2p |
| Earl Shilton Albion | v | Ibstock United | 2-3 |
| Lutterworth Town | v | Coalville Town Dev. | 3-1 |

**SEMI FINALS**

| | | | |
|---|---|---|---|
| Birstall United | v | Blaby & Whetstone Athletic | 1-3 |
| Ibstock United | v | Lutterworth Town | 3-1 |

**FINAL**

| | | | |
|---|---|---|---|
| Blaby & Whetstone Athletic | v | Ibstock United | 2-3 |

## PRESIDENT'S TROPHY

**HOLDERS:** AYLESTONE PARK OB RESERVES

**FINAL**

| | | | |
|---|---|---|---|
| Lutterworth Town Reserves | v | Friar Lane & Epworth Reserves | 1-2 |

| | PREMIER DIVISION | 1 | 2 | 3 | 4 | 5 | 6 | 7 | 8 | 9 | 10 | 11 | 12 | 13 | 14 | 15 | 16 | 17 |
|---|---|---|---|---|---|---|---|---|---|---|---|---|---|---|---|---|---|---|
| 1 | Allexton & New Parks | | 1-4 | 2-3 | 0-3 | 2-3 | 4-2 | 3-1 | 2-2 | 1-8 | 3-7 | 1-3 | 1-2 | 4-6 | 0-3 | 3-1 | 3-1 | 1-2 |
| 2 | Ashby Ivanhoe Reserves | 1-4 | | 3-2 | 2-3 | 2-1 | 3-1 | 0-3 | 3-2 | 0-3 | 1-1 | 0-3 | 1-2 | 0-1 | 3-6 | 6-2 | 3-4 | 0-1 |
| 3 | Barlestone St Giles | 0-6 | 2-1 | | 0-4 | 0-2 | 3-1 | 1-0 | 2-1 | 7-0 | 2-1 | 1-2 | 0-3 | 4-0 | 2-3 | - | 2-2 | 0-1 |
| 4 | Birstall United | 8-1 | 4-0 | 1-0 | | 1-0 | 3-1 | 2-1 | 5-0 | 4-0 | 2-0 | 1-0 | 4-0 | 5-1 | 2-3 | 3-2 | 0-1 | 1-1 |
| 5 | Blaby & Whetstone Athletic Reserves | 5-0 | 1-4 | 5-2 | 0-1 | | 4-0 | 5-2 | 3-0 | 3-2 | 6-2 | 4-0 | 1-0 | 1-0 | 0-5 | 9-2 | 1-3 | 2-1 |
| 6 | Cottesmore Amateurs | 3-0 | 6-2 | 1-1 | 2-2 | 0-2 | | 4-0 | 2-1 | 2-2 | 0-1 | 2-4 | 1-1 | 1-1 | 3-3 | 2-1 | 2-2 | 0-2 |
| 7 | Desford | 2-3 | 3-1 | 1-1 | 1-5 | 2-7 | 0-3 | | 1-2 | 1-3 | 0-6 | 1-3 | 1-3 | 4-0 | 0-5 | 1-4 | 2-1 | 1-3 |
| 8 | Earl Shilton Albion | 4-1 | 0-0 | 1-5 | 1-0 | 2-1 | 4-0 | 3-2 | | 1-5 | 2-3 | 1-5 | 4-0 | 1-0 | 0-4 | - | 1-4 | 3-5 |
| 9 | Friar Lane & Epworth | 2-2 | 2-1 | 1-4 | 1-2 | 1-2 | 2-0 | 9-0 | 2-3 | | 1-2 | 1-2 | 2-2 | 5-4 | 2-2 | 1-1 | 0-5 | 2-2 |
| 10 | GNG | 2-2 | 2-1 | 2-1 | 1-6 | 4-3 | 1-1 | 1-0 | 0-1 | 4-2 | | 1-1 | 5-2 | 2-2 | 1-4 | 1-1 | 2-4 | 0-5 |
| 11 | Ingles | 5-0 | 2-1 | 3-1 | 2-5 | 1-1 | 3-1 | 7-1 | 3-1 | 2-1 | 4-1 | | 1-2 | 5-0 | 1-2 | 5-2 | 2-2 | 0-0 |
| 12 | Kirby Muxloe Reserves | 2-1 | 3-5 | 0-7 | 0-2 | 2-2 | 0-4 | 2-1 | 1-4 | 2-1 | 2-4 | 0-6 | | 1-3 | 1-4 | 5-2 | 1-1 | 2-3 |
| 13 | Lutterworth Athletic Reserves | 1-4 | 1-2 | 1-3 | 1-4 | 0-4 | 0-1 | 4-1 | 1-3 | 6-2 | 3-3 | 1-2 | 2-1 | | 4-4 | 2-5 | 4-0 | 3-8 |
| 14 | Melton Mowbray | 5-2 | 3-0 | 5-1 | 0-2 | 0-1 | 5-1 | 8-2 | 6-1 | 7-1 | 4-0 | 2-1 | 4-0 | 4-1 | | 3-0 | 7-0 | 0-3 |
| 15 | Rothley Imperial | 2-3 | 4-1 | 0-1 | 0-1 | - | 1-3 | 4-2 | 1-3 | 4-3 | 1-2 | 0-3 | 2-1 | 0-4 | 5-1 | | - | 1-2 |
| 16 | Saffron Dynamo | 1-1 | 1-0 | 0-1 | 0-5 | 0-4 | 0-3 | 5-1 | 3-3 | 2-0 | 3-0 | 1-0 | 1-1 | 1-2 | 3-2 | 3-2 | | 2-4 |
| 17 | Sileby Town | 7-1 | 5-1 | 1-1 | 4-2 | 0-1 | 6-1 | 6-0 | 5-0 | 3-1 | 3-2 | 1-0 | 10-1 | 7-0 | 0-0 | 3-0 | 2-2 | |

## Leicestershire Senior League Premier Division

| | | |
|---|---|---|
| **ALLEXTON & NEW PARKS** | New College, Glenfield Road, Leicester LE3 6DN | 0116 287 1759 |
| **ASHBY IVANHOE RESERVES** | The NFU Sports Ground, Lower Packington Rd, Ashby de la Zouch, LE65 1TS | 01530 413 140 |
| **BARDON HILL** | Bardon Close, Coalville, Leicester LE67 4BS | 01530 815 569 |
| **BARLESTONE ST GILES** | Barton Road, Barlestone, Nuneaton CV13 0EP | 01455 291 392 |
| **BLABY & WHETSTONE ATH. RES.** | Blaby & Whetstone Boys Club, Warwick Road, Whetstone, Leicestershire LE8 6LW | 01162 286 852 |
| **COALVILLE TOWN DEV.** | Owen Street Sports Ground, Owen St, Coalville LE67 3DA | 01530 833 365 |
| **COTTESMORE AMATEURS** | Rogues Park, Main Street, Cottesmore, Oakham LE15 4DH | 07764 193 475 |
| **EARL SHILTON ALBION** | Stoneycroft Park, New Street, Earl Shilton LE9 7FR | 01455 844 277 |
| **FRIAR LANE & EPWORTH** | Whittier Road, Leicester. LE2 6FT | 0116 283 3629 |
| **GNG** | Riverside Football Ground, Braunstone Lane East, Leicester LE3 2FW | 07968 829 858 |
| **INGLES** | The Dovecote, Butthole Lane, Shepshed, Leicestershire. LE12 9BN | 01509 650 992 |
| **KIRBY MUXLOE SC RESERVES** | Ratby Lane, Kirby Muxloe, Leicester LE9 9AQ | 0116 239 2301 |
| **LUTTERWORTH TOWN** | Dunley Way, Lutterworth, Leicestershire, LE17 4NP | 07855 836 489 |
| **SAFFRON DYNAMO** | Cambridge Road, Whetstone LE8 3LG | 07957 151 630 |
| **SHELTHORPE DYNAMO** | Nanpantan Sports Ground Watermead Lane, Loughborough, Leics. LE11 3YE | 07582 293 807 |
| **SILEBY TOWN** | Sileby Sports Club, 3 Southfield Avenue, Sileby, Leicestershire LE12 7WL | 07708 231 563 |

**CLUB MOVEMENTS**

**Premier Division**

In: Bardon Hill (R - Midland Football League), Coalville Town Development (P), Lutterworth Town (P), Shelthorpe Dynamo (P),

**Out:** Birstall United (P - East Midlands County), Desford (R), Lutterworth Athletic Reserves (W),

Melton Mowbray (P - United Counties League / NC to Melton Town), Rothley Imperial (W),

**Championahip Division One**

In: Birstall United Reserves (P), County Hall (Leicester & District), Desford (R), Loughborough FC (North Leicestershire)

**Out:** Coalville Town Development (P), Lutterworth Town (P), NKF Burbage, Shelthorpe Dynamo (P).

**Division One**

In: Ibstock United Reserves. Loughborough FC Reserves (North Leicestershire), Melton Town Reserves (NC from Melton Mowbray Reserves).

**Out:** Birstall United (P), Hathern Reserves, Melton Mowbray Reserves (NC to Melton Town Reserves).

# LIVERPOOL COUNTY PREMIER LEAGUE

**Sponsored by:** No sponsor
**Founded:** 2006
**Recent Champions:**
**2013:** West Everton Xaviers
**2014:** Aigburth Peoples Hall
**2015:** Aigburth Peoples Hall

| PREMIER DIVISION | | P | W | D | L | F | A | GD | Pts |
|---|---|---|---|---|---|---|---|---|---|
| 1 | Aigburth Peoples Hall | 26 | 19 | 3 | 4 | 84 | 37 | 47 | 60 |
| 2 | Waterloo Dock | 26 | 19 | 1 | 6 | 94 | 42 | 52 | 58 |
| 3 | Lower Breck | 26 | 14 | 7 | 5 | 67 | 36 | 31 | 49 |
| 4 | Warbreck | 26 | 13 | 7 | 6 | 65 | 36 | 29 | 46 |
| 5 | Alder (-3) | 26 | 14 | 5 | 7 | 54 | 38 | 16 | 44 |
| 6 | West Everton Xaviers | 26 | 13 | 5 | 8 | 68 | 56 | 12 | 44 |
| 7 | Page Celtic | 26 | 13 | 3 | 10 | 84 | 66 | 18 | 42 |
| 8 | Waterloo Grammar School O.B. (+3) | 26 | 11 | 3 | 12 | 60 | 52 | 8 | 39 |
| 9 | East Villa | 26 | 11 | 3 | 12 | 51 | 58 | -7 | 36 |
| 10 | Old Xaverians | 26 | 9 | 7 | 10 | 58 | 57 | 1 | 34 |
| 11 | Byrom | 26 | 9 | 7 | 10 | 58 | 72 | -14 | 34 |
| 12 | South Sefton Borough (+3) | 26 | 5 | 3 | 18 | 37 | 71 | -34 | 21 |
| 13 | Stoneycroft | 26 | 1 | 3 | 22 | 21 | 94 | -73 | 6 |
| 14 | ROMA | 26 | 1 | 3 | 22 | 16 | 102 | -86 | 6 |

**In:** Alumni (P), Walton Community (P), MSB Woolton.

## ZINGARI CUP

**HOLDERS:** EAST VILLA

**ROUND 1**

| | | | |
|---|---|---|---|
| Byrom | v | Old Xaverians | 2-6 |
| Alder | v | Lower Breck | 3-2 |
| Waterloo Dock | v | Page Celtic | 1-2 |
| Waterloo Grammar School OB | v | ROMA | 10-1 |
| Warbreck | v | Stoneycroft | HW |
| West Everton Xaviers | v | East Villa | HW |

**QUARTER FINALS**

| | | | |
|---|---|---|---|
| Old Xaverians | v | Alder | 4-3 |
| Waterloo Grammar School OB | v | Page Celtic | 1-4 |
| Aigburth Peoples Hall | v | West Everton Xaviers | 3-0 |
| South Sefton Borough | v | Warbreck | 0-3 |

**SEMI FINALS**

| | | | |
|---|---|---|---|
| Warbreck | v | Aigburth Peoples Hall | 1-3 |
| Old Xaverians | v | Page Celtic | 0-6 |

**FINAL**

| | | | |
|---|---|---|---|
| Aigburth Peoples Hall | v | Page Celtic | 6-1 |

| DIVISION ONE | | P | W | D | L | F | A | GD | Pts |
|---|---|---|---|---|---|---|---|---|---|
| 1 | Old Xaverians Reserves | 20 | 14 | 3 | 3 | 47 | 19 | 28 | 45 |
| 2 | Alumni | 20 | 14 | 1 | 5 | 64 | 30 | 34 | 43 |
| 3 | Walton Community | 20 | 12 | 3 | 5 | 50 | 32 | 18 | 39 |
| 4 | MSB Woolton | 20 | 11 | 3 | 6 | 47 | 38 | 9 | 36 |
| 5 | Salisbury Athletic | 20 | 11 | 2 | 7 | 46 | 40 | 6 | 35 |
| 6 | Copperas Hill | 20 | 8 | 6 | 6 | 49 | 41 | 8 | 30 |
| 7 | Leyfield | 20 | 8 | 5 | 7 | 50 | 28 | 22 | 29 |
| 8 | BRNESC (+3) | 20 | 3 | 4 | 13 | 34 | 58 | -24 | 16 |
| 9 | St Michaels (-1) | 20 | 4 | 3 | 13 | 36 | 49 | -13 | 14 |
| 10 | Eli Lilly (-3) | 20 | 5 | 2 | 13 | 38 | 73 | -35 | 14 |
| 11 | Edge Hill Boys Club O.B. (+2) | 20 | 3 | 2 | 15 | 23 | 76 | -53 | 13 |

| DIVISION TWO | | P | W | D | L | F | A | GD | Pts |
|---|---|---|---|---|---|---|---|---|---|
| 1 | BRNESC Reserves | 24 | 17 | 5 | 2 | 93 | 39 | 54 | 56 |
| 2 | Alder Reserves | 24 | 18 | 2 | 4 | 64 | 35 | 29 | 56 |
| 3 | Warbreck Reserves | 24 | 16 | 4 | 4 | 62 | 39 | 23 | 52 |
| 4 | Litherland REMYCA Res. | 24 | 14 | 2 | 8 | 67 | 57 | 10 | 44 |
| 5 | Wood Street Res. (+3) | 24 | 8 | 1 | 15 | 31 | 77 | -46 | 28 |
| 6 | Liver Academy Res. (-1) | 24 | 7 | 3 | 14 | 60 | 32 | 28 | 23 |
| 7 | Aintree Villa | 24 | 6 | 3 | 15 | 51 | 91 | -40 | 21 |
| 8 | Liverpool Hibernia (-1) | 24 | 4 | 3 | 17 | 38 | 88 | -50 | 14 |
| 9 | Red Rum (-6) | 24 | 5 | 3 | 16 | 40 | 48 | -8 | 12 |

| PREMIER DIVISION | | 1 | 2 | 3 | 4 | 5 | 6 | 7 | 8 | 9 | 10 | 11 | 12 | 13 | 1 |
|---|---|---|---|---|---|---|---|---|---|---|---|---|---|---|---|
| 1 | Aigburth Peoples Hall | | 2-2 | 9-5 | 2-1 | 2-2 | 4-0 | 1-0 | 6-0 | 4-0 | HW | 2-1 | 0-2 | 2-0 | 2- |
| 2 | Alder | 0-2 | | 6-1 | 7-1 | 4-1 | 3-2 | 1-6 | 4-1 | 3-1 | 1-1 | 0-2 | 2-1 | 3-2 | 4- |
| 3 | Byrom | 3-2 | 0-0 | | 2-2 | 1-0 | 4-5 | 4-3 | 3-0 | 3-3 | 2-1 | 2-2 | 0-4 | 2-1 | 0- |
| 4 | East Villa | 2-3 | 1-2 | 7-3 | | 1-2 | 2-0 | 3-3 | 3-0 | 3-2 | 1-0 | 1-5 | 0-3 | 2-1 | 4- |
| 5 | Lower Breck | 2-2 | 3-0 | 1-2 | 4-1 | | 0-0 | 3-2 | 4-0 | 4-1 | 4-0 | 2-2 | 6-2 | 4-0 | 0- |
| 6 | Old Xaverians | 1-3 | 2-0 | 5-4 | 0-2 | 2-2 | | 2-0 | 1-1 | 9-1 | 3-3 | 1-1 | 2-3 | 3-2 | 4- |
| 7 | Page Celtic | 2-5 | 1-4 | 5-5 | 5-2 | 2-2 | 3-0 | | 4-1 | 3-1 | 4-1 | 3-0 | 4-1 | 2-5 | 7- |
| 8 | ROMA | 0-6 | 0-1 | 0-2 | 1-1 | 2-4 | 0-5 | 1-7 | | 0-2 | 2-0 | 0-11 | 1-10 | 0-2 | 1- |
| 9 | South Sefton Borough | 1-3 | 0-1 | 1-1 | 0-2 | 1-5 | 1-1 | 1-5 | 6-2 | | 4-1 | 1-2 | 2-1 | 0-2 | 2- |
| 10 | Stoneycroft | 2-8 | 1-3 | 1-4 | 0-3 | 1-7 | 0-4 | 1-4 | 0-0 | 1-3 | | 1-9 | 0-2 | 1-2 | 0- |
| 11 | Warbreck | 2-0 | 0-0 | HW | 5-1 | 2-2 | 2-1 | 2-4 | 3-2 | 3-2 | 4-1 | | 1-4 | 2-2 | 1- |
| 12 | Waterloo Dock | 3-1 | 2-1 | 3-1 | 3-1 | 1-3 | 6-3 | 6-2 | 7-0 | 5-0 | 9-1 | 1-5 | | 5-1 | 3- |
| 13 | Waterloo Grammar School Old Boys | 3-5 | 3-0 | 3-3 | 0-3 | 4-0 | 8-0 | 3-1 | 2-1 | 5-2 | 2-3 | 1-0 | 1-2 | | 2- |
| 14 | West Everton Xaviers | 2-8 | 2-2 | 3-1 | 2-1 | 3-2 | 2-2 | 5-2 | 5-0 | 2-1 | 3-0 | 1-1 | 1-5 | 4-3 | |

| DIVISION THREE | P | W | D | L | F | A | GD | Pts |
|---|---|---|---|---|---|---|---|---|
| 1 Custys | 18 | 13 | 0 | 5 | 65 | 39 | 26 | 39 |
| 2 Netherley Wood Lane Legion | 18 | 11 | 2 | 5 | 68 | 34 | 34 | 35 |
| 3 Jacobs FC (-3) | 18 | 11 | 2 | 5 | 55 | 39 | 16 | 32 |
| 4 The Parky (+3) | 18 | 9 | 1 | 8 | 57 | 42 | 15 | 31 |
| 5 Garston Derby | 18 | 9 | 1 | 8 | 49 | 47 | 2 | 28 |
| 6 Lower Breck Reserves | 18 | 5 | 2 | 11 | 49 | 79 | -30 | 17 |
| 7 Botanic | 18 | 1 | 0 | 17 | 25 | 88 | -63 | 3 |

| Youth Division (U18) | P | W | D | L | F | A | GD | Pts |
|---|---|---|---|---|---|---|---|---|
| 1 Waterloo Dock U18 | 22 | 19 | 2 | 1 | 124 | 12 | 112 | 59 |
| 2 Bootle Bucks | 22 | 18 | 0 | 4 | 76 | 22 | 54 | 54 |
| 3 MSB Woolton Okell | 22 | 16 | 3 | 3 | 87 | 25 | 62 | 51 |
| 4 Finn Harps | 22 | 13 | 3 | 6 | 57 | 38 | 19 | 42 |
| 5 Pex Hill | 22 | 12 | 2 | 8 | 65 | 31 | 34 | 38 |
| 6 Mags JFL | 22 | 10 | 3 | 9 | 51 | 35 | 16 | 33 |
| 7 Westpool | 22 | 10 | 3 | 9 | 62 | 61 | 1 | 33 |
| 8 Liverton (+3) | 22 | 6 | 1 | 15 | 48 | 73 | -25 | 22 |
| 9 Commitar | 22 | 6 | 3 | 13 | 38 | 73 | -35 | 21 |
| 10 Mersey Batteries (-3) | 22 | 5 | 5 | 12 | 30 | 57 | -27 | 17 |
| 11 MSB Woolton U18 | 22 | 3 | 1 | 18 | 37 | 93 | -56 | 10 |
| 12 Sweeps Tropicana | 22 | 1 | 0 | 21 | 15 | 170 | -155 | 3 |

## GEORGE MAHON CUP

**HOLDERS:** PAGE CELTIC

**PRELIMINARY ROUND**

| | | | |
|---|---|---|---|
| Botanic | v | Aintree Villa | 3-3, 8-7p |
| Liver Academy Reserves | v | Litherland REMYCA Res. | 5-1 |
| Strand United | v | Liverpool Hibernia | 7-5 |
| Woodstreet | v | Garston Derby | 2-1 |
| The Parky | v | Red Rum | 4-2 |

**ROUND 1**

| | | | |
|---|---|---|---|
| Aigburth Peoples Hall | v | Byrom | 5-0 |
| Custys | v | Copperas Hill | 4-1 |
| Edge Hill Boys Club Old Boys | v | BRNESC | HW |
| Jacobs | v | Salisbury Athletic | 1-4 |
| Leyfield | v | Page Celtic | 3-6 |
| MSB Woolton | v | Eli Lilly | 5-2 |
| ROMA | v | Old Xaverians | 0-3 |
| Stoneycroft | v | The Parky | 2-3 |
| Strand United | v | Liver Academy Reserves | 4-1 |
| Warbreck | v | West Everton Xaviers | 1-2 |
| Waterloo Grammar School OB | v | St Michaels | 1-3 |
| Woodstreet | v | Botanic | 3-0 |
| Alumni | v | East Villa | 3-0 |
| Waterloo Dock | v | Lower Breck | 1-3 |
| South Sefton Borough | v | Walton Community | 4-1 |
| Netherley Wood Lane Legion | v | Alder | 2-3 |

**ROUND 2**

| | | | |
|---|---|---|---|
| Alumni | v | Old Xaverians | AW |
| Custys | v | Aigburth Peoples Hall | 2-6 |
| Alder | v | Edge Hill Boys Club Old Boys | HW |
| The Parky | v | Page Celtic | 1-5 |
| Strand United | v | South Sefton Borough | 1-4 |
| St Michaels | v | Lower Breck | 1-8 |
| Woodstreet | v | West Everton Xaviers | 1-3 |
| MSB Woolton | v | Salisbury Athletic | 0-3 |

**QUARTER FINALS**

| | | | |
|---|---|---|---|
| Alder | v | Aigburth Peoples Hall | 0-2 |
| South Sefton Borough | v | Page Celtic | 2-3 |
| West Everton Xaviers | v | Lower Breck | 3-2 |
| Old Xaverians | v | Salisbury Athletic | 6-3 |

SEMI FINALS

| | | | |
|---|---|---|---|
| Old Xaverians | v | Page Celtic | 3-1 |
| West Everton Xaviers | v | Aigburth Peoples Hall | 4-0 |

**FINAL**

| | | | |
|---|---|---|---|
| Old Xaverians | v | West Everton Xaviers | 0-3 |

## Liverpool County Premier League Premier Division

| | | |
|---|---|---|
| **AIGBURTH PEOPLE'S HALL** | Wavertree Sports Park 3G pitch, Wellington Road L15 4LE | |
| **ALUMNI** | Wavertree Sports Park 3G pitch, Wellington Road L15 4LE | |
| **BYROM** | Archbishop Beck | |
| **EAST VILLA** | Scargreen Park, Scargreen Avenue, Liverpool | |
| **LIVERPOOL NALGO** | Alder Sports Club, Alder Road, Liverpool L12 2BA | 0151 228 5250 |
| **LOWER BRECK** | Lower Breck 3G | |
| **MSB WOOLTON** | Wavertree Sports Park 3G pitch, Wellington Road L15 4LE | |
| **OLD XAVERIANS** | St Francis Xaviers College, Beconsfield Road, Liverpool L25 6EG | 0151 428 2829 |
| **PAGE CELTIC** | Lord Derby Memorial Ground, Seel Road, Huyton, Liverpool L36 6DG | |
| **SOUTH SEFTON BOROUGH** | Mill Dam Field behind the Punch Bowl Pub, Bridges Lane, Sefton L29 7WA | |
| **WALTON COMMUNITY** | Walton Hall Park, Walton Hall Avenue, Liverpool L4 9XP | |
| **WARBRECK** | St John Bosco 3G | |
| **WATERLOO DOCK** | Lower Breck 3G | |
| **WATERLOO GSOB** | Archbishop Beck | |
| **WEST EVERTON XAVERIANS** | William Collins Memorial Ground, Commercial Road, Liverpool, Merseyside L5 7QY | |

# MANCHESTER LEAGUE

**Sponsored by:** FBT Europe
**Founded:** 1893
**Recent Champions:**
**2013:** Hindsford
**2014:** Hindsford
**2015:** Stockport Georgians

| PREMIER DIVISION | P | W | D | L | F | A | GD | Pts |
|---|---|---|---|---|---|---|---|---|
| 1 Prestwich Heys | 30 | 23 | 4 | 3 | 91 | 29 | 62 | 73 |
| 2 Royton Town | 30 | 19 | 3 | 8 | 92 | 53 | 39 | 60 |
| 3 Springhead | 30 | 18 | 5 | 7 | 70 | 41 | 29 | 59 |
| 4 Rochdale Sacred Heart | 30 | 18 | 4 | 8 | 102 | 73 | 29 | 58 |
| 5 Dukinfield Town | 30 | 18 | 3 | 9 | 70 | 39 | 31 | 57 |
| 6 Hindsford (-1) | 30 | 14 | 7 | 9 | 71 | 65 | 6 | 48 |
| 7 AFC Monton | 30 | 13 | 7 | 10 | 47 | 47 | 0 | 46 |
| 8 Old Altrinchamians | 30 | 12 | 7 | 11 | 47 | 49 | -2 | 43 |
| 9 AVRO | 30 | 12 | 6 | 12 | 51 | 55 | -4 | 42 |
| 10 Wythenshawe Amateurs | 30 | 11 | 7 | 12 | 54 | 58 | -4 | 40 |
| 11 Manchester Gregorians | 30 | 9 | 8 | 13 | 49 | 61 | -12 | 35 |
| 12 Walshaw Sports | 30 | 9 | 5 | 16 | 67 | 70 | -3 | 32 |
| 13 Stockport Georgians | 30 | 7 | 9 | 14 | 50 | 65 | -15 | 30 |
| 14 Atherton Town | 30 | 7 | 8 | 15 | 36 | 65 | -29 | 29 |
| 15 Boothstown | 30 | 3 | 4 | 23 | 45 | 101 | -56 | 13 |
| 16 Uppermill | 30 | 1 | 5 | 24 | 22 | 93 | -71 | 8 |

## GILGRYST CUP

**HOLDERS:** AVRO

**ROUND 1**

| | | | |
|---|---|---|---|
| Springhead | v | Dukinfield Town | 5-4 |
| Royton Town | v | AFC Monton | 2-0 |
| AVRO | v | Atherton Town | 3-2 |
| Wythenshawe Amateurs | v | Manchester Gregorians | 1-2 |
| Boothstown | v | Stockport Georgians | 1-2 |
| Rochdale Sacred Heart | v | Walshaw Sports | 3-1 |
| Uppermill | v | Prestwich Heys | 0-2 |
| Old Altrinchamians | v | Hindsford | 5-1 |

**QUARTER FINALS**

| | | | |
|---|---|---|---|
| Springhead | v | Royton Town | 0-0, 2-3p |
| AVRO | v | Manchester Gregorians | 1-2 |
| Stockport Georgians | v | Rochdale Sacred Heart | 1-0 |
| Prestwich Heys | v | Old Altrinchamians | 4-0 |

**SEMI FINALS**

| | | | |
|---|---|---|---|
| Royton Town | v | Manchester Gregorians | 0-1 |
| Stockport Georgians | v | Prestwich Heys | 1-1, 2-4p |

**FINAL**

| | | | |
|---|---|---|---|
| Manchester Gregorians | v | Prestwich Heys | 0-1 |

| DIVISION ONE | P | W | D | L | F | A | GD | Pts |
|---|---|---|---|---|---|---|---|---|
| 1 East Manchester | 24 | 18 | 4 | 2 | 103 | 32 | 71 | 58 |
| 2 Elton Vale | 24 | 15 | 4 | 5 | 68 | 39 | 29 | 49 |
| 3 Wilmslow Albion | 24 | 10 | 6 | 8 | 43 | 41 | 2 | 36 |
| 4 Chapel Town | 24 | 10 | 6 | 8 | 42 | 43 | -1 | 36 |
| 5 Leigh Athletic | 24 | 10 | 5 | 9 | 73 | 56 | 17 | 35 |
| 6 Heywood St James | 24 | 10 | 4 | 10 | 64 | 54 | 10 | 34 |
| 7 Irlam Steel | 24 | 9 | 7 | 8 | 49 | 52 | -3 | 34 |
| 8 Pennington | 24 | 9 | 5 | 10 | 53 | 61 | -8 | 32 |
| 9 Beechfield United | 24 | 10 | 2 | 12 | 57 | 69 | -12 | 32 |
| 10 Breightmet United | 24 | 8 | 7 | 9 | 42 | 57 | -15 | 31 |
| 11 Chadderton Reserves | 24 | 6 | 5 | 13 | 42 | 60 | -18 | 23 |
| 12 Westbury Sports Club | 24 | 5 | 6 | 13 | 65 | 89 | -24 | 21 |
| 13 Hollinwood (-4) | 24 | 4 | 3 | 17 | 46 | 94 | -48 | 11 |

| DIVISION TWO | P | W | D | L | F | A | GD | Pts |
|---|---|---|---|---|---|---|---|---|
| 1 Prestwich Heys Res. | 30 | 24 | 4 | 2 | 124 | 42 | 82 | 76 |
| 2 Stockport Georgians Res. | 30 | 24 | 2 | 4 | 118 | 36 | 82 | 74 |
| 3 Rochdale Sacred Heart Res. | 30 | 18 | 5 | 7 | 88 | 61 | 27 | 59 |
| 4 Walshaw Sports Res. | 30 | 16 | 4 | 10 | 90 | 79 | 11 | 52 |
| 5 Royton Town Reserves | 30 | 16 | 3 | 11 | 91 | 61 | 30 | 51 |
| 6 Dukinfield Town Res. | 30 | 15 | 4 | 11 | 78 | 48 | 30 | 49 |
| 7 Manchester Gregorians Res. | 30 | 15 | 4 | 11 | 66 | 44 | 22 | 49 |
| 8 Hindsford Reserves (-3) | 30 | 15 | 6 | 9 | 83 | 68 | 15 | 48 |
| 9 Elton Vale Reserves | 30 | 11 | 3 | 16 | 76 | 82 | -6 | 36 |
| 10 Springhead Reserves | 30 | 10 | 4 | 16 | 69 | 80 | -11 | 34 |
| 11 AFC Monton Reserves | 30 | 9 | 5 | 16 | 54 | 74 | -20 | 32 |
| 12 Wythenshawe Amateurs Res. | 30 | 9 | 4 | 17 | 48 | 59 | -11 | 31 |
| 13 Hollinwood Reserves | 30 | 9 | 0 | 21 | 51 | 126 | -75 | 27 |
| 14 AVRO Reserves | 30 | 7 | 5 | 18 | 66 | 110 | -44 | 26 |
| 15 East Manchester Academy | 30 | 7 | 4 | 19 | 48 | 96 | -48 | 25 |
| 16 Leigh Athletic Reserves | 30 | 6 | 1 | 23 | 52 | 136 | -84 | 19 |

| PREMIER DIVISION | 1 | 2 | 3 | 4 | 5 | 6 | 7 | 8 | 9 | 10 | 11 | 12 | 13 | 14 | 15 | 16 |
|---|---|---|---|---|---|---|---|---|---|---|---|---|---|---|---|---|
| 1 AFC Monton | | 1-1 | 0-2 | 2-1 | 1-3 | 2-1 | 2-0 | 0-1 | 0-1 | 2-1 | 1-2 | 3-1 | 4-3 | 3-0 | 3-3 | 0-0 |
| 2 Atherton Town | 1-2 | | 2-2 | 1-3 | 0-7 | 1-1 | 1-2 | 0-3 | 0-0 | 1-5 | 4-1 | 0-1 | 2-2 | 1-2 | 0-0 | 3-2 |
| 3 AVRO | 1-1 | 2-0 | | 3-1 | 0-1 | 3-3 | 1-0 | 0-1 | 1-3 | 4-6 | 0-1 | 1-1 | 3-2 | 4-3 | 3-2 | 0-1 |
| 4 Boothstown | 2-2 | 1-2 | 1-4 | | 1-1 | 2-3 | 1-3 | 1-2 | 0-5 | 3-6 | 1-2 | 1-3 | 2-3 | 2-0 | 0-2 | 3-4 |
| 5 Dukinfield Town | 4-0 | 2-1 | 1-0 | 5-1 | | 4-0 | 0-1 | 1-1 | 0-3 | 1-3 | 3-2 | 2-6 | 3-0 | 3-0 | 3-1 | 2-0 |
| 6 Hindsford | 4-3 | 2-2 | 2-3 | 3-1 | 1-0 | | 4-1 | 0-2 | 0-3 | 3-2 | 2-0 | 3-3 | 5-4 | 4-0 | 2-1 | 4-1 |
| 7 Manchester Gregorians | 0-1 | 3-0 | 2-2 | 2-2 | 2-3 | 2-4 | | 1-1 | 0-1 | 1-2 | 3-4 | 1-0 | 2-6 | 2-0 | 3-3 | 1-2 |
| 8 Old Altrinchamians | 0-2 | 0-1 | 1-0 | 0-4 | 1-0 | 3-3 | 0-0 | | 1-4 | 4-2 | 1-3 | 3-5 | 2-3 | 5-1 | 2-1 | 1-1 |
| 9 Prestwich Heys | 2-3 | 7-1 | 4-0 | 4-0 | 2-0 | 6-3 | 6-1 | 3-2 | | 5-0 | 2-2 | 0-0 | 2-1 | 5-0 | 6-4 | 3-0 |
| 10 Rochdale Sacred Heart | 2-0 | 4-0 | 5-1 | 7-1 | 3-3 | 4-5 | 4-4 | 1-1 | 1-3 | | 5-4 | 2-1 | 3-0 | 6-2 | 7-4 | 2-0 |
| 11 Royton Town | 4-0 | 1-3 | 4-0 | 9-2 | 4-0 | 3-1 | 3-3 | 5-2 | 4-1 | 8-1 | | 1-0 | 4-0 | 2-0 | 0-3 | 1-3 |
| 12 Springhead | 4-1 | 2-2 | 0-3 | 4-1 | 2-1 | 3-1 | 1-1 | 3-1 | 4-2 | 7-4 | 3-0 | | 3-1 | 5-0 | 2-1 | 2-1 |
| 13 Stockport Georgians | 1-1 | 2-0 | 1-1 | 4-2 | 0-2 | 1-1 | 3-4 | 1-1 | 0-2 | 2-2 | 1-4 | 0-1 | | H-W | 2-3 | 2-2 |
| 14 Uppermill | 1-5 | 0-2 | A-W | 3-3 | 1-6 | 0-0 | 0-1 | 0-2 | 0-2 | 0-6 | 3-7 | 0-2 | 1-1 | | 2-2 | 3-4 |
| 15 Walshaw Sports | 0-1 | 1-2 | 3-5 | 6-1 | 1-5 | 2-6 | 2-0 | 2-1 | 0-3 | 1-2 | 3-3 | 1-0 | 2-3 | 8-0 | | 1-2 |
| 16 Wythenshawe Amateurs | 1-1 | 4-2 | 3-2 | 6-1 | 1-4 | 3-0 | 2-3 | 1-2 | 1-1 | 2-4 | 2-4 | 3-1 | 1-1 | 0-0 | 1-4 | |

| DIVISION THREE | P | W | D | L | F | A | GD | Pts |
|---|---|---|---|---|---|---|---|---|
| 1 Walshaw Sports A | 27 | 21 | 2 | 4 | 136 | 53 | 83 | 65 |
| 2 Wilmslow Albion Res. | 28 | 18 | 4 | 6 | 79 | 43 | 36 | 58 |
| 3 Royton Town A | 28 | 17 | 7 | 4 | 76 | 49 | 27 | 58 |
| 4 Atherton Town Reserves | 28 | 15 | 4 | 9 | 79 | 66 | 13 | 49 |
| 5 Hollinwood A | 28 | 13 | 6 | 9 | 103 | 70 | 33 | 45 |
| 6 Irlam Steel Reserves | 28 | 13 | 6 | 9 | 77 | 64 | 13 | 45 |
| 7 Chapel Town Reserves | 28 | 14 | 1 | 13 | 80 | 72 | 8 | 43 |
| 8 Old Altrinchamians Res. | 28 | 13 | 3 | 12 | 85 | 61 | 24 | 42 |
| 9 Boothstown Reserves | 27 | 12 | 4 | 11 | 77 | 68 | 9 | 40 |
| 10 Pennington Reserves | 28 | 11 | 3 | 14 | 68 | 69 | -1 | 36 |
| 11 Uppermill Reserves (-3) | 28 | 12 | 2 | 14 | 81 | 80 | 1 | 35 |
| 12 Breightmet United Res. | 28 | 9 | 4 | 15 | 58 | 115 | -57 | 31 |
| 13 Heywood St James Res. | 28 | 7 | 3 | 18 | 62 | 124 | -62 | 24 |
| 14 Atherton Town A | 28 | 5 | 1 | 22 | 47 | 122 | -75 | 16 |
| 15 Dukinfield Town A | 28 | 4 | 0 | 24 | 39 | 91 | -52 | 12 |

**CLUB MOVEMENTS**

**Premier Division**

**In:** Rochdale Town (R - North West Counties D1 - due to ground grading) .

**Out:** Prestwich Heys (P - North west Counties D1).

**Division One**

**In:** Altrincham Hale, Bolton County, Govan Athletic, Heyside, Manchester Central.

**Division Three**

**In:** Bolton County Reserves; Govan Athletic Reserves; Rochdale Sacred Heart 'A'; Springhead 'A'; Westbury Sports Club Reserves.

**Out:** Atherton Town Reserves (P); Dukinfield Town 'A'; Hollinwood 'A' (W); Royton Town 'A' (P); Uppermill Reserves (W); Walshaw Sports 'A' (W); Wimslow Albion Reserves (P).

## NORMAN NODEN CUP

**HOLDERS:** AFC MONTON

**FINAL -** Premier Division Winners v Gilcrist Cup Winners 08/08/15

Stockport Georgians v AVRO 3-2

## TERRY WOOD CUP

**HOLDERS:** ELTON VALE

**FINAL -** Division One Winners v Murray Shield Winners 08/08/15

Old Altrinchamians v Boothstown 3-0

## MURRAY SHIELD

**HOLDERS:** BOOTHSTOWN

**FINAL**

Elton Vale v East Manchester 1-3

## OPEN CUP

**HOLDERS:** STOCKPORT GEORGIANS RESERVES

**FINAL**

Rochdale Sacred Heart Res. v Prestwich Heys Res. 3-3, 4-5p

## BRIDGWATER CUP

**HOLDERS:** WALSHAW SPORTS 'A'

**FINAL**

Uppermill Reserves v Wilmslow Albion Reserves 1-0

## Manchester League Premier Division

| | | |
|---|---|---|
| **AFC MONTON** | New Alder Park, Off Worlsey Road, Winton, Salford M30 8JN | 07836 321 193 |
| **AVRO** | Lancaster Club, Broadway, Failsworth, Oldham M35 0BH | 07900 192 467 |
| **DUKINFIELD TOWN** | Woodhams Park, Birch Lane, Dukinfield SK16 5AP | 07748 634 862 |
| **EAST MANCHESTER** | Wright Robinson Sports College, Abbey Hey Lane, Gorton M18 8RL | |
| **ELTON VALE** | Elton Vale Sports Club, Elton Vale Road, Bury BL8 2RZ | 07971 007486 |
| **HINDSFORD** | Squires Lane, Tyldesley M29 8JF | |
| **MANCHESTER GREGORIANS** | MCFC, Platt Lane Complex, Yew Tree Road, Fallowfield M14 7UU | |
| **OLD ALTRINCHAMIANS** | Crossford Bridge Sports Ground, Danefield Road, Sale M33 7WR | |
| **ROCHDALE SACRED HEART** | Fox Park, Belfield Mill Lane, Rochdale OL16 2UB | 01706 869 640 |
| **ROCHDALE TOWN** | Kingsway Park Sports Centre 3G, Turf Hill Road, ROCHDALE, Lancashire OL16 4XA | |
| **ROYTON TOWN** | Oldham Academy North, Broadway OL2 5BF | |
| **SPRINGHEAD** | Ashfield Crescent PF, St John Street, Lees, Oldham OL4 3DR | |
| **STOCKPORT GEORGIANS** | Cromley Road, Woodsmoor, Stockport SK2 7DT | |
| **WALSHAW SPORTS** | Walshaw Sports Club, Sycamore Road, Tottington, Bury BL8 3EG | 07843 761 182 |
| **WILMSLOW ALBION** | Oakwood Farm, Styal Road, Wilmslow, Cheshire SK9 4HP | 07747 112 672 |
| **WYTHENSHAWE AMATEUR** | St Pauls Catholic High School, Fairbanks Road, Wythenshawe, Manchester M23 2YS | |

# MIDDLESEX COUNTY LEAGUE

**Sponsored by:** Cherry Red Books
**Founded:** 1984
**Recent Champions:**
**2013:** British Airways
**2014:** Sporting Hackney
**2015:** Hillingdon

| PREMIER DIVISION | P | W | D | L | F | A | GD | Pts |
|---|---|---|---|---|---|---|---|---|
| 1 West Essex | 34 | 22 | 10 | 2 | 77 | 30 | 47 | 76 |
| 2 LPOSSA | 34 | 22 | 8 | 4 | 116 | 43 | 73 | 74 |
| 3 New Hanford | 34 | 23 | 4 | 7 | 89 | 43 | 46 | 73 |
| 4 Pitshanger Dynamo | 34 | 22 | 1 | 11 | 104 | 61 | 43 | 67 |
| 5 Indian Gymkhana Club | 34 | 21 | 3 | 10 | 85 | 56 | 29 | 66 |
| 6 British Airways | 34 | 18 | 6 | 10 | 80 | 58 | 22 | 60 |
| 7 Kilburn | 34 | 18 | 3 | 13 | 99 | 61 | 38 | 57 |
| 8 Hillingdon | 34 | 16 | 7 | 11 | 73 | 53 | 20 | 55 |
| 9 FC Assyria | 34 | 17 | 2 | 15 | 72 | 58 | 14 | 53 |
| 10 AFC Wembley | 34 | 13 | 11 | 10 | 62 | 55 | 7 | 50 |
| 11 Kensington Dragons | 34 | 15 | 2 | 17 | 58 | 45 | 13 | 47 |
| 12 Cricklewood Wanderers | 34 | 14 | 2 | 18 | 65 | 94 | -29 | 44 |
| 13 FC Deportivo Galicia | 34 | 10 | 8 | 16 | 66 | 74 | -8 | 38 |
| 14 Sporting Hackney | 34 | 7 | 6 | 21 | 45 | 84 | -39 | 27 |
| 15 C.B. Hounslow United Res. | 34 | 7 | 3 | 24 | 45 | 99 | -54 | 24 |
| 16 Tooting & Mitcham Wanderers | 34 | 6 | 5 | 23 | 55 | 133 | -78 | 23 |
| 17 Southall Reserves | 34 | 6 | 4 | 24 | 36 | 135 | -99 | 22 |
| 18 South Kilburn | 34 | 5 | 3 | 26 | 34 | 79 | -45 | 18 |

## ALEC SMITH PREMIER DIVISION CUP

**HOLDERS:** SPORTING HACKNEY

**PRELIMINARY ROUND**

| | | | |
|---|---|---|---|
| Tooting & Mitcham Wanderers | v | Hillingdon | 1-5 |
| AFC Wembley | v | South Kilburn | 1-2 |

**ROUND 1**

| | | | |
|---|---|---|---|
| Sporting Hackney | v | Hillingdon | 0-5 |
| New Hanford | v | South Kilburn | 2-1 |
| CB Hounslow United Res. | v | West Essex | 1-2 |
| Pitshanger Dynamo | v | FC Assyria | 3-5 |
| LPOSSA | v | Cricklewood Wanderers | 1-4 |
| Southall Reserves | v | Kilburn | 1-4 |
| Indian Gymkhana Club | v | FC Deportivo Galicia | 3-2 |
| Kensington Dragons | v | British Airways | 2-1 |

**QUARTER FINALS**

| | | | |
|---|---|---|---|
| Hillingdon | v | Indian Gymkhana Club | 2-1 |
| FC Assyria | v | New Hanford | 2-3 |
| Kensington Dragons | v | West Essex | 0-1 |
| Cricklewood Wanderers | v | Kilburn | 1-3 |

**SEMI FINALS**

| | | | |
|---|---|---|---|
| Kilburn | v | Hillingdon | 0-2 |
| New Hanford | v | West Essex | AW |

**FINAL**

| | | | |
|---|---|---|---|
| West Essex | v | Hillingdon | 3-3, 2-4p |

| | PREMIER DIVISION | 1 | 2 | 3 | 4 | 5 | 6 | 7 | 8 | 9 | 10 | 11 | 12 | 13 | 14 | 15 | 16 | 17 | 18 |
|---|---|---|---|---|---|---|---|---|---|---|---|---|---|---|---|---|---|---|---|
| 1 | AFC Wembley | | 4-5 | 4-0 | 1-1 | AW | 3-2 | 3-2 | AW | 2-1 | 1-1 | 0-3 | 2-1 | 2-3 | 4-2 | 3-0 | 1-1 | 2-2 | 0-0 |
| 2 | British Airways | 0-0 | | 3-2 | 1-2 | 2-2 | 2-1 | 1-2 | 4-1 | 3-2 | 4-3 | 1-2 | 2-0 | 1-2 | 3-2 | 4-1 | 2-2 | 6-0 | 2-3 |
| 3 | C.B. Hounslow United Reserves | 3-3 | 2-5 | | 0-3 | 3-0 | 5-1 | 0-3 | 2-7 | 1-3 | 0-2 | 0-5 | 1-8 | 2-1 | 4-0 | 0-2 | HW | 1-4 | 0-4 |
| 4 | Cricklewood Wanderers | 3-4 | 3-2 | 2-1 | | 4-1 | 4-4 | 0-3 | 7-0 | 0-3 | 1-0 | 1-8 | 2-0 | 3-5 | 2-3 | 2-0 | 2-0 | 1-0 | 1-4 |
| 5 | FC Assyria | 1-2 | 0-2 | 2-1 | 9-1 | | 3-2 | 5-1 | 2-1 | 1-2 | 3-1 | 2-3 | 2-3 | 2-1 | 2-0 | 5-1 | 4-0 | 1-2 | 0-2 |
| 6 | FC Deportivo Galicia | 1-1 | 0-2 | 2-3 | 2-3 | 2-3 | | 1-0 | 0-0 | 1-2 | 3-7 | 2-2 | 1-3 | 2-4 | 1-0 | 3-0 | 0-0 | 6-4 | 1-2 |
| 7 | Hillingdon | 2-0 | 2-2 | 0-0 | 1-3 | 3-3 | 1-1 | | 4-5 | 2-1 | 1-1 | 1-1 | 0-1 | 1-3 | 4-0 | 3-0 | 2-0 | 14-1 | 1-1 |
| 8 | Indian Gymkhana Club | 4-3 | 2-0 | 5-1 | 5-2 | 3-2 | 4-0 | 6-0 | | 1-0 | 1-3 | 2-2 | 4-1 | 2-4 | 3-4 | 4-0 | 3-0 | 3-0 | 2-3 |
| 9 | Kensington Dragons | 2-1 | 1-1 | 2-0 | 1-3 | 0-1 | 2-3 | 1-4 | 2-0 | | 0-2 | 1-3 | 1-2 | 0-1 | 1-0 | 8-0 | 5-0 | 2-0 | 1-0 |
| 10 | Kilburn | 2-0 | 2-3 | 2-1 | 4-1 | 2-4 | 3-2 | 2-1 | 1-0 | 0-2 | | 2-1 | 1-4 | 2-3 | 2-0 | 1-1 | 3-6 | 4-1 | 2-4 |
| 11 | LPOSSA | 1-1 | 3-0 | 5-1 | 6-2 | 3-1 | 5-1 | 2-0 | 1-2 | 2-1 | 2-0 | | 4-1 | 1-2 | 5-0 | 6-0 | 5-0 | 6-1 | 0-4 |
| 12 | New Hanford | 3-2 | 1-0 | 3-2 | 6-2 | 3-1 | 0-0 | 0-3 | 1-1 | 1-1 | 3-1 | 3-3 | | 3-0 | 2-1 | 9-0 | 1-0 | 5-0 | 1-0 |
| 13 | Pitshanger Dynamo | 2-3 | 3-1 | 7-1 | 5-2 | 2-1 | 2-4 | 1-2 | 0-1 | 2-1 | 1-2 | 2-6 | 1-5 | | 3-1 | 9-0 | 6-0 | 11-1 | 1-1 |
| 14 | South Kilburn | 1-2 | 1-5 | 3-1 | 3-0 | 0-2 | 1-3 | 0-1 | AW | 0-2 | 1-3 | 1-5 | 0-2 | 3-4 | | 1-1 | 1-1 | 2-0 | AW |
| 15 | Southall Res | 0-1 | 1-3 | 2-1 | 4-1 | 1-3 | 0-4 | 3-5 | 2-7 | 1-0 | 1-17 | 2-2 | 2-5 | 1-5 | 5-0 | | 2-1 | 0-4 | 0-4 |
| 16 | Sporting Hackney | 1-1 | 2-3 | 6-0 | 2-0 | 1-2 | 1-6 | 0-1 | 0-1 | HW | 0-7 | 1-8 | 1-4 | 2-3 | 3-0 | 4-1 | | 5-2 | 2-2 |
| 17 | Tooting & Mitcham Wanderers | 3-4 | 2-3 | 0-6 | 2-1 | 4-2 | 2-4 | 2-3 | 1-4 | 3-5 | 1-12 | 3-3 | 0-3 | 0-4 | 3-3 | 2-2 | 3-2 | | 1-2 |
| 18 | West Essex | 2-2 | 2-2 | 0-0 | 4-0 | HW | 0-0 | 3-0 | 4-1 | 4-2 | 4-2 | 2-2 | 2-1 | 2-1 | HW | 8-0 | 3-1 | 1-1 | |

| DIVISION ONE CENTRAL & EAST | P | W | D | L | F | A | GD | Pts |
|---|---|---|---|---|---|---|---|---|
| 1 Tottenham Hale Rangers | 16 | 11 | 3 | 2 | 38 | 11 | 27 | 36 |
| 2 Mile End Park Rangers | 16 | 10 | 6 | 0 | 41 | 20 | 21 | 36 |
| 3 The Wilberforce Wanderers | 16 | 8 | 4 | 4 | 34 | 26 | 8 | 28 |
| 4 FC Krystal | 16 | 7 | 3 | 6 | 48 | 30 | 18 | 24 |
| 5 J L Rovers | 16 | 6 | 4 | 6 | 29 | 29 | 0 | 22 |
| 6 Paddington Elite | 16 | 4 | 4 | 8 | 20 | 31 | -11 | 16 |
| 7 Stonewall | 16 | 4 | 4 | 8 | 19 | 33 | -14 | 16 |
| 8 Imperial College Old Boys | 16 | 4 | 4 | 8 | 24 | 39 | -15 | 16 |
| 9 Hackney Wick | 16 | 1 | 2 | 13 | 25 | 59 | -34 | 5 |

| DIVISION ONE WEST | P | W | D | L | F | A | GD | Pt |
|---|---|---|---|---|---|---|---|---|
| 1 Brentham | 16 | 11 | 3 | 2 | 47 | 14 | 33 | 3 |
| 2 Greenford Celtic | 16 | 11 | 3 | 2 | 43 | 21 | 22 | 3 |
| 3 British Airways (Speedbird) | 16 | 11 | 2 | 3 | 46 | 15 | 31 | 3 |
| 4 Kodak (Harrow) | 16 | 9 | 2 | 5 | 33 | 32 | 1 | 2 |
| 5 Hounslow Wanderers | 16 | 6 | 1 | 9 | 26 | 48 | -22 | 1 |
| 6 Larkspur Rovers | 16 | 6 | 0 | 10 | 33 | 39 | -6 | 1 |
| 7 AEK London | 16 | 4 | 3 | 9 | 30 | 38 | -8 | 1 |
| 8 Spartan Youth | 16 | 4 | 1 | 11 | 32 | 41 | -9 | 1 |
| 9 Hillingdon Abbots | 16 | 2 | 1 | 13 | 17 | 59 | -42 | |

| DIVISION TWO | P | W | D | L | F | A | GD | Pts |
|---|---|---|---|---|---|---|---|---|
| 1 Lampton Park | 16 | 15 | 1 | 0 | 61 | 16 | 45 | 46 |
| 2 Best 72 | 16 | 14 | 1 | 1 | 73 | 27 | 46 | 43 |
| 3 Victoria | 16 | 10 | 1 | 5 | 40 | 37 | 3 | 31 |
| 4 Heston Bombers | 16 | 9 | 0 | 7 | 35 | 24 | 11 | 27 |
| 5 C.B. Hounslow United 3rds | 16 | 6 | 1 | 9 | 22 | 39 | -17 | 19 |
| 6 AMU | 16 | 5 | 1 | 10 | 29 | 60 | -31 | 16 |
| 7 Harrow Rangers | 16 | 4 | 3 | 9 | 32 | 48 | -16 | 15 |
| 8 Cranford Park | 16 | 2 | 2 | 12 | 24 | 48 | -24 | 8 |
| 9 Hilltop | 16 | 2 | 0 | 14 | 32 | 49 | -17 | 6 |

| MCFL COMBINATION | P | W | D | L | F | A | GD | Pts |
|---|---|---|---|---|---|---|---|---|
| 1 AFC Hanwell & Hayes | 16 | 16 | 0 | 0 | 64 | 12 | 52 | 48 |
| 2 Centenary Park | 16 | 10 | 4 | 2 | 60 | 24 | 36 | 34 |
| 3 Speedy Utd | 16 | 9 | 4 | 3 | 43 | 24 | 19 | 31 |
| 4 Windmill Wanderers | 16 | 8 | 3 | 5 | 39 | 33 | 6 | 27 |
| 5 Harrow | 16 | 6 | 3 | 7 | 20 | 20 | 0 | 21 |
| 6 Philippine | 16 | 4 | 2 | 10 | 26 | 47 | -21 | 14 |
| 7 C.B. Hounslow United 5ths | 16 | 4 | 1 | 11 | 18 | 37 | -19 | 13 |
| 8 Hillingdon 3rds | 16 | 4 | 1 | 11 | 15 | 43 | -28 | 13 |
| 9 AFC London | 16 | 1 | 2 | 13 | 13 | 58 | -45 | 5 |

| SENIOR RESERVE DIVISION | P | W | D | L | F | A | GD | Pts |
|---|---|---|---|---|---|---|---|---|
| 1 Indian Gymkhana Club Res. | 16 | 13 | 1 | 2 | 56 | 27 | 29 | 40 |
| 2 FC Deportivo Galicia Res. | 16 | 12 | 1 | 3 | 53 | 26 | 27 | 37 |
| 3 Pitshanger Dynamo Res. | 16 | 9 | 2 | 5 | 52 | 30 | 22 | 29 |
| 4 Kensington Dragons Res. | 16 | 9 | 2 | 5 | 51 | 32 | 19 | 29 |
| 5 Hillingdon Reserves | 16 | 7 | 3 | 6 | 32 | 29 | 3 | 24 |
| 6 Sporting Hackney Res. | 16 | 5 | 1 | 10 | 27 | 44 | -17 | 16 |
| 7 Brentham Reserves | 16 | 4 | 3 | 9 | 32 | 47 | -15 | 15 |
| 8 C.B. Hounslow United 4ths | 16 | 4 | 1 | 11 | 28 | 40 | -12 | 13 |
| 9 LPOSSA Reserves | 16 | 1 | 2 | 13 | 15 | 71 | -56 | 5 |

## Middlesex County League Premier Division

|  |  |
|---|---|
| AFC WEMBLEY | GEC Sports Ground, Pellatt Road off Preston Raod, Wembley, Middlesex HA9 8FB |
| BRETHAM | Meadvale Road, Ealing, London W5 1NP |
| BRITISH AIRWAYS | Robert Parker Stadium, Stanwell, Staines TW19 7BH |
| C.B. HOUNSLOW UNITED RES. | Osterley Sports Club, Tentelow Lane, Norwood Green UB2 4LW |
| CRICKLEWOOD WANDERERS | Vale Farm Sports Centre, Watford Road, North Wembley, London HA0 3HE |
| FC ASSYRIA | Northolt Rugby Club, Cayton Road, Greenford UB6 8B |
| FC DEPORTIVO GALICIA | Siver Jubilee Park, Townsend Lane, London NW9 7NE |
| HILLINGDON | Brunel Uni. Sports Complex, Kingston Park, Kingston Lane, Hillingdon UB8 3PW |
| INDIAN GYMKHANA | Indian Gymkhana Club, Thornbury Avenue, Osterley TW7 4NQ |
| KENSINGTON DRAGONS | Linford Christie Stadium, Artillery Lane, off Du Cane Road W12 0DF |
| LPOSSA | AFC Hayes, Farm Park, Kingsmill Avenue, Hayes UB4 8DD |
| PITSHANGER DYNAMO | West London Sports Ground, Argyle Road, West Ealing, London W13 0AY |
| SOUTH KILBURN | Vale Farm, Watford Road, North Wembley HA0 3HE |
| SOUTHALL RESERVES | Bedfont Sports Club, Hatton Road, Bedfont TW14 8JA |
| SPORTING HACKNEY | Hackney Marshes, Homerton Road, Hackney, London E9 5PF |
| TOOTING & MITCHAM WANDERERS | Whyteleafe FC, Chruch Road, Whyteleafe, Surrey CR3 0AR |

**CLUB MOVEMENTS**

**Premier Division - In:** Brentham (P). **Out:** Kilburn (W); New Hanford (R - D1W)

**Division One Central & East - In:** Alpha/Omega (N); Camden Town (N). **Out:** Paddington Elite (W); Imperial College Old Boys (W).

**Division One West - In:** Evergreen (N); Lampton Park (P); New Hanford (R); **Out:** Brentham (P).

**Division Two - In:** PCF Victoria; Victoria; West London E Benfica (N); **Out:** Lampton Park (P - D1W).

# NORTH BERKSHIRE LEAGUE

**Sponsored by:** No sponsor
**Founded:** 1909
**Recent Champions:**
**2013:** Saxton Rovers
**2014:** Kintbury Rangers
**2015:** Berinsfield
**nbfl.co.uk**

| | DIVISION ONE | P | W | D | L | F | A | GD | Pts |
|---|---|---|---|---|---|---|---|---|---|
| 1 | Kintbury Rangers | 20 | 15 | 2 | 3 | 57 | 20 | 37 | 47 |
| 2 | Berinsfield | 20 | 14 | 2 | 4 | 62 | 31 | 31 | 44 |
| 3 | Saxton Rovers | 19 | 14 | 0 | 5 | 70 | 29 | 41 | 42 |
| 4 | Lambourn Sports | 19 | 13 | 2 | 4 | 44 | 27 | 17 | 41 |
| 5 | Abingdon Town | 20 | 12 | 2 | 6 | 38 | 29 | 9 | 38 |
| 6 | Wallingford Town | 20 | 11 | 2 | 7 | 40 | 25 | 15 | 35 |
| 7 | Long Wittenham Athletic | 20 | 7 | 4 | 9 | 29 | 39 | -10 | 25 |
| 8 | Crowmarsh Gifford | 20 | 4 | 6 | 10 | 21 | 34 | -13 | 18 |
| 9 | East Hendred | 20 | 4 | 3 | 13 | 32 | 54 | -22 | 15 |
| 10 | Faringdon Town | 20 | 3 | 0 | 17 | 23 | 65 | -42 | 9 |
| 11 | Dorchester | 20 | 0 | 1 | 19 | 26 | 89 | -63 | 1 |

Drayton withdrew - record expunged (Re-formed in Div4 2016-17).

**In:** Burghclere (R), Stanford-in-the-Vale (P), Turnpike Sports (P).

**Out:** Abingdon Town (W), Crowmarsh Gifford (W),

Faringdon Town (S - Hellenic D2W), Turnpike Sports (W).

## NORTH BERKS CUP

**HOLDERS:** BERINSFIELD

**ROUND 1**

| | | | |
|---|---|---|---|
| Benson Lions | v | Turnpike Sports | 0-12 |
| Steventon | v | Hanney United | 5-1 |
| Hagbourne United | v | North Oxford | 0-4 |
| Hungerford Town Swifts | v | Sutton Courtney | 6-1 |
| Kennington Athletic | v | Compton FC | 2-2, 3-5p |
| Hanney 66 Club | v | Grove Rangers | 2-7 |
| Harwell Village | v | Blewbury | 2-3 |
| Union Street | v | Uffington United | 0-3 |

**ROUND 2**

| | | | |
|---|---|---|---|
| Burghclere FC | v | Crowmarsh Gifford | 0-1 |
| Turnpike Sports | v | Lambourn Sports | 2-0 |
| Steventon | v | Drayton | 0-3 |
| Stratford-in-the-Vale | v | Westminster | 1-3 |
| Dorchester | v | Watlington Town | 1-2 |
| North Oxford | v | Marcham | 3-2 |
| Hungerford Town Swifts | v | Faringdon Town | 1-0 |
| Compton FC | v | Grove Rangers | 1-5 |
| Saxton Rovers | v | East Hendred | 2-1 aet |
| Blewbury | v | Uffington United | 1-1, 5-6p |

**ROUND 3**

| | | | |
|---|---|---|---|
| Kintbury Rangers | v | Crowmarsh Gifford | 2-0 |
| Turnpike Sports | v | Abingdon Town | 0-2 |
| Long Wittenham Athletic | v | Drayton | 2-1 |
| Westminster | v | Watlington Town | 4-3 |
| Hungerford Town Swifts | v | Wallingford Town | 2-0 |
| Grove Rangers | v | Saxton Rovers | 0-4 |
| Berinsfield | v | Uffington United | 4-0 |
| North Oxford | - | Bye | |

**QUARTER FINALS**

| | | | |
|---|---|---|---|
| Kintbury Rangers | v | Abingdon Town | 3-0 |
| Long Wittenham Athletic | v | Westminster | 2-1 |
| North Oxford | v | Hungerford Town Swifts | 0-2 |
| Saxton Rovers | v | Berinsfield | 6-0 |

**SEMI FINALS**

| | | | |
|---|---|---|---|
| Kintbury Rangers | v | Long Wittenham Athletic | 0-1 |
| Hungerford Town Swifts | v | Saxton Rovers | 1-4 |

**FINAL**

| | | | |
|---|---|---|---|
| Long Wittenham Athletic | v | Saxton Rovers | 5-3 aet |

| | DIVISION ONE | 1 | 2 | 3 | 4 | 5 | 6 | 7 | 8 | 9 | 10 | 11 |
|---|---|---|---|---|---|---|---|---|---|---|---|---|
| 1 | Abingdon Town | | 2-0 | H-W | 4-1 | 4-2 | 2-1 | 3-3 | H-W | 1-1 | 2-0 | 1-2 |
| 2 | Berinsfield | 3-0 | | 1-1 | 4-1 | 5-0 | 3-0 | 2-1 | 6-2 | 4-0 | 4-1 | 0-0 |
| 3 | Crowmarsh Gifford | 1-3 | 0-4 | | 1-1 | 2-2 | 3-2 | A-W | A-W | 1-1 | 0-5 | 2-2 |
| 4 | Dorchester | 1-4 | 1-5 | 1-3 | | 1-2 | 1-3 | 2-9 | 2-3 | 2-3 | 4-7 | 0-1 |
| 5 | East Hendred | 2-3 | 3-7 | 1-1 | 4-3 | | 4-0 | 0-1 | 4-5 | 1-1 | 3-5 | 0-3 |
| 6 | Faringdon Town | 0-2 | 3-5 | 1-2 | 4-2 | 2-1 | | 2-4 | 0-6 | 0-2 | 0-10 | 1-3 |
| 7 | Kintbury Rangers | 2-1 | 5-0 | 2-1 | 7-0 | 4-1 | 3-1 | | 2-2 | 2-1 | 0-1 | 2-0 |
| 8 | Lambourn Sports | 4-1 | 3-2 | H-W | 5-2 | 1-0 | 3-0 | 1-2 | | 4-0 | V-V | 1-0 |
| 9 | Long Wittenham Athletic | 2-1 | 2-3 | 0-2 | 6-1 | 2-0 | 2-1 | 1-0 | 1-1 | | 0-5 | 3-6 |
| 10 | Saxton Rovers | 4-3 | 4-1 | 5-0 | 8-0 | 0-2 | 5-1 | 1-4 | 4-1 | 2-1 | | 1-2 |
| 11 | Wallingford Town | 0-1 | 2-3 | 3-1 | 6-0 | 4-0 | 2-1 | 0-4 | 1-2 | 2-0 | 1-2 | |

## NORTH BERKS CHARITY SHIELD

**HOLDERS:** WALLINGFORD TOWN

**ROUND 1**

| | | | |
|---|---|---|---|
| Long Wittenham Athletic | v | Abingdon Town | 2-2, 3-4p |
| Kintbury Rangers | v | Wallingford Town | 4-2 |
| East Hendred | v | Burghclere FC | 1-3 |
| Saxton Rovers | v | Stanford-in-the-Vale | 1-1, 1-3p |
| Westminster | v | Dorchester | 2-2, 5-6p |
| Drayton | v | Crowmarsh Gifford | 0-2 |
| Berinsfield | v | Faringdon Town | AW |
| Watlington Town | v | Lambourn Sports | 0-4 |

**QUARTER FINALS**

| | | | |
|---|---|---|---|
| Abingdon Town | v | Kintbury Rangers | 2-1 aet |
| Burghclere FC | v | Stanford-in-the-Vale | 3-0 |
| Dorchester | v | Crowmarsh Gifford | 1-2 |
| Faringdon Town | v | Lambourn Sports | 1-6 |

**SEMI FINALS**

| | | | |
|---|---|---|---|
| Abingdon Town | v | Burghclere FC | 1-4 |
| Crowmarsh Gifford | v | Lambourn Sports | 0-1 |

**FINAL**

| | | | |
|---|---|---|---|
| Burghclere FC | v | Lambourn Sports | 3-4 aet |

## North Berkshire League Division One

|  |  |  |
|---|---|---|
| **BERINSFIELD** | Lay Avenue, Berinsfield OX10 7N | 07983 399 992 |
| **BURGHCLERE** | Burghclere Sports Club, Harts Lane RG20 9JD | 07826 757 175 |
| **EAST HENDRED** | Mill Lane, East Hendred OX12 8JS | 07816 480 578 |
| **KINTBURY RANGERS** | Inkpen Road, Kintbury, Hungerford RG17 9UA | 07771 636 594 |
| **LAMBOURN SPORTS** | Bockhampton Road, Lambourn RG17 8PS | 07799 890 841 |
| **LONG WITTENHAM ATHLETIC** | Bodkins Sports Field, East End of Village, Long Wittenham | 07947 309 120 |
| **SAXTON ROVERS** | Recreation Ground, Caldecott Road, Abingdon OX14 5HR | 07752 390 039 |
| **STANFORD-IN-THE-VALE** | Cottage Road, off Faringdon/Wantage Road, Stanford-in-the-Vale SN7 8HX | 07715 015 991 |
| **WALLINGFORD TOWN** | Wallingford Sports Park , Hithercroft Road , Wallingford OX10 9RB | 077950 998 952 |

| DIVISION TWO | | P | W | D | L | F | A | GD | Pts |
|---|---|---|---|---|---|---|---|---|---|
| 1 | Burghclere FC | 20 | 17 | 1 | 2 | 62 | 17 | 45 | 52 |
| 2 | Kintbury Reserves | 20 | 12 | 4 | 4 | 43 | 27 | 16 | 40 |
| 3 | Stanford-in-the-Vale | 20 | 12 | 3 | 5 | 48 | 25 | 23 | 39 |
| 4 | Turnpike Sports | 20 | 10 | 4 | 6 | 63 | 37 | 26 | 34 |
| 5 | Westminster | 20 | 9 | 3 | 8 | 44 | 42 | 2 | 30 |
| 6 | Steventon | 20 | 8 | 3 | 9 | 33 | 36 | -3 | 27 |
| 7 | Sutton Courtenay | 20 | 7 | 2 | 11 | 28 | 59 | -31 | 23 |
| 8 | Hanney Utd | 20 | 7 | 1 | 12 | 34 | 46 | -12 | 22 |
| 9 | Faringdon Town Res. | 20 | 5 | 3 | 12 | 30 | 44 | -14 | 18 |
| 10 | Watlington Town | 20 | 4 | 3 | 13 | 27 | 46 | -19 | 15 |
| 11 | Marcham | 20 | 4 | 3 | 13 | 35 | 68 | -33 | 15 |

| DIVISION THREE | | P | W | D | L | F | A | GD | Pts |
|---|---|---|---|---|---|---|---|---|---|
| | Harwell Village | 20 | 16 | 1 | 3 | 70 | 23 | 47 | 49 |
| | North Oxford | 20 | 15 | 2 | 3 | 58 | 26 | 32 | 47 |
| | Hungerford Town Swifts | 20 | 15 | 0 | 5 | 55 | 22 | 33 | 45 |
| | Grove Rangers | 20 | 10 | 4 | 6 | 48 | 35 | 13 | 34 |
| | Uffington United | 20 | 8 | 3 | 9 | 49 | 47 | 2 | 27 |
| | Newbury Reserves | 20 | 8 | 3 | 9 | 29 | 62 | -33 | 27 |
| | Benson Lions | 20 | 8 | 1 | 11 | 51 | 49 | 2 | 25 |
| | Compton FC | 20 | 6 | 3 | 11 | 34 | 40 | -6 | 21 |
| | Saxton Rovers Reserves | 20 | 3 | 5 | 12 | 34 | 52 | -18 | 14 |
| 10 | Dorchester Reserves | 20 | 3 | 4 | 13 | 27 | 50 | -23 | 13 |
| 11 | Union Street | 20 | 3 | 4 | 13 | 22 | 71 | -49 | 13 |

**In:** Ardington & Lockinge (N); Highworth Town Dev. (Cirencester League).
**Out:** Union Street (W).

| DIVISION FOUR | | P | W | D | L | F | A | GD | Pts |
|---|---|---|---|---|---|---|---|---|---|
| | East Hendred Reserves | 20 | 17 | 1 | 2 | 73 | 23 | 50 | 52 |
| | Wallingford Town Res. | 20 | 14 | 3 | 3 | 77 | 27 | 50 | 45 |
| | Stanford-in-the-Vale Res. | 20 | 12 | 3 | 5 | 53 | 31 | 22 | 39 |
| | Long Wittenham Res. | 20 | 10 | 4 | 6 | 37 | 36 | 1 | 34 |
| | Berinsfield Reserves | 20 | 10 | 0 | 10 | 43 | 62 | -19 | 30 |
| | Lambourn Sports Res. | 20 | 8 | 4 | 8 | 48 | 50 | -2 | 28 |
| | Blewbury | 20 | 8 | 2 | 10 | 36 | 51 | -15 | 26 |
| | Kennington Athletic | 20 | 8 | 1 | 11 | 35 | 44 | -9 | 25 |
| | Abingdon Town Res. | 20 | 4 | 4 | 12 | 29 | 38 | -9 | 16 |
| 10 | Hagbourne United | 20 | 3 | 3 | 14 | 27 | 66 | -39 | 12 |
| | Faringdon Town A | 20 | 2 | 3 | 15 | 19 | 49 | -30 | 9 |

**In:** Coleshill United (N).

| DIVISION FIVE | | P | W | D | L | F | A | GD | Pts |
|---|---|---|---|---|---|---|---|---|---|
| 1 | Hungerford Town Swifts Res. | 24 | 21 | 3 | 0 | 117 | 25 | 92 | 66 |
| 2 | Burghclere Reserves | 24 | 16 | 5 | 3 | 82 | 31 | 51 | 53 |
| 3 | North Oxford Reserves | 24 | 15 | 1 | 8 | 71 | 53 | 18 | 46 |
| 4 | Didcot Eagles | 24 | 15 | 0 | 9 | 76 | 52 | 24 | 45 |
| 5 | Sutton Courtenay Res. | 24 | 12 | 5 | 7 | 76 | 48 | 28 | 41 |
| 6 | Wallingford Town 'A' | 24 | 12 | 3 | 9 | 65 | 66 | -1 | 39 |
| 7 | Grove Rangers Res. | 24 | 11 | 2 | 11 | 49 | 39 | 10 | 35 |
| 8 | Uffington Utd. Reserves | 24 | 9 | 4 | 11 | 56 | 68 | -12 | 31 |
| 9 | Marcham Reserves | 24 | 10 | 0 | 14 | 66 | 76 | -10 | 30 |
| 10 | Steventon Reserves | 24 | 7 | 3 | 14 | 57 | 62 | -5 | 24 |
| 11 | Watlington Town Res | 24 | 8 | 0 | 16 | 35 | 82 | -47 | 24 |
| 12 | Hagbourne Utd. Res. | 24 | 4 | 0 | 20 | 33 | 101 | -68 | 12 |
| 13 | Hanney 66 Club | 24 | 2 | 2 | 20 | 31 | 111 | -80 | 8 |

**In:** Cumnor Minors (N).

### WAR MEMORIAL TROPHY

**FINAL** — **HOLDERS:** BURGHCLERE FC

North Oxford v Burghclere FC 3-2 aet

### LEAGUE CUP

**FINAL** — **HOLDERS:** WALLIGFORD TOWN RESERVES

Hungerford Town Swifts Res. v East Hendred Reserves 1-3

### AG KINGHAM CUP

**FINAL** — **HOLDERS:** KINTBURY RESERVES

Kintbury Reserves v East Hendred Reserves 3-2 aet

### NAIRNE PAUL TROPHY

**FINAL** — **HOLDERS:** ARDINGTON RESERVES

Kintbury Reserves v Wallingford Town Reserves 3-0

# NORTHAMPTONSHIRE COMBINATION

**Sponsored by:** MDH Teamwear
**Founded:** N/K
**Recent Champions:**
**2013:** Harpole
**2014:** Brixworth All Saints
**2015:** Corby Eagles
**northantscombination.co.uk**

| PREMIER DIVISION | P | W | D | L | F | A | GD | Pts |
|---|---|---|---|---|---|---|---|---|
| 1 James King Blisworth | 26 | 23 | 2 | 1 | 113 | 34 | 79 | 71 |
| 2 Harpole | 26 | 21 | 2 | 3 | 76 | 16 | 60 | 65 |
| 3 Weldon United | 26 | 18 | 5 | 3 | 62 | 26 | 36 | 59 |
| 4 Roade | 26 | 17 | 4 | 5 | 76 | 32 | 44 | 55 |
| 5 Kettering Nomads | 26 | 10 | 9 | 7 | 62 | 46 | 16 | 39 |
| 6 Heyford Athletic | 26 | 10 | 5 | 11 | 43 | 53 | -10 | 35 |
| 7 Milton | 26 | 9 | 6 | 11 | 49 | 60 | -11 | 33 |
| 8 Moulton | 26 | 10 | 2 | 14 | 50 | 51 | -1 | 32 |
| 9 Brixworth All Saints | 26 | 9 | 4 | 13 | 45 | 59 | -14 | 31 |
| 10 Corby S&L Khalsa | 26 | 7 | 6 | 13 | 52 | 65 | -13 | 27 |
| 11 Earls Barton United | 26 | 7 | 5 | 14 | 48 | 63 | -15 | 26 |
| 12 Daventry Drayton Grange (-3) | 26 | 7 | 2 | 17 | 45 | 64 | -19 | 20 |
| 13 Clipston | 26 | 4 | 7 | 15 | 49 | 73 | -24 | 19 |
| 14 Stanion United (-6) | 26 | 0 | 1 | 25 | 17 | 145 | -128 | -5 |
| Ringstead withdrew | | | | | | | | |

## PREMIER DIVISION CUP

**HOLDERS:** JAMES KING BLISWORTH

**ROUND 1**

| | | | |
|---|---|---|---|
| Earls Barton United | v | Stanion United | 5-0 |
| Moulton | v | Ringstead Rangers | HW |
| Harpole | v | James King Blisworth | 1-0 |
| Milton | v | Kettering Nomads | 0-2 |
| Roade | v | Weldon United | 6-1 |
| Brixworth All Saints | v | Daventry Drayton Grange | 0-1 aet |
| Corby S&L Khalsa | - | Bye | |
| Clipston | v | Heyford Athletic | 2-5 |

**QUARTER FINALS**

| | | | |
|---|---|---|---|
| Earls Barton United | v | Moulton | 2-1 |
| Harpole | v | Kettering Nomads | 4-0 |
| Roade | v | Daventry Drayton Grange | 6-0 |
| Corby S&L Khalsa | v | Heyford Athletic | 2-1 |

**SEMI FINALS**

| | | | |
|---|---|---|---|
| Earls Barton United | v | Harpole | 1-5 |
| Roade | v | Corby S&L Khalsa | 2-0 |

**FINAL**

| | | | |
|---|---|---|---|
| Harpole | v | Roade | 1-0 |

| PREMIER DIVISION | 1 | 2 | 3 | 4 | 5 | 6 | 7 | 8 | 9 | 10 | 11 | 12 | 13 | 14 |
|---|---|---|---|---|---|---|---|---|---|---|---|---|---|---|
| 1 Brixworth All Saints | | 3-1 | 4-4 | 4-2 | 2-0 | 1-2 | 4-2 | 1-6 | 1-4 | 0-0 | 0-4 | 0-6 | 3-0 | 1-3 |
| 2 Clipston | 4-4 | | 2-3 | 2-2 | 2-3 | 0-3 | 2-2 | 1-4 | 1-1 | 3-4 | 2-4 | 1-4 | 11-0 | 1-2 |
| 3 Corby S&L Khalsa | 1-2 | 1-3 | | 2-3 | H-W | 0-2 | 0-0 | 2-4 | 2-2 | 1-4 | 1-4 | 2-1 | 8-1 | 1-1 |
| 4 Daventry Drayton Grange | 1-3 | 1-0 | 2-1 | | 1-2 | 1-6 | 3-1 | 2-4 | 1-2 | 3-4 | 2-3 | 0-4 | 5-0 | 2-4 |
| 5 Earls Barton United | 0-3 | 1-1 | 2-2 | 1-3 | | 0-3 | 1-2 | 2-6 | 3-3 | 4-2 | 2-1 | 1-3 | 9-0 | 1-3 |
| 6 Harpole | 2-1 | 4-0 | 2-1 | 1-0 | 3-0 | | 3-0 | 3-0 | 0-0 | 1-2 | 5-0 | 2-1 | 15-0 | 1-0 |
| 7 Heyford Athletic | 3-1 | 2-3 | 4-1 | 2-0 | 3-3 | 1-2 | | 1-5 | 1-0 | 3-1 | 1-3 | 1-1 | 3-0 | 0-2 |
| 8 James King Blisworth | 5-2 | 8-1 | 7-4 | H-W | 9-1 | 5-4 | 5-1 | | 5-2 | 8-0 | 2-0 | 2-2 | H-W | 3-2 |
| 9 Kettering Nomads | 2-1 | 5-0 | 4-1 | 4-4 | 3-0 | 1-2 | 1-1 | 2-4 | | 0-0 | 2-1 | 0-0 | 11-0 | 1-6 |
| 10 Milton | 0-0 | 2-2 | 1-5 | 5-3 | 2-2 | 0-1 | 1-2 | 0-6 | 2-2 | | 1-4 | 1-2 | 7-1 | 1-3 |
| 11 Moulton | 4-0 | 4-1 | 1-2 | 2-0 | 0-2 | 1-3 | 2-3 | 0-4 | 3-4 | 1-3 | | 1-2 | H-W | 1-2 |
| 12 Roade | 2-1 | 3-1 | 6-2 | 3-0 | 2-1 | 0-0 | 4-0 | 1-3 | 4-0 | 2-3 | 3-2 | | 11-1 | 2-1 |
| 13 Stanion United | 0-3 | 1-2 | 1-3 | 1-3 | 2-6 | 0-6 | 2-4 | 0-8 | 0-5 | 1-3 | 3-3 | 2-5 | | 1-2 |
| 14 Weldon United | 1-0 | 2-2 | 2-2 | 3-1 | 2-1 | 1-0 | 3-0 | 0-0 | 3-1 | H-W | 1-1 | 4-2 | 9-0 | |

| DIVISION ONE | P | W | D | L | F | A | GD | Pts |
|---|---|---|---|---|---|---|---|---|
| 1 Wellingborough Rising Sun | 26 | 22 | 1 | 3 | 108 | 37 | 71 | 67 |
| 2 Corby Pegasus | 26 | 18 | 2 | 6 | 84 | 57 | 27 | 56 |
| 3 Medbourne | 26 | 15 | 5 | 6 | 84 | 35 | 49 | 50 |
| 4 Wollaston Victoria | 26 | 14 | 3 | 9 | 68 | 44 | 24 | 45 |
| 5 Gretton | 26 | 11 | 8 | 7 | 64 | 52 | 12 | 41 |
| 6 Spratton | 26 | 11 | 7 | 8 | 61 | 63 | -2 | 40 |
| 7 Burton United | 26 | 10 | 7 | 9 | 47 | 49 | -2 | 37 |
| 8 Corby Eagles (-3) | 26 | 12 | 3 | 11 | 61 | 59 | 2 | 36 |
| 9 AFC Corby Shamrock | 26 | 10 | 3 | 13 | 68 | 74 | -6 | 33 |
| 10 Higham Ferrers (-3) | 26 | 10 | 2 | 14 | 55 | 88 | -33 | 29 |
| 11 Wootton St George (-6) | 26 | 10 | 2 | 14 | 70 | 49 | 21 | 26 |
| 12 Finedon Volta | 26 | 7 | 5 | 14 | 52 | 60 | -8 | 26 |
| 13 Kettering Orchard Park | 26 | 5 | 3 | 18 | 42 | 93 | -51 | 18 |
| 14 Weedon (-6) | 26 | 1 | 1 | 24 | 19 | 123 | -104 | -2 |

| DIVISION TWO | P | W | D | L | F | A | GD | Pts |
|---|---|---|---|---|---|---|---|---|
| 1 Desborough & Rothwell United | 24 | 21 | 0 | 3 | 69 | 23 | 46 | 6 |
| 2 Weldon United Reserves | 24 | 16 | 4 | 4 | 69 | 47 | 22 | 5 |
| 3 Roade Reserves | 24 | 13 | 7 | 4 | 67 | 43 | 24 | 4 |
| 4 Woodford Wolves | 24 | 11 | 3 | 10 | 54 | 57 | -3 | 3 |
| 5 West Haddon Albion | 24 | 11 | 3 | 10 | 43 | 49 | -6 | 3 |
| 6 Kislingbury | 24 | 8 | 8 | 8 | 44 | 43 | 1 | 3 |
| 7 Northampton Spartak | 24 | 9 | 3 | 12 | 52 | 49 | 3 | 3 |
| 8 Bugbrooke St Michaels 'A' | 24 | 8 | 3 | 13 | 46 | 63 | -17 | 2 |
| 9 Wellingborough Aztecs (-6) | 24 | 10 | 2 | 12 | 44 | 46 | -2 | 2 |
| 10 James King Blisworth Res. (-6) | 24 | 9 | 4 | 11 | 46 | 45 | 1 | 2 |
| 11 Kettering Park Rovers | 24 | 6 | 6 | 12 | 57 | 69 | -12 | |
| 12 Higham Town | 24 | 6 | 2 | 16 | 35 | 67 | -32 | 2 |
| 13 Corby Locos | 24 | 4 | 3 | 17 | 43 | 68 | -25 | |

## Northamptonshire Combination Premier Division

| | |
|---|---|
| **BRIXWORTH ALL SAINTS** | St Davids Close, off Froxhill Crescent, Brixworth NN6 9EA |
| **CORBY PEGASUS** | West Glebe South Pitch 3 NN17 1SZ |
| **CORBY S&L KHALSA** | Occupation Road, Corby, Northants. NN17 1EH |
| **EARLS BARTON UNITED** | The Grange, Northampton Road, Earls Barton, Northants NN6 0HA |
| **HARPOLE** | Playing Field, Larkhall Lane, Harpole NN7 4DP |
| **HEYFORD ATHLETIC** | Nether Heyford PF NN7 3LL |
| **JAMES KING BLISWORTH** | Blisworth Playing Field, Courteenhall Road, Blisworth NN7 3DD |
| **KETTERING NOMADS** | Isham Cricket Club NN14 1HW |
| **MEDBOURNE** | Medbourne S&S Club LE16 8DR |
| **MILTON** | Milton PF NN7 3AU |
| **MOULTON** | Brunting Road, Moulton, Northampton NN3 7QF |
| **ROADE** | Connolly Way, Hyde Road, Roade NN7 2LU |
| **SPRATTON** | Smith Street, Spratton NN6 8HW |
| **WELLINGBOROUGH RISING SUN** | Old Grammarians Memorial Sports Ground, Sywell Road, Wellingborough NN8 6BS |
| **WOLLASTON VICTORIA** | Wollaston PF NN29 7QP |

| DIVISION THREE | P | W | D | L | F | A | GD | Pts |
|---|---|---|---|---|---|---|---|---|
| AFC Houghton Magna | 24 | 20 | 3 | 1 | 96 | 29 | 67 | 63 |
| Mereway | 24 | 18 | 2 | 4 | 104 | 27 | 77 | 56 |
| Grange Park Rangers | 24 | 17 | 1 | 6 | 92 | 40 | 52 | 52 |
| Corby Kingswood | 24 | 16 | 3 | 5 | 80 | 36 | 44 | 51 |
| Northampton Falcons (-3) | 24 | 13 | 0 | 11 | 62 | 48 | 14 | 36 |
| Corby Strip Mills | 24 | 10 | 1 | 13 | 48 | 68 | -20 | 31 |
| JLB FC | 24 | 9 | 2 | 13 | 61 | 58 | 3 | 29 |
| Corby Ravens | 24 | 8 | 2 | 14 | 64 | 94 | -30 | 26 |
| Irthlingborough Town | 24 | 7 | 5 | 12 | 35 | 66 | -31 | 26 |
| 0 Kettering Nomads Res. | 24 | 6 | 5 | 13 | 39 | 65 | -26 | 23 |
| 1 Wilby | 24 | 6 | 4 | 14 | 44 | 90 | -46 | 22 |
| 2 Wollaston Victoria Res. (-3) | 24 | 7 | 2 | 15 | 40 | 55 | -15 | 20 |
| 3 Stanwick Rovers | 24 | 2 | 4 | 18 | 31 | 120 | -89 | 10 |

| DIVISION FOUR | P | W | D | L | F | A | GD | Pts |
|---|---|---|---|---|---|---|---|---|
| Corby Pegasus Res. | 24 | 16 | 5 | 3 | 55 | 29 | 26 | 53 |
| Bugbrooke St Michaels 'B' | 24 | 15 | 3 | 6 | 66 | 43 | 23 | 48 |
| Gretton Reserves | 24 | 13 | 5 | 6 | 47 | 30 | 17 | 44 |
| Medbourne Reserves | 24 | 13 | 1 | 10 | 61 | 59 | 2 | 40 |
| Earls Barton United Res.(-3) | 24 | 13 | 3 | 8 | 52 | 43 | 9 | 39 |
| Daventry Drayton Grange Res. (-3) | 24 | 12 | 4 | 8 | 64 | 37 | 27 | 37 |
| Brixworth All Saints Res. | 24 | 12 | 1 | 11 | 47 | 50 | -3 | 37 |
| Weldon United 'A' | 24 | 9 | 4 | 11 | 67 | 50 | 17 | 31 |
| Desborough & Rothwell Utd Res. | 24 | 9 | 3 | 12 | 52 | 60 | -8 | 30 |
| ) AFC Corby Shamrock Res. (-6) | 24 | 7 | 5 | 12 | 52 | 65 | -13 | 20 |
| Harpole Reserves | 24 | 5 | 3 | 16 | 32 | 52 | -20 | 18 |
| 2 Corby United | 24 | 5 | 3 | 16 | 39 | 74 | -35 | 18 |
| 3 Irthlingborough Rangers (-6) | 24 | 6 | 2 | 16 | 36 | 78 | -42 | 14 |

| DIVISION FIVE | P | W | D | L | F | A | GD | Pts |
|---|---|---|---|---|---|---|---|---|
| 1 FC FotoGold | 22 | 18 | 1 | 3 | 86 | 24 | 62 | 52 |
| 2 Daventry Rangers | 22 | 14 | 4 | 4 | 68 | 36 | 32 | 46 |
| 3 Corby Domino | 22 | 13 | 3 | 6 | 56 | 40 | 16 | 42 |
| 4 Heyford Athletic Res. | 22 | 13 | 3 | 6 | 51 | 36 | 15 | 42 |
| 5 West Haddon Albion Res. (-3) | 22 | 11 | 2 | 9 | 58 | 48 | 10 | 32 |
| 6 Kettering Ise Lodge | 22 | 10 | 2 | 10 | 44 | 43 | 1 | 32 |
| 7 Finedon Falcons Res. | 22 | 8 | 4 | 10 | 54 | 51 | 3 | 28 |
| 8 Finedon Volta Reserves | 22 | 8 | 4 | 10 | 45 | 59 | -14 | 28 |
| 9 Corby United Reserves | 22 | 5 | 6 | 11 | 38 | 62 | -24 | 21 |
| 10 Spratton Reserves (-6) | 22 | 6 | 5 | 11 | 29 | 45 | -16 | 17 |
| 11 Higham Town Reserves | 22 | 3 | 4 | 15 | 34 | 73 | -39 | 13 |
| 12 Wootton Rhinos (-3) | 22 | 1 | 6 | 15 | 44 | 90 | -46 | 6 |

**ADDITIONAL CLUB MOVEMENTS**

**Premier Division**

**In:** Spratton (P).

**Out:** Clipston (F); Daventry Drayton Grange (W); Weldon United (F - Adult teams only).

**Division One**

**In:** Desborough & Rothwell United (P); Roade Reserves (P); West Haddon Albion (P); Woodford Wolves (P).

**Out:** Spratton (P); Weedon (R - D3).

**Division Two**

**In:** Corby Strip Mills (P).

**Out:** Weldon United Reserves (F).

**Division Three**

**In:** Brixworth All Saints Reserves (P); Bugbrooke St Michaels (P); Daventry Rangers (P - D5); Earls Barton United Reserves (P); FC FotoGold (P - D5), Gretton Reserves (P); Medbourne Reserves (P); Weedon (R - D1)

**Out:** Corby Strip Mills (P); Northampton Falcons (R); Wilby (R).

**Division Four**

**In:** Finedon Volta Reserves (P); Heyford Athletic Reserves (P); Kettering Ise Lodge (P); Northampton Falcons (R); Wilby (R); Yelvertoft (N).

**Out:** Bugbrooke St Michaels (P); Earls Barton United Reserves (P); Gretton Reserves (P0; Medbourne Reserves (P): Weldon United 'A' (F)

**Division Five**

**In:** . Corby Hellenic Fisher (N); Corby Ravens Reserves (N); Corby Strip Mills Reserves (N); Corby Trades & Labour (N); Corby United Reserves (N); Daventry Rangers Reserves (N); Great Doddington (N); Irthlingborough Rangers (N); Moulton Reserves (N); Stanion United Reserves (N);

**Out:** Corby Domino (W); Daventry Rangers (P - D3); FC FotoGold (P - D3); Finedon Falcons Reserves (W); Finedon Volta Reserves (P); Heyford Athletic Reserves (P); Wootton Rhinos (W).

# NORTHERN ALLIANCE

**Sponsored by:** Pin Point Recruitment
**Founded:** 1890
**Recent Champions:**
**2013:** Heaton Stannington
**2014:** Blyth Town **2015:** Blyth Town

| PREMIER DIVISION | P | W | D | L | F | A | GD | Pts |
|---|---|---|---|---|---|---|---|---|
| 1 Blyth Town | 28 | 22 | 4 | 2 | 95 | 19 | 76 | 70 |
| 2 Whitley Bay A | 28 | 22 | 1 | 5 | 72 | 38 | 34 | 67 |
| 3 Carlisle City | 28 | 16 | 3 | 9 | 56 | 39 | 17 | 51 |
| 4 Seaton Delaval Amateurs | 28 | 16 | 3 | 9 | 55 | 50 | 5 | 51 |
| 5 Walker Central | 28 | 14 | 3 | 11 | 51 | 51 | 0 | 45 |
| 6 Killingworth Town (-3) | 28 | 13 | 6 | 9 | 63 | 52 | 11 | 42 |
| 7 Wallington | 28 | 12 | 4 | 12 | 58 | 55 | 3 | 40 |
| 8 Percy Main Amateurs | 28 | 9 | 6 | 13 | 61 | 68 | -7 | 33 |
| 9 AFC Newbiggin | 28 | 9 | 6 | 13 | 38 | 56 | -18 | 33 |
| 10 Gateshead Rutherford | 28 | 9 | 4 | 15 | 53 | 67 | -14 | 31 |
| 11 North Shields Athletic | 28 | 8 | 4 | 16 | 54 | 70 | -16 | 28 |
| 12 Shankhouse | 28 | 8 | 3 | 17 | 40 | 66 | -26 | 27 |
| 13 Ashington Colliers | 28 | 7 | 6 | 15 | 43 | 72 | -29 | 27 |
| 14 Northbank | 28 | 6 | 7 | 15 | 40 | 60 | -20 | 25 |
| 15 Red House Farm (-3) | 28 | 7 | 4 | 17 | 49 | 65 | -16 | 22 |

Whickham Sporting Club withdrew - record expunged.

**In:** Birtley Town (R - Northern).

**Out:** Blyth Town (P -Northern); Carlisle City (P - NWC).

**NB:** At the time of going to press, Shilbottle CW (promoted from D1) resigned from the Northern Alliance, at the time the League were yet to decide on whether it would change the constitution.

## CHALLENGE CUP

**HOLDERS:** BLYTH TOWN

**ROUND 1**

| | | | |
|---|---|---|---|
| Gateshead Rutherford | v | Killingworth Town | 0-10 |
| Seaton Delaval AFC | v | Ashington Colliers | 7-0 |
| Whickham Sporting Club | v | North Shields Athletic | 3-2 |
| Blyth Town | v | Wallington | 3-0 |
| Whitley Bay A | v | Red House Farm | 5-0 |
| Percy Main Amateurs | v | AFC Newbiggin | 1-2 |
| Carlisle City | v | Walker Central | 4-0 |
| Northbank Carlisle | v | Shankhouse | 2-5 |

QUARTER FINALS

| | | | |
|---|---|---|---|
| Killingworth Town | v | Seaton Delaval AFC | 2-1 |
| Blyth Town | Bye | | |
| Whitley Bay A | v | AFC Newbiggin | 2-1 |
| Carlisle City | v | Shankhouse | 3-0 |

SEMI FINALS

| | | | |
|---|---|---|---|
| Killingworth Town | v | Blyth Town | 1-3 |
| Whitley Bay A | v | Carlisle City | 0-1 |

FINAL

| | | | |
|---|---|---|---|
| Blyth Town | v | Carlisle City | 3-1 |

| PREMIER DIVISION | 1 | 2 | 3 | 4 | 5 | 6 | 7 | 8 | 9 | 10 | 11 | 12 | 13 | 14 | 15 |
|---|---|---|---|---|---|---|---|---|---|---|---|---|---|---|---|
| 1 AFC Newbiggin | | 2-2 | 0-1 | 1-2 | 2-1 | 2-2 | 1-1 | 1-0 | 2-0 | 2-1 | 4-1 | 2-1 | 2-2 | 0-2 | 2-5 |
| 2 Ashington Colliers | 3-1 | | 1-1 | 0-5 | 1-3 | 1-2 | 1-2 | 1-1 | 1-4 | 2-0 | 2-1 | 2-2 | 0-1 | 1-1 | 2-3 |
| 3 Blyth Town | 7-0 | 9-3 | | 1-2 | 3-0 | 0-0 | 4-0 | 5-1 | 2-0 | 4-1 | 2-0 | 5-0 | 2-0 | 2-4 | 4-2 |
| 4 Carlisle City | 3-1 | 1-1 | 1-1 | | 1-0 | 2-0 | 4-1 | 0-3 | 4-1 | 3-0 | 1-4 | 3-0 | 1-3 | 2-0 | 1-2 |
| 5 Gateshead Rutherford | 2-3 | 1-4 | 0-4 | 3-4 | | 1-3 | 2-0 | 5-1 | 1-1 | 0-0 | 1-2 | 2-2 | 3-4 | 2-5 | 0-3 |
| 6 Killingworth Town | 1-2 | 3-0 | 2-2 | 3-0 | 2-5 | | 0-1 | 4-1 | 3-2 | 3-3 | 1-5 | 3-1 | 1-4 | 3-2 | 0-1 |
| 7 North Shields Athletic | 3-2 | 1-2 | 2-3 | 2-4 | 7-4 | 1-7 | | 1-0 | 3-3 | 7-0 | 2-3 | 2-4 | 1-2 | 0-2 | 1-3 |
| 8 Northbank Carlisle | 1-1 | 7-1 | 0-2 | 2-2 | 0-2 | 0-0 | 0-2 | | 4-1 | 3-2 | 1-1 | 1-2 | 2-0 | 2-2 | 2-3 |
| 9 Percy Main Amateurs | 2-2 | 4-1 | 0-10 | 0-3 | 3-1 | 1-3 | 2-1 | 8-2 | | 1-1 | 2-3 | 2-1 | 2-2 | 1-3 | 2-2 |
| 10 Red House Farm | 3-1 | 5-0 | 0-1 | 2-1 | 2-3 | 2-4 | 2-2 | 3-0 | 1-3 | | 1-2 | 2-1 | 1-2 | 2-3 | 1-2 |
| 11 Seaton Delaval AFC | 2-0 | 4-3 | 0-3 | 0-2 | 1-4 | 0-4 | 2-2 | 3-1 | 0-6 | 6-0 | | 1-0 | 2-0 | 3-0 | 2-1 |
| 12 Shankhouse | 1-2 | 3-2 | 0-8 | 1-0 | 2-3 | 2-2 | 1-4 | 3-0 | 3-2 | 1-3 | 4-1 | | 4-1 | 1-2 | 0-1 |
| 13 Walker Central | 2-0 | 2-3 | 0-4 | 3-1 | 0-2 | 0-1 | 4-2 | 3-3 | 0-4 | 4-3 | 0-2 | 2-0 | | 2-0 | 3-0 |
| 14 Wallington | 1-0 | 1-3 | 0-2 | 2-3 | 2-2 | 8-4 | 4-0 | 0-2 | 4-2 | 0-6 | 1-1 | 6-0 | 1-4 | | 1-2 |
| 15 Whitley Bay A | 4-0 | 2-0 | 0-3 | 2-0 | 5-0 | 3-2 | 4-3 | 2-0 | 5-2 | 4-2 | 2-3 | 2-0 | 4-1 | 3-1 | |

| DIVISION ONE | P | W | D | L | F | A | GD | Pts |
|---|---|---|---|---|---|---|---|---|
| 1 Shilbottle C W | 28 | 21 | 3 | 4 | 98 | 33 | 65 | 66 |
| 2 Newcastle University | 28 | 20 | 3 | 5 | 111 | 33 | 78 | 63 |
| 3 Ponteland United | 28 | 17 | 3 | 8 | 88 | 55 | 33 | 54 |
| 4 Birtley St Josephs | 28 | 14 | 5 | 9 | 63 | 52 | 11 | 47 |
| 5 Felling Magpies | 28 | 14 | 3 | 11 | 56 | 50 | 6 | 45 |
| 6 New Fordley | 28 | 14 | 3 | 11 | 57 | 59 | -2 | 45 |
| 7 Hexham (-6) | 28 | 14 | 2 | 12 | 56 | 52 | 4 | 38 |
| 8 Wallsend Boys Club (-3) | 28 | 10 | 10 | 8 | 63 | 55 | 8 | 37 |
| 9 Cramlington Town (-3) | 28 | 13 | 1 | 14 | 52 | 53 | -1 | 37 |
| 10 Lindisfarne Custom Planet | 28 | 11 | 4 | 13 | 49 | 70 | -21 | 37 |
| 11 Hebburn Reyrolle (-3) | 28 | 9 | 3 | 16 | 50 | 95 | -45 | 27 |
| 12 Gosforth Bohemian | 28 | 8 | 2 | 18 | 56 | 82 | -26 | 26 |
| 13 Newcastle Chemfica Ind | 28 | 7 | 3 | 18 | 44 | 76 | -32 | 24 |
| 14 Cullercoats (-3) | 28 | 6 | 5 | 17 | 57 | 84 | -27 | 20 |
| 15 Blyth Isabella | 28 | 6 | 2 | 20 | 35 | 86 | -51 | 20 |

**In:** Heaton Stannington A (Merger with Newcastle Chemfica Ind & Heaton Stannington), Monkseaton (NC from Lindisfarne C.P.)

**Out:** Blyth Isabella (W). Newcastle Chemfica Ind (Merged with Heaton Stannington)

| DIVISION TWO | P | W | D | L | F | A | GD | Pts |
|---|---|---|---|---|---|---|---|---|
| 1 Gateshead FC A | 28 | 24 | 1 | 3 | 142 | 27 | 115 | [illegible] |
| 2 Grainger Park Boys Club (-3) | 28 | 20 | 3 | 5 | 96 | 56 | 40 | [illegible] |
| 3 Seaton Burn | 28 | 18 | 5 | 5 | 62 | 34 | 28 | [illegible] |
| 4 Wallsend Labour Club | 28 | 14 | 7 | 7 | 65 | 49 | 16 | [illegible] |
| 5 Alnmouth United | 28 | 15 | 3 | 10 | 68 | 49 | 19 | [illegible] |
| 6 Gateshead Redheugh 1957 | 28 | 14 | 5 | 9 | 53 | 55 | -2 | [illegible] |
| 7 Hazlerigg Victory | 28 | 12 | 6 | 10 | 72 | 54 | 18 | [illegible] |
| 8 Forest Hall | 28 | 10 | 4 | 14 | 53 | 62 | -9 | [illegible] |
| 9 Prudhoe Youth Club Senior | 28 | 8 | 8 | 12 | 68 | 78 | -10 | [illegible] |
| 10 Whitburn Athletic | 28 | 8 | 7 | 13 | 55 | 72 | -17 | [illegible] |
| 11 Cramlington United | 28 | 8 | 6 | 14 | 50 | 69 | -19 | [illegible] |
| 12 Wideopen & District | 28 | 8 | 4 | 16 | 53 | 95 | -42 | [illegible] |
| 13 Swalwell | 28 | 6 | 5 | 17 | 48 | 93 | -45 | [illegible] |
| 14 Whitley Bay BC Seniors | 28 | 5 | 4 | 19 | 35 | 85 | -50 | [illegible] |
| 15 Willington Quay Saints | 28 | 2 | 8 | 18 | 48 | 90 | -42 | [illegible] |
| 16 Wideopen An District | 30 | 4 | 0 | 26 | 36 | 130 | -94 | [illegible] |

Wooler withdrew - record expunged.

**In:** Bedlington Town (N), Blyth FC (Newcastle Corinthians League), Blyth Town A (N), Killingworth YPC (Durham Alliance Combination), Red Row Welfare (North Northumberland League), Raton & Crawcrook A (Tyneside Amateur), Spittal Rovers (North Northumberland).

## Northern Alliance Premier Division

| | | |
|---|---|---|
| **AFC NEWBIGGIN** | Newbiggin Sports Centre, Newbiggin by the Sea NE64 6HG | 07528 608 807 |
| **ASHINGTON COLLIERS** | Ashington FC, Hirst Welfare, Alexandra Road, Ashington NE63 9HF | 07745 344 502 |
| **BIRTLEY TOWN** | Birtley Sports Complex, Durham Road, Birtley DH3 2TB | 07958 540 389 |
| **GATESHEAD RUTHERFORD** | Eslington Park, Gateshead NE8 2TQ | 07538 837 130 |
| **KILLINGWORTH TOWN** | West Moor Community Centre, Benton Lane, West Moor, Newcastle NE12 7NP | 07896 262 944 |
| **NEWCASTLE UNIVERSITY** | Cochrane Park, Etherstone Avenue, Newcastle upon Tyne NE7 7JX | 07971 852 468 |
| **NORTH SHIELDS ATHLETIC** | John Spence Community High School, Preston Road, North Shields NE29 9PU | 07813 590 965 |
| **NORTHBANK CARLISLE** | Sheepmount Sports Complex, Sheepmount, Carlisle CA3 8XL | 07761 416 331 |
| **PERCY MAIN AMATEURS** | Purvis Park, St Johns Green, Percy Main, North Shields NE29 6HS | 07960 189 667 |
| **RED HOUSE FARM** | Kingston Park Road, Newcastle-upon-Tyne NE3 2HY | 07770 943 120 |
| **SEATON DELAVAL AMATEURS** | Wheatridge Park, Seaton Delaval, Whitley Bay NE25 0QH | 07969 551 513 |
| **SHANKHOUSE** | Action Park, Dudley NE23 7HY | 01670 361 929 |
| **WALKER CENTRAL** | Peggy Shepherd Pavillion, Monkchester Road, Newcastle-upon-Tyne NE6 2LJ | 07858 721 828 |
| **WALLINGTON** | Oakford Park, Scots Gap, Morpeth NE61 4EJ | 07920 099 416 |
| **WHITLEY BAY A** | Hillheads Park, Rink Way, off Hillheads Road, Whitley Bay NE25 8HR | 07534 711 921 |

## GEORGE DOBBIN LEAGUE CUP

**HOLDERS:** BLYTH TOWN

**ROUND 1**

| | | | |
|---|---|---|---|
| New Fordley | v | Prudhoe Youth Club Senior | 2-1 |
| Cramlington United | v | Whickham Sporting Club | 2-3 |
| Forest Hall | v | Willington Quay Saints | 2-1 |
| Felling Magpies | v | Newcastle Chemfica Ind | 3-2 |
| Ashington Colliers | v | Killingworth Town | 3-6 |
| Birtley St Josephs | v | Northbank Carlisle | 1-0 |
| Percy Main Amateurs | v | Seaton Delaval AFC | 2-3 |
| Swalwell | v | Wallington | 2-3 |
| Longbenton | v | Gateshead Redheugh 1957 | 2-3 |
| Newcastle University | v | Hexham | 4-2 |
| Hazlerigg Victory | v | AFC Newbiggin | 3-5 |
| Whitley Bay A | v | Carlisle City | 3-2 |
| Cramlington Town | v | Gateshead Rutherford | 2-1 |
| Ponteland United | v | North Shields Athletic | 2-0 |
| Whitley Bay Boys Club Senior | v | Hebburn Reyrolle | 1-3 |

**ROUND 2**

| | | | |
|---|---|---|---|
| New Fordley | v | Grainger Park B C | 3-6 |
| Gateshead FC A | v | Whickham Sporting Club | 2-1 |
| Forest Hall | v | Wallsend Labour Club | 0-3 |
| Wideopen & District | v | Shankhouse | 0-4 |
| Felling Magpies | v | Blyth Town | 1-0 |
| Alnmouth United | v | Red House Farm | 3-0 |
| Cullercoats | v | Wallsend Boys Club | 3-2 |
| Killingworth Town | v | Birtley St Josephs | 5-4 |
| Lindisfarne Custon Planet | v | Shilbottle C W | 1-3 |
| Seaton Delaval AFC | v | Wallington | 4-3 |
| Whitburn Athletic | v | Gateshead Redheugh 1957 | 6-4 |
| Newcastle University | v | Blyth Isabella | 2-0 |
| Seaton Burn | v | AFC Newbiggin | 2-1 |
| Walker Central | v | Whitley Bay A | 4-5 |
| Cramlington Town | v | Ponteland United | 4-7 |
| Gosforth Bohemians | v | Hebburn Reyrolle | 2-4 |

**ROUND 3**

| | | | |
|---|---|---|---|
| Grainger Park B C | v | Gateshead FC A | 3-2 |
| Wallsend Labour Club | v | Shankhouse | 1-0 |
| Felling Magpies | v | Alnmouth United | 2-1 |
| Cullercoats | v | Killingworth Town | 2-1 |
| Shilbottle C W | v | Seaton Delaval AFC | 0-1 |
| Whitburn Athletic | v | Newcastle University | 1-3 |
| Seaton Burn | v | Whitley Bay A | 1-0 |
| Ponteland United | v | Hebburn Reyrolle | 5-1 |

**QUARTER FINALS**

| | | | |
|---|---|---|---|
| Grainger Park B C | v | Wallsend Labour Club | 3-1 |
| Felling Magpies | v | Cullercoats | 2-1 |
| Seaton Delaval AFC | v | Newcastle University | 5-3 |
| Seaton Burn | v | Ponteland United | 0-3 |

**SEMI FINALS**

| | | | |
|---|---|---|---|
| Grainger Park B C | v | Felling Magpies | 1-0 |
| Seaton Delaval AFC | v | Ponteland United | 0-1 |

**FINAL**

| | | | |
|---|---|---|---|
| Grainger Park B C | v | Ponteland United | 0-3 |

## COMBINATION CUP

**FINAL** **HOLDERS:** AFC NEWBIGGIN

| | | | |
|---|---|---|---|
| Cramlington Town | v | Newcastle University | 1-2 |

## AMATEUR CUP

**FINAL**

| | | | |
|---|---|---|---|
| Gateshead FC A | v | Grainger Park B C | 1-0 |

## BILL GARDNER CUP

**FINAL**

| | | | |
|---|---|---|---|
| Carlisle City | v | Percy Main Amateurs | 3-1 |

# NOTTINGHAMSHIRE SENIOR LEAGUE

**Sponsored by:** Precision
**Founded:** 2004
**Recent Champions:**
**2013:** Bulwell FC
**2014:** Selston **2015:** Wollaton

| SENIOR DIVISION | P | W | D | L | F | A | GD | Pts |
|---|---|---|---|---|---|---|---|---|
| 1 Ruddington Village | 34 | 26 | 3 | 5 | 104 | 46 | 58 | 81 |
| 2 Wollaton | 34 | 25 | 5 | 4 | 86 | 37 | 49 | 80 |
| 3 West Bridgford | 34 | 23 | 6 | 5 | 103 | 39 | 64 | 75 |
| 4 Unity (-1) | 34 | 21 | 8 | 5 | 122 | 51 | 71 | 70 |
| 5 Awsworth Villa | 34 | 22 | 4 | 8 | 87 | 50 | 37 | 70 |
| 6 Clifton All Whites | 34 | 18 | 9 | 7 | 95 | 53 | 42 | 63 |
| 7 Real United (-3) | 34 | 19 | 7 | 8 | 115 | 45 | 70 | 61 |
| 8 Dunkirk AFC | 34 | 13 | 7 | 14 | 73 | 58 | 15 | 46 |
| 9 Bilborough Town | 34 | 12 | 7 | 15 | 73 | 87 | -14 | 43 |
| 10 Burton Joyce | 34 | 13 | 4 | 17 | 70 | 105 | -35 | 43 |
| 11 Attenborough | 34 | 11 | 5 | 18 | 51 | 75 | -24 | 38 |
| 12 Bingham Town (-3) | 34 | 9 | 7 | 18 | 55 | 72 | -17 | 31 |
| 13 Cotgrave | 34 | 8 | 6 | 20 | 54 | 83 | -29 | 30 |
| 14 Underwood Villa | 34 | 7 | 7 | 20 | 48 | 79 | -31 | 28 |
| 15 FC Cavaliers | 34 | 7 | 7 | 20 | 39 | 86 | -47 | 28 |
| 16 Newark Flowserve | 34 | 7 | 7 | 20 | 40 | 96 | -56 | 28 |
| 17 Beeston | 34 | 7 | 6 | 21 | 37 | 84 | -47 | 27 |
| 18 Sandhurst | 34 | 4 | 3 | 27 | 41 | 147 | -106 | 15 |

## SENIOR CUP

**HOLDERS:** WOLLATON

**ROUND 1**

| | | | |
|---|---|---|---|
| Calverton Miners Welfare | v | Sandhurst | 3-3, 4-5p |
| Attenborough | v | Clifton All Whites | 1-6 |
| Wollaton | v | Magdala Amateurs | 5-0 |
| Bilborough United | v | Burton Joyce | 2-1 |
| Kirton Brickworks | v | AFC Clifton | 4-1 |
| Bilborough Town | v | Gedling Southbank | 5-2 |
| Real United | v | Ashland Rovers | 5-0 |
| Bingham Town | v | West Bridgford | 0-1 |
| Nottinghamshire | v | Watnall Athletic | 4-2 |
| Unity | Bye | | |
| Awsworth Villa | Bye | | |
| Aspley Park | v | Underwood Villa | 1-8 |
| Netherfield Albion | Bye | | |
| Cotgrave | v | Dunkirk AFC | 2-2, 6-5p |
| Beeston | v | FC Cavaliers | 2-1 |
| Newark Flowserve | v | Ruddington Village | 1-0 |

**ROUND 2**

| | | | |
|---|---|---|---|
| Sandhurst | v | Clifton All Whites | 2-3 |
| Wollaton | v | Bilborough United | 5-0 |
| Kirton Brickworks | v | Bilborough Town | 0-3 |
| Real United | v | West Bridgford | 3-1 |
| Nottinghamshire | v | Unity | 0-3 |

| SENIOR DIVISION | 1 | 2 | 3 | 4 | 5 | 6 | 7 | 8 | 9 | 10 | 11 | 12 | 13 | 14 | 15 | 16 | 17 | 18 |
|---|---|---|---|---|---|---|---|---|---|---|---|---|---|---|---|---|---|---|
| 1 Attenborough | | 5-1 | 0-0 | 3-4 | 1-2 | 2-1 | 0-3 | 0-4 | 3-1 | 1-1 | 3-1 | 1-5 | 0-1 | 2-0 | 0-0 | 0-5 | 0-3 | 1-2 |
| 2 Awsworth Villa | 3-0 | | 6-1 | 3-2 | 6-0 | 4-1 | 4-3 | 3-0 | 3-1 | 2-1 | 3-1 | H-W | 3-0 | 2-0 | 3-2 | 2-2 | 3-5 | 2-4 |
| 3 Beeston | 1-0 | 0-3 | | 2-2 | 3-1 | 1-2 | 1-2 | 1-0 | 0-1 | 1-0 | 0-1 | 0-3 | 0-4 | 3-1 | 0-0 | 1-3 | 0-1 | 0-3 |
| 4 Bilborough Town | 0-3 | 3-2 | 2-2 | | 2-5 | 1-1 | 1-3 | 6-1 | 0-4 | 4-0 | 2-0 | 1-5 | 0-2 | 4-2 | 3-2 | 1-6 | 3-3 | 4-4 |
| 5 Bingham Town | 0-1 | 3-3 | 2-0 | 3-1 | | 1-3 | 0-1 | 1-2 | 0-4 | 3-1 | 1-1 | 1-5 | 2-2 | 3-2 | 7-1 | 4-6 | 1-3 | 0-1 |
| 6 Burton Joyce | 8-2 | 2-3 | 1-1 | 1-5 | 3-1 | | 1-5 | 3-2 | 2-1 | 0-2 | 2-1 | 5-2 | 2-5 | 1-2 | 3-2 | 1-10 | 1-7 | 2-4 |
| 7 Clifton All Whites | 3-0 | 3-0 | 0-1 | 1-5 | 4-1 | 4-1 | | 2-2 | 0-2 | 3-0 | 4-2 | 2-2 | 2-2 | 10-0 | 0-0 | 1-5 | 5-1 | 0-2 |
| 8 Cotgrave | 1-1 | 0-1 | 3-2 | 3-1 | 0-1 | 2-2 | 0-2 | | 1-4 | 1-0 | 6-0 | 1-3 | 2-3 | 3-3 | 2-3 | 1-3 | 0-2 | 3-1 |
| 9 Dunkirk AFC | 2-1 | 2-2 | 3-3 | 3-3 | 2-2 | 3-1 | 2-2 | 4-2 | | 2-0 | 7-2 | 1-3 | 1-2 | 9-0 | 1-4 | 2-3 | 0-1 | 2-1 |
| 10 FC Cavaliers | 2-2 | 2-5 | 5-1 | 0-3 | 2-1 | 0-2 | 1-2 | 1-1 | 1-1 | | 2-2 | 0-6 | 2-7 | 2-0 | 4-3 | 2-2 | 0-5 | 0-3 |
| 11 Newark Flowserve | 0-5 | 1-0 | 3-0 | 0-0 | 1-1 | 1-3 | 2-8 | 3-0 | 1-0 | 0-1 | | 0-5 | 0-3 | 2-5 | 3-5 | 1-1 | 0-4 | 1-1 |
| 12 Real United | 4-1 | 0-3 | 9-0 | 5-1 | 1-1 | 4-2 | 4-4 | 5-0 | 4-3 | 3-2 | 8-1 | | 1-2 | 6-0 | 5-0 | 1-1 | 2-2 | 2-3 |
| 13 Ruddington Village | 5-2 | 2-1 | 4-3 | 2-1 | 2-1 | 5-1 | 3-4 | 5-0 | 3-0 | 5-1 | 5-2 | 3-2 | | 5-0 | 3-1 | 1-2 | 0-3 | 2-1 |
| 14 Sandhurst | 2-6 | 0-5 | 4-6 | 0-2 | 1-1 | 3-7 | 1-6 | 1-8 | 2-1 | 1-1 | 3-4 | 0-8 | 1-6 | | 2-1 | 2-5 | 0-8 | 0-4 |
| 15 Underwood Villa | 1-2 | 2-1 | 4-1 | 0-1 | 1-0 | 0-3 | 3-3 | 1-1 | 1-2 | 1-3 | 1-2 | 1-1 | 1-3 | 2-1 | | 2-3 | 0-0 | 1-2 |
| 16 Unity | 1-2 | 2-2 | 4-0 | 9-2 | 2-1 | 8-0 | 2-2 | 8-0 | 0-0 | 6-0 | 2-0 | 1-0 | 0-4 | 6-2 | 6-0 | | 1-2 | 3-5 |
| 17 West Bridgford | 6-0 | 0-1 | 5-1 | 3-1 | 2-4 | 9-0 | 2-1 | 3-2 | 3-2 | 4-0 | 4-0 | 0-0 | 2-2 | 3-0 | 4-2 | 2-2 | | 1-3 |
| 18 Wollaton | 2-1 | 0-2 | 2-1 | 4-2 | 2-0 | 2-2 | 0-0 | 4-0 | 2-0 | 3-0 | 1-1 | 2-1 | 2-1 | 5-0 | 4-0 | 5-2 | 2-0 | |

| DIVISION ONE | P | W | D | L | F | A | GD | Pts |
|---|---|---|---|---|---|---|---|---|
| 1 South Normanton Town | 32 | 28 | 2 | 2 | 124 | 42 | 82 | 86 |
| 2 Ruddington Village Res. | 32 | 19 | 5 | 8 | 105 | 70 | 35 | 62 |
| 3 Magdala Amateurs | 32 | 19 | 3 | 10 | 96 | 64 | 32 | 60 |
| 4 Hucknall Rolls Leisure Res. | 32 | 18 | 3 | 11 | 66 | 55 | 11 | 57 |
| 5 Ashland Rovers | 32 | 17 | 4 | 11 | 75 | 62 | 13 | 55 |
| 6 Wollaton Reserves | 32 | 15 | 8 | 9 | 66 | 54 | 12 | 53 |
| 7 Bilborough United | 32 | 15 | 4 | 13 | 67 | 49 | 18 | 49 |
| 8 Calverton Miners Welfare | 32 | 13 | 10 | 9 | 84 | 67 | 17 | 49 |
| 9 Gedling Southbank | 32 | 14 | 6 | 12 | 68 | 75 | -7 | 48 |
| 10 Aspley Park (-1) | 32 | 14 | 6 | 12 | 72 | 69 | 3 | 47 |
| 11 Kimberley Miners Welfare Res. | 32 | 13 | 3 | 16 | 59 | 52 | 7 | 42 |
| 12 Clifton All Whites Res. | 32 | 11 | 4 | 17 | 67 | 103 | -36 | 37 |
| 13 Linby Colliery Welfare Res. | 32 | 11 | 3 | 18 | 54 | 92 | -38 | 36 |
| 14 Netherfield Albion | 32 | 10 | 4 | 18 | 51 | 72 | -21 | 34 |
| 15 Nottinghamshire | 32 | 8 | 3 | 21 | 55 | 96 | -41 | 27 |
| 16 Southwell City Reserves | 32 | 5 | 4 | 23 | 53 | 98 | -45 | 19 |
| 17 Kirton Brickworks | 32 | 3 | 6 | 23 | 41 | 83 | -42 | 15 |

| DIVISION TWO | P | W | D | L | F | A | GD | Pts |
|---|---|---|---|---|---|---|---|---|
| 1 Awsworth Villa Reserves | 22 | 14 | 3 | 5 | 68 | 31 | 37 | 45 |
| 2 Keyworth United Res. | 22 | 14 | 2 | 6 | 77 | 36 | 41 | 44 |
| 3 Bilsthorpe Reserves | 22 | 13 | 5 | 4 | 63 | 27 | 36 | 4[illegible] |
| 4 AFC Clifton | 22 | 14 | 1 | 7 | 65 | 41 | 24 | 4[illegible] |
| 5 Watnall Athletic | 22 | 13 | 2 | 7 | 62 | 32 | 30 | 4[illegible] |
| 6 Selston Reserves | 22 | 11 | 2 | 9 | 65 | 33 | 32 | 3[illegible] |
| 7 Aspley Park Reserves | 22 | 10 | 2 | 10 | 44 | 39 | 5 | 3[illegible] |
| 8 Underwood Villa Res. | 22 | 9 | 3 | 10 | 44 | 53 | -9 | 3[illegible] |
| 9 Bingham Town Reserves | 22 | 9 | 2 | 11 | 45 | 44 | 1 | 2[illegible] |
| 10 Cotgrave Reserves | 22 | 8 | 4 | 10 | 58 | 52 | 6 | 2[illegible] |
| 11 Nottinghamshire Res. | 22 | 3 | 2 | 17 | 30 | 120 | -90 | 1[illegible] |
| 12 Bilborough Town Res. | 22 | 0 | 0 | 22 | 22 | 135 | -113 | |

## SENIOR CUP

| | | | |
|---|---|---|---|
| Awsworth Villa | v | Underwood Villa | 1-0 |
| Netherfield Albion | v | Cotgrave | 1-4 |
| Beeston | v | Newark Flowserve | 2-3 aet |

**QUARTER FINALS**

| | | | |
|---|---|---|---|
| Clifton All Whites | v | Wollaton | HW |
| Bilborough Town | v | Real United | 1-1, 4-6p |
| Unity | v | Awsworth Villa | 4-5 |
| Cotgrave | v | Newark Flowserve | 0-1 |

**SEMI FINALS**

| | | | |
|---|---|---|---|
| Clifton All Whites | v | Real United | 1-3 |
| Awsworth Villa | v | Newark Flowserve | 2-1 |

**FINAL**

| | | | |
|---|---|---|---|
| Real United | v | Awsworth Villa | 1-2 |

## Nottinghamshire Senior Premier Division

| | | |
|---|---|---|
| **AFC DUNKIRK** | Ron Steel Sports Ground, Lenton Lane, Nottingham NG7 2SA | |
| **ASTON UNITED** | Ilkeston Football Club New Manor Ground, Awsworth Road, Ilkeston DE7 8JF | 0115 944 4428 |
| **ATTENBOROUGH** | Village Green, The Strand, Attenborough, Nottingham NG9 6AU | 0115 9257 439 |
| **AWSWORTH VILLA** | The Shilo, Attewell Road, Awsworth, Nottingham NG16 2SY | |
| **BASFORD UNITED COMMUNITY** | Greenwich Avenue | |
| **BEESTON AFC** | Hetley Pearson Rec. Grd, Cartwright Way, Queens Road, Beeston NG9 1RL | |
| **BILBOROUGH TOWN** | Harvey Hadden | |
| **BINGHAM TOWN** | Butt Field, Bingham, Nottingham NG13 8GG | |
| **CLIFTON ALL WHITES** | Green Lane, Clifton, Nottingham NG11 9AZ | |
| **COTGRAVE** | Woodview, Cotgrave Welfare, Woodview, Cotgrave, Nottingham NG12 | |
| **FC CAVALIERS** | The Forest. #1, Gregory Boulevard, Nottingham NG7 2SA | |
| **MAGDALA AMATEURS** | Roko, Wilford Lane, West Bridgford, Nottingham NG2 7RN | |
| **NEWARK FLOWSERVE** | Hawton Lane, Newark, Nottinghamshire NG24 3BU | |
| **NOTTINGHAM TRENT UNIVERSITY** | Clifton Campas, lifton Lane, Clifton, Nottingham NG11 8NS | |
| **REAL UNITED** | Inspire Stadium, Stoke Lane, Stoke Bardolph, Nottingham. NG14 5HX | |
| **RUDDINGTON VILLAGE** | Elms Park, Ruddington, Nottingham | 07545 388439 |
| **SANDIACRE TOWN** | St Giles | |
| **UNDERWOOD VILLA** | Bracken Park, Felly Mill Lane, North, Off Mansfield Road, Underwood NG16 5FG | |
| **UNITY** | Greenwood Meadows, Lenton Lane | |
| **WOLLATON** | Wollaton Sports Association, 753 Wollaton Road, Wollaton, NG8 2AN | |

**LUB MOVEMENTS**
**remier Division**
: Aston United (Midlands Regional Alliance), Basford United Community, Magdala Amateurs (P), Sandiacre Town (Midlands Regional Alliance), ottingham Trent University.
**ut:** Burton Joyce (W), Sandhurst (W), West Bridgford (P - East Midlands Counties).

**vision One**
: AFC Bridgford (Notts Amateur Alliance); AFC Clifton (P); Awsworth Villa Reserves (P); Keyworth United Reserves (P); Watnall (P).
**ut:** Hucknall Rolls Leisure Reserves (W); Linby CW Reserves (W); South Normanton Town

**vision Two**
: Aslockton Cranmers (N); Basford United Community Reserves (N); Beeston Reserves (N); Greyhounders (Grantham League); Ravenshead (Midnds Amateur Alliance); Team DNF (J); The Rock (Derby Churches League); West Bridgford Reserves (N).
**ut:** Cotgrave Reserves (W).

# OXFORDSHIRE SENIOR LEAGUE

**Sponsored by:** No sponsor

**Founded:** N/K

**Recent Champions:**

**2013:** Riverside

**2014:** Oakley United

**2015:** Oakley United

| PREMIER DIVISION | P | W | D | L | F | A | GD | Pts |
|---|---|---|---|---|---|---|---|---|
| 1 OUP | 22 | 17 | 4 | 1 | 89 | 24 | 65 | 55 |
| 2 Mansfield Road | 22 | 14 | 5 | 3 | 52 | 29 | 23 | 47 |
| 3 Garsington | 22 | 12 | 2 | 8 | 53 | 56 | -3 | 38 |
| 4 Adderbury Park | 22 | 11 | 3 | 8 | 35 | 34 | 1 | 36 |
| 5 Freeland | 22 | 9 | 6 | 7 | 49 | 43 | 6 | 33 |
| 6 Chalgrove | 22 | 10 | 2 | 10 | 36 | 45 | -9 | 32 |
| 7 Kidlington Old Boys | 22 | 8 | 6 | 8 | 31 | 44 | -13 | 30 |
| 8 Launton Sports | 22 | 8 | 5 | 9 | 33 | 41 | -8 | 29 |
| 9 Horspath | 22 | 7 | 3 | 12 | 39 | 44 | -5 | 24 |
| 10 Eynsham | 22 | 6 | 2 | 14 | 36 | 48 | -12 | 20 |
| 11 Marston Saints | 22 | 6 | 2 | 14 | 26 | 48 | -22 | 20 |
| 12 Middleton Cheney | 22 | 3 | 2 | 17 | 24 | 47 | -23 | 11 |

**In:** Cropedy (P), Heyford Athletic (P - Banbury District & Lord Jersey FA), Yarnton (P).

## PRESIDENTS CUP

**HOLDERS:** EYNSHAM

**ROUND 1**

| | | | |
|---|---|---|---|
| Oakley United | v | OUP | 0-18 |
| Oxford Irish | v | Eynsham | 0-7 |
| Middleton Cheney | v | Chalgrove | 2-0 |
| Charlton | v | Adderbury Park | 1-7 |
| Freeland | v | Mansfield Road | 5-1 |
| Cropedy | v | Marston Saints | 3-1 |
| Northway | v | Kidlington Old Boys | 1-2 |
| Horspath | - | Bye | |
| Blackbird Rovers | v | Garsington | 3-4 |
| Yarnton | v | Launton Sports | 1-2 |

**ROUND 2**

| | | | |
|---|---|---|---|
| OUP | v | Eynsham | 2-0 |
| Middleton Cheney | - | Bye | |
| Adderbury Park | - | Bye | |
| Freeland | - | Bye | |
| Cropedy | v | Kidlington Old Boys | 2-2, 3-1p |
| Horspath | - | Bye | |
| Garsington | - | Bye | |
| Launton Sports | - | Bye | |

**QUARTER FINALS**

| | | | |
|---|---|---|---|
| OUP | v | Middleton Cheney | HW |
| Adderbury Park | v | Freeland | 3-2 |
| Cropedy | v | Horspath | 3-2 |
| Garsington | v | Launton Sports | 6-1 |

**SEMI FINALS**

| | | | |
|---|---|---|---|
| OUP | v | Adderbury Park | 2-3 |
| Cropedy | v | Garsington | 1-3 aet |

**FINAL**

| | | | |
|---|---|---|---|
| Adderbury Park | v | Garsington | 3-2 |

| PREMIER DIVISION | 1 | 2 | 3 | 4 | 5 | 6 | 7 | 8 | 9 | 10 | 11 | 12 |
|---|---|---|---|---|---|---|---|---|---|---|---|---|
| 1 Adderbury Park | | 2-1 | 2-1 | 0-2 | H-W | 2-1 | 1-1 | 1-1 | H-W | 0-1 | 2-1 | 0-1 |
| 2 Chalgrove | 1-3 | | 2-0 | 2-1 | 2-1 | 2-1 | H-W | 2-1 | 1-2 | 2-1 | H-W | 1-6 |
| 3 Eynsham | 4-0 | 1-3 | | 0-2 | 3-4 | 2-2 | 1-3 | 3-1 | 0-2 | 0-1 | 5-3 | 0-3 |
| 4 Freeland | 2-4 | 1-1 | 1-2 | | 10-2 | 3-2 | 2-2 | 2-0 | 2-2 | 4-1 | 6-1 | 2-2 |
| 5 Garsington | 5-2 | 2-1 | 2-2 | 4-0 | | 4-1 | 2-3 | 3-3 | 0-7 | 3-2 | H-W | 2-3 |
| 6 Horspath | 2-0 | 4-1 | 3-2 | 1-3 | 4-5 | | 3-1 | 1-3 | 2-2 | 0-0 | 0-2 | 2-4 |
| 7 Kidlington Old Boys | 2-2 | 3-1 | 1-3 | 0-0 | 0-1 | H-W | | 1-1 | 0-2 | 4-0 | 2-1 | 0-7 |
| 8 Launton Sports | 0-3 | 3-2 | 2-0 | 1-1 | 1-0 | 3-4 | 2-2 | | 1-2 | 2-1 | 3-0 | 0-5 |
| 9 Mansfield Rd | 4-2 | 3-2 | 4-3 | 4-2 | 1-4 | 3-1 | 1-3 | 4-1 | | 1-0 | 1-1 | 1- |
| 10 Marston Saints | 0-6 | 4-1 | 2-1 | 4-1 | 0-3 | 2-3 | 2-3 | 0-2 | 0-2 | | 3-1 | 0- |
| 11 Middleton Cheney | 0-2 | 2-4 | 4-0 | A-W | 2-3 | 0-2 | 2-0 | 0-2 | 1-2 | 2-2 | | 1- |
| 12 OUP | 4-1 | 4-4 | 1-3 | 8-2 | 9-3 | H-W | 10-0 | 4-0 | 2-2 | H-W | 4-0 | |

| DIVISION ONE | P | W | D | L | F | A | GD | Pts |
|---|---|---|---|---|---|---|---|---|
| 1 Blackbird Rovers | 15 | 12 | 2 | 1 | 51 | 21 | 30 | 38 |
| 2 Cropedy | 15 | 10 | 2 | 3 | 44 | 25 | 19 | 32 |
| 3 Yarnton | 15 | 8 | 4 | 3 | 40 | 21 | 19 | 28 |
| 4 Northway | 16 | 9 | 1 | 6 | 42 | 41 | 1 | 28 |
| 5 OUP Reserves | 15 | 8 | 1 | 6 | 31 | 24 | 7 | 25 |
| 6 Charlton | 16 | 7 | 3 | 6 | 20 | 21 | -1 | 24 |
| 7 Oxford Irish | 16 | 3 | 2 | 11 | 25 | 39 | -14 | 11 |
| 8 Marston Saints Reserves | 16 | 3 | 1 | 12 | 21 | 46 | -25 | 10 |
| 9 Horspath Reserves | 16 | 2 | 0 | 14 | 25 | 61 | -36 | 6 |

**In:** Chinnor Reserves (Hellenic 2E), Kennington Athletic (N), Wheatley Youth, Woodstock Town Reserves (Hellenic 2W), Zubry Oxford (N).

**Out:** Cropedy (P), OUP Reserves (R), Yarnton (P).

| DIVISION TWO | P | W | D | L | F | A | GD | P |
|---|---|---|---|---|---|---|---|---|
| 1 Adderbury Reserves | 18 | 18 | 0 | 0 | 61 | 15 | 46 | |
| 2 Mansfield Rd Reserves | 18 | 11 | 1 | 6 | 42 | 23 | 19 | |
| 3 Launton Sports Reserves | 18 | 8 | 4 | 6 | 44 | 29 | 15 | |
| 4 Cropedy Reserves | 18 | 9 | 0 | 9 | 45 | 40 | 5 | |
| 5 Chalgrove Reserves | 18 | 8 | 2 | 8 | 33 | 36 | -3 | |
| 6 Yarnton Reserves | 18 | 8 | 2 | 8 | 42 | 46 | -4 | |
| 7 Freeland Reserves | 18 | 7 | 2 | 9 | 30 | 37 | -7 | |
| 8 Eynsham Reserves | 18 | 5 | 2 | 11 | 38 | 47 | -9 | |
| 9 Garsington Reserves | 18 | 4 | 3 | 11 | 26 | 43 | -17 | |
| 10 Charlton Reserves | 18 | 4 | 0 | 14 | 18 | 63 | -45 | |

**In:** OUP Reserves (R).

# PETERBOROUGH & DISTRICT LEAGUE

**Sponsored by:** ChromaSport
**Founded:** 1902
**Recent Champions:**
**2013:** Moulton Harrox
**2014:** Kings Lynn Town Res. **2015:** Oakham United

| PREMIER DIVISION | P | W | D | L | F | A | GD | Pts |
|---|---|---|---|---|---|---|---|---|
| 1 Moulton Harrox (+3) | 34 | 29 | 2 | 2 | 144 | 28 | 116 | 92 |
| 2 Whittlesey Athletic | 34 | 27 | 3 | 4 | 113 | 17 | 96 | 84 |
| 3 Pinchbeck United (+3) | 34 | 25 | 3 | 5 | 103 | 39 | 64 | 81 |
| 4 Netherton United (+3) | 34 | 23 | 8 | 2 | 123 | 32 | 91 | 80 |
| 5 Peterborough Sports Res. (-8) | 34 | 23 | 5 | 6 | 108 | 41 | 67 | 66 |
| 6 Peterborough ICA Sports | 34 | 17 | 5 | 12 | 77 | 56 | 21 | 56 |
| 7 Ketton | 34 | 15 | 8 | 11 | 76 | 57 | 19 | 53 |
| 8 Holbeach United Res. | 34 | 15 | 5 | 14 | 84 | 56 | 28 | 50 |
| 9 Langtoft United (+3) | 34 | 13 | 4 | 16 | 50 | 65 | -15 | 46 |
| 10 Stilton United | 34 | 12 | 4 | 18 | 73 | 87 | -14 | 40 |
| 11 Thorney (-1) | 34 | 11 | 6 | 16 | 65 | 74 | -9 | 38 |
| 12 AFC Stanground | 34 | 11 | 4 | 19 | 89 | 105 | -16 | 37 |
| 13 Deeping Rangers Res. (-1) | 34 | 10 | 4 | 19 | 68 | 96 | -28 | 33 |
| 14 Uppingham Town (-3) | 34 | 10 | 4 | 20 | 57 | 99 | -42 | 31 |
| 15 Sawtry (-3) | 34 | 8 | 5 | 21 | 37 | 100 | -63 | 26 |
| 16 Crowland Town (-1) | 34 | 7 | 4 | 22 | 47 | 125 | -78 | 24 |
| 17 Leverington Sports | 34 | 5 | 3 | 26 | 40 | 137 | -97 | 18 |
| 18 Riverside (-1) | 34 | 1 | 3 | 29 | 31 | 171 | -140 | 5 |

**Out:** Whittlesey Athletic (P - United Counties League)

## PREMIER SHIELD

**HOLDERS:** OAKHAM UNITED

**ROUND 1**

| | | | |
|---|---|---|---|
| Whittlesey Athletic | v | Peterborough Sports Res. | 2-1 |
| Langtoft United | v | Deeping Rangers Res. | 1-1, 6-7p |
| Sawtry | v | Moulton Harrox | 1-4 |
| Uppingham Town | v | Stilton United | 4-3 aet |
| Ketton | v | Whittlesey Athletic | 1-3 aet |
| Netherton United | v | Deeping Rangers Reserves | 8-3 |
| Peterborough ICA Sports | v | AFC Stanground | 0-1 |
| Crowland Town | v | Holbeach United Reserves | 2-3 |
| Pinchbeck United | v | Riverside | 8-1 |
| Thorney | v | Leverington Sports | 5-1 |

ROUND 2

| | | | |
|---|---|---|---|
| Sawtry | v | Moulton Harrox | 1-4 |
| Uppingham Town | v | Stilton United | 4-3 aet |
| Ketton | v | Whittlesey Athletic | 1-3 aet |
| Netherton United | v | Deeping Rangers Reserves | 8-3 |
| Peterborough ICA Sports | v | AFC Stanground | 0-1 |
| Crowland Town | v | Holbeach United Reserves | 2-3 |
| Pinchbeck United | v | Riverside | 8-1 |
| Thorney | v | Leverington Sports | 5-1 |

QUARTER FINALS

| | | | |
|---|---|---|---|
| Moulton Harrox | v | Uppingham Town | 3-0 |
| Whittlesey Athletic | v | Netherton United | 0-5 |
| AFC Stanground | v | Holbeach United Reserves | 3-1 |
| Pinchbeck United | v | Thorney | 5-2 |

SEMI FINALS

| | | | |
|---|---|---|---|
| Moulton Harrox | v | Netherton United | 3-0 |
| AFC Stanground | v | Pinchbeck United | 0-4 |

FINAL

| | | | |
|---|---|---|---|
| Moulton Harrox | v | Pinchbeck United | 0-1 |

| PREMIER DIVISION | 1 | 2 | 3 | 4 | 5 | 6 | 7 | 8 | 9 | 10 | 11 | 12 | 13 | 14 | 15 | 16 | 17 | 18 |
|---|---|---|---|---|---|---|---|---|---|---|---|---|---|---|---|---|---|---|
| 1 AFC Stanground | | 7-2 | 3-2 | 2-1 | 2-3 | 2-2 | 8-1 | 0-4 | 0-4 | 4-4 | 1-4 | 1-3 | 11-0 | 5-3 | 4-8 | 2-2 | 4-1 | 0-3 |
| 2 Crowland Town | 0-4 | | 2-1 | 1-0 | 0-3 | 1-1 | 2-3 | 0-7 | 1-4 | 1-10 | 2-8 | 2-6 | 7-0 | 1-1 | 1-1 | 4-5 | 1-6 | 1-3 |
| 3 Deeping Rangers Reserves | 2-1 | 1-1 | | 2-0 | 9-0 | 1-2 | 7-2 | V-V | 1-3 | 0-3 | 1-4 | 0-6 | 9-3 | 4-2 | 1-3 | 1-3 | 7-1 | 1-3 |
| 4 Holbeach United Reserves | 4-2 | 4-0 | 8-1 | | 2-2 | 1-3 | 6-1 | 0-3 | 3-2 | 0-1 | 1-3 | 2-2 | 5-0 | 2-0 | 5-2 | 3-1 | 3-0 | 2-1 |
| 5 Ketton | 4-0 | 5-2 | 3-0 | 2-2 | | 0-3 | 9-0 | 1-4 | 2-2 | 0-0 | 1-2 | 1-2 | 5-2 | 4-0 | 1-1 | 3-1 | 1-1 | 1-3 |
| 6 Langtoft United | 1-3 | V-V | 3-0 | 1-0 | 1-2 | | 2-1 | 1-2 | 1-6 | 0-2 | 1-0 | 0-2 | 1-1 | 2-2 | 3-0 | 0-2 | 2-4 | 1-5 |
| 7 Leverington Sports | 3-1 | 1-4 | 2-2 | 0-8 | 2-2 | 1-4 | | 1-7 | 1-2 | 0-1 | 0-5 | 0-1 | 5-1 | 1-2 | 0-3 | 0-5 | 0-1 | 0-6 |
| 8 Moulton Harrox | 5-1 | 5-0 | 11-0 | 3-1 | 5-0 | 3-0 | 8-0 | | 1-1 | 4-0 | 4-2 | 4-1 | 5-4 | 4-0 | 6-1 | 3-0 | 7-0 | 0-3 |
| 9 Netherton United | 7-0 | 7-2 | 2-1 | 7-0 | 2-0 | 4-0 | 10-0 | 1-1 | | 5-1 | 2-3 | 3-2 | 1-0 | 9-2 | 5-0 | 1-1 | 1-1 | 0-0 |
| 10 Peterborough ICA Sports | 0-4 | 9-1 | 1-1 | 1-0 | 2-1 | 0-3 | 6-0 | 3-6 | 0-3 | | 1-2 | 1-4 | 5-0 | 4-1 | 1-0 | 2-2 | 4-0 | 0-3 |
| 11 Peterborough Sports Reserves | 11-0 | 6-0 | 3-1 | 2-2 | 1-1 | 2-0 | 3-1 | 1-2 | 1-3 | 0-0 | | 3-0 | 2-0 | 2-2 | 7-1 | 5-1 | 3-1 | 0-2 |
| 12 Pinchbeck United | 4-1 | 4-1 | 6-0 | 3-1 | 2-0 | 5-3 | 2-0 | 2-1 | 2-2 | 3-2 | 1-1 | | V-V | 7-0 | 5-0 | 1-3 | 5-1 | 0-1 |
| 13 Riverside | 0-11 | 0-1 | 0-1 | 2-9 | 0-6 | 1-4 | 0-9 | 1-5 | 0-10 | 0-2 | 2-3 | 0-6 | | 2-2 | 0-4 | 3-4 | 0-4 | 0-9 |
| 14 Sawtry | 1-0 | 3-0 | 1-3 | 1-2 | 1-2 | 0-2 | 1-0 | 0-9 | 2-6 | 2-5 | 0-4 | 0-2 | 1-1 | | 2-1 | 1-0 | 0-2 | 0-5 |
| 15 Stilton United | 3-1 | 0-2 | 1-1 | 3-2 | 0-1 | 6-1 | 2-2 | 1-5 | 2-6 | 2-1 | 0-1 | 3-5 | 8-2 | 4-0 | | 3-4 | 4-1 | 0-2 |
| 16 Thorney | 3-1 | 2-3 | 2-4 | 1-1 | 0-2 | 1-0 | 2-3 | 1-3 | V-V | 1-2 | 4-8 | 1-3 | 4-0 | 1-2 | 4-1 | | 2-4 | 0-3 |
| 17 Uppingham Town | 2-2 | 2-1 | 5-3 | 0-4 | 1-8 | 1-2 | 9-0 | 1-5 | 1-2 | 0-3 | 0-6 | 1-5 | 3-5 | 1-2 | 2-1 | 0-0 | | 0-3 |
| 18 Whittlesey Athletic | 8-1 | 6-0 | 6-0 | 1-0 | 2-0 | 4-0 | 5-0 | 0-2 | 0-0 | 3-0 | 3-0 | 0-1 | 9-1 | 3-0 | 3-4 | 2-2 | 3-0 | |

| DIVISION ONE | P | W | D | L | F | A | GD | Pts |
|---|---|---|---|---|---|---|---|---|
| Stamford Lions | 30 | 24 | 4 | 2 | 105 | 30 | 75 | 76 |
| Wisbech Town Reserves | 30 | 23 | 1 | 6 | 93 | 38 | 55 | 70 |
| Sutton Bridge United | 30 | 19 | 7 | 4 | 90 | 49 | 41 | 64 |
| Moulton Harrox Res. | 30 | 12 | 10 | 8 | 71 | 48 | 23 | 46 |
| Oundle Town | 30 | 14 | 3 | 13 | 77 | 69 | 8 | 45 |
| Wittering | 30 | 13 | 5 | 12 | 71 | 63 | 8 | 44 |
| Warboys Town (-3) | 30 | 13 | 6 | 9 | 69 | 61 | 8 | 42 |
| Baston | 30 | 12 | 4 | 14 | 63 | 66 | -3 | 40 |
| Spalding United Res. | 30 | 12 | 3 | 15 | 66 | 70 | -4 | 39 |
| Kings Cliffe (+3) | 30 | 9 | 8 | 12 | 41 | 59 | -18 | 38 |
| Netherton United Res. | 30 | 11 | 4 | 15 | 54 | 55 | -1 | 37 |
| Long Sutton Athletic | 30 | 9 | 6 | 15 | 64 | 69 | -5 | 33 |
| Stamford Belvedere (-1) | 30 | 9 | 6 | 14 | 48 | 66 | -18 | 32 |
| Whittlesey Athletic Res.(-5) | 30 | 10 | 3 | 17 | 44 | 65 | -21 | 28 |
| Peterborough ICA Sports Res. (-1) | 30 | 4 | 3 | 22 | 37 | 128 | -91 | 14 |
| Langtoft United Res. (-6) | 30 | 5 | 3 | 21 | 44 | 101 | -57 | 12 |

| DIVISION TWO | P | W | D | L | F | A | GD | Pts |
|---|---|---|---|---|---|---|---|---|
| 1 Oakham United Res. (+3) | 26 | 22 | 2 | 1 | 98 | 30 | 68 | 71 |
| 2 Glinton & Northborough | 26 | 19 | 3 | 4 | 99 | 39 | 60 | 60 |
| 3 Spalding Town (+6) | 26 | 17 | 0 | 7 | 102 | 34 | 68 | 57 |
| 4 Whittlesey Athletic 'A' (+6) | 26 | 12 | 2 | 10 | 59 | 47 | 12 | 44 |
| 5 Peterborough Polonia FC (-6) | 26 | 15 | 2 | 8 | 82 | 43 | 39 | 41 |
| 6 Ketton Reserves (+2) | 26 | 10 | 3 | 11 | 43 | 47 | -4 | 35 |
| 7 Parkway Eagles | 26 | 11 | 1 | 14 | 72 | 77 | -5 | 34 |
| 8 Netherton United 'A' (+3) | 26 | 7 | 8 | 10 | 35 | 51 | -16 | 32 |
| 9 Hampton Sport (+1) | 26 | 8 | 2 | 13 | 63 | 74 | -11 | 27 |
| 10 Pinchbeck United Res. | 26 | 7 | 4 | 15 | 53 | 87 | -34 | 25 |
| 11 Crowland Town Res. (-10) | 26 | 10 | 3 | 12 | 51 | 54 | -3 | 23 |
| 12 Thorney Reserves (-2) | 26 | 6 | 3 | 15 | 49 | 112 | -63 | 19 |
| 13 Leverington Sports Res. (-3) | 26 | 4 | 6 | 16 | 35 | 89 | -54 | 15 |
| 14 Sawtry Reserves (-3) | 26 | 4 | 3 | 16 | 34 | 91 | -57 | 12 |

## Peterborough & District League Premier Division

| | | |
|---|---|---|
| **AFC STANGROUND SPORTS** | In2itive Park, Leading Drove, Holme Road Yaxley, PE7 3NA | 01733 244 928 |
| **CROWLAND TOWN** | Snowden Field, Thorney Road, Crowland PE6 0AL | 07786 994 921 |
| **DEEPING RANGERS RESERVES** | Haydon Whitham Stadium, Outgang Road, Market Deeping, Lincolnshire, PE6 8LQ | 01778 344 701 |
| **HOLBEACH UNITED RESERVES** | Carters Park, Park Road, Holbeach Spalding PE12 7EE | 01406 424 761 |
| **KETTON** | Ketton Sports and Community Centre, Pit Lane, Ketton, Stamford, PE9 3SZ | 01780 721 507 |
| **LANGTOFT UNITED** | Manor Way, Sports Ground, Langtoft, Peterborough PE6 9NB | 01778 347 253 |
| **LEVERINGTON SPORTS** | Church Road, Leverington, Wisbech PE13 5DE | 01945 465 082 |
| **MOULTON HARROX** | Broad Lane, Moulton, Spalding PE12 6PN | 07714 700 940 |
| **NETHERTON UNITED** | The Grange, Charlotte Way, Peterborough PE3 9TT | 07808 774 302 |
| **PETERBOROUGH ICA SPORTS** | Ringwood, South Bretton PE3 9SH | 07827 446 844 |
| **PETERBOROUGH SPORTS RES.** | 651 Lincoln Road, Peterborough PE1 3HA | 07894 445 991 |
| **PINCHBECK UNITED** | Glebe Playing Fields, Knight Street, Pinchbeck, Spalding PE11 3RB | 07508 809 96 |
| **SAWTRY** | Greenfield, Straight Drove, Sawtry, Cambridgeshire PE28 5XE | 01487 831 79 |
| **STAMFORD LIONS** | Borderville Sports Centre, Ryhall Road, Stamford, Lincolnshire, PE9 1US | 07739 005 34 |
| **STILTON UNITED** | Stilton Recreation Ground, High Street, Stilton, PE7 | 07756 778 15 |
| **THORNEY** | Thorney Park, Tavistock Close, Thorney PE6 0SP | 07743 296 505 |
| **UPPINGHAM TOWN** | Todd's Piece, North Street East, Uppingham, Rutland, LE15 9QJ | 01572 821 44 |
| **WISBECH TOWN RESERVES** | The Elgoods Fenland Stadium, Lynn Road, Wisbech, PE14 7AL | 01945 581 51 |

| | DIVISION THREE | P | W | D | L | F | A | GD | Pts |
|---|---|---|---|---|---|---|---|---|---|
| 1 | Stanground Sports FC | 24 | 18 | 4 | 2 | 96 | 29 | 67 | 58 |
| 2 | Ramsey Town | 24 | 14 | 3 | 5 | 72 | 36 | 36 | 51 |
| 3 | Stamford Lions Res. | 24 | 16 | 3 | 5 | 76 | 49 | 27 | 51 |
| 4 | Eye United | 24 | 16 | 2 | 6 | 87 | 40 | 47 | 50 |
| 5 | Bretton North End (-3) | 24 | 17 | 0 | 6 | 78 | 42 | 36 | 48 |
| 6 | Tydd St Mary (+9) | 24 | 11 | 2 | 8 | 70 | 46 | 24 | 44 |
| 7 | Thorpe Wood Rangers (+6) | 24 | 11 | 2 | 9 | 63 | 40 | 23 | 41 |
| 8 | Oundle Town Res. (+3) | 24 | 10 | 0 | 13 | 53 | 76 | -23 | 33 |
| 9 | Farcet United (+3) | 24 | 9 | 0 | 14 | 65 | 61 | 4 | 30 |
| 10 | Baston Reserves (-1) | 24 | 6 | 3 | 14 | 36 | 67 | -31 | 20 |
| 11 | Whittlesey Athletic 'B' (+3) | 24 | 2 | 0 | 21 | 33 | 101 | -68 | 9 |
| 12 | Uppingham Town Res. (-1) | 24 | 2 | 0 | 21 | 30 | 119 | -89 | 5 |
| 13 | Stilton United Res. (-9) | 24 | 3 | 1 | 11 | 24 | 77 | -53 | 1 |

| | DIVISION FOUR | P | W | D | L | F | A | GD | Pts |
|---|---|---|---|---|---|---|---|---|---|
| 1 | Brotherhood Sports (+3) | 28 | 22 | 1 | 4 | 113 | 42 | 71 | 70 |
| 2 | FC Peterborough (+3) | 28 | 18 | 3 | 6 | 95 | 44 | 51 | 60 |
| 3 | AFC Stanground Res. | 28 | 16 | 7 | 5 | 102 | 45 | 57 | 55 |
| 4 | Stamford Belvedere Res. (+6) | 28 | 15 | 2 | 9 | 55 | 43 | 12 | 53 |
| 5 | Rutland DR | 28 | 15 | 4 | 9 | 101 | 77 | 24 | 49 |
| 6 | Sutton Bridge United Res. (+3) | 28 | 13 | 2 | 12 | 80 | 70 | 10 | 44 |
| 7 | Long Sutton Athletic Res. (+1) | 28 | 12 | 3 | 10 | 64 | 44 | 20 | 40 |
| 8 | Holbeach Bank FC (-2) | 28 | 13 | 2 | 13 | 64 | 74 | -10 | 39 |
| 9 | Tydd St Mary Res. (+3) | 28 | 11 | 3 | 13 | 50 | 73 | -23 | 39 |
| 10 | Warboys Town Reserves | 28 | 11 | 1 | 12 | 55 | 62 | -7 | 34 |
| 11 | Parkside | 28 | 10 | 2 | 16 | 57 | 69 | -12 | 32 |
| 12 | Whaplode Drove | 28 | 9 | 4 | 15 | 59 | 69 | -10 | 31 |
| 13 | Netherton United 'B' | 28 | 8 | 2 | 18 | 62 | 95 | -33 | 26 |
| 14 | Huntingdon Rovers | 28 | 7 | 0 | 21 | 56 | 135 | -79 | 21 |
| 15 | Parkway Eagles Res. (-5) | 28 | 3 | 2 | 20 | 38 | 109 | -71 | 6 |

**In:** FC Peterborough Reserves (P); Feeder (P); Stanground Sports 'B' (P); Stamford Lions 'A' (P); Whittlesey Athletic 'C' (P): Withering Reserves (P).

| | DIVISION FIVE | P | W | D | L | F | A | GD | Pts |
|---|---|---|---|---|---|---|---|---|---|
| 1 | Limetree UTR | 22 | 20 | 1 | 1 | 154 | 32 | 122 | 6 |
| 2 | Harrowby United Res. | 22 | 17 | 1 | 4 | 71 | 19 | 52 | 5 |
| 3 | Feeder | 22 | 17 | 0 | 5 | 111 | 34 | 77 | 5 |
| 4 | Stanground Sports Res. | 22 | 13 | 1 | 8 | 56 | 34 | 22 | 4 |
| 5 | Whittlesey Athletic 'C' | 22 | 11 | 2 | 9 | 51 | 46 | 5 | 3 |
| 6 | Stamford Lions 'A' (+3) | 22 | 9 | 3 | 9 | 52 | 45 | 7 | 3 |
| 7 | Parkside Reserves (+3) | 22 | 8 | 3 | 10 | 46 | 73 | -27 | 3 |
| 8 | Wittering Reserves (+1) | 22 | 7 | 2 | 12 | 40 | 58 | -18 | 2 |
| 9 | FC Peterborough Res. | 22 | 7 | 3 | 12 | 45 | 74 | -29 | 2 |
| 10 | Holbeach United 'A' | 22 | 6 | 1 | 15 | 40 | 82 | -42 | 1 |
| 11 | KRC Deeping | 22 | 1 | 2 | 19 | 21 | 147 | -126 | |
| 12 | Leverington Sports 'A' (-5) | 22 | 2 | 3 | 14 | 32 | 75 | -43 | |

**Division Five 2016-17**

AFC Orton
British School of Sports Football Club
Eunice Huntingdon Football Club
FC Peterborough 'A'
Feeder Reserves
Glinton & Northborough Reserves
Holbeach United 'A'
Kings Cliffe Reserves
Leverington Sports 'A'
NECI Peterborough Football Club
Orton Rangers Football Club
Ramsey Town Reserves
Riverside Reserves
Wisbech Town Acorns Football Club

# SHEFFIELD & HALLAMSHIRE SENIOR LEAGUE

**Sponsored by:** Windsor Food Services
**Founded:** N/K
**Recent Champions:**
**2013:** Shaw Lane Aqua Force Barnsley
**2014:** Handsworth FC **2015:** Swinton Athletic

| PREMIER DIVISION | P | W | D | L | F | A | GD | Pts |
|---|---|---|---|---|---|---|---|---|
| 1 Frecheville CA FC | 26 | 19 | 3 | 4 | 69 | 38 | 31 | 60 |
| 2 Swinton Athletic | 26 | 16 | 4 | 6 | 60 | 31 | 29 | 52 |
| 3 Houghton Main | 26 | 15 | 4 | 7 | 54 | 31 | 23 | 49 |
| 4 AFC Penistone Church | 26 | 12 | 7 | 7 | 51 | 41 | 10 | 43 |
| 5 Stocksbridge Park Steels Res. | 26 | 12 | 7 | 7 | 44 | 35 | 9 | 43 |
| 6 North Gawber Colliery | 26 | 11 | 5 | 10 | 52 | 51 | 1 | 38 |
| 7 Swallownest FC | 26 | 10 | 3 | 13 | 47 | 49 | -2 | 33 |
| 8 Millmoor Juniors | 26 | 9 | 5 | 12 | 61 | 67 | -6 | 32 |
| 9 Athersley Recreation Res. | 26 | 9 | 4 | 13 | 34 | 45 | -11 | 31 |
| 10 Jubilee Sports | 26 | 8 | 6 | 12 | 40 | 54 | -14 | 30 |
| 11 Handsworth Parramore Res. | 26 | 7 | 7 | 12 | 46 | 54 | -8 | 28 |
| 12 Oughtibridge WMFC | 26 | 9 | 1 | 16 | 33 | 64 | -31 | 28 |
| 13 Wickersley FC | 26 | 7 | 4 | 15 | 53 | 63 | -10 | 25 |
| 14 Thorpe Hesley | 26 | 5 | 6 | 15 | 38 | 59 | -21 | 21 |

**Out:** Thorpe Hesley (W).

| DIVISION ONE | P | W | D | L | F | A | GD | Pts |
|---|---|---|---|---|---|---|---|---|
| 1 Denaby United | 24 | 16 | 5 | 3 | 76 | 36 | 40 | 53 |
| 2 Wombwell Main | 24 | 16 | 2 | 6 | 81 | 45 | 36 | 50 |
| 3 Denaby Main JFC | 24 | 14 | 7 | 3 | 54 | 29 | 25 | 49 |
| 4 Caribbean Sports | 24 | 15 | 2 | 7 | 64 | 43 | 21 | 47 |
| 5 Silkstone United | 24 | 14 | 1 | 9 | 73 | 55 | 18 | 43 |
| 6 Ecclesfield Red Rose 1915 | 24 | 12 | 4 | 8 | 62 | 47 | 15 | 40 |
| 7 South Kirkby Colliery | 24 | 11 | 2 | 11 | 54 | 50 | 4 | 35 |
| 8 Sheffield Bankers | 24 | 9 | 6 | 9 | 43 | 49 | -6 | 33 |
| 9 AFC Dronfield | 24 | 9 | 4 | 11 | 65 | 60 | 5 | 31 |
| 10 Davy FC | 24 | 7 | 3 | 14 | 45 | 65 | -20 | 24 |
| 11 Byron House | 24 | 5 | 4 | 15 | 48 | 71 | -23 | 19 |
| 12 High Green Villa | 24 | 3 | 4 | 17 | 35 | 83 | -48 | 13 |
| 13 Millmoor Juniors Res. | 24 | 2 | 2 | 20 | 30 | 97 | -67 | 8 |

**Out:** Byron House (W).

| DIVISION TWO | P | W | D | L | F | A | GD | Pts |
|---|---|---|---|---|---|---|---|---|
| 1 Hemsworth Miners Welfare Res. | 20 | 16 | 2 | 2 | 75 | 21 | 54 | 50 |
| 2 Grimethorpe Sports | 20 | 15 | 2 | 3 | 80 | 26 | 54 | 47 |
| 3 Brinsworth Whitehill | 20 | 12 | 3 | 5 | 63 | 35 | 28 | 39 |
| 4 North Gawber Colliery Res. | 20 | 10 | 5 | 5 | 40 | 41 | -1 | 35 |
| 5 Houghton Main Res. | 20 | 10 | 3 | 7 | 46 | 41 | 5 | 33 |
| 6 Swallownest FC Res. | 20 | 10 | 1 | 9 | 58 | 39 | 19 | 31 |
| 7 New Bohemians | 20 | 9 | 4 | 7 | 48 | 37 | 11 | 31 |
| 8 Kiveton Park | 20 | 8 | 2 | 10 | 37 | 37 | 0 | 26 |
| 9 Worsbrough Bridge Athletic Res. | 20 | 3 | 4 | 13 | 22 | 61 | -39 | 13 |
| 10 Bawtry Town FC | 20 | 1 | 3 | 16 | 28 | 102 | -74 | 6 |
| 11 Sheffield Lane Top | 20 | 1 | 1 | 18 | 26 | 83 | -57 | 4 |

**Out:** Swallownest FC Reserves (W),

## LEAGUE CUP

**HOLDERS:** OUGHTIBRIDGE WMFC

**ROUND 1**

| | | | |
|---|---|---|---|
| Grimethorpe Sports | v | Brinsworth Whitehill | 5 - 3 aet |
| Handsworth Parramore Res. | v | Denaby United | 6 - 5 |
| Jubilee Sports | v | Davy U21 | 8 - 0 |
| Maltby Main Reserves | v | Stocksbridge Park U21 | 1 - 3 |
| Millmoor Juniors | v | Athersley Recreation Res. | 4 - 0 |
| North Gawber Colliery | v | Wombwell Main U21 | 6 - 2 |
| Sheffield Bankers | v | Kiveton Park | 0 - 4 |
| South Kirkby Colliery U21 | v | Denaby Main JFC | 0 - 1 |
| Thorpe Hesley | v | Frecheville CA FC | 2 - 1 |
| Treeton Terriers | v | Kingstone United | 5 - 6 |
| Wickersley FC | v | Davy FC | 6 - 1 |
| Wombwell Main | v | AFC Dronfield | 5 - 2 |
| Worsbrough Bridge Athletic Res. | v | Swinton Athletic | 1 - 3 |
| AFC Penistone Church | v | Caribbean Sports | 3 - 1 |
| Athersley Recreation U21 | v | Sheffield Lane Top | 2 - 3 |
| Bawtry Town U21 | v | Handsworth Parramore U21 | HW |
| Caribbean Sports U21 | v | Stocksbridge Park Steels Res. | 0 - 8 |
| South Kirkby Colliery | v | Silkstone United | 1 - 6 |

**ROUND 2**

| | | | |
|---|---|---|---|
| Byron House | v | Denaby Main JFC | 7 - 1 |
| High Green Villa | v | Millmoor Juniors Reserves | 4 - 9 |
| Houghton Main | v | Bawtry Town FC | HW |
| Jubilee Sports | v | Wombwell Main | 5 - 2 |
| Kingstone United | v | Stocksbridge Park Steels Res. | 2 - 4 |
| Kiveton Park | v | Millmoor Juniors | 2 - 6 |
| Swallownest FC | v | New Bohemians | 6 - 1 |
| Wickersley FC | v | Hemsworth Miners Welfare Res. | 6 - 2 |
| North Gawber Colliery Res, | v | AFC Penistone Church | 1 - 8 |
| Swinton Athletic | v | Houghton Main Reserves | 10 - 0 |
| Grimethorpe Sports | v | Ecclesfield Red Rose 1915 | 4-1 aet |
| Millmoor Juniors U21 | v | Stocksbridge Park U21 | 0 - 6 |
| Sheffield Lane Top | v | Handsworth Parramore Res. | 1 - 4 |
| Swallownest FC Reserves | v | Bawtry Town U21 | 3 - 6 |
| Thorpe Hesley | v | Silkstone United | 3 - 6 |
| North Gawber Colliery | v | Oughtibridge WMFC | 1 - 4 |

**ROUND 3**

| | | | |
|---|---|---|---|
| Silkstone United | v | Houghton Main | 1 - 4 |
| Millmoor Juniors Reserves | v | Oughtibridge WMFC | 3 - 4 |
| Swinton Athletic | v | Bawtry Town U21 | 7 - 0 |
| Byron House | v | Grimethorpe Sports | 1 - 3 |
| Millmoor Juniors | v | Stocksbridge Park Steels Res. | 5 - 0 |
| Stocksbridge Park U21 | v | Swallownest FC | 2-2, 3-1p |
| Jubilee Sports | v | Handsworth Parramore Res. | 3 - 2 |
| Wickersley FC | v | AFC Penistone Church | 2 - 1 |

**QUARTER FINALS**

| | | | |
|---|---|---|---|
| Jubilee Sports | v | Houghton Main | 3-3, 6-5p |
| Oughtibridge WMFC | v | Wickersley FC | 0 - 2 |
| Millmoor Juniors | v | Grimethorpe Sports | 3 - 5 |
| Swinton Athletic | v | Stocksbridge Park U21 | 2 - 1 |

**SEMI FINALS**

| | | | |
|---|---|---|---|
| Wickersley FC | v | Jubilee Sports | 0 - 2 |
| Swinton Athletic | v | Grimethorpe Sports | 1 - 3 |

**FINAL**

| | | | |
|---|---|---|---|
| Grimethorpe Sports | v | Jubilee Sports | 4-5 aet |

| SENIOR DIVISION | 1 | 2 | 3 | 4 | 5 | 6 | 7 | 8 | 9 | 10 | 11 | 12 | 13 | 14 |
|---|---|---|---|---|---|---|---|---|---|---|---|---|---|---|
| 1 AFC Penistone Church | | 3-1 | 0-2 | 1-4 | 1-2 | 1-1 | 3-2 | 4-0 | 3-1 | 1-1 | 2-2 | 3-2 | 2-1 | 1-0 |
| 2 Athersley Recreation Reserves | 1-0 | | 0-0 | 2-1 | 0-2 | 1-2 | 2-2 | 0-2 | 0-1 | 1-3 | 0-2 | 2-1 | 0-0 | 2-3 |
| 3 Frecheville CA FC | 0-4 | 5-3 | | 4-2 | 2-0 | 1-0 | 2-1 | 3-1 | 5-2 | 1-0 | 3-2 | 3-4 | 4-1 | 7-5 |
| 4 Handsworth Parramore Reserves | 3-5 | 1-1 | 0-3 | | 1-1 | 4-2 | 4-4 | 2-2 | 1-2 | 2-2 | 2-0 | 0-1 | 1-1 | 2-1 |
| 5 Houghton Main | 2-1 | 3-2 | 1-2 | 1-0 | | 3-0 | 3-0 | 6-0 | 4-1 | 2-2 | 1-2 | 1-4 | 5-1 | 3-2 |
| 6 Jubilee Sports | 1-1 | 0-2 | 2-5 | 2-0 | 2-2 | | 5-1 | 0-2 | 2-0 | 1-0 | 1-2 | 0-5 | 2-2 | 1-1 |
| 7 Millmoor Juniors | 6-2 | 2-3 | 4-2 | 1-1 | 4-1 | 1-1 | | 3-2 | 0-4 | 4-5 | 2-1 | 1-5 | 3-0 | 3-3 |
| 8 North Gawber Colliery | 1-1 | 2-1 | 1-3 | 1-4 | 0-1 | 3-1 | 7-0 | | 3-0 | 1-3 | 3-2 | 2-3 | 1-1 | 5-3 |
| 9 Oughtibridge WMFC | 1-4 | 0-1 | 1-6 | 4-2 | 1-0 | 4-2 | 2-1 | 1-1 | | 1-2 | 0-4 | 1-0 | 2-1 | 1-2 |
| 10 Stocksbridge Park Steels Reserves | 3-2 | 2-0 | 0-0 | 1-2 | 1-1 | 3-0 | 1-0 | 1-2 | 1-0 | | 3-1 | 0-0 | 0-3 | 3-1 |
| 11 Swallownest FC | 1-2 | 2-4 | 0-2 | 1-2 | 2-1 | 1-4 | 4-3 | 1-2 | 6-1 | 3-1 | | 2-2 | 1-1 | 0-2 |
| 12 Swinton Athletic | 1-1 | 4-0 | 1-0 | 1-0 | 0-2 | 5-0 | 3-6 | 2-2 | 2-0 | 4-1 | 2-0 | | 1-0 | 2-0 |
| 13 Thorpe Hesley | 1-2 | 2-3 | 3-3 | 5-1 | 0-3 | 2-5 | 0-3 | 1-3 | 3-2 | 1-4 | 1-2 | 3-1 | | 1-4 |
| 14 Wickersley FC | 1-1 | 0-2 | 0-1 | 5-4 | 0-3 | 2-3 | 1-4 | 4-3 | 8-0 | 1-1 | 2-3 | 1-4 | 1-3 | |

# SOMERSET COUNTY LEAGUE

**Sponsored by:** Errea
**Founded:** 1890
**Recent Champions:**
**2013:** Nailsea United. **2014:** Nailsea United. **2015:** Shirehampton.

| PREMIER DIVISION | | P | W | D | L | F | A | GD | Pts |
|---|---|---|---|---|---|---|---|---|---|
| 1 | Bishops Lydeard | 32 | 22 | 8 | 2 | 90 | 28 | 62 | 74 |
| 2 | Nailsea and Tickenham FC | 32 | 21 | 7 | 4 | 77 | 27 | 50 | 70 |
| 3 | Watchet Town | 32 | 22 | 2 | 8 | 76 | 33 | 43 | 68 |
| 4 | Shirehampton | 32 | 20 | 6 | 6 | 101 | 47 | 54 | 66 |
| 5 | Odd Down Reserves (-3) | 31 | 18 | 5 | 8 | 63 | 44 | 19 | 56 |
| 6 | Nailsea United | 32 | 17 | 3 | 12 | 79 | 53 | 26 | 54 |
| 7 | Fry Club | 32 | 14 | 7 | 11 | 82 | 49 | 33 | 49 |
| 8 | Bridgwater Town Res. (-2) | 32 | 13 | 6 | 13 | 79 | 74 | 5 | 43 |
| 9 | Wrington Redhill (-5) | 32 | 13 | 7 | 12 | 59 | 53 | 6 | 41 |
| 10 | Yatton Athletic | 32 | 13 | 2 | 17 | 61 | 83 | -22 | 41 |
| 11 | Staplegrove | 32 | 12 | 4 | 16 | 58 | 59 | -1 | 40 |
| 12 | Clevedon United | 32 | 10 | 4 | 18 | 49 | 62 | -13 | 34 |
| 13 | Chilcompton Sports | 31 | 9 | 5 | 17 | 72 | 74 | -2 | 32 |
| 14 | Berrow | 32 | 10 | 1 | 21 | 56 | 77 | -21 | 31 |
| 15 | Dundry Athletic | 32 | 8 | 7 | 17 | 42 | 73 | -31 | 31 |
| 16 | Clutton | 32 | 8 | 4 | 20 | 43 | 95 | -52 | 28 |
| 17 | Cutters Friday | 32 | 1 | 2 | 29 | 21 | 177 | -156 | 5 |

Frome Collegians withdrew - record expunged.

**Out:** Bishops Lydeard (P - Western League).

| | PREMIER DIVISION | 1 | 2 | 3 | 4 | 5 | 6 | 7 | 8 | 9 | 10 | 11 | 12 | 13 | 14 | 15 | 16 | 17 |
|---|---|---|---|---|---|---|---|---|---|---|---|---|---|---|---|---|---|---|
| 1 | Berrow | | 1-3 | 1-3 | 3-2 | 1-0 | 4-0 | 2-0 | 0-4 | 3-1 | 2-4 | 2-3 | 2-2 | 0-1 | 3-1 | 0-1 | 2-1 | 3-2 |
| 2 | Bishops Lydeard | 4-2 | | 4-0 | 2-1 | 2-0 | 5-0 | 12-0 | 0-0 | 2-2 | 2-0 | 3-0 | 3-2 | 4-2 | 2-0 | 3-1 | 2-0 | 6-1 |
| 3 | Bridgwater Town Res | 6-2 | 2-2 | | 4-2 | 1-0 | 5-2 | 6-1 | 6-1 | 1-1 | 0-1 | 4-3 | 1-4 | 2-2 | 2-1 | 4-5 | 1-4 | 7-0 |
| 4 | Chilcompton Sports | 3-1 | 0-1 | 2-2 | | 2-2 | 6-2 | 10-0 | 4-5 | 3-1 | 0-2 | 3-4 | 3-4 | 4-5 | 1-0 | 1-2 | 1-1 | 4-1 |
| 5 | Clevedon United | 2-7 | 2-2 | 0-2 | 1-3 | | 1-3 | 3-0 | 2-0 | 1-3 | 0-0 | 2-3 | 2-5 | 0-3 | 0-2 | 2-0 | 1-1 | 2-0 |
| 6 | Clutton | 4-1 | 2-7 | 2-1 | 2-0 | 3-2 | | 1-0 | 2-0 | 1-4 | 1-2 | 1-1 | 0-1 | 0-6 | 1-3 | 1-5 | 3-3 | 1-2 |
| 7 | Cutters Friday | 0-2 | 0-4 | 3-5 | 3-3 | 1-4 | 1-1 | | 1-3 | 2-0 | 0-9 | 0-3 | 1-2 | 2-7 | 1-3 | 0-3 | 1-5 | 1-3 |
| 8 | Dundry Athletic | 2-1 | 0-0 | 1-1 | 3-2 | 0-1 | 4-1 | 6-0 | | 0-0 | 0-3 | 0-3 | 1-1 | 2-2 | 3-1 | 0-4 | 1-1 | 1-6 |
| 9 | Fry Club | 3-1 | 3-2 | 4-1 | 4-1 | 2-1 | 6-1 | 23-0 | 4-1 | | 2-2 | 2-0 | 0-1 | 1-2 | 1-2 | 0-2 | 2-2 | 4-4 |
| 10 | Nailsea and Tickenham FC | 3-1 | 0-1 | 3-0 | 2-1 | 3-0 | 2-1 | 7-1 | 7-0 | 1-2 | | 1-1 | 2-2 | 1-1 | 3-0 | 1-0 | 2-0 | 3-0 |
| 11 | Nailsea United | 2-1 | 0-3 | 5-3 | 9-0 | 1-3 | 5-0 | 10-0 | 4-2 | 0-2 | 0-2 | | 2-0 | 3-1 | 0-4 | 0-1 | 2-4 | 3-0 |
| 12 | Odd Down Res | 3-2 | 1-1 | 3-1 | V-V | 2-4 | 5-0 | 4-1 | 3-1 | 1-4 | 2-0 | 2-1 | | 2-0 | 4-2 | 1-1 | 0-1 | 0-1 |
| 13 | Shirehampton | 3-1 | 1-1 | 6-2 | 2-2 | 1-2 | 5-1 | 8-0 | 5-0 | 3-0 | 1-1 | 4-2 | 0-1 | | 5-1 | 3-1 | 4-2 | 5-0 |
| 14 | Staplegrove | 3-1 | 2-2 | 1-1 | 1-2 | 2-0 | 1-1 | 5-1 | 2-0 | 2-0 | 2-3 | 2-2 | 3-0 | 4-3 | | 0-1 | 0-2 | 3-4 |
| 15 | Watchet Town | 4-0 | 2-0 | 3-1 | 2-0 | 2-1 | 4-1 | 8-0 | 3-1 | 2-0 | 1-2 | 0-2 | 2-3 | 0-3 | 4-1 | | 4-0 | 2-0 |
| 16 | Wrington Redhill | 3-2 | 1-3 | 0-2 | 3-1 | 5-3 | 1-0 | 6-0 | 1-0 | 1-1 | 1-3 | 0-1 | 0-1 | 3-4 | 3-2 | 2-2 | | 0-1 |
| 17 | Yatton Athletic | 4-2 | 0-2 | 5-2 | 0-5 | 0-5 | 2-4 | 9-0 | 2-0 | 3-0 | 2-2 | 1-4 | 2-1 | 2-3 | 3-2 | 0-4 | 1-2 | |

| DIVISION ONE EAST | | P | W | D | L | F | A | GD | Pts |
|---|---|---|---|---|---|---|---|---|---|
| 1 | Shepton Mallet Reserves | 26 | 22 | 3 | 1 | 68 | 16 | 52 | 69 |
| 2 | Stockwood Wanderers | 26 | 22 | 1 | 3 | 73 | 28 | 45 | 67 |
| 3 | Larkhall Athletic Reserves | 26 | 17 | 5 | 4 | 73 | 34 | 39 | 56 |
| 4 | Peasedown Athletic | 26 | 12 | 5 | 9 | 59 | 36 | 23 | 41 |
| 5 | Stockwood Green | 26 | 10 | 8 | 8 | 49 | 38 | 11 | 38 |
| 6 | Frome Town Sports | 26 | 10 | 4 | 12 | 48 | 55 | -7 | 34 |
| 7 | Broad Plain House | 26 | 10 | 3 | 13 | 56 | 54 | 2 | 33 |
| 8 | Westfield FC | 26 | 9 | 4 | 13 | 70 | 68 | 2 | 31 |
| 9 | Brislington Res | 26 | 8 | 7 | 11 | 47 | 54 | -7 | 31 |
| 10 | Purnells Sports FC | 26 | 8 | 4 | 14 | 33 | 53 | -20 | 28 |
| 11 | Keynsham Town Res. | 26 | 7 | 6 | 13 | 41 | 56 | -15 | 27 |
| 12 | Timsbury Athletic | 26 | 6 | 7 | 13 | 27 | 46 | -19 | 25 |
| 13 | Castle Cary (-4) | 26 | 7 | 5 | 14 | 42 | 69 | -27 | 22 |
| 14 | Welton Rovers Reserves | 26 | 2 | 2 | 22 | 24 | 103 | -79 | 8 |

**In:** Clutton (R); Cutters Friday (R); Imperial (P).

| DIVISION ONE WEST | | P | W | D | L | F | A | GD | Pts |
|---|---|---|---|---|---|---|---|---|---|
| 1 | Middlezoy Rovers | 24 | 20 | 4 | 0 | 77 | 16 | 61 | 64 |
| 2 | Wells City Reserves | 24 | 14 | 4 | 6 | 48 | 22 | 26 | 46 |
| 3 | Minehead | 24 | 13 | 4 | 7 | 57 | 36 | 21 | 4 |
| 4 | Street Res | 24 | 10 | 6 | 8 | 40 | 49 | -9 | 36 |
| 5 | Winscombe | 24 | 11 | 2 | 11 | 49 | 50 | -1 | 35 |
| 6 | Cleeve West Town | 24 | 10 | 4 | 10 | 49 | 44 | 5 | 3 |
| 7 | Ilminster Town | 24 | 10 | 4 | 10 | 42 | 47 | -5 | 3 |
| 8 | Glastonbury FC | 24 | 8 | 7 | 9 | 29 | 33 | -4 | 3 |
| 9 | Congresbury (-8) | 24 | 12 | 2 | 10 | 45 | 40 | 5 | 3 |
| 10 | Portishead Town Res. (-4) | 24 | 7 | 6 | 11 | 39 | 54 | -15 | 2 |
| 11 | Combe St Nicholas (-7) | 24 | 7 | 3 | 14 | 48 | 58 | -10 | 1 |
| 12 | Burnham United | 24 | 3 | 8 | 13 | 32 | 49 | -17 | 1 |
| 13 | St George Easton in Gordano (-8) | 24 | 3 | 2 | 19 | 27 | 84 | -57 | |

**In:** Heybridge Town (P); Somerton (P); Uphill Castle (P).

| DIVISION TWO EAST | P | W | D | L | F | A | GD | Pts |
|---|---|---|---|---|---|---|---|---|
| 1 Somerton | 26 | 19 | 5 | 2 | 72 | 24 | 48 | 62 |
| 2 Imperial FC | 26 | 15 | 7 | 4 | 64 | 43 | 21 | 52 |
| 3 Long Ashton | 26 | 16 | 3 | 7 | 75 | 44 | 31 | 51 |
| 4 Chew Magna | 26 | 14 | 2 | 10 | 68 | 51 | 17 | 44 |
| 5 Saltford | 26 | 13 | 4 | 9 | 56 | 30 | 26 | 43 |
| 6 Pensford | 26 | 12 | 6 | 8 | 46 | 36 | 10 | 42 |
| 7 AFC Brislington (-4) | 26 | 13 | 6 | 7 | 55 | 30 | 25 | 41 |
| 8 Fry Club Reserves | 26 | 11 | 5 | 10 | 36 | 36 | 0 | 38 |
| 9 Farrington Gurney | 26 | 10 | 5 | 11 | 47 | 46 | 1 | 35 |
| 10 Hengrove Athletic Res. | 26 | 10 | 4 | 12 | 48 | 56 | -8 | 34 |
| 11 Radstock Town Reserves | 26 | 6 | 7 | 13 | 28 | 50 | -22 | 25 |
| 12 Stockwood Green Res. | 26 | 3 | 9 | 14 | 39 | 64 | -25 | 18 |
| 13 Cutters Friday Reserves | 26 | 2 | 5 | 19 | 27 | 100 | -73 | 11 |
| 14 Tunley Athletic (-3) | 26 | 2 | 4 | 20 | 42 | 93 | -51 | 7 |

**In:** Mendip Broadwalk.

| DIVISION TWO WEST | P | W | D | L | F | A | GD | Pts |
|---|---|---|---|---|---|---|---|---|
| 1 Uphill Castle | 26 | 19 | 3 | 4 | 86 | 28 | 58 | 60 |
| 2 Highbridge Town | 26 | 19 | 2 | 5 | 94 | 45 | 49 | 59 |
| 3 Worle | 26 | 16 | 7 | 3 | 75 | 30 | 45 | 55 |
| 4 1610 Taunton United | 26 | 15 | 1 | 10 | 77 | 50 | 27 | 46 |
| 5 Nailsea and Tickenham Res. | 26 | 13 | 7 | 6 | 71 | 48 | 23 | 46 |
| 6 Kewstoke Lions | 26 | 14 | 4 | 8 | 55 | 57 | -2 | 46 |
| 7 Ashton and Backwell United Res. | 26 | 9 | 7 | 10 | 60 | 61 | -1 | 34 |
| 8 Banwell | 26 | 7 | 9 | 10 | 47 | 67 | -20 | 30 |
| 9 Cheddar Reserves (-1) | 26 | 8 | 6 | 12 | 56 | 53 | 3 | 29 |
| 10 Churchill Club 70 | 26 | 8 | 3 | 15 | 49 | 62 | -13 | 27 |
| 11 Nailsea United Reserves | 26 | 6 | 7 | 13 | 39 | 56 | -17 | 25 |
| 12 Clevedon Utd Res | 26 | 6 | 5 | 15 | 47 | 70 | -23 | 23 |
| 13 Weston St Johns | 26 | 5 | 4 | 17 | 42 | 101 | -59 | 19 |
| 14 Burnham United Res. | 26 | 2 | 5 | 19 | 27 | 97 | -70 | 11 |

**In:** Winscombe Reserves.

## Somerset County League Premier Division

|  |  |  |
|---|---|---|
| BERROW | Red Road Playing Fields, Berrow, Burnham-on-Sea TA8 2LY | |
| BRIDGWATER TOWN RESEVES | Fairfax Park, College Way, Bath Road, Bridgwater TA6 4TZ | 01278 446 899 |
| CHILCOMPTON SPORTS | Chilcompton Sports Ground, Bennell Wells Road, Chilcompton BA3 4EZ | |
| CLEVEDON UNITED | Coleridge Vale, Clevedon, North Somerset | 01275 871 878 |
| DUNDRY ATHLETIC | Dundry Playing Fields, Crabtree Lane, Dundry, Nr Bristol BS41 8LN | 0117 9645 536 |
| FRY CLUB | Cadbury's, Somerdale, Keynsham, Bristol BS31 2AU | 0117 9376 500 |
| MIDDLEZOY ROVERS | The Aerodrome, Westonzoyland, Somerset TA7 0ES | |
| NAILSEA AND TICKENHAM | Fryth Way, Pound Lane, Nailsea BS48 2AS | 07763 925 811 |
| NAILSEA UNITED | Grove Sports Ground, Old Church, Nailsea BS48 4ND | 01275 856 892 |
| ODD DOWN RESERVES | Lew Hill Memorial Ground, Combe Hay Lane, Odd Down, Bath BA2 8PH | 01225 832 491 |
| SHEPTON MALLET RESERVES | Playing Fields, Old Wells Road, West Shepton, Shepton Mallet BA4 5XN | 01749 344 609 |
| SHIREHAMPTON | Recreation Ground, Penpole Lane, Shirehampton, Bristol BS11 0EA | 0117 923 5461 |
| STAPLEGROVE | Staplegrove Sports Ground, Manor Road, Staplegrove, Taunton TA2 6EG | |
| STOCKWOOD WANDERERS | Stockers Stadium, Stockwood lane, Bristol BS14 9BP | |
| WATCHET TOWN | Memorial Ground, Doniford Road, Watchet TA23 0TG | 01984 631 041 |
| WELLS CITY RESERVES | Athletic Ground, Rowdens Road, Wells, Somerset BA5 1TU | 01749 679 971 |
| WRINGTON REDHILL | The Recreation Field, Silver Street, Wrington, Bristol BS40 5QN | 07918 192 544 |
| YATTON ATHLETIC | Hangstones Playing Fields, Stowey Road, Yatton, North Somerset BS49 4HS | |

# STAFFORDSHIRE COUNTY SENIOR LEAGUE

**Sponsored by:** No sponsor
**Founded:** 1957
**Recent Champions:**
**2013:** Hanley Town
**2014:** Wolstanton United **2015:** Wolstanton United.

| PREMIER DIVISION | P | W | D | L | F | A | GD | Pts |
|---|---|---|---|---|---|---|---|---|
| 1 Leek CSOB | 32 | 26 | 5 | 1 | 90 | 19 | 71 | 83 |
| 2 Wolstanton United | 32 | 22 | 3 | 7 | 93 | 33 | 60 | 69 |
| 3 Redgate Clayton | 32 | 22 | 3 | 7 | 79 | 39 | 40 | 69 |
| 4 Florence | 32 | 19 | 7 | 6 | 75 | 40 | 35 | 64 |
| 5 Hilton Harriers | 32 | 18 | 2 | 12 | 57 | 47 | 10 | 56 |
| 6 Uttoxeter Town | 32 | 17 | 4 | 11 | 71 | 43 | 28 | 55 |
| 7 Silverdale Athletic | 31 | 14 | 9 | 8 | 62 | 41 | 21 | 51 |
| 8 Abbey Hulton United | 31 | 15 | 3 | 13 | 58 | 48 | 10 | 48 |
| 9 Knypersley Victoria | 32 | 14 | 6 | 12 | 63 | 73 | -10 | 48 |
| 10 Cheadle Town | 32 | 11 | 8 | 13 | 38 | 35 | 3 | 41 |
| 11 Ball Haye Green | 32 | 11 | 5 | 16 | 65 | 62 | 3 | 38 |
| 12 Hanley Town Reserves | 32 | 10 | 8 | 14 | 35 | 57 | -22 | 38 |
| 13 Audley & District | 32 | 7 | 8 | 17 | 29 | 41 | -12 | 29 |
| 14 Cheadle SMU | 31 | 6 | 7 | 18 | 29 | 69 | -40 | 25 |
| 15 Alsager Town Reserves | 32 | 5 | 7 | 20 | 33 | 77 | -44 | 22 |
| 16 Eccleshall Reserves | 32 | 5 | 6 | 21 | 33 | 71 | -38 | 21 |
| 17 Leek Town Reserves | 31 | 2 | 1 | 28 | 20 | 135 | -115 | 7 |
| Kidsgrove Athletic Reserves withdrew | | | | | | | | |

| DIVISION ONE | P | W | D | L | F | A | GD | Pts |
|---|---|---|---|---|---|---|---|---|
| 1 Redgate Clayton Res. | 26 | 20 | 2 | 4 | 68 | 25 | 43 | 62 |
| 2 Ashbourne | 24 | 17 | 2 | 5 | 77 | 25 | 52 | 53 |
| 3 Walsall Phoenix | 26 | 14 | 8 | 4 | 66 | 41 | 25 | 50 |
| 4 Stone Dominoes | 26 | 15 | 4 | 7 | 79 | 35 | 44 | 49 |
| 5 MMU Cheshire | 26 | 14 | 6 | 6 | 56 | 43 | 13 | 48 |
| 6 Keele University | 26 | 11 | 9 | 6 | 72 | 46 | 26 | 42 |
| 7 Market Drayton Tigers | 25 | 10 | 7 | 8 | 59 | 62 | -3 | 37 |
| 8 Milton United | 26 | 10 | 6 | 10 | 57 | 51 | 6 | 36 |
| 9 Wolverhampton SC U21 | 24 | 9 | 1 | 14 | 44 | 59 | -15 | 28 |
| 10 Cheadle Town Reserves | 26 | 6 | 6 | 14 | 40 | 74 | -34 | 24 |
| 11 Foley Meir | 26 | 5 | 6 | 15 | 46 | 80 | -34 | 21 |
| 12 Staffordshire LA | 26 | 5 | 4 | 17 | 45 | 86 | -41 | 19 |
| 13 Hawkins Sports | 23 | 3 | 5 | 15 | 36 | 83 | -47 | 17 |
| 14 Abbey Hulton United Res. | 26 | 3 | 6 | 17 | 47 | 82 | -35 | 15 |
| Betley withdrew | | | | | | | | |
| Whittington withdrew | | | | | | | | |

| Division Two North | P | W | D | L | F | A | GD | Pts |
|---|---|---|---|---|---|---|---|---|
| 1 Eastwood Hanley | 20 | 18 | 1 | 1 | 68 | 15 | 53 | 55 |
| 2 Audley & District Res. | 20 | 13 | 2 | 5 | 61 | 34 | 27 | 41 |
| 3 Leek CSOB Reserves | 20 | 12 | 2 | 6 | 48 | 28 | 20 | 38 |
| 4 Norton | 20 | 10 | 4 | 6 | 62 | 49 | 13 | 34 |
| 5 Goldenhill Wanderers | 20 | 10 | 2 | 8 | 52 | 33 | 19 | 32 |
| 6 Hardman Development Centre | 20 | 9 | 1 | 10 | 44 | 41 | 3 | 28 |
| 7 AFC Alsager | 20 | 8 | 3 | 9 | 49 | 65 | -16 | 27 |
| 8 Keele University Res. | 20 | 6 | 2 | 12 | 46 | 57 | -11 | 20 |
| 9 Congleton Rovers | 20 | 5 | 3 | 12 | 52 | 57 | -5 | 18 |
| 10 Chesterton | 20 | 5 | 3 | 12 | 31 | 58 | -27 | 18 |
| 11 Tunstall Town | 20 | 2 | 1 | 17 | 25 | 101 | -76 | 7 |
| Betley Reserves - withdrew | | | | | | | | |

| Division Two South | P | W | D | L | F | A | GD | Pts |
|---|---|---|---|---|---|---|---|---|
| 1 Penkridge | 20 | 16 | 1 | 3 | 77 | 29 | 48 | 49 |
| 2 Shenstone Pathfinder Res. | 20 | 15 | 3 | 2 | 83 | 24 | 59 | 48 |
| 3 Brereton Social U21s | 20 | 14 | 1 | 5 | 76 | 18 | 58 | 43 |
| 4 Stone Old Alleynians Res. | 20 | 11 | 2 | 7 | 48 | 29 | 19 | 3[illegible] |
| 5 Cannock United | 20 | 9 | 5 | 6 | 37 | 41 | -4 | 3[illegible] |
| 6 Hilton Harriers Reserves | 20 | 8 | 4 | 8 | 44 | 34 | 10 | 2[illegible] |
| 7 Whittington Reserves | 20 | 7 | 3 | 10 | 37 | 53 | -16 | 2[illegible] |
| 8 Walsall Phoenix U21s | 20 | 6 | 0 | 14 | 34 | 62 | -28 | 1[illegible] |
| 9 Barton United Reserves | 20 | 4 | 6 | 10 | 26 | 58 | -32 | 1[illegible] |
| 10 Acorn Albion | 20 | 3 | 5 | 12 | 23 | 54 | -31 | 1[illegible] |
| 11 Eastfield | 20 | 1 | 2 | 17 | 15 | 98 | -83 | [illegible] |

# SUFFOLK & IPSWICH LEAGUE

**Sponsored by:** TouchlineSIL

**Founded:** 1896

**Recent Champions:**

**2013:** Ipswich Valley Rangers

**2014:** Achilles

**2015:** Crane Sports

| | SENIOR DIVISION | P | W | D | L | F | A | GD | Pts |
|---|---|---|---|---|---|---|---|---|---|
| 1 | Crane Sports | 30 | 23 | 4 | 3 | 83 | 32 | 51 | 73 |
| 2 | Achilles | 30 | 22 | 4 | 4 | 109 | 34 | 75 | 70 |
| 3 | East Bergholt United | 30 | 18 | 5 | 7 | 77 | 44 | 33 | 59 |
| 4 | Bramford United | 30 | 18 | 3 | 9 | 74 | 43 | 31 | 57 |
| 5 | Framlingham Town | 30 | 16 | 3 | 11 | 61 | 40 | 21 | 51 |
| 6 | Haughley United | 30 | 15 | 5 | 10 | 80 | 47 | 33 | 50 |
| 7 | Capel Plough | 30 | 14 | 3 | 13 | 46 | 39 | 7 | 45 |
| 8 | Westerfield United | 30 | 12 | 7 | 11 | 57 | 70 | -13 | 43 |
| 9 | Felixstowe Harpers United | 30 | 13 | 4 | 13 | 41 | 67 | -26 | 43 |
| 10 | Ipswich Athletic | 30 | 12 | 5 | 13 | 59 | 57 | 2 | 41 |
| 11 | Grundisburgh | 30 | 13 | 1 | 16 | 58 | 60 | -2 | 40 |
| 12 | Wenhaston United | 30 | 12 | 3 | 15 | 48 | 54 | -6 | 39 |
| 13 | Stanton | 30 | 10 | 3 | 17 | 50 | 58 | -8 | 33 |
| 14 | Leiston St Margarets | 30 | 9 | 4 | 17 | 46 | 72 | -26 | 31 |
| 15 | Wickham Market | 30 | 3 | 4 | 23 | 38 | 91 | -53 | 13 |
| 16 | Ipswich Valley Rangers | 30 | 0 | 2 | 28 | 19 | 138 | -119 | 2 |

| | DIVISION ONE | P | W | D | L | F | A | GD | Pts |
|---|---|---|---|---|---|---|---|---|---|
| | Ransomes Sports (-1) | 24 | 17 | 6 | 1 | 86 | 32 | 54 | 56 |
| | Coplestonians | 24 | 16 | 5 | 3 | 69 | 27 | 42 | 53 |
| | Henley Athletic | 24 | 16 | 3 | 5 | 68 | 36 | 32 | 51 |
| | AFC Hoxne | 24 | 14 | 2 | 8 | 57 | 34 | 23 | 44 |
| | Benhall St Mary (-1) | 24 | 11 | 5 | 8 | 48 | 45 | 3 | 37 |
| | Mendlesham | 24 | 11 | 3 | 10 | 46 | 42 | 4 | 36 |
| | Old Newton United | 24 | 11 | 2 | 11 | 54 | 60 | -6 | 35 |
| | Bacton United 89 | 24 | 8 | 9 | 7 | 41 | 37 | 4 | 33 |
| | Sporting 87 | 24 | 7 | 2 | 15 | 32 | 49 | -17 | 23 |
| 10 | Trimley Athletic | 24 | 5 | 5 | 14 | 33 | 61 | -28 | 20 |
| 11 | Claydon | 24 | 5 | 4 | 15 | 35 | 57 | -22 | 19 |
| 12 | Ipswich Exiles | 24 | 5 | 2 | 17 | 36 | 73 | -37 | 17 |
| 13 | Somersham | 24 | 5 | 2 | 17 | 31 | 83 | -52 | 17 |

## BOB COLEMAN CUP

**HOLDERS:** IPSWICH ATHLETIC

**ROUND 1**

| | | | |
|---|---|---|---|
| Coddenham Athletic | v | Cockfield United | 1-0 |
| Saxmundham Sports | v | Halesworth Town | 1-7 |
| Shotley | v | Chantry Grasshoppers | 5-2 |
| Sizewell Associates | v | AFC Kesgrove & Willis | 1-11 |
| Sproughton United | v | Tattingstone United | 1-6 |
| Ufford Sports | v | Bramford Road Old Boys | 3-2 |
| Witnesham Wasps | v | Tacket Street BBOB | 0-2 |

**ROUND 2**

| | | | |
|---|---|---|---|
| Barham Athletic | v | Sporting 87 | 5-5, 5-4p |
| Bartons | v | Trimley Athletic | 0-4 |
| Benhall St Mary | v | Tacket Street BBOB | 4-1 |
| Boxford Rovers | v | Cedars Park | 0-1 |
| Claydon | v | Ufford Sports | 5-0 |
| Coplestonians | v | Bacton United 89 | 4-1 |
| Elmswell | v | Henley Athletic | 0-9 |
| Halesworth Town | v | Stowupland Falcons | 2-4 |
| Old Newton United | v | Ipswich Exiles | 7-2 |
| Ransomes Sports | v | AFC Hoxne | 1-2 |
| Salvation Army | v | Stonham Aspal | 1-4 |
| Shotley | v | AFC Kesgrave & Willis | 3-4 |
| Somersham | v | Bildeston Rangers | 3-1 |
| Tattingstone United | v | Sproughton Sports | 1-1, 6-7p |
| Trimley Red Devils | v | Mendlesham | 0-1 |

**ROUND 3**

| | | | |
|---|---|---|---|
| Achilles | v | Barham Athletic | 10-0 |
| AFC Hoxne | v | Coddenham Athletic | 3-2 |
| Benhall St Mary | v | Cedars Park | 3-0 |
| Capel Plough | v | Old Newton United | 3-0 |
| Claydon | v | Leiston St Margarets | 2-4 |
| Coplestonians | v | Bramford United | 1-6 |
| Crane Sports | v | Mendlesham | 3-0 |
| East Bergholt United | v | Ipswich Valley Rangers | 2-1 |
| Felixstowe Harpers United | v | Stanton | 2-1 |
| Framlingham Town | v | Wickham Market | 1-3 |
| Grundisburgh | v | Wenhaston United | 2-4 |
| Haughley United | v | Ipswich Athletic | 4-1 |
| Henley Athletic | v | Sproughton Sports | 3-0 |
| Somersham | v | AFC Kesgrave & Willis | 1-2 |
| Trimley Athletic | v | Stonham Aspal | 5-3 |
| Westerfield United | v | Stowupland Falcons | 4-4, 5-4p |

| | SENIOR DIVISION | 1 | 2 | 3 | 4 | 5 | 6 | 7 | 8 | 9 | 10 | 11 | 12 | 13 | 14 | 15 | 16 |
|---|---|---|---|---|---|---|---|---|---|---|---|---|---|---|---|---|---|
| 1 | Achilles | | 1-0 | 4-2 | 4-1 | 3-3 | 2-0 | 5-3 | 1-3 | 1-1 | 1-0 | 4-2 | 1-3 | 3-0 | 2-2 | 5-0 | 6-1 |
| 2 | Bramford United | 1-3 | | 1-0 | 1-2 | 3-0 | 4-0 | 1-1 | 1-0 | 2-1 | 0-0 | 4-3 | 4-1 | 2-1 | 3-4 | 5-2 | 3-0 |
| 3 | Capel Plough | 1-1 | 2-0 | | 1-3 | 1-2 | 0-2 | 0-1 | 3-0 | 1-2 | 2-0 | 3-1 | 3-2 | 2-5 | 2-1 | 1-2 | 3-1 |
| 4 | Crane Sports | 3-2 | 3-0 | 1-2 | | 2-0 | 2-0 | 3-2 | 3-1 | 0-0 | 6-1 | 5-0 | 4-0 | 7-1 | 1-0 | 6-2 | 2-0 |
| 5 | East Bergholt United | 0-4 | 3-0 | 1-0 | 1-1 | | 1-2 | 2-1 | 2-1 | 2-2 | 1-3 | 4-0 | 6-1 | 3-2 | 1-0 | 2-2 | 7-1 |
| 6 | Felixstowe Harpers United | 0-6 | 1-6 | 0-2 | 1-1 | 2-8 | | 1-0 | 3-1 | 0-4 | 2-1 | 1-1 | 3-2 | 2-1 | 0-5 | 2-2 | 3-1 |
| 7 | Framlingham Town | 0-1 | 4-3 | 1-0 | 0-1 | 1-4 | 4-1 | | 0-2 | 3-1 | 2-2 | 3-0 | 3-1 | 3-1 | 0-1 | 2-0 | 2-0 |
| 8 | Grundisburgh | 1-2 | 3-5 | 0-4 | 0-3 | 3-1 | 2-4 | 0-1 | | 1-0 | 3-2 | 1-1 | 2-1 | 1-3 | 0-1 | 2-1 | 5-0 |
| 9 | Haughley United | 4-2 | 0-1 | 1-2 | 4-2 | 2-5 | 0-1 | 2-7 | 5-0 | | 0-3 | 7-1 | 3-1 | 0-0 | 1-0 | 3-1 | 6-2 |
| 10 | Ipswich Athletic | 0-9 | 1-1 | 1-1 | 2-3 | 4-1 | 3-1 | 2-0 | 0-6 | 0-3 | | 12-0 | 3-1 | 3-0 | 1-2 | 3-0 | 1-4 |
| 11 | Ipswich Valley Rangers | 1-10 | 0-6 | 1-4 | 1-3 | 1-4 | 0-1 | 0-7 | 1-6 | 2-11 | 0-1 | | 0-3 | 0-2 | 0-4 | 0-4 | 0-3 |
| 12 | Leiston St Margarets | 1-3 | 0-5 | 1-0 | 1-5 | 0-4 | 2-4 | 0-1 | 4-2 | 1-4 | 2-2 | 3-0 | | 2-0 | 0-0 | 0-0 | 4-3 |
| 13 | Stanton | 0-2 | 1-3 | 0-1 | 2-4 | 0-1 | 2-0 | 0-3 | 3-4 | 3-2 | 2-0 | 5-0 | 2-2 | | 4-0 | 1-3 | 2-1 |
| 14 | Wenhaston United | 0-8 | 3-2 | 0-1 | 1-2 | 0-1 | 2-2 | 1-2 | 2-4 | 2-5 | 2-1 | 3-1 | 1-2 | 2-1 | | 0-2 | 3-0 |
| 15 | Westerfield United | 0-10 | 2-3 | 4-2 | 2-2 | 2-2 | 2-1 | 2-1 | 3-2 | 0-0 | 1-3 | 8-2 | 3-2 | 0-4 | 3-1 | | 1-1 |
| 16 | Wickham Market | 1-3 | 1-4 | 0-0 | 0-2 | 0-5 | 0-1 | 3-3 | 0-2 | 1-6 | 1-4 | 6-0 | 1-3 | 2-2 | 2-5 | 2-3 | |

## SUFFOLK & IPSWICH LEAGUE - STEP 7

| DIVISION TWO | P | W | D | L | F | A | GD | Pts |
|---|---|---|---|---|---|---|---|---|
| 1 AFC Kesgrave & Willis | 22 | 18 | 1 | 3 | 100 | 26 | 74 | 55 |
| 2 Trimley Red Devils | 22 | 17 | 2 | 3 | 77 | 24 | 53 | 53 |
| 3 Stowupland Falcons | 22 | 15 | 3 | 4 | 86 | 27 | 59 | 48 |
| 4 Cedars Park | 22 | 13 | 3 | 6 | 55 | 33 | 22 | 42 |
| 5 Stonham Aspal | 22 | 12 | 3 | 7 | 59 | 47 | 12 | 39 |
| 6 Barham Athletic | 22 | 11 | 2 | 9 | 74 | 54 | 20 | 35 |
| 7 Sproughton Sports | 22 | 9 | 4 | 9 | 48 | 44 | 4 | 31 |
| 8 Witnesham Wasps | 22 | 7 | 4 | 11 | 54 | 55 | -1 | 25 |
| 9 Bramford Road Old Boys | 22 | 6 | 3 | 13 | 63 | 89 | -26 | 21 |
| 10 Bartons (-2) | 22 | 6 | 2 | 14 | 36 | 57 | -21 | 18 |
| 11 Bildeston Rangers (-6) | 22 | 4 | 1 | 17 | 33 | 103 | -70 | 7 |
| 12 Salvation Army | 22 | 0 | 0 | 22 | 16 | 142 | -126 | 0 |

| DIVISION THREE | P | W | D | L | F | A | GD | Pts |
|---|---|---|---|---|---|---|---|---|
| 1 Coddenham Athletic | 22 | 18 | 1 | 3 | 94 | 25 | 69 | 55 |
| 2 Shotley | 22 | 17 | 1 | 4 | 78 | 36 | 42 | 52 |
| 3 Tacket Street BBOB | 22 | 16 | 0 | 6 | 76 | 35 | 41 | 48 |
| 4 Chantry Grasshoppers | 22 | 14 | 2 | 6 | 78 | 47 | 31 | 44 |
| 5 Halesworth Town | 21 | 12 | 5 | 4 | 57 | 32 | 25 | 41 |
| 6 Cockfield United | 22 | 13 | 2 | 7 | 51 | 40 | 11 | 41 |
| 7 Sizewell Associates | 22 | 6 | 4 | 12 | 48 | 75 | -27 | 22 |
| 8 Ufford Sports | 22 | 4 | 7 | 11 | 39 | 60 | -21 | 19 |
| 9 Saxmundham Sports | 22 | 5 | 4 | 13 | 35 | 72 | -37 | 19 |
| 10 Tattingstone United (-3) | 21 | 5 | 3 | 13 | 48 | 78 | -30 | 15 |
| 11 Elmswell (-6) | 22 | 5 | 3 | 14 | 52 | 70 | -18 | 12 |
| 12 Sproughton United (-2) | 22 | 0 | 0 | 22 | 29 | 115 | -86 | -2 |

**In:** Adastral Park (P - Div.5), Newton Road formerly AFC Titans (P - Div.5), Stage Event Security (P - Div.5), Sutton Heath Saxons (P - Div.5), Stradbrooke (P).

| DIVISION FOUR | P | W | D | L | F | A | GD | Pts |
|---|---|---|---|---|---|---|---|---|
| 1 Woolverstone United | 20 | 15 | 2 | 3 | 73 | 24 | 49 | 47 |
| 2 Kesgrave Kestrels | 20 | 14 | 2 | 4 | 69 | 36 | 33 | 44 |
| 3 AFC Kesgrave & Willis Res. | 20 | 12 | 2 | 6 | 61 | 43 | 18 | 38 |
| 4 Witnesham Wasps Res. | 20 | 12 | 2 | 6 | 49 | 42 | 7 | 38 |
| 5 Stradbroke United | 20 | 10 | 2 | 8 | 72 | 42 | 30 | 32 |
| 6 Cockfield United Res. | 20 | 8 | 5 | 7 | 34 | 30 | 4 | 29 |
| 7 Sporting 87 'A' | 20 | 6 | 5 | 9 | 46 | 51 | -5 | 23 |
| 8 Halesworth Town Res. | 20 | 6 | 3 | 11 | 42 | 70 | -28 | 21 |
| 9 AFC Elmsett (-2) | 20 | 6 | 4 | 10 | 61 | 61 | 0 | 20 |
| 10 Stowupland Falcons 'A' (-4) | 20 | 4 | 2 | 14 | 28 | 80 | -52 | 10 |
| 11 Stonham Aspal 'A' (-2) | 20 | 1 | 3 | 16 | 32 | 88 | -56 | 4 |

| DIVISION FIVE | P | W | D | L | F | A | GD | Pts |
|---|---|---|---|---|---|---|---|---|
| 1 Adastral Park | 20 | 17 | 0 | 3 | 105 | 17 | 88 | 51 |
| 2 Stage Event Security (-7) | 20 | 16 | 2 | 2 | 88 | 21 | 67 | 43 |
| 3 Sproughton Sports Res | 20 | 14 | 1 | 5 | 62 | 41 | 21 | 43 |
| 4 AFC Titans (-2) | 20 | 11 | 1 | 8 | 70 | 54 | 16 | 32 |
| 5 Cedars Park 'A' | 20 | 10 | 1 | 9 | 47 | 55 | -8 | 31 |
| 6 Sutton Heath Saxons (-1) | 20 | 7 | 4 | 9 | 41 | 42 | -1 | 24 |
| 7 Needham Market Phoenix | 20 | 6 | 3 | 11 | 47 | 80 | -33 | 21 |
| 8 Bacton United 89 'A' | 20 | 6 | 2 | 12 | 51 | 69 | -18 | 20 |
| 9 Kesgrave Kestrels Res. | 20 | 5 | 4 | 11 | 35 | 72 | -37 | 19 |
| 10 Ufford Sports Res. (-3) | 20 | 5 | 1 | 14 | 35 | 63 | -28 | 13 |
| 11 Chantry Grasshoppers Res. (-2) | 20 | 3 | 1 | 16 | 29 | 96 | -67 | 8 |

See Division 3 for promoted clubs.

### BOB COLEMAN CUP

**ROUND 4**

| | | | |
|---|---|---|---|
| AFC Hoxne | v | Henley Athletic | 2-3 |
| AFC Kesgrave & Willis | v | Benhall St Mary | 5-1 |
| Bramford United | v | Wenhaston United | 5-1 |
| Crane Sports | v | Capel Plough | 2-1 |
| East Bergholt United | v | Westerfield United | 2-0 |
| Felixstowe Harpers United | v | Achilles | 2-3 |
| Leiston St Margarets | v | Trimley Athletic | 1-0 |
| Wickham Market | v | Haughley United | 0-10 |

**QUARTER FINALS**

| | | | |
|---|---|---|---|
| AFC Kesgrave & Willis | v | Bramford United | 2-2, 5-4p |
| Crane Sports | v | Henley Athletic | 3-1 |
| East Bergholt United | v | Achilles | 2-3 |
| Haughley United | v | Leiston St Margarets | 2-0 |

**SEMI FINALS**

| | | | |
|---|---|---|---|
| Achilles | v | AFC Kesgrave & Willis | 5-0 |
| Haughley United | v | Crane Sports | 1-0 |

**FINAL**

| | | | |
|---|---|---|---|
| Achilles | v | Haughley United | 4-2 |

| INTERMEDIATE A | P | W | D | L | F | A | GD | Pts |
|---|---|---|---|---|---|---|---|---|
| 1 Achilles Reserves | 22 | 19 | 1 | 2 | 85 | 21 | 64 | [illegible] |
| 2 East Bergholt United Res. | 22 | 11 | 7 | 4 | 67 | 41 | 26 | [illegible] |
| 3 Coplestonians Reserves | 22 | 12 | 4 | 6 | 57 | 36 | 21 | [illegible] |
| 4 Westerfield United Res. | 21 | 11 | 3 | 7 | 67 | 46 | 21 | [illegible] |
| 5 Crane Sports Reserves | 22 | 10 | 3 | 9 | 65 | 41 | 24 | [illegible] |
| 6 Sporting 87 Reserves | 22 | 8 | 3 | 11 | 51 | 50 | 1 | [illegible] |
| 7 Wenhaston United Res. | 21 | 8 | 3 | 10 | 33 | 44 | -11 | [illegible] |
| 8 Mendlesham Reserves | 22 | 7 | 5 | 10 | 41 | 60 | -19 | [illegible] |
| 9 Felixstowe Harpers United Res. | 22 | 7 | 4 | 11 | 53 | 77 | -24 | [illegible] |
| 10 Grundisburgh Res. (-2) | 22 | 7 | 1 | 14 | 43 | 71 | -28 | [illegible] |
| 11 Old Newton United Res. (-3) | 21 | 6 | 4 | 11 | 28 | 66 | -38 | [illegible] |
| 12 Capel Plough Res. (-8) | 21 | 4 | 2 | 15 | 24 | 61 | -37 | [illegible] |

| INTERMEDIATE B | P | W | D | L | F | A | GD | Pts |
|---|---|---|---|---|---|---|---|---|
| 1 Ipswich Athletic Res. (2) | 24 | 18 | 4 | 2 | 85 | 30 | 55 | [illegible] |
| 2 Framlingham Town Res. | 24 | 19 | 2 | 3 | 113 | 34 | 79 | [illegible] |
| 3 AFC Hoxne Reserves | 24 | 15 | 3 | 6 | 74 | 32 | 42 | [illegible] |
| 4 Haughley United Res. | 24 | 13 | 6 | 5 | 59 | 43 | 16 | [illegible] |
| 5 Henley Athletic Reserves (-1) | 24 | 11 | 3 | 10 | 37 | 37 | 0 | [illegible] |
| 6 Ipswich Exiles Res. (-4) | 24 | 10 | 6 | 8 | 65 | 50 | 15 | [illegible] |
| 7 Claydon Reserves (2) | 24 | 8 | 4 | 12 | 49 | 56 | -7 | [illegible] |
| 8 Bramford United Res. | 24 | 8 | 5 | 11 | 44 | 45 | -1 | [illegible] |
| 9 Benhall St Mary Res. | 24 | 7 | 4 | 13 | 32 | 63 | -31 | [illegible] |
| 10 Coplestonians 'A' (-3) | 24 | 6 | 7 | 11 | 41 | 62 | -21 | [illegible] |
| 11 Trimley Athletic Res. (-2) | 24 | 6 | 5 | 13 | 50 | 81 | -31 | [illegible] |
| 12 Wickham Market Res. (-2) | 24 | 6 | 1 | 17 | 36 | 76 | -40 | [illegible] |
| 13 Ipswich Wanderers Res. (-6) | 24 | 2 | 4 | 18 | 26 | 102 | -76 | [illegible] |

| INTERMEDIATE C | P | W | D | L | F | A | GD | Pts |
|---|---|---|---|---|---|---|---|---|
| 1 Bacton United 89 Reserves | 22 | 14 | 4 | 4 | 64 | 30 | 34 | [illegible] |
| 2 Stowupland Falcons Res. | 22 | 14 | 3 | 5 | 57 | 32 | 25 | [illegible] |
| 3 East Bergholt United 'A' | 22 | 13 | 2 | 7 | 64 | 27 | 37 | [illegible] |
| 4 Trimley Red Devils Res. | 22 | 10 | 3 | 9 | 60 | 56 | 4 | [illegible] |
| 5 Stonham Aspal Res. | 22 | 9 | 5 | 8 | 59 | 56 | 3 | [illegible] |
| 6 Cedars Park Reserves | 22 | 8 | 6 | 8 | 44 | 43 | 1 | [illegible] |
| 7 Ransomes Sports Res. (-3) | 21 | 9 | 2 | 10 | 57 | 59 | -2 | [illegible] |
| 8 Debenham LC Res. (-3) | 22 | 8 | 5 | 9 | 44 | 51 | -7 | [illegible] |
| 9 Somersham Res. (-2) | 22 | 7 | 3 | 12 | 38 | 56 | -18 | [illegible] |
| 10 Old Newton United 'A' (-8) | 22 | 9 | 2 | 11 | 46 | 56 | -10 | [illegible] |
| 11 Leiston St Margarets Res. (-2) | 21 | 6 | 5 | 10 | 43 | 55 | -12 | [illegible] |
| 12 Bramford Road Old Boys Res. (-2) | 22 | 3 | 2 | 17 | 38 | 93 | -55 | [illegible] |

# SURREY ELITE INTERMEDIATE LEAGUE

**Sponsored by:** No Sponsor
**Founded:** 2008
**Recent Champions:**
**2013:** Yateley Green **2014:** N P L **2015:** Horsley

| INTERMEDIATE DIVISION | P | W | D | L | F | A | GD | Pts |
|---|---|---|---|---|---|---|---|---|
| 1 Horsley | 30 | 20 | 8 | 2 | 97 | 36 | 61 | 68 |
| 2 Balham | 30 | 20 | 3 | 7 | 91 | 34 | 57 | 63 |
| 3 Merrow | 30 | 18 | 5 | 7 | 69 | 43 | 26 | 59 |
| 4 Project Clapham | 30 | 16 | 8 | 6 | 58 | 36 | 22 | 56 |
| 5 Virginia Water | 30 | 16 | 8 | 6 | 53 | 42 | 11 | 56 |
| 6 Battersea Ironsides | 30 | 15 | 8 | 7 | 72 | 42 | 30 | 53 |
| 7 Tooting Bec | 30 | 14 | 4 | 12 | 64 | 53 | 11 | 46 |
| 8 AFC Spelthorne Sports | 30 | 12 | 8 | 10 | 48 | 52 | -4 | 44 |
| 9 AFC Cubo | 30 | 12 | 5 | 13 | 45 | 72 | -27 | 41 |
| 10 Godalming & Farncombe Athletic | 30 | 11 | 3 | 16 | 59 | 62 | -3 | 36 |
| 11 Chobham Burymead (-3) | 30 | 8 | 9 | 13 | 53 | 52 | 1 | 30 |
| 12 N P L | 30 | 8 | 6 | 16 | 57 | 74 | -17 | 30 |
| 13 Ripley Village | 30 | 6 | 8 | 16 | 42 | 75 | -33 | 26 |
| 14 Warlingham | 30 | 7 | 5 | 18 | 49 | 104 | -55 | 26 |
| 15 Reigate Priory (+3) | 30 | 4 | 5 | 21 | 45 | 83 | -38 | 20 |
| 16 Yateley United | 30 | 4 | 5 | 21 | 30 | 72 | -42 | 17 |

**In:** Laleham (P - Surrey County Intermediate - Western), Westside (P - Surrey South Eastern Combination). **Out:** Balham (P - Combined Counties), Chobham Burymead (R)

## INTERMEDIATE LEAGUE CHALLENGE CUP

**HOLDERS:** HORSLEY

**ROUND 1**

| | | | |
|---|---|---|---|
| Balham | v | AFC Cubo | HW |
| Battersea Ironsides | v | N P L | 2-1 |
| Godalming & Farncombe Athletic | v | Project Clapham | 1-2 |
| Tooting Bec | v | Ripley Village | 3-2 |
| Reigate Priory | v | Yateley United | 2-3 |
| Merrow | v | Warlingham | 2-3 |
| Horlsey | v | Virginia Water | 1-0 |
| AFC Spelthorne Sports | v | Chobham Burymead | 0-2 |

**QUARTER FINALS**

| | | | |
|---|---|---|---|
| Yateley United | v | Warlingham | 4-2 |
| Battersea Ironsides | v | Chobham Burymead | 4-2 |
| Tooting Bec | v | Horsley | 2-4 |
| Project Clapham | v | Balham | 1-0 |

**SEMI FINALS**

| | | | |
|---|---|---|---|
| Battersea Ironsides | v | Yateley United | 1-0 |
| Horlsey | v | Project Clapham | 3-0 |

**FINAL**

| | | | |
|---|---|---|---|
| Battersea Ironsides | v | Horsley | 0-3 |

| INTERMEDIATE DIVISION | 1 | 2 | 3 | 4 | 5 | 6 | 7 | 8 | 9 | 10 | 11 | 12 | 13 | 14 | 15 | 16 |
|---|---|---|---|---|---|---|---|---|---|---|---|---|---|---|---|---|
| 1 AFC Cubo | | 2-3 | 3-1 | 3-0 | 2-2 | 3-0 | 1-1 | 0-5 | 2-0 | 1-4 | 3-2 | 0-2 | 2-1 | 2-2 | 2-1 | 1-2 |
| 2 AFC Spelthorne Sports | 0-1 | | 0-0 | 3-2 | 3-2 | HW | 2-3 | 2-2 | 4-2 | 3-0 | 1-0 | 4-2 | 4-1 | 1-1 | 4-4 | 1-1 |
| 3 Balham | 0-1 | 6-1 | | 4-0 | 6-1 | 0-4 | 2-4 | 3-1 | 7-1 | 0-0 | 9-1 | 4-0 | 2-1 | 2-0 | 9-0 | 4-2 |
| 4 Battersea Ironsides | 1-1 | 4-0 | 1-2 | | 2-2 | 4-0 | 1-1 | 2-0 | 1-0 | 5-1 | 4-1 | 2-0 | 1-1 | 4-0 | 3-2 | 6-2 |
| 5 Chobham Burymead | 7-0 | 0-2 | 0-1 | 0-0 | | 2-0 | 1-2 | 1-3 | 3-3 | D-D | 1-3 | 2-2 | 3-2 | 0-0 | 8-2 | 1-0 |
| 6 Godalming & Farncombe Athletic | 5-0 | 2-0 | 1-3 | 1-0 | 0-1 | | 2-4 | 0-3 | 5-1 | 1-2 | 3-2 | 2-2 | 4-3 | 1-2 | 2-3 | 1-3 |
| 7 Horsley | 11-0 | 2-0 | 0-0 | 4-2 | 3-1 | 4-1 | | 2-0 | 4-0 | 1-1 | 3-1 | 3-1 | 3-0 | 1-1 | 11-2 | 2-2 |
| 8 Merrow | 4-0 | 2-0 | 1-3 | 0-3 | HW | 3-2 | 3-2 | | 3-1 | 3-1 | 2-1 | 3-0 | 1-1 | 3-1 | 3-3 | 5-1 |
| 9 N P L | 7-2 | 2-3 | 2-0 | 2-3 | 4-1 | 3-3 | 3-3 | 2-2 | | 0-1 | 3-3 | 1-2 | 0-1 | 1-3 | 4-2 | 3-0 |
| 10 Project Clapham | 3-0 | 3-0 | 3-1 | 2-2 | 2-0 | 1-2 | 1-2 | 2-2 | 1-1 | | 2-2 | 5-1 | 2-2 | 1-0 | 4-1 | 2-1 |
| 11 Reigate Priory | 1-1 | 1-2 | 1-8 | 2-3 | 1-3 | 3-4 | 2-4 | 0-1 | 3-4 | 2-3 | | 2-2 | 1-2 | 0-1 | 0-4 | 2-1 |
| 12 Ripley Village | 1-0 | 2-2 | 1-3 | 3-3 | 1-6 | 2-2 | 0-4 | 2-3 | 0-1 | 1-4 | 3-1 | | 1-2 | 1-4 | 4-3 | 1-1 |
| 13 Tooting Bec | 0-3 | 2-1 | 0-1 | 4-1 | 5-2 | 2-3 | 1-0 | 1-4 | 3-1 | 1-2 | 2-2 | 5-0 | | 2-4 | 3-1 | 4-0 |
| 14 Virginia Water | 3-2 | 2-1 | 0-1 | 1-1 | 2-2 | 3-1 | 5-5 | 2-1 | 2-1 | 1-0 | 2-0 | 3-2 | 1-4 | | 2-2 | 2-0 |
| 15 Warlingham | 1-4 | 1-1 | 2-9 | 0-6 | HW | 0-5 | 0-6 | 4-3 | 5-1 | 0-1 | 1-2 | 0-0 | 2-4 | 0-2 | | 1-0 |
| 16 Yateley United | 2-3 | 0-0 | 2-0 | 0-5 | 1-1 | 3-2 | 0-2 | 1-3 | 2-3 | 0-4 | 1-3 | 0-3 | 1-4 | 0-1 | 1-2 | |

D-D: Match postponed due to waterlogged pitch and the season was not extended to replay so match awarded as a draw.

## Surrey Elite Intermediate League

| | |
|---|---|
| **AFC CUBO** | Barn Elms Sports Ground, Queen Elizabeth Walk, Barnes SW13 0DG |
| **AFC SPELTHORNE SPORTS** | 296 Staines Road West, Ahford Common, Ashford TW15 1RY |
| **BATTERSEA IRONSIDES** | Battersea Ironsides S&S Club, Burntwood Lane, Earlsfield SW17 0AW |
| **GODALMING & FARNCOMBE ATH** | From Surrey County League (Western) |
| **HORSLEY** | Toms Field, Long Reach, West Horsley KT14 6PG |
| **LALEHAM** | Laleham Recreation Ground, The Broadway, Laleham, Staines. TW18 1RZ |
| **MERROW** | The Urnfield, Downside Road, Guildford, Surrey, GU4 8PH |
| **NPL** | NPL Sports Club, Queens Road, Teddington, TW11 0LW |
| **PROJECT CLAPHAM** | Denning Mews, Clapham, SW12 8QT |
| **REIGATE PRIORY** | Reigate Priory Cricket Club, off Park Lane, Reigate RH2 8JX |
| **RIPLEY VILLAGE** | The Green, Ripley, Woking GU23 6AN |
| **TOOTING BEC** | Raynes Park Sports Ground, Taunton Avenue SW20 0BH |
| **VIRGINIA WATER** | The Timbers, Crown Road, Virginia Water GU25 4HS |
| **WARLINGHAM** | Verdayne Sports Ground, Warlingham, Surrey |
| **WESTSIDE** | The Memorial Ground, Westway Close, Raynes Park SW20 9LN |
| **YATELEY UNITED** | Chandlers Lane, Yateley, Hampshire GU46 7SZ |

# TEESSIDE LEAGUE

| DIVISION ONE | | P | W | D | L | F | A | GD | Pts |
|---|---|---|---|---|---|---|---|---|---|
| 1 | Boro Rangers | 30 | 26 | 3 | 1 | 125 | 26 | 99 | 81 |
| 2 | Stockton West End | 30 | 23 | 2 | 5 | 147 | 50 | 97 | 71 |
| 3 | Whinney Banks YCC | 30 | 22 | 3 | 5 | 97 | 51 | 46 | 69 |
| 4 | Thornaby Dubliners | 30 | 21 | 3 | 6 | 82 | 38 | 44 | 66 |
| 5 | Fishburn Park | 30 | 15 | 4 | 11 | 80 | 55 | 25 | 49 |
| 6 | Redcar Newmarket | 30 | 14 | 4 | 12 | 90 | 62 | 28 | 46 |
| 7 | Thirsk Falcons (-6) | 30 | 14 | 3 | 13 | 80 | 67 | 13 | 39 |
| 8 | BEADS FC | 30 | 11 | 5 | 14 | 72 | 75 | -3 | 38 |
| 9 | Grangetown BC | 30 | 12 | 2 | 16 | 68 | 82 | -14 | 38 |
| 10 | Redcar Town | 30 | 8 | 10 | 12 | 49 | 58 | -9 | 34 |
| 11 | Staithes Athletic (-3) | 30 | 11 | 2 | 17 | 62 | 72 | -10 | 32 |
| 12 | St Mary's College | 30 | 9 | 5 | 16 | 59 | 73 | -14 | 32 |
| 13 | Nunthorpe Athletic | 30 | 9 | 1 | 20 | 63 | 118 | -55 | 28 |
| 14 | Lingdale FC | 30 | 8 | 3 | 19 | 50 | 113 | -63 | 27 |
| 15 | Yarm FC (-3) | 30 | 8 | 1 | 21 | 43 | 100 | -57 | 22 |
| 16 | Billingham Football Club (-3) | 30 | 3 | 1 | 26 | 38 | 165 | -127 | 7 |

Billingham Synthonia Reserves withdrew - record expunged.
Cargo Fleet withdrew - record expunged.
Middleton Rangers withdrew - record expunged.

**In:** Billingham Town Reserves (Durham Alliance Combination), Guisborough Three Fiddles (N), St Mary's Yarm (Formed by the merger of St Mary's College and Yarm FC.) **Out:** Billingham FC (R - Durham Alliance Combination), Lingdale (F), Thirsk Falcons (W - Harrogate and District League Div.1)

**Sponsored by:** Jack Hatfield Sports
**Founded:** 1891
**Recent Champions: 2013:** Endeavor
**2014:** Whinney Banks YCC **2015:** Whinney Banks YCC

## MACMILLAN BOWL LEAGUE CUP

| | | | |
|---|---|---|---|
| **QUARTER FINALS** | | | |
| Grangetown BC | v | Redcar Newmarket | 0-3 |
| Thirsk Falcons | v | Boro Rangers | 1-2 |
| Fishburn Park | v | Staithes Athletic | 1-1, 3-1p |
| Whinney Banks YCC | v | Stockton West End | 4-2 |
| **SEMI FINALS** | | | |
| Redcar Newmarket | v | Boro Rangers | 2-3 |
| Fishburn Park | v | Whinney Banks YCC | 1-4 |
| **FINAL** | | | |
| Boro Rangers | v | Whinney Banks YCC | 0-2 |

## LOU MOORE MEMORIAL TROPHY

| | | | |
|---|---|---|---|
| **FINAL** | | | |
| Redcar Newmarket | v | Stockton West End | 2-0 |

| | DIVISION ONE | 1 | 2 | 3 | 4 | 5 | 6 | 7 | 8 | 9 | 10 | 11 | 12 | 13 | 14 | 15 | 16 |
|---|---|---|---|---|---|---|---|---|---|---|---|---|---|---|---|---|---|
| 1 | BEADS FC | | 7-2 | 1-3 | 1-3 | 1-4 | 4-1 | 1-2 | 2-2 | 2-0 | 1-2 | 4-2 | 3-5 | 1-5 | 0-2 | 2-1 | 4-3 |
| 2 | Billingham Football Club | 1-2 | | 0-5 | 2-7 | 2-1 | 4-5 | 3-4 | 0-6 | 3-3 | 1-7 | 0-11 | 0-7 | 0-7 | 0-4 | A-W | 1-4 |
| 3 | Boro Rangers | 3-1 | 14-0 | | 2-1 | 5-1 | 11-2 | 15-0 | 4-2 | 6-2 | 2-0 | 5-1 | 1-0 | 4-1 | 3-1 | 0-1 | 3-0 |
| 4 | Fishburn Park | 6-0 | 4-0 | 1-1 | | 2-5 | 3-0 | 5-1 | 1-3 | 1-2 | 5-3 | 0-1 | 4-5 | 2-3 | 2-0 | 4-2 | 4-0 |
| 5 | Grangetown BC | 4-2 | 3-1 | 0-2 | 0-4 | | 4-1 | 4-2 | 3-1 | 4-3 | 1-3 | 1-2 | 3-5 | 6-2 | 1-3 | 0-3 | 0-1 |
| 6 | Lingdale FC | 1-7 | 2-4 | 0-3 | 2-2 | 2-3 | | 3-5 | 3-0 | 1-3 | 1-3 | 2-3 | 1-0 | 0-3 | 3-2 | 2-4 | 4-1 |
| 7 | Nunthorpe Ath | 2-5 | 4-3 | 2-3 | 5-3 | 1-6 | 3-1 | | 3-8 | 1-1 | 0-5 | 1-2 | 1-5 | H-W | 1-3 | 2-5 | 3-4 |
| 8 | Redcar Newmarket | 3-5 | 7-1 | 1-1 | 3-0 | 4-1 | 9-1 | 3-2 | | 1-1 | 3-2 | 2-1 | 1-5 | 3-1 | 1-2 | 1-3 | 10-0 |
| 9 | Redcar Town | 1-1 | 5-1 | 0-0 | 1-1 | 5-2 | 1-3 | 1-0 | 3-3 | | 1-1 | 2-1 | 2-4 | 0-3 | 0-1 | 0-4 | 2-0 |
| 10 | St Mary's College | 0-5 | 3-0 | 1-2 | 2-2 | 2-2 | 2-2 | 0-4 | 1-7 | 1-0 | | 2-0 | 1-4 | 2-6 | A-W | 1-2 | 1-5 |
| 11 | Staithes Athletic | 1-1 | 2-0 | 1-2 | 1-2 | 4-1 | 0-2 | 1-6 | 2-1 | 2-2 | 4-2 | | 3-4 | 2-3 | 1-2 | 3-4 | 3-2 |
| 12 | Stockton West End | 6-2 | 10-0 | 2-3 | 3-0 | 7-1 | 14-1 | 9-2 | 2-0 | 6-1 | 5-2 | 7-1 | | 3-0 | 3-3 | 2-4 | 9-0 |
| 13 | Thirsk Falcons | 4-4 | 5-2 | 2-8 | 0-3 | 7-1 | 1-1 | 4-2 | 5-2 | 0-5 | 5-2 | 6-2 | 0-0 | | 0-1 | 0-2 | 4-0 |
| 14 | Thornaby Dubliners | 1-0 | 13-1 | 1-4 | 4-1 | 1-1 | 4-0 | 5-1 | 3-0 | 2-1 | 1-0 | 4-2 | 5-1 | 6-2 | | 2-2 | 1-3 |
| 15 | Whinney Banks YCC | 3-1 | 11-3 | 1-10 | 2-3 | 2-1 | 8-0 | 7-1 | 3-1 | 1-1 | 2-2 | H-W | 4-6 | 3-1 | 3-1 | | 3-0 |
| 16 | Yarm FC | 2-2 | 2-3 | A-W | 1-4 | 2-4 | 2-3 | 3-2 | 1-2 | 2-0 | 0-6 | 2-3 | 1-8 | H-W | 1-4 | 1-7 | |

## Teesside League Division One

| | | |
|---|---|---|
| **BEADS FC** | Beechwood & Easterside Social Club, Marton Road, Middlesbrough TS4 3PP | |
| **BILLINGHAM TOWN RESERVES** | Bedford Terrace, Billingham, Cleveland TS23 4AE | |
| **BORO RANGERS** | Eston Leisure Complex #2, Normanby Road, Eston, Middlesbrough TS6 9AE | |
| **FISHBURN PARK** | Eskdale School, Broomfield Park, Whitby, N Yorkshire YO22 4EB | |
| **GRANGETOWN BOYS CLUB** | Grangetown Youth & C. Centre 1,Trunk Road, Grangetown, Middlesbrough TS6 7HP | |
| **GUISBOROUGH THREE FIDDLES** | King George V Playing Fields 1, Howlbeck Road, Guisborough TS14 6LE | |
| **NUNTHORPE ATHLETIC** | Nunthorpe Recreation Club, Guisborough Road, Nunthorpe, Middlesbrough TS7 0LE | |
| **REDCAR NEWMARKET** | Rye Hill School, Redcar Lane, Redcar TS10 2HN | |
| **REDCAR TOWN** | Mo Mowlam Park #2, Trunk Road, Redcar TS10 5BW | |
| **ST MARY'S YARM** | Conyers School #1, Green Lane, Yarm TS15 9ET | |
| **STAITHES ATHLETIC** | Staithes Athletic Social Club, Seaton Crescent, Staithes, Saltburn TS13 5AY | 01947 840 88 |
| **STOCKTON WEST END** | North Shore Health Academy, Talbot Street, Stockton TS20 2AY | |
| **THORNABY DUBLINERS** | Harold Wilson Sports Complex, Bader Avenue, Thornaby TS17 8PH | |
| **WHINNEY BANKS YCC** | Outwood Academy, Hall Drive, Middlesbrough TS5 7JX | |

# THAMES VALLEY PREMIER LEAGUE

**Formerly the Reading Football League > 2014**
**Founded:** 1988
**Recent Champions:**
**2013:** Reading YMCA
**2014:** Highmoor Ibis Reserves **2015:** Marlow United

| PREMIER DIVISION | P | W | D | L | F | A | GD | Pts |
|---|---|---|---|---|---|---|---|---|
| 1 Reading YMCA | 26 | 20 | 2 | 4 | 106 | 24 | 82 | 62 |
| 2 Marlow United | 26 | 18 | 3 | 5 | 82 | 43 | 39 | 57 |
| 3 Cookham Dean (-1) | 26 | 16 | 7 | 3 | 69 | 37 | 32 | 54 |
| 4 Woodcote Stoke Row | 26 | 16 | 4 | 6 | 64 | 51 | 13 | 52 |
| 5 Newbury FC | 26 | 14 | 4 | 8 | 64 | 61 | 3 | 46 |
| 6 Mortimer (-3) | 26 | 14 | 3 | 9 | 56 | 43 | 13 | 42 |
| 7 AFC Aldermaston | 26 | 10 | 7 | 9 | 57 | 62 | -5 | 37 |
| 8 Taplow United | 26 | 9 | 3 | 14 | 54 | 65 | -11 | 30 |
| 9 Rotherfield United | 26 | 7 | 6 | 13 | 39 | 59 | -20 | 27 |
| 10 Hurst | 26 | 8 | 2 | 16 | 39 | 65 | -26 | 26 |
| 11 Woodley United Reserves | 26 | 7 | 3 | 16 | 39 | 70 | -31 | 24 |
| 12 Unity | 26 | 7 | 2 | 17 | 43 | 63 | -20 | 23 |
| 13 Berks County FC | 26 | 7 | 1 | 18 | 41 | 68 | -27 | 22 |
| 14 Highmoor Ibis Reserves | 26 | 4 | 3 | 19 | 27 | 69 | -42 | 15 |

**In:** Wraysbury Village (Re-formed)
**Out:** AFC Aldermaston (P - Hellenic Div.1E)

| DIVISION ONE | P | W | D | L | F | A | GD | Pts |
|---|---|---|---|---|---|---|---|---|
| 1 Westwood United | 16 | 13 | 2 | 1 | 47 | 13 | 34 | 41 |
| 2 Winnersh Rangers | 16 | 10 | 1 | 5 | 40 | 22 | 18 | 31 |
| 3 Maidenhead Magpies (-3) | 16 | 10 | 3 | 3 | 60 | 33 | 27 | 30 |
| 4 Reading YMCA Rapids | 15 | 7 | 4 | 4 | 30 | 19 | 11 | 25 |
| 5 Mortimer Reserves | 16 | 7 | 3 | 6 | 35 | 27 | 8 | 24 |
| 6 Frilsham & Yattendon | 16 | 6 | 1 | 9 | 33 | 36 | -3 | 19 |
| 7 Cookham Dean Reserves | 16 | 5 | 2 | 9 | 21 | 41 | -20 | 17 |
| 8 Highmoor U21 | 15 | 3 | 0 | 12 | 23 | 44 | -21 | 9 |
| 9 AFC Corinthians | 16 | 2 | 0 | 14 | 16 | 70 | -54 | 6 |

**Out:** Highmoor U21 (R)

## SENIOR CUP

**HOLDERS:** MARLOW UNITED

**ROUND 1**

| | | | |
|---|---|---|---|
| Reading YMCA | v | Newbury FC | 6-0 |
| Highmoor Ibis Reserves | v | Hurst | 1-0 |
| Winnersh Rangers | v | Westwood United | 2-7 |

**ROUND 2**

| | | | |
|---|---|---|---|
| AFC Corinthians | v | Reading YMCA | 2-13 |
| Berks County FC | v | Maidenhead Magpies | 6-6, 5-4p |
| Woodley United Reserves | v | Mortimer | 0-5 |
| Rotherfield United | v | AFC Aldermaston | 2-3 |
| Cookham Dean | v | Frilsham & Yattendon | 3-1 |
| Taplow United | v | Unity | 1-3 |
| Marlow United | v | Woodcote Stoke Row | 3-2 aet |
| Highmoor Ibis Reserves | v | Westwood United | 2-4 |

**QUARTER FINALS**

| | | | |
|---|---|---|---|
| Reading YMCA | v | Berks County FC | 3-1 |
| Mortimer | v | AFC Aldermaston | 2-3 aet |
| Cookham Dean | v | Unity | 5-1 |
| Marlow United | v | Westwood United | 1-3 |

**SEMI FINALS**

| | | | |
|---|---|---|---|
| Reading YMCA | v | AFC Aldermaston | 0-1 |
| Cookham Dean | v | Westwood United | 3-2 |

**FINAL**

| | | | |
|---|---|---|---|
| AFC Aldermaston | v | Cookham Dean | 0-1 |

## INTERMEDIATE CUP

**FINAL**

| | | | |
|---|---|---|---|
| FC Imaan Lions | v | Mortimer Reserves | 3-1 |

## JUNIOR CUP

**FINAL**

| | | | |
|---|---|---|---|
| Hurst Reserves | v | Woodley United 'A' | 2-0 |

| SENIOR DIVISION | 1 | 2 | 3 | 4 | 5 | 6 | 7 | 8 | 9 | 10 | 11 | 12 | 13 | 14 |
|---|---|---|---|---|---|---|---|---|---|---|---|---|---|---|
| 1 AFC Aldermaston | | 4-3 | 2-3 | 7-1 | 2-2 | 3-1 | 1-0 | 3-5 | 0-4 | 3-3 | 3-2 | 0-8 | 2-2 | 2-1 |
| 2 Berks County FC | 2-5 | | 1-2 | 2-1 | 1-0 | 1-2 | 2-1 | 1-5 | 0-4 | 1-2 | 2-2 | 2-1 | 0-1 | 1-2 |
| 3 Cookham Dean | 0-0 | 7-3 | | 5-0 | 3-1 | 0-1 | 4-3 | 3-2 | 1-1 | 1-1 | 4-2 | 5-0 | 2-1 | 0-5 |
| 4 Highmoor Ibis Reserves | 2-2 | 0-6 | 2-2 | | 0-5 | 1-2 | 0-3 | 0-3 | A-W | 2-4 | 2-0 | 4-2 | 1-4 | 4-1 |
| 5 Hurst | 1-3 | 2-0 | 0-2 | 5-0 | | 0-8 | 1-2 | 1-3 | 1-7 | 2-1 | 1-4 | 2-1 | 2-0 | 1-0 |
| 6 Marlow United | 4-0 | 4-1 | 3-3 | 2-1 | 8-3 | | 2-2 | 6-1 | 2-1 | 2-2 | 3-1 | 5-0 | 1-2 | 6-3 |
| 7 Mortimer | 4-2 | 2-1 | 1-1 | 2-1 | 5-2 | 2-3 | | 1-1 | 4-3 | 0-1 | 0-1 | 6-1 | 2-3 | 1-2 |
| 8 Newbury FC | 1-1 | 1-2 | 0-5 | 1-0 | 3-2 | 2-0 | 1-2 | | 2-5 | 3-2 | 2-2 | 1-0 | 3-4 | 2-0 |
| 9 Reading YMCA | 2-2 | 7-0 | 0-2 | 2-1 | 7-1 | 5-0 | 7-0 | 10-1 | | 3-0 | 4-1 | 3-0 | 2-1 | 5-0 |
| 10 Rotherfield United | 1-5 | 2-1 | 2-2 | 0-1 | 1-0 | 1-3 | 0-2 | 0-3 | 0-7 | | 2-2 | 3-2 | 1-4 | 2-3 |
| 11 Taplow United | 5-1 | 2-4 | 0-4 | H-W | 1-0 | 2-6 | 1-4 | 3-5 | 3-4 | 3-1 | | 0-2 | 1-7 | 5-1 |
| 12 Unity | 4-1 | 2-0 | 1-2 | 2-1 | 0-2 | 1-2 | 2-3 | 4-6 | 1-0 | 1-1 | 0-4 | | 2-2 | 3-2 |
| 13 Woodcote Stoke Row | 1-3 | 2-0 | 5-1 | 4-1 | 2-1 | 2-1 | 0-1 | 3-3 | 1-13 | 3-1 | 2-1 | 2-1 | | 3-2 |
| 14 Woodley United Reserves | H-W | 5-4 | 0-5 | 0-0 | 1-1 | 3-5 | 0-3 | 1-4 | A-W | 0-5 | 0-3 | 4-2 | 3-3 | |

## THAMES VALLEY LEAGUE - STEP 7

| DIVISION TWO | P | W | D | L | F | A | GD | Pts |
|---|---|---|---|---|---|---|---|---|
| 1 Westwood United Res. | 18 | 13 | 4 | 1 | 69 | 18 | 51 | 43 |
| 2 Marlow United Reserves | 18 | 11 | 4 | 3 | 52 | 23 | 29 | 37 |
| 3 Eldon Celtic | 18 | 11 | 4 | 3 | 51 | 28 | 23 | 37 |
| 4 FC Imaan Lions (-3) | 18 | 12 | 3 | 3 | 59 | 31 | 28 | 36 |
| 5 Woodcote Stoke Row Res. | 18 | 7 | 2 | 9 | 33 | 36 | -3 | 23 |
| 6 Wargrave | 18 | 7 | 0 | 11 | 35 | 65 | -30 | 21 |
| 7 Goring United | 18 | 5 | 5 | 8 | 37 | 48 | -11 | 20 |
| 8 Barkham Athletic | 18 | 5 | 3 | 10 | 25 | 38 | -13 | 18 |
| 9 Ashridge Park | 18 | 2 | 3 | 13 | 28 | 66 | -38 | 9 |
| 10 Sonning | 18 | 2 | 2 | 14 | 29 | 65 | -36 | 8 |

**Out:** Ashridge Park (R); Sonning (W).

| DIVISION THREE | P | W | D | L | F | A | GD | Pts |
|---|---|---|---|---|---|---|---|---|
| 1 S.R.C.C. | 18 | 13 | 3 | 2 | 43 | 20 | 23 | 42 |
| 2 White Eagles | 18 | 12 | 4 | 2 | 75 | 28 | 47 | 40 |
| 3 Finchampstead Res. | 18 | 10 | 2 | 6 | 47 | 27 | 20 | 32 |
| 4 Taplow United Reserves | 18 | 10 | 1 | 7 | 53 | 42 | 11 | 31 |
| 5 Baughurst AFC | 18 | 9 | 2 | 7 | 45 | 49 | -4 | 29 |
| 6 "Woodley United ""A"" | 18 | 8 | 1 | 9 | 45 | 54 | -9 | 25 |
| 7 Unity Reserves | 18 | 5 | 6 | 7 | 29 | 33 | -4 | 21 |
| 8 AFC Aldermaston Res. | 18 | 3 | 4 | 11 | 31 | 52 | -21 | 13 |
| 9 Wargrave Reserves | 18 | 4 | 1 | 13 | 24 | 48 | -24 | 13 |
| 10 Twyford & Ruscombe | 18 | 1 | 6 | 11 | 22 | 61 | -39 | 9 |

| DIVISION FOUR | P | W | D | L | F | A | GD | Pts |
|---|---|---|---|---|---|---|---|---|
| 1 Maidenhead Magpies Res. | 18 | 13 | 2 | 3 | 42 | 21 | 21 | 41 |
| 2 Burghfield FC (-3) | 18 | 13 | 1 | 4 | 67 | 20 | 47 | 37 |
| 3 Berks County Reserves | 18 | 11 | 2 | 5 | 69 | 37 | 32 | 35 |
| 4 Hurst Reserves | 18 | 10 | 2 | 6 | 36 | 33 | 3 | 32 |
| 5 Harchester Hawks | 18 | 9 | 3 | 6 | 33 | 25 | 8 | 30 |
| 6 Rotherfield United Res. | 18 | 8 | 4 | 6 | 38 | 33 | 5 | 28 |
| 7 Highmoor Knights | 18 | 7 | 2 | 9 | 30 | 39 | -9 | 23 |
| 8 AFC Corinthians Res. | 18 | 3 | 2 | 13 | 32 | 66 | -34 | 11 |
| 9 FC Reading Dons | 18 | 3 | 2 | 13 | 30 | 65 | -35 | 11 |
| 10 Theale | 18 | 2 | 2 | 14 | 17 | 55 | -38 | 8 |

| DIVISION FIVE | P | W | D | L | F | A | GD | Pts |
|---|---|---|---|---|---|---|---|---|
| 1 TDC Knights | 18 | 14 | 1 | 3 | 72 | 27 | 45 | 43 |
| 2 Berks County FC Rovers | 18 | 11 | 1 | 6 | 43 | 29 | 14 | 34 |
| 3 The Hop Leaf | 18 | 11 | 1 | 6 | 52 | 39 | 13 | 34 |
| 4 Shinfield Rangers Mens (-3) | 17 | 12 | 0 | 5 | 40 | 27 | 13 | 33 |
| 5 "Hurst ""A"" | 17 | 9 | 2 | 6 | 65 | 38 | 27 | 29 |
| 6 Sonning Sports | 18 | 9 | 0 | 9 | 40 | 45 | -5 | 27 |
| 7 "Woodley United ""B"" | 18 | 6 | 2 | 10 | 40 | 42 | -2 | 20 |
| 8 Baughurst AFC Res. | 18 | 5 | 0 | 13 | 32 | 78 | -46 | 15 |
| 9 Goring Utd Reserves | 18 | 4 | 1 | 13 | 26 | 57 | -31 | 13 |
| 10 "Taplow United ""A"" | 18 | 3 | 2 | 13 | 38 | 66 | -28 | 11 |

| Thames Valley Premier League Senior Division | | |
|---|---|---|
| BERKS COUNTY | Bracknell Leisure Centre | |
| COOKHAM DEAN | Alfred Major Rec Ground, Hillcrest Avenue, Cookham Rise , Maidenhead SL6 9NB | |
| HIGHMOOR-IBIS RESERVES | Palmer Park Stadium, Wokingham Road, Reading RG6 1LF | |
| HURST | Cantley Park, Wokingham | |
| MARLOW UNITED | Bisham Abbey National Sports Centre, Abbey Way, Marlow, Bucks SL7 1RR | |
| MORTIMER | Alfred Palmer Memorial PF, West End Road, Mortimer, Reading RG7 3TW | |
| NEWBURY | Faraday Road, Newbury RG14 2AD | 01635 41031 |
| READING YMCA | Padworth Village Hall, Padworth, Reading, Berkshire RG7 4HY | |
| ROTHERFIELD UNITED | Bishopswood Sports Ground, Horsepond Rd, Gallowstree Common RG4 9BT | |
| TAPLOW UNITED | Stanley Jones Field, Berry Hill, Taplow SL6 0DA | |
| UNITY | Cintra Park, Cintra Avenue, Reading RG2 7AU | |
| WOODCOTE & STOKE ROW | Woodcote Recreation Ground, Woodcote, Reading RG8 0QY | |
| WOODLEY UNITED RESERVES | | |
| WRAYSBURY ATHLETIC | | |

# WEARSIDE LEAGUE

**Sponsored by:** No Sponsor
**Founded:** 1892
**Recent Champions:**
**2013:** Stockton Town
**2014:** Stockton Town **2015:** Stockton Town

| | | P | W | D | L | F | A | GD | Pts |
|---|---|---|---|---|---|---|---|---|---|
| 1 | Stockton Town | 38 | 33 | 2 | 3 | 164 | 26 | 138 | 101 |
| 2 | Redcar Athletic | 38 | 29 | 4 | 5 | 169 | 46 | 123 | 91 |
| 3 | Sunderland West End | 38 | 29 | 3 | 6 | 97 | 37 | 60 | 90 |
| 4 | Cleator Moor Celtic | 38 | 24 | 4 | 10 | 114 | 46 | 68 | 76 |
| 5 | Hartlepool | 38 | 21 | 1 | 16 | 106 | 76 | 30 | 64 |
| 6 | Horden CW | 38 | 20 | 4 | 14 | 84 | 85 | -1 | 64 |
| 7 | Richmond Town | 38 | 19 | 4 | 15 | 107 | 62 | 45 | 61 |
| 8 | Jarrow | 38 | 18 | 7 | 13 | 84 | 79 | 5 | 61 |
| 9 | Spennymoor Town Res. | 38 | 16 | 11 | 11 | 93 | 63 | 30 | 59 |
| 10 | Ashbrooke Belford House (-3) | 38 | 17 | 6 | 15 | 90 | 108 | -18 | 57 |
| 11 | Boldon CA | 38 | 15 | 7 | 16 | 85 | 87 | -2 | 52 |
| 12 | Whitehaven | 38 | 14 | 7 | 17 | 80 | 87 | -7 | 49 |
| 13 | Silksworth Colliery Welfare | 38 | 13 | 7 | 18 | 71 | 79 | -8 | 46 |
| 14 | Prudhoe Town | 38 | 12 | 9 | 17 | 81 | 101 | -20 | 45 |
| 15 | Harton and Westoe CW | 38 | 12 | 5 | 21 | 68 | 110 | -42 | 41 |
| 16 | Gateshead Leam Rangers | 38 | 11 | 6 | 21 | 50 | 98 | -48 | 39 |
| 17 | Wolviston | 38 | 8 | 8 | 22 | 57 | 91 | -34 | 32 |
| 18 | Annfield Plain | 38 | 8 | 4 | 26 | 57 | 143 | -86 | 28 |
| 19 | Seaham Red Star Res. | 38 | 8 | 2 | 28 | 56 | 134 | -78 | 26 |
| 20 | Murton | 38 | 1 | 3 | 34 | 28 | 183 | -155 | 6 |

**In:** Coxhoe Athletic (NC from Spennymoor Town Reserves), South Shields Reserves (N), Stokesley Sports Club (R - Northern), Windscale (N)

**Out:** Murton AFC (W), Spennymoor Town Reserves (NC to Coxhoe Athletic), Stockton Town (P - Northern), Whitehaven (S - West Lancashire)

## LEAGUE CUP

**HOLDERS:** STOCKTON TOWN

**ROUND 1**

| | | | |
|---|---|---|---|
| Richmond Town | v | Prudhoe Town | 3-1 |
| Stockton Town | v | Jarrow | 5-4 |
| Cleator Moor Celtic | v | Murton | 15-0 |
| Redcar Athletic | v | Whitehaven | 6-0 |
| Spennymoor Town Res. | v | Horden CW | 7-1 |
| Boldon CA | v | Annfield Plain | 3-2 |
| Silksworth Colliery Welfare | v | Hartlepool | 2-3 |
| Sunderland West End | v | Ashbrooke Belford House | 3-1 |

**QUARTER FINALS**

| | | | |
|---|---|---|---|
| Boldon CA | v | Stockton Town | 0-3 |
| Hartlepool | v | Cleator Moor Celtic | 0-4 |
| Redcar Athletic | v | Sunderland West End | 5-1 |
| Richmond Town | v | Spennymoor Town Res. | 0-0, 6-5p |

**SEMI FINALS**

| | | | |
|---|---|---|---|
| Richmond Town | v | Redcar Athletic | 1-2 |
| Stockton Town | v | Cleator Moor Celtic | 3-1 |

**FINAL**

| | | | |
|---|---|---|---|
| Redcar Athletic | v | Stockton Town | 1-3 |

## MONKWEARMOUTH CHARITY CUP

**FINAL** **HOLDERS:** STOCKTON TOWN

Stockton Town v Cleator Moor Celtic 1-0

## SUNDERLAND SHIPOWNERS CUP

**FINAL** **HOLDERS:** STOCKTON TOWN

Stockton Town v Ashbrooke Belford House 2-0

## DURHAM TROPHY

**FINAL** **HOLDERS:** SILKSWORTH COLLIERY WELFARE

Hartlepool v Seaham Red Star Reserves 1-3

## Wearside League

| | |
|---|---|
| **ANNFIELD PLAIN** | Derwent Park , West Road , Annfield Plain DH9 8PZ |
| **ASHBROOKE BELFORD HOUSE** | Silksworth Park, Blind Lane, Silksworth, Sunderland SR3 1AX |
| **BOLDON COMMUNITY ASSOC.** | Boldon Colliery Welfare, New Road, Boldon Colliery NE35 9DS |
| **CLEATOR MOOR CELTIC** | McGrath Park |
| **COXHOE ATHLETIC** | Beechfield Park Commercial Road East Coxhoe County Durham DH6 4LF |
| **GATESHEAD LEAM RANGERS** | Hilltop Playing Field |
| **HARTLEPOOL** | Grayfields Enclosure, Jesmond Gardens, Hartlepool TS24 8QS |
| **HARTON AND WESTOE** | Welfare Ground, Low Lane, South Shields NE34 ONA |
| **HORDEN C.W.** | Grayfields Enclosure, Jesmond Gardens, Hartlepool TS24 8QS |
| **JARROW** | Perth Green Community Assoc., Inverness Road, Jarrow NE32 4AQ |
| **PRUDHOE TOWN** | Kimberley Park, Broomhouse Road, Prudhoe NE42 5EH |
| **REDCAR ATHLETIC** | Green Lane, Redcar TS10 3RW |
| **RICHMOND TOWN** | Earls Orchard Playing Field. DL10 4RH |
| **SEAHAM RED STAR RESERVES** | Seaham Town Park |
| **SILKSWORTH COLLIERY WELFARE** | Silksworth Welfare Park, Blind Lane, Sliksworth, Sunderland SR3 1AX |
| **SOUTH SHIELDS RESERVES** | Harton & Westoe FC, Welfare Ground, Low Lane, South Shields NE34 ONA |

# WEST CHESHIRE LEAGUE

**Sponsored by:** Carlsberg

**Founded:** 1892

**Recent Champions:**

**2013:** Maghull

**2014:** Maghull

**2015:** South Liverpool

| DIVISION ONE | P | W | D | L | F | A | GD | Pts |
|---|---|---|---|---|---|---|---|---|
| 1 South Liverpool | 30 | 21 | 4 | 5 | 79 | 37 | 42 | 67 |
| 2 Chester Nomads | 30 | 18 | 6 | 6 | 57 | 26 | 31 | 60 |
| 3 Maghull | 30 | 17 | 7 | 6 | 72 | 35 | 37 | 58 |
| 4 Vauxhall Motors | 30 | 16 | 5 | 9 | 61 | 40 | 21 | 53 |
| 5 Upton A.A. | 30 | 14 | 6 | 10 | 72 | 57 | 15 | 48 |
| 6 Rainhill Town (-6) | 30 | 15 | 5 | 10 | 68 | 59 | 9 | 44 |
| 7 Mossley Hill Athletic | 30 | 12 | 7 | 11 | 61 | 54 | 7 | 43 |
| 8 West Kirby & Wasps | 30 | 11 | 7 | 12 | 51 | 55 | -4 | 40 |
| 9 Newton | 30 | 13 | 1 | 16 | 56 | 66 | -10 | 40 |
| 10 Hale | 30 | 12 | 3 | 15 | 58 | 69 | -11 | 39 |
| 11 Capenhurst Villa | 30 | 11 | 5 | 14 | 52 | 69 | -17 | 38 |
| 12 Helsby | 30 | 9 | 8 | 13 | 55 | 59 | -4 | 35 |
| 13 Heswall | 30 | 9 | 7 | 14 | 36 | 55 | -19 | 34 |
| 14 Cammell Laird 1907 Res. | 30 | 7 | 7 | 16 | 47 | 68 | -21 | 28 |
| 15 Mallaby (+3) | 30 | 7 | 2 | 21 | 40 | 68 | -28 | 26 |
| 16 Blacon Youth Club (-3) | 30 | 6 | 4 | 20 | 48 | 96 | -48 | 19 |

**Out:** Hale (R)

## PYKE CUP

**HOLDERS:** CAMMELL LAIRD RESERVES

**ROUND 1**

| | | | |
|---|---|---|---|
| Cammell Laird 1907 Res. | v | Helsby | 4-1 |
| Heswall | v | Mossley Hill Athletic | 0-2 |
| Capenhurst Villa | v | West Kirby & Wasps | 2-3 |
| Chester Nomads | v | Maghull | 2-2, 3-2p |
| Rainhill Town | v | Blacon Youth Club | 4-0 |
| Mallaby | v | Vauxhall Motors | 1-2 |
| Newton | v | Upton A.A. | 5-3 |
| Hale | v | South Liverpool | 2-3 |

QUARTER FINALS

Cammell Laird 1907 Reserves v

Mossley Hill Athletic 3-4

| | | | |
|---|---|---|---|
| West Kirby & Wasps | v | Chester Nomads | 1-2 |
| Rainhill Town | v | Vauxhall Motors | 6-0 |
| Newton | v | South Liverpool | 0-5 |

SEMI FINALS

| | | | |
|---|---|---|---|
| Mossley Hill Athletic | v | Chester Nomads | 1-0 |
| Rainhill Town | v | South Liverpool | 0-2 |

FINAL

| | | | |
|---|---|---|---|
| Mossley Hill Athletic | v | South Liverpool | 1-2 |

| DIVISION ONE | 1 | 2 | 3 | 4 | 5 | 6 | 7 | 8 | 9 | 10 | 11 | 12 | 13 | 14 | 15 | 16 |
|---|---|---|---|---|---|---|---|---|---|---|---|---|---|---|---|---|
| 1 Blacon Youth Club | | 1-4 | 3-1 | 0-1 | 0-1 | 2-2 | 0-0 | 2-4 | 5-4 | 4-1 | 1-3 | 1-4 | 1-3 | 2-2 | 2-7 | 1-1 |
| 2 Cammell Laird 1907 Reserves | 0-4 | | 3-2 | 1-0 | 5-1 | 1-1 | 2-2 | 3-3 | 2-7 | 2-0 | 1-2 | 1-2 | 1-4 | 3-3 | 1-2 | 1-1 |
| 3 Capenhurst Villa | 3-2 | 1-2 | | 1-3 | 1-1 | 2-1 | 0-2 | 1-1 | 3-0 | 4-5 | H-W | 2-2 | 2-9 | 3-2 | 2-0 | 3-2 |
| 4 Chester Nomads | 4-1 | 1-0 | 4-1 | | 3-3 | 2-0 | 3-0 | 1-2 | 3-0 | 2-1 | 4-0 | 2-1 | 0-1 | 1-1 | 1-2 | 1-0 |
| 5 Hale | 7-5 | 2-1 | 2-2 | 2-4 | | 1-3 | 4-1 | 4-3 | H-W | 5-1 | 4-3 | 3-2 | 0-2 | 2-3 | 2-0 | 0-2 |
| 6 Helsby | 6-0 | 3-1 | 0-1 | 1-1 | H-W | | 6-3 | 1-0 | 1-2 | 1-1 | 2-3 | 2-3 | 1-4 | 2-2 | 2-2 | 3-2 |
| 7 Heswall | 0-2 | 1-1 | 1-1 | 1-2 | 3-1 | 1-3 | | 1-0 | H-W | 1-1 | 1-4 | 2-1 | 1-4 | 0-0 | 1-2 | 1-2 |
| 8 Maghull | 4-2 | 7-0 | 4-0 | 0-0 | 6-1 | 2-2 | 1-0 | | 2-2 | 2-2 | 3-1 | 0-2 | 2-1 | 6-1 | 2-0 | 2-1 |
| 9 Mallaby | 1-0 | 4-1 | 1-3 | 0-5 | 3-1 | 2-5 | 1-5 | 1-3 | | 1-0 | 0-2 | 0-2 | 0-1 | 0-4 | 2-3 | 3-1 |
| 10 Mossley Hill Athletic | 10-0 | 3-2 | 3-1 | 3-1 | 1-2 | 4-0 | 2-0 | 0-3 | 5-1 | | 3-3 | 2-2 | 2-3 | 2-1 | 0-0 | 1-1 |
| 11 Newton | 6-0 | 0-5 | 3-1 | 3-2 | 3-1 | 3-1 | 0-1 | 2-1 | 2-1 | 0-1 | | 4-1 | 0-3 | 2-3 | 0-5 | 3-4 |
| 12 Rainhill Town | 6-3 | 1-1 | 1-3 | 0-1 | 4-3 | 3-3 | 2-0 | 1-1 | H-W | 2-0 | 5-1 | | 0-5 | 4-3 | 3-4 | 5-2 |
| 13 South Liverpool | H-W | 3-1 | 3-0 | 0-0 | 0-4 | 3-2 | 7-1 | 2-1 | 2-1 | 1-3 | 4-2 | 4-2 | | 2-2 | 1-1 | 2-2 |
| 14 Upton A.A. | 1-2 | 1-0 | 4-2 | 0-3 | 6-1 | 1-0 | 2-4 | 1-2 | 3-2 | 4-0 | 3-0 | 3-4 | 3-2 | | 2-3 | 3-1 |
| 15 Vauxhall Motors | 5-1 | 3-1 | 1-3 | 1-2 | 2-0 | 4-1 | 0-0 | 0-1 | 3-0 | 2-0 | 3-0 | 3-1 | 0-2 | 1-3 | | 1-1 |
| 16 West Kirby & Wasps | 5-1 | 3-0 | 4-3 | 0-0 | H-W | 3-0 | 1-2 | 0-4 | 1-1 | 3-4 | 2-1 | 0-2 | 2-1 | 1-5 | 3-1 | |

## West Cheshire League Division One

| | | |
|---|---|---|
| **CAMMELL LAIRD RESERVES** | MBS Stadium, St Peters Road, Rock Ferry, Wirral CH42 1PY | |
| **CAPENHURST VILLA** | Capenhurst Sports Ground, Capenhurst, South Wirral | |
| **CHESTER NOMADS** | Boughton Hall Cricket Club, Boughton, Chester, CH3 5EL | |
| **HELSBY** | Helsby Sports & Social club, Helsby, Cheshire | |
| **HESWALL** | Gayton Park, Brimstage Road, Heswall CH60 1XG | |
| **MAGHULL** | Old Hall Field, Hall Lane, Maghull L31 7DY | |
| **MALLABY** | Wirral Tennis Centre, Valley Road, Birkenhead, Wirral CH41 7EJ | 0151 606 2010 |
| **MOSSLEY HILL ATHLETIC** | Mossley Hill Athletic Club, Mossley Hill Road, Liverpool L18 8BX | |
| **NEWTON** | Millcroft, Frankby Road, Greasby CH49 3PE | |
| **RAINHILL TOWN** | JMO Sports Park, Blaguegate Playing Fields, Liverpool Road, Skelmersdale WN8 8BX | |
| **REDGATE ROVERS** | Riversdale Police Ground, Liverpool | |
| **RICHMOND RAITH ROVERS** | St John Bosco School, Storrington Avenue, Liverpool L11 9DQ | 0151 235 1620 |
| **SOUTH LIVERPOOL** | North Field, Jericho Lane, Aigburth, Liverpool L17 5AR | |
| **UPTON A.A.** | Chester County Sports & Social Club, Plas Newton Lane, Chester CH2 1PR | |
| **VAUXHALL MOTORS** | Vauxhall Sports Ground, Rivacre Road, Hooton, Ellesmere Port CH66 1NJ | |
| **WEST KIRBY & WASPS** | Marine Park, Greenbank Road, West Kirby CH48 5HL | |

| DIVISION TWO | P | W | D | L | F | A | GD | Pts |
|---|---|---|---|---|---|---|---|---|
| 1 Richmond Raith Rovers | 28 | 21 | 4 | 3 | 90 | 37 | 53 | 67 |
| 2 Redgate Rovers | 28 | 18 | 5 | 5 | 98 | 39 | 59 | 59 |
| 3 Hales Reserves | 28 | 18 | 4 | 6 | 56 | 35 | 21 | 58 |
| 4 Ashville | 28 | 17 | 5 | 6 | 86 | 46 | 40 | 56 |
| 5 South Liverpool Res. | 28 | 15 | 8 | 5 | 62 | 44 | 18 | 53 |
| 6 Neston Nomads | 28 | 16 | 4 | 8 | 71 | 51 | 20 | 52 |
| 7 Kirkby Town Railway | 28 | 11 | 8 | 9 | 65 | 56 | 9 | 41 |
| 8 Willaston | 28 | 9 | 6 | 13 | 52 | 80 | -28 | 33 |
| 9 Maghull Reserves | 28 | 9 | 5 | 14 | 51 | 56 | -5 | 32 |
| 10 Vauxhall Motors Res. | 28 | 9 | 2 | 17 | 51 | 77 | -26 | 29 |
| 11 Marshalls | 28 | 8 | 4 | 16 | 44 | 71 | -27 | 28 |
| 12 Southport Trinity | 28 | 7 | 5 | 16 | 56 | 70 | -14 | 26 |
| 13 West Kirby & Wasps Res. | 28 | 5 | 6 | 17 | 44 | 95 | -51 | 21 |
| 14 Mossley Hill Athletic Res. | 28 | 5 | 4 | 19 | 48 | 80 | -32 | 19 |
| 15 Prescot Cables Res. | 28 | 4 | 6 | 18 | 33 | 70 | -37 | 18 |

**Out:** Hale Reserves (W).

| DIVISION THREE | P | W | D | L | F | A | GD | Pts |
|---|---|---|---|---|---|---|---|---|
| 1 Bootle Reserves | 28 | 19 | 3 | 6 | 80 | 32 | 48 | 60 |
| 2 Heswall Reserves | 28 | 17 | 5 | 6 | 72 | 46 | 26 | 56 |
| 3 Mersey Royal | 28 | 17 | 4 | 7 | 56 | 44 | 12 | 55 |
| 4 Ford Motors | 28 | 15 | 7 | 6 | 83 | 47 | 36 | 52 |
| 5 Redgate Rovers Res. | 28 | 14 | 4 | 10 | 89 | 70 | 19 | 46 |
| 6 Helsby Reserves | 28 | 14 | 4 | 10 | 59 | 56 | 3 | 46 |
| 7 Upton A.A. Reserves | 28 | 13 | 6 | 9 | 55 | 50 | 5 | 45 |
| 8 Rainhill Town Reserves | 28 | 13 | 5 | 10 | 66 | 43 | 23 | 44 |
| 9 Ashville Reserves | 28 | 12 | 4 | 12 | 65 | 66 | -1 | 40 |
| 10 Chester Nomads Res. | 28 | 9 | 8 | 11 | 46 | 43 | 3 | 35 |
| 11 Cheshire Lines | 28 | 8 | 6 | 14 | 62 | 70 | -8 | 30 |
| 12 Marshalls Reserves | 28 | 8 | 5 | 15 | 41 | 71 | -30 | 29 |
| 13 Ellesmere Port Town | 28 | 6 | 4 | 18 | 35 | 64 | -29 | 22 |
| 14 Capenhurst Villa Res. | 28 | 5 | 6 | 17 | 33 | 82 | -49 | 21 |
| 15 Newton Reserves | 28 | 3 | 3 | 22 | 37 | 95 | -58 | 12 |
| Belfry withdrew | | | | | | | | |

**In:** Cammell Laird 1907 Dev.; City of Liverpool Reserves; Litherland REMYCA Reserves; Neston Nomads Reserves.

**Out:** Ford Motors (W); Newton Reserves (W).

# WEST LANCASHIRE LEAGUE

**Sponsored by:** Bay Radio
**Founded:** 1904
**Recent Champions:**
**2013:** Charnock Richard **2014:** Charnock Richard **2015:** Charnock Richard

| PREMIER DIVISION | P | W | D | L | F | A | GD | Pts |
|---|---|---|---|---|---|---|---|---|
| 1 Blackpool Wren Rovers | 30 | 21 | 6 | 3 | 107 | 36 | 71 | 69 |
| 2 Charnock Richard | 30 | 21 | 5 | 4 | 97 | 37 | 60 | 68 |
| 3 Fulwood Amateurs | 30 | 21 | 2 | 7 | 78 | 39 | 39 | 65 |
| 4 Longridge Town (-6) | 30 | 21 | 3 | 6 | 90 | 35 | 55 | 60 |
| 5 Thornton Cleveleys | 30 | 15 | 3 | 12 | 59 | 53 | 6 | 48 |
| 6 Euxton Villa | 30 | 14 | 5 | 11 | 48 | 46 | 2 | 47 |
| 7 Hesketh Bank | 30 | 13 | 3 | 14 | 65 | 76 | -11 | 42 |
| 8 Coppull United (-6) | 30 | 14 | 4 | 12 | 69 | 68 | 1 | 40 |
| 9 Garstang | 30 | 11 | 7 | 12 | 49 | 49 | 0 | 40 |
| 10 Southport Hesketh | 30 | 11 | 3 | 16 | 51 | 70 | -19 | 36 |
| 11 Slyne with Hest | 30 | 10 | 5 | 15 | 61 | 62 | -1 | 35 |
| 12 Lostock St Gerards | 30 | 9 | 2 | 19 | 54 | 92 | -38 | 29 |
| 13 Burnley United | 30 | 6 | 7 | 17 | 52 | 72 | -20 | 25 |
| 14 Vickerstown | 30 | 6 | 7 | 17 | 38 | 82 | -44 | 25 |
| 15 Crooklands Casuals | 30 | 7 | 2 | 21 | 34 | 94 | -60 | 23 |
| 16 Eagley | 30 | 5 | 6 | 19 | 50 | 91 | -41 | 21 |

**Out:** Burnley United (W - East Lancashire Lge); Charnock Richard (P - NWC).

| DIVISION ONE | P | W | D | L | F | A | GD | Pts |
|---|---|---|---|---|---|---|---|---|
| 1 Turton | 26 | 19 | 3 | 4 | 74 | 31 | 43 | 60 |
| 2 Tempest United | 26 | 13 | 7 | 6 | 60 | 36 | 24 | 46 |
| 3 Hawcoat Park | 26 | 14 | 3 | 9 | 51 | 40 | 11 | 45 |
| 4 Burscough Richmond | 26 | 13 | 5 | 8 | 44 | 33 | 11 | 44 |
| 5 Poulton | 26 | 13 | 3 | 10 | 52 | 54 | -2 | 42 |
| 6 Ladybridge | 25 | 12 | 4 | 9 | 61 | 53 | 8 | 40 |
| 7 Lytham Town | 26 | 12 | 3 | 11 | 68 | 54 | 14 | 39 |
| 8 Haslingden St Marys | 26 | 10 | 6 | 10 | 49 | 44 | 5 | 36 |
| 9 Wyre Villa | 26 | 8 | 9 | 9 | 48 | 64 | -16 | 33 |
| 10 Hurst Green | 26 | 8 | 5 | 13 | 42 | 51 | -9 | 29 |
| 11 GSK Ulverston Rangers | 25 | 7 | 8 | 10 | 28 | 50 | -22 | 29 |
| 12 Askam United | 26 | 5 | 10 | 11 | 49 | 63 | -14 | 25 |
| 13 Mill Hill St Peters | 26 | 4 | 7 | 15 | 39 | 65 | -26 | 19 |
| 14 Dalton United | 26 | 5 | 3 | 18 | 42 | 69 | -27 | 18 |

| DIVISION TWO | P | W | D | L | F | A | GD | Pts |
|---|---|---|---|---|---|---|---|---|
| 1 CMB | 22 | 17 | 3 | 2 | 82 | 36 | 46 | 54 |
| 2 Milnthorpe Corinthians | 22 | 13 | 5 | 4 | 77 | 37 | 40 | 44 |
| 3 Stoneclough | 22 | 12 | 5 | 5 | 64 | 32 | 32 | 41 |
| 4 Kendal County | 22 | 12 | 5 | 5 | 42 | 31 | 11 | 41 |
| 5 Furness Rovers | 22 | 10 | 3 | 9 | 38 | 39 | -1 | 33 |
| 6 Bolton County | 22 | 10 | 1 | 11 | 49 | 50 | -1 | 31 |
| 7 Croston Sports | 22 | 9 | 2 | 11 | 41 | 45 | -4 | 29 |
| 8 Millom | 22 | 9 | 2 | 11 | 36 | 48 | -12 | 29 |
| 9 Furness Cavaliers | 22 | 8 | 1 | 13 | 34 | 58 | -24 | 25 |
| 10 Walney Island | 22 | 7 | 0 | 15 | 38 | 58 | -20 | 21 |
| 11 Leyland United | 22 | 6 | 3 | 13 | 37 | 59 | -22 | 21 |
| 12 Swarthmoor Social | 22 | 4 | 0 | 18 | 24 | 69 | -45 | 12 |

**Out:** Bolton County (W).

| RESERVE DIVISION ONE | P | W | D | L | F | A | GD | Pts |
|---|---|---|---|---|---|---|---|---|
| 1 Fulwood Amateurs Res. | 24 | 18 | 1 | 5 | 66 | 28 | 38 | 55 |
| 2 Blackpool Wren Rovers Res. | 24 | 16 | 4 | 4 | 60 | 30 | 30 | 52 |
| 3 Charnock Richard Res. | 24 | 15 | 2 | 7 | 50 | 39 | 11 | 47 |
| 4 Garstang Reserves | 24 | 13 | 3 | 8 | 52 | 42 | 10 | 42 |
| 5 Hurst Green Reserves | 24 | 9 | 7 | 8 | 47 | 49 | -2 | 34 |
| 6 Coppull United Reserves | 24 | 9 | 6 | 9 | 46 | 40 | 6 | 33 |
| 7 Euxton Villa Reserves | 24 | 10 | 2 | 12 | 50 | 57 | -7 | 32 |
| 8 Burscough Richmond Res. | 24 | 10 | 2 | 12 | 47 | 55 | -8 | 32 |
| 9 Thornton Cleveleys Res. | 24 | 8 | 6 | 10 | 45 | 49 | -4 | 30 |
| 10 Lostock St Gerards Res. | 24 | 9 | 3 | 12 | 50 | 57 | -7 | 30 |
| 11 Tempest United Res. | 24 | 7 | 6 | 11 | 55 | 59 | -4 | 27 |
| 12 Hesketh Bank Reserves | 24 | 6 | 6 | 12 | 37 | 50 | -13 | 24 |
| 13 Haslingden St Marys Res. | 24 | 1 | 2 | 21 | 18 | 68 | -50 | 5 |
| Leyland United Reserves withdrew | | | | | | | | |

**Out:** Burscough Richmond Res. (P); Coppull United Res. (P); Euxton Villa Res. (P); Garstang Res. (P); Hurst Green Res. (P); Thornton Cleveleys Res. (P);

| RESERVE DIVISION TWO | P | W | D | L | F | A | GD | Pts |
|---|---|---|---|---|---|---|---|---|
| 1 Lytham Town Reserves | 20 | 18 | 0 | 2 | 73 | 17 | 56 | 54 |
| 2 CMB Reserves | 20 | 13 | 2 | 5 | 62 | 31 | 31 | 41 |
| 3 Turton Reserves | 20 | 12 | 2 | 6 | 55 | 35 | 20 | 38 |
| 4 Mill Hill St Peters Res. | 20 | 11 | 2 | 7 | 52 | 41 | 11 | 35 |
| 5 Poulton Reserves | 20 | 11 | 0 | 9 | 52 | 48 | 4 | 33 |
| 6 Ladybridge Res. (-3) | 20 | 9 | 5 | 6 | 58 | 46 | 12 | 29 |
| 7 Croston Sports Res. | 20 | 8 | 2 | 10 | 45 | 53 | -8 | 26 |
| 8 Eagley Reserves (-3) | 20 | 9 | 0 | 11 | 46 | 59 | -13 | 24 |
| 9 Milnthorpe Corinthians Res. | 20 | 5 | 1 | 14 | 47 | 61 | -14 | 16 |
| 10 Stoneclough Reserves | 20 | 4 | 1 | 15 | 44 | 73 | -29 | 13 |
| 11 Wyre Villa Reserves | 20 | 2 | 1 | 17 | 27 | 97 | -70 | 7 |

**In:** Fulwood Amateurs Res. 'A'; Haslingden St Marys Res.; Hesketh Bank Res.; Lostock St Gerards Res.; Tempest United Res.

## West Lancashire League Premier Division

| | | |
|---|---|---|
| **BLACKPOOL WREN ROVERS** | Bruce Park, School Road, Marton, Blackpool FY4 5DX | 07876 013 181 |
| **COPPULL UNITED** | Springfield Road, Coppull PR7 5EJ | |
| **CROOKLANDS CASUALS** | Longlands Park, Greystone Lane, Dalton-in-Furness LA15 8JF | 07966 660 428 |
| **EAGLEY** | Eagley Sports Complex, Dunscar Bridge, Bolton BL7 9PQ | |
| **EUXTON VILLA** | Jim Fowler Memorial Ground, Runshaw Hall Lane, Euxton, Chorley PR7 6HH | 07851 603 350 |
| **FULWOOD AMATEURS** | Lightfoot Lane, Fulwood, Preston PR2 3LP | 07952 743 475 |
| **GARSTANG** | The Riverside, High Street, Garstang PR3 1EB | 07967 337 411 |
| **HESKETH BANK** | Centenary Sports Ground, Station Road, Hesketh Bank, Preston PR4 6SR | 07713 158 393 |
| **LONGRIDGE TOWN** | Inglewhite Road, Longridge, Preston PR3 2NA | |
| **LOSTOCK ST. GERARD'S** | Wateringpool Lane, Lostock Hall, Preston Lancs PR5 5UA | 01772 610 636 |
| **SLYNE WITH HEST** | Bottomdale Road, Slyne, Lancaster LA2 6BG | 07775 777 835 |
| **SOUTHPORT HESKETH** | Bankfield Lane, Southport, Merseyside PR9 7NJ | 07927 325 585 |
| **TEMPEST UNITED** | Tempest Road, Chew Moor Village, Lostock, Bolton BL6 4HL | 01942 811 938 |
| **THORNTON CLEVELEYS** | Bourne Road, Cleveleys, Thornton Cleveleys FY5 4QA | |
| **TURTON** | Thomasson Fold, Turton, Bolton BL7 0PD | 07814 317 295 |
| **VICKERSTOWN CC** | Park Vale, Mill Lane, Walney, Barrow-in-Furness LA14 3NB | 07446 112 716 |
| **WHITEHAVEN** | Focus Scaffolding Sports Complex, Coach Road, Whitehaven, CA28 9DB | 07876 612 277 |

# WEST YORKSHIRE LEAGUE

**Sponsored by:** Active 8
**Founded:** 1928
**Recent Champions:**
**2013:** Bardsey
**2014:** Bardsey **2015:** Field

| PREMIER DIVISION | P | W | D | L | F | A | GD | Pts |
|---|---|---|---|---|---|---|---|---|
| 1 Beeston St Anthony's | 28 | 23 | 2 | 3 | 96 | 36 | 60 | 71 |
| 2 Carlton Athletic | 28 | 19 | 6 | 3 | 84 | 36 | 48 | 63 |
| 3 Field | 28 | 20 | 2 | 6 | 74 | 43 | 31 | 62 |
| 4 Leeds City | 28 | 18 | 6 | 4 | 76 | 44 | 32 | 60 |
| 5 Wetherby Athletic | 28 | 13 | 2 | 13 | 76 | 57 | 19 | 41 |
| 6 Horbury Town | 28 | 12 | 3 | 13 | 57 | 55 | 2 | 39 |
| 7 Hunslet Club | 28 | 11 | 5 | 12 | 55 | 61 | -6 | 38 |
| 8 Brighouse Old Boys | 28 | 11 | 2 | 15 | 52 | 56 | -4 | 35 |
| 9 Robin Hood Athletic | 28 | 11 | 2 | 15 | 45 | 63 | -18 | 35 |
| 10 Pool | 28 | 11 | 2 | 15 | 46 | 65 | -19 | 35 |
| 11 Shelley | 28 | 10 | 3 | 15 | 49 | 71 | -22 | 33 |
| 12 Oxenhope Recreation | 28 | 9 | 5 | 14 | 52 | 67 | -15 | 32 |
| 13 Knaresborough Town | 28 | 7 | 5 | 16 | 48 | 58 | -10 | 26 |
| 14 Wyke Wanderers | 28 | 5 | 3 | 20 | 28 | 85 | -57 | 18 |
| 15 Otley Town | 28 | 4 | 4 | 20 | 26 | 67 | -41 | 16 |

| DIVISION ONE | P | W | D | L | F | A | GD | Pts |
|---|---|---|---|---|---|---|---|---|
| 1 Stanley United | 30 | 21 | 5 | 4 | 90 | 32 | 58 | 68 |
| 2 Headingley | 30 | 17 | 7 | 6 | 70 | 46 | 24 | 58 |
| 3 Sherburn White Rose | 30 | 17 | 7 | 6 | 72 | 52 | 20 | 58 |
| 4 Ilkley Town | 30 | 17 | 4 | 9 | 65 | 52 | 13 | 55 |
| 5 East End Park | 30 | 15 | 7 | 8 | 74 | 51 | 23 | 52 |
| 6 Whitkirk Wanderers | 30 | 14 | 6 | 10 | 51 | 51 | 0 | 48 |
| 7 Aberford Albion | 30 | 14 | 5 | 11 | 72 | 52 | 20 | 47 |
| 8 Hartshead | 30 | 14 | 3 | 13 | 82 | 64 | 18 | 45 |
| 9 Boroughbridge | 30 | 10 | 11 | 9 | 52 | 42 | 10 | 41 |
| 10 Featherstone Colliery | 30 | 11 | 5 | 14 | 55 | 63 | -8 | 38 |
| 11 Old Centralians | 30 | 10 | 7 | 13 | 39 | 45 | -6 | 37 |
| 12 Leeds Modernians | 30 | 8 | 10 | 12 | 68 | 79 | -11 | 34 |
| 13 Kippax | 30 | 9 | 5 | 16 | 54 | 76 | -22 | 32 |
| 14 Thornhill | 30 | 7 | 5 | 18 | 65 | 118 | -53 | 26 |
| 15 Baildon Trinity Athletic | 30 | 4 | 7 | 19 | 52 | 74 | -22 | 19 |
| 16 Ripon City | 30 | 3 | 4 | 23 | 39 | 103 | -64 | 13 |

**Out:** Headingley (P); Ilkley Town (P); Sherburn White Rose (P); Stanley United (W).

| DIVISION TWO | P | W | D | L | F | A | GD | Pts |
|---|---|---|---|---|---|---|---|---|
| 1 Huddersfield Amateur | 24 | 17 | 1 | 6 | 93 | 36 | 57 | 52 |
| 2 Hall Green United | 24 | 16 | 2 | 6 | 88 | 48 | 40 | 50 |
| 3 Howden Clough | 24 | 16 | 2 | 6 | 84 | 46 | 38 | 50 |
| 4 Swillington Saints | 24 | 14 | 6 | 4 | 70 | 43 | 27 | 48 |
| 5 Altofts | 24 | 13 | 4 | 7 | 58 | 44 | 14 | 43 |
| 6 Ossett Albion | 24 | 12 | 2 | 10 | 75 | 65 | 10 | 38 |
| 7 Mount St. Mary's | 24 | 12 | 1 | 11 | 65 | 47 | 18 | 37 |
| 8 Kellingley Welfare | 24 | 10 | 2 | 12 | 72 | 84 | -12 | 32 |
| 9 Great Preston (-3) | 24 | 10 | 3 | 11 | 58 | 67 | -9 | 30 |
| 10 Normanton Woodhouse Hill (-3) | 24 | 8 | 2 | 14 | 54 | 91 | -37 | 23 |
| 11 Middleton Park | 24 | 5 | 4 | 15 | 37 | 73 | -36 | 19 |
| 12 Ossett Common Rovers (-3) | 24 | 7 | 0 | 17 | 52 | 72 | -20 | 18 |
| 13 Garforth Rangers (-3) | 24 | 0 | 3 | 21 | 32 | 122 | -90 | 0 |

**In:** AFC Horsforth; Nostell Miners Welfare; Rawdon Old Boys; Rothwell.
**Out:** Mount St Mary's (W).

## LEAGUE CUP

**HOLDERS:** LEEDS CITY

**ROUND 1**

| | | | |
|---|---|---|---|
| Garforth Rangers | v | Howden Clough | 0-11 |
| Old Centralians | v | Thornhill | 4-1 |
| Baildon Trinity Athletic | v | Middleton Park | 1-2 |
| Barwick | v | Hall Green United | 7-5 aet |
| Normanton Woodhouse Hill | v | Ripon City | 7-7, 2-4p |
| Ossett Albion | v | Hartshead | 7-2 |
| Aberford Albion | v | Leeds Modemians | 4-2 |
| Ossett Common Rovers | v | Swillington Saints | 2-5 |
| Headingley | v | Boroughbridge | 2-1 |
| Stanley United | v | Kellingley Welfare | 1-0 |
| Rothwell Town | v | Kippax | 3-0 |
| Sherburn White Rose | v | Yorkshire Amateur | 3-0 |
| Huddersfield Amateur | v | Great Preston | 5-2 |
| Featherstone Colliery | v | East End Park | 2-1 |
| Ilkley Town | v | Altofts | 2-0 |
| Mount St Mary's | v | Whitkirk Wanderers | 3-1 aet |

**ROUND 2**

| | | | |
|---|---|---|---|
| Otley Town | v | Howden Clough | 3-1 |
| Brighouse Old Boys | v | Old Centralians | 9-1 |
| Middleton Park | v | Shelley | 0-7 |
| Robin Hood Athletic | v | Barwick | 7-1 |
| Carlton Athletic | v | Ripon City | 5-0 |
| Ossett Albion | v | Knaresborough Town | 2-1 |
| Leeds City | v | Wyke Wanderers | 3-0 |
| Aberford Albion | v | Pool | 1-2 |
| Swillington Saints | v | Headingley | 0-2 |
| Stanley United | v | Horbury Town | 1-3 |
| Bardsey | v | Hunslet Club | AW |
| Rothwell Town | v | Sherburn White Rose | 2-7 |
| Huddersfield Amateur | v | Featherstone Colliery | 2-1 |
| Ilkley Town | v | Field | 1-4 |
| Wetherby Athletic | v | Mount St Mary's | 1-0 |
| Oxenhope Recreation | v | Beeston St Anthony's | 0-1 |

**ROUND 3**

| | | | |
|---|---|---|---|
| Otley Town | v | Brighouse Old Boys | 3-4 |
| Shelley | v | Robin Hood Athletic | 1-1, 1-3p |
| Carlton Athletic | v | Ossett Albion | 3-2 |
| Leeds City | v | Pool | 5-1 |
| Headingley | v | Horbury Town | 3-4 |
| Hunslet Club | v | Sherburn White Rose | 3-1 |
| Huddersfield Amateur | v | Field | 0-1 |
| Wetherby Athletic | v | Beeston St Anthony's | 0-1 |

**QUARTER FINALS**

| | | | |
|---|---|---|---|
| Brighouse Old Boys | v | Robin Hood Athletic | 1-1, 4-1p |
| Carlton Athletic | v | Leeds City | 4-4, 5-4p |
| Horbury Town | v | Hunslet Club | 1-0 |
| Field | v | Beeston St Anthony's | 1-3 aet |

**SEMI FINALS**

| | | | |
|---|---|---|---|
| Brighouse Old Boys | v | Carlton Athletic | 1-4 |
| Horbury Town | v | Beeston St Anthony's | 0-1 |

**FINAL**

| | | | |
|---|---|---|---|
| Carlton Athletic | v | Beeston St Anthony's | 1-1, 2-4p |

| PREMIER DIVISION | 1 | 2 | 3 | 4 | 5 | 6 | 7 | 8 | 9 | 10 | 11 | 12 | 13 | 14 | 15 |
|---|---|---|---|---|---|---|---|---|---|---|---|---|---|---|---|
| 1 Beeston St Anthony's | | 4-2 | 4-4 | 4-1 | 2-3 | 3-2 | 3-1 | 1-2 | 6-0 | 7-0 | 1-1 | 4-3 | 2-1 | 5-4 | 2-1 |
| 2 Brighouse Old Boys | 1-4 | | 2-3 | 0-2 | 3-1 | 1-2 | 4-2 | 0-5 | 5-0 | 2-0 | 2-0 | 1-2 | 2-0 | 3-1 | 3-4 |
| 3 Carlton Athletic | 3-1 | 3-0 | | 4-2 | 5-3 | 5-0 | 3-0 | 1-3 | 2-0 | 11-0 | 4-1 | 5-1 | 1-1 | 4-3 | 4-0 |
| 4 Field | 0-1 | 2-1 | 3-0 | | 2-1 | 0-2 | 2-1 | 1-3 | 2-2 | 4-1 | 5-1 | 3-2 | 8-2 | 1-0 | 2-1 |
| 5 Horbury Town | 1-5 | 4-1 | 1-4 | 1-4 | | 1-1 | 2-1 | 0-3 | 2-0 | 3-0 | 2-1 | 3-1 | 2-3 | 0-2 | 6-0 |
| 6 Hunslet Club | 1-4 | 1-3 | 2-0 | 1-3 | 2-2 | | 1-4 | 2-2 | 3-1 | 4-2 | 3-4 | 2-1 | 4-0 | 3-2 | 2-5 |
| 7 Knaresborough Town | 0-5 | 1-2 | 2-2 | 0-2 | 1-4 | 1-3 | | 3-3 | 0-1 | 2-1 | 5-1 | 0-1 | 1-2 | 0-1 | 7-2 |
| 8 Leeds City | 1-5 | 2-1 | 4-6 | 2-2 | 4-2 | 4-1 | 2-2 | | 3-0 | 0-0 | 0-3 | 3-4 | 1-1 | 4-3 | 4-1 |
| 9 Otley Town | 0-3 | 0-2 | 0-1 | 1-4 | 0-2 | 0-0 | 2-3 | 0-3 | | 3-3 | 2-3 | 0-1 | 3-1 | 4-2 | 0-1 |
| 10 Oxenhope Recreation | 2-4 | 2-4 | 1-2 | 2-4 | 1-1 | 3-1 | 1-1 | 1-3 | 3-1 | | 8-0 | 0-1 | 2-1 | 1-1 | 5-0 |
| 11 Pool | 0-3 | 1-0 | 0-1 | 4-3 | 2-1 | 4-2 | 2-0 | 1-3 | 1-1 | 2-3 | | 1-3 | 1-2 | 0-2 | 2-0 |
| 12 Robin Hood Athletic | 0-2 | 1-1 | 0-0 | 0-1 | 3-2 | 0-5 | 0-3 | 0-3 | 2-4 | 2-1 | 2-4 | | 3-1 | 0-5 | 2-3 |
| 13 Shelley | 0-4 | 4-2 | 1-1 | 1-2 | 3-4 | 3-1 | 2-5 | 1-2 | 3-0 | 1-3 | 3-2 | 1-3 | | 3-2 | 5-0 |
| 14 Wetherby Athletic | 2-4 | 3-2 | 0-4 | 3-5 | 1-0 | 2-2 | 4-2 | 1-3 | 5-1 | 1-4 | 4-0 | 5-2 | 9-0 | | 6-0 |
| 15 Wyke Wanderers | 0-3 | 2-2 | 1-1 | 2-4 | 0-3 | 1-2 | 0-0 | 1-4 | 1-0 | 1-2 | 0-4 | 0-5 | 1-3 | 0-2 | |

## West Yorkshire League Premier Division

|  |  |
|---|---|
| **BEESTON ST ANTHONY'S** | St Antony's Road, Beeston, Leeds LS11 8DP |
| **BRIGHOUSE OLD BOYS** | Hipperholme & Lightcliffe School, Stoney Lane, Lightcliffe, Halifax HX3 8TL |
| **CARLTON ATHLETIC** | Carlton Cricket Club, Town Street, Carlton WF3 3QU |
| **FIELD** | Field Sports & Social Club, Hollingwood Lane, Bradford BD7 2RE |
| **HEADINGLEY** | Weetwood Playing Fields, Weetwood, Leeds LS16 5AU |
| **HORBURY TOWN** | Slazengers Sports Complex, Southfields, Horbury WF4 5BH |
| **HUNSLET CLUB** | The Hunslet Club, Hillidge Road LS10 1BP |
| **ILKLEY TOWN** | Ben Rhydding Sports Club, Leeds Road, ILKLEY LS29 8AW |
| **KNARESBOROUGH TOWN** | Knaresborough Town A.F.C., Manse Lane, Knaresborough HG5 8LF |
| **LEEDS CITY** | Adel War Memorial Association, Church Lane, Adel, Leeds LS16 8DE |
| **OXENHOPE RECREATION** | The Recreation ground, Hebden Bridge Road, Oxenhope BD22 9LY |
| **POOL** | Arthington Lane, Pool-in-Wharfedale LS21 1LE |
| **ROBIN HOOD ATHLETIC** | Behind Coach & Horses Hotel, Rothwell Haigh LS26 0SF |
| **SHELLEY** | Storthes Hall, Huddersfield HD8 0WA |
| **SHERBURN WHITE ROSE** | Finkle Hill, Recreation Ground, Finkle Hill, Sherburn-in-Elmet LS25 6EL |
| **WETHERBY ATHLETIC** | The Ings, Wetherby LS22 5HA |

| ALLIANCE DIVISION ONE | P | W | D | L | F | A | GD | Pts |
|---|---|---|---|---|---|---|---|---|
| 1 Beeston St. Anthony's Res. | 26 | 24 | 0 | 2 | 94 | 27 | 67 | 72 |
| 2 Oxenhope Recreation Res. | 26 | 23 | 1 | 2 | 91 | 21 | 70 | 70 |
| 3 Field Reserves | 26 | 17 | 1 | 8 | 86 | 44 | 42 | 52 |
| 4 Leeds City Reserves | 26 | 16 | 3 | 7 | 104 | 50 | 54 | 51 |
| 5 Robin Hood Athletic Res. | 26 | 13 | 2 | 11 | 77 | 60 | 17 | 41 |
| 6 Horbury Town Res. (-6) | 26 | 13 | 6 | 7 | 63 | 53 | 10 | 39 |
| 7 Hunslet Club Reserves | 26 | 10 | 5 | 11 | 73 | 66 | 7 | 35 |
| 8 East End Park Res. (-3) | 26 | 9 | 1 | 16 | 39 | 59 | -20 | 25 |
| 9 Pool Reserves | 26 | 7 | 4 | 15 | 36 | 75 | -39 | 25 |
| 10 Headingley Reserves | 26 | 6 | 6 | 14 | 44 | 75 | -31 | 24 |
| 11 Boroughbridge Reserves | 26 | 6 | 5 | 15 | 38 | 67 | -29 | 23 |
| 12 Brighouse Old Boys Res. | 26 | 7 | 2 | 17 | 54 | 86 | -32 | 23 |
| 13 Wyke Wanderers Res. | 26 | 5 | 2 | 19 | 28 | 98 | -70 | 17 |
| 14 Otley Town Res. (-3) | 26 | 5 | 4 | 17 | 37 | 83 | -46 | 16 |

| ALLIANCE DIVISION TWO | P | W | D | L | F | A | GD | Pts |
|---|---|---|---|---|---|---|---|---|
| 1 Huddersfield Amateur Res. | 20 | 17 | 3 | 0 | 80 | 20 | 60 | 54 |
| 2 Leeds Modernians Res. | 20 | 10 | 3 | 7 | 53 | 44 | 9 | 33 |
| 3 Carlton Athletic Res. | 20 | 10 | 1 | 9 | 57 | 46 | 11 | 31 |
| 4 Old Centralians Res. | 20 | 9 | 4 | 7 | 45 | 38 | 7 | 31 |
| 5 Ilkley Town Reserves | 20 | 9 | 2 | 9 | 58 | 46 | 12 | 29 |
| 6 Altofts Reserves | 20 | 7 | 5 | 8 | 38 | 42 | -4 | 26 |
| 7 Howden Clough Res. | 20 | 7 | 4 | 9 | 47 | 59 | -12 | 25 |
| 8 Hall Green United Res. | 20 | 7 | 3 | 10 | 47 | 51 | -4 | 24 |
| 9 Kippax Reserves (-6) | 20 | 9 | 1 | 10 | 37 | 58 | -21 | 22 |
| 10 Aberford Albion Res. | 20 | 7 | 1 | 12 | 35 | 57 | -22 | 22 |
| 11 Middleton Park Res. | 20 | 4 | 1 | 15 | 33 | 69 | -36 | 13 |

# WILTSHIRE LEAGUE

**Sponsored by:** No sponsor
**Founded:** 1928
**Recent Champions:**
**2013:** Wilts Calne Town
**2014:** Southbrook **2015:** Malmesbury Victoria

| PREMIER DIVISION | P | W | D | L | F | A | GD | Pts |
|---|---|---|---|---|---|---|---|---|
| 1 Trowbridge Town | 28 | 22 | 4 | 2 | 109 | 27 | 82 | 70 |
| 2 Shrewton United | 28 | 19 | 2 | 7 | 92 | 46 | 46 | 59 |
| 3 Malmesbury Victoria | 28 | 19 | 1 | 8 | 85 | 44 | 41 | 58 |
| 4 Melksham Town Res. | 28 | 17 | 2 | 9 | 69 | 37 | 32 | 53 |
| 5 Ludgershall Sports | 28 | 13 | 6 | 9 | 66 | 52 | 14 | 45 |
| 6 Trowbridge Wanderers | 28 | 14 | 3 | 11 | 60 | 46 | 14 | 45 |
| 7 Wroughton | 28 | 13 | 4 | 11 | 59 | 53 | 6 | 43 |
| 8 Chippenham Park Dev. | 28 | 13 | 1 | 14 | 56 | 55 | 1 | 40 |
| 9 Marlborough Town | 28 | 10 | 8 | 10 | 58 | 56 | 2 | 38 |
| 10 Devizes Town Reserves | 28 | 11 | 3 | 14 | 44 | 63 | -19 | 36 |
| 11 Royal Wootton Bassett Town Res. | 28 | 10 | 5 | 13 | 58 | 62 | -4 | 35 |
| 12 Corsham Town Res. | 28 | 11 | 1 | 16 | 53 | 69 | -16 | 34 |
| 13 Wilts Calne Town | 28 | 5 | 7 | 16 | 45 | 81 | -36 | 22 |
| 14 Vale of Pewsey | 28 | 4 | 6 | 18 | 24 | 106 | -82 | 18 |
| 15 Sarum Youth | 28 | 1 | 3 | 24 | 24 | 105 | -81 | 6 |

Andover New Street Swifts withdrew - record expunged.

## SENIOR CUP

**ROUND 1** **HOLDERS:** MELKSHAM TOWN RESERVES

| | | | |
|---|---|---|---|
| Devizes Town Reserves | v | Corsham Town Reserves | 0-2 |
| Chippenham Park Dev. | v | Marlborough Town | 5-0 |
| Trowbridge Town | v | Trowbridge Wanderers | 1-0 |
| Andover New Street Swifts | v | Melksham Town Reserves | AW |
| Wroughton | v | Sarum Youth | 3-0 |
| Royal Wootton Bassett Town | v | Wilts Calne Town | 2-1 |
| Ludgershall Sports | v | Malmesbury Victoria | 3-2 |
| Vale of Pewsey | v | Shrewton United | 0-4 |

**QUARTER FINALS**

| | | | |
|---|---|---|---|
| Corsham Town Reserves | v | Chippenham Park Dev. | 1-2 |
| Trowbridge Town | v | Melksham Town Res. | 1-3 aet |
| Wroughton | v | Royal Wootton Bassett Town | 1-0 |
| Ludgershall Sports | v | Shrewton United | 4-2 |

**SEMI FINALS**

| | | | |
|---|---|---|---|
| Chippenham Park Dev. | v | Melksham Town Res. | 1-1, 5-4p |
| Wroughton | v | Ludgershall Sports | 1-1, 8-7p |

FINAL

| | | | |
|---|---|---|---|
| Chippenham Park Dev. | v | Wroughton | 1-2 |

## CLUB MOVEMENTS

**In:** Broham (reformed); Cricklade Town (reformed); Lydiard Millicent (N); Malmesbury Victoria FC Dev. (N); Pewsey Vale FC Dev. (N);

**Out:** Malmesbury Victoria (P - Western); Sarum Youth (Salisbury & Dist.); Trowbridge Wanderers (W); Vale of Pewsey (W).

| PREMIER DIVISION | 1 | 2 | 3 | 4 | 5 | 6 | 7 | 8 | 9 | 10 | 11 | 12 | 13 | 14 | 15 |
|---|---|---|---|---|---|---|---|---|---|---|---|---|---|---|---|
| 1 Chippenham Park Development | | 2-3 | 0-2 | 1-2 | 4-2 | 2-1 | 0-2 | 3-2 | 5-0 | 1-2 | 3-8 | 1-2 | 2-1 | 2-1 | 0-2 |
| 2 Corsham Town Reserves | 2-3 | | 4-2 | 3-2 | 3-2 | 1-4 | 4-2 | 1-1 | 5-2 | 1-4 | 0-3 | 0-2 | 1-3 | 0-2 | 0-4 |
| 3 Devizes Town Reserves | 1-2 | 3-2 | | 0-5 | 0-4 | 2-2 | 0-1 | 1-0 | 2-1 | 1-5 | 0-5 | 2-2 | 2-3 | 1-5 | 1-0 |
| 4 Ludgershall Sports | 4-0 | 3-2 | 1-4 | | 1-3 | 1-5 | 6-2 | 2-2 | 5-1 | 1-1 | 0-0 | 4-1 | 4-0 | 4-3 | 3-1 |
| 5 Malmesbury Victoria | 3-2 | 3-0 | 4-0 | 3-1 | | 3-3 | 1-0 | 0-1 | 4-1 | 4-2 | 0-2 | 3-0 | 10-0 | 3-2 | 4-2 |
| 6 Marlborough Town | 1-5 | 3-0 | 0-1 | 1-1 | 3-4 | | 1-2 | 2-2 | 4-1 | 0-5 | 2-7 | 2-0 | 3-0 | 1-1 | 0-2 |
| 7 Melksham Town Reserves | 2-0 | 3-1 | 5-2 | 4-0 | 0-4 | 4-0 | | 1-0 | 7-0 | 1-3 | 1-3 | 2-1 | 6-0 | 2-0 | 1-1 |
| 8 Royal Wootton Bassett Town Reserves | 3-1 | 4-3 | 2-4 | 2-3 | 5-2 | 1-2 | 2-2 | | 3-1 | 5-4 | 1-2 | 2-3 | 5-1 | 1-0 | 4-5 |
| 9 Sarum Youth | 2-2 | 0-2 | 0-4 | 1-1 | 1-8 | 1-6 | 1-4 | 4-0 | | 1-4 | 0-6 | 1-1 | 0-2 | 2-5 | 1-3 |
| 10 Shrewton United | 3-0 | 3-4 | 4-1 | 2-1 | 3-0 | 1-4 | 0-2 | 6-1 | 7-2 | | 2-3 | 3-2 | 7-0 | 7-3 | 2-1 |
| 11 Trowbridge Town | 4-0 | 3-1 | 1-3 | 4-1 | 3-2 | 2-2 | 2-0 | 3-0 | 6-0 | 1-3 | | 3-0 | 9-0 | 8-1 | 7-1 |
| 12 Trowbridge Wanderers | 0-1 | 4-1 | 3-0 | 2-4 | 1-2 | 3-1 | 2-1 | 0-2 | 2-0 | 2-1 | 1-3 | | 9-1 | 0-0 | 7-3 |
| 13 Vale of Pewsey | 0-4 | 1-3 | 0-4 | 0-5 | 1-2 | 1-1 | 0-7 | 1-1 | 2-0 | 2-2 | 1-1 | 1-5 | | 1-1 | 0-3 |
| 14 Wilts Calne Town | 0-6 | 1-2 | 1-1 | 1-1 | 3-2 | 1-2 | 0-4 | 2-4 | 4-0 | 1-4 | 1-9 | 2-3 | 2-2 | | 1-1 |
| 15 Wroughton | 0-4 | 0-4 | 1-0 | 3-0 | 0-3 | 2-2 | 3-1 | 3-2 | 1-0 | 1-2 | 1-1 | 0-2 | 7-0 | 8-1 | |

## Wiltshire League Premier Division

| | |
|---|---|
| **BROMHAM** | Station Road, Sway, Lymington SO41 6BE |
| **CHIPPENHAM PARK DEV.** | Stanley Park, Chippenham |
| **CORSHAM TOWN RESERVES** | Southbank Ground, Lacock Road, Corsham |
| **CRICKLADE TOWN** | Cricklade Leisure Centre, Stones Lane, Cricklade SN6 6JW |
| **DEVIZES TOWN RESERVES** | Nursteed Road, Devizes SN10 3DX |
| **LUDGERSHALL SPORTS** | Astor Crescent, Ludgershall SP11 9QE |
| **LYDIARD MILLICENT** | Beversbrook Sports Centre, Beversbrook Road, Calne, Wiltshire SN11 9FL |
| **MALMESBURY VICTORIA DEV.** | Flying Monk Ground Gloucester Road SN16 9JS |
| **MARLBOROUGH TOWN** | Elcot Lane, Marlborough, SN8 2BG |
| **MELKSHAM TOWN RESERVES** | The Conigre, Melksham |
| **PEWSEY VALE DEVELOPMENT** | |
| **SHREWTON UNITED** | Shrewton Recreation Ground, Mill Lane, Shrewton SP3 4JY |
| **TROWBRIDGE TOWN** | Woodmarsh, Bradley Road, Trowbridge BA14 0SB |
| **WILTS CALNE TOWN** | Bremhill View, Calne SN11 9EE |
| **WOOTTON BASSETT TOWN RES.** | Gerrard Buxton Sports Ground, Rylands Way, Royal Wootton Bassett SN4 8AW |
| **WROUGHTON** | The Weir Field Ground, Devizes Road, Wroughton, Wiltshire |

## A lot has changed in 40 years!

*Believe it or not next year's edition (2018) will be the 40th.*

*We'd liked to hear from you, in your view how has non-League football changed, for the better or worse.*

*Share with us some of your high points, and memories the game has brought you.*

*And anything you'd like to change about the Directory itself, please get in touch by emailing to* ***tw.publications@btinternet.com***

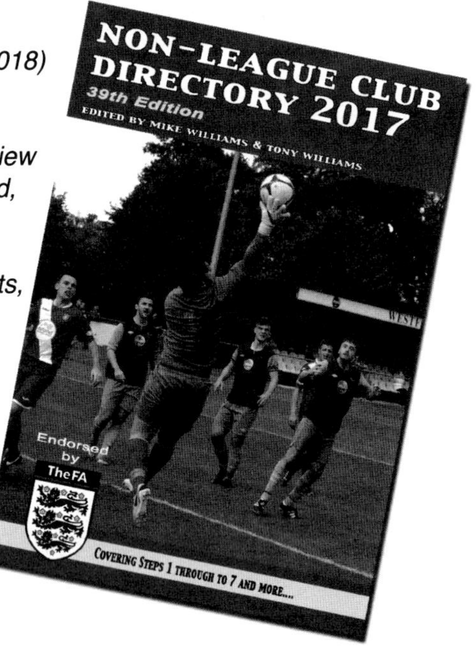

# LEAGUE TABLES 2015-16

## ACCRINGTON & DISTRICT LEAGUE

| Division One | P | W | D | L | F | A | GD | Pts |
|---|---|---|---|---|---|---|---|---|
| 1 Black Dog | 24 | 19 | 3 | 2 | 124 | 36 | 88 | 60 |
| 2 Great Harwood Town . | 22 | 12 | 6 | 4 | 78 | 36 | 42 | 42 |
| 3 Water . | 23 | 14 | 0 | 9 | 65 | 52 | 13 | 42 |
| 4 Haslingden (-3) | 24 | 12 | 2 | 10 | 61 | 39 | 22 | 35 |
| 5 Hapton | 24 | 11 | 1 | 12 | 55 | 60 | -5 | 34 |
| 6 AFC Accy | 24 | 9 | 2 | 13 | 55 | 118 | -63 | 29 |
| 7 Bay Horse . (-3) | 23 | 7 | 3 | 13 | 71 | 89 | -18 | 21 |
| 8 St Mary's Coll. OB | 24 | 5 | 4 | 15 | 43 | 71 | -28 | 19 |
| 9 Globe Bullough Park | 24 | 6 | 1 | 17 | 63 | 114 | -51 | 19 |

## ALDERSHOT & DISTRICT LEAGUE

| Senior Division | P | W | D | L | F | A | GD | Pts |
|---|---|---|---|---|---|---|---|---|
| 1 Bagshot | 18 | 15 | 0 | 3 | 73 | 32 | 41 | 45 |
| 2 Eversley & California Res. | 18 | 13 | 0 | 5 | 55 | 29 | 26 | 39 |
| 3 Sandhurst Town Res. | 18 | 12 | 0 | 6 | 31 | 26 | 5 | 36 |
| 4 Rushmoor Community | 18 | 11 | 0 | 7 | 23 | 13 | 10 | 33 |
| 5 Wey Valley | 18 | 9 | 1 | 8 | 37 | 46 | -9 | 28 |
| 6 Frimley Select | 18 | 9 | 0 | 9 | 54 | 44 | 10 | 27 |
| 7 Alton United | 18 | 8 | 0 | 10 | 30 | 46 | -16 | 24 |
| 8 Spartans | 18 | 6 | 0 | 12 | 48 | 47 | 1 | 18 |
| 9 Fleet Spurs Res. | 18 | 3 | 1 | 14 | 26 | 65 | -39 | 10 |
| 10 Sandhurst Sports | 18 | 3 | 0 | 15 | 22 | 51 | -29 | 9 |

| Division One | P | W | D | L | F | A | GD | Pts |
|---|---|---|---|---|---|---|---|---|
| 1 Fleet Spurs A | 18 | 13 | 3 | 2 | 53 | 25 | 28 | 42 |
| 2 Ropley | 18 | 13 | 2 | 3 | 55 | 23 | 32 | 41 |
| 3 Yateley United A | 18 | 11 | 0 | 7 | 54 | 40 | 14 | 33 |
| 4 AFC Laffans | 18 | 10 | 2 | 6 | 39 | 26 | 13 | 32 |
| 5 Mytchett Athletic | 18 | 10 | 1 | 7 | 38 | 24 | 14 | 31 |
| 6 Hartley Wintney A | 18 | 9 | 0 | 9 | 39 | 35 | 4 | 27 |
| 7 Four Marks Res. | 18 | 6 | 2 | 10 | 33 | 47 | -14 | 20 |
| 8 Farnham Park | 18 | 6 | 0 | 12 | 33 | 57 | -24 | 18 |
| 9 Hindhead Athletic | 18 | 5 | 2 | 11 | 18 | 34 | -16 | 17 |
| 10 South Farnborough | 18 | 0 | 2 | 16 | 27 | 78 | -51 | 2 |

| Division Two | P | W | D | L | F | A | GD | Pts |
|---|---|---|---|---|---|---|---|---|
| 1 Bagshot Res. | 12 | 10 | 0 | 2 | 48 | 11 | 37 | 30 |
| 2 Yateley United B | 12 | 9 | 0 | 3 | 32 | 18 | 14 | 27 |
| 3 Normandy Res. | 12 | 6 | 1 | 5 | 31 | 26 | 5 | 19 |
| 4 BOSC Rovers | 12 | 5 | 1 | 6 | 24 | 26 | -2 | 16 |
| 5 Fleet Spurs Vet | 12 | 4 | 1 | 7 | 16 | 31 | -15 | 13 |
| 6 Letef Select | 12 | 4 | 0 | 8 | 16 | 21 | -5 | 12 |
| 7 Wey Valley Res. | 12 | 2 | 1 | 9 | 18 | 52 | -34 | 7 |

## ALTRINCHAM & DISTRICT AMATEUR LEAGUE

| Division One | P | W | D | L | F | A | GD | Pts |
|---|---|---|---|---|---|---|---|---|
| 1 Broadheath Central | 16 | 15 | 1 | 0 | 57 | 6 | 51 | 46 |
| 2 Old Altrinchamians | 16 | 10 | 3 | 3 | 37 | 29 | 8 | 33 |
| 3 Altrincham Hale | 16 | 9 | 3 | 4 | 36 | 22 | 14 | 30 |
| 4 Sale Amateurs | 16 | 7 | 4 | 5 | 36 | 40 | -4 | 25 |
| 5 Sale UNT | 16 | 5 | 2 | 9 | 35 | 35 | 0 | 17 |
| 6 Moorlands | 16 | 5 | 2 | 9 | 40 | 51 | -11 | 17 |
| 7 Railway Hale | 16 | 4 | 3 | 9 | 26 | 46 | -20 | 15 |
| 8 Kartel Sports | 16 | 2 | 5 | 9 | 38 | 47 | -9 | 11 |
| 9 Club AZ | 16 | 2 | 3 | 11 | 24 | 53 | -29 | 9 |

| Division Two | P | W | D | L | F | A | GD | Pts |
|---|---|---|---|---|---|---|---|---|
| 1 Northenden Victoria | 16 | 13 | 0 | 3 | 54 | 28 | 26 | 39 |
| 2 Altrincham Hale Res. | 16 | 11 | 1 | 4 | 36 | 18 | 18 | 34 |
| 3 Prestbury | 16 | 11 | 0 | 5 | 35 | 27 | 8 | 33 |
| 4 Broadheath Central Res. | 16 | 10 | 2 | 4 | 51 | 28 | 23 | 32 |
| 5 APFC | 16 | 9 | 1 | 6 | 43 | 34 | 9 | 28 |
| 6 Wythenshawe Amateur | 16 | 7 | 0 | 9 | 42 | 33 | 9 | 21 |
| 7 Unicorn Athletic | 16 | 4 | 1 | 11 | 24 | 43 | -19 | 13 |
| 8 Flixton AFC | 16 | 3 | 1 | 12 | 30 | 54 | -24 | 10 |
| 9 Wythenshawe Celtic | 16 | 1 | 0 | 15 | 17 | 67 | -50 | 3 |

## AMATEUR FOOTBALL COMBINATION

| Premier | P | W | D | L | F | A | GD | Pts |
|---|---|---|---|---|---|---|---|---|
| 1 Old Hamptonians | 16 | 14 | 0 | 4 | 68 | 22 | 46 | 42 |
| 2 Old Meadonians | 18 | 13 | 2 | 3 | 43 | 15 | 28 | 41 |
| 3 Old Suttonians | 18 | 10 | 1 | 7 | 37 | 26 | 11 | 31 |
| 4 Dorkinians | 18 | 9 | 2 | 7 | 43 | 30 | 13 | 29 |
| 5 Old Minchendenians | 18 | 8 | 4 | 6 | 30 | 35 | -5 | 28 |
| 6 Old Thorntonians | 18 | 7 | 5 | 6 | 37 | 35 | 2 | 26 |
| 7 Honorable Artillery Company | 18 | 8 | 2 | 8 | 37 | 39 | -2 | 26 |
| 8 Old Salvatorians | 18 | 5 | 3 | 10 | 33 | 45 | -12 | 18 |
| 9 Kings Old Boys | 18 | 4 | 2 | 12 | 27 | 58 | -31 | 14 |
| 10 Enfield Old Grammarians | 18 | 0 | 3 | 15 | 12 | 62 | -50 | 3 |

| Senior One | P | W | D | L | F | A | GD | Pts |
|---|---|---|---|---|---|---|---|---|
| 1 Old Wokingians | 20 | 16 | 4 | 0 | 43 | 18 | 25 | 52 |
| 2 Old Parmiterians | 20 | 15 | 5 | 0 | 85 | 22 | 63 | 50 |
| 3 UCL Academicals | 20 | 8 | 8 | 4 | 48 | 27 | 21 | 32 |
| 4 Bealonians | 20 | 9 | 5 | 6 | 48 | 38 | 10 | 32 |
| 5 Old Ignatians | 20 | 9 | 2 | 9 | 61 | 47 | 14 | 29 |
| 6 Economicals | 20 | 6 | 4 | 10 | 38 | 52 | -14 | 22 |
| 7 Old Pauline | 20 | 6 | 4 | 10 | 27 | 53 | -26 | 22 |
| 8 London Lawyers | 20 | 4 | 7 | 9 | 37 | 49 | -12 | 19 |
| 9 Old Aloysians (-3) | 20 | 6 | 2 | 12 | 35 | 66 | -31 | 17 |
| 10 Albanian | 20 | 3 | 6 | 11 | 33 | 52 | -19 | 15 |
| 11 Old Minchendenians II | 20 | 2 | 5 | 13 | 28 | 59 | -31 | 11 |

| | Senior Two North | P | W | D | L | F | A | GD | Pts |
|---|---|---|---|---|---|---|---|---|---|
| 1 | Park View | 14 | 10 | 2 | 2 | 43 | 19 | 24 | 32 |
| 2 | Southgate Olympic | 14 | 6 | 6 | 2 | 35 | 30 | 5 | 24 |
| 3 | Queen Mary College Old Boys | 14 | 6 | 5 | 3 | 43 | 26 | 17 | 23 |
| 4 | Latymer Old Boys | 14 | 6 | 2 | 6 | 31 | 36 | -5 | 20 |
| 5 | Sloane | 14 | 5 | 2 | 7 | 39 | 38 | 1 | 17 |
| 6 | Mayfield Athletic | 14 | 4 | 4 | 6 | 29 | 27 | 2 | 16 |
| 7 | Old Woodhouseians | 14 | 5 | 0 | 9 | 24 | 35 | -11 | 15 |
| 8 | Lea Valley | 14 | 3 | 1 | 10 | 25 | 58 | -33 | 10 |

| | **Senior Two South** | P | W | D | L | F | A | GD | Pts |
|---|---|---|---|---|---|---|---|---|---|
| 1 | Fulham Compton Old Boys | 20 | 13 | 4 | 3 | 59 | 23 | 36 | 43 |
| 2 | Clapham Old Xaverians | 20 | 12 | 4 | 4 | 51 | 34 | 17 | 40 |
| 3 | Old Meadonians II | 20 | 10 | 2 | 8 | 28 | 29 | -1 | 32 |
| 4 | Reigatians | 20 | 9 | 4 | 7 | 49 | 41 | 8 | 31 |
| 5 | Honorable Artillery Company II | 20 | 7 | 6 | 7 | 39 | 44 | -5 | 27 |
| 6 | Shene Old Grammarians | 20 | 6 | 7 | 7 | 29 | 29 | 0 | 25 |
| 7 | Glyn Old Boys | 20 | 6 | 7 | 7 | 42 | 43 | -1 | 25 |
| 8 | Economicals II | 20 | 6 | 6 | 8 | 38 | 38 | 0 | 24 |
| 9 | Old Tenisonians | 20 | 5 | 4 | 11 | 26 | 38 | -12 | 19 |
| 10 | Wandsworth Borough | 20 | 3 | 9 | 8 | 33 | 37 | -4 | 18 |
| 11 | Sinjuns Grammarians | 20 | 4 | 5 | 11 | 20 | 58 | -38 | 17 |

| | **Senior Three North** | P | W | D | L | F | A | GD | Pts |
|---|---|---|---|---|---|---|---|---|---|
| 1 | Old Manorians | 18 | 15 | 1 | 2 | 67 | 18 | 49 | 46 |
| 2 | Old Aloysians II | 18 | 13 | 1 | 4 | 57 | 37 | 20 | 40 |
| 3 | Hale End Athletic | 18 | 9 | 1 | 8 | 50 | 34 | 16 | 28 |
| 4 | Old Salvatorians II | 18 | 9 | 1 | 8 | 35 | 35 | 0 | 28 |
| | Southgate County | 18 | 8 | 2 | 8 | 42 | 31 | 11 | 26 |
| 6 | Albanian II | 18 | 7 | 5 | 6 | 51 | 53 | -2 | 26 |
| 7 | UCL Academicals II | 18 | 8 | 2 | 8 | 31 | 33 | -2 | 26 |
| 8 | Old Tollingtonians | 18 | 5 | 1 | 12 | 39 | 56 | -17 | 16 |
| | Old Minchendenians III | 18 | 4 | 1 | 13 | 31 | 66 | -35 | 13 |
| 10 | Old Edmontonians (-4) | 18 | 4 | 1 | 13 | 37 | 77 | -40 | 9 |

| | **Senior Three South** | P | W | D | L | F | A | GD | Pts |
|---|---|---|---|---|---|---|---|---|---|
| | Fitzwilliam Old Boys | 18 | 15 | 1 | 2 | 56 | 20 | 36 | 46 |
| | Worcester College Old Boys | 18 | 11 | 2 | 5 | 48 | 31 | 17 | 35 |
| | Old Sedcopians | 18 | 9 | 2 | 7 | 49 | 33 | 16 | 29 |
| | Mickleham Old Boxhillians | 18 | 7 | 3 | 8 | 48 | 46 | 2 | 24 |
| | Old Meadonians III | 18 | 7 | 3 | 8 | 35 | 43 | -8 | 24 |
| | Citigroup | 18 | 7 | 2 | 9 | 41 | 54 | -13 | 23 |
| | Old Vaughanians | 18 | 6 | 3 | 9 | 41 | 50 | -9 | 21 |
| | Old Suttonians II | 18 | 6 | 3 | 9 | 23 | 47 | -24 | 21 |
| | Old Thorntonians II | 18 | 5 | 5 | 8 | 30 | 42 | -12 | 20 |
| 10 | Economicals III | 18 | 4 | 2 | 12 | 30 | 35 | -5 | 14 |

| | **Intermediate South** | P | W | D | L | F | A | GD | Pts |
|---|---|---|---|---|---|---|---|---|---|
| 1 | Old Hamptonians II | 20 | 16 | 1 | 3 | 63 | 25 | 38 | 49 |
| 2 | Economicals IV | 20 | 14 | 4 | 2 | 62 | 26 | 36 | 46 |
| 3 | Old Strand Academicals | 20 | 12 | 2 | 6 | 62 | 32 | 30 | 38 |
| 4 | Old St Marys | 20 | 10 | 3 | 7 | 47 | 38 | 9 | 33 |
| 5 | Dorkinians II | 20 | 10 | 1 | 9 | 43 | 36 | 7 | 31 |
| 6 | Old Isleworthians (-1) | 20 | 10 | 2 | 8 | 43 | 51 | -8 | 31 |
| 7 | Royal Bank of Scotland | 20 | 9 | 3 | 8 | 45 | 44 | 1 | 30 |
| 8 | Hampstead Heathens (-1) | 20 | 5 | 3 | 12 | 29 | 42 | -13 | 17 |
| 9 | New-Magdalen AFC | 20 | 4 | 3 | 13 | 26 | 55 | -29 | 15 |
| 10 | Old Suttonians III | 20 | 2 | 5 | 13 | 28 | 67 | -39 | 11 |
| 11 | Glyn Old Boys II (-3) | 20 | 2 | 5 | 13 | 42 | 74 | -32 | 8 |

| | **Intermediate North** | P | W | D | L | F | A | GD | Pts |
|---|---|---|---|---|---|---|---|---|---|
| 1 | Globe Rangers | 18 | 11 | 3 | 4 | 72 | 40 | 32 | 36 |
| 2 | Old Ignatians II | 18 | 11 | 2 | 5 | 38 | 28 | 10 | 35 |
| 3 | Hale End Athletic II | 18 | 8 | 6 | 4 | 43 | 32 | 11 | 30 |
| 4 | Bealonians II | 18 | 8 | 4 | 6 | 37 | 37 | 0 | 28 |
| 5 | Wood Green Old Boys | 18 | 7 | 5 | 6 | 41 | 41 | 0 | 26 |
| 6 | Old Uffingtonians | 18 | 6 | 5 | 7 | 44 | 44 | 0 | 23 |
| 7 | Old Parmiterians II | 18 | 5 | 6 | 7 | 38 | 36 | 2 | 21 |
| 8 | Old Manorians II | 18 | 5 | 4 | 9 | 36 | 43 | -7 | 19 |
| 9 | UCL Academicals III | 18 | 5 | 2 | 11 | 33 | 53 | -20 | 17 |
| 10 | Old Magdalenians | 18 | 5 | 1 | 12 | 32 | 60 | -28 | 16 |

| | **One North** | P | W | D | L | F | A | GD | Pts |
|---|---|---|---|---|---|---|---|---|---|
| 1 | Oakhill Tigers II | 16 | 12 | 2 | 2 | 65 | 20 | 45 | 38 |
| 2 | Enfield Old Grammarians II | 16 | 10 | 4 | 2 | 41 | 19 | 22 | 34 |
| 3 | Old Salvatorians III | 16 | 10 | 2 | 4 | 44 | 27 | 17 | 32 |
| 4 | Old Woodhouseians II | 16 | 8 | 3 | 5 | 38 | 39 | -1 | 27 |
| 5 | Old Parmiterians III | 16 | 7 | 2 | 7 | 38 | 30 | 8 | 23 |
| 6 | Leyton County Old Boys | 16 | 5 | 2 | 9 | 32 | 44 | -12 | 17 |
| 7 | Egbertian | 16 | 4 | 3 | 9 | 33 | 41 | -8 | 15 |
| 8 | University of Hertfordshire | 16 | 3 | 1 | 12 | 28 | 48 | -20 | 10 |
| 9 | Albanian III | 16 | 3 | 1 | 12 | 23 | 74 | -51 | 10 |

| | **One South** | P | W | D | L | F | A | GD | Pts |
|---|---|---|---|---|---|---|---|---|---|
| 1 | Royal Bank of Scotland II | 18 | 14 | 2 | 2 | 65 | 28 | 37 | 44 |
| 2 | London Lawyers II | 18 | 11 | 5 | 2 | 49 | 27 | 22 | 38 |
| 3 | Old Wokingians II | 18 | 10 | 3 | 5 | 37 | 41 | -4 | 33 |
| 4 | Witan | 18 | 7 | 3 | 8 | 37 | 37 | 0 | 24 |
| 5 | City of London | 18 | 6 | 3 | 9 | 44 | 46 | -2 | 21 |
| 6 | Old Thorntonians III | 18 | 6 | 3 | 9 | 35 | 41 | -6 | 21 |
| 7 | Old Sedcopians II | 18 | 5 | 5 | 8 | 31 | 38 | -7 | 20 |
| 8 | Old Tiffinians | 18 | 5 | 3 | 10 | 31 | 40 | -9 | 18 |
| 9 | Old Pauline II | 18 | 5 | 3 | 10 | 41 | 53 | -12 | 18 |
| 10 | Tilburg Regents (-3) | 18 | 4 | 4 | 10 | 33 | 52 | -19 | 13 |

## LEAGUE TABLES

| Two North | P | W | D | L | F | A | GD | Pts |
|---|---|---|---|---|---|---|---|---|
| 1 Somerville Old Boys | 14 | 9 | 1 | 4 | 43 | 33 | 10 | 28 |
| 2 Old Manorians III | 14 | 9 | 0 | 5 | 54 | 34 | 20 | 27 |
| 3 Bealonians III | 14 | 7 | 2 | 5 | 35 | 27 | 8 | 23 |
| 4 Latymer Old Boys II | 14 | 7 | 1 | 6 | 40 | 36 | 4 | 22 |
| 5 Queen Mary College Old Boys II | 14 | 6 | 4 | 4 | 35 | 36 | -1 | 22 |
| 6 Old Salvatorians IV | 14 | 7 | 0 | 7 | 54 | 31 | 23 | 21 |
| 7 Old Parmiterians IV | 14 | 5 | 1 | 8 | 44 | 48 | -4 | 16 |
| 8 Old Ignatians III | 14 | 1 | 1 | 12 | 25 | 85 | -60 | 4 |

| Two South | P | W | D | L | F | A | GD | Pts |
|---|---|---|---|---|---|---|---|---|
| 1 Old Pauline III | 20 | 15 | 2 | 3 | 52 | 22 | 30 | 47 |
| 2 Economicals V | 20 | 13 | 4 | 3 | 52 | 25 | 27 | 43 |
| 3 Old Meadonians IV | 20 | 12 | 1 | 7 | 53 | 36 | 17 | 37 |
| 4 Reigatians II | 20 | 10 | 2 | 8 | 45 | 36 | 9 | 32 |
| 5 Heathrow Seniors | 20 | 10 | 1 | 9 | 44 | 37 | 7 | 31 |
| 6 Clapham Old Xaverians II | 20 | 8 | 4 | 8 | 39 | 39 | 0 | 28 |
| 7 Old Tenisonians II (-3) | 20 | 8 | 5 | 7 | 43 | 47 | -4 | 26 |
| 8 Kings Old Boys II | 20 | 5 | 5 | 10 | 25 | 38 | -13 | 20 |
| 9 Sinjuns Grammarians II | 20 | 5 | 2 | 13 | 45 | 69 | -24 | 17 |
| 10 Wandsworth Borough II | 20 | 4 | 4 | 12 | 36 | 63 | -27 | 16 |
| 11 National Westminster Bank II (-3) | 20 | 4 | 2 | 14 | 30 | 52 | -22 | 11 |

| Three North | P | W | D | L | F | A | GD | Pts |
|---|---|---|---|---|---|---|---|---|
| 1 UCL Academicals IV | 18 | 16 | 0 | 2 | 78 | 25 | 53 | 48 |
| 2 Old Kingsburians | 18 | 13 | 2 | 3 | 58 | 28 | 30 | 41 |
| 3 Hale End Athletic III | 18 | 10 | 3 | 5 | 52 | 32 | 20 | 33 |
| 4 Egbertian II | 18 | 9 | 2 | 7 | 43 | 41 | 2 | 29 |
| 5 Old Minchendenians IV | 18 | 6 | 3 | 9 | 49 | 56 | -7 | 21 |
| 6 Hinton & Finchley Revolution OB | 18 | 6 | 1 | 11 | 45 | 50 | -5 | 19 |
| 7 Southgate Olympic II | 18 | 5 | 4 | 9 | 35 | 59 | -24 | 19 |
| 8 Old Aloysians IV (-3) | 18 | 6 | 2 | 10 | 30 | 47 | -17 | 17 |
| 9 Enfield Old Grammarians IV (-2) | 18 | 5 | 1 | 12 | 43 | 52 | -9 | 14 |
| 10 Parkfield | 18 | 4 | 2 | 12 | 32 | 75 | -43 | 14 |

| Three South | P | W | D | L | F | A | GD | Pts |
|---|---|---|---|---|---|---|---|---|
| 1 London Welsh | 18 | 14 | 2 | 2 | 46 | 25 | 21 | 44 |
| 2 Brent | 18 | 11 | 3 | 4 | 54 | 28 | 26 | 36 |
| 3 Old Meadonians V | 18 | 9 | 4 | 5 | 41 | 31 | 10 | 31 |
| 4 Old Whitgiftian | 18 | 8 | 1 | 9 | 41 | 39 | 2 | 25 |
| 5 Old Crosbeians | 18 | 6 | 4 | 8 | 28 | 28 | 0 | 22 |
| 6 Fulham Compton Old Boys II | 18 | 6 | 3 | 9 | 25 | 35 | -10 | 21 |
| 7 Old Suttonians IV | 18 | 6 | 2 | 10 | 41 | 50 | -9 | 20 |
| 8 Old Wokingians III | 18 | 6 | 2 | 10 | 23 | 37 | -14 | 20 |
| 9 Old Thorntonians IV | 18 | 5 | 4 | 9 | 33 | 51 | -18 | 19 |
| 10 Old Boilers | 18 | 5 | 3 | 10 | 49 | 57 | -8 | 18 |

| Four North | P | W | D | L | F | A | GD | Pts |
|---|---|---|---|---|---|---|---|---|
| 1 Old Parmiterians V | 18 | 14 | 1 | 3 | 71 | 28 | 43 | 43 |
| 2 Mayfield Athletic II | 18 | 14 | 1 | 3 | 73 | 37 | 36 | 43 |
| 3 Mill Hill Village | 18 | 12 | 1 | 5 | 80 | 42 | 38 | 37 |
| 4 Queen Mary College Old Boys III | 18 | 11 | 2 | 5 | 55 | 41 | 14 | 35 |
| 5 UCL Academicals V | 18 | 9 | 1 | 8 | 50 | 39 | 11 | 28 |
| 6 Southgate County II | 18 | 7 | 3 | 8 | 51 | 57 | -6 | 24 |
| 7 Old Woodhouseians III | 18 | 7 | 1 | 10 | 37 | 47 | -10 | 22 |
| 8 Latymer Old Boys III | 18 | 6 | 0 | 12 | 34 | 53 | -19 | 18 |
| 9 Old Magdalenians II | 18 | 4 | 1 | 13 | 26 | 55 | -29 | 13 |
| 10 Egbertian III | 18 | 0 | 1 | 17 | 22 | 100 | -78 | 1 |

| Four South | P | W | D | L | F | A | GD | Pts |
|---|---|---|---|---|---|---|---|---|
| 1 Old Guildfordians | 18 | 15 | 1 | 2 | 57 | 19 | 38 | 46 |
| 2 Reigatians III | 18 | 10 | 4 | 4 | 49 | 33 | 16 | 34 |
| 3 Old St Marys II | 18 | 10 | 3 | 5 | 36 | 37 | -1 | 33 |
| 4 Old Meadonians VI | 18 | 9 | 4 | 5 | 45 | 32 | 13 | 31 |
| 5 Fulham Compton Old Boys III | 18 | 9 | 3 | 6 | 40 | 36 | 4 | 30 |
| 6 Shene Old Grammarians II | 18 | 7 | 3 | 8 | 48 | 44 | 4 | 24 |
| 7 Old Hamptonians III | 18 | 6 | 4 | 8 | 42 | 43 | -1 | 22 |
| 8 City of London II | 18 | 6 | 3 | 9 | 35 | 38 | -3 | 21 |
| 9 Dorkinians III | 18 | 2 | 3 | 13 | 32 | 61 | -29 | 9 |
| 10 Old Wokingians IV | 18 | 2 | 0 | 16 | 24 | 65 | -41 | 6 |

| Five North | P | W | D | L | F | A | GD | Pts |
|---|---|---|---|---|---|---|---|---|
| 1 Oakhill Tigers III | 16 | 14 | 0 | 2 | 51 | 20 | 31 | 42 |
| 2 Old Challoners | 16 | 11 | 2 | 3 | 46 | 18 | 28 | 35 |
| 3 Egbertian IV (-3) | 16 | 8 | 3 | 5 | 37 | 32 | 5 | 24 |
| 4 Albanian IV | 16 | 6 | 4 | 6 | 47 | 44 | 3 | 22 |
| 5 Old Salvatorians V | 16 | 6 | 1 | 9 | 32 | 37 | -5 | 19 |
| 6 Wood Green Old Boys II | 16 | 5 | 3 | 8 | 40 | 47 | -7 | 18 |
| 7 Mayfield Athletic III | 16 | 5 | 3 | 8 | 33 | 53 | -20 | 18 |
| 8 Old Tollingtonians II | 16 | 4 | 2 | 10 | 28 | 41 | -13 | 14 |
| 9 Southgate Olympic III | 16 | 2 | 4 | 10 | 28 | 50 | -22 | 10 |

| Five South | P | W | D | L | F | A | GD | Pts |
|---|---|---|---|---|---|---|---|---|
| 1 Royal Sun Alliance | 16 | 12 | 2 | 2 | 75 | 24 | 51 | 38 |
| 2 Wandsworth Borough III | 16 | 10 | 2 | 4 | 37 | 34 | 3 | 32 |
| 3 Old Meadonians VII | 16 | 6 | 5 | 5 | 43 | 41 | 2 | 23 |
| 4 Shene Old Grammarians III | 16 | 5 | 7 | 4 | 43 | 29 | 14 | 22 |
| 5 Old Thorntonians V | 16 | 6 | 2 | 8 | 33 | 43 | -10 | 2[illegible] |
| 6 Witan II | 16 | 5 | 4 | 7 | 48 | 39 | 9 | 1[illegible] |
| 7 Clapham Old Xaverians III | 16 | 5 | 3 | 8 | 36 | 44 | -8 | 1[illegible] |
| 8 Glyn Old Boys III (-3) | 16 | 5 | 2 | 9 | 31 | 68 | -37 | 1[illegible] |
| 9 John Fisher Old Boys | 16 | 3 | 3 | 10 | 22 | 46 | -24 | 1[illegible] |

| Six North | P | W | D | L | F | A | GD | Pts |
|---|---|---|---|---|---|---|---|---|
| 1 Old Kingsburians II | 16 | 14 | 0 | 2 | 74 | 21 | 53 | 4[illegible] |
| 2 Old Vaughanians II | 16 | 12 | 2 | 2 | 71 | 25 | 46 | 3[illegible] |
| 3 Bealonians IV | 16 | 10 | 3 | 3 | 31 | 26 | 5 | 3[illegible] |
| 4 Old Manorians IV | 16 | 9 | 2 | 5 | 51 | 47 | 4 | 2[illegible] |
| 5 Old Aloysians V | 16 | 5 | 2 | 9 | 43 | 60 | -17 | 1[illegible] |
| 6 Latymer Old Boys IV | 16 | 4 | 4 | 8 | 41 | 43 | -2 | 1[illegible] |
| 7 London Hospital Old Boys (-1) | 16 | 2 | 5 | 9 | 26 | 60 | -34 | 1[illegible] |
| 8 Wood Green Old Boys III | 16 | 2 | 3 | 11 | 23 | 57 | -34 | |
| 9 Old Pegasonians (-4) | 16 | 1 | 5 | 10 | 24 | 45 | -21 | |

| Six South | | P | W | D | L | F | A | GD | Pts |
|---|---|---|---|---|---|---|---|---|---|
| 1 | Old Sedcopians III | 18 | 14 | 2 | 2 | 45 | 24 | 21 | 44 |
| 2 | Old Tiffinians II | 18 | 8 | 6 | 4 | 50 | 37 | 13 | 30 |
| 3 | Old Wokingians V | 18 | 9 | 3 | 6 | 51 | 39 | 12 | 30 |
| 4 | London Welsh II | 18 | 8 | 4 | 6 | 34 | 43 | -9 | 28 |
| 5 | Clapham Old Xaverians IV | 18 | 9 | 0 | 9 | 42 | 32 | 10 | 27 |
| 6 | Old Suttonians V | 18 | 7 | 6 | 5 | 37 | 28 | 9 | 27 |
| 7 | Glyn Old Boys IV (-3) | 18 | 8 | 2 | 8 | 41 | 40 | 1 | 23 |
| 8 | Old Meadonians VIII | 18 | 5 | 2 | 11 | 41 | 55 | -14 | 17 |
| 9 | Mickleham Old Boxhillians II | 18 | 3 | 6 | 9 | 34 | 45 | -11 | 15 |
| 10 | Brent II | 18 | 2 | 3 | 13 | 23 | 55 | -32 | 9 |

| Seven North | | P | W | D | L | F | A | GD | Pts |
|---|---|---|---|---|---|---|---|---|---|
| 1 | Old Parmiterians VI | 16 | 10 | 6 | 0 | 58 | 17 | 41 | 36 |
| 2 | Bealonians V | 16 | 11 | 2 | 3 | 54 | 29 | 25 | 35 |
| 3 | Old Ignatians IV | 16 | 9 | 4 | 3 | 46 | 32 | 14 | 31 |
| 4 | Old Woodhouseians IV | 16 | 7 | 3 | 6 | 40 | 33 | 7 | 24 |
| 5 | Old Tollingtonians III | 16 | 6 | 2 | 8 | 49 | 55 | -6 | 20 |
| 6 | Mill Hill Village II | 16 | 5 | 5 | 6 | 27 | 35 | -8 | 20 |
| 7 | Leyton County Old Boys II (-1) | 16 | 4 | 3 | 9 | 41 | 53 | -12 | 14 |
| 8 | Oakhill Tigers IV | 16 | 4 | 2 | 10 | 34 | 66 | -32 | 14 |
| 9 | Southgate Olympic IV | 16 | 2 | 1 | 13 | 37 | 66 | -29 | 7 |

| Seven South | | P | W | D | L | F | A | GD | Pts |
|---|---|---|---|---|---|---|---|---|---|
| 1 | Old Grantonians | 16 | 11 | 2 | 3 | 52 | 33 | 19 | 35 |
| 2 | Old Wokingians VI | 16 | 9 | 1 | 6 | 46 | 37 | 9 | 28 |
| 3 | Old Suttonians VI | 16 | 9 | 1 | 6 | 39 | 32 | 7 | 28 |
| 4 | Old Sedcopians IV | 16 | 8 | 3 | 5 | 55 | 29 | 26 | 27 |
| 5 | John Fisher Old Boys II | 16 | 8 | 2 | 6 | 44 | 35 | 9 | 26 |
| 6 | Reigatians IV | 16 | 7 | 1 | 8 | 31 | 35 | -4 | 22 |
| 7 | Old Thorntonians VI | 16 | 7 | 0 | 9 | 39 | 33 | 6 | 21 |
| 8 | Sinjuns Grammarians III | 16 | 5 | 3 | 8 | 37 | 52 | -15 | 18 |
| 9 | Old Meadonians IX | 16 | 1 | 1 | 14 | 20 | 77 | -57 | 4 |

| Eight North | | P | W | D | L | F | A | GD | Pts |
|---|---|---|---|---|---|---|---|---|---|
| 1 | Old Manorians V | 16 | 14 | 1 | 1 | 75 | 16 | 59 | 43 |
| 2 | Old Parmiterians VII | 16 | 11 | 1 | 4 | 66 | 41 | 25 | 34 |
| 3 | Old Kingsburians III | 16 | 7 | 3 | 6 | 42 | 35 | 7 | 24 |
| 4 | Old Salvatorians VI | 16 | 7 | 2 | 7 | 44 | 40 | 4 | 23 |
| 5 | Egbertian V (-3) | 16 | 7 | 3 | 6 | 41 | 32 | 9 | 21 |
| 6 | Latymer Old Boys V | 16 | 5 | 3 | 8 | 26 | 56 | -30 | 18 |
| 7 | Old Woodhouseians V | 16 | 5 | 2 | 9 | 30 | 51 | -21 | 17 |
| 8 | Old Minchendenians V | 16 | 4 | 1 | 11 | 38 | 72 | -34 | 13 |
| 9 | Enfield Old Grammarians V (-1) | 16 | 4 | 0 | 12 | 42 | 61 | -19 | 11 |

| Eight South | | P | W | D | L | F | A | GD | Pts |
|---|---|---|---|---|---|---|---|---|---|
| 1 | Old Suttonians VII | 18 | 15 | 1 | 2 | 68 | 18 | 50 | 46 |
| 2 | Old Pauline IV | 18 | 10 | 4 | 4 | 52 | 31 | 21 | 34 |
| 3 | Wandsworth Borough IV | 18 | 7 | 6 | 5 | 52 | 46 | 6 | 27 |
| 4 | Reigatians V | 18 | 7 | 3 | 8 | 45 | 51 | -6 | 24 |
| 5 | Old Wokingians VII | 18 | 8 | 0 | 10 | 44 | 55 | -11 | 24 |
| 6 | City of London III (-6) | 18 | 9 | 1 | 8 | 49 | 46 | 3 | 22 |
| 7 | Old Sedcopians V | 18 | 7 | 1 | 10 | 53 | 61 | -8 | 22 |
| 8 | Old Guildfordians II | 18 | 6 | 4 | 8 | 41 | 51 | -10 | 22 |
| 9 | Dorkinians IV | 18 | 5 | 3 | 10 | 40 | 49 | -9 | 18 |
| 10 | Old Tiffinians III | 18 | 3 | 3 | 12 | 32 | 68 | -36 | 12 |

| Nine North | | P | W | D | L | F | A | GD | Pts |
|---|---|---|---|---|---|---|---|---|---|
| 1 | Bealonians VI | 18 | 16 | 2 | 0 | 109 | 14 | 95 | 50 |
| 2 | University of Hertfordshire II | 18 | 13 | 2 | 3 | 75 | 29 | 46 | 41 |
| 3 | Old Kingsburians IV | 18 | 13 | 1 | 4 | 75 | 36 | 39 | 40 |
| 4 | UCL Academicals VI | 18 | 12 | 1 | 5 | 61 | 26 | 35 | 37 |
| 5 | Old Parmiterians VIII | 18 | 9 | 3 | 6 | 59 | 41 | 18 | 30 |
| 6 | Ravenscroft Old Boys | 18 | 7 | 0 | 11 | 47 | 76 | -29 | 21 |
| 7 | Old Vaughanians III | 18 | 5 | 2 | 11 | 42 | 77 | -35 | 17 |
| 8 | Southgate County III | 18 | 4 | 1 | 13 | 39 | 82 | -43 | 13 |
| 9 | Old Ignatians V | 18 | 3 | 1 | 14 | 31 | 86 | -55 | 10 |
| 10 | Old Challoners II | 18 | 1 | 1 | 16 | 23 | 94 | -71 | 4 |

| Nine South | | P | W | D | L | F | A | GD | Pts |
|---|---|---|---|---|---|---|---|---|---|
| 1 | Brent III | 18 | 13 | 4 | 1 | 76 | 29 | 47 | 43 |
| 2 | Dorkinians V | 18 | 12 | 2 | 4 | 55 | 29 | 26 | 38 |
| 3 | Old Whitgiftian II | 18 | 11 | 1 | 6 | 59 | 36 | 23 | 34 |
| 4 | Old Suttonians VIII | 18 | 10 | 3 | 5 | 42 | 35 | 7 | 33 |
| 5 | Wandsworth Borough V | 18 | 9 | 4 | 5 | 48 | 37 | 11 | 31 |
| 6 | Old Wokingians VIII | 18 | 8 | 2 | 8 | 70 | 57 | 13 | 26 |
| 7 | Reigatians VI | 18 | 6 | 1 | 11 | 31 | 52 | -21 | 19 |
| 8 | Old Tiffinians IV | 18 | 4 | 4 | 10 | 36 | 58 | -22 | 16 |
| 9 | Old Guildfordians III | 18 | 4 | 1 | 13 | 24 | 83 | -59 | 12 * |
| 10 | Old St Marys III | 18 | 2 | 0 | 16 | 35 | 60 | -25 | 6 |

## ANDOVER & DISTRICT LEAGUE

| Division One | | P | W | D | L | F | A | GD | Pts |
|---|---|---|---|---|---|---|---|---|---|
| 1 | Sutton Scotney | 18 | 14 | 2 | 2 | 46 | 23 | 23 | 44 |
| 2 | South Wonston Swifts | 18 | 14 | 1 | 3 | 76 | 22 | 54 | 43 |
| 3 | Sparten | 18 | 11 | 2 | 5 | 74 | 40 | 34 | 35 |
| 4 | Kings Somborne | 18 | 10 | 4 | 4 | 59 | 34 | 25 | 34 |
| 5 | Over Wallop | 18 | 7 | 7 | 4 | 47 | 40 | 7 | 28 |
| 6 | Kingsclere | 18 | 6 | 3 | 9 | 39 | 31 | 8 | 21 |
| 7 | Andover New Street Swifts Res. | 18 | 4 | 2 | 12 | 30 | 64 | -34 | 14 |
| 8 | Broughton Res. | 18 | 4 | 1 | 13 | 35 | 61 | -26 | 13 |
| 9 | Andover Lions Res. | 18 | 4 | 1 | 13 | 29 | 75 | -46 | 13 |
| 10 | CK Andover | 18 | 3 | 3 | 12 | 26 | 71 | -45 | 12 |

## ARMY ASSOCIATION

| Massey Trophy - Division One | | P | W | D | L | F | A | GD | Pts |
|---|---|---|---|---|---|---|---|---|---|
| 1 | RLC | 12 | 10 | 1 | 1 | 48 | 10 | 38 | 31 |
| 2 | RE | 12 | 8 | 2 | 2 | 37 | 17 | 20 | 26 |
| 3 | R Sigs | 12 | 7 | 1 | 4 | 47 | 22 | 25 | 22 |
| 4 | REME | 12 | 7 | 0 | 5 | 27 | 18 | 9 | 21 |
| 5 | RA | 12 | 4 | 0 | 8 | 21 | 37 | -16 | 12 |
| 6 | RAPTC | 12 | 3 | 0 | 9 | 11 | 38 | -27 | 9 |
| 7 | INT CORPS | 12 | 1 | 0 | 11 | 14 | 63 | -49 | 3 |

| Massey Trophy - Division Two | | P | W | D | L | F | A | GD | Pts |
|---|---|---|---|---|---|---|---|---|---|
| 1 | AAC | 8 | 5 | 0 | 3 | 17 | 6 | 11 | 15 |
| 2 | AGC | 8 | 5 | 0 | 3 | 24 | 15 | 9 | 15 |
| 3 | INF | 8 | 3 | 2 | 3 | 12 | 12 | 0 | 11 |
| 4 | AMS | 8 | 3 | 0 | 5 | 12 | 15 | -3 | 9 |
| 5 | RAC | 8 | 2 | 2 | 4 | 13 | 30 | -17 | 8 |

## ARTHURIAN LEAGUE

| Premeir Division | P | W | D | L | F | A | GD | Pts |
|---|---|---|---|---|---|---|---|---|
| 1 Old Tonbridgians I | 18 | 14 | 3 | 1 | 56 | 29 | 27 | 45 |
| 2 Old Carthusians I | 18 | 12 | 4 | 2 | 51 | 24 | 27 | 40 |
| 3 Old Foresters I | 18 | 12 | 3 | 3 | 46 | 21 | 25 | 39 |
| 4 Old Etonians I | 18 | 8 | 3 | 7 | 30 | 24 | 6 | 27 |
| 5 Old Salopians I | 18 | 7 | 4 | 7 | 42 | 32 | 10 | 25 |
| 6 Lancing Old Boys I | 18 | 5 | 5 | 8 | 27 | 39 | -12 | 20 |
| 7 Kings College Wimbledon I | 18 | 5 | 3 | 10 | 32 | 36 | -4 | 18 |
| 8 Old Marlburians | 18 | 5 | 1 | 12 | 27 | 52 | -25 | 16 |
| 9 Old Chigwellians I | 18 | 3 | 4 | 11 | 29 | 56 | -27 | 13 |
| 10 Old Cholmeleians I | 18 | 2 | 4 | 12 | 23 | 50 | -27 | 10 |

| Division One | P | W | D | L | F | A | GD | Pts |
|---|---|---|---|---|---|---|---|---|
| 1 Old Brentwoods I | 18 | 16 | 1 | 1 | 95 | 22 | 73 | 49 |
| 2 Old Harrovians I | 18 | 12 | 2 | 4 | 48 | 18 | 30 | 38 |
| 3 Old Radleians (-3) | 18 | 9 | 3 | 6 | 44 | 43 | 1 | 27 |
| 4 Old Reptonians | 18 | 8 | 3 | 7 | 33 | 32 | 1 | 27 |
| 5 Old Bradfieldians I | 18 | 8 | 2 | 8 | 46 | 42 | 4 | 26 |
| 6 Old Wellingtonians (-3) | 18 | 8 | 3 | 7 | 46 | 36 | 10 | 21 |
| 7 Old Malvernians I | 18 | 6 | 3 | 9 | 37 | 46 | -9 | 21 |
| 8 Old Wykehamists I | 18 | 5 | 1 | 12 | 42 | 57 | -15 | 16 |
| 9 Old Aldenhamians I | 18 | 4 | 3 | 11 | 34 | 56 | -22 | 15 |
| 10 Old Haileyburians | 18 | 3 | 1 | 14 | 21 | 94 | -73 | 10 |

| Division Two | P | W | D | L | F | A | GD | Pts |
|---|---|---|---|---|---|---|---|---|
| 1 Old Carthusians III | 16 | 10 | 3 | 3 | 42 | 19 | 23 | 33 |
| 2 Lancing Old Boys II | 16 | 9 | 3 | 4 | 32 | 19 | 13 | 30 |
| 3 Old Millfieldians | 16 | 7 | 7 | 2 | 50 | 36 | 14 | 28 |
| 4 Old Berkhamstedians | 16 | 7 | 6 | 3 | 40 | 28 | 12 | 27 |
| 5 Old Carthusians II | 16 | 8 | 3 | 5 | 37 | 32 | 5 | 27 |
| 6 Old Westminsters I (-3) | 16 | 7 | 5 | 4 | 42 | 39 | 3 | 23 |
| 7 Old Etonians II | 16 | 2 | 5 | 9 | 21 | 43 | -22 | 11 |
| 8 Old Foresters II | 16 | 2 | 4 | 10 | 23 | 36 | -13 | 10 |
| 9 Old Chigwellians II (-3) | 16 | 1 | 2 | 13 | 11 | 46 | -35 | 2 |

| Division Three | P | W | D | L | F | A | GD | Pts |
|---|---|---|---|---|---|---|---|---|
| 1 Kings College Wimbledon II | 14 | 8 | 4 | 2 | 32 | 21 | 11 | 28 |
| 2 Old Epsomians | 14 | 7 | 6 | 1 | 41 | 21 | 20 | 27 |
| 3 Old Sennockians | 14 | 8 | 1 | 5 | 28 | 23 | 5 | 25 |
| 4 Old Harrovians II | 14 | 5 | 2 | 7 | 34 | 38 | -4 | 17 |
| 5 Old Citizens (-3) | 14 | 6 | 3 | 5 | 33 | 25 | 8 | 15 |
| 6 Old Salopians II | 14 | 2 | 6 | 6 | 26 | 35 | -9 | 12 |
| 7 Old Eastbournians (-3) | 14 | 3 | 5 | 6 | 25 | 33 | -8 | 11 |
| 8 Old Haberdashers (-3) | 14 | 2 | 3 | 9 | 24 | 47 | -23 | 6 |

| Division Four | P | W | D | L | F | A | GD | Pts |
|---|---|---|---|---|---|---|---|---|
| 1 Old Alleynians AFC | 12 | 7 | 3 | 2 | 44 | 13 | 31 | 24 |
| 2 Old Aldenhamians II | 12 | 6 | 4 | 2 | 20 | 18 | 2 | 22 |
| 3 Old Wykehamists II | 12 | 5 | 2 | 5 | 33 | 36 | -3 | 17 |
| 4 Old Millhillians (-6) | 12 | 7 | 1 | 4 | 37 | 24 | 13 | 16 |
| 5 Old Stoics | 12 | 4 | 3 | 5 | 26 | 34 | -8 | 15 |
| 6 Old Chigwellians III | 12 | 4 | 2 | 6 | 20 | 25 | -5 | 14 |
| 7 Old Cholmeleians III | 12 | 1 | 1 | 10 | 16 | 46 | -30 | 4 |

| Division Five North | P | W | D | L | F | A | GD | Pts |
|---|---|---|---|---|---|---|---|---|
| 1 Old Bancroftians AFC | 10 | 9 | 1 | 0 | 37 | 5 | 32 | 28 |
| 2 Old Merchant Taylors | 10 | 5 | 4 | 1 | 36 | 15 | 21 | 19 |
| 3 Old Harrovians III | 10 | 4 | 3 | 3 | 20 | 18 | 2 | 15 |
| 4 Old Foresters III | 10 | 3 | 4 | 3 | 20 | 22 | -2 | 13 |
| 5 Old Cholmeleians IV | 10 | 1 | 2 | 7 | 16 | 53 | -37 | 5 |
| 6 Old Brentwoods III | 10 | 1 | 0 | 9 | 15 | 31 | -16 | 3 |

| Division Five South | P | W | D | L | F | A | GD | Pts |
|---|---|---|---|---|---|---|---|---|
| 1 Old Oundelians | 10 | 9 | 0 | 1 | 36 | 12 | 24 | 27 |
| 2 Old Tonbridgians II | 10 | 6 | 1 | 3 | 25 | 10 | 15 | 19 |
| 3 Old Amplefordians | 10 | 4 | 2 | 4 | 16 | 23 | -7 | 14 |
| 4 Old Rugbeians | 10 | 4 | 0 | 6 | 27 | 30 | -3 | 12 |
| 5 Old Westminsters II | 10 | 4 | 0 | 6 | 14 | 26 | -12 | 12 |
| 6 Old Malvernians II | 10 | 1 | 1 | 8 | 12 | 29 | -17 | 4 |

## AYLESBURY & DISTRICT LEAGUE

| Premier Division | P | W | D | L | F | A | GD | Pts |
|---|---|---|---|---|---|---|---|---|
| 1 APBS | 17 | 14 | 2 | 1 | 68 | 26 | 42 | 44 |
| 2 Haddenham United | 17 | 13 | 1 | 3 | 69 | 25 | 44 | 40 |
| 3 Aylesbury Dynamos | 18 | 7 | 7 | 4 | 63 | 41 | 22 | 28 |
| 4 Wendover | 18 | 9 | 1 | 8 | 47 | 37 | 10 | 28 |
| 5 FC Mandeville | 18 | 8 | 2 | 8 | 47 | 54 | -7 | 26 |
| 6 Walton Court Wanderers | 18 | 7 | 4 | 7 | 42 | 42 | 0 | 25 |
| 7 Bucks CC | 18 | 6 | 4 | 8 | 43 | 47 | -4 | 22 |
| 8 Long Marston | 18 | 4 | 3 | 11 | 35 | 50 | -15 | 15 |
| 9 Pond Park Rangers | 18 | 4 | 1 | 13 | 36 | 90 | -54 | 13 |
| 10 Elmhurst | 18 | 3 | 3 | 12 | 33 | 71 | -38 | 12 |

| Division One | P | W | D | L | F | A | GD | Pts |
|---|---|---|---|---|---|---|---|---|
| 1 St Johns Sports | 18 | 13 | 3 | 2 | 84 | 35 | 49 | 42 |
| 2 Long Crendon | 18 | 13 | 3 | 2 | 56 | 24 | 32 | 42 |
| 3 New Zealand | 18 | 10 | 3 | 5 | 72 | 43 | 29 | 33 |
| 4 FC Spandits | 18 | 8 | 5 | 5 | 53 | 34 | 19 | 29 |
| 5 Tring Town AFC | 18 | 6 | 9 | 3 | 33 | 25 | 8 | 27 |
| 6 Wingrave | 18 | 7 | 3 | 8 | 48 | 41 | 7 | 24 |
| 7 Bucks CC Res. | 18 | 5 | 5 | 8 | 31 | 47 | -16 | 20 |
| 8 Oving | 18 | 4 | 6 | 8 | 40 | 59 | -19 | 18 |
| 9 Bedgrove Dynamos | 18 | 1 | 4 | 13 | 25 | 75 | -50 | 7 |
| 10 Tetsworth | 18 | 1 | 3 | 14 | 23 | 82 | -59 | 6 |

| Division Two | P | W | D | L | F | A | GD | Pts |
|---|---|---|---|---|---|---|---|---|
| 1 Quainton | 22 | 18 | 4 | 0 | 92 | 26 | 66 | 58 |
| 2 Ludgershall | 22 | 15 | 3 | 4 | 52 | 23 | 29 | 48 |
| 3 Rivets Sports | 22 | 12 | 5 | 5 | 68 | 31 | 37 | 41 |
| 4 FC Mandeville Res. | 22 | 12 | 1 | 9 | 52 | 52 | 0 | 37 |
| 5 Haddenham United Res. | 22 | 10 | 6 | 6 | 55 | 41 | 14 | 36 |
| 6 Wendover Res. | 22 | 9 | 4 | 9 | 70 | 78 | -8 | 31 |
| 7 Waddesdon | 22 | 9 | 0 | 13 | 48 | 56 | -8 | 27 |
| 8 FC Spandits Res. | 22 | 8 | 2 | 12 | 53 | 61 | -8 | 26 |
| 9 Long Marston Res. | 22 | 7 | 4 | 11 | 57 | 82 | -25 | 25 |
| 10 Long Crendon Res. | 22 | 7 | 2 | 13 | 40 | 48 | -8 | 23 |
| 11 Bedgrove United | 22 | 4 | 4 | 14 | 37 | 68 | -31 | 16 |
| 12 Wingrave Res. | 22 | 3 | 1 | 18 | 26 | 84 | -58 | 10 |

| Division Three | P | W | D | L | F | A | GD | Pts |
|---|---|---|---|---|---|---|---|---|
| 1 Rivets Sports Res. | 20 | 18 | 1 | 1 | 95 | 15 | 80 | 55 |
| 2 Quainton Res. | 20 | 15 | 1 | 4 | 62 | 38 | 24 | 46 |
| 3 Aylesbury Dynamos Res. | 20 | 15 | 1 | 4 | 51 | 31 | 20 | 46 |
| 4 AC Meadowcroft | 20 | 12 | 2 | 6 | 67 | 31 | 36 | 38 |
| 5 Waddesdon Res. | 20 | 9 | 5 | 5 | 46 | 52 | -6 | 32 |
| 6 Tring Town AFC Res. | 20 | 10 | 1 | 9 | 32 | 36 | -4 | 31 |
| 7 Great Milton | 20 | 8 | 3 | 8 | 57 | 47 | 10 | 27 |
| 8 The Kennedy FC | 20 | 4 | 2 | 14 | 33 | 55 | -22 | 14 |
| 9 Oving Res. | 20 | 4 | 2 | 14 | 27 | 62 | -35 | 14 |
| 10 Ludgershall Res. | 20 | 2 | 1 | 17 | 22 | 83 | -61 | 7 |
| 11 Bedgrove Dynamos Res. | 20 | 1 | 3 | 16 | 27 | 69 | -42 | 6 |

## BANBURY DISTRICT & LORD JERSEY LEAGUE

| **Premier Division** | P | W | D | L | F | A | GD | Pts |
|---|---|---|---|---|---|---|---|---|
| 1 Heyford Athletic | 18 | 15 | 2 | 1 | 61 | 6 | 55 | 47 |
| 2 KEA | 18 | 12 | 4 | 1 | 60 | 18 | 42 | 40 |
| 3 Croughton | 18 | 9 | 5 | 4 | 43 | 32 | 11 | 32 |
| 4 Deddington Town | 18 | 8 | 6 | 4 | 40 | 30 | 10 | 30 |
| 5 Ashton Villa | 18 | 8 | 4 | 5 | 48 | 35 | 13 | 28 |
| 6 Broughton & North Newington | 18 | 6 | 3 | 9 | 34 | 43 | -9 | 21 |
| 7 Woodford United | 18 | 5 | 3 | 10 | 29 | 35 | -6 | 18 |
| 8 Hornton | 18 | 4 | 2 | 12 | 32 | 64 | -32 | 14 |
| 9 Bishops Itchington | 18 | 3 | 1 | 14 | 24 | 64 | -40 | 10 |
| 10 MIddleton Cheney | 18 | 2 | 4 | 12 | 13 | 57 | -44 | 10 |

| **Division One** | P | W | D | L | F | A | GD | Pts |
|---|---|---|---|---|---|---|---|---|
| 1 Diverse | 20 | 17 | 3 | 0 | 76 | 23 | 53 | 54 |
| 2 Sinclair United | 20 | 12 | 1 | 7 | 61 | 42 | 19 | 37 |
| 3 Banbury United Youth | 20 | 10 | 2 | 8 | 54 | 49 | 5 | 32 |
| 4 AFC BIcester | 20 | 9 | 3 | 8 | 50 | 40 | 10 | 30 |
| 5 Wroxton Sports | 20 | 9 | 1 | 10 | 44 | 50 | -6 | 28 |
| 6 Bloxham | 20 | 8 | 2 | 10 | 45 | 45 | 0 | 26 |
| 7 FC Langford | 20 | 7 | 4 | 9 | 44 | 60 | -16 | 25 |
| 8 Finmere | 20 | 7 | 3 | 10 | 53 | 55 | -2 | 24 |
| 9 Chesterton | 20 | 7 | 3 | 10 | 30 | 52 | -22 | 24 |
| 10 Deddington Town Res. | 20 | 5 | 3 | 12 | 40 | 60 | -20 | 18 |
| 11 Bodicote Sports | 20 | 5 | 3 | 12 | 46 | 67 | -21 | 18 |

| **Division Two** | P | W | D | L | F | A | GD | Pts |
|---|---|---|---|---|---|---|---|---|
| 1 Chasewell Park | 26 | 22 | 2 | 2 | 120 | 31 | 89 | 68 |
| 2 Heyford Athletic Res. | 26 | 19 | 2 | 5 | 92 | 34 | 58 | 59 |
| 3 Chacombe | 26 | 19 | 1 | 6 | 87 | 40 | 47 | 58 |
| 4 Byfield Athletic | 26 | 16 | 4 | 6 | 55 | 39 | 16 | 52 |
| 5 Steeple Aston | 26 | 15 | 1 | 10 | 48 | 48 | 0 | 46 |
| 6 Souldern | 26 | 13 | 5 | 8 | 67 | 51 | 16 | 44 |
| 7 Bishops Itchington Res. | 26 | 12 | 2 | 12 | 54 | 63 | -9 | 38 |
| 8 Swis FC | 26 | 11 | 3 | 12 | 66 | 66 | 0 | 36 |
| 9 Bloxham Res. | 26 | 9 | 2 | 15 | 51 | 66 | -15 | 29 |
| 10 Banbury Sports | 26 | 7 | 4 | 15 | 43 | 67 | -24 | 25 |
| 11 AFC Banbury | 26 | 7 | 2 | 17 | 51 | 91 | -40 | 23 |
| 12 Brill United | 26 | 6 | 3 | 17 | 53 | 87 | -34 | 21 |
| 13 Kings Sutton | 26 | 4 | 3 | 19 | 35 | 79 | -44 | 15 |
| 14 Heyford United | 26 | 4 | 2 | 20 | 42 | 102 | -60 | 14 |

| Division Three | P | W | D | L | F | A | GD | Pts |
|---|---|---|---|---|---|---|---|---|
| 1 Bicester United | 24 | 21 | 1 | 2 | 165 | 22 | 143 | 64 |
| 2 KEA Res. | 24 | 20 | 2 | 2 | 113 | 33 | 80 | 62 |
| 3 Banbury Galaxy | 24 | 15 | 4 | 5 | 84 | 43 | 41 | 49 |
| 4 Priors Marston | 24 | 13 | 2 | 9 | 90 | 57 | 33 | 41 |
| 5 Wroxton Sports Res. | 24 | 12 | 5 | 7 | 45 | 31 | 14 | 41 |
| 6 Bloxbury Athletic | 24 | 13 | 1 | 10 | 74 | 53 | 21 | 40 |
| 7 Bodicote Sports Res. | 24 | 11 | 3 | 10 | 64 | 66 | -2 | 36 |
| 8 Broughton & North Newington Res. | 24 | 7 | 7 | 10 | 52 | 65 | -13 | 28 |
| 9 Swis FC Res. | 24 | 8 | 4 | 12 | 54 | 72 | -18 | 28 |
| 10 Chasewell Park Res. | 24 | 7 | 2 | 15 | 49 | 95 | -46 | 23 |
| 11 Finmere Res. | 24 | 7 | 0 | 17 | 40 | 82 | -42 | 21 |
| 12 Kings Sutton Res. | 24 | 4 | 3 | 17 | 34 | 96 | -62 | 15 |
| 13 Brill United Res. | 24 | 1 | 0 | 23 | 22 | 171 | -149 | 3 |

## BASINGSTOKE & DISTRICT LEAGUE

| **Division One** | P | W | D | L | F | A | GD | Pts |
|---|---|---|---|---|---|---|---|---|
| 1 Hook | 16 | 13 | 0 | 3 | 56 | 19 | 37 | 39 |
| 2 Tadley Calleva 'A' | 16 | 11 | 1 | 4 | 65 | 26 | 39 | 34 |
| 3 Sherborne St John | 16 | 8 | 1 | 7 | 49 | 41 | 8 | 25 |
| 4 TwentyTen | 16 | 7 | 3 | 6 | 32 | 26 | 6 | 24 |
| 5 DJS Telecoms | 16 | 8 | 0 | 8 | 51 | 57 | -6 | 24 |
| 6 Overton United FC 'A' | 16 | 5 | 4 | 7 | 30 | 40 | -10 | 19 |
| 7 Basingstoke Athletic | 16 | 6 | 1 | 9 | 36 | 64 | -28 | 19 |
| 8 Basingstoke Labour Club | 16 | 5 | 1 | 10 | 42 | 69 | -27 | 16 |
| 9 Hampshire Irons | 16 | 3 | 1 | 12 | 27 | 46 | -19 | 10 |

| **Division Two** | P | W | D | L | F | A | GD | Pts |
|---|---|---|---|---|---|---|---|---|
| 1 Tron | 18 | 15 | 3 | 0 | 76 | 21 | 55 | 48 |
| 2 Basingstoke United | 18 | 12 | 2 | 4 | 56 | 31 | 25 | 38 |
| 3 Bounty United (-1) | 18 | 10 | 6 | 2 | 63 | 38 | 25 | 35 |
| 4 Herriard Sports | 18 | 10 | 2 | 6 | 57 | 40 | 17 | 32 |
| 5 AFC Aldermaston 'A' | 18 | 8 | 2 | 8 | 35 | 35 | 0 | 26 |
| 6 Winklebury Wizards | 18 | 7 | 1 | 10 | 40 | 37 | 3 | 22 |
| 7 Overton United 'B' | 18 | 7 | 1 | 10 | 44 | 43 | 1 | 22 |
| 8 TDI Group (-1) | 18 | 4 | 2 | 12 | 32 | 66 | -34 | 13 |
| 9 Basingstoke Athletic Res. | 18 | 4 | 0 | 14 | 21 | 72 | -51 | 12 |
| 10 AFC Berg | 18 | 3 | 1 | 14 | 27 | 68 | -41 | 10 |

## BIRMINGHAM & DISTRICT FOOTBALL LEAGUE

| **Premier Division** | P | W | D | L | F | A | GD | Pts |
|---|---|---|---|---|---|---|---|---|
| 1 Wake Green Amateurs 'A' | 24 | 20 | 2 | 2 | 76 | 29 | 47 | 62 |
| 2 Silhill 'A' | 24 | 15 | 3 | 6 | 64 | 36 | 28 | 48 |
| 3 CPA 1sts | 24 | 13 | 7 | 4 | 50 | 34 | 16 | 46 |
| 4 Kings Heath Old Boys | 24 | 13 | 5 | 6 | 60 | 35 | 25 | 44 |
| 5 Village A | 24 | 13 | 0 | 11 | 58 | 45 | 13 | 39 |
| 6 AFC Somers | 24 | 9 | 7 | 8 | 43 | 46 | -3 | 34 |
| 7 Old Hill | 24 | 11 | 1 | 12 | 48 | 52 | -4 | 34 |
| 8 Premier A | 24 | 9 | 6 | 9 | 44 | 36 | 8 | 33 |
| 9 Athletic Sparkhill | 24 | 9 | 3 | 12 | 52 | 48 | 4 | 30 |
| 10 BT | 24 | 7 | 4 | 13 | 42 | 73 | -31 | 25 |
| 11 Handsworth GSOB 'A' | 24 | 6 | 0 | 18 | 34 | 73 | -39 | 18 |
| 12 Crusaders | 24 | 4 | 5 | 15 | 39 | 72 | -33 | 17 |
| 13 Parkfield Amateurs A F.C | 24 | 4 | 3 | 17 | 40 | 71 | -31 | 15 |

| Division One | P | W | D | L | F | A | GD | Pts |
|---|---|---|---|---|---|---|---|---|
| 1 Birmingham Irish | 21 | 14 | 4 | 3 | 68 | 22 | 46 | 46 |
| 2 Alvechurch Res. | 22 | 12 | 6 | 4 | 54 | 33 | 21 | 42 |
| 3 Old Wulfrunians 'A' | 22 | 12 | 4 | 6 | 53 | 37 | 16 | 40 |
| 4 Silhill B | 22 | 11 | 2 | 9 | 44 | 38 | 6 | 35 |
| 5 Wake Green Amateurs B | 22 | 9 | 7 | 6 | 40 | 41 | -1 | 34 |
| 6 Village B | 22 | 9 | 5 | 8 | 39 | 37 | 2 | 32 |
| 7 Coldlands | 22 | 9 | 5 | 8 | 42 | 44 | -2 | 32 |
| 8 Sutton United A F.C | 22 | 7 | 5 | 10 | 44 | 57 | -13 | 26 |
| 9 CT Shush | 21 | 7 | 3 | 11 | 44 | 55 | -11 | 24 |
| 10 Two Gates (-1) | 21 | 6 | 6 | 9 | 44 | 56 | -12 | 23 |
| 11 BNJS | 21 | 6 | 3 | 12 | 43 | 62 | -19 | 21 |
| 12 Flamengo | 22 | 1 | 4 | 17 | 37 | 70 | -33 | 7 |

| Division Two | P | W | D | L | F | A | GD | Pts |
|---|---|---|---|---|---|---|---|---|
| 1 Bearwood Athletic | 16 | 12 | 2 | 2 | 55 | 19 | 36 | 38 |
| 2 Birmingham Medics A | 16 | 12 | 0 | 4 | 47 | 24 | 23 | 36 |
| 3 Calthorpe United | 16 | 8 | 2 | 6 | 48 | 42 | 6 | 26 |
| 4 Dosthill Rovers | 16 | 7 | 4 | 5 | 44 | 28 | 16 | 25 |
| 5 Boldmere Sports & Social 'A' | 16 | 6 | 2 | 8 | 29 | 32 | -3 | 20 |
| 6 St Georges Warriors | 16 | 6 | 0 | 10 | 32 | 47 | -15 | 18 |
| 7 Castlecroft Rangers | 16 | 5 | 2 | 9 | 29 | 42 | -13 | 17 |
| 8 Shere Punjab (-4) | 16 | 4 | 4 | 8 | 33 | 51 | -18 | 12 |
| 9 Desi | 16 | 4 | 0 | 12 | 36 | 68 | -32 | 12 |

| Division Three | P | W | D | L | F | A | GD | Pts |
|---|---|---|---|---|---|---|---|---|
| 1 Kinver (-3) | 18 | 12 | 3 | 3 | 57 | 18 | 39 | 36 |
| 2 Sportsco | 18 | 10 | 3 | 5 | 52 | 30 | 22 | 33 |
| 3 Halesowen Zion | 18 | 9 | 4 | 5 | 49 | 40 | 9 | 31 |
| 4 Wake Green Amateurs C | 18 | 9 | 1 | 8 | 44 | 44 | 0 | 28 |
| 5 Amanah | 18 | 9 | 0 | 9 | 69 | 47 | 22 | 27 |
| 6 Aston (-1) | 18 | 7 | 2 | 9 | 49 | 55 | -6 | 22 |
| 7 Lodgefield Park | 18 | 6 | 4 | 8 | 31 | 39 | -8 | 22 |
| 8 Cresconians (-3) | 18 | 7 | 2 | 9 | 41 | 48 | -7 | 20 |
| 9 Premier B | 18 | 6 | 2 | 10 | 35 | 59 | -24 | 20 |
| 10 Parkfield Amateurs B | 18 | 3 | 3 | 12 | 35 | 82 | -47 | 12 |

| Division Four | P | W | D | L | F | A | GD | Pts |
|---|---|---|---|---|---|---|---|---|
| 1 Wake Green Amateurs D | 22 | 18 | 1 | 3 | 78 | 25 | 53 | 55 |
| 2 Birmingham Tigers (-3) | 22 | 15 | 3 | 4 | 67 | 25 | 42 | 45 |
| 3 West Hagley | 22 | 14 | 2 | 6 | 69 | 30 | 39 | 44 |
| 4 CPA 2nds | 22 | 13 | 2 | 7 | 44 | 39 | 5 | 41 |
| 5 Silhill C | 22 | 13 | 1 | 8 | 66 | 39 | 27 | 40 |
| 6 Wood Wanderers | 22 | 10 | 2 | 10 | 47 | 41 | 6 | 32 |
| 7 Real Riverside A F.C | 22 | 8 | 2 | 12 | 40 | 57 | -17 | 26 |
| 8 Village D | 22 | 7 | 1 | 14 | 28 | 55 | -27 | 22 |
| 9 Old Wulfrunians B | 22 | 6 | 1 | 15 | 29 | 60 | -31 | 19 |
| 10 Birmingham Citadel (-6) | 22 | 6 | 5 | 11 | 39 | 61 | -22 | 17 |
| 11 Hall Green United | 22 | 5 | 2 | 15 | 42 | 78 | -36 | 17 |
| 12 Sutton United B (-3) | 22 | 5 | 2 | 15 | 28 | 67 | -39 | 14 |

| Division Five | P | W | D | L | F | A | GD | Pts |
|---|---|---|---|---|---|---|---|---|
| 1 Crown F.M.N | 15 | 12 | 2 | 1 | 66 | 15 | 51 | 38 |
| 2 Kingstanding Allstars | 17 | 10 | 2 | 5 | 64 | 55 | 9 | 32 |
| 3 AFC Vesey | 18 | 8 | 4 | 6 | 46 | 41 | 5 | 28 |
| 4 Lapal Athletic | 18 | 7 | 6 | 5 | 36 | 26 | 10 | 27 |
| 5 AFC Glebe United (-3) | 17 | 8 | 3 | 6 | 51 | 41 | 10 | 24 |
| 6 Silhill D | 18 | 6 | 5 | 7 | 60 | 54 | 6 | 23 |
| 7 RL 2012 | 18 | 6 | 5 | 7 | 56 | 58 | -2 | 23 |
| 8 Coldfield Rangers | 18 | 6 | 4 | 8 | 34 | 44 | -10 | 22 |
| 9 Dudley Athletic | 18 | 5 | 0 | 13 | 33 | 73 | -40 | 15 |
| 10 Birchmoor United | 17 | 3 | 1 | 13 | 30 | 69 | -39 | 10 |

| Division Six | P | W | D | L | F | A | GD | Pts |
|---|---|---|---|---|---|---|---|---|
| 1 Chelmsley Wood | 18 | 17 | 0 | 1 | 104 | 14 | 90 | 51 |
| 2 Coleshill North Warwick | 18 | 14 | 1 | 3 | 70 | 26 | 44 | 43 |
| 3 Hampton | 18 | 12 | 0 | 6 | 73 | 27 | 46 | 36 |
| 4 Handsworth GSOB B | 18 | 11 | 3 | 4 | 57 | 38 | 19 | 36 |
| 5 Norton Canes | 18 | 9 | 1 | 8 | 34 | 37 | -3 | 28 |
| 6 Wednesbury Athletic | 18 | 7 | 3 | 8 | 51 | 47 | 4 | 24 |
| 7 Birmingham Medics B | 18 | 5 | 0 | 13 | 41 | 79 | -38 | 15 |
| 8 Garden House Rangers | 18 | 3 | 2 | 13 | 23 | 70 | -47 | 11 |
| 9 Walsall Phoenix (-3) | 18 | 3 | 1 | 14 | 27 | 65 | -38 | 7 |
| 10 Whittington (-3) | 18 | 3 | 1 | 14 | 34 | 111 | -77 | 7 |

| Division Seven | P | W | D | L | F | A | GD | Pts |
|---|---|---|---|---|---|---|---|---|
| 1 Sporting Sandwell | 18 | 15 | 2 | 1 | 48 | 17 | 31 | 47 |
| 2 Real Riverside B | 18 | 14 | 2 | 2 | 71 | 31 | 40 | 44 |
| 3 Wake Green Amateurs E | 17 | 10 | 2 | 5 | 48 | 25 | 23 | 32 |
| 4 FC Birmingham | 18 | 10 | 2 | 6 | 47 | 33 | 14 | 32 |
| 5 Rest (-6) | 17 | 8 | 5 | 4 | 56 | 42 | 14 | 23 |
| 6 Village E (-3) | 18 | 6 | 3 | 9 | 38 | 46 | -8 | 18 |
| 7 Bluepool | 18 | 4 | 4 | 10 | 38 | 59 | -21 | 16 |
| 8 Silhill E | 18 | 3 | 3 | 12 | 31 | 59 | -28 | 12 |
| 9 Manchester Wanderers | 18 | 3 | 2 | 13 | 27 | 61 | -34 | 11 |
| 10 Handsworth GSOB C | 18 | 2 | 3 | 13 | 23 | 54 | -31 | 9 |

| Under 21 League | P | W | D | L | F | A | GD | Pts |
|---|---|---|---|---|---|---|---|---|
| 1 Lichfield City U21 | 16 | 14 | 0 | 2 | 70 | 12 | 58 | 42 |
| 2 Whittington U21 | 16 | 9 | 3 | 4 | 56 | 33 | 23 | 30 |
| 3 Smethwick Raiders | 16 | 8 | 1 | 7 | 41 | 26 | 15 | 25 |
| 4 Cresconians U21 (-3) | 16 | 3 | 3 | 10 | 37 | 82 | -45 | 9 |
| 5 FC Birmingham U21 (-3) | 16 | 2 | 1 | 13 | 27 | 78 | -51 | 4 |

## BISHOP'S STORTFORD, STANSTED & DISTRICT LEAGUE

| Premier Division | P | W | D | L | F | A | GD | Pts |
|---|---|---|---|---|---|---|---|---|
| 1 Atletico Corinthians | 14 | 11 | 1 | 2 | 36 | 11 | 25 | 34 |
| 2 Alemite Athletic | 14 | 10 | 1 | 3 | 49 | 24 | 25 | 31 |
| 3 Northolt | 14 | 10 | 0 | 4 | 46 | 34 | 12 | 30 |
| 4 North Weald | 14 | 8 | 1 | 5 | 42 | 35 | 7 | 25 |
| 5 Town Mead | 14 | 6 | 1 | 7 | 37 | 33 | 4 | 19 |
| 6 Sheering | 14 | 5 | 0 | 9 | 24 | 43 | -19 | 15 |
| 7 Hatfield Heath | 14 | 2 | 0 | 12 | 15 | 41 | -26 | [illegible] |
| 8 Hertfordshire Rangers | 14 | 2 | 0 | 12 | 19 | 47 | -28 | [illegible] |

| ivision One | P | W | D | L | F | A | GD | Pts |
|---|---|---|---|---|---|---|---|---|
| Alemite Athletic Res. | 21 | 15 | 5 | 1 | 48 | 14 | 34 | 50 |
| Avondale Rangers | 21 | 12 | 4 | 5 | 60 | 30 | 30 | 40 |
| Heath Rovers Stansted | 21 | 10 | 3 | 8 | 33 | 31 | 2 | 33 |
| Lower Street | 21 | 10 | 2 | 9 | 59 | 53 | 6 | 32 |
| E F Lakers | 21 | 8 | 5 | 8 | 37 | 55 | -18 | 29 |
| Albury | 21 | 8 | 3 | 10 | 38 | 50 | -12 | 27 |
| Social Club Birchanger | 21 | 6 | 3 | 12 | 40 | 53 | -13 | 21 |
| Sheering Res. | 21 | 2 | 1 | 18 | 21 | 50 | -29 | 7 |

## BLACKBURN & DISTRICT FOOTBALL COMBINATION

| remier Division | P | W | D | L | F | A | GD | Pts |
|---|---|---|---|---|---|---|---|---|
| The Ivy | 24 | 19 | 1 | 4 | 96 | 28 | 68 | 58 |
| Cabin End | 24 | 17 | 1 | 6 | 83 | 34 | 49 | 52 |
| Anchor | 24 | 12 | 2 | 10 | 61 | 70 | -9 | 38 |
| Euro Garages | 24 | 12 | 1 | 11 | 56 | 50 | 6 | 37 |
| Clifton | 24 | 11 | 1 | 12 | 58 | 90 | -32 | 34 |
| Blackburn United | 24 | 10 | 1 | 13 | 40 | 58 | -18 | 31 |
| Rishton United (-3) | 24 | 10 | 3 | 11 | 54 | 37 | 17 | 30 |
| Clayton Park Rangers | 24 | 9 | 1 | 14 | 53 | 69 | -16 | 28 |
| Islington | 24 | 1 | 3 | 20 | 29 | 94 | -65 | 6 |

| vision Two | P | W | D | L | F | A | GD | Pts |
|---|---|---|---|---|---|---|---|---|
| The Ivy Veterans | 22 | 19 | 0 | 3 | 119 | 29 | 90 | 57 |
| Longshaw (-1) | 22 | 18 | 2 | 2 | 133 | 37 | 96 | 55 |
| Blackburn Olympic | 22 | 11 | 3 | 8 | 80 | 71 | 9 | 36 |
| Walker Preston (+2) | 22 | 8 | 5 | 9 | 58 | 72 | -14 | 31 |
| The Lion | 22 | 9 | 1 | 12 | 77 | 76 | 1 | 28 |
| Lord Raglan (-1) | 22 | 12 | 1 | 9 | 68 | 74 | -6 | 36 |
| Blackburn United Res. (-5) | 22 | 11 | 4 | 7 | 58 | 46 | 12 | 32 |
| Rishton Rovers (+2) | 22 | 5 | 2 | 15 | 44 | 61 | -17 | 19 |
| Worth Avenue (-3) | 22 | 5 | 0 | 17 | 45 | 103 | -58 | 12 |
| Blackburn Eagles (-3) | 22 | 3 | 0 | 19 | 38 | 151 | -113 | 6 |

## BOURNEMOUTH HAYWARD SATURDAY LEAGUE

| emier Division | P | W | D | L | F | A | GD | Pts |
|---|---|---|---|---|---|---|---|---|
| Bournemouth Manor | 20 | 20 | 0 | 0 | 73 | 16 | 57 | 60 |
| Bournemouth Electric | 20 | 15 | 3 | 2 | 60 | 28 | 32 | 48 |
| Bournemouth Sports | 20 | 15 | 1 | 4 | 65 | 17 | 48 | 46 |
| Allendale | 20 | 10 | 3 | 7 | 45 | 47 | -2 | 33 |
| Parley Sports | 20 | 7 | 6 | 7 | 47 | 57 | -10 | 27 |
| Ferndown Sports (-1) | 20 | 5 | 5 | 10 | 33 | 57 | -24 | 19 |
| Westover Bournemouth | 20 | 5 | 3 | 12 | 33 | 44 | -11 | 18 |
| Hamworthy Recreation | 20 | 5 | 2 | 13 | 37 | 51 | -14 | 17 |
| Gotham | 20 | 4 | 4 | 12 | 24 | 55 | -31 | 16 |
| Alderholt (-1) | 20 | 3 | 6 | 11 | 24 | 40 | -16 | 14 |
| Merley Cobham Res. | 20 | 2 | 5 | 13 | 31 | 60 | -29 | 11 |

| Division One | P | W | D | L | F | A | GD | Pts |
|---|---|---|---|---|---|---|---|---|
| 1 AFC Burton | 16 | 12 | 2 | 2 | 48 | 21 | 27 | 38 |
| 2 Bournemouth Manor Res. | 16 | 11 | 2 | 3 | 45 | 23 | 22 | 35 |
| 3 Redlynch and Woodfalls | 16 | 8 | 1 | 7 | 40 | 27 | 13 | 25 |
| 4 Bournemouth Sports Res. | 16 | 7 | 3 | 6 | 34 | 27 | 7 | 24 |
| 5 Sway Res. | 16 | 6 | 3 | 7 | 32 | 31 | 1 | 21 |
| 6 Holt Utd Res. | 16 | 6 | 3 | 7 | 21 | 35 | -14 | 21 |
| 7 Bournemouth Poppies Res. | 16 | 4 | 5 | 7 | 30 | 28 | 2 | 17 |
| 8 Bisterne United | 16 | 5 | 1 | 10 | 36 | 51 | -15 | 16 |
| 9 Ferndown Sports Res. | 16 | 2 | 2 | 12 | 16 | 59 | -43 | 8 |

| Division Two | P | W | D | L | F | A | GD | Pts |
|---|---|---|---|---|---|---|---|---|
| 1 Portcastrian | 20 | 15 | 4 | 1 | 70 | 28 | 42 | 49 |
| 2 Bournemouth Electric Res. | 20 | 14 | 1 | 5 | 71 | 38 | 33 | 43 |
| 3 Queens Park Athletic | 20 | 14 | 1 | 5 | 61 | 31 | 30 | 43 |
| 4 Lower Parkstone CFC | 20 | 12 | 3 | 5 | 65 | 25 | 40 | 39 |
| 5 Alderholt Res. | 20 | 10 | 1 | 9 | 34 | 42 | -8 | 31 |
| 6 Mudeford Mens Club | 20 | 8 | 4 | 8 | 48 | 49 | -1 | 28 |
| 7 Allendale Res. | 20 | 6 | 5 | 9 | 54 | 48 | 6 | 23 |
| 8 Poole Borough Res. | 20 | 6 | 0 | 14 | 29 | 41 | -12 | 18 |
| 9 Westover Bournemouth Res. | 20 | 6 | 0 | 14 | 30 | 65 | -35 | 18 |
| 10 West Howe | 20 | 4 | 3 | 13 | 24 | 50 | -26 | 15 |
| 11 Talbot Rise | 20 | 4 | 0 | 16 | 25 | 94 | -69 | 12 |

| Division Three | P | W | D | L | F | A | GD | Pts |
|---|---|---|---|---|---|---|---|---|
| 1 Throop United | 18 | 15 | 2 | 1 | 72 | 24 | 48 | 47 |
| 2 Boldre Royals | 18 | 13 | 2 | 3 | 74 | 28 | 46 | 41 |
| 3 Fordingbridge Turks | 18 | 8 | 6 | 4 | 51 | 29 | 22 | 30 |
| 4 Bisterne United Res. | 18 | 9 | 2 | 7 | 46 | 44 | 2 | 29 |
| 5 New Milton Eagles | 18 | 8 | 3 | 7 | 44 | 49 | -5 | 27 |
| 6 Milford | 18 | 6 | 6 | 6 | 38 | 46 | -8 | 24 |
| 7 Bournemouth Electric A | 18 | 3 | 7 | 8 | 24 | 45 | -21 | 16 |
| 8 Bournemouth Manor A (-3) | 18 | 5 | 3 | 10 | 36 | 55 | -19 | 15 |
| 9 Cherry Bees | 18 | 3 | 4 | 11 | 34 | 57 | -23 | 13 |
| 10 Magpies | 18 | 2 | 1 | 15 | 27 | 69 | -42 | 7 |

| Division Four | P | W | D | L | F | A | GD | Pts |
|---|---|---|---|---|---|---|---|---|
| 1 AFC Burton Res. | 18 | 11 | 1 | 6 | 58 | 42 | 16 | 34 |
| 2 AFC Bransgore | 18 | 9 | 6 | 3 | 52 | 35 | 17 | 33 |
| 3 Bransgore Utd | 18 | 9 | 5 | 4 | 53 | 39 | 14 | 32 |
| 4 New Milton Rovers | 18 | 8 | 5 | 5 | 53 | 36 | 17 | 29 |
| 5 FC Barolo | 18 | 9 | 2 | 7 | 43 | 37 | 6 | 29 |
| 6 Milford Club AFC | 18 | 7 | 4 | 7 | 44 | 38 | 6 | 25 |
| 7 Alderholt A | 18 | 6 | 5 | 7 | 34 | 41 | -7 | 23 |
| 8 Redlynch and Woodfalls Res. (-3) | 18 | 7 | 3 | 8 | 53 | 42 | 11 | 21 |
| 9 Burley | 18 | 5 | 5 | 8 | 32 | 46 | -14 | 20 |
| 10 Parkstone Athletic | 18 | 1 | 0 | 17 | 25 | 91 | -66 | 3 |

# NATIONAL STRIKE FORCE - TOP 106!

on this page and continued on pages 672 and 692

| | Club | League | Lge | FAC | FAT | Pens | Hat Tricks | Consec Scoring Games | Scoring Games | Total |
|---|---|---|---|---|---|---|---|---|---|---|
| Sam Higgins | East Thurrock United | Isthmian Prem | 38 | 5 | 2 | 9 | 3 | 8 | 28 | 45 |
| Jason Prior | Bognor Regis Town | Isthmian Prem | 35 | 2 | 4 | 7 | 4 | 5 | 25 | 41 |
| Padraig Amond | Grimsby Town | National Prem | 30+1PO | 4 | 2 | 3 | 2 | 5 | 24 | 37 |
| Danny Rowe | AFC Fylde | National North | 23+1PO | 3 | 7 | 1 | 3 | 7 | 24 | 34 |
| Danny Mills | Whitehawk | National South | 23+2PO | 8 | | | 2 | 6 | 25 | 33 |
| Karl Hawley | Stourbridge | N.P.L. | 27 | 2 | 2 | 4 | | 4 | 28 | 31 |
| Kristian Dennis | Macclesfield Town | National Prem | 22 | 3 | 5 | 4 | 1 | 5 | 22 | 30 |
| Matt Godden | Ebbsfleet United | National South | 26 | 1 | 3 | | 3 | 7 | 19 | 30 |
| Dan Holman | Woking & Cheltenham T | National Prem | 14+16 | | | 0+1 | | 3+3 | 10+10 | 30 |
| Martin Pilkington | Ashton United | N.P.L. | 25 | 2 | 2 | 1 | | 2 | 22 | 29 |
| Justin Bennett | Gosport Borough | National South | 23 | 5 | | 2 | 3 | 3 | 18 | 28 |
| Elliott Buchanan | Bishop's Stortford | National South | 28 | | | 5 | 3 | 3 | 17 | 28 |
| Nathan Elder | Tonbridge Angels | Isthmian Prem | 24 | 2 | 1 | | | 4 | 22 | 27 |
| Pat Cox | Staines Town | Isthmian Prem | 17 | 8 | 1 | 7 | 2 | 4 | 17 | 26 |
| Robbie Dale | Blyth Spartans | N.P.L. | 23 | | 2 | 5 | 1 | 3 | 18 | 25 |
| Charlie Griffin | Cirencester Town | Southern Prem | 20 | 2 | 3 | 1 | 1 | 3 | 18 | 25 |
| Ross Hannah | Chester | National Prem | 22 | | 3 | 2 | | 3 | 19 | 25 |
| Danny Wright | Cheltenham Town | National Prem | 22 | 3 | | 3 | | 3 | 20 | 25 |
| Bradley Bubb | Oxford City | National South | 18 | 2 | 4 | 5 | | 4 | 22 | 24 |
| Liam Hardy | Buxton | N.P.L. | 19 | 4 | 1 | 7 | 3 | 4 | 16 | 24 |
| Tom Meecham | St Neots Town | Southern Prem | 22 | 2 | | 3 | 1 | 4 | 16 | 24 |
| Dayle Southwell | Boston United | National North | 24 | | | 5 | 1 | 3 | 20 | 24 |
| Martin Tuohy | Canvey Island | Isthmian Prem | 24 | | | | | 3 | 19 | 24 |
| Brendon Daniels | Harrogate Town | National North. | 21 | 2 | | 2 | | 5 | 18 | 23 |
| Andy Cook | Barrow | National Prem | 23 | | | 1 | | 2 | 20 | 23 |
| Daniel Mitchley | Skelm Utd & Marine | N.P.L. | 9+13 | | 0+1 | 2+3 | | 7+4 | 9+14 | 23 |
| Stefan Payne | Dover Athletic | National Prem | 18 | 1 | 4 | | | 2 | 18 | 23 |
| Nat Pinney | Eastbourne Borough | National South | 18 | 3 | 2 | 1 | | 2 | 17 | 23 |
| Matt Rhead | Lincoln City | National Prem | 20 | 3 | | 5 | | 3 | 16 | 23 |
| Michael Roberts | Whitby Town | N.P.L. | 23 | | | 7 | 1 | 3 | 18 | 23 |
| Andy Sandell | Chippenham Town | Southern Prem | 22 | 1 | | 5 | | 4 | 15 | 23 |
| Scott Spencer | Hyde United | N.P.L. | 20 | 3 | | 2 | 3 | 6 | 14 | 23 |
| Corey Whitely | Enfield Town | Isthmian Prem | 21 | | 2 | 2 | 1 | 4 | 16 | 23 |
| Scott Wilson | Weston-s-Mare | National South | 18 | 1 | 4 | 2 | 1 | 3 | 19 | 23 |
| Luke Benbow | Rushall Olympic | N.P.L. | 20 | 1 | 1 | 2 | | 6 | 17 | 22 |

## BRIGHTON, WORTHING & DISTRICT LEAGUE

| Premier Division | P | W | D | L | F | A | GD | Pts |
|---|---|---|---|---|---|---|---|---|
| 1 Worthing Leisure | 20 | 16 | 0 | 4 | 64 | 22 | 42 | 48 |
| 2 Sompting | 20 | 14 | 1 | 5 | 59 | 24 | 35 | 43 |
| 3 Worthing BCOB | 20 | 13 | 3 | 4 | 72 | 29 | 43 | 42 |
| 4 Goring Cricket Club | 20 | 12 | 3 | 5 | 54 | 30 | 24 | 39 |
| 5 Brighton Electricity | 20 | 11 | 3 | 6 | 42 | 37 | 5 | 36 |
| 6 George & Dragon | 20 | 10 | 2 | 8 | 45 | 41 | 4 | 32 |
| 7 Romans United | 20 | 7 | 1 | 12 | 34 | 29 | 5 | 22 |
| 8 C.C.K | 20 | 7 | 1 | 12 | 36 | 70 | -34 | 22 |
| 9 Ovingdean | 20 | 6 | 2 | 12 | 35 | 57 | -22 | 20 |
| 10 Fiveways | 20 | 5 | 1 | 14 | 26 | 44 | -18 | 16 |
| 11 Boys Brigade Old Boys | 20 | 0 | 1 | 19 | 22 | 106 | -84 | 1 |

| Division One East | P | W | D | L | F | A | GD | Pts |
|---|---|---|---|---|---|---|---|---|
| Southwick Rangers A | 24 | 17 | 6 | 1 | 100 | 29 | 71 | 57 |
| Midway | 24 | 18 | 3 | 3 | 88 | 34 | 54 | 57 |
| Hangleton Athletic | 24 | 17 | 5 | 2 | 91 | 27 | 64 | 56 |
| Woodingdean Wanderers | 24 | 16 | 4 | 4 | 80 | 26 | 54 | 52 |
| The Lectern | 24 | 13 | 4 | 7 | 91 | 43 | 48 | 43 |
| Rottingdean Village Res. | 24 | 14 | 0 | 10 | 72 | 55 | 17 | 42 |
| The View | 24 | 11 | 3 | 10 | 79 | 45 | 34 | 36 |
| Unity | 24 | 10 | 2 | 12 | 60 | 47 | 13 | 32 |
| St Peters | 24 | 9 | 0 | 15 | 39 | 78 | -39 | 27 |
| 10 Racing King & Queen | 24 | 7 | 3 | 14 | 42 | 37 | 5 | 24 |
| 11 Southwick Rangers A | 24 | 6 | 0 | 18 | 39 | 120 | -81 | 18 |
| 12 C.C.K II | 24 | 2 | 1 | 21 | 43 | 118 | -75 | 7 |
| 13 Lansdowne United | 24 | 0 | 1 | 23 | 13 | 178 | -165 | 1 |

| Division One West | P | W | D | L | F | A | GD | Pts |
|---|---|---|---|---|---|---|---|---|
| Worthing Dynamos | 16 | 13 | 1 | 2 | 66 | 17 | 49 | 40 |
| Worthing Leisure II | 16 | 9 | 3 | 4 | 63 | 28 | 35 | 30 |
| Sompting II | 16 | 9 | 3 | 4 | 51 | 36 | 15 | 30 |
| Northbrook | 16 | 7 | 3 | 6 | 47 | 30 | 17 | 24 |
| Hangleton Athletic II | 16 | 8 | 0 | 8 | 45 | 53 | -8 | 24 |
| Real Rustington | 16 | 6 | 4 | 6 | 36 | 39 | -3 | 22 |
| Broadwater Athletic | 16 | 6 | 1 | 9 | 35 | 61 | -26 | 19 |
| Maybridge | 16 | 4 | 2 | 10 | 28 | 49 | -21 | 14 |
| St Marys | 16 | 1 | 1 | 14 | 20 | 78 | -58 | 4 |

| Division Two West | P | W | D | L | F | A | GD | Pts |
|---|---|---|---|---|---|---|---|---|
| AFC Sparta | 18 | 14 | 2 | 2 | 65 | 18 | 47 | 44 |
| Worthing Town | 18 | 12 | 2 | 4 | 40 | 33 | 7 | 38 |
| George & Dragon II | 18 | 11 | 0 | 7 | 80 | 46 | 34 | 33 |
| Worthing BCOB II | 18 | 10 | 2 | 6 | 47 | 36 | 11 | 32 |
| AFC Broadwater | 18 | 9 | 4 | 5 | 50 | 39 | 11 | 31 |
| Adur Athletic | 18 | 8 | 2 | 8 | 46 | 48 | -2 | 26 |
| Goring Cricket Club II | 18 | 7 | 2 | 9 | 49 | 45 | 4 | 23 |
| Del United | 18 | 4 | 3 | 11 | 40 | 68 | -28 | 15 |
| FC MSR All Stars | 18 | 2 | 6 | 10 | 29 | 54 | -25 | 12 |
| Goring St Theresas | 18 | 0 | 3 | 15 | 23 | 82 | -59 | 3 |

## BRISTOL AND DISTRICT LEAGUE

| Senior Division | P | W | D | L | F | A | GD | Pts |
|---|---|---|---|---|---|---|---|---|
| 1 Chipping Sodbury Town Res. | 26 | 17 | 4 | 5 | 72 | 51 | 21 | 55 |
| 2 De Veys | 26 | 16 | 4 | 6 | 89 | 47 | 42 | 52 |
| 3 St Pancras | 26 | 15 | 6 | 5 | 80 | 49 | 31 | 51 |
| 4 Bristol Barcelona | 26 | 14 | 5 | 7 | 70 | 42 | 28 | 47 |
| 5 Bradley Stoke Town | 26 | 13 | 5 | 8 | 62 | 45 | 17 | 44 |
| 6 Pucklechurch Sports | 26 | 13 | 3 | 10 | 64 | 51 | 13 | 42 |
| 7 Shirehampton Res. | 26 | 12 | 3 | 11 | 71 | 52 | 19 | 39 |
| 8 Wick Res. | 26 | 11 | 4 | 11 | 55 | 75 | -20 | 37 |
| 9 Iron Acton | 26 | 11 | 3 | 12 | 64 | 68 | -4 | 36 |
| 10 Mendip Broadwalk Res. | 26 | 9 | 4 | 13 | 45 | 61 | -16 | 31 |
| 11 Longwell Green Sports 'A' | 26 | 9 | 3 | 14 | 49 | 70 | -21 | 30 |
| 12 Lebeq (Saturday) FC.Res. | 26 | 8 | 2 | 16 | 58 | 92 | -34 | 26 |
| 13 Patchway Town Res. | 26 | 6 | 0 | 20 | 25 | 49 | -24 | 18 |
| 14 Rangeworthy | 26 | 3 | 4 | 19 | 36 | 88 | -52 | 13 |

| **Division One** | P | W | D | L | F | A | GD | Pts |
|---|---|---|---|---|---|---|---|---|
| 1 Stapleton | 24 | 18 | 3 | 3 | 71 | 27 | 44 | 57 |
| 2 Cribbs 'A' | 24 | 17 | 4 | 3 | 60 | 25 | 35 | 55 |
| 3 Nicholas Wanderers Res. | 24 | 15 | 2 | 7 | 61 | 34 | 27 | 47 |
| 4 AEK Boco 'A' | 24 | 13 | 7 | 4 | 67 | 36 | 31 | 46 |
| 5 Port of Bristol | 24 | 14 | 2 | 8 | 80 | 42 | 38 | 44 |
| 6 Hanham Athletic Res. | 24 | 13 | 4 | 7 | 54 | 24 | 30 | 43 |
| 7 Frys Club 'A' | 24 | 11 | 0 | 13 | 49 | 60 | -11 | 33 |
| 8 Henbury Res. | 24 | 9 | 2 | 13 | 38 | 49 | -11 | 29 |
| 9 Greyfriars Athletic Res. | 24 | 8 | 1 | 15 | 43 | 58 | -15 | 25 |
| 10 Totterdown United Res. | 24 | 7 | 4 | 13 | 29 | 51 | -22 | 25 |
| 11 Frampton Athletic Res. | 24 | 5 | 3 | 16 | 34 | 64 | -30 | 18 |
| 12 Seymour United Res. | 24 | 5 | 2 | 17 | 27 | 86 | -59 | 17 |
| 13 Soundwell Victoria | 24 | 3 | 2 | 19 | 32 | 89 | -57 | 11 |

| **Division Two** | P | W | D | L | F | A | GD | Pts |
|---|---|---|---|---|---|---|---|---|
| 1 Hillfields Old Boys | 28 | 23 | 2 | 3 | 126 | 39 | 87 | 71 |
| 2 Made for Ever | 28 | 21 | 3 | 4 | 75 | 30 | 45 | 66 |
| 3 Staple Hill Orient | 28 | 21 | 0 | 7 | 83 | 36 | 47 | 63 |
| 4 Horfield United | 28 | 14 | 3 | 11 | 63 | 58 | 5 | 45 |
| 5 Yate Athletic | 27 | 14 | 3 | 10 | 64 | 65 | -1 | 45 |
| 6 Hartcliffe | 28 | 13 | 3 | 12 | 54 | 68 | -14 | 42 |
| 7 Iron Acton Res. | 28 | 12 | 5 | 11 | 56 | 55 | 1 | 41 |
| 8 Bendix | 28 | 11 | 4 | 13 | 64 | 78 | -14 | 37 |
| 9 Old Sodbury Res. (-1) | 28 | 10 | 7 | 11 | 58 | 53 | 5 | 36 |
| 10 Chipping Sodbury Town 'A' | 28 | 11 | 3 | 14 | 43 | 51 | -8 | 36 |
| 11 Highridge United Res. | 27 | 10 | 4 | 13 | 58 | 54 | 4 | 34 |
| 12 Nicholas Wanderers 'A' | 28 | 9 | 5 | 14 | 50 | 77 | -27 | 32 |
| 13 Olveston United Res. | 27 | 7 | 2 | 18 | 49 | 63 | -14 | 23 |
| 14 Hambrook Res. | 28 | 2 | 7 | 19 | 18 | 67 | -49 | 13 |
| 15 Bristol Barcelona Res. | 27 | 3 | 3 | 21 | 31 | 98 | -67 | 12 |

| Division Three | P | W | D | L | F | A | GD | Pts |
|---|---|---|---|---|---|---|---|---|
| 1 Stoke Lane | 26 | 20 | 5 | 1 | 107 | 42 | 65 | 65 |
| 2 Sea Mills Park Res. | 26 | 19 | 1 | 6 | 97 | 37 | 60 | 58 |
| 3 Tormarton | 26 | 17 | 4 | 5 | 65 | 32 | 33 | 55 |
| 4 Stapleton Res. | 26 | 17 | 4 | 5 | 70 | 44 | 26 | 55 |
| 5 Westerleigh Sports | 26 | 15 | 6 | 5 | 62 | 34 | 28 | 51 |
| 6 Bromley Heath United (Fishponds) | 26 | 14 | 3 | 9 | 59 | 48 | 11 | 45 |
| 7 Wick 'A' | 26 | 10 | 6 | 10 | 47 | 49 | -2 | 36 |
| 8 Bradley Stoke Town Res. | 26 | 11 | 0 | 15 | 71 | 58 | 13 | 33 |
| 9 Talbot Knowle United | 26 | 9 | 5 | 12 | 48 | 63 | -15 | 32 |
| 10 Frys Club 'B' | 26 | 8 | 5 | 13 | 47 | 45 | 2 | 29 |
| 11 Pucklechurch Sports Res. | 26 | 8 | 2 | 16 | 45 | 50 | -5 | 26 |
| 12 Roman Glass St George 'A' | 26 | 5 | 4 | 17 | 42 | 83 | -41 | 19 |
| 13 Greyfriars Athletic 'A' | 26 | 2 | 4 | 20 | 28 | 102 | -74 | 10 |
| 14 DRG Frenchay Res. | 26 | 2 | 1 | 23 | 27 | 128 | -101 | 7 |

| Division Four | P | W | D | L | F | A | GD | Pts |
|---|---|---|---|---|---|---|---|---|
| 1 Rangeworthy Res. | 24 | 16 | 2 | 6 | 72 | 50 | 22 | 50 |
| 2 Lawrence Rovers Res. | 24 | 14 | 6 | 4 | 70 | 33 | 37 | 48 |
| 3 Mendip Broadwalk 'A' | 24 | 13 | 5 | 6 | 57 | 42 | 15 | 44 |
| 4 Cribbs 'B' | 24 | 13 | 3 | 8 | 59 | 40 | 19 | 42 |
| 5 Crosscourt United | 22 | 12 | 4 | 6 | 63 | 52 | 11 | 40 |
| 6 Iron Acton 'A' | 24 | 12 | 4 | 8 | 72 | 70 | 2 | 40 |
| 7 Stanton Drew Res. | 24 | 12 | 1 | 11 | 58 | 52 | 6 | 37 |
| 8 Highridge United 'A' | 23 | 11 | 3 | 9 | 49 | 53 | -4 | 36 |
| 9 Yate Athletic Res. | 24 | 10 | 1 | 13 | 47 | 49 | -2 | 31 |
| 10 Frampton Ath 'A' | 23 | 6 | 3 | 14 | 43 | 63 | -20 | 21 |
| 11 Port of Bristol Res. | 22 | 4 | 4 | 14 | 38 | 50 | -12 | 16 |
| 12 Cutters Friday | 22 | 5 | 1 | 16 | 33 | 71 | -38 | 16 |
| 13 Sea Mills Park 'A' | 22 | 3 | 3 | 16 | 28 | 64 | -36 | 12 |

| Division Five | P | W | D | L | F | A | GD | Pts |
|---|---|---|---|---|---|---|---|---|
| 1 Winterbourne United 'A' | 26 | 20 | 2 | 4 | 120 | 36 | 84 | 62 |
| 2 De Veys Res. | 26 | 20 | 1 | 5 | 99 | 48 | 51 | 61 |
| 3 Real Thornbury Res. | 26 | 19 | 3 | 4 | 78 | 36 | 42 | 60 |
| 4 Hillfields OB Res. | 26 | 17 | 1 | 8 | 98 | 69 | 29 | 52 |
| 5 Longwell Green 'B' | 26 | 15 | 3 | 8 | 68 | 49 | 19 | 48 |
| 6 Shaftesbury Crusade Res. | 26 | 14 | 5 | 7 | 84 | 51 | 33 | 47 |
| 7 Hanham Athletic Colts | 26 | 12 | 3 | 11 | 59 | 36 | 23 | 39 |
| 8 Seymour United 'A' | 26 | 10 | 2 | 14 | 67 | 68 | -1 | 32 |
| 9 Bradley Stoke 'A' | 26 | 9 | 4 | 13 | 54 | 82 | -28 | 31 |
| 10 AFC Grace | 26 | 8 | 4 | 14 | 53 | 75 | -22 | 28 |
| 11 Bristol Barcelona 'A' | 26 | 8 | 3 | 15 | 52 | 63 | -11 | 27 |
| 12 Brimsham Green Res. | 26 | 7 | 2 | 17 | 40 | 77 | -37 | 23 |
| 13 Greyfriars Athletic 'B' | 26 | 2 | 4 | 20 | 27 | 128 | -101 | 10 |
| 14 Bristol City Deaf | 26 | 1 | 3 | 22 | 18 | 99 | -81 | 6 |

## BRISTOL DOWNS ASSOCIATION FOOTBALL LEAGUE

| Division One | P | W | D | L | F | A | GD | Pts |
|---|---|---|---|---|---|---|---|---|
| 1 Torpedo | 26 | 18 | 6 | 2 | 69 | 26 | 43 | 60 |
| 2 Ashley | 26 | 19 | 3 | 4 | 65 | 23 | 42 | 60 |
| 3 Clifton St Vincents | 26 | 16 | 7 | 3 | 69 | 29 | 40 | 55 |
| 4 Sneyd Park | 26 | 14 | 7 | 5 | 62 | 36 | 26 | 49 |
| 5 Old Cliftonians | 26 | 13 | 5 | 8 | 60 | 40 | 20 | 44 |
| 6 Wellington Wanderers | 26 | 13 | 3 | 10 | 69 | 58 | 11 | 42 |
| 7 AFC Bohemia | 26 | 9 | 6 | 11 | 45 | 41 | 4 | 33 |
| 8 Easton Cowboys | 26 | 9 | 5 | 12 | 51 | 57 | -6 | 32 |
| 9 Saints Old Boys | 26 | 8 | 6 | 12 | 48 | 73 | -25 | 3[illegible] |
| 10 Portland Old Boys | 26 | 8 | 4 | 14 | 40 | 63 | -23 | 2[illegible] |
| 11 Sporting Greyhound | 26 | 5 | 7 | 14 | 33 | 59 | -26 | 22 |
| 12 St Andrews | 26 | 5 | 6 | 15 | 51 | 77 | -26 | 2[illegible] |
| 13 Jamaica Bell | 26 | 4 | 5 | 17 | 33 | 73 | -40 | 1[illegible] |
| 14 DAC Beachcroft | 26 | 3 | 6 | 17 | 32 | 72 | -40 | 15 |

| Division Two | P | W | D | L | F | A | GD | Pts |
|---|---|---|---|---|---|---|---|---|
| 1 Old Elizabethans AFC | 26 | 20 | 3 | 3 | 126 | 38 | 88 | 6[illegible] |
| 2 Torpedo Res. | 26 | 19 | 5 | 2 | 98 | 20 | 78 | 6[illegible] |
| 3 Sneyd Park Res. | 26 | 17 | 6 | 3 | 65 | 26 | 39 | 5[illegible] |
| 4 Jersey Rangers | 26 | 16 | 2 | 8 | 87 | 58 | 29 | 5[illegible] |
| 5 Clifton St Vincents Res. | 26 | 15 | 5 | 6 | 64 | 46 | 18 | 5[illegible] |
| 6 Evergreen | 26 | 12 | 4 | 10 | 72 | 56 | 16 | 4[illegible] |
| 7 Clifton Rockets | 26 | 11 | 4 | 11 | 64 | 66 | -2 | 3[illegible] |
| 8 Saints Old Boys Res. | 26 | 10 | 5 | 11 | 65 | 62 | 3 | 3[illegible] |
| 9 Tebby AFC | 26 | 9 | 4 | 13 | 41 | 56 | -15 | 3[illegible] |
| 10 Easton Cowboys Res. | 26 | 7 | 4 | 15 | 41 | 78 | -37 | 2[illegible] |
| 11 Lion FC | 26 | 6 | 5 | 15 | 33 | 79 | -46 | 2[illegible] |
| 12 Retainers | 26 | 6 | 4 | 16 | 53 | 73 | -20 | 2[illegible] |
| 13 Greens Park Rangers | 26 | 2 | 5 | 19 | 33 | 94 | -61 | 1[illegible] |
| 14 Bengal Tigers | 26 | 3 | 2 | 21 | 49 | 139 | -90 | 1[illegible] |

| Division Three | P | W | D | L | F | A | GD | Pts |
|---|---|---|---|---|---|---|---|---|
| 1 Sneyd Park A | 26 | 18 | 5 | 3 | 73 | 20 | 53 | 5[illegible] |
| 2 Torpedo A | 26 | 15 | 7 | 4 | 83 | 43 | 40 | 5[illegible] |
| 3 Durdham Down Adult School | 26 | 14 | 8 | 4 | 64 | 34 | 30 | [illegible] |
| 4 Sporting Greyhound Res. | 26 | 12 | 6 | 8 | 66 | 40 | 26 | [illegible] |
| 5 Clifton St Vincents A | 26 | 12 | 6 | 8 | 57 | 44 | 13 | [illegible] |
| 6 Ashley Res. | 26 | 12 | 4 | 10 | 56 | 54 | 2 | [illegible] |
| 7 Helios FC | 26 | 9 | 6 | 11 | 70 | 63 | 7 | [illegible] |
| 8 Portland Old Boys Res. | 26 | 9 | 6 | 11 | 59 | 60 | -1 | [illegible] |
| 9 Old Cliftonians Res. | 26 | 7 | 11 | 8 | 54 | 57 | -3 | [illegible] |
| 10 Clifton Rockets Res. | 26 | 9 | 3 | 14 | 51 | 79 | -28 | [illegible] |
| 11 Corinthians | 26 | 9 | 2 | 15 | 60 | 63 | -3 | [illegible] |
| 12 West Town United | 26 | 8 | 4 | 14 | 54 | 74 | -20 | [illegible] |
| 13 Clifton Vale | 26 | 5 | 5 | 16 | 38 | 106 | -68 | [illegible] |
| 14 Cotham Old Boys | 26 | 5 | 3 | 18 | 42 | 90 | -48 | [illegible] |

| | Division Four | P | W | D | L | F | A | GD | Pts |
|---|---|---|---|---|---|---|---|---|---|
| 1 | Saints Old Boys A | 22 | 17 | 3 | 2 | 73 | 25 | 48 | 54 |
| 2 | Old Elizabethans Res. | 22 | 17 | 2 | 3 | 70 | 31 | 39 | 53 |
| 3 | Sneyd Park B | 22 | 12 | 3 | 7 | 63 | 36 | 27 | 39 |
| 4 | Tebby AFC Res. | 22 | 9 | 5 | 8 | 63 | 53 | 10 | 32 |
| 5 | Torpedo B | 22 | 9 | 5 | 8 | 45 | 55 | -10 | 32 |
| 6 | Lion FC Res. | 22 | 9 | 4 | 9 | 47 | 51 | -4 | 31 |
| 7 | Jersey Rangers Res. | 22 | 8 | 3 | 11 | 61 | 59 | 2 | 27 |
| 8 | Racing Mouse | 22 | 7 | 5 | 10 | 49 | 55 | -6 | 26 |
| 9 | Clifton St Vincents B | 22 | 6 | 7 | 9 | 53 | 55 | -2 | 25 |
| 10 | NCSF United | 22 | 4 | 8 | 10 | 33 | 65 | -32 | 20 |
| 11 | Retainers Res. | 22 | 5 | 2 | 15 | 43 | 64 | -21 | 17 |
| 12 | Durdham Down Adult School Res. | 22 | 4 | 3 | 15 | 21 | 72 | -51 | 15 |

## BRISTOL PREMIER COMBINATION

| remier Division | P | W | D | L | F | A | GD | Pts |
|---|---|---|---|---|---|---|---|---|
| Mendip Broadwalk | 24 | 15 | 5 | 4 | 75 | 30 | 45 | 50 |
| Cribbs Res. | 24 | 15 | 3 | 6 | 68 | 37 | 31 | 48 |
| Highridge United | 24 | 12 | 6 | 6 | 51 | 36 | 15 | 42 |
| Old Sodbury | 24 | 12 | 3 | 9 | 51 | 41 | 10 | 39 |
| Winterbourne United | 24 | 11 | 5 | 8 | 63 | 46 | 17 | 38 |
| Wick | 24 | 11 | 4 | 9 | 52 | 51 | 1 | 37 |
| Olveston United | 24 | 10 | 4 | 10 | 42 | 49 | -7 | 34 |
| Hallen Res. | 24 | 10 | 2 | 12 | 46 | 40 | 6 | 32 |
| Totterdown United | 24 | 8 | 4 | 12 | 46 | 45 | 1 | 28 |
| Longwell Green Res. | 24 | 7 | 5 | 12 | 33 | 58 | -25 | 26 |
| Bitton Res. | 24 | 8 | 1 | 15 | 38 | 85 | -47 | 25 |
| Lebeq (Saturday) FC | 24 | 7 | 2 | 15 | 51 | 79 | -28 | 23 |
| Bristol Manor Farm Res. | 24 | 6 | 4 | 14 | 47 | 66 | -19 | 22 |

| remier One | P | W | D | L | F | A | GD | Pts |
|---|---|---|---|---|---|---|---|---|
| Talbot Knowle United | 26 | 19 | 5 | 2 | 60 | 21 | 39 | 62 |
| A.E.K. Boco Res. | 26 | 18 | 5 | 3 | 81 | 22 | 59 | 59 |
| Sea Mills Park | 26 | 17 | 7 | 2 | 83 | 30 | 53 | 58 |
| Real Thornbury | 26 | 16 | 3 | 7 | 76 | 45 | 31 | 51 |
| Shaftesbury Crusade | 26 | 13 | 7 | 6 | 73 | 46 | 27 | 46 |
| Greyfriars Athletic | 26 | 10 | 9 | 7 | 58 | 42 | 16 | 39 |
| Frampton Athletic | 26 | 11 | 6 | 9 | 54 | 48 | 6 | 39 |
| Hambrook | 26 | 10 | 6 | 10 | 36 | 39 | -3 | 36 |
| Seymour United | 26 | 11 | 3 | 12 | 41 | 47 | -6 | 36 |
| Roman Glass/St George Res. | 26 | 8 | 5 | 13 | 48 | 42 | 6 | 29 |
| Lawrence Rovers | 26 | 5 | 4 | 17 | 35 | 68 | -33 | 19 |
| Oldland Abbotonians Res. (-3) | 26 | 6 | 3 | 17 | 34 | 81 | -47 | 18 |
| D R G (Frenchay) | 26 | 3 | 2 | 21 | 24 | 106 | -82 | 11 |
| Brimsham Green | 26 | 1 | 3 | 22 | 23 | 89 | -66 | 6 |

## BRISTOL & SUBURBAN LEAGUE

| remier Division One | P | W | D | L | F | A | GD | Pts |
|---|---|---|---|---|---|---|---|---|
| Lebeq United | 24 | 19 | 4 | 1 | 64 | 23 | 41 | 61 |
| Little Stoke | 24 | 15 | 5 | 4 | 51 | 30 | 21 | 50 |
| Easton Cowboys Suburbia | 24 | 14 | 4 | 6 | 51 | 29 | 22 | 46 |
| Avonmouth | 24 | 13 | 3 | 8 | 59 | 43 | 16 | 42 |
| AFC Mangotsfield | 24 | 11 | 8 | 5 | 41 | 28 | 13 | 41 |
| Downend | 24 | 11 | 2 | 11 | 43 | 43 | 0 | 35 |
| Filton Athletic | 24 | 9 | 6 | 9 | 30 | 33 | -3 | 33 |
| St Aldhelms | 24 | 8 | 5 | 11 | 51 | 58 | -7 | 29 |
| Mangotsfield Sports | 24 | 8 | 3 | 13 | 30 | 43 | -13 | 27 |
| Stoke Gifford United | 24 | 6 | 5 | 13 | 33 | 54 | -21 | 23 |
| Ashton United | 24 | 6 | 4 | 14 | 33 | 49 | -16 | 22 |
| Lawrence Weston | 24 | 3 | 6 | 15 | 25 | 48 | -23 | 15 |
| Fishponds Old Boys | 24 | 4 | 3 | 17 | 33 | 63 | -30 | 15 |

| | Premier Division Two | P | W | D | L | F | A | GD | Pts |
|---|---|---|---|---|---|---|---|---|---|
| 1 | Bristol Bilbao | 20 | 14 | 3 | 3 | 69 | 24 | 45 | 45 |
| 2 | Sartan United | 20 | 13 | 4 | 3 | 56 | 26 | 30 | 43 |
| 3 | Old Georgians | 20 | 13 | 3 | 4 | 42 | 28 | 14 | 42 |
| 4 | Rockleaze Rangers Res | 20 | 10 | 5 | 5 | 42 | 26 | 16 | 35 |
| 5 | Almondsbury UWE Res | 20 | 10 | 5 | 5 | 45 | 35 | 10 | 35 |
| 6 | Old Cothamians | 20 | 9 | 1 | 10 | 49 | 39 | 10 | 28 |
| 7 | Brislington A | 20 | 8 | 5 | 7 | 43 | 51 | -8 | 28 |
| 8 | Cadbury Heath Res. | 20 | 5 | 3 | 12 | 26 | 50 | -24 | 18 |
| 9 | Ridings High | 20 | 5 | 2 | 13 | 29 | 54 | -25 | 16 |
| 10 | Glenside 5 Old Boys | 20 | 3 | 4 | 13 | 28 | 59 | -31 | 13 |
| 11 | AFC Hartcliffe | 20 | 2 | 1 | 17 | 18 | 55 | -37 | 7 |

| | Division One | P | W | D | L | F | A | GD | Pts |
|---|---|---|---|---|---|---|---|---|---|
| 1 | Rockleaze Rangers 'A' | 26 | 21 | 2 | 3 | 76 | 21 | 55 | 65 |
| 2 | AFC Brislington Res. | 26 | 17 | 2 | 7 | 74 | 39 | 35 | 53 |
| 3 | Parson Street Old Boys | 26 | 16 | 2 | 8 | 71 | 51 | 20 | 50 |
| 4 | St Aldhelms Res. | 26 | 14 | 5 | 7 | 50 | 38 | 12 | 47 |
| 5 | Kellaway Rangers | 26 | 12 | 2 | 12 | 46 | 51 | -5 | 38 |
| 6 | Fry's Club OB | 26 | 11 | 4 | 11 | 65 | 61 | 4 | 37 |
| 7 | Wanderers | 26 | 11 | 4 | 11 | 57 | 55 | 2 | 37 |
| 8 | Stoke Gifford United Res. | 26 | 11 | 2 | 13 | 48 | 61 | -13 | 35 |
| 9 | Ridings High Res. | 26 | 9 | 5 | 12 | 45 | 42 | 3 | 32 |
| 10 | Bristol Telephones Res. | 26 | 9 | 5 | 12 | 34 | 34 | 0 | 32 |
| 11 | Avonmouth Res. | 26 | 8 | 4 | 14 | 46 | 64 | -18 | 28 |
| 12 | Broad Plain House Res. | 26 | 8 | 3 | 15 | 45 | 67 | -22 | 27 |
| 13 | Ashton Backwell Colts | 26 | 8 | 1 | 17 | 45 | 75 | -30 | 25 |
| 14 | Lawrence Weston Res. | 26 | 4 | 5 | 17 | 39 | 82 | -43 | 17 |

| | Division Two | P | W | D | L | F | A | GD | Pts |
|---|---|---|---|---|---|---|---|---|---|
| 1 | Bromley Heath United | 26 | 21 | 4 | 1 | 79 | 21 | 58 | 67 |
| 2 | Ashton United Res. | 26 | 20 | 1 | 5 | 69 | 33 | 36 | 61 |
| 3 | AFC Mangotsfield Res. | 26 | 19 | 3 | 4 | 66 | 32 | 34 | 60 |
| 4 | North Bristol United | 26 | 15 | 3 | 8 | 74 | 53 | 21 | 48 |
| 5 | Long Ashton Res. | 26 | 14 | 3 | 9 | 74 | 44 | 30 | 45 |
| 6 | Old Cothamians Res. | 26 | 12 | 4 | 10 | 56 | 51 | 5 | 40 |
| 7 | Oldbury FC | 26 | 11 | 5 | 10 | 47 | 52 | -5 | 38 |
| 8 | Wessex Wanderers | 26 | 11 | 5 | 10 | 38 | 46 | -8 | 38 |
| 9 | AEK Boco Colts | 26 | 8 | 3 | 15 | 49 | 70 | -21 | 27 |
| 10 | Almondsbury UWE A | 26 | 7 | 2 | 17 | 56 | 69 | -13 | 23 |
| 11 | Hydez Futebol Clube | 26 | 7 | 2 | 17 | 36 | 57 | -21 | 23 |
| 12 | Fishponds Old Boys Res. | 26 | 7 | 2 | 17 | 40 | 72 | -32 | 23 |
| 13 | Keynsham Town A | 26 | 6 | 4 | 16 | 33 | 70 | -37 | 22 |
| 14 | Park Knowle | 26 | 2 | 3 | 21 | 29 | 76 | -47 | 9 |

## LEAGUE TABLES

| Division Three | P | W | D | L | F | A | GD | Pts |
|---|---|---|---|---|---|---|---|---|
| 1 Bristol Spartak | 24 | 19 | 1 | 4 | 73 | 33 | 40 | 58 |
| 2 Sartan United Res. | 24 | 15 | 4 | 5 | 70 | 40 | 30 | 49 |
| 3 Stockwood Wanderers Res. | 24 | 13 | 5 | 6 | 78 | 39 | 39 | 44 |
| 4 Lockleaze Community | 24 | 12 | 6 | 6 | 63 | 44 | 19 | 42 |
| 5 Rockleaze Rangers B | 24 | 12 | 6 | 6 | 43 | 38 | 5 | 42 |
| 6 Corinthian Sports | 24 | 11 | 2 | 11 | 47 | 61 | -14 | 35 |
| 7 Filton Athletic Res. | 24 | 10 | 1 | 13 | 47 | 50 | -3 | 31 |
| 8 Lawrence Weston A | 24 | 10 | 1 | 13 | 53 | 65 | -12 | 31 |
| 9 Hanham Athletic Suburbia | 24 | 8 | 4 | 12 | 33 | 31 | 2 | 28 |
| 10 Avon Plate | 24 | 9 | 5 | 10 | 48 | 73 | -25 | 25 |
| 11 Bromley Heath United Res. | 24 | 6 | 3 | 15 | 40 | 54 | -14 | 21 |
| 12 Glenside 5 Old Boys Res. | 24 | 5 | 3 | 16 | 39 | 72 | -33 | 18 |
| 13 Old Georgians Res. | 24 | 5 | 1 | 18 | 32 | 66 | -34 | 15 |

| Division Four | P | W | D | L | F | A | GD | Pts |
|---|---|---|---|---|---|---|---|---|
| 1 North Bristol Trust | 22 | 18 | 3 | 1 | 81 | 24 | 57 | 57 |
| 2 AFC Filwood | 22 | 17 | 1 | 4 | 80 | 40 | 40 | 52 |
| 3 Brandon Sports | 22 | 13 | 6 | 3 | 57 | 36 | 21 | 45 |
| 4 Fry's Club OB Res. | 22 | 11 | 6 | 5 | 69 | 45 | 24 | 39 |
| 5 Long Ashton 'A' | 22 | 10 | 4 | 8 | 60 | 49 | 11 | 34 |
| 6 Cosmos | 22 | 8 | 7 | 7 | 61 | 48 | 13 | 31 |
| 7 AFC Mangotsfield 'A' | 22 | 9 | 4 | 9 | 51 | 60 | -9 | 31 |
| 8 Imperial Res. | 22 | 9 | 2 | 11 | 44 | 59 | -15 | 29 |
| 9 AFC Brislington A | 22 | 5 | 1 | 16 | 31 | 65 | -34 | 16 |
| 10 Avonmouth 'A' | 22 | 4 | 4 | 14 | 49 | 85 | -36 | 16 |
| 11 Stoke Gifford United A | 22 | 5 | 0 | 17 | 24 | 69 | -45 | 15 |
| 12 Kellaway Rangers Res. | 22 | 4 | 0 | 18 | 29 | 56 | -27 | 12 |

| Division Five | P | W | D | L | F | A | GD | Pts |
|---|---|---|---|---|---|---|---|---|
| 1 Kingswood | 22 | 19 | 1 | 2 | 118 | 35 | 83 | 58 |
| 2 Bedminster Cricketers | 22 | 16 | 0 | 6 | 113 | 33 | 80 | 48 |
| 3 RR Athletic | 22 | 15 | 2 | 5 | 104 | 43 | 61 | 47 |
| 4 Lockleaze Community Res. | 22 | 14 | 3 | 5 | 59 | 44 | 15 | 45 |
| 5 AFC Mangotsfield B | 22 | 13 | 4 | 5 | 75 | 42 | 33 | 43 |
| 6 North Bristol Trust Res. | 22 | 11 | 2 | 9 | 58 | 38 | 20 | 35 |
| 7 St Aldhelms A | 22 | 11 | 2 | 9 | 54 | 42 | 12 | 32 |
| 8 Cosmos Res. | 22 | 8 | 1 | 13 | 40 | 98 | -58 | 25 |
| 9 Oldbury FC Res. | 22 | 6 | 1 | 15 | 30 | 73 | -43 | 19 |
| 10 Parson Street OB Res. | 22 | 4 | 1 | 17 | 42 | 93 | -51 | 13 |
| 11 Wessex Wanderers Res. | 22 | 3 | 1 | 18 | 32 | 92 | -60 | 10 |
| 12 TC Sports | 22 | 2 | 2 | 18 | 32 | 124 | -92 | 8 |

### BROMLEY AND DISTRICT FOOTBALL LEAGUE

| Premier Division | P | W | D | L | F | A | GD | Pts |
|---|---|---|---|---|---|---|---|---|
| 1 Baldon Sports | 20 | 16 | 3 | 1 | 85 | 27 | 58 | 51 |
| 2 Centresports FC | 20 | 13 | 1 | 6 | 63 | 36 | 27 | 40 |
| 3 AFC Bexley | 20 | 12 | 4 | 4 | 61 | 41 | 20 | 40 |
| 4 Ten Em Bee FC | 19 | 9 | 4 | 6 | 63 | 40 | 23 | 31 |
| 5 Real Mayo FC | 20 | 8 | 3 | 9 | 47 | 45 | 2 | 27 |
| 6 Eden Park Rangers | 17 | 7 | 5 | 5 | 47 | 48 | -1 | 26 |
| 7 Farnborough OBG | 20 | 7 | 2 | 11 | 37 | 51 | -14 | 23 |
| 8 Chislehurst Town FC | 18 | 5 | 5 | 8 | 37 | 58 | -21 | 20 |
| 9 Colfeians | 19 | 5 | 3 | 11 | 36 | 53 | -17 | 18 |
| 10 Old Colfeians CFC | 20 | 4 | 3 | 13 | 43 | 71 | -28 | 15 |
| 11 River Plate FC | 19 | 3 | 1 | 15 | 35 | 84 | -49 | 10 |

| Division One | P | W | D | L | F | A | GD | Pts |
|---|---|---|---|---|---|---|---|---|
| 1 Knights Old Boys FC | 20 | 16 | 2 | 2 | 77 | 29 | 48 | 50 |
| 2 South East Athletic Res. | 20 | 16 | 2 | 2 | 76 | 29 | 47 | 50 |
| 3 TW AFC | 19 | 14 | 2 | 3 | 68 | 22 | 46 | 44 |
| 4 Rutland Rangers FC | 20 | 12 | 2 | 6 | 82 | 45 | 37 | 38 |
| 5 "Welling Park ""A"" FC" | 19 | 12 | 2 | 5 | 73 | 36 | 37 | 38 |
| 6 Highfield & Welling FC | 20 | 11 | 1 | 8 | 63 | 50 | 13 | 34 |
| 7 Charlton Athletic Deaf | 20 | 6 | 1 | 13 | 37 | 58 | -21 | 19 |
| 8 Chislehurst Royals | 20 | 3 | 3 | 14 | 43 | 93 | -50 | 12 |
| 9 Columbas FC | 20 | 3 | 2 | 15 | 28 | 61 | -33 | 11 |
| 10 King's Stairs Gardens FC | 20 | 3 | 2 | 15 | 42 | 93 | -51 | [illegible] |
| 11 Latter-Day Saints FC | 20 | 3 | 1 | 16 | 36 | 109 | -73 | 10 |

### CENTRAL & SOUTH NORFOLK LEAGUE

| **Division One** | P | W | D | L | F | A | GD | Pts |
|---|---|---|---|---|---|---|---|---|
| 1 Castle Acre Swifts | 14 | 12 | 1 | 1 | 51 | 12 | 39 | [illegible] |
| 2 Tacolneston | 14 | 12 | 0 | 2 | 63 | 12 | 51 | [illegible] |
| 3 Narborough | 14 | 8 | 2 | 4 | 38 | 23 | 15 | [illegible] |
| 4 North Elmham | 14 | 5 | 1 | 8 | 22 | 41 | -19 | [illegible] |
| 5 Shipdham | 14 | 5 | 1 | 8 | 24 | 45 | -21 | [illegible] |
| 6 Beetley Bees | 14 | 4 | 2 | 8 | 21 | 39 | -18 | [illegible] |
| 7 Mulbarton Wanderers A | 14 | 3 | 1 | 10 | 18 | 35 | -17 | [illegible] |
| 8 Gressenhall | 14 | 2 | 2 | 10 | 15 | 45 | -30 | [illegible] |

| **Division Two** | P | W | D | L | F | A | GD | Pts |
|---|---|---|---|---|---|---|---|---|
| 1 Marham Wanderers | 16 | 12 | 3 | 1 | 56 | 23 | 33 | [illegible] |
| 2 Morley Village | 16 | 9 | 4 | 3 | 58 | 23 | 35 | [illegible] |
| 3 Hethersett Athletic | 16 | 8 | 3 | 5 | 36 | 26 | 10 | [illegible] |
| 4 Rockland United | 16 | 7 | 4 | 5 | 38 | 32 | 6 | [illegible] |
| 5 Attleborough Town A | 16 | 7 | 3 | 6 | 38 | 29 | 9 | [illegible] |
| 6 Sporle | 16 | 6 | 3 | 7 | 64 | 52 | 12 | [illegible] |
| 7 Tacolneston Res. | 16 | 5 | 2 | 9 | 29 | 63 | -34 | [illegible] |
| 8 Castle Acre Swifts Res. | 16 | 3 | 3 | 10 | 33 | 71 | -38 | [illegible] |
| 9 Bridgham United | 16 | 2 | 1 | 13 | 28 | 61 | -33 | [illegible] |

| **Division Three** | P | W | D | L | F | A | GD | Pts |
|---|---|---|---|---|---|---|---|---|
| 1 Dereham Taverners | 20 | 18 | 2 | 0 | 104 | 16 | 88 | [illegible] |
| 2 Billingford | 20 | 15 | 2 | 3 | 78 | 17 | 61 | [illegible] |
| 3 Longham | 20 | 14 | 0 | 6 | 104 | 56 | 48 | [illegible] |
| 4 Watton United Res. | 20 | 11 | 3 | 6 | 78 | 38 | 40 | [illegible] |
| 5 Walsingham United | 20 | 10 | 3 | 7 | 59 | 60 | -1 | [illegible] |
| 6 Colkirk | 20 | 10 | 1 | 9 | 70 | 75 | -5 | [illegible] |
| 7 Northwold | 20 | 9 | 1 | 10 | 76 | 60 | 16 | [illegible] |
| 8 Yaxham Res. | 20 | 6 | 4 | 10 | 52 | 53 | -1 | [illegible] |
| 9 Feltwell United Res. | 20 | 4 | 0 | 16 | 40 | 94 | -54 | [illegible] |
| 10 Cockers | 20 | 3 | 1 | 16 | 27 | 104 | -77 | [illegible] |
| 11 Rampant Horse | 20 | 1 | 1 | 18 | 21 | 136 | -115 | [illegible] |

| **Division Four** | P | W | D | L | F | A | GD | Pts |
|---|---|---|---|---|---|---|---|---|
| 1 Bar 33 | 16 | 10 | 3 | 3 | 65 | 31 | 34 | [illegible] |
| 2 Beetley Bees Res. | 16 | 9 | 3 | 4 | 53 | 41 | 12 | [illegible] |
| 3 Rockland United. Res. | 16 | 9 | 2 | 5 | 59 | 41 | 18 | [illegible] |
| 4 Scarning United | 16 | 8 | 2 | 6 | 65 | 53 | 12 | [illegible] |
| 5 Scole United A | 16 | 8 | 1 | 7 | 67 | 51 | 16 | [illegible] |
| 6 Shipdham Res. | 16 | 8 | 1 | 7 | 40 | 48 | -8 | [illegible] |
| 7 Narborough Res. | 16 | 5 | 2 | 9 | 35 | 48 | -13 | [illegible] |
| 8 Necton Res. | 16 | 4 | 1 | 11 | 30 | 78 | -48 | [illegible] |
| 9 Gressenhall Res. | 16 | 3 | 1 | 12 | 29 | 52 | -23 | [illegible] |

## CHELTENHAM ASSOCIATION FOOTBALL LEAGUE

| Division One | | P | W | D | L | F | A | GD | Pts |
|---|---|---|---|---|---|---|---|---|---|
| 1 | FC Lakeside | 22 | 19 | 1 | 2 | 98 | 21 | 77 | 58 |
| 2 | Chelt Civil Service Res. (-1) | 22 | 11 | 7 | 4 | 42 | 34 | 8 | 39 |
| 3 | Churchdown Panthers | 22 | 11 | 4 | 7 | 70 | 57 | 13 | 37 |
| 4 | Falcons | 22 | 9 | 6 | 7 | 56 | 38 | 18 | 33 |
| 5 | Gala Wilton Res. | 22 | 8 | 6 | 8 | 30 | 34 | -4 | 30 |
| 6 | Bishops Cleeve III | 22 | 8 | 5 | 9 | 38 | 42 | -4 | 29 |
| 7 | Kings FC | 22 | 8 | 5 | 9 | 41 | 48 | -7 | 29 |
| 8 | R.S.G. | 22 | 8 | 5 | 9 | 36 | 48 | -12 | 29 |
| 9 | Staunton & Corse | 22 | 7 | 7 | 8 | 36 | 46 | -10 | 28 |
| 10 | Upton Town | 22 | 6 | 6 | 10 | 33 | 50 | -17 | 24 |
| 11 | FC Barometrics Res. | 22 | 5 | 4 | 13 | 40 | 47 | -7 | 19 |
| 12 | Newton FC | 22 | 2 | 4 | 16 | 29 | 84 | -55 | 10 |

| Division Two | | P | W | D | L | F | A | GD | Pts |
|---|---|---|---|---|---|---|---|---|---|
| 1 | Welland FC | 22 | 16 | 4 | 2 | 60 | 24 | 36 | 52 |
| 2 | Leckhampton Rovers | 22 | 14 | 3 | 5 | 89 | 47 | 42 | 45 |
| 3 | Whaddon United Res. | 22 | 13 | 1 | 8 | 44 | 36 | 8 | 40 |
| 4 | Andoversford (-3) | 22 | 13 | 3 | 6 | 74 | 46 | 28 | 39 |
| 5 | AFC Worcester Olympic (-3) | 22 | 11 | 2 | 9 | 71 | 56 | 15 | 32 |
| 6 | Gloucester Elmleaze | 22 | 9 | 5 | 8 | 51 | 51 | 0 | 32 |
| 7 | Dowty Dynamos | 22 | 9 | 5 | 8 | 45 | 51 | -6 | 32 |
| 8 | Prestbury Rovers | 22 | 9 | 1 | 12 | 46 | 54 | -8 | 28 |
| 9 | Southside Star FC Res. (-1) | 22 | 8 | 3 | 11 | 45 | 76 | -31 | 26 |
| 10 | Tewkesbury Town | 22 | 5 | 4 | 13 | 45 | 61 | -16 | 19 |
| 11 | Brockworth Albion Res. (-3) | 22 | 4 | 5 | 13 | 38 | 56 | -18 | 14 |
| 12 | Hanley Swan | 22 | 2 | 2 | 18 | 30 | 80 | -50 | 8 |

| Division Three | | P | W | D | L | F | A | GD | Pts |
|---|---|---|---|---|---|---|---|---|---|
| | Shurdington Rovers | 22 | 19 | 1 | 2 | 70 | 20 | 50 | 58 |
| | Chelt Civil Service III | 22 | 14 | 4 | 4 | 62 | 27 | 35 | 46 |
| | Newlands Athletic | 22 | 13 | 1 | 8 | 70 | 34 | 36 | 40 |
| | Smiths Athletic Res. (-1) | 22 | 11 | 7 | 4 | 46 | 37 | 9 | 39 |
| | Apperley | 22 | 8 | 7 | 7 | 55 | 41 | 14 | 31 |
| | Fintan | 22 | 8 | 7 | 7 | 42 | 42 | 0 | 31 |
| | Gala Wilton III | 22 | 5 | 10 | 7 | 44 | 44 | 0 | 25 |
| | Falcons Res. (-3) | 22 | 7 | 6 | 9 | 43 | 58 | -15 | 24 |
| | Southside Star FC III | 22 | 6 | 5 | 11 | 42 | 58 | -16 | 23 |
| 10 | Kings FC Res. | 22 | 4 | 7 | 11 | 32 | 61 | -29 | 19 |
| 11 | Pittville United | 22 | 4 | 3 | 15 | 38 | 72 | -34 | 15 |
| 12 | Leckhampton Rovers Res. | 22 | 2 | 4 | 16 | 30 | 80 | -50 | 10 |

| Division Four | | P | W | D | L | F | A | GD | Pts |
|---|---|---|---|---|---|---|---|---|---|
| | Bredon Res. (-3) | 20 | 18 | 2 | 0 | 88 | 13 | 75 | 53 |
| | Bourton Rovers III | 20 | 13 | 5 | 2 | 67 | 24 | 43 | 44 |
| | Andoversford Res. | 20 | 12 | 2 | 6 | 69 | 53 | 16 | 38 |
| | FC Barometrics III | 20 | 10 | 4 | 6 | 80 | 43 | 37 | 34 |
| | Malvern Vale | 20 | 7 | 5 | 8 | 47 | 54 | -7 | 26 |
| | FC Lakeside Res. | 20 | 6 | 4 | 10 | 49 | 52 | -3 | 22 |
| | Chelt Civil Service IV | 20 | 7 | 1 | 12 | 48 | 60 | -12 | 22 |
| | Charlton Rovers Res. (-4) | 20 | 7 | 3 | 10 | 61 | 73 | -12 | 20 |
| | Staunton & Corse Res. (-1) | 20 | 6 | 3 | 11 | 32 | 89 | -57 | 20 |
| | Hatherley FC | 20 | 5 | 2 | 13 | 47 | 79 | -32 | 17 |
| | Shurdington Rovers Res. (-3) | 20 | 3 | 1 | 16 | 41 | 89 | -48 | 7 |

| Division Five | | P | W | D | L | F | A | GD | Pts |
|---|---|---|---|---|---|---|---|---|---|
| 1 | Apperley Res. | 24 | 19 | 2 | 3 | 112 | 42 | 70 | 59 |
| 2 | Cheltenham United | 24 | 18 | 4 | 2 | 108 | 44 | 64 | 58 |
| 3 | Windyridge Rovers | 24 | 17 | 1 | 6 | 116 | 54 | 62 | 52 |
| 4 | Regency Town | 24 | 15 | 4 | 5 | 88 | 48 | 40 | 49 |
| 5 | Chelt Saracens III | 24 | 9 | 4 | 11 | 57 | 72 | -15 | 31 |
| 6 | Winchcombe Town Res. (-3) | 24 | 9 | 6 | 9 | 54 | 69 | -15 | 30 |
| 7 | Welland FC Res. | 24 | 8 | 4 | 12 | 66 | 80 | -14 | 28 |
| 8 | Gala Wilton IV (-5) | 24 | 8 | 5 | 11 | 51 | 72 | -21 | 24 |
| 9 | Malvern Vale Res. | 24 | 6 | 4 | 14 | 41 | 75 | -34 | 22 |
| 10 | Andoversford III | 24 | 6 | 4 | 14 | 41 | 87 | -46 | 22 |
| 11 | Fintan Res. (-4) | 24 | 6 | 7 | 11 | 47 | 60 | -13 | 21 |
| 12 | Charlton Rovers III | 24 | 4 | 4 | 16 | 55 | 98 | -43 | 16 |
| 13 | Prestbury Rovers Res. (-6) | 24 | 3 | 7 | 14 | 51 | 86 | -35 | 10 |

## CHESTER & WIRRAL FOOTBALL LEAGUE

| Premier Division | | P | W | D | L | F | A | GD | Pts |
|---|---|---|---|---|---|---|---|---|---|
| 1 | Lache | 22 | 19 | 1 | 2 | 83 | 29 | 54 | 58 |
| 2 | Birkenhead Town | 22 | 16 | 4 | 2 | 57 | 18 | 39 | 52 |
| 3 | Deva Athletic | 22 | 14 | 5 | 3 | 78 | 26 | 52 | 47 |
| 4 | Ellesmere Port | 22 | 14 | 2 | 6 | 83 | 38 | 45 | 44 |
| 5 | Lodge Bar | 22 | 13 | 2 | 7 | 61 | 47 | 14 | 41 |
| 6 | Higher Bebington Kelma | 22 | 10 | 2 | 10 | 55 | 52 | 3 | 32 |
| 7 | Shaftsbury Youth | 22 | 7 | 7 | 8 | 45 | 51 | -6 | 28 |
| 8 | Christleton Celtic | 22 | 5 | 4 | 13 | 44 | 67 | -23 | 19 |
| 9 | Kelsall | 22 | 6 | 1 | 15 | 40 | 70 | -30 | 19 |
| 10 | Whitby Athletic | 22 | 5 | 2 | 15 | 53 | 71 | -18 | 17 |
| 11 | Uberlube | 22 | 4 | 1 | 17 | 31 | 103 | -72 | 13 |
| 12 | Ellesmere Port Town Res. | 22 | 3 | 1 | 18 | 41 | 99 | -58 | 10 |

| Division One | | P | W | D | L | F | A | GD | Pts |
|---|---|---|---|---|---|---|---|---|---|
| 1 | Blacon Thistle | 18 | 18 | 0 | 0 | 85 | 16 | 69 | 54 |
| 2 | Newton Athletic | 18 | 15 | 0 | 3 | 45 | 20 | 25 | 45 |
| 3 | Franklyn's | 18 | 11 | 1 | 6 | 49 | 30 | 19 | 34 |
| 4 | Neston Nomads Res. | 18 | 10 | 1 | 7 | 36 | 35 | 1 | 31 |
| 5 | Chester Nomads III | 18 | 8 | 0 | 10 | 29 | 35 | -6 | 24 |
| 6 | Lodge Bar II | 18 | 7 | 1 | 10 | 35 | 69 | -34 | 22 |
| 7 | Ashton | 18 | 5 | 2 | 11 | 33 | 41 | -8 | 17 |
| 8 | Whitby Athletic Res. | 18 | 4 | 3 | 11 | 25 | 25 | 0 | 15 |
| 9 | Elton Athletic | 18 | 3 | 2 | 13 | 33 | 61 | -28 | 11 |
| 10 | Cestrian Alex | 18 | 3 | 2 | 13 | 33 | 71 | -38 | 11 |

| Division Two | | P | W | D | L | F | A | GD | Pts |
|---|---|---|---|---|---|---|---|---|---|
| 1 | MBNA | 22 | 17 | 4 | 1 | 84 | 28 | 56 | 55 |
| 2 | Woodchurch Athletic | 22 | 17 | 2 | 3 | 91 | 34 | 57 | 53 |
| 3 | Samba | 22 | 15 | 2 | 5 | 91 | 32 | 59 | 47 |
| 4 | New Ferry Rangers AFC | 22 | 11 | 6 | 5 | 68 | 39 | 29 | 39 |
| 5 | Crossway | 22 | 10 | 3 | 9 | 45 | 48 | -3 | 33 |
| 6 | Clubbies AFC | 22 | 9 | 5 | 8 | 57 | 41 | 16 | 32 |
| 7 | Eastham Athletic | 22 | 8 | 4 | 10 | 42 | 55 | -13 | 28 |
| 8 | Hoole Rangers | 22 | 7 | 4 | 11 | 57 | 79 | -22 | 25 |
| 9 | Elton Rigger AFC | 22 | 6 | 3 | 13 | 35 | 73 | -38 | 21 |
| 10 | Orange Athletic Chester | 22 | 6 | 1 | 15 | 38 | 80 | -42 | 19 |
| 11 | Ellesmere Port Town III | 22 | 5 | 2 | 15 | 38 | 78 | -40 | 17 |
| 12 | Ellesmere Port Spartans | 22 | 2 | 2 | 18 | 31 | 90 | -59 | 8 |

## CIRENCESTER & DISTRICT LEAGUE

| Division One | P | W | D | L | F | A | GD | Pts |
|---|---|---|---|---|---|---|---|---|
| 1 Intel FC | 22 | 16 | 2 | 4 | 70 | 25 | 45 | 50 |
| 2 Bibury Res. | 22 | 14 | 1 | 7 | 59 | 53 | 6 | 43 |
| 3 South Cerney (-1) | 22 | 13 | 3 | 6 | 49 | 28 | 21 | 41 |
| 4 Highworth Town Development | 22 | 12 | 1 | 9 | 39 | 44 | -5 | 37 |
| 5 Wroughton Town FC Res. (-4) | 22 | 12 | 4 | 6 | 45 | 31 | 14 | 36 |
| 6 Ashton Keynes (-4) | 22 | 12 | 3 | 7 | 73 | 54 | 19 | 35 |
| 7 Poulton | 22 | 9 | 7 | 6 | 62 | 44 | 18 | 34 |
| 8 Malmesbury Vics FC Res. (-6) | 22 | 9 | 3 | 10 | 44 | 59 | -15 | 24 |
| 9 Lechlade FC 87 (-9) | 22 | 8 | 2 | 12 | 35 | 44 | -9 | 17 |
| 10 CHQ United (-6) | 22 | 7 | 2 | 13 | 29 | 40 | -11 | 17 |
| 11 Siddington | 22 | 3 | 1 | 18 | 26 | 70 | -44 | 10 |
| 12 Oaksey | 22 | 2 | 1 | 19 | 33 | 72 | -39 | 7 |

| Division Two | P | W | D | L | F | A | GD | Pts |
|---|---|---|---|---|---|---|---|---|
| 1 The Beeches | 26 | 24 | 0 | 2 | 142 | 16 | 126 | 72 |
| 2 Hatherop | 26 | 22 | 1 | 3 | 145 | 49 | 96 | 67 |
| 3 Siddington Sports Vets | 26 | 20 | 2 | 4 | 137 | 39 | 98 | 62 |
| 4 South Cerney Res. | 26 | 15 | 4 | 7 | 81 | 41 | 40 | 49 |
| 5 Blunsdon FC | 26 | 15 | 2 | 9 | 69 | 50 | 19 | 47 |
| 6 Kingshill Sports (+3) | 26 | 13 | 2 | 11 | 90 | 76 | 14 | 44 |
| 7 Lechlade FC 87 Res. | 26 | 10 | 3 | 13 | 61 | 71 | -10 | 33 |
| 8 Minety | 26 | 9 | 5 | 12 | 50 | 78 | -28 | 32 |
| 9 Oaksey Res. (-1) | 26 | 9 | 2 | 15 | 69 | 89 | -20 | 28 |
| 10 Stratton United (-1) | 26 | 8 | 3 | 15 | 64 | 94 | -30 | 26 |
| 11 Sherston (-1) | 26 | 7 | 3 | 16 | 52 | 111 | -59 | 23 |
| 12 Sherborne Harriers | 26 | 4 | 3 | 19 | 54 | 107 | -53 | 15 |
| 13 Ashton Keynes Res. (-1) | 26 | 4 | 3 | 19 | 43 | 136 | -93 | 14 |
| 14 Tetbury Town 3rds (-4) | 26 | 3 | 5 | 18 | 34 | 134 | -100 | 10 |

## COLCHESTER & EAST ESSEX FOOTBALL LEAGUE

| Premier Division | P | W | D | L | F | A | GD | Pts |
|---|---|---|---|---|---|---|---|---|
| 1 Belle Vue Social | 16 | 13 | 1 | 2 | 63 | 20 | 43 | 40 |
| 2 Connaught Red Star | 16 | 12 | 2 | 2 | 56 | 9 | 47 | 38 |
| 3 University of Essex 'A' | 16 | 10 | 0 | 6 | 39 | 37 | 2 | 30 |
| 4 Bures United | 16 | 6 | 4 | 6 | 18 | 17 | 1 | 22 |
| 5 Tollesbury Res. | 16 | 7 | 1 | 8 | 23 | 25 | -2 | 22 |
| 6 New Field | 16 | 6 | 2 | 8 | 29 | 29 | 0 | 20 |
| 7 Oyster | 16 | 5 | 4 | 7 | 30 | 30 | 0 | 19 |
| 8 Mistley | 16 | 3 | 1 | 12 | 22 | 63 | -41 | 10 |
| 9 Whitehall | 16 | 2 | 1 | 13 | 20 | 70 | -50 | 7 |

| Division One | P | W | D | L | F | A | GD | Pts |
|---|---|---|---|---|---|---|---|---|
| 1 Harwich Rangers | 20 | 16 | 0 | 4 | 69 | 31 | 38 | 48 |
| 2 Sporting Rebels | 20 | 14 | 4 | 2 | 85 | 32 | 53 | 46 |
| 3 University of Essex 'B' | 20 | 11 | 4 | 5 | 81 | 35 | 46 | 37 |
| 4 Cavendish | 20 | 10 | 2 | 8 | 65 | 30 | 35 | 32 |
| 5 Langham Lodgers | 20 | 9 | 3 | 8 | 54 | 58 | -4 | 30 |
| 6 Wormingford Wanderers Res. | 20 | 8 | 4 | 8 | 51 | 46 | 5 | 28 |
| 7 Nayland Rangers | 20 | 8 | 2 | 10 | 46 | 61 | -15 | 26 |
| 8 Abbey Fields | 20 | 7 | 2 | 11 | 47 | 59 | -12 | 23 |
| 9 Riverbank Athletic | 20 | 7 | 2 | 11 | 40 | 58 | -18 | 23 |
| 10 Stoke-by-Nayland | 20 | 4 | 6 | 10 | 43 | 66 | -23 | 18 |
| 11 Beacon Hill Rovers 'A' | 20 | 0 | 3 | 17 | 26 | 131 | -105 | 3 |

| Division Two | P | W | D | L | F | A | GD | Pts |
|---|---|---|---|---|---|---|---|---|
| 1 Colne Engaine | 18 | 15 | 1 | 2 | 77 | 22 | 55 | 46 |
| 2 Weeley Athletic Res. | 18 | 14 | 1 | 3 | 71 | 18 | 53 | 43 |
| 3 Brantham Athletic Colts | 18 | 12 | 1 | 5 | 55 | 27 | 28 | 37 |
| 4 Monkwick Wanderers | 18 | 11 | 2 | 5 | 47 | 26 | 21 | 35 |
| 5 Cinque Port Res. | 18 | 9 | 0 | 9 | 48 | 47 | 1 | 27 |
| 6 Tiptree Park Res. | 18 | 8 | 2 | 8 | 48 | 47 | 1 | 26 |
| 7 Kelvedon Social 'A' | 18 | 5 | 0 | 13 | 14 | 71 | -57 | 15 |
| 8 New Field Res. | 18 | 4 | 1 | 13 | 34 | 57 | -23 | 13 |
| 9 Marks Tey | 18 | 4 | 0 | 14 | 29 | 67 | -38 | 12 |
| 10 Cavendish Res. | 18 | 3 | 2 | 13 | 29 | 70 | -41 | 11 |

## CORNWALL COMBINATION

| | P | W | D | L | F | A | GD | Pts |
|---|---|---|---|---|---|---|---|---|
| 1 Ludgvan | 38 | 30 | 3 | 5 | 131 | 33 | 98 | 93 |
| 2 Carharrack | 38 | 29 | 2 | 7 | 126 | 53 | 73 | 89 |
| 3 St Agnes | 38 | 25 | 2 | 11 | 102 | 51 | 51 | 77 |
| 4 St Ives Town | 38 | 23 | 5 | 10 | 105 | 53 | 52 | 74 |
| 5 Perranwell | 38 | 23 | 2 | 13 | 101 | 68 | 33 | 71 |
| 6 Redruth United (-3) | 38 | 21 | 8 | 9 | 73 | 49 | 24 | 68 |
| 7 St Just | 38 | 20 | 6 | 12 | 106 | 66 | 40 | 66 |
| 8 Hayle | 38 | 20 | 5 | 13 | 90 | 64 | 26 | 65 |
| 9 Newquay Res. | 38 | 21 | 2 | 15 | 92 | 80 | 12 | 65 |
| 10 Mullion (-3) | 38 | 20 | 1 | 17 | 83 | 60 | 23 | 58 |
| 11 Helston Athletic Res. | 38 | 18 | 3 | 17 | 89 | 84 | 5 | 57 |
| 12 RNAS Culdrose | 38 | 16 | 5 | 17 | 79 | 84 | -5 | 53 |
| 13 Perranporth | 38 | 15 | 3 | 20 | 89 | 122 | -33 | 48 |
| 14 Penryn Athletic Res. | 38 | 14 | 3 | 21 | 84 | 82 | 2 | 45 |
| 15 Holman SC | 38 | 13 | 2 | 23 | 80 | 110 | -30 | 4[illegible] |
| 16 Falmouth Town Res. | 38 | 11 | 5 | 22 | 56 | 103 | -47 | 3[illegible] |
| 17 Goonhavern Athletic | 38 | 8 | 7 | 23 | 60 | 98 | -38 | 3[illegible] |
| 18 St Day | 38 | 9 | 2 | 27 | 89 | 125 | -36 | 2[illegible] |
| 19 Illogan RBL Res. | 38 | 7 | 2 | 29 | 49 | 143 | -94 | 2[illegible] |
| 20 Porthleven Res. | 38 | 3 | 0 | 35 | 35 | 191 | -156 | [illegible] |

## CRAVEN & DISTRICT FOOTBALL LEAGUE

| Premier Division | P | W | D | L | F | A | GD | Pts |
|---|---|---|---|---|---|---|---|---|
| 1 Skipton LMS | 20 | 18 | 2 | 0 | 82 | 29 | 53 | 5[illegible] |
| 2 Trawden Celtic | 20 | 13 | 5 | 2 | 47 | 24 | 23 | 4[illegible] |
| 3 Settle Utd | 20 | 13 | 4 | 3 | 49 | 17 | 32 | 4[illegible] |
| 4 Rolls | 20 | 11 | 2 | 7 | 81 | 44 | 37 | 3[illegible] |
| 5 Grassington Utd | 20 | 10 | 4 | 6 | 44 | 41 | 3 | 3[illegible] |
| 6 Wilsden Athletic | 20 | 9 | 2 | 9 | 45 | 49 | -4 | 2[illegible] |
| 7 Silsden Whitestar | 20 | 6 | 4 | 10 | 34 | 42 | -8 | 2[illegible] |
| 8 Cross Hills | 20 | 6 | 1 | 13 | 34 | 63 | -29 | 1[illegible] |
| 9 Earby Town | 20 | 4 | 1 | 15 | 27 | 57 | -30 | 1[illegible] |
| 10 Gargrave | 20 | 3 | 2 | 15 | 28 | 59 | -31 | 1[illegible] |
| 11 Grindleton | 20 | 3 | 1 | 16 | 21 | 67 | -46 | 1[illegible] |

| | Division One | P | W | D | L | F | A | GD | Pts |
|---|---|---|---|---|---|---|---|---|---|
| 1 | Pendle Renegades | 22 | 20 | 0 | 2 | 87 | 35 | 52 | 60 |
| 2 | FC Sporting Keighley | 22 | 14 | 2 | 6 | 65 | 41 | 24 | 44 |
| 3 | Cowling | 22 | 14 | 1 | 7 | 67 | 36 | 31 | 43 |
| 4 | Rolls Res. | 22 | 12 | 1 | 9 | 66 | 48 | 18 | 37 |
| 5 | Chatburn | 22 | 11 | 4 | 7 | 41 | 42 | -1 | 37 |
| 6 | AFC Colne | 22 | 10 | 5 | 7 | 55 | 48 | 7 | 35 |
| 7 | Skipton Town | 22 | 9 | 5 | 8 | 63 | 58 | 5 | 32 |
| 8 | Oxenhope Recreation | 22 | 8 | 3 | 11 | 41 | 58 | -17 | 27 |
| 9 | Ingrow and Worth Valley | 22 | 5 | 5 | 12 | 45 | 43 | 2 | 20 |
| 10 | Bingley Town | 22 | 6 | 1 | 15 | 38 | 70 | -32 | 19 |
| 11 | Embsay | 22 | 5 | 3 | 14 | 31 | 54 | -23 | 18 |
| 12 | Bradley | 22 | 3 | 0 | 19 | 15 | 81 | -66 | 9 |

| | Division Two | P | W | D | L | F | A | GD | Pts |
|---|---|---|---|---|---|---|---|---|---|
| 1 | Carleton | 22 | 17 | 1 | 4 | 99 | 43 | 56 | 52 |
| 2 | Broomhill | 22 | 16 | 4 | 2 | 58 | 20 | 38 | 52 |
| 3 | Manningham All Stars | 22 | 16 | 1 | 5 | 80 | 49 | 31 | 49 |
| 4 | F.C. Polonia | 22 | 15 | 3 | 4 | 113 | 49 | 64 | 48 |
| 5 | Settle Utd Res. | 22 | 10 | 3 | 9 | 51 | 65 | -14 | 33 |
| 6 | Salts | 22 | 9 | 3 | 10 | 51 | 52 | -1 | 30 |
| 7 | Skipton Town Res. | 22 | 8 | 2 | 12 | 39 | 65 | -26 | 26 |
| 8 | Cononley Sports Res. | 22 | 7 | 3 | 12 | 56 | 78 | -22 | 24 |
| 9 | Grassington Utd Res. | 22 | 6 | 4 | 12 | 62 | 74 | -12 | 22 |
| 10 | Trawden Celtic Res. | 22 | 4 | 4 | 14 | 34 | 76 | -42 | 16 |
| 11 | Pendle Renegades Res. | 22 | 4 | 2 | 16 | 38 | 68 | -30 | 14 |
| 12 | Cross Hills Res. | 22 | 3 | 4 | 15 | 34 | 76 | -42 | 13 |

| | Division Three | P | W | D | L | F | A | GD | Pts |
|---|---|---|---|---|---|---|---|---|---|
| 1 | Hellifield | 24 | 20 | 0 | 4 | 86 | 31 | 55 | 60 |
| 2 | Barnoldswick Barons | 24 | 15 | 5 | 4 | 85 | 42 | 43 | 50 |
| 3 | AFC Barnoldswick | 24 | 14 | 4 | 6 | 62 | 41 | 21 | 46 |
| 4 | Otley Town | 24 | 13 | 4 | 7 | 72 | 47 | 25 | 43 |
| 5 | Addingham | 24 | 12 | 2 | 10 | 48 | 50 | -2 | 38 |
| 6 | Ilkley | 24 | 10 | 7 | 7 | 57 | 52 | 5 | 37 |
| 7 | Horton | 24 | 9 | 8 | 7 | 57 | 43 | 14 | 35 |
| 8 | Barlick Wanderers | 24 | 9 | 4 | 11 | 55 | 88 | -33 | 31 |
| 9 | Bingley Town Res. | 24 | 6 | 5 | 13 | 51 | 56 | -5 | 23 |
| 10 | Sutton | 24 | 6 | 4 | 14 | 68 | 78 | -10 | 22 |
| 11 | Cowling Res. | 24 | 6 | 4 | 14 | 38 | 68 | -30 | 22 |
| 12 | Ingrow and Worth Valley Res. | 24 | 5 | 4 | 15 | 47 | 100 | -53 | 19 |
| 13 | Broomhill Res. | 24 | 3 | 5 | 16 | 38 | 68 | -30 | 14 |

## CREWE & DISTRICT FOOTBALL LEAGUE

| | Premier Division | P | W | D | L | F | A | GD | Pts |
|---|---|---|---|---|---|---|---|---|---|
| | Winsford Saxons FC | 20 | 14 | 4 | 2 | 84 | 27 | 57 | 46 |
| | Barnton Wanderers | 20 | 14 | 3 | 3 | 77 | 41 | 36 | 45 |
| | Sandbach Curshaws | 20 | 11 | 3 | 6 | 67 | 52 | 15 | 36 |
| | Sandbach Town | 20 | 11 | 3 | 6 | 49 | 46 | 3 | 36 |
| | Winnington Avenue 1994 | 20 | 9 | 6 | 5 | 49 | 32 | 17 | 33 |
| | Tarporley Victoria Res. | 20 | 9 | 3 | 8 | 36 | 49 | -13 | 30 |
| | Tarvin | 20 | 6 | 2 | 12 | 42 | 60 | -18 | 20 |
| | Winnington Avenue | 20 | 6 | 1 | 13 | 32 | 49 | -17 | 19 |
| | Crewe FC Res. | 20 | 5 | 4 | 11 | 30 | 61 | -31 | 19 |
| 10 | Knights Grange (The Grange) | 20 | 3 | 6 | 11 | 33 | 54 | -21 | 15 |
| 11 | Mary Dendy | 20 | 3 | 3 | 14 | 41 | 69 | -28 | 12 |

## CROOK & DISTRICT LEAGUE

| | Division One | P | W | D | L | F | A | GD | Pts |
|---|---|---|---|---|---|---|---|---|---|
| 1 | Bowes | 18 | 16 | 0 | 2 | 59 | 17 | 42 | 48 |
| 2 | Shildon Railway (-3) | 18 | 12 | 2 | 4 | 54 | 23 | 31 | 35 |
| 3 | Wear Valley | 18 | 9 | 4 | 5 | 44 | 25 | 19 | 31 |
| 4 | West Auckland | 18 | 10 | 1 | 7 | 48 | 42 | 6 | 31 |
| 5 | Bishop Auckland Hogans | 18 | 9 | 1 | 8 | 43 | 37 | 6 | 28 |
| 6 | Willington W.M.C. | 18 | 7 | 4 | 7 | 44 | 49 | -5 | 25 |
| 7 | Middlestone Moor Masons Arms | 18 | 6 | 1 | 11 | 36 | 47 | -11 | 19 |
| 8 | Bowden-Le-Wear Australia | 18 | 6 | 2 | 10 | 26 | 38 | -12 | 14 |
| 9 | Heighington | 18 | 3 | 2 | 13 | 22 | 49 | -27 | 8 |
| 10 | Darlington D.S.R.M. Social Club | 18 | 1 | 5 | 12 | 35 | 84 | -49 | 8 |

| | **Division Two** | P | W | D | L | F | A | GD | Pts |
|---|---|---|---|---|---|---|---|---|---|
| 1 | Bishop Auckland Welcome | 22 | 19 | 1 | 2 | 122 | 30 | 92 | 58 |
| 2 | Alston Moor Sports Club | 22 | 18 | 0 | 4 | 63 | 25 | 38 | 54 |
| 3 | Evenwood Town | 22 | 17 | 2 | 3 | 82 | 35 | 47 | 53 |
| 4 | Newton Aycliffe Turbina | 22 | 12 | 1 | 9 | 54 | 42 | 12 | 37 |
| 5 | Ferryhill Town | 22 | 9 | 3 | 10 | 58 | 65 | -7 | 30 |
| 6 | Wolsingham | 22 | 9 | 3 | 10 | 45 | 58 | -13 | 30 |
| 7 | Crook Albion | 22 | 9 | 2 | 11 | 54 | 52 | 2 | 29 |
| 8 | Darlington Travellers Rest (-3) | 22 | 9 | 2 | 11 | 72 | 61 | 11 | 26 |
| 9 | Crook Town Wanderers | 22 | 6 | 3 | 13 | 35 | 63 | -28 | 21 |
| 10 | Stanhope Town Sports & SC | 22 | 6 | 0 | 16 | 36 | 81 | -45 | 18 |
| 11 | Barnard Castle Glaxo Rangers (-3) | 22 | 5 | 5 | 12 | 41 | 66 | -25 | 17 |
| 12 | Wearhead United (-3) | 22 | 0 | 4 | 18 | 20 | 104 | -84 | 1 |

## DEVON & EXETER FOOTBALL LEAGUE

| | Premier Division | P | W | D | L | F | A | GD | Pts |
|---|---|---|---|---|---|---|---|---|---|
| 1 | Topsham Town | 28 | 20 | 5 | 3 | 78 | 23 | 55 | 65 |
| 2 | Newtown | 28 | 20 | 4 | 4 | 77 | 44 | 33 | 64 |
| 3 | Honiton Town | 28 | 19 | 5 | 4 | 83 | 37 | 46 | 62 |
| 4 | Feniton | 28 | 17 | 4 | 7 | 83 | 44 | 39 | 55 |
| 5 | Elmore | 28 | 14 | 6 | 8 | 63 | 39 | 24 | 48 |
| 6 | Seaton Town | 28 | 12 | 4 | 12 | 59 | 55 | 4 | 40 |
| 7 | Newton St Cyres | 28 | 10 | 7 | 11 | 41 | 48 | -7 | 37 |
| 8 | Hatherleigh Town | 28 | 9 | 8 | 11 | 45 | 51 | -6 | 35 |
| 9 | Heavitree United | 28 | 10 | 3 | 15 | 57 | 67 | -10 | 33 |
| 10 | Exwick Villa 2nds | 28 | 8 | 7 | 13 | 55 | 60 | -5 | 31 |
| 11 | Clyst Valley | 28 | 9 | 4 | 15 | 41 | 69 | -28 | 31 |
| 12 | Beer Albion | 28 | 8 | 4 | 16 | 38 | 63 | -25 | 28 |
| 13 | Bow AAC | 28 | 6 | 6 | 16 | 54 | 71 | -17 | 24 |
| 14 | Chard Town 2nds | 28 | 6 | 6 | 16 | 46 | 81 | -35 | 24 |
| 15 | Willand Rovers 2nds | 28 | 3 | 5 | 20 | 31 | 99 | -68 | 14 |

16 Sidbury United withdrew - record expunged

## LEAGUE TABLES

| Division One | P | W | D | L | F | A | GD | Pts |
|---|---|---|---|---|---|---|---|---|
| 1 Exmouth Amateurs | 24 | 19 | 3 | 2 | 70 | 15 | 55 | 60 |
| 2 University 2nds | 24 | 17 | 5 | 2 | 86 | 21 | 65 | 56 |
| 3 Upottery | 24 | 15 | 5 | 4 | 70 | 29 | 41 | 50 |
| 4 Sidmouth Town 2nds | 24 | 14 | 3 | 7 | 64 | 50 | 14 | 45 |
| 5 Bickleigh | 24 | 13 | 5 | 6 | 55 | 27 | 28 | 44 |
| 6 Westexe Rovers | 24 | 9 | 4 | 11 | 48 | 72 | -24 | 31 |
| 7 Colyton | 24 | 8 | 5 | 11 | 47 | 51 | -4 | 29 |
| 8 Wellington Town 2nds | 24 | 6 | 7 | 11 | 47 | 54 | -7 | 25 |
| 9 Witheridge 2nds | 24 | 6 | 4 | 14 | 42 | 63 | -21 | 22 |
| 10 Alphington 2nds | 24 | 5 | 6 | 13 | 36 | 53 | -17 | 21 |
| 11 Heavitree United 2nds (-1) | 24 | 6 | 4 | 14 | 25 | 61 | -36 | 21 |
| 12 Budleigh Salterton 2nds | 24 | 4 | 7 | 13 | 29 | 68 | -39 | 19 |
| 13 Lympstone | 24 | 2 | 6 | 16 | 24 | 79 | -55 | 12 |

14 Chulmleigh withdrew - record expunged.

| Division Two | P | W | D | L | F | A | GD | Pts |
|---|---|---|---|---|---|---|---|---|
| 1 Henry's Cronies | 24 | 21 | 3 | 0 | 109 | 16 | 93 | 66 |
| 2 Lyme Regis | 24 | 17 | 1 | 6 | 96 | 39 | 57 | 52 |
| 3 Chulmleigh | 24 | 16 | 3 | 5 | 95 | 36 | 59 | 51 |
| 4 Exmouth Town 2nds | 24 | 14 | 2 | 8 | 56 | 37 | 19 | 44 |
| 5 Dawlish United | 24 | 14 | 1 | 9 | 49 | 37 | 12 | 43 |
| 6 University 3rds | 24 | 14 | 0 | 10 | 64 | 46 | 18 | 42 |
| 7 Cullompton Rangers 2nds | 24 | 13 | 2 | 9 | 54 | 33 | 21 | 41 |
| 8 Newtown 2nds | 24 | 12 | 1 | 11 | 52 | 64 | -12 | 37 |
| 9 Halwill | 24 | 7 | 2 | 15 | 45 | 67 | -22 | 23 |
| 10 Tipton St John | 24 | 6 | 2 | 16 | 41 | 97 | -56 | 20 |
| 11 Hemyock (-2) | 24 | 5 | 2 | 17 | 26 | 77 | -51 | 15 |
| 12 East Budleigh | 24 | 4 | 2 | 18 | 25 | 77 | -52 | 14 |
| 13 Culm United | 24 | 2 | 1 | 21 | 29 | 115 | -86 | 7 |

| Division Three | P | W | D | L | F | A | GD | Pts |
|---|---|---|---|---|---|---|---|---|
| 1 Lapford | 26 | 22 | 1 | 3 | 123 | 23 | 100 | 67 |
| 2 Chagford | 26 | 18 | 4 | 4 | 90 | 44 | 46 | 58 |
| 3 Woodbury | 26 | 17 | 4 | 5 | 95 | 38 | 57 | 55 |
| 4 Axmouth United | 26 | 14 | 4 | 8 | 62 | 37 | 25 | 46 |
| 5 University 4ths (-1) | 26 | 15 | 2 | 9 | 66 | 45 | 21 | 46 |
| 6 Dawlish Town | 26 | 11 | 3 | 12 | 61 | 64 | -3 | 36 |
| 7 Exmouth Amateurs 2nds (-1) | 26 | 10 | 5 | 11 | 45 | 62 | -17 | 34 |
| 8 Newton Poppleford | 26 | 9 | 5 | 12 | 80 | 90 | -10 | 32 |
| 9 Cheriton Fitzpaine (-1) | 26 | 10 | 2 | 14 | 56 | 59 | -3 | 31 |
| 10 Topsham Town 2nds (-4) | 26 | 10 | 5 | 11 | 49 | 59 | -10 | 31 |
| 11 Tedburn St Mary | 26 | 8 | 5 | 13 | 40 | 67 | -27 | 29 |
| 12 Clyst Valley 2nds | 26 | 7 | 3 | 16 | 47 | 83 | -36 | 24 |
| 13 St Martins 2nds (-2) | 26 | 6 | 2 | 18 | 42 | 94 | -52 | 18 |
| 14 Thorverton (-1) | 26 | 1 | 3 | 22 | 37 | 128 | -91 | 5 |

| Division Four | P | W | D | L | F | A | GD | Pts |
|---|---|---|---|---|---|---|---|---|
| 1 Axminster Town 2nds | 22 | 17 | 1 | 4 | 96 | 45 | 51 | 52 |
| 2 Bampton | 22 | 15 | 2 | 5 | 79 | 47 | 32 | 47 |
| 3 Honiton Town 2nds | 22 | 13 | 3 | 6 | 53 | 37 | 16 | 42 |
| 4 University 5ths (-2) | 22 | 10 | 6 | 6 | 66 | 40 | 26 | 34 |
| 5 Bow AAC 2nds (-3) | 22 | 9 | 4 | 9 | 38 | 36 | 2 | 30 |
| 6 Fluxton | 22 | 8 | 5 | 9 | 43 | 53 | -10 | 29 |
| 7 Morchard Bishop | 22 | 9 | 2 | 11 | 56 | 69 | -13 | 29 |
| 8 Lord's XI | 22 | 8 | 1 | 13 | 52 | 56 | -4 | 25 |
| 9 Sampford Peverell | 22 | 6 | 6 | 10 | 35 | 44 | -9 | 24 |
| 10 Countess Wear Dynamoes | 22 | 7 | 3 | 12 | 35 | 72 | -37 | 24 |
| 11 Pinhoe | 22 | 5 | 7 | 10 | 49 | 68 | -19 | 22 |
| 12 North Tawton | 22 | 3 | 4 | 15 | 43 | 78 | -35 | 13 |

| Division Five | P | W | D | L | F | A | GD | Pts |
|---|---|---|---|---|---|---|---|---|
| 1 Uplowman Athletic | 24 | 19 | 1 | 4 | 96 | 29 | 67 | 58 |
| 2 Otterton | 24 | 18 | 2 | 4 | 83 | 32 | 51 | 56 |
| 3 Kentisbeare | 24 | 17 | 0 | 7 | 78 | 35 | 43 | 51 |
| 4 Sandford | 24 | 15 | 4 | 5 | 66 | 37 | 29 | 49 |
| 5 Ottery St Mary | 24 | 15 | 2 | 7 | 66 | 40 | 26 | 47 |
| 6 Priory | 24 | 10 | 3 | 11 | 66 | 55 | 11 | 33 |
| 7 Feniton 2nds | 24 | 10 | 3 | 11 | 75 | 66 | 9 | 33 |
| 8 Awliscombe United | 24 | 10 | 3 | 11 | 63 | 57 | 6 | 33 |
| 9 Alphington 3rds | 24 | 10 | 3 | 11 | 65 | 65 | 0 | 33 |
| 10 Beer Albion 2nds (-1) | 24 | 8 | 1 | 15 | 42 | 56 | -14 | 24 |
| 11 Starcross Generals | 24 | 5 | 5 | 14 | 46 | 101 | -55 | 20 |
| 12 Halwill 2nds | 24 | 3 | 2 | 19 | 30 | 104 | -74 | 11 |
| 13 Hatherleigh Town 2nds | 24 | 1 | 1 | 22 | 35 | 134 | -99 | 4 |

| Division Six | P | W | D | L | F | A | GD | Pts |
|---|---|---|---|---|---|---|---|---|
| 1 Whipton & Pinhoe | 24 | 20 | 2 | 2 | 109 | 42 | 67 | 62 |
| 2 Millwey Rise | 24 | 19 | 0 | 5 | 107 | 35 | 72 | 57 |
| 3 Winchester | 24 | 18 | 1 | 5 | 99 | 39 | 60 | 55 |
| 4 Royal Oak | 24 | 15 | 3 | 6 | 78 | 54 | 24 | 48 |
| 5 South Zeal United | 24 | 12 | 2 | 10 | 90 | 84 | 6 | 38 |
| 6 Newton St Cyres 2nds | 24 | 11 | 3 | 10 | 72 | 73 | -1 | 36 |
| 7 Exwick Village | 24 | 11 | 3 | 10 | 63 | 69 | -6 | 36 |
| 8 Winkleigh | 24 | 10 | 5 | 9 | 59 | 59 | 0 | 35 |
| 9 Stoke Hill | 24 | 7 | 2 | 15 | 43 | 68 | -25 | 23 |
| 10 Dunkeswell Rovers | 24 | 6 | 2 | 16 | 49 | 79 | -30 | 2[illegible] |
| 11 Silverton | 24 | 5 | 2 | 17 | 51 | 90 | -39 | 1[illegible] |
| 12 Ilminster Town 2nds (-1) | 24 | 4 | 2 | 18 | 42 | 95 | -53 | 1[illegible] |
| 13 Woodbury 2nds | 24 | 4 | 1 | 19 | 37 | 112 | -75 | 1[illegible] |

14 East Budleigh 2nds withdrew - record expandged.

| Division Seven | P | W | D | L | F | A | GD | Pts |
|---|---|---|---|---|---|---|---|---|
| 1 Tivvy Park Rangers | 22 | 15 | 5 | 2 | 86 | 37 | 49 | 5[illegible] |
| 2 Central FC | 22 | 15 | 4 | 3 | 89 | 35 | 54 | 4[illegible] |
| 3 Elmore 2nds | 22 | 13 | 6 | 3 | 72 | 44 | 28 | 4[illegible] |
| 4 Offwell Rangers | 22 | 13 | 5 | 4 | 68 | 38 | 30 | 4[illegible] |
| 5 Pinhoe 2nds (-1) | 22 | 12 | 3 | 7 | 60 | 42 | 18 | 3[illegible] |
| 6 Lyme Regis 2nds | 22 | 9 | 6 | 7 | 61 | 43 | 18 | 3[illegible] |
| 7 Wellington Town 3rds (-1) | 22 | 10 | 1 | 11 | 51 | 53 | -2 | 3[illegible] |
| 8 Colyton 2nds | 22 | 8 | 3 | 11 | 32 | 44 | -12 | 2[illegible] |
| 9 Cheriton Fitzpaine 2nds | 22 | 6 | 3 | 13 | 51 | 58 | -7 | 2[illegible] |
| 10 Seaton Town 2nds | 22 | 5 | 2 | 15 | 33 | 68 | -35 | 1[illegible] |
| 11 H T Dons | 22 | 4 | 2 | 16 | 39 | 84 | -45 | 1[illegible] |
| 12 Bradninch (-3) | 22 | 2 | 0 | 20 | 19 | 115 | -96 | [illegible] |

| Division Eight | P | W | D | L | F | A | GD | Pts |
|---|---|---|---|---|---|---|---|---|
| 1 Cranbrook | 20 | 13 | 6 | 1 | 64 | 23 | 41 | 45 |
| 2 Bickleigh 2nds | 20 | 14 | 3 | 3 | 60 | 30 | 30 | 45 |
| 3 Exmouth Spartans | 20 | 13 | 3 | 4 | 74 | 49 | 25 | 42 |
| 4 Sidmouth Town 3rds | 20 | 13 | 2 | 5 | 60 | 39 | 21 | 41 |
| 5 K&M Polonia Exeter | 20 | 9 | 4 | 7 | 49 | 41 | 8 | 31 |
| 6 Ashwater (-1) | 20 | 7 | 1 | 12 | 42 | 54 | -12 | 21 |
| 7 Queens Head | 20 | 6 | 3 | 11 | 37 | 57 | -20 | 21 |
| 8 Sandford 2nds | 20 | 6 | 3 | 11 | 39 | 67 | -28 | 21 |
| 9 Bampton 2nds | 20 | 5 | 3 | 12 | 29 | 50 | -21 | 18 |
| 10 Lympstone 2nds | 20 | 4 | 2 | 14 | 44 | 62 | -18 | 14 |
| 11 Chagford 2nds | 20 | 4 | 2 | 14 | 25 | 51 | -26 | 14 |

12 Ottery St Mary 2nds withdrew - record expunged.

| Division Nine | P | W | D | L | F | A | GD | Pts |
|---|---|---|---|---|---|---|---|---|
| 1 Upottery 2nds | 22 | 19 | 2 | 1 | 84 | 19 | 65 | 59 |
| 2 Lapford 2nds | 22 | 12 | 6 | 4 | 47 | 31 | 16 | 42 |
| 3 Newton Poppleford 2nds | 22 | 13 | 2 | 7 | 60 | 54 | 6 | 41 |
| 4 Kentisbeare 2nds | 22 | 11 | 5 | 6 | 62 | 39 | 23 | 38 |
| 5 Axminster Town 3rds | 22 | 10 | 6 | 6 | 51 | 34 | 17 | 36 |
| 6 Amory Green Rovers | 22 | 10 | 4 | 8 | 49 | 39 | 10 | 34 |
| 7 Honiton Town 3rds | 22 | 8 | 4 | 10 | 51 | 49 | 2 | 28 |
| 8 Witheridge 3rds | 22 | 7 | 7 | 8 | 37 | 55 | -18 | 28 |
| 9 Exmouth Amateurs 3rds (-2) | 22 | 6 | 7 | 9 | 46 | 48 | -2 | 23 |
| 10 Feniton 3rds | 22 | 5 | 1 | 16 | 32 | 78 | -46 | 16 |
| 11 Millwey Rise 2nds | 22 | 3 | 4 | 15 | 27 | 60 | -33 | 13 |
| 12 Tedburn St Mary 2nds | 22 | 3 | 2 | 17 | 28 | 68 | -40 | 11 |

## DORSET FOOTBALL LEAGUE

| Senior | P | W | D | L | F | A | GD | Pts |
|---|---|---|---|---|---|---|---|---|
| 1 Chickerell United | 20 | 13 | 5 | 2 | 51 | 22 | 29 | 44 |
| 2 Gillingham Town Res. | 20 | 13 | 4 | 3 | 47 | 23 | 24 | 43 |
| 3 Dorchester Sports | 20 | 12 | 5 | 3 | 60 | 27 | 33 | 41 |
| 4 Witchampton United (-1) | 20 | 10 | 5 | 5 | 50 | 30 | 20 | 34 * |
| 5 Sturminster Newton United | 20 | 8 | 5 | 7 | 44 | 39 | 5 | 29 |
| 6 Westland Sports Res. | 20 | 7 | 3 | 10 | 42 | 49 | -7 | 24 |
| 7 Corfe Mullen United | 20 | 7 | 2 | 11 | 39 | 53 | -14 | 23 |
| 8 Blandford United Res. | 20 | 6 | 2 | 12 | 39 | 56 | -17 | 20 |
| 9 Portland United Res. | 20 | 6 | 2 | 12 | 35 | 52 | -17 | 20 |
| 10 Piddletrenthide Spartans | 20 | 4 | 4 | 12 | 36 | 56 | -20 | 16 |
| 11 Poole Borough | 20 | 4 | 3 | 13 | 27 | 63 | -36 | 15 |

| Division One | P | W | D | L | F | A | GD | Pts |
|---|---|---|---|---|---|---|---|---|
| 1 Milborne Port | 16 | 12 | 2 | 2 | 55 | 19 | 36 | 38 |
| 2 Boscombe Polonia | 16 | 10 | 3 | 3 | 50 | 30 | 20 | 33 |
| 3 Shaftesbury Town Res. | 16 | 8 | 5 | 3 | 41 | 29 | 12 | 29 |
| 4 Wincanton Town Res. | 16 | 7 | 4 | 5 | 42 | 31 | 11 | 25 |
| 5 Dorchester Sports Res. | 16 | 6 | 6 | 4 | 30 | 24 | 6 | 24 |
| 6 Canford United | 16 | 6 | 4 | 6 | 31 | 30 | 1 | 22 |
| 7 Swanage Town & Herston Res. | 16 | 4 | 2 | 10 | 38 | 59 | -21 | 14 |
| 8 Portland Town | 16 | 2 | 3 | 11 | 22 | 55 | -33 | 9 |
| 9 Gillingham Town A | 16 | 1 | 3 | 12 | 20 | 52 | -32 | 6 |

| Division Two | P | W | D | L | F | A | GD | Pts |
|---|---|---|---|---|---|---|---|---|
| 1 Chickerell United Res. | 24 | 17 | 6 | 1 | 79 | 28 | 51 | 57 |
| 2 Broadstone | 24 | 14 | 6 | 4 | 67 | 27 | 40 | 48 |
| 3 Corfe Castle | 24 | 12 | 7 | 5 | 68 | 42 | 26 | 43 |
| 4 Parley Sports Res. | 24 | 12 | 6 | 6 | 66 | 40 | 26 | 42 |
| 5 AFC Blandford | 24 | 12 | 4 | 8 | 52 | 51 | 1 | 40 |
| 6 Tisbury (-1) | 24 | 10 | 6 | 8 | 51 | 37 | 14 | 35 |
| 7 Wool & Winfrith | 24 | 9 | 7 | 8 | 59 | 51 | 8 | 34 |
| 8 Mere Town Res. (-1) | 24 | 9 | 6 | 9 | 51 | 51 | 0 | 32 |
| 9 AFC Milborne | 24 | 8 | 4 | 12 | 49 | 64 | -15 | 28 |
| 10 Puddletown | 24 | 8 | 3 | 13 | 53 | 58 | -5 | 27 |
| 11 Wareham Rangers Res. | 24 | 4 | 6 | 14 | 48 | 70 | -22 | 18 |
| 12 Portesham United (-1) | 24 | 5 | 3 | 16 | 31 | 80 | -49 | 17 |
| 13 Piddlehinton United | 24 | 2 | 4 | 18 | 25 | 100 | -75 | 10 |

| Division Three | P | W | D | L | F | A | GD | Pts |
|---|---|---|---|---|---|---|---|---|
| 1 Portland United Youth | 16 | 13 | 3 | 0 | 68 | 22 | 46 | 42 |
| 2 Milborne Port Res. | 16 | 8 | 5 | 3 | 38 | 19 | 19 | 29 |
| 3 Portland Town Res. | 16 | 7 | 4 | 5 | 42 | 34 | 8 | 25 |
| 4 Maiden Newton & Catistock | 16 | 7 | 3 | 6 | 34 | 27 | 7 | 24 |
| 5 Sturminster Newton United Res. | 16 | 7 | 1 | 8 | 27 | 36 | -9 | 22 |
| 6 Broadstone Res. | 16 | 5 | 4 | 7 | 32 | 41 | -9 | 19 |
| 7 Owermoigne | 16 | 5 | 3 | 8 | 36 | 35 | 1 | 18 |
| 8 Stalbridge | 16 | 5 | 1 | 10 | 26 | 46 | -20 | 16 |
| 9 Handley Sports | 16 | 3 | 0 | 13 | 24 | 67 | -43 | 9 |

| Division Four | P | W | D | L | F | A | GD | Pts |
|---|---|---|---|---|---|---|---|---|
| 1 Marnhull | 20 | 17 | 1 | 2 | 66 | 22 | 44 | 52 |
| 2 Sturminster Marshall | 20 | 13 | 2 | 5 | 67 | 31 | 36 | 41 |
| 3 Donhead United | 20 | 12 | 2 | 6 | 42 | 22 | 20 | 38 |
| 4 Portland Town A | 20 | 9 | 2 | 9 | 42 | 45 | -3 | 29 |
| 5 AFC Blandford Res. | 20 | 8 | 3 | 9 | 46 | 45 | 1 | 27 |
| 6 Pimperne Sports Society | 20 | 8 | 3 | 9 | 44 | 44 | 0 | 27 |
| 7 South Cheriton United | 20 | 8 | 2 | 10 | 45 | 58 | -13 | 26 |
| 8 United Football Club of Poundbury | 20 | 7 | 3 | 10 | 40 | 44 | -4 | 24 |
| 9 Corfe Mullen United Res. | 20 | 6 | 2 | 12 | 25 | 53 | -28 | 20 |
| 10 Wool & Winfrith Res. | 20 | 6 | 1 | 13 | 39 | 63 | -24 | 19 |
| 11 Kangaroos | 20 | 5 | 1 | 14 | 38 | 67 | -29 | 16 |

| Division Five | P | W | D | L | F | A | GD | Pts |
|---|---|---|---|---|---|---|---|---|
| 1 Okeford United | 21 | 15 | 5 | 1 | 57 | 15 | 42 | 50 |
| 2 Portland Town B | 21 | 16 | 1 | 4 | 88 | 20 | 68 | 49 |
| 3 Marnhull Res. | 21 | 11 | 5 | 5 | 67 | 36 | 31 | 38 |
| 4 Lytchett and Upton Red Triangle (-4) | 21 | 11 | 2 | 8 | 54 | 38 | 16 | 31 |
| 5 Corfe Castle Res. | 21 | 9 | 3 | 9 | 62 | 36 | 26 | 30 |
| 6 Chickerell United A | 21 | 8 | 3 | 10 | 69 | 35 | 34 | 27 |
| 7 Crossways Spitfires | 21 | 2 | 0 | 19 | 17 | 146 | -129 | 6 |
| 8 Wool & Winfrith A (-1) | 21 | 1 | 3 | 17 | 24 | 112 | -88 | 5 |

## DUCHY LEAGUE

| Premier Division | P | W | D | L | F | A | GD | Pts |
|---|---|---|---|---|---|---|---|---|
| 1 Looe Town | 24 | 19 | 4 | 1 | 76 | 29 | 47 | 61 |
| 2 St Minver (-3) | 24 | 19 | 2 | 3 | 84 | 27 | 57 | 56 |
| 3 Edgcumbe FC | 24 | 14 | 2 | 8 | 63 | 47 | 16 | 44 |
| 4 St Stephen | 24 | 13 | 3 | 8 | 72 | 50 | 22 | 42 |
| 5 Torpoint Athletic | 24 | 11 | 4 | 9 | 53 | 48 | 5 | 37 |
| 6 Saltash United | 24 | 9 | 4 | 11 | 49 | 54 | -5 | 31 |
| 7 Biscovey (-3) | 24 | 11 | 0 | 13 | 52 | 49 | 3 | 30 |
| 8 Lostwithiel | 24 | 9 | 3 | 12 | 54 | 63 | -9 | 30 |
| 9 Foxhole Stars | 24 | 9 | 2 | 13 | 58 | 77 | -19 | 29 |
| 10 Pelynt | 24 | 8 | 2 | 14 | 53 | 77 | -24 | 26 |
| 11 North Petherwin | 24 | 6 | 4 | 14 | 52 | 60 | -8 | 22 |
| 12 St Mawgan | 24 | 5 | 4 | 15 | 40 | 76 | -36 | 19 |
| 13 St Dominick | 24 | 5 | 2 | 17 | 39 | 88 | -49 | 17 |

## DURHAM FOOTBALL ALLIANCE

| | P | W | D | L | F | A | GD | Pts |
|---|---|---|---|---|---|---|---|---|
| 1 Sunderland Oddies | 30 | 25 | 4 | 1 | 139 | 29 | 110 | 79 |
| 2 Durham City Res. | 30 | 21 | 2 | 7 | 126 | 33 | 93 | 65 |
| 3 Coundon and Leeholm Youth | 30 | 19 | 4 | 7 | 117 | 29 | 88 | 61 |
| 4 Redcar Town (-6) | 30 | 20 | 6 | 4 | 136 | 28 | 108 | 60 |
| 5 Sherburn Village WMC | 30 | 19 | 3 | 8 | 102 | 42 | 60 | 60 |
| 6 Wheatley Hill WMC | 30 | 17 | 4 | 9 | 114 | 60 | 54 | 55 |
| 7 Hartlepool Res. (-3) | 30 | 17 | 4 | 9 | 102 | 45 | 57 | 52 |
| 8 Sunderland Hall Farm | 30 | 14 | 6 | 10 | 75 | 48 | 27 | 48 |
| 9 Bishop Auckland Res. | 30 | 13 | 5 | 12 | 86 | 51 | 35 | 44 |
| 10 Killingworth YPC (-6) | 30 | 14 | 7 | 9 | 74 | 59 | 15 | 43 |
| 11 Wallsend Town | 30 | 11 | 0 | 19 | 63 | 172 | -109 | 33 |
| 12 Brandon United Development (-3) | 30 | 10 | 3 | 17 | 78 | 85 | -7 | 30 |
| 13 Blackhill and Ebchester | 30 | 9 | 1 | 20 | 99 | 122 | -23 | 28 |
| 14 Sunderland Farringdon Detached (-3) | 30 | 4 | 1 | 25 | 59 | 137 | -78 | 10 |
| 15 Washington AFC | 30 | 0 | 1 | 29 | 23 | 192 | -169 | 1 |
| 16 Seaham New Westlea (-3) | 30 | 1 | 1 | 28 | 15 | 276 | -261 | 1 |

| Division One | P | W | D | L | F | A | GD | Pts |
|---|---|---|---|---|---|---|---|---|
| 1 Callington Town | 22 | 20 | 1 | 1 | 82 | 14 | 68 | 61 |
| 2 LC Phoenix | 22 | 13 | 4 | 5 | 68 | 33 | 35 | 43 |
| 3 Sticker | 22 | 11 | 5 | 6 | 72 | 36 | 36 | 38 |
| 4 Gerrans & St Mawes Utd | 22 | 10 | 6 | 6 | 81 | 51 | 30 | 36 |
| 5 St Dennis | 22 | 9 | 8 | 5 | 89 | 50 | 39 | 35 |
| 6 St Columb Major | 22 | 10 | 3 | 9 | 66 | 44 | 22 | 33 |
| 7 AFC Bodmin | 22 | 8 | 4 | 10 | 44 | 34 | 10 | 28 |
| 8 Gunnislake | 22 | 8 | 3 | 11 | 45 | 55 | -10 | 27 |
| 9 Grampound (-3) | 22 | 8 | 4 | 10 | 59 | 62 | -3 | 25 |
| 10 Altarnun | 22 | 5 | 5 | 12 | 46 | 63 | -17 | 20 |
| 11 Premier Sixes (-6) | 22 | 6 | 2 | 14 | 45 | 80 | -35 | 14 |
| 12 St Newlyn East (-6) | 22 | 1 | 1 | 20 | 18 | 193 | -175 | -2 |

| Division Two | P | W | D | L | F | A | GD | Pts |
|---|---|---|---|---|---|---|---|---|
| 1 Veryan | 22 | 20 | 2 | 0 | 111 | 8 | 103 | 62 |
| 2 Holywell and Cubert | 22 | 13 | 4 | 5 | 60 | 40 | 20 | 43 |
| 3 Tintagel | 22 | 12 | 4 | 6 | 56 | 35 | 21 | 40 |
| 4 North Hill | 22 | 12 | 1 | 9 | 44 | 41 | 3 | 37 |
| 5 Lifton | 22 | 9 | 6 | 7 | 44 | 49 | -5 | 33 |
| 6 Queens Rangers | 22 | 10 | 2 | 10 | 47 | 64 | -17 | 32 |
| 7 St Breward | 22 | 7 | 4 | 11 | 30 | 43 | -13 | 25 |
| 8 Boscastle | 22 | 7 | 3 | 12 | 41 | 40 | 1 | 24 |
| 9 St Cleer | 22 | 6 | 5 | 11 | 44 | 58 | -14 | 23 |
| 10 Godolphin Atlantic (-3) | 22 | 6 | 6 | 10 | 39 | 52 | -13 | 21 |
| 11 Calstock (-3) | 22 | 7 | 2 | 13 | 45 | 60 | -15 | 20 |
| 12 Stoke Climsland (-3) | 22 | 1 | 5 | 16 | 29 | 100 | -71 | 5 |

| Division Three | P | W | D | L | F | A | GD | Pts |
|---|---|---|---|---|---|---|---|---|
| 1 Tregrehan Mills | 24 | 18 | 3 | 3 | 80 | 30 | 50 | 57 |
| 2 Mevagissey | 23 | 16 | 4 | 3 | 100 | 35 | 65 | 52 |
| 3 St Merryn | 24 | 13 | 7 | 4 | 69 | 37 | 32 | 46 |
| 4 Gorran | 23 | 12 | 4 | 7 | 55 | 36 | 19 | 40 |
| 5 Delabole United | 24 | 12 | 3 | 9 | 67 | 54 | 13 | 39 |
| 6 St Minver Res. | 24 | 11 | 3 | 10 | 63 | 55 | 8 | 36 |
| 7 Lanivet Inn | 24 | 10 | 4 | 10 | 63 | 62 | 1 | 34 |
| 8 High Street (-3) | 24 | 11 | 2 | 11 | 42 | 49 | -7 | 32 |
| 9 North Petherwin Res. | 24 | 8 | 3 | 13 | 56 | 70 | -14 | 27 |
| 10 Grampound Res. | 24 | 8 | 3 | 13 | 47 | 67 | -20 | 27 |
| 11 Tregony | 24 | 6 | 3 | 15 | 44 | 78 | -34 | 21 |
| 12 Packhorse Athletic | 24 | 6 | 2 | 16 | 42 | 77 | -35 | 20 |
| 13 Pelynt Res. | 24 | 3 | 1 | 20 | 34 | 112 | -78 | 10 |

| Division Four | P | W | D | L | F | A | GD | Pts |
|---|---|---|---|---|---|---|---|---|
| 1 Pensilva | 22 | 16 | 1 | 5 | 91 | 25 | 66 | 49 |
| 2 Saltash United Res. | 22 | 14 | 6 | 2 | 58 | 28 | 30 | 48 |
| 3 St Dennis Res. | 22 | 13 | 3 | 6 | 55 | 33 | 22 | 42 |
| 4 Real Saltash (-6) | 22 | 14 | 3 | 5 | 76 | 40 | 36 | 39 |
| 5 Roche | 22 | 10 | 5 | 7 | 49 | 40 | 9 | 35 |
| 6 St Stephen Res. | 22 | 11 | 2 | 9 | 45 | 52 | -7 | 35 |
| 7 Padstow United (-3) | 22 | 11 | 4 | 7 | 42 | 35 | 7 | 34 |
| 8 Rame Peninsula FC | 22 | 9 | 5 | 8 | 59 | 50 | 9 | 32 |
| 9 St Teath (-6) | 22 | 8 | 0 | 14 | 40 | 57 | -17 | 18 |
| 10 St Mawgan Res. | 22 | 4 | 2 | 16 | 38 | 71 | -33 | 14 |
| 11 Southgate Seniors | 22 | 2 | 3 | 17 | 31 | 87 | -56 | 9 |
| 12 Kilkhampton | 22 | 3 | 0 | 19 | 31 | 97 | -66 | 9 |

| Division Five | P | W | D | L | F | A | GD | Pts |
|---|---|---|---|---|---|---|---|---|
| 1 Foxhole Stars Res. | 18 | 14 | 2 | 2 | 67 | 26 | 41 | 44 |
| 2 Dobwalls | 18 | 11 | 4 | 3 | 63 | 30 | 33 | 37 |
| 3 Lanreath | 18 | 10 | 5 | 3 | 55 | 22 | 33 | 35 |
| 4 Liskeard Athletic | 18 | 8 | 5 | 5 | 59 | 40 | 19 | 29 |
| 5 Boscastle Res. | 18 | 9 | 2 | 7 | 40 | 56 | -16 | 29 |
| 6 Week St Mary (-3) | 18 | 9 | 4 | 5 | 60 | 39 | 21 | 28 |
| 7 St Eval Spitfires | 18 | 8 | 2 | 8 | 49 | 49 | 0 | 26 |
| 8 Looe Town Res. (-3) | 18 | 4 | 0 | 14 | 34 | 64 | -30 | 9 |
| 9 Lostwithiel Res. | 18 | 2 | 2 | 14 | 21 | 59 | -38 | 8 |
| 10 Wadebridge Town | 18 | 1 | 2 | 15 | 26 | 89 | -63 | 5 |

Premier Sixes Res. withdrew

## EAST BERKSHIRE FOOTBALL LEAGUE

| Premier Division | P | W | D | L | F | A | GD | Pts |
|---|---|---|---|---|---|---|---|---|
| 1 Lynchpin | 15 | 14 | 0 | 1 | 38 | 18 | 20 | 42 |
| 2 Chalvey (WMC) Sports | 16 | 11 | 2 | 3 | 59 | 29 | 30 | 35 |
| 3 Iver Heath Rovers | 16 | 10 | 3 | 3 | 41 | 22 | 19 | 33 |
| 4 Langley FC | 15 | 7 | 0 | 8 | 31 | 29 | 2 | 21 |
| 5 Slough Heating Laurencians | 16 | 6 | 1 | 9 | 33 | 42 | -9 | 19 |
| 6 Windsor FC Res. | 16 | 6 | 0 | 10 | 38 | 45 | -7 | 18 |
| 7 Eton Wick | 16 | 5 | 2 | 9 | 30 | 36 | -6 | 17 |
| 8 Old Windsor | 16 | 4 | 3 | 9 | 19 | 36 | -17 | 15 |
| 9 KS Gryf | 16 | 1 | 3 | 12 | 23 | 55 | -32 | 6 |

| | Division One | P | W | D | L | F | A | GD | Pts |
|---|---|---|---|---|---|---|---|---|---|
| 1 | FC Beaconsfield | 14 | 10 | 3 | 1 | 40 | 14 | 26 | 33 |
| 2 | Richings Park | 14 | 11 | 0 | 3 | 49 | 29 | 20 | 33 |
| 3 | Burnham Beeches | 14 | 10 | 0 | 4 | 27 | 27 | 0 | 30 |
| 4 | Stoke Poges Saints FC | 14 | 5 | 2 | 7 | 30 | 33 | -3 | 17 |
| 5 | Slough Heating Laurencians Res. | 14 | 5 | 1 | 8 | 24 | 38 | -14 | 16 |
| 6 | Maidenhead Town | 14 | 4 | 1 | 9 | 32 | 34 | -2 | 13 |
| 7 | Robertswood | 14 | 3 | 2 | 9 | 29 | 42 | -13 | 11 |
| 8 | Frontline | 14 | 3 | 1 | 10 | 21 | 35 | -14 | 10 |

| Division Two | P | W | D | L | F | A | GD | Pts |
|---|---|---|---|---|---|---|---|---|
| Chalvey (WMC) Sports Res. | 16 | 15 | 0 | 1 | 69 | 25 | 44 | 45 |
| Iver Heath Rovers Res. | 16 | 14 | 1 | 1 | 54 | 22 | 32 | 43 |
| Richings Park Res. | 16 | 10 | 0 | 6 | 49 | 42 | 7 | 30 |
| Fulmer | 16 | 8 | 1 | 7 | 32 | 32 | 0 | 25 |
| LA Micro FC (-3) | 16 | 8 | 2 | 6 | 49 | 33 | 16 | 23 |
| Real Saracens (+3) | 16 | 4 | 2 | 10 | 25 | 47 | -22 | 17 |
| AFC Ascot | 16 | 4 | 1 | 11 | 31 | 54 | -23 | 13 |
| Hurley | 16 | 2 | 2 | 12 | 31 | 57 | -26 | 8 |
| Braybrooke | 16 | 2 | 1 | 13 | 21 | 49 | -28 | 7 |

| Division Three | P | W | D | L | F | A | GD | Pts |
|---|---|---|---|---|---|---|---|---|
| Maidenhead Town Res. | 22 | 18 | 3 | 1 | 73 | 33 | 40 | 57 |
| Langley Galaxy | 22 | 17 | 3 | 2 | 89 | 38 | 51 | 54 |
| Signcraft FC | 21 | 13 | 3 | 5 | 70 | 42 | 28 | 42 |
| Britwell | 21 | 11 | 3 | 7 | 57 | 41 | 16 | 36 |
| Delaford | 20 | 11 | 2 | 7 | 70 | 41 | 29 | 35 |
| Old Windsor Res. | 21 | 10 | 2 | 9 | 38 | 47 | -9 | 32 |
| Falcons (-3) | 21 | 9 | 4 | 8 | 59 | 60 | -1 | 28 |
| Eton Wick Res. (+3) | 21 | 7 | 3 | 11 | 49 | 65 | -16 | 27 |
| Phoenix Old Boys FC | 22 | 5 | 3 | 14 | 42 | 60 | -18 | 18 |
| Langley Eagles | 20 | 3 | 7 | 10 | 41 | 57 | -16 | 16 |
| Harefield St Mary's | 21 | 5 | 1 | 15 | 55 | 78 | -23 | 16 |
| Stoke Poges Saints FC Res. | 22 | 1 | 0 | 21 | 30 | 111 | -81 | 3 |

| | Division Four | P | W | D | L | F | A | GD | Pts |
|---|---|---|---|---|---|---|---|---|---|
| 1 | Willow Wanderers | 18 | 12 | 2 | 4 | 54 | 41 | 13 | 38 |
| 2 | West Drayton | 17 | 11 | 3 | 3 | 54 | 29 | 25 | 36 |
| 3 | Chalvey (WMC) Sports A | 17 | 9 | 4 | 4 | 59 | 35 | 24 | 31 |
| 4 | St Peter's Iver | 18 | 8 | 4 | 6 | 53 | 49 | 4 | 28 |
| 5 | Mercian United | 18 | 9 | 0 | 9 | 45 | 35 | 10 | 27 |
| 6 | Frontline Res. | 17 | 7 | 4 | 6 | 32 | 32 | 0 | 25 |
| 7 | Townmead | 18 | 6 | 2 | 10 | 39 | 41 | -2 | 20 |
| 8 | KS Gryf Res. | 17 | 4 | 5 | 8 | 45 | 44 | 1 | 17 |
| 9 | Upton Park Rangers | 18 | 5 | 2 | 11 | 34 | 67 | -33 | 17 |
| 10 | Langley Hornets | 18 | 2 | 4 | 12 | 23 | 65 | -42 | 10 |

## EAST RIDING AMATEUR LEAGUE

| | Premier Division | P | W | D | L | F | A | GD | Pts |
|---|---|---|---|---|---|---|---|---|---|
| 1 | Cavalier FC | 20 | 17 | 1 | 2 | 109 | 21 | 88 | 52 |
| 2 | Pinefleet Wolf'n Ath | 20 | 15 | 2 | 3 | 68 | 14 | 54 | 47 |
| 3 | West Hull United | 20 | 14 | 2 | 4 | 65 | 32 | 33 | 44 |
| 4 | Longhill Ravens | 20 | 13 | 1 | 6 | 96 | 45 | 51 | 40 |
| 5 | Apollo Rangers | 20 | 11 | 2 | 7 | 96 | 57 | 39 | 35 |
| 6 | AFC Hawthorn | 20 | 10 | 2 | 8 | 80 | 52 | 28 | 32 |
| 7 | Griffin Athletic | 20 | 9 | 3 | 8 | 38 | 41 | -3 | 30 |
| 8 | Kingston Hull FC | 20 | 7 | 1 | 12 | 43 | 83 | -40 | 22 |
| 9 | C-Force Utd | 20 | 3 | 1 | 16 | 32 | 91 | -59 | 10 |
| 10 | AFC Hawthorn Acad | 20 | 2 | 2 | 16 | 22 | 89 | -67 | 8 |
| 11 | Cockerill United | 20 | 0 | 1 | 19 | 22 | 146 | -124 | 1 |

## EAST RIDING COUNTY LEAGUE

| | Premier Division | P | W | D | L | F | A | GD | Pts |
|---|---|---|---|---|---|---|---|---|---|
| 1 | Bridlington Town Res. | 20 | 16 | 2 | 2 | 54 | 22 | 32 | 50 |
| 2 | Swinefleet Vikings | 20 | 11 | 7 | 2 | 67 | 35 | 32 | 40 |
| 3 | St George's FC | 20 | 12 | 2 | 6 | 52 | 45 | 7 | 38 |
| 4 | Beverley Town Res. | 20 | 11 | 1 | 8 | 52 | 46 | 6 | 34 |
| 5 | North Ferriby United Academy | 20 | 10 | 2 | 8 | 51 | 41 | 10 | 32 |
| 6 | Holme Rovers | 20 | 8 | 5 | 7 | 44 | 43 | 1 | 29 |
| 7 | Eddie Beedle AFC | 20 | 6 | 7 | 7 | 34 | 40 | -6 | 25 |
| 8 | Sculcoates Amateurs Res. | 20 | 7 | 3 | 10 | 39 | 54 | -15 | 24 |
| 9 | Bridlington SC County | 20 | 6 | 4 | 10 | 45 | 52 | -7 | 22 |
| 10 | Goole United Res. | 20 | 3 | 1 | 16 | 25 | 61 | -36 | 10 |
| 11 | North Cave | 20 | 2 | 2 | 16 | 34 | 58 | -24 | 8 |

| | Division One | P | W | D | L | F | A | GD | Pts |
|---|---|---|---|---|---|---|---|---|---|
| 1 | AFC Orchard | 16 | 12 | 1 | 3 | 55 | 32 | 23 | 37 |
| 2 | Leven Members Club | 16 | 9 | 5 | 2 | 48 | 27 | 21 | 32 |
| 3 | Hodgsons AFC | 16 | 8 | 4 | 4 | 49 | 28 | 21 | 28 |
| 4 | West Hull Amateurs | 16 | 8 | 3 | 5 | 46 | 34 | 12 | 27 |
| 5 | East Riding Rangers Res. | 16 | 6 | 2 | 8 | 35 | 39 | -4 | 20 |
| 6 | Beverley Town Academy | 16 | 5 | 2 | 9 | 31 | 33 | -2 | 17 |
| 7 | Hedon Rangers Res. | 16 | 4 | 3 | 9 | 27 | 47 | -20 | 15 |
| 8 | Hornsea Town Res. | 16 | 4 | 2 | 10 | 31 | 55 | -24 | 14 |
| 9 | Hunters FC Res. | 16 | 3 | 4 | 9 | 38 | 65 | -27 | 13 |

| Division Two | P | W | D | L | F | A | GD | Pts |
|---|---|---|---|---|---|---|---|---|
| 1 Hutton Cranswick SRA | 22 | 18 | 2 | 2 | 62 | 22 | 40 | 56 |
| 2 Queens County | 22 | 17 | 3 | 2 | 92 | 34 | 58 | 54 |
| 3 Middleton Rovers | 22 | 16 | 2 | 4 | 71 | 25 | 46 | 50 |
| 4 Eastern Raiders | 22 | 10 | 5 | 7 | 41 | 62 | -21 | 35 |
| 5 Haltemprice | 22 | 10 | 4 | 8 | 59 | 43 | 16 | 34 |
| 6 Apollo Rangers | 22 | 9 | 2 | 11 | 72 | 65 | 7 | 29 |
| 7 Wawne United Res. | 22 | 8 | 5 | 9 | 47 | 56 | -9 | 29 |
| 8 Roos | 22 | 8 | 3 | 11 | 60 | 59 | 1 | 27 |
| 9 Driffield Evening Institute Res. | 22 | 7 | 3 | 12 | 45 | 66 | -21 | 24 |
| 10 Skirlaugh | 22 | 6 | 5 | 11 | 34 | 44 | -10 | 23 |
| 11 Newland St John's | 22 | 2 | 2 | 18 | 38 | 81 | -43 | 8 |
| 12 Orchard Park | 22 | 2 | 2 | 18 | 44 | 108 | -64 | 8 |

| Division Three | P | W | D | L | F | A | GD | Pts |
|---|---|---|---|---|---|---|---|---|
| 1 AFC North | 20 | 15 | 1 | 4 | 68 | 35 | 33 | 46 |
| 2 Wawne United 3rd Team | 20 | 13 | 4 | 3 | 68 | 41 | 27 | 43 |
| 3 Harchester United | 20 | 12 | 4 | 4 | 71 | 27 | 44 | 40 |
| 4 South Cave Utd Res. | 20 | 12 | 1 | 7 | 48 | 51 | -3 | 37 |
| 5 AFC Longhill | 20 | 11 | 1 | 8 | 46 | 40 | 6 | 34 |
| 6 Waterloo | 20 | 10 | 2 | 8 | 68 | 47 | 21 | 32 |
| 7 Easington United Res. | 20 | 9 | 2 | 9 | 38 | 61 | -23 | 29 |
| 8 FC Georgies Bar | 20 | 7 | 2 | 11 | 34 | 57 | -23 | 23 |
| 9 Gilberdyke Phoenix | 20 | 6 | 1 | 13 | 46 | 64 | -18 | 19 |
| 10 South Park Rangers | 20 | 5 | 2 | 13 | 39 | 51 | -12 | 17 |
| 11 Howden Res. | 20 | 0 | 0 | 20 | 10 | 62 | -52 | 0 |

| Division Four | P | W | D | L | F | A | GD | Pts |
|---|---|---|---|---|---|---|---|---|
| 1 Withernsea | 22 | 19 | 2 | 1 | 88 | 27 | 61 | 59 |
| 2 Skirlaugh Res. | 22 | 17 | 2 | 3 | 84 | 31 | 53 | 53 |
| 3 AFC Duke of York | 22 | 11 | 4 | 7 | 61 | 48 | 13 | 37 |
| 4 East Riding Rangers 3rds | 21 | 10 | 5 | 6 | 46 | 38 | 8 | 35 |
| 5 Holme Rovers Res. | 22 | 9 | 3 | 10 | 53 | 59 | -6 | 30 |
| 6 Langtoft | 22 | 8 | 6 | 8 | 42 | 56 | -14 | 30 |
| 7 AFC Northfield Res. | 22 | 7 | 7 | 8 | 36 | 53 | -17 | 28 |
| 8 Driffield Red Lion | 22 | 8 | 3 | 11 | 54 | 69 | -15 | 27 |
| 9 Eastrington Village | 22 | 8 | 2 | 12 | 67 | 50 | 17 | 26 |
| 10 Long Riston | 22 | 6 | 3 | 13 | 50 | 76 | -26 | 21 |
| 11 Hornsea Town 3rd Team | 22 | 4 | 2 | 16 | 45 | 98 | -53 | 14 |
| 12 Westella& Willerby County | 21 | 3 | 3 | 15 | 47 | 68 | -21 | 12 |

| Division Five | P | W | D | L | F | A | GD | Pts |
|---|---|---|---|---|---|---|---|---|
| 1 Hedon Rangers 3rds | 22 | 16 | 3 | 3 | 82 | 41 | 41 | 51 |
| 2 Little Driffield AFC | 22 | 14 | 6 | 2 | 67 | 38 | 29 | 48 |
| 3 AFC Hawthorn | 22 | 14 | 4 | 4 | 64 | 29 | 35 | 46 |
| 4 AFC North Res. | 22 | 12 | 4 | 6 | 65 | 52 | 13 | 40 |
| 5 Patrington Res. | 22 | 11 | 4 | 7 | 50 | 49 | 1 | 37 |
| 6 Market Weighton United | 22 | 9 | 4 | 9 | 73 | 61 | 12 | 31 |
| 7 Kingston Hull | 22 | 10 | 1 | 11 | 65 | 68 | -3 | 31 |
| 8 West Hull Amateurs Res. | 22 | 9 | 2 | 11 | 59 | 72 | -13 | 29 |
| 9 Leven Members Club Res. | 22 | 6 | 4 | 12 | 43 | 60 | -17 | 22 |
| 10 C-Force Utd | 22 | 5 | 3 | 14 | 34 | 32 | 2 | 18 |
| 11 Orchard Park Res. | 22 | 5 | 1 | 16 | 63 | 106 | -43 | 16 |
| 12 Easington United Casuals | 22 | 3 | 0 | 19 | 24 | 81 | -57 | 9 |

| Division Six | P | W | D | L | F | A | GD | Pts |
|---|---|---|---|---|---|---|---|---|
| 1 Brandesburton Res. | 18 | 15 | 0 | 3 | 57 | 30 | 27 | 45 |
| 2 Cottingham Rangers | 18 | 12 | 1 | 5 | 58 | 38 | 20 | 37 |
| 3 Market Weighton United Res. | 18 | 12 | 0 | 6 | 76 | 50 | 26 | 36 |
| 4 Banks Harbour | 18 | 11 | 3 | 4 | 71 | 52 | 19 | 36 |
| 5 East Riding Rangers 4ths | 18 | 9 | 3 | 6 | 65 | 50 | 15 | 30 |
| 6 New Cleveland Wolves | 18 | 7 | 2 | 9 | 42 | 51 | -9 | 23 |
| 7 Griffin Athletic | 18 | 7 | 1 | 10 | 42 | 38 | 4 | 22 |
| 8 Withernsea Res. | 18 | 5 | 2 | 11 | 54 | 63 | -9 | 17 |
| 9 South Park Rangers Juniors | 18 | 4 | 1 | 13 | 44 | 87 | -43 | 13 |
| 10 Molescroft Rangers Res. | 18 | 1 | 1 | 16 | 34 | 84 | -50 | 4 |

## ESKVALE & CLEVELAND FOOTBALL LEAGUE

| Division One | P | W | D | L | F | A | GD | Pts |
|---|---|---|---|---|---|---|---|---|
| 1 Great Ayton United Royals | 20 | 17 | 1 | 2 | 90 | 25 | 65 | [illegible] |
| 2 Redcar Athletic | 20 | 15 | 1 | 4 | 85 | 26 | 59 | [illegible] |
| 3 Dormanstown (-3) | 20 | 12 | 4 | 4 | 55 | 37 | 18 | [illegible] |
| 4 Loftus Athletic | 20 | 11 | 3 | 6 | 61 | 40 | 21 | [illegible] |
| 5 Great Ayton Utd | 20 | 9 | 1 | 10 | 52 | 39 | 13 | [illegible] |
| 6 Stokesley SC (-6) | 20 | 11 | 0 | 9 | 50 | 44 | 6 | [illegible] |
| 7 Boosbeck Utd AFC (-3) | 20 | 9 | 2 | 9 | 36 | 44 | -8 | [illegible] |
| 8 Brotton Railway Arms FC | 20 | 8 | 1 | 11 | 47 | 67 | -20 | [illegible] |
| 9 Lealholm FC | 20 | 7 | 1 | 12 | 38 | 55 | -17 | [illegible] |
| 10 Hinderwell F.C. | 20 | 3 | 0 | 17 | 23 | 90 | -67 | [illegible] |
| 11 Lakes United (-3) | 20 | 1 | 0 | 19 | 23 | 93 | -70 | [illegible] |

## FURNESS PREMIER LEAGUE

| Premier Division | P | W | D | L | F | A | GD | Pts |
|---|---|---|---|---|---|---|---|---|
| 1 Kirkby United | 28 | 22 | 1 | 5 | 85 | 43 | 42 | [illegible] |
| 2 Vickerstown CC Res. | 28 | 20 | 2 | 6 | 86 | 48 | 38 | [illegible] |
| 3 Hawcoat Park Res. | 28 | 18 | 3 | 7 | 84 | 48 | 36 | [illegible] |
| 4 Haverigg United | 28 | 17 | 3 | 8 | 79 | 44 | 35 | [illegible] |
| 5 Holker Old Boys Res. | 28 | 16 | 3 | 9 | 94 | 46 | 48 | [illegible] |
| 6 GSK Ulverston Rangers Res. | 28 | 12 | 6 | 10 | 54 | 55 | -1 | [illegible] |
| 7 Barrow Celtic | 28 | 11 | 2 | 15 | 66 | 76 | -10 | [illegible] |
| 8 Furness Rovers Res. | 28 | 10 | 5 | 13 | 47 | 63 | -16 | [illegible] |
| 9 Furness Cavaliers Res. | 28 | 10 | 4 | 14 | 42 | 69 | -27 | [illegible] |
| 10 Britannia (-6) | 28 | 12 | 2 | 14 | 55 | 71 | -16 | [illegible] |
| 11 Swarthmoor Social Res. | 28 | 8 | 5 | 15 | 49 | 73 | -24 | [illegible] |
| 12 Millom Res. | 28 | 9 | 1 | 18 | 61 | 75 | -14 | [illegible] |
| 13 Bootle | 28 | 7 | 5 | 16 | 42 | 64 | -22 | [illegible] |
| 14 Askam United Res. (-6) | 28 | 9 | 3 | 16 | 55 | 77 | -22 | [illegible] |
| 15 Barrow Wanderers (-3) | 28 | 5 | 3 | 20 | 42 | 89 | -47 | [illegible] |

| Division One | P | W | D | L | F | A | GD | Pts |
|---|---|---|---|---|---|---|---|---|
| 1 Croftlands Park | 20 | 16 | 2 | 2 | 116 | 19 | 97 | [illegible] |
| 2 Walney Island Res. | 20 | 13 | 2 | 5 | 41 | 27 | 14 | [illegible] |
| 3 Dalton United Res. | 20 | 12 | 2 | 6 | 59 | 39 | 20 | [illegible] |
| 4 Crooklands Casuals Res. | 20 | 10 | 4 | 6 | 48 | 39 | 9 | [illegible] |
| 5 Vickerstown CC A | 20 | 9 | 4 | 7 | 48 | 49 | -1 | [illegible] |
| 6 Hawcoat Park A | 20 | 9 | 3 | 8 | 45 | 44 | 1 | [illegible] |
| 7 Holker Old Boys A (-3) | 20 | 8 | 2 | 10 | 63 | 48 | 15 | [illegible] |
| 8 Haverigg United Res. | 20 | 7 | 1 | 12 | 29 | 73 | -44 | [illegible] |
| 9 Barrow Celtic Res. | 20 | 6 | 2 | 12 | 56 | 75 | -19 | [illegible] |
| 10 Barrow Wanderers Res. (-3) | 20 | 5 | 1 | 14 | 38 | 82 | -44 | [illegible] |
| 11 GSK Ulverston Rangers A | 20 | 3 | 1 | 16 | 35 | 83 | -48 | [illegible] |

| | Division Two | P | W | D | L | F | A | GD | Pts |
|---|---|---|---|---|---|---|---|---|---|
| 1 | Ormsgill North End | 16 | 13 | 1 | 2 | 68 | 14 | 54 | 40 |
| 2 | Millom A | 16 | 10 | 1 | 5 | 62 | 38 | 24 | 31 |
| 3 | Kirkby United Res. | 16 | 8 | 2 | 6 | 45 | 37 | 8 | 26 |
| 4 | Britannia Res. | 16 | 8 | 1 | 7 | 48 | 35 | 13 | 25 |
| 5 | Dalton United A | 16 | 8 | 1 | 7 | 42 | 48 | -6 | 25 |
| 6 | Bootle Res. | 16 | 7 | 1 | 8 | 29 | 44 | -15 | 22 |
| 7 | FC Barrow Island (-9) | 16 | 10 | 0 | 6 | 60 | 44 | 16 | 21 |
| 8 | Walney Island A | 16 | 2 | 2 | 12 | 19 | 62 | -43 | 8 |
| 9 | Coniston Res. (-3) | 16 | 1 | 1 | 14 | 18 | 69 | -51 | 1 |

## GLOUCESTERSHIRE NORTHERN SENIOR LEAGUE

| | Division One | P | W | D | L | F | A | GD | Pts |
|---|---|---|---|---|---|---|---|---|---|
| 1 | Sharpness | 28 | 22 | 2 | 4 | 78 | 37 | 41 | 68 |
| 2 | Stonehouse Town | 28 | 20 | 4 | 4 | 66 | 29 | 37 | 64 |
| 3 | Newent Town | 28 | 16 | 5 | 7 | 69 | 42 | 27 | 53 |
| 4 | Taverners | 28 | 14 | 5 | 9 | 68 | 53 | 15 | 47 |
| 5 | FC Barometrics (-3) | 28 | 15 | 3 | 10 | 69 | 51 | 18 | 45 |
| 6 | Charlton Rovers | 28 | 11 | 8 | 9 | 44 | 33 | 11 | 41 |
| 7 | Cam Bulldogs | 28 | 12 | 4 | 12 | 54 | 57 | -3 | 40 |
| 8 | Ruardean Hill Rangers | 28 | 11 | 6 | 11 | 53 | 64 | -11 | 39 |
| 9 | Brockworth Albion | 28 | 9 | 10 | 9 | 46 | 47 | -1 | 37 |
| 10 | Tuffley Rovers Res. (-3) | 28 | 10 | 4 | 14 | 56 | 68 | -12 | 31 |
| 11 | Harrow Hill | 28 | 7 | 7 | 14 | 46 | 55 | -9 | 28 |
| 12 | Berkeley Town (-3) | 28 | 9 | 4 | 15 | 51 | 65 | -14 | 28 |
| 13 | Southside Star | 28 | 7 | 7 | 14 | 43 | 69 | -26 | 28 |
| 14 | Avonvale United | 28 | 7 | 2 | 19 | 49 | 74 | -25 | 23 |
| 15 | Dursley Town | 28 | 2 | 5 | 21 | 32 | 81 | -49 | 11 |

| Division Two | P | W | D | L | F | A | GD | Pts |
|---|---|---|---|---|---|---|---|---|
| Bibury | 30 | 25 | 2 | 3 | 113 | 36 | 77 | 77 |
| Bredon | 30 | 19 | 7 | 4 | 66 | 27 | 39 | 64 |
| Leonard Stanley | 30 | 19 | 3 | 8 | 88 | 49 | 39 | 60 |
| Quedgeley Wanderers | 30 | 13 | 9 | 8 | 64 | 45 | 19 | 48 |
| Chalford | 30 | 14 | 5 | 11 | 69 | 34 | 35 | 47 |
| Whaddon United | 30 | 13 | 8 | 9 | 73 | 51 | 22 | 47 |
| Lydney Town Res. | 30 | 14 | 4 | 12 | 78 | 43 | 35 | 46 |
| Woolaston | 30 | 12 | 6 | 12 | 52 | 51 | 1 | 42 |
| Longlevens Res. (-3) | 30 | 13 | 5 | 12 | 62 | 43 | 19 | 41 |
| English Bicknor | 30 | 12 | 4 | 14 | 53 | 50 | 3 | 40 |
| Smiths Athletic | 30 | 10 | 9 | 11 | 46 | 54 | -8 | 39 |
| Lydbrook Athletic | 30 | 9 | 9 | 12 | 47 | 64 | -17 | 36 |
| Winchcombe Town | 30 | 9 | 6 | 15 | 61 | 68 | -7 | 33 |
| Wotton Rovers | 30 | 8 | 5 | 17 | 35 | 64 | -29 | 29 |
| Abbeymead Rovers | 30 | 8 | 2 | 20 | 54 | 66 | -12 | 26 |
| Longford | 30 | 0 | 0 | 30 | 10 | 226 | -216 | 0 |

## GUILDFORD & WOKING ALLIANCE LEAGUE

| | Premier Division | P | W | D | L | F | A | GD | Pts |
|---|---|---|---|---|---|---|---|---|---|
| 1 | Lyne Youth (Mens) | 16 | 14 | 2 | 0 | 41 | 11 | 30 | 44 |
| 2 | Parkside United | 16 | 13 | 0 | 3 | 56 | 20 | 36 | 39 |
| 3 | Holmbury St Mary | 16 | 11 | 2 | 3 | 46 | 22 | 24 | 35 |
| 4 | Guildford Rangers | 16 | 8 | 1 | 7 | 37 | 30 | 7 | 25 |
| 5 | Manorcroft United | 16 | 7 | 3 | 6 | 30 | 26 | 4 | 24 |
| 6 | Chertsey Old Salesians | 16 | 5 | 3 | 8 | 23 | 36 | -13 | 18 |
| 7 | AFC Westend | 16 | 4 | 0 | 12 | 17 | 43 | -26 | 12 |
| 8 | Shalford | 16 | 2 | 1 | 13 | 21 | 48 | -27 | 7 |
| 9 | N.L.U. | 16 | 2 | 0 | 14 | 18 | 53 | -35 | 6 |

| | Division One | P | W | D | L | F | A | GD | Pts |
|---|---|---|---|---|---|---|---|---|---|
| 1 | Worplesdon Phoenix 'A' | 18 | 16 | 1 | 1 | 70 | 20 | 50 | 49 |
| 2 | Burpham | 18 | 10 | 3 | 5 | 42 | 34 | 8 | 33 |
| 3 | Weysiders | 18 | 9 | 4 | 5 | 42 | 31 | 11 | 31 |
| 4 | AFC Westend Res. (-3) | 18 | 9 | 4 | 5 | 43 | 30 | 13 | 28 |
| 5 | Swinley Forest | 18 | 7 | 4 | 7 | 51 | 49 | 2 | 25 |
| 6 | Heathervale | 18 | 7 | 1 | 10 | 25 | 36 | -11 | 22 |
| 7 | University of Surrey 'A' | 18 | 7 | 1 | 10 | 40 | 55 | -15 | 22 |
| 8 | Woking United Sports Club. | 18 | 4 | 3 | 11 | 32 | 45 | -13 | 15 |
| 9 | Allianz | 18 | 4 | 3 | 11 | 29 | 48 | -19 | 15 |
| 10 | Woking & Maybury | 18 | 4 | 2 | 12 | 44 | 70 | -26 | 14 |

| | Division Two | P | W | D | L | F | A | GD | Pts |
|---|---|---|---|---|---|---|---|---|---|
| 1 | Elstead | 18 | 14 | 1 | 3 | 52 | 23 | 29 | 43 |
| 2 | AFC Bedfont Green | 18 | 14 | 1 | 3 | 40 | 20 | 20 | 43 |
| 3 | West Byfleet Albion | 18 | 12 | 3 | 3 | 44 | 21 | 23 | 39 |
| 4 | Ockham | 18 | 10 | 1 | 7 | 35 | 30 | 5 | 31 |
| 5 | Chertsey Curfews | 18 | 7 | 1 | 10 | 43 | 45 | -2 | 22 |
| 6 | Bourne Blades | 18 | 6 | 2 | 10 | 38 | 53 | -15 | 20 |
| 7 | Puttenham United | 18 | 6 | 1 | 11 | 32 | 41 | -9 | 19 |
| 8 | Merrow 'A' | 18 | 5 | 2 | 11 | 36 | 56 | -20 | 17 |
| 9 | FC Shepperton | 18 | 4 | 3 | 11 | 27 | 35 | -8 | 15 |
| 10 | Surrey Athletic | 18 | 4 | 1 | 13 | 29 | 52 | -23 | 13 |

| | Division Three | P | W | D | L | F | A | GD | Pts |
|---|---|---|---|---|---|---|---|---|---|
| 1 | Deepcut Community | 18 | 15 | 1 | 2 | 68 | 15 | 53 | 46 |
| 2 | Woking Tigers | 18 | 15 | 1 | 2 | 70 | 32 | 38 | 46 |
| 3 | UFC Farnham | 18 | 13 | 2 | 3 | 67 | 31 | 36 | 41 |
| 4 | Farncombe Athletic | 18 | 10 | 2 | 6 | 70 | 43 | 27 | 32 |
| 5 | Dunsfold | 18 | 8 | 0 | 10 | 44 | 35 | 9 | 24 |
| 6 | Woking Corinthians | 18 | 7 | 0 | 11 | 35 | 52 | -17 | 21 |
| 7 | Burpham Res. | 18 | 5 | 4 | 9 | 34 | 40 | -6 | 19 |
| 8 | Blackwater Royals | 18 | 5 | 2 | 11 | 25 | 61 | -36 | 17 |
| 9 | Shottermill & Haslemere 'A' | 18 | 3 | 1 | 14 | 19 | 76 | -57 | 10 |
| 10 | Addlestone United | 18 | 1 | 3 | 14 | 18 | 65 | -47 | 6 |

| Division Four | P | W | D | L | F | A | GD | Pts |
|---|---|---|---|---|---|---|---|---|
| 1 Byfleet | 16 | 13 | 0 | 3 | 63 | 24 | 39 | 39 |
| 2 Staines Lammas Res. | 16 | 12 | 3 | 1 | 61 | 26 | 35 | 39 |
| 3 Laleham Athletic | 16 | 10 | 1 | 5 | 60 | 27 | 33 | 31 |
| 4 FC Staines | 16 | 7 | 2 | 7 | 27 | 33 | -6 | 23 |
| 5 Hersham Sports & Social | 16 | 7 | 1 | 8 | 45 | 35 | 10 | 22 |
| 6 Ockham Res. | 16 | 6 | 3 | 7 | 31 | 30 | 1 | 21 |
| 7 Shalford Res. | 16 | 5 | 0 | 11 | 27 | 54 | -27 | 15 |
| 8 Woking & Horsell 'A' | 16 | 4 | 3 | 9 | 23 | 51 | -28 | 15 |
| 9 Knaphill Athletic 'A' | 16 | 1 | 1 | 14 | 24 | 81 | -57 | 4 |

| Division Five | P | W | D | L | F | A | GD | Pts |
|---|---|---|---|---|---|---|---|---|
| 1 Farncombe Athletic Res. | 16 | 13 | 1 | 2 | 52 | 24 | 28 | 40 |
| 2 Walton Comrades | 16 | 12 | 1 | 3 | 66 | 17 | 49 | 37 |
| 3 University of Surrey 'B' | 16 | 9 | 3 | 4 | 54 | 24 | 30 | 30 |
| 4 Hambledon 'A' | 16 | 8 | 1 | 7 | 30 | 35 | -5 | 25 |
| 5 Weysiders Res. | 16 | 7 | 1 | 8 | 32 | 28 | 4 | 22 |
| 6 Guildford Barbarians | 16 | 6 | 3 | 7 | 30 | 40 | -10 | 21 |
| 7 Burpham 'A' | 16 | 4 | 1 | 11 | 26 | 48 | -22 | 13 |
| 8 Hersham | 16 | 4 | 0 | 12 | 20 | 58 | -38 | 12 |
| 9 UFC Farnham Res. | 16 | 2 | 3 | 11 | 26 | 62 | -36 | 9 |

## GREAT YARMOUTH & DISTRICT LEAGUE

| | P | W | D | L | F | A | GD | Pts |
|---|---|---|---|---|---|---|---|---|
| 1 Catfield (-1) | 22 | 20 | 1 | 1 | 172 | 18 | 154 | 60 |
| 2 Great Yarmouth Town Hall FC | 22 | 18 | 1 | 3 | 90 | 24 | 66 | 55 |
| 3 Belton FC | 22 | 16 | 3 | 3 | 104 | 43 | 61 | 51 |
| 4 Caister FC A | 22 | 12 | 4 | 6 | 62 | 36 | 26 | 40 |
| 5 Prostar Windows | 22 | 12 | 3 | 7 | 72 | 62 | 10 | 39 |
| 6 Mariners FC (-1) | 22 | 10 | 1 | 11 | 68 | 60 | 8 | 30 |
| 7 Bohemians | 22 | 8 | 4 | 10 | 46 | 52 | -6 | 28 |
| 8 Hemsby Res. (-1) | 22 | 7 | 2 | 13 | 52 | 72 | -20 | 22 |
| 9 Bohemians Res. (-1) | 22 | 6 | 3 | 13 | 40 | 80 | -40 | 20 |
| 10 Sportsmans FC | 22 | 6 | 1 | 15 | 50 | 87 | -37 | 19 |
| 11 Filby and Runham | 22 | 1 | 4 | 17 | 24 | 91 | -67 | 7 |
| 12 Caister FC B | 22 | 1 | 3 | 18 | 14 | 169 | -155 | 6 |

## GUERNSEY FOOTBALL ASSOCIATION LEAGUE

| Priaulx League | P | W | D | L | F | A | GD | Pts |
|---|---|---|---|---|---|---|---|---|
| 1 North A C | 18 | 15 | 1 | 2 | 69 | 24 | 45 | 46 |
| 2 Rovers AC | 18 | 13 | 1 | 4 | 53 | 25 | 28 | 40 |
| 3 Vale Recreation | 18 | 12 | 2 | 4 | 57 | 25 | 32 | 38 |
| 4 UCF Sylvans | 18 | 8 | 0 | 10 | 31 | 49 | -18 | 24 |
| 5 St Martins FC | 18 | 7 | 1 | 10 | 29 | 44 | -15 | 22 |
| 6 Belgrave Wanderers | 18 | 5 | 0 | 13 | 29 | 53 | -24 | 15 |
| 7 Rangers F C | 18 | 0 | 1 | 17 | 18 | 66 | -48 | 1 |

| Jackson League | P | W | D | L | F | A | GD | Pts |
|---|---|---|---|---|---|---|---|---|
| 1 North AC | 12 | 10 | 2 | 0 | 48 | 26 | 22 | 32 |
| 2 Rovers AC | 12 | 8 | 2 | 2 | 43 | 24 | 19 | 26 |
| 3 Vale Recreation | 12 | 7 | 1 | 4 | 45 | 25 | 20 | 22 |
| 4 Belgrave Wanderers | 12 | 5 | 1 | 6 | 31 | 36 | -5 | 16 |
| 5 UCF Sylvans | 12 | 5 | 0 | 7 | 35 | 38 | -3 | 15 |
| 6 St Martins AC | 12 | 2 | 0 | 10 | 26 | 39 | -13 | 6 |
| 7 Rangers FC | 12 | 2 | 0 | 10 | 23 | 63 | -40 | 6 |

| Railway League | P | W | D | L | F | A | GD | Pts |
|---|---|---|---|---|---|---|---|---|
| 1 Captains | 24 | 22 | 0 | 2 | 109 | 18 | 91 | 66 |
| 2 Manzur | 24 | 21 | 0 | 3 | 100 | 25 | 75 | 63 |
| 3 Vale Recreation | 24 | 18 | 0 | 6 | 104 | 34 | 70 | 54 |
| 4 Fusion Rangers | 24 | 14 | 3 | 7 | 56 | 49 | 7 | 45 |
| 5 Rising Bet | 24 | 14 | 1 | 9 | 55 | 50 | 5 | 43 |
| 6 Northerners | 24 | 12 | 2 | 10 | 72 | 61 | 11 | 38 |
| 7 UCF Sylvans | 24 | 12 | 1 | 11 | 60 | 51 | 9 | 37 |
| 8 Rovers AC | 24 | 10 | 5 | 9 | 60 | 62 | -2 | 35 |
| 9 Richmond Wanderers | 24 | 10 | 1 | 13 | 58 | 76 | -18 | 31 |
| 10 Manor Farm Saints | 24 | 6 | 1 | 17 | 37 | 79 | -42 | 19 |
| 11 Centrals | 24 | 5 | 2 | 17 | 42 | 91 | -49 | 17 |
| 12 United F C | 24 | 3 | 2 | 19 | 26 | 111 | -85 | 11 |
| 13 Herm | 24 | 0 | 0 | 24 | 0 | 72 | -72 | 0 |

## HALIFAX & DISTRICT AFL

| Premier Division | P | W | D | L | F | A | GD | Pts |
|---|---|---|---|---|---|---|---|---|
| 1 Calder 76 | 20 | 17 | 0 | 3 | 69 | 22 | 47 | 51 |
| 2 Ryburn United | 20 | 15 | 0 | 5 | 75 | 30 | 45 | 45 |
| 3 Mixenden United | 20 | 14 | 2 | 4 | 45 | 32 | 13 | 44 |
| 4 Midgley United | 20 | 10 | 3 | 7 | 45 | 40 | 5 | 33 |
| 5 Shelf United | 20 | 9 | 3 | 8 | 49 | 48 | 1 | 30 |
| 6 Warley Rangers Halifax | 20 | 8 | 5 | 7 | 56 | 41 | 15 | 29 |
| 7 Hebden Royd RS | 20 | 7 | 3 | 10 | 47 | 58 | -11 | 24 |
| 8 Greetland AFC | 20 | 6 | 2 | 12 | 37 | 51 | -14 | 20 |
| 9 Northowram | 20 | 5 | 5 | 10 | 35 | 50 | -15 | [illegible] |
| 10 Copley United | 20 | 5 | 1 | 14 | 39 | 68 | -29 | 16 |
| 11 Holmfield | 20 | 0 | 4 | 16 | 23 | 80 | -57 | 4 |

| Division One | P | W | D | L | F | A | GD | Pts |
|---|---|---|---|---|---|---|---|---|
| 1 Illingworth St Marys | 24 | 24 | 0 | 0 | 181 | 25 | 156 | [illegible] |
| 2 Sowerby United | 24 | 18 | 1 | 5 | 89 | 43 | 46 | [illegible] |
| 3 Brighouse Sports AFC | 24 | 18 | 1 | 5 | 80 | 37 | 43 | [illegible] |
| 4 Denholme United | 24 | 16 | 4 | 4 | 72 | 51 | 21 | [illegible] |
| 5 Sowerby Bridge | 24 | 12 | 4 | 8 | 60 | 55 | 5 | [illegible] |
| 6 Ryburn United Res. | 24 | 11 | 1 | 12 | 72 | 75 | -3 | [illegible] |
| 7 Elland United | 24 | 9 | 2 | 13 | 62 | 57 | 5 | [illegible] |
| 8 Elland Allstars | 24 | 7 | 4 | 13 | 50 | 73 | -23 | [illegible] |
| 9 Calder 76 Res. | 24 | 5 | 7 | 12 | 32 | 62 | -30 | [illegible] |
| 10 AFC Crossleys | 24 | 7 | 1 | 16 | 66 | 111 | -45 | [illegible] |
| 11 Salem | 24 | 7 | 1 | 16 | 47 | 110 | -63 | [illegible] |
| 12 Midgley United Res. | 24 | 5 | 3 | 16 | 34 | 59 | -25 | [illegible] |
| 13 Halifax Irish Centre | 24 | 1 | 3 | 20 | 30 | 117 | -87 | [illegible] |

| Division Two | P | W | D | L | F | A | GD | Pts |
|---|---|---|---|---|---|---|---|---|
| 1 Greetland AFC Res. | 22 | 18 | 2 | 2 | 96 | 30 | 66 | [illegible] |
| 2 Shelf FC | 22 | 16 | 3 | 3 | 78 | 40 | 38 | [illegible] |
| 3 St Columbas | 22 | 15 | 3 | 4 | 68 | 39 | 29 | [illegible] |
| 4 Illingworth St Marys Res. | 22 | 14 | 2 | 6 | 75 | 37 | 38 | [illegible] |
| 5 Sowerby United Res. | 22 | 12 | 2 | 8 | 62 | 52 | 10 | [illegible] |
| 6 Northowram Res. | 22 | 11 | 2 | 9 | 69 | 60 | 9 | [illegible] |
| 7 Denholme United Res. | 22 | 7 | 4 | 11 | 34 | 52 | -18 | [illegible] |
| 8 Sowerby Bridge Res. | 22 | 6 | 3 | 13 | 58 | 76 | -18 | [illegible] |
| 9 Shelf United Res. | 22 | 4 | 7 | 11 | 52 | 76 | -24 | [illegible] |
| 10 Hebden Royd RS Res. | 22 | 5 | 3 | 14 | 48 | 77 | -29 | [illegible] |
| 11 Salem Res. | 22 | 3 | 3 | 16 | 41 | 88 | -47 | [illegible] |
| 12 AFC Crossleys Res. | 22 | 4 | 0 | 18 | 30 | 84 | -54 | [illegible] |

## HARROGATE AND DISTRICT FOOTBALL LEAGUE

| Premier Division | | P | W | D | L | F | A | GD | Pts |
|---|---|---|---|---|---|---|---|---|---|
| 1 | Bedale Town | 20 | 18 | 1 | 1 | 65 | 27 | 38 | 55 |
| 2 | Rawdon Old Boys | 20 | 18 | 0 | 2 | 60 | 13 | 47 | 54 |
| 3 | Clifford | 20 | 10 | 3 | 7 | 54 | 44 | 10 | 33 |
| 4 | Wetherby Athletic A | 20 | 10 | 2 | 8 | 39 | 40 | -1 | 32 |
| 5 | Knaresborough Celtic | 20 | 9 | 2 | 9 | 49 | 45 | 4 | 29 |
| 6 | Kirk Deighton Rangers | 20 | 8 | 2 | 10 | 40 | 41 | -1 | 26 |
| 7 | Hampsthwaite United | 20 | 6 | 4 | 10 | 40 | 46 | -6 | 22 |
| 8 | Harlow Hill | 20 | 6 | 0 | 14 | 42 | 61 | -19 | 18 |
| 9 | Beckwithshaw Saints | 20 | 4 | 5 | 11 | 27 | 45 | -18 | 17 |
| 10 | Kirkstall Crusaders FC | 20 | 5 | 2 | 13 | 36 | 61 | -25 | 17 |
| 11 | Kirkby Malzeard | 20 | 5 | 1 | 14 | 27 | 56 | -29 | 16 |

| Division One | | P | W | D | L | F | A | GD | Pts |
|---|---|---|---|---|---|---|---|---|---|
| 1 | AFC Horsforth | 24 | 23 | 0 | 1 | 90 | 19 | 71 | 69 |
| 2 | Pannal Sports | 24 | 17 | 5 | 2 | 72 | 37 | 35 | 56 |
| 3 | Bramham | 24 | 14 | 3 | 7 | 60 | 48 | 12 | 45 |
| 4 | Burley Trojans | 24 | 12 | 6 | 6 | 64 | 53 | 11 | 42 |
| 5 | Dalton Athletic | 24 | 10 | 5 | 9 | 73 | 57 | 16 | 35 |
| 6 | Boroughbridge A | 24 | 10 | 4 | 10 | 68 | 61 | 7 | 34 |
| 7 | Beckwithshaw Saints Res. | 24 | 8 | 5 | 11 | 40 | 75 | -35 | 29 |
| 8 | Pateley Bridge | 24 | 8 | 4 | 12 | 63 | 62 | 1 | 28 |
| 9 | Thirsk Falcons Res. | 24 | 8 | 3 | 13 | 47 | 56 | -9 | 27 |
| 10 | Hampsthwaite HC | 24 | 8 | 0 | 16 | 51 | 88 | -37 | 24 |
| 11 | Harlow Hill Res. | 24 | 4 | 6 | 14 | 31 | 39 | -8 | 18 |
| 12 | Ripon Red Arrows | 24 | 5 | 3 | 16 | 45 | 77 | -32 | 18 |
| 13 | Kirk Deighton Rangers Res. | 24 | 4 | 6 | 14 | 34 | 66 | -32 | 18 |

| Division Two | | P | W | D | L | F | A | GD | Pts |
|---|---|---|---|---|---|---|---|---|---|
| | Knaresborough Celtic Res. | 24 | 20 | 1 | 3 | 101 | 39 | 62 | 61 |
| 2 | Helperby United | 24 | 18 | 1 | 5 | 91 | 45 | 46 | 55 |
| 3 | Bramhope | 24 | 15 | 3 | 6 | 78 | 45 | 33 | 48 |
| | Addingham | 24 | 14 | 1 | 9 | 70 | 56 | 14 | 43 |
| | FC Harrogate | 24 | 13 | 3 | 8 | 59 | 54 | 5 | 42 |
| | Bardsey Res. | 24 | 11 | 3 | 10 | 57 | 52 | 5 | 36 |
| | AFC Horsforth Res. | 24 | 9 | 3 | 12 | 56 | 65 | -9 | 30 |
| | Westbrook YMCA Res. | 24 | 8 | 5 | 11 | 42 | 59 | -17 | 29 |
| | FC United Knaresborough | 24 | 8 | 3 | 13 | 59 | 85 | -26 | 27 |
| 0 | Kirkby Malzeard Res. | 24 | 8 | 2 | 14 | 49 | 56 | -7 | 26 |
| 1 | Hampsthwaite United Res. | 24 | 8 | 0 | 16 | 47 | 62 | -15 | 24 |
| 2 | Pannal Sports Res. | 24 | 6 | 2 | 16 | 42 | 82 | -40 | 20 |
| 3 | Pool A | 24 | 4 | 1 | 19 | 38 | 89 | -51 | 13 |

## HEREFORDSHIRE FOOTBALL LEAGUE

| Premier Division | | P | W | D | L | F | A | GD | Pts |
|---|---|---|---|---|---|---|---|---|---|
| | Wellington Res. | 20 | 16 | 2 | 2 | 64 | 25 | 39 | 50 |
| | Tenbury United | 20 | 13 | 4 | 3 | 57 | 35 | 22 | 43 |
| | Ewyas Harold | 20 | 12 | 4 | 4 | 53 | 33 | 20 | 40 |
| | Fownhope | 20 | 11 | 5 | 4 | 54 | 31 | 23 | 38 |
| | Orleton Colts | 20 | 7 | 4 | 9 | 45 | 53 | -8 | 25 |
| | Hinton | 20 | 6 | 5 | 9 | 40 | 41 | -1 | 23 |
| | Leominster Town | 20 | 7 | 1 | 12 | 50 | 61 | -11 | 22 |
| | Pegasus Res. | 20 | 5 | 4 | 11 | 49 | 60 | -11 | 19 |
| | Lads Club Res. | 20 | 5 | 3 | 12 | 39 | 53 | -14 | 18 |
| 0 | Westfields F.C | 20 | 5 | 3 | 12 | 31 | 66 | -35 | 18 |
| | Ledbury Town (-3) | 20 | 4 | 3 | 13 | 34 | 58 | -24 | 12 |

| Division One | | P | W | D | L | F | A | GD | Pts |
|---|---|---|---|---|---|---|---|---|---|
| 1 | Holme Lacy | 20 | 14 | 3 | 3 | 73 | 31 | 42 | 45 |
| 2 | Sinkum | 20 | 14 | 0 | 6 | 75 | 48 | 27 | 42 |
| 3 | Wellington Colts | 20 | 10 | 6 | 4 | 58 | 44 | 14 | 36 |
| 4 | Woofferton | 20 | 10 | 2 | 8 | 49 | 43 | 6 | 32 |
| 5 | Bromyard FC | 20 | 8 | 3 | 9 | 53 | 53 | 0 | 27 |
| 6 | Ewyas Harold Res. | 20 | 8 | 3 | 9 | 48 | 54 | -6 | 27 |
| 7 | Tenbury Town | 20 | 8 | 2 | 10 | 55 | 61 | -6 | 26 |
| 8 | Fownhope Res. | 20 | 7 | 5 | 8 | 39 | 51 | -12 | 26 |
| 9 | Hinton Res. | 20 | 6 | 7 | 7 | 42 | 42 | 0 | 25 |
| 10 | Kingstone Harriers | 20 | 4 | 2 | 14 | 32 | 76 | -44 | 14 |
| 11 | Orleton Colts Res. | 20 | 4 | 1 | 15 | 38 | 59 | -21 | 13 |

| Division Two | | P | W | D | L | F | A | GD | Pts |
|---|---|---|---|---|---|---|---|---|---|
| 1 | Ledbury Town Res. | 24 | 20 | 2 | 2 | 82 | 30 | 52 | 62 |
| 2 | Weobley | 24 | 15 | 4 | 5 | 76 | 37 | 39 | 49 |
| 3 | Hereford City | 24 | 16 | 1 | 7 | 58 | 33 | 25 | 49 |
| 4 | Holme Lacy Res. | 24 | 15 | 3 | 6 | 93 | 42 | 51 | 48 |
| 5 | Kington Town Res. | 24 | 15 | 1 | 8 | 91 | 33 | 58 | 46 |
| 6 | Civil Service | 24 | 12 | 2 | 10 | 63 | 58 | 5 | 38 |
| 7 | Dore Valley | 24 | 11 | 4 | 9 | 58 | 43 | 15 | 37 |
| 8 | Leominster Town Colts | 24 | 11 | 2 | 11 | 60 | 75 | -15 | 35 |
| 9 | Bartestree Res. | 24 | 8 | 3 | 13 | 53 | 57 | -4 | 27 |
| 10 | Kingstone Rovers | 24 | 7 | 4 | 13 | 59 | 71 | -12 | 25 |
| 11 | Shobdon | 24 | 5 | 8 | 11 | 37 | 49 | -12 | 23 |
| 12 | Withington F.C | 24 | 1 | 3 | 20 | 18 | 101 | -83 | 6 |
| 13 | Burghill | 24 | 1 | 1 | 22 | 26 | 145 | -119 | 4 |

## HOPE VALLEY AMATEUR LEAGUE

| Premier Division | | P | W | D | L | F | A | GD | Pts |
|---|---|---|---|---|---|---|---|---|---|
| 1 | Bradwell | 20 | 18 | 0 | 2 | 71 | 24 | 47 | 54 |
| 2 | Furness Vale | 20 | 17 | 0 | 3 | 74 | 24 | 50 | 51 |
| 3 | Bakewell Town | 20 | 12 | 4 | 4 | 46 | 27 | 19 | 40 |
| 4 | High Lane | 20 | 10 | 3 | 7 | 56 | 42 | 14 | 33 |
| 5 | Dove Holes | 20 | 9 | 2 | 9 | 55 | 26 | 29 | 29 |
| 6 | Hathersage | 20 | 7 | 4 | 9 | 42 | 49 | -7 | 25 |
| 7 | Ashover | 20 | 7 | 4 | 9 | 38 | 57 | -19 | 25 |
| 8 | Buxworth | 20 | 7 | 0 | 13 | 36 | 69 | -33 | 21 |
| 9 | Dronfield Town A | 20 | 5 | 2 | 13 | 42 | 55 | -13 | 17 |
| 10 | AFC Dronfield | 20 | 4 | 3 | 13 | 30 | 69 | -39 | 15 |

| A Division | | P | W | D | L | F | A | GD | Pts |
|---|---|---|---|---|---|---|---|---|---|
| 1 | Dronfield Old Boys | 20 | 18 | 0 | 2 | 83 | 26 | 57 | 54 |
| 2 | Tideswell United Res. | 20 | 11 | 4 | 5 | 60 | 45 | 15 | 37 |
| 3 | Youlgrave United | 20 | 10 | 1 | 8 | 55 | 52 | 3 | 34 |
| 4 | Buxton Town | 20 | 10 | 3 | 7 | 59 | 51 | 8 | 33 |
| 5 | Darley Dale Lions | 20 | 9 | 1 | 10 | 50 | 51 | -1 | 28 |
| 6 | Blazing Rag | 20 | 8 | 4 | 8 | 48 | 61 | -13 | 28 |
| 7 | Dove Holes Res. | 20 | 7 | 2 | 11 | 49 | 55 | -6 | 23 |
| 8 | Baslow | 20 | 9 | 4 | 6 | 62 | 42 | 20 | 22 |
| 9 | Grindleford | 20 | 5 | 3 | 12 | 42 | 74 | -32 | 18 |
| 10 | Dronfield Woodhouse | 20 | 5 | 2 | 13 | 48 | 57 | -9 | 17 |
| 11 | Bamford | 20 | 4 | 2 | 14 | 28 | 68 | -40 | 14 |

Hope Athletic withdrew - record expunged.
Railway FC withdrew - record expunged.

# LEAGUE TABLES

## HUDDERSFIELD AND DISTRICT ASSOCIATION FOOTBALL LEAGUE

| Division One | P | W | D | L | F | A | GD | Pts |
|---|---|---|---|---|---|---|---|---|
| 1 Hepworth United | 22 | 18 | 3 | 1 | 64 | 39 | 25 | 57 |
| 2 Shepley | 22 | 14 | 3 | 5 | 60 | 37 | 23 | 45 |
| 3 Heyside FC | 22 | 14 | 2 | 6 | 66 | 38 | 28 | 44 |
| 4 Shelley | 22 | 11 | 4 | 7 | 54 | 34 | 20 | 37 |
| 5 Heywood Irish Centre FC | 22 | 9 | 5 | 8 | 49 | 45 | 4 | 32 |
| 6 Diggle | 22 | 10 | 2 | 10 | 53 | 54 | -1 | 32 |
| 7 Holmbridge | 22 | 9 | 3 | 10 | 33 | 43 | -10 | 30 |
| 8 Newsome | 22 | 7 | 5 | 10 | 64 | 55 | 9 | 26 |
| 9 Britannia Sports | 22 | 8 | 0 | 14 | 41 | 56 | -15 | 24 |
| 10 Skelmanthorpe | 22 | 6 | 5 | 11 | 42 | 47 | -5 | 23 |
| 11 Berry Brow | 22 | 7 | 2 | 13 | 43 | 54 | -11 | 23 |
| 12 Holmfirth Town | 22 | 1 | 2 | 19 | 21 | 88 | -67 | 5 |

| Division Two | P | W | D | L | F | A | GD | Pts |
|---|---|---|---|---|---|---|---|---|
| 1 Aimbry | 22 | 14 | 4 | 4 | 65 | 46 | 19 | 46 |
| 2 Meltham Athletic | 22 | 14 | 3 | 5 | 84 | 34 | 50 | 45 |
| 3 Kirkheaton Rovers | 22 | 13 | 2 | 7 | 49 | 27 | 22 | 41 |
| 4 H.V.Academicals | 22 | 12 | 4 | 6 | 48 | 43 | 5 | 40 |
| 5 Marsden | 22 | 12 | 2 | 8 | 64 | 56 | 8 | 38 |
| 6 Linthwaite Athletic | 22 | 9 | 7 | 6 | 68 | 72 | -4 | 34 |
| 7 AFC Lindley | 22 | 8 | 5 | 9 | 57 | 52 | 5 | 29 |
| 8 Scholes | 22 | 7 | 6 | 9 | 37 | 44 | -7 | 27 |
| 9 Netherton | 22 | 7 | 4 | 11 | 48 | 59 | -11 | 25 |
| 10 Honley | 22 | 5 | 2 | 15 | 45 | 68 | -23 | 17 |
| 11 Cumberworth | 22 | 4 | 5 | 13 | 36 | 62 | -26 | 17 |
| 12 KKS Spartans | 22 | 4 | 2 | 16 | 32 | 70 | -38 | 14 |

| Division Three | P | W | D | L | F | A | GD | Pts |
|---|---|---|---|---|---|---|---|---|
| 1 Slaithwaite United | 22 | 19 | 2 | 1 | 71 | 20 | 51 | 59 |
| 2 Colne Valley | 22 | 17 | 3 | 2 | 79 | 28 | 51 | 54 |
| 3 Scissett | 22 | 16 | 2 | 4 | 65 | 31 | 34 | 50 |
| 4 Lepton Highlanders | 22 | 13 | 4 | 5 | 74 | 44 | 30 | 43 |
| 5 Moorside | 22 | 11 | 3 | 8 | 68 | 51 | 17 | 36 |
| 6 Grange Moor | 22 | 10 | 3 | 9 | 46 | 39 | 7 | 33 |
| 7 Brook Motors | 22 | 8 | 5 | 9 | 54 | 60 | -6 | 29 |
| 8 Hade Edge | 22 | 6 | 1 | 15 | 35 | 46 | -11 | 19 |
| 9 Paddock Rangers | 22 | 5 | 3 | 14 | 34 | 55 | -21 | 18 |
| 10 Flockton FC | 22 | 4 | 4 | 14 | 31 | 72 | -41 | 16 |
| 11 Wooldale Wanderers | 22 | 3 | 3 | 16 | 31 | 73 | -42 | 12 |
| 12 Uppermill | 22 | 2 | 3 | 17 | 32 | 101 | -69 | 9 |

| Division Four | P | W | D | L | F | A | GD | Pts |
|---|---|---|---|---|---|---|---|---|
| 1 Almondbury Woolpack | 24 | 17 | 5 | 2 | 97 | 39 | 58 | 56 |
| 2 Black Horse | 24 | 17 | 2 | 5 | 111 | 35 | 76 | 53 |
| 3 3D Dynamos | 24 | 16 | 3 | 5 | 82 | 47 | 35 | 51 |
| 4 Junction | 24 | 16 | 2 | 6 | 90 | 41 | 49 | 50 |
| 5 Storthes Hall | 24 | 15 | 4 | 5 | 66 | 28 | 38 | 49 |
| 6 Almondbury WMC | 24 | 13 | 4 | 7 | 87 | 54 | 33 | 43 |
| 7 Lindley Saddle | 24 | 13 | 1 | 10 | 93 | 60 | 33 | 40 |
| 8 Brighouse Athletic | 24 | 11 | 5 | 8 | 93 | 64 | 29 | 38 |
| 9 Thornhill United | 24 | 8 | 4 | 12 | 77 | 87 | -10 | 28 |
| 10 Cartworth Moor | 24 | 5 | 1 | 18 | 33 | 119 | -86 | 16 |
| 11 Golcar United | 24 | 3 | 3 | 18 | 52 | 97 | -45 | 12 |
| 12 Railway Berry Brow | 24 | 3 | 0 | 21 | 46 | 155 | -109 | 9 |
| 13 Mount | 24 | 2 | 0 | 22 | 28 | 129 | -101 | 6 |

## ISLE OF MAN SENIOR LEAGUES

| Premier Division | P | W | D | L | F | A | GD | Pts |
|---|---|---|---|---|---|---|---|---|
| 1 St Georges | 24 | 23 | 1 | 0 | 162 | 14 | 148 | 70 |
| 2 Peel | 24 | 21 | 2 | 1 | 136 | 26 | 110 | 65 |
| 3 Rushen United | 24 | 14 | 3 | 7 | 70 | 37 | 33 | 45 |
| 4 DHSOB | 24 | 14 | 2 | 8 | 83 | 44 | 39 | 44 |
| 5 Corinthians | 24 | 13 | 4 | 7 | 72 | 48 | 24 | 43 |
| 6 Laxey | 24 | 13 | 3 | 8 | 64 | 74 | -10 | 42 |
| 7 St Johns United | 24 | 13 | 1 | 10 | 59 | 52 | 7 | 40 |
| 8 St Marys | 24 | 9 | 1 | 14 | 54 | 88 | -34 | 28 |
| 9 Ayre United | 24 | 8 | 0 | 16 | 48 | 108 | -60 | 24 |
| 10 Ramsey | 24 | 6 | 1 | 17 | 33 | 93 | -60 | 19 |
| 11 Union Mills | 24 | 6 | 0 | 18 | 42 | 108 | -66 | 18 |
| 12 Marown | 24 | 5 | 0 | 19 | 31 | 92 | -61 | 15 |
| 13 RYCOB | 24 | 1 | 2 | 21 | 30 | 100 | -70 | 5 |

| Division Two | P | W | D | L | F | A | GD | Pts |
|---|---|---|---|---|---|---|---|---|
| 1 Douglas Athletic | 24 | 21 | 3 | 0 | 123 | 23 | 100 | 66 |
| 2 Colby | 24 | 16 | 3 | 5 | 90 | 42 | 48 | 51 |
| 3 Castletown | 24 | 15 | 4 | 5 | 88 | 37 | 51 | 49 |
| 4 Gymnasium | 24 | 15 | 4 | 5 | 79 | 34 | 45 | 49 |
| 5 Braddan | 24 | 14 | 6 | 4 | 77 | 30 | 47 | 48 |
| 6 Pulrose United | 24 | 14 | 3 | 7 | 90 | 64 | 26 | 45 |
| 7 Douglas Royal | 24 | 11 | 4 | 9 | 92 | 69 | 23 | 37 |
| 8 Michael United | 24 | 7 | 4 | 13 | 46 | 92 | -46 | 25 |
| 9 Foxdale | 24 | 7 | 3 | 14 | 52 | 88 | -36 | 24 |
| 10 Malew | 24 | 5 | 4 | 15 | 42 | 82 | -40 | 19 |
| 11 Onchan | 24 | 4 | 4 | 16 | 41 | 90 | -49 | 16 |
| 12 Douglas & District | 24 | 3 | 5 | 16 | 47 | 97 | -50 | 14 |
| 13 Governors Athletic | 24 | 0 | 1 | 23 | 35 | 154 | -119 | 1 |

## ISLE OF WIGHT SATURDAY LEAGUE

| Division One | P | W | D | L | F | A | GD | Pts |
|---|---|---|---|---|---|---|---|---|
| 1 Whitecroft & Barton Sports FC | 20 | 18 | 1 | 1 | 68 | 10 | 58 | 55 |
| 2 Shanklin | 20 | 11 | 7 | 2 | 45 | 31 | 14 | 40 |
| 3 West Wight | 20 | 9 | 7 | 4 | 43 | 19 | 24 | 34 |
| 4 E.C.S. | 20 | 10 | 3 | 7 | 53 | 33 | 20 | 33 |
| 5 Brading Town | 20 | 8 | 7 | 5 | 45 | 36 | 9 | 31 |
| 6 Ventnor FC | 20 | 8 | 4 | 8 | 37 | 35 | 2 | 28 |
| 7 Cowes Sports Res. | 20 | 6 | 8 | 6 | 36 | 37 | -1 | 26 |
| 8 Oakfield | 20 | 5 | 2 | 13 | 32 | 66 | -34 | 17 |
| 9 Bembridge | 20 | 4 | 4 | 12 | 25 | 68 | -43 | 16 |
| 10 Binstead & COB | 20 | 2 | 7 | 11 | 26 | 43 | -17 | 13 |
| 11 Northwood St Johns | 20 | 2 | 4 | 14 | 20 | 52 | -32 | 10 |

| Division Two | P | W | D | L | F | A | GD | Pts |
|---|---|---|---|---|---|---|---|---|
| 1 Brighstone | 20 | 15 | 4 | 1 | 63 | 14 | 49 | 49 |
| 2 Ryde Saints | 20 | 15 | 4 | 1 | 52 | 23 | 29 | 49 |
| 3 Osborne Coburg | 20 | 13 | 5 | 2 | 57 | 15 | 42 | 4[illegible] |
| 4 High Park | 20 | 9 | 5 | 6 | 58 | 30 | 28 | 3[illegible] |
| 5 East Cowes Vics Res. | 20 | 9 | 2 | 9 | 39 | 51 | -12 | 2[illegible] |
| 6 Sandown | 20 | 7 | 4 | 9 | 40 | 38 | 2 | 2[illegible] |
| 7 Yarmouth & Calb | 20 | 7 | 1 | 12 | 45 | 59 | -14 | 2[illegible] |
| 8 Carisbrooke United | 20 | 6 | 3 | 11 | 34 | 41 | -7 | 2[illegible] |
| 9 Niton | 20 | 6 | 2 | 12 | 31 | 65 | -34 | 2[illegible] |
| 10 Newport IOW A | 20 | 5 | 3 | 12 | 30 | 54 | -24 | 1[illegible] |
| 11 Newchurch | 20 | 1 | 1 | 18 | 12 | 71 | -59 | [illegible] |

| Division Three | | P | W | D | L | F | A | GD | Pts |
|---|---|---|---|---|---|---|---|---|---|
| 1 | Pan Sports | 24 | 21 | 1 | 2 | 83 | 20 | 63 | 64 |
| 2 | Cowes Sports A | 24 | 18 | 3 | 3 | 105 | 15 | 90 | 57 |
| 3 | AFC Wootton | 24 | 16 | 1 | 7 | 60 | 39 | 21 | 49 |
| 4 | Brading Town A | 24 | 14 | 2 | 8 | 52 | 49 | 3 | 44 |
| 5 | Kyngs Towne (-9) | 24 | 15 | 0 | 9 | 55 | 34 | 21 | 36 |
| 6 | Shanklin A | 24 | 9 | 5 | 10 | 48 | 48 | 0 | 32 |
| 7 | St Helens Blue Star (-7) | 24 | 11 | 5 | 8 | 68 | 48 | 20 | 31 |
| 8 | Rookley | 24 | 9 | 0 | 15 | 50 | 44 | 6 | 27 |
| 9 | Seaview FC | 24 | 7 | 5 | 12 | 44 | 51 | -7 | 26 |
| 10 | Seaclose | 24 | 8 | 1 | 15 | 35 | 54 | -19 | 25 |
| 11 | Bembridge A | 24 | 5 | 4 | 15 | 39 | 110 | -71 | 19 |
| 12 | Wroxall | 24 | 5 | 2 | 17 | 35 | 91 | -56 | 17 |
| 13 | Ryde Saints A | 24 | 2 | 3 | 19 | 38 | 109 | -71 | 9 |

## JERSEY FOOTBALL COMBINATION

| Premiership (First half of the season) | | P | W | D | L | F | A | GD | Pts |
|---|---|---|---|---|---|---|---|---|---|
| 1 | Jersey Scottish | 14 | 14 | 0 | 0 | 62 | 11 | 51 | 42 |
| 2 | St Paul's | 14 | 12 | 1 | 1 | 90 | 13 | 77 | 37 |
| 3 | JTC Jersey Wanderers | 14 | 11 | 2 | 1 | 66 | 17 | 49 | 35 |
| 4 | St Ouen | 14 | 9 | 2 | 3 | 37 | 17 | 20 | 29 |
| 5 | Trinity | 14 | 9 | 1 | 4 | 50 | 25 | 25 | 28 |
| 6 | St Peter | 14 | 7 | 2 | 5 | 39 | 27 | 12 | 23 |
| 7 | St Clement | 14 | 7 | 1 | 6 | 34 | 25 | 9 | 22 |
| 8 | St John | 14 | 7 | 1 | 6 | 20 | 28 | -8 | 22 |
| 9 | Jersey Portuguese | 14 | 6 | 0 | 8 | 33 | 36 | -3 | 18 |
| 10 | Rozel Rovers | 14 | 5 | 2 | 7 | 23 | 31 | -8 | 17 |
| 11 | Grouville | 14 | 4 | 1 | 9 | 16 | 44 | -28 | 13 |
| 12 | St Brelade | 14 | 4 | 0 | 10 | 24 | 33 | -9 | 12 |
| 13 | Sporting Academics | 14 | 2 | 1 | 11 | 19 | 80 | -61 | 7 |
| 14 | St Lawrence | 14 | 1 | 0 | 13 | 15 | 46 | -31 | 3 |
| 15 | Beeches OB | 14 | 0 | 0 | 14 | 5 | 100 | -95 | 0 |

| Premiership (Second half of the season) | | P | W | D | L | F | A | GD | Pts |
|---|---|---|---|---|---|---|---|---|---|
| 1 | St Paul's | 14 | 11 | 1 | 2 | 47 | 14 | 33 | 34 |
| 2 | Jersey Scottish | 14 | 11 | 1 | 2 | 42 | 16 | 26 | 34 |
| 3 | JTC Jersey Wanderers | 14 | 7 | 3 | 4 | 30 | 21 | 9 | 24 |
| 4 | St Ouen | 14 | 7 | 1 | 6 | 32 | 21 | 11 | 22 |
| 5 | Trinity | 14 | 6 | 2 | 6 | 29 | 27 | 2 | 20 |
| 6 | St Peter | 14 | 4 | 3 | 7 | 21 | 31 | -10 | 15 |
| 7 | St John | 14 | 2 | 2 | 10 | 12 | 44 | -32 | 8 |
| 8 | St Clement | 14 | 1 | 1 | 12 | 12 | 51 | -39 | 4 |

| Championship | | P | W | D | L | F | A | GD | Pts |
|---|---|---|---|---|---|---|---|---|---|
| 1 | Rozel Rovers | 18 | 15 | 1 | 2 | 66 | 10 | 56 | 46 |
| 2 | Jersey Portuguese | 18 | 14 | 1 | 3 | 63 | 17 | 46 | 43 |
| 3 | Grouville | 18 | 10 | 4 | 4 | 38 | 28 | 10 | 34 |
| 4 | St Brelade | 18 | 10 | 0 | 8 | 52 | 28 | 24 | 30 |
| 5 | St Lawrence | 18 | 4 | 3 | 11 | 22 | 32 | -10 | 15 |
| 6 | Sporting Academics | 18 | 3 | 3 | 12 | 23 | 72 | -49 | 12 |
| 7 | Beeches OB | 18 | 1 | 0 | 17 | 10 | 87 | -77 | 3 |

| Division One | | P | W | D | L | F | A | GD | Pts |
|---|---|---|---|---|---|---|---|---|---|
| 1 | St Ouen Res. | 18 | 14 | 2 | 2 | 57 | 15 | 42 | 44 |
| 2 | St Paul's Res. | 18 | 14 | 1 | 3 | 56 | 23 | 33 | 43 |
| 3 | St Peter Res. | 18 | 11 | 2 | 5 | 45 | 30 | 15 | 35 |
| 4 | JTC Jersey Wanderers Res. | 18 | 10 | 3 | 5 | 66 | 41 | 25 | 33 |
| 5 | St Clement Res. | 18 | 10 | 3 | 5 | 48 | 26 | 22 | 33 |
| 6 | St John Res. | 18 | 8 | 1 | 9 | 51 | 46 | 5 | 25 |
| 7 | Jersey Scottish Res. | 18 | 7 | 1 | 10 | 35 | 39 | -4 | 22 |
| 8 | Jersey Portuguese Res. | 17 | 4 | 1 | 12 | 19 | 39 | -20 | 13 |
| 9 | Grouville Res. | 17 | 3 | 0 | 14 | 25 | 72 | -47 | 9 |
| 10 | Rozel Rovers Res. | 18 | 1 | 0 | 17 | 17 | 88 | -71 | 3 |

| Division Two | | P | W | D | L | F | A | GD | Pts |
|---|---|---|---|---|---|---|---|---|---|
| 1 | St Peter C | 16 | 15 | 1 | 0 | 72 | 13 | 59 | 46 |
| 2 | St Ouen C | 16 | 8 | 5 | 3 | 56 | 28 | 28 | 29 |
| 3 | First Tower United Res | 16 | 8 | 1 | 7 | 34 | 38 | -4 | 25 |
| 4 | Trinity Res | 16 | 7 | 3 | 6 | 42 | 44 | -2 | 24 |
| 5 | Sporting Academics Res | 16 | 7 | 2 | 7 | 50 | 55 | -5 | 23 |
| 6 | St Brelade Res | 16 | 6 | 1 | 9 | 48 | 47 | 1 | 19 |
| 7 | St Clement C | 16 | 4 | 5 | 7 | 40 | 50 | -10 | 17 |
| 8 | St Lawrence Res | 16 | 5 | 1 | 10 | 35 | 51 | -16 | 16 |
| 9 | St John C | 16 | 2 | 1 | 13 | 21 | 72 | -51 | 7 |

## LANCASHIRE & CHESHIRE AFL

| Premier Division | | P | W | D | L | F | A | GD | Pts |
|---|---|---|---|---|---|---|---|---|---|
| 1 | Rochdalians | 24 | 20 | 1 | 3 | 105 | 31 | 74 | 61 |
| 2 | Mellor | 24 | 19 | 3 | 2 | 98 | 29 | 69 | 60 |
| 3 | Old Trafford and Gorse Hill | 24 | 15 | 3 | 6 | 65 | 39 | 26 | 48 |
| 4 | Whalley Range (-3) | 24 | 14 | 5 | 5 | 79 | 54 | 25 | 44 |
| 5 | Abacus Media | 24 | 13 | 1 | 10 | 60 | 57 | 3 | 40 |
| 6 | Newton | 24 | 10 | 2 | 12 | 47 | 51 | -4 | 32 |
| 7 | South Manchester | 24 | 7 | 7 | 10 | 49 | 72 | -23 | 28 |
| 8 | Moston Brook | 24 | 7 | 6 | 11 | 50 | 60 | -10 | 27 |
| 9 | Parrswood Celtic | 24 | 6 | 7 | 11 | 47 | 67 | -20 | 25 |
| 10 | Bedians | 24 | 7 | 3 | 14 | 46 | 66 | -20 | 24 |
| 11 | Chorltonians | 24 | 7 | 2 | 15 | 40 | 65 | -25 | 23 |
| 12 | Old Ashtonians | 24 | 5 | 5 | 14 | 43 | 69 | -26 | 20 |
| 13 | Bury Amateur AFC 1st | 24 | 3 | 1 | 20 | 32 | 101 | -69 | 10 |

| Division One | | P | W | D | L | F | A | GD | Pts |
|---|---|---|---|---|---|---|---|---|---|
| 1 | Tintwistle Athletic FC | 20 | 14 | 2 | 4 | 62 | 33 | 29 | 44 |
| 2 | High Lane 1st | 20 | 13 | 3 | 4 | 69 | 39 | 30 | 42 |
| 3 | Moorside Rangers FC (-3) | 20 | 12 | 4 | 4 | 59 | 33 | 26 | 37 |
| 4 | Salford Victoria FC 1st | 20 | 9 | 4 | 7 | 54 | 48 | 6 | 31 |
| 5 | Govan Athletic | 20 | 7 | 8 | 5 | 55 | 40 | 15 | 29 |
| 6 | Signol Athletic FC First | 20 | 8 | 2 | 10 | 47 | 55 | -8 | 26 |
| 7 | Burnage Metro | 20 | 6 | 4 | 10 | 47 | 61 | -14 | 22 |
| 8 | Old Stretfordians | 20 | 7 | 1 | 12 | 36 | 58 | -22 | 22 |
| 9 | Newton Heath (-3) | 20 | 6 | 4 | 10 | 65 | 77 | -12 | 19 |
| 10 | Milton FC | 20 | 4 | 4 | 12 | 29 | 49 | -20 | 16 |
| 11 | Hooley Bridge Celtic | 20 | 4 | 4 | 12 | 43 | 73 | -30 | 16 |

## LEAGUE TABLES

| Division Two | P | W | D | L | F | A | GD | Pts |
|---|---|---|---|---|---|---|---|---|
| 1 Whalley Range Res. | 20 | 17 | 1 | 2 | 87 | 37 | 50 | 52 |
| 2 Parrswood Celtic Res. | 20 | 15 | 2 | 3 | 75 | 35 | 40 | 47 |
| 3 Stoconians 1st | 20 | 11 | 4 | 5 | 68 | 50 | 18 | 37 |
| 4 Chorltonians Res. | 20 | 12 | 1 | 7 | 49 | 38 | 11 | 37 |
| 5 Old Stretfordians Res. | 20 | 10 | 3 | 7 | 62 | 52 | 10 | 33 |
| 6 Mellor Res. (-3) | 20 | 6 | 5 | 9 | 45 | 52 | -7 | 20 |
| 7 Staly Lions FC | 20 | 5 | 3 | 12 | 37 | 56 | -19 | 18 |
| 8 Spurley Hey | 20 | 5 | 2 | 13 | 49 | 64 | -15 | 17 |
| 9 Rochdalians Res. (-3) | 20 | 6 | 2 | 12 | 38 | 65 | -27 | 17 |
| 10 Urmston Sports Club | 20 | 5 | 2 | 13 | 33 | 64 | -31 | 17 |
| 11 AFC Oldham 2005 | 20 | 4 | 3 | 13 | 34 | 64 | -30 | 15 |

| Division Three | P | W | D | L | F | A | GD | Pts |
|---|---|---|---|---|---|---|---|---|
| 1 Chorltonians Town | 20 | 17 | 1 | 2 | 116 | 27 | 89 | 52 |
| 2 Swinton FC | 20 | 15 | 1 | 4 | 71 | 34 | 37 | 46 |
| 3 Trafford United 1st | 20 | 13 | 4 | 3 | 53 | 31 | 22 | 43 |
| 4 Oldham Victoria | 20 | 11 | 4 | 5 | 81 | 57 | 24 | 37 |
| 5 Moston Brook Res. | 20 | 9 | 1 | 10 | 59 | 64 | -5 | 28 |
| 6 Newton Res. | 20 | 8 | 2 | 10 | 44 | 48 | -4 | 26 |
| 7 Newton Heath Res. (-3) | 20 | 8 | 3 | 9 | 85 | 81 | 4 | 24 |
| 8 Cheadle Hulme Athletic | 20 | 5 | 4 | 11 | 35 | 52 | -17 | 19 |
| 9 Heaton Mersey | 20 | 5 | 3 | 12 | 36 | 73 | -37 | 18 |
| 10 Hooley Bridge Celtic Res. (-3) | 20 | 4 | 3 | 13 | 44 | 78 | -34 | 12 |
| 11 AFC Stockport | 20 | 2 | 0 | 18 | 20 | 99 | -79 | 6 |

### LANCASHIRE AMATEUR LEAGUE

| Premier Division | P | W | D | L | F | A | GD | Pts |
|---|---|---|---|---|---|---|---|---|
| 1 Failsworth Dynamos | 22 | 19 | 2 | 1 | 74 | 27 | 47 | 59 |
| 2 Old Boltonians | 22 | 19 | 0 | 3 | 76 | 28 | 48 | 57 |
| 3 Rochdale St Clements | 22 | 12 | 2 | 8 | 42 | 29 | 13 | 38 |
| 4 Mostonians | 22 | 11 | 4 | 7 | 52 | 28 | 24 | 37 |
| 5 Horwich St Mary's Victoria | 22 | 10 | 3 | 9 | 49 | 31 | 18 | 33 |
| 6 Bury GSOB | 22 | 10 | 3 | 9 | 53 | 48 | 5 | 33 |
| 7 Little Lever SC | 22 | 9 | 5 | 8 | 50 | 47 | 3 | 32 |
| 8 Tottington United | 22 | 10 | 1 | 11 | 53 | 55 | -2 | 31 |
| 9 Old Mancunians | 22 | 7 | 3 | 12 | 38 | 44 | -6 | 24 |
| 10 Howe Bridge Mills | 22 | 4 | 3 | 15 | 36 | 95 | -59 | 15 |
| 11 Chaddertonians (-4) | 22 | 5 | 2 | 15 | 28 | 62 | -34 | 13 |
| 12 Wardle | 22 | 1 | 2 | 19 | 36 | 93 | -57 | 5 |

| Division One | P | W | D | L | F | A | GD | Pts |
|---|---|---|---|---|---|---|---|---|
| 1 Oldham Hulmeians | 26 | 20 | 3 | 3 | 92 | 24 | 68 | 63 |
| 2 Blackrod Town | 26 | 17 | 6 | 3 | 81 | 38 | 43 | 57 |
| 3 Whitworth Valley | 26 | 16 | 5 | 5 | 86 | 48 | 38 | 53 |
| 4 Prestwich | 26 | 14 | 4 | 8 | 81 | 52 | 29 | 46 |
| 5 Old Blackburnians | 26 | 12 | 7 | 7 | 59 | 44 | 15 | 43 |
| 6 Rossendale FC | 26 | 10 | 7 | 9 | 60 | 57 | 3 | 37 |
| 7 Roach Dynamos | 26 | 10 | 4 | 12 | 63 | 60 | 3 | 34 |
| 8 Accrington Amateurs | 26 | 10 | 3 | 13 | 55 | 58 | -3 | 33 |
| 9 Bolton Wyresdale | 26 | 9 | 3 | 14 | 43 | 58 | -15 | 30 |
| 10 Farnworth Town | 26 | 8 | 5 | 13 | 49 | 82 | -33 | 29 |
| 11 Castle Hill | 26 | 7 | 5 | 14 | 48 | 78 | -30 | 26 |
| 12 Hesketh Casuals | 26 | 7 | 4 | 15 | 59 | 75 | -16 | 25 |
| 13 Rochdale St Clements Res. | 26 | 7 | 3 | 16 | 31 | 71 | -40 | 24 |
| 14 Ainsworth | 26 | 4 | 3 | 19 | 46 | 108 | -62 | 15 |

| Division Two | P | W | D | L | F | A | GD | Pts |
|---|---|---|---|---|---|---|---|---|
| 1 Thornleigh | 22 | 18 | 2 | 2 | 93 | 26 | 67 | 56 |
| 2 Ashtonians | 22 | 16 | 1 | 5 | 62 | 36 | 26 | 49 |
| 3 Failsworth Dynamos Res. | 22 | 13 | 3 | 6 | 67 | 28 | 39 | 42 |
| 4 Old Boltonians Res. | 22 | 11 | 5 | 6 | 77 | 66 | 11 | 38 |
| 5 Radcliffe Town | 22 | 10 | 4 | 8 | 65 | 47 | 18 | 34 |
| 6 Bury GSOB Res. | 22 | 9 | 4 | 9 | 54 | 64 | -10 | 31 |
| 7 AFC Dobbies (-4) | 22 | 9 | 4 | 9 | 64 | 60 | 4 | 27 |
| 8 Oldham Hulmeians Res. | 22 | 8 | 3 | 11 | 48 | 65 | -17 | 27 |
| 9 Mostonians Res. | 22 | 7 | 4 | 11 | 56 | 57 | -1 | 25 |
| 10 Horwich RMI | 22 | 6 | 3 | 13 | 39 | 58 | -19 | 21 |
| 11 Old Blackburnians Res. | 22 | 6 | 3 | 13 | 44 | 73 | -29 | 21 |
| 12 Hesketh Casuals Res. | 22 | 1 | 0 | 21 | 27 | 116 | -89 | [illegible] |

| Division Three | P | W | D | L | F | A | GD | Pts |
|---|---|---|---|---|---|---|---|---|
| 1 Accrington Amateurs Res. | 22 | 15 | 4 | 3 | 100 | 41 | 59 | [illegible] |
| 2 Rossendale FC Res. | 22 | 13 | 4 | 5 | 61 | 42 | 19 | [illegible] |
| 3 Radcliffe Boys | 22 | 12 | 6 | 4 | 75 | 31 | 44 | [illegible] |
| 4 Radcliffe Town Res. | 22 | 12 | 3 | 7 | 46 | 49 | -3 | [illegible] |
| 5 Old Mancunians Res. | 22 | 12 | 2 | 8 | 50 | 43 | 7 | [illegible] |
| 6 Old Boltonians A | 22 | 9 | 6 | 7 | 49 | 50 | -1 | [illegible] |
| 7 Rochdale St Clements A | 22 | 9 | 5 | 8 | 46 | 35 | 11 | [illegible] |
| 8 Howe Bridge Mills Res. | 22 | 9 | 0 | 13 | 57 | 62 | -5 | [illegible] |
| 9 Little Lever SC Res. | 22 | 7 | 3 | 12 | 44 | 53 | -9 | [illegible] |
| 10 Thornleigh Res. | 22 | 7 | 3 | 12 | 42 | 68 | -26 | [illegible] |
| 11 Bacup United (-8) | 22 | 6 | 1 | 15 | 50 | 78 | -28 | [illegible] |
| 12 Chaddertonians Res. | 22 | 1 | 3 | 18 | 26 | 94 | -68 | [illegible] |

| Division Four | P | W | D | L | F | A | GD | Pts |
|---|---|---|---|---|---|---|---|---|
| 1 Horwich St Mary's Victoria Res. | 18 | 13 | 3 | 2 | 58 | 19 | 39 | [illegible] |
| 2 Old Blackburnians A | 18 | 12 | 2 | 4 | 55 | 29 | 26 | [illegible] |
| 3 Bolton Lads Club | 18 | 11 | 3 | 4 | 46 | 24 | 22 | [illegible] |
| 4 Mostonians A | 18 | 10 | 3 | 5 | 43 | 24 | 19 | [illegible] |
| 5 Lymm | 18 | 6 | 3 | 9 | 38 | 40 | -2 | [illegible] |
| 6 Wardle Res. | 18 | 6 | 3 | 9 | 40 | 57 | -17 | [illegible] |
| 7 Ainsworth Res. | 18 | 5 | 4 | 9 | 37 | 49 | -12 | [illegible] |
| 8 Old Mancunians A | 18 | 5 | 4 | 9 | 31 | 44 | -13 | [illegible] |
| 9 Horwich RMI Res. | 18 | 4 | 7 | 7 | 34 | 49 | -15 | [illegible] |
| 10 Bolton Wyresdale Res. | 18 | 1 | 2 | 15 | 32 | 79 | -47 | [illegible] |

| Division Five | P | W | D | L | F | A | GD | Pts |
|---|---|---|---|---|---|---|---|---|
| 1 Thornleigh A | 22 | 18 | 3 | 1 | 113 | 35 | 78 | [illegible] |
| 2 Whitworth Valley Res. | 22 | 17 | 2 | 3 | 99 | 35 | 64 | [illegible] |
| 3 Ashtonians Res. | 22 | 11 | 4 | 7 | 43 | 39 | 4 | [illegible] |
| 4 Little Lever SC A | 22 | 11 | 3 | 8 | 64 | 61 | 3 | [illegible] |
| 5 Oldham Hulmeians A | 22 | 11 | 3 | 8 | 56 | 56 | 0 | [illegible] |
| 6 Radcliffe Town A | 22 | 10 | 2 | 10 | 61 | 69 | -8 | [illegible] |
| 7 Tottington United Res. | 22 | 9 | 2 | 11 | 55 | 56 | -1 | [illegible] |
| 8 Bolton Wyresdale A | 22 | 7 | 5 | 10 | 46 | 54 | -8 | [illegible] |
| 9 Bury GSOB A | 22 | 8 | 2 | 12 | 43 | 61 | -18 | [illegible] |
| 10 Rochdale St Clements B | 22 | 6 | 6 | 10 | 52 | 54 | -2 | [illegible] |
| 11 Old Boltonians B | 22 | 4 | 5 | 13 | 31 | 73 | -42 | [illegible] |
| 12 Radcliffe Boys Res. | 22 | 1 | 1 | 20 | 22 | 92 | -70 | [illegible] |

| Division Six | | P | W | D | L | F | A | GD | Pts |
|---|---|---|---|---|---|---|---|---|---|
| 1 | Howe Bridge Mills A | 18 | 13 | 2 | 3 | 98 | 40 | 58 | 41 |
| 2 | Lymm Res. | 18 | 12 | 2 | 4 | 71 | 33 | 38 | 38 |
| 3 | Old Mancunians B | 18 | 10 | 2 | 6 | 52 | 35 | 17 | 32 |
| 4 | Tottington United A | 18 | 9 | 2 | 7 | 52 | 41 | 11 | 29 |
| 5 | Bury GSOB B | 18 | 9 | 2 | 7 | 51 | 50 | 1 | 29 |
| 6 | Oldham Hulmeians B | 18 | 8 | 1 | 9 | 46 | 50 | -4 | 25 |
| 7 | Hesketh Casuals A | 18 | 7 | 3 | 8 | 51 | 62 | -11 | 24 |
| 8 | Radcliffe Town B | 18 | 6 | 2 | 10 | 48 | 54 | -6 | 20 |
| 9 | Thornleigh B | 18 | 4 | 1 | 13 | 41 | 91 | -50 | 13 |
| 10 | Horwich RMI A | 18 | 2 | 3 | 13 | 32 | 86 | -54 | 9 |

## LANCASHIRE FOOTBALL LEAGUE

| East | | P | W | D | L | F | A | GD | Pts |
|---|---|---|---|---|---|---|---|---|---|
| | Brighouse Town | 14 | 9 | 3 | 2 | 49 | 22 | 27 | 30 |
| | Thackley | 14 | 8 | 2 | 4 | 37 | 27 | 10 | 26 |
| | AFC Emley | 14 | 8 | 2 | 4 | 35 | 25 | 10 | 26 |
| | Ossett Town | 14 | 8 | 1 | 5 | 31 | 16 | 15 | 25 |
| | RIASA East | 14 | 7 | 1 | 6 | 33 | 26 | 7 | 22 |
| | Silsden | 14 | 3 | 4 | 7 | 34 | 41 | -7 | 13 |
| | Pontefract Collieries | 14 | 3 | 3 | 8 | 26 | 49 | -23 | 12 |
| | Goole | 14 | 1 | 2 | 11 | 18 | 57 | -39 | 5 |

| West | | P | W | D | L | F | A | GD | Pts |
|---|---|---|---|---|---|---|---|---|---|
| | Colne | 14 | 10 | 1 | 3 | 40 | 25 | 15 | 31 |
| | Workington | 14 | 8 | 2 | 4 | 48 | 27 | 21 | 26 |
| | Padiham | 14 | 8 | 2 | 4 | 32 | 22 | 10 | 26 |
| | AFC Fylde | 14 | 8 | 1 | 5 | 38 | 29 | 9 | 25 |
| | Ashton Athletic | 14 | 7 | 1 | 6 | 38 | 30 | 8 | 22 |
| | Bamber Bridge | 14 | 4 | 1 | 9 | 26 | 38 | -12 | 13 |
| | Squires Gate | 14 | 3 | 2 | 9 | 22 | 44 | -22 | 11 |
| | Skelmersdale United | 14 | 3 | 0 | 11 | 18 | 47 | -29 | 9 |

| South | | P | W | D | L | F | A | GD | Pts |
|---|---|---|---|---|---|---|---|---|---|
| | Curzon Ashton Dev | 20 | 17 | 0 | 3 | 91 | 27 | 64 | 51 |
| | FC United of Manchester | 20 | 14 | 2 | 4 | 73 | 34 | 39 | 44 |
| | Stockport County | 20 | 14 | 2 | 4 | 68 | 51 | 17 | 44 |
| | Bradford RIASA | 20 | 11 | 2 | 7 | 61 | 40 | 21 | 35 |
| | Hyde | 20 | 8 | 3 | 9 | 42 | 33 | 9 | 27 |
| | Ashton United | 20 | 8 | 1 | 11 | 50 | 62 | -12 | 25 |
| | Buxton | 20 | 8 | 0 | 12 | 44 | 57 | -13 | 24 |
| | Witton Albion Dev | 20 | 8 | 0 | 12 | 40 | 60 | -20 | 24 |
| | New Mills | 20 | 7 | 2 | 11 | 44 | 63 | -19 | 23 |
| | RIASA South | 20 | 6 | 1 | 13 | 41 | 62 | -21 | 19 |
| | Stalybridge Celtic | 20 | 1 | 3 | 16 | 28 | 93 | -65 | 6 |

| Division | | P | W | D | L | F | A | GD | Pts |
|---|---|---|---|---|---|---|---|---|---|
| | Cote Heath | 20 | 16 | 3 | 1 | 78 | 22 | 56 | 51 |
| | Eyam | 20 | 14 | 2 | 4 | 54 | 33 | 21 | 44 |
| | Bradwell Res. | 20 | 13 | 4 | 3 | 66 | 30 | 36 | 43 |
| | Bakewell Town Res. | 20 | 10 | 4 | 6 | 54 | 39 | 15 | 34 |
| | Calver | 20 | 9 | 7 | 4 | 71 | 47 | 24 | 30 |
| | Stoney Middleton | 20 | 7 | 4 | 9 | 42 | 44 | -2 | 25 |
| | Fairfield FC | 20 | 6 | 5 | 9 | 34 | 59 | -25 | 23 |
| | Edale | 20 | 6 | 3 | 11 | 49 | 59 | -10 | 21 |
| | Buxworth Res. | 20 | 5 | 4 | 11 | 26 | 52 | -26 | 19 |
| | Chinley | 20 | 3 | 2 | 15 | 26 | 73 | -47 | 11 |
| | Bakewell Manners (-3) | 20 | 2 | 4 | 14 | 23 | 65 | -42 | 7 |

## LEICESTER & DISTRICT FOOTBALL LEAGUE

| Premier Division | | P | W | D | L | F | A | GD | Pts |
|---|---|---|---|---|---|---|---|---|---|
| 1 | County Hall | 18 | 15 | 1 | 2 | 57 | 20 | 37 | 46 |
| 2 | Cosby United | 18 | 14 | 1 | 3 | 61 | 16 | 45 | 43 |
| 3 | Magna 73 | 18 | 12 | 0 | 6 | 43 | 31 | 12 | 36 |
| 4 | Kibworth Town | 18 | 9 | 1 | 8 | 38 | 37 | 1 | 28 |
| 5 | Kingsway Rangers | 18 | 8 | 3 | 7 | 35 | 32 | 3 | 27 |
| 6 | Leicester Three Lions | 18 | 7 | 1 | 10 | 40 | 44 | -4 | 22 |
| 7 | Beaumont Town | 18 | 4 | 5 | 9 | 38 | 48 | -10 | 17 |
| 8 | Huncote | 18 | 5 | 1 | 12 | 29 | 42 | -13 | 16 |
| 9 | Burbage Old Boys | 18 | 4 | 2 | 12 | 27 | 41 | -14 | 14 |
| 10 | Queniborough | 18 | 3 | 3 | 12 | 23 | 80 | -57 | 12 |

| Division One | | P | W | D | L | F | A | GD | Pts |
|---|---|---|---|---|---|---|---|---|---|
| 1 | Thurnby Rangers | 20 | 16 | 0 | 4 | 108 | 31 | 77 | 48 |
| 2 | Houghton Rangers | 20 | 16 | 0 | 4 | 88 | 26 | 62 | 48 |
| 3 | Glen Villa | 20 | 14 | 0 | 6 | 66 | 42 | 24 | 42 |
| 4 | Glenfield Town | 19 | 12 | 0 | 7 | 60 | 48 | 12 | 36 |
| 5 | Thurlaston | 19 | 9 | 2 | 8 | 38 | 45 | -7 | 29 |
| 6 | Broughton Astley | 20 | 9 | 2 | 9 | 42 | 61 | -19 | 29 |
| 7 | Belgrave | 20 | 9 | 1 | 10 | 54 | 57 | -3 | 28 |
| 8 | Fleckney Athletic | 20 | 8 | 2 | 10 | 51 | 50 | 1 | 26 |
| 9 | Ashby Road | 20 | 5 | 2 | 13 | 40 | 67 | -27 | 17 |
| 10 | Magna 73 Res. | 20 | 3 | 3 | 14 | 33 | 86 | -53 | 12 |
| 11 | North Kilworth | 20 | 1 | 2 | 17 | 28 | 95 | -67 | 5 |

| Division Two | | P | W | D | L | F | A | GD | Pts |
|---|---|---|---|---|---|---|---|---|---|
| 1 | Birstall RBL | 22 | 15 | 4 | 3 | 85 | 32 | 53 | 49 |
| 2 | New Parks Social 2015 | 22 | 15 | 1 | 6 | 95 | 41 | 54 | 46 |
| 3 | Old Aylestone | 22 | 14 | 0 | 8 | 87 | 61 | 26 | 42 |
| 4 | Cosby United Res. | 22 | 13 | 2 | 7 | 70 | 41 | 29 | 41 |
| 5 | Huncote Res. | 22 | 13 | 1 | 8 | 59 | 40 | 19 | 40 |
| 6 | Forest East | 22 | 11 | 4 | 7 | 68 | 32 | 36 | 37 |
| 7 | Dunton & Broughton Rangers Res. | 22 | 10 | 4 | 8 | 59 | 47 | 12 | 34 |
| 8 | St Patricks | 22 | 10 | 1 | 11 | 60 | 52 | 8 | 31 |
| 9 | Northfield Emerald 2013 | 22 | 10 | 0 | 12 | 70 | 58 | 12 | 30 |
| 10 | Leicester Polska | 22 | 9 | 1 | 12 | 59 | 66 | -7 | 28 |
| 11 | North Kilworth Res. | 22 | 3 | 0 | 19 | 33 | 94 | -61 | 9 |
| 12 | CFA FC | 22 | 0 | 0 | 22 | 11 | 192 | -181 | 0 |

| Division Three | | P | W | D | L | F | A | GD | Pts |
|---|---|---|---|---|---|---|---|---|---|
| 1 | Studs FC | 22 | 17 | 4 | 1 | 78 | 33 | 45 | 55 |
| 2 | Belgrave Res. (-1) | 22 | 16 | 4 | 2 | 81 | 39 | 42 | 51 |
| 3 | Leicester Three Lions Res. | 22 | 11 | 3 | 8 | 68 | 51 | 17 | 36 |
| 4 | Glenfield Town Res. | 22 | 10 | 3 | 9 | 43 | 39 | 4 | 33 |
| 5 | Kibworth Town Res. | 22 | 9 | 5 | 8 | 44 | 51 | -7 | 32 |
| 6 | Northfield Emerald 2013 Res. | 22 | 8 | 5 | 9 | 61 | 56 | 5 | 29 |
| 7 | Glen Villa Res. (-3) | 22 | 10 | 2 | 10 | 52 | 49 | 3 | 29 |
| 8 | Broughton Astley Res. | 22 | 8 | 3 | 11 | 62 | 58 | 4 | 27 |
| 9 | AFC Andrews | 22 | 7 | 3 | 12 | 32 | 50 | -18 | 24 |
| 10 | Queniborough Res. (-8) | 22 | 8 | 3 | 11 | 55 | 61 | -6 | 19 |
| 11 | Park End 74 | 22 | 4 | 4 | 14 | 46 | 77 | -31 | 16 |
| 12 | A+United (-3) | 22 | 3 | 3 | 16 | 29 | 87 | -58 | 9 |

# NATIONAL STRIKE FORCE - TOP 106!

on this page and starts on page 652 and continued on pages 692

| | | | | | | | | | | |
|---|---|---|---|---|---|---|---|---|---|---|
| Luke Blewden | Tonbridge Angels | Isthmian Prem | 20 | | 2 | 2 | 1 | 4 | 16 | 22 |
| Tom Denton | North Ferriby United | National North | 20+1PO | | 1 | | | 3 | 19 | 22 |
| Dan Fitchett | Sutton United | National South | 20 | | 2 | 2 | 1 | 3 | 16 | 22 |
| Billy Healey | Wingate & Finchley | Isthmian Prem | 20 | 2 | | 3 | | 3 | 15 | 22 |
| Lee Hughes | Ilkeston T & Worcester C | National North | 3+18 | 0+1 | | | | 3+4 | 3+15 | 3+19 |
| Ben Mackey | Leamington | Southern Prem | 16 | | 6 | 1 | | 3 | 18 | 22 |
| James Norwood | Tranmere Rovers | National Prem | 20 | 2 | | 4 | | 2 | 17 | 22 |
| Tom Wraight | East Thurrock United | Isthmian Prem | 21 | | 1 | | | 2 | 20 | 22 |
| Scott Allison | Workington | N.P.L. | 18 | 3 | | | 2 | 2 | 12 | 21 |
| Ryan Bowman | Gateshead | National Prem | 16 | 1 | 3 | 3 | | 3 | 17 | 21 |
| Dumebi Dumaka | Grays Athletic | Isthmian Prem | 17 | 4 | | 1 | 1 | 3 | 13 | 21 |
| Ricky Miller | Dover Athletic | National Prem | 20 | | 1 | | | 3 | 16 | 21 |
| Dave Tarpey | Maidenhead United | National South | 16 | 3 | 2 | | 2 | 2 | 14 | 21 |
| Akwasi Asante | Solihull Moors | National North | 18 | 1 | 1 | 1 | 1 | 3 | 15 | 20 |
| Moses Emmanuel | Bromley | National Prem | 19 | | | 1 | 1 | 4 | 16 | 20 |
| Jacob Hazel | Frickley Athletic | N.P.L. | 19 | 1 | | | 1 | 3 | 18 | 20 |
| Alex Reid | Rushall Olympic | N.P.L. | 16 | 3 | 1 | | 1 | 3 | 16 | 20 |
| Liam Shotton | Nantwich Town | N.P.L. | 16 | | 4 | | 2 | 3 | 16 | 20 |
| Lewis Smith | East Thurrock United | Isthmian Prem | 14 | 2 | 4 | 5 | 1 | 3 | 14 | 20 |
| Nathan Cartman | Darlington 1883 | N.P.L. | 18 | | 1 | 1 | | 2 | 17 | 19 |
| Marc Charles-Smith | Harrow Borough | Isthmian Prem | 19 | | | 2 | 1 | 2 | 13 | 19 |
| Brad Fortnam-Tomlinson | Grays Athletic | Isthmian Prem | 15 | 3 | 1 | 1 | 2 | 3 | 13 | 19 |
| Darren Stephenson | Chorley | National North | 18 | 1 | | 1 | | 3 | 17 | 19 |
| Greg Mills | Corby Town | National North | 17 | | 2 | 7 | 1 | 2 | 14 | 19 |
| James Poole | Salford City | N.P.L. | 15 | 4 | | | 2 | 4 | 10 | 19 |
| Dayle Southwell | Boston United | National North | 19 | | | 4 | | 3 | 16 | 19 |
| Danny Webber | Salford City | N.P.L. | 16 | 3 | | 1 | | 2 | 16 | 19 |
| Chris Almond | Skelmersdale United | N.P.L. | 15 | | 3 | 2 | 1 | 2 | 12 | 18 |
| Omar Bogle | Grimsby Town | National Prem | 12+3PO | 1 | 2 | 4 | | 3 | 15 | 18 |
| Jordan Burrow | FC Halifax Town | National Prem | 14 | | 4 | 4 | | 3 | 14 | 18 |
| Chib Chilaka | Bradford PA | National North | 16 | 1 | 1 | | 1 | 2 | 12 | 18 |
| Steve Diggin | Brackley Town | National North | 14 | 4 | | | | 2 | 15 | 18 |
| Nat Jarvis | Hungerford Town | Southern Prem | 17 | | 1 | 1 | 1 | | 13 | 18 |
| Elliott Osborne | Nantwich Town | N.P.L. | 13 | | 5 | 8 | | 2 | 16 | 18 |
| Richard Allen | Salford City | N.P.L. | 15 | 2 | | 4 | | 2 | 14 | 17 |
| Elliott Brabrook | Dartford | National South | 17 | | | 3 | | 3 | 15 | 17 |
| Marvin Brooks | Poole Town | Southern Prem | 16 | 1 | | | | 3 | 13 | 17 |

## LINCOLNSHIRE FOOTBALL LEAGUE

| Premier Division | P | W | D | L | F | A | GD | Pts |
|---|---|---|---|---|---|---|---|---|
| 1 Skegness Town | 22 | 17 | 2 | 3 | 78 | 20 | 58 | 53 |
| 2 Hykeham Town | 22 | 15 | 2 | 5 | 69 | 27 | 42 | 47 |
| 3 Wyberton | 22 | 14 | 4 | 4 | 56 | 25 | 31 | 46 |
| 4 Sleaford Town Res. | 22 | 12 | 2 | 8 | 51 | 38 | 13 | 38 |
| 5 Brigg Town Res. | 22 | 11 | 3 | 8 | 40 | 40 | 0 | 36 |
| 6 Lincoln Railway A.F.C. | 22 | 9 | 6 | 7 | 49 | 52 | -3 | 33 |
| 7 Cleethorpes Town D.S. | 22 | 8 | 8 | 6 | 40 | 35 | 5 | 32 |
| 8 Horncastle Town | 22 | 8 | 5 | 9 | 22 | 37 | -15 | 29 |
| 9 Skegness United | 22 | 5 | 5 | 12 | 29 | 46 | -17 | 20 |
| 10 CGB Humbertherm | 22 | 5 | 3 | 14 | 31 | 55 | -24 | 18 |
| 11 Market Rasen Town | 22 | 4 | 2 | 16 | 25 | 64 | -39 | 14 |
| 12 Ruston Sports | 22 | 2 | 2 | 18 | 17 | 68 | -51 | 8 |

## LONDON COMMERCIAL FOOTBALL LEAGUE

| | P | W | D | L | F | A | GD | Pts |
|---|---|---|---|---|---|---|---|---|
| 1 Manor Boys FC | 12 | 7 | 3 | 2 | 40 | 22 | 18 | 24 |
| 2 LNER Sports | 12 | 7 | 1 | 4 | 43 | 35 | 8 | 22 |
| 3 Lampton Park II | 12 | 6 | 2 | 4 | 24 | 25 | -1 | 20 |
| 4 British Airways ( Coaches ) | 12 | 5 | 4 | 3 | 41 | 33 | 8 | 19 |
| 5 Sudbury Court | 12 | 4 | 3 | 5 | 25 | 21 | 4 | 15 |
| 6 Chiswick Homefields | 12 | 4 | 2 | 6 | 37 | 34 | 3 | 14 |
| 7 Old Alpertonians | 12 | 0 | 3 | 9 | 17 | 57 | -40 | 3 |

## LUTON DISTRICT & SOUTH BEDS FOOTBALL LEAGUE

| Premier Division | P | W | D | L | F | A | GD | Pts |
|---|---|---|---|---|---|---|---|---|
| Sporting Lewsey Park | 14 | 12 | 0 | 2 | 71 | 19 | 52 | 36 |
| Farley Boys | 14 | 9 | 2 | 3 | 70 | 23 | 47 | 29 |
| St Josephs | 14 | 7 | 3 | 4 | 37 | 28 | 9 | 24 |
| Christians in Sport | 14 | 6 | 3 | 5 | 34 | 40 | -6 | 21 |
| YP Community FC | 13 | 6 | 2 | 5 | 31 | 35 | -4 | 20 |
| Square FC | 14 | 5 | 2 | 7 | 38 | 51 | -13 | 17 |
| Luton Hussars | 14 | 2 | 1 | 11 | 21 | 65 | -44 | 7 |
| Jedenastka | 13 | 1 | 1 | 11 | 15 | 56 | -41 | 4 |

| Division One | P | W | D | L | F | A | GD | Pts |
|---|---|---|---|---|---|---|---|---|
| Luton Leagrave AFC | 14 | 12 | 2 | 0 | 60 | 14 | 46 | 38 |
| Farley Boys 2nd X1 | 14 | 8 | 3 | 3 | 43 | 29 | 14 | 27 |
| North Sundon Wanderers | 14 | 7 | 4 | 3 | 27 | 19 | 8 | 25 |
| FC Kokan | 14 | 7 | 2 | 5 | 32 | 35 | -3 | 23 |
| FC Polonia | 14 | 6 | 2 | 6 | 39 | 39 | 0 | 20 |
| Square FC 2nd X1 | 14 | 5 | 1 | 8 | 32 | 30 | 2 | 16 |
| Luton Aces | 13 | 2 | 2 | 9 | 22 | 55 | -33 | 8 |
| Brache Sparta (2015) Res. | 13 | 0 | 0 | 13 | 8 | 42 | -34 | 0 |

## MERCIAN REGIONAL FOOTBALL LEAGUE

| Premier Division | P | W | D | L | F | A | GD | Pts |
|---|---|---|---|---|---|---|---|---|
| 1 FC Oswestry Town | 26 | 20 | 3 | 3 | 96 | 40 | 56 | 63 |
| 2 Allscott | 26 | 18 | 2 | 6 | 102 | 30 | 72 | 56 |
| 3 Rock Rovers | 26 | 13 | 6 | 7 | 62 | 51 | 11 | 45 |
| 4 AFC Broseley | 26 | 12 | 5 | 9 | 59 | 50 | 9 | 41 |
| 5 Church Stretton | 26 | 13 | 2 | 11 | 56 | 49 | 7 | 41 |
| 6 Wroxeter Rovers | 26 | 12 | 4 | 10 | 76 | 70 | 6 | 40 |
| 7 Childs Ercall | 26 | 11 | 4 | 11 | 58 | 59 | -1 | 37 |
| 8 AFC Bridgnorth Res. | 26 | 10 | 7 | 9 | 50 | 58 | -8 | 37 |
| 9 Oakengates Athletic | 26 | 11 | 3 | 12 | 57 | 57 | 0 | 36 |
| 10 Madeley Sports | 26 | 10 | 3 | 13 | 44 | 56 | -12 | 33 |
| 11 Wrockwardine Wood | 26 | 7 | 6 | 13 | 45 | 74 | -29 | 27 |
| 12 FC Hodnet | 26 | 7 | 4 | 15 | 37 | 54 | -17 | 25 |
| 13 Prees | 26 | 6 | 3 | 17 | 33 | 77 | -44 | 21 |
| 14 Shifnal United 97 | 26 | 5 | 2 | 19 | 37 | 87 | -50 | 17 |

| Division One | P | W | D | L | F | A | GD | Pts |
|---|---|---|---|---|---|---|---|---|
| 1 Stoke Heath 1st | 12 | 10 | 0 | 2 | 38 | 16 | 22 | 30 |
| 2 Clee Hill United | 12 | 8 | 0 | 4 | 46 | 18 | 28 | 24 |
| 3 Gobowen Celtic | 12 | 7 | 1 | 4 | 36 | 30 | 6 | 22 |
| 4 Bishops Castle Town FC | 12 | 6 | 1 | 5 | 41 | 31 | 10 | 19 |
| 5 AFC Wellington | 12 | 6 | 0 | 6 | 21 | 21 | 0 | 18 |
| 6 Oakengates Rangers | 12 | 2 | 0 | 10 | 16 | 40 | -24 | 6 |
| 7 Brown Clee | 12 | 2 | 0 | 10 | 15 | 57 | -42 | 6 |

| Division Two | P | W | D | L | F | A | GD | Pts |
|---|---|---|---|---|---|---|---|---|
| 1 Madeley Sports Res. | 18 | 13 | 3 | 2 | 72 | 22 | 50 | 42 |
| 2 Claverley | 18 | 13 | 2 | 3 | 71 | 22 | 49 | 41 |
| 3 Coven United | 18 | 11 | 2 | 5 | 55 | 24 | 31 | 35 |
| 4 Craven Arms Town | 18 | 11 | 2 | 5 | 63 | 37 | 26 | 35 |
| 5 St Martins Res. | 18 | 9 | 2 | 7 | 53 | 30 | 23 | 29 |
| 6 Riverside | 18 | 8 | 3 | 7 | 35 | 32 | 3 | 27 |
| 7 Albrighton Juniors FC | 18 | 6 | 1 | 11 | 60 | 43 | 17 | 19 |
| 8 AFC Broseley Res. | 18 | 5 | 2 | 11 | 26 | 63 | -37 | 17 |
| 9 FC Oswestry Res. | 18 | 5 | 1 | 12 | 44 | 66 | -22 | 16 |
| 10 Denso | 18 | 0 | 0 | 18 | 14 | 154 | -140 | 0 |

## MID ESSEX FOOTBALL LEAGUE

| Premier Division | P | W | D | L | F | A | GD | Pts |
|---|---|---|---|---|---|---|---|---|
| 1 Pro Essex | 18 | 12 | 4 | 2 | 60 | 26 | 34 | 40 |
| 2 CT 66 | 18 | 12 | 1 | 5 | 63 | 35 | 28 | 37 |
| 3 Haver Town | 18 | 12 | 1 | 5 | 48 | 28 | 20 | 37 |
| 4 Beacon Hill Rovers | 17 | 11 | 0 | 6 | 33 | 26 | 7 | 33 |
| 5 Sandon Royals | 18 | 9 | 3 | 6 | 42 | 31 | 11 | 30 |
| 6 Stifford Town | 17 | 6 | 3 | 8 | 33 | 33 | 0 | 21 |
| 7 Iona | 18 | 6 | 1 | 11 | 25 | 26 | -1 | 19 |
| 8 Harold Wood Athletic A | 18 | 4 | 3 | 11 | 20 | 58 | -38 | 15 |
| 9 Braintree and Bocking United | 18 | 4 | 2 | 12 | 32 | 52 | -20 | 14 |
| 10 Academy Soccer | 18 | 4 | 0 | 14 | 19 | 60 | -41 | 12 |

## LEAGUE TABLES

| Division One | P | W | D | L | F | A | GD | Pts |
|---|---|---|---|---|---|---|---|---|
| 1 Pro Athletic | 22 | 16 | 2 | 4 | 68 | 31 | 37 | 50 |
| 2 Flitch United | 22 | 16 | 1 | 5 | 63 | 23 | 40 | 49 |
| 3 Dunmow Rhodes | 22 | 13 | 4 | 5 | 74 | 46 | 28 | 43 |
| 4 Great Leighs Athletic (-1) | 22 | 12 | 4 | 6 | 61 | 43 | 18 | 39 |
| 5 Focus Ferrers | 22 | 10 | 5 | 7 | 49 | 39 | 10 | 35 |
| 6 Real Maldon | 22 | 10 | 3 | 9 | 46 | 44 | 2 | 33 |
| 7 Battlesbridge and Rayleigh Town | 22 | 9 | 3 | 10 | 47 | 55 | -8 | 30 |
| 8 Frenford Senior A | 22 | 8 | 4 | 10 | 32 | 45 | -13 | 28 |
| 9 Great Baddow Res. | 22 | 6 | 5 | 11 | 36 | 40 | -4 | 23 |
| 10 Boreham | 22 | 6 | 1 | 15 | 36 | 73 | -37 | 19 |
| 11 Sandon Royals Res. | 22 | 4 | 4 | 14 | 30 | 63 | -33 | 16 |
| 12 Stock United | 22 | 2 | 4 | 16 | 35 | 75 | -40 | 10 |

| Division Two | P | W | D | L | F | A | GD | Pts |
|---|---|---|---|---|---|---|---|---|
| 1 St.Clere's | 20 | 17 | 2 | 1 | 60 | 17 | 43 | 53 |
| 2 Felsted Rovers | 20 | 13 | 2 | 5 | 50 | 28 | 22 | 41 |
| 3 United Chelmsford Churches | 20 | 12 | 2 | 6 | 52 | 31 | 21 | 38 |
| 4 Mayland Village | 20 | 10 | 2 | 8 | 41 | 32 | 9 | 32 |
| 5 Gosfield United (-1) | 20 | 9 | 3 | 8 | 41 | 33 | 8 | 29 |
| 6 Extreme United | 20 | 8 | 2 | 10 | 40 | 40 | 0 | 26 |
| 7 Durning | 20 | 7 | 4 | 9 | 33 | 43 | -10 | 25 |
| 8 Mundon Vics | 20 | 7 | 2 | 11 | 39 | 42 | -3 | 23 |
| 9 Hutton A | 20 | 6 | 4 | 10 | 35 | 48 | -13 | 22 |
| 10 Writtle | 20 | 5 | 4 | 11 | 35 | 59 | -24 | 19 |
| 11 White Notley Res. | 20 | 2 | 1 | 17 | 23 | 76 | -53 | 7 |

| Division Three | P | W | D | L | F | A | GD | Pts |
|---|---|---|---|---|---|---|---|---|
| 1 Harold Wood Athletic B | 14 | 9 | 4 | 1 | 36 | 22 | 14 | 31 |
| 2 Haver Town Res. | 14 | 8 | 3 | 3 | 40 | 25 | 15 | 27 |
| 3 Sparta Basildon | 14 | 8 | 1 | 5 | 35 | 20 | 15 | 25 |
| 4 Writtle Res. | 14 | 7 | 4 | 3 | 36 | 26 | 10 | 25 |
| 5 Kenson | 14 | 7 | 3 | 4 | 35 | 26 | 9 | 24 |
| 6 CT 66 Res. | 14 | 4 | 4 | 6 | 36 | 48 | -12 | 16 |
| 7 Flitch United Res. | 14 | 2 | 0 | 12 | 14 | 51 | -37 | 6 |
| 8 AFC Horndon | 14 | 1 | 1 | 12 | 18 | 32 | -14 | 4 |

| Division Four | P | W | D | L | F | A | GD | Pts |
|---|---|---|---|---|---|---|---|---|
| 1 Elgar Eagles (-3) | 20 | 18 | 0 | 2 | 107 | 32 | 75 | 51 |
| 2 Southminster St. Leonards | 20 | 14 | 1 | 5 | 71 | 35 | 36 | 43 |
| 3 Dunmow Rhodes Res. | 20 | 13 | 0 | 7 | 56 | 41 | 15 | 39 |
| 4 Focus Ferrers Res. | 20 | 11 | 1 | 8 | 49 | 43 | 6 | 34 |
| 5 Beacon Hill Rovers Res. | 20 | 10 | 2 | 8 | 49 | 74 | -25 | 32 |
| 6 Brendans | 20 | 7 | 5 | 8 | 57 | 50 | 7 | 26 |
| 7 Valley Green | 20 | 7 | 2 | 11 | 51 | 73 | -22 | 23 |
| 8 Writtle Manor | 20 | 6 | 3 | 11 | 42 | 56 | -14 | 21 |
| 9 Leigh Ramblers A | 20 | 6 | 2 | 12 | 28 | 55 | -27 | 20 |
| 10 Gosfield United Res. | 20 | 4 | 6 | 10 | 40 | 50 | -10 | 18 |
| 11 Marconi Athletic | 20 | 2 | 2 | 16 | 35 | 76 | -41 | 8 |

| Division Five | P | W | D | L | F | A | GD | Pts |
|---|---|---|---|---|---|---|---|---|
| 1 Royal Oak (-1) | 26 | 19 | 4 | 3 | 68 | 26 | 42 | 60 |
| 2 Maldon Saints | 26 | 18 | 4 | 4 | 53 | 31 | 22 | 58 |
| 3 Baddow Athletic (-1) | 26 | 15 | 5 | 6 | 77 | 46 | 31 | 49 |
| 4 Tillingham Hotspur | 26 | 16 | 1 | 9 | 88 | 59 | 29 | 49 |
| 5 Pro Athletic Res. | 26 | 16 | 0 | 10 | 71 | 35 | 36 | 48 |
| 6 Braintree & Bocking Utd Res. | 26 | 12 | 6 | 8 | 64 | 55 | 9 | 42 |
| 7 Felsted Rovers Res. (-1) | 26 | 12 | 3 | 11 | 65 | 57 | 8 | 38 |
| 8 Old Chelmsfordians A | 26 | 11 | 4 | 11 | 77 | 53 | 24 | 37 |
| 9 United Chelsmford Churches Res. | 26 | 11 | 4 | 11 | 56 | 44 | 12 | 37 |
| 10 Burnham Ramblers Res. (-3) | 26 | 10 | 1 | 15 | 50 | 63 | -13 | 28 |
| 11 Southminster St. Leonards Res. | 26 | 6 | 5 | 15 | 44 | 78 | -34 | 23 |
| 12 Valley Green Res. | 26 | 6 | 4 | 16 | 44 | 71 | -27 | 22 |
| 13 Mundon Vics Res. | 26 | 4 | 6 | 16 | 43 | 93 | -50 | 18 |
| 14 Marconi Athletic Res. | 26 | 2 | 1 | 23 | 22 | 111 | -89 | 7 |

### MAIDSTONE & DISTRICT FOOTBALL LEAGUE

| Premier Division | P | W | D | L | F | A | GD | Pts |
|---|---|---|---|---|---|---|---|---|
| 1 Wateringbury FC | 12 | 9 | 1 | 2 | 27 | 11 | 16 | 28 |
| 2 Malgo | 12 | 7 | 2 | 3 | 26 | 20 | 6 | 23 |
| 3 Larkfield & New Hythe Res. | 12 | 7 | 0 | 5 | 30 | 22 | 8 | 21 |
| 4 Eccles | 12 | 6 | 1 | 5 | 28 | 26 | 2 | 19 |
| 5 Lenham Wanderers | 12 | 3 | 2 | 7 | 26 | 38 | -12 | 11 |
| 6 Marden Minors | 12 | 3 | 1 | 8 | 35 | 41 | -6 | 10 |
| 7 Three Suttons | 12 | 3 | 1 | 8 | 22 | 36 | -14 | 10 |

| Division One | P | W | D | L | F | A | GD | Pts |
|---|---|---|---|---|---|---|---|---|
| 1 Hollingbourne | 16 | 15 | 0 | 1 | 79 | 12 | 67 | 45 |
| 2 Leybourne Athletic | 16 | 10 | 1 | 5 | 42 | 25 | 17 | 31 |
| 3 Headcorn (-1) | 16 | 10 | 0 | 6 | 35 | 44 | -9 | 29 |
| 4 Eccles Res. (-1) | 16 | 9 | 2 | 5 | 43 | 26 | 17 | 28 |
| 5 Trisports (-2) | 16 | 9 | 2 | 5 | 46 | 39 | 7 | 27 |
| 6 Lenham Wanderers Res. | 16 | 5 | 3 | 8 | 36 | 35 | 1 | 18 |
| 7 Town Malling Club | 16 | 4 | 2 | 10 | 38 | 41 | -3 | 14 |
| 8 Kings Hill Res. | 16 | 3 | 3 | 10 | 37 | 54 | -17 | 1[illegible] |
| 9 Phoenix United (-1) | 16 | 0 | 1 | 15 | 17 | 97 | -80 | [illegible] |

| Division Two | P | W | D | L | F | A | GD | Pts |
|---|---|---|---|---|---|---|---|---|
| 1 Mangravet | 16 | 12 | 4 | 0 | 65 | 15 | 50 | 4[illegible] |
| 2 Hunton | 16 | 12 | 1 | 3 | 50 | 20 | 30 | 3[illegible] |
| 3 Kilnbarn FC | 16 | 11 | 3 | 2 | 59 | 22 | 37 | 3[illegible] |
| 4 Ashford Ath | 16 | 8 | 3 | 5 | 38 | 28 | 10 | 2[illegible] |
| 5 West Farleigh Res | 16 | 7 | 2 | 7 | 27 | 37 | -10 | 2[illegible] |
| 6 Maidstone Athletic | 16 | 5 | 1 | 10 | 33 | 52 | -19 | 1[illegible] |
| 7 Ditton Minors (-2) | 16 | 4 | 3 | 9 | 26 | 39 | -13 | 1[illegible] |
| 8 Aylesford Res. (-1) | 16 | 3 | 0 | 13 | 28 | 63 | -35 | [illegible] |
| 9 Parkwood Jupitors | 16 | 1 | 1 | 14 | 22 | 72 | -50 | [illegible] |

## MID LANCS FOOTBALL LEAGUE

| [P]remier Division | P | W | D | L | F | A | GD | Pts |
|---|---|---|---|---|---|---|---|---|
| Southport & Ainsdale Amateurs | 20 | 14 | 4 | 2 | 76 | 22 | 54 | 46 |
| Preston Wanderers | 20 | 14 | 3 | 3 | 97 | 37 | 60 | 45 |
| Eccleston & Heskin | 20 | 13 | 2 | 5 | 69 | 39 | 30 | 41 |
| Bolton United (-3) | 20 | 9 | 7 | 4 | 50 | 25 | 25 | 31 |
| Hoole United | 20 | 7 | 8 | 5 | 51 | 37 | 14 | 29 |
| Broughton Amateurs | 20 | 7 | 7 | 6 | 43 | 42 | 1 | 28 |
| Newman College | 20 | 7 | 6 | 7 | 46 | 43 | 3 | 27 |
| Walmer Bridge | 20 | 8 | 3 | 9 | 59 | 71 | -12 | 27 |
| Penwortham Town | 20 | 6 | 3 | 11 | 58 | 84 | -26 | 21 |
| Anchorsholme | 20 | 2 | 1 | 17 | 24 | 89 | -65 | 7 |
| Baxters | 20 | 0 | 2 | 18 | 19 | 103 | -84 | 2 |

| [D]ivision One | P | W | D | L | F | A | GD | Pts |
|---|---|---|---|---|---|---|---|---|
| Fleetwood Hesketh | 20 | 16 | 1 | 3 | 107 | 36 | 71 | 49 |
| Ribble Wanderers | 20 | 15 | 2 | 3 | 77 | 35 | 42 | 47 |
| Walton-Le-Dale | 20 | 11 | 3 | 6 | 65 | 34 | 31 | 36 |
| Wilbraham Club | 20 | 10 | 2 | 8 | 54 | 67 | -13 | 32 |
| Chipping | 20 | 8 | 5 | 7 | 37 | 32 | 5 | 29 |
| Charnock Richard Academy | 20 | 8 | 2 | 10 | 50 | 58 | -8 | 26 |
| Bolton Nomads | 20 | 8 | 2 | 10 | 28 | 51 | -23 | 26 |
| Eccleston & Heskin Res. | 20 | 7 | 4 | 9 | 39 | 63 | -24 | 25 |
| Southport Trinity Res. | 20 | 5 | 4 | 11 | 30 | 54 | -24 | 19 |
| Tarleton Corinthians | 20 | 4 | 4 | 12 | 40 | 50 | -10 | 16 |
| New Longton Rovers FC | 20 | 1 | 5 | 14 | 31 | 78 | -47 | 8 |

| [Di]vision Two | P | W | D | L | F | A | GD | Pts |
|---|---|---|---|---|---|---|---|---|
| Ribchester Rovers | 24 | 19 | 1 | 4 | 59 | 33 | 26 | 58 |
| AFC Preston | 24 | 17 | 3 | 4 | 68 | 34 | 34 | 54 |
| Farington Villa (-3) | 24 | 15 | 2 | 7 | 70 | 46 | 24 | 44 |
| Broughton Amateurs Res. (-6) | 24 | 15 | 3 | 6 | 76 | 38 | 38 | 42 |
| Chorley Athletic | 24 | 12 | 3 | 9 | 73 | 65 | 8 | 39 |
| FC Ribbleton | 24 | 12 | 1 | 11 | 65 | 58 | 7 | 37 |
| Lytham | 24 | 10 | 4 | 10 | 48 | 57 | -9 | 34 |
| FC Bolton | 24 | 9 | 3 | 12 | 59 | 64 | -5 | 30 |
| Whittle | 24 | 9 | 3 | 12 | 69 | 81 | -12 | 30 |
| Eagle | 24 | 8 | 2 | 14 | 51 | 55 | -4 | 26 |
| Springfields | 24 | 6 | 3 | 15 | 40 | 62 | -22 | 21 |
| Cottam Corinthians | 24 | 6 | 3 | 15 | 48 | 72 | -24 | 21 |
| Newman College Res. | 24 | 2 | 1 | 21 | 24 | 85 | -61 | 7 |

| | Division Three | P | W | D | L | F | A | GD | Pts |
|---|---|---|---|---|---|---|---|---|---|
| 1 | Tarleton Corinthians Res. | 26 | 21 | 3 | 2 | 91 | 27 | 64 | 66 |
| 2 | Walmer Bridge Res. | 26 | 18 | 2 | 6 | 96 | 53 | 43 | 56 |
| 3 | Cottam Corinthians Res. | 26 | 17 | 2 | 7 | 72 | 57 | 15 | 53 |
| 4 | Southport & Ainsdale Amateurs Res. (-1) | 26 | 15 | 6 | 5 | 86 | 45 | 41 | 50 |
| 5 | Hoole United Res. | 26 | 14 | 5 | 7 | 83 | 45 | 38 | 47 |
| 6 | Broughton Amateurs A | 26 | 14 | 5 | 7 | 84 | 60 | 24 | 47 |
| 7 | Appley Bridge | 26 | 12 | 7 | 7 | 72 | 56 | 16 | 43 |
| 8 | Burscough Dynamo | 26 | 12 | 5 | 9 | 73 | 48 | 25 | 41 |
| 9 | International Allstars | 26 | 11 | 6 | 9 | 71 | 54 | 17 | 39 |
| 10 | Penwortham Town Res. | 26 | 6 | 3 | 17 | 56 | 90 | -34 | 21 |
| 11 | Adlington | 26 | 6 | 2 | 18 | 45 | 77 | -32 | 20 |
| 12 | New Longton Rovers Res. | 26 | 5 | 2 | 19 | 54 | 102 | -48 | 17 |
| 13 | Eccleston & Heskin 'A' | 26 | 3 | 5 | 18 | 33 | 73 | -40 | 14 |
| 14 | Chorley Town | 26 | 1 | 1 | 24 | 31 | 160 | -129 | 4 |

## MID-SOMERSET LEAGUE

| | Premier Division | P | W | D | L | F | A | GD | Pts |
|---|---|---|---|---|---|---|---|---|---|
| 1 | Coleford Athletic, | 18 | 15 | 2 | 1 | 75 | 16 | 59 | 47 |
| 2 | Stoke Rovers, | 18 | 11 | 4 | 3 | 54 | 27 | 27 | 37 |
| 3 | Interhound, | 18 | 9 | 3 | 6 | 52 | 37 | 15 | 30 |
| 4 | Westfield Res., | 18 | 8 | 2 | 8 | 48 | 43 | 5 | 26 |
| 5 | Welton Arsenal, (-2) | 18 | 7 | 5 | 6 | 46 | 51 | -5 | 24 |
| 6 | Mells & Vobster United, | 18 | 7 | 2 | 9 | 44 | 39 | 5 | 23 |
| 7 | Clutton Res., (-2) | 18 | 5 | 6 | 7 | 37 | 43 | -6 | 19 |
| 8 | Wells City A, | 18 | 4 | 5 | 9 | 36 | 50 | -14 | 17 |
| 9 | Meadow Rangers, | 18 | 4 | 4 | 10 | 29 | 64 | -35 | 16 |
| 10 | Pilton United, (-3) | 18 | 1 | 5 | 12 | 32 | 83 | -51 | 5 |

| | Division One | P | W | D | L | F | A | GD | Pts |
|---|---|---|---|---|---|---|---|---|---|
| 1 | Radstock Town A, | 20 | 16 | 1 | 3 | 74 | 28 | 46 | 49 |
| 2 | Frome Collegians Res., | 20 | 14 | 4 | 2 | 68 | 21 | 47 | 46 |
| 3 | Temple Cloud, | 20 | 14 | 1 | 5 | 68 | 32 | 36 | 43 |
| 4 | Peasedown Athletic Res. | 20 | 11 | 4 | 5 | 49 | 26 | 23 | 37 |
| 5 | Glastonbury Res., (-1) | 20 | 10 | 1 | 9 | 43 | 39 | 4 | 30 |
| 6 | Belrose , | 20 | 8 | 3 | 9 | 42 | 42 | 0 | 27 |
| 7 | Purnells Sports Res. (-3) | 20 | 7 | 2 | 11 | 44 | 46 | -2 | 20 |
| 8 | High Littleton FC | 20 | 5 | 5 | 10 | 37 | 51 | -14 | 20 |
| 9 | Evercreech Rovers, | 20 | 5 | 1 | 14 | 37 | 66 | -29 | 16 |
| 10 | Camerton Athletic, (-2) | 20 | 3 | 3 | 14 | 31 | 86 | -55 | 10 |
| 11 | Westfield A, (-4) | 20 | 3 | 3 | 14 | 28 | 84 | -56 | 8 |

| | Division Two | P | W | D | L | F | A | GD | Pts |
|---|---|---|---|---|---|---|---|---|---|
| 1 | Baltonsborough | 16 | 13 | 0 | 3 | 84 | 27 | 57 | 39 |
| 2 | Westhill Sports FC | 16 | 12 | 2 | 2 | 67 | 23 | 44 | 38 |
| 3 | Mells & Vobster United Res., | 16 | 9 | 3 | 4 | 59 | 41 | 18 | 30 |
| 4 | Farrington Gurney Res., | 16 | 7 | 3 | 6 | 53 | 55 | -2 | 24 |
| 5 | Pensford Res. (-1) | 16 | 7 | 4 | 5 | 41 | 44 | -3 | 24 |
| 6 | Chilcompton Sports Res., (-3) | 16 | 6 | 2 | 8 | 37 | 43 | -6 | 17 |
| 7 | Coleford Athletic Res., (-1) | 16 | 4 | 3 | 9 | 34 | 55 | -21 | 14 |
| 8 | Frome Town Sports Res., (-1) | 16 | 2 | 2 | 12 | 24 | 59 | -35 | 7 |
| 9 | Tunley Athletic Reserve, (-5) | 16 | 2 | 1 | 13 | 24 | 76 | -52 | 2 |

## LEAGUE TABLES

| Division Three | P | W | D | L | F | A | GD | Pts |
|---|---|---|---|---|---|---|---|---|
| 1 Victoria Sports (-1) | 22 | 18 | 4 | 0 | 96 | 14 | 82 | 57 |
| 2 Chew Magna Res | 22 | 17 | 2 | 3 | 106 | 37 | 69 | 53 |
| 3 Somer Valley FC | 22 | 14 | 1 | 7 | 79 | 53 | 26 | 43 |
| 4 Saltford Res. (-1) | 22 | 11 | 3 | 8 | 51 | 42 | 9 | 35 |
| 5 Timsbury Athletic Res | 22 | 10 | 1 | 11 | 46 | 53 | -7 | 31 |
| 6 Chilcompton Sports A | 22 | 9 | 3 | 10 | 53 | 68 | -15 | 30 |
| 7 Westhill Sports Res. (-6) | 22 | 11 | 1 | 10 | 48 | 52 | -4 | 28 |
| 8 Chilcompton United, | 22 | 7 | 1 | 14 | 43 | 63 | -20 | 22 |
| 9 Midsomer Norton Athletic (-2) | 22 | 7 | 3 | 12 | 37 | 63 | -26 | 22 |
| 10 Purnells Sports A | 22 | 5 | 5 | 12 | 38 | 58 | -20 | 20 |
| 11 Baltonsborough Res. FC | 22 | 5 | 3 | 14 | 46 | 91 | -45 | 18 |
| 12 Pilton United Res., | 22 | 4 | 1 | 17 | 43 | 92 | -49 | 13 |

### MID SUSSEX FOOTBALL LEAGUE

| Premier Division | P | W | D | L | F | A | GD | Pts |
|---|---|---|---|---|---|---|---|---|
| 1 Jarvis Brook | 26 | 19 | 5 | 2 | 59 | 23 | 36 | 62 |
| 2 Lindfield | 26 | 15 | 4 | 7 | 66 | 43 | 23 | 49 |
| 3 Smallfield | 26 | 12 | 7 | 7 | 50 | 45 | 5 | 43 |
| 4 Peacehaven United | 26 | 13 | 3 | 10 | 49 | 37 | 12 | 42 |
| 5 Willingdon Athletic | 26 | 13 | 2 | 11 | 45 | 36 | 9 | 41 |
| 6 Balcombe | 26 | 11 | 7 | 8 | 55 | 41 | 14 | 40 |
| 7 Copthorne | 26 | 11 | 6 | 9 | 57 | 48 | 9 | 39 |
| 8 Rotherfield | 26 | 10 | 5 | 11 | 44 | 41 | 3 | 35 |
| 9 AFC Varndeanians II | 26 | 9 | 4 | 13 | 40 | 51 | -11 | 31 |
| 10 Forest Row | 26 | 8 | 5 | 13 | 42 | 63 | -21 | 29 |
| 11 East Grinstead United | 26 | 7 | 6 | 13 | 38 | 70 | -32 | 27 |
| 12 Cuckfield Rangers | 26 | 6 | 7 | 13 | 37 | 40 | -3 | 25 |
| 13 Portslade Athletic | 26 | 6 | 6 | 14 | 40 | 55 | -15 | 24 |
| 14 Buxted | 26 | 7 | 3 | 16 | 31 | 60 | -29 | 24 |

| Championship | P | W | D | L | F | A | GD | Pts |
|---|---|---|---|---|---|---|---|---|
| 1 Dormansland Rockets | 22 | 18 | 1 | 3 | 82 | 23 | 59 | 55 |
| 2 AFC Ringmer | 22 | 17 | 2 | 3 | 63 | 30 | 33 | 53 |
| 3 AFC Haywards | 22 | 14 | 4 | 4 | 51 | 23 | 28 | 46 |
| 4 Ditchling | 22 | 14 | 3 | 5 | 50 | 25 | 25 | 45 |
| 5 Barcombe | 22 | 9 | 5 | 8 | 37 | 35 | 2 | 32 |
| 6 Polegate Town | 22 | 9 | 4 | 9 | 38 | 49 | -11 | 31 |
| 7 Ashurst Wood | 22 | 9 | 3 | 10 | 54 | 58 | -4 | 30 |
| 8 Phoenix United | 22 | 6 | 3 | 13 | 39 | 59 | -20 | 21 |
| 9 Sporting Lindfield | 22 | 5 | 4 | 13 | 36 | 53 | -17 | 19 |
| 10 Framfield & Blackboys United | 22 | 4 | 3 | 15 | 25 | 45 | -20 | 15 |
| 11 Cuckfield Town | 22 | 4 | 3 | 15 | 40 | 73 | -33 | 15 |
| 12 Furnace Green Rovers | 22 | 3 | 5 | 14 | 26 | 68 | -42 | 14 |

| Division One | P | W | D | L | F | A | GD | Pts |
|---|---|---|---|---|---|---|---|---|
| 1 Nutley | 20 | 15 | 4 | 1 | 72 | 23 | 49 | 49 |
| 2 AFC Uckfield Town III | 20 | 15 | 3 | 2 | 68 | 29 | 39 | 48 |
| 3 Montpelier Villa II | 20 | 10 | 3 | 7 | 43 | 41 | 2 | 33 |
| 4 Alliance | 20 | 10 | 2 | 8 | 51 | 55 | -4 | 32 |
| 5 AFC Varndeanians III | 20 | 9 | 4 | 7 | 50 | 42 | 8 | 31 |
| 6 Ansty Sports & Social | 20 | 8 | 3 | 9 | 45 | 42 | 3 | 27 |
| 7 Sporting Elite | 20 | 6 | 5 | 9 | 42 | 40 | 2 | 23 |
| 8 Wivelsfield Green Pilgrims | 20 | 6 | 4 | 10 | 49 | 60 | -11 | 22 |
| 9 Ardingly | 20 | 5 | 2 | 13 | 33 | 67 | -34 | 17 |
| 10 Felbridge | 20 | 4 | 3 | 13 | 27 | 51 | -24 | 15 |
| 11 East Court | 20 | 4 | 3 | 13 | 30 | 60 | -30 | 15 |

| Division Two | P | W | D | L | F | A | GD | Pts |
|---|---|---|---|---|---|---|---|---|
| 1 Copthorne II | 18 | 14 | 1 | 3 | 60 | 26 | 34 | 43 |
| 2 Burgess Hill Albion | 18 | 11 | 4 | 3 | 53 | 24 | 29 | 37 |
| 3 Buxted II | 18 | 8 | 8 | 2 | 42 | 24 | 18 | 32 |
| 4 United Services | 18 | 10 | 1 | 7 | 39 | 41 | -2 | 31 |
| 5 Handcross Village | 18 | 6 | 6 | 6 | 37 | 42 | -5 | 24 |
| 6 West Hoathly | 18 | 6 | 3 | 9 | 36 | 41 | -5 | 21 |
| 7 Crawley Cobras | 18 | 4 | 7 | 7 | 28 | 34 | -6 | [illegible] |
| 8 Crawley Athletic FC | 18 | 4 | 5 | 9 | 26 | 43 | -17 | [illegible] |
| 9 Balcombe II | 18 | 4 | 1 | 13 | 23 | 45 | -22 | [illegible] |
| 10 Willingdon Athletic II | 18 | 3 | 4 | 11 | 25 | 49 | -24 | [illegible] |

| Division Three | P | W | D | L | F | A | GD | Pts |
|---|---|---|---|---|---|---|---|---|
| 1 DCK Copthorne | 14 | 12 | 0 | 2 | 44 | 19 | 25 | [illegible] |
| 2 Crawley Devils | 14 | 8 | 3 | 3 | 47 | 29 | 18 | [illegible] |
| 3 Plumpton Athletic (+3) | 14 | 7 | 2 | 5 | 33 | 34 | -1 | [illegible] |
| 4 Copthorne III | 14 | 7 | 3 | 4 | 34 | 29 | 5 | [illegible] |
| 5 Lindfield II | 14 | 4 | 2 | 8 | 36 | 37 | -1 | [illegible] |
| 6 Dormansland Rockets II | 14 | 3 | 4 | 7 | 21 | 44 | -23 | [illegible] |
| 7 Cuckfield Rangers II (-3) | 14 | 4 | 3 | 7 | 28 | 30 | -2 | [illegible] |
| 8 Ifield Galaxy II | 14 | 2 | 1 | 11 | 19 | 40 | -21 | [illegible] |

| Division Four | P | W | D | L | F | A | GD | Pts |
|---|---|---|---|---|---|---|---|---|
| 1 Eastbourne Rangers II | 15 | 12 | 1 | 2 | 46 | 17 | 29 | [illegible] |
| 2 Jarvis Brook II | 15 | 10 | 2 | 3 | 50 | 22 | 28 | [illegible] |
| 3 Peacehaven United II | 15 | 7 | 1 | 7 | 38 | 36 | 2 | [illegible] |
| 4 AFC Hurst | 15 | 5 | 2 | 8 | 27 | 30 | -3 | [illegible] |
| 5 Rotherfield II | 15 | 3 | 3 | 9 | 24 | 47 | -23 | [illegible] |
| 6 Polegate Town II | 15 | 3 | 1 | 11 | 21 | 54 | -33 | [illegible] |

| Division Five | P | W | D | L | F | A | GD | Pts |
|---|---|---|---|---|---|---|---|---|
| 1 AFC Haywards II | 16 | 11 | 2 | 3 | 41 | 14 | 27 | [illegible] |
| 2 Portslade Athletic II | 16 | 8 | 4 | 4 | 36 | 25 | 11 | [illegible] |
| 3 Stones | 16 | 9 | 1 | 6 | 34 | 26 | 8 | [illegible] |
| 4 Montpelier Villa III | 16 | 8 | 2 | 6 | 41 | 32 | 9 | [illegible] |
| 5 Wisdom Sports | 16 | 6 | 7 | 3 | 33 | 28 | 5 | [illegible] |
| 6 Copthorne IV | 16 | 6 | 4 | 6 | 32 | 35 | -3 | [illegible] |
| 7 Ashurst Wood II | 16 | 6 | 2 | 8 | 42 | 47 | -5 | [illegible] |
| 8 Sporting Elite II | 16 | 3 | 1 | 12 | 29 | 52 | -23 | [illegible] |
| 9 Ansty Sports & Social II | 16 | 2 | 3 | 11 | 22 | 51 | -29 | [illegible] |

| | Division Six | P | W | D | L | F | A | GD | Pts |
|---|---|---|---|---|---|---|---|---|---|
| 1 | Ridgewood | 18 | 14 | 3 | 1 | 55 | 15 | 40 | 45 |
| 2 | Fletching | 18 | 13 | 3 | 2 | 62 | 26 | 36 | 42 |
| 3 | Burgess Hill Rhinos | 18 | 12 | 1 | 5 | 50 | 26 | 24 | 37 |
| 4 | Willingdon Athletic III | 18 | 11 | 1 | 6 | 42 | 31 | 11 | 34 |
| 5 | Roffey III | 18 | 9 | 4 | 5 | 42 | 26 | 16 | 31 |
| 6 | Fairwarp | 18 | 5 | 4 | 9 | 29 | 40 | -11 | 19 |
| 7 | Newick | 18 | 3 | 5 | 10 | 28 | 48 | -20 | 14 |
| 8 | Ditchling II | 18 | 4 | 2 | 12 | 22 | 57 | -35 | 14 |
| 9 | Bolney Rovers | 18 | 3 | 2 | 13 | 26 | 59 | -33 | 11 |
| 10 | Forest Row II | 18 | 3 | 1 | 14 | 36 | 64 | -28 | 10 |

| | Division Seven | P | W | D | L | F | A | GD | Pts |
|---|---|---|---|---|---|---|---|---|---|
| | AFC Ringmer II | 18 | 14 | 1 | 3 | 60 | 24 | 36 | 43 |
| | Fairfield | 18 | 10 | 1 | 7 | 56 | 41 | 15 | 31 |
| | Plumpton Athletic II | 18 | 10 | 1 | 7 | 52 | 37 | 15 | 31 |
| | Hartfield | 18 | 9 | 3 | 6 | 42 | 28 | 14 | 30 |
| | Ardingly II | 18 | 9 | 2 | 7 | 32 | 37 | -5 | 29 |
| | Maresfield Village II | 18 | 8 | 3 | 7 | 48 | 33 | 15 | 27 |
| | Ifield Galaxy III | 18 | 8 | 2 | 8 | 57 | 55 | 2 | 26 |
| | Lindfield III | 18 | 6 | 2 | 10 | 41 | 60 | -19 | 20 |
| | Handcross Village II | 18 | 5 | 1 | 12 | 32 | 47 | -15 | 16 |
| 10 | Wivelsfield Green Pilgrims II | 18 | 1 | 4 | 13 | 26 | 84 | -58 | 7 |

| | Division Eight | P | W | D | L | F | A | GD | Pts |
|---|---|---|---|---|---|---|---|---|---|
| | Scaynes Hill | 18 | 14 | 1 | 3 | 42 | 15 | 27 | 43 |
| | Burgess Hill Albion II | 18 | 13 | 3 | 2 | 56 | 21 | 35 | 42 |
| | East Grinstead Mavericks | 18 | 11 | 3 | 4 | 42 | 21 | 21 | 36 |
| | Furngate | 18 | 9 | 1 | 8 | 65 | 46 | 19 | 28 |
| | Lindfield IV (-3) | 18 | 8 | 7 | 3 | 42 | 26 | 16 | 28 |
| | Cuckfield Rangers III | 18 | 6 | 4 | 8 | 34 | 65 | -31 | 22 |
| | Barcombe II | 18 | 5 | 6 | 7 | 24 | 33 | -9 | 21 |
| | East Grinstead Town III (+3) | 18 | 3 | 4 | 11 | 24 | 44 | -20 | 16 |
| | Crawley Panthers | 18 | 2 | 3 | 13 | 31 | 50 | -19 | 9 |
| 10 | Handcross Village III | 18 | 2 | 2 | 14 | 31 | 70 | -39 | 8 |

| | Division Nine | P | W | D | L | F | A | GD | Pts |
|---|---|---|---|---|---|---|---|---|---|
| | AFC Uckfield Town IV (+3) | 18 | 13 | 1 | 4 | 61 | 32 | 29 | 43 |
| | Jarvis Brook III (-6) | 18 | 14 | 3 | 1 | 83 | 20 | 63 | 39 |
| | AFC Bolnore | 18 | 11 | 6 | 1 | 51 | 21 | 30 | 39 |
| | East Grinstead Meads | 18 | 10 | 3 | 5 | 53 | 48 | 5 | 33 |
| | Crawley United | 18 | 7 | 5 | 6 | 40 | 34 | 6 | 26 |
| | Crawley Cobras II | 18 | 7 | 4 | 7 | 46 | 51 | -5 | 25 |
| | West Hoathly II | 18 | 3 | 4 | 11 | 25 | 53 | -28 | 16 |
| | Cuckfield Rangers Dev. | 18 | 3 | 4 | 11 | 33 | 55 | -22 | 13 |
| | Heath Rangers | 18 | 4 | 0 | 14 | 34 | 82 | -48 | 12 |
| | Buxted III | 18 | 2 | 2 | 14 | 27 | 57 | -30 | 8 |

| | Division Ten | P | W | D | L | F | A | GD | Pts |
|---|---|---|---|---|---|---|---|---|---|
| | Nutley II | 14 | 12 | 0 | 2 | 52 | 16 | 36 | 36 |
| | Keymer & Hassocks | 14 | 11 | 0 | 3 | 55 | 23 | 32 | 33 |
| | Ringmer III | 14 | 10 | 0 | 4 | 65 | 29 | 36 | 30 |
| | Ashurst Wood III | 14 | 8 | 2 | 4 | 54 | 30 | 24 | 26 |
| | Stones II | 14 | 5 | 0 | 9 | 41 | 50 | -9 | 15 |
| | Rotherfield III | 14 | 3 | 1 | 10 | 23 | 51 | -28 | 10 |
| | Scaynes Hill II | 14 | 3 | 1 | 10 | 20 | 72 | -52 | 10 |
| | Fairwarp II | 14 | 1 | 2 | 11 | 23 | 62 | -39 | 5 |

## MIDLAND AMATEUR ALLIANCE

| | Premier Division | P | W | D | L | F | A | GD | Pts |
|---|---|---|---|---|---|---|---|---|---|
| 1 | Old Elizabethans | 16 | 11 | 3 | 2 | 60 | 18 | 42 | 36 |
| 2 | A S Plant United | 16 | 10 | 4 | 2 | 39 | 22 | 17 | 34 |
| 3 | Ravenshead | 16 | 8 | 5 | 3 | 44 | 24 | 20 | 29 |
| 4 | Woodborough United | 16 | 8 | 4 | 4 | 34 | 29 | 5 | 28 |
| 5 | Beeston Old Boys Association | 16 | 7 | 3 | 6 | 36 | 38 | -2 | 24 |
| 6 | Trinity Renatus | 16 | 6 | 4 | 6 | 36 | 30 | 6 | 22 |
| 7 | AFC South Wingfield 93 | 16 | 5 | 2 | 9 | 35 | 46 | -11 | 17 |
| 8 | Derbyshire Amateurs (-1) | 16 | 2 | 2 | 12 | 20 | 48 | -28 | 7 |
| 9 | Trent Vineyard | 16 | 1 | 1 | 14 | 15 | 64 | -49 | 4 |

| | Division One | P | W | D | L | F | A | GD | Pts |
|---|---|---|---|---|---|---|---|---|---|
| 1 | Sutton Travellers | 22 | 15 | 2 | 5 | 69 | 32 | 37 | 47 |
| 2 | Ravenshead II | 22 | 15 | 2 | 5 | 66 | 29 | 37 | 47 |
| 3 | Alvaston United | 22 | 14 | 3 | 5 | 74 | 35 | 39 | 45 |
| 4 | Old Bemrosians | 22 | 13 | 4 | 5 | 72 | 42 | 30 | 43 |
| 5 | Kirkby Athletic | 22 | 12 | 5 | 5 | 81 | 50 | 31 | 41 |
| 6 | Wollaton III | 22 | 13 | 2 | 7 | 73 | 54 | 19 | 41 |
| 7 | ASHA FC | 22 | 12 | 4 | 6 | 59 | 43 | 16 | 40 |
| 8 | Mansfield Hosiery Mills | 22 | 7 | 2 | 13 | 47 | 66 | -19 | 23 |
| 9 | Wollaton IV | 22 | 5 | 2 | 15 | 48 | 81 | -33 | 17 |
| 10 | Derbyshire Amateurs II | 22 | 4 | 4 | 14 | 43 | 73 | -30 | 16 |
| 11 | Ashfield FC | 22 | 2 | 4 | 16 | 38 | 116 | -78 | 10 |
| 12 | Blidworth Welfare Red | 22 | 2 | 2 | 18 | 39 | 88 | -49 | 8 |

## MIDLANDS REGIONAL ALLIANCE

| | Premier Division | P | W | D | L | F | A | GD | Pts |
|---|---|---|---|---|---|---|---|---|---|
| 1 | Aston United | 22 | 20 | 1 | 1 | 72 | 23 | 49 | 61 |
| 2 | Sandiacre Town | 22 | 15 | 2 | 5 | 75 | 40 | 35 | 47 |
| 3 | Rowsley 86 | 22 | 14 | 3 | 5 | 84 | 24 | 60 | 45 |
| 4 | FC Stockbrook Rangers | 22 | 14 | 3 | 5 | 56 | 30 | 26 | 45 |
| 5 | Wirksworth Ivanhoe | 22 | 10 | 4 | 8 | 39 | 47 | -8 | 34 |
| 6 | Wirksworth Town | 22 | 9 | 5 | 8 | 48 | 41 | 7 | 32 |
| 7 | Cromford | 22 | 8 | 6 | 8 | 44 | 44 | 0 | 30 |
| 8 | Newhall United | 22 | 9 | 3 | 10 | 38 | 43 | -5 | 30 |
| 9 | Bestwood Miners Welfare | 22 | 7 | 4 | 11 | 42 | 43 | -1 | 25 |
| 10 | Allestree | 22 | 3 | 5 | 14 | 29 | 63 | -34 | 14 |
| 11 | Tibshelf | 22 | 3 | 2 | 17 | 27 | 82 | -55 | 11 |
| 12 | Little Eaton | 22 | 0 | 2 | 20 | 22 | 96 | -74 | 2 |

| | Division One | P | W | D | L | F | A | GD | Pts |
|---|---|---|---|---|---|---|---|---|---|
| 1 | Derby Singh Brothers (-1) | 20 | 16 | 1 | 3 | 70 | 31 | 39 | 48 |
| 2 | Rowsley 86 Res. | 20 | 13 | 4 | 3 | 59 | 28 | 31 | 43 |
| 3 | Shirebrook Rangers | 20 | 13 | 4 | 3 | 44 | 22 | 22 | 43 |
| 4 | Matlock United | 20 | 13 | 3 | 4 | 59 | 31 | 28 | 42 |
| 5 | Melbourne Dynamo | 20 | 11 | 3 | 6 | 45 | 36 | 9 | 36 |
| 6 | Sherwin | 20 | 8 | 2 | 10 | 45 | 44 | 1 | 26 |
| 7 | Ripley Town | 20 | 7 | 4 | 9 | 28 | 46 | -18 | 25 |
| 8 | Doe Lea AFC | 20 | 6 | 5 | 9 | 51 | 54 | -3 | 23 |
| 9 | Wirksworth Town Res. | 20 | 4 | 3 | 13 | 22 | 53 | -31 | 15 |
| 10 | Newhall United Res. | 20 | 2 | 2 | 16 | 33 | 91 | -58 | 8 |
| 11 | Matlock Town (C.F.A) | 20 | 1 | 1 | 18 | 19 | 39 | -20 | 4 |

| Division Two | P | W | D | L | F | A | GD | Pts |
|---|---|---|---|---|---|---|---|---|
| 1 Ambergate | 18 | 14 | 4 | 0 | 74 | 16 | 58 | 46 |
| 2 Chesterfield Town | 18 | 12 | 2 | 4 | 72 | 29 | 43 | 38 |
| 3 Shirebrook Rangers Res. | 18 | 12 | 0 | 6 | 48 | 26 | 22 | 36 |
| 4 Punjab United | 18 | 7 | 4 | 7 | 52 | 44 | 8 | 25 |
| 5 Real Medina | 18 | 7 | 1 | 10 | 51 | 60 | -9 | 22 |
| 6 Sherwin Res. | 18 | 5 | 4 | 9 | 36 | 56 | -20 | 19 |
| 7 Little Eaton Development (-1) | 18 | 6 | 2 | 10 | 29 | 50 | -21 | 19 |
| 8 Wirksworth Ivanhoe Res. | 18 | 6 | 1 | 11 | 31 | 63 | -32 | 19 |
| 9 Ripley Town Res. | 18 | 5 | 2 | 11 | 34 | 58 | -24 | 17 |
| 10 Willington Sports | 18 | 5 | 2 | 11 | 27 | 52 | -25 | 17 |

## NORTH BUCKS AND DISTRICT FOOTBALL LEAGUE

| Premier Division | P | W | D | L | F | A | GD | Pts |
|---|---|---|---|---|---|---|---|---|
| 1 Potterspury | 24 | 21 | 2 | 1 | 85 | 21 | 64 | 65 |
| 2 Great Horwood | 24 | 19 | 1 | 4 | 80 | 27 | 53 | 58 |
| 3 Silverstone | 24 | 15 | 5 | 4 | 51 | 34 | 17 | 50 |
| 4 Towcester Town | 24 | 14 | 4 | 6 | 56 | 36 | 20 | 46 |
| 5 Stewkley | 24 | 13 | 4 | 7 | 65 | 30 | 35 | 43 |
| 6 Marsh Gibbon | 24 | 11 | 2 | 11 | 46 | 48 | -2 | 35 |
| 7 Deanshanger Athletic | 24 | 11 | 1 | 12 | 45 | 48 | -3 | 34 |
| 8 Hanslope | 24 | 7 | 8 | 9 | 36 | 46 | -10 | 29 |
| 9 MK Titans | 24 | 6 | 7 | 11 | 54 | 80 | -26 | 25 |
| 10 Great Linford | 24 | 6 | 6 | 12 | 38 | 58 | -20 | 24 |
| 11 Brackley Sports | 24 | 3 | 6 | 15 | 32 | 61 | -29 | 15 |
| 12 Syresham | 24 | 2 | 6 | 16 | 22 | 54 | -32 | 12 |
| 13 MK Wanderers | 24 | 1 | 2 | 21 | 26 | 93 | -67 | 5 |

| Intermediate Division | P | W | D | L | F | A | GD | Pts |
|---|---|---|---|---|---|---|---|---|
| 1 MK Gallactico | 20 | 19 | 0 | 1 | 95 | 20 | 75 | 57 |
| 2 Southcott Village R.A. | 20 | 15 | 3 | 2 | 81 | 22 | 59 | 48 |
| 3 Twyford United | 20 | 15 | 1 | 4 | 63 | 33 | 30 | 46 |
| 4 Stoke Hammond Wanderers | 20 | 11 | 2 | 7 | 68 | 58 | 10 | 35 |
| 5 AFC Santander | 20 | 10 | 2 | 8 | 38 | 42 | -4 | 32 |
| 6 Yardley Gobion | 20 | 10 | 2 | 8 | 44 | 49 | -5 | 32 |
| 7 Great Horwood Res. | 20 | 6 | 3 | 11 | 29 | 73 | -44 | 21 |
| 8 Wicken Sports | 20 | 6 | 2 | 12 | 43 | 65 | -22 | 20 |
| 9 Potterspury Res. | 20 | 1 | 7 | 12 | 30 | 56 | -26 | 10 |
| 10 Charlton & District | 20 | 2 | 2 | 16 | 36 | 74 | -38 | 8 |
| 11 Clean Slate Res. | 20 | 1 | 4 | 15 | 28 | 63 | -35 | 7 |

| Division One | P | W | D | L | F | A | GD | Pts |
|---|---|---|---|---|---|---|---|---|
| 1 Wing Village | 22 | 16 | 3 | 3 | 79 | 26 | 53 | 51 |
| 2 Willen | 22 | 16 | 2 | 4 | 91 | 47 | 44 | 50 |
| 3 Padbury Village | 22 | 12 | 3 | 7 | 45 | 37 | 8 | 39 |
| 4 City Colts | 22 | 12 | 2 | 8 | 52 | 39 | 13 | 38 |
| 5 Tattenhoe | 22 | 11 | 1 | 10 | 43 | 34 | 9 | 34 |
| 6 Brackley Old Boy | 22 | 11 | 1 | 10 | 39 | 39 | 0 | 34 |
| 7 Steeple Claydon | 22 | 10 | 2 | 10 | 47 | 53 | -6 | 32 |
| 8 Olney | 22 | 8 | 5 | 9 | 38 | 34 | 4 | 29 |
| 9 Great Linford Res. | 22 | 6 | 5 | 11 | 29 | 47 | -18 | 23 |
| 10 Stewkley Res. | 22 | 6 | 2 | 14 | 36 | 67 | -31 | 20 |
| 11 University of Buckingham | 22 | 5 | 1 | 16 | 46 | 81 | -35 | 16 |
| 12 Deanshanger Athletic Res. | 22 | 4 | 3 | 15 | 27 | 68 | -41 | 15 |

| Division Two | P | W | D | L | F | A | GD | Pts |
|---|---|---|---|---|---|---|---|---|
| 1 Southcott Village R.A. Res. | 20 | 16 | 2 | 2 | 63 | 31 | 32 | 50 |
| 2 Towcester Town Res. | 20 | 15 | 2 | 3 | 50 | 26 | 24 | 47 |
| 3 Wing Village Res. | 20 | 14 | 3 | 3 | 62 | 41 | 21 | 45 |
| 4 Scot | 20 | 11 | 2 | 7 | 58 | 36 | 22 | 35 |
| 5 Westbury | 20 | 11 | 1 | 8 | 68 | 52 | 16 | 34 |
| 6 Silverstone Res. | 20 | 10 | 1 | 9 | 48 | 41 | 7 | 31 |
| 7 Brackley Sports Res. | 20 | 6 | 3 | 11 | 35 | 47 | -12 | 21 |
| 8 Hanslope Res. | 20 | 6 | 0 | 14 | 38 | 50 | -12 | 18 |
| 9 Marsh Gibbon Res. | 20 | 4 | 3 | 13 | 16 | 45 | -29 | 15 |
| 10 Yardley Gobion Res. | 20 | 4 | 1 | 15 | 35 | 61 | -26 | 13 |
| 11 Padbury Village Res. | 20 | 4 | 0 | 16 | 20 | 63 | -43 | 12 |

## NORTH DEVON FOOTBALL LEAGUE

| Premier Division | P | W | D | L | F | A | GD | Pts |
|---|---|---|---|---|---|---|---|---|
| 1 Braunton | 28 | 27 | 0 | 1 | 122 | 18 | 104 | [illegible] |
| 2 Torridgeside | 28 | 24 | 1 | 3 | 138 | 35 | 103 | [illegible] |
| 3 Boca Seniors | 28 | 20 | 2 | 6 | 100 | 38 | 62 | [illegible] |
| 4 Torrington | 28 | 18 | 2 | 8 | 89 | 59 | 30 | [illegible] |
| 5 Bideford CAFC | 28 | 16 | 3 | 9 | 84 | 55 | 29 | [illegible] |
| 6 Ilfracombe Town | 28 | 15 | 1 | 12 | 88 | 60 | 28 | [illegible] |
| 7 Landkey Town | 28 | 12 | 3 | 13 | 85 | 80 | 5 | [illegible] |
| 8 Bradworthy | 28 | 11 | 2 | 15 | 59 | 77 | -18 | [illegible] |
| 9 Park United (-3) | 28 | 10 | 6 | 12 | 68 | 67 | 1 | [illegible] |
| 10 Shamwickshire Rovers | 28 | 8 | 7 | 13 | 46 | 68 | -22 | [illegible] |
| 11 North Molton Sports Club | 28 | 9 | 3 | 16 | 55 | 101 | -46 | [illegible] |
| 12 Fremington (-3) | 28 | 8 | 1 | 19 | 48 | 111 | -63 | [illegible] |
| 13 Shebbear United | 28 | 7 | 1 | 20 | 56 | 127 | -71 | [illegible] |
| 14 Barnstaple FC | 28 | 5 | 3 | 20 | 45 | 112 | -67 | [illegible] |
| 15 Appledore Res. (-3) | 28 | 1 | 3 | 24 | 32 | 107 | -75 | [illegible] |

| Senior Division | P | W | D | L | F | A | GD | Pts |
|---|---|---|---|---|---|---|---|---|
| 1 Hartland | 30 | 27 | 2 | 1 | 134 | 35 | 99 | [illegible] |
| 2 Braunton Res. | 30 | 25 | 2 | 3 | 122 | 38 | 84 | [illegible] |
| 3 Georgeham & Croyde | 30 | 21 | 2 | 7 | 123 | 36 | 87 | [illegible] |
| 4 Torridgeside Res. | 30 | 20 | 3 | 7 | 86 | 32 | 54 | [illegible] |
| 5 Pilton Academicals | 30 | 18 | 5 | 7 | 107 | 61 | 46 | [illegible] |
| 6 Chittlehampton (-3) | 30 | 16 | 4 | 10 | 108 | 57 | 51 | [illegible] |
| 7 Northam Lions | 30 | 14 | 5 | 11 | 88 | 65 | 23 | [illegible] |
| 8 Chivenor (-3) | 30 | 15 | 5 | 10 | 80 | 66 | 14 | [illegible] |
| 9 Barnstaple AAC (-3) | 30 | 13 | 7 | 10 | 76 | 58 | 18 | [illegible] |
| 10 Combe Martin | 30 | 8 | 6 | 16 | 72 | 86 | -14 | [illegible] |
| 11 Shamwickshire Rovers Res. (-3) | 30 | 10 | 2 | 18 | 68 | 99 | -31 | [illegible] |
| 12 Merton | 30 | 7 | 1 | 22 | 41 | 102 | -61 | [illegible] |
| 13 Putford | 30 | 6 | 4 | 20 | 42 | 106 | -64 | [illegible] |
| 14 Woolacombe & Mortehoe (-6) | 30 | 7 | 2 | 21 | 56 | 123 | -67 | [illegible] |
| 15 North Molton Sports Club Res. | 30 | 4 | 1 | 25 | 28 | 142 | -114 | [illegible] |
| 16 Lynton & Lynmouth (-3) | 30 | 2 | 3 | 25 | 31 | 156 | -125 | [illegible] |

| Intermediate One | | P | W | D | L | F | A | GD | Pts |
|---|---|---|---|---|---|---|---|---|---|
| 1 | Sporting Barum | 24 | 24 | 0 | 0 | 169 | 19 | 150 | 72 |
| 2 | Ilfracombe Town Res. | 24 | 19 | 0 | 5 | 85 | 35 | 50 | 57 |
| 3 | Braunton Thirds | 24 | 18 | 2 | 4 | 98 | 39 | 59 | 56 |
| 4 | High Bickington | 24 | 13 | 2 | 9 | 47 | 33 | 14 | 41 |
| 5 | Appledore 3rds (-3) | 24 | 14 | 2 | 8 | 66 | 55 | 11 | 41 |
| 6 | Morwenstow Res. | 24 | 11 | 5 | 8 | 51 | 49 | 2 | 38 |
| 7 | Clovelly | 24 | 11 | 1 | 12 | 67 | 74 | -7 | 34 |
| 8 | Haxton Rangers (-3) | 24 | 8 | 2 | 14 | 52 | 75 | -23 | 23 |
| 9 | Landkey Town Res. | 24 | 7 | 2 | 15 | 55 | 81 | -26 | 23 |
| 10 | Barnstaple FC Res. | 24 | 5 | 4 | 15 | 52 | 80 | -28 | 19 |
| 11 | Torrington Res. | 24 | 6 | 1 | 17 | 42 | 103 | -61 | 19 |
| 12 | South Molton | 24 | 5 | 4 | 15 | 32 | 97 | -65 | 19 |
| 13 | Equalizers | 24 | 2 | 1 | 21 | 44 | 120 | -76 | 7 |

| Intermediate Two | | P | W | D | L | F | A | GD | Pts |
|---|---|---|---|---|---|---|---|---|---|
| | Ilfracombe Town Thirds | 22 | 21 | 1 | 0 | 147 | 26 | 121 | 64 |
| 2 | Fremington Res. | 22 | 17 | 2 | 3 | 108 | 34 | 74 | 53 |
| | Bideford CAFC Res. | 22 | 16 | 0 | 6 | 110 | 34 | 76 | 48 |
| | Hartland Res. | 22 | 11 | 5 | 6 | 76 | 59 | 17 | 38 |
| | Appledore Lions | 22 | 11 | 3 | 8 | 69 | 58 | 11 | 36 |
| | Combe Martin Res. | 22 | 11 | 2 | 9 | 70 | 61 | 9 | 35 |
| | Braunton Fourths | 22 | 9 | 2 | 11 | 53 | 79 | -26 | 29 |
| | Woolsery Res. | 22 | 5 | 6 | 11 | 48 | 91 | -43 | 21 |
| | Georgeham & Croyde Res. | 22 | 5 | 5 | 12 | 54 | 59 | -5 | 20 |
| 0 | Northam Lions Res. (-6) | 22 | 6 | 2 | 14 | 34 | 67 | -33 | 14 |
| 1 | Merton Res. | 22 | 2 | 2 | 18 | 30 | 117 | -87 | 8 |
| 2 | Putford Res. | 22 | 1 | 4 | 17 | 19 | 133 | -114 | 7 |

## NORTH EAST NORFOLK LEAGUE

| ivision One | | P | W | D | L | F | A | GD | Pts |
|---|---|---|---|---|---|---|---|---|---|
| | Runton FC | 22 | 22 | 0 | 0 | 98 | 15 | 83 | 66 |
| | Haisboro Atheltic FC (-2) | 22 | 16 | 1 | 5 | 73 | 28 | 45 | 47 |
| | East Ruston FC (-1) | 22 | 12 | 4 | 6 | 43 | 36 | 7 | 39 |
| | Sheringham A | 22 | 10 | 3 | 9 | 63 | 60 | 3 | 33 |
| | Lyng F.C. (-1) | 22 | 9 | 5 | 8 | 45 | 43 | 2 | 31 |
| | Gimingham FC (-1) | 22 | 10 | 1 | 11 | 54 | 38 | 16 | 30 |
| | Cromer YOB | 22 | 7 | 9 | 6 | 44 | 43 | 1 | 30 |
| | Southrepps FC | 22 | 8 | 5 | 9 | 46 | 49 | -3 | 29 |
| | Hickling F,C, | 22 | 7 | 2 | 13 | 31 | 62 | -31 | 23 |
| | Felmingham FC (-3) | 22 | 5 | 3 | 14 | 32 | 55 | -23 | 15 |
| | Erpingham FC | 22 | 4 | 2 | 16 | 48 | 84 | -36 | 14 |
| 2 | Holt Res FC (-1) | 22 | 3 | 3 | 16 | 27 | 91 | -64 | 11 |

| ivision Two | | P | W | D | L | F | A | GD | Pts |
|---|---|---|---|---|---|---|---|---|---|
| | Blakeney | 14 | 12 | 1 | 1 | 68 | 20 | 48 | 37 |
| | Aylsham A | 14 | 12 | 1 | 1 | 65 | 19 | 46 | 37 |
| | Stalham A (-1) | 14 | 8 | 0 | 6 | 30 | 35 | -5 | 23 |
| | Holt Colts (-1) | 14 | 6 | 0 | 8 | 31 | 56 | -25 | 17 |
| | Plumstead Res. (-3) | 14 | 5 | 1 | 8 | 26 | 32 | -6 | 13 |
| | Southrepps Res. (-1) | 14 | 4 | 1 | 9 | 25 | 56 | -31 | 12 |
| | Gimingham Res. (-3) | 14 | 4 | 1 | 9 | 35 | 37 | -2 | 10 |
| | Erpingham Res. (-2) | 14 | 2 | 1 | 11 | 26 | 51 | -25 | 5 |

## NORTH GLOUCESTERSHIRE ASSOCIATION FOOTBALL LEAGUE

| Premier Division | | P | W | D | L | F | A | GD | Pts |
|---|---|---|---|---|---|---|---|---|---|
| 1 | Mitcheldean | 26 | 22 | 2 | 2 | 80 | 21 | 59 | 68 |
| 2 | Whitecroft | 26 | 17 | 1 | 8 | 102 | 38 | 64 | 52 |
| 3 | Soudley | 26 | 15 | 4 | 7 | 73 | 43 | 30 | 49 |
| 4 | Viney St Swithins | 26 | 14 | 5 | 7 | 61 | 51 | 10 | 47 |
| 5 | Redbrook Rovers | 26 | 15 | 1 | 10 | 96 | 54 | 42 | 46 |
| 6 | Ellwood Res. | 26 | 13 | 5 | 8 | 67 | 40 | 27 | 44 |
| 7 | Coleford United | 26 | 12 | 1 | 13 | 66 | 51 | 15 | 37 |
| 8 | Broadwell Res. | 26 | 11 | 4 | 11 | 56 | 61 | -5 | 37 |
| 9 | Bream Amts | 26 | 11 | 2 | 13 | 56 | 70 | -14 | 35 |
| 10 | Ruardean Hill Rangers Res. | 26 | 11 | 2 | 13 | 44 | 70 | -26 | 35 |
| 11 | Huntley | 26 | 10 | 4 | 12 | 53 | 53 | 0 | 34 |
| 12 | Westbury United | 26 | 10 | 3 | 13 | 51 | 67 | -16 | 33 |
| 13 | Blakeney | 26 | 3 | 0 | 23 | 30 | 111 | -81 | 9 |
| 14 | Lydbrook Athletic Res. | 26 | 1 | 0 | 25 | 22 | 127 | -105 | 3 |

| Division One | | P | W | D | L | F | A | GD | Pts |
|---|---|---|---|---|---|---|---|---|---|
| 1 | Yorkley | 22 | 17 | 5 | 0 | 60 | 17 | 43 | 56 |
| 2 | Whitecroft Res. | 22 | 13 | 5 | 4 | 58 | 28 | 30 | 44 |
| 3 | Howle Hill | 22 | 13 | 2 | 7 | 58 | 35 | 23 | 41 |
| 4 | Tidenham | 22 | 10 | 4 | 8 | 56 | 45 | 11 | 34 |
| 5 | Soudley Res. | 22 | 10 | 3 | 9 | 41 | 37 | 4 | 33 |
| 6 | Redmarley | 22 | 9 | 5 | 8 | 51 | 42 | 9 | 32 |
| 7 | Harrow Hill Res. | 22 | 8 | 5 | 9 | 38 | 39 | -1 | 29 |
| 8 | Westbury United Res. | 22 | 7 | 6 | 9 | 29 | 39 | -10 | 27 |
| 9 | Lydney Town A | 22 | 8 | 3 | 11 | 40 | 53 | -13 | 27 |
| 10 | Puma FC | 22 | 7 | 4 | 11 | 36 | 41 | -5 | 25 |
| 11 | Woolaston Res. | 22 | 4 | 3 | 15 | 34 | 66 | -32 | 15 |
| 12 | United Longhope | 22 | 2 | 3 | 17 | 23 | 82 | -59 | 9 |

| Division Two | | P | W | D | L | F | A | GD | Pts |
|---|---|---|---|---|---|---|---|---|---|
| 1 | Mushet & Coalway United | 22 | 20 | 1 | 1 | 75 | 13 | 62 | 61 |
| 2 | Redside | 22 | 15 | 5 | 2 | 62 | 36 | 26 | 50 |
| 3 | Newent Town Res. | 22 | 14 | 2 | 6 | 65 | 34 | 31 | 44 |
| 4 | Harrow Hill A | 22 | 10 | 5 | 7 | 34 | 30 | 4 | 35 |
| 5 | Whitecroft A | 22 | 9 | 3 | 10 | 49 | 38 | 11 | 30 |
| 6 | English Bicknor Res. | 22 | 8 | 5 | 9 | 39 | 36 | 3 | 29 |
| 7 | Viney St Swithins Res. | 22 | 8 | 3 | 11 | 42 | 50 | -8 | 27 |
| 8 | Ruardean Hill Rangers A | 22 | 8 | 3 | 11 | 34 | 47 | -13 | 27 |
| 9 | Aylburton Rovers | 22 | 8 | 2 | 12 | 54 | 38 | 16 | 26 |
| 10 | Ruardean United | 22 | 7 | 4 | 11 | 30 | 56 | -26 | 25 |
| 11 | Lydbrook Athletic A | 22 | 4 | 2 | 16 | 26 | 76 | -50 | 14 |
| 12 | Bream Amts Res. | 22 | 3 | 1 | 18 | 20 | 76 | -56 | 10 |

| Division Three | | P | W | D | L | F | A | GD | Pts |
|---|---|---|---|---|---|---|---|---|---|
| 1 | Worrall Hill | 20 | 19 | 0 | 1 | 108 | 20 | 88 | 57 |
| 2 | Mitcheldean Res. | 20 | 15 | 2 | 3 | 63 | 24 | 39 | 47 |
| 3 | Coleford United Res. | 20 | 14 | 0 | 6 | 69 | 29 | 40 | 42 |
| 4 | Rank Outsiders | 20 | 12 | 2 | 6 | 70 | 31 | 39 | 38 |
| 5 | Milkwall | 20 | 8 | 2 | 10 | 54 | 60 | -6 | 26 |
| 6 | Newent Town A | 20 | 7 | 3 | 10 | 35 | 61 | -26 | 24 |
| 7 | Yorkley Res. | 20 | 7 | 2 | 11 | 50 | 52 | -2 | 23 |
| 8 | Mushet & Coalway United Res. | 20 | 5 | 6 | 9 | 36 | 59 | -23 | 21 |
| 9 | Redbrook Rovers Res. | 20 | 5 | 3 | 12 | 41 | 102 | -61 | 18 |
| 10 | Broadwell A | 20 | 2 | 5 | 13 | 28 | 53 | -25 | 11 |
| 11 | Puma FC Res. | 20 | 3 | 1 | 16 | 27 | 90 | -63 | 10 |

| Division Four | P | W | D | L | F | A | GD | Pts |
|---|---|---|---|---|---|---|---|---|
| 1 Weston | 22 | 20 | 0 | 2 | 103 | 25 | 78 | 60 |
| 2 Ross Juniors | 22 | 19 | 0 | 3 | 132 | 27 | 105 | 57 |
| 3 St Briavels | 22 | 14 | 3 | 5 | 66 | 51 | 15 | 45 |
| 4 Sling United | 22 | 13 | 3 | 6 | 67 | 38 | 29 | 42 |
| 5 Sedbury United | 22 | 11 | 2 | 9 | 70 | 44 | 26 | 35 |
| 6 Gloster Rovers | 22 | 9 | 6 | 7 | 80 | 61 | 19 | 33 |
| 7 Lydney Town B | 22 | 9 | 2 | 11 | 58 | 52 | 6 | 29 |
| 8 Blakeney Res | 22 | 5 | 5 | 12 | 31 | 37 | -6 | 20 |
| 9 Harrow Hill B | 22 | 6 | 2 | 14 | 41 | 85 | -44 | 20 |
| 10 Milkwall Res. | 22 | 4 | 5 | 13 | 31 | 72 | -41 | 17 |
| 11 Littledean | 22 | 1 | 7 | 14 | 27 | 92 | -65 | 10 |
| 12 Rank Outsiders Res. | 22 | 2 | 3 | 17 | 19 | 141 | -122 | 9 |

## NORTH LANCASHIRE & DISTRICT LEAGUE

| Premier Division | P | W | D | L | F | A | GD | Pts |
|---|---|---|---|---|---|---|---|---|
| 1 Carnforth Rangers | 26 | 21 | 2 | 3 | 85 | 20 | 65 | 65 |
| 2 Cartmel & District | 26 | 20 | 1 | 5 | 91 | 27 | 64 | 61 |
| 3 Ingleton | 26 | 19 | 2 | 5 | 85 | 40 | 45 | 59 |
| 4 Caton United | 26 | 17 | 6 | 3 | 70 | 28 | 42 | 57 |
| 5 Trimpell & Bare Rangers | 26 | 15 | 3 | 8 | 57 | 44 | 13 | 48 |
| 6 Mayfield United | 26 | 13 | 3 | 10 | 47 | 43 | 4 | 42 |
| 7 Highgrove (-3) | 26 | 11 | 3 | 12 | 49 | 49 | 0 | 33 |
| 8 Marsh United | 26 | 9 | 4 | 13 | 46 | 67 | -21 | 31 |
| 9 Arnside | 26 | 8 | 4 | 14 | 52 | 77 | -25 | 28 |
| 10 Galgate (-3) | 26 | 9 | 2 | 15 | 31 | 64 | -33 | 26 |
| 11 Lancaster Rovers | 26 | 6 | 4 | 16 | 41 | 67 | -26 | 22 |
| 12 Bowerham | 26 | 6 | 3 | 17 | 38 | 65 | -27 | 21 |
| 13 Storeys | 26 | 5 | 3 | 18 | 32 | 71 | -39 | 18 |
| 14 Bentham | 26 | 1 | 4 | 21 | 25 | 87 | -62 | 7 |

| Division One | P | W | D | L | F | A | GD | Pts |
|---|---|---|---|---|---|---|---|---|
| 1 Westgate Wanderers | 24 | 19 | 1 | 4 | 94 | 45 | 49 | 58 |
| 2 Cartmel & District Res. | 24 | 18 | 3 | 3 | 68 | 24 | 44 | 57 |
| 3 College AFC | 24 | 15 | 4 | 5 | 76 | 35 | 41 | 49 |
| 4 Boys Club | 24 | 15 | 3 | 6 | 62 | 38 | 24 | 48 |
| 5 Carnforth Rangers Res. | 24 | 13 | 0 | 11 | 64 | 72 | -8 | 39 |
| 6 TIC Dynamos of Overton and Middleton | 24 | 11 | 4 | 9 | 59 | 44 | 15 | 37 |
| 7 Freehold | 24 | 8 | 4 | 12 | 44 | 64 | -20 | 28 |
| 8 Millhead | 24 | 8 | 2 | 14 | 51 | 77 | -26 | 26 |
| 9 Morecambe Royals | 24 | 7 | 3 | 14 | 35 | 54 | -19 | 24 |
| 10 Ingleton Res. | 24 | 7 | 3 | 14 | 47 | 67 | -20 | 24 |
| 11 AFC Moorlands | 24 | 7 | 3 | 14 | 68 | 89 | -21 | 24 |
| 12 Caton United Res. | 24 | 7 | 2 | 15 | 40 | 58 | -18 | 23 |
| 13 Heysham (-3) | 24 | 3 | 4 | 17 | 38 | 79 | -41 | 10 |

| Division Two | P | W | D | L | F | A | GD | Pts |
|---|---|---|---|---|---|---|---|---|
| 1 Highgrove Res. | 26 | 17 | 4 | 5 | 74 | 34 | 40 | 55 |
| 2 Grange | 26 | 16 | 5 | 5 | 65 | 33 | 32 | 53 |
| 3 Preesall & Pilling | 26 | 14 | 5 | 7 | 75 | 44 | 31 | 47 |
| 4 FC Britannia | 26 | 12 | 6 | 8 | 66 | 49 | 17 | 42 |
| 5 Burton Thistle | 26 | 12 | 4 | 10 | 61 | 43 | 18 | 40 |
| 6 Mayfield United Res. (-3) | 26 | 13 | 3 | 10 | 60 | 52 | 8 | 39 |
| 7 Marsh United Res. | 26 | 11 | 5 | 10 | 56 | 47 | 9 | 38 |
| 8 Trimpell & Bare Rangers Res. | 26 | 10 | 7 | 9 | 63 | 64 | -1 | 37 |
| 9 Torrisholme | 26 | 9 | 7 | 10 | 57 | 57 | 0 | 34 |
| 10 Lancaster Rovers Res. | 26 | 11 | 1 | 14 | 54 | 60 | -6 | 34 |
| 11 Carnforth Rangers A | 26 | 7 | 8 | 11 | 47 | 68 | -21 | 29 |
| 12 Boys Club Res. | 26 | 8 | 4 | 14 | 40 | 58 | -18 | 28 |
| 13 Bolton Le Sands | 26 | 7 | 6 | 13 | 52 | 60 | -8 | 27 |
| 14 Galgate Res. | 26 | 1 | 3 | 22 | 33 | 134 | -101 | 6 |

| Division Three | P | W | D | L | F | A | GD | Pts |
|---|---|---|---|---|---|---|---|---|
| 1 Heysham Res. | 24 | 17 | 1 | 6 | 89 | 47 | 42 | 52 |
| 2 College AFC Res. (-4) | 24 | 18 | 1 | 5 | 88 | 29 | 59 | 51 |
| 3 Cartmel & District A | 24 | 15 | 6 | 3 | 54 | 21 | 33 | 51 |
| 4 AFC Moorlands Res. (-3) | 24 | 15 | 3 | 6 | 84 | 41 | 43 | 45 |
| 5 Westgate Wanderers Res. | 24 | 14 | 0 | 10 | 64 | 45 | 19 | 42 |
| 6 Kirkby Lonsdale | 24 | 12 | 3 | 9 | 69 | 36 | 33 | 39 |
| 7 Storeys Res. | 24 | 9 | 3 | 12 | 46 | 51 | -5 | 30 |
| 8 TIC Dynamos of Overton & Middleton Res | 24 | 9 | 2 | 13 | 58 | 70 | -12 | 29 |
| 9 Millhead Res. | 24 | 7 | 5 | 12 | 39 | 70 | -31 | 26 |
| 10 Arnside Res. (-3) | 24 | 8 | 3 | 13 | 31 | 59 | -28 | 2[illegible] |
| 11 Carnforth Rangers Youth (-3) | 24 | 5 | 3 | 16 | 35 | 73 | -38 | 15 |
| 12 FC Britannia Res. | 24 | 3 | 3 | 18 | 31 | 100 | -69 | 1[illegible] |
| 13 AFC Burton United (-12) | 24 | 6 | 3 | 15 | 33 | 79 | -46 | [illegible] |

## NORTH LEICESTERSHIRE FOOTBALL LEAGUE

| Premier Division | P | W | D | L | F | A | GD | Pts |
|---|---|---|---|---|---|---|---|---|
| 1 Ravenstone United | 18 | 14 | 0 | 4 | 67 | 22 | 45 | 4[illegible] |
| 2 Greenhill YC | 18 | 12 | 1 | 5 | 62 | 36 | 26 | 3[illegible] |
| 3 Loughborough FC | 18 | 11 | 2 | 5 | 53 | 36 | 17 | 3[illegible] |
| 4 Falcons FC | 18 | 11 | 2 | 5 | 40 | 29 | 11 | 3[illegible] |
| 5 Castle Donington (-3) | 18 | 11 | 2 | 5 | 58 | 27 | 31 | 3[illegible] |
| 6 Mountsorrel Amateurs | 18 | 9 | 3 | 6 | 42 | 35 | 7 | 3[illegible] |
| 7 Sileby Victoria | 18 | 7 | 1 | 10 | 36 | 39 | -3 | 2[illegible] |
| 8 Thringstone MW (-1) | 18 | 5 | 0 | 13 | 24 | 67 | -43 | 1[illegible] |
| 9 Sutton Bonington Academicals | 18 | 2 | 0 | 16 | 17 | 71 | -54 | [illegible] |
| 10 Wymeswold FC (-3) | 18 | 2 | 1 | 15 | 32 | 69 | -37 | [illegible] |

| Division One | P | W | D | L | F | A | GD | Pts |
|---|---|---|---|---|---|---|---|---|
| 1 Bottesford FC | 18 | 11 | 4 | 3 | 57 | 21 | 36 | 3[illegible] |
| 2 Greenhill YC Res. | 18 | 11 | 3 | 4 | 55 | 28 | 27 | 3[illegible] |
| 3 Sutton Bonington | 18 | 11 | 1 | 6 | 60 | 40 | 20 | 3[illegible] |
| 4 Loughborough United | 18 | 7 | 5 | 6 | 40 | 51 | -11 | 2[illegible] |
| 5 Belton Villa | 18 | 7 | 4 | 7 | 37 | 36 | 1 | 2[illegible] |
| 6 Loughborough FC Res. (-1) | 18 | 7 | 3 | 8 | 57 | 49 | 8 | 2[illegible] |
| 7 Sileby Saints | 18 | 7 | 2 | 9 | 47 | 62 | -15 | 2[illegible] |
| 8 Genesis FC | 18 | 6 | 4 | 8 | 54 | 70 | -16 | 2[illegible] |
| 9 Anstey Crown (-1) | 18 | 4 | 4 | 10 | 33 | 55 | -22 | [illegible] |
| 10 Ashby Ivanhoe Dev. Team | 18 | 3 | 2 | 13 | 37 | 65 | -28 | [illegible] |

| Division Two | P | W | D | L | F | A | GD | Pts |
|---|---|---|---|---|---|---|---|---|
| 1 Birstall Old Boys | 18 | 16 | 0 | 2 | 112 | 31 | 81 | 48 |
| 2 Shepshed Amateurs | 18 | 11 | 2 | 5 | 53 | 35 | 18 | 35 |
| 3 Mountsorrel Amateurs Res. | 18 | 10 | 2 | 6 | 61 | 45 | 16 | 32 |
| 4 Ravenstone United Res. | 18 | 9 | 3 | 6 | 56 | 48 | 8 | 30 |
| 5 Kegworth Imperial | 18 | 8 | 4 | 6 | 54 | 38 | 16 | 28 |
| 6 Measham Imperial | 18 | 8 | 1 | 9 | 50 | 57 | -7 | 25 |
| 7 Shelthorpe Dynamo FC Res. | 18 | 7 | 3 | 8 | 52 | 59 | -7 | 24 |
| 8 Market Bosworth | 18 | 6 | 1 | 11 | 38 | 72 | -34 | 19 |
| 9 Woodhouse Imperial | 18 | 2 | 3 | 13 | 28 | 84 | -56 | 9 |
| 10 Sileby Victoria Res. (-1) | 18 | 1 | 5 | 12 | 25 | 60 | -35 | 7 |

| Division Three | P | W | D | L | F | A | GD | Pts |
|---|---|---|---|---|---|---|---|---|
| 1 Sporting Markfield | 20 | 20 | 0 | 0 | 140 | 14 | 126 | 60 |
| 2 Castle Donington Res. | 20 | 15 | 0 | 5 | 105 | 39 | 66 | 45 |
| 3 FC Coalville | 20 | 11 | 1 | 8 | 76 | 46 | 30 | 34 |
| 4 Shepshed Amateurs Res. | 20 | 10 | 1 | 9 | 48 | 57 | -9 | 31 |
| 5 Woodhouse Imperial Res. (-1) | 20 | 9 | 2 | 9 | 48 | 64 | -16 | 28 |
| 6 Birstall Old Boys Res. (-3) | 20 | 9 | 2 | 9 | 47 | 56 | -9 | 26 |
| 7 Loughborough Emmanuel (-1) | 20 | 8 | 2 | 10 | 45 | 58 | -13 | 25 |
| 8 Loughborough FC 'A' | 20 | 6 | 4 | 10 | 63 | 97 | -34 | 22 |
| 9 Mountsorrel FC | 20 | 6 | 3 | 11 | 40 | 69 | -29 | 21 |
| 10 Loughborough United Res. (-1) | 20 | 5 | 2 | 13 | 63 | 99 | -36 | 16 |
| 11 Shepborough United | 20 | 2 | 1 | 17 | 22 | 98 | -76 | 7 |

## NORTH WEST NORFOLK LEAGUE

| Division One | P | W | D | L | F | A | GD | Pts |
|---|---|---|---|---|---|---|---|---|
| 1 Watlington | 20 | 14 | 3 | 3 | 67 | 31 | 36 | 45 |
| 2 Heacham | 20 | 13 | 3 | 4 | 76 | 31 | 45 | 42 |
| 3 Birchwood | 20 | 13 | 1 | 6 | 79 | 37 | 42 | 40 |
| 4 Gayton United Res. | 20 | 10 | 6 | 4 | 57 | 37 | 20 | 36 |
| 5 Bishops Lynn | 20 | 9 | 4 | 7 | 59 | 54 | 5 | 31 |
| 6 West Lynn | 20 | 9 | 3 | 8 | 58 | 58 | 0 | 30 |
| 7 Ingoldisthorpe | 20 | 8 | 4 | 8 | 70 | 45 | 25 | 28 |
| 8 Castle Rising | 20 | 8 | 4 | 8 | 47 | 41 | 6 | 28 |
| 9 Dersingham Rovers A | 20 | 7 | 3 | 10 | 43 | 60 | -17 | 24 |
| 10 The Woottons | 20 | 3 | 1 | 16 | 32 | 103 | -71 | 10 |
| 11 Discovery Royals | 20 | 0 | 0 | 20 | 19 | 110 | -91 | 0 |

| Division Two | P | W | D | L | F | A | GD | Pts |
|---|---|---|---|---|---|---|---|---|
| 1 Thornham | 18 | 14 | 3 | 1 | 61 | 21 | 40 | 45 |
| 2 River Lane Rangers | 18 | 13 | 3 | 2 | 59 | 25 | 34 | 42 |
| 3 Redgate Rangers Res. | 18 | 13 | 2 | 3 | 64 | 15 | 49 | 41 |
| 4 Terrington | 18 | 10 | 0 | 8 | 41 | 29 | 12 | 30 |
| 5 Marshland Saints | 18 | 8 | 3 | 7 | 46 | 37 | 9 | 27 |
| 6 Heacham Res. | 18 | 8 | 3 | 7 | 48 | 50 | -2 | 27 |
| 7 Great Massingham | 18 | 6 | 1 | 11 | 45 | 56 | -11 | 19 |
| 8 Docking | 18 | 4 | 1 | 13 | 26 | 53 | -27 | 13 |
| 9 Hunstanton | 18 | 3 | 0 | 15 | 16 | 62 | -46 | 9 |
| 10 Ingoldisthorpe Res. | 18 | 2 | 2 | 14 | 18 | 76 | -58 | 8 |

| Division Three | P | W | D | L | F | A | GD | Pts |
|---|---|---|---|---|---|---|---|---|
| 1 South Creake | 20 | 16 | 3 | 1 | 86 | 28 | 58 | 51 |
| 2 Denver | 20 | 16 | 2 | 2 | 80 | 15 | 65 | 50 |
| 3 Upwell Town A | 20 | 14 | 2 | 4 | 73 | 34 | 39 | 44 |
| 4 Springwood | 20 | 10 | 1 | 9 | 73 | 47 | 26 | 31 |
| 5 The Woottons Res. | 20 | 8 | 4 | 8 | 40 | 61 | -21 | 28 |
| 6 Birchwood Res. | 20 | 9 | 0 | 11 | 49 | 60 | -11 | 27 |
| 7 Watlington Res. | 20 | 8 | 2 | 10 | 65 | 60 | 5 | 26 |
| 8 Heacham A | 20 | 8 | 2 | 10 | 49 | 53 | -4 | 26 |
| 9 Pentney | 20 | 7 | 2 | 11 | 40 | 64 | -24 | 23 |
| 10 Hungate | 20 | 2 | 1 | 17 | 33 | 83 | -50 | 7 |
| 11 Hunstanton Res. | 20 | 2 | 1 | 17 | 30 | 113 | -83 | 7 |

## NORTHAMPTON TOWN AND DISTRICT LEAGUE

| Premier Division | P | W | D | L | F | A | GD | Pts |
|---|---|---|---|---|---|---|---|---|
| 1 Sporting Bat & Wickets | 18 | 12 | 3 | 3 | 68 | 28 | 40 | 39 |
| 2 Duston Dynamo | 18 | 12 | 0 | 6 | 73 | 34 | 39 | 36 |
| 3 FC Shelley Road | 18 | 11 | 1 | 6 | 72 | 52 | 20 | 34 |
| 4 Liberty Stars | 18 | 9 | 2 | 7 | 77 | 45 | 32 | 29 |
| 5 James King Blisworth A | 18 | 8 | 1 | 9 | 51 | 64 | -13 | 25 |
| 6 Thorplands Club 81 | 18 | 7 | 1 | 10 | 71 | 49 | 22 | 22 |
| 7 Thorplands Club 81 Res. | 18 | 0 | 0 | 18 | 15 | 155 | -140 | 0 |

## NORWICH & DISTRICT SATURDAY FOOTBALL LEAGUE

| Division One | P | W | D | L | F | A | GD | Pts |
|---|---|---|---|---|---|---|---|---|
| 1 Hethersett Old Boys | 16 | 12 | 1 | 3 | 59 | 23 | 36 | 37 |
| 2 Yelverton Res. | 16 | 10 | 4 | 2 | 38 | 23 | 15 | 34 |
| 3 One Love United | 16 | 10 | 3 | 3 | 70 | 33 | 37 | 33 |
| 4 Earlham Colney | 16 | 9 | 1 | 6 | 46 | 25 | 21 | 28 |
| 5 Norman Wanderers | 16 | 7 | 2 | 7 | 47 | 43 | 4 | 23 |
| 6 UEA A | 16 | 6 | 3 | 7 | 35 | 34 | 1 | 21 |
| 7 Norwich Medics | 16 | 5 | 2 | 9 | 45 | 47 | -2 | 17 |
| 8 Mattishall A | 16 | 2 | 1 | 13 | 20 | 58 | -38 | 7 |
| 9 Homecare United | 16 | 2 | 1 | 13 | 17 | 91 | -74 | 7 |

| Division Two | P | W | D | L | F | A | GD | Pts |
|---|---|---|---|---|---|---|---|---|
| 1 Wensum Albion | 14 | 12 | 0 | 2 | 46 | 19 | 27 | 36 |
| 2 BGS | 14 | 8 | 4 | 2 | 48 | 25 | 23 | 28 |
| 3 Drayton | 14 | 8 | 2 | 4 | 33 | 28 | 5 | 26 |
| 4 Taverham | 14 | 7 | 3 | 4 | 32 | 26 | 6 | 24 |
| 5 Blofield United A | 14 | 5 | 2 | 7 | 42 | 43 | -1 | 17 |
| 6 Heartsease Athletic | 14 | 4 | 1 | 9 | 22 | 31 | -9 | 13 |
| 7 Earlham Colney Res. | 14 | 3 | 1 | 10 | 32 | 45 | -13 | 10 |
| 8 Dyers Arms | 14 | 2 | 1 | 11 | 13 | 51 | -38 | 7 |

## NOTTS AMATEUR ALLIANCE

| Premier Division | P | W | D | L | F | A | GD | Pts |
|---|---|---|---|---|---|---|---|---|
| 1 Strelley Rose | 16 | 13 | 3 | 0 | 67 | 19 | 48 | 42 |
| 2 AFC Bridgford | 16 | 10 | 5 | 1 | 57 | 22 | 35 | 35 |
| 3 Ashfield Athletic | 16 | 9 | 3 | 4 | 45 | 21 | 24 | 30 |
| 4 Nottingham Sikh Lions | 16 | 9 | 2 | 5 | 51 | 44 | 7 | 29 |
| 5 Beeston Res. | 16 | 5 | 4 | 7 | 30 | 40 | -10 | 19 |
| 6 FC Geordie | 16 | 5 | 3 | 8 | 33 | 35 | -2 | 18 |
| 7 West 8 | 16 | 4 | 1 | 11 | 37 | 51 | -14 | 13 |
| 8 Vernon Villa | 16 | 3 | 1 | 12 | 14 | 43 | -29 | 10 |
| 9 Robin Hood Colts | 16 | 2 | 2 | 12 | 16 | 75 | -59 | 8 |

| Division One | P | W | D | L | F | A | GD | Pts |
|---|---|---|---|---|---|---|---|---|
| 1 Arnold Saints | 20 | 15 | 2 | 3 | 66 | 30 | 36 | 47 |
| 2 Skegby United | 20 | 12 | 3 | 5 | 63 | 35 | 28 | 39 |
| 3 Netherfield Albion A | 20 | 12 | 3 | 5 | 50 | 44 | 6 | 39 |
| 4 Rainworth Archers | 20 | 11 | 3 | 6 | 54 | 41 | 13 | 36 |
| 5 Gedling Southbank Colts | 20 | 8 | 4 | 8 | 44 | 37 | 7 | 28 |
| 6 Beeston Rylands | 20 | 8 | 4 | 8 | 48 | 54 | -6 | 28 |
| 7 Arnold Samba | 20 | 9 | 1 | 10 | 33 | 48 | -15 | 28 |
| 8 Nottingham Riverside United | 20 | 7 | 5 | 8 | 55 | 48 | 7 | 26 |
| 9 Nottingham Community | 20 | 6 | 4 | 10 | 27 | 38 | -11 | 22 |
| 10 Gedling Southbank A | 20 | 4 | 1 | 15 | 27 | 55 | -28 | 13 |
| 11 FC Cavaliers Res. | 20 | 2 | 2 | 16 | 24 | 61 | -37 | 8 |

| Division Two | P | W | D | L | F | A | GD | Pts |
|---|---|---|---|---|---|---|---|---|
| 1 Premium | 18 | 17 | 1 | 0 | 100 | 16 | 84 | 52 |
| 2 Netherfield Seniors | 18 | 12 | 2 | 4 | 82 | 29 | 53 | 38 |
| 3 AC Wollaton | 18 | 12 | 0 | 6 | 81 | 50 | 31 | 36 |
| 4 AFC Villa | 18 | 10 | 2 | 6 | 66 | 36 | 30 | 32 |
| 5 Sneinton Town | 18 | 9 | 2 | 7 | 58 | 58 | 0 | 29 |
| 6 Beeston A | 18 | 7 | 3 | 8 | 72 | 62 | 10 | 24 |
| 7 AFC Bridgford Res. | 18 | 7 | 2 | 9 | 50 | 48 | 2 | 23 |
| 8 Forest Park | 18 | 5 | 5 | 8 | 53 | 59 | -6 | 20 |
| 9 Mapperley | 18 | 1 | 1 | 16 | 23 | 91 | -68 | 4 |
| 10 Steve Marshall | 18 | 1 | 0 | 17 | 15 | 151 | -136 | 3 |

## PERRY STREET AND DISTRICT LEAGUE

| Premier Division | P | W | D | L | F | A | GD | Pts |
|---|---|---|---|---|---|---|---|---|
| 1 Perry Street | 22 | 18 | 4 | 0 | 94 | 20 | 74 | 58 |
| 2 South Petherton | 22 | 17 | 2 | 3 | 95 | 25 | 70 | 53 |
| 3 Shepton Beauchamp | 22 | 15 | 3 | 4 | 80 | 18 | 62 | 48 |
| 4 Barrington | 22 | 14 | 2 | 6 | 72 | 42 | 30 | 44 |
| 5 Beaminster | 22 | 14 | 1 | 7 | 66 | 48 | 18 | 43 |
| 6 Winsham | 22 | 7 | 4 | 11 | 37 | 48 | -11 | 25 |
| 7 Netherbury | 22 | 7 | 3 | 12 | 45 | 54 | -9 | 24 |
| 8 West & Middle Chinnock | 22 | 7 | 2 | 13 | 43 | 79 | -36 | 23 |
| 9 Combe Res. | 22 | 7 | 1 | 14 | 38 | 49 | -11 | 22 |
| 10 Chard United | 22 | 6 | 3 | 13 | 41 | 76 | -35 | 21 |
| 11 Forton Rangers (-3) | 22 | 4 | 2 | 16 | 25 | 80 | -55 | 11 |
| 12 Crewkerne Town (-1) | 22 | 2 | 1 | 19 | 30 | 127 | -97 | 6 |

| Division One | P | W | D | L | F | A | GD | Pts |
|---|---|---|---|---|---|---|---|---|
| 1 Misterton | 18 | 15 | 0 | 3 | 56 | 17 | 39 | 45 |
| 2 Drimpton | 18 | 14 | 0 | 4 | 68 | 30 | 38 | 42 |
| 3 Hawkchurch | 18 | 12 | 1 | 5 | 55 | 31 | 24 | 37 |
| 4 Waytown Hounds | 18 | 9 | 3 | 6 | 37 | 30 | 7 | 30 |
| 5 Pymore | 18 | 8 | 2 | 8 | 39 | 35 | 4 | 26 |
| 6 Uplyme | 18 | 8 | 1 | 9 | 47 | 38 | 9 | 25 |
| 7 Combe A | 18 | 8 | 1 | 9 | 32 | 36 | -4 | 25 |
| 8 Ilminster Colts | 18 | 5 | 1 | 12 | 24 | 52 | -28 | 16 |
| 9 Thorncombe | 18 | 2 | 3 | 13 | 25 | 76 | -51 | 9 |
| 10 Crewkerne Rangers | 18 | 2 | 2 | 14 | 27 | 65 | -38 | 8 |

| Division Two | P | W | D | L | F | A | GD | Pts |
|---|---|---|---|---|---|---|---|---|
| 1 South Petherton Res. | 20 | 18 | 0 | 2 | 113 | 32 | 81 | 54 |
| 2 Merriott Rovers | 20 | 17 | 1 | 2 | 87 | 16 | 71 | 52 |
| 3 Shepton Res. | 20 | 11 | 4 | 5 | 58 | 37 | 21 | 37 |
| 4 Farway United | 20 | 12 | 1 | 7 | 56 | 44 | 12 | 37 |
| 5 Winsham Res. | 20 | 10 | 1 | 9 | 53 | 50 | 3 | 31 |
| 6 Combe B (-9) | 20 | 12 | 0 | 8 | 50 | 43 | 7 | 27 |
| 7 Chard Rangers | 20 | 8 | 2 | 10 | 46 | 50 | -4 | 26 |
| 8 Chard United Res. | 20 | 7 | 2 | 11 | 38 | 51 | -13 | 23 |
| 9 Kingsbury | 20 | 5 | 1 | 14 | 30 | 60 | -30 | 16 |
| 10 Hinton St George | 20 | 4 | 0 | 16 | 32 | 82 | -50 | 12 |
| 11 Thorncombe Res. | 20 | 0 | 0 | 20 | 12 | 110 | -98 | 0 |

| Division Three | P | W | D | L | F | A | GD | Pts |
|---|---|---|---|---|---|---|---|---|
| 1 Halstock | 24 | 21 | 1 | 2 | 114 | 14 | 100 | 64 |
| 2 Perry Street Res. (-1) | 24 | 19 | 2 | 3 | 86 | 27 | 59 | 58 |
| 3 Dowlish & Donyatt | 24 | 17 | 1 | 6 | 125 | 38 | 87 | 52 |
| 4 Charmouth | 24 | 14 | 5 | 5 | 68 | 36 | 32 | 47 |
| 5 Netherbury Res. | 24 | 13 | 3 | 8 | 65 | 53 | 12 | 42 |
| 6 Fivehead | 24 | 12 | 1 | 11 | 75 | 66 | 9 | 37 |
| 7 Uplyme Res. | 24 | 9 | 4 | 11 | 52 | 66 | -14 | 31 |
| 8 Chard Rangers Res. (-3) | 24 | 8 | 6 | 10 | 40 | 56 | -16 | 27 |
| 9 Drimpton Res. (-3) | 24 | 9 | 2 | 13 | 58 | 86 | -28 | 26 |
| 10 Crewkerne Rangers Res. (-3) | 24 | 7 | 3 | 14 | 47 | 96 | -49 | 21 |
| 11 Chard United All Stars | 24 | 5 | 2 | 17 | 32 | 101 | -69 | 17 |
| 12 Farway Res. | 24 | 3 | 4 | 17 | 31 | 80 | -49 | 13 |
| 13 Ilminster Town A (-3) | 24 | 2 | 0 | 22 | 23 | 97 | -74 | 3 |

## PLYMOUTH & WEST DEVON LEAGUE

| Premier Division | P | W | D | L | F | A | GD | Pts |
|---|---|---|---|---|---|---|---|---|
| 1 Plymouth Marjons (-3) | 22 | 18 | 3 | 1 | 67 | 24 | 43 | 54 |
| 2 The Windmill | 22 | 15 | 3 | 4 | 77 | 35 | 42 | 48 |
| 3 Mount Gould | 22 | 14 | 4 | 4 | 99 | 49 | 50 | 46 |
| 4 Ernesettle DRDE Trust | 22 | 12 | 4 | 6 | 70 | 46 | 24 | 40 |
| 5 Roborough | 22 | 12 | 4 | 6 | 57 | 41 | 16 | 40 |
| 6 Bar Sol Ona | 22 | 8 | 6 | 8 | 51 | 48 | 3 | 30 |
| 7 Chaddlewood Miners Old Boys (-3) | 22 | 9 | 2 | 11 | 42 | 58 | -16 | 29 |
| 8 Millbridge | 22 | 6 | 3 | 13 | 37 | 75 | -38 | 21 |
| 9 Chaddlewood RBL | 22 | 7 | 2 | 13 | 69 | 70 | -1 | 20 |
| 10 University of Plymouth | 22 | 6 | 2 | 14 | 54 | 88 | -34 | 20 |
| 11 Plympton Athletic | 22 | 3 | 5 | 14 | 28 | 66 | -38 | 14 |
| 12 Morley Rangers | 22 | 2 | 2 | 18 | 32 | 83 | -51 | 8 |

Devonport Services withdrew - record expunged.
Hideaway Cafe withdrew - record expunged.

| Division One | P | W | D | L | F | A | GD | Pts |
|---|---|---|---|---|---|---|---|---|
| 1 Millbridge Res. | 20 | 15 | 3 | 2 | 78 | 24 | 54 | 48 |
| 2 Navy Inn | 20 | 15 | 1 | 4 | 72 | 36 | 36 | 46 |
| 3 Maristow | 20 | 14 | 3 | 3 | 72 | 33 | 39 | 45 |
| 4 Bar Sol Ona Res. | 19 | 12 | 3 | 4 | 93 | 30 | 63 | 39 |
| 5 Tavistock Community | 20 | 9 | 3 | 8 | 69 | 55 | 14 | 30 |
| 6 D&C Auto Repairs | 20 | 8 | 3 | 9 | 46 | 45 | 1 | 27 |
| 7 Princetown | 20 | 7 | 3 | 10 | 43 | 63 | -20 | 24 |
| 8 Belgrave | 20 | 5 | 5 | 10 | 42 | 66 | -24 | 20 |
| 9 Morley Rangers Res. | 20 | 6 | 1 | 13 | 57 | 66 | -9 | 19 |
| 10 Plymouth Hope | 19 | 5 | 1 | 13 | 42 | 55 | -13 | 16 |
| 11 Plymouth Falcons | 20 | 0 | 0 | 20 | 23 | 164 | -141 | 0 |

| Division Two | P | W | D | L | F | A | GD | Pts |
|---|---|---|---|---|---|---|---|---|
| 1 Lakeside Ath | 18 | 17 | 1 | 0 | 83 | 19 | +64 | 52 |
| 2 Hooe Rovers | 18 | 11 | 4 | 3 | 51 | 39 | +12 | 37 |
| 3 Pennycross SC | 18 | 9 | 6 | 3 | 50 | 27 | +23 | 33 |
| 4 Melbourne Inn (-3) | 18 | 11 | 2 | 5 | 63 | 42 | +21 | 32 |
| 5 SB Frankfort | 18 | 9 | 2 | 7 | 54 | 44 | +10 | 29 |
| 6 Millbridge 'B' | 18 | 5 | 3 | 10 | 43 | 62 | -19 | 18 |
| 7 Roborough 'B' | 18 | 5 | 3 | 10 | 41 | 69 | -28 | 18 |
| 8 Weston Mill OV | 18 | 5 | 1 | 12 | 37 | 57 | -20 | 16 |
| 9 Woodford (-3) | 18 | 4 | 1 | 13 | 30 | 67 | -37 | 10 |
| 10 Staddiscombe Colts | 18 | 2 | 1 | 15 | 38 | 64 | -26 | 7 |

| Division Three | P | W | D | L | F | A | GD | Pts |
|---|---|---|---|---|---|---|---|---|
| 1 West Hart Rangers | 18 | 14 | 1 | 3 | 60 | 22 | 38 | 43 |
| 2 Plympton Athletic Res. | 18 | 12 | 1 | 5 | 57 | 34 | 23 | 37 |
| 3 Chaddlewood Inn (-6) | 18 | 13 | 3 | 2 | 77 | 28 | 49 | 36 |
| 4 Kitto FC | 18 | 11 | 3 | 4 | 57 | 34 | 23 | 36 |
| 5 SB Frankfort 'B' | 18 | 7 | 2 | 9 | 35 | 46 | -11 | 23 |
| 6 Friary Vaults | 18 | 6 | 3 | 9 | 45 | 44 | 1 | 21 |
| 7 Maristow 'B' | 18 | 6 | 3 | 9 | 34 | 45 | -11 | 21 |
| 8 Princetown Res. | 18 | 4 | 1 | 13 | 37 | 83 | -46 | 13 |
| 9 Belgrave FC Res. | 18 | 1 | 3 | 14 | 30 | 77 | -47 | 6 |
| 10 FC Colwill & Davey (-12) | 18 | 5 | 2 | 11 | 33 | 52 | -19 | 5 |

## PORTSMOUTH SATURDAY FOOTBALL LEAGUE

| **Premier Division** | P | W | D | L | F | A | GD | Pts |
|---|---|---|---|---|---|---|---|---|
| 1 Horndean Hawks | 21 | 18 | 1 | 2 | 83 | 26 | 57 | 55 |
| 2 Widley Wanderers | 21 | 13 | 4 | 4 | 60 | 35 | 25 | 43 |
| 3 Wymering | 21 | 11 | 2 | 8 | 59 | 41 | 18 | 35 |
| 4 Southsea Utd | 21 | 8 | 3 | 10 | 52 | 55 | -3 | 27 |
| 5 Widbrook Utd | 21 | 8 | 2 | 11 | 42 | 47 | -5 | 26 |
| 6 Budd AFC | 21 | 7 | 3 | 11 | 28 | 55 | -27 | 24 |
| 7 Carberry | 21 | 6 | 0 | 15 | 25 | 55 | -30 | 18 |
| 8 Horndean Utd | 21 | 5 | 1 | 15 | 34 | 69 | -35 | 16 |

| **Division One** | P | W | D | L | F | A | GD | Pts |
|---|---|---|---|---|---|---|---|---|
| 1 Bishops Waltham Dynamos | 21 | 19 | 1 | 1 | 98 | 24 | 74 | 58 |
| 2 Portsmouth Water FC | 21 | 14 | 3 | 4 | 101 | 40 | 61 | 45 |
| 3 Portchester Rovers | 21 | 9 | 5 | 7 | 44 | 43 | 1 | 32 |
| 4 Segensworth FC | 21 | 10 | 1 | 10 | 63 | 58 | 5 | 31 |
| 5 AFC Ventora | 21 | 6 | 4 | 11 | 49 | 58 | -9 | 22 |
| 6 Fareport Town | 21 | 7 | 1 | 13 | 35 | 81 | -46 | 22 |
| 7 Burrfields FC (-3) | 21 | 7 | 2 | 12 | 55 | 73 | -18 | 20 |
| 8 Drayton Town | 21 | 2 | 3 | 16 | 28 | 96 | -68 | 9 |

## REDHILL & DISTRICT LEAGUE

| **Premier Division** | P | W | D | L | F | A | GD | Pts |
|---|---|---|---|---|---|---|---|---|
| 1 South Park 'A' | 16 | 14 | 1 | 1 | 49 | 10 | 39 | 43 |
| 2 Frenches Athletic | 16 | 10 | 4 | 2 | 36 | 21 | 15 | 34 |
| 3 Holland Sports | 16 | 10 | 3 | 3 | 30 | 19 | 11 | 33 |
| 4 Woodmansterne Hyde | 16 | 9 | 1 | 6 | 51 | 25 | 26 | 28 |
| 5 Brockham | 16 | 7 | 3 | 6 | 43 | 36 | 7 | 24 |
| 6 Racing Epsom | 16 | 5 | 3 | 8 | 25 | 39 | -14 | 18 |
| 7 Farleigh Rovers 'A' | 16 | 5 | 1 | 10 | 22 | 43 | -21 | 16 |
| 8 Overton Athletic | 16 | 2 | 2 | 12 | 15 | 35 | -20 | 8 |
| 9 RH Athletic | 16 | 1 | 0 | 15 | 17 | 60 | -43 | 3 |

| **Division One** | P | W | D | L | F | A | GD | Pts |
|---|---|---|---|---|---|---|---|---|
| 1 South Godstone | 14 | 10 | 2 | 2 | 51 | 29 | 22 | 32 |
| 2 Nutfield | 14 | 10 | 0 | 4 | 45 | 31 | 14 | 30 |
| 3 Charlwood | 14 | 9 | 2 | 3 | 46 | 25 | 21 | 29 |
| 4 AFC Walcountians | 14 | 5 | 3 | 6 | 27 | 32 | -5 | 18 |
| 5 South Park 'B' | 14 | 5 | 1 | 8 | 30 | 33 | -3 | 16 |
| 6 Walton Heath | 14 | 5 | 1 | 8 | 32 | 42 | -10 | 16 |
| 7 Horley AFC | 14 | 4 | 2 | 8 | 29 | 43 | -14 | 14 |
| 8 Warlingham 'A' | 14 | 2 | 1 | 11 | 21 | 46 | -25 | 7 |

| **Division Two** | P | W | D | L | F | A | GD | Pts |
|---|---|---|---|---|---|---|---|---|
| 1 Priory OB | 18 | 16 | 0 | 2 | 83 | 22 | 61 | 48 |
| 2 Warlingham 'B' | 18 | 15 | 0 | 3 | 49 | 21 | 28 | 45 |
| 3 Walton Heath Res. | 18 | 11 | 2 | 5 | 46 | 26 | 20 | 35 |
| 4 Perrywood Sports Seniors | 18 | 8 | 2 | 8 | 41 | 36 | 5 | 26 |
| 5 Nomads Res. | 18 | 8 | 2 | 8 | 38 | 49 | -11 | 26 |
| 6 Reigate OB | 18 | 6 | 4 | 8 | 38 | 37 | 1 | 22 |
| 7 RH Athletic Res. | 18 | 6 | 2 | 10 | 17 | 41 | -24 | 20 |
| 8 AC Carshalton Select | 18 | 5 | 2 | 11 | 29 | 50 | -21 | 17 |
| 9 Westcott 35 | 18 | 4 | 3 | 11 | 42 | 54 | -12 | 15 |
| 10 Reigate Priory 'A' | 18 | 2 | 1 | 15 | 17 | 64 | -47 | 7 |

| **Division Three** | P | W | D | L | F | A | GD | Pts |
|---|---|---|---|---|---|---|---|---|
| 1 AFC Hamsey Rangers | 18 | 16 | 1 | 1 | 101 | 27 | 74 | 49 |
| 2 Woodmansterne Hyde 'A' | 18 | 13 | 3 | 2 | 66 | 19 | 47 | 42 |
| 3 RH Athletic 'A' | 18 | 11 | 2 | 5 | 45 | 40 | 5 | 35 |
| 4 Horley AFC Res. | 18 | 10 | 2 | 6 | 51 | 39 | 12 | 32 |
| 5 Oxted & District 'A' | 18 | 9 | 2 | 7 | 54 | 49 | 5 | 29 |
| 6 Brockham Res. | 18 | 9 | 1 | 8 | 40 | 46 | -6 | 28 |
| 7 Frenches Athletic Res. | 18 | 7 | 4 | 7 | 36 | 52 | -16 | 25 |
| 8 Reigate Priory 'B' | 18 | 2 | 2 | 14 | 13 | 42 | -29 | 8 |
| 9 Monotype Res. | 18 | 2 | 1 | 15 | 13 | 43 | -30 | 7 |
| 10 Nomads 'A' | 18 | 1 | 2 | 15 | 21 | 83 | -62 | 5 |

## ROMFORD & DISTRICT FOOTBALL LEAGUE

| Premier Division | P | W | D | L | F | A | GD | Pts |
|---|---|---|---|---|---|---|---|---|
| 1 Ferns Seniors | 14 | 9 | 3 | 2 | 31 | 15 | 16 | 30 |
| 2 Brentwood United | 14 | 9 | 2 | 3 | 31 | 20 | 11 | 29 |
| 3 East Ham Working Mens Club | 14 | 7 | 3 | 4 | 29 | 28 | 1 | 24 |
| 4 Havering Oak | 14 | 7 | 2 | 5 | 17 | 23 | -6 | 23 |
| 5 Colebrook Royals | 14 | 5 | 2 | 7 | 32 | 21 | 11 | 17 |
| 6 Emeronians | 13 | 5 | 2 | 6 | 29 | 25 | 4 | 17 |
| 7 Roneo Colts | 14 | 3 | 3 | 8 | 26 | 46 | -20 | 12 |
| 8 New Star Soccer FC | 13 | 1 | 1 | 11 | 20 | 37 | -17 | 4 |

| Division One | P | W | D | L | F | A | GD | Pts |
|---|---|---|---|---|---|---|---|---|
| 1 Lionside United | 12 | 12 | 0 | 0 | 47 | 6 | 41 | 36 |
| 2 AAH Romford | 12 | 8 | 1 | 3 | 45 | 21 | 24 | 25 |
| 3 Colebrook Royals Res. | 12 | 8 | 0 | 4 | 22 | 14 | 8 | 24 |
| 4 Gatcliffe FC | 12 | 4 | 0 | 8 | 21 | 33 | -12 | 12 |
| 5 Brentwood United Res. | 12 | 3 | 1 | 8 | 21 | 39 | -18 | 10 |
| 6 Upminster FC | 12 | 3 | 1 | 8 | 20 | 52 | -32 | 10 |
| 7 Harold Wood Hospital | 12 | 2 | 1 | 9 | 21 | 32 | -11 | 7 |

## SALISBURY & DISTRICT LEAGUE

| Premier Division | P | W | D | L | F | A | GD | Pts |
|---|---|---|---|---|---|---|---|---|
| 1 Alderbury | 14 | 12 | 0 | 2 | 48 | 19 | 29 | 36 |
| 2 Stockton & Codford | 14 | 9 | 2 | 3 | 55 | 13 | 42 | 29 |
| 3 Porton Sports | 14 | 7 | 4 | 3 | 33 | 28 | 5 | 25 |
| 4 D.I.UTD | 14 | 7 | 3 | 4 | 32 | 23 | 9 | 24 |
| 5 South Newton & Wishford | 14 | 3 | 5 | 6 | 32 | 33 | -1 | 14 |
| 6 Chalke Valley | 14 | 4 | 1 | 9 | 20 | 34 | -14 | 13 |
| 7 Amesbury Kings Arms | 14 | 3 | 1 | 10 | 21 | 45 | -24 | 10 |
| 8 West Harnham | 14 | 2 | 2 | 10 | 21 | 67 | -46 | 8 |

| Division One | P | W | D | L | F | A | GD | Pts |
|---|---|---|---|---|---|---|---|---|
| 1 RCFC | 16 | 14 | 0 | 2 | 70 | 26 | 44 | 42 |
| 2 South Newton & Wishford Res | 16 | 10 | 1 | 5 | 55 | 27 | 28 | 31 |
| 3 Railway Social Club | 16 | 9 | 1 | 6 | 39 | 38 | 1 | 28 |
| 4 Value Cars | 16 | 3 | 1 | 12 | 22 | 70 | -48 | 10 |
| 5 Fordingbridge Turks | 16 | 2 | 1 | 13 | 18 | 43 | -25 | 7 |

## SCUNTHORPE & DISTRICT FOOTBALL LEAGUE

| Division One | P | W | D | L | F | A | GD | Pts |
|---|---|---|---|---|---|---|---|---|
| 1 Limestone Rangers | 16 | 14 | 2 | 0 | 69 | 7 | 62 | 44 |
| 2 Epworth Town | 16 | 11 | 3 | 2 | 60 | 12 | 48 | 36 |
| 3 Brumby | 16 | 10 | 2 | 4 | 96 | 23 | 73 | 32 |
| 4 College Wanderers | 16 | 10 | 2 | 4 | 48 | 21 | 27 | 32 |
| 5 Barnetby United | 16 | 8 | 4 | 4 | 41 | 28 | 13 | 28 |
| 6 Broughton Colts (-3) | 16 | 5 | 1 | 10 | 26 | 64 | -38 | 13 |
| 7 Bottesford Town Res. | 16 | 4 | 0 | 12 | 38 | 69 | -31 | 12 |
| 8 Scotter United (+3) | 16 | 1 | 2 | 13 | 21 | 75 | -54 | 8 |
| 9 Crosby Colts | 16 | 0 | 2 | 14 | 14 | 114 | -100 | 2 |

| Division Two | P | W | D | L | F | A | GD | Pts |
|---|---|---|---|---|---|---|---|---|
| 1 Crowle Town Colts | 14 | 14 | 0 | 0 | 79 | 10 | 69 | 42 |
| 2 Scunthonians | 14 | 7 | 3 | 4 | 55 | 35 | 20 | 24 |
| 3 Westwoodside Rangers (-6) | 14 | 8 | 3 | 3 | 53 | 41 | 12 | 21 |
| 4 East Drayton (+3) | 14 | 5 | 2 | 7 | 34 | 43 | -9 | 20 |
| 5 Ashby RAOB | 14 | 5 | 3 | 6 | 39 | 58 | -19 | 18 |
| 6 Epworth Town Res. | 14 | 4 | 2 | 8 | 46 | 52 | -6 | 14 |
| 7 New Holland Villa (+3) | 14 | 2 | 2 | 10 | 15 | 49 | -34 | 11 |
| 8 Crosby Colts Res. | 14 | 2 | 3 | 9 | 28 | 61 | -33 | 9 |

| Division Three | P | W | D | L | F | A | GD | Pts |
|---|---|---|---|---|---|---|---|---|
| 1 The Butchers Arms | 18 | 15 | 2 | 1 | 74 | 11 | 63 | 47 |
| 2 Limestone Rangers Res. | 18 | 10 | 4 | 4 | 50 | 30 | 20 | 34 |
| 3 College Wanderers Res. (-3) | 18 | 11 | 3 | 4 | 50 | 35 | 15 | 33 |
| 4 Barnetby United Res. | 18 | 9 | 4 | 5 | 52 | 43 | 9 | 31 |
| 5 Briggensians | 18 | 8 | 3 | 7 | 39 | 33 | 6 | 27 |
| 6 A. Queensway (+3) | 18 | 7 | 2 | 9 | 52 | 39 | 13 | 26 |
| 7 Crowle Town Colts Res. | 18 | 6 | 5 | 7 | 36 | 52 | -16 | 23 |
| 8 Scotter United Res. | 18 | 6 | 4 | 8 | 41 | 49 | -8 | 22 |
| 9 Santon | 18 | 2 | 1 | 15 | 21 | 88 | -67 | 7 |
| 10 Midtown United | 18 | 1 | 2 | 15 | 17 | 52 | -35 | 5 |

## SOUTH DEVON FOOTBALL LEAGUE

| Premier Division | P | W | D | L | F | A | GD | Pts |
|---|---|---|---|---|---|---|---|---|
| 1 Buckland Athletic 2nd | 24 | 19 | 4 | 1 | 83 | 21 | 62 | 61 |
| 2 Dartmouth AFC | 24 | 18 | 5 | 1 | 76 | 16 | 60 | 59 |
| 3 Watcombe Wanderers | 24 | 17 | 4 | 3 | 74 | 35 | 39 | 55 |
| 4 East Allington United | 24 | 11 | 5 | 8 | 37 | 39 | -2 | 38 |
| 5 Waldon Athletic | 24 | 11 | 4 | 9 | 66 | 52 | 14 | 37 |
| 6 Ivybridge Town 2nd | 24 | 10 | 2 | 12 | 46 | 45 | 1 | 32 |
| 7 Kingsteignton Athletic | 24 | 8 | 5 | 11 | 40 | 39 | 1 | 29 |
| 8 Upton Athletic | 24 | 9 | 2 | 13 | 48 | 53 | -5 | 29 |
| 9 Brixham AFC 2nds | 24 | 8 | 5 | 11 | 32 | 52 | -20 | 29 |
| 10 Newton Abbot Spurs 2nd | 24 | 7 | 2 | 15 | 36 | 73 | -37 | 23 |
| 11 Kingskerswell & Chelston | 24 | 6 | 3 | 15 | 32 | 58 | -26 | 21 |
| 12 Loddiswell Athletic | 24 | 5 | 3 | 16 | 27 | 56 | -29 | 18 |
| 13 Stoke Gabriel 2nd (-3) | 24 | 4 | 2 | 18 | 31 | 89 | -58 | 11 |

| Division One | P | W | D | L | F | A | GD | Pts |
|---|---|---|---|---|---|---|---|---|
| 1 Ashburton | 24 | 19 | 2 | 3 | 88 | 26 | 62 | 59 |
| 2 Buckland Athletic 3rd | 24 | 18 | 4 | 2 | 81 | 28 | 53 | 58 |
| 3 Ipplepen Athletic | 24 | 17 | 2 | 5 | 67 | 26 | 41 | 53 |
| 4 Newton Abbot 66 | 24 | 17 | 0 | 7 | 73 | 35 | 38 | 51 |
| 5 Chudleigh Athletic | 24 | 11 | 4 | 9 | 62 | 58 | 4 | 37 |
| 6 Beesands Rovers | 24 | 11 | 1 | 12 | 49 | 50 | -1 | 34 |
| 7 Babbacombe Corinthians | 24 | 10 | 2 | 12 | 58 | 51 | 7 | 32 |
| 8 Bovey Tracey 2nds | 24 | 10 | 2 | 12 | 47 | 54 | -7 | 32 |
| 9 Totnes & Dartington 2nds (-3) | 24 | 10 | 2 | 12 | 41 | 44 | -3 | 29 |
| 10 Stoke Gabriel 3rds | 24 | 8 | 4 | 12 | 47 | 62 | -15 | 28 |
| 11 Paignton Villa | 24 | 7 | 2 | 15 | 52 | 72 | -20 | 23 |
| 12 Buckland & Milber | 24 | 4 | 1 | 19 | 30 | 113 | -83 | 13 |
| 13 Kingskerswell & Chelston 2nd | 24 | 1 | 0 | 23 | 23 | 99 | -76 | 3 |

| Division Two | P | W | D | L | F | A | GD | Pts |
|---|---|---|---|---|---|---|---|---|
| 1 Roselands | 24 | 19 | 1 | 4 | 131 | 38 | 93 | 58 |
| 2 Watcombe Wanderers 2nds | 24 | 19 | 0 | 5 | 120 | 42 | 78 | 57 |
| 3 Harbertonford | 24 | 18 | 0 | 6 | 98 | 40 | 58 | 54 |
| 4 Buckfastleigh Rangers | 24 | 16 | 4 | 4 | 88 | 57 | 31 | 52 |
| 5 Hookhills United | 24 | 12 | 2 | 10 | 45 | 57 | -12 | 38 |
| 6 Teignmouth 2nd (-3) | 24 | 12 | 2 | 10 | 85 | 71 | 14 | 35 |
| 7 Kingsteignton Athletic 2nds | 24 | 11 | 2 | 11 | 69 | 62 | 7 | 35 |
| 8 Brixham Town | 24 | 9 | 3 | 12 | 56 | 76 | -20 | 30 |
| 9 Paignton Saints | 24 | 6 | 6 | 12 | 42 | 86 | -44 | 24 |
| 10 Newton United | 24 | 5 | 5 | 14 | 42 | 70 | -28 | 20 |
| 11 Bishopsteignton United | 24 | 6 | 0 | 18 | 49 | 110 | -61 | 18 |
| 12 Waldon Athletic 2nd | 24 | 5 | 2 | 17 | 38 | 86 | -48 | 17 |
| 13 Abbotskerswell | 24 | 3 | 3 | 18 | 35 | 103 | -68 | 12 |

| Division Three | P | W | D | L | F | A | GD | Pts |
|---|---|---|---|---|---|---|---|---|
| 1 Dartmouth AFC 2nd | 26 | 24 | 1 | 1 | 97 | 19 | 78 | 73 |
| 2 Salcombe Town | 26 | 18 | 2 | 6 | 108 | 44 | 64 | 56 |
| 3 AFC Staverton | 26 | 17 | 4 | 5 | 73 | 33 | 40 | 55 |
| 4 Liverton United 2nd (-3) | 26 | 18 | 1 | 7 | 92 | 41 | 51 | 52 |
| 5 Harbertonford 2nd | 26 | 15 | 4 | 7 | 71 | 52 | 19 | 49 |
| 6 East Allington United 2nd | 26 | 10 | 9 | 7 | 50 | 47 | 3 | 39 |
| 7 Torbay Police (-3) | 26 | 11 | 6 | 9 | 77 | 59 | 18 | 36 |
| 8 Chudleigh Athletic 2nds | 26 | 8 | 8 | 10 | 44 | 66 | -22 | 32 |
| 9 Ipplepen Athletic 2nds (-3) | 26 | 9 | 5 | 12 | 46 | 52 | -6 | 29 |
| 10 Teign Village | 26 | 6 | 4 | 16 | 40 | 75 | -35 | 22 |
| 11 Upton Athletic 2nds | 26 | 5 | 4 | 17 | 49 | 88 | -39 | 19 |
| 12 Buckfastleigh Rangers 2nds (-3) | 26 | 5 | 3 | 18 | 26 | 101 | -75 | 15 |
| 13 Waldon Athletic 3rds (-9) | 26 | 4 | 4 | 18 | 38 | 84 | -46 | 7 |
| 14 Dittisham United (-6) | 26 | 3 | 3 | 20 | 41 | 91 | -50 | 6 |

| Division Four | P | W | D | L | F | A | GD | Pts |
|---|---|---|---|---|---|---|---|---|
| 1 Watcombe Wanderers 3rds | 26 | 21 | 3 | 2 | 112 | 27 | 85 | 66 |
| 2 Roselands 2nds | 26 | 20 | 1 | 5 | 101 | 31 | 70 | 61 |
| 3 Riviera United | 26 | 16 | 3 | 7 | 75 | 49 | 26 | 51 |
| 4 Broadmeadow | 26 | 14 | 4 | 8 | 60 | 57 | 3 | 46 |
| 5 Meadowbrook Athletic | 26 | 14 | 1 | 11 | 56 | 51 | 5 | 43 |
| 6 Barton Athletic | 26 | 13 | 3 | 10 | 79 | 63 | 16 | 42 |
| 7 Paignton Villa 2nds | 26 | 11 | 2 | 13 | 48 | 67 | -19 | 35 |
| 8 Newton Rovers | 26 | 10 | 3 | 13 | 48 | 51 | -3 | 33 |
| 9 Newton Abbot 66 2nd | 26 | 9 | 5 | 12 | 48 | 76 | -28 | 32 |
| 10 Ashburton 2nd (-3) | 26 | 9 | 4 | 13 | 59 | 67 | -8 | 28 |
| 11 Kingsbridge & Kellaton United | 26 | 7 | 5 | 14 | 41 | 86 | -45 | 26 |
| 12 Torquay Town (-9) | 26 | 9 | 2 | 15 | 49 | 62 | -13 | 20 |
| 13 Babbacombe Corinthians 2nd | 26 | 4 | 4 | 18 | 37 | 72 | -35 | 16 |
| 14 Ilsington Villa | 26 | 2 | 6 | 18 | 34 | 88 | -54 | 12 |

| Division Five | P | W | D | L | F | A | GD | Pts |
|---|---|---|---|---|---|---|---|---|
| 1 Torbay Police 2nds | 24 | 20 | 1 | 3 | 107 | 23 | 84 | 61 |
| 2 Buckland & Milber 2nds | 24 | 18 | 2 | 4 | 99 | 38 | 61 | 56 |
| 3 Broadhempston United 2nd | 24 | 17 | 4 | 3 | 96 | 58 | 38 | 55 |
| 4 Moretonhampstead | 24 | 17 | 2 | 5 | 92 | 50 | 42 | 53 |
| 5 Riviera United 2nds | 24 | 14 | 4 | 6 | 69 | 45 | 24 | 46 |
| 6 Newton United 2nd | 24 | 9 | 6 | 9 | 53 | 47 | 6 | 33 |
| 7 Paignton Saints 2nds | 24 | 9 | 2 | 13 | 62 | 86 | -24 | 29 |
| 8 Newton Rovers 2nds | 24 | 8 | 2 | 14 | 48 | 87 | -39 | 26 |
| 9 Stoke Fleming & Strete | 24 | 8 | 1 | 15 | 41 | 62 | -21 | 25 |
| 10 Barton Athletic 2nds (-3) | 24 | 8 | 3 | 13 | 51 | 83 | -32 | 24 |
| 11 Watts Blake & Bearne AFC | 24 | 7 | 0 | 17 | 52 | 87 | -35 | 21 |
| 12 Malborough United | 24 | 4 | 2 | 18 | 50 | 85 | -35 | 14 |
| 13 Chudleigh Athletic 3rds | 24 | 2 | 1 | 21 | 25 | 94 | -69 | 7 |

## SOUTH LONDON FOOTBALL ALLIANCE

| Premier Division | P | W | D | L | F | A | GD | Pts |
|---|---|---|---|---|---|---|---|---|
| 1 Wickham Park | 18 | 14 | 3 | 1 | 50 | 16 | 34 | 45 |
| 2 Long Lane A | 18 | 13 | 2 | 3 | 52 | 23 | 29 | 41 |
| 3 Drummond Athletic | 18 | 10 | 2 | 6 | 44 | 30 | 14 | 32 |
| 4 Red Velvet | 18 | 9 | 5 | 4 | 29 | 33 | -4 | 32 |
| 5 Lewisham Athletic Res. | 18 | 7 | 4 | 7 | 26 | 31 | -5 | 25 |
| 6 Erith 147 Res. | 18 | 7 | 0 | 11 | 27 | 13 | 14 | 21 |
| 7 Blackheath Wanderers | 18 | 6 | 2 | 10 | 33 | 38 | -5 | 20 |
| 8 Southwark Borough | 18 | 4 | 4 | 10 | 22 | 35 | -13 | 16 |
| 9 Croydon BR | 18 | 4 | 2 | 12 | 22 | 59 | -37 | 14 |
| 10 Acorns | 18 | 3 | 2 | 13 | 8 | 35 | -27 | 11 |
| 11 Old Roan A withdrew - record expunged. | | | | | | | | |

| Division One | P | W | D | L | F | A | GD | Pts |
|---|---|---|---|---|---|---|---|---|
| 1 Red Velvet Res. | 21 | 18 | 1 | 2 | 81 | 13 | 68 | 55 |
| 2 West Bromley Albion | 21 | 14 | 3 | 4 | 44 | 27 | 17 | 45 |
| 3 Our Lady Seniors | 21 | 9 | 5 | 7 | 44 | 43 | 1 | 32 |
| 4 Stansfeld Oxford & Bermonsey | 21 | 8 | 4 | 9 | 37 | 38 | -1 | 28 |
| 5 Seven Acre Sports | 21 | 7 | 5 | 9 | 48 | 52 | -4 | 26 |
| 6 Old Colfeians | 21 | 5 | 3 | 13 | 37 | 59 | -22 | 18 |
| 7 Farnborough O.B.G. 'A' | 21 | 5 | 3 | 13 | 33 | 65 | -32 | 18 |
| 8 Old Bromleians Res. | 21 | 3 | 6 | 12 | 31 | 58 | -27 | 15 |
| 9 Beaverwood withdrew - record expunged. | | | | | | | | |

| Division Two | P | W | D | L | F | A | GD | Pts |
|---|---|---|---|---|---|---|---|---|
| 1 Golden Lion | 24 | 17 | 4 | 3 | 82 | 35 | 47 | 55 |
| 2 Kingsdale | 24 | 17 | 2 | 5 | 65 | 27 | 38 | 53 |
| 3 New Saints | 24 | 14 | 4 | 6 | 71 | 61 | 10 | 46 |
| 4 Shirley Town | 24 | 12 | 3 | 9 | 49 | 41 | 8 | 39 |
| 5 Johnson and Philips Res. | 24 | 9 | 5 | 10 | 45 | 48 | -3 | 32 |
| 6 Iron Tugboat City | 24 | 7 | 4 | 13 | 47 | 59 | -12 | 25 |
| 7 London Falcons | 24 | 8 | 1 | 15 | 47 | 67 | -20 | 25 |
| 8 Southern Seaters | 24 | 7 | 2 | 15 | 48 | 46 | 2 | 23 |
| 9 Old Bromleians 'A' | 24 | 3 | 3 | 18 | 27 | 97 | -70 | 12 |
| 10 Lewisham Tigers withdrew - record expunged. | | | | | | | | |

## SOUTH YORKSHIRE AMATEUR FOOTBALL LEAGUE

| Premier Division | P | W | D | L | F | A | GD | Pts |
|---|---|---|---|---|---|---|---|---|
| 1 Sheffield Medics | 16 | 13 | 2 | 1 | 75 | 19 | 56 | 41 |
| 2 Swinton Athletic | 16 | 12 | 2 | 2 | 73 | 30 | 43 | 38 |
| 3 Dale Dynamos | 16 | 8 | 2 | 6 | 61 | 39 | 22 | 26 |
| 4 Three Feathers Prince Of Wales | 16 | 8 | 1 | 7 | 59 | 45 | 14 | 25 |
| 5 Euroglaze | 16 | 7 | 3 | 6 | 49 | 40 | 9 | 24 |
| 6 Working Wonders | 16 | 7 | 2 | 7 | 54 | 46 | 8 | 23 |
| 7 Sheffield West End | 16 | 6 | 1 | 9 | 44 | 63 | -19 | 19 |
| 8 Sheffield Bankers | 16 | 3 | 1 | 12 | 24 | 75 | -51 | 10 |
| 9 Davys Res. | 16 | 1 | 0 | 15 | 22 | 104 | -82 | 3 |

## SOUTHAMPTON SATURDAY FOOTBALL LEAGUE

| | Premier Division | P | W | D | L | F | A | GD | Pts |
|---|---|---|---|---|---|---|---|---|---|
| 1 | Comrades | 16 | 10 | 2 | 4 | 50 | 21 | 29 | 32 |
| 2 | AFC Gulf Western | 16 | 10 | 2 | 4 | 40 | 26 | 14 | 32 |
| 3 | Hedge End Town | 16 | 10 | 1 | 5 | 40 | 37 | 3 | 31 |
| 4 | BTC Southampton | 16 | 10 | 0 | 6 | 60 | 25 | 35 | 30 |
| 5 | Southampton University | 16 | 9 | 1 | 6 | 47 | 35 | 12 | 28 |
| 6 | Nursling | 16 | 6 | 4 | 6 | 44 | 39 | 5 | 22 |
| 7 | Braishfield | 16 | 6 | 2 | 8 | 28 | 40 | -12 | 20 |
| 8 | Durley | 16 | 1 | 4 | 11 | 21 | 39 | -18 | 7 |
| 9 | Cadnam United | 16 | 1 | 2 | 13 | 14 | 82 | -68 | 5 |

| | Senior One | P | W | D | L | F | A | GD | Pts |
|---|---|---|---|---|---|---|---|---|---|
| 1 | Park Sports | 14 | 11 | 0 | 3 | 51 | 23 | 28 | 33 |
| 2 | Chamberlayne Athletic | 14 | 10 | 3 | 1 | 42 | 18 | 24 | 33 |
| 3 | Bishops Waltham Dynamo's | 14 | 8 | 2 | 4 | 47 | 29 | 18 | 26 |
| 4 | Montefiore Halls | 14 | 7 | 1 | 6 | 36 | 34 | 2 | 22 |
| 5 | Warsash Wasps | 14 | 6 | 2 | 6 | 31 | 29 | 2 | 20 |
| 6 | AFC Botley | 14 | 6 | 0 | 8 | 33 | 36 | -3 | 18 |
| 7 | Comrades Res. | 14 | 3 | 0 | 11 | 23 | 38 | -15 | 9 |
| 8 | BTC Soton Res. | 14 | 1 | 0 | 13 | 13 | 69 | -56 | 3 |

| | Junior One | P | W | D | L | F | A | GD | Pts |
|---|---|---|---|---|---|---|---|---|---|
| 1 | Athletico Romsey | 14 | 9 | 2 | 3 | 46 | 19 | 27 | 29 |
| 2 | Priory Rovers | 14 | 7 | 2 | 5 | 26 | 26 | 0 | 23 |
| 3 | Sporting BTC | 14 | 6 | 4 | 4 | 41 | 36 | 5 | 22 |
| 4 | Nursling Vets | 14 | 6 | 3 | 5 | 25 | 25 | 0 | 21 |
| 5 | Compton Res. | 14 | 6 | 2 | 6 | 16 | 19 | -3 | 20 |
| 6 | BTC Soton A | 14 | 5 | 3 | 6 | 36 | 35 | 1 | 18 |
| 7 | Langley Manor | 14 | 4 | 2 | 8 | 23 | 39 | -16 | 14 |
| 8 | Capital | 14 | 3 | 2 | 9 | 26 | 40 | -14 | 11 |

| | Junior Two | P | W | D | L | F | A | GD | Pts |
|---|---|---|---|---|---|---|---|---|---|
| 1 | Park Phoenix | 16 | 12 | 2 | 2 | 45 | 18 | 27 | 38 |
| 2 | Shamblehurst | 16 | 12 | 1 | 3 | 53 | 19 | 34 | 37 |
| 3 | Knightwood Utd | 16 | 8 | 4 | 4 | 47 | 32 | 15 | 28 |
| 4 | London Airways | 16 | 7 | 2 | 7 | 31 | 32 | -1 | 23 |
| 5 | FC White Horse | 16 | 6 | 4 | 6 | 26 | 34 | -8 | 22 |
| 6 | Shiza's Stars | 16 | 6 | 3 | 7 | 32 | 37 | -5 | 21 |
| 7 | Durley Res. | 16 | 4 | 2 | 10 | 29 | 46 | -17 | 14 |
| 8 | Hamble United | 16 | 4 | 2 | 10 | 24 | 46 | -22 | 14 |
| 9 | AFC Testwood | 16 | 2 | 2 | 12 | 26 | 49 | -23 | 8 |

| | Junior Three | P | W | D | L | F | A | GD | Pts |
|---|---|---|---|---|---|---|---|---|---|
| 1 | Upham Res. | 18 | 15 | 3 | 0 | 69 | 16 | 53 | 48 |
| 2 | AFC Phoenix XI | 18 | 14 | 2 | 2 | 78 | 21 | 57 | 44 |
| 3 | Waltham Wolves | 18 | 12 | 1 | 5 | 63 | 38 | 25 | 37 |
| 4 | Hedge End Tn Res. | 18 | 10 | 2 | 6 | 38 | 37 | 1 | 32 |
| 5 | Hythe Aztecs | 18 | 9 | 1 | 8 | 48 | 43 | 5 | 28 |
| 6 | AFC Hiltingbury | 18 | 6 | 3 | 9 | 28 | 52 | -24 | 21 |
| 7 | Inmar | 18 | 6 | 1 | 11 | 34 | 52 | -18 | 19 |
| 8 | Shield FC | 18 | 5 | 1 | 12 | 32 | 52 | -20 | 16 |
| 9 | AFC Station | 18 | 4 | 1 | 13 | 18 | 55 | -37 | 13 |
| 10 | Weston City | 18 | 1 | 1 | 16 | 26 | 68 | -42 | 4 |

| | Junior Four | P | W | D | L | F | A | GD | Pts |
|---|---|---|---|---|---|---|---|---|---|
| 1 | Kings Park Rangers | 18 | 10 | 5 | 3 | 51 | 37 | 14 | 35 |
| 2 | West End Rovers | 18 | 10 | 4 | 4 | 67 | 34 | 33 | 34 |
| 3 | Athletico Romsey Res. | 18 | 9 | 6 | 3 | 42 | 23 | 19 | 33 |
| 4 | Hythe Aztecs Res. | 18 | 8 | 3 | 7 | 53 | 31 | 22 | 27 |
| 5 | Michelmersh & T Res. | 18 | 7 | 4 | 7 | 52 | 50 | 2 | 25 |
| 6 | Sporting Wessex | 18 | 6 | 2 | 10 | 39 | 60 | -21 | 20 |
| 7 | Braishfield Res. | 18 | 1 | 0 | 17 | 22 | 91 | -69 | 3 |

## SOUTHERN AMATEUR LEAGUE

| | Senior Division One | P | W | D | L | F | A | GD | Pts |
|---|---|---|---|---|---|---|---|---|---|
| 1 | Polytechnic | 20 | 13 | 5 | 2 | 53 | 24 | 29 | 44 |
| 2 | Nottsborough | 20 | 11 | 6 | 3 | 46 | 26 | 20 | 39 |
| 3 | Alleyn Old Boys | 20 | 11 | 5 | 4 | 48 | 20 | 28 | 38 |
| 4 | West Wickham | 20 | 10 | 5 | 5 | 38 | 23 | 15 | 35 |
| 5 | Old Wilsonians | 20 | 9 | 6 | 5 | 38 | 29 | 9 | 33 |
| 6 | NUFC Oilers | 20 | 10 | 2 | 8 | 35 | 32 | 3 | 32 |
| 7 | Old Garchonians (-3) | 20 | 9 | 4 | 7 | 31 | 34 | -3 | 28 |
| 8 | Old Owens | 20 | 7 | 2 | 11 | 25 | 43 | -18 | 23 |
| 9 | Winchmore Hill | 20 | 5 | 2 | 13 | 31 | 40 | -9 | 17 |
| 10 | Civil Service | 20 | 4 | 3 | 13 | 20 | 47 | -27 | 15 |
| 11 | Alexandra Park | 20 | 0 | 2 | 18 | 13 | 60 | -47 | 2 |

| | Senior Division Two | P | W | D | L | F | A | GD | Pts |
|---|---|---|---|---|---|---|---|---|---|
| 1 | Old Parkonians | 22 | 16 | 3 | 3 | 74 | 18 | 56 | 51 |
| 2 | Crouch End Vampires | 22 | 14 | 5 | 3 | 57 | 20 | 37 | 47 |
| 3 | Bank of England | 22 | 14 | 2 | 6 | 47 | 27 | 20 | 44 |
| 4 | Actonians Association | 22 | 12 | 6 | 4 | 53 | 18 | 35 | 42 |
| 5 | East Barnet Old Grammarians | 22 | 11 | 4 | 7 | 53 | 44 | 9 | 37 |
| 6 | Old Finchleians | 22 | 9 | 2 | 11 | 46 | 44 | 2 | 29 |
| 7 | Weirside Rangers | 22 | 8 | 4 | 10 | 37 | 42 | -5 | 28 |
| 8 | Ibis Eagles | 22 | 8 | 3 | 11 | 46 | 49 | -3 | 27 |
| 9 | Lloyds Warren | 22 | 7 | 5 | 10 | 35 | 42 | -7 | 26 |
| 10 | Merton | 22 | 6 | 4 | 12 | 31 | 44 | -13 | 22 |
| 11 | Old Esthameians (-3) | 22 | 4 | 2 | 16 | 35 | 80 | -45 | 11 |
| 12 | Old Salesians | 22 | 2 | 2 | 18 | 19 | 105 | -86 | 8 |

| | Senior Division Three | P | W | D | L | F | A | GD | Pts |
|---|---|---|---|---|---|---|---|---|---|
| 1 | HSBC | 18 | 14 | 2 | 2 | 47 | 18 | 29 | 44 |
| 2 | South Bank Cuaco | 18 | 12 | 2 | 4 | 42 | 26 | 16 | 38 |
| 3 | Norsemen | 18 | 11 | 3 | 4 | 53 | 32 | 21 | 36 |
| 4 | Kew Association | 18 | 9 | 4 | 5 | 46 | 30 | 16 | 31 |
| 5 | Old Lyonians | 18 | 6 | 5 | 7 | 39 | 43 | -4 | 23 |
| 6 | Carshalton (-3) | 18 | 7 | 3 | 8 | 33 | 33 | 0 | 21 |
| 7 | Old Stationers | 18 | 6 | 2 | 10 | 36 | 53 | -17 | 20 |
| 8 | Broomfield | 18 | 6 | 0 | 12 | 29 | 41 | -12 | 18 |
| 9 | Old Blues | 18 | 4 | 5 | 9 | 28 | 46 | -18 | 17 |
| 10 | AFC Oldsmiths | 18 | 1 | 2 | 15 | 20 | 51 | -31 | 5 |

| Intermediate Division One | | P | W | D | L | F | A | GD | Pts |
|---|---|---|---|---|---|---|---|---|---|
| 1 | Nottsborough Res. | 20 | 15 | 3 | 2 | 58 | 17 | 41 | 48 |
| 2 | Old Wilsonians Res. | 20 | 9 | 5 | 6 | 43 | 35 | 8 | 32 |
| 3 | NUFC Oilers Res. | 20 | 8 | 6 | 6 | 52 | 37 | 15 | 30 |
| 4 | Alleyn Old Boys Res. | 20 | 9 | 3 | 8 | 39 | 44 | -5 | 30 |
| 5 | West Wickham Res. | 20 | 9 | 2 | 9 | 32 | 27 | 5 | 29 |
| 6 | Old Parkonians Res. | 20 | 9 | 2 | 9 | 42 | 46 | -4 | 29 |
| 7 | Old Garchonians Res. | 20 | 6 | 7 | 7 | 44 | 48 | -4 | 25 |
| 8 | Old Owens Res. | 20 | 7 | 4 | 9 | 36 | 44 | -8 | 25 |
| 9 | Civil Service Res. | 20 | 7 | 3 | 10 | 39 | 37 | 2 | 24 |
| 10 | Winchmore Hill Res. | 20 | 7 | 3 | 10 | 41 | 55 | -14 | 24 |
| 11 | Norsemen Res. | 20 | 3 | 4 | 13 | 29 | 65 | -36 | 13 |

| Intermediate Division Two | | P | W | D | L | F | A | GD | Pts |
|---|---|---|---|---|---|---|---|---|---|
| 1 | Polytechnic Res. | 20 | 13 | 5 | 2 | 44 | 21 | 23 | 44 |
| 2 | Actonians Association Res. | 20 | 13 | 5 | 2 | 43 | 20 | 23 | 44 |
| 3 | Old Esthameians Res. (-1) | 20 | 12 | 3 | 5 | 58 | 40 | 18 | 38 |
| 4 | Carshalton Res. | 20 | 12 | 2 | 6 | 45 | 33 | 12 | 38 |
| 5 | East Barnet Old Grammarians Res. | 20 | 9 | 6 | 5 | 49 | 36 | 13 | 33 |
| 6 | Bank of England Res. | 20 | 8 | 3 | 9 | 45 | 48 | -3 | 27 |
| 7 | Old Finchleians Res. | 20 | 8 | 2 | 10 | 42 | 49 | -7 | 26 |
| 8 | Alexandra Park Res. | 20 | 5 | 4 | 11 | 41 | 60 | -19 | 19 |
| 9 | Merton Res. | 20 | 3 | 5 | 12 | 26 | 42 | -16 | 14 |
| 10 | Crouch End Vampires Res. (-3) | 20 | 4 | 5 | 11 | 25 | 49 | -24 | 14 |
| 11 | Old Stationers Res. | 20 | 3 | 0 | 17 | 18 | 38 | -20 | 9 |

| Intermediate Division Three | | P | W | D | L | F | A | GD | Pts |
|---|---|---|---|---|---|---|---|---|---|
| 1 | Ibis Eagles Res. | 20 | 15 | 1 | 4 | 64 | 32 | 32 | 46 |
| 2 | Old Lyonians Res. | 20 | 13 | 1 | 6 | 62 | 31 | 31 | 40 |
| 3 | Kew Association Res. (-3) | 20 | 12 | 3 | 5 | 59 | 39 | 20 | 36 |
| 4 | Broomfield Res. | 20 | 11 | 2 | 7 | 58 | 39 | 19 | 35 |
| 5 | Lloyds Warren Res. | 20 | 9 | 5 | 6 | 50 | 33 | 17 | 32 |
| 6 | Weirside Rangers Res. | 20 | 10 | 2 | 8 | 43 | 43 | 0 | 32 |
| 7 | South Bank Cuaco Res. | 20 | 8 | 4 | 8 | 35 | 38 | -3 | 28 |
| 8 | Old Blues Res. | 20 | 8 | 0 | 12 | 45 | 55 | -10 | 24 |
| 9 | AFC Oldsmiths Res. | 20 | 6 | 4 | 10 | 41 | 50 | -9 | 22 |
| 10 | HSBC Res. | 20 | 4 | 3 | 13 | 44 | 59 | -15 | 15 |
| 11 | St. James' Old Boys (-3) | 20 | 0 | 3 | 17 | 25 | 107 | -82 | 0 |

| Junior Division One | | P | W | D | L | F | A | GD | Pts |
|---|---|---|---|---|---|---|---|---|---|
| 1 | Civil Service 3rd | 18 | 12 | 3 | 3 | 31 | 21 | 10 | 39 |
| 2 | Nottsborough 3rd | 18 | 11 | 4 | 3 | 52 | 22 | 30 | 37 |
| 3 | Winchmore Hill 3rd (-3) | 18 | 11 | 3 | 4 | 53 | 25 | 28 | 33 |
| 4 | Polytechnic 3rd | 18 | 8 | 4 | 6 | 37 | 37 | 0 | 28 |
| 5 | West Wickham 3rd | 18 | 8 | 3 | 7 | 39 | 31 | 8 | 27 |
| 6 | Old Parkonians 3rd | 18 | 5 | 4 | 9 | 30 | 40 | -10 | 19 |
| 7 | Actonians Association 3rd | 18 | 4 | 6 | 8 | 36 | 47 | -11 | 18 |
| 8 | East Barnet Old Grammarians 3rd | 18 | 6 | 0 | 12 | 35 | 57 | -22 | 18 |
| 9 | Old Garchonians 3rd | 18 | 5 | 2 | 11 | 27 | 40 | -13 | 17 |
| 10 | Alexandra Park 3rd | 18 | 4 | 3 | 11 | 23 | 43 | -20 | 15 |

| Junior Division Two | | P | W | D | L | F | A | GD | Pts |
|---|---|---|---|---|---|---|---|---|---|
| 1 | Alleyn Old Boys 3rd | 21 | 15 | 4 | 2 | 63 | 29 | 34 | 49 |
| 2 | Civil Service 4th | 21 | 14 | 4 | 3 | 66 | 22 | 44 | 46 |
| 3 | Old Finchleians 3rd | 21 | 8 | 7 | 6 | 45 | 42 | 3 | 31 |
| 4 | Old Owens 3rd | 21 | 8 | 4 | 9 | 47 | 41 | 6 | 28 |
| 5 | Norsemen 3rd (-3) | 21 | 8 | 5 | 8 | 50 | 42 | 8 | 26 |
| 6 | Carshalton 3rd | 21 | 5 | 4 | 12 | 41 | 66 | -25 | 19 |
| 7 | Old Wilsonians 3rd | 21 | 4 | 7 | 10 | 34 | 59 | -25 | 19 |
| 8 | HSBC 3rd | 21 | 3 | 3 | 15 | 38 | 83 | -45 | 12 |

| Junior Division Three | | P | W | D | L | F | A | GD | Pts |
|---|---|---|---|---|---|---|---|---|---|
| 1 | Nottsborough 4th | 18 | 16 | 1 | 1 | 92 | 20 | 72 | 49 |
| 2 | Old Parkonians 4th | 18 | 16 | 1 | 1 | 64 | 20 | 44 | 49 |
| 3 | Merton 3rd | 18 | 9 | 4 | 5 | 49 | 29 | 20 | 31 |
| 4 | Old Finchleians 4th | 18 | 10 | 1 | 7 | 54 | 39 | 15 | 31 |
| 5 | Winchmore Hill 4th | 18 | 6 | 3 | 9 | 38 | 55 | -17 | 21 |
| 6 | East Barnet Old Grammarians 4th | 18 | 5 | 4 | 9 | 44 | 65 | -21 | 19 |
| 7 | Crouch End Vampires 3rd | 18 | 5 | 3 | 10 | 32 | 53 | -21 | 18 |
| 8 | Old Blues 3rd | 18 | 4 | 2 | 12 | 22 | 60 | -38 | 14 |
| 9 | South Bank Cuaco 3rd | 18 | 3 | 4 | 11 | 33 | 42 | -9 | 13 |
| 10 | St. James' Old Boys Res. | 18 | 3 | 3 | 12 | 32 | 77 | -45 | 12 |

| Junior Division Four | | P | W | D | L | F | A | GD | Pts |
|---|---|---|---|---|---|---|---|---|---|
| 1 | Actonians Association 4th | 18 | 12 | 4 | 2 | 52 | 19 | 33 | 40 |
| 2 | Bank of England 3rd | 18 | 12 | 2 | 4 | 65 | 37 | 28 | 38 |
| 3 | Old Garchonians 4th | 18 | 12 | 2 | 4 | 51 | 24 | 27 | 38 |
| 4 | Civil Service 5th | 18 | 11 | 3 | 4 | 52 | 28 | 24 | 36 |
| 5 | Winchmore Hill 5th | 18 | 8 | 3 | 7 | 52 | 34 | 18 | 27 |
| 6 | Ibis Eagles 3rd | 18 | 7 | 4 | 7 | 30 | 38 | -8 | 25 |
| 7 | Polytechnic 4th | 18 | 6 | 6 | 6 | 53 | 40 | 13 | 24 |
| 8 | AFC Oldsmiths 3rd | 18 | 4 | 3 | 11 | 25 | 45 | -20 | 15 |
| 9 | Lloyds Warren 3rd | 18 | 2 | 1 | 15 | 13 | 62 | -49 | 7 |
| 10 | Old Owens 4th | 18 | 1 | 2 | 15 | 24 | 90 | -66 | 5 |

## SOUTHEND BOROUGH & DISTRICT FOOTBALL COMBINATION

| Premier Division | | P | W | D | L | F | A | GD | Pts |
|---|---|---|---|---|---|---|---|---|---|
| 1 | Shoebury Town | 18 | 15 | 2 | 1 | 49 | 19 | 30 | 47 |
| 2 | Corinthians | 18 | 14 | 0 | 4 | 51 | 30 | 21 | 42 |
| 3 | Christchurch | 18 | 11 | 3 | 4 | 53 | 31 | 22 | 36 |
| 4 | Leigh Town | 18 | 11 | 2 | 5 | 55 | 27 | 28 | 35 |
| 5 | Laindon Orient | 18 | 9 | 3 | 6 | 66 | 31 | 35 | 30 |
| 6 | Southend Sports Res. | 18 | 6 | 4 | 8 | 32 | 44 | -12 | 22 |
| 7 | Wakering Wanderers | 18 | 5 | 2 | 11 | 36 | 49 | -13 | 17 |
| 8 | Hadleigh & Thundersley | 18 | 4 | 4 | 10 | 30 | 48 | -18 | 16 |
| 9 | Earls Hall United | 18 | 1 | 4 | 13 | 23 | 61 | -38 | 7 |
| 10 | Ashingdon | 18 | 1 | 2 | 15 | 10 | 65 | -55 | 5 |

11 Railway Academicals withdrew - record expunged.

12 Southend Collegians withdrew - record expunged.

| Division One | P | W | D | L | F | A | GD | Pts |
|---|---|---|---|---|---|---|---|---|
| 1 Brit Academicals | 18 | 16 | 1 | 1 | 50 | 17 | 33 | 49 |
| 2 Bridgemarsh | 18 | 14 | 0 | 4 | 44 | 23 | 21 | 42 |
| 3 Leigh Town Res. | 18 | 10 | 1 | 7 | 57 | 39 | 18 | 31 |
| 4 Elmwood | 18 | 9 | 2 | 7 | 38 | 30 | 8 | 29 |
| 5 Rochford Town Res. | 18 | 9 | 2 | 7 | 40 | 39 | 1 | 29 |
| 6 Ashingdon Res. | 18 | 8 | 2 | 8 | 42 | 40 | 2 | 26 |
| 7 Hadleigh & Thundersley Res. | 18 | 8 | 1 | 9 | 38 | 32 | 6 | 25 |
| 8 White Ensign A | 18 | 4 | 1 | 13 | 36 | 42 | -6 | 13 |
| 9 Shoebury Town Res. | 18 | 4 | 1 | 13 | 30 | 73 | -43 | 13 |
| 10 Old Southendian A | 18 | 2 | 1 | 15 | 31 | 71 | -40 | 7 |

| Division Two | P | W | D | L | F | A | GD | Pts |
|---|---|---|---|---|---|---|---|---|
| 1 Shoebury Town A | 16 | 14 | 0 | 2 | 54 | 13 | 41 | 42 |
| 2 Laindon Orient Res. | 16 | 12 | 1 | 3 | 71 | 16 | 55 | 37 |
| 3 Southend Rangers | 16 | 11 | 0 | 5 | 33 | 22 | 11 | 33 |
| 4 B.K.S. Sports | 16 | 8 | 2 | 6 | 44 | 31 | 13 | 26 |
| 5 Papillon FC | 16 | 8 | 0 | 8 | 27 | 35 | -8 | 24 |
| 6 Corinthians Res. | 16 | 6 | 2 | 8 | 31 | 46 | -15 | 20 |
| 7 Weir Sports | 16 | 6 | 1 | 9 | 38 | 43 | -5 | 19 |
| 8 Ashingdon A | 16 | 3 | 1 | 12 | 39 | 80 | -41 | 10 |
| 9 Southend Collegians Res. | 16 | 0 | 1 | 15 | 10 | 61 | -51 | 1 |

10 Catholic United A withdrew - record expunged.
11 Westcliff United withdrew - record expunged.

| Division Three | P | W | D | L | F | A | GD | Pts |
|---|---|---|---|---|---|---|---|---|
| 1 Parkway Sports | 20 | 17 | 2 | 1 | 68 | 25 | 43 | 53 |
| 2 Pitsea Athletic | 20 | 15 | 2 | 3 | 99 | 32 | 67 | 47 |
| 3 Rochford Town A | 20 | 12 | 2 | 6 | 66 | 42 | 24 | 38 |
| 4 Ekco Whitecaps | 20 | 10 | 3 | 7 | 46 | 41 | 5 | 33 |
| 5 Southend Sports A | 20 | 9 | 1 | 10 | 41 | 53 | -12 | 28 |
| 6 Southend Collegians A | 20 | 9 | 1 | 10 | 55 | 75 | -20 | 28 |
| 7 Benfleet Amateurs | 20 | 8 | 2 | 10 | 59 | 47 | 12 | 26 |
| 8 Leigh Town A | 20 | 7 | 3 | 10 | 48 | 72 | -24 | 24 |
| 9 Earls Hall United Res. | 20 | 4 | 3 | 13 | 29 | 55 | -26 | 15 |
| 10 Rayford Athletic | 20 | 5 | 0 | 15 | 44 | 82 | -38 | 15 |
| 11 Old Southendian B | 20 | 3 | 3 | 14 | 42 | 73 | -31 | 12 |

| Division Four | P | W | D | L | F | A | GD | Pts |
|---|---|---|---|---|---|---|---|---|
| 1 Laindon Orient A | 18 | 16 | 2 | 0 | 77 | 23 | 54 | 50 |
| 2 Railway Academicals Res. | 18 | 13 | 0 | 5 | 62 | 34 | 28 | 39 |
| 3 B.K.S. Sports Res. | 18 | 10 | 3 | 5 | 55 | 32 | 23 | 33 |
| 4 Ashingdon B | 18 | 9 | 4 | 5 | 52 | 42 | 10 | 31 |
| 5 Southend Sports B | 18 | 8 | 2 | 8 | 39 | 42 | -3 | 26 |
| 6 Leigh Town B | 18 | 8 | 1 | 9 | 52 | 39 | 13 | 25 |
| 7 Landwick | 18 | 6 | 2 | 10 | 38 | 45 | -7 | 20 |
| 8 Southend Rangers Res. | 18 | 5 | 3 | 10 | 35 | 59 | -24 | 18 |
| 9 Southend Collegians B | 18 | 3 | 2 | 13 | 30 | 84 | -54 | 11 |
| 10 J.M.C. Athletic | 18 | 2 | 1 | 15 | 28 | 68 | -40 | 7 |

11 Westcliff United Res. withdrew - record expunged.

## ST HELENS AND DISTRICT COMBINATION LEAGUE

| Premier Division | P | W | D | L | F | A | GD | Pts |
|---|---|---|---|---|---|---|---|---|
| 1 New Street Res. FC | 23 | 18 | 1 | 4 | 91 | 39 | 52 | 55 |
| 2 Tanner Athletic FC | 23 | 14 | 6 | 3 | 65 | 40 | 25 | 48 |
| 3 Boilermakers Arms FC | 24 | 10 | 4 | 10 | 67 | 70 | -3 | 34 |
| 4 West Park FC | 24 | 7 | 7 | 10 | 50 | 59 | -9 | 28 |
| 5 Old Mill FC | 24 | 8 | 4 | 12 | 58 | 75 | -17 | 28 |
| 6 Prescot Sun FC | 24 | 8 | 1 | 15 | 70 | 82 | -12 | 25 |
| 7 Clock Face Miners FC | 24 | 5 | 3 | 16 | 57 | 93 | -36 | 18 |

| Division One | P | W | D | L | F | A | GD | Pts |
|---|---|---|---|---|---|---|---|---|
| 1 Cheshire Lines Res. (+3) | 24 | 18 | 2 | 4 | 101 | 38 | 63 | 59 |
| 2 Ecclesfield FC | 24 | 18 | 3 | 3 | 146 | 35 | 111 | 57 |
| 3 West Park Res. FC | 24 | 17 | 1 | 6 | 99 | 46 | 53 | 52 |
| 4 Bold Rangers JFC (-3) | 24 | 12 | 0 | 12 | 72 | 68 | 4 | 33 |
| 5 Rockware FC | 24 | 9 | 1 | 14 | 47 | 72 | -25 | 28 |
| 6 Manor Athletic FC | 24 | 5 | 1 | 18 | 39 | 72 | -33 | 16 |
| 7 Sutton Junction Third | 24 | 1 | 0 | 23 | 24 | 197 | -173 | 3 |

## STROUD & DISTRICT FOOTBALL LEAGUE

| Division One | P | W | D | L | F | A | GD | Pts |
|---|---|---|---|---|---|---|---|---|
| 1 Stroud Harriers | 22 | 17 | 3 | 2 | 78 | 30 | 48 | 54 |
| 2 Kings Stanley Res. | 22 | 12 | 5 | 5 | 48 | 33 | 15 | 41 |
| 3 Barnwood United | 22 | 12 | 5 | 5 | 42 | 28 | 14 | 41 |
| 4 Upton St Leonards | 22 | 12 | 1 | 9 | 51 | 42 | 9 | 37 |
| 5 Whitminster | 22 | 11 | 2 | 9 | 48 | 45 | 3 | 35 |
| 6 Old Richians | 22 | 10 | 5 | 7 | 42 | 41 | 1 | 35 |
| 7 Tetbury Town | 22 | 10 | 3 | 9 | 36 | 39 | -3 | 33 |
| 8 Stonehouse Town Res. | 22 | 8 | 3 | 11 | 35 | 49 | -14 | 27 |
| 9 Frampton United Res. (-3) | 22 | 9 | 1 | 12 | 43 | 47 | -4 | 25 |
| 10 Randwick | 22 | 7 | 3 | 12 | 36 | 44 | -8 | 24 |
| 11 Charfield | 22 | 5 | 1 | 16 | 41 | 57 | -16 | 16 |
| 12 Didmarton | 22 | 1 | 4 | 17 | 28 | 73 | -45 | 7 |

| Division Two | P | W | D | L | F | A | GD | Pts |
|---|---|---|---|---|---|---|---|---|
| 1 Stroud United | 24 | 19 | 2 | 3 | 89 | 30 | 59 | 59 |
| 2 Tredworth Tigers | 24 | 18 | 3 | 3 | 88 | 36 | 52 | 57 |
| 3 St Nicholas Old Boys | 24 | 16 | 1 | 7 | 79 | 45 | 34 | 49 |
| 4 Horsley United | 24 | 15 | 0 | 9 | 68 | 35 | 33 | 45 |
| 5 Quedgeley Wanderers Res. | 24 | 14 | 1 | 9 | 54 | 48 | 6 | 43 |
| 6 Hardwicke Res. (-3) | 24 | 13 | 5 | 6 | 73 | 35 | 38 | 41 |
| 7 Sharpness Res. | 24 | 9 | 6 | 9 | 53 | 52 | 1 | 33 |
| 8 AFC Phoenix | 24 | 9 | 0 | 15 | 48 | 65 | -17 | 27 |
| 9 Tibberton United | 24 | 6 | 2 | 16 | 43 | 64 | -21 | 20 |
| 10 AC Royals (-3) | 24 | 6 | 5 | 13 | 33 | 74 | -41 | 20 |
| 11 Kingswood Res. (-12) | 24 | 9 | 2 | 13 | 44 | 57 | -13 | 17 |
| 12 Dursley Town Res. | 24 | 5 | 2 | 17 | 37 | 82 | -45 | 17 |
| 13 Slimbridge Res. | 24 | 2 | 1 | 21 | 27 | 113 | -86 | 7 |

| Division Three | P | W | D | L | F | A | GD | Pts |
|---|---|---|---|---|---|---|---|---|
| 1 Cam Bulldogs Res. | 24 | 18 | 4 | 2 | 63 | 16 | 47 | 58 |
| 2 Bush FC | 24 | 18 | 0 | 6 | 69 | 33 | 36 | 54 |
| 3 Tuffley Rovers 3rds | 24 | 16 | 5 | 3 | 78 | 34 | 44 | 53 |
| 4 Longlevens 3rds | 24 | 14 | 5 | 5 | 66 | 37 | 29 | 47 |
| 5 Eastcombe | 24 | 15 | 0 | 9 | 62 | 50 | 12 | 45 |
| 6 Tetbury Town Res. | 24 | 10 | 5 | 9 | 48 | 47 | 1 | 35 |
| 7 Arlingham | 24 | 8 | 8 | 8 | 60 | 55 | 5 | 32 |
| 8 Thornbury Town Res. | 24 | 7 | 5 | 12 | 52 | 58 | -6 | 26 |
| 9 Uley | 24 | 6 | 6 | 12 | 26 | 41 | -15 | 24 |
| 10 McCadam (-3) | 24 | 7 | 3 | 14 | 37 | 51 | -14 | 21 |
| 11 Coaley Rovers | 24 | 6 | 3 | 15 | 39 | 79 | -40 | 21 |
| 12 Abbeymead Rovers Res. | 24 | 4 | 4 | 16 | 46 | 82 | -36 | 16 |
| 13 Nympsfield (-3) | 24 | 2 | 2 | 20 | 34 | 97 | -63 | 5 |

| Division Four | P | W | D | L | F | A | GD | Pts |
|---|---|---|---|---|---|---|---|---|
| 1 Rodborough Old Boys | 22 | 18 | 2 | 2 | 131 | 32 | 99 | 56 |
| 2 Minchinhampton | 22 | 18 | 2 | 2 | 70 | 18 | 52 | 56 |
| 3 Trident | 22 | 16 | 4 | 2 | 96 | 31 | 65 | 52 |
| 4 Chalford Res. | 22 | 15 | 2 | 5 | 72 | 28 | 44 | 47 |
| 5 Cotswold Rangers | 22 | 13 | 1 | 8 | 58 | 30 | 28 | 40 |
| 6 Whitminster Res. | 22 | 9 | 5 | 8 | 64 | 48 | 16 | 32 |
| 7 Old Richians Res. | 22 | 6 | 7 | 9 | 39 | 47 | -8 | 25 |
| 8 Alkerton Rangers | 22 | 5 | 3 | 14 | 38 | 61 | -23 | 18 |
| 9 Upton St Leonards Res. (-3) | 22 | 5 | 3 | 14 | 35 | 66 | -31 | 15 |
| 10 Longford Res. (-12) | 22 | 7 | 2 | 13 | 34 | 121 | -87 | 11 |
| 11 Avonvale United Res. (-3) | 22 | 2 | 2 | 18 | 36 | 84 | -48 | 5 |
| 12 Wotton Rovers Res. (-6) | 22 | 1 | 1 | 20 | 14 | 121 | -107 | -2 |

| Division Five | P | W | D | L | F | A | GD | Pts |
|---|---|---|---|---|---|---|---|---|
| 1 Wickwar Wanderers | 24 | 16 | 5 | 3 | 98 | 46 | 52 | 53 |
| 2 Quedgeley Wanderers 3rds | 24 | 16 | 4 | 4 | 75 | 34 | 41 | 52 |
| 3 Hardwicke 3rds | 24 | 16 | 3 | 5 | 97 | 47 | 50 | 51 |
| 4 Ramblers Res. | 24 | 16 | 0 | 8 | 74 | 42 | 32 | 48 |
| 5 Frampton United 3rds | 24 | 15 | 1 | 8 | 52 | 35 | 17 | 46 |
| 6 Taverners Res. | 24 | 11 | 5 | 8 | 77 | 70 | 7 | 38 |
| 7 Stonehouse Town 3rds (-3) | 24 | 9 | 4 | 11 | 49 | 65 | -16 | 28 |
| 8 Randwick Res. | 24 | 7 | 7 | 10 | 43 | 61 | -18 | 28 |
| 9 Barnwood United Res. | 24 | 8 | 3 | 13 | 47 | 55 | -8 | 27 |
| 10 Leonard Stanley Res. (-3) | 24 | 6 | 4 | 14 | 46 | 76 | -30 | 19 |
| 11 Berkeley Town Res. | 24 | 4 | 3 | 17 | 47 | 96 | -49 | 15 |
| 12 Brockworth Albion 3rds (-3) | 24 | 4 | 2 | 18 | 39 | 78 | -39 | 11 |
| 13 Dursley Town 3rds (-12) | 24 | 7 | 1 | 16 | 49 | 88 | -39 | 10 |

| Division Six | P | W | D | L | F | A | GD | Pts |
|---|---|---|---|---|---|---|---|---|
| 1 Longlevens 4ths | 22 | 17 | 3 | 2 | 85 | 33 | 52 | 54 |
| 2 Chalford 3rds | 22 | 16 | 1 | 5 | 96 | 34 | 62 | 49 |
| 3 Tredworth Tigers Res. | 22 | 16 | 1 | 5 | 88 | 40 | 48 | 49 |
| 4 Charfield Res. | 22 | 13 | 3 | 6 | 83 | 37 | 46 | 42 |
| 5 Tuffley Rovers 4ths | 22 | 13 | 2 | 7 | 84 | 38 | 46 | 41 |
| 6 Saintbridge | 22 | 10 | 4 | 8 | 61 | 46 | 15 | 34 |
| 7 Horsley United Res. | 22 | 7 | 6 | 9 | 56 | 71 | -15 | 27 |
| 8 Stroud United Res. (-6) | 22 | 7 | 5 | 10 | 55 | 67 | -12 | 20 |
| 9 Cam Bulldogs 3rds (-3) | 22 | 6 | 4 | 12 | 53 | 52 | 1 | 19 |
| 10 Sharpness 3rds (-9) | 22 | 6 | 4 | 12 | 48 | 75 | -27 | 13 |
| 11 Uley Res. | 22 | 4 | 1 | 17 | 30 | 89 | -59 | 13 |
| 12 Coaley Rovers Res. (-9) | 22 | 0 | 0 | 22 | 6 | 163 | -157 | -9 |

| Division Seven | P | W | D | L | F | A | GD | Pts |
|---|---|---|---|---|---|---|---|---|
| 1 Kingsway Rovers | 26 | 24 | 2 | 0 | 146 | 18 | 128 | 74 |
| 2 Painswick | 26 | 18 | 5 | 3 | 120 | 29 | 91 | 59 |
| 3 Minchinhampton Res. | 26 | 17 | 3 | 6 | 104 | 57 | 47 | 54 |
| 4 Eastcombe Res. | 26 | 17 | 0 | 9 | 100 | 56 | 44 | 51 |
| 5 North Nibley | 26 | 15 | 5 | 6 | 74 | 36 | 38 | 50 |
| 6 Longlevens 5ths | 26 | 15 | 3 | 8 | 81 | 43 | 38 | 48 |
| 7 Rodborough Old Boys Res. | 26 | 13 | 4 | 9 | 71 | 55 | 16 | 43 |
| 8 Stonehouse Town 4ths (-3) | 26 | 11 | 3 | 12 | 79 | 69 | 10 | 33 |
| 9 Cotswold Rangers Res. (-3) | 26 | 10 | 3 | 13 | 66 | 75 | -9 | 30 |
| 10 Abbeymead Rovers 3rds | 26 | 6 | 5 | 15 | 49 | 70 | -21 | 23 |
| 11 Randwick 3rds | 26 | 6 | 4 | 16 | 43 | 97 | -54 | 22 |
| 12 Woodchester | 26 | 5 | 2 | 19 | 28 | 118 | -90 | 17 |
| 13 Kingsway Wanderers (-6) | 26 | 2 | 6 | 18 | 29 | 143 | -114 | 6 |
| 14 Uley 3rds (-3) | 26 | 0 | 1 | 25 | 15 | 139 | -124 | -2 |

## STRATFORD UPON AVON FOOTBALL ALLIANCE

| Division One | P | W | D | L | F | A | GD | Pts |
|---|---|---|---|---|---|---|---|---|
| 1 Badsey United | 18 | 15 | 3 | 0 | 69 | 21 | 48 | 48 |
| 2 Henley Forest | 18 | 13 | 1 | 4 | 62 | 25 | 37 | 40 |
| 3 Studley United | 18 | 11 | 0 | 7 | 46 | 38 | 8 | 33 |
| 4 FISSC | 18 | 6 | 6 | 6 | 34 | 37 | -3 | 24 |
| 5 Badsey Rangers | 18 | 5 | 5 | 8 | 37 | 47 | -10 | 20 |
| 6 Alveston | 18 | 6 | 2 | 10 | 36 | 49 | -13 | 20 |
| 7 Inkberrow Res. | 18 | 6 | 2 | 10 | 32 | 47 | -15 | 20 |
| 8 South Redditch Athletic | 18 | 6 | 2 | 10 | 31 | 54 | -23 | 20 |
| 9 Northfield Athletic | 18 | 5 | 3 | 10 | 43 | 41 | 2 | 18 |
| 10 Welford | 18 | 4 | 2 | 12 | 25 | 56 | -31 | 14 |

| Division Two | P | W | D | L | F | A | GD | Pts |
|---|---|---|---|---|---|---|---|---|
| 1 Alcester Town Res. | 16 | 13 | 2 | 1 | 68 | 16 | 52 | 41 |
| 2 Quinton | 16 | 12 | 2 | 2 | 51 | 24 | 27 | 38 |
| 3 Shipston Res. | 16 | 9 | 3 | 4 | 46 | 18 | 28 | 30 |
| 4 Studley Rangers | 16 | 8 | 1 | 7 | 51 | 44 | 7 | 25 |
| 5 AFC Solihull Hayes Res. | 16 | 7 | 0 | 9 | 42 | 37 | 5 | 21 |
| 6 Blockley Sports | 16 | 4 | 3 | 9 | 35 | 50 | -15 | 15 |
| 7 Henley Forest Res. (-3) | 16 | 5 | 1 | 10 | 40 | 61 | -21 | 13 |
| 8 Tysoe United | 16 | 4 | 1 | 11 | 36 | 66 | -30 | 13 |
| 9 Inkberrow Res. | 16 | 3 | 1 | 12 | 20 | 73 | -53 | 10 |

| Division Three | P | W | D | L | F | A | GD | Pts |
|---|---|---|---|---|---|---|---|---|
| 1 Claverdon AFC | 18 | 14 | 3 | 1 | 95 | 32 | 63 | 45 |
| 2 Ilmington United | 18 | 15 | 0 | 3 | 66 | 29 | 37 | 45 |
| 3 Astwood Bank | 18 | 10 | 4 | 4 | 79 | 43 | 36 | 34 |
| 4 AFC Solihull A | 18 | 8 | 1 | 9 | 54 | 59 | -5 | 25 |
| 5 White Eagles | 18 | 8 | 1 | 9 | 44 | 68 | -24 | 25 |
| 6 Redditch Athletic | 18 | 7 | 1 | 10 | 67 | 63 | 4 | 22 |
| 7 Bretforton Old Boys | 18 | 6 | 3 | 9 | 42 | 51 | -9 | 21 |
| 8 FISSC Res. | 18 | 6 | 2 | 10 | 44 | 61 | -17 | 20 |
| 9 Shipston Excelsior Colts | 18 | 3 | 5 | 10 | 41 | 81 | -40 | 14 |
| 10 Central Ajax | 18 | 2 | 2 | 14 | 33 | 78 | -45 | 8 |

## SURREY COUNTY INTERMEDIATE LEAGUE (WESTERN)

| Premier Division | P | W | D | L | F | A | GD | Pts |
|---|---|---|---|---|---|---|---|---|
| 1 Laleham | 22 | 21 | 0 | 1 | 90 | 12 | 78 | 63 |
| 2 Farnborough North End | 22 | 15 | 2 | 5 | 69 | 33 | 36 | 47 |
| 3 Shottermill & Haslemere | 22 | 14 | 3 | 5 | 62 | 35 | 27 | 45 |
| 4 University of Surrey | 22 | 13 | 3 | 6 | 67 | 21 | 46 | 42 |
| 5 Woking & Horsell (-1) | 22 | 10 | 7 | 5 | 45 | 28 | 17 | 36 |
| 6 Milford & Witley | 22 | 9 | 3 | 10 | 39 | 49 | -10 | 30 |
| 7 Royal Holloway Old Boys | 22 | 6 | 5 | 11 | 42 | 63 | -21 | 23 |
| 8 Chiddingfold | 22 | 6 | 5 | 11 | 36 | 64 | -28 | 23 |
| 9 Lightwater United | 22 | 5 | 7 | 10 | 37 | 58 | -21 | 22 |
| 10 Cranleigh | 22 | 5 | 3 | 14 | 22 | 56 | -34 | 18 |
| 11 Tongham | 22 | 3 | 6 | 13 | 28 | 65 | -37 | 15 |
| 12 Millmead | 22 | 1 | 4 | 17 | 19 | 72 | -53 | 7 |

| Division One | P | W | D | L | F | A | GD | Pts |
|---|---|---|---|---|---|---|---|---|
| 1 Chertsey Curfews | 22 | 20 | 0 | 2 | 80 | 31 | 49 | 60 |
| 2 West End Village | 22 | 13 | 5 | 4 | 64 | 33 | 31 | 44 |
| 3 Knaphill Athletic | 22 | 13 | 4 | 5 | 56 | 33 | 23 | 43 |
| 4 Guildford Park | 22 | 11 | 1 | 10 | 53 | 51 | 2 | 34 |
| 5 Hambledon | 22 | 10 | 2 | 10 | 49 | 54 | -5 | 32 |
| 6 Egham Athletic | 22 | 8 | 7 | 7 | 54 | 49 | 5 | 31 |
| 7 Windlesham United | 22 | 9 | 3 | 10 | 34 | 56 | -22 | 30 |
| 8 Keens Park Rangers (-3) | 22 | 10 | 2 | 10 | 58 | 49 | 9 | 29 |
| 9 Old Salesians | 22 | 7 | 3 | 12 | 37 | 49 | -12 | 24 |
| 10 Guildford United | 22 | 5 | 7 | 10 | 52 | 57 | -5 | 22 |
| 11 Worplesdon Phoenix | 22 | 5 | 0 | 17 | 36 | 75 | -39 | 15 |
| 12 Woking Cougars | 22 | 3 | 2 | 17 | 27 | 63 | -36 | 11 |

## SWINDON & DISTRICT FOOTBALL LEAGUE

| Premier Division | P | W | D | L | F | A | GD | Pts |
|---|---|---|---|---|---|---|---|---|
| 1 Tawny Owl | 16 | 16 | 0 | 0 | 99 | 24 | 75 | 48 |
| 2 Avtar Construction | 16 | 11 | 1 | 4 | 55 | 20 | 35 | 34 |
| 3 Sheild & Dagger | 16 | 10 | 2 | 4 | 44 | 29 | 15 | 32 |
| 4 Village Inn | 15 | 8 | 1 | 6 | 34 | 39 | -5 | 25 |
| 5 KS Miltax | 16 | 6 | 1 | 9 | 41 | 58 | -17 | 19 |
| 6 Spectrum | 16 | 5 | 1 | 10 | 31 | 54 | -23 | 16 |
| 7 Old Town United | 16 | 5 | 0 | 11 | 25 | 47 | -22 | 15 |
| 8 DJC Marlborough | 16 | 5 | 0 | 11 | 23 | 54 | -31 | 15 |
| 9 Lower Stratton | 15 | 2 | 0 | 13 | 17 | 44 | -27 | 6 |

| Division One | P | W | D | L | F | A | GD | Pts |
|---|---|---|---|---|---|---|---|---|
| 1 Swindon Spitfires | 20 | 16 | 1 | 3 | 96 | 25 | 71 | 49 |
| 2 Swindon Centurians | 20 | 14 | 6 | 0 | 85 | 27 | 58 | 48 |
| 3 Bassett Bulldogs | 20 | 12 | 2 | 6 | 57 | 35 | 22 | 38 |
| 4 Ramsbury | 20 | 10 | 1 | 9 | 42 | 51 | -9 | 31 |
| 5 North Swindon WMC | 20 | 10 | 1 | 9 | 46 | 71 | -25 | 31 |
| 6 Moredon | 20 | 9 | 3 | 8 | 43 | 41 | 2 | 30 |
| 7 Chiseldon | 20 | 8 | 1 | 11 | 43 | 47 | -4 | 25 |
| 8 Sport 4 Pinehurst | 20 | 6 | 5 | 9 | 60 | 61 | -1 | 23 |
| 9 Core Construction | 20 | 7 | 2 | 11 | 41 | 57 | -16 | 23 |
| 10 Morris Street | 20 | 6 | 2 | 12 | 45 | 35 | 10 | 20 |
| 11 R & D United | 20 | 0 | 0 | 20 | 19 | 127 | -108 | 0 |

Wheatie Wanderers withdrew - record expunged.

## TAUNTON & DISTRICT SATURDAY FOOTBALL LEAGUE

| Division One | P | W | D | L | F | A | GD | Pts |
|---|---|---|---|---|---|---|---|---|
| 1 Bridgwater Sports | 12 | 9 | 2 | 1 | 38 | 10 | 28 | 29 |
| 2 The Gallery | 12 | 8 | 2 | 2 | 36 | 18 | 18 | 26 |
| 3 Alcombe Rovers | 12 | 5 | 2 | 5 | 24 | 20 | 4 | 17 |
| 4 Middlezoy Rovers Res. | 12 | 4 | 4 | 4 | 20 | 24 | -4 | 16 |
| 5 Porlock | 12 | 3 | 4 | 5 | 19 | 26 | -7 | 13 |
| 6 Bishops Lydeard Res. | 12 | 2 | 4 | 6 | 21 | 30 | -9 | 10 |
| 7 Staplegrove Res. (-6) | 12 | 0 | 4 | 8 | 11 | 41 | -30 | -2 |

| Division Two | P | W | D | L | F | A | GD | Pts |
|---|---|---|---|---|---|---|---|---|
| 1 Sydenham Rangers | 16 | 15 | 1 | 0 | 66 | 17 | 49 | 46 |
| 2 Morganians | 16 | 11 | 1 | 4 | 40 | 18 | 22 | 34 |
| 3 Westonzoyland | 16 | 10 | 2 | 4 | 53 | 18 | 35 | 32 |
| 4 Bridgwater Sports Res. | 16 | 5 | 3 | 8 | 32 | 43 | -11 | 18 |
| 5 Wembdon | 16 | 5 | 3 | 8 | 23 | 34 | -11 | 18 |
| 6 Watchet Town Res. | 16 | 4 | 4 | 8 | 23 | 43 | -20 | 16 |
| 7 Milverton Rangers | 16 | 3 | 5 | 8 | 28 | 43 | -15 | 14 |
| 8 Dulverton Town | 16 | 3 | 4 | 9 | 22 | 34 | -12 | 13 |
| 9 Stogursey (-3) | 16 | 3 | 3 | 10 | 17 | 54 | -37 | 9 |

10 Tone Youth Res. withdrew - record expunged.

| Division Three | P | W | D | L | F | A | GD | Pts |
|---|---|---|---|---|---|---|---|---|
| 1 Ash Rangers | 16 | 13 | 1 | 2 | 77 | 23 | 54 | 40 |
| 2 Woolavington | 16 | 12 | 3 | 1 | 72 | 28 | 44 | 39 |
| 3 Creech FC | 16 | 9 | 3 | 4 | 45 | 30 | 15 | 30 |
| 4 North Petherton Res. | 16 | 7 | 5 | 4 | 37 | 25 | 12 | 26 |
| 5 Norton Fitzwarren | 16 | 6 | 3 | 7 | 33 | 36 | -3 | 21 |
| 6 Redgate | 16 | 6 | 1 | 9 | 25 | 42 | -17 | 19 |
| 7 Exmoor Rangers | 16 | 3 | 1 | 12 | 20 | 71 | -51 | 10 |
| 8 Galmington Dragons | 16 | 2 | 3 | 11 | 30 | 62 | -32 | 9 |
| 9 Minehead Res. (-3) | 16 | 3 | 2 | 11 | 27 | 49 | -22 | 8 |

| Division Four | P | W | D | L | F | A | GD | Pts |
|---|---|---|---|---|---|---|---|---|
| 1 Bishops Lydeard Colts | 16 | 12 | 2 | 2 | 71 | 30 | 41 | 38 |
| 2 Bridgwater Grasshoppers | 16 | 10 | 2 | 4 | 66 | 30 | 36 | 32 |
| 3 Bridgwater Wolves | 16 | 10 | 1 | 5 | 48 | 43 | 5 | 31 |
| 4 Williton | 16 | 7 | 2 | 7 | 40 | 49 | -9 | 23 |
| 5 Middlezoy Athletic | 16 | 7 | 1 | 8 | 45 | 36 | 9 | 22 |
| 6 The Gallery Res. | 16 | 6 | 2 | 8 | 44 | 48 | -4 | 20 |
| 7 Porlock Res. | 16 | 6 | 0 | 10 | 31 | 48 | -17 | 18 |
| 8 East Bower | 16 | 5 | 1 | 10 | 32 | 54 | -22 | 16 |
| 9 Highbridge Town Res. | 16 | 2 | 3 | 11 | 31 | 70 | -39 | 9 |

| Division Five | P | W | D | L | F | A | GD | Pts |
|---|---|---|---|---|---|---|---|---|
| 1 FC Boca Seniors | 18 | 16 | 1 | 1 | 88 | 17 | 71 | 49 |
| 2 Butlins FC | 18 | 13 | 2 | 3 | 66 | 22 | 44 | 41 |
| 3 Bridgwater Sports Colts | 18 | 10 | 5 | 3 | 53 | 18 | 35 | 35 |
| 4 North Curry | 18 | 11 | 2 | 5 | 54 | 38 | 16 | 35 |
| 5 White Eagles FC | 18 | 9 | 3 | 6 | 56 | 37 | 19 | 30 |
| 6 Galmington Dragons Res. | 18 | 7 | 2 | 9 | 52 | 42 | 10 | 23 |
| 7 Nether Stowey | 18 | 4 | 4 | 10 | 25 | 66 | -41 | 16 |
| 8 Hamilton Athletic Foxes | 18 | 4 | 0 | 14 | 42 | 84 | -42 | 12 |
| 9 Morganians Res. | 18 | 3 | 1 | 14 | 27 | 61 | -34 | 10 |
| 10 Norton Fitzwarren Res. | 18 | 2 | 2 | 14 | 25 | 103 | -78 | 8 |

## WAKEFIELD & DISTRICT FA LEAGUE

| Premier Division | P | W | D | L | F | A | GD | Pts |
|---|---|---|---|---|---|---|---|---|
| 1 Beechwood Gate (Sat) FC | 20 | 19 | 0 | 1 | 105 | 24 | 81 | 57 |
| 2 FC Gawthorpe | 20 | 13 | 4 | 3 | 74 | 39 | 35 | 43 |
| 3 Crofton Sports FC | 20 | 14 | 1 | 5 | 64 | 35 | 29 | 43 |
| 4 Prince of Wales FC (OCR) | 19 | 9 | 2 | 8 | 56 | 43 | 13 | 29 |
| 5 Walton FC (-6) | 20 | 11 | 0 | 9 | 78 | 52 | 26 | 27 |
| 6 Crackenedge FC | 20 | 7 | 3 | 10 | 59 | 59 | 0 | 24 |
| 7 Halton Moor FC (-3) | 19 | 8 | 1 | 10 | 54 | 54 | 0 | 22 |
| 8 AFC Kettlethorpe | 20 | 6 | 3 | 11 | 50 | 75 | -25 | 21 |
| 9 AFC Ossett | 20 | 7 | 0 | 13 | 45 | 78 | -33 | 21 |
| 10 Fieldhead Hospital | 20 | 5 | 0 | 15 | 34 | 99 | -65 | 15 |
| 11 Snydale Athletic | 20 | 3 | 0 | 17 | 45 | 106 | -61 | 9 |

| Division One | P | W | D | L | F | A | GD | Pts |
|---|---|---|---|---|---|---|---|---|
| 1 Eastmoor FC | 18 | 15 | 2 | 1 | 61 | 23 | 38 | 47 |
| 2 Healdfield FC | 18 | 11 | 1 | 6 | 76 | 42 | 34 | 34 |
| 3 Nostell Miners Welfare | 18 | 11 | 1 | 6 | 49 | 34 | 15 | 34 |
| 4 Featherstone Colliery FC (-3) | 18 | 10 | 1 | 7 | 70 | 56 | 14 | 28 |
| 5 Royston Cross FC | 18 | 9 | 1 | 8 | 62 | 53 | 9 | 28 |
| 6 Marsh FC (-3) | 18 | 8 | 1 | 9 | 49 | 55 | -6 | 22 |
| 7 Ossett Dynamos | 18 | 7 | 0 | 11 | 36 | 57 | -21 | 21 |
| 8 Pontefract Sports & Social | 18 | 5 | 3 | 10 | 38 | 65 | -27 | 18 |
| 9 Old Bank WMC | 18 | 4 | 2 | 12 | 47 | 65 | -18 | 14 |
| 10 New Pot Oil | 18 | 2 | 4 | 12 | 41 | 79 | -38 | 10 |

| Division Two | P | W | D | L | F | A | GD | Pts |
|---|---|---|---|---|---|---|---|---|
| 1 Red Lion Alverthorpe FC | 16 | 12 | 2 | 2 | 70 | 29 | 41 | 38 |
| 2 FC Prince | 16 | 11 | 1 | 4 | 103 | 31 | 72 | 34 |
| 3 Ryhill FC | 16 | 8 | 4 | 4 | 54 | 31 | 23 | 28 |
| 4 Durkar FC | 16 | 8 | 3 | 5 | 76 | 48 | 28 | 27 |
| 5 Stanley United (-3) | 16 | 8 | 3 | 5 | 58 | 31 | 27 | 24 |
| 6 Horbury Athletic | 16 | 7 | 3 | 6 | 68 | 42 | 26 | 24 |
| 7 Fox & Hounds (Batley) FC (-1) | 16 | 7 | 2 | 7 | 111 | 55 | 56 | 22 |
| 8 Wakefield City | 16 | 2 | 0 | 14 | 41 | 132 | -91 | 6 |
| 9 Queen (Wakefield) FC | 16 | 0 | 0 | 16 | 18 | 200 | -182 | 0 |

| Division THree | P | W | D | L | F | A | GD | Pts |
|---|---|---|---|---|---|---|---|---|
| 1 AFC Junction (Normanton) | 20 | 18 | 1 | 1 | 105 | 27 | 78 | 55 |
| 2 Henry Boons FC | 20 | 13 | 3 | 4 | 77 | 42 | 35 | 42 |
| 3 Waterloo FC (-3) | 20 | 12 | 4 | 4 | 74 | 42 | 32 | 37 |
| 4 Overthorpe SC (Wfd) (-3) | 20 | 12 | 1 | 7 | 53 | 47 | 6 | 34 |
| 5 Snydale Athletic Res | 20 | 11 | 0 | 9 | 57 | 37 | 20 | 33 |
| 6 Crofton Sports FC Res | 20 | 10 | 1 | 9 | 42 | 48 | -6 | 31 |
| 7 Eastmoor FC Res | 20 | 7 | 3 | 10 | 39 | 52 | -13 | 24 |
| 8 Fleece FC (-6) | 20 | 7 | 2 | 11 | 44 | 57 | -13 | 17 |
| 9 New Carlton FC (-3) | 20 | 4 | 3 | 13 | 33 | 58 | -25 | 12 |
| 10 Middleton Old Boys (-3) | 20 | 2 | 4 | 14 | 35 | 76 | -41 | 7 |
| 11 Wheatsheaf FC (-6) | 20 | 2 | 2 | 16 | 22 | 95 | -73 | 2 |

## WEST RIDING COUNTY AMATEUR FOOTBALL LEAGUE

| Premier Division | P | W | D | L | F | A | GD | Pts |
|---|---|---|---|---|---|---|---|---|
| 1 Huddersfield YMCA | 24 | 20 | 2 | 2 | 91 | 22 | 69 | 62 |
| 2 Lepton Highlanders | 24 | 18 | 2 | 4 | 98 | 37 | 61 | 56 |
| 3 Campion | 24 | 14 | 4 | 6 | 85 | 38 | 47 | 46 |
| 4 Halifax Irish | 24 | 14 | 4 | 6 | 105 | 61 | 44 | 46 |
| 5 Salts | 24 | 13 | 2 | 9 | 70 | 48 | 22 | 41 |
| 6 Ovenden West Riding | 24 | 12 | 4 | 8 | 86 | 38 | 48 | 40 |
| 7 Golcar United | 24 | 12 | 2 | 10 | 68 | 56 | 12 | 38 |
| 8 Littletown | 24 | 9 | 4 | 11 | 70 | 74 | -4 | 31 |
| 9 Lower Hopton | 24 | 8 | 6 | 10 | 66 | 58 | 8 | 30 |
| 10 Steeton | 24 | 8 | 6 | 10 | 48 | 56 | -8 | 30 |
| 11 Kirkburton | 24 | 5 | 3 | 16 | 44 | 73 | -29 | 18 |
| 12 Tyersal | 24 | 3 | 0 | 21 | 31 | 159 | -128 | 9 |
| 13 Hunsworth | 24 | 0 | 1 | 23 | 21 | 163 | -142 | 1 |

| Division One | P | W | D | L | F | A | GD | Pts |
|---|---|---|---|---|---|---|---|---|
| 1 Newsome FC | 20 | 15 | 3 | 2 | 85 | 25 | 60 | 48 |
| 2 Overthorpe Sports Club | 20 | 14 | 2 | 4 | 57 | 32 | 25 | 44 |
| 3 D.R.A.M. Community FC | 20 | 14 | 1 | 5 | 64 | 45 | 19 | 43 |
| 4 Honley FC | 20 | 12 | 2 | 6 | 49 | 32 | 17 | 38 |
| 5 Campion Res. | 20 | 10 | 4 | 6 | 48 | 38 | 10 | 34 |
| 6 Holmfirth Town FC | 19 | 7 | 6 | 6 | 40 | 39 | 1 | 27 |
| 7 Ventus/Yeadon Celtic | 20 | 5 | 5 | 10 | 40 | 55 | -15 | 20 |
| 8 West Horton | 20 | 5 | 4 | 11 | 41 | 52 | -11 | 19 |
| 9 Wibsey | 19 | 3 | 5 | 11 | 37 | 62 | -25 | 14 |
| 10 Steeton Res. | 20 | 4 | 1 | 15 | 37 | 72 | -35 | 13 |
| 11 Westbrook YMCA | 20 | 2 | 3 | 15 | 21 | 67 | -46 | 9 |

| Division Two | P | W | D | L | F | A | GD | Pts |
|---|---|---|---|---|---|---|---|---|
| 1 Thornton United | 21 | 18 | 0 | 3 | 105 | 35 | 70 | 54 |
| 2 Golcar United Res. | 21 | 15 | 2 | 4 | 85 | 35 | 50 | 47 |
| 3 Route One Rovers | 21 | 13 | 2 | 6 | 63 | 47 | 16 | 41 |
| 4 Salts Res. | 21 | 9 | 1 | 11 | 46 | 41 | 5 | 28 |
| 5 T V R United | 21 | 8 | 3 | 10 | 60 | 75 | -15 | 27 |
| 6 Littletown Res. | 21 | 8 | 1 | 12 | 48 | 70 | -22 | 25 |
| 7 Bradford FC | 21 | 7 | 2 | 12 | 34 | 66 | -32 | 23 |
| 8 Lower Hopton Res. | 21 | 0 | 1 | 20 | 32 | 104 | -72 | 1 |

## WEST SUSSEX FOOTBALL LEAGUE

| **Premier Division** | P | W | D | L | F | A | GD | Pts |
|---|---|---|---|---|---|---|---|---|
| 1 Lancing United | 18 | 12 | 5 | 1 | 48 | 27 | 21 | 41 |
| 2 Lavant | 18 | 10 | 4 | 4 | 50 | 30 | 20 | 34 |
| 3 West Chiltington | 18 | 10 | 2 | 6 | 40 | 31 | 9 | 32 |
| 4 Nyetimber Pirates | 18 | 9 | 1 | 8 | 36 | 32 | 4 | 28 |
| 5 Newtown Villa | 18 | 7 | 4 | 7 | 33 | 32 | 1 | 25 |
| 6 Predators (-1) | 18 | 5 | 6 | 7 | 47 | 35 | 12 | 20 |
| 7 Holbrook | 18 | 6 | 2 | 10 | 33 | 45 | -12 | 20 |
| 8 Petworth | 18 | 5 | 4 | 9 | 31 | 45 | -14 | 19 |
| 9 Henfield | 18 | 4 | 6 | 8 | 25 | 41 | -16 | 18 |
| 10 Southwater | 18 | 4 | 2 | 12 | 24 | 49 | -25 | 14 |

# NATIONAL STRIKE FORCE - TOP 106!

ends on this page and was started on page 652

| | | | | | | | | | | |
|---|---|---|---|---|---|---|---|---|---|---|
| Ashley Carew | Dulwich Hamlet | Isthmian Prem | 14 | 2 | 1 | 7 | | 2 | 15 | 17 |
| MIchael Cheek | Braintree Town | National Prem | 15 | 2 | | | | 2 | 12 | 17 |
| James Constable | Eastleigh | National Prem | 15 | 1 | 1 | | | 4 | 14 | 17 |
| Bobby Devyne | Enfield Town | Isthmian Prem | 15 | 1 | 1 | | | 3 | 15 | 17 |
| Brady Hickey | Barwell | N.P.L. | 13 | 4 | | | 1 | | 11 | 17 |
| Nicke Kabamba | Hampton & Richmond | Isthmian Prem | 17 | | | 1 | | 2 | 13 | 17 |
| Liam King | North Ferriby Utd | National North | 16 | 1 | | 2 | | 4 | 13 | 17 |
| Jonny McNamara | Hitchin Town | Southern Prem | 16 | 1 | | | | 2 | 15 | 17 |
| Dave Pearce | Chesham United | Southern Prem | 14 | 2 | 1 | 6 | | 2 | 13 | 17 |
| Charlie Penny | Merstham | Isthmian Prem | 17 | | | 3 | 2 | 3 | 10 | 17 |
| Louie Theophanous | St Albans City | National South | 15 | 2 | | | | 1 | 9 | 17 |
| Ryan Blake | Chesham United | Southern Prem | 10 | 4 | 2 | | | 2 | 12 | 16 |
| Anthony Carney | Barwell | N.P.L. | 12 | 3 | 1 | 1 | 1 | 3 | 11 | 16 |
| Anthony Carew | Dulwich Hamlet | Isthmian Prem | 13 | 2 | 1 | 10 | | 2 | 15 | 16 |
| Dion Charles | AFC Fylde | National North | 14 | 2 | | | | 2 | 14 | 16 |
| Bradley Hudson-Odei | Wealdstone | National South | 11 | 2 | 3 | | | 2 | 12 | 16 |
| Jordan Hulme | Salford City | N.P.L. | 15 | 1 | | | | 2 | 13 | 16 |
| Chris Lait | Stourbridge | N.P.L. | 11 | 3 | 2 | | | 3 | 15 | 16 |
| Joel Purkiss | Matlock Town | N.P.L. | 14 | 1 | 1 | | | 2 | 13 | 16 |
| Jake Reed | Lowestoft Town | National North | 15 | | 1 | 1 | | 2 | 14 | 16 |
| Alfie Rutherford | Bognor Regis Town | Isthmian Prem | 13 | | 1 | | 1 | 2 | 11 | 16 |
| Ben Wright | Maidenhead United | National South | 14 | 1 | 1 | 3 | | 2 | 13 | 16 |
| Billy Bricknell | Chelmsford City | National South | 14 | | 1 | | | 3 | 9 | 15 |
| Chib Chilaka | Bradford PA | National North | 14 | 1 | | | 1 | 2 | 12 | 15 |
| Nick Deverdics | Dover Athletic | National Prem | 14 | | 1 | 2 | | 2 | 14 | 15 |
| Elliott Durrell | Tamworth | National North | 14 | 1 | 1 | 3 | | 3 | 14 | 15 |
| Inih Effiong | Biggleswade Town | Southern Prem | 15 | | | | 1 | 3 | 10 | 15 |
| Gareth Finch | Leiston | Isthmian Prem | 15 | | | 2 | | 2 | 11 | 15 |
| Nathan Jarman | Gainsborough Trinity | National North | 11 | 4 | | | | 2 | 12 | 15 |
| Danny Kedwell | Ebbsfleet United | National South | 12+2PO | | 1 | 2 | | 2 | 8 | 15 |
| Sam Merson | Biggleswade Town | Southern Prem | 14 | 1 | | | | 3 | 13 | 15 |
| Sean Reid | Blyth Spartans | N.P.L. | 15 | | | | | 3 | 12 | 15 |
| Justin Richards | Stourbridge | N.P.L. | 12 | 2 | 1 | | | 3 | 14 | 15 |
| Charlie Walker | Aldershot Town | National Prem | 15 | | | | | 2 | 13 | 15 |

| Championship | | P | W | D | L | F | A | GD | Pts |
|---|---|---|---|---|---|---|---|---|---|
| 1 | Hunston Community Club | 20 | 15 | 3 | 2 | 67 | 26 | 41 | 48 |
| 2 | T D Shipley | 20 | 12 | 5 | 3 | 61 | 33 | 28 | 41 |
| 3 | Wisborough Green | 20 | 9 | 5 | 6 | 38 | 29 | 9 | 32 |
| 4 | Rogate 08 FC | 20 | 8 | 6 | 6 | 49 | 31 | 18 | 30 |
| 5 | Wittering United | 20 | 7 | 7 | 6 | 33 | 39 | -6 | 28 |
| 6 | Fernhurst Sports | 20 | 8 | 3 | 9 | 46 | 44 | 2 | 27 |
| 7 | Newtown Villa Res. | 20 | 5 | 7 | 8 | 34 | 44 | -10 | 22 |
| 8 | Partridge Green | 20 | 5 | 6 | 9 | 32 | 51 | -19 | 21 |
| 9 | Cowfold Res. | 20 | 6 | 3 | 11 | 28 | 48 | -20 | 21 |
| 10 | Stedham United | 20 | 5 | 5 | 10 | 43 | 59 | -16 | 20 |
| 11 | Rudgwick | 20 | 3 | 4 | 13 | 32 | 59 | -27 | 13 |

| Division Two North | | P | W | D | L | F | A | GD | Pts |
|---|---|---|---|---|---|---|---|---|---|
| 1 | Ashington Rovers | 20 | 16 | 1 | 3 | 70 | 16 | 54 | 49 |
| 2 | Pulborough | 20 | 14 | 1 | 5 | 68 | 34 | 34 | 43 |
| 3 | Horsham Trinity | 20 | 12 | 3 | 5 | 56 | 46 | 10 | 39 |
| 4 | Upper Beeding Res. | 20 | 11 | 3 | 6 | 56 | 36 | 20 | 36 |
| 5 | Border Wanderers | 20 | 9 | 2 | 9 | 38 | 39 | -1 | 29 |
| 6 | Billinghurst Thirds | 20 | 9 | 2 | 9 | 38 | 46 | -8 | 29 |
| 7 | Faygate United | 20 | 8 | 3 | 9 | 41 | 46 | -5 | 27 |
| 8 | Holbrook Res. | 20 | 7 | 2 | 11 | 38 | 51 | -13 | 23 |
| 9 | Barns Green | 20 | 6 | 2 | 12 | 28 | 42 | -14 | 20 |
| 10 | Ewhurst | 20 | 6 | 1 | 13 | 26 | 38 | -12 | 19 |
| 11 | Slinfold | 20 | 2 | 0 | 18 | 30 | 95 | -65 | 6 |

| Division Two South | | P | W | D | L | F | A | GD | Pts |
|---|---|---|---|---|---|---|---|---|---|
| | Angmering Seniors | 18 | 16 | 0 | 2 | 91 | 22 | 69 | 48 |
| | East Dean | 18 | 13 | 3 | 2 | 56 | 31 | 25 | 42 |
| | Harting | 18 | 10 | 3 | 5 | 62 | 38 | 24 | 33 |
| | Coal Exchange | 18 | 9 | 1 | 8 | 54 | 49 | 5 | 28 |
| | Yapton | 18 | 9 | 1 | 8 | 58 | 58 | 0 | 28 |
| | The Crown FC | 18 | 7 | 3 | 8 | 44 | 51 | -7 | 24 |
| | Lodsworth | 18 | 7 | 2 | 9 | 48 | 48 | 0 | 23 |
| | Hammer United | 18 | 6 | 1 | 11 | 37 | 51 | -14 | 19 |
| | Beaumont Park | 18 | 4 | 0 | 14 | 30 | 68 | -38 | 12 |
| 10 | Felpham Colts | 18 | 2 | 0 | 16 | 23 | 87 | -64 | 6 |

| Division Three North | | P | W | D | L | F | A | GD | Pts |
|---|---|---|---|---|---|---|---|---|---|
| | Horsham Crusaders | 18 | 13 | 4 | 1 | 38 | 22 | 16 | 43 |
| | Alfold Res. | 18 | 12 | 4 | 2 | 48 | 22 | 26 | 40 |
| | Capel | 18 | 12 | 2 | 4 | 53 | 30 | 23 | 38 |
| | Horsham Olympic | 18 | 10 | 6 | 2 | 42 | 24 | 18 | 36 |
| | Newdigate | 18 | 7 | 2 | 9 | 30 | 36 | -6 | 23 |
| | Horsham Bap & Am | 18 | 5 | 4 | 9 | 36 | 42 | -6 | 19 |
| | Cowfold Thirds | 18 | 6 | 1 | 11 | 25 | 32 | -7 | 19 |
| | Pulborough Res. | 18 | 5 | 2 | 11 | 25 | 36 | -11 | 17 |
| | Henfield Res. | 18 | 4 | 1 | 13 | 28 | 42 | -14 | 13 |
| 10 | Rowfant Village | 18 | 3 | 0 | 15 | 28 | 67 | -39 | 9 |

| Division Three South | | P | W | D | L | F | A | GD | Pts |
|---|---|---|---|---|---|---|---|---|---|
| 1 | Worthing Borough | 18 | 12 | 4 | 2 | 75 | 30 | 45 | 40 |
| 2 | Lavant Res. | 18 | 10 | 3 | 5 | 41 | 26 | 15 | 33 |
| 3 | The Unicorn | 18 | 10 | 2 | 6 | 56 | 32 | 24 | 32 |
| 4 | Whyke United | 18 | 10 | 2 | 6 | 48 | 32 | 16 | 32 |
| 5 | Hunston Community Club Res. | 18 | 9 | 2 | 7 | 42 | 39 | 3 | 29 |
| 6 | Nyetimber Pirates Res. | 18 | 8 | 4 | 6 | 53 | 44 | 9 | 28 |
| 7 | Predators Res. | 18 | 7 | 3 | 8 | 36 | 36 | 0 | 24 |
| 8 | West Chiltington Res. | 18 | 6 | 4 | 8 | 34 | 48 | -14 | 22 |
| 9 | Ambassadors | 18 | 3 | 1 | 14 | 27 | 78 | -51 | 10 |
| 10 | Fittleworth | 18 | 2 | 1 | 15 | 16 | 63 | -47 | 7 |

| Division Four North | | P | W | D | L | F | A | GD | Pts |
|---|---|---|---|---|---|---|---|---|---|
| 1 | Thakeham Village | 20 | 15 | 2 | 3 | 67 | 31 | 36 | 47 |
| 2 | Southwater Res. | 20 | 13 | 4 | 3 | 86 | 42 | 44 | 43 |
| 3 | Holbrook Thirds | 20 | 13 | 1 | 6 | 56 | 32 | 24 | 40 |
| 4 | Partridge Green Res. | 20 | 11 | 3 | 6 | 68 | 39 | 29 | 36 |
| 5 | Plaistow | 20 | 10 | 6 | 4 | 60 | 32 | 28 | 36 |
| 6 | Rudgwick Res. | 20 | 8 | 2 | 10 | 45 | 64 | -19 | 26 |
| 7 | Wisborough Green Res. | 20 | 7 | 4 | 9 | 48 | 64 | -16 | 25 |
| 8 | Newdigate Res. | 20 | 5 | 8 | 7 | 40 | 47 | -7 | 23 |
| 9 | Border Wanderers Res. | 20 | 7 | 2 | 11 | 53 | 63 | -10 | 23 |
| 10 | Horsham Bap & Am Res. | 20 | 3 | 1 | 16 | 25 | 68 | -43 | 10 |
| 11 | Barns Green Res. | 20 | 1 | 1 | 18 | 18 | 84 | -66 | 4 |

| Division Four South | | P | W | D | L | F | A | GD | Pts |
|---|---|---|---|---|---|---|---|---|---|
| 1 | Elmer FC | 18 | 14 | 1 | 3 | 59 | 18 | 41 | 43 |
| 2 | Yapton Res. | 18 | 14 | 0 | 4 | 60 | 37 | 23 | 42 |
| 3 | Real Milland | 18 | 11 | 2 | 5 | 63 | 38 | 25 | 35 |
| 4 | Watersfield | 18 | 9 | 2 | 7 | 58 | 34 | 24 | 29 |
| 5 | Fernhurst Sports Res. | 18 | 9 | 1 | 8 | 66 | 50 | 16 | 28 |
| 6 | Chapel | 18 | 7 | 4 | 7 | 48 | 47 | 1 | 25 |
| 7 | Petworth Res. | 18 | 6 | 4 | 8 | 44 | 48 | -4 | 22 |
| 8 | Stedham United Res. (-3) | 18 | 6 | 3 | 9 | 27 | 50 | -23 | 18 |
| 9 | Whyke United Res. | 18 | 4 | 0 | 14 | 41 | 69 | -28 | 12 |
| 10 | Fittleworth Res. | 18 | 1 | 1 | 16 | 14 | 89 | -75 | 4 |

| Division Five North | | P | W | D | L | F | A | GD | Pts |
|---|---|---|---|---|---|---|---|---|---|
| 1 | Ewhurst Res. | 18 | 14 | 2 | 2 | 43 | 14 | 29 | 44 |
| 2 | T D Shipley Res. | 18 | 14 | 0 | 4 | 51 | 23 | 28 | 42 |
| 3 | Royal United | 18 | 10 | 5 | 3 | 32 | 20 | 12 | 35 |
| 4 | Southwater Thirds | 18 | 8 | 3 | 7 | 46 | 32 | 14 | 27 |
| 5 | Capel Res. | 18 | 8 | 3 | 7 | 45 | 36 | 9 | 27 |
| 6 | Henfield Thirds | 18 | 6 | 5 | 7 | 32 | 39 | -7 | 23 |
| 7 | Horsham Crusaders Res. | 18 | 5 | 4 | 9 | 40 | 47 | -7 | 19 |
| 8 | Horsham Olympic Res. | 18 | 5 | 4 | 9 | 36 | 47 | -11 | 19 |
| 9 | Holbrook Fourths | 18 | 3 | 3 | 12 | 18 | 51 | -33 | 12 |
| 10 | Slinfold Res. | 18 | 2 | 1 | 15 | 18 | 52 | -34 | 7 |

**Division Five South**

| | Division Five South | P | W | D | L | F | A | GD | Pts |
|---|---|---|---|---|---|---|---|---|---|
| 1 | Tangmere | 18 | 18 | 0 | 0 | 92 | 23 | 69 | 54 |
| 2 | Lancing United Res. | 18 | 16 | 0 | 2 | 72 | 18 | 54 | 48 |
| 3 | Felpham Colts Res. | 18 | 10 | 1 | 7 | 40 | 49 | -9 | 31 |
| 4 | Trojans FC | 18 | 9 | 1 | 8 | 45 | 31 | 14 | 28 |
| 5 | Harting Res. | 18 | 7 | 2 | 9 | 35 | 52 | -17 | 23 |
| 6 | Littlehampton Town Athletic | 18 | 6 | 2 | 10 | 43 | 50 | -7 | 20 |
| 7 | Rogate 08 FC Res. | 18 | 6 | 1 | 11 | 38 | 51 | -13 | 19 |
| 8 | Pulborough Patriots | 18 | 6 | 1 | 11 | 38 | 60 | -22 | 19 |
| 9 | Lodsworth Res. | 18 | 4 | 1 | 13 | 18 | 47 | -29 | 13 |
| 10 | Watersfield Res. | 18 | 3 | 1 | 14 | 24 | 64 | -40 | 10 |

## WESTMORLAND ASSOCIATION FOOTBALL LEAGUE

| | Division One | P | W | D | L | F | A | GD | Pts |
|---|---|---|---|---|---|---|---|---|---|
| 1 | Keswick | 24 | 22 | 2 | 0 | 107 | 20 | 87 | 68 |
| 2 | Kendal Utd | 24 | 16 | 4 | 4 | 60 | 28 | 32 | 52 |
| 3 | Appleby | 24 | 13 | 7 | 4 | 67 | 40 | 27 | 46 |
| 4 | Windermere SC | 24 | 12 | 4 | 8 | 61 | 47 | 14 | 40 |
| 5 | Sedbergh Wanderers | 24 | 11 | 6 | 7 | 66 | 50 | 16 | 39 |
| 6 | Kirkoswald | 24 | 11 | 4 | 9 | 69 | 53 | 16 | 37 |
| 7 | Ibis | 24 | 8 | 8 | 8 | 37 | 49 | -12 | 32 |
| 8 | Ambleside Utd | 24 | 9 | 5 | 10 | 46 | 60 | -14 | 32 |
| 9 | Wetheriggs Utd | 24 | 9 | 2 | 13 | 46 | 53 | -7 | 29 |
| 10 | Lunesdale Utd | 24 | 9 | 1 | 14 | 52 | 80 | -28 | 28 |
| 11 | Penrith Res. | 24 | 5 | 1 | 18 | 49 | 94 | -45 | 16 |
| 12 | Kendal County Res. | 24 | 3 | 5 | 16 | 29 | 73 | -44 | 14 |
| 13 | Unisun Athletic | 24 | 2 | 3 | 19 | 28 | 70 | -42 | 9 |

| | Division Two | P | W | D | L | F | A | GD | Pts |
|---|---|---|---|---|---|---|---|---|---|
| 1 | Wetheriggs Utd Res. (+2) | 28 | 17 | 5 | 6 | 78 | 55 | 23 | 58 |
| 2 | Pirelli (-4) | 28 | 18 | 5 | 5 | 103 | 47 | 56 | 55 |
| 3 | Kendal Utd Res. (+3) | 28 | 15 | 5 | 8 | 66 | 56 | 10 | 53 |
| 4 | Burneside | 28 | 16 | 3 | 9 | 74 | 42 | 32 | 51 |
| 5 | Coniston | 28 | 16 | 0 | 12 | 93 | 76 | 17 | 48 |
| 6 | Langwathby Utd | 28 | 13 | 4 | 11 | 64 | 66 | -2 | 43 |
| 7 | Dent | 28 | 12 | 4 | 12 | 63 | 57 | 6 | 40 |
| 8 | Endmoor KGR | 28 | 11 | 6 | 11 | 58 | 52 | 6 | 39 |
| 9 | Carleton Banks | 28 | 11 | 5 | 12 | 53 | 54 | -1 | 38 |
| 10 | Braithwaite | 28 | 11 | 4 | 13 | 54 | 66 | -12 | 37 |
| 11 | Shap | 28 | 10 | 4 | 14 | 68 | 85 | -17 | 34 |
| 12 | Keswick Res. (-6) | 28 | 11 | 4 | 13 | 57 | 61 | -4 | 31 |
| 13 | Staveley Utd | 28 | 8 | 6 | 14 | 49 | 71 | -22 | 30 |
| 14 | Greystoke | 28 | 5 | 5 | 18 | 49 | 79 | -30 | 20 |
| 15 | Ambleside Utd Res. (-12) | 28 | 4 | 4 | 20 | 49 | 111 | -62 | 4 |

| | Division Three | P | W | D | L | F | A | GD | Pts |
|---|---|---|---|---|---|---|---|---|---|
| 1 | Eden Thistle | 28 | 23 | 1 | 4 | 104 | 30 | 74 | 70 |
| 2 | Kirkoswald Res. | 28 | 22 | 2 | 4 | 118 | 49 | 69 | 68 |
| 3 | Windermere SC Res. | 28 | 20 | 2 | 6 | 88 | 43 | 45 | 62 |
| 4 | Ullswater Utd | 28 | 16 | 4 | 8 | 91 | 67 | 24 | 52 |
| 5 | AFC Carlisle | 28 | 16 | 3 | 9 | 116 | 50 | 66 | 51 |
| 6 | Ibis Res. | 28 | 15 | 5 | 8 | 80 | 66 | 14 | 50 |
| 7 | Appleby Res. | 28 | 13 | 7 | 8 | 77 | 39 | 38 | 46 |
| 8 | Burneside Res. (-9) | 28 | 14 | 3 | 11 | 82 | 78 | 4 | 36 |
| 9 | Lunesdale Utd Res. | 28 | 11 | 3 | 14 | 70 | 70 | 0 | 36 |
| 10 | Penrith Royal | 28 | 9 | 4 | 15 | 73 | 70 | 3 | 31 |
| 11 | Endmoor KGR Res. (-3) | 28 | 10 | 2 | 16 | 63 | 99 | -36 | 29 |
| 12 | Penrith Academy | 28 | 8 | 1 | 19 | 48 | 104 | -56 | 25 |
| 13 | Dent Res. | 28 | 7 | 2 | 19 | 37 | 71 | -34 | 23 |
| 14 | Greystoke Res. | 28 | 3 | 3 | 22 | 43 | 116 | -73 | 12 |
| 15 | Penrith Saints | 28 | 2 | 0 | 26 | 40 | 178 | -138 | 6 |

## WESTON SUPER MARE AND DISTRICT FOOTBALL LEAGUE

| | Division One | P | W | D | L | F | A | GD | Pts |
|---|---|---|---|---|---|---|---|---|---|
| 1 | Portishead Town A | 20 | 15 | 2 | 3 | 71 | 24 | 47 | 47 |
| 2 | Winscombe Res. | 20 | 15 | 1 | 4 | 66 | 29 | 37 | 46 |
| 3 | Draycott (-3) | 20 | 14 | 1 | 5 | 64 | 44 | 20 | 40 |
| 4 | Cleeve West Town Res. | 20 | 9 | 5 | 6 | 43 | 38 | 5 | 32 |
| 5 | Weston Super Seagulls (-3) | 20 | 9 | 3 | 8 | 43 | 36 | 7 | 27 |
| 6 | Hutton | 20 | 8 | 2 | 10 | 45 | 47 | -2 | 26 |
| 7 | Locking Park | 20 | 7 | 4 | 9 | 42 | 50 | -8 | 25 |
| 8 | Nailsea Utd A | 20 | 7 | 3 | 10 | 56 | 56 | 0 | 24 |
| 9 | St George (EIG) Res. (-1) | 20 | 6 | 1 | 13 | 33 | 52 | -19 | 18 |
| 10 | Worle Rangers | 20 | 5 | 3 | 12 | 35 | 65 | -30 | 18 |
| 11 | Clevedon Utd A | 20 | 2 | 1 | 17 | 28 | 85 | -57 | 7 |

| | Division Two | P | W | D | L | F | A | GD | Pts |
|---|---|---|---|---|---|---|---|---|---|
| 1 | K V F C | 20 | 16 | 2 | 2 | 58 | 20 | 38 | 50 |
| 2 | Wrington Red Hill Res. | 20 | 13 | 1 | 6 | 54 | 35 | 19 | 40 |
| 3 | Sporting Weston (-1) | 20 | 12 | 3 | 5 | 55 | 31 | 24 | 38 |
| 4 | Uphill Castle Res. | 20 | 11 | 2 | 7 | 57 | 37 | 20 | 35 |
| 5 | Westend | 20 | 11 | 1 | 8 | 60 | 48 | 12 | 34 |
| 6 | Yatton Ath Res. (-6) | 20 | 13 | 1 | 6 | 60 | 50 | 10 | 34 |
| 7 | Berrow Res. (-1) | 20 | 10 | 2 | 8 | 46 | 49 | -3 | 31 |
| 8 | Wedmore | 20 | 6 | 1 | 13 | 39 | 68 | -29 | 19 |
| 9 | Congresbury Res. | 20 | 5 | 2 | 13 | 33 | 55 | -22 | 17 |
| 10 | Axbridge Town | 20 | 3 | 1 | 16 | 28 | 54 | -26 | 10 |
| 11 | AFC Nailsea | 20 | 2 | 0 | 18 | 26 | 69 | -43 | 6 |

| | Division Three | P | W | D | L | F | A | GD | Pts |
|---|---|---|---|---|---|---|---|---|---|
| 1 | Portishead Caledonian Thistle | 22 | 21 | 0 | 1 | 133 | 21 | 112 | 63 |
| 2 | Winscombe A | 22 | 18 | 2 | 2 | 68 | 23 | 45 | 56 |
| 3 | Clapton in Gordano | 22 | 13 | 2 | 7 | 84 | 35 | 49 | 41 |
| 4 | South Park Rangers | 22 | 12 | 1 | 9 | 60 | 55 | 5 | 37 |
| 5 | Banwell Res | 22 | 9 | 3 | 10 | 61 | 64 | -3 | 30 |
| 6 | Churchill Club 70 Res. | 22 | 8 | 3 | 11 | 52 | 62 | -10 | 27 |
| 7 | Kewstoke Lions Res. | 22 | 8 | 3 | 11 | 47 | 74 | -27 | 27 |
| 8 | Worle Res. | 22 | 8 | 2 | 12 | 49 | 47 | 2 | 26 |
| 9 | Cleeve West Town A | 22 | 7 | 1 | 14 | 36 | 80 | -44 | 22 |
| 10 | Nailsea Utd B | 22 | 6 | 2 | 14 | 35 | 80 | -45 | 20 |
| 11 | Cheddar A | 22 | 6 | 1 | 15 | 39 | 80 | -41 | 19 |
| 12 | Burnham Utd A (-1) | 22 | 5 | 2 | 15 | 44 | 87 | -43 | 1[illegible] |

| | Division Four | P | W | D | L | F | A | GD | Pts |
|---|---|---|---|---|---|---|---|---|---|
| 1 | Worle Rangers Res. | 18 | 12 | 3 | 3 | 65 | 56 | 9 | 39 |
| 2 | Dynamo Locking | 18 | 11 | 4 | 3 | 53 | 32 | 21 | 3[illegible] |
| 3 | Westend Res. (-4) | 18 | 12 | 4 | 2 | 72 | 26 | 46 | 3[illegible] |
| 4 | Portishead Town B (-3) | 18 | 7 | 6 | 5 | 58 | 41 | 17 | 2[illegible] |
| 5 | AFC Nailsea Res. | 18 | 6 | 2 | 10 | 28 | 54 | -26 | 2[illegible] |
| 6 | St George (EIG) A (-3) | 18 | 6 | 4 | 8 | 32 | 51 | -19 | 1[illegible] |
| 7 | Shipham | 18 | 5 | 3 | 10 | 37 | 55 | -18 | 1[illegible] |
| 8 | Clapton in Gordano Res. (-5) | 18 | 6 | 4 | 8 | 61 | 47 | 14 | [illegible] |
| 9 | Uphill Castle A (-1) | 18 | 4 | 3 | 11 | 32 | 56 | -24 | [illegible] |
| 10 | Hutton Res. | 18 | 3 | 3 | 12 | 33 | 53 | -20 | [illegible] |
| 11 | Clevedon United B withdrew - record expunged. | | | | | | | | |

| | Division Five | P | W | D | L | F | A | GD | Pts |
|---|---|---|---|---|---|---|---|---|---|
| 1 | Selkirk Utd (-1) | 18 | 15 | 2 | 1 | 73 | 16 | 57 | 46 |
| 2 | Portishead Town Colts | 18 | 11 | 3 | 4 | 67 | 36 | 31 | 36 |
| 3 | Wrington Redhill A (-1) | 18 | 9 | 3 | 6 | 54 | 36 | 18 | 29 |
| 4 | South Park Rangers Res. (-3) | 18 | 9 | 3 | 6 | 59 | 51 | 8 | 27 |
| 5 | Axbridge Town Res. | 18 | 6 | 3 | 9 | 53 | 63 | -10 | 21 |
| 6 | Clapton in Gordano A (-1) | 18 | 6 | 3 | 9 | 41 | 57 | -16 | 20 |
| 7 | Congresbury A (-1) | 18 | 6 | 2 | 10 | 39 | 56 | -17 | 19 |
| 8 | St Pauls Church FC | 18 | 6 | 1 | 11 | 53 | 71 | -18 | 19 |
| 9 | Banwell A (-1) | 18 | 6 | 1 | 11 | 42 | 56 | -14 | 18 |
| 10 | Wedmore Res. | 18 | 4 | 3 | 11 | 32 | 71 | -39 | 15 |

## WIGAN & DISTRICT AMATEUR LEAGUE

| | Premier Division | P | W | D | L | F | A | GD | Pts |
|---|---|---|---|---|---|---|---|---|---|
| 1 | Winstanley St.Aidans | 22 | 21 | 0 | 1 | 77 | 19 | 58 | 63 |
| 2 | Ormskirk Town | 22 | 17 | 1 | 4 | 66 | 27 | 39 | 52 |
| 3 | Newburgh Harrock United | 22 | 13 | 2 | 7 | 43 | 30 | 13 | 41 |
| 4 | Shevington | 22 | 12 | 1 | 9 | 48 | 46 | 2 | 37 |
| 5 | Bickerstaffe | 22 | 9 | 3 | 10 | 34 | 54 | -20 | 30 |
| 6 | Wigan Rovers | 22 | 8 | 3 | 11 | 40 | 49 | -9 | 27 |
| 7 | Hindley Town | 22 | 8 | 2 | 12 | 44 | 60 | -16 | 26 |
| 8 | Pemberton | 22 | 8 | 0 | 14 | 44 | 49 | -5 | 24 |
| 9 | Ince Central | 22 | 8 | 0 | 14 | 32 | 47 | -15 | 24 |
| 10 | Standish St.Wilfrid's | 22 | 7 | 2 | 13 | 43 | 48 | -5 | 23 |
| 11 | St.Judes | 22 | 6 | 2 | 14 | 39 | 57 | -18 | 20 |
| 12 | Gidlow Athletic | 22 | 4 | 6 | 12 | 33 | 57 | -24 | 18 |

| | Division One | P | W | D | L | F | A | GD | Pts |
|---|---|---|---|---|---|---|---|---|---|
| 1 | Digmoor | 24 | 22 | 1 | 1 | 95 | 28 | 67 | 67 |
| 2 | Hurlston Hall | 24 | 18 | 2 | 4 | 71 | 28 | 43 | 56 |
| 3 | Higher Ince | 24 | 15 | 5 | 4 | 58 | 31 | 27 | 50 |
| 4 | AFC Scholes | 24 | 10 | 4 | 10 | 67 | 56 | 11 | 34 |
| 5 | Astley and Tyldesey | 24 | 9 | 7 | 8 | 49 | 49 | 0 | 34 |
| 6 | Bickerstaffe Res. | 24 | 9 | 5 | 10 | 44 | 46 | -2 | 32 |
| 7 | AFC Tyldesley | 24 | 8 | 7 | 9 | 64 | 52 | 12 | 31 |
| 8 | Winstanley Warriors | 24 | 9 | 4 | 11 | 51 | 69 | -18 | 31 |
| 9 | Leigh Foundry | 24 | 8 | 5 | 11 | 56 | 58 | -2 | 29 |
| 10 | Goose Green United | 24 | 8 | 5 | 11 | 39 | 52 | -13 | 29 |
| 11 | Standish St.Wilfrid's Res. | 24 | 6 | 2 | 16 | 35 | 81 | -46 | 20 |
| 12 | Mitch FC | 24 | 5 | 3 | 16 | 45 | 72 | -27 | 18 |
| 13 | Rope FC | 24 | 3 | 2 | 19 | 34 | 86 | -52 | 11 |

| | Division Two | P | W | D | L | F | A | GD | Pts |
|---|---|---|---|---|---|---|---|---|---|
| 1 | Leigh Rangers | 22 | 17 | 1 | 4 | 54 | 35 | 19 | 52 |
| 2 | Sutton Junction | 22 | 16 | 3 | 3 | 62 | 27 | 35 | 51 |
| 3 | Punchbowl | 22 | 12 | 2 | 8 | 67 | 40 | 27 | 38 |
| 4 | Black Bull | 22 | 12 | 1 | 9 | 75 | 53 | 22 | 37 |
| 5 | Hag Fold | 22 | 12 | 1 | 9 | 47 | 33 | 14 | 37 |
| 6 | Winstanley Warriors Res. | 22 | 9 | 5 | 8 | 61 | 47 | 14 | 32 |
| 7 | Atherleigh United | 22 | 9 | 4 | 9 | 53 | 57 | -4 | 31 |
| 8 | Daten 3rd | 22 | 9 | 3 | 10 | 56 | 57 | -1 | 30 |
| 9 | The Village Inn | 22 | 7 | 4 | 11 | 33 | 35 | -2 | 25 |
| 10 | Whelley | 22 | 7 | 4 | 11 | 54 | 69 | -15 | 25 |
| 11 | Hindley Town Res. | 22 | 4 | 3 | 15 | 33 | 76 | -43 | 15 |
| 12 | Ashton Villa | 22 | 2 | 1 | 19 | 21 | 87 | -66 | 7 |

| | Divisiion Three | P | W | D | L | F | A | GD | Pts |
|---|---|---|---|---|---|---|---|---|---|
| 1 | HMP Hindley | 20 | 16 | 1 | 3 | 71 | 26 | 45 | 49 |
| 2 | Golborne Parkside | 20 | 11 | 4 | 5 | 44 | 35 | 9 | 37 |
| 3 | Ormskirk | 20 | 11 | 3 | 6 | 54 | 36 | 18 | 36 |
| 4 | Sutton Junction Res. | 20 | 10 | 4 | 6 | 74 | 55 | 19 | 34 |
| 5 | Mitch FC Res. | 20 | 10 | 4 | 6 | 49 | 44 | 5 | 34 |
| 6 | Abram | 20 | 7 | 6 | 7 | 68 | 57 | 11 | 27 |
| 7 | Daten 4th | 20 | 7 | 5 | 8 | 55 | 51 | 4 | 26 |
| 8 | Astley and Tyldesley Res. | 20 | 7 | 1 | 12 | 35 | 57 | -22 | 22 |
| 9 | Wigan Rovers Res. | 20 | 6 | 3 | 11 | 46 | 74 | -28 | 21 |
| 10 | Gidlow Athletic Res. | 20 | 3 | 4 | 13 | 39 | 59 | -20 | 13 |
| 11 | Billinge Community | 20 | 3 | 3 | 14 | 36 | 77 | -41 | 12 |

## WOLVERHAMPTON FOOTBALL COMBINATION

| | | P | W | D | L | F | A | GD | Pts |
|---|---|---|---|---|---|---|---|---|---|
| 1 | Tipton Town Res. | 15 | 11 | 2 | 2 | 40 | 10 | 30 | 35 |
| 2 | Azaad Sports | 15 | 9 | 2 | 4 | 44 | 38 | 6 | 29 |
| 3 | Emerald Athletic | 15 | 9 | 1 | 5 | 38 | 28 | 10 | 28 |
| 4 | Shere Punjab | 15 | 5 | 4 | 6 | 38 | 32 | 6 | 19 |
| 5 | West Park Rangers | 15 | 4 | 1 | 10 | 23 | 46 | -23 | 13 |
| 6 | Whitmore Reans | 15 | 1 | 2 | 12 | 23 | 52 | -29 | 5 |

## YEOVIL AND DISTRICT LEAGUE

| | Premier Division | P | W | D | L | F | A | GD | Pts |
|---|---|---|---|---|---|---|---|---|---|
| 1 | Normalair | 16 | 11 | 4 | 1 | 45 | 21 | 24 | 37 |
| 2 | Montacute | 16 | 11 | 1 | 4 | 42 | 22 | 20 | 34 |
| 3 | East Coker | 16 | 10 | 4 | 2 | 33 | 23 | 10 | 34 |
| 4 | Templecombe Rovers | 16 | 9 | 2 | 5 | 42 | 25 | 17 | 29 |
| 5 | Martock United | 16 | 4 | 3 | 9 | 33 | 49 | -16 | 15 |
| 6 | Stoke | 16 | 4 | 2 | 10 | 29 | 45 | -16 | 14 |
| 7 | Castle Cary Res. (-1) | 16 | 4 | 3 | 9 | 22 | 42 | -20 | 14 |
| 8 | Huish AFC | 16 | 3 | 4 | 9 | 29 | 36 | -7 | 13 |
| 9 | Ashcott | 16 | 3 | 3 | 10 | 31 | 43 | -12 | 12 |

| | Division One | P | W | D | L | F | A | GD | Pts |
|---|---|---|---|---|---|---|---|---|---|
| 1 | Wagtail Athletic | 20 | 16 | 2 | 2 | 75 | 30 | 45 | 50 |
| 2 | Ilchester | 20 | 15 | 1 | 4 | 71 | 40 | 31 | 46 |
| 3 | Somerton Town Res. | 20 | 13 | 2 | 5 | 57 | 31 | 26 | 41 |
| 4 | Bradford Abbas | 20 | 10 | 3 | 7 | 57 | 51 | 6 | 33 |
| 5 | AFC Camel | 20 | 10 | 1 | 9 | 49 | 44 | 5 | 31 |
| 6 | Aller Park Rangers | 20 | 10 | 0 | 10 | 45 | 36 | 9 | 30 |
| 7 | Manor Athletic | 20 | 7 | 1 | 12 | 46 | 73 | -27 | 22 |
| 8 | Barwick & Stoford | 20 | 5 | 5 | 10 | 39 | 50 | -11 | 20 |
| 9 | Ashcott Res. | 20 | 5 | 3 | 12 | 33 | 64 | -31 | 18 |
| 10 | Bruton United | 20 | 3 | 5 | 12 | 31 | 57 | -26 | 14 |
| 11 | Normalair Res. | 20 | 3 | 3 | 14 | 34 | 61 | -27 | 12 |

| Division Two | P | W | D | L | F | A | GD | Pts |
|---|---|---|---|---|---|---|---|---|
| 1 Keinton Park Rangers | 20 | 15 | 5 | 0 | 80 | 20 | 60 | 50 |
| 2 Mudford | 20 | 15 | 4 | 1 | 86 | 29 | 57 | 49 |
| 3 Charlton | 20 | 11 | 4 | 5 | 71 | 30 | 41 | 37 |
| 4 Pen Mill | 20 | 11 | 2 | 7 | 50 | 41 | 9 | 35 |
| 5 Milborne Port A | 20 | 7 | 6 | 7 | 29 | 36 | -7 | 27 |
| 6 Odcombe | 20 | 6 | 8 | 6 | 33 | 32 | 1 | 26 |
| 7 AFC Huish Res. | 20 | 7 | 1 | 12 | 48 | 54 | -6 | 22 |
| 8 Stoke Res. | 20 | 6 | 1 | 13 | 37 | 93 | -56 | 19 |
| 9 Ashcott A | 20 | 5 | 3 | 12 | 35 | 56 | -21 | 18 |
| 10 Aller Park Rangers Res. (-3) | 20 | 5 | 4 | 11 | 36 | 58 | -22 | 16 |
| 11 Martock United Res. | 20 | 2 | 2 | 16 | 24 | 80 | -56 | 8 |

## YORKSHIRE AMATEUR LEAGUE

| Premier Division | P | W | D | L | F | A | GD | Pts |
|---|---|---|---|---|---|---|---|---|
| 1 Farsley Celtic Juniors | 18 | 14 | 2 | 2 | 64 | 23 | 41 | 44 |
| 2 Ealandians | 18 | 12 | 3 | 3 | 53 | 36 | 17 | 39 |
| 3 Alwoodley FC | 18 | 11 | 1 | 6 | 62 | 35 | 27 | 34 |
| 4 Leeds Medics & Dentists | 18 | 9 | 5 | 4 | 57 | 33 | 24 | 32 |
| 5 Farnley Sports | 18 | 9 | 2 | 7 | 32 | 32 | 0 | 29 |
| 6 Grangefield OB | 18 | 6 | 4 | 8 | 31 | 37 | -6 | 22 |
| 7 Stanningley OB | 18 | 6 | 1 | 11 | 35 | 47 | -12 | 19 |
| 8 Trinity & All Saints COB | 18 | 5 | 2 | 11 | 23 | 54 | -31 | 17 |
| 9 Wigton Moor | 18 | 4 | 2 | 12 | 35 | 63 | -28 | 14 |
| 10 Rodillian | 18 | 2 | 2 | 14 | 25 | 57 | -32 | 8 |

| Championship | P | W | D | L | F | A | GD | Pts |
|---|---|---|---|---|---|---|---|---|
| 1 St. Nicholas | 22 | 16 | 4 | 2 | 68 | 15 | 53 | 52 |
| 2 Leeds Medics & Dentists Res. | 22 | 15 | 4 | 3 | 56 | 28 | 28 | 49 |
| 3 Beeston Juniors (+3) | 22 | 14 | 3 | 5 | 70 | 40 | 30 | 48 |
| 4 Alwoodley FC Res. | 21 | 9 | 4 | 8 | 55 | 51 | 4 | 31 |
| 5 Shire Academics | 22 | 9 | 3 | 10 | 67 | 48 | 19 | 30 |
| 6 Morley Town AFC | 22 | 9 | 3 | 10 | 67 | 67 | 0 | 30 |
| 7 Beeston St. Anthony's (-3) | 21 | 8 | 7 | 6 | 42 | 36 | 6 | 28 |
| 8 Thornesians | 22 | 8 | 4 | 10 | 51 | 68 | -17 | 28 |
| 9 Stanningley OB Res. | 22 | 7 | 6 | 9 | 44 | 57 | -13 | 27 |
| 10 Collingham Juniors OB | 22 | 6 | 4 | 12 | 40 | 55 | -15 | 22 |
| 11 Old Batelians | 22 | 5 | 1 | 16 | 52 | 96 | -44 | 16 |
| 12 Leeds Independent | 22 | 2 | 3 | 17 | 38 | 89 | -51 | 9 |

| Division One | P | W | D | L | F | A | GD | Pts |
|---|---|---|---|---|---|---|---|---|
| 1 Drighlington FC | 22 | 15 | 4 | 3 | 83 | 26 | 57 | 49 |
| 2 Calverley United | 22 | 14 | 2 | 6 | 41 | 32 | 9 | 44 |
| 3 Amaranth | 22 | 13 | 1 | 8 | 47 | 41 | 6 | 40 |
| 4 Wortley | 22 | 12 | 2 | 8 | 67 | 43 | 24 | 38 |
| 5 Leeds Medics & Dentists III | 22 | 11 | 3 | 8 | 42 | 43 | -1 | 36 |
| 6 Garforth Rangers | 22 | 10 | 3 | 9 | 50 | 39 | 11 | 33 |
| 7 Dewsbury Rangers FC | 22 | 10 | 3 | 9 | 48 | 43 | 5 | 33 |
| 8 Rothwell Res. (-3) | 22 | 9 | 2 | 11 | 55 | 60 | -5 | 26 |
| 9 St. Bedes AFC | 22 | 8 | 2 | 12 | 59 | 80 | -21 | 26 |
| 10 Grangefield OB Res. (-9) | 22 | 8 | 3 | 11 | 48 | 58 | -10 | 18 |
| 11 Wheelwright OB (-3) | 22 | 4 | 3 | 15 | 45 | 72 | -27 | 12 |
| 12 Colton Athletic | 22 | 2 | 4 | 16 | 37 | 85 | -48 | 10 |

| Division Two | P | W | D | L | F | A | GD | Pts |
|---|---|---|---|---|---|---|---|---|
| 1 Gildersome Spurs OB | 20 | 17 | 0 | 3 | 98 | 31 | 67 | 51 |
| 2 Huddersfield YMCA | 20 | 16 | 1 | 3 | 89 | 34 | 55 | 49 |
| 3 Farsley Celtic Juniors Res. | 20 | 14 | 1 | 5 | 70 | 31 | 39 | 43 |
| 4 Churwell Lions | 20 | 13 | 2 | 5 | 61 | 35 | 26 | 41 |
| 5 Woodkirk Valley | 20 | 12 | 0 | 8 | 69 | 44 | 25 | 36 |
| 6 Sandal Wanderers | 20 | 9 | 4 | 7 | 61 | 61 | 0 | 31 |
| 7 Collegians | 20 | 7 | 2 | 11 | 52 | 57 | -5 | 23 |
| 8 Morley Town AFC Res. | 20 | 6 | 1 | 13 | 60 | 72 | -12 | 19 |
| 9 Old Centralians | 20 | 5 | 0 | 15 | 37 | 104 | -67 | 15 |
| 10 Leeds Medics & Dentists IV (-3) | 20 | 3 | 1 | 16 | 38 | 75 | -37 | 7 |
| 11 Old Batelians Res. | 20 | 2 | 0 | 18 | 33 | 124 | -91 | 6 |

| Division Three | P | W | D | L | F | A | GD | Pts |
|---|---|---|---|---|---|---|---|---|
| 1 Horsforth St. Margaret's | 21 | 18 | 1 | 2 | 85 | 22 | 63 | 55 |
| 2 Kippax Athletic | 22 | 16 | 3 | 3 | 77 | 29 | 48 | 51 |
| 3 Leeds City OB | 22 | 15 | 1 | 6 | 79 | 33 | 46 | 46 |
| 4 Norristhorpe | 22 | 13 | 1 | 8 | 87 | 49 | 38 | 40 |
| 5 Ealandians Res. | 21 | 12 | 3 | 6 | 70 | 38 | 32 | 39 |
| 6 Fairbank United | 22 | 8 | 4 | 10 | 59 | 70 | -11 | 28 |
| 7 FC Headingley (-3) | 22 | 8 | 2 | 12 | 42 | 63 | -21 | 23 |
| 8 Churwell Lions Res. (-3) | 22 | 8 | 1 | 13 | 54 | 58 | -4 | 22 |
| 9 Leeds Modernians | 22 | 6 | 2 | 14 | 59 | 78 | -19 | 20 |
| 10 Thornesians Res. | 22 | 6 | 2 | 14 | 33 | 89 | -56 | 20 |
| 11 Woodhouse Moor Methodists (-3) | 22 | 5 | 4 | 13 | 33 | 66 | -33 | 16 |
| 12 Middleton Park | 22 | 2 | 4 | 16 | 32 | 115 | -83 | 10 |

| Division Four | P | W | D | L | F | A | GD | Pts |
|---|---|---|---|---|---|---|---|---|
| 1 Amaranth Res | 20 | 13 | 3 | 4 | 90 | 45 | 45 | 42 |
| 2 Shire Academics Res | 20 | 13 | 3 | 4 | 84 | 41 | 43 | 42 |
| 3 Leeds City OB Res | 20 | 11 | 2 | 7 | 63 | 60 | 3 | 35 |
| 4 Farnley Sports Res | 19 | 11 | 1 | 7 | 49 | 52 | -3 | 34 |
| 5 Beeston Juniors Res | 20 | 7 | 5 | 8 | 66 | 78 | -12 | 26 |
| 6 Alwoodley FC III | 20 | 6 | 6 | 8 | 44 | 48 | -4 | 24 |
| 7 Wigton Moor Res | 20 | 7 | 2 | 11 | 51 | 70 | -19 | 23 |
| 8 Colton Athletic Res | 20 | 6 | 4 | 10 | 65 | 63 | 2 | 22 |
| 9 North Leeds | 20 | 6 | 4 | 10 | 46 | 51 | -5 | 22 |
| 10 Ealandians III | 20 | 6 | 3 | 11 | 49 | 74 | -25 | 21 |
| 11 Horsforth St. Margaret's Res. (-6) | 19 | 5 | 3 | 11 | 41 | 66 | -25 | 12 |

| Division Five | P | W | D | L | F | A | GD | Pts |
|---|---|---|---|---|---|---|---|---|
| 1 Huddersfield Amateur | 20 | 16 | 1 | 3 | 95 | 33 | 62 | 49 |
| 2 East Ardsley Wanderers | 20 | 14 | 2 | 4 | 91 | 48 | 43 | 44 |
| 3 Trinity & All Saints COB Res | 20 | 14 | 1 | 5 | 70 | 40 | 30 | 43 |
| 4 Rodillian Res | 20 | 14 | 0 | 6 | 64 | 38 | 26 | 42 |
| 5 Drighlington FC Res | 20 | 9 | 4 | 7 | 48 | 39 | 9 | 31 |
| 6 Woodkirk Valley Mens Res | 20 | 8 | 4 | 8 | 57 | 53 | 4 | 28 |
| 7 Shire Academics III | 20 | 8 | 4 | 8 | 54 | 54 | 0 | 28 |
| 8 Dewsbury Rangers FC Res | 20 | 9 | 1 | 10 | 46 | 47 | -1 | 28 |
| 9 Methley United | 20 | 4 | 0 | 16 | 36 | 101 | -65 | 12 |
| 10 North Leeds Res | 20 | 3 | 1 | 16 | 24 | 62 | -38 | 10 |
| 11 Thornesians III | 20 | 1 | 2 | 17 | 28 | 98 | -70 | 5 |

| Division Six | P | W | D | L | F | A | GD | Pts |
|---|---|---|---|---|---|---|---|---|
| 1 Morley Town AFC III | 20 | 17 | 1 | 2 | 87 | 26 | 61 | 52 |
| 2 Norristhorpe Res. | 20 | 16 | 0 | 4 | 85 | 32 | 53 | 48 |
| 3 St. Bedes AFC Res. | 20 | 13 | 2 | 5 | 64 | 44 | 20 | 41 |
| 4 Rothwell III | 20 | 8 | 3 | 9 | 63 | 49 | 14 | 27 |
| 5 Shire Academics IV | 20 | 8 | 2 | 10 | 43 | 49 | -6 | 26 |
| 6 Old Batelians III (-6) | 20 | 10 | 1 | 9 | 43 | 49 | -6 | 25 |
| 7 Leeds Modernians Res. | 20 | 7 | 4 | 9 | 29 | 44 | -15 | 25 |
| 8 Huddersfield Amateur Res. | 20 | 6 | 5 | 9 | 42 | 58 | -16 | 23 |
| 9 Old Centralians Res. (-3) | 20 | 8 | 0 | 12 | 38 | 57 | -19 | 21 |
| 10 Leeds City OB III | 20 | 6 | 2 | 12 | 32 | 60 | -28 | 20 |
| 11 Thornesians IV (-3) | 20 | 0 | 2 | 18 | 16 | 74 | -58 | -1 |

# NORTHERN IRELAND TABLES 2015-16

## IRELAND FOOTBALL ASSOCIATION

| Premiership | | P | W | D | L | F | A | GD | Pts |
|---|---|---|---|---|---|---|---|---|---|
| 1 | Crusaders | 38 | 28 | 7 | 3 | 79 | 28 | 51 | 91 |
| 2 | Linfield | 38 | 26 | 5 | 7 | 91 | 35 | 56 | 83 |
| 3 | Glenavon | 38 | 20 | 9 | 9 | 72 | 40 | 32 | 69 |
| 4 | Cliftonville | 38 | 18 | 10 | 10 | 58 | 53 | 5 | 64 |
| 5 | Coleraine | 38 | 18 | 4 | 16 | 47 | 46 | 1 | 58 |
| 6 | Glentoran | 38 | 15 | 7 | 16 | 46 | 55 | -9 | 52 |
| 7 | Dungannon Swifts | 38 | 12 | 7 | 19 | 51 | 66 | -15 | 43 |
| 8 | Ballymena United | 38 | 11 | 7 | 20 | 57 | 81 | -24 | 40 |
| 9 | Portadown | 38 | 11 | 5 | 22 | 43 | 67 | -24 | 38 |
| 10 | Carrick Rangers | 38 | 8 | 11 | 19 | 43 | 68 | -25 | 35 |
| 11 | Ballinamallard United | 38 | 9 | 7 | 22 | 39 | 59 | -20 | 34 |
| 12 | Warrenpoint Town | 38 | 9 | 7 | 22 | 45 | 73 | -28 | 34 |

| Championship 1 | | P | W | D | L | F | A | GD | Pts |
|---|---|---|---|---|---|---|---|---|---|
| 1 | Ards | 26 | 17 | 3 | 6 | 59 | 35 | 24 | 54 |
| 2 | HW Welders | 26 | 15 | 6 | 5 | 54 | 28 | 26 | 51 |
| 3 | Armagh City | 26 | 13 | 5 | 8 | 64 | 36 | 28 | 44 |
| 4 | Knockbreda | 26 | 12 | 7 | 7 | 48 | 32 | 16 | 43 |
| 5 | Institute | 26 | 12 | 6 | 8 | 40 | 20 | 20 | 42 |
| 6 | Larne | 26 | 12 | 6 | 8 | 64 | 45 | 19 | 42 |
| 7 | Lurgan Celtic | 26 | 11 | 6 | 9 | 40 | 40 | 0 | 39 |
| 8 | Ballyclare Comrades | 26 | 9 | 10 | 7 | 44 | 40 | 4 | 37 |
| 9 | Loughgall | 26 | 10 | 6 | 10 | 45 | 54 | -9 | 36 |
| 10 | Bangor | 26 | 10 | 5 | 11 | 44 | 40 | 4 | 35 |
| 11 | Dergview | 26 | 9 | 8 | 9 | 41 | 40 | 1 | 35 |
| 12 | Annagh United | 26 | 7 | 6 | 13 | 37 | 57 | -20 | 27 |
| 13 | Donegal Celtic | 26 | 2 | 4 | 20 | 34 | 80 | -46 | 10 |
| 14 | Lisburn Distillery | 26 | 2 | 4 | 20 | 18 | 85 | -67 | 10 |

| Championship 2 | | P | W | D | L | F | A | GD | Pts |
|---|---|---|---|---|---|---|---|---|---|
| 1 | Limavady United | 26 | 18 | 5 | 3 | 66 | 27 | 39 | 59 |
| 2 | PSNI | 26 | 18 | 5 | 3 | 59 | 23 | 36 | 59 |
| 3 | Sport and Leisure Swifts | 26 | 13 | 8 | 5 | 59 | 28 | 31 | 47 |
| 4 | Tobermore United | 26 | 13 | 5 | 8 | 38 | 31 | 7 | 44 |
| 5 | Moyola Park | 26 | 12 | 5 | 9 | 40 | 34 | 6 | 41 |
| 6 | Banbridge Town | 26 | 9 | 9 | 8 | 35 | 34 | 1 | 36 |
| 7 | Queens University | 26 | 10 | 6 | 10 | 35 | 37 | -2 | 36 |
| 8 | Dundela | 26 | 11 | 3 | 12 | 38 | 47 | -9 | 36 |
| 9 | Newington YC | 26 | 9 | 7 | 10 | 38 | 38 | 0 | 34 |
| 10 | Dollingstown | 26 | 9 | 7 | 10 | 46 | 51 | -5 | 34 |
| 11 | Glebe Rangers | 26 | 9 | 5 | 12 | 34 | 46 | -12 | 32 |
| 12 | Coagh United | 26 | 6 | 4 | 16 | 28 | 54 | -26 | 22 |
| 13 | Portstewart | 26 | 6 | 3 | 17 | 34 | 58 | -24 | 21 |
| 14 | Wakehurst | 26 | 1 | 4 | 21 | 25 | 67 | -42 | 7 |

## BALLYMENA & PROVINCIAL LEAGUE

| Premier Division | | P | W | D | L | F | A | GD | Pts |
|---|---|---|---|---|---|---|---|---|---|
| 1 | Newtowne | 18 | 16 | 1 | 1 | 73 | 13 | 60 | 49 |
| 2 | Ballynure Old Boys | 17 | 13 | 2 | 2 | 69 | 17 | 52 | 41 |
| 3 | Brantwood | 17 | 11 | 3 | 3 | 45 | 16 | 29 | 36 |
| 4 | Dunloy | 18 | 8 | 5 | 5 | 65 | 31 | 34 | 29 |
| 5 | Chimney Corner | 18 | 8 | 1 | 9 | 37 | 26 | 11 | 25 |
| 6 | Desertmartin | 18 | 8 | 1 | 9 | 37 | 34 | 3 | 25 |
| 7 | Magherafelt Sky Blues | 18 | 8 | 0 | 10 | 52 | 46 | 6 | 24 |
| 8 | Killymoon Rangers | 18 | 5 | 1 | 12 | 19 | 70 | -51 | 16 |
| 9 | Rathcoole | 17 | 2 | 2 | 13 | 26 | 58 | -32 | 8 |
| 10 | Sofia Farm | 17 | 0 | 2 | 15 | 13 | 125 | -112 | 2 |

| Junior Division One | | P | W | D | L | F | A | GD | Pts |
|---|---|---|---|---|---|---|---|---|---|
| 1 | Newington YC II | 18 | 17 | 0 | 1 | 76 | 16 | 60 | 51 |
| 2 | Ballyclare Comrades Res. | 19 | 16 | 2 | 1 | 99 | 15 | 84 | 50 |
| 3 | Antrim Rovers | 20 | 9 | 4 | 7 | 42 | 48 | -6 | 31 |
| 4 | Sport & Leisure Swifts II | 20 | 9 | 2 | 9 | 59 | 54 | 5 | 29 |
| 5 | Mallusk Athletic | 20 | 9 | 2 | 9 | 45 | 42 | 3 | 29 |
| 6 | Cookstown Olympic | 20 | 6 | 4 | 10 | 46 | 62 | -16 | 22 |
| 7 | Desertmartin Swifts | 20 | 6 | 4 | 10 | 47 | 64 | -17 | 22 |
| 8 | FC Whiteabbey | 19 | 7 | 1 | 11 | 45 | 63 | -18 | 22 |
| 9 | Woodlands | 20 | 5 | 6 | 9 | 50 | 55 | -5 | 21 |
| 10 | Cookstown RBL | 20 | 5 | 6 | 9 | 32 | 56 | -24 | 21 |
| 11 | Carnmoney | 20 | 2 | 3 | 15 | 35 | 101 | -66 | 9 |

| Junior Division Two | | P | W | D | L | F | A | GD | Pts |
|---|---|---|---|---|---|---|---|---|---|
| 1 | Brantwood Reserves | 17 | 13 | 1 | 3 | 75 | 33 | 42 | 40 |
| 2 | Cookstown Youth | 15 | 12 | 2 | 1 | 67 | 19 | 48 | 38 |
| 3 | Larne Olympic | 17 | 10 | 2 | 5 | 64 | 30 | 34 | 32 |
| 4 | Wakehurst Strollers | 18 | 10 | 1 | 7 | 57 | 36 | 21 | 31 |
| 5 | Mountainview | 16 | 9 | 1 | 6 | 45 | 36 | 9 | 28 |
| 6 | Ballynure Old Boys B | 17 | 8 | 3 | 6 | 55 | 42 | 13 | 27 |
| 7 | Remo | 18 | 7 | 1 | 10 | 33 | 59 | -26 | 22 |
| 8 | Clough Rangers Athletic | 18 | 6 | 0 | 12 | 39 | 73 | -34 | 18 |
| 9 | Moyola Park Olympic | 18 | 3 | 2 | 13 | 32 | 80 | -48 | 11 |
| 10 | Ballyclare North End | 18 | 1 | 1 | 16 | 21 | 80 | -59 | 4 |

| Junior Division Three | | P | W | D | L | F | A | GD | Pts |
|---|---|---|---|---|---|---|---|---|---|
| 1 | 3rd Ballyclare OB | 18 | 15 | 2 | 1 | 73 | 13 | 60 | 47 |
| 2 | Castle Star | 17 | 14 | 1 | 2 | 80 | 18 | 62 | 43 |
| 3 | Whitehead Rangers | 17 | 8 | 5 | 4 | 46 | 34 | 12 | 29 |
| 4 | Antrim Rovers Swifts | 18 | 9 | 2 | 7 | 40 | 47 | -7 | 29 |
| 5 | 1st Carrickfergus OB | 17 | 8 | 4 | 5 | 45 | 31 | 14 | 28 |
| 6 | Carrick Thistle | 17 | 8 | 3 | 6 | 46 | 37 | 9 | 27 |
| 7 | Hillhead Eagles U18 | 17 | 4 | 3 | 10 | 26 | 49 | -23 | 15 |
| 8 | Carnlough Swifts II | 17 | 3 | 2 | 12 | 23 | 60 | -37 | 11 |
| 9 | Brantwood III | 17 | 1 | 4 | 12 | 20 | 75 | -55 | 7 |
| 10 | Red Star | 15 | 1 | 2 | 12 | 10 | 45 | -35 | 5 |
| 11 | KCC Athletic withdrew | | | | | | | | |

## MID ULSTER LEAGUE

| Intermediate A | | P | W | D | L | F | A | GD | Pts |
|---|---|---|---|---|---|---|---|---|---|
| 1 | Newry City | 26 | 22 | 3 | 1 | 101 | 21 | 80 | 69 |
| 2 | Valley Rangers | 26 | 18 | 3 | 5 | 96 | 49 | 47 | 57 |
| 3 | Hanover | 25 | 16 | 5 | 4 | 74 | 28 | 46 | 53 |
| 4 | St Marys YC | 26 | 15 | 3 | 8 | 48 | 32 | 16 | 48 |
| 5 | Crewe United | 26 | 12 | 8 | 6 | 62 | 42 | 20 | 44 |
| 6 | Tandragee Rovers | 26 | 13 | 4 | 9 | 53 | 40 | 13 | 43 |
| 7 | Camlough Rovers | 25 | 13 | 3 | 9 | 64 | 51 | 13 | 42 |
| 8 | Ballymacash Rangers | 26 | 9 | 5 | 12 | 51 | 57 | -6 | 32 |
| 9 | Banbridge Rangers | 26 | 9 | 5 | 12 | 46 | 53 | -7 | 32 |
| 10 | Broomhill | 25 | 8 | 3 | 14 | 49 | 75 | -26 | 27 |
| 11 | Fivemiletown United | 25 | 5 | 7 | 13 | 45 | 61 | -16 | 22 |
| 12 | Seapatrick | 26 | 5 | 3 | 18 | 28 | 92 | -64 | 18 |
| 13 | Lower Maze | 26 | 5 | 1 | 20 | 56 | 94 | -38 | 16 |
| 14 | AFC Craigavon | 26 | 2 | 3 | 21 | 17 | 95 | -78 | 9 |

| Intermediate B | | P | W | D | L | F | A | GD | Pts |
|---|---|---|---|---|---|---|---|---|---|
| 1 | Windmill Stars | 24 | 23 | 1 | 0 | 98 | 18 | 80 | 70 |
| 2 | Moneyslane | 24 | 19 | 1 | 4 | 118 | 31 | 87 | 58 |
| 3 | Richhill | 26 | 15 | 3 | 8 | 53 | 40 | 13 | 48 |
| 4 | Dungannon Tigers | 26 | 15 | 3 | 8 | 59 | 50 | 9 | 48 |
| 5 | Tullyvallen | 26 | 13 | 3 | 10 | 59 | 54 | 5 | 42 |
| 6 | Craigavon City | 26 | 13 | 2 | 11 | 41 | 43 | -2 | 41 |
| 7 | Bourneview Mill | 25 | 12 | 4 | 9 | 52 | 51 | 1 | 40 |
| 8 | Seagoe | 23 | 10 | 4 | 9 | 47 | 38 | 9 | 34 |
| 9 | Markethill Swifts | 24 | 9 | 3 | 12 | 53 | 38 | 15 | 30 |
| 10 | Lurgan Town | 26 | 7 | 6 | 13 | 42 | 52 | -10 | 27 |
| 11 | Dungannon Rovers | 25 | 7 | 3 | 15 | 48 | 78 | -30 | 24 |
| 12 | Broomhedge | 23 | 4 | 4 | 15 | 31 | 69 | -38 | 16 |
| 13 | Laurelvale | 24 | 3 | 5 | 16 | 34 | 88 | -54 | 14 |
| 14 | Oxford Sunnyside | 26 | 2 | 2 | 22 | 22 | 107 | -85 | 8 |

| Division One | | P | W | D | L | F | A | GD | Pts |
|---|---|---|---|---|---|---|---|---|---|
| 1 | Hill Street | 20 | 15 | 2 | 3 | 95 | 32 | 63 | 47 |
| 2 | Silverwood United | 19 | 14 | 4 | 1 | 72 | 23 | 49 | 46 |
| 3 | Coalisland Athletic | 20 | 12 | 3 | 5 | 71 | 44 | 27 | 39 |
| 4 | Ballyoran | 20 | 9 | 5 | 6 | 80 | 50 | 30 | 32 |
| 5 | Sandy Hill | 20 | 9 | 4 | 7 | 54 | 35 | 19 | 31 |
| 6 | Cookstown Celtic | 20 | 9 | 1 | 10 | 60 | 56 | 4 | 28 |
| 7 | Red Star FC | 20 | 8 | 2 | 10 | 47 | 77 | -30 | 26 |
| 8 | Ambassadors | 20 | 7 | 4 | 9 | 59 | 52 | 7 | 25 |
| 9 | Derryhirk United | 19 | 5 | 3 | 11 | 41 | 70 | -29 | 18 |
| 10 | Armagh Rovers | 20 | 5 | 2 | 13 | 43 | 64 | -21 | 17 |
| 11 | Lurgan Institute | 20 | 1 | 0 | 19 | 8 | 127 | -119 | 3 |
| 12 | Riverdale FC withdrew | | | | | | | | |

| Division Two | | P | W | D | L | F | A | GD | Pts |
|---|---|---|---|---|---|---|---|---|---|
| 1 | Rectory Rangers | 22 | 19 | 1 | 2 | 95 | 33 | 62 | 58 |
| 2 | Portadown BBOB | 21 | 15 | 2 | 4 | 67 | 31 | 36 | 47 |
| 3 | Donaghamore | 21 | 14 | 1 | 6 | 66 | 34 | 32 | 43 |
| 4 | Armagh Celtic | 22 | 12 | 3 | 7 | 63 | 39 | 24 | 39 |
| 5 | Keady Celtic | 21 | 11 | 2 | 8 | 59 | 40 | 19 | 35 |
| 6 | Glenavy | 22 | 10 | 3 | 9 | 47 | 44 | 3 | 33 |
| 7 | Castlecaufield | 22 | 9 | 4 | 9 | 43 | 43 | 0 | 31 |
| 8 | Knockmenagh Swifts | 22 | 9 | 1 | 12 | 50 | 58 | -8 | 28 |
| 9 | Scarva Rangers | 22 | 7 | 1 | 14 | 36 | 66 | -30 | 22 |
| 10 | Lurgan BBOB | 21 | 6 | 3 | 12 | 35 | 61 | -26 | 21 |
| 11 | Stranmillis | 22 | 3 | 3 | 16 | 32 | 92 | -60 | 12 |
| 12 | Gilford Crusaders | 22 | 2 | 2 | 18 | 31 | 83 | -52 | 8 |

| Division Three | | P | W | D | L | F | A | GD | Pts |
|---|---|---|---|---|---|---|---|---|---|
| 1 | Caledon Rovers | 20 | 19 | 0 | 1 | 88 | 19 | 69 | 57 |
| 2 | Lurgan United | 20 | 13 | 2 | 5 | 71 | 33 | 38 | 41 |
| 3 | Goodyear | 20 | 12 | 5 | 3 | 66 | 50 | 16 | 41 |
| 4 | Aghalee Village | 20 | 10 | 6 | 4 | 67 | 40 | 27 | 36 |
| 5 | Newmills | 20 | 11 | 2 | 7 | 76 | 54 | 22 | 35 |
| 6 | Hillsborough Boys | 20 | 9 | 2 | 9 | 46 | 61 | -15 | 29 |
| 7 | Donacloney | 20 | 7 | 2 | 11 | 32 | 38 | -6 | 23 |
| 8 | White City | 20 | 7 | 1 | 12 | 49 | 69 | -20 | 22 |
| 9 | Moira Albion | 20 | 5 | 1 | 14 | 45 | 62 | -17 | 16 |
| 10 | Union Luasa | 20 | 3 | 1 | 16 | 34 | 90 | -56 | 10 |
| 11 | Armagh Blues | 20 | 3 | 0 | 17 | 21 | 79 | -58 | 9 |
| 12 | Orchard City withdrew | | | | | | | | |

| Division Four | | P | W | D | L | F | A | GD | Pts |
|---|---|---|---|---|---|---|---|---|---|
| 1 | West End Hibs | 16 | 13 | 2 | 1 | 55 | 22 | 33 | 41 |
| 2 | Millbrook | 16 | 12 | 2 | 2 | 63 | 27 | 36 | 38 |
| 3 | Santos | 16 | 10 | 0 | 6 | 62 | 37 | 25 | 30 |
| 4 | Banbridge YCOB | 16 | 9 | 1 | 6 | 51 | 15 | 36 | 28 |
| 5 | Sporting Lisburn | 16 | 8 | 2 | 6 | 42 | 35 | 7 | 26 |
| 6 | Damolly United | 16 | 6 | 1 | 9 | 44 | 52 | -8 | 19 |
| 7 | Southside | 16 | 5 | 2 | 9 | 40 | 63 | -23 | 17 |
| 8 | The Dons | 16 | 1 | 2 | 13 | 21 | 69 | -48 | 5 |
| 9 | Lurgyvallen 12 | 16 | 1 | 2 | 13 | 15 | 73 | -58 | 5 |

## NORTHERN AMATEUR LEAGUE

| Premier Division | | P | W | D | L | F | A | GD | Pts |
|---|---|---|---|---|---|---|---|---|---|
| 1 | Immaculata | 26 | 23 | 2 | 1 | 95 | 22 | 73 | 71 |
| 2 | Ards Rangers | 26 | 21 | 1 | 4 | 96 | 35 | 61 | 64 |
| 3 | Crumlin Star | 25 | 16 | 4 | 5 | 59 | 32 | 27 | 52 |
| 4 | Downpatrick | 26 | 15 | 5 | 6 | 85 | 42 | 43 | 50 |
| 5 | Albert Foundry | 26 | 14 | 5 | 7 | 75 | 38 | 37 | 47 |
| 6 | Shankill United | 26 | 14 | 3 | 9 | 69 | 43 | 26 | 45 |
| 7 | Nortel | 26 | 10 | 3 | 13 | 50 | 54 | -4 | 33 |
| 8 | Crumlin United | 26 | 9 | 5 | 12 | 49 | 54 | -5 | 32 |
| 9 | Drumaness Mills | 25 | 8 | 6 | 11 | 35 | 56 | -21 | 30 |
| 10 | Derriaghy CC | 26 | 6 | 6 | 14 | 37 | 61 | -24 | 24 |
| 11 | Malachians | 26 | 6 | 3 | 17 | 33 | 68 | -35 | 21 |
| 12 | Ardglass | 26 | 4 | 8 | 14 | 31 | 76 | -45 | 20 |
| 13 | Islandmagee | 26 | 3 | 6 | 17 | 24 | 97 | -73 | 15 |
| 14 | Kilmore Rec | 26 | 2 | 3 | 21 | 18 | 78 | -60 | 9 |

| Division One A | | P | W | D | L | F | A | GD | Pts |
|---|---|---|---|---|---|---|---|---|---|
| 1 | Rathfriland Rangers | 25 | 20 | 2 | 3 | 79 | 22 | 57 | 62 |
| 2 | Lisburn Rangers | 26 | 19 | 1 | 6 | 68 | 39 | 29 | 58 |
| 3 | East Belfast | 26 | 17 | 3 | 6 | 76 | 45 | 31 | 54 |
| 4 | Comber Rec | 26 | 16 | 5 | 5 | 58 | 38 | 20 | 53 |
| 5 | Dunmurry Rec | 26 | 13 | 4 | 9 | 53 | 45 | 8 | 43 |
| 6 | Larne Tech OB | 26 | 12 | 1 | 13 | 51 | 44 | 7 | 37 |
| 7 | Abbey Villa (-3) | 25 | 11 | 5 | 9 | 49 | 45 | 4 | 35 |
| 8 | St Patricks YM | 26 | 10 | 5 | 11 | 51 | 54 | -3 | 35 |
| 9 | 1st Bangor OB | 26 | 10 | 2 | 14 | 34 | 48 | -14 | 32 |
| 10 | Killyleagh YC | 25 | 7 | 3 | 15 | 30 | 56 | -26 | 24 |
| 11 | Orangefield OB | 26 | 6 | 5 | 15 | 36 | 64 | -28 | 23 |
| 12 | Dundonald | 26 | 7 | 1 | 18 | 42 | 59 | -17 | 22 |
| 13 | Dromara Village (-3) | 25 | 7 | 1 | 17 | 31 | 59 | -28 | 19 |
| 14 | Barn United | 26 | 3 | 6 | 17 | 32 | 72 | -40 | 15 |

| Division One B | P | W | D | L | F | A | GD | Pts |
|---|---|---|---|---|---|---|---|---|
| Ballynahinch Olympic | 26 | 20 | 3 | 3 | 72 | 27 | 45 | 63 |
| Newcastle | 26 | 16 | 3 | 7 | 68 | 45 | 23 | 51 |
| Wellington Rec | 26 | 13 | 8 | 5 | 52 | 41 | 11 | 47 |
| Rosario YC | 26 | 13 | 6 | 7 | 47 | 39 | 8 | 45 |
| Colin Valley | 26 | 13 | 5 | 8 | 54 | 37 | 17 | 44 |
| Ballynahinch United | 26 | 12 | 8 | 6 | 47 | 31 | 16 | 44 |
| Sirocco Works | 26 | 13 | 2 | 11 | 53 | 36 | 17 | 41 |
| Portaferry Rovers | 26 | 8 | 4 | 14 | 52 | 58 | -6 | 28 |
| Rathfern Rangers | 26 | 7 | 4 | 15 | 55 | 73 | -18 | 25 |
| Ballywalter Rec | 26 | 6 | 6 | 14 | 41 | 74 | -33 | 24 |
| UUJ | 26 | 5 | 8 | 13 | 41 | 54 | -13 | 23 |
| Grove United (-13) | 26 | 10 | 5 | 11 | 47 | 46 | 1 | 22 |
| Bloomfield | 26 | 6 | 4 | 16 | 38 | 66 | -28 | 22 |
| Donard Hospital | 26 | 5 | 4 | 17 | 23 | 63 | -40 | 19 |

| Division One C | P | W | D | L | F | A | GD | Pts |
|---|---|---|---|---|---|---|---|---|
| Downshire YM | 26 | 20 | 4 | 2 | 100 | 23 | 77 | 64 |
| Mossley | 26 | 20 | 2 | 4 | 84 | 37 | 47 | 62 |
| Bangor Amateurs | 26 | 17 | 3 | 6 | 77 | 35 | 42 | 54 |
| Bryansburn Rangers | 26 | 15 | 5 | 6 | 84 | 42 | 42 | 50 |
| 18th Newtownabbey OB | 26 | 15 | 4 | 7 | 69 | 46 | 23 | 49 |
| Shorts | 26 | 15 | 3 | 8 | 74 | 50 | 24 | 48 |
| Bangor Swifts | 26 | 11 | 6 | 9 | 73 | 61 | 12 | 39 |
| Dunmurry YM (-15) | 26 | 14 | 4 | 8 | 83 | 43 | 40 | 31 |
| Holywood | 26 | 8 | 4 | 14 | 56 | 82 | -26 | 28 |
| Saintfield United | 26 | 7 | 4 | 15 | 45 | 56 | -11 | 25 |
| Iveagh United | 26 | 5 | 3 | 18 | 44 | 75 | -31 | 18 |
| Dromore Amateurs | 26 | 3 | 6 | 17 | 38 | 76 | -38 | 15 |
| Groomsport | 26 | 4 | 1 | 21 | 33 | 109 | -76 | 13 |
| Newington Rangers | 26 | 3 | 1 | 22 | 27 | 152 | -125 | 10 |

## NORTHERN IRELAND INTERMEDIATE LEAGUE

| | P | W | D | L | F | A | GD | Pts |
|---|---|---|---|---|---|---|---|---|
| Ballymoney United | 17 | 11 | 3 | 3 | 48 | 28 | 20 | 36 |
| Trojans | 15 | 8 | 4 | 3 | 33 | 20 | 13 | 28 |
| Strabane Athletic | 16 | 7 | 5 | 4 | 26 | 16 | 10 | 26 |
| Newbuildings United | 17 | 7 | 3 | 7 | 42 | 34 | 8 | 24 |
| Oxford United Stars | 16 | 7 | 2 | 7 | 22 | 21 | 1 | 23 |
| Ardstraw | 17 | 4 | 2 | 11 | 22 | 39 | -17 | 14 |
| Dungiven | 16 | 2 | 3 | 11 | 19 | 54 | -35 | 9 |

## BELFAST & DISTRICT LEAGUE

| Premier Division | P | W | D | L | F | A | GD | Pts |
|---|---|---|---|---|---|---|---|---|
| 1 Cumann Spoirt an Phobail | 18 | 12 | 4 | 2 | 65 | 26 | 39 | 40 |
| 2 Willowbank | 18 | 12 | 3 | 3 | 55 | 32 | 23 | 39 |
| 3 Tullymore Swifts | 18 | 10 | 3 | 5 | 43 | 33 | 10 | 33 |
| 4 St Matthews | 18 | 9 | 4 | 5 | 47 | 37 | 10 | 31 |
| 5 St Marys | 18 | 9 | 2 | 7 | 47 | 40 | 7 | 29 |
| 6 Bheann Mhadigan | 18 | 9 | 1 | 8 | 45 | 41 | 4 | 28 |
| 7 Berlin Swifts | 18 | 8 | 4 | 6 | 41 | 38 | 3 | 28 |
| 8 New Santos | 18 | 2 | 5 | 11 | 27 | 56 | -29 | 11 |
| 9 St James Swifts | 18 | 3 | 1 | 14 | 34 | 60 | -26 | 10 |
| 10 Kashmir Bilbao | 18 | 2 | 1 | 15 | 26 | 67 | -41 | 7 |

| Division One | P | W | D | L | F | A | GD | Pts |
|---|---|---|---|---|---|---|---|---|
| 1 Belfast Celtic | 22 | 14 | 6 | 2 | 100 | 34 | 66 | 48 |
| 2 Ligoniel WMC | 22 | 15 | 2 | 5 | 61 | 47 | 14 | 47 |
| 3 Newhill | 22 | 15 | 1 | 6 | 73 | 45 | 28 | 46 |
| 4 Cumann Spoirt an Phobail II | 22 | 11 | 6 | 5 | 80 | 51 | 29 | 39 |
| 5 22nd OB | 22 | 12 | 3 | 7 | 50 | 34 | 16 | 39 |
| 6 Realtá | 22 | 10 | 2 | 10 | 54 | 59 | -5 | 32 |
| 7 St Malachys OB | 22 | 9 | 2 | 11 | 40 | 45 | -5 | 29 |
| 8 Tullymore Swifts II | 22 | 9 | 1 | 12 | 51 | 54 | -3 | 28 |
| 9 St Matthews II | 22 | 8 | 3 | 11 | 50 | 43 | 7 | 27 |
| 10 Holylands | 22 | 6 | 2 | 14 | 47 | 68 | -21 | 20 |
| 11 Glenpark | 22 | 5 | 1 | 16 | 46 | 102 | -56 | 16 |
| 12 Colin Bhoys | 22 | 3 | 1 | 18 | 26 | 96 | -70 | 10 |

| Division Two | P | W | D | L | F | A | GD | Pts |
|---|---|---|---|---|---|---|---|---|
| 1 Willowbank II | 22 | 19 | 2 | 1 | 98 | 29 | 69 | 59 |
| 2 Belfast Celtic II | 22 | 17 | 0 | 5 | 73 | 38 | 35 | 51 |
| 3 Bheann Mhadigan II | 22 | 15 | 2 | 5 | 71 | 31 | 40 | 47 |
| 4 St Marys II | 22 | 12 | 5 | 5 | 69 | 51 | 18 | 41 |
| 5 Berlin Swifts Reserves | 22 | 11 | 4 | 7 | 44 | 39 | 5 | 37 |
| 6 22nd OB B | 22 | 7 | 5 | 10 | 38 | 43 | -5 | 26 |
| 7 Sparta Belfast | 22 | 7 | 5 | 10 | 46 | 58 | -12 | 26 |
| 8 Rock Athletic | 22 | 7 | 4 | 11 | 45 | 52 | -7 | 25 |
| 9 Solway Stars | 22 | 7 | 2 | 13 | 52 | 73 | -21 | 23 |
| 10 New Santos II | 22 | 6 | 2 | 14 | 35 | 56 | -21 | 20 |
| 11 Glanville Rec | 22 | 4 | 4 | 14 | 35 | 71 | -36 | 16 |
| 12 St Malachys OB II | 22 | 1 | 3 | 18 | 17 | 82 | -65 | 6 |

| Division Three | P | W | D | L | F | A | GD | Pts |
|---|---|---|---|---|---|---|---|---|
| 1 Westland YM | 22 | 18 | 2 | 2 | 83 | 38 | 45 | 56 |
| 2 Newhill II | 22 | 15 | 2 | 5 | 83 | 36 | 47 | 47 |
| 3 St James Swifts II | 22 | 13 | 5 | 4 | 61 | 27 | 34 | 44 |
| 4 Sporting Belfast | 22 | 10 | 3 | 9 | 65 | 42 | 23 | 33 |
| 5 Glencairn | 22 | 9 | 4 | 9 | 47 | 50 | -3 | 31 |
| 6 Ballysillan Swifts III | 22 | 9 | 2 | 11 | 38 | 41 | -3 | 29 |
| 7 Realtá II | 22 | 9 | 2 | 11 | 42 | 49 | -7 | 29 |
| 8 Shankill Elim | 22 | 8 | 4 | 10 | 41 | 55 | -14 | 28 |
| 9 Belfast Deaf United | 22 | 8 | 2 | 12 | 51 | 68 | -17 | 26 |
| 10 Rock Athletic II | 22 | 6 | 5 | 11 | 48 | 70 | -22 | 23 |
| 11 Solway Stars II | 22 | 5 | 6 | 11 | 42 | 77 | -35 | 21 |
| 12 Glengormley | 22 | 2 | 3 | 17 | 34 | 82 | -48 | 9 |

## IRISH CUP

**HOLDERS:** GLENAVON

**FIRST ROUND**

**Tuesday 18th August 2015**

Newcastle 3-2 Ballynahinch United

**Thursday 20th August 2015**

Drumaness Mills 1-4 Dunloy

**Friday 21st August, 2015**

Ballynure OB 1-2 Sirocco Works

**Saturday 22nd August 2015**

Abbey Villa 4-1 UUJ

Ardstraw 1-5 Newry City AFC

Ballynahinch United 2-4 Valley Rangers

Ballynure OB 1-2 Sirocco Works

Ballywalter Rec 4-2 Iveagh United

Bloomfield 1-4 Desertmartin

Chimney Corner 3-3 (4-5p) Downshire YM

Comber Rec. 3-0 Windmill Stars

Craigavon City 3-4 Lower Maze

Crumlin Star 3-0 Shorts

Crumlin United 3-2 Nortel

Derriaghy CC 4-1 Orangefield OB

Donard Hospital 2-4 Shankill United

Dromara Village 2-1 Colin Valley

Dromore Amateurs 0-3 Lisburn Rangers

Dundonald 3-2 Broomhill

Dungiven 1-5 Newtowne

Dunmurry YM 8-1 Laurelvale

East Belfast 1-2 Ards Rangers

Trojans 2-1 Islandmagee

Fivemiletown United 2-3 St. Mary's YC

Grove United 2-3 Malachians

Hanover 5-1 Ballymoney United

Immaculata 2-1 1st Bangor

Killyleagh YC 3-2 Bryansburn Rangers

Lurgan Town 0-1 Wellington Rec.

Magherafelt Sky Blues 1-2 Brantwood

Moneyslane 1-2 Barn United

Mossley 1-3 18th Newtownabbey OB

Newbuildings United 2-3 Crewe United

Newcastle 3-2 Ballynahinch Olympic

Oxford Sunnyside 2-7 Rosario YC

Portaferry Rovers 0-3 Banbridge Rangers

Rathcoole 3-2 Ballymacash Rangers

Rathfern Rangers 4-2 Richhill

Saintfield United 1-2 Ardglass

Seapatrick 1-0 Killymoon Rangers

St. Patrick's 2-1 Markethill Swifts

Strabane Athletic 11-0 Kilmore Rec.

Tandragee Rovers 1-0 Albert Foundry

Trojans 2-1 Islandmagee

**SECOND ROUND**

**Saturday 3rd October 2015**

18th Newtownabbey OB 1-3 Abbey Villa

Ardglass 3-1 Killyleagh YC

Ards Rangers 4-1 Strabane Athletic

Ballywalter Rec 0-4 Tandragee Rovers

Banbridge Rangers 2-0 Seapatrick

Brantwood 2-3 Sirocco Works

Crumlin Star 2-1 Newry City AFC

Crumlin United 9-1 Seagoe

Derriaghy CC 1-6 Trojans

Desertmartin 1-2 Lisburn Rangers

Downshire YM 4-2 Moneyslane

Dromara Village 2-1 Newcastle

Dunloy 2-10 Dundonald

Dunmurry Rec. 5-3 Hanover

Groomsport 1-4 Newtowne

Immaculata 10-0 Dunmurry YM

Larne Tech. OB 2-2 (4-5p) Oxford United Stars

Malachians 0-1 Comber Rec.

Rathcoole 1-2 Lower Maze

Rathfriland Rangers 1-0 Crewe United

St. Mary's YC 3-1 Downpatrick

Valley Rangers 3-1 Rathfern Rangers

Wellington Rec. 2-1 Rosario YC

**THIRD ROUND**

**Saturday 7th November 2015**

Abbey Villa 1-1 Dunmurry Rec.

Ards Rangers 4-1 St. Mary's YC

Comber Rec. 3-4 Ardglass

Crumlin Star 5-0 Dundonald

Downshire YM 2-3 Crumlin United

Immaculata 4-2 Lower Maze

Lisburn Rangers 3-0 Tandragee Rovers

Newtowne 3-2 Dromara Village

Oxford United Stars 1-0 St. Patrick's

Rathfriland Rangers 4-2 Sirocco Works

Trojans 5-1 Banbridge Rangers

Valley Rangers 0-2 Wellington Rec.

**FOURTH ROUND**

**Saturday 5th December 2015**

Annagh United 2-1 Dollingstown

Ards 7-0 Donegal Celtic

Ards Rangers 2-3 Oxford United Stars

Armagh City 3-0 Lisburn Rangers

Ballyclare Comrades 0-1 Crumlin Star

Banbridge Town 3-3 (3-2p) Crumlin United

Dundela 0-2 Immaculata

H&W Welders 3-2 Wellington Rec.

Loughgall 2-1 Trojans

Lurgan Celtic 4-0 Ardglass

Newington 1-2 PSNI

Queen's University 1-2 Tobermore United

Wakehurst 1-1 (3-2p) Glebe Rangers

**Tuesday 8th December 2015**

Bangor 5-0 Coagh United

**Wednesday 9th December 2015**

Institute 1-1 (5-4p) Newtowne

**Saturday 19th December 2015**

Dergview 1-6 Sport & Leisure Swifts

Larne 2-0 Limavady United

Lisburn Distillery 2-3 Knockbreda

Portstewart 3-1 Moyola ParkSaturday

**2nd January 2016**

Abbey Villa 0-4 Rathfriland Rangers

**FIFTH ROUND**

**Saturday 9th January 2016**

rmagh City 3-3 (4-1p) Portstewart

anbridge Town 0-2 Carrick Rangers

Cliftonville 2-0 Immaculata

Coleraine 2-2 Ballinamallard United

Crumlin Star 3-2 Oxford United Stars

rusaders 3-0 Rathfriland Rangers

Dungannon Swifts 4-3 Warrenpoint Town

&W Welders 1-4 Glenavon

Linfield 2-1 Ballymena United

oughgall 5-2 Larne

Lurgan Celtic 2-1 Bangor

Portadown 6-1 Wakehurst

Sport & Leisure Swifts 3-2 Institute

obermore United 0-2 PSNI

**uesday 19th January 2016**

nnagh United 1-5 Knockbreda

Glentoran 4-1 Ards

**SIXTH ROUND**

**Saturday 6th February 2016**

Cliftonville 4-0 Sport & Leisure Swifts

Dungannon Swifts 1-3 Crusaders

Glentoran 1-4 Glenavon

Linfield 7-0 Armagh City

Loughgall 2-0 PSNI

Lurgan Celtic 1-0 Knockbreda

Portadown 3-1 Coleraine

**Monday 15th February 2016**

Carrick Rangers 1-0 Crumlin Star

**QUARTER FINALS**

**Saturday 5th March 2016**

Carrick Rangers 0-3 Crusaders

Cliftonville 0-3 Linfield

Glenavon 2-1 Loughgall

Portadown 2-3 Lurgan Celtic

**SEMI FINALS**

**Friday 1st April 2016**

Glenavon 4-3 Crusaders

**Saturday 2nd April 2016**

Linfield 3-0 Lurgan Celtic

**FINAL**

**Saturday 7th May 2016**

Glenavon 2-0 Linfield

# SCOTTISH TABLES 2015-16

## HIGHLAND LEAGUE

| | | P | W | D | L | F | A | GD | Pts |
|---|---|---|---|---|---|---|---|---|---|
| 1 | Cove Rangers | 34 | 29 | 2 | 3 | 98 | 28 | 70 | 89 |
| 2 | Formartine United | 34 | 27 | 4 | 3 | 137 | 35 | 102 | 85 |
| 3 | Brora Rangers | 34 | 27 | 4 | 3 | 128 | 35 | 93 | 85 |
| 4 | Turriff United | 34 | 20 | 8 | 6 | 88 | 31 | 57 | 68 |
| 5 | Wick Academy | 34 | 18 | 6 | 10 | 76 | 42 | 34 | 60 |
| 6 | Inverurie Loco Works | 34 | 18 | 4 | 12 | 71 | 43 | 28 | 58 |
| 7 | Buckie Thistle | 34 | 18 | 4 | 12 | 80 | 77 | 3 | 58 |
| 8 | Nairn County | 34 | 17 | 6 | 11 | 75 | 55 | 20 | 57 |
| 9 | Fraserburgh | 34 | 15 | 8 | 11 | 63 | 49 | 14 | 53 |
| 10 | Keith | 34 | 17 | 1 | 16 | 70 | 76 | -6 | 52 |
| 11 | Forres Mechanics | 34 | 15 | 4 | 15 | 60 | 65 | -5 | 49 |
| 12 | Lossiemouth | 34 | 12 | 2 | 20 | 46 | 70 | -24 | 38 |
| 13 | Deveronvale | 34 | 8 | 8 | 18 | 46 | 64 | -18 | 32 |
| 14 | Clachnacuddin | 34 | 10 | 2 | 22 | 59 | 80 | -21 | 32 |
| 15 | Huntly | 34 | 7 | 5 | 22 | 49 | 89 | -40 | 26 |
| 16 | Strathspey Thistle | 34 | 6 | 2 | 26 | 38 | 118 | -80 | 20 |
| 17 | Fort William | 34 | 5 | 1 | 28 | 38 | 116 | -78 | 16 |
| 18 | Rothes | 34 | 1 | 1 | 32 | 16 | 165 | -149 | 4 |

## LOWLAND LEAGUE

| | | P | W | D | L | F | A | GD | Pts |
|---|---|---|---|---|---|---|---|---|---|
| 1 | Edinburgh City | 28 | 24 | 1 | 3 | 74 | 28 | +46 | 73 |
| 2 | Spartans | 28 | 18 | 4 | 6 | 74 | 36 | +38 | 58 |
| 3 | University of Stirling | 28 | 17 | 5 | 6 | 65 | 32 | +33 | 56 |
| 4 | Cumbernauld Colts | 28 | 15 | 6 | 7 | 60 | 42 | +18 | 51 |
| 5 | East Kilbride | 28 | 14 | 7 | 7 | 68 | 44 | +24 | 49 |
| 6 | Edinburgh University | 28 | 13 | 3 | 12 | 51 | 46 | +5 | 42 |
| 7 | BSC Glasgow | 28 | 12 | 5 | 11 | 54 | 51 | +3 | 41 |
| 8 | Whitehill Welfare | 28 | 12 | 4 | 12 | 47 | 43 | +4 | 40 |
| 9 | Dalbeattie Star | 28 | 10 | 6 | 12 | 54 | 50 | +4 | 36 |
| 10 | Gretna 2008 | 28 | 11 | 3 | 14 | 38 | 50 | -12 | 36 |
| 11 | Gala Fairydean Rovers | 28 | 10 | 2 | 16 | 53 | 61 | -8 | 32 |
| 12 | Selkirk | 28 | 9 | 2 | 17 | 52 | 70 | -18 | 29 |
| 13 | Vale of Leithen | 28 | 7 | 5 | 16 | 38 | 67 | -29 | 26 |
| 14 | Preston Athletic | 28 | 6 | 4 | 18 | 28 | 70 | -42 | 22 |
| 15 | Threave Rovers | 28 | 3 | 1 | 24 | 30 | 96 | -66 | 10 |

## NORTH CALEDONIAN LEAGUE

| | | P | W | D | L | F | A | GD | Pts |
|---|---|---|---|---|---|---|---|---|---|
| 1 | Halkirk United (-3) | 10 | 8 | 0 | 2 | 23 | 12 | 11 | 21 |
| 2 | Golspie Sutherland | 10 | 5 | 4 | 1 | 27 | 15 | 12 | 19 |
| 3 | Thurso (+3) | 10 | 3 | 4 | 3 | 17 | 14 | 3 | 16 |
| 4 | Orkney | 10 | 4 | 2 | 4 | 16 | 19 | -3 | 14 |
| 5 | Invergordon | 10 | 2 | 3 | 5 | 11 | 17 | -6 | 9 |
| 6 | Alness United | 10 | 0 | 3 | 7 | 10 | 27 | -17 | 3 |

## EAST OF SCOTLAND LEAGUE

| Premier Division | | P | W | D | L | F | A | GD | Pts |
|---|---|---|---|---|---|---|---|---|---|
| 1 | Leith Athletic | 28 | 24 | 0 | 4 | 103 | 23 | 80 | 72 |
| 2 | Lothian Thistle Hutchison Vale | 28 | 20 | 3 | 5 | 98 | 41 | 57 | 63 |
| 3 | Civil Service Strollers | 28 | 18 | 1 | 9 | 74 | 49 | 25 | 55 |
| 4 | Tynecastle | 28 | 16 | 4 | 8 | 72 | 71 | 1 | 5[illegible] |
| 5 | Hawick Royal Albert | 28 | 15 | 3 | 10 | 70 | 50 | +20 | 4[illegible] |
| 6 | Peebles Rovers | 28 | 13 | 4 | 11 | 57 | 60 | -3 | 4[illegible] |
| 7 | Spartans Reserves (-3) | 28 | 14 | 2 | 12 | 67 | 61 | 6 | 4[illegible] |
| 8 | Ormiston | 28 | 12 | 5 | 11 | 70 | 70 | 0 | 4[illegible] |
| 9 | University of Stirling Res. | 28 | 10 | 5 | 13 | 65 | 55 | 10 | 3[illegible] |
| 10 | Heriot-Watt University | 28 | 9 | 6 | 13 | 61 | 65 | -4 | 3[illegible] |
| 11 | Coldstream | 28 | 10 | 2 | 16 | 63 | 87 | -24 | 3[illegible] |
| 12 | Craigroyston | 28 | 10 | 2 | 16 | 48 | 74 | -26 | 3[illegible] |
| 13 | Burntisland Shipyard | 28 | 8 | 3 | 17 | 43 | 67 | -24 | 2[illegible] |
| 14 | Eyemouth United | 28 | 5 | 2 | 21 | 39 | 115 | -76 | 1[illegible] |
| 15 | Duns | 28 | 4 | 2 | 22 | 45 | 87 | -42 | 1[illegible] |

## SJFA EAST REGION

| Superleague | | P | W | D | L | F | A | GD | Pts |
|---|---|---|---|---|---|---|---|---|---|
| 1 | Bonnyrigg Rose Athletic | 30 | 23 | 4 | 3 | 85 | 31 | 54 | 7[illegible] |
| 2 | Kelty Hearts | 30 | 19 | 5 | 6 | 59 | 30 | 29 | 6[illegible] |
| 3 | Linlithgow Rose | 30 | 18 | 6 | 6 | 64 | 39 | 25 | 6[illegible] |
| 4 | Bo'ness United | 30 | 17 | 5 | 8 | 60 | 36 | 24 | 5[illegible] |
| 5 | Newtongrange Star | 30 | 15 | 2 | 13 | 45 | 38 | 7 | 4[illegible] |
| 6 | Broxburn Athletic | 30 | 13 | 5 | 12 | 51 | 54 | -3 | 4[illegible] |
| 7 | Musselburgh Athletic | 30 | 13 | 4 | 13 | 56 | 54 | 2 | 4[illegible] |
| 8 | Hill of Beath Hawthorn | 30 | 12 | 5 | 13 | 54 | 48 | 6 | 4[illegible] |
| 9 | Penicuik Athletic | 30 | 12 | 5 | 13 | 47 | 56 | -9 | 4[illegible] |
| 10 | Broughty Athletic | 30 | 12 | 3 | 15 | 49 | 54 | -5 | 3[illegible] |
| 11 | Camelon Juniors | 30 | 10 | 6 | 14 | 49 | 57 | -8 | [illegible] |
| 12 | Carnoustie Panmure | 30 | 11 | 1 | 18 | 50 | 63 | -13 | 3[illegible] |
| 13 | Fauldhouse United | 30 | 9 | 5 | 16 | 44 | 61 | -17 | 3[illegible] |
| 14 | Sauchie Juniors | 30 | 9 | 5 | 16 | 52 | 70 | -18 | 3[illegible] |
| 15 | St Andrews United | 30 | 7 | 3 | 20 | 38 | 68 | -30 | [illegible] |
| 16 | Tayport | 30 | 7 | 2 | 21 | 32 | 76 | -44 | [illegible] |

Play-offs

Sauchie 0-5 Lochee United

Lochee United 5-0 Sauchie

Lochee United win 10-0 on aggregate. Lochee United are promoted to the Superleague whilst Sauchie are relegated to the Premier League.

| remier Division | | P | W | D | L | F | A | GD | Pts |
|---|---|---|---|---|---|---|---|---|---|
| | Jeanfield Swifts | 30 | 21 | 7 | 2 | 88 | 44 | 44 | 70 |
| | Dundonald Bluebell | 30 | 19 | 7 | 4 | 75 | 33 | 42 | 64 |
| | Lochee United | 30 | 18 | 7 | 5 | 88 | 45 | 43 | 61 |
| | Arniston Rangers | 30 | 15 | 8 | 7 | 62 | 41 | 21 | 53 |
| | Haddington Athletic | 30 | 16 | 4 | 10 | 66 | 47 | 19 | 52 |
| | Bathgate Thistle | 30 | 13 | 4 | 13 | 63 | 58 | 5 | 43 |
| | Dalkeith Thistle | 30 | 12 | 4 | 14 | 49 | 58 | -9 | 40 |
| | Forfar West End | 30 | 9 | 11 | 10 | 46 | 44 | 2 | 38 |
| | Kennoway Star Hearts | 30 | 9 | 9 | 12 | 61 | 59 | 2 | 36 |
| 0 | Falkirk Juniors | 30 | 10 | 5 | 15 | 60 | 72 | -12 | 35 |
| 1 | Montrose Roselea | 30 | 9 | 7 | 14 | 40 | 54 | -14 | 34 |
| 2 | Dundee Violet | 30 | 9 | 6 | 15 | 45 | 62 | -17 | 33 |
| 3 | Armadale Thistle | 30 | 8 | 7 | 15 | 55 | 70 | -15 | 31 |
| 4 | Thornton Hibs | 30 | 6 | 8 | 16 | 44 | 71 | -27 | 26 |
| 5 | Edinburgh United | 30 | 7 | 5 | 18 | 43 | 88 | -45 | 26 |
| 6 | Oakley United | 30 | 6 | 7 | 17 | 27 | 66 | -39 | 25 |

| orth Division | | P | W | D | L | F | A | GD | Pts |
|---|---|---|---|---|---|---|---|---|---|
| | Downfield Juniors | 28 | 21 | 5 | 2 | 86 | 27 | 59 | 68 |
| | Glenrothes Juniors | 28 | 20 | 5 | 3 | 82 | 19 | 63 | 65 |
| | Kirriemuir Thistle | 28 | 19 | 5 | 4 | 87 | 35 | 52 | 62 |
| | Blairgowrie Juniors | 28 | 18 | 7 | 3 | 75 | 43 | 32 | 61 |
| | Dundee North End | 28 | 15 | 3 | 10 | 66 | 41 | 25 | 48 |
| | Lochore Welfare | 28 | 13 | 4 | 11 | 78 | 56 | 22 | 43 |
| | Kinnoull Juniors | 28 | 13 | 4 | 11 | 61 | 52 | 9 | 43 |
| | Dundee East Craigie | 28 | 13 | 3 | 12 | 53 | 53 | 0 | 42 |
| | Coupar Angus | 28 | 10 | 3 | 15 | 59 | 69 | -10 | 33 |
| | Scone Thistle | 28 | 8 | 7 | 13 | 49 | 59 | -10 | 31 |
| | Lochee Harp | 28 | 9 | 4 | 15 | 58 | 77 | -19 | 31 |
| | Arbroath Victoria | 28 | 9 | 2 | 17 | 46 | 79 | -33 | 29 |
| | Brechin Victoria | 28 | 9 | 1 | 18 | 39 | 58 | -19 | 28 |
| | Newburgh Juniors | 28 | 3 | 3 | 22 | 33 | 94 | -61 | 12 |
| | Forfar Albion | 28 | 1 | 2 | 25 | 25 | 135 | -110 | 5 |

| uth Division | | P | W | D | L | F | A | GD | Pts |
|---|---|---|---|---|---|---|---|---|---|
| | Tranent Juniors | 22 | 16 | 5 | 1 | 68 | 22 | 46 | 53 |
| | Whitburn Juniors | 22 | 16 | 2 | 4 | 73 | 26 | 47 | 50 |
| | Blackburn United | 22 | 12 | 8 | 2 | 52 | 21 | 31 | 44 |
| | Dunbar United | 22 | 11 | 4 | 7 | 55 | 46 | 9 | 37 |
| | Lochgelly Albert | 22 | 10 | 4 | 8 | 45 | 34 | 11 | 34 |
| | Easthouses Lily Miners Welfare | 22 | 10 | 2 | 10 | 45 | 45 | 0 | 32 |
| | Rosyth | 22 | 9 | 2 | 11 | 47 | 47 | 0 | 29 |
| | West Calder United | 22 | 8 | 3 | 11 | 34 | 43 | -9 | 27 |
| | Kirkcaldy YM | 22 | 8 | 2 | 12 | 36 | 59 | -23 | 26 |
| | Pumpherston Juniors | 22 | 5 | 6 | 11 | 36 | 57 | -21 | 21 |
| | Livingston United | 22 | 4 | 2 | 16 | 27 | 74 | -47 | 14 |
| | Stoneyburn Juniors | 22 | 2 | 2 | 18 | 17 | 61 | -44 | 8 |
| | Crossgates Primrose withdrew | | | | | | | | |

## SJFA NORTH REGION

| Superleague | P | W | D | L | F | A | GD | Pts |
|---|---|---|---|---|---|---|---|---|
| 1 Banks o' Dee | 26 | 20 | 1 | 5 | 87 | 23 | 64 | 61 |
| 2 Hermes | 26 | 16 | 7 | 3 | 56 | 30 | 26 | 55 |
| 3 Stonehaven Juniors | 26 | 15 | 6 | 5 | 52 | 31 | 21 | 51 |
| 4 Dyce Juniors | 26 | 16 | 1 | 9 | 49 | 33 | 16 | 49 |
| 5 Culter | 26 | 13 | 6 | 7 | 62 | 48 | 14 | 45 |
| 6 Inverness City | 26 | 11 | 4 | 11 | 47 | 45 | 2 | 37 |
| 7 Hall Russell United (2) | 26 | 9 | 7 | 10 | 31 | 37 | -6 | 36 |
| 8 Dufftown | 26 | 9 | 5 | 12 | 45 | 52 | -7 | 32 |
| 9 Maud Juniors | 26 | 8 | 4 | 14 | 39 | 66 | -27 | 28 |
| 10 Deveronside | 26 | 8 | 3 | 15 | 40 | 59 | -19 | 27 |
| 11 Newburgh Thistle | 26 | 7 | 5 | 14 | 42 | 55 | -13 | 26 |
| 12 Banchory St Ternan | 26 | 7 | 4 | 15 | 59 | 77 | -18 | 25 |
| 13 Ellon United | 26 | 7 | 4 | 15 | 41 | 70 | -29 | 25 |
| 14 FC Stoneywood (-4) | 26 | 6 | 3 | 17 | 34 | 58 | -24 | 17 |

| Division One East | P | W | D | L | F | A | GD | Pts |
|---|---|---|---|---|---|---|---|---|
| 1 Colony Park | 22 | 19 | 3 | 0 | 78 | 16 | 62 | 60 |
| 2 Fraserburgh United | 22 | 15 | 2 | 5 | 66 | 28 | 38 | 47 |
| 3 Buchanhaven Hearts | 22 | 14 | 4 | 4 | 72 | 40 | 32 | 46 |
| 4 East End | 22 | 12 | 4 | 6 | 53 | 37 | 16 | 40 |
| 5 Lewis United | 22 | 9 | 6 | 7 | 48 | 40 | 8 | 33 |
| 6 Parkvale | 22 | 8 | 8 | 6 | 49 | 35 | 14 | 32 |
| 7 Longside | 22 | 7 | 7 | 8 | 45 | 52 | -7 | 28 |
| 8 Newmachar United | 22 | 8 | 2 | 12 | 47 | 61 | -14 | 26 |
| 9 Aberdeen University | 22 | 6 | 3 | 13 | 39 | 60 | -21 | 21 |
| 10 Sunnybank | 22 | 4 | 5 | 13 | 25 | 53 | -28 | 17 |
| 11 Glentanar | 22 | 5 | 1 | 16 | 34 | 80 | -46 | 16 |
| 12 Cruden Bay Juniors | 22 | 1 | 3 | 18 | 22 | 76 | -54 | 6 |

| Division One West | P | W | D | L | F | A | GD | Pts |
|---|---|---|---|---|---|---|---|---|
| 1 Buckie Rovers | 16 | 13 | 0 | 3 | 47 | 20 | 27 | 39 |
| 2 Forres Thistle | 16 | 10 | 2 | 4 | 27 | 15 | 12 | 32 |
| 3 Nairn St Ninian | 16 | 9 | 2 | 5 | 35 | 27 | 8 | 29 |
| 4 Islavale | 16 | 8 | 4 | 4 | 46 | 28 | 18 | 28 |
| 5 Spey Valley | 16 | 6 | 1 | 9 | 30 | 39 | -9 | 19 |
| 6 New Elgin | 16 | 5 | 3 | 8 | 26 | 32 | -6 | 18 |
| 7 Grantown | 16 | 4 | 4 | 8 | 30 | 35 | -5 | 16 |
| 8 Fochabers Juniors | 16 | 3 | 4 | 9 | 30 | 50 | -20 | 13 |
| 9 Burghead Thistle | 16 | 3 | 2 | 11 | 24 | 49 | -25 | 11 |
| 10 Lossiemouth United wthdrew | | | | | | | | |

## SJFA WESTERN REGION

| Superleague Premier | P | W | D | L | F | A | GD | Pts |
|---|---|---|---|---|---|---|---|---|
| 1 Auchinleck Talbot | 22 | 14 | 3 | 5 | 42 | 17 | 25 | 45 |
| 2 Hurlford United | 22 | 12 | 5 | 5 | 40 | 22 | 18 | 41 |
| 3 Kilbirnie Ladeside | 22 | 12 | 4 | 6 | 42 | 25 | 17 | 40 |
| 4 Troon | 22 | 12 | 1 | 9 | 51 | 31 | 20 | 37 |
| 5 Pollok | 22 | 10 | 4 | 8 | 38 | 31 | 7 | 34 |
| 6 Glenafton Athletic | 22 | 9 | 4 | 9 | 31 | 35 | -4 | 31 |
| 7 Beith Juniors | 22 | 8 | 6 | 8 | 34 | 40 | -6 | 30 |
| 8 Kirkintilloch Rob Roy | 22 | 7 | 6 | 9 | 27 | 39 | -12 | 27 |
| 9 Arthurlie | 22 | 7 | 5 | 10 | 35 | 40 | -5 | 26 |
| 10 Shettleston | 22 | 7 | 4 | 11 | 26 | 32 | -6 | 25 |
| 11 Petershill | 22 | 5 | 6 | 11 | 27 | 50 | -23 | 21 |
| 12 Irvine Meadow XI | 22 | 3 | 4 | 15 | 30 | 61 | -31 | 13 |

## SCOTTISH FOOTBALL

| Division One | | P | W | D | L | F | A | GD | Pts |
|---|---|---|---|---|---|---|---|---|---|
| 1 | Cumnock Juniors | 26 | 17 | 3 | 6 | 72 | 42 | 30 | 54 |
| 2 | Largs Thistle | 26 | 16 | 6 | 4 | 47 | 26 | 21 | 54 |
| 3 | Kilwinning Rangers | 26 | 16 | 5 | 5 | 72 | 34 | 38 | 53 |
| 4 | Clydebank | 26 | 14 | 8 | 4 | 56 | 30 | 26 | 50 |
| 5 | Blantyre Victoria | 26 | 12 | 4 | 10 | 33 | 40 | -7 | 40 |
| 6 | Kilsyth Rangers | 26 | 12 | 3 | 11 | 46 | 45 | 1 | 39 |
| 7 | Rutherglen Glencairn | 26 | 9 | 7 | 10 | 38 | 43 | -5 | 34 |
| 8 | Cumbernauld United | 26 | 10 | 4 | 12 | 46 | 56 | -10 | 34 |
| 9 | Shotts Bon Accord | 26 | 10 | 2 | 14 | 34 | 46 | -12 | 32 |
| 10 | Yoker Athletic | 26 | 8 | 7 | 11 | 52 | 52 | 0 | 31 |
| 11 | Greenock Juniors | 26 | 9 | 4 | 13 | 34 | 39 | -5 | 31 |
| 12 | Ardrossan Winton Rovers | 26 | 8 | 2 | 16 | 34 | 52 | -18 | 26 |
| 13 | Bellshill Athletic | 26 | 7 | 3 | 16 | 30 | 53 | -23 | 24 |
| 14 | Maybole Juniors | 26 | 4 | 2 | 20 | 30 | 66 | -36 | 14 |

| Central District Division One | | P | W | D | L | F | A | GD | Pts |
|---|---|---|---|---|---|---|---|---|---|
| 1 | Renfrew | 26 | 17 | 5 | 4 | 50 | 25 | 25 | 56 |
| 2 | Maryhill | 26 | 17 | 2 | 7 | 54 | 34 | 20 | 53 |
| 3 | Wishaw Juniors | 26 | 16 | 4 | 6 | 69 | 41 | 28 | 52 |
| 4 | Rossvale | 26 | 13 | 5 | 8 | 61 | 42 | 19 | 44 |
| 5 | St Roch's | 26 | 12 | 6 | 8 | 60 | 46 | 14 | 42 |
| 6 | Larkhall Thistle | 26 | 12 | 5 | 9 | 60 | 53 | 7 | 41 |
| 7 | Johnstone Burgh | 26 | 12 | 2 | 12 | 50 | 54 | -4 | 38 |
| 8 | Vale of Clyde | 26 | 10 | 6 | 10 | 46 | 45 | 1 | 36 |
| 9 | Lesmahagow Juniors | 26 | 10 | 2 | 14 | 48 | 46 | 2 | 32 |
| 10 | Thorniewood United | 26 | 9 | 5 | 12 | 51 | 51 | 0 | 32 |
| 11 | Neilston Juniors | 26 | 9 | 4 | 13 | 42 | 49 | -7 | 31 |
| 12 | Carluke Rovers | 26 | 8 | 5 | 13 | 49 | 63 | -14 | 29 |
| 13 | St Anthony's | 26 | 4 | 7 | 15 | 32 | 65 | -33 | 19 |
| 14 | Dunipace Juniors | 26 | 2 | 4 | 20 | 26 | 84 | -58 | 10 |

| Central District Division Two | | P | W | D | L | F | A | GD | Pts |
|---|---|---|---|---|---|---|---|---|---|
| 1 | Forth Wanderers | 22 | 15 | 3 | 4 | 54 | 34 | 20 | 48 |
| 2 | Benburb | 22 | 11 | 7 | 4 | 56 | 40 | 16 | 40 |
| 3 | Cambuslang Rangers | 22 | 13 | 1 | 8 | 53 | 45 | 8 | 40 |
| 4 | Port Glasgow Juniors | 22 | 11 | 6 | 5 | 50 | 32 | 18 | 39 |
| 5 | Gartcairn Juniors | 22 | 11 | 5 | 6 | 51 | 34 | 17 | 38 |
| 6 | Lanark United | 22 | 9 | 6 | 7 | 40 | 28 | 12 | 33 |
| 7 | East Kilbride Thistle | 22 | 9 | 3 | 10 | 50 | 49 | 1 | 30 |
| 8 | Glasgow Perthshire | 22 | 6 | 7 | 9 | 42 | 55 | -13 | 25 |
| 9 | Newmains United | 22 | 7 | 4 | 11 | 35 | 49 | -14 | 25 |
| 10 | Vale of Leven | 22 | 6 | 3 | 13 | 31 | 48 | -17 | 21 |
| 11 | Ashfield | 22 | 4 | 4 | 14 | 29 | 42 | -13 | 16 |
| 12 | Royal Albert | 22 | 2 | 7 | 13 | 27 | 62 | -35 | 13 |

| Ayrshire District League | | P | W | D | L | F | A | GD | Pts |
|---|---|---|---|---|---|---|---|---|---|
| 1 | Girvan | 22 | 18 | 4 | 0 | 77 | 19 | 58 | 58 |
| 2 | Irvine Victoria | 22 | 17 | 3 | 2 | 66 | 25 | 41 | 54 |
| 3 | Darvel | 22 | 15 | 1 | 6 | 61 | 32 | 29 | 46 |
| 4 | Whitletts Victoria | 22 | 10 | 6 | 6 | 57 | 33 | 24 | 36 |
| 5 | Lugar Boswell Thistle | 22 | 9 | 7 | 6 | 57 | 41 | 16 | 34 |
| 6 | Kello Rovers | 22 | 10 | 4 | 8 | 37 | 34 | 3 | 34 |
| 7 | Craigmark Burntonians | 22 | 9 | 3 | 10 | 48 | 52 | -4 | 30 |
| 8 | Dalry Thistle | 22 | 6 | 3 | 13 | 37 | 61 | -24 | 21 |
| 9 | Annbank United | 22 | 6 | 2 | 14 | 35 | 61 | -26 | 20 |
| 10 | Muirkirk Juniors | 22 | 5 | 3 | 14 | 20 | 58 | -38 | 18 |
| 11 | Ardeer Thistle | 22 | 3 | 4 | 15 | 23 | 57 | -34 | 13 |
| 12 | Saltcoats Victoria | 22 | 3 | 2 | 17 | 31 | 76 | -45 | 11 |

### SOUTH OF SCOTLAND LEAGUE

| | | P | W | D | L | F | A | GD | Pts |
|---|---|---|---|---|---|---|---|---|---|
| 1 | St Cuthbert Wanderers | 26 | 24 | 1 | 1 | 120 | 34 | 86 | 73 |
| 2 | Edusports Academy | 26 | 20 | 3 | 3 | 96 | 22 | 74 | 63 |
| 3 | Wigtown & Bladnoch | 26 | 15 | 4 | 7 | 67 | 49 | 18 | 49 |
| 4 | Lochmaben | 26 | 14 | 5 | 7 | 76 | 54 | 22 | 47 |
| 5 | Heston Rovers | 26 | 13 | 5 | 8 | 68 | 52 | 16 | 44 |
| 6 | Upper Annandale | 26 | 13 | 1 | 12 | 54 | 57 | -3 | 40 |
| 7 | Lochar Thistle | 26 | 12 | 2 | 12 | 68 | 56 | 12 | 3[illegible] |
| 8 | Mid-Annandale | 26 | 10 | 4 | 12 | 57 | 51 | 6 | 3[illegible] |
| 9 | Newton Stewart | 26 | 10 | 3 | 13 | 54 | 62 | -8 | 3[illegible] |
| 10 | Creetown | 26 | 9 | 2 | 15 | 54 | 68 | -14 | 2[illegible] |
| 11 | Abbey Vale | 26 | 8 | 2 | 16 | 48 | 76 | -28 | 2[illegible] |
| 12 | Nithsdale Wanderers | 26 | 7 | 5 | 14 | 43 | 74 | -31 | 2[illegible] |
| 13 | Fleet Star | 26 | 5 | 3 | 18 | 43 | 87 | -44 | 1[illegible] |
| 14 | Dumfries YMCA | 26 | 2 | 0 | 24 | 32 | 138 | -106 | |

### SCOTTISH AMATEUR FOOTBALL LEAGUE

| Premier Division | | P | W | D | L | F | A | GD | Pts |
|---|---|---|---|---|---|---|---|---|---|
| 1 | East Kilbride FC | 18 | 14 | 3 | 1 | 51 | 16 | 35 | [illegible] |
| 2 | Goldenhill AFC | 18 | 10 | 4 | 4 | 48 | 30 | 18 | [illegible] |
| 3 | St. Josephs FP AFC | 18 | 11 | 0 | 7 | 43 | 37 | 6 | [illegible] |
| 4 | Oban Saints AFC | 18 | 7 | 6 | 5 | 36 | 28 | 8 | [illegible] |
| 5 | Finnart AFC | 18 | 7 | 3 | 8 | 34 | 31 | 3 | [illegible] |
| 6 | Shawlands FP AFC | 18 | 7 | 3 | 8 | 37 | 39 | -2 | [illegible] |
| 7 | Inverclyde AFC | 18 | 7 | 0 | 11 | 35 | 42 | -7 | [illegible] |
| 8 | Campbeltown Pupils AFC (+3) | 18 | 5 | 3 | 10 | 27 | 44 | -17 | [illegible] |
| 9 | Alba Thistle AFC | 18 | 5 | 3 | 10 | 23 | 42 | -19 | [illegible] |
| 10 | EKRR AFC | 18 | 3 | 3 | 12 | 22 | 47 | -25 | [illegible] |

### ABERDEENSHIRE AMATEUR FOOTBALL ASSOCIATION

| Premier Division | | P | W | D | L | F | A | GD | Pts |
|---|---|---|---|---|---|---|---|---|---|
| 1 | RGU | 26 | 19 | 6 | 1 | 84 | 28 | 56 | [illegible] |
| 2 | Woodside | 26 | 20 | 2 | 4 | 87 | 30 | 57 | [illegible] |
| 3 | Sportsmans Club | 26 | 16 | 5 | 5 | 86 | 48 | 38 | [illegible] |
| 4 | MS United | 26 | 14 | 1 | 11 | 67 | 74 | -7 | [illegible] |
| 5 | Echt | 26 | 11 | 3 | 12 | 54 | 53 | 1 | [illegible] |
| 6 | Torry Select | 26 | 11 | 3 | 12 | 62 | 75 | -13 | [illegible] |
| 7 | Ellon Amateurs | 26 | 10 | 6 | 10 | 56 | 58 | -2 | [illegible] |
| 8 | University | 26 | 9 | 4 | 13 | 47 | 56 | -9 | [illegible] |
| 9 | Westdyke | 26 | 9 | 4 | 13 | 46 | 59 | -13 | [illegible] |
| 10 | Rothie Rovers | 26 | 9 | 4 | 13 | 49 | 68 | -19 | [illegible] |
| 11 | Cove Thistle (-6) | 26 | 10 | 4 | 12 | 57 | 63 | -6 | [illegible] |
| 12 | Cowie Thistle | 26 | 6 | 5 | 15 | 49 | 87 | -38 | [illegible] |
| 13 | Beacon Rangers | 26 | 5 | 4 | 17 | 51 | 72 | -21 | [illegible] |
| 14 | Alford (-6) | 26 | 6 | 3 | 17 | 40 | 64 | -24 | [illegible] |

| Division One North | | P | W | D | L | F | A | GD | Pts |
|---|---|---|---|---|---|---|---|---|---|
| 1 | Westhill | 24 | 17 | 3 | 4 | 67 | 29 | 38 | 54 |
| 2 | Kincorth | 24 | 15 | 2 | 7 | 68 | 49 | 19 | 47 |
| 3 | Nicolls Amateurs | 24 | 13 | 5 | 6 | 57 | 45 | 12 | 44 |
| 4 | Insch | 24 | 12 | 3 | 9 | 63 | 43 | 20 | 39 |
| 5 | Glendale | 24 | 10 | 8 | 6 | 46 | 40 | 6 | 38 |
| 6 | Tarves (-4) | 24 | 12 | 4 | 8 | 73 | 56 | 17 | 36 |
| 7 | Bervie Caledonian | 24 | 10 | 5 | 9 | 58 | 41 | 17 | 35 |
| 8 | Stoneywood Amateurs | 24 | 10 | 4 | 10 | 52 | 41 | 11 | 34 |
| 9 | Stonehaven Athletic | 24 | 8 | 6 | 10 | 47 | 56 | -9 | 30 |
| 10 | Great Western United | 24 | 8 | 3 | 13 | 40 | 68 | -28 | 27 |
| 11 | West End | 24 | 7 | 3 | 14 | 41 | 67 | -26 | 24 |
| 12 | Don Athletic | 24 | 6 | 3 | 15 | 56 | 75 | -19 | 21 |
| 13 | Glentanar Reflex | 24 | 2 | 3 | 19 | 37 | 95 | -58 | 9 |

| Division One East | | P | W | D | L | F | A | GD | Pts |
|---|---|---|---|---|---|---|---|---|---|
| 1 | AC Mill Inn | 24 | 16 | 6 | 2 | 78 | 37 | 41 | 54 |
| 2 | Newtonhill | 24 | 16 | 2 | 6 | 60 | 40 | 20 | 50 |
| 3 | Blackburn (-3) | 24 | 13 | 3 | 8 | 60 | 56 | 4 | 39 |
| 4 | Granite City | 24 | 11 | 4 | 9 | 56 | 45 | 11 | 37 |
| 5 | Dee Amateurs | 24 | 10 | 4 | 10 | 71 | 61 | 10 | 34 |
| 6 | Old Aberdonians | 24 | 10 | 4 | 10 | 55 | 55 | 0 | 34 |
| 7 | Banchory Amateurs | 24 | 10 | 4 | 10 | 47 | 51 | -4 | 34 |
| | Kaimhill United | 24 | 9 | 5 | 10 | 59 | 65 | -6 | 32 |
| | Halliburton | 24 | 8 | 5 | 11 | 41 | 55 | -14 | 29 |
| 0 | Dyce ITC Hydraulics | 24 | 8 | 2 | 14 | 41 | 46 | -5 | 26 |
| 1 | Formartine United | 24 | 7 | 4 | 13 | 48 | 66 | -18 | 25 |
| 2 | Bridge of Don | 24 | 7 | 2 | 15 | 49 | 75 | -26 | 23 |
| 3 | Northern United | 24 | 6 | 5 | 13 | 46 | 59 | -13 | 23 |

| ivision Two North | | P | W | D | L | F | A | GD | Pts |
|---|---|---|---|---|---|---|---|---|---|
| | Bon Accord City | 26 | 20 | 4 | 2 | 89 | 46 | 43 | 64 |
| | Cammachmore | 26 | 18 | 1 | 7 | 84 | 44 | 40 | 55 |
| | St Laurence | 26 | 15 | 5 | 6 | 85 | 37 | 48 | 50 |
| | Fintray Thistle | 26 | 14 | 6 | 6 | 74 | 45 | 29 | 48 |
| | University Strollers | 26 | 15 | 2 | 9 | 56 | 52 | 4 | 47 |
| | Newburgh Thistle | 26 | 13 | 6 | 7 | 61 | 43 | 18 | 45 |
| | Lads Club Amateurs | 26 | 13 | 4 | 9 | 68 | 51 | 17 | 43 |
| | Burghmuir | 26 | 12 | 3 | 11 | 56 | 48 | 8 | 39 |
| | Sheddocksley (-9) | 26 | 12 | 3 | 11 | 62 | 51 | 11 | 30 |
| ) | FC Polska | 26 | 8 | 4 | 14 | 67 | 82 | -15 | 28 |
| | Torphins | 26 | 7 | 3 | 16 | 48 | 83 | -35 | 24 |
| 2 | AFC Murdos (-6) | 26 | 5 | 2 | 19 | 41 | 88 | -47 | 11 |
| | CBC Hilton (-6) | 26 | 4 | 3 | 19 | 40 | 93 | -53 | 9 |
| 4 | Postal ALC | 26 | 2 | 2 | 22 | 27 | 95 | -68 | 8 |

| Division Two East | | P | W | D | L | F | A | GD | Pts |
|---|---|---|---|---|---|---|---|---|---|
| 1 | Rattrays XI | 26 | 18 | 5 | 3 | 80 | 36 | 44 | 59 |
| 2 | Turriff Thistle | 26 | 17 | 6 | 3 | 76 | 31 | 45 | 57 |
| 3 | Ellon Thistle | 26 | 17 | 5 | 4 | 62 | 26 | 36 | 56 |
| 4 | Westdyce | 26 | 16 | 5 | 5 | 88 | 44 | 44 | 53 |
| 5 | Huntly Amateurs | 26 | 11 | 4 | 11 | 52 | 55 | -3 | 37 |
| 6 | Glendale Youth (-9) | 26 | 13 | 5 | 8 | 68 | 59 | 9 | 35 |
| 7 | Kintore | 26 | 11 | 2 | 13 | 57 | 69 | -12 | 35 |
| 8 | Grammar FPs | 26 | 9 | 6 | 11 | 61 | 72 | -11 | 33 |
| 9 | BSFC | 26 | 7 | 9 | 10 | 53 | 62 | -9 | 30 |
| 10 | JS XI | 26 | 7 | 5 | 14 | 52 | 70 | -18 | 26 |
| 11 | Theologians | 26 | 6 | 6 | 14 | 46 | 63 | -17 | 24 |
| 12 | Feughside | 26 | 7 | 2 | 17 | 43 | 68 | -25 | 23 |
| 13 | Middlefield Wasps (-3) | 26 | 7 | 4 | 15 | 56 | 80 | -24 | 22 |
| 14 | Continental (-4) | 26 | 2 | 4 | 20 | 35 | 94 | -59 | 6 |

| Division Three | | P | W | D | L | F | A | GD | Pts |
|---|---|---|---|---|---|---|---|---|---|
| 1 | Balmedie | 24 | 16 | 5 | 3 | 70 | 34 | 36 | 53 |
| 2 | Auchnagatt Barons | 24 | 15 | 5 | 4 | 70 | 34 | 36 | 50 |
| 3 | Monymusk | 24 | 13 | 6 | 5 | 54 | 38 | 16 | 45 |
| 4 | Aboyne | 24 | 13 | 3 | 8 | 67 | 49 | 18 | 42 |
| 5 | Glendale XI | 24 | 12 | 6 | 6 | 74 | 46 | 28 | 42 |
| 6 | Jesus House (-3) | 24 | 12 | 5 | 7 | 51 | 45 | 6 | 38 |
| 7 | Kemnay Youth | 24 | 11 | 5 | 8 | 48 | 36 | 12 | 38 |
| 8 | Highland Hotel | 24 | 9 | 5 | 10 | 47 | 48 | -1 | 32 |
| 9 | University Colts | 24 | 9 | 3 | 12 | 36 | 40 | -4 | 30 |
| 10 | Colony Park | 24 | 7 | 2 | 15 | 37 | 73 | -36 | 23 |
| 11 | McTeagle | 24 | 7 | 0 | 17 | 34 | 73 | -39 | 21 |
| 12 | Bon Accord Thistle (-6) | 24 | 6 | 3 | 15 | 50 | 69 | -19 | 15 |
| 13 | Ferryhill (-3) | 24 | 1 | 2 | 21 | 16 | 69 | -53 | 2 |

## BORDER AMATEUR LEAGUE

| A League | | P | W | D | L | F | A | GD | Pts |
|---|---|---|---|---|---|---|---|---|---|
| 1 | West Barns Star | 18 | 13 | 2 | 3 | 64 | 26 | 38 | 41 |
| 2 | Gordon | 18 | 10 | 5 | 3 | 50 | 28 | 22 | 35 |
| 3 | Jed Legion | 18 | 10 | 3 | 5 | 40 | 24 | 16 | 33 |
| 4 | Stow | 18 | 8 | 5 | 5 | 35 | 27 | 8 | 29 |
| 5 | Chirnside United | 18 | 9 | 1 | 8 | 47 | 42 | 5 | 28 |
| 6 | Greenlaw | 18 | 6 | 5 | 7 | 39 | 35 | 4 | 23 |
| 7 | Langholm Legion | 18 | 7 | 2 | 9 | 37 | 45 | -8 | 23 |
| 8 | Hawick Waverley | 18 | 6 | 2 | 10 | 33 | 50 | -17 | 20 |
| 9 | Hawick Legion | 18 | 5 | 3 | 10 | 39 | 51 | -12 | 18 |
| 10 | Leithen Rovers | 18 | 1 | 2 | 15 | 18 | 74 | -56 | 5 |

## SCOTTISH JUNIOR CUP

### ROUND 1

| | | | |
|---|---|---|---|
| Larkhall Thistle | v | Haddington Athletic | 3-2 |
| East Kilbride Thistle | v | Armadale Thistle | 0-4 |
| Inverness City | v | FC Stoneywood | 2-1 |
| Kilwinning Rangers | v | Dalry Thistle | 3-1 |
| Newmains United | v | Fraserburgh United | 1-8 |
| Bonnyrigg Rose Athletic | v | Thorniewood United | 3-0 |
| Ardeer Thistle | v | West Calder United | 3-3 |
| Nairn St. Ninian | v | Oakley United | 1-1 |
| Crossgates Primrose | v | Lanark United | 1-4 |
| Sunnybank | v | Yoker Athletic | 1-5 |
| Stoneyburn | v | Dyce Juniors | 1-0 |
| Whitletts Victoria | v | Lochgelly Albert | 3-1 |
| Glenafton Athletic | v | Newmachar United | 14-0 |
| Hall Russell United | v | Vale of Clyde | 1-2 |
| Bridge of Don Thistle | v | Rosyth | 2-2 |
| Vale of Leven | v | Kennoway Star Hearts | 0-0 |
| Newtongrange Star | v | Edinburgh United | 5-1 |
| Newburgh | v | Kilbirnie Ladeside | 0-6 |
| Irvine Victoria | v | Camelon Juniors | 1-7 |
| Maybole | v | Broxburn Athletic | 0-0 |
| Ardrossan Winton Rovers | v | Whitburn | 2-1 |
| Montrose Roselea | v | Forfar Albion | 4-0 |
| Lochee Harp | v | Tayport | 1-2 |
| Banchory St. Ternan | v | East End | 1-2 |
| Buckie Rovers | v | Hill of Beath Hawthorn | 0-3 |
| Burghead Thistle | v | Kilsyth Rangers | 1-5 |
| Cumnock Juniors | v | Broughty Athletic | 3-0 |
| Neilston Juniors | v | Dufftown | 3-1 |
| Bellshill Athletic | v | Wishaw Juniors | 0-0 |
| Port Glasgow | v | Benburb | 1-1 |

**Replays**

| | | | |
|---|---|---|---|
| West Calder United | v | Ardeer Thistle | 2-1 |
| Oakley United | v | Nairn St. Ninian | 4-0 |
| Rosyth | v | Bridge of Don Thistle | 7-0 |
| Kennoway Star Hearts | v | Vale of Leven | 4-1 |
| Broxburn Athletic | v | Maybole | 4-0 |
| Wishaw Juniors | v | Bellshill Athletic | 1-0 |
| Benburb | v | Port Glasgow | 2-1 |

### ROUND 2

| | | | |
|---|---|---|---|
| St Andrews United | | Oakley United | 2-2 |
| Thornton Hibs | v | East Craigie | 1-1 |
| Dundee Violet | v | Forth | 7-1 |
| Kilwinning Rangers | v | Ashfield | 4-2 |
| Stonehaven | v | Shotts Bon Accord | 2-0 |
| Forfar West End | v | Clydebank | 0-2 |
| Arbroath Victoria | v | Dundonald Bluebell | 2-3 |
| Shettleston | v | Kilbirnie Ladeside | 1-1 |
| Kirkcaldy YM | v | Royal Albert | 0-3 |
| Lesmahagow | v | Hill of Beath Hawthorn | 3-4 |
| Saltcoats Victoria | v | Easthouses Lily MW | 3-3 |
| Tranent Juniors | v | Auchinleck Talbot | 0-2 |
| Beith Juniors | v | Vale of Clyde | 10-2 |
| Linlithgow Rose | v | Annbank United | 7-2 |
| Lochee United | v | Maryhill | 4-3 |
| West Calder United | v | Dunipace Juniors | 1-3 |
| Kelty Hearts | v | Stoneyburn | 5-0 |
| Kilsyth Rangers | v | Culter | 3-2 |
| Bathgate Thistle | v | Greenock Juniors | 2-2 |
| Coupar Angus | v | Lossiemouth United | 0-0 |
| Ellon United | v | St Roch's | 0-3 |
| Aberdeen University | v | Dundee North End | 0-3 |
| Livingston United | v | Largs Thistle | 2-1 |
| Dunbar United | v | Irvine Meadow | 0-3 |
| Brechin Victoria | v | Penicuik Athletic | 1-2 |
| Kirkintilloch Rob Roy | v | Wishaw Juniors | 0-3 |
| Fochabers | v | Kennoway Star Hearts | 0-2 |
| Renfrew | v | Maud | 4-0 |
| Larkhall Thistle | v | Arniston Rangers | 2-2 |
| Camelon Juniors | v | Banks O' Dee | 3-2 |
| Blantyre Victoria | v | Rosyth | 1-5 |
| Neilston Juniors | v | Rutherglen Glencairn | 2-0 |
| Lochore Welfare | v | Darvel | 0-1 |
| Musselburgh Athletic | v | Johnstone Burgh | 7-1 |
| Buchanhaven Hearts | v | Arthurlie | 0-4 |
| Parkvale | v | Tayport | 4-5 |
| Fauldhouse United | v | Hurlford United | 2-2 |
| Lewis United | v | Troon | 0-4 |
| St Anthony's | v | Forres Thistle | 6-0 |
| Bonnyrigg Rose Athletic | v | Montrose Roselea | 6-1 |
| Blackburn United | v | Downfield | 2-1 |
| Rossvale | v | Pumpherston | 2-0 |
| Bo'ness United | v | East End | 5-0 |
| Falkirk Juniors | v | Longside | 4-0 |
| Girvan | v | Cambuslang Rangers | 7-1 |
| Broxburn Athletic | v | Whitletts Victoria | 1-3 |
| Pollok | v | Yoker Athletic | 3-1 |
| Inverness City | v | Sauchie Juniors | 1-3 |
| Gartcairn FA Juniors | v | Hermes | 3-3 |
| Scone Thistle | v | Benburb | 1-1 |
| Colony Park | v | Carnoustie Panmure | 0-7 |
| Spey Valley | v | Cumbernauld United | 1-8 |
| Glenafton Athletic | v | Jeanfield Swifts | 1-3 |
| Fraserburgh United | v | Kinnoull | 1-3 |
| Kello Rovers | v | Cumnock Juniors | 2-3 |
| Grantown | v | Blairgowrie | 2-3 |
| Carluke Rovers | v | Lugar Boswell Thistle | 4-2 |
| Petershill | v | Newtongrange Star | 1-1 |
| Dalkeith Thistle | v | Kirriemuir Thistle | 1-0 |
| Ardrossan Winton Rovers | v | Deveronside | 7-3 |
| Glasgow Perthshire | v | Lanark United | 0-4 |
| Cruden Bay | v | Armadale Thistle | 0-7 |
| Muirkirk Juniors | v | Craigmark Burntonians | 3-2 |
| New Elgin | v | Glenrothes | 0-5 |

**Replays**

| | | | |
|---|---|---|---|
| Oakley United | v | St Andrews United | 1-0 |
| East Craigie | v | Thornton Hibs | 3-2 |
| Kilbirnie Ladeside | v | Shettleston | 2-0 |
| Easthouses Lily MW | v | Saltcoats Victoria | 1-3 |
| Greenock Juniors | v | Bathgate Thistle | 1-1, 3-4p |
| Lossiemouth United | v | Coupar Angus | 1-4 |

### ROUND 3

| | | | |
|---|---|---|---|
| Cumnock Juniors | v | Dundonald Bluebell | 3-2 |
| Lochee United | v | Penicuik Athletic | 4-2 |
| Whitletts Victoria | v | Dalkeith Thistle | 1-5 |
| Carnoustie Panmure | v | Livingston United | 5-0 |
| Linlithgow Rose | v | Cumbernauld United | 5-0 |
| Wishaw Juniors | v | Armadale Thistle | 1-1 |
| Royal Albert | v | Pollok | 1-41 |
| Bathgate Thistle | v | Oakley United | 1-4 |
| Hurlford United | v | Falkirk Juniors | 4-1 |
| Troon | v | Bo'ness United | 2-1 |
| Girvan | v | Beith Juniors | 0-0 |
| Lanark United | v | Rossvale | 0-5 |
| Hill of Beath Hawthorn | v | Ardrossan Winton Rovers | 3-1 |
| Scone Thistle | v | Saltcoats Victoria | 3-1 |
| St Roch's | v | Kennoway Star Hearts | 1-1 |
| Kinnoull | v | Auchinleck Talbot | 2-8 |
| Renfrew | v | East Craigie | 4-1 |
| Glenrothes | v | Rosyth | 2-2 |
| Jeanfield Swifts | v | Bonnyrigg Rose Athletic | 1-3 |
| Kilbirnie Ladeside | v | Dundee Violet | 0-0 |
| Petershill | v | Musselburgh Athletic | 1-0 |
| Neilston Juniors | v | Arniston Rangers | 1-1 |
| Tayport | v | Muirkirk | 0-0 |
| Irvine Meadow | v | Blackburn United | 6-2 |
| Blairgowrie | v | Darvel | 2-3 |
| Kilwinning Rangers | v | Sauchie Juniors | 2-1 |
| Stonehaven | v | St Anthony's | 3-1 |
| Arthurlie | v | Dunipace Juniors | 4-1 |
| Clydebank | v | Kelty Hearts | 0-1 |
| Dundee North End | v | Carluke Rovers | 2-0 |
| Kilsyth Rangers | v | Camelon Juniors | 1-4 |
| Coupar Angus | v | Hermes | 1-4 |

**Replays**

| | | | |
|---|---|---|---|
| Armadale Thistle | v | Wishaw Juniors | 2-2, 3-5p |
| Beith Juniors | v | Girvan | 2-1 |
| Kennoway Star Hearts | v | St Roch's | 3-3, 4-3p |

| | | | |
|---|---|---|---|
| Rosyth | v | Glenrothes | 0-0, 3-4p |
| Dundee Violet | v | Kilbirnie Ladeside | 1-4 |
| Arniston Rangers | v | Neilston Juniors | 2-1 2 |
| Muirkirk Juniors | v | Tayport | 0-5 |

**ROUND 4**

| | | | |
|---|---|---|---|
| Kennoway Star Hearts | v | Pollok | 2-7 |
| Kelty Hearts | v | Renfrew | 8-0 |
| Auchinleck Talbot | v | Cumnock Juniors | 3-0 |
| Linlithgow Rose | v | Irvine Meadow | 1-1 |
| Kilwinning Rangers | v | Arniston Rangers | 3-0 |
| Camelon Juniors | v | Dundee North End | 1-0 |
| Kilbirnie Ladeside | v | Tayport | 3-0 |
| Glenrothes | v | Hermes | 4-5 |
| Oakley United | v | Carnoustie Panmure | 0-1 |
| Darvel Juniors | v | Troon | 2-1 |
| Scone Thistle | v | Beith Juniors | 1-5 |
| Hill of Beath Hawthorn | v | Petershill | 0-3 |
| Hurlford United | v | Dalkeith Thistle | 5-3 |
| Rossvale | v | Stonehaven | 6-1 |
| Bonnyrigg Rose Athletic | v | Lochee United | 2-0 |
| Arthurlie | v | Wishaw Juniors | 4-1 |
| **Replay** | | | |
| Irvine Meadow | v | Linlithgow Rose | 0-2 |

**ROUND 5**

| | | | |
|---|---|---|---|
| Beith Juniors | v | Petershill | 3-1 |
| Bonnyrigg Rose Athletic | v | Pollok | 0-5 |
| Hermes | v | Kilbirnie Ladeside | 0-2 |
| Kilwinning Rangers | v | Linlithgow Rose | 4-1 |
| Camelon Juniors | v | Kelty Hearts | 4-1 |
| Carnoustie Panmure | v | Auchinleck Talbot | 2-3 |
| Darvel Juniors | v | Arthurlie | 0-3 |
| Hurlford United | v | Rossvale | 4-0 |

**QUARTER FINALS**

| | | | |
|---|---|---|---|
| Beith Juniors | v | Arthurlie | 3-1 |
| Kilwinning Rangers | v | Camelon Juniors | 3-3 |
| Hurlford United | v | Auchinleck Talbot | 2-0 |
| Pollok | v | Kilbirnie Ladeside | 1-0 |
| Replay | | | |
| Camelon Juniors | v | Kilwinning Rangers | 1-4 |

**SEMI FINALS 1st LEG**

| | | | |
|---|---|---|---|
| Beith Juniors | v | Kilwinning Rangers | 3-0 |
| Hurlford United | v | Pollok | 0-0 |

**SEMI FINALS 2nd LEG**

| | | | |
|---|---|---|---|
| Kilwinning Rangers | v | Beith Juniors | 1-0 |
| Pollok | v | Hurlford United | 0-0, 4-3p |

**FINAL**

| | | | |
|---|---|---|---|
| Beith Juniors | v | Pollok | 1-1, 4-3p |

# WELSH TABLES 2015-16

## WELSH PREMIER

| | | P | W | D | L | F | A | GD | Pts |
|---|---|---|---|---|---|---|---|---|---|
| 1 | The New Saints | 32 | 18 | 10 | 4 | 72 | 24 | +48 | 64 |
| 2 | Bala Town | 32 | 15 | 12 | 5 | 48 | 27 | +21 | 57 |
| 3 | Llandudno | 32 | 15 | 7 | 10 | 53 | 46 | +7 | 52 |
| 4 | Connah's Quay Nomads | 32 | 15 | 3 | 14 | 50 | 42 | +8 | 48 |
| 5 | Newtown | 32 | 11 | 9 | 12 | 46 | 54 | -8 | 42 |
| 6 | Airbus UK Broughton | 32 | 12 | 6 | 14 | 46 | 55 | -9 | 42 |
| 7 | Carmarthen Town | 32 | 14 | 5 | 13 | 45 | 52 | -7 | 47 |
| 8 | Aberystwyth Town | 32 | 13 | 7 | 12 | 51 | 47 | +4 | 46 |
| 9 | Bangor City | 32 | 13 | 6 | 13 | 49 | 52 | -3 | 45 |
| 10 | Port Talbot Town | 32 | 10 | 9 | 13 | 39 | 56 | -17 | 39 |
| 11 | Rhyl | 32 | 5 | 12 | 15 | 36 | 50 | -14 | 27 |
| 12 | Haverfordwest County | 32 | 5 | 6 | 21 | 27 | 57 | -30 | 21 |

Ater 22 games the League splits into two. The top six then play each other twice again and the bottom six do the same. However, once split, no team can climb back into the top six no matter what points they finish on.

## CYMRU ALLIANCE

| | | P | W | D | L | F | A | GD | Pts |
|---|---|---|---|---|---|---|---|---|---|
| 1 | Caernarfon Town | 30 | 24 | 3 | 3 | 95 | 23 | 72 | 75 |
| 2 | Cefn Druids | 30 | 21 | 3 | 6 | 62 | 33 | 29 | 66 |
| 3 | Denbigh Town | 30 | 20 | 3 | 7 | 72 | 46 | 26 | 63 |
| 4 | Guilsfield | 30 | 17 | 2 | 11 | 60 | 44 | 16 | 53 |
| 5 | Holywell Town | 30 | 15 | 7 | 8 | 55 | 34 | 21 | 52 |
| 6 | Gresford Athletic | 30 | 15 | 4 | 11 | 45 | 44 | 1 | 49 |
| 7 | Holyhead Hotspur | 30 | 13 | 7 | 10 | 44 | 40 | 4 | 46 |
| 8 | Prestatyn Town | 30 | 14 | 3 | 13 | 61 | 50 | 11 | 45 |
| 9 | Flint Town United | 30 | 13 | 3 | 14 | 54 | 45 | 9 | 42 |
| 10 | Porthmadog | 30 | 13 | 2 | 15 | 47 | 54 | -7 | 41 |
| 11 | Conwy Borough | 30 | 11 | 3 | 16 | 47 | 54 | -7 | 36 |
| 12 | Buckley Town | 30 | 9 | 5 | 16 | 45 | 65 | -20 | 32 |
| 13 | Mold Alexandra | 30 | 9 | 4 | 17 | 38 | 59 | -21 | 31 |
| 14 | Caersws | 30 | 8 | 2 | 20 | 40 | 67 | -27 | 26 |
| 15 | Llanfair United | 30 | 7 | 0 | 23 | 35 | 70 | -35 | 21 |
| 16 | Rhayader Town | 30 | 4 | 3 | 23 | 24 | 96 | -72 | 15 |

## WELSH LEAGUE

| Division One | | P | W | D | L | F | A | GD | Pts |
|---|---|---|---|---|---|---|---|---|---|
| 1 | Cardiff Met University | 30 | 19 | 5 | 6 | 63 | 26 | 37 | 62 |
| 2 | Barry Town United | 30 | 16 | 10 | 4 | 62 | 33 | 29 | 58 |
| 3 | Goytre | 30 | 17 | 5 | 8 | 72 | 36 | 36 | 56 |
| 4 | Caerau (Ely) | 30 | 15 | 5 | 10 | 59 | 43 | 16 | 50 |
| 5 | Cambrian & Clydach | 30 | 15 | 5 | 10 | 48 | 39 | 9 | 50 |
| 6 | Taffs Well | 30 | 14 | 5 | 11 | 57 | 51 | 6 | 47 |
| 7 | Goytre United | 30 | 13 | 4 | 13 | 45 | 47 | -2 | 43 |
| 8 | Afan Lido | 30 | 11 | 9 | 10 | 53 | 53 | 0 | 42 |
| 9 | Ton Pentre | 30 | 12 | 4 | 14 | 45 | 52 | -7 | 40 |
| 10 | Risca United | 30 | 12 | 3 | 15 | 48 | 48 | 0 | 39 |
| 11 | Penybont | 30 | 11 | 6 | 13 | 53 | 56 | -3 | 39 |
| 12 | Monmouth Town | 30 | 10 | 9 | 11 | 56 | 60 | -4 | 39 |
| 13 | Briton Ferry Llansawel | 30 | 10 | 9 | 11 | 41 | 49 | -8 | 39 |
| 14 | Aberdare Town | 30 | 11 | 4 | 15 | 34 | 56 | -22 | 37 |
| 15 | Aberbargoed Buds | 30 | 8 | 3 | 19 | 42 | 63 | -21 | 27 |
| 16 | Garden Village | 30 | 1 | 4 | 25 | 27 | 93 | -66 | 7 |
| 15 | Pontardawe Town | 30 | 4 | 6 | 20 | 28 | 66 | -38 | 18 |
| 16 | AFC Porth | 30 | 0 | 1 | 29 | 16 | 131 | -115 | 1 |

| Division Two | | P | W | D | L | F | A | GD | Pts |
|---|---|---|---|---|---|---|---|---|---|
| 1 | Caldicot Town | 30 | 24 | 1 | 5 | 68 | 28 | 40 | 73 |
| 2 | Cwmbran Celtic | 30 | 24 | 0 | 6 | 89 | 33 | 56 | 72 |
| 3 | Undy Athletic | 30 | 22 | 5 | 3 | 76 | 24 | 52 | 71 |
| 4 | Pontardawe Town | 30 | 16 | 9 | 5 | 55 | 37 | 18 | 57 |
| 5 | Ammanford | 30 | 16 | 3 | 11 | 59 | 44 | 15 | 51 |
| 6 | Cwmamman United | 30 | 15 | 5 | 10 | 71 | 48 | 23 | 50 |
| 7 | Llanelli Town | 30 | 15 | 3 | 12 | 59 | 44 | 15 | 48 |
| 8 | AFC Llwydcoed | 30 | 13 | 4 | 13 | 52 | 52 | 0 | 43 |
| 9 | AFC Porth | 30 | 11 | 4 | 15 | 49 | 51 | -2 | 37 |
| 10 | Tata Steel | 30 | 9 | 8 | 13 | 42 | 60 | -18 | 35 |
| 11 | West End | 30 | 9 | 5 | 16 | 46 | 76 | -30 | 32 |
| 12 | Croesyceilog | 30 | 8 | 6 | 16 | 38 | 60 | -22 | 30 |
| 13 | Llanwern | 30 | 8 | 5 | 17 | 43 | 55 | -12 | 29 |
| 14 | Dinas Powys | 30 | 8 | 2 | 20 | 36 | 70 | -34 | 26 |
| 15 | Penrhiwceiber Rangers | 30 | 4 | 6 | 20 | 46 | 91 | -45 | 18 |
| 16 | Chepstow Town | 30 | 3 | 4 | 23 | 37 | 93 | -56 | 13 |

| Division Three | | P | W | D | L | F | A | GD | Pts |
|---|---|---|---|---|---|---|---|---|---|
| 1 | Pontypridd Town | 34 | 25 | 6 | 3 | 99 | 31 | 68 | 8 |
| 2 | Abergavenny Town | 34 | 24 | 5 | 5 | 98 | 48 | 50 | 7 |
| 3 | Bridgend Street | 34 | 22 | 6 | 6 | 81 | 50 | 31 | 7 |
| 4 | STM Sports | 34 | 21 | 4 | 9 | 103 | 65 | 38 | 6 |
| 5 | Caerau | 34 | 20 | 5 | 9 | 108 | 69 | 39 | 6 |
| 6 | Llantwit Major | 34 | 18 | 11 | 5 | 71 | 39 | 32 | 6 |
| 7 | Panteg | 34 | 17 | 6 | 11 | 88 | 67 | 21 | 5 |
| 8 | Cwm Welfare | 34 | 15 | 5 | 14 | 79 | 71 | 8 | 5 |
| 9 | Treharris Athletic Western | 34 | 13 | 6 | 15 | 72 | 60 | 12 | 4 |
| 10 | Tredegar Town | 34 | 12 | 7 | 15 | 51 | 51 | 0 | 4 |
| 11 | Treowen Stars | 34 | 12 | 7 | 15 | 53 | 77 | -24 | 4 |
| 12 | Caerleon | 34 | 11 | 8 | 15 | 62 | 72 | -10 | 4 |
| 13 | Ely Rangers | 34 | 11 | 8 | 15 | 64 | 77 | -13 | 4 |
| 14 | Bettws | 34 | 10 | 5 | 19 | 65 | 87 | -22 | 3 |
| 15 | Lliswerry | 34 | 9 | 3 | 22 | 47 | 71 | -24 | 3 |
| 16 | Newport YMCA | 34 | 7 | 6 | 21 | 44 | 91 | -47 | 2 |
| 17 | Cardiff Corinthians | 34 | 3 | 8 | 23 | 45 | 104 | -59 | [illegible] |
| 18 | Newport Civil Service | 34 | 2 | 2 | 30 | 39 | 139 | -100 | |

## WELSH NATIONAL LEAGUE

| | Premier | P | W | D | L | F | A | GD | Pts |
|---|---|---|---|---|---|---|---|---|---|
| 1 | FC Nomads of Connah's Quay | 26 | 18 | 4 | 4 | 95 | 33 | 62 | 58 |
| 2 | Ruthin Town | 26 | 17 | 4 | 5 | 70 | 35 | 35 | 55 |
| 3 | FC Queens Park | 26 | 17 | 2 | 7 | 89 | 38 | 51 | 53 |
| 4 | Chirk AAA | 26 | 15 | 6 | 5 | 77 | 30 | 47 | 51 |
| 5 | Brymbo | 26 | 16 | 2 | 8 | 71 | 37 | 34 | 47 |
| 6 | Hawarden Rangers | 26 | 13 | 3 | 10 | 56 | 38 | 18 | 42 |
| 7 | Corwen | 26 | 12 | 4 | 10 | 68 | 48 | 20 | 40 |
| 8 | Saltney Town | 26 | 12 | 3 | 11 | 71 | 58 | 13 | 39 |
| 9 | Penycae | 26 | 12 | 2 | 12 | 64 | 67 | -3 | 38 |
| 10 | Brickfield Rangers | 26 | 11 | 3 | 12 | 50 | 65 | -15 | 36 |
| 11 | Overton Recreational | 26 | 7 | 3 | 16 | 49 | 70 | -21 | 24 |
| 12 | Llay Welfare | 26 | 5 | 4 | 17 | 38 | 87 | -49 | 19 |
| 13 | Penyffordd | 26 | 4 | 3 | 19 | 31 | 133 | -102 | 15 |
| 14 | Coedpoeth United | 26 | 1 | 1 | 24 | 21 | 111 | -90 | 4 |
| 15 | Borras Park Albion withdrew - record expunged. | | | | | | | | |

| | Division One | P | W | D | L | F | A | GD | Pts |
|---|---|---|---|---|---|---|---|---|---|
| 1 | Cefn Albion | 24 | 19 | 1 | 4 | 122 | 35 | 87 | 58 |
| 2 | Llanuwchllyn | 24 | 18 | 3 | 3 | 119 | 26 | 93 | 57 |
| 3 | Rhos Aelwyd | 24 | 17 | 3 | 4 | 62 | 22 | 40 | 54 |
| 4 | Lex Glyndwr | 24 | 15 | 2 | 7 | 67 | 41 | 26 | 47 |
| 5 | Llangollen Town | 24 | 14 | 4 | 6 | 76 | 32 | 44 | 46 |
| 6 | Penley | 24 | 12 | 5 | 7 | 73 | 52 | 21 | 41 |
| 7 | AFC Brynford | 24 | 12 | 2 | 10 | 85 | 58 | 27 | 38 |
| 8 | Point of Ayr | 24 | 11 | 0 | 13 | 81 | 78 | 3 | 33 |
| 9 | Castell Alun Colts | 24 | 10 | 1 | 13 | 55 | 53 | 2 | 31 |
| 10 | New Brighton Villa | 24 | 9 | 2 | 13 | 60 | 64 | -4 | 29 |
| 11 | Johnstown Youth | 24 | 2 | 2 | 20 | 30 | 130 | -100 | 8 |
| 12 | Acrefair Youth | 24 | 2 | 1 | 21 | 33 | 163 | -130 | 7 |
| 13 | Garden Village (-6) | 24 | 1 | 2 | 21 | 19 | 128 | -109 | -1 |
| 14 | Argoed United withdrew - record expunged. | | | | | | | | |
| 15 | CPD Caerwys withdrew - record expunged. | | | | | | | | |

## NORTH EAST WALES LEAGUE

| | Division One | P | W | D | L | F | A | GD | Pts |
|---|---|---|---|---|---|---|---|---|---|
| | Rhostyllen | 20 | 16 | 3 | 1 | 121 | 31 | 90 | 51 |
| 2 | CPD Sychdyn | 20 | 11 | 5 | 4 | 59 | 24 | 35 | 38 |
| | Mold Town United | 20 | 11 | 2 | 7 | 51 | 48 | 3 | 35 |
| | Gap Connah's Quay Res. (-3) | 20 | 11 | 4 | 5 | 55 | 44 | 11 | 34 |
| | Offa Athletic (-3) | 20 | 9 | 4 | 7 | 55 | 58 | -3 | 28 |
| | Connah's Quay Tigers | 20 | 9 | 1 | 10 | 54 | 60 | -6 | 28 |
| | Ewloe Spartans | 20 | 7 | 6 | 7 | 38 | 46 | -8 | 27 |
| | Maesgwyn | 20 | 6 | 5 | 9 | 44 | 79 | -35 | 23 |
| | Flint Mountain | 20 | 4 | 6 | 10 | 48 | 59 | -11 | 18 |
| 0 | Aston Park Rangers | 20 | 3 | 5 | 12 | 42 | 81 | -39 | 14 |
| | Acton | 20 | 2 | 1 | 17 | 36 | 73 | -37 | 7 |
| 2 | Castle Park withdrew - record expunged. | | | | | | | | |

## WELSH ALLIANCE

| | Division One | P | W | D | L | F | A | GD | Pts |
|---|---|---|---|---|---|---|---|---|---|
| 1 | Trearddur Bay | 30 | 22 | 7 | 1 | 85 | 31 | 54 | 73 |
| 2 | Llandudno Junction | 30 | 21 | 7 | 2 | 86 | 37 | 49 | 70 |
| 3 | Llangefni Town | 30 | 19 | 5 | 6 | 65 | 44 | 21 | 62 |
| 4 | Glantraeth (-3) | 30 | 18 | 6 | 6 | 65 | 42 | 23 | 57 |
| 5 | Llanrug United | 30 | 16 | 7 | 7 | 68 | 36 | 32 | 55 |
| 6 | Penrhyndeudraeth | 30 | 15 | 5 | 10 | 81 | 53 | 28 | 50 |
| 7 | Glan Conwy | 30 | 13 | 2 | 15 | 71 | 67 | 4 | 41 |
| 8 | Abergele Town | 30 | 12 | 3 | 15 | 41 | 51 | -10 | 39 |
| 9 | Gwalchmai | 30 | 11 | 3 | 16 | 43 | 61 | -18 | 36 |
| 10 | Barmouth & Dyffryn United | 30 | 11 | 2 | 17 | 37 | 59 | -22 | 35 |
| 11 | Llanberis | 30 | 8 | 9 | 13 | 46 | 48 | -2 | 33 |
| 12 | St Asaph City | 30 | 10 | 3 | 17 | 57 | 65 | -8 | 33 |
| 13 | Llanrwst United | 30 | 9 | 5 | 16 | 39 | 61 | -22 | 32 |
| 14 | Pwllheli (-3) | 30 | 7 | 8 | 15 | 45 | 66 | -21 | 26 |
| 15 | Llandyrnog United (-3) | 30 | 7 | 5 | 18 | 41 | 72 | -31 | 23 |
| 16 | Llanfairpwll | 30 | 1 | 3 | 26 | 20 | 97 | -77 | 6 |

| | Division Two | P | W | D | L | F | A | GD | Pts |
|---|---|---|---|---|---|---|---|---|---|
| 1 | Greenfield | 24 | 21 | 2 | 1 | 94 | 36 | 58 | 65 |
| 2 | Nantlle Vale | 24 | 18 | 2 | 4 | 77 | 39 | 38 | 56 |
| 3 | Llanllyfni | 24 | 13 | 7 | 4 | 76 | 46 | 30 | 46 |
| 4 | Mynydd Llandegai | 24 | 13 | 3 | 8 | 59 | 61 | -2 | 42 |
| 5 | Pentraeth | 24 | 11 | 5 | 8 | 75 | 47 | 28 | 38 |
| 6 | Prestatyn Sports | 24 | 11 | 4 | 9 | 72 | 57 | 15 | 37 |
| 7 | Mochdre Sports | 24 | 8 | 6 | 10 | 46 | 59 | -13 | 30 |
| 8 | Meliden | 24 | 9 | 2 | 13 | 59 | 65 | -6 | 29 |
| 9 | Amlwch Town | 24 | 8 | 4 | 12 | 44 | 59 | -15 | 28 |
| 10 | Penmaenmawr Phoenix | 24 | 7 | 5 | 12 | 49 | 54 | -5 | 26 |
| 11 | Llanerchymedd | 24 | 7 | 3 | 14 | 33 | 58 | -25 | 24 |
| 12 | Blaenau Ffestiniog Amt | 24 | 7 | 0 | 17 | 55 | 100 | -45 | 21 |
| 13 | Gaerwen (-3) | 24 | 0 | 3 | 21 | 35 | 93 | -58 | 0 |
| 14 | Halkyn United withdrew - record expunged. | | | | | | | | |

## GWYNEDD LEAGUE

| | | P | W | D | L | F | A | GD | Pts |
|---|---|---|---|---|---|---|---|---|---|
| 1 | Y Felinheli | 24 | 17 | 2 | 5 | 64 | 39 | 25 | 53 |
| 2 | Llanystumdwy | 24 | 15 | 4 | 5 | 78 | 42 | 36 | 49 |
| 3 | Cemaes Bay | 24 | 14 | 3 | 7 | 63 | 34 | 29 | 45 |
| 4 | Menai Bridge Tigers | 24 | 14 | 3 | 7 | 69 | 47 | 22 | 45 |
| 5 | Nefyn United | 24 | 14 | 2 | 8 | 70 | 39 | 31 | 44 |
| 6 | Aberffraw | 24 | 13 | 3 | 8 | 62 | 41 | 21 | 42 |
| 7 | Bodedern Athletic | 24 | 11 | 6 | 7 | 66 | 37 | 29 | 39 |
| 8 | Waunfawr | 24 | 11 | 2 | 11 | 57 | 47 | 10 | 35 |
| 9 | Bontnewydd | 24 | 10 | 4 | 10 | 57 | 60 | -3 | 34 |
| 10 | Talysarn Celts | 24 | 8 | 5 | 11 | 52 | 68 | -16 | 29 |
| 11 | Beaumaris Town | 24 | 4 | 3 | 17 | 48 | 118 | -70 | 15 |
| 12 | Harlech Town | 24 | 4 | 2 | 18 | 39 | 86 | -47 | 14 |
| 13 | Bangor University | 24 | 1 | 1 | 22 | 34 | 101 | -67 | 4 |

## ANGLESEY LEAGUE

| | | P | W | D | L | F | A | GD | Pts |
|---|---|---|---|---|---|---|---|---|---|
| 1 | Bro Goronwy | 14 | 13 | 1 | 0 | 64 | 11 | 53 | 40 |
| 2 | Llanfairpwll Reserves | 14 | 12 | 0 | 2 | 64 | 16 | 48 | 36 |
| 3 | Maes y Bryn | 14 | 8 | 0 | 6 | 37 | 40 | -3 | 24 |
| 4 | Valley Athletic | 14 | 5 | 2 | 7 | 22 | 38 | -16 | 17 |
| 5 | Llangoed & District | 14 | 5 | 1 | 8 | 31 | 39 | -8 | 16 |
| 6 | Pentraeth Reserves | 14 | 4 | 1 | 9 | 40 | 35 | 5 | 13 |
| 7 | Llanfairfechan Town Reserves | 14 | 3 | 2 | 9 | 18 | 50 | -32 | 11 |
| 8 | Bodorgan | 14 | 2 | 1 | 11 | 23 | 70 | -47 | 7 |

## MID WALES LEAGUE

| Division One | P | W | D | L | F | A | GD | Pts |
|---|---|---|---|---|---|---|---|---|
| 1 Penrhyncoch | 26 | 20 | 3 | 3 | 67 | 27 | 40 | 63 |
| 2 Knighton Town | 26 | 20 | 2 | 4 | 72 | 21 | 51 | 62 |
| 3 Carno | 26 | 17 | 3 | 6 | 59 | 24 | 35 | 54 |
| 4 Hay St Mary's | 26 | 16 | 1 | 9 | 68 | 49 | 19 | 49 |
| 5 Llanrhaeadr Ym Mochant | 26 | 14 | 3 | 9 | 71 | 51 | 20 | 45 |
| 6 Llandrindod Wells | 26 | 14 | 1 | 11 | 50 | 38 | 12 | 43 |
| 7 Llanidloes Town | 26 | 11 | 1 | 14 | 42 | 57 | -15 | 34 |
| 8 Welshpool Town | 26 | 9 | 4 | 13 | 36 | 47 | -11 | 31 |
| 9 Aberaeron | 26 | 9 | 4 | 13 | 42 | 60 | -18 | 31 |
| 10 Bow Street | 26 | 9 | 2 | 15 | 43 | 59 | -16 | 29 |
| 11 Machynlleth | 26 | 7 | 5 | 14 | 49 | 76 | -27 | 26 |
| 12 Waterloo Rovers | 26 | 7 | 4 | 15 | 41 | 61 | -20 | 25 |
| 13 Tywyn Bryncrug | 26 | 7 | 1 | 18 | 50 | 76 | -26 | 22 |
| 14 Montgomery Town | 26 | 3 | 4 | 19 | 24 | 68 | -44 | 10 |

| Division Two | P | W | D | L | F | A | GD | Pts |
|---|---|---|---|---|---|---|---|---|
| 1 Berriew | 28 | 25 | 1 | 2 | 108 | 28 | 80 | 76 |
| 2 Radnor Valley | 28 | 20 | 0 | 8 | 79 | 39 | 40 | 60 |
| 3 Kerry | 28 | 19 | 1 | 8 | 105 | 36 | 69 | 58 |
| 4 Aberystwyth University | 28 | 17 | 6 | 5 | 76 | 43 | 33 | 57 |
| 5 Builth Wells | 28 | 14 | 3 | 11 | 61 | 55 | 6 | 45 |
| 6 Bettws | 28 | 12 | 7 | 9 | 53 | 60 | -7 | 43 |
| 7 Churchstoke | 28 | 13 | 3 | 12 | 70 | 60 | 10 | 42 |
| 8 Borth United | 28 | 12 | 4 | 12 | 61 | 49 | 12 | 40 |
| 9 Abermule (-3) | 28 | 12 | 3 | 13 | 57 | 68 | -11 | 36 |
| 10 Dyffryn Banw | 28 | 10 | 4 | 14 | 46 | 52 | -6 | 34 |
| 11 Presteigne St. Andrews | 28 | 7 | 5 | 16 | 41 | 77 | -36 | 26 |
| 12 Newbridge-on-Wye (-3) | 28 | 9 | 2 | 17 | 49 | 91 | -42 | 26 |
| 13 Bont (-3) | 28 | 6 | 4 | 18 | 28 | 75 | -47 | 19 |
| 14 Four Crosses | 28 | 5 | 4 | 19 | 45 | 101 | -56 | 19 |
| 15 Penybont | 28 | 4 | 3 | 21 | 36 | 81 | -45 | 15 |

## VALE OF CLYWD & CONWY LEAGUE

| Premier Division | P | W | D | L | F | A | GD | Pts |
|---|---|---|---|---|---|---|---|---|
| 1 Prestatyn Sports | 20 | 19 | 0 | 1 | 107 | 20 | 87 | 57 |
| 2 Conwy Legion United | 20 | 13 | 5 | 2 | 64 | 34 | 30 | 44 |
| 3 Rhyl Athletic | 20 | 7 | 8 | 5 | 47 | 37 | 10 | 29 |
| 4 Rhos United | 20 | 9 | 1 | 10 | 30 | 48 | -18 | 28 |
| 5 Llanefydd | 20 | 7 | 5 | 8 | 48 | 54 | -6 | 26 |
| 6 Rhyl Rovers | 20 | 7 | 4 | 9 | 47 | 66 | -19 | 25 |
| 7 Machno United | 20 | 7 | 3 | 10 | 59 | 63 | -4 | 24 |
| 8 Llansannan | 20 | 7 | 3 | 10 | 41 | 64 | -23 | 24 |
| 9 Rhyl Town AFC | 20 | 6 | 5 | 9 | 37 | 42 | -5 | 23 |
| 10 Old Colwyn | 20 | 7 | 2 | 11 | 48 | 61 | -13 | 23 |
| 11 Bro Cernyw | 20 | 1 | 4 | 15 | 18 | 57 | -39 | 7 |

| Division One | P | W | D | L | F | A | GD | PTS |
|---|---|---|---|---|---|---|---|---|
| 1 Prestatyn Sports Reserves | 18 | 15 | 2 | 1 | 83 | 27 | 56 | 47 |
| 2 Llandudno Albion | 18 | 14 | 3 | 1 | 112 | 18 | 94 | 45 |
| 3 Trefnant | 18 | 12 | 2 | 4 | 84 | 40 | 44 | 38 |
| 4 Llanfairfechan Town | 18 | 12 | 1 | 5 | 87 | 32 | 55 | 37 |
| 5 Llandudno United | 18 | 11 | 3 | 4 | 88 | 32 | 56 | 36 |
| 6 Y Glannau | 18 | 4 | 4 | 10 | 35 | 63 | -28 | 16 |
| 7 Betws-y-Coed | 18 | 5 | 0 | 13 | 34 | 82 | -48 | 15 |
| 8 Cerrig-y-Drudion | 18 | 3 | 4 | 11 | 29 | 56 | -27 | 13 |
| 9 Llysfaen | 18 | 3 | 2 | 13 | 28 | 78 | -50 | 11 |
| 10 Llandudno Athletic | 18 | 0 | 1 | 17 | 14 | 166 | -152 | 1 |

## NEWPORT & DISTRICT FOOTBALL LEAGUE

| Premier X | P | W | D | L | F | A | GD | Pts |
|---|---|---|---|---|---|---|---|---|
| 1 Machen FC | 24 | 24 | 0 | 0 | 111 | 25 | 86 | 72 |
| 2 Cwmcarn Athletic | 24 | 16 | 3 | 5 | 85 | 41 | 44 | 51 |
| 3 FC Boilermaker | 24 | 16 | 1 | 7 | 77 | 50 | 27 | 49 |
| 4 Docks Cons | 24 | 13 | 4 | 7 | 68 | 56 | 12 | 43 |
| 5 Cwmbran Centre FC | 24 | 13 | 2 | 9 | 72 | 63 | 9 | 41 |
| 6 Malpas United | 24 | 12 | 2 | 10 | 70 | 63 | 7 | 38 |
| 7 Fairwater FC | 24 | 11 | 3 | 10 | 64 | 67 | -3 | 36 |
| 8 Villa Dino Christchurch | 24 | 8 | 4 | 12 | 58 | 64 | -6 | 28 |
| 9 Llanyrafon AFC | 24 | 8 | 4 | 12 | 46 | 61 | -15 | 28 |
| 10 Riverside Rovers | 24 | 6 | 5 | 13 | 53 | 75 | -22 | 23 |
| 11 Cwmbran Celtic | 24 | 6 | 3 | 15 | 50 | 80 | -30 | 21 |
| 12 Whiteheads United | 24 | 3 | 2 | 19 | 44 | 81 | -37 | 11 |
| 13 Croesyceiliog Athletic | 24 | 3 | 1 | 20 | 36 | 108 | -72 | 10 |
| 14 Newport Civil Service withdrawn from the League. | | | | | | | | |

| Premier Y | P | W | D | L | F | A | Gd | Pts |
|---|---|---|---|---|---|---|---|---|
| 1 Albion Rovers | 14 | 11 | 1 | 2 | 55 | 19 | 36 | 34 |
| 2 AC Pontymister | 14 | 9 | 2 | 3 | 46 | 19 | 27 | 29 |
| 3 Trethomas Bluebirds | 14 | 8 | 2 | 4 | 42 | 26 | 16 | 26 |
| 4 Coed Eva Athletic | 14 | 8 | 1 | 5 | 49 | 31 | 18 | 25 |
| 5 Cromwell AFC | 14 | 6 | 1 | 7 | 35 | 53 | -18 | 19 |
| 6 Newport Corinthians | 14 | 5 | 1 | 8 | 25 | 43 | -18 | 16 |
| 7 West of St Julians | 14 | 3 | 1 | 10 | 25 | 45 | -20 | 10 |
| 8 Lucas Cwmbran | 14 | 1 | 1 | 12 | 18 | 59 | -41 | 4 |

9 Cwmbran Town withdrawn from league.
10 Ponthir FC withdrawn from league.
11 Pill AFC withdrawn from league.
12 Spencer Boys Club withdrawn from league.

| Division One | P | W | D | L | F | A | Gd | Pts |
|---|---|---|---|---|---|---|---|---|
| 1 Rogerstone | 24 | 17 | 6 | 1 | 102 | 41 | 61 | 57 |
| 2 Spencer Boys club | 24 | 15 | 9 | 2 | 90 | 41 | 49 | 52 |
| 3 Marshfield AFC | 24 | 13 | 3 | 8 | 81 | 51 | 30 | 42 |
| 4 Albion Rovers | 24 | 13 | 3 | 8 | 77 | 65 | 12 | 42 |
| 5 Villa Dino C/Church | 24 | 12 | 2 | 10 | 76 | 71 | 5 | 38 |
| 6 AC Pontymister | 24 | 10 | 6 | 8 | 74 | 62 | 12 | 36 |
| 7 Cwmcarn Athletic | 24 | 10 | 5 | 9 | 71 | 72 | 11 | 35 |
| 8 Cromwell Youth | 24 | 10 | 3 | 11 | 78 | 92 | -14 | 33 |
| 9 Caerleon Town | 24 | 10 | 4 | 10 | 76 | 77 | -1 | 34 |
| 10 The Docks Cons | 24 | 7 | 5 | 12 | 57 | 70 | -13 | 26 |
| 11 Upper Cwmbran | 24 | 7 | 3 | 14 | 64 | 72 | -8 | 24 |
| 12 Riverside Rovers | 24 | 4 | 6 | 14 | 53 | 74 | -21 | 18 |
| 13 Glenside Rovers FC | 24 | 1 | 1 | 22 | 38 | 149 | -111 | 4 |
| 14 Machen FC withdrawn from league. | | | | | | | | |

| Division Two | P | W | D | L | F | A | Gd | Pts |
|---|---|---|---|---|---|---|---|---|
| 1 Cross Hands FC | 17 | 16 | 1 | 0 | 101 | 12 | 89 | 49 |
| 2 Newport Cricket FC | 18 | 14 | 2 | 2 | 102 | 27 | 75 | 44 |
| 3 Risca Athletic | 17 | 11 | 2 | 4 | 65 | 45 | 20 | 35 |
| 4 Newport Corinthians | 18 | 10 | 2 | 6 | 50 | 41 | 9 | 32 |
| 5 Coed Eva Athletic | 18 | 6 | 3 | 9 | 46 | 71 | -25 | 2[illegible] |
| 6 Malpas United | 18 | 6 | 2 | 10 | 52 | 54 | -2 | 20 |
| 7 Lliswerry FC | 18 | 6 | 2 | 10 | 49 | 56 | -7 | 20 |
| 8 Albion Rovers | 18 | 5 | 2 | 11 | 40 | 80 | -40 | 1[illegible] |
| 9 Newport Eagles | 18 | 4 | 2 | 12 | 56 | 88 | -32 | 1[illegible] |
| 10 Rogerstone AFC | 18 | 1 | 2 | 15 | 22 | 109 | -87 | [illegible] |

*Nothing better than a good old fashioned shoulder to shoulder battle to get to the ball first, demonstrated here by Edwards (Guilsfield) and Roberts (Buckley).*

***Above:*** *Lloyd (Holywell) gets the ball over Jones (Llanfair) to equalise.*

***Left:*** *Great block from Hesp (Cefn) to prevent Davies (Porthmadog) getting a shot in.*

***Bottom left:*** *Bromley (Guilsfield) and Jamie Roberts (Holyhead) keep their eyes on the ball.*

***Below:*** *Breese (Caernarfon) gets his shot away before Cunningham (Flint) can block.*

***Photos: Keith Clayton***

## PEMBROKESHIRE LEAGUE

| Division One | P | W | D | L | F | A | GD | Pts |
|---|---|---|---|---|---|---|---|---|
| 1 Goodwick United | 26 | 20 | 5 | 1 | 79 | 20 | 59 | 65 |
| 2 Hakin United | 26 | 20 | 4 | 2 | 119 | 34 | 85 | 64 |
| 3 West Dragons | 26 | 15 | 7 | 4 | 71 | 49 | 22 | 52 |
| 4 Johnston | 26 | 15 | 4 | 7 | 77 | 55 | 22 | 49 |
| 5 Neyland | 26 | 13 | 3 | 10 | 70 | 48 | 22 | 42 |
| 6 Narberth | 25 | 11 | 3 | 11 | 44 | 53 | -9 | 36 |
| 7 Merlins Bridge | 26 | 10 | 4 | 12 | 63 | 56 | 7 | 34 |
| 8 Tenby (-3) | 26 | 11 | 2 | 13 | 67 | 71 | -4 | 32 |
| 9 Angle | 26 | 9 | 3 | 14 | 46 | 74 | -28 | 30 |
| 10 Milford United | 26 | 7 | 6 | 13 | 39 | 61 | -22 | 27 |
| 11 Pennar Robins | 26 | 7 | 5 | 14 | 39 | 75 | -36 | 26 |
| 12 Carew | 25 | 7 | 3 | 15 | 29 | 62 | -33 | 24 |
| 13 Herbrandston | 26 | 4 | 4 | 18 | 44 | 75 | -31 | 16 |
| 14 St Clears | 26 | 4 | 3 | 19 | 32 | 86 | -54 | 15 |

| Division Two | P | W | D | L | F | A | GD | Pts |
|---|---|---|---|---|---|---|---|---|
| 1 Monkton Swifts | 24 | 19 | 2 | 3 | 114 | 36 | 78 | 59 |
| 2 Lamphey | 24 | 18 | 4 | 2 | 109 | 38 | 71 | 58 |
| 3 Clarbeston Road | 24 | 18 | 2 | 4 | 104 | 46 | 58 | 56 |
| 4 Hundleton | 24 | 12 | 5 | 7 | 57 | 40 | 17 | 41 |
| 5 Fishguard Sports | 24 | 11 | 5 | 8 | 67 | 50 | 17 | 38 |
| 6 Solva | 24 | 10 | 6 | 8 | 78 | 66 | 12 | 36 |
| 7 St Ishmaels | 24 | 11 | 1 | 12 | 60 | 54 | 6 | 34 |
| 8 Saundersfoot Sports | 24 | 7 | 7 | 10 | 51 | 48 | 3 | 28 |
| 9 Prendergast Villa | 24 | 8 | 2 | 14 | 49 | 81 | -32 | 26 |
| 10 Lawrenny | 24 | 8 | 1 | 15 | 42 | 89 | -47 | 25 |
| 11 Goodwick United II | 24 | 5 | 3 | 16 | 41 | 94 | -53 | 18 |
| 12 Letterston | 24 | 5 | 1 | 18 | 37 | 100 | -63 | 16 |
| 13 Milford Athletic | 24 | 3 | 3 | 18 | 34 | 101 | -67 | 12 |

| Division Three | P | W | D | L | F | A | GD | Pts |
|---|---|---|---|---|---|---|---|---|
| 1 Hakin United II | 30 | 21 | 4 | 5 | 127 | 37 | 90 | 67 |
| 2 Merlins Bridge II | 30 | 20 | 3 | 7 | 106 | 57 | 49 | 63 |
| 3 Camrose | 30 | 19 | 4 | 7 | 104 | 41 | 63 | 61 |
| 4 Narberth II | 30 | 18 | 6 | 6 | 83 | 38 | 45 | 60 |
| 5 Broad Haven | 30 | 18 | 6 | 6 | 83 | 46 | 37 | 60 |
| 6 Kilgetty | 30 | 16 | 3 | 11 | 63 | 47 | 16 | 51 |
| 7 Pennar Robins II | 30 | 15 | 3 | 12 | 69 | 59 | 10 | 48 |
| 8 Milford United II | 30 | 14 | 3 | 13 | 63 | 52 | 11 | 45 |
| 9 Clarbeston Road II | 30 | 12 | 5 | 13 | 76 | 72 | 4 | 41 |
| 10 Carew II | 30 | 11 | 8 | 11 | 59 | 66 | -7 | 41 |
| 11 Cosheston Cougars | 30 | 11 | 7 | 12 | 76 | 81 | -5 | 40 |
| 12 Johnston II | 30 | 9 | 2 | 19 | 50 | 104 | -54 | 29 |
| 13 Saundersfoot Sports II | 30 | 6 | 8 | 16 | 54 | 93 | -39 | 23 |
| 14 Manorbier United | 30 | 6 | 6 | 18 | 55 | 139 | -84 | 21 |
| 15 Herbrandston II | 30 | 4 | 3 | 23 | 29 | 87 | -58 | 12 |
| 16 Hubberston | 30 | 3 | 3 | 24 | 47 | 125 | -78 | 9 |

| Division Four | P | W | D | L | F | A | GD | Pts |
|---|---|---|---|---|---|---|---|---|
| 1 Llangwm | 30 | 26 | 4 | 0 | 120 | 33 | 87 | 82 |
| 2 Pendine | 30 | 23 | 3 | 4 | 134 | 38 | 96 | 72 |
| 3 Angle II | 30 | 21 | 5 | 4 | 124 | 51 | 73 | 68 |
| 4 Pembroke Boro | 30 | 16 | 2 | 12 | 90 | 72 | 18 | 53 |
| 5 Pennar Robins III | 30 | 16 | 4 | 10 | 99 | 59 | 40 | 52 |
| 6 Prendergast Villa II | 30 | 15 | 6 | 9 | 80 | 58 | 22 | 51 |
| 7 Fishguard Sports II | 30 | 15 | 5 | 10 | 88 | 69 | 19 | 50 |
| 8 St Clears II | 30 | 12 | 6 | 12 | 57 | 54 | 3 | 42 |
| 9 Neyland II | 30 | 12 | 4 | 14 | 74 | 97 | -23 | 40 |
| 10 St Ishmaels II | 30 | 7 | 7 | 16 | 51 | 106 | -55 | 28 |
| 11 Solva II | 30 | 7 | 5 | 18 | 60 | 95 | -35 | 26 |
| 12 St Florence | 30 | 6 | 7 | 17 | 66 | 104 | -38 | 25 |
| 13 Narberth III | 30 | 7 | 6 | 17 | 43 | 113 | -70 | 24 |
| 14 Carew III (-3) | 30 | 6 | 7 | 17 | 52 | 101 | -49 | 2[illegible] |
| 15 Milford Athletic II | 30 | 4 | 7 | 19 | 44 | 84 | -40 | 1[illegible] |
| 16 Letterston II (-6) | 30 | 7 | 2 | 21 | 44 | 92 | -48 | 1[illegible] |

| Division Five | P | W | D | L | F | A | GD | Pts |
|---|---|---|---|---|---|---|---|---|
| 1 Lamphey II | 20 | 16 | 2 | 2 | 98 | 33 | 65 | 5[illegible] |
| 2 West Dragons II | 20 | 16 | 0 | 4 | 84 | 27 | 57 | 4[illegible] |
| 3 Hundleton II | 20 | 13 | 0 | 7 | 73 | 53 | 20 | 3[illegible] |
| 4 Broad Haven II | 20 | 12 | 2 | 6 | 50 | 29 | 21 | 3[illegible] |
| 5 Monkton Swifts II | 20 | 11 | 4 | 5 | 71 | 37 | 34 | 3[illegible] |
| 6 Pembroke Boro II | 20 | 12 | 1 | 7 | 71 | 55 | 16 | 3[illegible] |
| 7 Kilgetty II | 20 | 7 | 0 | 13 | 38 | 66 | -28 | 2[illegible] |
| 8 Milford United III | 20 | 6 | 5 | 9 | 44 | 54 | -10 | 2[illegible] |
| 9 Lawrenny II | 20 | 5 | 1 | 14 | 27 | 82 | -55 | 1[illegible] |
| 10 Llangwm II | 20 | 1 | 3 | 16 | 30 | 75 | -45 | |
| 11 Camrose II | 20 | 1 | 2 | 17 | 26 | 101 | -75 | |

## WELSH CUP

### FIRST QUALIFYING ROUND

| | | | |
|---|---|---|---|
| Aberaeron | v | Abermule | 6-1 |
| Berriew | v | Newbridge on Wye | 11-2 |
| Hay St Mary | v | Llansantffraid Village | 1-1, 5-4p |
| Knighton Town | v | Kerry | 4-0 |
| Llanfyllin Town | v | Machynlleth | 2-4 |
| Montgomery Town | v | Pontrhydfendigaid | 3-0 |
| Presteigne St. Andrews | v | Tywyn Bryncrug | 2-4 |
| Welshpool Town | v | Borth United | 5-4 |
| Aberffraw | v | Gaerwen | 4-1 aet |
| Amlwch Town | v | Meliden | 3-2 aet |
| Aston Park Rangers | v | Llandyrnog United | 2-4 |
| Blaenau Ffestiniog | v | Prestatyn Sports | 0-6 |
| Brymbo | v | Halkyn United | 4-1 |
| Caerwys | v | Castell Alun Colts | 1-3 |
| Cefn Albion | v | Llanuwchllyn | 5-2 |
| CPD Sychdyn | v | Argoed United | 2-1 |
| Ewloe Harriers | v | Lex Glyndwr | 2-3 |
| Greenfield | v | Overton Recreational | 2-1 |
| Llanerch y medd | v | Talysarn Celts FC | 8-0 |
| Llanfairpwll | v | Llanberis | 2-4 |
| Llangollen Town | v | Llay Miners Welfare | 9-1 |
| Llanystumdwy | v | Dyffryn Nantlle Vale | 0-1 |
| Mochdre Sports | v | Llanllyfni | 3-2 |
| Penley | v | Brickfield Rangers FC | 4-3 |
| Penmaenmawr Phoenix | v | Pwllheli | 3-1 |

| | | | |
|---|---|---|---|
| 'entraeth | v | Menai Bridge Tigers | 7-1 |
| 'enyffordd | v | Coedpoeth United | 8-0 |
| Rhostyllen FC | v | AFC Brynford | 6-0 |
| Saltney Town | v | Queens Park | 1-4 |
| St Asaph City FC | v | Llanrwst United | 0-2 |
| Trearddur Bay United | v | Glan Conwy | 5-2 |
| 'anteg | v | Newport YMCA | 2-1 |
| AFC Butetown | v | Blaenrhondda | 4-1 |
| AFC Perthcelyn | v | Llantwit Fardre FC | 1-2 |
| 3ettws | v | Newcastle Emlyn | 6-2 |
| 3recon Corinthians FC | v | Penrhiwfer FC | 3-0 |
| 3ridgend Street | v | Cardiff Corinthians | 2-3 |
| ;anton Liberal FC | v | Pontypridd Town | 1-2 |
| ;ardiff Hibernians | v | Treharris Athletic Western | 3-5 |
| ;arnetown | v | Pontyclun | 1-7 |
| ;ornelly United | v | Penlan FC | 2-4 |
| ;wmbach Royal Stars | v | Ely Rangers | 2-0 |
| 'C Tredegar | v | Dynamo Aber FC | 4-4, 1-4p |
| ;arw | v | Ynysygerwn | 3-0 |
| ;raig | v | Cwm Welfare FC | 2-4 |
| .langynwyd Rangers | v | Trefelin | 4-2 |
| .lantwit Major | v | Cefn Cribwr | 5-0 |
| .liswerry FC | v | Newport Civil Service | 1-1, 4-3p |
| Aerthyr Saints | v | Cogan Coronation | 5-2 |
| enrhiwceiber Constitutional Athletic | v | Clwb Cymric | 2-1 |
| 'orthcawl Town Athletic | v | Caerau | 3-1 |
| ?TB Ebbw Vale | v | Aberfan | 6-2 |
| TM Sports | v | West of StJulians | 6-0 |
| ully Sports | v | Treforest | 3-0 |
| redegar Town | v | Caerleon | 0-2 |
| reowen Stars | v | Aber Valley YMCA | 3-2 |
| rethomas Bluebirds | v | Cwmbran Town | 2-3, aet |
| 'nysddu Welfare | v | Machen AFC | 4-0 |

**ECOND QUALIFYING ROUND**

| | | | |
|---|---|---|---|
| beraeron | v | Montgomery Town | 4-2 |
| erriew | v | Machynlleth | 2-1 |
| ow Street FC | v | Hay St Mary | 2-1 |
| arno | v | Llanrhaeadr Ym Mochant | 5-0 |
| nighton Town | v | Welshpool Town | 2-1 |
| enrhyncoch | v | Llanidloes Town | 5-1 |
| 'aterloo Rovers | v | Tywyn Bryncrug | 3-1 |
| armouth & Dyffryn United | v | Llandudno Junction | 1-1, 1-3p |
| efn Albion | v | Llannerch y Medd | 3-2 |
| yffryn Nantlle Vale | v | Penley | 4-3 aet |
| walchmai | v | Greenfield | 5-3 aet |
| ex Glyndwr | v | Ruthin Town | 1-2 |
| angefni Town | v | Glantraeth | 0-1 |
| angollen Town | v | Chirk AAA | 0-1 |
| anrug United | v | Llanberis | 3-1 |
| anrwst United | v | Aberffraw | 1-2 |
| ochdre Sports | v | FC Nomads of Connah's Quay | 1-7 |
| enrhyndeudraeth | v | Abergele Town | 2-0 |
| entraeth | v | Castell Alun Colts | 3-1 |
| enycae | v | Penmaenmawr Phoenix | 2-5 |
| enyffordd | v | Corwen | 1-3 |
| estatyn Sports | v | Sychdyn | 3-1 |
| ueens Park | v | Llandyrnog United | 2-1 |
| hostyllen FC | v | Brymbo | 1-0 aet |
| earddur Bay United | v | Amlwch Town | 8-1 |
| 'C Butetown | v | Chepstow Town FC | 5-0 |
| 'C Llwydcoed | v | Bettws | 5-2 |
| 'C Porth | v | Undy Athletic | 1-4 |
| rdiff Corinthians | v | West End | 2-3 aet |
| oesyceiliog | v | Llanelli Town AFC | 0-4 |
| wm Welfare FC | v | Brecon Corries | 1-2 |
| wmamman United | v | Garw | 4-2 |
| Cwmbach Royal Stars | v | Newport Civil Service | 3-2 aet |
| Cwmbran Celtic | v | Llanwern | 3-0 |
| Cwmbran Town | v | Penrhiwceiber Rangers | 7-3 |
| Dynamo Aber FC | v | Treowen Stars | 4-5 aet |
| Llantwit Fardre | v | Merthyr Saints | 1-1, 6-5p |
| Llantwit Major | v | Tata Steel | 3-2 |
| Panteg | v | Ammanford | 2-1 aet |
| Penlan FC | v | Caldicot Town | 1-2 aet |
| Penrhiwceiber Constitutional Athletic | v | Llandrindod Wells | 2-4 |
| Pontardawe Town | v | RTB Ebbw Vale | 1-2 |
| Pontyclun | v | Caerleon | 1-2 aet |
| Pontypridd Town | v | Sully Sports | 4-2 |
| STM Sports | v | Porthcawl Utd | 5-1 |
| Treharris Athletic Western | v | Llangynwyd Rangers | 2-0 |
| Ynysddu Welfare | v | Dinas Powys | 2-6 |

**ROUND 1**

| | | | |
|---|---|---|---|
| Aberffraw | v | Penrhyncoch | 0-5 |
| Caersws | v | Llandudno Junction | 1-6 |
| Carno | v | Flint Town United | 0-4 |
| Cefn Druids | v | Gresford Athletic | 4-0 |
| Chirk AAA | v | Prestatyn Sports | 5-0 |
| Conwy Borough FC | v | Cefn Albion | 5-3 |
| Corwen | v | Prestatyn Town | 2-3 |
| Dyffryn Nantlle Vale | v | Knighton Town | 1-2 |
| FC Nomads of Connah's Quay | v | Denbigh Town | 1-3 |
| Guilsfield | v | Glantraeth | 4-2, aet |
| Gwalchmai | v | Mold Alexandra | 0-3 |
| Hawarden Rangers | v | Llanfair United | 0-4 |
| Holyhead Hotspur | v | Pentraeth | 8-0 |
| Llanrug United | v | Caernarfon Town | 2-3 aet |
| Penmaenmawr Phoenix | v | Buckley Town | 0-1 |
| Penrhyndeudraeth | v | Queens Park | 2-0 |
| Porthmadog | v | Bow Street FC | 3-1 |
| Rhostyllen FC | v | Berriew | 2-1 |
| Ruthin Town | v | Holywell Town | 0-1 |
| Waterloo Rovers | v | Trearddur Bay United | 1-7 |
| Aberaeron | v | Brecon Corries | 0-1 |
| Afan Lido | v | AFC Butetown | 5-1 |
| Briton Ferry Llansawel | v | Barry Town United | 2-3 |
| Caerau Ely | v | Undy Athletic | 4-0 |
| Caerleon | v | Treharris Athletic Western | 2-1 aet |
| Cambrian & Clydach Vale | v | AFC Llwydcoed | 3-0 |
| Cwmamman United | v | Taffs Well | 2-1 |
| Cwmbach Royal Stars | v | Aberdare Town | 0-3 |
| Dinas Powys | v | Cwmbran Town | 4-1 |
| Garden Village | v | Rhayader Town | 2-1 |
| Goytre (Gwent) | v | Llantwit Major FC | 2-0 |
| Goytre United | v | Monmouth Town | 4-2, aet |
| Llandrindod Wells | v | Cwmbran Celtic | 0-3 |
| Llanelli Town AFC | v | Panteg | 6-3 |
| Llantwit Fardre | v | Cardiff Metropolitan | 0-1 |
| Pontypridd Town | v | Penybont FC | 0-2 |
| Ton Pentre | v | STM Sports | 0-4 |
| Treowen Stars | v | West End | 2-3 |
| Risca United | v | Aberbargoed Buds | 2-3 |
| RTB Ebbw Vale | v | Caldicot Town | 1-1, 4-5p |

## WELSH FOOTBALL

### ROUND 2

| | | | |
|---|---|---|---|
| Caernarfon Town | v | Llandudno Junction | 4-0 |
| Cefn Druids | v | Porthmadog | 2-0 |
| Denbigh Town | v | Conwy Borough FC | 4-1 |
| Guilsfield | v | Penrhyndeudraeth FC | 3-2 |
| Holyhead Hotspur | v | Chirk AAA | 4-0 |
| Holywell Town | v | Knighton Town | 6-3 |
| Llanfair United | v | Prestatyn Town | 3-5 |
| Mold Alexandra | v | Buckley Town | 0-1 |
| Penrhyncoch | v | Trearddur Bay United | 4-0 |
| Rhostyllen FC | v | Flint Town United | 0-2 |
| Afan Lido | v | Caerleon | 2-0 |
| Barry Town United | v | Aberdare Town | 7-2 |
| Brecon Corries | v | Aberbargoed Buds | 3-0 |
| Cardiff Metropolitan | v | Penybont FC | 4-2 |
| Cwmamman United | v | Caldicot Town | 4-2 |
| Garden Village | v | STM Sports | 1-4 |
| Goytre (Gwent) | v | Dinas Powys | 4-1 |
| Goytre United | v | Caerau Ely | 1-4 |
| West End | v | Cwmbran Celtic | 2-3 |
| Llanelli Town AFC | v | Cambrian & Clydach Vale | 0-2 |

### ROUND 3

| | | | |
|---|---|---|---|
| Cwmamman United | v | Guilsfield | 0-3 |
| Goytre (Gwent) | v | Caernarfon Town | 4-2 |
| Holyhead Hotspur | v | Bangor City | 2-1 |
| Afan Lido | v | Holywell Town | 1-0 |
| Barry Town United | v | Denbigh Town | 6-1 |
| Caerau Ely | v | Brecon Corries JFC | 4-0 |
| Cardiff Metropolitan | v | STM Sports | 2-0 |
| Carmarthen Town | v | Bala Town | 1-3 |
| Cefn Druids | v | Rhyl | 1-0 aet |
| Flint Town United | v | Newtown | 0-2 |
| Haverfordwest County | v | Airbus UK Broughton | 0-2 |
| MBi Llandudno FC | v | Buckley Town | 0-0, 3-4p |
| Penrhyncoch | v | Cwmbran Celtic | 2-3 |
| Prestatyn Town | v | Gap Connahs Quay | 0-3 |
| The New Saints | v | Aberystwyth Town | 3-0 |
| Port Talbot Town | v | Cambrian & Clydach Vale | 2-1 aet |

### ROUND 4

| | | | |
|---|---|---|---|
| Airbus UK Broughton | v | Guilsfield | 3-0 |
| Cwmbran Celtic | v | Goytre (Gwent) | 5-3 |
| Afan Lido | v | Cardiff Metropolitan | 0-2 |
| Barry Town United | v | The New Saints | 2-5 |
| Holyhead Hotspur | v | Bala Town | 1-3 |
| Newtown | v | Cefn Druids | 6-0 |
| Port Talbot Town | v | Caerau Ely | 3-0 |
| Gap Connahs Quay | v | Buckley Town | 4-1 |

### QUARTER FINALS

| | | | |
|---|---|---|---|
| Airbus UK Broughton | v | Bala Town | 3-0 |
| Cardiff Metropolitan | v | Gap Connahs Quay | 0-2 |
| Cwmbran Celtic | v | Port Talbot Town | 1-2 |
| The New Saints | v | Newtown | 1-0 |

### SEMI FINALS

| | | | |
|---|---|---|---|
| Port Talbot | v | Airbus UK Broughton | 0-7 |
| The New Saints | v | Gap Connahs Quay | 5-0 |

### FINAL

| | | | |
|---|---|---|---|
| Airbus UK Broughton | v | The New Saints | 0-2 |

## WELSH TROPHY

### ROUND 1

| | | | |
|---|---|---|---|
| Aston Park | v | Llanfairfechan | 2-5 |
| Rhos United FC | v | Ewloe Spartans | 1-3 |
| Sychdyn | v | Rhostyllen FC | 0-4 |
| Talysarn Celts FC | v | Llanystumdwy | 1-3 |
| Blaen y Maes FC | v | Rockspur FC | 0-5 |
| Bryn Rovers | v | West End Rangers | 0-4 |
| Bwlch Rangers | v | Ynystawe Athletic | 3-2 aet |
| Canton Liberal FC | v | Mardy | 7-1 |
| Cardiff Draconians | v | Llanrumney United Old Boys | 7-1 |
| Carnetown | v | Tonyrefail BGC | 3-4 |
| Cefn Cribwr | v | Baglan Dragons | 4-1 |
| Cowbridge Town | v | Lucas Cwmbran | 2-2, 4-5p |
| Dynamo Aber FC | v | Clydach Wasps | 1-3 aet |
| FC Tredegar | v | Clwb Cymric | 6-2 |
| Garw SBGC | v | CRC Rangers | 4-6 |
| Hirwaun Sports | v | Cardiff Hibernian | 3-0 |
| Llangynwyd Rangers | v | Maerdy Social FC | 3-1 |
| Merthyr Saints | v | Cwmaman Institute | 3-2 |
| Nelson Cavaliers | v | Ton & Gelli | 3-2 |
| Penrhiwceiber Constitutional Athletic | v | Machen AFC | 3-1 |
| Penrhiwfer FC | v | Cogan Coronation | 2-3 |
| Porth Tywyn Suburbs | v | North End | 2-6 |
| RTB Ebbw Vale | v | AFC Perthcelyn | 3-2 |
| Sporting Marvels FC | v | Blaenrhondda | 1-0 aet |
| Tynte Rovers | v | Brecon Corinthians FC | 3-1 |
| Wainfelin Bluebirds | v | Grange Albion | 0-5 |
| West of StJulians | v | Hirwaun Welfare | 2-2, 5-3 |
| Whiteheads United | v | Llanbradach Junior FC | 2-5 aet |

### ROUND 2

| | | | |
|---|---|---|---|
| Bow Street FC | v | Llanidloes Town | 1-5 |
| Carno | v | Presteigne St. Andrews | 3-1 |
| Llanrhaeadr Ym Mochant | v | Llansantffraid Village | 3-0 |
| Machynlleth | v | Knighton Town | 1-2 |
| Montgomery Town | v | Llangollen Town | 2-4 |
| Penrhyncoch | v | Berriew | 2-1 |
| Tywyn Bryncrug | v | Llanfyllin Town | 3-0 |
| Aberffraw | v | Abergele Town | 2-0 |
| Acrefair Youth | v | New Brighton Villa | 1-9 |
| Amlwch Town | v | Dyffryn Nantlle Vale | 1-7 |
| Beaumaris Town FC | v | Llanystumdwy | 2-8 |
| Blaenau Ffestiniog | v | Llanrug United | 4-4, 4-6p |
| Castell Alun Colts | v | AFC Brynford | 2-1 |
| Cefn Albion | v | Ewloe Spartans | 13-0 |
| Coedpoeth United | v | Penycae | 0-4 |
| Corwen | v | St Asaph City FC | 2-1 |
| FC Nomads of Connah's Quay | v | Greenfield | 2-3 |
| Glan Conwy | v | Llangefni Town | 2-1 |
| Gwalchmai | - | Bye | |
| Lex Glyndwr | v | Chirk AAA | 0-5 |
| Llandudno Junction | v | Barmouth & Dyffryn United | 2-0 aet |
| Llandyrnog United | v | Trearddur Bay United | 0-3 |
| Llanfairfechan | v | Argoed United | 4-2 |
| Llanfairpwll | v | Gaerwen | 2-5 |
| Llanrwst United | v | Y Felinheli | 1-2 |
| Llay Miners Welfare | v | Saltney Town | 1-3 |
| Meliden | v | Pwllheli | 2-1 |
| Mynydd Llandegai | v | Llannerch y Medd | 2-4 |
| Offa Athletic | v | Ruthin Town | 0-2 |
| Overton Recreational | v | Penyffordd | 2-3 |

| | | | |
|---|---|---|---|
| Penley | v | Brymbo | 0-2 |
| Penmaenmawr Phoenix | v | Llanberis | 1-4 |
| Pentraeth | v | Mochdre Sports | 3-2 |
| Prestatyn Sports | v | Llanllyfni | 0-3 |
| Queens Park | v | Halkyn United | 5-3 |
| Rhos Aelwyd | v | Caerwys | 4-1 |
| Rhostyllen FC | v | Brickfield Rangers FC | 4-2 |
| Aber Valley YMCA | v | Tonyrefail BGC | 0-2 |
| Abercarn United | v | Cogan Coronation | 2-3 |
| AC Pontymister | v | Penrhiwceiber Constitutional Athletic | 3-1 |
| Bonymaen Colts | v | Penlan FC | 1-6 |
| Bwlch Rangers | v | Pengelli United | 1-1, 4-1p |
| Cardiff Draconians | v | Cwmbach Royal Stars | 5-2 |
| Clydach Wasps | v | Marshfield | 5-2 |
| FC Tredegar | v | Abertillery Excelsiors | 2-3 |
| Hakin United | v | Goodwick United | 3-1 |
| Llanbradach | v | RTB Ebbw Vale | 2-1 |
| Lucas Cwmbran | v | Llandrindod Wells | 1-8 |
| Maltsters Sports | v | Cwmfelin Press | 3-1 |
| Merthyr Saints | v | Canton Liberal FC | 5-5, 5-6p |
| Morriston Olympic FC | v | Dafen Welfare | 2-0 |
| Nelson Cavaliers | v | Sporting Marvels FC | 1-2 |
| Pencoed Athletic Amateur FC | v | Sully Sports | 1-8 |
| Pentwynmawr Athletic | v | Llangynwyd Rangers | 0-3 |
| Ragged School | v | North End | 2-5 |
| Rockspur FC | v | Cefn Cribwr | 1-2 |
| Team Swansea | v | CRC Rangers | 3-2 |
| Trethomas Bluebirds | v | Grange Albion | 1-2 |
| Tynte Rovers | v | Hirwaun Sports | 3-3, 2-4p |
| West End Rangers | v | Trefelin | 2-4 |
| West of StJulians | v | Llantwit Fardre | 2-3 |

**ROUND 3**

| | | | |
|---|---|---|---|
| Brymbo | v | Llandrindod Wells | 1-0 |
| Carno | v | Penycae | 3-3, HWp |
| Cefn Albion | v | Castell Alun Colts | 2-4 aet |
| Corwen | v | Llangollen Town | 1-0 |
| Gaerwen | v | Llandudno Junction | 3-8 |
| Glan Conwy | v | Y Felinheli | 4-0 |
| Greenfield | v | Knighton Town | 3-2 aet |
| Gwalchmai | v | Meliden | 6-1 |
| Llanberis | v | Dyffryn Nantlle Vale | 2-1 |
| Llanfairfechan | v | Aberffraw | 1-3 aet |
| Llanidloes Town | v | Queens Park | 2-4 |
| Llanllyfni | v | Glantraeth | 3-4 |
| Llanrhaeadr Ym Mochant | v | Chirk AAA | 4-1 |
| Llanrug United | v | Trearddur Bay United | 3-3, 3-4p |
| Llanystumdwy | v | Penrhyndeudraeth FC | 0-3 |
| Penrhyncoch | v | Llannerch y Medd | 3-2 |
| Rhos Aelwyd | v | New Brighton Villa | 2-1 |
| Ruthin Town | v | Penyffordd | 5-4 |
| Saltney Town | v | Rhostyllen FC | 2-3 |
| Tywyn Bryncrug | v | Pentraeth | 1-5 |
| Abergavenny Town | v | Tonyrefail BGC | 3-0 |
| Bwlch Rangers | v | Sully Sports | 2-4 aet |
| Canton Liberal FC | v | Penlan FC | 4-1 |
| Cardiff Draconians | v | Cefn Cribwr | 2-0 |
| Clydach Wasps | v | AC Pontymister | 0-2 |
| Llanbradach | v | Llantwit Fardre | 2-0 |
| Maltsters Sports | v | Grange Albion | 1-0 |
| Morriston Olympic FC | v | Hakin United | 1-2 |
| North End | v | Llangynwyd Rangers | 1-3 |
| Sporting Marvels FC | v | Abertillery Excelsiors | 5-1 |
| Team Swansea | v | Hirwaun Sports | 6-2 |
| Trefelin | v | Cogan Coronation | 2-2, 5-6p |

**ROUND 4**

| | | | |
|---|---|---|---|
| Brymbo | v | Llanrhaeadr Ym Mochant | 1-2 |
| Carno | v | Castell Alun Colts | 6-0 |
| Glantraeth | v | Corwen | 2-3 |
| Greenfield | v | Llanberis | 4-1 |
| Gwalchmai | v | Trearddur Bay United | 2-3 |
| Llandudno Junction | v | Aberffraw | 6-1 |
| Penrhyncoch | v | Penrhyndeudraeth FC | 1-0 |
| Queens Park | v | Rhos Aelwyd | 4-3 |
| Rhostyllen FC | v | Pentraeth | 3-1 |
| Ruthin Town | v | Glan Conwy | 2-1 |
| Cardiff Draconians | v | Sporting Marvels FC | 1-2 |
| AC Pontymister | v | Hakin United | 5-1 |
| Llanbradach | v | Sully Sports | 1-5 |
| Llangynwyd Rangers | v | Canton Liberal FC | 1-0 |
| Maltsters Sports | v | Cogan Coronation | 3-2 |
| Team Swansea | v | Abergavenny Town | 3-4 |

**ROUND 5**

| | | | |
|---|---|---|---|
| Greenfield | v | Llanrhaeadr Ym Mochant | 2-3 |
| Llandudno Junction | v | Corwen | 3-2 |
| Queens Park | v | Penrhyncoch | 1-0 |
| Rhostyllen FC | v | Ruthin Town | 2-0 |
| Trearddur Bay United | v | Carno | 2-5 |
| Llangynwyd Rangers | v | AC Pontymister | 1-2 |
| Maltsters Sports | v | Sully Sports | 2-4 |
| Sporting Marvels FC | v | Abergavenny Town | 1-2 |

**QUARTER FINALS**

| | | | |
|---|---|---|---|
| Carno | v | Sully Sports | 0-2 |
| Abergavenny Town | v | Llanrhaeadr Ym Mochant | 6-1 |
| AC Pontymister | v | Rhostyllen FC | 3-4 aet |
| Queens Park | v | Llandudno Junction | 3-1 |

**SEMI FINALS**

| | | | |
|---|---|---|---|
| Abergavenny Town | v | Queens Park | 7-0 |
| Sully Sports | v | Rhostyllen FC | 1-0 |

**FINAL**

| | | | |
|---|---|---|---|
| Abergavenny Town | v | Sully Sports | 1-0 |

the
# FOOTBALL ASSOCIATION COMPETITIONS

# ENGLAND C

## RESULTS 2015-16

International Challenge Trophy Group Match
22 March 2016

| | | | | |
|---|---|---|---|---|
| Ukraine | v | England C | 0-2 | |
| | | *Guthrie 35, Jackson 45* | | |

International Challenge Trophy Group Match
5 June 2016 (Pictured right - Photo: Keith Clayton)

| | | | | |
|---|---|---|---|---|
| England C | v | Slovakia U21 | 3-4 | 1572 |
| *Holland 28* | | *Haraslin 18, Huk 55* | | |
| *John 38, 52* | | Fasko 75, 90+7 | | |

## ENGLAND'S RESULTS 1979 - 2016

| | | |
|---|---|---|
| **BARBADOS** | | |
| 02.06.08 | Bridgetown | 2 - 0 |
| **BELGIUM** | | |
| 11.02.03 | KV Ostend | 1 - 3 |
| 04.11.03 | Darlington | 2 - 2 |
| 15.11.05 | FC Racing Jets | 2 - 0 |
| 19.05.09 | Oxford United | 0 - 1 |
| 09.02.11 | Luton Town | 1 - 0 |
| 12.09.12 | Gemeentalijk Sportstadion | 2 - 1 |
| **BERMUDA** | | |
| 04.06.13 | Hamilton | 6 - 1 |
| **BOSNIA & HERZEGOVINA** | | |
| 16.09.08 | Grbavia Stadium | 2 - 6 |
| **CYPRUS U21** | | |
| 17.02.15 | Larnaca | 1 - 2 |
| **CZECH REPUBLIC UNDER-21** | | |
| 19.11.13 | Home | 2 - 2 |
| **ESTONIA** | | |
| 12.10.10 | | 1 - 0 |
| **UNDER-23** | | |
| 18.11.14 | FC Halifax Town | 4 - 2 |
| **FINLAND UNDER-21** | | |
| 14.04.93 | Woking | 1 - 3 |
| 30.05.94 | Aanekoski | 0 - 2 |
| 01.06.07 | FC Hakka | 1 - 0 |
| 15.11.07 | Helsinki | 2 - 0 |
| **GIBRALTAR** | | |
| 27.04.82 | Gibraltar | 3 - 2 |
| 31.05.95 | Gibraltar | 3 - 2 |
| 21.05.08 | Colwyn Bay | 1 - 0 |
| 15.11.11 | Gibraltar | 1 - 3 |
| **GRENADA** | | |
| 31.05.08 | St. George's | 1 - 1 |
| **HOLLAND** | | |
| 03.06.79 | Stafford | 1 - 0 |
| 07.06.80 | Zeist | 2 - 1 |
| 09.06.81 | Lucca | 2 - 0 |
| 03.06.82 | Aberdeen | 1 - 0 |
| 02.06.83 | Scarborough | 6 - 0 |
| 05.06.84 | Palma | 3 - 3 |
| 13.06.85 | Vleuten | 3 - 0 |
| 20.05.87 | Kirkaldy | 4 - 0 |
| 11.04.95 | Aalsmeer | 0 - 0 |
| 02.04.96 | Irthlingborough | 3 - 1 |
| 18.04.97 | Appingedam | 0 - 0 |
| 03.03.98 | Crawley | 2 - 1 |
| 30.03.99 | Genemuiden | 1 - 1 |
| 21.03.00 | Northwich | 1 - 0 |
| 22.03.01 | Wihemina FC | 3 - 0 |
| 24.04.02 | Yeovil Town | 1 - 0 |
| 25.03.03 | BV Sparta 25 | 0 - 0 |
| 16.02.05 | Woking | 3 - 0 |
| 29.11.06 | Burton Albion | 4 - 1 |

| | | |
|---|---|---|
| **HUNGARY** | | |
| 15.09.09 | Szekesfehervar | 1 - 1 |
| 28.05.14 | Budapest | 2 - 4 |
| **IRAQ** | | |
| 27.05.04 | Macclesfield | 1 - 5 |
| **IRISH PREMIER LEAGUE XI** | | |
| 13.02.07 | Glenavon FC | 1 - 3 |
| **ITALY** | | |
| 03.06.80 | Zeist | 2 - 0 |
| 13.06.81 | Montecatini | 1 - 1 |
| 01.06.82 | Aberdeen | 0 - 0 |
| 31.05.83 | Scarborough | 2 - 0 |
| 09.06.84 | Reggio Emilia | 0 - 1 |
| 11.06.85 | Houten | 2 - 2 |
| 18.05.87 | Dunfermline | 1 - 2 |
| 29.01.89 | La Spezia | 1 - 1 |
| 25.02.90 | Solerno | 0 - 2 |
| 05.03.91 | Kettering | 0 - 0 |
| 01.03.99 | Hayes | 4 - 1 |
| 01.03.00 | Padova | 1 - 1 |
| 20.11.02 | AC Cremonese | 3 - 2 |
| 11.02.04 | Shrewsbury | 1 - 4 |
| 10.11.04 | US Ivrea FC | 1 - 0 |
| 15.02.06 | Cambridge United | 3 - 1 |
| 12.11.08 | Benevento | 2 - 2 |
| 28.02.12 | Fleetwood Town | 1 - 1 |
| **JORDAN UNDER-23** | | |
| 04.03.14 | Jordan | 1 - 0 |
| **LATVIA UNDER-23** | | |
| 10.09.13 | Latvia | 0 - 1 |
| **MALTA UNDER-21** | | |
| 17.02.09 | Malta | 4 - 0 |
| **NORWAY UNDER-21** | | |
| 01.06.94 | Slemmestad | 1 - 2 |
| **POLAND** | | |
| 17.11.09 | Gradiszk Wielpolski | 2 - 1 |
| **PORTUGAL** | | |
| 19.05.11 | Sixfields Stadium | 0 - 1 |
| **REPUBLIC OF IRELAND** | | |
| 24.05.86 | Kidderminster | 2 - 1 |
| 26.05.86 | Nuneaton | 2 - 1 |
| 25.05.90 | Dublin | 2 - 1 |
| 27.05.90 | Cork | 3 - 0 |
| 27.02.96 | Kidderminster | 4 - 0 |
| 25.02.97 | Dublin | 0 - 2 |
| 16.05.02 | Boston | 1 - 2 |
| 20.05.03 | Merthyr Tydfil | 4 - 0 |
| 18.05.04 | Deverondale | 2 - 3 |
| 24.05.05 | Cork | 1 - 0 |
| 23.05.06 | Eastbourne Boro' | 2 - 0 |
| 22.05.07 | Clachnacuddin | 5 - 0 |
| 26.05.10 | Waterford United | 2 - 1 |
| **UNDER-21** | | |
| 01.06.15 | Galway | 2 - 1 |

| | | |
|---|---|---|
| **RUSSIA** | | |
| 05.06.12 | Russia | 0 - 4 |
| **SCOTLAND** | | |
| 31.05.79 | Stafford | 5 - 1 |
| 05.06.80 | Zeist | 2 - 4 |
| 11.06.81 | Empoli | 0 - 0 |
| 05.06.82 | Aberdeen | 1 - 1 |
| 04.06.83 | Scarborough | 2 - 1 |
| 07.06.84 | Modena | 2 - 0 |
| 15.06.85 | Harderwijk | 1 - 3 |
| 23.05.87 | Dunfermline | 2 - 1 |
| 18.05.02 | Kettering | 2 - 0 |
| 24.05.03 | Carmarthen Town | 0 - 0 |
| 23.05.04 | Deverondale | 3 - 1 |
| 28.05.05 | Cork | 3 - 2 |
| 27.05.06 | Eastbourne Boro' | 2 - 0 |
| 25.05.07 | Ross County | 3 - 0 |
| 22.05.08 | Colwyn Bay | 1 - 0 |
| **SLOVAKIA UNDER-21/23** | | |
| 24.05.14 | Slovakia | 0 - 1 |
| 05.06.16 | Sutton United | 3 - 4 |
| **SPARTA PRAGUE B** | | |
| 21.05.14 | Prague | 2 - 2 |
| **TURKEY U23** | | |
| 05.02.13 | Dartford FC | 0 - 1 |
| 14.10.14 | Istanbul | 0 - 2 |
| **UKRAINE** | | |
| 22.03.16 | Kiev | 2 - 0 |
| **USA** | | |
| 20.03.02 | Stevenage Boro. | 2 - 1 |
| 09.06.04 | Charleston USA | 0 - 0 |
| **WALES** | | |
| 27.03.84 | Newtown | 1 - 2 |
| 26.03.85 | Telford | 1 - 0 |
| 18.03.86 | Merthyr Tydfil | 1 - 3 |
| 17.03.87 | Gloucester | 2 - 2 |
| 15.03.88 | Rhyl | 2 - 0 |
| 21.03.89 | Kidderminster | 2 - 0 |
| 06.03.90 | Merthyr Tydfil | 0 - 0 |
| 17.05.91 | Stafford | 1 - 2 |
| 03.03.92 | Aberystwyth | 1 - 0 |
| 02.03.93 | Cheltenham | 2 - 1 |
| 22.02.94 | Bangor | 2 - 1 |
| 28.02.95 | Yeovil Town | 1 - 0 |
| 23.05.99 | St Albans | 2 - 1 |
| 16.05.00 | Llanelli | 1 - 1 |
| 13.02.01 | Rushden & Dia. | 0 - 0 |
| 14.05.02 | Boston | 1 - 1 |
| 22.05.03 | Merthyr Tydfil | 2 - 0 |
| 20.05.04 | Keith FC | 0 - 2 |
| 26.05.05 | Cork | 1 - 0 |
| 25.05.06 | Eastbourne Boro' | 1 - 1 |
| 27.05.07 | Clachnacuddin | 3 - 0 |
| 21.02.08 | Exeter City | 2 - 1 |
| 24.05.08 | Rhyl | 3 - 0 |
| 15.09.10 | Newtown FC | 2 - 2 |

| RESULTS SUMMARY 1979 - 2016 | P | W | D | L | F | A |
|---|---|---|---|---|---|---|
| Barbados | 1 | 1 | 0 | 0 | 2 | 0 |
| Belgium | 6 | 3 | 1 | 2 | 8 | 7 |
| Bermuda | 1 | 1 | 0 | 0 | 6 | 1 |
| Bosnia & Herzegovina | 1 | 0 | 0 | 1 | 2 | 6 |
| Cyprus U21 | 1 | 0 | 0 | 1 | 1 | 2 |
| Czech Republic U21 | 1 | 0 | 2 | 0 | 2 | 2 |
| Finland Under-21 | 4 | 2 | 0 | 2 | 4 | 5 |
| Estonia | 1 | 1 | 0 | 0 | 1 | 0 |
| Estonia Under-23 | 1 | 1 | 0 | 0 | 4 | 2 |
| Grenada | 1 | 0 | 1 | 0 | 1 | 1 |
| Gibraltar | 4 | 3 | 0 | 1 | 8 | 7 |
| Holland | 19 | 14 | 5 | 0 | 40 | 8 |
| Hungary | 2 | 0 | 1 | 1 | 3 | 5 |
| Iraq | 1 | 0 | 0 | 1 | 1 | 5 |
| Irish Premier League XI | 1 | 0 | 0 | 1 | 1 | 3 |
| Italy | 18 | 5 | 8 | 4 | 24 | 22 |
| Jordan U23 | 1 | 1 | 0 | 0 | 1 | 0 |
| Latvia U23 | 1 | 0 | 0 | 1 | 0 | 1 |
| Malta | 1 | 1 | 0 | 0 | 4 | 0 |
| Norway Under-21 | 1 | 0 | 0 | 1 | 1 | 2 |
| Poland | 1 | 1 | 0 | 0 | 2 | 1 |
| Portugal | 1 | 0 | 0 | 1 | 0 | 1 |
| Republic of Ireland | 13 | 10 | 0 | 3 | 30 | 11 |
| Republic of Ireland U21 | 1 | 1 | 0 | 0 | 2 | 1 |
| Russia | 1 | 0 | 0 | 1 | 0 | 4 |
| Scotland | 15 | 10 | 3 | 2 | 30 | 15 |
| Slovakia U21/U23 | 2 | 0 | 0 | 2 | 3 | 5 |
| Sparta Prague B | 1 | 0 | 2 | 0 | 2 | 2 |
| Turkey U23 | 2 | 0 | 0 | 2 | 0 | 3 |
| Ukraine | 1 | 1 | 0 | 0 | 2 | 0 |
| USA | 2 | 1 | 1 | 0 | 2 | 1 |
| Wales | 24 | 13 | 7 | 4 | 34 | 20 |
| **TOTALS** | **131** | **70** | **31** | **31** | **221** | **143** |

## MANAGERS 1979 - 2016

| | | P | W | D | L | F | A | *Win% |
|---|---|---|---|---|---|---|---|---|
| 1979 | Howard Wilkinson | 2 | 2 | 0 | 0 | 6 | 1 | - |
| 1980 - 1984 | Keith Wright | 17 | 9 | 5 | 3 | 30 | 16 | 53 |
| 1985 - 1988 | Kevin Verity | 12 | 7 | 2 | 3 | 23 | 15 | 58 |
| 1989 - 1996 | Tony Jennings | 19 | 10 | 4 | 5 | 27 | 18 | 53 |
| 1997 | Ron Reid | 2 | 0 | 1 | 1 | 0 | 2 | - |
| 1998 - 2002 | John Owens | 14 | 8 | 5 | 1 | 22 | 10 | 57 |
| 2002 - | Paul Fairclough | 65 | 35 | 12 | 19 | 113 | 79 | 54 |

*Calculated for those who managed for 10 games or more.

## GOALSCORERS 1979 - 2016

**13 GOALS...**
Carter, Mark

**7 GOALS...**
Cole, Mitchell

**6 GOALS...**
Ashford, Noel

**5 GOALS...**
Davison, Jon
Williams, Colin

**4 GOALS...**
Culpin, Paul
D'Sane, Roscoe
Johnson, Jeff
Mackhail-Smith, Craig
Norwood, James

**3 GOALS...**
Adamson, David
Guinan, Steve
Grayson,Neil
Hatch, Liam
Kirk, Jackson
Morison, Steve
Morrison, Michael
Opponents
Taylor, Matt
Watkins, Dale

**2 GOALS...**
Alford, Carl
Barnes-Homer, Matthew
Barrett, Keith
Bishop, Andrew
Burgess, Andrew
Casey, Kim
Cordice, Neil
Elding, Anthony
Gray, Andre
Hayles, Barry
Hill, Kenny
Howell, David
John, Louis
Mutrie, Les
Patmore, Warren
Pearson, Matty
Richards, Justin
Seddon, Gareth
Southam, Glen
Watson, John
Weatherstone, Simon
Whitbread, Barry
Yiadom, Andy

**1 GOAL...**
Agana, Tony
Anderson, Dale
Ashton, John
Beautyman, Harry
Benson, Paul
Berry
Blackburn, Chris
Boardman, Jon
Bogle, Omar
Bolton, Jimmy
Boyd, George
Bradshaw, Mark
Briscoe, Louis
Brown, Paul
Browne, Corey
Carey-Bertram, Daniel
Carr, Michael
Cavell, Paul
Charles, Lee
Charley, Ken
Charnock, Kieran
Constable, James
Crittenden, Nick
Davies, Paul
Day, Matt
Densmore, Shaun
Drummond, Stewart
Fleming, Andrew
Franks, Franks
Furlong, Paul
Grant, John
Guthrie, Kurtis
Harrad, Shaun
Hine, Mark
Holland, Jack
Holroyd, Chris
Humphreys, Delwyn
Howells, Jake
Jackson, Kayden
Jackson, Marlon
James, Kingsley
Jennings, Connor
Kennedy, John
Kerr, Scott
Kimmins,Ged
King, Simon
Leworthy, David
McDougald, Junior
McFadzean, Kyle
Mayes, Bobby
Moore, Neil
Moore, Luke
Newton, Sean
O'Keefe, Eamon
Oli, Dennis
Penn, Russell
Pitcher, Geoff
Porter, Max
Ricketts, Sam
Robbins, Terry
Roberts, Jordan
Robinson, Mark
Roddis,Nick
Rodgers, Luke
Rodman, Alex
Rogers, Paul
Ryan, Tim
Sarcevic, Antoni
Sellars, Neil
Shaw, John
Sheldon, Gareth
Simpson, Josh
Sinclair, Dean
Smith, Ian
Smith, Ossie
Spencer, Scott
Stansfield, Adam
Stephens, Mickey
Stott, Steve
Taylor, Steve
Thurgood, Stuart
Tubbs, Matthew
Venables, David
Watkins, Adam
Way, Darren
Webb, Paul
Wilcox, Russ

# THE FA CUP 2015-16

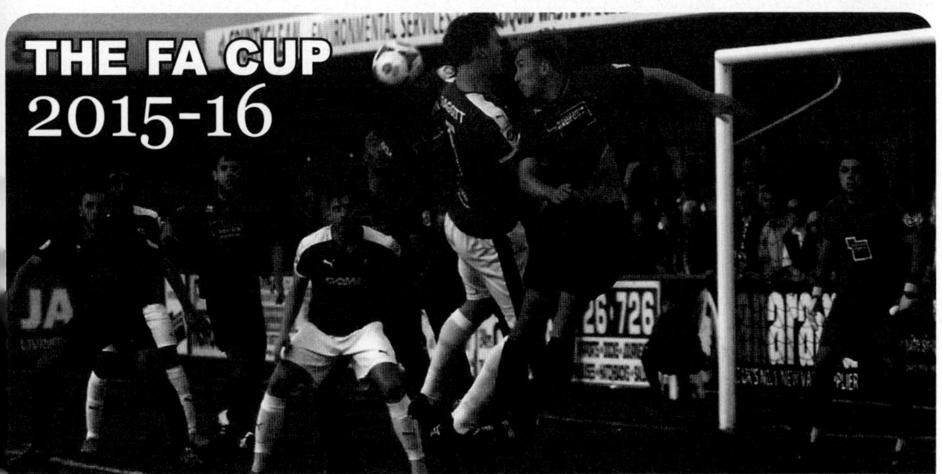

Eastbourne Borough's defence under pressure during their Fourth Qualifying Round tie against Dover Athletic. Photo: Roger Turner

## EXTRA PRELIMINARY ROUND

Every year the fact that the first round of the FA Cup ties is played in mid August, probably means that some clubs will have lost their involvement with the famous knock-out competition after their first match of the season. Many clubs will also lose interest in the competition before some players return from holidays.

This season, The Extra Preliminary Round contained 184 ties and involved some clubs with great FA Cup memories. Bishop Auckland and Crook Town (North East), Alvechurch and Bedford (Midlands) and Wisbech Town (Eastern Counties) were all drawn at home.

Times have changed for at least two of these ex-non-league giants, as Crook Town conceded six goals at home to Dunston UTS and Bedford also lost 0-6 to Cogenhoe United. This massive round of 184 ties produced 32 replays and some very high scoring performances, including some impressive away victories.
Chadderton 2  AFC Liverpool 9
Wellingborough 1  Ashford Town 8
Bishop Sutton 0  Street 6
and some high scoring home victories were also achieved:-
Coleshill Town 11  Ellesmere Rangers 0
Shoreham 8  St Francis Rangers 0
Horley Town 7  Wick & Barnham United 0
AFC Emley 7  Parkgate 1
Deeping Rangers 6  Boston Town 0
Newport Pagnell Town 6  Holmer Green 0

## PRELIMINARY ROUND

With another 160 FA Cup ties decided in this round, 244 non-league clubs will have already sampled the thrill of competing in the most famous club knock out competition, but sadly will not be involved in the First Qualifying Round.

With many clubs changing their names in recent years, new titles need to be accepted and many powerful new clubs are developing.

Certainly, Jarrow Roofing Bolden are proving to be a regular challenger and they achieved a fine away win at the more traditionally famous Bishop Auckland.

Scarborough Athletic lost away to Consett and Spennymoor Town won a home replay against Harrogate Railway Athletic. Runcorn Linnets achieved an impressive 6-0 victory over Pontefract Colliers, while Runcorn Town lost 2-3 at home to Northwich Victoria FC and 1874 Northwich FC lost at home to Maltby Main!

Its not easy to follow is it?

In the Midlands, Bromsgrove Sporting FC lost heavily at home to Hinckley FC, Rugby Town beat Coventry Sphinx 1-0 and Gresley FC drew at home with Coalville Town while Leicester Nirvana lost at home to Belper Town.

An Eastern Counties club that may not be well known nationally is Kirkley and Pakefield, but their supporters will be thrilled with a fine 3-0 away victory at Whitton United. East Midlands football was given a great boost when Rushden & Diamonds first took non-league football by storm and now the modern AFC Rushden & Diamonds would be featuring in the next FA Cup round after a 1-0 away win at Kings Langley.

South Park Football Club will remember this seasons FA Cup competition, as they probably will never score ten goals away from home again, as they did at Holmesdale FC.
Some other high scoring winners were:-

Dorking Wanderers 6 Canterbury City 2
Molesey 7 East Grinstead Town 1
Cove 0 North Leigh 7
Runcorn Linnets 6 Pontefract Collieries 0
FC Clacton 2 Aveley 6

There were some high scoring battles which were possibly more exciting:-

Thetford Town 3 Bury Town 5
Congleton Town 4 Handsworth Parramore 3
Newmarket Town 3 Peterborough Sports 5
Biggleswade United 5 Chalfont St Peter 3

After earning a draw away from home, one would imagine the replays would usually produce home victories, but in this Round of the FA Cup,15 of the 33 replays were won away from home.

## FIRST QUALIFYING ROUND

The clubs from the Premier Divisions of the Southern, Isthmian and Northern Premier Leagues enter the competition, all with their supporters hoping it will be their club's year for some exciting giant killing.

However, at least three victories will be needed before they qualify for a chance to meet a Football League club and in this First Qualifying Round they will of course act as the 'giants' to be challenged by the little clubs who have earned their place after the qualifying rounds.

Some results that caught the eye included clubs who are not usually in the national headlines such as:

Sporting Khalsa (Midland League)
Peterborough Sports (United Counties League)
AFC Portchester (Wessex League)
Tuffley Rovers (Hellenic League)

These Leagues have all produced their Cup heroes in the past and two of them moved on to the next round.

One of the Southern League's leading clubs this season has been Hungerford Town and a home draw for them against Bradford Town from the Western League may have been considered a good pairing. But an away draw and a home win saw the West Country club through and their excited supporters looking forward to the next challenge.

Once again famous clubs having experienced financial problems and a name change, could be seen battling to regain the reputations of their predecessors:- Runcorn Linnets left the

Jamie Salvidge, Halsham Town's No.8, has his shot saved by Eastbourne United's 'keeper Callum Christie in the Extra Preliminary Round. Photo: Roger Turner.

# EXTRA PRELIMINARY ROUND

## SATURDAY 15 AUGUST 2015 - WINNING CLUBS TO RECEIVE £1,500

| No | Home | | Away | Score | Att |
|---|---|---|---|---|---|
| 1 | Penrith | v | Jarrow Roofing Boldon CA | 1-2 | 110 |
| 2 | Silsden | v | West Allotment Celtic | 2-1 | 53 |
| 3 | Ashington | v | Albion Sports | 2-2 | 310 |
| | Albion Sports | v | Ashington (19/8) | 2-3 | 121 |
| 4 | AFC Darwen | v | Washington | 1-2 | 203 |
| 5 | Newcastle Benfield | v | Yorkshire Amateur | 4-2 | 80 |
| 6 | Nelson | v | Newton Aycliffe | 0-4 | 96 |
| 7 | Bedlington Terriers | v | West Auckland Town | 1-1 | 84 |
| | West Auckland Town | v | Bedlington Terriers (18/8) | 4-0 | |
| 8 | Barnoldswick Town | v | Colne | 0-5 | 333 |
| 9 | Billingham Synthonia | v | Consett | 0-0 | 147 |
| | Consett | v | Billingham Synthonia (18/8) | 8-0 | 188 |
| 10 | Hebburn Town | v | Tadcaster Albion | 1-3 | 83 |
| 11 | Bishop Auckland | v | Shildon | 1-1 | |
| | Shildon | v | Bishop Auckland (19/8) | 2-4 | |
| 12 | Sunderland RCA | v | Guisborough Town | 4-4 | 65 |
| | Guisborough Town | v | Sunderland RCA (19/8) | 3-2 | |
| 13 | Crook Town | v | Dunston UTS | 0-6 | 118 |
| 14 | Holker Old Boys | v | Liversedge | 4-0 | 89 |
| 15 | Pickering Town | v | Thornaby (16/8) | 4-0 | 159 |
| 16 | Seaham Red Star | v | Marske United | 2-2 | 145 |
| | Marske United | v | Seaham Red Star (18/8) | 3-1 | 104 |
| 17 | Garforth Town | v | Morpeth Town | 1-4 | 121 |
| 18 | Heaton Stannington | v | Norton & Stockton Ancients | 3-1 | 203 |
| 19 | Bridlington Town | v | North Shields | 0-2 | 351 |
| 20 | Whitley Bay | v | Sunderland Ryhope CW | 1-1 | 287 |
| | Sunderland Ryhope CW | v | Whitley Bay (18/8) | 2-3 | 127 |
| 21 | Whickham | v | Padiham (16/8) | 1-2 | 130 |
| 22 | Durham City | v | Thackley | 1-3 | 108 |
| 23 | Glasshoughton Welfare | v | Runcorn Linnets | 2-2 | 180 |
| | Runcorn Linnets | v | Glasshoughton Welfare (18/8) | 6-1 | 252 |
| 24 | Chadderton | v | AFC Liverpool | 2-9 | 75 |
| 25 | Congleton Town | v | Nostell MW | 0-0 | 163 |
| | Nostell MW | v | Congleton Town (18/8) | 0-4 | 56 |
| 6 | Alsager Town | v | Athersley Recreation | 1-0 | 110 |
| 7 | Winsford United | v | AFC Blackpool | 1-1 | 134 |
| | AFC Blackpool | v | Winsford United (18/8) | 3-2 | |
| 8 | AFC Emley | v | Parkgate (16/8) | 7-1 | 249 |
| 9 | Ashton Athletic | v | Maltby Main | 2-2 | 82 |
| | Maltby Main | v | Ashton Athletic (19/8) | 0-6 | |
| 0 | Penistone Church | v | Pontefract Collieries | 0-2 | 220 |
| 1 | Maine Road | v | St Helens Town | 2-1 | 103 |
| 2 | Handsworth Parramore | v | Staveley MW | 6-0 | 122 |
| 3 | 1874 Northwich | v | West Didsbury & Chorlton (14/8) | 3-0 | 350 |
| 4 | Barton Town Old Boys | v | Squires Gate | 2-2 | 122 |
| | Squires Gate | v | Barton Town Old Boys (18/8) | 2-4aet | |
| 5 | Abbey Hey | v | Worksop Town | 3-1 | 180 |
| 6 | Runcorn Town | v | Bacup Borough | 3-0 | 65 |
| 7 | Hemsworth MW | v | Armthorpe Welfare | 1-2 | 68 |
| 8 | Bootle | v | Atherton Collieries | 0-2 | 195 |
| 9 | Hanley Town | v | Shawbury United | 4-2 | 118 |
| 0 | Continental Star | v | Bolehall Swifts (16/8) | 2-2 | 69 |
| | (at Rushall Olympic FC) | | | | |
| | Bolehall Swifts | v | Continental Star (18/8) | 1-3 | 48 |
| | Boldmere St Michaels | v | Rocester | 3-3 | 123 |
| | Rocester | v | Boldmere St Michaels (18/8) | 4-0 | |
| 2 | Hinckley | v | Walsall Wood | 0-0 | 241 |
| | Walsall Wood | v | Hinckley (18/8) | 1-3 | |
| 3 | Brocton | v | Stourport Swifts | 1-5 | 92 |
| 44 | Southam United | v | AFC Wulfrunians | 0-2 | 68 |
| 45 | Alvechurch | v | Heath Hayes | 3-0 | 88 |
| 46 | Tipton Town | v | Cadbury Athletic | 0-2 | 85 |
| 47 | AFC Bridgnorth | v | Wolverhampton Casuals | 1-0 | 80 |
| 48 | Malvern Town | v | Sporting Khalsa | 0-5 | 108 |
| 49 | Westfields | v | Pegasus Juniors | 1-0 | 247 |
| 50 | Gornal Athletic | v | Bromsgrove Sporting | 1-2 | 128 |
| 51 | Lye Town | v | Coventry Sphinx | 2-2 | 80 |
| | (at Bromsgrove Sporting FC) | | | | |
| | Coventry Sphinx | v | Lye Town (17/8) | 2-1 | 90 |
| 52 | Coleshill Town | v | Ellesmere Rangers (14/8) | 11-0 | 121 |
| | (at Tamworth FC) | | | | |
| 53 | Cleethorpes Town | v | Brigg Town | 5-1 | 116 |
| 54 | Harborough Town | v | Shirebrook Town | 3-2 | 81 |
| 55 | South Normanton Athletic | v | AFC Mansfield | 2-1 | 75 |
| 56 | Shepshed Dynamo | v | Retford United | 1-0 | 185 |
| 57 | Bottesford Town | v | Rainworth MW | 2-2 | 63 |
| | Rainworth MW | v | Bottesford Town (18/8) | 1-5 | 62 |
| 58 | Kirby Muxloe | v | Heanor Town | 3-1 | 98 |
| 59 | Long Eaton United | v | Harrowby United | 2-1 | 111 |
| 60 | Loughborough University | v | Barrow Town | 4-1 | 74 |
| 61 | St Andrews | v | Clipstone Welfare | 2-3 | 32 |
| 62 | Radford | v | Sleaford Town | 3-2 | 105 |
| 63 | Quorn | v | Oadby Town | 1-3 | 161 |
| 64 | Bardon Hill Sports | v | Dunkirk | 0-1 | 61 |
| 65 | Ellistown & Ibstock United | v | Holwell Sports | 0-5 | 54 |
| 66 | Blaby & Whetstone Athletic | v | Leicester Nirvana | 0-5 | 68 |
| 67 | Walsham Le Willows | v | Godmanchester Rovers | 0-3 | 107 |
| 68 | Wisbech Town | v | Diss Town | 1-0 | 226 |
| 69 | Yaxley | v | Gorleston | 2-1 | 62 |
| 70 | Peterborough Northern Star | v | Newmarket Town | 1-2 | 48 |
| 71 | Haverhill Rovers | v | Mildenhall Town | 0-1 | 152 |
| 72 | Fakenham Town | v | Huntingdon Town | 0-0 | 92 |
| | Huntingdon Town | v | Fakenham Town (19/8) | 1-1 | 67 |
| 73 | Eynesbury Rovers | v | Peterborough Sports | 0-1 | 110 |
| 74 | Swaffham Town | v | Thetford Town | 2-4 | 109 |
| 75 | Great Yarmouth Town | v | Norwich United | 0-3 | 143 |
| 76 | Deeping Rangers | v | Boston Town | 6-1 | 110 |
| 77 | Holbeach United | v | Ely City | 1-1 | 137 |
| | Ely City | v | Holbeach United (18/8) | 0-4 | 108 |
| 78 | Welwyn Garden City | v | Haverhill Borough | 3-1 | 96 |
| 79 | Hoddesdon Town | v | Sawbridgeworth Town (14/8) | 4-0 | 216 |
| 80 | FC Romania | v | Whitton United | 0-3 | 34 |
| | (at Whitton United FC) | | | | |
| 81 | Southend Manor | v | Codicote | 3-1 | 60 |
| 82 | Wivenhoe Town | v | Tower Hamlets | 1-5 | 99 |
| 83 | Cockfosters | v | Burnham Ramblers | 4-0 | 88 |
| 84 | Hadley | v | Saffron Walden Town | 1-2 | 70 |
| 85 | Hertford Town | v | Kirkley & Pakefield | 2-2 | 111 |
| | Kirkley & Pakefield | v | Hertford Town (18/8) | 2-1 | 78 |
| 86 | Debenham LC | v | Ipswich Wanderers | 0-1 | 86 |
| 87 | Bowers & Pitsea | v | Ilford | 0-1 | 66 |
| 88 | Basildon United | v | Sporting Bengal United | 3-1 | 68 |
| 89 | FC Broxbourne Borough | v | Brantham Athletic | 1-2 | 41 |
| 90 | Long Melford | v | London Bari | 3-0 | 108 |
| 91 | FC Clacton | v | Eton Manor | 3-1 | 139 |
| 92 | Hullbridge Sports | v | Hadleigh United | 2-1 | 56 |
| 93 | Clapton | v | Stanway Rovers | 1-2 | |
| 94 | Stansted | v | Takeley | 2-1 | 187 |

Jason Taylor, Eastbourne Town's No.7, head's the ball into the back of the net against Whyteleafe during this Preliminary Round tie. Photo: Roger Turner.

competition, but Enfield Town, Kettering, AFC Rushden & Diamonds and Northwich all earned their place in the next round.

Cup ties come every two weeks early in the season, and the excitement will build if any of the successful clubs in this Round can manage another three victories.

## SECOND QUALIFYING ROUND

The National North and South clubs are welcomed to the FA Cup and there are still three rounds before The Football League clubs give the non-league 'family' a chance to hit the headlines.

The luck of the draw is very prominent in this round as can be seen from two of the very best clubs being drawn together, with Ebbsfleet beating Chelmsford City after a replay. While senior club Gosport Borough thrashed struggling Bideford 7-0, with on form striker Justin Bennett scoring four goals - his third hat trick already this season.

Basingstoke Town were paired with near neighbours Slough Town, winning a thriller 4-2 while Bath City enjoyed a victory over the comparatively easier opposition at Bodmin.

Two of the lesser known clubs mentioned in the previous rounds review were AFC Portchester who lost this time by the only goal at Brockenhurst but Sporting Khalsa won 3-2 away at Basford United and are obviously a club to watch.

Two famous clubs with a new 'image' revived some special memories for their fans, as Kettering beat AFC Telford United 2-1 at home.

While one of the best results of the round was achieved by Uxbridge who won 1-0 at Dartford and Petersfield Town will be pleased with their 3-1 defeat of Cirencester Town

A club who had already scored 28 goals in the first four weeks of the season was Stamford of the Northern Premier League, but amazingly, they failed to score in their cup tie at Coleshill Town and lost 0-2. In Stamford's twelve games this season their fans had seen 65 goals - that's entertainment !

Another club scoring plenty of goals is East Thurrock United, who like Stamford, are also in the lower half of their Premier Division, but have scored 26 goals including five away to Carshalton Athletic in this round. At least this match provided them with their first clean sheet of the campaign.

Two Rounds to go before the qualifying non-league clubs will be in the draw for the First Round Proper with The Football League clubs.

# EXTRA PRELIMINARY ROUND

## SATURDAY 15 AUGUST 2015 - WINNING CLUBS TO RECEIVE £1,500

| No | Home | | Away | Score | Att |
|---|---|---|---|---|---|
| | (at Bishop's Stortford FC) | | | | |
| 95 | Enfield 1893 | v | London Colney | 0-4 | |
| 96 | Felixstowe & Walton United | v | Barking | 1-1 | 130 |
| | Barking | v | Felixstowe & Walton United (18/8) | 3-1aet | |
| 97 | Waltham Forest | v | St Margaretsbury | 0-3 | 63 |
| 98 | AFC Hayes | v | Flackwell Heath | 3-2 | 58 |
| 99 | Wellingborough Town | v | Ashford Town (Middx) | 1-8 | 101 |
| 100 | Berkhamsted | v | Hanworth Villa | 3-2 | 73 |
| 101 | Oxhey Jets | v | AFC Kempston Rovers | 0-0 | 58 |
| | AFC Kempston Rovers | v | Oxhey Jets (18/8) | 3-2 | 43 |
| | (at Biggleswade Town FC) | | | | |
| 102 | Spelthorne Sports | v | Stotfold | 2-1 | 80 |
| 103 | Windsor | v | AFC Dunstable | 0-1 | 127 |
| 104 | Ampthill Town | v | Risborough Rangers | 0-3 | 140 |
| 105 | Rothwell Corinthians | v | Thrapston Town | 1-2 | 109 |
| 106 | Hillingdon Borough | v | Wembley | 1-1 | 58 |
| | Wembley | v | Hillingdon Borough (18/8) | 2-1 | 73 |
| 107 | Northampton Sileby Rangers | v | Sun Postal Sports | 2-1 | 72 |
| 108 | Wellingborough Whitworths | v | Northampton Spencer | 0-3 | 61 |
| 109 | Newport Pagnell Town | v | Holmer Green | 6-2 | 98 |
| 110 | Biggleswade United | v | Desborough Town | 2-1 | 98 |
| 111 | Potton United | v | Bedfont Sports | 0-2 | 91 |
| 112 | London Tigers | v | Bedfont & Feltham | 1-1 | 30 |
| | Bedfont & Feltham | v | London Tigers (18/8) | 2-2aet | |
| | (Bedfont & Feltham won 8-7 on kicks from the penalty mark) | | | | |
| 113 | Tring Athletic | v | Leverstock Green | 2-1 | 107 |
| 114 | Bedford | v | Cogenhoe United | 0-6 | 57 |
| 115 | Raunds Town | v | Crawley Green | 1-0 | 89 |
| 116 | Harefield United | v | Long Buckby | 2-2 | 102 |
| | Long Buckby | v | Harefield United (18/8) | 1-0 | |
| 117 | Royal Wootton Bassett Town | v | Bracknell Town | 0-2 | 121 |
| 118 | Ardley United | v | Tuffley Rovers | 1-4 | 41 |
| 119 | Binfield | v | Westfield | 1-1 | 94 |
| | Westfield | v | Binfield (18/8) | 0-1 | 120 |
| 120 | Ascot United | v | Kidlington | 1-2 | 53 |
| | (at Bracknell Town FC) | | | | |
| 121 | Holyport | v | Milton United | 1-3 | 67 |
| 122 | Hook Norton | v | Frimley Green | 5-0 | 44 |
| 123 | Reading Town | v | Chertsey Town | 0-5 | 53 |
| 124 | Knaphill | v | Highworth Town | 1-3 | 86 |
| 125 | Chinnor | v | Hartley Wintney | 0-2 | |
| 126 | Thame United | v | Farnham Town (16/8) | 1-1 | |
| | Farnham Town | v | Thame United (18/8) | 1-1aet | |
| | (Farnham Town won 4-3 on kicks from the penalty mark) | | | | |
| 127 | Abingdon United | v | Brimscombe & Thrupp | 0-3 | 117 |
| 128 | Cheltenham Saracens | v | Winterbourne United | 1-0 | 25 |
| 129 | Tadley Calleva | v | Guildford City | 2-3 | 110 |
| 130 | Highmoor Ibis | v | Thatcham Town | 1-2 | 102 |
| | (at Thatcham Town FC) | | | | |
| 131 | Badshot Lea | v | Camberley Town | 2-1 | 190 |
| 132 | Cove | v | Shrivenham | 5-4 | 61 |
| 133 | Banstead Athletic | v | Rochester United | 1-1 | 61 |
| | Rochester United | v | Banstead Athletic (18/8) | 2-1 | 54 |
| 134 | Hailsham Town | v | Eastbourne United | 2-3 | 172 |
| 135 | Worthing United | v | Deal Town | 0-0 | 68 |
| | Deal Town | v | Worthing United (18/8) | 7-1 | 84 |
| 136 | Arundel | v | Raynes Park Vale | 3-1 | 98 |
| 137 | Horsham YMCA | v | AFC Croydon Athletic | 2-0 | |
| 138 | Fisher | v | Corinthian | 0-3 | 74 |
| 139 | Crawley Down Gatwick | v | Chichester City | 1-3 | 53 |
| 140 | Tunbridge Wells | v | Glebe | | |
| | (walkover for Tunbridge Wells – Glebe not accepted into the Competition) | | | | |
| 141 | Shoreham | v | St Francis Rangers | 8-0 | 80 |
| 142 | East Preston | v | Littlehampton Town (16/8) | 1-2 | 186 |
| 143 | Horsham | v | Lancing (16/8) | 1-0 | 244 |
| 144 | Colliers Wood United | v | Eastbourne Town | 0-2 | 56 |
| 145 | Redhill | v | Pagham | 1-2 | 73 |
| 146 | Holmesdale | v | Mile Oak | 2-0 | 60 |
| 147 | Selsey | v | Erith Town | 1-5 | 95 |
| 148 | Croydon | v | Sutton Common Rovers | 5-1 | 68 |
| 149 | Sevenoaks Town | v | Seven Acre & Sidcup | 1-1 | 88 |
| | Seven Acre & Sidcup | v | Sevenoaks Town (19/8) | 1-1aet | 124 |
| | (Seven Acre & Sidcup won 4-2 on kicks from the penalty mark) | | | | |
| 150 | Cray Valley (PM) | v | Ashford United | 5-1 | 100 |
| 151 | Chessington & Hook United | v | Crowborough Athletic | 1-1 | 102 |
| | Crowborough Athletic | v | Chessington & Hook United (18/8) | 1-2aet | 105 |
| 152 | Bexhill United | v | Loxwood | 3-1 | 41 |
| | (at Eastbourne United FC) | | | | |
| 153 | Ringmer | v | Beckenham Town | 1-4 | 47 |
| 154 | Lingfield | v | Canterbury City (14/8) | 0-3 | 145 |
| | (at Whyteleafe FC) | | | | |
| 155 | Greenwich Borough | v | Lordswood (16/8) | 1-0 | 123 |
| 156 | Epsom & Ewell | v | Erith & Belvedere (16/8) | 0-4 | 151 |
| 157 | Horley Town | v | Wick & Barnham United | 7-0 | 87 |
| 158 | Christchurch | v | Cadbury Heath (16/8) | 2-1 | 92 |
| 159 | Melksham Town | v | Cowes Sports | 2-2 | 114 |
| | Cowes Sports | v | Melksham Town (18/8) | 3-1 | |
| 160 | Longwell Green Sports | v | Folland Sports | 2-1 | 77 |
| 161 | Andover Town | v | Gillingham Town | 2-0 | 142 |
| 162 | Lymington Town | v | Bitton | 0-3 | 45 |
| | (at New Milton Town FC) | | | | |
| 163 | Alresford Town | v | Bridport | 0-1 | 57 |
| 164 | Hamworthy United | v | Hallen | 1-1 | 84 |
| | Hallan | v | Hamworth United (18/8) | 0-1 | 69 |
| 165 | Amesbury Town | v | Bemerton Heath Harlequins | 1-2 | 150 |
| 166 | Hythe & Dibden | v | Moneyfields | 1-4 | |
| 167 | Team Solent | v | Blackfield & Langley | 3-4 | 59 |
| 168 | Bradford Town | v | United Services Portsmouth | 2-0 | 81 |
| 169 | Cribbs | v | Bristol Manor Farm | 0-5 | 88 |
| 170 | Verwood Town | v | Newport (IW) | 2-0 | |
| 171 | Almondsbury UWE | v | Fawley | 3-2 | 42 |
| 172 | Brockenhurst | v | Fareham Town | 2-0 | 88 |
| 173 | Bournemouth | v | AFC Portchester | 0-3 | 77 |
| 174 | Sherborne Town | v | New Milton Town | 2-0 | 68 |
| 175 | Whitchurch United | v | Wincanton Town | 1-1 | 62 |
| | Wincanton Town | v | Whitchurch United (18/8) | 3-1 | |
| 176 | Horndean | v | Sholing | 1-3 | 80 |
| 177 | Buckland Athletic | v | Clevedon Town | 3-0 | 133 |
| 178 | Saltash United | v | AFC St Austell | 0-4 | 128 |
| 179 | Bishop Sutton | v | Street | 0-6 | 43 |
| 180 | Witheridge | v | Welton Rovers | 2-0 | 77 |
| 181 | Shepton Mallet | v | Plymouth Parkway | 0-2 | 128 |
| 182 | Bodmin Town | v | Brislington | 3-1 | 88 |
| 183 | Odd Down | v | Ashton & Backwell United | 3-1 | 87 |
| 184 | Barnstaple Town | v | Willand Rovers | 2-0 | 237 |

Molesey's Matt Baxter (white kit) puts his effort over the Croydon bar in the First Qualifying Round. Photo: Alan Coomes.

## THIRD QUALIFYING ROUND

This is the time that 40 clubs anxiously wait to see the draw for the final round before The Football League clubs enter the competition. They have won their way through the Third Round and are joined by the 24 National Premier clubs, meaning 32 clubs will then represent the non-league World in the First Round Proper.

Members of the National North and South divisions joined the competition in the Third Qualifying Round, and between them, 23 of their members survived. AFC Fylde produced a staggering 9-0 victory over Coleshill Town and there was a high scoring battle at East Thurrock where the recently improving Staines Town beat the high scoring United club 6-3.

Another thriller between two form clubs saw Bognor Regis Town beat Oxford City 4-2 and Alfreton Town triumphed by the same score at Hednesford Town.

Clubs below the Premier level also enjoyed the headlines, as AFC Rushden & Diamonds beat Ashton United 2-0 at home, Northwich Victoria won at Hyde United and Harlow Town won a replay away to Bath City.

However, the name that really stands out is Sporting Khalsa, a club that gained promotion from the The West Midlands (Regional) League to The Midland League at the end of last season So far, they have beaten Cadbury Athletic 4-0 (home), Old Wulfrunians 3-2 (home), Basford United 3-2 (away) and after a last minute equalizer at Spalding United, a 2-1 victory at home gave them the exciting prospect of a home tie against FC United of Manchester.

Clubs with cup tradition or encouraging form wh will be looking forward to one more vital FA Cup victory, include three Uniteds from North Ferriby Maidstone and Sutton. But before any non-league clubs can consider senior giant killing, some excellent local pairings will have to be decided in a Round full of potentially thrilling traditional FA Cup ties.

| **National North - 11** | **National South - 12** | **NPL Premier - 3** | **Southern Premier - 3** | **Isthmian Premier - 4** |
|---|---|---|---|---|
| AFC Fylde | Basingstoke Town | Barwell | Chesham United | Bognor Regis Town |
| Alfreton Town | Chelmsford City | Salford City | Chippenham Town | Brentwood Town |
| Brackley Town | Eastbourne Borough | Stourbridge | Poole Town | Enfield Town |
| Chorley | Havant & Waterlooville | | | Grays Athletic |
| FC United | Maidenhead United | **NPL Div.1 N - 2** | **Sth Div.1 SW - 1** | Staines Town |
| Gainsborough T | Maidstone United | Bamber Bridge | Didcot Town | |
| Gloucester City | Margate | Northwich Victoria | | **Isthmian Div.1 N - 2** |
| Harrogate Town | St Albans City | | **Sth Div.1 Cen.** | Harlow Town |
| North Ferriby Utd | Sutton United | | AFC Rushden & Dia | AFC Hornchurch |
| Stalybridge Celtic | Wealdstone | | | |
| Worcester City | Weston-s-Mare | **Midland League -1** | | |
| | Whitehawk | Sporting Khaba | | |

# PRELIMINARY ROUND

## SATURDAY 29 AUGUST 2015 - WINNERS RECEIVE £1,925

| No | Home | | Away | Score | Att |
|---|---|---|---|---|---|
| 1 | Whitley Bay | v | Heaton Stannington | 2-1 | 346 |
| 2 | West Auckland Town | v | Washington | 2-3 | 98 |
| 3 | Ashington | v | Thackley | 1-2 | 236 |
| 4 | Pickering Town | v | Clitheroe (30/8) | 1-5 | 231 |
| 5 | North Shields | v | Kendal Town | 1-1 | 356 |
| | Kendal Town | v | North Shields (1/9) | 2-0 | 201 |
| 6 | Bishop Auckland | v | Jarrow Roofing Boldon CA | 1-2 | |
| 7 | Silsden | v | Padiham | 0-2 | 107 |
| 8 | Guisborough Town | v | Newcastle Benfield | 4-2 | |
| 9 | Marske United | v | Lancaster City | 1-1 | 216 |
| | Lancaster City | v | Marske United (1/9) | 1-0 | 187 |
| 10 | Harrogate Railway Athletic | v | Spennymoor Town | 0-0 | 172 |
| | Spennymoor Town | v | Harrogate Railway Athletic (1/9) | 2-0 | 388 |
| 11 | Holker Old Boys | v | Dunston UTS | 0-2 | 125 |
| 12 | Consett | v | Scarborough Athletic | 2-0 | 334 |
| 13 | Tadcaster Albion | v | Colne | 2-5 | 243 |
| 14 | Newton Aycliffe | v | Morpeth Town | 2-0 | |
| 15 | Congleton Town | v | Handsworth Parramore | 4-3 | 143 |
| 16 | Runcorn Linnets | v | Pontefract Collieries | 6-0 | 272 |
| 17 | Armthorpe Welfare | v | New Mills | 1-0 | 51 |
| 18 | Runcorn Town | v | Northwich Victoria | 2-3 | 82 |
| 19 | Alsager Town | v | Shaw Lane Aquaforce | 2-1 | 99 |
| 20 | Ossett Albion | v | Maine Road | 3-0 | 117 |
| 21 | Mossley | v | Bamber Bridge | 1-1 | 169 |
| | Bamber Bridge | v | Mossley (1/9) | 3-1 | 204 |
| 22 | Burscough | v | AFC Emley | 3-1 | 110 |
| 23 | Barton Town OBs | v | Droylsden | 1-2 | 142 |
| 24 | 1874 Northwich | v | Maltby Main | 1-2 | 260 |
| 25 | Abbey Hey | v | Warrington Town | 3-2 | 152 |
| 26 | AFC Blackpool | v | Ossett Town | 1-0 | 100 |
| 27 | Brighouse Town | v | Atherton Collieries | 1-1 | 139 |
| | Atherton Collieries | v | Brighouse Town (31/8) | 1-2 | 220 |
| 28 | AFC Liverpool | v | Radcliffe Borough (28/8) | 3-2 | 213 |
| 29 | Stocksbridge Park Steels | v | Farsley Celtic | 1-1 | 109 |
| | Farsley Celtic | v | Stocksbridge Park Steels (1/9) | 3-0 | 137 |
| 30 | Glossop North End | v | Prescot Cables | 2-1 | 327 |
| 31 | Goole | v | Sheffield | 1-1 | 143 |
| | Sheffield | v | Goole (1/9) | 0-3 | 197 |
| 32 | Trafford | v | Witton Albion | 1-2 | 259 |
| 33 | Market Drayton Town | v | AFC Bridgnorth | 2-0 | 102 |
| 34 | Bromsgrove Sporting | v | Hinckley | 2-6 | 386 |
| 35 | Newcastle Town | v | Continental Star | 4-0 | 77 |
| 36 | Leek Town | v | Rocester | 1-1 | 198 |
| | Rocester | v | Leek Town (1/9) | 1-2 | 260 |
| 37 | Rugby Town | v | Coventry Sphinx | 1-0 | 239 |
| 38 | Coleshill Town | v | Stafford Rangers | 2-1 | 358 |
| | (at Stafford Rangers FC) | | | | |
| 9 | Sporting Khalsa | v | Cadbury Athletic | 4-0 | |
| 0 | Chasetown | v | Evesham United | 2-0 | 168 |
| 1 | Westfields | v | Kidsgrove Athletic | 1-1 | 118 |
| | Kidsgrove Athletic | v | Westfields (2/9) | 5-6aet | 175 |
| 42 | Stourport Swifts | v | Alvechurch | 1-0 | 138 |
| 43 | AFC Wulfrunians | v | Romulus | 2-0 | 93 |
| 44 | Tividale | v | Hanley Town | 1-0 | 87 |
| 45 | Carlton Town | v | Shepshed Dynamo | 1-2 | 100 |
| 46 | Harborough Town | v | Oadby Town | 0-2 | |
| 47 | Kirby Muxloe | v | Holwell Sports | 0-0 | |
| | Holwell Sports | v | Kirby Muxloe (1/9) | 1-0 | |
| 48 | Loughborough Dynamo | v | Basford United | 1-3 | 102 |
| 49 | Radford | v | Spalding United | 1-2 | 110 |
| 50 | Dunkirk | v | Bottesford Town | 4-1 | 49 |
| 51 | South Normanton Athletic | v | Lincoln United | 1-1 | 109 |
| | Lincoln United | v | South Normanton Athletic (1/9) | 2-1 | |
| 52 | Gresley | v | Coalville Town | 2-2 | 351 |
| | Coalville Town | v | Gresley (1/9) | 5-0 | 234 |
| 53 | Leicester Nirvana | v | Belper Town | 2-4 | 96 |
| 54 | Loughborough University | v | Long Eaton United | 1-2 | 143 |
| 55 | Clipstone Welfare | v | Cleethorpes Town | 1-0 | 109 |
| 56 | Mildenhall Town | v | Soham Town Rangers | 5-2 | 182 |
| 57 | Yaxley | v | Godmanchester Rovers | 4-1 | 112 |
| 58 | Deeping Rangers | v | Dereham Town | 1-0 | 140 |
| 59 | Thetford Town | v | Bury Town (30/8) | 3-5 | 276 |
| 60 | Wroxham | v | Fakenham Town | 3-2 | 141 |
| 61 | Wisbech Town | v | Holbeach United | 0-1 | 287 |
| 62 | St Ives Town | v | Norwich United (28/8) | 1-1 | 216 |
| | Norwich United | v | St Ives Town (2/9) | 2-6 | 125 |
| 63 | Newmarket Town | v | Peterborough Sports | 3-5 | 192 |
| 64 | London Colney | v | Potters Bar Town | 1-3 | 102 |
| 65 | St Margaretsbury | v | AFC Hornchurch | 1-5 | 91 |
| 66 | Welwyn Garden City | v | Waltham Abbey | 1-0 | 203 |
| 67 | Ilford | v | Stanway Rovers | 0-2 | |
| 68 | Hullbridge Sports | v | Maldon & Tiptree | 2-0 | 83 |
| 69 | Harlow Town | v | Southend Manor | 5-1 | 230 |
| 70 | Barkingside | v | Ipswich Wanderers (30/8) | 1-2 | 110 |
| 71 | Barking | v | Haringey Borough | 0-0 | 162 |
| | Haringey Borough | v | Barking (1/9) | 2-1 | 83 |
| 72 | AFC Sudbury | v | Ware | 4-0 | 166 |
| 73 | Whitton United | v | Kirkley & Pakefield | 0-3 | 77 |
| 74 | Hoddesdon Town | v | Romford | 0-0 | 98 |
| | Romford | v | Hoddesdon Town (2/9) | 1-1aet | 121 |
| | (Hoddesdon Town won 5-4 on kicks from the penalty mark) | | | | |
| 75 | Stansted | v | Tilbury (30/8) | 0-0 | 189 |
| | Tilbury | v | Stansted (1/9) | 3-0 | 95 |
| 76 | Redbridge | v | Heybridge Swifts | 1-2 | 61 |
| 77 | Cockfosters | v | Tower Hamlets | 3-3 | |
| | Tower Hamlets | v | Cockfosters (31/8) | 1-5 | 76 |
| 78 | Saffron Walden Town | v | Cheshunt | 2-0 | 263 |
| 79 | Great Wakering Rovers | v | Brantham Athletic | 0-2 | 115 |
| 80 | Basildon United | v | Long Melford | 1-0 | 50 |
| 81 | Thurrock | v | Royston Town | 2-2 | 80 |
| | Royston Town | v | Thurrock (1/9) | 1-3 | 115 |
| 82 | Witham Town | v | Brightlingsea Regent | 1-1 | 117 |

## FOURTH QUALIFYING ROUND

When the dust settled after one of the most exciting and rewarding rounds of the FA Cup, the thrilling run of Sporting Khaba from the Midland League had come to an honourable end. A superb crowd of 2,252 attended their 1-3 home defeat against the glamourous FC United from The National North and their very special cup run will be remembered by their supporters for the rest of their lives.

Their place as the competition's special 'underdog' in the next round will be taken by Didcot Town from The Southern League Division One South West although they were joined by Northwich Victoria (N.P.L. Div 1 North), who of course had built an impressive reputation as Founder Members of the Alliance and Conference.

Exeter City were watched by the country, live on television, as they lost away to Wakefield who became national giant killing heroes. The pressure, atmosphere and general worry about losing to non-league opposition proved too much on the day for 'The Grecians'.
So how have they been rewarded for their suffering?

They have been drawn away to Didcot Town and the match will once again by live on Television!

The excellent television programmes featuring Salford City has been great for non-league football. The involvement of so many famous and wealthy ex Manchester United footballers does make them a little different from the average club at their level although their supporters will surely enjoy their First Round match against Notts County and the publicity on and off the field.

A second junior member of the Manchester Football Family will also be featured on television as FC United will be hosts to Chesterfield on the Monday before the successful ones will find out just how famous their opponents will be in the last round before the real giants join the competition.

32 Qualifyers for The FACup 1st Round Proper were:

**National - 13 (Lge Position at the time)**
Forest Green Rovers (1), Cheltenham Town (2), Dover Athletic (3), Braintree Town (5), Eastleigh (7), Grimsby Town (9), Lincoln City (11), Aldershot Town (12), Macclesfield Town (13), Welling United (18), Altrincham (19), Boreham Wood (20), and FC Halifax Town (23).

**National North - 6**
AFC Fylde (1), Stalybridge Celtic (10), Gainsborough trinity (14), FC United (15), Brackley Town (16) and Worcester City (18).

**National South - 6**
Whitehawk (3), Maidstone United (4), Maidenhead United (5), Weladstone (17), St Albans City (20) and Basingstoke Town (22).

**NPL Premier - 3**
Salford City (4), Stourbridge (5) and Barwell (15)
**NPL Division 1 North**
Northwich Victoria (3)

**Southern Premier**
Chesham United (14)
**Southern Division 1 South & West**
Didcot Town (15)

**Isthmian Premier**
Staines Town (17)

Nathan Pinney scores against AFC Sudbury for Eastbourne Borough in the Second Qualifying Round. Photo: Roger Turner

# PRELIMINARY ROUND

## SATURDAY 29 AUGUST 2015 - WINNERS RECEIVE £1,925

| No. | Home | | Away | Score | Att |
|---|---|---|---|---|---|
| | Brightlingsea Regent | v | Witham Town (1/9) | 2-3 | 135 |
| 83 | FC Clacton | v | Aveley | 2-6 | 149 |
| 84 | Ashford Town (Middx) | v | AFC Kempston Rovers | 1-0 | 105 |
| 85 | Long Buckby | v | Daventry Town | 2-1 | 124 |
| 86 | Beaconsfield SYCOB | v | Raunds Town (30/8) | 3-0 | 143 |
| 87 | Barton Rovers | v | Berkhamsted | 3-1 | 120 |
| 88 | Biggleswade United | v | Chalfont St Peter | 5-3 | 112 |
| 89 | Risborough Rangers | v | Aylesbury | 0-3 | 388 |
| 90 | Wembley | v | North Greenford United | 1-1 | 63 |
| | North Greenford United | v | Wembley (1/9) | 5-1 | 87 |
| 91 | Northampton Sileby Rangers | v | Leighton Town | 0-3 | 79 |
| 92 | Bedfont & Feltham | v | AFC Hayes | 1-1 | 55 |
| | AFC Hayes | v | Bedfont & Feltham (1/9) | 1-3 | |
| 93 | Newport Pagnell Town | v | AFC Dunstable | 1-1 | |
| | AFC Dunstable | v | Newport Pagnell Town (1/9) | 2-1 | 138 |
| 94 | Bedfont Sports | v | Hanwell Town | 1-2 | 76 |
| 95 | Uxbridge | v | Northampton Spencer | 1-0 | 77 |
| 96 | Aylesbury United | v | Northwood | 1-2 | 141 |
| 97 | Bedford Town | v | Thrapston Town | 2-1 | 187 |
| 98 | Cogenhoe United | v | Spelthorne Sports | 3-0 | 78 |
| 99 | Tring Athletic | v | Arlesey Town | 0-2 | 116 |
| 100 | Kings Langley | v | AFC Rushden & Diamonds | 0-1 | 205 |
| 101 | Wantage Town | v | Didcot Town (28/8) | 3-4 | |
| 102 | Chertsey Town | v | Kidlington | 1-4 | 112 |
| 103 | Binfield | v | Shortwood United | 1-2 | 126 |
| 104 | Badshot Lea | v | Fleet Town | 2-4 | 75 |
| 105 | Marlow | v | Godalming Town | 1-1 | 116 |
| | Godalming Town | v | Marlow (1/9) | 2-1aet | 139 |
| 106 | Brimscombe & Thrupp | v | Bracknell Town | 2-2 | 79 |
| | Bracknell Town | v | Brimscombe & Thrupp (1/9) | 1-0 | 141 |
| 107 | Tuffley Rovers | v | Bishop's Cleeve | 1-0 | 149 |
| 108 | Cheltenham Saracens | v | Milton United | 1-0 | 32 |
| 109 | Cove | v | North Leigh | 0-7 | 162 |
| 110 | Egham Town | v | Slimbridge | 2-2 | 71 |
| | Slimbridge | v | Egham Town (1/9) | 3-2aet | 92 |
| 111 | Thatcham Town | v | Guildford City | 3-2 | 138 |
| 112 | Hartley Wintney | v | Banbury United | 5-2 | 186 |
| 113 | Farnham Town | v | Highworth Town | 4-2 | 56 |
| 114 | Hook Norton | v | Burnham | 1-1 | 100 |
| | Burnham | v | Hook Norton (1/9) | 2-4aet | 76 |
| 115 | Molesey | v | East Grinstead Town | 7-1 | 64 |
| 116 | Chipstead | v | Rochester United | 0-1 | 55 |
| 117 | Deal Town | v | Horsham | 1-1 | |
| | Horsham | v | Deal Town (31/8) | 1-2 | 241 |
| 118 | Seven Acre & Sidcup | v | Sittingbourne (28/8) | 1-2 | 152 |
| 119 | Ramsgate | v | Tooting & Mitcham United | 0-1 | 216 |
| 120 | Folkestone Invicta | v | Corinthian | 3-1 | 281 |
| 121 | Herne Bay | v | Peacehaven & Telscombe | 1-0 | 117 |
| 122 | Hythe Town | v | Chessington & Hook United | 0-2 | 140 |
| 123 | Tunbridge Wells | v | Croydon | 1-1 | 255 |
| | Croydon | v | Tunbridge Wells (2/9) | 2-1 | 110 |
| 124 | Cray Valley (PM) | v | Hastings United | 0-3 | 117 |
| 125 | Holmesdale | v | South Park | 1-10 | 40 |
| 126 | Whitstable Town | v | Walton Casuals | 3-0 | 152 |
| 127 | Three Bridges | v | Cray Wanderers | 0-1 | 125 |
| 128 | Bexhill United | v | Faversham Town | 0-5 | 150 |
| | (at Faversham Town FC) | | | | |
| 129 | Eastbourne United | v | Arundel | 1-1 | 63 |
| | Arundel | v | Eastbourne United (1/9) | 1-4 | |
| 130 | Littlehampton Town | v | Thamesmead Town | 0-1 | 70 |
| | (at Worthing United FC) | | | | |
| 131 | Chichester City | v | Chatham Town | 0-4 | 72 |
| 132 | Shoreham | v | Horley Town | 1-1 | 142 |
| | Horley Town | v | Shoreham (1/9) | 2-3 | |
| 133 | Beckenham Town | v | Greenwich Borough | 0-4 | 75 |
| 134 | Pagham | v | Corinthian Casuals | 3-1 | 116 |
| 135 | Erith Town | v | Horsham YMCA (30/8) | 2-4 | 110 |
| 136 | Worthing | v | Walton & Hersham | 4-2 | 306 |
| 137 | Eastbourne Town | v | Whyteleafe | 1-1 | 113 |
| | Whyteleafe | v | Eastbourne Town (1/9) | 2-3 | 113 |
| 138 | Phoenix Sports | v | Guernsey | 2-2 | 160 |
| | Guernsey | v | Phoenix Sports (2/9) | 1-2 | 121 |
| | (at Lewes FC) | | | | |
| 139 | Dorking Wanderers | v | Canterbury City | 6-2 | 73 |
| 140 | Erith & Belvedere | v | Carshalton Athletic (30/8) | 1-3 | 115 |
| 141 | Winchester City | v | Wincanton Town | 5-1 | 136 |
| 142 | Hamworthy United | v | Andover Town (12/9) | 4-1 | 103 |
| | (29/8 – tie ordered to be replayed) | | | | |
| | Hamworthy United | v | Andover Town (12/9) | 2-1 | 87 |
| 143 | Longwell Green Sports | v | Cinderford Town | 0-1 | 112 |
| 144 | Brockenhurst | v | Yate Town | 2-1 | 82 |
| 145 | Sholing | v | Swindon Supermarine (28/8) | 2-4 | 141 |
| 146 | Bradford Town | v | Christchurch | 6-3 | 77 |
| 147 | Cowes Sports | v | Wimborne Town | 0-5 | |
| 148 | Bristol Manor Farm | v | Bitton | 3-2 | 126 |
| 149 | AFC Portchester | v | AFC Totton | 3-1 | 145 |
| 150 | Bashley | v | Mangotsfield United | 0-4 | 100 |
| 151 | Almondsbury UWE | v | Verwood Town | 3-1 | 48 |
| 152 | Moneyfields | v | Petersfield Town | 1-2 | 108 |
| 153 | Blackfield & Langley | v | Bemerton Heath Harlequins | 1-0 | 73 |
| 154 | Bridport | v | Sherborne Town | 3-3 | |
| | Sherborne Town | v | Bridport (2/9) | 0-1aet | |
| 155 | Plymouth Parkway | v | Tiverton Town | 4-1 | 213 |
| 156 | Larkhall Athletic | v | Buckland Athletic | 3-2 | 135 |
| 157 | AFC St Austell | v | Bodmin Town | 0-1 | 351 |
| 158 | Barnstaple Town | v | Bridgwater Town | 2-0 | 237 |
| 159 | Street | v | Witheridge | 1-2 | 118 |
| 160 | Taunton Town | v | Odd Down | 5-1 | 228 |

### THE FA CUP

Since the formation of senior regional divisions beneath the National Premier Division in 2004, the quality of the senior clubs representing The Isthmian, Southern and Northern Premier senior divisions have suffered on and off the field.

This is reflected in their FA Cup achievements and its sad to see so few of their representatives will be featuring in the First Round Proper this season.

On the other hand, the majority of clubs in the National League's Premier Division are Football League 'old boys' and consider themselves still on a par with their ex colleagues in League Two. So a cup victory is hardly described as giant killing and their supporters are deprived of the old fashioned but, extremely exciting, cup fever.

However, a positive feature of the thirteen Senior non-league qualifiers is the fact that Boreham Wood, Braintree Town, Dover Athletic, Eastleigh and Forest Green Rovers are still obviously ambitious to achieve new levels and experiences in the game.

Interesting to see which clubs obviously took their FA Cup ties seriously. One can imagine that club officials at National North and South clubs might consider promotion more important. So one can also imagine the attitudes in National North, as only AFC Fylde, who appeared to be better than any of their challengers anyway, reached the First Round Stage, whereas in the South the six qualifiers represented clubs in both halves of their table.

Supporters who travel up and down the country, love a cup run and nothing upsets them more after a days travel to find the manager has picked a weaker side to save his players for their league challenge. Players should be fit enough to play two games a week all through the season. There is nothing more uplifting at a club than an exciting cup run, with victories and meetings with opposition from senior leagues. Morale throughout the club is boosted and inspired to complete a special season.

Didcot clear this Exeter City attack during their First Round Proper tie which attracted a record crowd of 2,707. Photo: Peter Barnes.

# FIRST QUALIFYING ROUND

## SATURDAY 12 SEPTEMBER 2015 - WINNERS RECEIVE £3,000

| | | | | | |
|---|---|---|---|---|---|
| 1 | Jarrow Roofing Boldon CA | v | Congleton Town | 3-4 | 106 |
| 2 | Buxton | v | Ramsbottom United | 2-1 | 207 |
| 3 | Washington | v | Runcorn Linnets | 1-0 | 129 |
| 4 | Padiham | v | Lancaster City | 0-2 | 197 |
| 5 | Spennymoor Town | v | Blyth Spartans | 2-1 | 132 |
| 6 | Droylsden | v | Ossett Albion | 2-1 | 132 |
| 7 | Northwich Victoria | v | AFC Blackpool (11/9) | 4-0 | 172 |
| 8 | Workington | v | Colwyn Bay | 5-0 | 438 |
| 9 | Consett | v | Colne | 3-1 | 383 |
| 10 | Matlock Town | v | Whitley Bay | 0-0 | 287 |
| | Whitley Bay | v | Matlock Town (15/9) | 3-3aet | 338 |
| | (Whitley Bay won 4-2 on kicks from the penalty mark) | | | | |
| 11 | Kendal Town | v | Dunston UTS | 5-2 | 240 |
| 12 | Glossop North End | v | Skelmersdale United | 1-1 | 339 |
| | Skelmersdale United | v | Glossop North End (15/9) | 2-1 | 248 |
| 13 | Maltby Main | v | Frickley Athletic | 0-2 | 202 |
| 14 | Salford City | v | Whitby Town | 1-1 | 255 |
| | Whitby Town | v | Salford City (16/9) | 0-5 | 244 |
| 15 | Darlington 1883 | v | Hyde United | 1-3 | 902 |
| 16 | AFC Liverpool | v | Armthorpe Welfare (13/9) | 3-4 | 201 |
| 17 | Ashton United | v | Guisborough Town | 0-0 | 133 |
| | Guisborough Town | v | Ashton United (16/9) | 2-3 | 220 |
| 18 | Thackley | v | Abbey Hey | 2-2 | 86 |
| | Abbey Hey | v | Thackley (15/9) | 1-0 | 60 |
| 19 | Alsager Town | v | Burscough | 1-2 | 112 |
| 20 | Witton Albion | v | Farsley Celtic | 2-1 | 204 |
| 21 | Brighouse Town | v | Newton Aycliffe | 0-2 | 147 |
| 22 | Marine | v | Clitheroe | 2-0 | 237 |
| 23 | Goole | v | Bamber Bridge | 2-2 | 176 |
| | Bamber Bridge | v | Goole (15/9) | 4-2 | 151 |
| 24 | Spalding United | v | Nantwich Town | 1-0 | 157 |
| 25 | Hinckley | v | Redditch United | 2-1 | 295 |
| 26 | Ilkeston | v | Rugby Town | 2-3 | 417 |
| 27 | Tividale | v | Stourbridge | 0-1 | 237 |
| 28 | Leamington | v | Stamford | 1-1 | 401 |
| | Stamford | v | Leamington (15/9) | 2-1 | 204 |
| 29 | Market Drayton Town | v | Kettering Town | 0-5 | 221 |
| 30 | Coleshill Town | v | Newcastle Town | 3-3 | 83 |
| | (at Tamworth FC) | | | | |
| | Newcastle Town | v | Coleshill Town (15/9) | 1-3 | 82 |
| 31 | Sutton Coldfield Town | v | Oadby Town | 0-1 | 140 |
| 32 | Sporting Khalsa | v | AFC Wulfrunians | 3-2 | 140 |
| 33 | Clipstone Welfare | v | Lincoln United | 1-2 | 113 |
| 34 | Shepshed Dynamo | v | Rushall Olympic | 0-0 | 212 |
| | Rushall Olympic | v | Shepshed Dynamo (15/9) | 4-1 | 151 |
| 35 | Holwell Sports | v | Bedworth United | 2-2 | 211 |
| | Bedworth United | v | Holwell Sports (15/9) | 2-0aet | 124 |
| 36 | Barwell | v | Westfields | 4-1 | 122 |
| 37 | Halesowen Town | v | Mickleover Sports | 2-1 | 252 |
| 38 | Basford United | v | Long Eaton United | 1-0 | 189 |
| 39 | Chasetown | v | Grantham Town | 3-0 | 191 |
| 40 | Stratford Town | v | Coalville Town | 0-2 | 239 |
| 41 | Holbeach United | v | Stourport Swifts | 2-2 | 152 |
| | Stourport Swifts | v | Holbeach United (15/9) | 0-1aet | |
| 42 | Belper Town | v | Dunkirk | 1-3 | 205 |
| 43 | Leek Town | v | Deeping Rangers | 2-2 | 239 |
| | Deeping Rangers | v | Leek Town (15/9) | 4-2 | 214 |
| 44 | Beaconsfield SYCOB | v | Kirkley & Pakefield | 1-2 | 96 |
| 45 | Long Buckby | v | Wingate & Finchley | 0-4 | 96 |
| 46 | Thurrock | v | Witham Town | 1-2 | 128 |
| 47 | Hanwell Town | v | Saffron Walden Town | 1-0 | 135 |
| 48 | Cogenhoe United | v | Leighton Town | 3-2 | 184 |
| 49 | Billericay Town | v | Enfield Town | 1-1 | 333 |
| | Enfield Town | v | Billericay Town (15/1) | 2-0 | 309 |
| 50 | Heybridge Swifts | v | Uxbridge | 1-3 | 109 |
| 51 | Potters Bar Town | v | Haringey Borough | 3-0 | 100 |
| 52 | Northwood | v | Harrow Borough | 0-0 | 173 |
| | Harrow Borough | v | Northwood (15/9) | 0-1 | 156 |
| 53 | Yaxley | v | East Thurrock United (15/9) | 1-3 | 76 |
| | (12/9 - tie abandoned after 85 mins, 0-0) | | | | |
| 54 | Leiston | v | AFC Dunstable | 1-0 | 161 |
| 55 | Peterborough Sports | v | Hitchin Town | 1-1 | 187 |
| | Hitchin Town | v | Peterborough Sports (14/9) | 4-2aet | 198 |
| 56 | Harlow Town | v | Bedford Town | 5-1 | 301 |
| 57 | AFC Sudbury | v | Hendon | 3-1 | 211 |
| 58 | Bury Town | v | Cockfosters | 2-1 | 275 |
| 59 | Bedfont & Feltham | v | AFC Rushden & Diamonds | 1-2 | 100 |
| 60 | Basildon United | v | Hullbridge Sports | 0-1 | 160 |
| 61 | AFC Hornchurch | v | Cambridge City | 2-1 | 235 |
| 62 | Ipswich Wanderers | v | Canvey Island | 1-0 | 208 |
| 63 | Dunstable Town | v | Barton Rovers | 2-1 | 181 |
| 64 | Brantham Athletic | v | Biggleswade Town | 1-2 | 108 |
| 65 | Brentwood Town | v | Arlesey Town | 2-0 | 109 |
| 66 | Hoddesdon Town | v | Ashford Town (Middx) | 3-1 | 158 |
| 67 | Histon | v | Aveley | 1-4 | 160 |
| 68 | North Greenford United | v | Mildenhall Town | 0-0 | 82 |
| | Mildenhall Town | v | North Greenford United (15/9) | 1-0 | 209 |
| 69 | Welwyn Garden City | v | St Ives Town | 0-1 | 257 |
| 70 | Tilbury | v | St Neots Town (22/9) | 2-5 | 97 |
| | (12/9 – tie ordered to be replayed) | | | | |
| 71 | King's Lynn Town | v | Wroxham | 4-1 | 617 |
| 72 | Chesham United | v | Aylesbury | 0-0 | 336 |
| | Aylesbury | v | Chesham United (15/9) | 1-2 | 163 |
| 73 | Needham Market | v | Stanway Rovers | 1-1 | 211 |
| | Stanway Rovers | v | Needham Market (15/9) | 3-0 | 240 |
| 74 | Grays Athletic | v | Biggleswade United | 5-0 | 182 |
| 75 | Tooting & Mitcham United | v | Farnham Town | 2-1 | 183 |
| 76 | Worthing | v | Thamesmead Town | 2-1 | 275 |
| 77 | Metropolitan Police | v | Sittingbourne | 0-0 | 66 |
| | Sittingbourne | v | Metropolitan Police (15/9) | 1-0 | 141 |
| 78 | Pagham | v | Carshalton Athletic | 1-2 | 141 |
| 79 | Rochester United | v | Herne Bay | 1-3 | 107 |
| 80 | Greenwich Borough | v | Slimbridge (13/9) | 2-3 | 154 |
| 81 | Croydon | v | Molesey | 1-0 | 71 |
| 82 | Horsham YMCA | v | Burgess Hill Town | 2-1 | 140 |
| 83 | South Park | v | Leatherhead | 1-1 | 148 |
| | Leatherhead | v | South Park (23/9) | 1-3 | 186 |
| 84 | Eastbourne United | v | Hook Norton | 0-1 | 127 |
| 85 | Godalming Town | v | Kidlington | 0-1 | 152 |
| 86 | Shoreham | v | Eastbourne Town | 2-3 | 105 |
| 87 | Tonbridge Angels | v | Folkestone Invicta | 1-1 | 574 |
| | Folkestone Invicta | v | Tonbridge Angels (15/9) | 1-2 | 365 |
| 88 | Hampton & Richmond Borough | v | Dulwich Hamlet | 0-1 | 404 |
| 89 | Phoenix Sports | v | Lewes | 2-0 | 136 |
| 90 | Whitstable Town | v | Deal Town | 1-1 | 247 |
| | Deal Town | v | Whitstable Town (15/9) | 2-0 | 137 |
| 91 | Dorking Wanderers | v | Slough Town | 0-1 | 184 |
| 92 | Bognor Regis Town | v | Merstham | 2-1 | 299 |
| 93 | VCD Athletic | v | Didcot Town | 1-1 | 106 |
| | Didcot Town | v | VCD Athletic (15/9) | 4-3 | 94 |
| 94 | Staines Town | v | Faversham Town | 2-2 | 188 |
| | Faversham Town | v | Staines Town (15/9) | 1-3 | 172 |
| 95 | Chessington & Hook United | v | North Leigh | 2-3 | 87 |
| 96 | Kingstonian | v | Farnborough | 1-1 | 282 |
| | Farnborough | v | Kingstonian (14/9) | 2-3 | 199 |
| 97 | Hartley Wintney | v | Fleet Town | 1-1 | 290 |
| | Fleet Town | v | Hartley Wintney (15/9) | 0-4 | 181 |
| 98 | Hastings United | v | Thatcham Town | 1-0 | 322 |
| 99 | Chatham Town | v | Cray Wanderers | 1-0 | 170 |
| 100 | Swindon Supermarine | v | Winchester City | 0-4 | 219 |
| 101 | Wimborne Town | v | Witheridge | 3-2 | 159 |
| 102 | Shortwood United | v | Bracknell Town | 4-3 | 85 |
| 103 | Cinderford Town | v | Paulton Rovers | 1-2 | 117 |
| 104 | Taunton Town | v | Tuffley Rovers | 3-0 | 310 |
| 105 | Dorchester Town | v | Cirencester Town | 1-1 | 320 |
| | Cirencester Town | v | Dorchester Town (15/9) | 3-1 | 132 |
| 106 | Bridport | v | Larkhall Athletic | 2-5 | 150 |
| 107 | Bristol Manor Farm | v | AFC Portchester | 0-3 | |
| 108 | Hungerford Town | v | Bradford Town | 1-1 | 132 |
| | Bradford Town | v | Hungerford Town (16/9) | 2-0 | 131 |
| 109 | Poole Town | v | Barnstaple Town | 1-0 | 306 |
| 110 | Frome Town | v | Chippenham Town (11/9) | 0-0 | 370 |
| | Chippenham Town | v | From Town (15/9) | 1-0 | 278 |
| 111 | Brockenhurst | v | Mangotsfield United | 3-0 | 100 |
| 112 | Plymouth Parkway | v | Merthyr Town | 0-2 | 221 |
| 113 | Cheltenham Saracens | v | Blackfield & Langley | 1-2 | 43 |
| 114 | Bodmin Town | v | Almondsbury UWE | 2-0 | 138 |
| 115 | Petersfield Town | v | Weymouth | 3-1 | 201 |
| 116 | Bideford | v | Hamworthy United (15/9) | 3-1 | 145 |

# SECOND QUALIFYING ROUND

## SATURDAY 26 SEPTEMBER 2015 - WINNERS RECEIVE £4,500

| | | | | | |
|---|---|---|---|---|---|
| 1 | Chorley | v | Frickley Athletic | 2-0 | 542 |
| 2 | Salford City | v | Curzon Ashton | 2-1 | 309 |
| 3 | Spennymoor Town | v | Burscough | 0-2 | 445 |
| 4 | Abbey Hey | v | Ashton United | 0-5 | 240 |
| 5 | Workington | v | Harrogate Town | 0-1 | 599 |
| 6 | Bamber Bridge | v | Skelmersdale United | 2-0 | 281 |
| 7 | Kendal Town | v | Stalybridge Celtic | 2-3 | 323 |
| 8 | FC United of Manchester | v | Witton Albion | 3-1 | 1648 |
| 9 | Hyde United | v | Northwich Victoria (10/10) | 1-2 | 374 |
| | (26/9 – tie ordered to be replayed, 0-1) | | | | |
| 10 | Whitley Bay | v | Congleton Town | 2-1 | 382 |
| 11 | Droylsden | v | Lancaster City | 2-0 | 185 |
| 12 | Consett | v | Bradford (Park Avenue) | 1-2 | 616 |
| 13 | Marine | v | Washington | 3-3 | 293 |
| | Washington | v | Marine (29/9) | 2-3aet | 318 |
| 14 | Armthorpe Welfare | v | Buxton | 1-6 | 253 |
| 15 | AFC Fylde | v | Stockport County | 1-0 | 651 |
| 16 | Newton Aycliffe | v | North Ferriby United | 0-0 | 254 |
| | North Ferriby United | v | Newton Aycliffe (29/9) | 3-0 | 186 |
| 17 | Holbeach United | v | Worcester City | 1-1 | 396 |
| | Worcester City | v | Holbeach United (29/9) | 2-0 | 403 |
| 18 | Barwell | v | Cogenhoe United | 5-0 | 128 |
| 19 | Basford United | v | Sporting Khalsa | 2-3 | 216 |
| 20 | Rugby Town | v | Lincoln United | 3-2 | 260 |
| 21 | Deeping Rangers | v | AFC Rushden & Diamonds | 0-3 | 635 |
| 22 | Halesowen Town | v | Nuneaton Town | 0-2 | 549 |
| 23 | Kettering Town | v | AFC Telford United | 2-1 | 693 |
| 24 | Gainsborough Trinity | v | Boston United | 2-0 | 725 |
| 25 | Coalville Town | v | Spalding United | 0-3 | 183 |
| 26 | Corby Town | v | Rushall Olympic | 1-1 | 439 |
| | Rushall Olympic | v | Corby Town (29/9) | 2-1 | 168 |
| 27 | Chasetown | v | Hinckley | 5-2 | 327 |
| 28 | Solihull Moors | v | Oadby Town | 3-1 | 341 |
| 29 | Hednesford Town | v | Bedworth United | 2-0 | 445 |
| 30 | Tamworth | v | Alfreton Town | 2-3 | 663 |
| 31 | Stourbridge | v | Dunkirk | 3-1 | 322 |
| 32 | Coleshill Town | v | Stamford (27/9) | 2-0 | 240 |
| | (at Tamworth FC) | | | | |
| 33 | Grays Athletic | v | Hullbridge Sports | 6-0 | 206 |
| 34 | Maidstone United | v | South Park | 6-2 | 1169 |
| 35 | Hanwell Town | v | Mildenhall Town | 1-0 | 139 |
| 36 | Chelmsford City | v | Ebbsfleet United | 0-0 | 823 |
| | Ebbsfleet United | v | Chelmsford City (29/9) | 1-2 | 790 |
| 37 | Phoenix Sports | v | AFC Hornchurch | 3-5 | 213 |
| 38 | Dunstable Town | v | Kingstonian | 2-0 | 173 |
| 39 | St Albans City | v | Deal Town | 2-1 | 351 |
| 40 | Dartford | v | Uxbridge | 0-1 | 503 |
| 41 | St Ives Town | v | Harlow Town | 0-3 | 345 |
| 42 | St Neots Town | v | Worthing | 1-1 | 342 |
| | Worthing | v | St Neots Town (6/10) | 2-2aet | 403 |
| | (Worthing won 6-5 on kicks from the penalty mark) | | | | |
| 43 | Carshalton Athletic | v | East Thurrock United | 0-5 | 227 |
| 44 | Wealdstone | v | Biggleswade Town | 1-1 | 320 |
| | Biggleswade Town | v | Wealdstone (29/9) | 0-2 | 264 |
| 45 | Potters Bar Town | v | Margate | 1-5 | 213 |
| 46 | Wingate & Finchley | v | Concord Rangers | 2-1 | 133 |
| 47 | Eastbourne Borough | v | AFC Sudbury | 2-1 | 404 |
| 48 | Bognor Regis Town | v | Lowestoft Town | 2-1 | 396 |
| 49 | Tooting & Mitcham United | v | Brackley Town | 1-3 | 249 |
| 50 | Whitehawk | v | Dulwich Hamlet | 4-2 | 355 |
| 51 | Bury Town | v | Hemel Hempstead Town | 0-3 | 408 |
| 52 | Horsham YMCA | v | Aveley | 2-2 | 168 |
| | Aveley | v | Horsham YMCA (30/9) | 4-1 | 83 |
| 53 | Stanway Rovers | v | Staines Town | 0-1 | 195 |
| 54 | Chatham Town | v | Eastbourne Town | 1-2 | 212 |
| 55 | Brentwood Town | v | Croydon | 3-1 | 175 |
| 56 | Sittingbourne | v | Hoddesdon Town | 1-2 | 205 |
| 57 | Enfield Town | v | Ipswich Wanderers | 1-0 | 342 |
| 58 | Bishop's Stortford | v | Sutton United | 0-2 | 347 |
| 59 | King's Lynn Town | v | Witham Town | 1-0 | 571 |
| 60 | Kirkley & Pakefield | v | Hitchin Town | 0-2 | 217 |
| 61 | Leiston | v | Tonbridge Angels | 3-1 | 212 |
| 62 | Northwood | v | Didcot Town | 1-2 | 154 |
| 63 | Herne Bay | v | Hastings United | 1-1 | 274 |
| | Hastings United | v | Herne Bay (29/9) | 3-2 | 301 |
| 64 | North Leigh | v | Slimbridge | 4-1 | 65 |
| 65 | Hook Norton | v | Weston Super Mare | 1-2 | 523 |
| 66 | Larkhall Athletic | v | Havant & Waterlooville | 1-1 | 210 |
| | Havant & Waterlooville | v | Larkhall Athletic (29/9) | 4-2 | 194 |
| 67 | Merthyr Town | v | Hartley Wintney | 0-1 | 280 |
| 68 | Bradford Town | v | Chippenham Town | 2-3 | 393 |
| 69 | Brockenhurst | v | AFC Portchester | 1-0 | 117 |
| 70 | Paulton Rovers | v | Chesham United | 0-2 | 123 |
| 71 | Bodmin Town | v | Bath City | 1-2 | 302 |
| 72 | Gosport Borough | v | Bideford | 7-0 | 325 |
| 73 | Winchester City | v | Maidenhead United | 1-1 | 245 |
| | Maidenhead United | v | Winchester City (29/9) | 4-2 | 256 |
| 74 | Taunton Town | v | Truro City | 2-2 | 481 |
| | Truro City | v | Taunton Town (29/9) | 3-1 | 236 |
| 75 | Oxford City | v | Shortwood United | 3-1 | 201 |
| 76 | Hayes & Yeading United | v | Poole Town | 2-3 | 185 |
| 77 | Wimborne Town | v | Blackfield & Langley | 1-6 | 209 |
| 78 | Gloucester City | v | Kidlington (27/9) | 4-2 | 393 |
| 79 | Basingstoke Town | v | Slough Town | 4-2 | 369 |
| 80 | Petersfield Town | v | Cirencester Town | 3-1 | 152 |

## THIRD QUALIFYING ROUND

### SATURDAY 10 OCTOBER 2015 - WINNERS RECEIVE £7,500

| | | | | | |
|---|---|---|---|---|---|
| 1 | Harrogate Town | v | Burscough | 3-0 | 513 |
| 2 | Salford City | v | Bradford (Park Avenue) | 1-1 | 534 |
| | Bradford (Park Avenue) | v | Salford City (14/10) | 0-1aet | 426 |
| 3 | Whitley Bay | v | Chorley | 2-3 | 782 |
| 4 | Stourbridge | v | Rushall Olympic | 1-0 | 773 |
| 5 | Solihull Moors | v | Worcester City | 1-1 | 923 |
| | Worcester City | v | Solihull Moors (13/10) | 1-0 | 652 |
| 6 | FC United of Manchester | v | Buxton (11/10) | 1-1 | 2357 |
| | Buxton | v | FC United Of Manchester (14/10) | 0-2 | 874 |
| 7 | Marine | v | Northwich Victoria (13/10) | 2-4 | 417 |
| 8 | Chasetown | v | Stalybridge Celtic | 1-1 | 443 |
| | Stalybridge Celtic | v | Chasetown (13/10) | 2-0 | 318 |
| 9 | North Ferriby United | v | Nuneaton Town | 2-1 | 531 |
| 10 | AFC Fylde | v | Coleshill Town | 9-0 | 390 |
| 11 | Barwell | v | King's Lynn Town | 1-0 | 292 |
| 12 | Hednesford Town | v | Alfreton Town | 2-4 | 569 |
| 13 | Droylsden | v | Gainsborough Trinity | 3-4 | 306 |
| 14 | Sporting Khalsa | v | Spalding United | 1-1 | 425 |
| | Spalding United | v | Sporting Khalsa (13/10) | 1-2 | 323 |
| 15 | Brackley Town | v | Rugby Town | 1-1 | 409 |
| | Rugby Town | v | Brackley Town (13/10) | 0-2 | 344 |
| 16 | Kettering Town | v | Bamber Bridge | 1-1 | 696 |
| | Bamber Bridge | v | Kettering Town (13/10) | 3-2 | 478 |
| 17 | AFC Rushden & Diamonds | v | Ashton United | 2-0 | 630 |
| 18 | Harlow Town | v | Bath City | 2-2 | 606 |
| | Bath City | v | Harlow Town (13/10) | 1-2 | 330 |
| 19 | East Thurrock United | v | Staines Town | 3-6 | 263 |
| 20 | Bognor Regis Town | v | Oxford City | 4-2 | 515 |
| 21 | Basingstoke Town | v | Chelmsford City | 4-2 | 488 |
| 22 | Maidstone United | v | Dunstable Town | 2-0 | 1583 |
| 23 | Eastbourne Borough | v | Hartley Wintney | 3-2 | 491 |
| 24 | Leiston | v | Gloucester City | 1-3 | 329 |
| 25 | Hastings United | v | Poole Town | 0-2 | 735 |
| 26 | Hoddesdon Town | v | Brentwood Town | 0-0 | 420 |
| | Brentwood Town | v | Hoddesdon Town (13/10) | 2-1 | 294 |
| 27 | Didcot Town | v | Eastbourne Town | 4-1 | 191 |
| 28 | Whitehawk | v | Gosport Borough | 2-2 | 410 |
| | Gosport Borough | v | Whitehawk (13/10) | 1-2 | 330 |
| 29 | Enfield Town | v | Hitchin Town | 0-0 | 883 |
| | Hitchin Town | v | Enfield Town (12/10) | 1-2 | 486 |
| 30 | Wingate & Finchley | v | Weston Super Mare | 1-3 | 337 |
| 31 | Chesham United | v | North Leigh | 2-0 | 390 |
| 32 | Hanwell Town | v | Grays Athletic | 1-2 | 311 |
| 33 | Margate | v | Truro City | 4-1 | 550 |
| 34 | Brockenhurst | v | Wealdstone | 1-5 | 477 |
| 35 | Uxbridge | v | Chippenham Town | 0-3 | 379 |
| 36 | Hemel Hempstead Town | v | Sutton United | 1-1 | 707 |
| | Sutton United | v | Hemel Hempstead Town (12/10) | 2-1 | 418 |
| 37 | Petersfield Town | v | St Albans City | 0-1 | 370 |
| 38 | Aveley | v | Havant & Waterlooville | 0-2 | 132 |
| 39 | Worthing | v | AFC Hornchurch | 1-4 | 757 |
| 40 | Blackfield & Langley | v | Maidenhead United | 0-1 | 189 |

## FOURTH QUALIFYING ROUND

### SATURDAY 24 OCTOBER 2015 - WINNERS RECEIVE £12,500

| | | | | | |
|---|---|---|---|---|---|
| 1 | Gateshead | v | Worcester City | 1-2 | 782 |
| 2 | AFC Fylde | v | Barrow | 1-0 | 901 |
| 3 | Wrexham | v | Gainsborough Trinity | 0-1 | 1841 |
| 4 | Northwich Victoria | v | Chorley (23/10) | 0-0 | 534 |
| | Chorley | v | Northwich Victoria (27/10) | 1-2 | 1020 |
| 5 | Harrogate Town | v | Grimsby Town | 1-4 | 1920 |
| 6 | Barwell | v | AFC Rushden & Diamonds | 2-2 | 819 |
| | AFC Rushden & Diamonds | v | Barwell (27/10) | 0-1 | 1162 |
| 7 | Salford City | v | Southport | 1-0 | 1019 |
| 8 | Sporting Khalsa | v | FC United of Manchester | 1-3 | 2252 |
| 9 | Stalybridge Celtic | v | North Ferriby United | 1-1 | 547 |
| | North Ferriby United | v | Stalybridge Celtic (28/10) | 0-0aet | 710 |
| | (Stalybridge Celtic won 8-7 on kicks from the penalty mark) | | | | |
| 10 | FC Halifax Town | v | Guiseley | 2-2 | 1078 |
| | Guiseley | v | FC Halifax Town (27/10) | 1-2 | 948 |
| 11 | Tranmere Rovers | v | Lincoln City | 0-0 | 3729 |
| | Lincoln City | v | Tranmere Rovers (27/10) | 2-0 | 2380 |
| 12 | Stourbridge | v | Kidderminster Harriers | 3-0 | 2032 |
| 13 | Macclesfield Town | v | Alfreton Town | 3-2 | 1041 |
| 14 | Brackley Town | v | Bamber Bridge | 3-0 | 451 |
| 15 | Altrincham | v | Chester | 1-0 | 1603 |
| 16 | Whitehawk | v | Poole Town | 2-0 | 450 |
| 17 | Maidenhead United | v | Woking | 3-0 | 867 |
| 18 | Basingstoke Town | v | Torquay United | 3-0 | 793 |
| 19 | Grays Athletic | v | Welling United (25/10) | 1-1 | 512 |
| | Welling United | v | Grays Athletic (27/10) | 4-0 | 733 |
| 20 | Boreham Wood | v | AFC Hornchurch | 2-1 | 307 |
| 21 | Wealdstone | v | Bognor Regis Town | 2-1 | 847 |
| 22 | Didcot Town | v | Brentwood Town | 4-2 | 347 |
| 23 | Eastbourne Borough | v | Dover Athletic | 1-2 | 821 |
| 24 | Chesham United | v | Enfield Town | 2-1 | 759 |
| 25 | Staines Town | v | Gloucester City | 2-1 | 417 |
| 26 | Aldershot Town | v | Sutton United | 1-0 | 1471 |
| 27 | Bromley | v | Eastleigh | 1-2 | 1110 |
| 28 | Margate | v | Forest Green Rovers | 1-2 | 1302 |
| | (Live on BT Sport) | | | | |
| 29 | Braintree Town | v | Harlow Town | 2-0 | 727 |
| 30 | Havant & Waterlooville | v | Cheltenham Town | 3-3 | 622 |
| | Cheltenham Town | v | Havant & Waterlooville (27/10) | 1-0 | 1628 |
| 31 | Chippenham Town | v | Maidstone United | 0-2 | 811 |
| 32 | St Albans City | v | Weston Super Mare | 2-1 | 829 |

# FIRST ROUND PROPER

## SATURDAY 7 NOVEMBER 2015 - WINNERS RECEIVE £18,000

| | | | | | |
|---|---|---|---|---|---|
| 1 | Burton Albion | v | Peterborough United | 0-3 | 2517 |
| 2 | Port Vale | v | Maidenhead United (8/11) | 1-1 | 3977 |
| | Maidenhead United (Live on BT Sport) | v | Port Vale (19/11) | 1-3 | 2212 |
| 3 | Barnet | v | Blackpool | 2-0 | 1869 |
| 4 | Bristol Rovers | v | Chesham United (8/11) | 0-1 | 5181 |
| 5 | Cambridge United | v | Basingstoke Town | 1-0 | 2974 |
| 6 | Mansfield Town | v | Oldham Athletic | 0-0 | 2886 |
| | Oldham Athletic | v | Mansfield Town (17/11) | 2-0 | 1893 |
| 7 | Altrincham | v | Barnsley | 1-0 | 2571 |
| 8 | Crewe Alexandra | v | Eastleigh | 0-1 | 3008 |
| 9 | Northwich Victoria | v | Boreham Wood | 1-1 | 502 |
| | Boreham Wood | v | Northwich Victoria (16/11) | 1-2 | 512 |
| 10 | Coventry City | v | Northampton Town | 1-2 | 9124 |
| 11 | Brackley Town | v | Newport County (8/11) | 2-2 | 1707 |
| | Newport County | v | Brackley Town (17/11) | 4-1 | 1511 |
| 12 | Grimsby Town | v | St Albans City | 5-1 | 2263 |
| 13 | Hartlepool United | v | Cheltenham Town | 1-0 | 2287 |
| 14 | Salford City (Live on BBC1) | v | Notts County (6/11) | 2-0 | 1400 |
| 15 | Dover Athletic | v | Stourbridge | 1-2 | 1392 |
| 16 | Stevenage | v | Gillingham | 3-0 | 1619 |
| 17 | Millwall | v | AFC Fylde | 3-1 | 3445 |
| 18 | Aldershot Town | v | Bradford City (8/11) | 0-0 | 2640 |
| | Bradford City (Live on BT Sport) | v | Aldershot Town (18/11) | 2-0 | 2930 |
| 19 | Walsall | v | Fleetwood Town | 2-0 | 2532 |
| 20 | Bury | v | Wigan Athletic | 4-0 | 3856 |
| 21 | Portsmouth | v | Macclesfield Town | 2-1 | 9834 |
| 22 | Sheffield United | v | Worcester City | 3-0 | 11108 |
| 23 | Barwell | v | Welling United | 0-2 | 843 |
| 24 | FC Halifax Town | v | Wycombe Wanderers (8/11) | 0-4 | 1789 |
| 25 | Crawley Town | v | Luton Town | 1-2 | 1929 |
| 26 | Doncaster Rovers | v | Stalybridge Celtic | 2-0 | 3991 |
| 27 | Didcot Town (Live on BT Sport) | v | Exeter City (8/11) | 0-3 | 2707 |
| 28 | Dagenham & Redbridge | v | Morecambe | 0-0 | 900 |
| | Morecambe | v | Dagenham & Redbridge (17/11) | 2-4 | 1176 |
| 29 | Leyton Orient | v | Staines Town | 6-1 | 2282 |
| 30 | Gainsborough Trinity | v | Shrewsbury Town (8/11) | 0-1 | 2180 |
| 31 | Maidstone United | v | Yeovil Town (8/11) | 0-1 | 2811 |
| 32 | Braintree Town | v | Oxford United (8/11) | 1-1 | 1248 |
| | Oxford United | v | Braintree Town (17/11) | 3-1 | 3265 |
| 33 | Whitehawk | v | Lincoln City (8/11) | 5-3 | 1342 |
| 34 | Accrington Stanley | v | York City | 3-2 | 1475 |
| 35 | Scunthorpe United | v | Southend United | 2-1 | 3335 |
| 36 | AFC Wimbledon | v | Forest Green Rovers | 1-2 | 2465 |
| 37 | Plymouth Argyle | v | Carlisle United | 0-2 | 6005 |
| 38 | FC United Of Manchester (Live on BT Sport) | v | Chesterfield (9/11) | 1-4 | 2916 |
| 39 | Rochdale | v | Swindon Town | 3-1 | 2060 |
| 40 | Wealdstone | v | Colchester United | 2-6 | 2469 |

# SECOND ROUND PROPER

## SATURDAY 5 DECEMBER 2015 - WINNERS RECEIVE £27,000

| | | | | | |
|---|---|---|---|---|---|
| 1 | Bradford City | v | Chesham United (6/12) | 4-0 | 6047 |
| 2 | Barnet | v | Newport County | 0-1 | 1767 |
| 3 | Peterborough United | v | Luton Town (6/12) | 2-0 | 8329 |
| 4 | Portsmouth | v | Accrington Stanley | 1-0 | 9258 |
| 5 | Stourbridge | v | Eastleigh | 0-2 | 2086 |
| 6 | Northampton Town | v | Northwich Victoria | 3-2 | 3837 |
| 7 | Exeter City | v | Port Vale (6/12) | 2-0 | 3565 |
| 8 | Cambridge United | v | Doncaster Rovers (6/12) | 1-3 | 3951 |
| 9 | Grimsby Town | v | Shrewsbury Town (7/12) | 0-0 | 3366 |
| | Shrewsbury Town | v | Grimsby Town (15/12) | 1-0 | 2730 |
| 10 | Yeovil Town | v | Stevenage | 1-0 | 2264 |
| 11 | Rochdale | v | Bury (6/12) | 0-1 | 4887 |
| 12 | Welling United | v | Carlisle United (6/12) | 0-5 | 2028 |
| 13 | Leyton Orient | v | Scunthorpe United | 0-0 | 2540 |
| | Scunthorpe United | v | Leyton Orient (15/12) | 3-0 | 3028 |
| 14 | Millwall | v | Wycombe Wanderers | 1-2 | 3960 |
| 15 | Colchester United | v | Altrincham (6/12) | 3-2 | 2592 |
| 16 | Chesterfield | v | Walsall | 1-1 | 4126 |
| | Walsall | v | Chesterfield (15/12) | 0-0aet | 2953 |
| | (Walsall won 5-3 on kicks from the penalty mark) | | | | |
| 17 | Sheffield United | v | Oldham Athletic | 1-0 | 6938 |
| 18 | Salford City | v | Hartlepool United (4/12) | 1-1 | |
| | Hartlepool United | v | Salford City (15/12) | 2-0aet | 4374 |
| 19 | Dagenham & Redbridge | v | Whitehawk (6/12) | 1-1 | 1953 |
| | Whitehawk | v | Dagenham & Redbridge (16/12) | 2-3aet | 2174 |
| 20 | Oxford United | v | Forest Green Rovers (6/12) | 1-0 | 4618 |

# THIRD ROUND PROPER

## SATURDAY 9 JANUARY 2016 - WINNERS RECEIVE £67,500

| | | | | | |
|---|---|---|---|---|---|
| 1 | Watford | v | Newcastle United | 1-0 | 18259 |
| 2 | West Bromwich Albion | v | Bristol City | 2-2 | 24917 |
| | Bristol City | v | West Bromwich Albion (19/1) | 0-1 | 15185 |
| 3 | West Ham United | v | Wolverhampton Wanderers | 1-0 | 34547 |
| 4 | Hartlepool United | v | Derby County | 1-2 | 4860 |
| 5 | Exeter City | v | Liverpool (8/1) | 2-2 | 8298 |
| | Liverpool | v | Exeter City (20/1) | 3-0 | 43292 |
| 6 | Tottenham Hotspur | v | Leicester City (10/1) | 2-2 | 35805 |
| | Leicester City | v | Tottenham Hotspur (20/1) | 0-2 | 30006 |
| 7 | Colchester United | v | Charlton Athletic | 2-1 | 5742 |
| 8 | Peterborough United | v | Preston North End | 2-0 | 7665 |
| 9 | Northampton Town | v | Milton Keynes Dons | 2-2 | 5878 |
| | Milton Keynes Dons | v | Northampton Town (19/1) | 3-0 | 15133 |
| 10 | Arsenal | v | Sunderland | 3-1 | 59349 |
| 11 | Newport County | v | Blackburn Rovers (18/1) | 1-2 | 5083 |
| 12 | Ipswich Town | v | Portsmouth | 2-2 | 17020 |
| | Portsmouth | v | Ipswich Town (19/1) | 2-1 | 15179 |
| 13 | Birmingham City | v | AFC Bournemouth | 1-2 | 13140 |
| 14 | Wycombe Wanderers | v | Aston Villa | 1-1 | 9298 |
| | Aston Villa | v | Wycombe Wanderers (19/1) | 2-0 | 20706 |
| 15 | Sheffield Wednesday | v | Fulham | 2-1 | 15244 |
| 16 | Oxford United | v | Swansea City (10/1) | 3-2 | 11673 |
| 17 | Brentford | v | Walsall | 0-1 | 7950 |
| 18 | Bury | v | Bradford City | 0-0 | 6962 |
| | Bradford City | v | Bury (19/1) | 0-0aet | 6227 |
| | (Bury won 4-2 on kicks from the penalty mark) | | | | |
| 19 | Manchester United | v | Sheffield United | 1-0 | 74284 |
| 20 | Everton | v | Dagenham & Redbridge | 2-0 | 30198 |
| 21 | Southampton | v | Crystal Palace | 1-2 | 30763 |
| 22 | Eastleigh | v | Bolton Wanderers | 1-1 | 5025 |
| | Bolton Wanderers | v | Eastleigh (19/1) | 3-2 | 8287 |
| 23 | Nottingham Forest | v | Queens Park Rangers | 1-0 | 14197 |
| 24 | Carlisle United | v | Yeovil Town (10/1) | 2-2 | 3357 |
| | Yeovil Town | v | Carlisle United (19/1) | 1-1aet | 4114 |
| | (Carlisle United won 5-4 on kicks from the penalty mark) | | | | |
| 25 | Chelsea | v | Scunthorpe United (10/1) | 2-0 | 41625 |
| 26 | Doncaster Rovers | v | Stoke City | 1-2 | 13299 |
| 27 | Leeds United | v | Rotherham United | 2-0 | 16039 |
| 28 | Cardiff City | v | Shrewsbury Town (10/1) | 0-1 | 4782 |
| 29 | Huddersfield Town | v | Reading | 2-2 | 9236 |
| | Reading | v | Huddersfield Town (19/1) | 5-2 | 8119 |
| 30 | Middlesbrough | v | Burnley | 1-2 | 18286 |
| 31 | Norwich City | v | Manchester City | 0-3 | 24507 |
| 32 | Hull City | v | Brighton & Hove Albion | 1-0 | 10706 |

## FOURTH ROUND PROPER

**SATURDAY 30 JANUARY 2016 - WINNERS RECEIVE £90,000**

| | | | | | |
|---|---|---|---|---|---|
| 1 | West Bromwich Albion | v | Peterborough United | 2-2 | 22517 |
| | Peterborough United | v | West Bromwich Albion (10/2) | 1-1aet | 10632 |
| | (West Bromwich Albion won 4-3 on kicks from the penalty mark) | | | | |
| 2 | Bolton Wanderers | v | Leeds United | 1-2 | 17336 |
| 3 | Arsenal | v | Burnley | 2-1 | 59932 |
| 4 | Derby County | v | Manchester United (29/1) | 1-3 | 31134 |
| 5 | Reading | v | Walsall | 4-0 | 13367 |
| 6 | Liverpool | v | West Ham United | 0-0 | 44060 |
| | West Ham United | v | Liverpool (9/2) | 2-1aet | 34433 |
| 7 | Aston Villa | v | Manchester City | 0-4 | 23636 |
| 8 | Shrewsbury Town | v | Sheffield Wednesday | 3-2 | 5699 |
| 9 | Nottingham Forest | v | Watford | 0-1 | 24703 |
| 10 | Carlisle United | v | Everton (31/1) | 0-3 | 17101 |
| 11 | Crystal Palace | v | Stoke City | 1-0 | 17062 |
| 12 | Oxford United | v | Blackburn Rovers | 0-3 | 11647 |
| 13 | Portsmouth | v | AFC Bournemouth | 1-2 | 18901 |
| 14 | Colchester United | v | Tottenham Hotspur | 1-4 | 9920 |
| 15 | Bury | v | Hull City | 1-3 | 7064 |
| 16 | Milton Keynes Dons | v | Chelsea (31/1) | 1-5 | 28127 |

## FIFTH ROUND PROPER

**SATURDAY 20 FEBRUARY 2016 - WINNERS RECEIVE £180,000**

| | | | | | |
|---|---|---|---|---|---|
| 1 | Chelsea | v | Manchester City (21/2) | 5-1 | 41594 |
| 2 | Reading | v | West Bromwich Albion | 3-1 | 19566 |
| 3 | Watford | v | Leeds United | 1-0 | 18336 |
| 4 | Shrewsbury Town | v | Manchester United (22/2) | 0-3 | 9370 |
| 5 | Blackburn Rovers | v | West Ham United (21/2) | 1-5 | 18793 |
| 6 | Tottenham Hotspur | v | Crystal Palace (21/2) | 0-1 | 35547 |
| 7 | Arsenal | v | Hull City | 0-0 | 59830 |
| | Hull City | v | Arsenal | 0-4 | 20993 |
| 8 | AFC Bournemouth | v | Everton | 0-2 | 11404 |

## SIXTH ROUND PROPER

**SATURDAY 12 MARCH 2016 - WINNERS RECEIVE £360,000**

| | | | | | |
|---|---|---|---|---|---|
| 1 | Reading | v | Crystal Palace (11/3) | 0-2 | 23110 |
| 2 | Everton | v | Chelsea | 2-0 | 37823 |
| 3 | Arsenal | v | Watford (13/3) | 1-2 | 58436 |
| 4 | Manchester United | v | West Ham United (13/3) | 1-1 | 74298 |
| | West Ham United | v | Manchester United (13/4) | 1-2 | 33505 |

## SEMI FINALS

**WINNERS RECEIVE £900,000 RUNNERS-UP £450,000**

SATURDAY 23 APRIL 2016 - at Wembley Stadium

| | | | | | |
|---|---|---|---|---|---|
| 1 | Crystal Palace | v | Watford | 2-1 | 79110 |

SUNDAY 24 APRIL 2016 - at Wembley Stadium

| | | | | | |
|---|---|---|---|---|---|
| 2 | Everton | v | Manchester United | 1-2 | 86064 |

## THE FINAL

**SATURDAY 21 MAY 2016 - at Wembley Stadium WINNERS RECEIVE £1.8m RUNNERS-UP £900,000**

| | | | | |
|---|---|---|---|---|
| CRYSTAL PALACE | 1 AET | 2 | MANCHESTER UNITED | 88619 |

Boldmere striker, Charisma Agbonlahor, rises to head a corner kick near the Rocester goal. The Extra Preliminary Round match ended in a 3-3 draw. Photo: Jonathan Holloway.

# PRELIMINARY ROUND DRAW

## SATURDAY 20 AUGUST 2016

1 Harrogate Railway Athletic v Whitley Bay or Norton & Stockton Ancients or Albion Sports
2 Durham City v Easington Colliery or Northallerton Town or Billingham Synthonia
3 Barnoldswick Town or Dunston UTS v Penrith or Sunderland RCA
4 Shildon or Bedlington Terriers v Kendal Town
5 Padiham or Team Northumbria v Newcastle Benfield or Thackley
6 Ashington or Nelson v Thornaby or Bishop Auckland
7 Chester-Le-Street Town v Marske United or South Shields or Garforth Town
8 Heaton Stannington v Lancaster City or West Auckland Town
9 Clitheroe v West Allotment Celtic or Consett
10 Liversedge or Guisborough Town v Bridlington Town or Silsden
11 Washington or Newton Aycliffe v Sunderland Ryhope CW or Pickering Town
12 Tadcaster Albion v Scarborough Athletic
13 North Shields v Seaham Red Star or Morpeth Town or Jarrow Roofing Boldon CA
14 Droylsden v Radcliffe Borough
15 Prescot Cables v Trafford
16 Armthorpe Welfare v Stocksbridge Park Steels or Handsworth Parramore
17 Congleton Town or New Mills v Farsley Celtic
18 Alsager Town v Staveley MW or Winsford United or Barton Town Old Boys
19 Ramsbottom United v Sheffield
20 Worksop Town or Hallam v AFC Blackpool or Ashton Athletic
21 Parkgate or Irlam v Burscough
22 Ossett Town v Goole
23 West Didsbury & Chorlton v Maltby Main or Squires Gate or AFC Liverpool
24 Atherton Collieries v Witton Albion or Bacup Borough
25 Mossley v Hemsworth MW or Runcorn Linnets
26 Hyde United v AFC Darwen or Cammell Laird 1907
27 Glossop North End v Brighouse Town
28 Maine Road or Nostell MW v AFC Emley or Athersley Recreation
29 Shaw Lane Association v Colwyn Bay
30 Colne v 1874 Northwich or Barnton
31 Northwich Victoria v Penistone Church or Cheadle Town
32 Bamber Bridge v Ossett Albion
33 Pontefract Collieries v Abbey Hey or Bootle or Runcorn Town
34 Coleshill Town or Cradley Town v Dudley Sports or Nuneaton Griff
35 Bedworth United v Malvern Town or Rocester
36 Kidsgrove Athletic v Lye Town or AFC Wulfrunians
37 Coventry United or Shawbury United v Lichfield City or Wolverhampton Casuals
38 Hereford v Haughmond or Alvechurch
39 Rugby Town v Heath Hayes or Bromsgrove Sporting
40 Leek Town v Newcastle Town
41 Coventry Sphinx or Highgate United v AFC Bridgnorth or Boldmere St Michaels
42 Market Drayton Town v Evesham United
43 Sporting Khalsa or Hanley Town v Romulus
44 Chasetown v Brocton or Walsall Wood
45 Stourport Swifts or Westfields v Tividale or Wolverhampton SC
46 Leicester Nirvana or Dunkirk v Rainworth MW or Cleethorpes Town
47 Hinckley or Heanor Town v Oadby Town or Long Eaton United
48 Lincoln United v Carlton Town
49 Loughborough Dynamo v Ashby Ivanhoe or Quorn
50 Basford United v Belper Town
51 Shepshed Dynamo v South Normanton Atheltic or Aylestone Park or AFC Mansfield
52 Brigg Town or Clipstone v Blaby & Whetstone Athletic or St Andrews
53 Retford United or Leicester Road v Anstey Nomads or Harborough Town
54 Bottesford Town or Radford v Bardon Hill or Kirby Muxloe
55 Loughborough University v Gresley or Shirebrook Town
56 Fakenham Town or Sleaford Town v Stamford
57 Yaxley or Huntingdon Town v Dereham Town
58 Soham Town Rangers v Harrowby United or Thetford Town
59 Kirkley & Pakefield v Holbeach United or Swaffham Town or Walsham Le Willows
60 Ely City or Deeping Rangers v Wroxham
61 Boston Town or Wisbech Town v Peterborough Sports or Gorleston
62 Norwich United v Histon
63 Eynesbury Rovers v Godmanchester Rovers or Great Yarmouth Town or Peterborough Northern Star
64 Bury Town v Spalding United
65 Ware v Maldon & Tiptree
66 Thurrock v Halstead Town or Newmarket Town
67 Witham Town v FC Clacton or Eton Manor
68 Redbridge or Waltham Forest v Hoddesdon Town or Stansted
69 Haringey Borough v Barkingside or Hadleigh United
70 Waltham Abbey v Bowers & Pitsea
71 Brentwood Town v Tilbury
72 Sporting Bengal United v London Bari or Clapton or Ipswich Wanderers
73 St Margaretsbury or Long Melford v Saffron Walden Town or Mildenhall Town
74 Romford v Wivenhoe Town or Hullbridge Sports
75 Barking or Takeley v Stanway Rovers or FC Romania
76 Ilford or Burnham Ramblers v FC Broxbourne Borough or Felixstowe & Walton United
77 Brightlingsea Regent v Great Wakering Rovers
78 Sawbridgeworth Town v Enfield 1893 or Tower Hamlets or Southend Manor
79 Aveley v AFC Hornchurch
80 Haverhill Rovers or Hertford Town v Brantham Athletic or Hadley
81 Royston Town v Heybridge Swifts
82 Cheshunt v Whitton United or Basildon United
83 Kempston Rovers v Burnham or Oxhey Jets
84 Wellingborough Town or Stotfold v Bedford or Welwyn Garden City
85 Crawley Green v Uxbridge or Rothwell Corinthians
86 Beford Town v AFC Dunstable
87 London Tigers or Sun Sports v Northwood
88 Arlesey Town v Potters Bar Town
89 AFC Rushden & Diamonds v Leighton Town or Northampton Sileby Rangers
90 Tring Athletic or Desborough Town v Leverstock Green or London Colney
91 Chalfont St Peter v Cockfosters or Harpenden Town
92 Edgware Town or Holmer Green v Barton Rovers
93 Aylesbury United v Newport Pagnell Town or Biggleswade United
94 Cogenhoe United or Berkhamsted v Flackwell Heath or Baldock Town
95 Beaconsfield SYCOB v Marlow
96 Aylesbury v Hanwell Town
97 Wembley or Daventry Town v Harefield United or Northampton On Chenecks
98 Bishop's Cleeve v Camberley Town or Cove
99 Carterton or Highmoor Ibis v Brimscombe & Thrupp or Henley Town
100 Thame United or Abbey Rangers v North Leigh
101 Wantage Town v Hanworth Villa or Knaphill
102 Binfield or North Greenford United v Kidlington

103 Fairford Town v Petersfield Town
or CB Hounslow United
104 Egham Town v Thatcham Town or Bracknell Town
105 Spelthorne Sports v Andover Town or Royal Wootton Bassett
or Hartley Wintney
106 Farnborough v Longlevens or Bedfont & Feltham
107 Ascot United or Milton United v Didcot Town
108 Slimbridge v Bedfont Sports or Windsor
109 Chertsey Town or Hook Norton v Abingdon United or AFC Hayes
110 Yate Town v Fleet Town
111 Shortwood United v Ashford Town (Middx)
112 Ardley United or Tuffley Rovers v Highworth Town or Tadley Calleva
113 Bridon Ropes or Canterbury City v Littlehampton Town or Pagham
114 Southwick or Cray Valley (PM) v Hastings United
115 Worthing United or Shoreham v Dorking Wanderers
116 Greenwich Borough v Westfield or Walton & Hersham
117 Horsham YMCA or Hollands & Blair v Whyteleafe
118 Peacehaven & Telscombe v Holmesdale or Haywards Heath Town
or Lordswood
119 Redhill or St Francis Rangers v Lewes
120 Sheppey United or Badshot Lea v Cray Wanderers
121 Hailsham Town v Corinthian Casuals
or Crawley Down Gatwick
122 Erith & Belvedere or Loxwood v Arundel or Chichester City
123 Carshalton Athletic v Crowborough Athletic or Farnham Town
124 Whitstable Town or Oakwood v Raynes Park Vale or Eastbourne Town
125 Chipstead v Beckenham Town or Lancing
126 South Park v Phoenix Sports
127 Tunbridge Wells v Newhaven or Rochester United
or Eastbourne United
128 Ashford United or Corinthian v Three Bridges
129 Herne Bay v East Grinstead Town
130 Molesey v Godalming Town
131 Faversham Town v Epsom & Ewell or Gravesham Borough
132 VCD Athletic v Croydon or AFC Uckfield Town

133 Sevenoaks Town v Horsham
or Sporting Club Thamesmead
134 Tooting & Mitcham United v East Preston or Horley Town
135 Guernsey v Thamesmead Town
136 Walton Casuals v Chatham Town
137 Ramsgate v Erith Town or Sutton Common Rovers
138 Deal Town or Banstead Athletic v Colliers Wood United or AFC Croydon Athletic
139 Sittingbourne v Hythe Town
140 Mile Oak or Guildford City v Chessington & Hook United or Wick
141 Bristol Manor Farm v AFC Totton
or Gillingham Town
142 Bashley or Horndean v Sholing or Bournemouth
143 Sherborne Town or Amesbury Town v Bemerton Heath Harlequins or Keynsham Town
144 Blackfield & Langley or Hallen v Paulton Rovers
145 Cadbury Heath or Folland Sports v Lydney Town or Team Solent
146 Fawley or AFC Portchester v Mangotsfield United
147 Whitchurch United or Cribbs v Moneyfields or Christchurch
148 Wimborne Town v Bridport or Alresford Town
149 United Services Portsmouth v Winchester City
or Melksham Town
150 Hengrove Athletic or Verwood Town v Bradford Town or Fareham Town
151 Swindon Supermarine v Odd Down or Longwell Green Sports
152 Oldland Abbotonians v Cowes Sports or Brislington
or Newport (IW)
153 Lymington Town v Brockenhurst or Laverstock & Ford
or Hamworthy United
154 Salisbury v Welton Rovers or Bitton
155 AFC St Austell or Street v Larkhall Athletic
156 Bideford v Bodmin Town or Cheddar
157 Taunton Town v Tiverton Town
158 Bridgwater Town v Buckland Athletic or Plymouth Parkway
159 Wells City or Portishead Town v Shepton Mallet or Willand Rovers
160 Clevedon Town v Barnstaple Town
or Ashton & Backwell United

Erith Town's Tom Garrick (stripes) beats Horsham YMCA's Matt Crane to the ball in last season's Preliminary Round. Photo: Alan Coomes.

# THE FA TROPHY 2015-16

The Slimbridge 'keeper plucks this cross out of the air before Egham Town's No.2 can get his head on it, which quite possibly would have resulted in a goal. Photo: Peter Barnes.

## PRELIMINARY ROUND

The knock out cup competition for the senior non-league clubs kicks off with a preliminary round of 64 ties at the beginning of October.

Having suffered financial problems in recent years, some famous FA Trophy names can be seen attempting to make a comeback in this round under their new names. Northwich Victoria and Stafford Rangers both have experience of FA Trophy Wembley finals.

AFC Rushden & Diamonds and Scarborough Athletic remind their supporters of better Trophy days under different titles, but sadly, both fall at their first hurdle to Basford United and Kendal Town respectively.

Many of these clubs starting their Trophy challenge in the Preliminary Round have had Wembley experience in the FA Vase and supporters who can remember the excitement of a Final at the famous stadium will know how important an exciting run in the knock out competition can be for all concerned.

Three such clubs, Barton Rovers, Rugby Town and Taunton Town survived the Preliminary Round but Sheffield FC and Spennymoor Town went out of the competition.

The most impressive results were achieved by Farsley Celtic who beat Prescot Cables, Kendal Town who eliminated Scarborough and Northwich Victoria who beat Lancaster City all by 4-0 while Tilbury United scored five without reply against Barkingside.

The competition is in its very early stages, but look out for a club with a not very well known name of Shaw Lane Aquaforce who have already enjoyed a fine 3-0 victory over New Mills.

## FIRST QUALIFYING ROUND

The Northern Premier League, Southern and Isthmian Premier clubs are all involved in the 72 ties in this round. The draw at this stage often sees the NPL clubs knocking each other out. While there are more clubs spread across the Southern counties from different leagues so they have more chance of avoiding members of their own competition.

However this round saw the seven top Isthmian clubs safely through, five of the top seven from The NPL and just three of the Southern League leaders. But its all about results, and unbelievably, the three Step Three Divisions will be represented by 13 winners each after 1st Qualifying Round replays were completed.

The most impressive results were victories for Harlow Town who beat Merstham 6-2 in a replay, Leamington 6-1 v Barwell and Mangotsfield Town 6-1 v Bashley. While there was also another victory for Shaw Lane Aquaforce FC (Northern Premier League Division One South) who beat Farsley Celtic 4-3.

## SECOND QUALIFYING ROUND

This is the last round before the clubs from the National North and South enter the competition in the Third Qualifying draw. The three senior regional leagues from the Isthmian, Southern and Northern Premier competitions are expected to provide most winners and this season certainly proved that the premier divisions of the three competitions are extremely well balanced.

**Step 3 clubs qualifying for the Third Qualifying Round:**

| Isthmian Premier | NPL Premier | Southern Premier |
|---|---|---|
| Bognor Regis Town | Ashton United | Bideford |
| Dulwich Hamlet | Blyth Spartans | Chesham Utd |
| East Thurrock Utd | Buxton | Cirencester Town |
| Grays Athletic | Marine | Frome Town |
| Hampton & R.B. | Matlock Town | Hitchin Town |
| Kingstonian | Nantwich Town | Hungerford Town |
| Met Police | Stourbridge | Leamington |
| | Skelmersdale Utd | Marlow |
| | Sutton Coldfield | Merthyr Town |
| | | Weymouth |

**Step 4**

**Divison One South**

| | |
|---|---|
| Corinthian Casuals | Burscough |
| Thamesmead Town | Spennymoor Town |
| Thurrock | Warrington Town |
| Tilbury | |
| Molesey | |

**Divison One North**

| | |
|---|---|
| Bury Town | Stocksbridge PS |

The survivors from the Division One Level (Step 4) seem to indicate that The Isthmian competition at that level is the strongest of the three at present, and it will be interesting to see how these qualifiers cope with the introduction of the National League clubs.

## THIRD QUALIFYING ROUND

Sees the Conference North and South clubs entering the competition and in this round the members of the Southern National Division outstripped their colleagues from the North by thirteen winners to nine.

From the senior qualifying clubs, The Northern Premier League (9 winners) outstripped The Southern Premier (4) and the Isthmian Premier (3), but there were special celebrations for 5 clubs who had qualified for their fifth FA Trophy tie of the campaign.

| | | | |
|---|---|---|---|
| Bury Town | 4 | Thurrock | 2 |
| Corinthian Casuals | 1 | Grays Athletic | 0 |
| Marine | 1 | Burscough | 2 |
| North Ferriby United | 1 | Stocksbridge Park Steels | 2 |
| Tilbury | 3 | Bishops Stortford | 0 |

## FIRST ROUND PROPER

In the modern football world no-one appears to be sure whether 'their club' is taking their cup ties seriously. The fact that a Wembley appearance would be remembered by their supporters and players all their lives is important. They also find it very disappointing if their special club doesn't appear to be selecting their best eleven and trying very hard to succeed in the cups, especially when they travel all over the country and spend money supporting their favourites.

Hopefully, the senior clubs are taking this season's FA Trophy competition seriously and judging from the First Round results, they certainly were!
Over half the clubs in the Second Round draw were National Premier members, with the National South leading their Northern colleagues by 7-3 and just five clubs from Step 3 had survived.

Isthmian's Bognor Regis Town and Dulwich Hamlet were joined by Nantwich Town and Stourbridge from the Northern Premier and Hungerford Town represented the Southern League.

## SECOND ROUND PROPER

With the National League's Premier Division dominating the Round, it was no surprise when over half the winners of the last 16 ties emerged from the senior league.

The urgency of regaining a place in the Football League may influence the amount of importance applied to their FA Trophy ties by promotion chasers, although most of their supporters do have the ambition of seeing their club competing in a Wembley Final.

With this in mind, perhaps the excellent 4-0 victory of Oxford City over National League Challengers Cheltenham Town can be understood. Impressive results were also achieved by Nantwich Town, who had already scored 66 Northern Premier League goals and beat National North club Bradford PA by a resounding 5-0 margin.

The last sixteen emerged from weather affected cup ties with nine National Premier clubs providing favourites, probably coming from Grimsby Town, Dover Athletic and Woking, depending on the draw.

# PRELIMINARY ROUND

## SATURDAY 3 OCTOBER 2015 - WINNERS RECEIVE £2,500

| | | | | | |
|---|---|---|---|---|---|
| 1 | Burscough | v | Bamber Bridge | 2-0 | 212 |
| 2 | Ossett Town | v | Warrington Town | 1-2 | 101 |
| 3 | Shaw Lane Aquaforce | v | New Mills (4/10) | 3-0 | 165 |
| 4 | Lancaster City | v | Northwich Victoria | 1-1 | 189 |
| | Northwich Victoria | v | Lancaster City (7/10) | 4-0 | 123 |
| 5 | Farsley Celtic | v | Prescot Cables | 4-0 | 115 |
| 6 | Witton Albion | v | Ossett Albion | 2-2 | 193 |
| | Ossett Albion | v | Witton United (6/10) | 0-2 | 101 |
| 7 | Sheffield | v | Trafford | 4-1 | 177 |
| 8 | Mossley | v | Harrogate Railway Athletic | 1-0 | 107 |
| 9 | Glossop North End | v | Spennymoor Town | 1-1 | 369 |
| | Spennymoor Town | v | Glossop North End (6/10) | 3-2 | 385 |
| 10 | Clitheroe | v | Stocksbridge Park Steels | 1-2 | 186 |
| 11 | Radcliffe Borough | v | Droylsden | 2-1 | 137 |
| 12 | Kendal Town | v | Scarborough Athletic | 4-0 | 213 |
| 13 | Newcastle Town | v | Spalding United | 5-4 | 60 |
| 14 | St Ives Town | v | Rugby Town (4/10) | 4-3 | 205 |
| 15 | Stafford Rangers | v | Tividale | 3-1 | 420 |
| 16 | Soham Town Rangers | v | Carlton Town | 1-3 | 75 |
| 17 | Leek Town | v | Lincoln United | 1-3 | 207 |
| 18 | Loughborough Dynamo | v | Kidsgrove Athletic | 0-3 | 90 |
| 19 | AFC Rushden & Diamonds | v | Basford United | 1-3 | 391 |
| 20 | Romulus | v | Gresley (2/10) | 0-0 | |
| | Gresley | v | Romulus (6/10) | 2-1 | 152 |
| 21 | Belper Town | v | Market Drayton Town | 1-0 | 168 |
| 22 | Coalville Town | v | Daventry Town | 3-2 | 128 |
| 23 | Chasetown | v | Evesham United | 1-1 | 203 |
| | Evesham United | v | Chasetown (6/10) | 2-1 | 163 |
| 24 | Northwood | v | Potters Bar Town | 1-1 | 96 |
| | Potters Bar Town | v | Northwood (6/10) | 0-1 | 69 |
| 25 | Thurrock | v | Guernsey | 2-0 | 122 |
| 26 | Witham Town | v | Herne Bay | 2-4 | 112 |
| 27 | Arlesey Town | v | Redbridge | 1-1 | 89 |
| | Redbridge | v | Arlesey Town (6/10) | 2-0 | 61 |
| 28 | Hanwell Town | v | Cheshunt | 1-2 | 48 |
| 29 | Walton Casuals | v | Sittingbourne (4/10) | 1-0 | |
| 30 | Chalfont St Peter | v | Beaconsfield SYCOB | 3-0 | 91 |
| 31 | Aylesbury United | v | Heybridge Swifts | 1-2 | 182 |
| 32 | Whyteleafe | v | Phoenix Sports | 0-1 | 86 |
| 33 | Corinthian Casuals | v | Three Bridges | 2-1 | 102 |
| 34 | Barton Rovers | v | AFC Sudbury | 1-1 | 121 |
| | AFC Sudbury | v | Barton Rovers (6/10) | 4-3 | 133 |
| 35 | Royston Town | v | Great Wakering Rovers | 3-0 | 108 |
| 36 | Wroxham | v | Hastings United | 2-3 | 112 |
| 37 | Maldon & Tiptree | v | Ramsgate | 2-3 | |
| 38 | Faversham Town | v | Bury Town | 0-1 | 174 |
| 39 | Carshalton Athletic | v | Leighton Town | 0-2 | 110 |
| 40 | Folkestone Invicta | v | Haringey Borough | 1-1 | 244 |
| | Haringey Borough | v | Folkestone Invicta (6/10) | 1-0 | 70 |
| 41 | Dereham Town | v | Waltham Abbey | 1-2 | 99 |
| 42 | Tooting & Mitcham United | v | Walton & Hersham | 3-2 | 136 |
| 43 | Tilbury | v | Barkingside | 5-0 | 54 |
| 44 | Chipstead | v | Uxbridge | 2-1 | 40 |
| 45 | Whitstable Town | v | Worthing | 2-4 | 154 |
| 46 | Harlow Town | v | Ware | 3-1 | 284 |
| 47 | Thamesmead Town | v | Brightlingsea Regent | 1-1 | 38 |
| | Brightlingsea Regent | v | Thamesmead Town (6/10) | 1-4 | 53 |
| 48 | Romford | v | North Greenford United (4/10) | 3-2 | 76 |
| 49 | Cray Wanderers | v | East Grinstead Town | 2-3 | 76 |
| 50 | Aveley | v | South Park | 1-4 | 42 |
| 51 | Aylesbury | v | Hythe Town | 3-0 | 78 |
| 52 | Tiverton Town | v | AFC Totton | 2-0 | 180 |
| 53 | Slimbridge | v | Egham Town | 0-1 | 45 |
| 54 | Taunton Town | v | Godalming Town | 4-1 | 215 |
| 55 | Bishop's Cleeve | v | North Leigh | 2-4 | 66 |
| 56 | Yate Town | v | Banbury United | 1-3 | 141 |
| 57 | Molesey | v | Fleet Town | 5-1 | 67 |
| 58 | Larkhall Athletic | v | Wimborne Town | 3-1 | 94 |
| 59 | Bashley | v | Cinderford Town | 1-0 | 75 |
| 60 | Mangotsfield United | v | Shortwood United | 4-3 | 103 |
| 61 | Marlow | v | Wantage Town | 5-2 | 86 |
| 62 | Didcot Town | v | Bridgwater Town | 0-0 | 118 |
| | Bridgwater Town | v | Didcot Town (6/10) | 1-3 | 107 |
| 63 | Burnham | v | Dorking Wanderers | 0-2 | 41 |
| 64 | Petersfield Town | v | Winchester City | 1-3 | 136 |

Just three clubs had survived from Step Three with The Northern Premier League represented by Nantwich Town (currently 5th) and Stourbridge (8th) while Bognor Regis Town (4th in The Isthmian Premier) continued their consistent cup form, having already enjoyed four FA Cup ties.

The Southern League's last representative Hungerford Town, lost at Chester, so the draw would probably underline the unlikely chances of any clubs challenging the FA Trophy dominance of the National Premier Division members.

## THIRD ROUND PROPER

In fact, six Step One clubs were drawn at home including the three aforementioned favourites, but Sutton United would host Bognor Regis Town and the two N.P.L. clubs would meet at Nantwich.

There were some potentially great ties in The Third Round with Grimsby Town probably the competition favourite. So just one surviver was expected from outside the top division.

The fixtures were spread over ten days with replays and waterlogged pitches creating a disjointed round.

As expected, Grimsby Town underlined their seniority by beating Havant & Waterlooville 3-0, Woking edged through 1-0 against the in form Oxford City club and Gateshead won at home by the same score against the equally confident AFC Fylde.

Every other tie was either postponed or drawn so the remaining winners had to fit their games and replays into the consistently changing playing surfaces and heavy rainstorms.

Torquay United, struggling badly at the foot of the National League were uplifted by winning an away replay at Macclesfield and a confident Dover Athletic were also held at home before beating Guiseley.

The result of the Round was achieved by Bognor Regis Town, who beat Sutton United 2-1 in their home replay and they joined Nantwich Town who had won their battle of the N.P.L. clubs by beating Stourbridge 1-0 in their delayed tie at home. Another delayed tie was also won by a single goal when FC Halifax eliminated Chester.

## FOURTH ROUND PROPER

| | | | |
|---|---|---|---|
| Nantwich Town | 2 | Dover Athletic | 1 |
| FC Halifax Town | 0 | Gateshead | 0 |
| Gateshead | 3, 4p | FC Halifax Town | 3, 5p |
| Grimsby Town | 2 | Woking | 0 |
| Bognore Regis Town | 1 | Torquay United | 0 |

The National League were well represented in the last eight but two Step Two clubs took advantage of being drawn at home to create exciting semi-finals.

Nantwich Town, with six marksmen, who reached double figures for the season, beat Dover Atletic 2-1 at home with a last minute goal. While Bognor Regis Town, another high scoring club on great form, beat Torquay United who were struggling to survive in the National League.

So The Northern Premier League and The Isthmian League had representatives set to compete in the semi-finals. They were joined by FC Halifax Town, who were still not in a comfortable National League position but managed to eliminate Gateshead away in a penalty shoot out after sharing six goals in a thrilling 3-3 replay, and Grimsby Town, another club with strikers on top form, led by Padraig Amold whose two goals eliminated Woking.

## SEMI FINALS

| *Isthmian Premier* | | *National League* | |
|---|---|---|---|
| Bognor Regis Town | 0 | Grimsby Town | 1 |
| Grimsby Town | 2 | Bognor Regis Town | 1 |

| *NPL Premier* | | *National League* | |
|---|---|---|---|
| Nantwich Town | 2 | FC HalifaxTown | 4 |
| FC Halifax Town | 2 | Nantwich Town | 2 |

The Semi-Final draw split the favourites and their seniority produced an all National League Final. Nantwich Town continued their scoring habit in both games against FC Halifax Town, but eventually lost a lively contest 2-4 (home) and 2-2 (away). Even in defeat Nantwich Town were good to watch, but the Yorkshire club, despite the worries of their League position, had reached Wembley.

Grimsby Town had enjoyed the reputation of a free scoring outfit all season and once again it was two of their regular marksmen, Nathan Arnold and Padraig Almond, who had already scored over 40 goals between them, who took the Mariners to the Final. After a tight 1-0 scoreline at Bognor, the Isthmian League promotion challengers produced a real battle in the second leg and eventually it was only two goals including a penalty, from top scorer Amond, that confirmed a Wembley Final for Grimsby Town.

So the senior clubs from The National League, both with Football League experience, would meet in the FA Trophy Final at Wembley. But strangely, although Grimsby Town were battling to gain promotion, FC Halifax Town were desperate to avoid relegation.

# FIRST QUALIFYING ROUND

## SATURDAY 31 OCTOBER 2015 - WINNERS RECEIVE £2,700

| | | | | | |
|---|---|---|---|---|---|
| 1 | Marine | v | Sheffield | 1-0 | 259 |
| 2 | Witton Albion | v | Radcliffe Borough | 1-2 | |
| 3 | Buxton | v | Frickley Athletic | 2-1 | 151 |
| 4 | Blyth Spartans | v | Kendal Town | 4-0 | 442 |
| 5 | Shaw Lane Aquaforce | v | Farsley Celtic | 4-3 | 182 |
| 6 | Workington | v | Whitby Town | 0-3 | 343 |
| 7 | Northwich Victoria | v | Stocksbridge Park Steels (1/11) 1-2 | | |
| 8 | Nantwich Town | v | Salford City (30/10) | 2-1 | 550 |
| 9 | Spennymoor Town | v | Goole | 6-3 | 411 |
| 10 | Ashton United | v | Ramsbottom United | 2-2 | 138 |
| | Ramsbottom United | v | Ashton United (3/11) | 2-2aet | |
| | (Ashton United won 10-9 on kicks from the penalty mark) | | | | |
| 11 | Skelmersdale United | v | Hyde United | 3-3 | |
| | Hyde United | v | Skelmersdale United (4/11) | 0-1 | 224 |
| | (2/11 - tie abandoned after 22 mins due to fog, 0-0) | | | | |
| 12 | Warrington Town | v | Brighouse Town | 2-0 | 235 |
| 13 | Burscough | v | Colwyn Bay | 1-0 | 156 |
| 14 | Darlington 1883 | v | Mossley | 3-2 | 635 |
| 15 | Leamington | v | Barwell | 6-1 | 291 |
| 16 | Cambridge City | v | Ilkeston | 0-1 | 232 |
| 17 | Sutton Coldfield Town | v | Coalville Town | 2-0 | 138 |
| 18 | Evesham United | v | Redditch United | 1-0 | 302 |
| 19 | Carlton Town | v | Stamford | 2-1 | 96 |
| 20 | Belper Town | v | King's Lynn Town | 1-1 | 236 |
| | King's Lynn Town | v | Belper Town (3/11) | 5-1 | 376 |
| 21 | Histon | v | Stratford Town | 0-0 | 187 |
| | Stratford Town | v | Histon (3/11) | 4-1 | 133 |
| 22 | Basford United | v | Grantham Town | 3-1 | 162 |
| 23 | St Ives Town | v | Kettering Town (30/10) | 0-1 | 325 |
| 24 | Rushall Olympic | v | Mickleover Sports | 1-0 | 101 |
| 25 | Stafford Rangers | v | Lincoln United | 1-1 | 414 |
| | Lincoln United | v | Stafford Rangers (3/11) | 1-1aet | 111 |
| | (Lincoln United won 5-4 on kicks from the penalty mark) | | | | |
| 26 | Halesowen Town | v | Stourbridge | 1-2 | 808 |
| 27 | Newcastle Town | v | Kidsgrove Athletic | 2-2 | 132 |
| | Kidsgrove Athletic | v | Newcastle Town (3/11) | 3-0 | 190 |
| 28 | Matlock Town | v | Gresley | 2-0 | 242 |
| 29 | St Neots Town | v | Bedworth United | 2-0 | 215 |
| 30 | Northwood | v | Bedford Town | 1-3 | 91 |
| 31 | East Thurrock United | v | South Park | 4-0 | |
| 32 | Corinthian Casuals | v | Redbridge | 4-1 | 76 |
| 33 | Chipstead | v | Hastings United | 1-2 | 94 |
| 34 | Leatherhead | v | Kingstonian | 1-5 | 260 |
| 35 | Enfield Town | v | Leighton Town | 4-0 | 311 |
| 36 | Aylesbury | v | Brentwood Town | 1-1 | 66 |
| | Brentwood Town | v | Aylesbury (3/11) | 2-0 | 89 |
| 37 | Phoenix Sports | v | Tonbridge Angels | 1-1 | |
| | Tonbridge Angels | v | Phoenix Sports (3/11) | 2-0 | |
| 38 | Herne Bay | v | Walton Casuals | 1-1 | |
| | Walton Casuals | v | Herne Bay (4/11) | 2-3 | |
| 39 | AFC Hornchurch | v | Metropolitan Police | 2-3 | 110 |
| 40 | Thurrock | v | Chatham Town | 3-0 | 84 |
| 41 | VCD Athletic | v | Staines Town | 2-1 | |
| 42 | Chalfont St Peter | v | Waltham Abbey | 1-3 | |
| 43 | Cheshunt | v | Heybridge Swifts | 2-0 | |
| 44 | Billericay Town | v | Chesham United | 0-2 | 271 |
| 45 | Thamesmead Town | v | Ramsgate (30/10) | 1-0 | 96 |
| 46 | East Grinstead Town | v | Bognor Regis Town+ | 0-3 | 249 |
| | (at Bognor Regis Town FC) | | | | |
| 47 | Tilbury | v | Tooting & Mitcham United | 2-1 | 101 |
| 48 | Dunstable Town | v | Haringey Borough | 1-3 | 76 |
| 49 | Hitchin Town | v | Burgess Hill Town | 3-2 | |
| 50 | Lewes | v | Hampton & Richmond Borough | 0-0 | 325 |
| | Hampton & Richmond Borough | v | Lewes (3/11) | 2-1 | |
| 51 | Grays Athletic | v | Biggleswade Town | 2-1 | |
| 52 | Romford | v | Slough Town (1/11) | 0-4 | 134 |
| 53 | Wingate & Finchley | v | Royston Town | 0-2 | |
| 54 | Harrow Borough | v | Dulwich Hamlet | 0-3 | 185 |
| 55 | Hendon | v | AFC Sudbury (1/11) | 0-1 | 182 |
| 56 | Worthing | v | Leiston | 1-3 | 311 |
| 57 | Merstham | v | Harlow Town | 0-0 | 123 |
| | Harlow Town | v | Merstham (3/11) | 6-2 | 210 |
| 58 | Bury Town | v | Kings Langley | 2-0 | 272 |
| 59 | Needham Market | v | Canvey Island | 0-2 | 191 |
| 60 | Paulton Rovers | v | Swindon Supermarine | 2-3 | 101 |
| 61 | Molesey | v | Didcot Town | 1-0 | |
| 62 | Taunton Town | v | Dorking Wanderers | 1-1 | 194 |
| | Dorking Wanderers | v | Taunton Town (3/11) | 1-3 | |
| 63 | Hungerford Town | v | Banbury United | 0-0 | 128 |
| | Banbury United | v | Hungerford Town (3/11) | 0-3 | 170 |
| 64 | Cirencester Town | v | North Leigh | 2-1 | 85 |
| 65 | Dorchester Town | v | Chippenham Town | 2-1 | 254 |
| 66 | Mangotsfield United | v | Bashley | 6-1 | 111 |
| 67 | Egham Town | v | Frome Town | 1-2 | 72 |
| 68 | Merthyr Town | v | Poole Town | 1-0 | 270 |
| 69 | Peacehaven & Telscombe | v | Tiverton Town | 0-3 | |
| 70 | Winchester City | v | Weymouth (30/10) | 1-2 | 349 |
| 71 | Bideford | v | Farnborough | 1-1 | 182 |
| | Farnborough | v | Bideford (2/11) | 2-2aet | |
| | (Bideford won 5-4 on kicks from the penalty mark) | | | | |
| 72 | Marlow | v | Larkhall Athletic | 3-0 | 105 |

## SECOND QUALIFYING ROUND

### SATURDAY 14 NOVEMBER 2015 - WINNERS RECEIVE £3,250

| No. | Home | | Away | Score | Att |
|---|---|---|---|---|---|
| 1 | Blyth Spartans | v | Whitby Town | 1-0 | 643 |
| 2 | Ashton United | v | Stratford Town | 2-1 | |
| 3 | Evesham United | v | Spennymoor Town | 1-2 | 294 |
| 4 | Buxton | v | Radcliffe Borough | 5-1 | 183 |
| 5 | Skelmersdale United | v | Lincoln United | 4-2 | 185 |
| 6 | Sutton Coldfield Town | v | Darlington 1883 | 1-0 | 360 |
| 7 | Nantwich Town | v | King's Lynn Town | 5-1 | 329 |
| 8 | Shaw Lane Aquaforce | v | Matlock Town | 1-2 | 232 |
| 9 | Leamington | v | Rushall Olympic | 0-0 | 296 |
| | Rushall Olympic | v | Leamington (24/11) | 2-3aet | |
| 10 | Warrington Town | v | Basford United | 3-0 | 202 |
| 11 | Marine | v | Kidsgrove Athletic | 2-2 | 274 |
| | Kidsgrove Athletic | v | Marine (1/12) | 0-1 | 156 |
| 12 | Ilkeston | v | Stocksbridge Park Steels | 1-1 | |
| | Stocksbridge Park Steels | v | Ilkeston (17/11) | 3-2 | 108 |
| 13 | Kettering Town | v | Burscough | 0-3 | 435 |
| 14 | Stourbridge | v | Carlton Town | 2-0 | 428 |
| 15 | Bideford | v | Brentwood Town | 3-2 | 185 |
| 16 | St Neots Town | v | Hungerford Town | 1-2 | 207 |
| 17 | Haringey Borough | v | Hitchin Town | 1-1 | |
| | Hitchin Town | v | Haringey Borough (16/11) | 3-0 | |
| 18 | Thurrock | v | Cheshunt | 3-1 | 77 |
| 19 | Tonbridge Angels | v | Cirencester Town | 1-2 | |
| 20 | Enfield Town | v | Thamesmead Town | 0-2 | 270 |
| 21 | Tilbury | v | Royston Town | 4-2 | 106 |
| 22 | Leiston | v | Corinthian Casuals | 1-2 | 185 |
| 23 | Bedford Town | v | Weymouth | 1-4 | 229 |
| 24 | Swindon Supermarine | v | Chesham United | 2-3 | |
| 25 | Taunton Town | v | Bognor Regis Town | 1-4 | 351 |
| 26 | Molesey | v | Harlow Town | 4-3 | |
| 27 | East Thurrock United | v | Tiverton Town | 5-0 | |
| 28 | Waltham Abbey | v | Grays Athletic | 0-2 | |
| 29 | Dulwich Hamlet | v | VCD Athletic | 2-0 | 795 |
| 30 | Frome Town | v | Slough Town | 2-1 | 151 |
| 31 | Hampton & Richmond Borough | v | AFC Sudbury | 3-1 | 212 |
| 32 | Dorchester Town | v | Kingstonian | 2-2 | |
| | Kingstonian | v | Dorchester Town (16/11) | 2-1 | 221 |
| 33 | Marlow | v | Mangotsfield United | 1-0 | 118 |
| 34 | Canvey Island | v | Metropolitan Police | 0-2 | 187 |
| 35 | Hastings United | v | Merthyr Town (17/11) | 1-2 | 150 |
| | (14/11 – tie abandoned after 45 mins due to waterlogged pitch, 0-2) | | | | |
| 36 | Bury Town | v | Herne Bay | 1-1 | |
| | Herne Bay | v | Bury Town (17/11) | 1-1aet | 131 |
| | (Bury Town won 4-3 on kicks from the penalty mark) | | | | |

## THIRD QUALIFYING ROUND

### SATURDAY 28 NOVEMBER 2015 - WINNERS RECEIVE £4,000

| No. | Home | | Away | Score | Att |
|---|---|---|---|---|---|
| 1 | FC United of Manchester | v | AFC Telford United (27/11) | 1-2 | 1034 |
| 2 | Solihull Moors | v | Boston United | 1-0 | 319 |
| 3 | Leamington | v | Hednesford Town | 4-2 | 308 |
| 4 | Stourbridge | v | Spennymoor Town | 4-2 | 393 |
| 5 | Harrogate Town | v | Curzon Ashton | 0-1 | |
| 6 | Marine | v | Burscough (8/12) | 1-2 | 294 |
| 7 | Corby Town | v | Tamworth | 2-6 | |
| 8 | Gainsborough Trinity | v | Ashton United | 0-0 | |
| | Ashton United | v | Gainsborough Trinity (1/12) | 3-1 | 106 |
| 9 | Brackley Town | v | Worcester City | 0-2 | 227 |
| 10 | Chorley | v | Skelmersdale United | 0-0 | 559 |
| | Skelmersdale United | v | Chorley (1/12) | 5-2 | 277 |
| 11 | Warrington Town | v | AFC Fylde | 0-2 | 297 |
| 12 | Buxton | v | Bradford (Park Avenue) (8/12) | 1-2 | 205 |
| | (28/11 - tie abandoned after 45 mins due to weather, 0-0) | | | | |
| 13 | Matlock Town | v | Blyth Spartans | 4-2 | 303 |
| 14 | Nuneaton Town | v | Alfreton Town | 2-0 | 467 |
| 15 | Sutton Coldfield Town | v | Stalybridge Celtic | 1-0 | |
| 16 | North Ferriby United | v | Stocksbridge Park Steels | 1-2 | 252 |
| 17 | Stockport County | v | Nantwich Town | 0-2 | 1022 |
| 18 | Merthyr Town | v | East Thurrock United | 1-1 | 225 |
| | East Thurrock United | v | Merthyr Town (1/12) | 3-1 | 162 |
| 19 | Hampton & Richmond Borough | v | Maidstone United (2.00) | 0-1 | 488 |
| 20 | Ebbsfleet United | v | Molesey | 4-1 | 672 |
| 21 | Maidenhead United | v | Bideford | 4-0 | 262 |
| 22 | Cirencester Town | v | Gosport Borough | 2-1 | 88 |
| 23 | Hungerford Town | v | Thamesmead Town | 3-0 | 120 |
| 24 | Tilbury | v | Bishop's Stortford | 3-0 | 132 |
| 25 | Weston Super Mare | v | Hitchin Town | 4-0 | |
| 26 | Oxford City | v | Marlow | 6-3 | |
| 27 | Chelmsford City | v | Gloucester City | 1-1 | 359 |
| | Gloucester City | v | Chelmsford City (1/12) | 0-1 | 238 |
| 28 | Lowestoft Town | v | St Albans City | 4-0 | 420 |
| 29 | Metropolitan Police | v | Wealdstone | 0-2 | |
| 30 | Hemel Hempstead Town | v | Weymouth | 1-0 | |
| 31 | Dartford | v | Whitehawk | 1-2 | 601 |
| 32 | Concord Rangers | v | Sutton United+ (21/12) | 0-2 | 251 |
| | (28/11 - tie ordered to be replayed, 3-1 - extra time & penalties agreed, no replay - at Sutton United FC) | | | | |
| 33 | Frome Town | v | Chesham United | 1-1 | 133 |
| | Chesham United | v | Frome Town (1/12) | 2-1 | 214 |
| 34 | Bury Town | v | Thurrock | 4-2 | 319 |
| 35 | Dulwich Hamlet | v | Margate | 2-1 | 1479 |
| 36 | Grays Athletic | v | Corinthian Casuals (29/11) | 0-0 | |
| | Corinthian Casuals | v | Grays Athletic (2/12) | 1-0 | 127 |
| 37 | Bognor Regis Town | v | Bath City | 1-0 | 362 |
| 38 | Havant & Waterlooville | v | Basingstoke Town | 2-1 | 277 |
| 39 | Hayes & Yeading United | v | Eastbourne Borough (29/11) | 2-2 | 158 |
| | Eastbourne Borough | v | Hayes & Yeading United (1/12) | 4-0 | 204 |
| 40 | Kingstonian | v | Truro City | 0-3 | 316 |

## FIRST ROUND PROPER

SATURDAY 12 DECEMBER 2015 - WINNERS RECEIVE £5,000

| | | | | | |
|---|---|---|---|---|---|
| 1 | FC Halifax Town | v | Tamworth (15/12) | 5-0 | 439 |
| 2 | Grimsby Town | v | Solihull Moors | 1-1 | 1071 |
| | Solihull Moors | v | Grimsby Town (22/12) | 2-3 | 479 |
| 3 | Sutton Coldfield Town | v | Barrow | 0-1 | 326 |
| 4 | Burscough | v | Guiseley | 2-2 | 227 |
| | Guiseley | v | Burscough (15/12) | 3-2 | |
| 5 | Macclesfield Town | v | Ashton United (22/12) | 4-0 | 610 |
| | (12/12 - abandoned after 45 mins, 0-2) | | | | |
| 6 | Nantwich Town | v | Matlock Town | 2-0 | 423 |
| 7 | Southport | v | Worcester City (15/12) | 0-0 | 270 |
| | Worcester City | v | Southport (22/12) | 2-3 | 452 |
| 8 | Curzon Ashton | v | Nuneaton Town (14/12) | 3-1 | |
| 9 | Altrincham | v | Leamington (15/12) | 1-1 | 355 |
| | Leamington | v | Altrincham (14/1) | 1-2aet | |
| 10 | AFC Telford United | v | Chester | 0-2 | 850 |
| 11 | Stourbridge | v | Kidderminster Harriers | 2-1 | 902 |
| 12 | Gateshead | v | Stocksbridge Park Steels (15/12) | 4-1 | 199 |
| 13 | AFC Fylde | v | Skelmersdale United (15/12) | 4-4 | |
| | Skelmersdale United | v | AFC Fylde (13/1) | 0-4 | 186 |
| | (at Salford Red Devils RFC) | | | | |
| 14 | Bradford (Park Avenue) | v | Lincoln City (21/12) | 2-1 | 365 |
| 15 | Tranmere Rovers | v | Wrexham | 2-4 | 3397 |
| 16 | Eastbourne Borough | v | Hemel Hempstead Town | 7-4 | 317 |
| 17 | Tilbury | v | Welling United | 3-4 | 186 |
| 18 | Truro City | v | Cirencester Town | 2-2 | |
| | Cirencester Town | v | Truro City (15/12) | 0-1 | 123 |
| 19 | Torquay United | v | Chesham United (13/12) | 0-0 | |
| | Chesham United | v | Torquay United (15/12) | 0-2 | 356 |
| 20 | Whitehawk | v | Dover Athletic | 1-3 | |
| 21 | Corinthian Casuals | v | Hungerford Town | 1-2 | 162 |
| 22 | Boreham Wood | v | Woking | 1-2 | 275 |
| 23 | Sutton United | v | Lowestoft Town (4/1) | 3-1 | 454 |
| 24 | Maidstone United | v | Bognor Regis Town | 0-1 | 892 |
| 25 | Cheltenham Town | v | Chelmsford City | 3-1 | 1124 |
| 26 | East Thurrock United | v | Maidenhead United | 1-4 | 156 |
| 27 | Oxford City | v | Ebbsfleet United | 3-1 | |
| 28 | Aldershot Town | v | Eastleigh | 0-1 | 877 |
| 29 | Weston Super Mare | v | Wealdstone (13/1) | 3-2 | 155 |
| | (at Paulton Rovers FC) | | | | |
| 30 | Havant & Waterlooville | v | Forest Green Rovers | 2-0 | 266 |
| 31 | Bury Town | v | Dulwich Hamlet | 1-2 | 441 |
| 32 | Braintree Town | v | Bromley (22/12) | 1-0 | 204 |

## SECOND ROUND PROPER

SATURDAY 16 JANUARY 2016 - WINNERS RECEIVE £6,000

| | | | | | |
|---|---|---|---|---|---|
| 1 | Dulwich Hamlet | v | Guiseley | 1-2 | 1949 |
| 2 | Dover Athletic | v | Southport | 2-1 | 629 |
| 3 | Havant & Waterlooville | v | Welling United | 2-1 | 371 |
| 4 | Truro City | v | Macclesfield Town | 2-2 | 665 |
| | Macclesfield Town | v | Truro City (19/1) | 2-0 | 507 |
| 5 | Braintree Town | v | Stourbridge | 0-1 | 244 |
| 6 | Chester | v | Hungerford Town | 4-0 | 1276 |
| 7 | Eastbourne Borough | v | AFC Fylde | 1-4 | 352 |
| 8 | Sutton United | v | Curzon Ashton | 1-0 | 605 |
| 9 | Torquay United | v | Wrexham | 1-0 | 1361 |
| 10 | Grimsby Town | v | Weston Super Mare | 3-1 | 1230 |
| 11 | FC Halifax Town | v | Barrow (19/1) | 1-0 | 673 |
| 12 | Eastleigh | v | Gateshead | 1-2 | |
| 13 | Bognor Regis Town | v | Altrincham (19/1) | 2-1 | 520 |
| 14 | Bradford (Park Avenue) | v | Nantwich Town (20/1) | 1-1 | 207 |
| | Nantwich Town | v | Bradford (Park Avenue) (26/1) | 5-0 | |
| 15 | Woking | v | Maidenhead United | 6-1 | |
| 16 | Oxford City | v | Cheltenham Town | 2-2 | 926 |
| | Cheltenham Town | v | Oxford City (26/1) | 0-3 | 776 |

## THIRD ROUND PROPER

SATURDAY 6 FEBRUARY 2016 - WINNERS RECEIVE £7,000

| | | | | | |
|---|---|---|---|---|---|
| 1 | Torquay United | v | Macclesfield Town (9/2) | 3-3 | 834 |
| | Macclesfield Town | v | Torquay United (16/2) | 0-1 | 566 |
| 2 | Grimsby Town | v | Havant & Waterlooville | 3-0 | 1613 |
| 3 | Gateshead | v | AFC Fylde | 1-0 | 485 |
| 4 | FC Halifax Town | v | Chester (10/2) | 1-0 | 878 |
| 5 | Woking | v | Oxford City | 1-0 | |
| 6 | Dover Athletic | v | Guiseley | 2-2 | |
| | Guiseley | v | Dover Athletic (16/2) | 0-3 | 476 |
| 7 | Sutton United | v | Bognor Regis Town | 0-0 | 1458 |
| | Bognor Regis Town | v | Sutton United (9/2) | 2-1 | 914 |
| 8 | Nantwich Town | v | Stourbidge (16/2) | 1-0 | 510 |

## FOURTH ROUND PROPER

SATURDAY 27 FEBRUARY 2016 - WINNERS RECEIVE £8,000

| | | | | | |
|---|---|---|---|---|---|
| 1 | Nantwich Town | v | Dover Athletic | 2-1 | 892 |
| 2 | FC Halifax Town | v | Gateshead | 0-0 | 1431 |
| | Gateshead | v | FC Halifax Town (2/3) | 3-3aet | 724 |
| | (FC Halifax Town won 5-4 on kicks from the penalty mark) | | | | |
| 3 | Grimsby Town | v | Woking | 2-0 | 1675 |
| 4 | Bognor Regis Town | v | Torquay United | 1-0 | 1821 |

## SEMI FINALS

1ST LEG SATURDAY 12 MARCH / 2ND LEG SATURDAY 19 MARCH 2016 - WINNERS RECEIVE £16,000

| | | | | |
|---|---|---|---|---|
| Nantwich Town | v | FC Halifax Town | 2-4 | 2078 |
| FC Halifax Town | v | Nantwich Town | 2-2 | 3009 |
| FC Halifax Town through 6-4 on aggregate. | | | | 5087 |
| Bognor Regis Town | v | Grimsby Town | 0-1 | 2629 |
| Grimsby Town | v | Bognor Regis Town | 2-1 | 2477 |
| Grimsby Town through 3-1 on aggregate. | | | | 5106 |

# THE FINAL...

**FC HALIFAX TOWN 1**
*(McManus 48)*
**GRIMSBY TOWN 0**

**Wembley Stadium Att: 46,781**
**combined Trophy/Vase attendance*

## THE SQUADS

| FC HALIFAX TOWN | GRIMSBY TOWN |
|---|---|
| Sam Johnson | James McKeown |
| Matty Brown | Richard Tait (sub 81) |
| Hamza Bencherif | Shaun Pearson |
| Kevin Roberts | Aristote Nsiala |
| James Bolton | Gregor Robertson |
| Nicky Wroe | Andy Monkhouse (sub 68) |
| Jake Hibbs | Craig Disley |
| Scott McManus (sub 73) | Craig Clay (sub 63) |
| Josh McDonald (sub 63) | Jon Nolan |
| Jordan Burrow | Omar Bogle |
| Richard Peniket (sub 86) | Padraig Amond |
| **Substitutes** | **Substitutes** |
| Sam Walker (63) | Nathan Arnold (63) |
| Kingsley James (73) | Jon-Paul Pitman (68) |
| Connor Hughes (86) | Danny East (81) |
| Jordan Porter | Josh Gowling |
| Shaquille McDonald | Josh Venney |

Referee Lee Mason (Lancashire FA).
Assisted by Adam Nunn and Matthew Wilkes.
Four official - Ross Joyce.

Having appeared at Wembley on the previous weekend in the National League play off final where, against Forest Green, victory had restored them to the Football League, Grimsby were hot favourites to defeat their northern opponents, F C Halifax Town, who were leaving the National League and heading in the opposite direction, after end of season relegation, to Step Two in the non-league pyramid..

As the teams entered for the pre-match rituals it was heartening to see that Halifax had included two disabled youngsters among their accompanying mascots. Only a few Hereford and Morpeth fans had stayed on to watch the Trophy final following the Vase so there was a smaller 'gate' for this tie, even though Halifax and Grimsby supporters also appeared in the main to have arrived only to see their own two teams in action. For those of us who had witnessed both finals this was certainly the more pedestrian of the two, the emphasis here quite distinctly on defence and security rather than providing much goalmouth action as the result of attacking football.

The first scoring chance fell to Halifax in the 8th minute when a Grimsby defender's header backwards fell short of his keeper James McKeown so that Jordan Burrow was able to pounce, although only able to shoot wide. The Mariners had the bulk of midfield possession but were certainly not firing on all cylinders. It definitely looked as if the previous week's efforts had left them bereft of both ambition and energy. Their supporters seemed also undemanding in the light of League status having been regained, treating this second outing to Wembley in a week as an everyday occurrence of little consequence.

The FC Halifax players move in on the Grimsby player. Photo: Peter Barnes.

It was the 18th minute before Halifax's Sam Johnson's keeping skills were brought into action, let alone tested, Padraig Almond tamely heading Jon Nolan's cross into Johnson's clutches. Full back Richard Tait then fired wide after some neat interplay with Omar Bogle. Shaun Pearson's header from Nolan's corner did cause Johnson some anxiety before he beat away the effort at the foot of a post. As the half neared its end players from both sides tried to 'con' referee Lee Mason into awarding free kicks and penalties but the official correctly waved away every imprecation with deserved disdain, before ending an easily forgettable forty five minutes.

The second half opened with the Shaymen's Burrow shooting over from about thirty yards while Mariners retaliated with high scoring Omar Bogle, of whom much had been expected, tearing away down the right but placing his pass slightly behind a fellow forward who could consequently get no power in his attempt to beat Johnson. Then, three minutes after the restart, came the moment of the match. Full back Scott McManus, having forsaken his duties in defence, raced into the opposition area hoping to capitalise on a Richard Peniket forage on that side. Craig Disley was robbed on the eighteen yard line and the ball ran loose to McManus who hit the sweetest of strikes to set the net bulging, leaving McKeown completely helpless. As McManus had shot with his supposedly weaker right foot – "he normally just stands on it," claimed his team mates afterwards - there was considerable jubilation and great astonishment at this wonderful strike. Even the scorer himself later honestly expressed incredulity at his achievement.

As Halifax came further to life, their spirits fted by McManus's strike, James Bolton and Burrow exchanged passes dangerously down he right before Nicky Wroe's shot was spilled by McKeown who recovered just before the nrushing strikers could pounce. Johnson, in he Halifax goal, had to make one save with his feet as Grimsby searched with slightly increasing rgency for an equaliser. Jake Hibbs blocked ne effort and as the final whistle approached the Mariners took to desperately pumping the ball

Pittman (Grimsby) gets a shot on target against Halifax. Photo: Keith Clayton.

into the Halifax area, even sending their keeper up for a corner. However it was the Shaymen's day and, despite seeing their hero McManus stretchered off with possible cruciate damage, they were not to be denied.

This was a sweet and sour victory for manager Jim Harvey who knew that his contract was ending and that his successor had already been lined up, an exact re-enactment of the previous day's F A Cup Final where Louis van Gaal faced the same ending, a cup winner but job loser. Ironically the man to replace Harvey will be Billy Heath manager of the previous year's Trophy winners, North Ferriby, also, in a further coincidence, one of the teams changing places with Halifax in the National League for the new season.

*Arthur Evans.*

# PAST FINALS

**1970 MACCLESFIELD TOWN** 2 (Lyons, B Fidler) — **TELFORD UNITED 0** — Att: 28,000
*Northern Premier League* — *Southern League*
Macclesfield: Cooke, Sievwright, Bennett, Beaumont, Collins, Roberts, Lyons, B Fidler,Young, Corfield, D Fidler.
Telford: Irvine, Harris, Croft, Flowers, Coton, Ray,Fudge, Hart, Bentley, Murray, Jagger. Ref: K Walker

**1971 TELFORD UTD** 3 (Owen, Bentley, Fudge) — **HILLINGDON BORO. 2 (Reeve, Bishop)** — Att: 29,500
*Southern League* — *Southern League*
Telford: Irvine, Harris, Croft, Ray, Coton, Carr, Fudge, Owen, Bentley, Jagger ,Murray.
Hillingdon B.: Lowe, Batt, Langley, Higginson, Newcombe, Moore, Fairchild,Bishop, Reeve, Carter, Knox. Ref: D Smith

**1972 STAFFORD RANGERS** 3 (Williams 2, Cullerton) — **BARNET 0** — Att: 24,000
*Northern Premier League* — *Southern League*
Stafford R.: Aleksic, Chadwick, Clayton, Sargeant, Aston, Machin, Cullerton, Chapman,Williams, Bayley, Jones.
Barnet: McClelland, Lye, Jenkins, Ward, Embrey, King, Powell, Ferry, Flatt, Easton, Plume . Ref: P Partridge

**1973 SCARBOROUGH** 2 (Leask, Thompson) — **WIGAN ATHLETIC 1 (Rogers) aet** — Att:23,000
*Northern Premier League* — *Northern Premier League*
Scarborough: Garrow, Appleton, Shoulder, Dunn, Siddle, Fagan, Donoghue, Franks,Leask (Barmby), Thompson, Hewitt.
Wigan: Reeves, Morris, Sutherland, Taylor,Jackson, Gillibrand, Clements, Oats (McCunnell), Rogers, King, Worswick. Ref: H Hackney

**1974 MORECAMBE** 2 (Richmond, Sutton) — **DARTFORD 1 (Cunningham)** — Att: 19,000
*Northern Premier League* — *Southern League*
Morecambe: Coates, Pearson, Bennett, Sutton, Street, Baldwin, Done, Webber,Roberts (Galley), Kershaw, Richmond.
Dartford: Morton, Read, Payne, Carr, Burns,Binks, Light, Glozier, Robinson (Hearne), Cunningham, Halleday. Ref: B Homewood

**1975(1) MATLOCK TOWN** 4 (Oxley, Dawson, T Fenoughty, N Fenoughy) — **SCARBOROUGH 0** — Att: 21,000
*Northern Premier League* — *Northern Premier League*
Matlock: Fell, McKay, Smith, Stuart, Dawson, Swan, Oxley, N Fenoughy, Scott, T Fenoughty, M Fenoughty.
Scarborough: Williams, Hewitt, Rettitt, Dunn, Marshall, Todd, Houghton, Woodall, Davidson, Barnby, Aveyard. Ref: K Styles

**1976 SCARBOROUGH** 3 (Woodall, Abbey, Marshall(p)) — **STAFFORD R. 2 (Jones 2) aet** — Att: 21,000
*Northern Premier League* — *Northern Premier League*
Scarborough: Barnard, Jackson, Marshall, H Dunn, Ayre (Donoghue), HA Dunn, Dale,Barmby, Woodall, Abbey, Hilley.
Stafford: Arnold, Ritchie, Richards, Sargeant,Seddon, Morris, Chapman, Lowe, Jones, Hutchinson, Chadwick. Ref: R Challis

**1977 SCARBOROUGH** 2 (Dunn(p), Abbey) — **DAGENHAM 1 (Harris)** — Att: 21,500
*Northern Premier League* — *Isthmian League*
Scarborough: Chapman, Smith, Marshall (Barmby), Dunn, Ayre, Deere, Aveyard,Donoghue, Woodall, Abbey, Dunn.
Dagenham: Hutley, Wellman, P Currie, Dunwell,Moore, W Currie, Harkins, Saul, Fox, Harris, Holder. Ref: G Courtney

**1978 ALTRINCHAM** 3 (King, Johnson, Rogers) — **LEATHERHEAD 1 (Cook)** — Att: 20,000
*Northern Premier League* — *Isthmian League*
Altrincham: Eales, Allan, Crossley, Bailey, Owens, King, Morris, Heathcote,Johnson, Rogers, Davidson (Flaherty).
Leatherhead: Swannell, Cooper, Eaton, Davies,Reid, Malley, Cook, Salkeld, Baker, Boyle (Bailey). Ref: A Grey

**1979 STAFFORD RANGERS** 2 (A Wood 2) — **KETTERING TOWN 0** — Att: 32,000
*Northern Premier League* — *Southern League*
Stafford: Arnold, F Wood, Willis, Sargeant, Seddon, Ritchie, Secker, Chapman, A Wood, Cullerton, Chadwick (Jones).
Kettering: Lane, Ashby, Lee, Eastell, Dixey,Suddards, Flannagan, Kellock, Phipps, Clayton, Evans (Hughes). Ref: D Richardson

**1980(2) DAGENHAM** 2 (Duck, Maycock) — **MOSSLEY 1 (Smith)** — Att: 26,000
*Isthmian League* — *Northern Premier League*
Dagenham: Huttley, Wellman, Scales, Dunwell, Moore, Durrell, Maycock, Horan,Duck, Kidd, Jones (Holder).
Mossley: Fitton, Brown, Vaughan, Gorman, Salter, Polliot, Smith, Moore, Skeete, O'Connor, Keelan (Wilson). Ref: K Baker

**1981(3) BISHOP'S STORTFORD** 1 (Sullivan) — **SUTTON UNITED 0** — Att: 22,578
*Isthmian League* — *Isthmian League*
Bishop's Stortford: Moore, Blackman, Brame, Smith (Worrell), Bradford, Abery, Sullivan,Knapman, Radford, Simmonds, Mitchell.
Sutton Utd.: Collyer, Rogers, Green, J Rains,T Rains, Stephens (Sunnucks), Waldon, Pritchard, Cornwell, Parsons, Dennis. Ref: J Worrall

**1982 ENFIELD** 1 (Taylor) — **ALTRINCHAM 0** — Att: 18,678
*Alliance Premier League* — *Alliance Premier League*
Enfield: Jacobs, Barrett, Tone, Jennings, Waite, Ironton, Ashford, Taylor,Holmes, Oliver (Flint), King. Ref: B Stevens
Altrincham: Connaughton, Crossley, Davison, Bailey, Cuddy, King (Whitbread), Allan, Heathcote, Johnson, Rogers, Howard.

**Notes:**
1 The only occasion three members of the same family played in the same FA Trophy Final team.
2 The first of the Amateurs from the Isthmian League to win the FA Trophy.
3 Goalkeeper Terry Moore had also won an Amateur Cup Winners Medal with Bishop's Stortford in 1974.
All games played at Wembley (old & new) unless stated.

1983 **TELFORD UTD** 2 (Mather 2) — NORTHWICH VICTORIA 1 (Bennett) — Att: 22,071
*Alliance Premier League* — *Alliance Premier League*
Telford: Charlton, Lewis, Turner, Mayman (Joseph), Walker, Easton, Barnett,Williams, Mather, Hogan, Alcock.
Northwich: Ryan, Fretwell, Murphy, Jones, Forshaw, Ward, Anderson, Abel (Bennett), Reid, Chesters, Wilson. Ref: B Hill

1984 NORTHWICH VICTORIA 1 (Chester) — BANGOR CITY 1 (Whelan) — Att: 14,200
Replay **NORTHWICH VICTORIA** 2 (Chesters(p), Anderson) — BANGOR CITY 1 (Lunn) — Att: 5,805 (at Stoke)
*Alliance Premier League* — *Alliance Premier League*
Northwich: Ryan, Fretwell, Dean, Jones, Forshaw (Power 65), Bennett, Anderson,Abel, Reid, Chesters, Wilson. Ref: J Martin
Bangor: Letheren, Cavanagh, Gray, Whelan, Banks,Lunn, Urqhart, Morris, Carter, Howat, Sutcliffe (Westwood 105) . Same in replay.

1985 **WEALDSTONE** 2 (Graham, Holmes) — BOSTON UNITED 1 (Cook) — Att: 20,775
*Alliance Premier League* — *Alliance Premier League*
Vealdstone: Iles, Perkins, Bowgett, Byatt, Davies, Greenaway, Holmes, Wainwright,Donnellan, Graham (N Cordice 89), A Cordice.
Boston: Blackwell, Casey, Ladd,Creane, O'Brien, Thommson, Laverick (Mallender 78), Simpsom, Gilbert, Lee, Cook. Ref: J Bray

1986 **ALTRINCHAM** 1 (Farrelly) — RUNCORN 0 — Att: 15,700
*Gola League* — *Gola League*
Altrincham: Wealands, Gardner, Densmore, Johnson, Farrelly, Conning, Cuddy,Davison, Reid, Ellis, Anderson. Sub: Newton.
Runcorn: McBride, Lee, Roberts,Jones, Fraser, Smith, S Crompton (A Crompton), Imrie, Carter, Mather, Carrodus. Ref: A Ward

1987 KIDDERMINSTER HARRIERS 0 — BURTON ALBION 0 — Att: 23,617
Replay **KIDDERMINSTER HARRIERS** 2 (Davies 2) — BURTON ALBION 1 (Groves) — Att: 15,685 (at West Brom)
*Conference* — *Southern League*
Kidderminster: Arnold, Barton, Boxall, Brazier (sub Hazlewood in rep), Collins (sub Pearson 90 at Wembley), Woodall, McKenzie, O'Dowd, Tuohy, Casey, Davies. sub:Jones.
Burton: New, Essex, Kamara, Vaughan, Simms, Groves, Bancroft, Land, Dorsett, Redfern, (sub Wood in replay), Gauden. Sub: Patterson. Ref: D Shaw

1988 ENFIELD 0 — TELFORD UNITED 0 — Att: 20,161
Replay **ENFIELD** 3 (Furlong 2, Howell) — TELFORD UNITED 2 (Biggins, Norris(p)) — Att: 6,912 (at W Brom)
*Conference* — *Conference*
Enfield: Pape, Cottington, Howell, Keen (sub Edmonds in rep), Sparrow (sub Hayzleden at Wembley), Lewis (sub Edmonds at Wembley), Harding, Cooper, King,Furlong, Francis.
Telford: Charlton, McGinty, Storton, Nelson, Wiggins, Mayman (sub Cunningham in rep (sub Hancock)), Sankey, Joseph, Stringer (sub Griffiths at Wembley, Griffiths in replay), Biggins, Norris. Ref: L Dilkes

1989 **TELFORD UNITED** 1 (Crawley) — MACCLESFIELD TOWN 0 — Att: 18,102
*Conference* — *Conference*
Telford: Charlton, Lee, Brindley, Hancock, Wiggins, Mayman, Grainger, Joseph, Nelson, Lloyd, Stringer. Subs: Crawley, Griffiths.
Macclesfield: Zelem, Roberts, Tobin, Edwards, Hardman, Askey, Lake, Hanton, Imrie, Burr, Timmons. Subs: Devonshire, Kendall.

1990 **BARROW** 3 (Gordon 2, Cowperthwaite) — LEEK TOWN 0 — Att: 19,011
*Conference* — *Northern Premier League*
Barrow: McDonnell, Higgins, Chilton, Skivington, Gordon, Proctor, Doherty (Burgess), Farrell (Gilmore), Cowperthwaite, Lowe, Ferris.
Leek: Simpson, Elsby (Smith), Pearce, McMullen, Clowes, Coleman (Russell),Mellor, Somerville, Sutton, Millington, Norris Ref: T Simpson

1991 **WYCOMBE W.** 2 (Scott, West) — KIDDERMINSTER HARRIERS 1 (Hadley) — Att: 34,842
*Conference* — *Conference*
Wycombe: Granville, Crossley, Cash, Kerr, Creaser, Carroll, Ryan, Stapleton,West, Scott, Guppy (Hutchinson). Ref: J Watson
Kidderminster: Jones, Kurila, McGrath, Weir, Barnett, Forsyth, Joseph (Wilcox), Howell (Whitehouse), Hadley, Lilwall, Humphries

1992 **COLCHESTER UTD*** 3 (Masters, Smith, McGavin) — WITTON ALBION 1 (Lutkevitch) — Att: 27,806
*Conference* — *Conference*
Colchester: Barrett, Donald, Roberts, Knsella, English, Martin, Cook, Masters,McDonough (Bennett 65), McGavin, Smith. Ref: K P Barratt
Witton: Mason, Halliday, Coathup, McNeilis, Jim Connor, Anderson, Thomas, Rose, Alford, Grimshaw (Joe Connor), Lutkevitch (McCluskie)

1993 **WYCOMBE W*.** 4 (Cousins, Kerr, Thompson, Carroll) — RUNCORN 1 (Shaughnessy) — Att: 32,968
*Conference* — *Conference*
Wycombe: Hyde, Cousins, Cooper, Kerr, Crossley, Thompson (Hayrettin 65),Carroll, Ryan, Hutchinson, Scott, Guppy. Sub: Casey.
Runcorn: Williams, Bates, Robertson, Hill, Harold (Connor 62), Anderson, Brady (Parker 72), Brown, Shaughnessy, McKenna, Brabin

1994 **WOKING** 2 (D Brown, Hay) — RUNCORN 1 (Shaw (pen)) — Att: 15,818
*Conference* — *Conference*
Woking: Batty, Tucker, L Wye, Berry, Brown, Clement, Brown (Rattray 32), Fielder, Steele, Hay (Puckett 46), Walker. Ref: Paul Durkin
Runcorn: Williams, Bates, Robertson, Shaw, Lee, Anderson, Thomas, Connor, McInerney (Hill 71), McKenna, Brabin. Sub: Parker

1995 **WOKING** 2 (Steele, Fielder) — KIDDERMINSTER HARRIERS 1 aet (Davies) — Att: 17,815
*Conference* — *Conference*
Woking: Batty, Tucker, L Wye, Fielder, Brown, Crumplin (Rattray 42), S Wye, Ellis, Steele, Hay (Newberry 112), Walker. (Sub: Read(gk)
Kidderminster: Rose, Hodson, Bancroft, Webb, Brindley (Cartwright 94), Forsyth, Deakin, Yates, Humphreys (Hughes 105), Davies, Purdie. Sub: Dearlove (gk) Ref: D J Gallagher

**1996** **MACCLESFIELD TOWN 3 (Payne, OG, Hemmings)** *Conference* — **NORTHWICH VICTORIA 1 (Williams)** *Conference* — **Att: 8,672**

Macclesfield: Price, Edey, Gardiner, Payne, Howarth(C), Sorvel, Lyons, Wood (Hulme 83), Coates, Power, Hemmings (Cavell 88).
Northwich: Greygoose, Ward, Duffy, Burgess (Simpson 87), Abel (Steele), Walters, Williams, Butler (C), Cooke, Humphries, Vicary.
Ref: M Reed

**1997** **WOKING 1 (Hay 112)** *Conference* — **DAGENHAM & REDBRIDGE 0** *Isthmian League* — **Att: 24,376**

Woking: Batty, Brown, Howard, Foster, Taylor, S Wye, Thompson (sub Jones 115), Ellis, Steele (L Wye 108), Walker, Jackson (Hay 77).
Dagenham: Gothard, Culverhouse, Connor, Creaser, Jacques (sub Double 75), Davidson, Pratt (Naylor 81), Parratt, Broom, Rogers, Stimson (John 65). Ref: J Winter

**1998** **CHELTENHAM TOWN 1 (Eaton 74)** *Conference* — **SOUTHPORT 0** *Conference* — **Att: 26,387**

Cheltenham: Book, Duff, Freeman, Banks, Victory, Knight (Smith 78), Howells, Bloomer, Walker (sub Milton 78), Eaton, Watkins. Sub: Wright.
Southport: Stewart, Horner, Futcher, Ryan, Farley, Kielty, Butler, Gamble, Formby (sub Whittaker 80), Thompson (sub Bollard 88), Ross. Sub: Mitten. Ref: G S Willard

**1999** **KINGSTONIAN 1 (Mustafa 49)** *Conference* — **FOREST GREEN ROVERS 0** *Conference* — **Att: 20,037**

Kingstonian: Farrelly, Mustafa, Luckett, Crossley, Stewart, Harris, Patterson, Pitcher, Rattray, Leworthy (Francis 87), Akuamoah. Subs (not used): John, Corbett, Brown, Tranter
Forest Green Rovers: Shuttlewood, Hedges, Forbes, Bailey (Smart 76), Kilgour, Wigg (Cook 58), Honor (Winter 58), Drysdale, McGregor, Mehew, Sykes. Subs (not used): Perrin, Coupe Ref: A B Wilkie

**2000** **KINGSTONIAN 3 (Akuamoah 40, 69, Simba 75)** *Conference* — **KETTERING TOWN 2 (Vowden 55, Norman 64p)** *Conference* — **Att: 20,034**

Kingstonian: Farelly, Mustafa, Luckett, Crossley, Stewart (Saunders 77), Harris, Kadi (Leworthy 83), Pitcher, Green (Basford 86), Smiba, Akuamoah. Subs (not used): Hurst, Allan
Kettering Town: Sollit, McNamara, Adams, Perkins, Vowden, Norman (Duik 76), Fisher, Brown, Shutt, Watkins (Hudson 46), Setchell (Hopkins 81). Subs (not used): Ridgway, Wilson Ref: S W Dunn

**2001** **CANVEY ISLAND 1 (Chenery)** *Isthmian League* — **FOREST GREEN ROVERS 0** *Conference* — **Att: 10,007 at Villa Park**

Forest Green Rovers: Perrin, Cousins, Lockwood, Foster, Clark, Burns, Daley, Drysdale (Bennett 46), Foster (Hunt 75), Meecham, Slater. Subs (not used): Hedges, Prince, Ghent
Canvey Island: Harrison, Duffy, Chenery, Bodley, Ward, Tilson, Stimson (Tanner 83), Gregory, Vaughan (Jones 76), Parmenter. Subs (not used): Bennett, Miller, Thompson. Ref: A G Wiley

**2002** **YEOVIL TOWN 2 (Alford, Stansfield)** *Conference* — **STEVENAGE BOROUGH 0** *Conference* — **Att: 18,809 at Villa Park**

Yeovil Town: Weale, Lockwood, Tonkin, Skiverton, Pluck (White 51), Way, Stansfield, Johnson, Alford (Giles 86), Crittenden (Lindegaard 83), McIndoe. Subs (not used): O'Brien, Sheffield
Stevenage Borough: Wilkerson, Hamsher, Goodliffe, Trott, Fraser, Fisher, Wormull (Stirling 71), Evers (Williams 56), Jackson, Sigere (Campbell 74), Clarke. Subs (not used): Campbell, Greygoose Ref: N S Barry

**2003** **BURSCOUGH 2 (Martindale 25, 55)** *Northern Premier* — **TAMWORTH 1 (Cooper 78)** *Southern Premier* — **Att: 14,265 at Villa Park**

Burscough: Taylor, Teale, Taylor, Macauley (White 77), Lawless, Bowen, Wright, Norman, Martindale (McHale 80), Byrne (Bluck 84), Burns. Subs (not used): McGuire (g/k) Molyneux.
Tamworth: Acton, Warner, Follett, Robinson, Walsh, Cooper, Colley, Evans (Turner 64), Rickards (Hatton 88), McGorry, Sale (Hallam 54). Subs (not used): Grocutt, Barnes (g/k). Ref: U D Rennie

**2004** **HEDNESFORD TOWN 3 (Maguire 28, Hines 53, Brindley 87)** *Southern Premier* — **CANVEY ISLAND 2 (Boylan 46, Brindley 48 og)** *Isthmian Premier Champions* — **Att: 6,635 at Villa Park**

Hednesford Town: Young, Simkin, Hines, King, Brindley, Ryder (Barrow 59), Palmer, Anthrobus, Danks (Piearce 78), Maguire, Charie (Evans 55). Subs (not used): Evans (g/k) McGhee.
Canvey Island: Potter, Kennedy, Duffy, Chenery, Cowan, Gooden (Dobinson 89), Minton, Gregory (McDougald 80), Boylan, Midgley (Berquez 73), Ward. Subs (not used): Theobald, Harrison (g/k).
Ref: M L Dean

**2005** **GRAYS ATHLETIC 1 (Martin 65) Pens: 6** *Conference South* — **HUCKNALL TOWN 1 (Ricketts 75) Pens: 5** *Conference North* — **Att: 8,116 at Villa Park**

Grays Athletic: Bayes, Brennan, Nutter, Stuart, Matthews, Thurgood, Oli (Powell 80), Hopper (Carthy 120), Battersby (sub West 61), Martin, Cole. Subs (not used): Emberson, Bruce..
Hucknall Town: Smith, Asher, Barrick (Plummer 30), Hunter, Timons, Cooke, Smith (Ward 120), Palmer (Heathcote 94), Ricketts, Bacon, Todd. Subs (not used): Winder, Lindley. Ref: P Dowd

**2006** **GRAYS ATHLETIC 2 (Oli, Poole)** *Conference* — **WOKING 0** *Conference* — **Att: 13,997 at Upton Park**

Grays Athletic: Bayes, Sambrook, Nutter, Stuart, Hanson, Kightly (Williamson 90), Thurgood, Martin, Poole, Oli, McLean. Subs (not used): Eyre (g/k), Hooper, Olayinka, Mawer.
Woking: Jalal, Jackson, MacDonald, Nethercott (Watson 60), Hutchinson, Murray, Smith (Cockerill 60), Evans (Blackman 85), Ferguson, McAllister, Justin Richards. Subs (not used): Davis (g/k), El-Salahi.
Ref: Howard Webb (Sheffield)

**2007 STEVENAGE BOROUGH** 3 (Cole, Dobson, Morrison) **KIDDERMINSTER HARRIERS 2 (Constable 2)** **Att: 53,262**
*Conference* *Conference* **(New Trophy record)**
Stevenage Borough: Julian, Fuller, Nutter, Oliver, Gaia, Miller, Cole, Morrison, Guppy (Dobson 63), Henry, Beard.
Subs not used: Potter, Slabber, Nurse, McMahon.
Kidderminster Harriers: Bevan, Kenna, Hurren, Creighton, Whitehead, Blackwood, Russell, Penn, Smikle (Reynolds 90), Christie (White 75) , Constable.
Subs not used: Taylor, Sedgemore, McGrath. Ref: Chris Foy (Merseyside)

**2008 EBBSFLEET UNITED 1 (McPhee)** **TORQUAY UNITED 0** **Att: 40,186**
*Blue Square Premier* *Blue Square Premier*
Ebbsfleet United: Cronin, Hawkins, McCarthy, Smith, Opinel, McPhee, Barrett, Bostwick, Long (MacDonald 84), Moore, Akinde.
Subs not used: Eribenne, Purcell, Ricketts, Mott.
Torquay United: Rice, Mansell, Todd, Woods, Nicholson, D'Sane (Benyon 66), Hargreaves, Adams, Zebroski, Sills (Hill 88), Phillips (Stevens 46). Subs not used: Hockley and Robertson. Ref: Martin Atkinson (West Riding)

**2009 STEVENAGE BOROUGH 2 (Morison, Boylan)** **YORK CITY 0** **Att: 27,102**
*Blue Square Premier* *Blue Square Premier*
Stevenage Borough: Day, Henry, Bostwick, Roberts, Wilson, Mills, Murphy, Drury, Vincenti (Anaclet 86), Boylan, Morison.
Subs not used: Bayes, Albrighton, Maamria and Willock.
York City:Ingham, Purkiss, McGurk, Parslow, Pejic, Mackin, Greaves(McWilliams 74), Rusk (Russell 80), Brodie, McBreen (Sodje 60), Boyes. Subs not used – Mimms and Robinson. Referee: Michael Jones.

**2010 BARROW 2 (McEvilly 79, Walker 117)** **STEVENAGE BOROUGH 1 (Drury 10)** **Att: 21,223**
*Blue Square Premier* *Blue Square Premier*
Barrow: Stuart Tomlinson, Simon Spender, Paul Jones, Phil Bolland, Paul Edwards, Simon Wiles (sub Carlos Logan 63rd min), Robin Hulbert, Andy Bond, Paul Rutherford (sub Mark Boyd 109th min), Jason Walker, Gregg Blundell (sub Lee McEvilly 73rd min).
Subs not used – Tim Deasy and Mike Pearson.
Stevenage Borough: Chris Day (sub Ashley Bayes 90th min), Ronnie Henry, Jon Ashton, Mark Roberts, Scott Laird, Joel Byrom (sub Lawrie Wilson 58th min), David Bridges, Michael Bostwick, Andy Drury, Chris Beardsley (sub Charlie Griffin 64th min), Yemi Odubade. Subs not used – Stacey Long and Peter Vincenti.
**Man of the match -** Paul Rutherford. Referee Lee Probert.

**2011 DARLINGTON 1 (Senior 120)** **MANSFIELD TOWN 0** **Att: 24,668**
*Blue Square Premier* *Blue Square Premier*
Darlington: Sam Russell, Paul Arnison, Ian Miller, Liam Hatch, Aaron Brown, Jamie Chandler, Chris Moore, Marc Bridge-Wilkinson (sub Paul Terry 100th min), Gary Smith (sub Arman Verma 38th min), John Campbell (sub Chris Senior 75th min), Tommy Wright.
Subs not used – Danzelle St Louis-Hamilton (gk) and Phil Gray.
Mansfield Town: Alan Marriott, Gary Silk, Stephen Foster, Tom Naylor, Dan Spence, Louis Briscoe, Tyrone Thompson, Kyle Nix, Adam Smith (sub Ashley Cain 95th min), Adam Murray (sub Danny Mitchley 108th min), Paul Connor
Subs not used – Paul Stonehouse and Neil Collett (gk)
**Man of the match -** Jamie Chandler. Referee Stuart Atwell

**2012 YORK CITY 2 (Blair 61, Oyebanjo 68)** **NEWPORT COUNTY 0** **Att: 19,844**
*Blue Square Premier* *Blue Square Premier*
York City: Michael Ingham, Jon Challinor, Chris Smith, Daniel Parslow, Ben Gibson, Matty Blair, Lanre Oyebanjo, Patrick McLaughlan (sub Jamal Fyfield 82nd min), James Meredith, Ashley Chambers (Adriano Moke (89th min), Jason Walker (Jamie Reed 90th min).
Subs not used – Paul Musselwhite (g/k), Michael Potts.
Newport County: Glyn Thompson, David Pipe, Ismail Yakubu, Gary Warren, Andrew Hughes, Sam Foley, Lee Evans, Nat Jarvis (sub Jake Harris 68th min), Max Porter (sub Darryl Knights 79th min), Romone Rose (sub Elliott Buchanan 68th min), Lee Minshull.
Subs not used – Matthew Swan (g/k), Paul Rodgers.
**Man of the match -** Lanre Oyebanjo. Referee Anthony Taylor

**2013 WREXHAM 1 (Thornton 82 (pen))** **GRIMSBY TOWN 1 (Cook 71)** **Att: 35,226**
*Wrexham won 4-1 on kicks from the penalty mark after extra time.*
*Blue Square Premier* *Blue Square Premier*
Wrexham: Chris Maxwell, Stephen Wright, Martin Riley, Jay Harris, Danny Wright, Brett Ormerod (Robert Ogleby 77 min), Andy Morrell (Adrian Cieslewicz 61 min), Dean Keates, Johnny Hunt, Chris Westwood, Kevin Thornton (Joe Clarke 89 min).
Subs not used - Andy Coughlin (gk) Glen Little.
Grimsby Town: Sam Hatton, Aswad Thomas, Shaun Pearson, Ian Miller, Joe Colbeck, Craig Disley, Frankie Artus, Andy Cook, James McKeown, Ross Hannah (Andi Thanoj 55 min), Marcus Marshall (Richard Brodie 87 min).
Subs not used - Jamie Devitt, Bradley Wood, Lenell John-Lewis. Referee Jonathan Moss

**2014 CAMBRIDGE UNITED 4** (Bird 38, Donaldson 50,59, Berry 78 (pen)) **GOSPORT BOROUGH 0** **Att: 18,120**
*Conference Premier* *Conference South*
Cambridge United: Will Norris, Greg Taylor, Jock Coulson (Tom Bonner 87 min), Ian Miller, Ryan Donaldson, Tom Champion, Richard Tait, Liam Hughes (Nathan Arnold 73 min), Luke Berry, Ryan Bird, Josh Gillies (Andy Pugh 61 min).
Subs not used - Kevin Roberts, Mitch Austin.
Gosport Borough: Nathan Ashmore, Lee Molyneaux, Andy Forbes, Jamie Brown (Rory Williams 57 min), Brett Poate, Sam Pearce, Josh Carmichael, Danny Smith, Tim Sills (Dan Woodward 57 min), Justin Bennett, Michael Gosney (Dan Wooden 72 min).
Subs not used - Ryan Scott, Adam Wilde.
Referee Craig Pawson

**2015** **NORTH FERRIBY UNITED** 3 (King 76 (pen), Kendall 86, 111) **WREXHAM** 3 (Moult 11, 118, Harris 59) **Att: 14,548**

*Conference North* *Conference National*

North Ferriby United: Adam Nicklin, Sam Topliss, Danny Hone, Matt Wilson, Josh Wilde (Nathan Peat 90), Liam King, Adam Bolder (Nathan Jarman 62), Russell Fry (Ryan Kendall 80), Danny Clarke, Tom Denton, Jason St Juste.
Subs not used - Tom Nicholson and Mark Gray.
Wrexham: Andy Coughlin, Steve Tomassen, Manny Smith, Blaine Hudson, Neil Ashton, Jay Harris, Dean Keates (Robbie Evans 73), Joe Clarke (Andy Bishop 102), Kieron Morris (Wes York 87), Louis Moult, Connor Jennings.
Subs not used - Mark Carrington and Luke Waterfall.

Referee Michael Oliver

*All Finals at Wembley unless otherwise stated.*

# PRELIMINARY ROUND 2016-17

## SATURDAY 8 OCTOBER 2016

| | | | |
|---|---|---|---|
| 1 | Witton Albion | v | Brighouse Town |
| 2 | Glossop North End | v | Tadcaster Albion |
| 3 | Prescot Cables | v | Ossett Albion |
| 4 | Colne | v | Trafford |
| 5 | Burscough | v | Kendal Town |
| 6 | Clitheroe | v | Stocksbridge Park Steels |
| 7 | Colwyn Bay | v | Hyde United |
| 8 | Northwich Victoria | v | Mossley |
| 9 | Shaw Lane Association | v | Scarborough Athletic |
| 10 | Belper Town | v | Goole |
| 11 | Radcliffe Borough | v | Farsley Celtic |
| 12 | Lancaster City | v | Droylsden |
| 13 | Ramsbottom United | v | Sheffield |
| 14 | Ossett Town | v | Bamber Bridge |
| 15 | Bedworth United | v | Rugby Town |
| 16 | Stamford | v | Basford United |
| 17 | AFC Rushden & Diamonds | v | Histon |
| 18 | Gresley | v | Spalding United |
| 19 | Carlton Town | v | Chasetown |
| 20 | Newcastle Town | v | Soham Town Rangers |
| 21 | Loughborough Dynamo | v | Leek Town |
| 22 | Lincoln United | v | Romulus |
| 23 | Aylesbury | v | Ware |
| 24 | Sittingbourne | v | Bury Town |
| 25 | Maldon & Tiptree | v | Great Wakering Rovers |
| 26 | East Grinstead Town | v | Three Bridges |
| 27 | Witham Town | v | Aveley |
| 28 | Cray Wanderers | v | Carshalton Athletic |
| 29 | Potters Bar Town | v | Horsham |
| 30 | Thurrock | v | Bowers & Pitsea |
| 31 | Chipstead | v | Kempston Rovers |
| 32 | Aylesbury United | v | Chatham Town |
| 33 | Uxbridge | v A | FC Dunstable |
| 34 | Lewes | v | Tilbury |
| 35 | South Park | v | Guernsey |
| 36 | Whyteleafe | v | Cheshunt |
| 37 | Haringey Borough | v | Hythe Town |
| 38 | Dorking Wanderers | v | Northwood |
| 39 | Wroxham | v | Godalming Town |
| 40 | Norwich United | v | Tooting & Mitcham United |
| 41 | Ramsgate | v | Hastings United |
| 42 | AFC Hornchurch | v | Ashford Town (Middx) |
| 43 | Molesey | v | Romford |
| 44 | Brentwood Town | v | Marlow |
| 45 | Arlesey Town | v | Chalfont St Peter |
| 46 | Corinthian Casuals | v | Thamesmead Town |
| 47 | Brightlingsea Regent | v | Dereham Town |
| 48 | VCD Athletic | v | Greenwich Borough |
| 49 | Royston Town | v | Egham Town |
| 50 | Hanwell Town | v | Bedford Town |
| 51 | Barton Rovers | v | Herne Bay |
| 52 | Slimbridge | v | Swindon Supermarine |
| 53 | Bridgwater Town | v | North Leigh |
| 54 | Winchester City | v | Petersfield Town |
| 55 | Wimborne Town | v | AFC Totton |
| 56 | Salisbury | v | Hereford |
| 57 | Paulton Rovers | v | Tiverton Town |
| 58 | Bishop's Cleeve | v | Didcot Town |
| 59 | Mangotsfield United | v | Yate Town |
| 60 | Farnborough | v | Barnstaple Town |
| 61 | Fleet Town | v | Bideford |
| 62 | Kidlington | v | Wantage Town |
| 63 | Taunton Town | v | Larkhall Athletic |
| 64 | Shortwood United | v | Evesham United |

# FIRST QUALIFYING ROUND 2016-17

## SATURDAY 29 OCTOBER 2016

| | | | |
|---|---|---|---|
| 1 | Belper Town or Goole | v | Blyth Spartans |
| 2 | Spennymoor Town | v | Matlock Town |
| 3 | Warrington Town | v | Nantwich Town |
| 4 | Clitheroe or Stocksbridge Park Steels | v | Lancaster City or Droylsden |
| 5 | Whitby Town | v | Workington |
| 6 | Skelmersdale United | v | Burscough or Kendal Town |
| 7 | Colwyn Bay or Hyde United | v | Witton Albion or Brighouse Town |
| 8 | Northwich Victoria or Mossley | v | Radcliffe Borough or Farsley Celtic |
| 9 | Ramsbottom United or Sheffield | v | Prescot Cables or Ossett Albion |
| 10 | Ossett Town or Bamber Bridge | v | Colne or Trafford |
| 11 | Buxton | v | Glossop North End or Tadcaster Albion |
| 12 | Ashton United | v | Marine |
| 13 | Shaw Lane Association or Scarborough Athletic | v | Frickley Athletic |
| 14 | Stratford Town | v | Grantham Town |
| 15 | Leamington | v | Mickleover Sports |
| 16 | Kidsgrove Athletic | v | Newcastle Town or Soham Town Rangers |
| 17 | Rushall Olympic | v | Halesowen Town |
| 18 | Ilkeston | v | Barwell |
| 19 | Carlton Town or Chasetown | v | St Ives Town |
| 20 | Stourbridge | v | King's Lynn Town |
| 21 | Corby Town | v | Stafford Rangers |
| 22 | Kettering Town | v | Market Drayton Town |
| 23 | Redditch United | v | Cambridge City |
| 24 | Stamford or Basford United | v | Hednesford Town |
| 25 | Loughborough Dynamo or Leek Town | v | Sutton Coldfield Town |
| 26 | AFC Rushden & Diamonds or Histon | v | Coalville Town |
| 27 | Bedworth United or Rugby Town | v | St Neots Town |
| 28 | Lincoln United or Romulus | v | Gresley or Spalding United |
| 29 | Potters Bar Town or Horsham | v | Molesey or Romford |
| 30 | East Grinstead Town or Three Bridges | v | Phoenix Sports |
| 31 | Kingstonian | v | Lewes or Tilbury |
| 32 | Ramsgate or Hastings United | v | Aylesbury United or Chatham Town |
| 33 | Haringey Borough or Hythe Town | v | Walton Casuals |
| 34 | Burgess Hill Town | v | Beaconsfield SYCOB |
| 35 | Leatherhead | v | Chesham United |
| 36 | Waltham Abbey | v | Merstham |
| 37 | Hanwell Town or Bedford Town | v | Sittingbourne or Bury Town |
| 38 | Metropolitan Police | v | Brightlingsea Regent or Dereham Town |
| 39 | Needham Market | v | Wroxham or Godalming Town |
| 40 | Slough Town | v | Bognor Regis Town |
| 41 | Grays Athletic | v | Wingate & Finchley |
| 42 | Worthing | v | Chipstead or Kempston Rovers |
| 43 | AFC Sudbury | v | Thurrock or Bowers & Pitsea |
| 44 | Tonbridge Angels | v | AFC Hornchurch or Ashford Town (Middx) |
| 45 | Kings Langley | v | Heybridge Swifts |
| 46 | Leiston | v | Hendon |
| 47 | VCD Athletic or Greenwich Borough | v | Aylesbury or Ware |
| 48 | Enfield Town | v | Canvey Island |
| 49 | Norwich United or Tooting & Mitcham United | v | Dunstable Town |
| 50 | Billericay Town | v | Maldon & Tiptree or Great Wakering Rovers |
| 51 | Arlesey Town or Chalfont St Peter | v | Corinthian Casuals or Thamesmead Town |
| 52 | Cray Wanderers or Carshalton Athletic | v | Brentwood Town or Marlow |
| 53 | Whyteleafe or Cheshunt | v | Folkestone Invicta |
| 54 | Royston Town or Egham Town | v | Dorking Wanderers or Northwood |
| 55 | Lowestoft Town | v | Dulwich Hamlet |
| 56 | Biggleswade Town | v | Witham Town or Aveley |
| 57 | Faversham Town | v | South Park or Guernsey |
| 58 | Uxbridge or AFC Dunstable | v | Harlow Town |
| 59 | Barton Rovers or Herne Bay | v | Harrow Borough |
| 60 | Hayes & Yeading United | v | Hitchin Town |
| 61 | Shortwood United or Evesham United | v | Frome Town |
| 62 | Mangotsfield United or Yate Town | v | Bridgwater Town or North Leigh |
| 63 | Salisbury or Hereford | v | Chippenham Town |
| 64 | Taunton Town or Larkhall Athletic | v | Slimbridge or Swindon Supermarine |
| 65 | Paulton Rovers or Tiverton Town | v | Wimborne Town or AFC Totton |
| 66 | Cirencester Town | v | Havant & Waterlooville |
| 67 | Merthyr Town | v | Cinderford Town |
| 68 | Banbury United | v | Bishop's Cleeve or Didcot Town |
| 69 | Fleet Town or Bideford | v | Winchester City or Petersfield Town |
| 70 | Weymouth | v | Kidlington or Wantage Town |
| 71 | Dorchester Town | v | Farnborough or Barnstaple Town |
| 72 | Staines Town | v | Basingstoke Town |

The North Leigh 'keeper looks set to save this Cirencester Town header during their First Qualifying Round match. Photo: Peter Barnes.

Goal mouth action during the Second Qualifying Round tie between Evesham United and Spennymoor Town. Photo: Peter Barnes.

# THE FA VASE 2015-16

The 'Cooks' celebrate their equaliser as Jack Bowen's effort is over the line, albeit in the 'keeper's hands. A late winner saw Cogenhoe United through 3-2 against Leighton Town in the First Qualifying Round. Photo: Gordon Whittington.

## FIRST QUALIFYING ROUND

The first round of this national competition at the qualifying stage has 176 ties, so for a large number of clubs, their involvement may be over practically before their season has started. Looking at the names of some of these clubs, they have had their great moments in the competition over the years and some have sampled a Wembley Final.

The North Eastern clubs playing in The Northern League, have dominated the competition in recent years, but to see the famous Whitley Bay (winners four times since 2003) competing in this qualifying round is a bit of a shock.

They beat Willington 6-2 away, but their hosts could also reminisce about a Wembley success, as they beat favourites Bishop Auckland 4-0 in the 1990 FA Amateur Cup Final in front of 88,000. Another clash between famous Northern League clubs saw West Auckland Town win at Crook Town by 2-0.

The fun of a successful run in a national knock out cup is the fact that opposition can be faced from all parts of the country. Obviously in the very early rounds this isn't the case, as the draw is made on a local basis, so sadly many clubs are knocked out by neighbours they know only too well.

Some clubs may have struggled to build a competitive squad by this early stage of the season and we can see some embarrassing results. But others will have been thrilled to have been able to compete in the famous national knock out competition. Even if they have suffered a hammering in their developing years, at least they have played in the famous FA Vase and they are getting valuable experience.

| | |
|---|---|
| Brandon United v Washington | 2-7 |
| Selby Town v Askern | 12-0 |
| Heather St Johns v Rocester | 1-8 |
| Ipswich Wanderers v London Bari | 7-0 |
| Hadleigh United v Eton Manor | 7-0 |
| Holmer Green v Wellington Town | 2-7 |
| Thatcham Town v New College Swindon | 7-0 |
| Tadley Valleva v Woodley United | 6-0 |
| Steyning Town v Wick & Barnham United | 6-2 |
| Wincanton Town v Salisbury FC | 1-8 |
| Andover Town v Fawley | 7-2 |
| Ivybridge Town v Porthleven | 7-0 |

One of the most intriguing results was in Lancashire where Rochdale Town beat Parkgate 6-5 with their winning goal in extra time. The club had been launched as St Gabriels, then changed their name to Castleton Gabriels and since 2008 have played as Rochdale Town. Perhaps they eventually hope to challenge their Football League neighbours.

The Round wasn't completed until thirteen replays had been decided but with the agreement of both clubs, there were some ties that were decided at the first meeting after extra time and a penalty shoot out if necessary.

Irchester United's Sam Dingel lifts the ball over the 'keeper and unfortunately over the bar, in one of the few chances they had during their First Qualifying Round defeat (0-4) to Risborough Rangers. Photo: Gordon Whittington.

## SECOND QUALIFYING ROUND

A huge round of 169 ties obviously sees the Vase ambitions of many clubs from all areas dramatically shattered for another season.

Some famous clubs with reputations in the national cups feature in this round. Surviving to enter the competition proper as usual, are a powerful group from The North East:-,Ashington, South Shields, Durham City, Seaham Red Star, Newcastle Benfield, West Auckland and Whitley Bay are some of the better known names throughout the country, but any clubs emerging from the Northern League will be respected throughout the competition.

Clubs from towns who are already represented by League Clubs include Coventry United, Sunderland RCA and Rochdale Town, all of whom won their ties at home in this round.

Some clubs at this level may not be well known in the national press, but the competition gives a chance to such clubs as Northwich Manchester Villa FC and Black Country Rangers to get their names some publicity and both clubs will feature in the next Round.

After some excitement in the FA Cup, Sporting Khalsa completed a sound 4-0 victory over Wellington FC, but some very one sided games may have proved a little embarrassing with two clubs actually reaching double figures. Witheridge with 10 and West Didsbury & Chorlton scoring 15 goals.

High scores are bound to occur in the early rounds but some famous and much feared names will be in the First Round draw and the ties will become tougher as the rounds are completed

## FIRST ROUND PROPER

The competition proper sees more of the traditional FA Vase challengers drawn against each other, but every year new names emerge to challenge in the 'smaller clubs' wonderful national knock out competition with a special Wembley Final.

Two exciting cup ties were provided by a couple of Northern clubs with nine goal thrillers, as Morpeth Town beat West Didsbury & Chorlton (away) and Handsworth Parramore beat Shildon at home.

The Northern section of the First Round certainly provided entertainment with 88 goals scored in 20 cup ties. Team Northumbria's 4-0 victory over Northern Division Two colleagues Darlington Railway Athletic and Hemsworth MW (Doncaster & District League) 3-2 win at home to West Auckland Town were impressive.

Two replays kept up the goalscoring standards with Black Country Rangers drawing with Coventry Sphinx and Beckenham Town being held by AFC Croydon Athletic, with both games standing at 3-3 after 90 minutes. The final scores were 6-3 in both games with victories to the Coventry and Beckenham clubs!

No doubt the usual favourites will emerge from the North East, but are there any Southern clubs strong enough to challenge? The strength of the new 'Hereford' is unknown but clubs like Norwich United (Eastern Counties), Salisbury and Newport IoW (Wessex League) plus Bodmin and St Austell from The South West Counties are all enjoying good starts to the season.

More traditional Vase battlers always looking forward to their cup ties include Buckland Athletic, Plymouth Parkway, Stotfold, Morpeth Town and Calne. All these clubs are still involved and perhaps we will see some new names battling for that treasured Wembley appearance as the FA Vase becomes more intense.

# FIRST QUALIFYING ROUND

## SATURDAY 5 SEPTEMBER 2015 - WINNERS RECEIVE £600

| No | Home | | Away | Score | Att |
|---|---|---|---|---|---|
| 1 | Garforth Town | v | Albion Sports | 4-1 | 89 |
| 2 | Willington | v | Whitley Bay | 2-6 | 128 |
| 3 | Norton & Stockton Ancients | v | Pickering Town | 2-1 | |
| 4 | Sunderland Ryhope CW | v | Darlington Railway Athletic | 1-4 | |
| 5 | Brandon United | v | Washington | 2-7 | 47 |
| 6 | Silsden | v | Thornaby | 3-1 | 83 |
| 7 | Crook Town | v | West Auckland Town | 0-2 | 146 |
| 8 | Hebburn Town | v | Knaresborough Town | 4-1 | 93 |
| 9 | Seaham Red Star | v | Billingham Town | 3-1 | 85 |
| 10 | Esh Winning | v | Hall Road Rangers | 2-3aet | |
| 11 | Morpeth Town | v | Padiham | 4-1 | 136 |
| 12 | Durham City | v | Northallerton Town | 3-1 | 100 |
| 13 | Billingham Synthonia | v | Alnwick Town | 2-2aet | |
| | Alnwick Town | v | Billingham Synthonia (8/9) | 1-3 | 100 |
| 14 | Ryton & Crawcrook Albion | v | Yorkshire Amateur | 1-2 | 67 |
| 15 | Eccleshill United | v | Heaton Stannington | 2-4 | 75 |
| 16 | Penrith | v | Bridlington Town | 1-2 | 110 |
| 17 | Thackley | v | Whickham | 0-0aet | 67 |
| | Whickham | v | Thackley (8/9) | 2-2aet | 92 |
| | (Whickham won 3-1 on kicks from the penalty mark) | | | | |
| 18 | Birtley Town | v | Chester-Le-Street Town | 0-5 | |
| 19 | Liversedge | v | Team Northumbria | 1-4 | |
| 20 | Brigg Town | v | Westella VIP | 3-4 | 80 |
| 21 | Vauxhall Motors | v | Glasshoughton Welfare | 5-0 | 65 |
| 22 | Staveley MW | v | Cheadle Town | 3-4 | 139 |
| 23 | Handsworth Parramore | v | AFC Liverpool | 1-0 | 105 |
| 24 | West Didsbury & Chorlton | v | Barton Town Old Boys | 2-1 | 82 |
| 25 | Bacup Borough | v | Worsbrough Bridge Athletic | 4-0 | 57 |
| 26 | Rossington Main | v | Pontefract Collieries | 4-2 | 122 |
| 27 | Winterton Rangers | v | St Helens Town | 0-4 | 37 |
| 28 | Bottesford Town | v | Appleby Frodingham | 4-1 | 88 |
| 29 | Hemsworth MW | v | Cammell Laird 1907 | 3-1 | 69 |
| 30 | AFC Blackpool | v | Maltby Main | 0-3 | 44 |
| 31 | Squires Gate | v | Irlam | 2-2aet | 37 |
| | Irlam | v | Squires Gate (8/9) | 1-3 | |
| 32 | Ashton Athletic | v | Atherton Collieries | 0-0aet | 134 |
| | Atherton Collieries | v | Ashton Athletic (7/9) | 3-1 | 190 |
| 33 | Selby Town | v | Askern | 12-0 | 98 |
| 34 | Runcorn Town | v | Litherland Remyca | 4-2 | 67 |
| 35 | Congleton Town | v | Nostell MW | 3-1 | 147 |
| 36 | Rochdale Town | v | Parkgate | 6-5aet | 52 |
| | (at Parkgate FC) | | | | |
| 37 | Ashby Ivanhoe | v | Racing Club Warwick | 0-2 | 131 |
| 38 | AFC Wulfrunians | v | Pershore Town | 2-1 | |
| 39 | Gornal Athletic | v | Littleton | 0-4 | 38 |
| 40 | Paget Rangers | v | Studley | 2-3 | 74 |
| 41 | Stafford Town | v | Wednesfield | 2-0 | 70 |
| 42 | Bewdley Town | v | Bilston Town | 1-2 | 63 |
| 43 | Lutterworth Athletic | v | Pilkington XXX | 0-5 | 68 |
| 44 | Heath Hayes | v | Bromsgrove Sporting | 1-4 | 135 |
| 45 | Wolverhampton Casuals | v | Southam United | 2-1 | |
| 46 | Pegasus Juniors | v | Stourport Swifts | 0-4 | 84 |
| 47 | Lye Town | v | Barnt Green Spartak | 3-0 | |
| 48 | Coventry Copsewood | v | Bardon Hill Sports | 1-4aet | |
| 49 | Wolverhampton SC | v | Hinckley | 0-5 | |
| 50 | Highgate United | v | Tipton Town | 5-0 | 69 |
| 51 | Westfields | v | Atherstone Town | 1-0 | |
| 52 | Cadbury Athletic | v | AFC Bridgnorth | 0-2 | 33 |
| 53 | Shawbury United | v | Nuneaton Griff | 2-3aet | 59 |
| | (at Nuneaton Griff FC) | | | | |
| 54 | Shifnal Town | v | Malvern Town | 1-4 | 69 |
| 55 | Hanley Town | v | Coventry United | 1-3aet | 114 |
| 56 | Dudley Town | v | Sporting Khalsa | 0-3 | 99 |
| 57 | Heather St Johns | v | Rocester | 1-8 | 50 |
| 58 | Aston | v | Black Country Rangers | | |
| | (walkover for Black Country Rangers – Aston removed) | | | | |
| 59 | Alvechurch | v | Lichfield City | 3-1 | |
| 60 | Continental Star | v | Ellistown & Ibstock United (6/9) | 2-3 | 46 |
| 61 | Anstey Nomads | v | Friar Lane & Epworth | 4-2 | 76 |
| 62 | Arnold Town | v | Gedling MW | 2-1 | 79 |
| 63 | Belper United | v | Clifton All Whites | 2-4aet | 58 |
| 64 | Blaby & Whetstone Athletic | v | Retford United | 1-4 | 52 |
| 65 | Shirebrook Town | v | Oakham United | 5-2 | 68 |
| 66 | Eastwood Community | v | Harrowby United | 1-3 | 86 |
| 67 | Borrowash Victoria | v | Kimberley MW | 3-1aet | 50 |
| 68 | Hucknall Town | v | Stapenhill | 4-0 | 109 |
| 69 | Ollerton Town | v | St Andrews | 1-2 | 85 |
| 70 | Quorn | v | Rainworth MW | 3-0 | 105 |
| 71 | Radcliffe Olympic | v | Holbrook Sports | 2-0 | |
| 72 | Shepshed Dynamo | v | Loughborough University | 1-3 | 136 |
| 73 | Leicester Road | v | Harborough Town | 2-0 | 55 |
| 74 | Peterborough Sports | v | Sleaford Town | 2-3aet | |
| 75 | Boston Town | v | Great Yarmouth Town | 2-4 | 65 |
| 76 | St Neots Town Saints | v | Team Bury | 2-1 | 42 |
| 77 | Downham Town | v | Huntingdon Town | 4-1 | 38 |
| 78 | Thetford Town | v | Blackstones | 2-3 | 62 |
| 79 | Ipswich Wanderers | v | London Bari | 7-0 | 119 |
| 80 | Tower Hamlets | v | Whitton United | 1-3 | 47 |
| | (at Whitton United FC) | | | | |
| 81 | Codicote | v | Clapton | 1-4 | |
| | (at Colney Heath FC) | | | | |
| 82 | Sporting Bengal United | v | Burnham Ramblers | 1-1aet | |
| | Burnham Ramblers | v | Sporting Bengal United (8/9) | 2-4 | |
| 83 | Baldock Town | v | St Margaretsbury (4/9) | 3-2 | 63 |
| 84 | Cockfosters | v | Greenhouse Sports | 3-3aet | |
| | Greenhouse Sports | v | Cockfosters (9/9) | 3-2 | |
| 85 | Welwyn Garden City | v | Haverhill Borough | 1-0aet | 105 |
| 86 | Debenham LC | v | Enfield 1893 | 3-1aet | 50 |
| 87 | FC Clacton | v | Stansted | 2-0 | 94 |
| 88 | Hadley | v | Felixstowe & Walton United | 2-1 | 38 |
| 89 | Brantham Athletic | v | Sawbridgeworth Town (6/9) | 1-0 | |
| 90 | Halstead Town | v | Haverhill Rovers | 1-0 | 118 |
| 91 | Hadleigh United | v | Eton Manor | 7-0 | 96 |
| 92 | Long Melford | v | Cornard United | 3-1 | 112 |
| 93 | Long Buckby | v | Spelthorne Sports | 3-1 | |
| 94 | Northampton On Chenecks | v | Sun Postal Sports | 2-1 | |
| 95 | Broadfields United | v | Harpenden Town | 2-4 | |
| 96 | Berkhamsted | v | Woodford United | 4-1 | 78 |
| 97 | Holmer Green | v | Wellingborough Town | 2-7 | 34 |
| 98 | Southall | v | Bedfont & Feltham | 2-1 | |
| 99 | Newport Pagnell Town | v | AFC Kempston Rovers | 0-2aet | |
| 100 | Wellingborough Whitworths | v | Edgware Town | 3-6 | 62 |
| 101 | Langford | v | Bedfont Sports | 0-3 | 40 |
| 102 | Thrapston Town | v | Northampton Sileby Rangers (4/9) | 1-3 | 80 |
| 103 | Hillingdon Borough | v | Potton United | 1-2 | 39 |
| 104 | Ampthill Town | v | London Tigers | 1-2 | |
| 105 | Burton Park Wanderers | v | Tring Athletic | 0-0aet | |
| | Tring Athletic | v | Burton Park Wanderers (8/9) | 4-0 | 107 |
| 106 | New Bradwell St Peter | v | Rushden & Higham United | 2-0aet | |
| 107 | Stotfold | v | Bugbrooke St Michaels | 3-1 | 52 |

Luke Fewsdale of Hollands & Blair tries to take the ball past AFC Croydon Athletic 'keeper Dan Burnett in the Second Qualifying round. Photo: Alan Coomes.

## SECOND ROUND

Extremely wet weather managed to disrupt this round of The FA Vase so to be successful clubs relied on a little luck and hoped to complete their ties on time and on reasonable surfaces.

Results that stood out on the original Second Round Saturday were:

| | | | |
|---|---|---|---|
| Walsall Wood | 4 | Holbeach United | 1 |
| Gorleston | 3 | FC Romania | 4 aet |
| Hertford Town | 3 | Barking | 2 |
| Eastbourne Town | 5 | Greenwich Borough | 4 |
| Buckland Athletic | 5 | Sholing | 2 |
| Bodmin Town | 3 | Melksham Town | 1 |
| Whitley Bay | 1 | Dunston UTS | 2 |
| Welton Rovers | 1 | Plymouth Parkway | 0 |

Some names, well known for their past achievements, are featuring under new ownership and we really cannot know what to expect from them. Hereford beat Houghmond 4-1 and Salisbury won 4-1 at home to AFC St Austell but clubs with consistent form in recent years include:-

Bradford Town who beat Cadbury Heath 6-3 and Runcorn Town with a 3-0 victory over Garforth Town are consistent FA Vase challengers so they are two to watch.

The postponed ties are sometimes badly affected by changes for away clubs' travelling plans and some unlucky clubs had their ties postponed more than once. However, South Shields won at Consett and Hullbridge Sports travelled to beat Norwich United and Tadcaster Albion eventually eliminated Worksop Town.

An awkward round was eventually, closed but these brave clubs were to face even more weather affected conditions in the 32 Third Round ties.

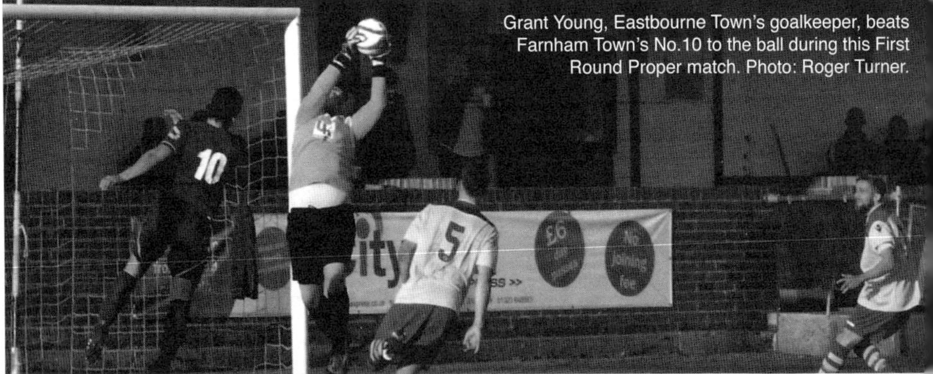

Grant Young, Eastbourne Town's goalkeeper, beats Farnham Town's No.10 to the ball during this First Round Proper match. Photo: Roger Turner.

# FIRST QUALIFYING ROUND

## SATURDAY 5 SEPTEMBER 2015 - WINNERS RECEIVE £600

| | | | | | |
|---|---|---|---|---|---|
| 108 | Hanworth Villa | v | Desborough Town | 1-0aet | 108 |
| 109 | Irchester United | v | Risborough Rangers (6/9) | 0-4 | |
| 110 | Rothwell Corinthians | v | Bedford | 1-0 | |
| 111 | Chertsey Town | v | Tuffley Rovers+ | 5-1 | 52 |
| 112 | Fairford Town | v | Ardley United | 3-0 | 39 |
| 113 | Shrivenham | v | Reading Town | 3-2 | 41 |
| 114 | Royal Wootton Bassett Town | v | Binfield | 1-1aet | 83 |
| | Binfield | v | Royal Wootton Bassett Town (7/9) | 3-4 | 122 |
| 115 | Bracknell Town | v | Hook Norton | 1-0 | 59 |
| 116 | Thatcham Town | v | New College Swindon | 7-0 | 129 |
| 117 | Abbey Rangers | v | Holyport | 0-0aet | 43 |
| | Holyport | v | Abbey Rangers (8/9) | 1-4 | |
| 118 | Oxford City Nomads | v | Buckingham Town (6/9) | 4-0 | 87 |
| 119 | Cheltenham Saracens | v | Brimscombe & Thrupp | 1-2 | 63 |
| 120 | Lydney Town | v | Abingdon United | 5-0 | 91 |
| 121 | Frimley Green | v | Fleet Spurs | 3-2 | 40 |
| 122 | Tadley Calleva | v | Woodley United | 7-0 | 71 |
| 123 | Hartley Wintney | v | Longlevens | 3-2 | 98 |
| 124 | Carterton | v | Chinnor | 6-0 | |
| 125 | Ash United | v | Windsor | 0-2 | 71 |
| 126 | Horsham | v | Epsom & Ewell (6/9) | 3-0 | 184 |
| 127 | Horsham YMCA | v | FC Elmstead | 3-2 | 55 |
| 128 | Deal Town | v | Dorking | 1-0 | 80 |
| 129 | Southwick | v | Lordswood | 0-3 | |
| 130 | Bexhill United | v | AFC Croydon Athletic | 0-2 | 67 |
| | (at Hailsham Town FC) | | | | |
| 31 | Raynes Park Vale | v | Croydon | 2-4 | 35 |
| 32 | Banstead Athletic | v | Seven Acre & Sidcup | 2-2aet | 55 |
| | Seven Acre & Sidcup | v | Banstead Athletic (9/9) | 1-2 | |
| 33 | Corinthian | v | Chessington & Hook United | 4-1 | 27 |
| 34 | Haywards Heath Town | v | Little Common | 2-1 | 76 |
| 35 | Chichester City | v | Erith Town | 0-2 | 58 |
| 36 | Worthing United | v | East Preston (6/9) | 2-1 | 1008 |
| 37 | Canterbury City | v | Ringmer | 1-0 | |
| | (at Ramsgate FC) | | | | |
| 38 | Cobham | v | Shoreham | 2-1aet | |
| 39 | Sevenoaks Town | v | Horley Town | 5-0 | 57 |
| 40 | Glebe | v | Eastbourne United | | |
| | (walkover for Eastbourne United – Glebe not accepted into the Competition) | | | | |
| 41 | AFC Uckfield Town | v | Beckenham Town | 1-5 | 60 |

| | | | | | |
|---|---|---|---|---|---|
| 142 | Steyning Town | v | Wick & Barnham United | 6-2 | 110 |
| 143 | Crawley Down Gatwick | v | Fisher | 1-3 | 61 |
| 144 | Mile Oak | v | Seaford Town | 3-1 | 46 |
| 145 | Loxwood | v | Crowborough Athletic | 2-0 | 53 |
| 146 | Newhaven | v | Guildford City | 1-0 | 74 |
| 147 | Bridon Ropes | v | Holmesdale | 1-1aet | |
| | Holmesdale | v | Bridon Ropes (9/9) | 1-3 | |
| 148 | Andover New Street | v | Bitton | 1-4 | 26 |
| 149 | Wincanton Town | v | Salisbury | 1-8 | 625 |
| | (at Salisbury FC) | | | | |
| 150 | Devizes Town | v | Shaftesbury Town | 0-2 | 68 |
| 151 | Team Solent | v | Christchurch | 4-1aet | |
| 152 | Alresford Town | v | Blackfield & Langley | 0-5 | 54 |
| 153 | Oldland Abbotonians | v | Downton | 3-0 | |
| 154 | Corsham Town | v | Westbury United | 5-1 | |
| 155 | Andover Town | v | Fawley | 7-2 | 92 |
| 156 | Bournemouth | v | Brockenhurst | 4-3 | 50 |
| 157 | East Cowes Victoria Athletic | v | Lymington Town | 0-9 | 39 |
| 158 | Whitchurch United | v | Hamworthy United | 3-0 | 28 |
| 159 | Cadbury Heath | v | Amesbury Town | 3-0 | 53 |
| 160 | Winterbourne United | v | Horndean | 4-4aet | 45 |
| | Horndean | v | Winterbourne United (8/9) | 3-0 | |
| 161 | Cribbs | v | Hallen | 1-2aet | 68 |
| 162 | Warminster Town | v | Pewsey Vale | 3-0 | 96 |
| 163 | Verwood Town | v | Fareham Town | 3-2aet | |
| 164 | Sherborne Town | v | Bemerton Heath Harlequins | 2-3 | 58 |
| 165 | Roman Glass St George | v | Calne Town (4/9) | 3-3aet | 65 |
| | Calne Town | v | Roman Glass St George (9/9) | 2-0aet | 42 |
| 166 | Witheridge | v | Cullompton Rangers | 1-0 | 73 |
| 167 | Falmouth Town | v | Newquay | 0-1 | 81 |
| 168 | Plymouth Parkway | v | Street | 5-1 | 134 |
| 169 | Ivybridge Town | v | Porthleven | 7-0 | 101 |
| 170 | Budleigh Salterton | v | Welton Rovers | 3-5 | 80 |
| 171 | Shepton Mallet | v | Cheddar | 3-1 | 98 |
| 172 | Ashton & Backwell United | v | Brislington | 2-1aet | 60 |
| 173 | St Blazey | v | Bovey Tracey | 2-0 | |
| 174 | Saltash United | v | Exmouth Town | 3-4aet | 49 |
| 175 | Portishead Town | v | Elburton Villa | 2-0 | 44 |
| 176 | Camelford | v | Clevedon Town | 2-1 | 51 |

# SECOND QUALIFYING ROUND

## SATURDAY 3 OCTOBER 2015 - WINNERS RECEIVE £800

| | | | | | |
|---|---|---|---|---|---|
| | Easington Colliery | v | Ashington | 1-3 | |
| | South Shields | v | Washington | 2-1 | 462 |
| | Tow Law Town | v | Stokesley | 0-3 | 60 |
| | Chester-Le-Street Town | v | Heaton Stannington | 4-3aet | 131 |
| | Darlington Railway Athletic | v | Hall Road Rangers | 3-1 | 42 |
| | Billingham Synthonia | v | Morpeth Town | 0-1 | 123 |
| | Sunderland RCA | v | Bridlington Town | 3-2aet | 84 |
| | Silsden | v | Daisy Hill | 6-0 | 74 |
| | Whickham | v | Garforth Town | 0-1 | 60 |
| 0 | Bedlington Terriers | v | Durham City | 2-4aet | |
| | Jarrow Roofing Boldon CA | v | Seaham Red Star | 0-1 | |
| 2 | Hebburn Town | v | Yorkshire Amateur | 3-1 | 53 |
| 3 | Bishop Auckland | v | Holker Old Boys (2/10) | 7-1 | 251 |
| 4 | Norton & Stockton Ancients | v | Newcastle Benfield | 1-4 | |
| 5 | AFC Darwen | v | West Auckland Town | 2-4aet | 116 |
| 6 | Whitley Bay | v | West Allotment Celtic | 5-1 | 312 |
| 7 | Newton Aycliffe | v | Barnoldswick Town | 3-0 | 63 |

| | | | | | |
|---|---|---|---|---|---|
| 18 | Nelson | v | Team Northumbria | 1-3aet | 100 |
| 19 | Runcorn Town | v | Barnton | 4-1 | 91 |
| 20 | Vauxhall Motors | v | Abbey Hey | 2-3 | 51 |
| 21 | AFC Emley | v | Congleton Town | 2-4 | 139 |
| 22 | Dronfield Town | v | Bootle | 2-1 | 63 |
| 23 | Handsworth Parramore | v | Cheadle Town | 3-2 | 86 |
| 24 | Armthorpe Welfare | v | Ashton Town | 3-2 | 41 |
| 25 | Rochdale Town | v | St Helens Town | 6-2 | 60 |
| 26 | Westella VIP | v | Selby Town | 1-3 | 73 |
| 27 | Bacup Borough | v | Hemsworth MW | 0-1 | 69 |
| 28 | Atherton Collieries | v | Atherton LR (2/10) | 6-2 | 429 |
| 29 | West Didsbury & Chorlton | v | Dinnington Town | 15-1 | 84 |
| 30 | Squires Gate | v | Winsford United | 0-2 | 36 |
| 31 | Northwich Manchester Villa | v | Rossington Main | 3-1 | 56 |
| | (at Irlam FC) | | | | |
| 32 | Penistone Church | v | Athersley Recreation | 0-2 | 184 |
| 33 | Maltby Main | v | Bottesford Town | 2-0 | |

## THIRD ROUND

With eleven of the thirty two ties postponed, the clubs who won their Vase ties on Saturday 12th December were certainly provided with a pre Christmas celebration.

Hereford and Salisbury received most national publicity, thanks to their disrupted previous years, but both won. Hereford with a 2-0 victory at home to Brocton and Salisbury a fine 5-1 triumph away to Highworth Town.

The most substantial victories were enjoyed by Bristol Manor Farm, 7-1 at home to Hengrove Athletic, while Ashford United and Leicester Nirvana both celebrated 5-1 away victories, at Lordswood and St Andrews respectively.

The North of England suffered most postponements but regular favourites North Shields eventually beat Ashington 3-0, South Shields won away to Consett and Team Northumbria travelled to beat Guisborough Town 2-1.

With bad weather, postponements and replays it was difficult to focus on the real favourites and the 16 ties in the Fourth Round were also given staggered match dates which created an obvious unfortunate disruption to a famous and very important competition.

FA Vase 3rd Round ties were contested on fourteen different days following the unpleasant weather. Much of the fun had gone out of the competition as the doubt over fixtures and the state of the pitches made results a lottery.

The best results were achieved by Sunderland RDA who beat Tadcaster Albion 4-0, Camberley Town who beat Ascot United 4-1 in a local derby and Newport (I.o.W) who won 4-2 at home to Tadley Calleva
Six ties were called off on 5th January but the holders had survived 1-0 away to Runcorn Town the day before.

The round was finally completed when South Shields and Morpeth Town drew 3-3 on Wednesday 20th January, and having agreed not to contest a replay, Morpeth survived after penalties

The North East, the home of most FA Vase favourites had suffered most from the weather with Morpeth Town the last club to qualify for the Fourth Round.

## FOURTH ROUND

Having survived an horrendous fixture programme in the previous round, the survivors were faced with equally bad weather which threatened the fixtures throughout the Round.

The sixteen matches were completely decimated by the weather with just four ties completed on the original date of 9th January. The'new Salisbury' won a the 'new Dunstable' as a Sunday fixture while Cleethorps Town, Nuneaton Griff and Camberley Tow had survived as winners on the original Saturday programme.

Eastbourne Town' Kenny Pogue an Greenwich Borough' Patrick O'Conno tussle for the ba during this Secon Round Proper tie Photo: Alan Coomes

# SECOND QUALIFYING ROUND

## SATURDAY 3 OCTOBER 2015 - WINNERS RECEIVE £800

| No | Home | | Away | Score | Att |
|---|---|---|---|---|---|
| 34 | Hallam | v | Harworth Colliery+ | 4-3 | 72 |
| 35 | Alsager Town | v | Maine Road | 3-1 | 81 |
| 36 | Bardon Hill Sports | v | Hereford | 0-1 | |
| 37 | Bilston Town | v | AFC Wulfrunians | 1-3 | 146 |
| 38 | Hinckley | v | Bromyard Town | 6-0 | 198 |
| 39 | Ellesmere Rangers | v | Malvern Town | 2-1 | 43 |
| 40 | Boldmere St Michaels | v | Stafford Town | 4-0 | |
| 41 | Coventry United | v | Studley (4/10) | 2-0 | 113 |
| 42 | Uttoxeter Town | v | Bolehall Swifts | 4-3aet | 70 |
| 43 | Stone Old Alleynians | v | Racing Club Warwick | 0-4 | |
| 44 | Sporting Khalsa | v | Wellington | 4-0 | 39 |
| 45 | Pilkington XXX | v | Alvechurch | 0-4 | |
| 46 | Stourport Swifts | v | Black Country Rangers | 1-3 | 99 |
| 47 | Eccleshall | v | Haughmond+ | 0-0aet | 63 |
| | (Haughmond won 4-1 on kicks from the penalty mark) | | | | |
| 48 | Highgate United | v | Wolverhampton Casuals | 5-2 | |
| 49 | AFC Bridgnorth | v | Willenhall Town | 5-2 | |
| 50 | Westfields | v | Littleton | 3-2 | 130 |
| 51 | Rocester | v | Kirby Muxloe | 5-1 | |
| 52 | Coton Green | v | Nuneaton Griff+ | 1-8 | |
| 53 | Bromsgrove Sporting | v | Dudley Sports | 3-1 | 261 |
| 54 | Lye Town | v | Cradley Town | 2-4 | 129 |
| 55 | Coventry Sphinx | v | Ellistown & Ibstock United | 4-3 | 67 |
| 56 | Retford United | v | Loughborough University | 0-2 | 72 |
| 57 | Anstey Nomads | v | Clifton All Whites | 2-0 | 86 |
| 58 | Holwell Sports | v | Dunkirk | 1-3 | 65 |
| 59 | Radford | v | South Normanton Athletic | 2-1 | 52 |
| 60 | Teversal | v | Radcliffe Olympic | 1-3 | 42 |
| 61 | Oadby Town | v | Borrowash Victoria | 1-4 | |
| 62 | Harrowby United | v | Leicester Road | 1-0 | 95 |
| 63 | Greenwood Meadows | v | Clipstone Welfare | 1-4 | 30 |
| 64 | Aylestone Park | v | St Andrews | 3-5 | 65 |
| 65 | Mickleover Royals | v | Shirebrook Town | | |
| | (walkover for Shirebrook Town – Mickleover Royals withdrawn) | | | | |
| 66 | Blidworth Welfare | v | Graham St Prims | 2-1 | |
| 67 | Lincoln Moorlands Railway | v | Pinxton | 1-4 | 35 |
| 68 | Barrow Town | v | Quorn | 0-3 | |
| 69 | Arnold Town | v | Hucknall Town | 0-2 | 134 |
| 70 | Blackstones | v | Peterborough Northern Star | 1-0aet | |
| 71 | Great Yarmouth Town | v | Deeping Rangers | 1-0aet | 104 |
| 72 | Mildenhall Town | v | St Neots Town Saints | 7-0 | 109 |
| 73 | Swaffham Town | v | Bourne Town | 2-1 | 66 |
| 74 | Gorleston | v | Walsham Le Willows | 3-2 | 112 |
| 75 | Wisbech St Mary | v | Diss Town | 1-3aet | 144 |
| 76 | Ely City | v | Newmarket Town | 1-2 | 103 |
| 77 | Downham Town | v | Sleaford Town | 0-2 | 65 |
| 78 | Eynesbury Rovers | v | Fakenham Town | 3-1 | 49 |
| 79 | Sporting Bengal United | v | Halstead Town | 4-0 | |
| 80 | Ipswich Wanderers | v | Clapton | 2-0 | 154 |
| 81 | Takeley | v | Hoddesdon Town | 1-1aet | |
| | Hoddesdon Town | v | Takeley (20/10) | 2-0 | |
| 82 | Woodbridge Town | v | Ilford | 2-3 | 74 |
| 83 | Brimsdown | v | Brantham Athletic+ | 2-4 | 60 |
| | (at Brantham Athletic FC) | | | | |
| 84 | Waltham Forest | v | Welwyn Garden City | 2-5 | |
| 85 | Greenhouse Sports | v | Hadleigh United | 3-0 | 42 |
| 86 | Stowmarket Town | v | Hertford Town | 1-4 | 105 |
| 87 | Newbury Forest | v | FC Clacton | 0-7 | 61 |
| 88 | FC Romania | v | Baldock Town+ | 2-1 | |
| 89 | FC Broxbourne Borough | v | Long Melford | 3-1 | 62 |
| 90 | Wivenhoe Town | v | Basildon United | 0-1 | 66 |
| 91 | Southend Manor | v | Hadley | 1-1aet | |
| | Hadley | v | Southend Manor (8/10) | 3-2 | |
| 92 | Whitton United | v | Debenham LC | 2-1aet | 55 |
| 93 | Raunds Town | v | Wellingborough Town | 1-0 | 71 |
| 94 | Edgware Town | v | Winslow United+ | 6-0 | 67 |
| 95 | AFC Kempston Rovers | v | Long Buckby | 3-0 | |
| | (at Biggleswade Town FC) | | | | |
| 96 | Wembley | v | Potton United | 3-2 | |
| 97 | Rothwell Corinthians | v | Tring Athletic | 3-3aet | |
| | Tring Athletic | v | Rothwell Corinthians (06/10) | 2-1 | 99 |
| 98 | Northampton Sileby Rangers | v | New Bradwell St Peter+ | 7-2 | 36 |
| 99 | Cricklewood Wanderers | v | Risborough Rangers (4/10) | 1-0 | |
| 100 | Hanworth Villa | v | Oxhey Jets | 2-1 | 62 |
| 101 | Southall | v | CB Hounslow United (4/10) | 2-0 | |
| 102 | Berkhamsted | v | Northampton On Chenecks | 2-1 | |
| 103 | London Tigers | v | Crawley Green+ | 4-2aet | |
| 104 | Rayners Lane | v | Stotfold | 1-3 | |
| 105 | Cogenhoe United | v | AFC Hayes | 3-1 | 47 |
| 106 | Bedfont Sports | v | Buckingham Athletic | 4-0 | |
| 107 | Biggleswade United | v | Leverstock Green | 2-1aet | |
| 108 | Northampton Spencer | v | Harpenden Town | 3-2 | |
| 109 | Westfield | v | Carterton | 1-2 | |
| 110 | Frimley Green | v | Thame United | 2-7 | 32 |
| 111 | Henley Town | v | Oxford City Nomads (2/10) | 1-5 | 83 |
| 112 | Alton Town | v | Bracknell Town | 1-1aet | |
| | Bracknell Town | v | Alton Town (06/10) | 0-3 | 81 |
| 113 | Abbey Rangers | v | Tytherington Rocks | 1-1aet | |
| | Tytherington Rocks | v | Abbey Rangers (7/10) | 0-3 | |
| 114 | Fairford Town | v | Badshot Lea | 4-2 | |
| 115 | Chertsey Town | v | Tadley Calleva | 0-2 | 82 |
| 116 | Windsor | v | Royal Wootton Bassett Town | 2-1aet | 106 |
| 117 | Wokingham & Emmbrook | v | Shrivenham | 6-1 | 48 |
| 118 | Hartley Wintney | v | Milton United | 4-1 | 102 |
| 119 | Thatcham Town | v | Brimscombe & Thrupp | 0-2 | |
| 120 | Malmesbury Victoria | v | Farnham Town | 2-2aet | 60 |
| | (Farnham Town won 4-2 on kicks from the penalty mark) | | | | |
| 121 | Knaphill | v | Lydney Town | 3-1 | 41 |
| 122 | Canterbury City | v | Tooting & Mitcham Wanderers+ | 2-0 | 40 |
| 123 | Croydon | v | Horsham YMCA | 2-1 | 63 |
| 124 | Cobham | v | Sutton Common Rovers | 0-3 | |
| 125 | Hailsham Town | v | Fisher | 3-0 | 74 |
| 126 | Hollands & Blair | v | AFC Croydon Athletic | 0-3 | 82 |
| 127 | Mile Oak | v | Lordswood | 2-4 | 47 |
| 128 | St Francis Rangers | v | Meridian | 2-7 | 20 |
| 129 | Selsey | v | Horsham | 0-3 | 152 |
| 130 | Loxwood | v | Arundel | 2-1 | 62 |
| 131 | Banstead Athletic | v | Cray Valley (PM) | 2-6 | 35 |
| 132 | Erith Town | v | Bridon Ropes | 1-2aet | 50 |
| 133 | Oakwood | v | Lancing | 4-9aet | 35 |
| 134 | Sevenoaks Town | v | Haywards Heath Town+ | 3-4aet | 88 |
| 135 | Beckenham Town | v | Redhill | 2-0 | 60 |
| 136 | Eastbourne United | v | Deal Town | 0-3 | 112 |
| 137 | Newhaven | v | Broadbridge Heath | 3-2 | 72 |
| 138 | Rochester United | v | Steyning Town | 0-1 | 60 |
| 139 | Corinthian | v | Lingfield | 4-0 | 41 |
| 140 | Worthing United | v | Epsom Athletic+ | 3-0 | 38 |
| 141 | Sheppey United | v | Gravesham Borough | 0-3 | 126 |
| 142 | Warminster Town | v | Gillingham Town | 0-5 | 116 |
| 143 | Salisbury | v | Folland Sports | 4-1 | 538 |
| 144 | New Milton Town | v | Verwood Town | 3-2 | |
| 145 | Romsey Town | v | Calne Town | 0-2 | 72 |
| 146 | Team Solent | v | Shaftesbury Town | 3-0 | |
| 147 | Laverstock & Ford | v | Cowes Sports | 2-0 | 40 |
| 148 | Bemerton Heath Harlequins | v | Andover Town | 0-3 | |
| 149 | Bitton | v | Hallen | 2-2 | 61 |
| 150 | Oldland Abbotonians | v | Lymington Town | 0-1aet | 34 |
| 151 | Horndean | v | Longwell Green Sports | 1-1aet | |
| | Longwell Green Sports | v | Horndean (06/10) | 1-3 | 61 |
| 152 | Blackfield & Langley | v | Ringwood Town | 6-2 | 64 |
| 153 | Cadbury Heath | v | Almondsbury UWE | 2-1aet | 50 |
| 154 | Swanage Town & Herston | v | Corsham Town | 3-4 | |
| 155 | Chippenham Park | v | Newport (IW) | 0-1 | 47 |
| 156 | Whitchurch United | v | Bournemouth | 6-0 | 52 |

**THE FA VASE**

With no mid week fixtures, the following weekend saw the 'new Hereford' underline their strength with a 6-0 victory over Leicester Nirvana, Dunston UTS and Ashford United survived after extra time and victories were also achieved by Kidlington, Bristol Manor Farm and Hartley Wintney.

In the third week Sunderland RCA,Newton Aycliffe and Bowers & Pitsea all won at home to leave just two Fourth Round ties to be decided. On 30th January, four weeks before the original fixture date Ipswich Wanderers won 3-1 deep in the West Country at Bodmin.

This left Morpeth Town who still hadn't fulfilled their Fourth Round fixture at home to North Shields. Finally on Monday 1st February the FA Vase holders were beaten 2-0 and Morpeth could start planning for their fixture away to Berkhamstead. Surely if they won in the home counties after this massive delay, it could be their year!

## FIFTH ROUND

To the relief of the surviving clubs, all of the eight matches in this round were played over the two weekends on Saturday 30th January and 6th February.

The first week proved to be lucky for the away clubs as only Camberley Town won at home, but at least they did it in style with a 5-0 victory over Newton Aycliffe. Salisbury, Kidlington and Bristol Manor Farm made it a rare success day for the South over the North at this level. They defeated Sunderland RCA, Cleethorps Town and Nuneaton Griff respectively.

In fact it was the away clubs' Round, as Morpeth Town (2-1), Ashford Athletic (3-2) and Hereford (4-1) all triumphed, while Bowers & Pitsea drew away to Ipswich Wanderers before eventually winning the replay.

Morpeth Town had once again been delayed by the weather but they were through to the last eight where they would proudly represent the Northern League.

## SIXTH ROUND - THE QUARTER FINALS

*Midland League* / *Combined Counties League*
Hereford 3 Camberley Town 2
*Bundu 62 (pen), Symons 74 Mills 119* / *Bunyan 21, 70* — *3,329*

*Wessex League* / *Combined Counties League*
Salisbury 3 Ashford Town 0
*O'Keefe 26, 47, Roberts 45* — *1,791*

*Northern League* / *Western League*
Morpeth Town 2 Bristol Manor Farm 0
*Swales 12, Pearson 90* — *718*

*Essex Senior League* / *Hellenic League*
Bowers & Pitsea 3 Kidlington 3
*Hilton 13, Stevens 56, Manor 67* / *Thomas 3, 9, Odhiambo 73* — *370*

Kidlington 0 Bowers & Pitsea 4
*Stevens 24, Wilson 50, Salmon 71, Adams 80* — *545*

Would the 'new' clubs be kept apart in the semi-final draw?

They would probably bring massive support to a Final.

This was considered, but as the two more famous names were actually drawn together, the remaining Northern League representative would of course always be dangerous.

This left Bowers & Pitsea as a definite 'outsider' which presumably gave them the advantage of less pressure.

## SEMI FINALS

Hereford 1 Salisbury 0
*Bundu 49* — *4,68.*

Salisbury 1 Hereford 2
*Walker 18* / *Symons 42, Turnelty 79* — *3,45*

Bowers & Pitsea 2 Morpeth Town 2
*Manor 61, Hilton 90* / *Taylor 10, Chilton 31* — *436*

Morpeth Town 2 Bowers & Pitsea 1
*Taylor 3, Carr 90* / *Manor 39* — *1,25*

Both two legged semi-finals were closely fought with superb attendances at the Salisbury v Hereford battles and both were won by Hereford by a single goal. Hopefully, their superb Vase runs this season will go a long way towards bringing the two famous clubs back to the levels they enjoyed in the past.

Bowers & Pitsea also battled brilliantly against the more experienced and well favoured Northern League representative Morpeth Town whose Vase run had already tested the courage and determination always associated with the northern club.

***Second Qualifying Round continued...***

| | | | | | |
|---|---|---|---|---|---|
| 157 | Sholing | v | US Portsmouth (2/10) | 1-1aet | |
| | US Portsmouth | v | Sholing (5/10) | 0-6 | 52 |
| 158 | Bridport | v | Hythe & Dibden | 5-1 | 75 |
| 159 | Radstock Town | v | Hengrove Athletic+ | 3-3aet | 58 |
| | (Hengrove Athletic won 5-4 on kicks from the penalty mark) | | | | |
| 160 | Shepton Mallet | v | Camelford | 1-2aet | 104 |
| 161 | Exmouth Town | v | Welton Rovers | 0-2 | 88 |
| 162 | Ivybridge Town | v | Barnstaple Town | 1-4 | 92 |
| 163 | Newquay | v | Odd Down+ | 1-1aet | |
| | (Odd Down won 5-4 on kicks from the penalty mark) | | | | |
| 164 | Wadebridge Town | v | Portishead Town | 2-5 | 51 |
| 165 | Crediton United | v | Bishop Sutton+ | 1-2 | 48 |
| 166 | Willand Rovers | v | Plymouth Parkway | 0-2 | |
| 167 | Ashton & Backwell United | v | Torpoint Athletic | 0-2 | 53 |
| 168 | Keynsham Town | v | Wells City | 2-2aet | |
| | Wells City | v | Keynsham Town (06/10) | 2-1aet | |
| 169 | Witheridge | v | St Blazey | 0-1 | 58 |

# FIRST ROUND PROPER

## SATURDAY 31 OCTOBER 2015 - WINNERS RECEIVE £900

| | | | | | |
|---|---|---|---|---|---|
| 1 | West Didsbury & Chorlton | v | Morpeth Town | 4-5 | 123 |
| 2 | Handsworth Parramore | v | Shildon | 5-4aet | |
| 3 | Guisborough Town | v | Armthorpe Welfare | 8-0 | 112 |
| 4 | Atherton Collieries | v | Newcastle Benfield | 2-0 | |
| 5 | Stokesley | v | Maltby Main | 1-4aet | |
| 6 | Silsden | v | Sunderland RCA | 2-4 | 115 |
| 7 | Rochdale Town | v | 1874 Northwich | 2-4 | 142 |
| 8 | Runcorn Linnets | v | Winsford United | 2-1 | 231 |
| 9 | Team Northumbria | v | Darlington RA | 4-0 | |
| 10 | Congleton Town | v | Marske United | 1-5 | 186 |
| 11 | Athersley Recreation | v | Colne+ | 1-5 | 90 |
| 12 | Durham City | v | Seaham Red Star | 0-1 | |
| | (at Consett AFC) | | | | |
| 13 | Dronfield Town | v | Ashington | 2-3aet | 90 |
| 14 | Chester-Le-Street Town | v | Newton Aycliffe | 0-4 | 154 |
| 15 | Selby Town | v | Hallam | 1-2 | 82 |
| 16 | Runcorn Town | v | Abbey Hey | 2-0 | 80 |
| 17 | Hemsworth MW | v | West Auckland Town | 3-2 | 189 |
| 18 | Northwich Manchester Villa | v | Whitley Bay | 1-1aet | 103 |
| | Whitley Bay | v | Northwich Manchester Villa (3/11) | 3-1 | 340 |
| 19 | Garforth Town | v | Hebburn Town | 1-0 | 109 |
| 20 | Bishop Auckland | v | South Shields (30/10) | 1-2 | 844 |
| 21 | Highgate United | v | Radcliffe Olympic | 3-1 | |
| 22 | Loughborough University | v | Uttoxeter Town | 0-0aet | |
| | Uttoxeter Town | v | Loughborough University (4/11) | 3-2 | 230 |
| 23 | Dunkirk | v | Bromsgrove Sporting | 2-1 | 111 |
| 24 | Pinxton | v | Cradley Town | 1-0 | 56 |
| 25 | Rocester | v | Hereford | 0-2 | |
| 26 | Coventry Sphinx | v | Black Country Rangers | 1-1aet | 47 |
| | Black Country Rangers | v | Coventry Sphinx (4/11) | 4-6aet | |
| 27 | Alsager Town | v | Borrowash Victoria | 2-2aet | |
| | (Alsager Town won 5-4 on kicks from the penalty mark) | | | | |
| 28 | Wisbech Town | v | Alvechurch | 0-4 | 221 |
| 29 | Cleethorpes Town | v | Westfields | 2-1 | 106 |
| 30 | Blackstones | v | Haughmond | 2-3aet | |
| 31 | Shirebrook Town | v | Sporting Khalsa | 2-0 | |
| 32 | Radford | v | AFC Bridgnorth | 1-3 | 70 |
| 33 | St Andrews | v | Blidworth Welfare | 3-3aet | 52 |
| | Blidworth Welfare | v | St Andrews (17/11) | 0-2aet | |
| | (3/11 - tie ordered to be replayed, 6-0 - to a conclusion at St Andrews FC) | | | | |
| 34 | Coleshill Town | v | Hucknall Town | 3-0 | 55 |
| 35 | AFC Wulfrunians | v | Harrowby United | 4-2aet | 102 |
| 36 | Racing Club Warwick | v | Ellesmere Rangers | 3-2 | 44 |
| 37 | Nuneaton Griff | v | Anstey Nomads (2.00) | 1-0 | 86 |
| 38 | Quorn | v | Clipstone Welfare | 1-0 | |
| 39 | Boldmere St Michaels | v | Coventry United | 0-2 | 114 |
| 40 | Long Eaton United | v | Hinckley | 2-1aet | |
| 41 | Stotfold | v | Newmarket Town (3/11) | 5-0 | |
| | (31/10 – tie abandoned after 42 mins, 2-1) | | | | |
| 42 | Cricklewood Wanderers | v | Welwyn Garden City | 1-0 | |
| 43 | Diss Town | v | Basildon United | 2-3 | 122 |
| 44 | Barking | v | Tring Athletic | 4-1 | |
| 45 | Bowers & Pitsea | v | Hanworth Villa | 3-2 | 54 |
| 46 | Hadley | v | FC Romania+ | 2-3 | |
| 47 | Northampton Sileby Rangers | v | Wembley | 5-4 | 52 |
| 48 | Brantham Athletic | v | Kirkley & Pakefield | 0-4 | 40 |
| 49 | Gorleston | v | London Tigers+ | 6-3aet | 102 |
| 50 | Ipswich Wanderers | v | Hoddesdon Town | 2-1 | |
| 51 | Berkhamsted | v | Northampton Spencer | 5-1 | 103 |
| 52 | London Colney | v | Great Yarmouth Town | 2-1 | |
| 53 | AFC Dunstable | v | FC Clacton (1/11) | 2-0aet | 181 |
| 54 | Raunds Town | v | Sleaford Town | 0-1 | 34 |
| 55 | Hertford Town | v | Eynesbury Rovers | 4-3 | |
| 56 | Godmanchester Rovers | v | Mildenhall Town | 1-1aet | 128 |
| | Mildenhall Town | v | Godmanchester Rovers (3/11) | 2-1 | 147 |
| 57 | Ilford | v | AFC Kempston Rovers | 0-1 | |
| 58 | Sporting Bengal United | v | Southall | 6-2 | |
| 59 | Swaffham Town | v | FC Broxbourne Borough | 1-2 | 94 |
| 60 | Edgware Town | v | Whitton United | 5-2 | |
| 61 | Cogenhoe United | v | Biggleswade United | 0-2 | 81 |
| | (at Biggleswade United FC) | | | | |
| 62 | Harefield United | v | Greenhouse Sports | 0-3 | |
| 63 | Eastbourne Town | v | Farnham Town | 3-2aet | 156 |
| 64 | Hartley Wintney | v | Wokingham & Emmbrook | 3-1 | 127 |
| 65 | Worthing United | v | Sutton Common Rovers | 0-1 | 53 |
| 66 | Knaphill | v | Cray Valley (PM) | 5-4aet | 89 |
| 67 | Deal Town | v | Oxford City Nomads | 4-2 | 120 |
| 68 | Littlehampton Town | v | Tadley Calleva | 1-2 | 90 |
| 69 | Andover Town | v | Newhaven | 1-2 | |
| 70 | Cove | v | Canterbury City | 0-5 | |
| 71 | Corinthian | v | Pagham | 2-3 | 60 |
| 72 | AFC Croydon Athletic | v | Beckenham Town | 2-2aet | |
| | Beckenham Town | v | AFC Croydon Athletic (4/11) | 6-3aet | |
| 73 | Loxwood | v | Highmoor Ibis | 3-1 | 47 |
| 74 | Haywards Heath Town | v | Alton Town | 1-0 | 115 |
| 75 | Kidlington | v | Ashford Town (Middx) | 2-2aet | 85 |
| | Ashford Town (Middx) | v | Kidlington (3/11) | 1-3 | 85 |
| 76 | Bedfont Sports | v | Carterton+ | 1-4 | |
| 77 | Lancing | v | Camberley Town | 1-2 | |
| 78 | Gravesham Borough | v | Hailsham Town | 0-1 | |
| | (at Hailsham Town FC) | | | | |
| 79 | Windsor | v | Croydon | 3-2 | 116 |
| 80 | Steyning Town | v | Horsham | 1-0aet | 280 |
| 81 | Thame United | v | Bridon Ropes | 4-3 | 91 |
| 82 | Meridian VP | v | Lordswood | 1-4 | |
| 83 | Bristol Manor Farm | v | Bridport | 3-0 | 93 |
| 84 | Plymouth Parkway | v | Blackfield & Langley (14/11) | 6-0 | |
| 85 | Moneyfields | v | Corsham Town | 1-0 | |
| 86 | Witheridge | v | Hallen | 0-1 | 90 |
| 87 | Horndean | v | Barnstaple Town | 1-3 | 85 |
| 88 | Lymington Town | v | Wells City | 2-0 | 71 |
| 89 | Calne Town | v | Salisbury | 2-6 | 303 |
| 90 | Whitchurch United | v | Welton Rovers | 2-2aet | 48 |
| | Welton Rovers | v | Whitchurch United (3/11) | 4-0 | 68 |
| 91 | Team Solent | v | Cadbury Heath | 2-3 | |
| 92 | Odd Down | v | Camelford+ | 2-1 | 44 |
| 93 | Portishead Town | v | Newport (IW) | 1-3 | 58 |
| 94 | AFC Portchester | v | Abbey Rangers | 1-2 | 189 |
| 95 | Gillingham Town | v | Hengrove Athletic+ | 0-0aet | 66 |
| | (Hengrove Athletic won 5-4 on kicks from the penalty mark) | | | | |
| 96 | New Milton Town | v | Buckland Athletic | 0-5 | 59 |
| 97 | Sholing | v | Laverstock & Ford | 3-1 | 123 |
| 98 | Bishop Sutton | v | Torpoint Athletic | 0-3 | 44 |
| 99 | Fairford Town | v | Brimscombe & Thrupp | 0-1 | 81 |

# SECOND ROUND PROPER

## SATURDAY 21 NOVEMBER 2015 - WINNERS RECEIVE £1,000

| | | | | | |
|---|---|---|---|---|---|
| 1 | Runcorn Town | v | Garforth Town | 3-0 | |
| 2 | North Shields | v | Ashington (25/11) | 3-0 | 464 |
| 3 | Atherton Collieries | v | Chadderton (23/11) | 3-0 | 128 |
| 4 | Morpeth Town | v | 1874 Northwich | | |
| | (walkover for Morpeth Town – 1874 Northwich unable to fulfil fixture – 25/11) | | | | |
| 5 | Colne | v | Newton Aycliffe | 3-5aet | 216 |
| 6 | Seaham Red Star | v | Maltby Main | 3-1 | |
| 7 | Handsworth Parramore | v | Hallam | 3-2 | 114 |
| 8 | Hemsworth MW | v | Sunderland RCA | 1-5 | 209 |
| 9 | Consett | v | South Shields (24/11) | 0-1aet | |
| 10 | Whitley Bay | v | Dunston UTS | 1-2 | 395 |
| 11 | Marske United | v | Runcorn Linnets (24/11) | 6-2 | 205 |
| 12 | Tadcaster Albion | v | Worksop Town (2/12) | 4-1 | 307 |
| 13 | Guisborough Town | v | Team Northumbria (25/11) | 1-2aet | 133 |
| 14 | AFC Mansfield | v | Alsager Town | 1-1aet | |
| | Alsager Town | v | AFC Mansfield (24/11) | 3-1 | 95 |
| 15 | Walsall Wood | v | Holbeach United | 4-1 | |
| 16 | AFC Bridgnorth | v | Alvechurch | 1-2 | 79 |
| 17 | Coventry Sphinx | v | Brocton | 2-3 | 54 |
| 18 | Coventry United | v | Uttoxeter Town (22/11) | 1-2 | 188 |
| 19 | Coleshill Town | v | Dunkirk | 4-2 | 57 |
| 20 | Hereford | v | Haughmond | 4-1 | 2170 |
| 21 | Long Eaton United | v | Pinxton | 2-3 | 96 |
| 22 | Heanor Town | v | Leicester Nirvana | 1-3 | 156 |
| 23 | Cleethorpes Town | v | Racing Club Warwick | 2-0 | 116 |
| 24 | Quorn | v | AFC Wulfunians | 1-2 | 99 |
| 25 | Nuneaton Griff | v | Highgate United | 1-1aet | |
| | Highgate United | v | Nuneaton Griff (1/12) | 2-4 | |
| | (at Coleshill Town FC) | | | | |
| 26 | St Andrews | v | Shirebrook Town | 4-0 | 88 |
| 27 | Stotfold | v | AFC Dunstable | 1-3 | 83 |
| 28 | Bowers & Pitsea | v | Flackwell Heath | 3-2 | 71 |
| 29 | Yaxley | v | London Colney | 3-2 | |
| 30 | Sporting Bengal United | v | Sleaford Town | 1-3aet | |
| 31 | Gorleston | v | FC Romania | 3-4aet | 110 |
| 32 | Ipswich Wanderers | v | Cricklewood Wanderers | 1-0 | |
| 33 | FC Broxbourne Borough | v | Greenhouse Sports (26/11) | 2-1aet | 39 |
| 34 | Norwich United | v | Hullbridge Sports (24/11) | 0-1aet | |
| 35 | Hertford Town | v | Barking | 3-2 | 202 |
| 36 | Biggleswade United | v | Saffron Walden Town | 1-3 | 116 |
| 37 | Kirkley & Pakefield | v | Edgware Town | 1-2 | |
| 38 | Basildon United | v | Northampton Sileby Rangers | 7-1 | 43 |
| 39 | Stanway Rovers | v | Mildenhall Town | 2-1 | |
| 40 | Berkhamsted | v | AFC Kempston Rovers | 3-1 | 116 |
| 41 | Sutton Common Rovers | v | Beckenham Town (20/11) | 3-2 | 123 |
| 42 | Knaphill | v | Tunbridge Wells | 3-0 | 154 |
| 43 | Newhaven | v | Camberley Town | 1-2 | |
| 44 | Ashford United | v | Steyning Town | 2-1 | |
| 45 | Eastbourne Town | v | Greenwich Borough | 5-4 | |
| 46 | Pagham | v | Thame United | 0-3 | 71 |
| 47 | Lordswood | v | Carterton | 4-1 | 46 |
| 48 | Hailsham Town | v | Ascot United | 1-4 | 75 |
| 49 | Canterbury City | v | Erith & Belvedere (22/11) | 3-2 | 70 |
| 50 | Tadley Calleva | v | Haywards Heath Town | 4-0 | 105 |
| 51 | Kidlington | v | Deal Town | 7-0 | 71 |
| 52 | Colliers Wood United | v | Loxwood | 2-0 | |
| 53 | Hartley Wintney | v | Windsor | 3-1 | 146 |
| 54 | Hallen | v | Moneyfields | 0-1 | 52 |
| 55 | Highworth Town | v | Odd Down | 2-1 | 94 |
| 56 | Salisbury | v | AFC St Austell | 4-0 | 854 |
| 57 | Bradford Town | v | Cadbury Heath | 6-3 | 81 |
| 58 | Buckland Athletic | v | Sholing | 2-1aet | |
| 59 | Welton Rovers | v | Plymouth Parkway | 1-0 | |
| 60 | Newport (IW) | v | Abbey Rangers | 3-1 | |
| 61 | Bodmin Town | v | Melksham Town | 3-1 | 147 |
| 62 | Bristol Manor Farm | v | Lymington Town | 2-1 | 79 |
| 63 | Hengrove Athletic | v | Barnstaple Town | 2-1 | 42 |
| 64 | Brimscombe & Thrupp | v | Torpoint Athletic | 3-2 | |

+ - penalties agreed, no replay

# THIRD ROUND PROPER

## SATURDAY 12 DECEMBER 2015 - WINNERS RECEIVE £1,300

| | | | | | |
|---|---|---|---|---|---|
| 1 | Marske United | v | Team Northumbria (9/1) | 2-1 | 193 |
| | (at Team Northumbria FC) | | | | |
| 2 | Sunderland RCA | v | Tadcaster Albion (15/12) | 4-0 | 165 |
| 3 | Newton Aycliffe | v | Atherton Collieries (12/1) | 1-0 | 127 |
| | (at Durham City FC) | | | | |
| 4 | South Shields | v | Morpeth Town+ (20/1) | 3-3aet | 359 |
| | (Morpeth Town won 10-9 on kicks from the penalty mark) | | | | |
| 5 | North Shields | v | Runcorn Town (16/12) | 1-1aet | 346 |
| | Runcorn Town | v | North Shields (4/1) | 0-1 | 178 |
| 6 | Dunston UTS | v | Seaham Red Star (9/1) | 1-0 | 207 |
| | (at Consett AFC) | | | | |
| 7 | Alsager Town | v | AFC Wulfunians | 0-2 | 132 |
| 8 | St Andrews | v | Leicester Nirvana | 1-5 | 153 |
| 9 | Handsworth Parramore | v | Cleethorpes Town (15/12) | 1-2 | 101 |
| 10 | Pinxton | v | Nuneaton Griff (17/12) | 3-4 | |
| 11 | Walsall Wood | v | Alvechurch | 0-3 | |
| 12 | Uttoxeter Town | v | Coleshill Town (16/12) | 3-4 | |
| 13 | Hereford | v | Brocton | 2-0 | 2025 |
| 14 | Saffron Walden Town | v | Berkhamsted | 2-3 | |
| 15 | FC Broxbourne Borough | v | Bowers & Pitsea+ (12/1) | 1-3 | |
| | (at Harlow Town FC) | | | | |
| 16 | Hullbridge Sports | v | Stanway Rovers | 2-0 | 89 |
| 17 | AFC Dunstable | v | Basildon United | 4-0 | 87 |
| 18 | Edgware Town | v | Ipswich Wanderers | 0-3 | 137 |
| 19 | Yaxley | v | Sleaford Town | 3-4aet | |
| 20 | Hertford Town | v | FC Romania | 0-2 | 231 |
| 21 | Colliers Wood United | v | Hartley Wintney | 1-3 | |
| 22 | Thame United | v | Kidlington | 1-2 | 132 |
| 23 | Ascot United | v | Camberley Town | 0-0aet | 240 |
| | Camberley Town | v | Ascot United (15/12) | 4-1 | |
| 24 | Lordswood | v | Ashford United | 1-5 | 90 |
| 25 | Eastbourne Town | v | Sutton Common Rovers | 2-3 | |
| 26 | Tadley Calleva | v | Newport (IW) | 2-2aet | |
| | Newport (IW) | v | Tadley Calleva (19/12) | 4-2aet | |
| 27 | Canterbury City | v | Knaphill | 1-3 | 81 |
| 28 | Moneyfields | v | Brimscombe & Thrupp | 0-0aet | |
| | Brimscombe & Thrupp | v | Moneyfields (29/12) | 0-2 | 152 |
| 29 | Buckland Athletic | v | Bradford Town | 1-2 | 149 |
| 30 | Highworth Town | v | Salisbury | 1-5 | 357 |
| 31 | Welton Rovers | v | Bodmin Town (12/1) | 0-2 | 117 |
| 32 | Bristol Manor Farm | v | Hengrove Athletic | 7-1 | 131 |

Action from the Second Round Proper match between Brimscombe & Thrupp and Torpoint Athletic. Photo: Peter Barnes.

## FOURTH ROUND PROPER

### SATURDAY 9 JANUARY 2016 - WINNERS RECEIVE £2,000

| No | Home | | Away | Score | Att |
|---|---|---|---|---|---|
| 1 | Cleethorpes Town | v | Alvechurch | 2-1 | 252 |
| 2 | Hereford | v | Leicester Nirvana (16/1) | 6-0 | 2842 |
| | (9/1 - tie abandoned after 45 mins, 3-1) | | | | |
| 3 | Morpeth Town | v | North Shields+ (1/2) | 2-0 | 479 |
| | (at North Shields FC) | | | | |
| 4 | Coleshill Town | v | Dunston UTS (16/1) | 1-3aet | 223 |
| 5 | AFC Wulfrunians | v | Nuneaton Griff | 2-3 | |
| 6 | Sunderland RCA | v | Sleaford Town (23/1) | 3-2 | 109 |
| 7 | Newton Aycliffe | v | Marske United (23/1) | 2-0 | 227 |
| 8 | Bowers & Pitsea | v | Sutton Common Rovers (23/1) | 3-0 | 121 |
| 9 | Kidlington | v | Knaphill (16/1) | 3-2 | 216 |
| 10 | Newport (IW) | v | Ashford United (16/1) | 1-2aet | |
| 11 | Moneyfields | v | Bristol Manor Farm (16/1) | 0-2 | 135 |
| 12 | FC Romania | v | Camberley Town | 1-2 | |
| 13 | AFC Dunstable | v | Salisbury (10/1) | 0-3 | 512 |
| 14 | Berkhamsted | v | Hullbridge Sports | 4-2 | 256 |
| 15 | Hartley & Wintney | v | Bradford Town (16/1) | 3-1 | 241 |
| 16 | Bodmin Town | v | Ipswich Wanderers+ (30/1) | 1-3 | 282 |

## FIFTH ROUND PROPER

### SATURDAY 30 JANUARY 2016 - WINNERS RECEIVE £2,500

| No | Home | | Away | Score | Att |
|---|---|---|---|---|---|
| 1 | Ipswich Wanderers | v | Bowers & Pitsea (6/2) | 1-1aet | |
| | Bowers & Pitsea | v | Ipswich Wanderers (17/2) | 2-1aet | 321 |
| | (at Canvey Island FC) | | | | |
| 2 | Sunderland RCA | v | Bristol Manor Farm | 2-3 | 329 |
| 3 | Camberley Town | v | Newton Aycliffe | 5-0 | 460 |
| 4 | Berkhamsted | v | Morpeth Town (6/2) | 1-2 | 327 |
| 5 | Cleethorpes Town | v | Kidlington | 1-2 | 274 |
| 6 | Nuneaton Griff | v | Salisbury | 0-3 | 870 |
| 7 | Ashford United | v | Dunston UTS | 1-1aet | 636 |
| | Dunston UTS | v | Ashford United (6/2) | 2-3 | 320 |
| 8 | Hartley Wintney | v | Hereford (6/2) | 1-4 | |

## SIXTH ROUND PROPER

### SATURDAY 20 FEBRUARY 2016 - WINNERS RECEIVE £4,500

| No | Home | | Away | Score | Att |
|---|---|---|---|---|---|
| 1 | Hereford | v | Camberley Town | 3-2aet | 3329 |
| 2 | Salisbury | v | Ashford United | 3-0 | 1797 |
| 3 | Morpeth Town | v | Bristol Manor Farm (27/2) | 2-0 | 718 |
| 4 | Bowers & Pitsea | v | Kidlington | 3-3aet | 370 |
| | Kidlington | v | Bowers & Pitsea (27/2) | 0-4 | 545 |

## SEMI FINALS

### 1ST LEG SATURDAY 16 MARCH / 2ND LEG SATURDAY 19 MARCH 2016 - WINNERS RECEIVE £6,000

| Home | | Away | Score | Att |
|---|---|---|---|---|
| Hereford | v | Salisbury | 1-0 | 4683 |
| Salisbury | v | Hereford | 1-2 | 3450 |
| Hereford through 3-1 on aggregate. | | | | 8133 |
| Bowers & Pitsea | v | Morpeth Town | 2-2 | 426 |
| Morpeth Town | v | Bowers & Pitsea | 2-1 | 1256 |
| Morpeth Town through 4-3 on aggregate. | | | | 1682 |

# THE FINAL...

## HEREFORD 1
*(Purdie 2)*

## MORPETH TOWN 4
*(Swailes 34, Carr 47, Taylor 59, Bell 92)*

**Wembley Stadium Att: 46,781***

**combined Trophy/Vase attendance*

Seven times in the last eight seasons a Northern League team has now won the Vase, a remarkable record. A small number of supporters moan that this is because most Northern League teams do not accept promotion to the next level in the pyramid but there are few gripes or jealousy about this from the real non-league enthusiasts who recognise the obstacles, chiefly concerning finance and player availability, faced by any teams from that area should they take promotion and confront the consequent increased cost of travel and likely exodus of players not able or wanting to devote hours to sitting on a motorway. Even so Northern League victory was not anticipated in this fixture against a team who had won their league comfortably and appear destined for eventual return much further up the pyramid. What a turn up for the betting fraternity the result was. Apparently the odds were fantastically so weighted Hereford's way that you could have gained 16 to 1 on a Morpeth victory, an achievement akin to Leicester City winning the Premier League. A count up of supporters present was said to reveal that Hereford fans outnumbered their North Eastern opponents by 6 to 1, 24 thousand versus 4 thousand, the disparity certainly not completely explained by the difference in the distances supporters had needed to travel to access the stadium.

The Morpeth Town goalscorers line up with the FA Vase. Photo: Roger Turner.

THE SQUADS

| HEREFORD | MORPETH TOWN |
|---|---|
| Martin Horsell | Karl Dryden |
| Jimmy Oates | Stephen Forster |
| Joel Edwards | James Novak |
| Rob Purdie | Ben Sayer |
| Ryan Green | Chris Swailes |
| Aaron Birch | Michael Hall |
| Pablo Haysham | Sean Taylor (sub 78) |
| Mike Symons | Keith Graydon |
| Jamie Willets (sub 70) | Luke Carr (sub 88) |
| Joe Tumelty (sub 55) | Michael Chilton (sub 69) |
| Sirdic Grant | Jordan Fry |
| **Substitutes** | **Substitutes** |
| Mustapha Bundu (55) | Steven Anderson (69) |
| John Mills (70) | Damien Mullen (78) |
| Nathan Summers | Shaun Bell (88) |
| Dylan Bonella | Dale Pearson |
| Ross Staley | Niall Harrison |

Referee Stuart Atwelly (Birmingham FA).
Assisted by Antony Coggins & James Mainwaring.
Four official - Peter Banks.

To begin with it appeared certain that the bookies had correctly assessed the odds on a Hereford victory. Barely twelve months ago, having risen from the ashes of Hereford United who had surprisingly never been to Wembley in their 90 year history, the Bulls, having paraded their lucky charm mascot, real bull Hawkesbury Ronaldo, round the stadium, took the earliest of leads. The score came from a second minute 25 yarder low to the right of keeper Karl Dryden struck by midfielder and long serving Rob Purdie making full use of Joe Tumelty's pass. Dryden was quickly again in action, spreading himself at the feet of Ghanaian winger Sirdic Grant to prevent a doubling of the Bulls' lead and then called into action to turn over, at the expense of a corner, a header from Pablo Haysham before Tumelty's shot fortuitously hit the keeper rather than being saved. At this stage Herford were rampant, for Morpeth had managed just one effort at goal, Sean Taylor's shot being turned over by Martin Horsell.

The lively Grant was proving a problem for the Morpeth defence, his effort from just inside the area hitting the cross bar before Aaron Birch was presented with a simple tap in. Unfortunately the ball was caught under his feet a matter of a few yards from goal. At the other end Ben Sayer's corner needed Ryan Green to deflect over his own bar before Sayer fired over a twenty yarder.

Then, in minute 33 came an unexpected event. Sayer's corner eluded keeper Horsell and fell 'ight by the oldest player ever to appear in a Wembley final, 45 year old defender Chris Swailes who bundled the ball over the line, before it was cleared but not before referee Attwell had rightly spotted the score. Amazingly Morpeth were level. With a six inch screw in his ankle, the survivor of four heart operations and wo previous retirements, twice previously a Vase winner, Swailes was the hero, later to be judged man of the match in what must have been a close contest with his inspirational skipper, Keith Graydon, also a previous Vase winner. Morpeth could in fact have gone in ahead at half time had Michael Chilton not pushed a chance wide, being only able to employ the outside of his boot rather than his full force, when faced with an open goal

The half ended with Morpeth miraculously level and Hereford ruing their many missed chances, yet within the first sixty seconds of the second half the Highwaymen were in the lead. Luke Carr seized the opportunity to place the ball well to the left of Horsell and 12 minutes later, almost unbelievably, put clear by Chilton, Taylor was

able to slide the ball past a helpless Horsell and Morpeth were 3-1 up. Hereford heads slumped further as sub John Mills was unable to gain control of a bouncing ball and a Haysham free kick lobbed well over the target. Morpeth's Carr, put through by Steven Anderson, shot straight at Horsell who also saved from Taylor

Bulls' sub Mustapha Bundu forged a chance but fired over and then went near with a header, while Mike Symons scuffed a chance to reduce the deficit when well placed, the ball rolling safely to Dryden's welcoming arms.

In the final minute Morpeth's jubilation soared even higher as sub Shaun Bell's shot deflected off a defender to roll gently into the net and complete the transformation from underdog to deserved victor. Recognising the spirited second half Morpeth fightback there was warm and generous applause from the Hereford supporters for the victors. Hereford players, no doubt disappointed and shocked, were still also most sporting, forming a spontaneous guard of honour to clap their opponents' return to the field following presentation of the Vase.

*Arthur Evans.*

Morpeth Town lift the FA Vase. Photo: Peter Barnes.

# PAST FINALS

**1975 HODDESDON TOWN** 2 *(South Midlands)* **EPSOM & EWELL 1** ***(Surrey Senior)*** **Att: 9,500**
**Sedgwick 2** **Wales** **Ref: Mr R Toseland**
Hoddesdon: Galvin, Green, Hickey, Maybury, Stevenson, Wilson, Bishop, Picking, Sedgwick, Nathan, Schofield
Epsom & Ewell: Page, Bennett, Webb, Wales, Worby, Jones, O'Connell, Walker, Tuite, Eales, Lee

**1976 BILLERICAY TOWN** 1 *(Essex Senior)* **STAMFORD 0 (aet)** ***(United Counties)*** **Att: 11,848**
**Aslett** **Ref: Mr A Robinson**
Billericay: Griffiths, Payne, Foreman, Pullin, Bone, Coughlan, Geddes, Aslett, Clayden, Scott, Smith
Stamford: Johnson, Kwiatowski, Marchant, Crawford, Downs, Hird, Barnes, Walpole, Smith, Russell, Broadbent

**1977 BILLERICAY TOWN 1** ***(Essex Senior)*** **SHEFFIELD 1 (aet)** ***(Yorkshire)*** **Att: 14,000**
**Clayden** **Coughlan og** **Ref: Mr J Worrall**
Billericay: Griffiths, Payne, Bone, Coughlan, Pullin, Scott, Wakefield, Aslett, Clayden,Woodhouse, McQueen. Sub: Whettell
Sheffield: Wing, Gilbody, Lodge, Hardisty, Watts, Skelton, Kay, Travis, Pugh, Thornhill,Haynes. Sub: Strutt
**Replay BILLERICAY TOWN** 2 **SHEFFIELD 1** **Att: 3,482**
**Aslett, Woodhouse** **Thornhill** **at Nottingham Forest**
Billericay: Griffiths, Payne, Pullin, Whettell, Bone, McQueen, Woodhouse, Aslett, Clayden, Scott, Wakefield
Sheffield: Wing, Gilbody, Lodge, Strutt, Watts, Skelton, Kay, Travis, Pugh, Thornhill, Haynes

**1978 NEWCASTLE BLUE STAR** 2 *(Wearside)* **BARTON ROVERS 1** ***(South Midlands)*** **Att: 16,858**
**Dunn, Crumplin** **Smith** **Ref: Mr T Morris**
Newcastle: Halbert, Feenan, Thompson, Davidson, S Dixon, Beynon, Storey, P Dixon, Crumplin, Callaghan, Dunn. Sub: Diamond
Barton Rovers: Blackwell, Stephens, Crossley, Evans, Harris, Dollimore, Dunn, Harnaman, Fossey, Turner, Smith. Sub: Cox

**1979 BILLERICAY TOWN** 4 *(Athenian)* **ALMONDSBURY GREENWAY 1** ***(Glos. Co)*** **Att: 17,500**
**Young 3, Clayden** **Price** **Ref: Mr C Steel**
Billericay: Norris, Blackaller, Bingham, Whettell, Bone, Reeves, Pullin, Scott, Clayden,Young, Groom. Sub: Carrigan
Almondsbury: Hamilton, Bowers, Scarrett, Sulllivan, Tudor, Wookey, Bowers, Shehean, Kerr, Butt, Price. Sub: Kilbaine

**1980 STAMFORD** 2 *(United Counties)* **GUISBOROUGH TOWN 0** ***(Northern Alliance)*** **Att: 11,500**
**Alexander, McGowan** **Ref: Neil Midgeley**
Stamford: Johnson, Kwiatkowski, Ladd, McGowan, Bliszczak I, Mackin, Broadhurst, Hall,Czarnecki, Potter, Alexander. Sub: Bliszczak S
Guisborough: Cutter, Scott, Thornton, Angus, Maltby, Percy, Skelton, Coleman, McElvaney,Sills, Dilworth. Sub: Harrison

**1981 WHICKHAM** 3 *(Wearside)* **WILLENHALL 2 (aet)** ***(West Midlands)*** **Att: 12,000**
**Scott, Williamson, Peck og** **Smith, Stringer** **Ref: Mr R Lewis**
Whickham: Thompson, Scott, Knox, Williamson, Cook, Ward, Carroll, Diamond, Cawthra,Robertson, Turnbull. Sub: Alton
Willenhall: Newton, White, Darris, Woodall, Heath, Fox, Peck, Price, Matthews, Smith,Stringer. Sub: Trevor

**1982 FOREST GREEN ROVERS** 3 *(Hellenic)* **RAINWORTH M.W 0** ***(Notts Alliance)*** **Att: 12,500**
**Leitch 2, Norman** **Ref: Mr K Walmsey**
Forest Green: Moss, Norman, Day, Turner, Higgins, Jenkins, Guest, Burns, Millard, Leitch, Doughty. Sub: Dangerfield
Rainworth M.W: Watson, Hallam, Hodgson, Slater, Sterland, Oliver, Knowles, Raine, Radzi, Reah, Comerford. Sub: Robinson

**1983 V.S. RUGBY** 1 *(West Midlands)* **HALESOWEN TOWN 0** ***(West Midlands)*** **Att: 13,700**
**Crawley** **Ref: Mr B Daniels**
VS Rugby: Burton, McGinty, Harrison, Preston, Knox, Evans, ingram, Setchell, Owen,Beecham, Crawley. Sub: Haskins
Halesowen Town: Coldicott, Penn, Edmonds, Lacey, Randall, Shilvock, Hazelwood, Moss, Woodhouse,P Joinson, L Joinson. Sub: Smith

**1984 STANSTED** 3 *(Essex Senior)* **STAMFORD 2** ***(United Counties)*** **Att: 8,125**
**Holt, Gillard, Reading** **Waddicore, Allen** **Ref: Mr T Bune**
Stanstead: Coe, Williams, Hilton, Simpson, Cooper, Reading, Callanan, Holt, Reevs,Doyle, Gillard. Sub: Williams
Stamford: Parslow, Smitheringate, Blades, McIlwain, Lyon, Mackin, Genovese, Waddicore,Allen, Robson, Beech. Sub: Chapman

**1985 HALESOWEN TOWN** 3 *(West Midlands)* **FLEETWOOD TOWN 1** ***(N W Counties)*** **Att: 16,715**
**L Joinson 2, Moss** **Moran** **Ref: Mr C Downey**
Halesowen: Coldicott, Penn, Sherwood, Warner, Randle, Heath, Hazlewood, Moss (Smith),Woodhouse, P Joinson, L Joinson
Fleetwood Town: Dobson, Moran, Hadgraft, Strachan, Robinson, Milligan, Hall, Trainor, Taylor(Whitehouse), Cain, Kennerley

**1986 HALESOWEN TOWN** 3 *(West Midlands)* **SOUTHALL 0** ***(Isthmian 2 South)*** **Att: 18,340**
**Moss 2, L Joinson** **Ref: Mr D Scott**
Halesowen: Pemberton, Moore, Lacey, Randle (Rhodes), Sherwood, Heath, Penn, Woodhouse, PJoinson, L Joinson, Moss
Southall: Mackenzie, James, McGovern, Croad, Holland, Powell (Richmond), Pierre,Richardson, Sweales, Ferdinand, Rowe

**1987** **ST. HELENS 3** ***(N W Counties)*** **WARRINGTON TOWN 2** ***(N W Counties)*** **Att: 4,254**
**Layhe 2, Rigby** **Reid, Cook** **Ref: Mr T Mills**
St Helens: Johnson, Benson, Lowe, Bendon, Wilson, McComb, Collins (Gledhill), O'Neill,Cummins, Lay, Rigby. Sub: Deakin
Warrington: O'Brien. Copeland, Hunter, Gratton, Whalley, Reid, Brownville (Woodyer), Cook,Kinsey, Looker (Hill), Hughes

**1988** **COLNE DYNAMOES 1** ***(N W Counties)*** **EMLEY 0** ***(Northern Counties East)*** **Att: 15,000**
**Anderson** **Ref: Mr A Seville**
Colne Dynamoes: Mason, McFafyen, Westwell, Bentley, Dunn, Roscoe, Rodaway, Whitehead (Burke),Diamond, Anderson, Wood (Coates)
Emley: Dennis, Fielding, Mellor, Codd, Hirst (Burrows), Gartland (Cook), Carmody,Green, Bramald, Devine, Francis

**1989** **TAMWORTH 1** ***(West Midlands)*** **SUDBURY TOWN 1 (aet)** ***(Eastern)*** **Att: 26,487**
**Devaney** **Hubbick** **Ref: Mr C Downey**
Tamworth: Bedford, Lockett, Atkins, Cartwright, McCormack, Myers, Finn, Devaney, Moores,Gordon, Stanton. Subs: Rathbone, Heaton
Sudbury Town: Garnham, Henry, G Barker, Boyland, Thorpe, Klug, D Barker, Barton, Oldfield,Smith, Hubbick. Subs: Money, Hunt
**Replay** **TAMWORTH 3** **SUDBURY TOWN 0** **Att: 11,201**
**Stanton 2, Moores** **at Peterborough**
Tamworth: Bedford, Lockett, Atkins, Cartwright, Finn, Myers, George, Devaney, Moores,Gordon, Stanton. Sub: Heaton
Sudbury Town: Garnham, Henry, G Barker, Boyland, Thorpe, Klug, D Barker, Barton, Oldfield,Smith, Hubbick. Subs: Money, Hunt

**1990** **YEADING 0** ***(Isthmian 2 South)*** **BRIDLINGTON TOWN 0 (aet)** ***(N Co East)*** **Att: 7,932**
**Ref: Mr R Groves**
Yeading: Mackenzie, Wickens, Turner, Whiskey (McCarthy), Croad, Denton, Matthews, James(Charles), Sweates, Impey, Cordery
Bridlington: Taylor, Pugh, Freeman, McNeill, Warburton, Brentano, Wilkes (Hall), Noteman,Gauden, Whiteman, Brattan (Brown)
**Replay** **YEADING 1** **BRIDLINGTON TOWN 0** **Att: 5,000**
**Sweales** **at Leeds Utd FC**
Yeading: Mackenzie, Wickens, Turner, Whiskey, Croad (McCarthy), Schwartz, Matthews,James, Sweates, Impey (Welsh), Cordery
Bridlington: Taylor, Pugh, Freeman, McNeill, Warburton, Brentano, Wilkes (Brown), Noteman,Gauden (Downing), Whiteman, Brattan

**1991** **GRESLEY ROVERS 4** ***(West Midlands)*** **GUISELEY 4 (aet)** ***(Northern Co East)*** **Att: 11,314**
**Rathbone, Smith 2, Stokes** **Tennison 2, Walling, A Roberts** **Ref: Mr C Trussell**
Gresley: Aston, Barry, Elliott (Adcock), Denby, Land, Astley, Stokes, K Smith, Acklam,Rathbone, Lovell (Weston)
Guiseley: Maxted, Bottomley, Hogarth, Tetley, Morgan, McKenzie, Atkinson (Annan),Tennison, Walling, A Roberts, B Roberts
**Replay** **GUISELEY 3** **GRESLEY ROVERS 1** **Att: 7,585**
**Tennison, Walling, Atkinson** **Astley** **at Bramall Lane**
Guiseley: Maxted, Annan, Hogarth, Tetley, Morgan, McKenzie (Bottomley), Atkinson,Tennison (Noteman), Walling, A Roberts, B Roberts
Gresley: Aston, Barry, Elliott, Denby, Land, Astley, Stokes (Weston), K Smith, Acklam, Rathbone, Lovell (Adcock)

**1992** **WIMBORNE TOWN 5** ***(Wessex)*** **GUISELEY 3** ***(Northern Premier Div 1)*** **Att: 10,772**
**Richardson, Sturgess 2, Killick 2** **Noteman 2, Colville** **Ref: Mr M J Bodenham**
Wimborne: Leonard, Langdown, Wilkins, Beacham, Allan, Taplin, Ames, Richardson, Bridle,Killick, Sturgess (Lovell), Lynn
Guiseley: Maxted, Atkinson, Hogarth, Tetley (Wilson), Morgan, Brockie, A Roberts,Tennison, Noteman (Colville), Annan, W Roberts

**1993** **BRIDLINGTON TOWN 1** ***(NPL Div 1)*** **TIVERTON TOWN 0** ***(Western)*** **Att: 9,061**
**Radford** **Ref: Mr R A Hart**
Bridlington: Taylor, Brentano, McKenzie, Harvey, Bottomley, Woodcock, Grocock, A Roberts, Jones, Radford (Tyrell), Parkinson. Sub: Swailes
Tiverton Town: Nott, J Smith, N Saunders, M Saunders, Short (Scott), Steele, Annunziata, KSmith, Everett, Daly, Hynds (Rogers)

**1994** **DISS TOWN 2** ***(Eastern)*** **TAUNTON TOWN 1** ***(Western)*** **Att: 13,450**
**Gibbs (p), Mendham** **Fowler** **Ref: Mr K. Morton**
Diss Town: Woodcock, Carter, Wolsey (Musgrave), Casey (Bugg), Hartle, Smith, Barth, Mendham, Miles, Warne, Gibbs
Taunton Town: Maloy, Morris, Walsh, Ewens, Graddon, Palfrey, West (Hendry), Fowler, Durham, Perrett (Ward), Jarvis

**1995** **ARLESEY TOWN 2** ***(South Midlands)*** **OXFORD CITY 1** ***(Ryman 2)*** **Att: 13,670**
**Palma, Gyalog** **S Fontaine** **Ref: Mr G S Willard**
Arlesey: Young, Cardines, Bambrick, Palma (Ward), Hull, Gonsalves, Gyalog, Cox, Kane,O'Keefe, Marshall (Nicholls). Sub: Dodwell
Oxford: Fleet, Brown (Fisher), Hume, Shepherd, Muttock, Hamilton (Kemp), Thomas, Spittle, Sherwood, S Fontaine, C Fontaine. Sub: Torres

**1996** **BRIGG TOWN 3** ***(N Co East)*** **CLITHEROE 0** ***(N W Counties)*** **Att: 7,340**
**Stead 2, Roach** **Ref: Mr S J Lodge**
Brigg: Gawthorpe, Thompson, Rogers, Greaves (Clay), Buckley (Mail), Elston, C Stead, McLean, N Stead (McNally), Flounders, Roach
Clitheroe: Nash, Lampkin, Rowbotham (Otley), Baron, Westwell, Rovine, Butcher, Taylor (Smith), Grimshaw, Darbyshire, Hill (Dunn)

**1997** **WHITBY TOWN 3** ***(Northern)*** **NORTH FERRIBY UTD. 0** ***(N Co East)*** **Att: 11,098**
**Williams, Logan, Toman** **Ref: Graham Poll**
North Ferriby: Sharp, Deacey, Smith, Brentano, Walmsley, M Smith, Harrison (Horne), Phillips (Milner), France (Newman), Flounders, Tennison
Whitby Town: Campbell, Williams, Logan, Goodchild, Pearson, Cook, Goodrick (Borthwick), Hodgson, Robinson, Toman (Pyle), Pitman (Hall)

**1998 TIVERTON TOWN** 1 *(Western)* — **TOW LAW TOWN 0** *(Northern Division 1)* — **Att: 13,139**
**Varley** — **Ref: M A Riley**

Tiverton Town: Edwards, Felton, Saunders, Tatterton, Smith J, Conning, Nancekivell (Rogers), Smith K (Varley), Everett, Daly, Leonard (Waters)
Tow Law Town: Dawson, Pickering, Darwent, Bailey, Hague, Moan, Johnson, Nelson, Suddick, Laidler (Bennett), Robinson.

**1999 TIVERTON TOWN** 1 *(Western)* — **BEDLINGTON TERRIERS 0** *(Northern)* — **Att: 13, 878**
**Rogers 88** — **Ref: W. C. Burns**

Bedlington Terriers: O'Connor, Bowes, Pike, Boon (Renforth), Melrose, Teasdale, Cross, Middleton (Ludlow), Gibb, Milner, Bond. Subs: Pearson, Cameron, Gowans
Tiverton Town: Edwards, Fallon, Saunders, Tatterton, Tallon, Conning (Rogers), Nancekivell (Pears), Varley, Everett, Daly, Leonard. Subs: Tucker, Hynds, Grimshaw

**2000 DEAL TOWN** 1 *(Kent)* — **CHIPPENHAM TOWN 0** *(Western)* — **Att: 20,000**
**Graham 87** — **Ref: D Laws**

Deal Town: Tucker, Kempster, Best, Ash, Martin, Seager, Monteith, Graham, Lovell, Marshall, Ribbens. Subs: Roberts, Warden, Turner
Chippenham Town: Jones, James, Andrews, Murphy, Burns, Woods, Brown, Charity, Tweddle, Collier, Godley. Subs: Tiley, Cutler

**2001 TAUNTON TOWN** 2 *(Western)* — **BERKHAMPSTED TOWN 1** *(Isthmian 2)* — **(at Villa Park) Att: 8,439**
**Fields 41, Laight 45** — **Lowe 71** — **Ref: E. K. Wolstenholme**

Taunton Town: Draper, Down, Chapman, West, Hawkings, Kelly, Fields (Groves), Laight, Cann (Tallon), Bastow, Lynch (Hapgood). Subs: Ayres, Parker
Berkhampsted Town: O'Connor, Mullins, Lowe, Aldridge, Coleman, Brockett, Yates, Adebowale, Richardson, Smith, Nightingale. Subs: Ringsell, Hall, Knight, Franklin, Osborne

**2002 WHITLEY BAY** 1 *(Northern)* — **TIPTREE UNITED 0** *(Eastern)* — **(at Villa Park) Att: 4742**
**Chandler 97** — **Ref: A Kaye**

Whitley Bay: Caffrey, Sunderland, Walmsley, Dixon (Neil), Anderson, Locker, Middleton, Bowes (Carr), Chandler, Walton, Fenwick (Cuggy). Subs: Cook, Livermore
Tiptree United: Haygreen, Battell, Wall, Houghton, Fish, Streetley (Gillespie), Wareham (Snow), Daly, Barefield, Aransibia (Parnell), Brady. Subs: Powell, Ford.

**2003 BRIGG TOWN** 2 *(Northern Co.East)* — **A.F.C SUDBURY 1** *(Eastern Counties)* — **(at Upton Park) Att: 6,634**
**Housham 2, Carter 68** — **Raynor 30** — **Ref: M Fletcher**

Brigg Town:- Steer, Raspin, Rowland, Thompson, Blanchard, Stones, Stead (Thompson 41), Housham, Borman (Drayton 87), Roach, Carter. Subs (not used) Nevis, Gawthorpe.
AFC Sudbury:- Greygoose, Head (Norfolk 63), Spearing, Tracey, Bishop, Anderson (Owen 73), Rayner, Gardiner (Banya 79), Bennett, Claydon, Betson. Subs (not used) Taylor, Hyde.

**2004 WINCHESTER CITY** 2 *(Wessex)* — **A.F.C SUDBURY 0** *(Eastern Counties)* — **(at St Andrews) Att: 5,080**
**Forbes 19, Smith 73 (pen)** — **Ref: P Crossley**

Winchester City:- Arthur, Dyke (Tate 83), Bicknell, Redwood, Goss, Blake, Webber, Green, Mancey, Forbes (Rogers 70), Smith (Green 90). Subs (not used) - Lang and Rastall.
AFC Sudbury:- Greygoose, Head, Wardley, Girling, Tracey, Norfolk, Owen (Banya 62), Hyde (Calver 57), Bennett, Claydon, Betson (Francis 73n). Subs (not used) - Rayner, Nower.

**2005 DIDCOT TOWN** 3 *(Hellenic)* — **A.F.C SUDBURY 2** *(Eastern Counties)* **(at White Hart Lane) Att: 8,66.**
**Beavon (2), Wardley (og)** — **Wardley, Calver (pen)** — **Ref: R Beeby**

Didcot Town:- Webb, Goodall, Heapy, Campbell, Green, Parrott, Hannigan, Ward, Concannon (Jones 88), Beavon (Bianchini 90), Powell. Subs (not used) – Cooper, Allen, Spurrett.
AFC Sudbury:- Greygoose, Girling, Wardley, Bennett, Hyde (Hayes 78), Owen (Norfolk 65), Claydon (Banya 59), Head, Calver, Betson, Terry Rayner. Subs (not used) – Howlett, Nower.

**2006 NANTWICH TOWN** 3 *(NWC 1)* — **HILLINGDON BOROUGH 1** *(Spartan S.Mids P.)***(at St Andrews) Att: 3,28**
**Kinsey (2), Scheuber** — **Nelson**

Nantwich Town:- Hackney, A.Taylor, T.Taylor, Smith, Davis, Donnelly, Beasley, Scheuber (Parkinson 69), Kinsey (Marrow 69), Blake (Scarlett 86) and Griggs. Subs (not used): O'Connor and Read.
Hillingdon Borough:- Brown, Rundell (Fenton 80),Kidson, Phillips, Croft, Lawrence, Duncan (Nelson 46), Tilbury, Hibbs, Wharton (Lyons 38). Subs (not used): O'Grady, White.

**2007 TRURO** 3 *(Western Division 1)* — **AFC TOTTON 1** *(Wessex Division 1)* — **Att: 27,754 (New Vase record)**
**Wills (2), Broad** — **Potter** — **Ref: P Joslin**

AFC Totton: Brunnschweiler, Reacord, Troon (Stevens 60), Potter (Gregory 82), Bottomley, Austen, Roden, Gosney, Hamodu (Goss 89), Osman, Byres. Subs not used: Zammit, McCormack.
Truro City: Stevenson, Ash, Power, Smith, Martin (Pope 84), Broad, Wills, Gosling, Yetton, Watkins, Walker (Ludlam 90). Subs not used: Butcher, Routledge, Reski.

2008 **KIRKHAM & WESHAM** 2 *(North West Co. Div.2)* LOWESTOFT TOWN 1 *(Eastern Co. Premier)* Att: 19,537
Walwyn (2) Thompson (og) Ref: A D'Urso
Kirkham and Wesham: Summerfield, Jackson (Walwyn 79), Keefe (Allen 55), Thompson, Shaw, Eastwood, Clark, Blackwell, Wane, Paterson (Sheppard 90), Smith. Subs not used: Moffat and Abbott
Lowestoft Town: Reynolds, Poppy, Potter, Woodrow, Saunders, Plaskett (McGee 79), Godbold, Darren Cockrill (Dale Cockrill 46), Stock, Hough, King (Hunn 55). Subs not used: McKenna and Rix.

2009 **WHITLEY BAY** 2 *(Northern Division One)* GLOSSOP NORTH END 0 *(North West Co. Prem)* Att: 12,212
Kerr, Chow Ref: K Friend
Whitley Bay: Burke, Taylor, Picton, McFarlane (Fawcett 60), Coulson, Ryan, Moore, Robson, Kerr, Chow (Robinson 73), Johnston (Bell 60). Subs not used: McLean and Reay.
Glossop North End: Cooper, Young, Kay, Lugsden, Yates, Gorton, Bailey (Hind 57), Morris, Allen (Balfe 65), Hamilton (Bailey 72), Hodges. Subs not used: Whelan and Parker.

2010 **WHITLEY BAY** 6 *(Northern Division One)* WROXHAM 1 *(Eastern Counties Premier Division)* Att: 8,920
Chow 21(sec), Easthaugh 16 (og), Kerr, Johnston, Robinson, Gillies Cook 12 Ref: A Taylor
Whitley Bay: Terry Burke, Craig McFarlane, Callum Anderson, Richard Hodgson, (sub Lee Picton 69th min), Darren Timmons, Leon Ryan, Adam Johnston (sub Joshua Gillies 77th min), Damon Robson, Lee Kerr, Paul Chow (sub Phillip Bell 61st min), Paul Robinson.
Subs not used – Tom Kindley and Chris Reid.
Wroxham: Scott Howie, Gavin Pauling (sub Ross Durrant 57th min), Shaun Howes, Graham Challen, Martin McNeil (sub Josh Carus 46th min), Andy Easthaugh (sub Owen Paynter 69th min), Steve Spriggs, Gavin Lemmon, Paul Cook, Danny White, Gary Gilmore.
Subs not used – Danny Self and Gareth Simpson.

2011 **WHITLEY BAY** 3 *(Northern Division One)* COALVILLE TOWN 2 *(Midland Alliance)* Att: 8,778
Chow 28, 90, Kerr 61 Moore 58, Goodby 80 Ref: S Mathieson
Whitley Bay: Terry Burke, Craig McFarlane (sub Steve Gibson 90th min), Callum Anderson, Darren Timmons, Gareth Williams (sub David Coulson 68th min), Damon Robson, Lee Kerr, Paul Chow, Paul Robinson, David Pounder (sub Brian Smith 68th min), Gary Ormston.
Subs not used – Kyle Hayes (gk) and Brian Rowe. Coalville Town: Sean Bowles, Ashley Brown (sub Matthew Gardner 88th min), Cameron Stuart, Adam Goodby, Zach Costello, Lee Miveld,
Callum Woodward, Anthony Carney (sub Craig Attwood 90th min), Ryan Robbins (sub Ashley Wells 66th min), Matt Moore, Jerome Murdock.
Subs not used – Richard Williams (gk) and James Dodd.

2012 **DUNSTON UTS** 2 *(Northern Division One)* WEST AUCKLAND TOWN 0 *(Northern Division One)* Att: 5,126
Bulford 32, 79 Ref: R East
Dunston UTS: Liam Connell, Ben Cattenach, Terry Galbraith, Michael Robson, Chris Swailes, Kane Young, Steven Shaw, Michael Dixon, Stephen Goddard (sub Sreven Preen 84th min), Andrew Bulford (sub Danny Craggs 88th min), Lee McAndrew.
*Subs not used* – Andrew Clark (g/k), Ian Herron, Jack Burns.
West Auckland Town: Mark Bell, Neil Pattinson, Andrew Green, Jonny Gibson, John Parker, Mark Stephenson (sub Daniel Hindmarsh 76th min), Stuart Banks, Mark Hudson, Mattie Moffatt, Michael Rae, Adam Nicholls (sub Martin Young 60th min).
*Subs not used* – Daryll Hall, Ross Preston, Matthew Coad.

2013 **SPENNYMOOR TOWN** 2 *(Northern Division One)* TUNBRIDGE WELLS 1 *(Kent League)* Att: 16,751
Cogdon 18, Graydon 80 Stanford 78 Ref: M Naylor
Spennymoor Town: Robert Dean, Kallum Griffiths, Leon Ryan, Chris Mason, Stephen Capper, Keith Graydon, Lewis Dodds, Wayne Phillips (Anthony Peacock [illegible] min), Joe Walton (Andrew Stephenson 73 min), Mark Davison, (Michael Rae 76 min), Gavin Congdon.
*Subs not used* - David Knight (g/k), Steven Richardson.
Tunbridge Wells: Chris Oladogba, Jason Bourne, Scott Whibley, Perry Spackman, Lewis Mingle, Jon Pilbeam (Richard Sinden 85 min), Andy McMath, Lee Fuller (Tom Davey 58 min), Andy Irvine, Carl Connell (Jack Harris 58 min), Josh Stanford.
*Subs not used* - Michael Czanner (gk), Andy Boyle.

2014 **SHOLING** 1 *(Wessex Premier Division - 1st)* WEST AUCKLAND TOWN 0 *(Northern Division One - 5th)* Att: 5,432
McLean 71 Ref: D Coote
Sholing: Matt Brown, Mike Carter, Marc Diaper, Peter Castle (Dan Miller 53 min), Lee Bright, Tyronne Bowers (Kevin Brewster 75 min), Barry Mason, Lewis Fennemore (Alex Sawyer 78 min), Lee Wort, Byron Mason, Marvin McLean.
*Subs not used* - Ashley Jarvis, Nick Watts.
West Auckland Town: Jordan Nixon, Neil Pattinson, Andrew Green (Jonathan Gibson 63 min), Daryll Hall, Lewis Galpin, Brian Close, Shaun Vipond (Stuart Banks 76 min), Robert Briggs, Mattie Moffat (Steven Richardson 74 min). John Campbell, Dennis Knight.
*Subs not used* - Paul Garthwaite, Adam Wilkinson..

2015 **NORTH SHIELDS** 2 *(Northern Division One - 4th)* GLOSSOP NORTH END 1 *(North West Co. Premier - 1st)* Att: 9,674
Bainbridge 80, Forster 96 Bailey 55 Ref: A Madley
North Shields: Christopher Bannon, Stuart Donnison, John Parker, Kevin Hughes, John Grey, James Luccock (Ryan Carr 59), Ben Richardson, Michael McKeown, Dean Holmes (Adam Forster 69), Denver Morris, Gareth Bainbridge (Kieran Wrightson 107).
*Subs not used* - Curtis Coppen and Marc Lancaster.
Glossop North End: Greg Hall, Michael Bowler, Matthew Russell, Kevin Lugsden, Dave Young, Martin Parker, Lee Blackshaw (Samuel Grimshaw 69), Samuel Hare (Samuel Hind 82), Tom Bailey, Kieran Lugsden, Eddie Moran (Daniel White 60).
*Subs not used* - Benjamin Richardson and Richard Gresty.

*All Finals at Wembley unless otherwise stated.*

# FIRST QUALIFYING ROUND 2016-17

## SATURDAY 10 SEPTEMBER 2016

| | | | |
|---|---|---|---|
| 1 | Bridlington Town | v | Yorkshire Amateur |
| 2 | Bedlington Terriers | v | Bishop Auckland |
| 3 | Albion Sports | v | Ashington |
| 4 | Knaresborough Town | v | Silsden |
| 5 | Stockton Town | v | Eccleshill United |
| 6 | Blyth Town | v | Ryton & Crawcrook Albion |
| 7 | Darlington Railway Athletic | v | Barnoldswick Town |
| 8 | Consett | v | Hebburn Town |
| 9 | Daisy Hill | v | Garforth Town |
| 10 | Penrith | v | Durham City |
| 11 | Billingham Town | v | Willington |
| 12 | West Allotment Celtic | v | Hall Road Rangers |
| 13 | Washington | v | Billingham Synthonia |
| 14 | Easington Colliery | v | Thackley |
| 15 | AFC Darwen | v | Pickering Town |
| 16 | Nelson | v | Heaton Stannington |
| 17 | West Auckland Town | v | Seaham Red Star |
| 18 | Crook Town | v | Esh Winning |
| 19 | Carlisle City | v | Team Northumbria |
| 20 | Brandon United | v | Chester-Le-Street Town |
| 21 | Tow Law Town | v | Norton & Stockton Ancients |
| 22 | Whickham | v | Charnock Richard |
| 23 | Thornaby | v | Liversedge |
| 24 | Newcastle Benfield | v | Alnwick Town |
| 25 | City of Liverpool | v | Litherland Remyca |
| 26 | Barton Town Old Boys | v | Grimsby Borough |
| 27 | Staveley MW | v | Cheadle Town |
| 28 | Maltby Main | v | Widnes |
| 29 | Alsager Town | v | Squires Gate |
| 30 | Ashton Town | v | Parkgate |
| 31 | Bootle | v | Maine Road |
| 32 | St Helens Town | v | Chadderton |
| 33 | Runcorn Town | v | Winsford United |
| 34 | Dronfield Town | v | Glasshoughton Welfare |
| 35 | Pontefract Collieries | v | Hemsworth MW |
| 36 | Irlam | v | Selby Town |
| 37 | Winterton Rangers | v | Penistone Church |
| 38 | Ashton Athletic | v | Athersley Recreation |
| 39 | Armthorpe Welfare | v | Congleton Town |
| 40 | Barnton | v | Harworth Colliery |
| 41 | Black Country Rangers | v | Stafford Town |
| 42 | Dudley Town | v | Wellington Amateurs |
| 43 | FC Oswestry Town | v | Walsall Wood |
| 44 | Coton Green | v | Kirby Muxloe |
| 45 | Ashby Ivanhoe | v | Pelsall Villa |
| 46 | Whitchurch Alport | v | Wellington |
| 47 | Highgate United | v | Lye Town |
| 48 | Bolehall Swifts | v | Heath Hayes |
| 49 | Bromyard Town | v | Atherstone Town |
| 50 | Cradley Town | v | Uttoxeter Town |
| 51 | Pershore Town | v | Bewdley Town |
| 52 | Chelmsley Town | v | Studley |
| 53 | Ellistown & Ibstock United | v | Bromsgrove Sporting |
| 54 | Redditch Borough | v | Rocester |
| 55 | AFC Bridgnorth | v | Boldmere St Michaels |
| 56 | Shawbury United | v | Heather St Johns |
| 57 | Shifnal Town | v | Gornal Athletic |
| 58 | Barnt Green Spartak | v | Cadbury Athletic |
| 59 | Racing Club Warwick | v | Coventry United |
| 60 | Malvern Town | v | Tividale |

| | | | |
|---|---|---|---|
| 61 | Bardon Hill | v | Littleton |
| 62 | Lutterworth Athletic | v | Stone Old Alleynians |
| 63 | Brocton | v | Eccleshall |
| 64 | Continental Star | v | Wolverhampton Casuals |
| 65 | Stourport Swifts | v | Smethwick |
| 66 | Ellesmere Rangers | v | Pegasus Juniors |
| 67 | Clay Cross Town | v | Leicester Road |
| 68 | Clifton All Whites | v | Oadby Town |
| 69 | Borrowash Victoria | v | Bottesford Town |
| 70 | Gedling MW | v | Oakham United |
| 71 | Loughborough University | v | Arnold Town |
| 72 | Ollerton Town | v | Retford United |
| 73 | Pinxton | v | Harrowby United |
| 74 | Rainworth MW | v | Heanor Town |
| 75 | Graham St Prims | v | Kimberley MW |
| 76 | Teversal | v | Blidworth Welfare |
| 77 | Aylestone Park | v | Stapenhill |
| 78 | Belper United | v | Radford |
| 79 | Barrow Town | v | St Andrews |
| 80 | Long Eaton United | v | South Normanton Athletic |
| 81 | Brigg Town | v | Harborough Town |
| 82 | Holbrook Sports | v | Hinckley |
| 83 | Thetford Town | v | Framlingham Town |
| 84 | Yaxley | v | Eynesbury Rovers |
| 85 | Great Yarmouth Town | v | Bourne Town |
| 86 | Wisbech Town | v | Mildenhall Town |
| 87 | Ely City | v | Kirkley & Pakefield |
| 88 | Walsham Le Willows | v | Deeping Rangers |
| 89 | Gorleston | v | Wisbech St Mary |
| 90 | Diss Town | v | Team Bury |
| 91 | London Bari | v | Newbury Forest |
| 92 | FC Clacton | v | Enfield 1893 |
| 93 | Wivenhoe Town | v | Wadham Lodge |
| 94 | FC Broxbourne Borough | v | Cornard United |
| 95 | Takeley | v | Tower Hamlets |
| 96 | Halstead Town | v | Hadley |
| 97 | Langford | v | Baldock Town |
| 98 | Stansted | v | Saffron Walden Town |
| 99 | Hadleigh United | v | Debenham LC |
| 100 | Burnham Ramblers | v | London Lions |
| 101 | Harpenden Town | v | Ilford |
| 102 | Whitton United | v | Biggleswade United |
| 103 | Woodbridge Town | v | Hatfield Town |
| 104 | Southend Manor | v | West Essex |
| 105 | Hertford Town | v | Clapton |
| 106 | Sporting Bengal United | v | Stowmarket Town |
| 107 | Codicote | v | St Margaretsbury |
| 108 | Redbridge | v | Eton Manor |
| 109 | Raunds Town | v | Northampton On Chenecks |
| 110 | Risborough Rangers | v | Broadfields United |
| 111 | Winslow United | v | Rushden & Higham United |
| 112 | Long Buckby | v | Hillingdon Borough |
| 113 | Bedfont & Feltham | v | Sandhurst Town |
| 114 | Ampthill Town | v | Northampton Sileby Rangers |
| 115 | Rothwell Corinthians | v | Burton Park Wanderers |
| 116 | AFC Hayes | v | Crawley Green |
| 117 | AFC Hillgate | v | Thrapston Town |
| 118 | Brackley Town Saints | v | Leighton Town |
| 119 | Spelthorne Sports | v | Tring Athletic |
| 120 | Cranfield United | v | Southall |

| | | | |
|---|---|---|---|
| 121 | Bicester Town | v | Potton United |
| 122 | FC Deportivo Galicia | v | Irchester United |
| 123 | London Tigers | v | Cogenhoe United |
| 124 | Daventry Town | v | Windsor |
| 125 | Stotfold | v | North Greenford United |
| 126 | Bedford | v | CB Hounslow United |
| 127 | Desborough Town | v | Woodford United |
| 128 | Stewarts & Lloyds Corby | v | Wellingborough Whitworths |
| 129 | Hanworth Villa | v | Bedfont Sports |
| 130 | Amersham Town | v | Highmoor Ibis |
| 131 | AFC Stoneham | v | Malmesbury Victoria |
| 132 | Buckingham Athletic | v | Binfield |
| 133 | Hook Norton | v | Bracknell Town |
| 134 | Shrivenham | v | Abbey Rangers |
| 135 | Ash United | v | Tytherington Rocks |
| 136 | Thame United | v | Tadley Calleva |
| 137 | Badshot Lea | v | Farnham Town |
| 138 | Fairford Town | v | Chipping Sodbury Town |
| 139 | Chertsey Town | v | Lydney Town |
| 140 | AFC Portchester | v | Holyport |
| 141 | Woodley United | v | Ardley United |
| 142 | Cove | v | Buckingham Town |
| 143 | Tunbridge Wells | v | Steyning Town |
| 144 | Hailsham Town | v | Lingfield |
| 145 | Croydon | v | Loxwood |
| 146 | Whitstable Town | v | Chichester City |
| 147 | Broadbridge Heath | v | Crowborough Athletic |
| 148 | Southwick | v | FC Elmstead |
| 149 | Bearsted | v | Pagham |
| 150 | Cray Valley (PM) | v | Glebe |
| 151 | St Francis Rangers | v | Ringmer |
| 152 | Raynes Park Vale | v | Haywards Heath Town |
| 153 | Arundel | v | Westfield |
| 154 | Horley Town | v | Hassocks |
| 155 | Sevenoaks Town | v | Crawley Down Gatwick |
| 156 | Little Common | v | Erith Town |
| 157 | Redhill | v | Deal Town |
| 158 | Guildford City | v | Eastbourne United |
| 159 | Chessington & Hook United | v | Rochester United |
| 160 | Bexhill United | v | Holmesdale |
| 161 | Shoreham | v | Meridian VP |
| 162 | Mile Oak | v | Erith & Belvedere |
| 163 | Littlehampton Town | v | Saltdean United |
| 164 | Worthing United | v | Peacehaven & Telscombe |
| 165 | Dorking | v | Beckenham Town |
| 166 | Bridon Ropes | v | Colliers Wood United |
| 167 | Langney Wanderers | v | Selsey |
| 168 | Brockenhurst | v | Ringwood Town |
| 169 | Corsham Town | v | United Services Portsmouth |
| 170 | Westbury United | v | Folland Sports |
| 171 | New Milton Town | v | Horndean |
| 172 | Oldland Abbotonians | v | Lymington Town |
| 173 | Whitchurch United | v | Laverstock & Ford |
| 174 | Hamworthy United | v | Amesbury Town |
| 175 | Cowes Sports | v | Cadbury Heath |
| 176 | Andover New Street | v | Gillingham Town |
| 177 | Hallen | v | Fawley |
| 178 | Bournemouth | v | Verwood Town |
| 179 | Hythe & Dibden | v | Team Solent |
| 180 | Bemerton Heath Harlequins | v | Downton |
| 181 | Romsey Town | v | Warminster Town |
| 182 | Christchurch | v | Swanage Town & Herston |
| 183 | Bridport | v | Cribbs |
| 184 | Alresford Town | v | Chippenham Park |
| 185 | Welton Rovers | v | Ashton & Backwell United |
| 186 | Liskeard Athletic | v | Portishead Town |
| 187 | Hengrove Athletic | v | Camelford |
| 188 | AFC St Austell | v | Crediton United |
| 189 | Cullompton Rangers | v | Wincanton Town |
| 190 | Shepton Mallet | v | Tavistock |
| 191 | Radstock Town | v | Torpoint Athletic |
| 192 | Wellington AFC | v | Bishop Sutton |
| 193 | Keynsham Town | v | Ivybridge Town |
| 194 | Cheddar | v | Elburton Villa |

## SECOND QUALIFYING ROUND 2016-17

### SATURDAY 24 SEPTEMBER 2016

| | | | |
|---|---|---|---|
| | Northallerton Town | v | Jarrow Roofing Boldon CA |
| | Whitley Bay | v | Stockton Town or Eccleshill United |
| | West Auckland Town or Seaham Red Star | v | Padiham |
| | Nelson or Heaton Stannington | v | Washington or Billingham Synthonia |
| | Crook Town or Esh Winning | v | South Shields |
| | Easington Colliery or Thackley | v | Albion Sports or Ashington |
| | Birtley Town | v | Holker Old Boys |
| | Brandon United or Chester-Le-Street Town | v | Tow Law Town or Norton & Stockton Ancients |
| | Bedlington Terriers or Bishop Auckland | v | Billingham Town or Willington |
| | Blyth Town or Ryton & Crawcrook Albion | v | Sunderland Ryhope CW |
| | Darlington Railway Athletic or Barnoldswick Town | v | Stokesley SC |
| | Bridlington Town or Yorkshire Amateur | v | Daisy Hill or Garforth Town |
| | Newcastle Benfield or Alnwick Town | v | Thornaby or Liversedge |
| | Penrith or Durham City | v | Carlisle City or Team Northumbria |
| | Knaresborough Town or Silsden | v | West Allotment Celtic or Hall Road Rangers |
| | Consett or Hebburn Town | v | AFC Darwen or Pickering Town |
| | Harrogate Railway Athletic | v | Whickham or Charnock Richard |
| | Westella VIP | v | Irlam or Selby Town |
| | Atherton LR | v | Cammell Laird 1907 |
| | Alsager Town or Squires Gate | v | Stockport Town |
| | AFC Liverpool | v | Abbey Hey |
| 22 | AFC Blackpool | v | Runcorn Town or Winsford United |
| 23 | Armthorpe Welfare or Congleton Town | v | Bacup Borough |
| 24 | Ashton Athletic or Athersley Recreation | v | AFC Emley |
| 25 | Hallam | v | Nostell MW |
| 26 | Staveley MW or Cheadle Town | v | Barton Town Old Boys or Grimsby Borough |
| 27 | Rossington Main | v | Bootle or Maine Road |
| 28 | Winterton Rangers or Penistone Church | v | West Didsbury & Chorlton |
| 29 | Ashton Town or Parkgate | v | Barnton or Harworth Colliery |
| 30 | City of Liverpool or Litherland Remyca | v | Vauxhall Motors |
| 31 | Maltby Main or Widnes | v | St Helens Town or Chadderton |
| 32 | Dronfield Town or Glasshoughton Welfare | v | Pontefract Collieries or Hemsworth MW |
| 33 | Hanley Town | v | AFC Bridgnorth or Boldmere St Michaels |
| 34 | Cradley Town or Uttoxeter Town | v | Dudley Town or Wellington Amateurs |
| 35 | Tipton Town | v | Ellistown & Ibstock United or Bromsgrove Sporting |
| 36 | Birstall United | v | Malvern Town or Tividale |
| 37 | Redditch Borough or Rocester | v | Black Country Rangers or Stafford Town |
| 38 | Willenhall Town | v | Haughmond |
| 39 | FC Oswestry Town or Walsall Wood | v | Ellesmere Rangers or Pegasus Juniors |
| 40 | Stourport Swifts or Smethwick | v | Barnt Green Spartak or Cadbury Athletic |
| 41 | Paget Rangers | v | Highgate United or Lye Town |
| 42 | Coventry Copsewood | v | Bromyard Town or Atherstone Town |

| | | | |
|---|---|---|---|
| 43 | Lutterworth Athletic or Stone Old Alleynians | v | Ashby Ivanhoe or Pelsall Villa |
| 44 | Racing Club Warwick or Coventry United | v | Wednesfield |
| 45 | Coton Green or Kirby Muxloe | v | Bardon Hill or Littleton |
| 46 | Shawbury United or Heather St Johns | v | Coventry Sphinx |
| 47 | Continental Star or Wolverhampton Casuals | v | Bilston Town |
| 48 | Brocton or Eccleshall | v | Chelmsley Town or Studley |
| 49 | Bolehall Swifts or Heath Hayes | v | Shifnal Town or Gornal Athletic |
| 50 | Westfields | v | Dudley Sports |
| 51 | Whitchurch Alport or Wellington | v | Lichfield City |
| 52 | Pershore Town or Bewdley Town | v | Wolverhampton SC |
| 53 | Clay Cross Town or Leicester Road | v | West Bridgford |
| 54 | Dunkirk | v | Borrowash Victoria or Bottesford Town |
| 55 | Rainworth MW or Heanor Town | v | Graham St Prims or Kimberley MW |
| 56 | Anstey Nomads | v | Quorn |
| 57 | Gedling MW or Oakham United | v | Ollerton Town or Retford United |
| 58 | Brigg Town or Harborough Town | v | Blaby & Whetstone Athletic |
| 59 | Teversal or Blidworth Welfare | v | Shirebrook Town |
| 60 | Hucknall Town | v | Eastwood Community |
| 61 | Pinxton or Harrowby United | v | Loughborough University or Arnold Town |
| 62 | Greenwood Meadows | v | Holbrook Sports or Hinckley |
| 63 | Clipstone | v | Sherwood Colliery |
| 64 | Aylestone Park or Stapenhill | v | Long Eaton United or South Normanton Athletic |
| 65 | Clifton All Whites or Oadby Town | v | Holwell Sports |
| 66 | AFC Mansfield | v | Radcliffe Olympic |
| 67 | New Mills | v | Belper United or Radford |
| 68 | Barrow Town or St Andrews | v | Retford |
| 69 | Yaxley or Eynesbury Rovers | v | Newmarket Town |
| 70 | Fakenham Town | v | Great Yarmouth Town or Bourne Town |
| 71 | Peterborough Northern Star | v | Blackstones |
| 72 | Thetford Town or Framlingham Town | v | Downham Town |
| 73 | Gorleston or Wisbech St Mary | v | March Town United |
| 74 | Ely City or Kirkley & Pakefield | v | Diss Town or Team Bury |
| 75 | Huntingdon Town | v | Swaffham Town |
| 76 | Wisbech Town or Mildenhall Town | v | Peterborough Sports |
| 77 | Boston Town | v | Walsham Le Willows or Deeping Rangers |
| 78 | Whitton United or Biggleswade United | v | Woodbridge Town or Hatfield Town |
| 79 | Colney Heath | v | Redbridge or Eton Manor |
| 80 | Takeley or Tower Hamlets | v | Biggleswade |
| 81 | Cockfosters | v | Hadley Wood & Wingate |
| 82 | Waltham Forest | v | Hadleigh United or Debenham LC |
| 83 | Sporting Bengal United or Stowmarket Town | v | Sawbridgeworth Town |
| 84 | Hertford Town or Clapton | v | Brantham Athletic |
| 85 | Haverhill Borough | v | Haverhill Rovers |
| 86 | Wivenhoe Town or Wadham Lodge | v | FC Clacton or Enfield 1893 |
| 87 | Long Melford | v | Langford or Baldock Town |
| 88 | Southend Manor or West Essex | v | Canning Town |
| 89 | Halstead Town or Hadley | v | Codicote or St Margaretsbury |
| 90 | London Bari or Newbury Forest | v | Barkingside |
| 91 | FC Broxbourne Borough or Cornard United | v | Stansted or Saffron Walden Town |
| 92 | Burnham Ramblers or London Lions | v | Harpenden Town or Ilford |
| 93 | Harefield United | v | Leverstock Green |
| 94 | Wembley | v | Long Buckby or Hillingdon Borough |
| 95 | Daventry Town or Windsor | v | Edgware Town |
| 96 | London Tigers or Cogenhoe United | v | Cranfield United or Southall |
| 97 | Stotfold or North Greenford United | v | Oxhey Jets |
| 98 | Bicester Town or Potton United | v | Risborough Rangers or Broadfields United |
| 99 | Holmer Green | v | Cricklewood Wanderers |
| 100 | Desborough Town or Woodford United or Wellingborough Whitworths | v | Stewarts & Lloyds Corby |
| 101 | Raunds Town or Northampton On Chenecks | v | Brackley Town Saints or Leighton Town |
| 102 | Bedfont & Feltham or Sandhurst Town | v | Sun Sports |
| 103 | Ampthill Town or Northampton Sileby Rangers | v | Rayners Lane |
| 104 | LPOSSA | v | AFC Hayes or Crawley Green |
| 105 | Burnham | v | Amersham Town or Highmoor Ibis |
| 106 | AFC Hillgate or Thrapston Town | v | Bedford or CB Hounslow United |
| 107 | Winslow United or Rushden & Higham United | v | Spelthorne Sports or Tring Athletic |
| 108 | Rothwell Corinthians or Burton Park Wanderers | v | FC Deportivo Galicia or Irchester United |
| 109 | Wellingborough Town | v | Hanworth Villa or Bedfont Sports |
| 110 | Tuffley Rovers | v | Woodley United or Ardley United |
| 111 | Carterton | v | Brimscombe & Thrupp |
| 112 | Ash United or Tytherington Rocks | v | Milton United |
| 113 | Frimley Green | v | Walton & Hersham |
| 114 | Fleet Spurs | v | Fairford Town or Chipping Sodbury Town |
| 115 | Alton Town | v | Henley Town |
| 116 | Bashley | v | Highworth Town |
| 117 | Melksham Town | v | New College Swindon |
| 118 | Hook Norton or Bracknell Town | v | Buckingham Athletic or Binfield |
| 119 | Royal Wootton Bassett | v | Thame United or Tadley Calleva |
| 120 | Cove or Buckingham Town | v | Eversley & California |
| 121 | Oxford City Nomads | v | Abingdon United |
| 122 | AFC Stoneham or Malmesbury Victoria | v | Longlevens |
| 123 | Shrivenham or Abbey Rangers | v | Badshot Lea or Farnham Town |
| 124 | Chertsey Town or Lydney Town | v | AFC Portchester or Holyport |
| 125 | Chessington & Hook United or Rochester United | v | Dorking or Beckenham Town |
| 126 | Cray Valley (PM) or Glebe | v | Redhill or Deal Town |
| 127 | Southwick or FC Elmstead | v | AFC Uckfield Town |
| 128 | St Francis Rangers or Ringmer | v | Sporting Club Thamesmead |
| 129 | Bexhill United or Holmesdale | v | Banstead Athletic |
| 130 | Mile Oak or Erith & Belvedere | v | Croydon or Loxwood |
| 131 | Oakwood | v | Shoreham or Meridian VP |
| 132 | Horley Town or Hassocks | v | Langney Wanderers or Selsey |
| 133 | Whitstable Town or Chichester City | v | Sheppey United |
| 134 | AC London | v | Littlehampton Town or Saltdean United |
| 135 | Little Common or Erith Town | v | Wick |
| 136 | Broadbridge Heath or Crowborough Athletic | v | Gravesham Borough |
| 137 | Corinthian | v | Sevenoaks Town or Crawley Down Gatwick |
| 138 | Cobham | v | Hailsham Town or Lingfield |
| 139 | Arundel or Westfield | v | Raynes Park Vale or Haywards Heath Town |
| 140 | East Preston | v | Tunbridge Wells or Steyning Town |
| 141 | Bridon Ropes or Colliers Wood United | v | Rusthall |
| 142 | Guildford City or Eastbourne United | v | AFC Croydon Athletic |
| 143 | Tooting & Mitcham Wanderers | v | Seaford Town |
| 144 | Canterbury City | v | Worthing United or Peacehaven & Telscombe |
| 145 | Bearsted or Pagham | v | Horsham YMCA |
| 146 | Westbury United or Folland Sports | v | Bridport or Cribbs |
| 147 | Whitchurch United or Laverstock & Ford | v | Hamworthy United or Amesbury Town |
| 148 | Devizes Town | v | Corsham Town or United Services Portsmout |
| 149 | Portland United | v | Almondsbury UWE |
| 150 | Shaftesbury Town | v | Fareham Town |
| 151 | Christchurch or Swanage Town & Herston | v | Romsey Town or Warminster Town |
| 152 | Hallen or Fawley | v | Hythe & Dibden or Team Solent |
| 153 | Bournemouth or Verwood Town | v | Brockenhurst or Ringwood Town |
| 154 | Bitton | v | Andover New Street or Gillingham Town |
| 155 | New Milton Town or Horndean | v | Oldland Abbotonians or Lymington Town |
| 156 | Calne Town | v | Roman Glass St George |
| 157 | Cowes Sports or Cadbury Heath | v | Alresford Town or Chippenham Park |
| 158 | Bemerton Heath Harlequins or Downton | v | Longwell Green Sports |
| 159 | East Cowes Victoria Athletic | v | Sherborne Town |
| 160 | Cullompton Rangers or Wincanton Town | v | Budleigh Salterton |
| 161 | Keynsham Town or Ivybridge Town | v | Shepton Mallet or Tavistock |
| 162 | Clevedon Town | v | Cheddar or Elburton Villa |
| 163 | AFC St Austell or Crediton United | v | Street |
| 164 | Exmouth | v | Witheridge |
| 165 | Hengrove Athletic or Camelford | v | Wellington AFC or Bishop Sutton |
| 166 | Wells City | v | Radstock Town or Torpoint Athletic |
| 167 | Welton Rovers or Ashton & Backwell United | v | Willand Rovers |
| 168 | Liskeard Athletic or Portishead Town | v | Helston Athletic |
| 169 | Brislington | v | Plymouth Parkway |

## PRELIMINARY ROUND

| | | | | | |
|---|---|---|---|---|---|
| 1 | Consett | v | Shildon | | |
| | (walkover for Shildon – Consett withdrawn) | | | | |
| 2 | Chester-Le-Street Town | v | Newcastle Benfield (10/9) | 1-7 | 122 |
| 3 | Radcliffe Borough | v | AFC Fylde (9/9) | 0-4 | |
| 4 | Vauxhall Motors | v | Bootle (8/9) | 8-1 | |
| 5 | Lancaster City | v | West Didsbury & Chorlton | | |
| | (walkover for West Didsbury & Chorlton – Lancaster City withdrawn) | | | | |
| 6 | Clitheroe | v | Ashton Athletic (9/9) | 3-8 | 111 |
| 7 | Irlam | v | Ashton Town (10/9) | 3-1 | 55 |
| 8 | Skelmersdale United | v | Marine (9/9) | 3-4 | 116 |
| 9 | AFC Liverpool | v | Cheadle Town (10/9) | 5-6 | 47 |
| 10 | Witton Albion | v | Salford City | | |
| | (walkover for Salford City – Witton Albion withdrawn) | | | | |
| 11 | Nantwich Town | v | Padiham (7/9) | 2-1 | 192 |
| 12 | Southport | v | FC United Of Manchester (9/9) | 2-6 | 294 |
| | (at FC United Of Manchester) | | | | |
| 13 | Macclesfield Town | v | Hyde United (10/9) | 0-1 | |
| 14 | Runcorn Town | v | Chester | | |
| | (walkover for Chester – Runcorn Town withdrawn) | | | | |
| 15 | Northwich Victoria | v | Prescot Cables | | |
| | (walkover for Prescot Cables – Northwich Victoria withdrawn) | | | | |
| 16 | Stalybridge Celtic | v | Burscough (10/9) | 2-0 | |
| 17 | Silsden | v | Hemsworth MW (10/9) | 5-2 | 35 |
| 18 | Hall Road Rangers | v | Handsworth Parramore (10/9) | 0-3 | |
| 19 | Staveley MW | v | Grimsby Town (11/9) | 0-1 | 122 |
| 20 | Brigg Town | v | Guiseley (10/9) | 0-6 | |
| 21 | Sheffield | v | Ossett Town (10/9) | 3-2 | |
| 22 | Selby Town | v | North Ferriby United (10/9) | 1-2 | 43 |
| 23 | Barton Town Old Boys | v | Pontefract Collieries | | |
| | (walkover for Pontefract Collieries – Barton Town Old Boys withdrawn) | | | | |
| 24 | Goole | v | Stocksbridge Park Steels (10/9) | 0-4 | 106 |
| 25 | Rossington Main | v | Cleethorpes Town (3/9) | 2-1aet | |
| 26 | Aylestone Park | v | Stamford (9/9) | 3-1 | |
| 27 | Leicester Nirvana | v | St Andrews (9/9) | 0-0aet | 56 |
| | (St Andrews won 3-2 on kicks from the penalty mark) | | | | |
| 28 | Mickleover Sports | v | Teversal (10/6) | 6-1 | |
| 29 | Bourne Town | v | Basford United (9/9) | 1-7 | 79 |
| 30 | Lincoln City | v | Matlock Town (9/9) | 9-1 | 12 |
| 31 | Lincoln United | v | Gresley (9/9) | 1-1aet | |
| | (Gresley won 5-4 on kicks from the penalty mark) | | | | |
| 32 | Long Eaton United | v | Loughborough Dynamo (9/9) | 1-2 | |
| 33 | Boldmere St Michaels | v | Studley (9/9) | 0-0aet | |
| | (Studley won 4-3 on kicks from the penalty mark) | | | | |
| 34 | Leek Town | v | Newcastle Town (10/9) | 0-4 | 115 |
| 35 | Ellesmere Rangers | v | Bromsgrove Sporting (10/9) | 2-0 | |
| 36 | Bilston Town | v | Pegasus Juniors (7/9) | 5-2 | 61 |
| 37 | Romulus | v | Nuneaton Griff (11/9) | 3-2 | 40 |
| 38 | Dudley Sports | v | Hereford (10/9) | 1-2 | |
| 39 | AFC Wulfrunians | v | Nuneaton Town (10/9) | 1-0 | 52 |
| 40 | Stratford Town | v | Coton Green (10/9) | 2-0 | 61 |
| 41 | Kidderminster Harriers | v | Evesham United (7/9) | 7-0 | 149 |
| 42 | Leamington | v | Stourbridge (21/9) | 2-3 | 31 |
| 43 | Halesowen Town | v | Bromyard Town (9/9) | 5-1 | 50 |
| 44 | Sutton Coldfield Town | v | AFC Telford United (7/9) | 0-6 | |
| 45 | Pilkington XXX | v | Solihull Moors (10/9) | 2-1 | 49 |
| 46 | Malvern Town | v | Coleshill Town (7/9) | 0-2 | 59 |
| 47 | Coventry Sphinx | v | Wednesfield | | |
| | (walkover for Wednesfield – Coventry Sphinx withdrawn) | | | | |
| 48 | Wisbech St Mary | v | Hadleigh United (8/9) | 4-1 | 76 |
| 49 | Ipswich Wanderers | v | Needham Market (8/9) | 2-3aet | 64 |
| 50 | Leiston | v | Stowmarket Town (10/9) | 1-4 | 53 |
| 51 | Histon | v | Walsham Le Willows (7/9) | 2-1 | 85 |
| 52 | Soham Town Rangers | v | Swaffham Town (10/9) | 1-3 | |
| 53 | Long Melford | v | Wroxham (10/9) | 0-1 | 27 |
| 54 | Norwich United | v | Great Yarmouth Town (10/9) | 2-1 | 54 |
| 55 | Cambridge City | v | Newmarket Town (10/9) | 4-0 | 69 |
| 56 | Yaxley | v | Brackley Town (8/9) | 0-2 | |
| 57 | St Neots Town | v | Bugbrooke St Michaels (10/9) | 5-1 | 45 |
| 58 | Cogenhoe United | v | AFC Rushden & Diamonds (10/9) | 0-1 | |
| 2 | | | | | |
| 59 | Biggleswade Town | v | Corby Town (10/9) | 8-1 | 65 |
| 60 | Rothwell Corinthians | v | Kettering Town (7/9) | 4-9 | 63 |
| 61 | Heybridge Swifts | v | Tower Hamlets (10/9) | 3-0 | 35 |
| 62 | Eton Manor | v | Billericay Town (10/9) | 2-2aet | |
| | (Eton Manor won 5-3 on kicks from the penalty mark – at Wadham Lodge FC) | | | | |
| 63 | Waltham Forest | v | Chelmsford City (9/9) | 1-9 | 70 |
| 64 | Romford | v | East Thurrock United (7/9) | 0-6 | 43 |
| 65 | Barkingside | v | Brentwood Town (7/9) | 0-2 | |
| 66 | Saffron Walden Town | v | Witham Town (10/9) | 1-2 | 90 |
| 67 | Clapton | v | AFC Hornchurch (10/9) | 1-3 | |
| 68 | Concord Rangers | v | Aveley (9/9) | 1-4 | 110 |
| 69 | Tilbury | v | Halstead Town (10/9) | 8-0 | 39 |
| 70 | Waltham Abbey | v | FC Broxbourne Borough (10/9) | 2-2aet | 92 |
| | (FC Broxbourne Borough won 0-3 on kicks from the penalty mark) | | | | |
| 71 | Hullbridge Sports | v | Bowers & Pitsea (10/9) | 1-3 | 58 |
| 72 | St Margaretsbury | v | Cheshunt (10/9) | 0-2 | 59 |
| 73 | Ilford | v | Bishop's Stortford (9/9) | 1-0 | |
| | (tie awarded to Bishop's Stortford - Ilford withdrawn) | | | | |
| 74 | Royston Town | v | Sawbridgeworth Town (9/9) | 6-1 | 75 |
| 75 | Chalfont St Peter | v | Hanworth Villa | | |
| | (walkover for Chalfont St Peter – Hanworth Villa withdrawn) | | | | |
| 76 | Hitchin Town | v | Aylesbury (9/9) | 5-3aet | |
| 77 | Hayes & Yeading United | v | Wingate & Finchley (10/9) | 1-1aet | 73 |
| | (at Wingate & Finchley FC) | | | | |
| | (Hayes & Yeading won 4-2 on kicks from the penalty mark) | | | | |
| 78 | Wealdstone | v | Buckingham Athletic (9/9) | 5-0 | |
| 79 | Welwyn Garden City | v | Enfield Town (8/9) | 0-1 | 80 |
| 80 | Boreham Wood | v | CB Hounslow United (9/9) | 1-0 | 68 |
| 81 | Potters Bar Town | v | Chesham United (7/9) | 3-1 | 53 |
| 82 | Newport Pagnell Town | v | Uxbridge (8/9) | 3-2 | 69 |
| 83 | Flackwell Heath | v | Bedfont Sports (10/9) | 3-4 | 62 |
| 84 | Harrow Borough | v | Staines Town (9/9) | 3-2aet | 68 |
| 85 | Dulwich Hamlet | v | Meridian (9/9) | 4-0 | 88 |
| 86 | Lordswood | v | Chipstead (9/9) | 0-5 | |
| 87 | VCD Athletic | v | Thamesmead Town (10/9) | 0-2 | 67 |
| 88 | Ramsgate | v | Phoenix Sports (10/9) | 4-0 | |
| 89 | Hastings United | v | Carshalton Athletic (10/9) | 6-3 | |
| 90 | Tooting & Mitcham United | v | Croydon (9/9) | 5-4aet | 52 |
| 91 | Welling United | v | Corinthian (8/9) | 4-2 | 104 |
| 92 | Margate | v | Little Common (8/9) | 9-0 | 93 |
| 93 | Dover Athletic | v | AFC Croydon Athletic (8/9) | 4-1 | 98 |
| 94 | Fisher | v | Eastbourne United | | |
| | (walkover for Fisher – Eastbourne United withdrawn) | | | | |
| 95 | Dartford | v | Cray Wanderers (9/9) | 9-0 | 128 |
| 96 | Erith & Belvedere | v | Cray Valley (PM) | | |
| | (walkover for Erith & Belvedere – Cray Valley (PM) withdrawn) | | | | |
| 97 | Ebbsfleet United | v | Lingfield (9/9) | 3-2 | 115 |
| 98 | Faversham Town | v | Colliers Wood United | | |
| | (walkover for Faversham Town – Colliers Wood United withdrawn) | | | | |
| 99 | Chertsey Town | v | Dorking Wanderers (10/9) | 4-3 | 67 |
| 100 | Sutton United | v | Worthing United (9/9) | 10-1 | 68 |
| 101 | Bognor Regis Town | v | Littlehampton Town (10/9) | 5-1 | 36 |
| 102 | Farnham Town | v | Raynes Park Vale (10/9) | 1-4 | |
| 103 | Kingstonian | v | Frimley Green | | |
| | (walkover for Kingstonian – Frimley Green withdrawn) | | | | |
| 104 | Dorking | v | Woking (9/9) | 0-3 | 46 |
| 105 | Wick & Barnham United | v | Oakwood (9/9) | 4-1 | 32 |
| 106 | Molesey | v | Chichester City (9/9) | 4-3 | |
| 107 | Metropolitan Police | v | South Park (10/9) | 7-1 | 40 |
| 108 | Pagham | v | Mile Oak (10/9) | 6-1 | 28 |
| 109 | Worthing | v | Loxwood (10/9) | 3-1aet | |
| 110 | Arundel | v | Horley Town (10/9) | 3-2 | |
| 111 | Three Bridges | v | Guildford City (7/9) | 1-1aet | 52 |
| | (Guildford City won 4-3 on kicks from the penalty mark) | | | | |
| 112 | Walton & Hersham | v | Camberley Town (7/9) | 0-5 | 43 |
| 113 | Lewes | v | Leatherhead (10/9) | 0-2 | 63 |
| 114 | Hampton & Richmond Borough | v | Haywards Heath Town (10/9) | 3-0 | 52 |
| 115 | Burnham | v | Aldershot Town (9/9) | 0-1 | |
| 116 | Andover Town | v | Fleet Town (10/9) | 3-1 | 59 |
| 117 | Basingstoke Town | v | Kidlington (9/9) | 2-4aet | 65 |
| 118 | Binfield | v | Thame United (9/9) | 2-2aet | 37 |
| | (Binfield won 7-6 on kicks from the penalty mark) | | | | |
| 119 | Bracknell Town | v | Milton United (10/9) | 2-1 | 31 |
| 120 | Farnborough | v | Reading Town (8/9) | 0-3 | |
| 121 | Marlow | v | Maidenhead United (9/9) | 1-4 | |
| 122 | Abingdon United | v | Hartley Wintney (10/9) | 1-3 | |
| 123 | Bournemouth | v | Poole Town (10/9) | 5-1 | 63 |
| 124 | Weymouth | v | Fareham Town (8/9) | 2-1 | 102 |
| 125 | Petersfield Town | v | Hamworthy United (9/9) | 1-0 | 82 |
| 126 | Winchester City | v | Moneyfields (8/9) | 1-3 | 21 |
| 127 | Gillingham Town | v | Havant & Waterlooville (10/9) | 1-9 | 49 |

| No | Home | | Away | Score | Att |
|---|---|---|---|---|---|
| 128 | Gloucester City | v | Chippenham Town (10/9) | 7-0 | 52 |
| | (at Tuffley Rovers FC) | | | | |
| 129 | Cheltenham Town | v | New College Swindon (7/9) | 6-0 | 126 |
| 130 | Forest Green Rovers | v | Bristol Manor Farm | 3-1 | 146 |
| 131 | Wells City | v | Clevedon Town (9/9) | 2-6 | |
| 132 | Torquay United | v | Larkhall Athletic | | |
| | (walkover for Larkhall Athletic – Torquay United withdrawn) | | | | |
| 133 | Tiverton Town | v | Bishop Sutton (10/9) | 4-1 | 81 |

## FIRST ROUND QUALIFYING

| No | Home | | Away | Score | Att |
|---|---|---|---|---|---|
| 1 | Hebburn Town | v | Workington (23/9) | 0-13 | |
| 2 | Ryton & Crawcrook Albion | v | Shildon (24/9) | 3-2 | 87 |
| 3 | Darlington RA | v | Newcastle Benfield (23/9) | 1-2 | 19 |
| 4 | Gateshead | v | Darlington 1883 (21/9) | 4-2 | 131 |
| 5 | Chester | v | Chadderton (22/9) | 9-1 | |
| 6 | Ashton Athletic | v | Marine (24/9) | 3-2 | 80 |
| 7 | AFC Fylde | v | Nelson (21/9) | 3-0 | 92 |
| 8 | Hyde United | v | Vauxhall Motors (30/9) | 3-1 | |
| 9 | Irlam | v | Curzon Ashton (24/9) | 0-2 | 55 |
| 10 | Warrington Town | v | Cheadle Town (22/9) | 2-4aet | 58 |
| 11 | Colne | v | Nantwich Town (23/9) | 1-3 | 72 |
| 12 | Salford City | v | Abbey Hey (22/9) | 1-2aet | 95 |
| 13 | FC United of Manchester | v | Altrincham (21/9) | 2-3 | 342 |
| 14 | Stalybridge Celtic | v | Prescot Cables (24/9) | 2-5 | 74 |
| 15 | West Didsbury & Chorlton | v | Wrexham (23/9) | 1-2 | 48 |
| 16 | Barnton | v | Tranmere Rovers (21/9) | 0-4 | |
| 17 | AFC Emley | v | Liversedge (21/9) | 1-2 | 96 |
| 18 | FC Halifax Town | v | Nostell MW (23/9) | 9-2 | 144 |
| 19 | Sheffield | v | Ossett Albion (24/9) | 0-3 | |
| 20 | Harrogate Town | v | Handsworth Parramore (23/9) | 2-3 | |
| 21 | Rossington Main | v | Stocksbridge Park Steels (24/9) | 3-1 | 80 |
| 22 | Silsden | v | Pontefract Collieries (23/9) | 3-1 | 37 |
| 23 | Farsley Celtic | v | Knaresborough Town (21/9) | 2-0 | 60 |
| 24 | Worksop Town | v | Guiseley (24/9) | 0-4 | 81 |
| 25 | Dinnington Town | v | Grimsby Town (24/9) | 0-4 | |
| 26 | Brighouse Town | v | North Ferriby United (24/9) | 3-4aet | 57 |
| 27 | Dunkirk | v | Basford United (21/9) | 0-2 | 91 |
| 28 | Ilkeston | v | Loughborough Dynamo (23/9) | 5-0 | 94 |
| 29 | Boston United | v | Anstey Nomads (23/9) | 4-2 | |
| 30 | Leicester Road | v | Lincoln City (23/9) | 0-10 | 35 |
| 31 | Mickleover Sports | v | Ashby Ivanhoe (24/9) | 2-1 | 43 |
| 32 | Aylestone Park | v | Oadby Town (23/9) | 1-3 | 49 |
| 33 | Belper Town | v | Gresley (23/9) | 0-4 | |
| 34 | St Andrews | v | Grantham Town (23/9) | 5-0 | 32 |
| 35 | AFC Telford United | v | Walsall Wood (21/9) | 2-1 | 149 |
| 36 | Bilston Town | v | Hereford (21/9) | 4-2 | 71 |
| 37 | Studley | v | Kidsgrove Athletic (23/9) | 3-0 | |
| 38 | Halesowen Town | v | Newcastle Town (21/9) | 2-1 | 92 |
| 39 | Romulus | v | Wolverhampton Casuals (22/9) | 2-0 | 41 |
| 40 | Rugby Town | v | AFC Wulfrunians (23/9) | 3-4 | 39 |
| 41 | Tipton Town | v | Kidderminster Harriers (21/9) | 2-4 | 45 |
| 42 | Stratford Town | v | Rushall Olympic (24/9) | 4-1 | 29 |
| 43 | Stourbridge | v | Wednesfield | | |
| | (walkover for Stourbridge – Wednesfield withdrawn) | | | | |
| 44 | Coleshill Town | v | Pilkington XXX (21/9) | 1-2aet | 39 |
| 45 | Ellesmere Rangers | v | Worcester City (24/9) | 0-5 | 22 |
| 46 | Bedworth United | v | Lye Town (23/9) | 3-1 | 43 |
| 47 | Dereham Town | v | Haverhill Rovers (24/9) | 4-1 | 43 |
| 48 | Bury Town | v | Gorleston (24/9) | 3-2 | 45 |
| 49 | Swaffham Town | v | Mildenhall Town (24/9) | 3-1 | 50 |
| 50 | Cornard United | v | Needham Market (23/9) | 0-2 | 55 |
| 51 | Ely City | v | Cambridge City (24/9) | 0-1 | 84 |
| 52 | Wisbech St Mary | v | Norwich United (22/9) | 1-2 | 89 |
| 53 | Woodbridge Town | v | Felixstowe & Walton United (21/9) | 8-1 | 38 |
| 54 | AFC Sudbury | v | Histon (24/9) | 2-1 | |
| 55 | Fakenham Town | v | Stowmarket Town (28/9) | 1-3 | 45 |
| | (21/9 - abandoned due to serious injury to player - 45 mins, 0-2) | | | | |
| 56 | Brantham Athletic | v | Wroxham (23/9) | 1-2 | |
| 57 | Eynesbury Rovers | v | Barton Rovers (24/9) | 0-3 | 67 |
| 58 | Kettering Town | v | Wellingborough Town (24/9) | 3-0 | 44 |
| 59 | Desborough Town | v | St Neots Town (23/9) | 1-2 | |
| 60 | Godmanchester Rovers | v | AFC Dunstable (24/9) | 2-6 | 42 |
| 61 | St Ives Town | v | Peterborough Northern Star (24/9) | 0-3 | 89 |
| 62 | Biggleswade Town | v | Wellingborough Whitworths | | |
| | (walkover for Biggleswade Town – Wellingborough Whitworths withdrawn) | | | | |
| 63 | Brackley Town | v | AFC Rushden & Diamonds (22/9) | 0-5 | 85 |
| 64 | Witham Town | v | Cheshunt (23/9) | 2-3 | |
| 65 | Heybridge Swifts | v | FC Broxbourne Borough (25/9) | 1-2aet | 55 |
| 66 | Tilbury | v | Aveley (24/9) | 1-2 | 79 |
| 67 | Barking | v | FC Clacton (29/9) | 5-3 | |
| | (23/9 – tie ordered to be replayed) | | | | |
| 68 | Grays Athletic | v | Eton Manor (28/9) | 4-0 | |
| 69 | AFC Hornchurch | v | Chelmsford City (24/9) | 4-3 | 80 |
| 70 | East Thurrock United | v | Braintree Town (21/9) | 0-3 | |
| 71 | Bowers & Pitsea | v | Thurrock (24/9) | 0-3 | 64 |
| 72 | Redbridge | v | Brentwood Town (21/9) | 0-3 | |
| 73 | Royston Town | v | Ware (23/9) | 3-2aet | |
| 74 | Great Wakering Rovers | v | Bishop's Stortford (23/9) | 3-0 | 70 |
| 75 | Boreham Wood | v | Leverstock Green (24/9) | 1-0 | 93 |
| 76 | Chalfont St Peter | v | Harrow Borough (22/9) | 1-4 | |
| 77 | Bedfont Sports | v | Newport Pagnell Town (24/9) | 9-0 | |
| 78 | Northwood | v | Ashford Town (Middx) (24/9) | 2-0 | 32 |
| 79 | Edgware Town | v | Hitchin Town (25/9) | 1-3 | 36 |
| 80 | Potters Bar Town | v | Hayes & Yeading United (22/9) | 0-3 | 33 |
| 81 | Wealdstone | v | Cockfosters (23/9) | 4-0 | |
| 82 | Beaconsfield SYCOB | v | Hendon (21/9) | 2-0 | |
| 83 | Spelthorne Sports | v | Enfield Town (23/9) | 1-2aet | |
| 84 | St Albans City | v | North Greenford United (21/9) | 5-3 | 41 |
| 85 | Harefield United | v | Tring Athletic | | |
| | (walkover for Harefield United – Tring Athletic withdrawn) | | | | |
| 86 | Erith & Belvedere | v | Eastbourne Borough (24/9) | 0-6 | 38 |
| 87 | Ramsgate | v | Tooting & Mitcham United (24/9) | 0-5 | 30 |
| 88 | Dulwich Hamlet | v | Whitstable Town (23/9) | 6-0 | 104 |
| 89 | Dartford | v | Chipstead (21/9) | 4-1 | |
| 90 | Hastings United | v | Eastbourne Town (25/9) | 0-2 | |
| 91 | Maidstone United | v | Welling United (21/9) | 2-0 | 224 |
| 92 | Tonbridge Angels | v | Dover Athletic (21/9) | 0-3 | |
| 93 | Margate | v | East Grinstead Town (24/9) | 8-2 | 91 |
| 94 | Fisher | v | Bromley | | |
| | (walkover for Bromley – Fisher withdrawn) | | | | |
| 95 | Faversham Town | v | Ebbsfleet United (25/9) | 0-5 | |
| 96 | Thamesmead Town | v | Ringmer (22/9) | 13-0 | |
| 97 | Chatham Town | v | Folkestone Invicta (1/10) | 0-2 | 53 |
| 98 | Sutton United | v | Westfield (21/9) | 11-0 | 65 |
| 99 | Metropolitan Police | v | Hampton & Richmond Borough (24/9) | 3-0 | 66 |
| 100 | Kingstonian | v | Chertsey Town (28/9) | 1-14 | 30 |
| | (at Banstead Athletic FC) | | | | |
| 101 | Shoreham | v | Camberley Town (24/9) | 0-4 | 33 |
| 102 | Woking | v | Corinthian Casuals (22/9) | 3-2 | 72 |
| 103 | Knaphill | v | Redhill (22/9) | 8-0 | |
| 104 | Guildford City | v | Burgess Hill Town (21/9) | 1-5 | |
| 105 | Wick & Barnham United | v | Worthing (23/9) | 0-10 | |
| 106 | Leatherhead | v | Arundel (24/9) | 5-2 | 35 |
| 107 | Bognor Regis Town | v | Molesey (23/9) | 1-1aet | 55 |
| | (Molesey won 4-2 on kicks from the penalty mark) | | | | |
| 108 | Pagham | v | East Preston | | |
| | (walkover for Pagham – East Preston withdrawn) | | | | |
| 109 | Crawley Down Gatwick | v | Whitehawk (24/9) | 1-6 | 55 |
| 110 | Raynes Park Vale | v | Horsham (24/9) | 6-0 | |
| 111 | Didcot Town | v | Alton Town (24/9) | 1-2 | 26 |
| 112 | Thatcham Town | v | Hungerford Town (23/9) | 0-6 | |
| 113 | Bracknell Town | v | Fleet Spurs (24/9) | 2-2aet | 44 |
| | (Fleet Spurs won 3-5 on kicks from the penalty mark) | | | | |
| 114 | Wantage Town | v | Andover Town (25/9) | 0-7 | |
| 115 | Ascot United | v | Hartley Wintney (24/9) | 8-3 | |
| 116 | Aldershot Town | v | Maidenhead United (21/9) | 2-1 | 54 |
| 117 | Oxford City | v | Windsor (21/9) | 10-0 | |
| 118 | Shrivenham | v | Binfield (21/9) | 2-3aet | |
| 119 | Highmoor Ibis | v | Kidlington (24/9) | 1-2 | 38 |
| | (at Reading Town FC) | | | | |
| 120 | Slough Town | v | Reading Town (24/9) | 1-7 | |
| | (tie awarded to Slough Town – Reading Town withdrawn) | | | | |
| 121 | Sholing | v | Salisbury (23/9) | 1-0 | 79 |
| 122 | Wimborne Town | v | Ringwood Town (23/9) | 4-2aet | |
| 123 | Petersfield Town | v | Weymouth (22/9) | 1-0 | 56 |
| 124 | Gosport Borough | v | Moneyfields (28/9) | 3-2 | 46 |
| 125 | Bournemouth | v | AFC Totton | | |
| | (walkover for Bournemouth – AFC Totton withdrawn) | | | | |
| 126 | Havant & Waterlooville | v | Eastleigh (24/9) | 3-2 | |
| 127 | Yate Town | v | Forest Green Rovers (23/9) | 0-2 | |
| 128 | Pewsey Vale | v | Gloucester City (24/9) | 1-7 | |
| 129 | Oldland Abbotonians | v | Cheltenham Town (23/9) | 0-17 | 50 |

| | | | | | |
|---|---|---|---|---|---|
| 130 | Tuffley Rovers | v | Cirencester Town (23/9) | 1-3 | 37 |
| 131 | Taunton Town | v | Weston Super Mare (21/9) | 2-1 | 107 |
| 132 | Bath City | v | Radstock Town (23/9) | 5-3 | 116 |
| 133 | Tiverton Town | v | Larkhall Athletic (24/9) | 3-3aet | 58 |
| | (Larkhall Athletic won 4-2 on kicks from the penalty mark) | | | | |
| 134 | Odd Down | v | Cullompton Rangers (24/9) | 2-1 | 31 |
| 135 | Clevedon Town | v | Bridgwater Town (24/9) | 3-1 | |
| 136 | Ashton & Backwell United | v | Brislington (24/9) | 2-1 | 66 |

## SECOND ROUND QUALIFYING

| | | | | | |
|---|---|---|---|---|---|
| 1 | Tranmere Rovers | v | Curzon Ashton (7/10) | 3-2 | 155 |
| 2 | Ashton Athletic | v | Hyde United (5/10) | 3-2 | 93 |
| 3 | Ryton & Crawcrook Albion | v | Prescot Cables (6/10) | 0-1aet | 100 |
| 4 | Wrexham | v | Abbey Hey (7/10) | 3-0 | 83 |
| 5 | Workington | v | Altrincham (8/10) | 2-4 | 99 |
| 6 | Gateshead | v | Newcastle Benfield (12/10) | 0-6 | 177 |
| 7 | Chester | v | Cheadle Town (7/10) | 7-0 | 175 |
| 8 | AFC Fylde | v | Nantwich Town (5/10) | 1-0 | 76 |
| 9 | Farsley Celtic | v | FC Halifax Town (9/10) | 0-5 | 99 |
| 10 | Handsworth Parramore | v | Guiseley (8/10) | 1-2 | 85 |
| 11 | Ossett Albion | v | Grimsby Town (5/10) | 3-2 | 89 |
| 12 | North Ferriby United | v | Liversedge (6/10) | 5-4aet | 80 |
| 13 | Silsden | v | Rossington Main (8/10) | 6-3 | 60 |
| 14 | Mickleover Sports | v | Basford United (8/10) | 2-3aet | 37 |
| 15 | Gresley | v | Oadby Town (7/10) | 2-6aet | 82 |
| 16 | St Andrews | v | Ilkeston (7/10) | 0-5 | 68 |
| 17 | Boston United | v | Lincoln City (7/10) | 2-3aet | |
| 18 | Stourbridge | v | Bilston Town (5/10) | 5-2 | |
| 19 | Bedworth United | v | AFC Telford United (7/10) | 2-4 | 53 |
| 20 | Stratford Town | v | Studley (8/10) | 2-3 | 53 |
| 21 | Halesowen Town | v | Kidderminster Harriers (7/10) | 0-7 | 153 |
| 22 | Worcester City | v | AFC Wulfrunians (6/10) | 1-3 | |
| 23 | Pilkington XXX | v | Romulus (8/10) | 0-3 | 46 |
| 24 | Woodbridge Town | v | Bury Town (5/10) | 3-1 | 35 |
| 25 | Needham Market | v | AFC Sudbury (8/10) | 0-0aet | |
| | (Needham Market won 3-1 on kicks from the penalty mark) | | | | |
| 26 | Swaffham Town | v | Stowmarket Town (8/10) | 1-3 | 54 |
| 27 | Wroxham | v | Dereham Town (8/10) | 2-8 | |
| 28 | Norwich United | v | Cambridge City (8/10) | 1-3 | 64 |
| 29 | Peterborough NS | v | Barton Rovers (8/10) | 2-3 | 59 |
| 30 | AFC Rushden & Diamonds | v | Biggleswade Town (5/10) | 1-4 | |
| 31 | Royston Town | v | Kettering Town (7/10) | 5-1 | 67 |
| 32 | St Neots Town | v | AFC Dunstable (8/10) | 0-7 | 63 |
| 33 | Braintree Town | v | FC Broxbourne Borough (5/10) | 2-1 | 86 |
| 34 | Barking | v | Thurrock (8/10) | 5-5aet | |
| | (Barking won 5-4 on kicks from the penalty mark) | | | | |
| 35 | Aveley | v | Brentwood Town (5/10) | 3-1 | 93 |
| 36 | Great Wakering Rovers | v | Cheshunt (7/10) | 3-2aet | 58 |
| 37 | AFC Hornchurch | v | Grays Athletic (8/10) | 2-0 | 42 |
| 38 | Beaconsfield SYCOB | v | Bedfont Sports (8/10) | 0-1 | 48 |
| 39 | Hitchin Town | v | Enfield Town (9/10) | 1-3 | 55 |
| 40 | Northwood | v | St Albans City (8/10) | 0-4 | 29 |
| 41 | Harefield United | v | Boreham Wood (8/10) | 0-3 | 74 |
| 42 | Wealdstone | v | Hayes & Yeading United (6/10) | 0-1 | 71 |
| 43 | Bromley | v | Tooting & Mitcham United (5/10) | 3-2 | 106 |
| 44 | Folkestone Invicta | v | Eastbourne Borough (8/10) | 1-0 | |
| 45 | Margate | v | Dulwich Hamlet (8/10) | 2-4 | 100 |
| 46 | Dartford | v | Dover Athletic (7/10) | 1-6 | 192 |
| 47 | Thamesmead Town | v | Maidstone United (6/10) | 1-5 | 81 |
| 48 | Ebbsfleet United | v | Eastbourne Town (5/10) | 3-2aet | |
| 49 | Slough Town | v | Pagham (12/10) | 4-4aet | |
| | (Pagham won 4-1 on kicks from the penalty mark) | | | | |
| 50 | Metropolitan Police | v | Knaphill (8/10) | 3-0 | |
| 51 | Sutton United | v | Raynes Park Vale (5/10) | 4-0 | 145 |
| 52 | Worthing | v | Leatherhead (8/10) | 3-1 | |
| 53 | Camberley Town | v | Chertsey Town (5/10) | 3-0 | |
| 54 | Molesey | v | Burgess Hill Town (7/10) | 1-5 | |
| 55 | Woking | v | Whitehawk (6/10) | 4-3aet | 89 |
| 56 | Aldershot Town | v | Alton Town (5/10) | 7-2 | 57 |
| | (at Godalming Town FC) | | | | |
| 57 | Fleet Spurs | v | Oxford City (5/10) | 0-4 | 56 |
| 58 | Hungerford Town | v | Binfield (7/10) | 4-0 | |
| 59 | Kidlington | v | Harrow Borough (8/10) | 4-1 | 70 |
| 60 | Ascot United | v | Andover Town (8/10) | 1-3 | |
| 61 | Wimborne Town | v | Sholing (7/10) | 1-4 | |
| 62 | Petersfield Town | v | Gosport Borough (6/10) | 0-4 | |
| 63 | Havant & Waterlooville | v | Bournemouth (14/10) | 1-2 | 81 |
| 64 | Larkhall Athletic | v | Gloucester City (5/10) | 0-3 | 36 |
| 65 | Cirencester Town | v | Odd Down (6/10) | 2-0 | 29 |
| 66 | Cheltenham Town | v | Clevedon Town (6/10) | 6-0 | |
| | (at Bishop's Cleeve FC) | | | | |
| 67 | Ashton & Backwell United | v | Forest Green Rovers (7/10) | 0-5 | 108 |
| 68 | Bath City | v | Taunton Town (6/10) | 3-2aet | |

## THIRD ROUND QUALIFYING

| | | | | | |
|---|---|---|---|---|---|
| 1 | AFC Fylde | v | Ashton Athletic (19/10) | 3-2 | 95 |
| 2 | Guiseley | v | North Ferriby United (19/10) | 1-2 | 124 |
| 3 | Basford United | v | FC Halifax Town (21/10) | 4-1 | 101 |
| 4 | Silsden | v | Chester (20/10) | 0-6 | 78 |
| 5 | Ossett Albion | v | Wrexham (19/10) | 0-6 | 97 |
| 6 | Newcastle Benfield | v | Altrincham (22/10) | 1-2 | 151 |
| 7 | Prescot Cables | v | Tranmere Rovers (22/10) | 1-4 | 235 |
| 8 | AFC Telford United | v | Kidderminster Harriers (20/10) | 2-1 | 168 |
| 9 | Oadby Town | v | Lincoln City (21/10) | 2-3 | |
| 10 | Romulus | v | Stourbridge (23/10) | 2-5 | 86 |
| 11 | AFC Wulfrunians | v | Cambridge City (22/10) | 1-4 | 76 |
| 12 | Studley | v | Ilkeston (21/10) | 1-4 | 81 |
| 13 | Aveley | v | Royston Town (19/10) | 2-1aet | |
| 14 | Needham Market | v | Biggleswade Town (19/10) | 2-7 | 93 |
| 15 | Boreham Wood | v | Great Wakering Rovers (22/10) | 2-1 | 98 |
| 16 | Barton Rovers | v | AFC Dunstable (16/10) | 5-4aet | 140 |
| 17 | Hayes & Yeading United | v | St Albans City (21/10) | 4-1 | 51 |
| | (at Hillingdon Borough FC) | | | | |
| 18 | AFC Hornchurch | v | Bedfont Sports (22/10) | 1-0 | 86 |
| 19 | Woodbridge Town | v | Braintree Town (22/10) | 3-0 | 72 |
| 20 | Barking | v | Enfield Town (22/10) | 0-3 | 31 |
| 21 | Stowmarket Town | v | Dereham Town (22/10) | 0-3 | 47 |
| 22 | Metropolitan Police | v | Folkestone Invicta (22/10) | 1-0 | |
| 23 | Worthing | v | Burgess Hill Town (22/10) | 5-2 | |
| 24 | Aldershot Town | v | Sutton United (19/10) | 1-2 | 63 |
| 25 | Woking | v | Pagham (19/10) | 4-1 | 103 |
| 26 | Camberley Town | v | Dover Athletic (19/10) | 2-4aet | 105 |
| 27 | Ebbsfleet United | v | Maidstone United (19/10) | 3-1 | 249 |
| 28 | Dulwich Hamlet | v | Bromley (21/10) | 3-1 | 178 |
| 29 | Sholing | v | Andover Town (20/10) | 1-0aet | 103 |
| 30 | Forest Green Rovers | v | Hungerford Town (28/10) | 1-0 | |
| | (20/10 - abandoned after 84 mins due to serious injury to player, 0-1) | | | | |
| 31 | Cheltenham Town | v | Gosport Borough (22/10) | 2-0 | 76 |
| | (at Bishop's Cleeve FC) | | | | |
| 32 | Bournemouth FC | v | Oxford City (22/10) | 3-3aet | 127 |
| | (Bournemouth won 5-4 on kicks from the penalty mark) | | | | |
| 33 | Kidlington | v | Bath City (22/10) | 1-0aet | 67 |
| 34 | Gloucester City | v | Cirencester Town | 3-2 | |
| | (at Tuffley Rovers FC) | | | | |

## FIRST ROUND PROPER

| | | | | | |
|---|---|---|---|---|---|
| 1 | Hartlepool United | v | Fleetwood Town (3/11) | 0-2 | 74 |
| 2 | ***North Ferriby United*** | v | Morecambe (3/11) | 1-2 | 110 |
| 3 | Scunthorpe United | v | ***Wrexham*** (3/11) | 2-1 | 163 |
| 4 | Accrington Stanley | v | ***Basford United*** (10/11) | 4-1 | 201 |
| 5 | Oldham Athletic | v | ***Chester*** (4/11) | 3-2aet | 353 |
| 6 | Altrincham | v | Rochdale (4/11) | 0-2 | |
| 7 | Doncaster Rovers | v | Barnsley (21/10) | 2-1aet | |
| 8 | Sheffield United | v | Bradford City (27/10) | 0-0aet | |
| | (Sheffield United won 4-2 on kicks from the penalty mark) | | | | |
| 9 | Blackpool | v | Crewe Alexandra (28/10) | 1-4aet | 392 |
| 10 | Wigan Athletic | v | York City (27/10) | 4-2 | 160 |
| 11 | Carlisle United | v | ***Tranmere Rovers*** (4/11) | 3-2aet | 166 |
| 12 | ***AFC Fylde*** | v | Bury (2/11) | 1-4 | 103 |
| 13 | ***Lincoln City*** | v | Port Vale (3/11) | 1-0 | 141 |
| 14 | ***Stourbridge*** | v | Chesterfield (4/11) | 2-3 | 151 |
| 15 | ***Ilkeston*** | v | Burton Albion (4/11) | 0-0aet | 198 |
| | (Ilkeston won 5-3 on kicks from the penalty mark) | | | | |
| 16 | Mansfield Town | v | ***Cambridge City*** (2/11) | 3-0 | 253 |
| 17 | Shrewsbury Town | v | ***AFC Telford United*** (27/10) | 2-1aet | 413 |
| 18 | Walsall | v | Coventry City (4/11) | 1-4 | 201 |
| 19 | Northampton Town | v | Notts County (27/10) | 0-2 | 284 |
| 20 | ***Aveley*** | v | Stevenage (2/11) | 0-3 | |
| 21 | ***Dereham Town*** | v | Peterborough United (5/11) | 2-1 | 199 |
| 22 | Luton Town | v | Colchester United (2/11) | 3-1 | 407 |
| 23 | ***Biggleswade Town*** | v | ***Enfield Town*** (5/11) | 6-1 | |
| 24 | Cambridge United | v | ***Hayes & Yeading United*** (4/11) | 5-0 | 187 |
| 25 | ***AFC Hornchurch*** | v | Leyton Orient (3/11) | 0-2 | 152 |
| 26 | ***Barton Rovers*** | v | Southend United (18/11) | 1-9 | 83 |
| | (3/11 - tie ordered to be replayed, 1-6) | | | | |
| 27 | ***Woodbridge Town*** | v | Dagenham & Redbridge (5/11) | 4-4aet | 140 |
| | (Woodbridge Town won 4-3 on kicks from the penalty mark) | | | | |
| 28 | ***Boreham Wood*** | v | Barnet (3/11) | 1-3 | 122 |

| | | | | | |
|---|---|---|---|---|---|
| 29 | ***Metropolitan Police*** | v | ***Dulwich Hamlet*** (2/11) | 2-2aet | 71 |
| | (Metropolitan Police won 4-2 on kicks from the penalty mark) | | | | |
| 30 | Gillingham | v | ***Ebbsfleet United*** (3/11) | 1-2 | |
| 31 | Millwall | v | ***Dover Athletic*** (3/11) | 2-0 | |
| 32 | ***Sutton United*** | v | ***Worthing*** (4/11) | 3-4aet | 114 |
| 33 | AFC Wimbledon | v | ***Woking*** (27/10) | 4-0 | 443 |
| 34 | ***Cheltenham Town*** | v | Swindon Town (3/11) | 5-1 | 172 |
| 35 | Bournemouth FC | v | Exeter City (4/11) | 1-6 | 116 |
| 36 | ***Gloucester City*** | v | Bristol Rovers (5/11) | 1-4 | |
| 37 | Oxford United | v | ***Kidlington*** (3/11) | 6-0 | 262 |
| 38 | Yeovil Town | v | ***Forest Green Rovers*** (3/11) | 4-0 | |
| 39 | ***Sholing*** | v | Newport County (3/11) | 0-0aet | 131 |
| | (Newport County won 4-2 on kicks from the penalty mark) | | | | |
| 40 | Plymouth Argyle | v | Portsmouth (28/10) | 0-3 | 340 |

## SECOND ROUND PROPER

| | | | | | |
|---|---|---|---|---|---|
| 1 | ***Lincoln City*** | v | Wigan Athletic (21/11) | 0-1 | 187 |
| 2 | ***Ilkeston*** | v | Shrewsbury Town (18/11) | 4-1 | 269 |
| 3 | Chesterfield | v | Sheffield United (24/11) | 0-3 | |
| 4 | Accrington Stanley | v | Fleetwood Town (17/11) | 2-1 | |
| 5 | Oldham Athletic | v | Morecambe (27/11) | 4-1 | 171 |
| 6 | Coventry City | v | Crewe Alexandra (23/11) | 2-0 | 223 |
| | (at Nuneaton Town FC) | | | | |
| 7 | Scunthorpe United | v | Bury (17/11) | 1-4 | 170 |
| 8 | Notts County | v | Rochdale (17/11) | 2-1 | 257 |
| 9 | Carlisle United | v | Doncaster Rovers (17/11) | 1-0aet | 197 |
| 10 | Mansfield Town | v | ***Dereham Town*** (13/11) | 4-3aet | 194 |
| 11 | AFC Wimbledon | v | ***Ebbsfleet United*** (26/11) | 2-0 | 344 |
| 12 | Exeter City | v | Oxford United (18/11) | 2-1 | 209 |
| 13 | ***Cheltenham Town*** | v | Barnet (17/11) | 3-2 | 139 |
| 14 | Cambridge United | v | Stevenage (18/11) | 0-0aet | 234 |
| | (Stevenage won 4-2 on kicks from the penalty mark) | | | | |
| 15 | Leyton Orient | v | Luton Town (16/11) | 0-1 | 337 |
| 16 | Yeovil Town | v | ***Metropolitan Police*** (18/11) | 1-1aet | 226 |
| | (Metropolitan Police won 7-6 on kicks from the penalty mark) | | | | |
| 17 | ***Biggleswade Town*** | v | ***Worthing*** (19/11) | 3-4 | 165 |
| 18 | Newport County | v | Southend United (25/11) | 1-2aet | 493 |
| 19 | Millwall | v | ***Woodbridge Town*** (16/11) | 9-1 | 273 |
| 20 | Bristol Rovers | v | Portsmouth (17/11) | 3-3aet | 204 |
| | (Portsmouth won 3-1 on kicks from the penalty mark | | | | |

## THIRD ROUND PROPER

| | | | | | |
|---|---|---|---|---|---|
| 1 | Wigan Athletic | v | Stevenage (17/12) | 3-1 | 220 |
| | (at Wigan Robin Park FC) | | | | |
| 2 | Coventry City | v | Stoke City (11/12) | 1-0 | 262 |
| | (at Leamington FC) | | | | |
| 3 | Manchester United | v | Queens Park Rangers (22/12) | 2-1aet | 1403 |
| | (at Leigh Sports Village) | | | | |
| 4 | Blackburn Rovers | v | Southend United (19/12) | 1-0 | 292 |
| 5 | Swansea City | v | Sheffield Wednesday (11/12) | 1-0 | 101 |
| | (at Llanelli FC) | | | | |
| 6 | Oldham Athletic | v | AFC Bournemouth (12/1) | 1-1aet | 248 |
| | (Oldham Athletic won 8-7 on kicks from the penalty mark) | | | | |
| 7 | Charlton Athletic | v | Millwall (2/12) | 1-1aet | 972 |
| | (Charlton Athletic won 4-2 on kicks from the penalty mark) | | | | |
| 8 | Notts County | v | Luton Town (15/12) | 1-3 | 260 |
| 9 | Arsenal | v | West Bromwich Albion (4/12) | 4-1 | |
| | (at Boreham Wood FC) | | | | |
| 10 | Nottingham Forest | v | Brighton & Hove Albion (10/12) | 1-1aet | 446 |
| | (Nottingham Forest won 4-3 on kicks from the penalty mark) | | | | |
| 11 | Derby County | v | West Ham United (18/12) | 3-1 | 545 |
| 12 | Mansfield Town | v | Sunderland (18/12) | 1-5 | 312 |
| 13 | Hull City | v | Norwich City (2/12) | 1-3 | |
| | (at North Ferriby United FC) | | | | |
| 14 | Exeter City | v | Bolton Wanderers (8/12) | 4-3 | |
| 15 | Ilkeston | v | Newcastle United (16/12) | 2-3 | |
| 16 | Tottenham Hotspur | v | Rotherham United (2/12) | 4-0 | 383 |
| | (at Stevenage FC) | | | | |
| 17 | Wolverhampton Wanderers | v | Milton Keynes Dons (7/12) | 3-0 | 381 |
| 18 | Reading | v | Sheffield United (15/12) | 3-1aet | 591 |
| 19 | Liverpool | v | Ipswich Town (16/12) | 2-1 | |
| 20 | ***Worthing*** | v | Middlesbrough (9/12) | 0-3 | |
| 21 | Southampton | v | Birmingham City (10/12) | 2-3 | 305 |
| 22 | Portsmouth | v | Manchester City (15/12) | 1-2 | 1779 |
| 23 | Everton | v | Aston Villa (11/12) | 0-1 | 289 |
| 24 | Carlisle United | v | Preston North End (1/12) | 1-2aet | |
| 25 | Leicester City | v | ***Cheltenham Town*** (16/12) | 5-0 | 416 |
| 26 | Burnley | v | ***Metropolitan Police*** (7/12) | 2-2aet | 215 |
| | (Metropolitan Police won 6-5 on kicks from the penalty mark) | | | | |
| 27 | Chelsea | v | Huddersfield Town (16/12) | 6-1 | 141 |
| | (at Aldershot Town FC) | | | | |
| 28 | Watford | v | AFC Wimbledon (11/12) | 2-2aet | 415 |
| | (AFC Wimbledon won 4-2 on kicks from the penalty mark) | | | | |
| 29 | Brentford | v | Leeds United (15/12) | 2-3 | 287 |
| 30 | Bristol City | v | Cardiff City (14/12) | 0-4 | 385 |
| 31 | Fulham | v | Bury (14/12) | 4-2 | |
| | (at Motspur Park) | | | | |
| 32 | Accrington Stanley | v | Crystal Palace (15/12) | 2-3aet | 215 |

## FOURTH ROUND PROPER

| | | | | | |
|---|---|---|---|---|---|
| 1 | Coventry City | v | Charlton Athletic (25/1) | 2-1 | |
| | (at Corby Town FC) | | | | |
| 2 | Newcastle United | v | AFC Wimbledon (6/1) | 1-2 | 915 |
| 3 | Blackburn Rovers | v | Leicester City (11/1) | 3-2aet | 291 |
| | (at Leigh Sports Village) | | | | |
| 4 | Wigan Athletic | v | Derby County (19/1) | 1-0 | 351 |
| 5 | Wolverhampton Wanderers | v | ***Metropolitan Police*** (22/1) | 5-0 | |
| 6 | Crystal Palace | v | Aston Villa (9/1) | 1-5 | 636 |
| 7 | Liverpool | v | Cardiff City (27/1) | 3-0 | |
| | (at Tranmere Rovers FC) | | | | |
| 8 | Sunderland | v | Norwich City (13/1) | 1-4 | 315 |
| 9 | Fulham | v | Reading (18/1) | 1-3 | 336 |
| | (at Motspur Park) | | | | |
| 10 | Exeter City | v | Preston North End (13/1) | 1-2 | |
| 11 | Oldham Athletic | v | Luton Town (27/1) | 0-1 | 378 |
| 12 | Manchester United | v | Chelsea (22/1) | 1-5 | 1104 |
| | (at Altrincham FC) | | | | |
| 13 | Tottenham Hotspur | v | Middlesbrough (6/1) | 1-3 | 389 |
| | (at Stevenage FC) | | | | |
| 14 | Leeds United | v | Manchester City (14/1) | 2-5 | 1477 |
| 15 | Nottingham Forest | v | Birmingham City (21/1) | 1-0 | 646 |
| 16 | Swansea City | v | Arsenal (15/1) | 1-3 | 428 |

## FIFTH ROUND PROPER

| | | | | | |
|---|---|---|---|---|---|
| 1 | Preston North End | v | Luton Town (10/2) | 1-1aet | 705 |
| | (Luton Town won 5-3 on kicks from the penalty mark) | | | | |
| 2 | Middlesbrough | v | Norwich City (3/2) | 4-5aet | |
| | (at Norwich City FC) | | | | |
| 3 | AFC Wimbledon | v | Chelsea (9/2) | 1-4 | 3455 |
| 4 | Wolverhampton Wanderers | v | Reading (5/2) | 0-3 | 350 |
| 5 | Wigan Athletic | v | Manchester City (2/2) | 1-3aet | 672 |
| 6 | Aston Villa | v | Blackburn Rovers (1/2) | 1-2 | 809 |
| 7 | Coventry City | v | Arsenal (15/2) | 2-2aet | 1828 |
| | (Arsenal won 7-6 on kicks from the penalty mark) | | | | |
| 8 | Nottingham Forest | v | Liverpool (4/2) | 1-2 | 1377 |

## SIXTH ROUND PROPER

| | | | | | |
|---|---|---|---|---|---|
| 1 | Chelsea | v | Reading (26/2) | 2-1 | 1755 |
| 2 | Blackburn Rovers | v | Luton Town (23/2) | 1-0 | 716 |
| 3 | Manchester City | v | Norwich City (29/2) | 2-0 | 1300 |
| | (at Academy Arena) | | | | |
| 4 | Arsenal | v | Liverpool (4/3) | 2-1 | 3293 |

## SEMI FINALS

| | | | | 1st Leg | | 2nd Leg | |
|---|---|---|---|---|---|---|---|
| 1 | Blackburn Rovers | v | Chelsea | 0-1 | 1007 | 1-3 | 3702 |
| 2 | Manchester City | v | Arsenal | 2-1 | 1321 | 2-2 | 4600 |

## THE FINAL

| | | | 1st Leg | | 2nd Leg | |
|---|---|---|---|---|---|---|
| Manchester City | v | Chelsea | 1-1 | 4084 | 1-3 | 8530 |

## PREVIOUS TEN FINALS

| | | | | Aggregate Score |
|---|---|---|---|---|
| 2015 | Chelsea | v | Manchester City | 5-2 |
| 2014 | Chelsea | v | Fulham | 7-6 |
| 2013 | Norwich City | v | Chelsea | 4-2 |
| 2012 | Chelsea | v | Blackburn Rovers | 4-1 |
| 2011 | Manchester Utd | v | Sheffield United | 4-1 |
| 2010 | Chelsea | v | Aston Villa | 3-2 |
| 2009 | Arsenal | v | Liverpool | 6-2 |
| 2008 | Manchester City | v | Chelsea | 4-2 |
| 2007 | Liverpool | v | Manchester Utd | 2-2* 4-3p |
| 2006 | Liverpool | v | Manchester City | 3-2 |

## FIRST ROUND

| | | | | | |
|---|---|---|---|---|---|
| 1 | Cumberland | v | Isle of Man (19/9) | 2-1 | |
| 2 | Westmorland | v | Northumberland (10/10) | 1-4 | |
| 3 | West Riding | v | Manchester (3/10) | 1-0 | |
| 4 | Cornwall | v | Guernsey (19/9) | 1-0 | |
| 5 | Essex | v | Somerset (10/10) | 9-2 | |
| 6 | Norfolk | v | Wiltshire (3/10) | 0-1 | |
| 7 | Worcestershire | v | Kent (4/10) | 4-3 | |
| 8 | Oxfordshire | v | London (11/10) | 2-1 | |

## SECOND ROUND

| | | | | | |
|---|---|---|---|---|---|
| 1 | Cheshire | v | Lincolnshire (7/11) | 2-1 | |
| 2 | East Riding | v | Leicestershire & Rutland (21/11) | 0-8 | |
| 3 | Cumberland | v | Sheffield & Hallamshire (28/11) | 1-2 | |
| 4 | Durham | v | Birmingham (31/10) | 3-1 | |
| 5 | Staffordshire | v | North Riding (31/10) | 1-0 | |
| 6 | West Riding | v | Lancashire (7/11) | 2-1aet | |
| 7 | Northumberland | v | Liverpool (21/11) | 2-3aet | |
| 8 | Oxfordshire | v | Bedfordshire (8/11) | 4-2 | |
| 9 | Gloucestershire | v | Cornwall (7/11) | 2-4 | 67 |
| 10 | Worcestershire | v | Suffolk (8/11) | 0-2 | 50 |
| 11 | Sussex | v | Cambridgeshire (7/11) | 5-0 | |
| 12 | Herefordshire | v | Jersey (7/11) | 3-3aet | |
| | (Herefordshire won 3-1 on kicks from the penalty mark) | | | | |
| 13 | Wiltshire | v | Hertfordshire (31/10) | 1-2 | |
| 14 | Devon | v | Middlesex (31/10) | 3-6 | |
| 15 | Essex | v | Berks & Bucks (8/11) | 3-0 | |
| 16 | Northamptonshire | v | Amateur Football Alliance (7/11) | 1-2 | |

## THIRD ROUND

| | | | | | |
|---|---|---|---|---|---|
| 1 | Herefordshire | v | Sussex (12/12) | 2-3 | |
| 2 | Suffolk | v | Middlesex (13/12) | 0-2 | 90 |
| 3 | Leicestershire & Rutland | v | Durham (12/12) | 2-1 | |
| 4 | Staffordshire | v | Hertfordshire (6/12) | 1-2 | |
| 5 | Amateur Football Alliance | v | Sheffield & Hallamshire (30/1) | 2-1 | |
| 6 | Liverpool | v | Oxfordshire (30/1) | 4-2 | |
| 7 | Cheshire | v | Essex (12/12) | 3-2 | |
| 8 | Cornwall | v | West Riding (5/12) | 0-3 | 81 |

## FOURTH ROUND

| | | | | | |
|---|---|---|---|---|---|
| 11 | Liverpool | v | Hertfordshire (20/1) | 2-0 | |
| 2 | Sussex | v | Middlesex (24/1) | 0-0aet | |
| | (Sussex won 7-6 on kicks from the penalty mark) | | | | |
| 3 | Amateur Football Alliance | v | Cheshire (27/2) | 0-4 | |
| 4 | West Riding | v | Leicestershire & Rutland (16/1) | 0-1 | 50 |

## SEMI FINALS

| | | | | |
|---|---|---|---|---|
| 1 | Sussex | v | Cheshire (12/3) | 3-2aet |
| | (at Sussex County FA) | | | |
| 2 | Leicestershire & Rutland | v | Liverpool (27/2) | 0-1 |

## THE FINAL

SUNDAY 10 APRIL 2016 @ Crawley Town FC

| | | | | |
|---|---|---|---|---|
| Sussex | v | Liverpool | 0-2 | 671 |

## PREVIOUS TEN FINALS

| | | | | |
|---|---|---|---|---|
| 2015 | Cheshire | v | Middlesex | 3-2 |
| 2014 | Lancashire | v | Suffolk | 3-2 aet |
| 2013 | Bedfordshire FA | v | Manchester FA | 4-4 aet |
| | (Bedfordshire FA won 4-2 on kicks from the penalty mark) | | | |
| 2012 | Essex FA | v | West Riding FA | 4-2 aet |
| 2011 | Norfolk FA | v | Staffordshire FA | 4-2 |
| 2010 | Kent FA | v | Sheffield & Hallamshire | 1-0 |
| 2009 | Birmingham FA | v | Kent FA | 2-1 |
| 2008 | Suffolk FA | v | Cambridgeshire FA | 2-1 |
| 2007 | West Riding FA | v | Suffolk FA | 1-1 aet, 4-3p |
| 2006 | Bedfordshire FA | v | Durham FA | 3-2 |

## CURRENT HOLDERS - CAMPFIELD

## FIRST ROUND

| | | | | | |
|---|---|---|---|---|---|
| 1 | Hardwick Social | v | Northallerton Police | 4-2 | |
| 2 | Hartlepool Lion Hillcarter | v | Burradon & New Fordley | 0-2 | 50 |
| 3 | Newton Aycliffe WMC | v | Seaton Carew | 8-1 | |
| 4 | Dawdon Welfare Park | v | South Bank | 9-3 | 70 |
| 5 | Windmill Kestrels | v | Seymour | 1-3 | 30 |
| 6 | Chapeltown Fforde Grene | v | AFC Blackburn Leisure | 7-1 | |
| 7 | West Bowling | v | Poulton Royal | 4-0 | |
| 8 | Bolton Woods | v | Fantail | 0-2 | 56 |
| 9 | Allerton | v | Pineapple | 2-1 | 91 |
| 10 | Thornton United | v | Alder | 0-5 | |
| 11 | Oyster Martyrs | v | BRNESC | 4-0 | 40 |
| 12 | Queens Park | v | HT Sports | 2-2aet | |
| | (Queens Park won 5-3 on kicks from the penalty mark) | | | | |
| 13 | Lobster | v | Garston | 1-2 | |
| 14 | Home & Bargain | v | LIV Supplies | | |
| | (walkover for Home & Bargain – LIV Supplies withdrawn) | | | | |
| 15 | Millhouse | v | Kirkdale | 1-2 | 80 |
| 16 | Dengo United | v | Canada | 0-1 | 60 |
| 17 | Frolesworth United | v | Oaks | 4-1 | 55 |
| 18 | Albion | v | Attenborough Cavaliers | 1-3 | 63 |
| 19 | Creation Builders | v | Mowmacre & Hoskins | 5-3 | 187 |
| 20 | RHP Sports & Social | v | Trentside | 1-2 | 49 |
| 21 | Quorn Royals 2008 | v | Halfway | 5-0 | 104 |
| 22 | Birstall Stamford | v | Punchbowl | 0-2 | |
| 23 | Riverside Rovers | v | Priory Sports | 0-4 | 105 |
| 24 | Falcons | v | Gym United | 4-2 | 26 |
| 25 | FC Bengals | v | Victoria Millers | 1-2 | |
| 26 | Club Lewsey | v | Two Touch | 5-6aet | 30 |
| 27 | Queens Head | v | FC Houghton | 1-12 | |
| 28 | North Wembley | v | Bushey Sports (Sunday) | 1-3 | |
| 29 | Belstone (Sunday) | v | Berkhamsted Athletic | | |
| | (walkover for Belstone (Sunday) – Berkhamsted Athletic withdrawn) | | | | |
| 30 | Hammer | v | AC Sportsman | 0-5 | |
| 31 | British Airways HEW | v | Brache Nation | 2-1 | |
| 32 | St Josephs (South Oxhey) | v | Comets Sports Club | 1-2 | |
| 33 | St Josephs (Sunday) | v | Aylesbury New Zealand (Sunday) | 2-1 | 22 |
| 34 | FC Morden | v | Lambeth All Stars | 5-2aet | |
| 35 | Barnes | v | Market Hotel | 6-0 | 24 |
| 36 | Polonia Reading | v | Lebeqs Tavern Courage | 0-8 | |
| 37 | Victoria Cross | v | Emmer Green (Sunday) | 4-0 | 35 |

25 Clubs with byes to the Second Round
AFC Kumazi Strikers, AFC Links, Ajax LA, Black Bull, Black Horse (Redditch), Broadfields United (Sunday), Custys, Green Man (Luton), Halton Moor, Hampton Blackwood, Hessle Rangers, Hundred Acre, Kennelwood, London St Georges, Mayfair, New Salamis, Nicosia, NLO, North Ormesby - WITHDRAWN, Nuthall, Sporting Dynamo, St John Fisher OB The Molly, Upshire, Witton Park Rose & Crown

2 Clubs exempt to the Second Round
Campfield, OJM

## SECOND ROUND

| | | | | | |
|---|---|---|---|---|---|
| 1 | Allerton | v | West Bowling (22/11) | 1-3 | |
| 2 | St John Fisher OB | v | Witton Park Rose & Crown (22/11) | 3-5 | 85 |
| 3 | Fantail | v | Home & Bargain (22/11) | 0-3 | |
| 4 | Alder | v | Mayfair | 0-6 | |
| 5 | The Molly | v | Kirkdale (22/11) | 4-0 | |
| 6 | Campfield | v | Dawdon Welfare Park | 2-1 | 102 |
| 7 | Newton Aycliffe WMC | v | Garston (22/11) | 1-1aet | |
| | (Newton Aycliffe won 4-2 on kicks from the penalty mark) | | | | |
| 8 | Halton Moor | v | Burradon & New Fordley (22/11) | 1-6 | |
| 9 | Oyster Martyrs | v | Nicosia | 2-0 | |
| 10 | Black Bull | v | Canada (22/11) | 2-2aet | |
| | (Black Bull won 4-2 on kicks from the penalty mark) | | | | |
| 11 | Seymour | v | Chapeltown Fforde Grene | 3-1 | |
| 12 | Custys | v | Kennelwood (22/11) | 2-0 | |
| 13 | Hessle Rangers | v | Hardwick Social | 0-3 | |
| 14 | Black Horse (Redditch) | v | Hundred Acre | 5-0 | 15 |
| 15 | Frolesworth United | v | Trentside | 5-3 | 18 |
| 16 | Attenborough Cavaliers | v | Punchbowl | | |
| | (walkover for Attenborough Cavaliers – Punchbowl failed to fulfil fixture) | | | | |
| 17 | Quorn Royals 2008 | v | Hampton Blackwood | 8-1 | 141 |
| 18 | Nuthall | v | OJM (22/11) | 0-6 | 47 |
| 19 | Sporting Dynamo | v | Creation Builders | 2-1 | 150 |
| 20 | AC Sportsman | v | Green Man (Luton) (22/11) | 0-4 | |
| 21 | St Josephs (Sunday) | v | Priory Sports | 3-0 | 15 |
| 22 | Two Touch | v | NLO | 2-2aet | 20 |
| | (NLO won 4-3 on kicks from the penalty mark) | | | | |
| 23 | Belstone (Sunday) | v | Broadfields United (Sunday) | 0-3 | 30 |
| 24 | Comets Sports Club | v | FC Houghton | 1-3 | |
| 25 | New Salamis | v | Falcons | 5-3 | |
| 26 | British Airways HEW | v | Bushey Sports (Sunday) | 2-1 | |
| 27 | Victoria Millers | v | Upshire | 3-0 | |
| 28 | Victoria Cross | v | London St Georges (22/11) | 8-4 | |
| 29 | FC Morden | v | AFC Links | 1-2 | 45 |
| 30 | Lebeqs Tavern Courage | v | AFC Kumazi Strikers (22/11) | 3-1 | 50 |
| 31 | Ajax LA | v | Barnes | 0-4 | |
| | Queens Park | - | BYE | | |

## THIRD ROUND

| | | | | | |
|---|---|---|---|---|---|
| 1 | Custys | v | Seymour (20/12) | 1-3 | |
| 2 | Queens Park | v | The Molly (20/12) | 0-2 | |
| 3 | Black Bull | v | Oyster Martyrs | 1-1aet | |
| | (Oyster Martyrs won 5-4 on kicks from the penalty mark) | | | | |
| 4 | Mayfair | v | Witton Park Rose & Crown (20/12) | 7-2 | |
| 5 | Home & Bargain | v | Campfield | 2-5 | |
| 6 | Newton Aycliffe WMC | v | Burradon & New Fordley (24/1) | 1-3 | |
| 7 | Hardwick Social | v | West Bowling (20/12) | 5-1aet | 35 |
| 8 | Attenborough Cavaliers | v | OJM (20/12) | 1-4 | 25 |
| 9 | Sporting Dynamo | v | Black Horse (Redditch) (20/12) | 0-5 | |
| 10 | Frolesworth United | v | Quorn Royals 2008 (20/12) | 2-1 | 70 |
| 11 | Victoria Millers | v | New Salamis | 3-6 | 78 |
| 12 | Broadfields United (Sunday) | v | NLO (20/12) | 0-1 | 12 |
| 13 | St Josephs (Sunday) | v | Green Man (Luton) (20/12) | 1-0aet | |
| 14 | FC Houghton | v | British Airways HEW | 6-4 | |
| 15 | Victoria Cross | v | Barnes | 1-3 | 55 |
| 16 | AFC Links | v | Lebeqs Tavern Courage | 0-1 | 30 |

## FOURTH ROUND

| | | | | | |
|---|---|---|---|---|---|
| 1 | Burradon & New Fordley | v | Hardwick Social (Sun 7 Feb 1.00) | 0-1 | |
| | (at Bedlington Terriers FC) | | | | |
| 2 | The Molly | v | Seymour (1.30) | 3-0 | 85 |
| 3 | Campfield | v | Oyster Martyrs (24/1) | 2-0aet | |
| 4 | OJM | v | Mayfair (24/1) | 1-0 | |
| 5 | Black Horse (Redditch) | v | FC Houghton (24/1) | 6-2 | |
| 6 | Lebeqs Tavern Courage | v | Barnes | 1-2aet | 40 |
| 7 | New Salamis | v | NLO (24/1) | 3-2 | |
| 8 | St Josephs (Sunday) | v | Frolesworth United (24/1) | 2-1aet | |

## FIFTH ROUND

| | | | | |
|---|---|---|---|---|
| 1 | The Molly | v | Campfield | 0-3 |
| 2 | OJM | v | Hardwick Social (21/2) | 1-0 |
| 3 | Barnes | v | Black Horse (Redditch) (21/2) | 1-0 |
| 4 | St Josephs (Sunday) | v | New Salamis | 2-3aet |

## SEMI FINALS

| | | | | | |
|---|---|---|---|---|---|
| 1 | Barnes | v | Campfield | 3-1 | 102 |
| | (at Hednesford Town FC) | | | | |
| 2 | OJM | v | New Salamis | 0-3 | 150 |
| | (at Nuneaton Town FC) | | | | |

## THE FINAL

SUNDAY 17APRIL 2016 @ Selhurst Park - Crystal Palace FC

| | | | | |
|---|---|---|---|---|
| Barnes | v | New Salamis | 1-1, 3-4p | 994 |

## PREVIOUS TEN FINALS

| | | | | |
|---|---|---|---|---|
| 2015 | Campfield | v | OJM | 2-0 |
| 2014 | Humbledon Plains Farm | v | Oyster Martyrs | 5-2 |
| 2013 | Oyster Martyrs | v | Barnes Albion | 4-3 |
| 2012 | Hetton Lyons C.C. | v | Canada | 5-1 |
| 2011 | Oyster Martyrs | v | Paddock | 1-0 |
| 2010 | Hetton Lyons C.C. | v | Magnet Tavern | 4-2 |
| 2009 | Scots Grey | v | Oyster Martyrs | 4-3 aet |
| 2008 | Hetton Lyons C.C. | v | Coundon Conservative | 3-2 |
| 2007 | Coundon Conservative | v | Lebeq Tavern Courage | 5-0 |
| 2006 | Hetton Lyons C.C. | v | St Joseph's (Luton) | 5-3 |

# THE WOMEN'S FA CUP

## FIRST QUALIFYING ROUND

| | | | | |
|---|---|---|---|---|
| 1 | Cleveland Ladies | v | Redcar Town | 0-7 |
| 2 | York City | v | Cramlington United | 7-0 |
| 3 | Birtley Town | v | Lowick United | 0-2 |
| 4 | Whitley Bay Women | v | Rutherford AFC Ladies | 9-0 |
| 5 | Ashington Woodhorn Lane | v | Hartlepool United | 2-3 |
| 6 | Sheffield United Community | v | Harrogate Railway | 4-2 |
| 7 | Wakefield FC Ladies | v | Brighouse Athletic | 0-3 |
| 8 | Oughtibridge War Memorial | v | Farsley Celtic | 2-1 |
| 9 | Brighouse Town | v | Ossett Albion | 4-1 |
| 10 | Winterton Rangers | v | Wetherby Athletic | 2-0 |
| 11 | Penrith AFC Ladies | v | Middleton Athletic | 3-0 |
| 12 | City Of Manchester | v | Blackburn Community Sports Club | 0-1 |
| 13 | AFC Urmston Meadowside | v | Accrington Girls & Ladies | 0-3 |
| 14 | Curzon Ashton | v | Chorltonians | 1-2aet |
| 15 | Woolton | v | Blackpool FC Ladies | 6-0 |
| 16 | Bolton Wanderers | v | Crewe Alexandra | 2-1 |
| 17 | Wigan Athletic | v | Chester City | 7-0 |
| 18 | Carlisle United | v | Burnley FC Ladies | 1-3 |
| 19 | CMB | v | Merseyrail Bootle | 5-1 |
| 20 | Workington Reds | v | Mersey Girls | 1-2 |
| 21 | Arnold Town | v | Dronfield Town | 2-1 |
| 22 | Rise Park | v | Mansfield Hosiery Mills | 2-2aet |
| | (Rise Park won 4-2 on kicks from the penalty mark) | | | |
| 23 | Ruddington Village | v | Sleaford Town | 6-2 |
| 24 | Teversal | v | AFC Leicester Ladies | 1-2 |
| 25 | Nettleham | v | Desford | 6-0 |
| 26 | Oadby & Wigston | v | Long Eaton United | 1-7 |
| 27 | Coleshill Town | v | Bradwell Belles | 3-1 |
| 28 | Bilbrook | v | Rubery | 3-1 |
| 29 | Stone Dominoes | v | Malvern Town | 5-1 |
| 30 | Leek CSOB | v | Stourbridge FC Ladies | 1-6 |
| 31 | Knowle | v | The New Saints | 0-3 |
| 32 | Crusaders | v | Burton Albion | 3-4 |
| 33 | Coundon Court | v | Shrewsbury Town | 1-4 |
| 34 | Lye Town | v | Leek Town | 4-2 |
| 35 | Kettering Town | v | Rothwell Corinthians | 5-0 |
| 36 | Great Shelford | v | March Town United | 6-1 |
| 37 | Huntingdon Town | v | Acle United | 0-9 |
| 38 | Northampton Town | v | Milton | 2-1 |
| 39 | Riverside | v | Fulbourn Institute Bluebirds | 4-0 |
| 40 | Moulton | v | Netherton United | 3-2 |
| 41 | Wymondham Town | v | Roade | 6-2 |
| 42 | Brentwood Town | v | Great Wakering Rovers | 0-4 |
| 43 | West Billericay | v | AFC Sudbury | 2-8 |
| 44 | Brandon Town | v | Bury Town | 2-5 |
| 45 | Haringey Borough | v | Leverstock Green | 6-0 |
| 46 | Garston | v | Colney Heath | 1-2 |
| 47 | Sherrardswood | v | Royston Town | 0-6 |
| 48 | AFC Dunstable | v | Leyton Orient | 1-3 |
| 49 | Hoddesdon Owls | v | Stevenage | 3-5 |
| 50 | Hampton & Richmond Borough | v | Bracknell Town | 11-5 |
| 51 | Marlow | v | Ascot United | 6-2 |
| 52 | Woodley United | v | Brentford | 2-0 |
| 53 | Wargrave | v | Headington | 3-1 |
| 54 | Oxford City | v | Barton United | |
| | (walkover for Oxford City – Barton United withdrawn) | | | |
| 55 | Wealdstone | v | Banbury United | 3-2 |
| 56 | Rottingdean Village | v | Crawley Wasps | 1-8 |
| 57 | Carshalton Athletic | v | Barming | 15-0 |
| 58 | Cowfold | v | Bexhill United | 1-3 |
| 59 | Aylesford | v | Eastbourne | 1-3 |
| 60 | Margate | v | Long Lane | 2-6 |
| 61 | London Corinthians | v | Parkwood Rangers | 3-0 |
| 62 | Abbey Rangers | v | Worthing Town | 10-1 |
| 63 | Herne Bay | v | Burgess Hill Town | 2-0 |
| 64 | Ashford Girls | v | Hassocks | 2-1 |
| 65 | AFC Wimbledon | v | Regents Park Rangers | 9-0 |
| 66 | Southampton Women | v | Winchester City Flyers | 7-2 |
| 67 | Royal Wootton Bassett Town | v | Downend Flyers | 1-5 |
| 68 | Torquay United | v | Brislington | 0-2 |
| 69 | Cheltenham Civil Service | v | Basingstoke Town | 1-3 |
| 70 | Ilminster Town | v | Bristol Ladies Union | 1-7 |
| 71 | Wimborne Town | v | Pen Mill | 8-0 |

## SECOND QUALIFYING ROUND

| | | | | | |
|---|---|---|---|---|---|
| 1 | Hartlepool United | v | Redcar Town | 0-0aet | 100 |
| | (Hartlepool United won 2-1 on kicks from the penalty mark) | | | | |
| 2 | Whitley Bay Women | v | York City | 3-3aet | |
| | (Whitley Bay won 4-3 on kicks from the penalty mark) | | | | |
| 3 | Boldon | v | Prudhoe Town | 5-0 | 42 |
| 4 | Lowick United | v | RACA Tynedale | 4-0 | 50 |
| 5 | Winterton Rangers | v | Bradford Park Avenue | 3-1 | |
| 6 | Sheffield United Community | v | Handsworth | 0-1 | |
| 7 | Oughtibridge War Memorial | v | Sheffield Wednesday | 4-1 | 200 |
| 8 | Brighouse Town | v | Brighouse Athletic | 4-0 | |
| 9 | North Ferriby United | v | Westella & Willerby | 0-9 | 55 |
| 10 | Woolton | v | Mersey Girls | 4-2 | |
| 11 | Penrith AFC Ladies | v | Burnley FC Ladies | 3-3aet | |
| | (Penrith won 4-3 on kicks from the penalty mark) | | | | |
| 12 | Accrington Girls & Ladies | v | CMB | 3-1 | |
| 13 | Chorltonians | v | Blackburn Community Sports Club | 1-3 | |
| 14 | Bolton Wanderers | v | Wigan Athletic | 0-2 | |
| 15 | AFC Leicester Ladies | v | Nettleham | 1-3 | |
| 16 | Long Eaton United | v | Rise Park | 5-0 | |
| 17 | Ruddington Village | v | Arnold Town | 8-3 | |
| 18 | Lye Town | v | Coleshill Town | 7-0 | |
| 19 | Coventry Ladies Development | v | Bedworth United | 3-2 | |
| 20 | Stockingford AA Pavilion | v | Shrewsbury Town | 1-4 | 74 |
| 21 | Wyrley | v | Stone Dominoes | 2-2aet | |
| | (Stone Dominoes won 2-3 on kicks from the penalty mark) | | | | |
| 22 | Burton Albion | v | Stourbridge FC Ladies | 3-0 | |
| 23 | The New Saints | v | Bilbrook | 5-1 | |
| 24 | Riverside | v | Daventry Town | 4-2 | |
| 25 | Kettering Town | v | Sandy | 5-0 | |
| 26 | Acle United | v | Newmarket Town | 11-1 | |
| 27 | Northampton Town | v | Great Shelford | 1-2aet | |
| 28 | Moulton | v | Wymondham Town | 0-3 | |
| 29 | Colchester Town | v | Silver End United | 5-0 | |
| 30 | Sawbridgeworth Town | v | AFC Sudbury | 1-0 | |
| 31 | Bury Town | v | Great Wakering Rovers | 1-5 | |
| 32 | Leyton Orient | v | Stevenage | 2-0 | |
| 33 | Hemel Hempstead Town | v | Colney Heath | 4-2 | |
| 34 | Royston Town | v | Haringey Borough | 0-2 | |
| 35 | Oxford City | v | Hampton & Richmond | 0-1 | |
| 36 | Wargrave | v | Marlow | 3-7 | |
| 37 | Wealdstone | v | Newbury | 3-1 | |
| 38 | Woodley United | v | Queens Park Rangers Girls | 0-4 | 79 |
| 39 | Ashford Girls | v | London Corinthians | 0-6 | 30 |
| 40 | Fulham Foundation | v | Carshalton Athletic | 2-1 | 50 |
| 41 | Herne Bay | v | Eastbourne (2.30) | 2-0 | 65 |
| 42 | Dartford Royals | v | Crawley Wasps | 0-6 | |
| 43 | Bexhill United | v | Surrey Eagles | 1-2 | |
| 44 | AFC Wimbledon | v | Abbey Rangers | 10-0 | 54 |
| 45 | Long Lane | v | Eastbourne Town | 4-0 | |
| 46 | Frome Town | v | AEK Boco | 1-2 | |
| 47 | Bristol Ladies Union | v | Middlezoy Rovers | 4-2 | |
| 48 | New Forest | v | Poole Town (27/9) | 0-12 | |
| 49 | Downend Flyers | v | Basingstoke Town | 0-4 | |
| 50 | Southampton Women | v | Wimborne Town | 4-0 | |
| 51 | Team Solent | v | Fleet Town | 7-0 | |
| 52 | Brislington | v | Keynsham Town Development | 6-2 | 63 |

## THIRD QUALIFYING ROUND

| | | | | |
|---|---|---|---|---|
| 1 | Blackburn Community Sports Club | v | Wigan Athletic | 4-3 |
| 2 | Whitley Bay Women | v | Westella & Willerby | 9-2 |
| 3 | Middlesbrough | v | Lowick United | 11-0 |
| 4 | Woolton | v | Boldon | 1-0 |
| 5 | Chester-Le-Street Town | v | Accrington Girls & Ladies | 3-0 |
| 6 | Mossley Hill | v | Penrith AFC Ladies | 4-0 |
| 7 | Brighouse Town | v | Winterton Rangers | 6-1 |
| 8 | Liverpool Marshall Feds | v | Chorley | 2-1 |
| 9 | Morecambe | v | Leeds | 5-0 |
| 10 | Hull City | v | Tranmere Rovers | 1-1aet |
| | (Tranmere Rovers won 5-4 on kicks from the penalty mark) | | | |
| 11 | Blackpool Wren Rovers | v | Hartlepool United | 1-2 |
| 12 | Rotherham United | v | Long Eaton United | 4-5 |
| 13 | The New Saints | v | Leafield Athletic | 4-3 |
| 14 | Lye Town | v | Nettleham | 3-6 |
| 15 | Wolverhampton Wanderers | v | Handsworth | 9-0 |
| 16 | Leicester City Ladies | v | Stockport County | 7-4 |
| 17 | Radcliffe Olympic | v | Oughtibridge War Memorial | 2-1aet |
| 18 | Burton Albion | v | Ruddington Village | 6-0 |
| 19 | Leicester City Women | v | Loughborough Students | 3-2 |
| 20 | Stone Dominoes | v | Kettering Town | 3-2aet |
| 21 | Coventry Ladies Development | v | Shrewsbury Town | 5-0 |
| 22 | Sporting Khalsa | v | Steel City Wanderers | 1-3 |
| 23 | Wealdstone | v | Bedford | 1-4 |
| 24 | Norwich City | v | Marlow | 0-1 |
| 25 | Sawbridgeworth Town | v | Ipswich Town | 0-6 |
| 26 | Luton Town | v | Acle United | 3-1 |
| 27 | Enfield Town | v | Haringey Borough | 4-0 |
| 28 | Wymondham Town | v | Cambridge United | 1-0 |
| 29 | Leyton Orient | v | Great Shelford | 0-2aet |
| 30 | Great Wakering Rovers | v | Milton Keynes Dons | 1-3 |
| 31 | Hampton & Richmond Borough | v | Peterborough Northern Star | 0-7 |
| 32 | Colchester Town | v | Hemel Hempstead Town | 1-2 |
| 33 | Riverside | v | Denham United | 0-4 |
| 34 | Queens Park Rangers Girls | v | Lowestoft Town | 1-5 |
| 35 | Southampton Women | v | London Corinthians | 2-2aet |
| | (London Corinthians won 5-4 on kicks from the penalty mark) | | | |
| 36 | Crystal Palace | v | Team Solent | 5-0 |
| 37 | Gloucester City | v | Southampton Saints | |
| | (walkover for Southampton Saints – Gloucester City withdrawn) | | | |
| 38 | AEK Boco | v | Shanklin | 1-0 |
| 39 | Gillingham | v | AFC Wimbledon | 7-0 |
| 40 | Keynsham Town | v | Cheltenham Town | 6-2 |
| 41 | Bristol Ladies Union | v | Herne Bay | 1-3 |
| 42 | Larkhall Athletic | v | Swindon Spitfires | 11-1 |
| 43 | Basingstoke Town | v | Fulham Foundation | 0-2 |
| 44 | St Nicholas | v | Surrey Eagles | 6-1 |
| 45 | Chichester City | v | Poole Town | 7-1 |
| 46 | Crawley Wasps | v | Old Actonians | 0-1 |
| 47 | Long Lane | v | Swindon Town | 0-12 |
| 48 | Brislington | v | Maidenhead United | 2-3 |

## FOURTH QUALIFYING ROUND

| | | | | | |
|---|---|---|---|---|---|
| 1 | Whitley Bay Women | v | Woolton | 1-0 | |
| 2 | Chester-Le-Street Town | v | Brighouse Town | 3-1 | |
| 3 | Morecambe | v | Hartlepool United (1.30) | 6-3 | 30 |
| 4 | Mossley Hill | v | Blackburn Community Sports Club | 4-2 | 25 |
| 5 | Middlesbrough | v | Liverpool Marshall Feds (2.00) | 1-3 | 76 |

| | | | | | |
|---|---|---|---|---|---|
| 6 | Tranmere Rovers | v | Steel City Wanderers (22/11) | 3-0 | |
| | (tie reversed – at Concord Sports Centre 3G, Sheffield) | | | | |
| 7 | Burton Albion | v | Radcliffe Olympic (15/11) | 1-1aet | |
| | (Radcliffe Olympic won 4-3 on kicks from the penalty mark) | | | | |
| 8 | The New Saints | v | Wolverhampton Wanderers | 0-3 | |
| 9 | Long Eaton United | v | Leicester City Ladies (2.00) | 4-1 | |
| 10 | Nettleham | v | Leicester City Women | | |
| | (walkover for Leicester City Women – Nettleham unable to fulfil fixture) | | | | |
| 11 | Coventry Ladies Development | v | Stone Dominoes (2.00) | 1-3 | |
| 12 | Marlow | v | Luton Town | 1-4 | |
| 13 | Enfield Town | v | Great Shelford (2.00) | 1-0 | |
| 14 | Peterborough Northern Star | v | Hemel Hempstead Town | 8-0 | 40 |
| 15 | Wymondham Town | v | Bedford | 0-2 | |
| 16 | Ipswich Town | v | Milton Keynes Dons (2.00) | 2-3 | |
| 17 | Lowestoft Town | v | London Corinthians | 1-8 | |
| 18 | Old Actonians | v | Southampton Saints (15/11) | 4-1 | |
| 19 | Denham United | v | Crystal Palace | 1-2 | |
| 20 | AEK Boco | v | Chichester City (15/11) | 0-10 | |
| 21 | Larkhall Athletic | v | Swindon Town (2.00) | 2-3 | 40 |
| 22 | Fulham Foundation | v | St Nicholas | 2-0 | 35 |
| 23 | Keynsham Town | v | Maidenhead United | 5-0 | 45 |
| 24 | Gillingham | v | Herne Bay (2.00) | 3-0 | |

## FIRST ROUND

| | | | | | |
|---|---|---|---|---|---|
| 1 | Tranmere Rovers | v | Whitley Bay Women (13/12) | 2-3 | |
| 2 | Morecambe | v | Chester-Le-Street Town (13/12) | 5-3aet | |
| 3 | Mossley Hill | v | Liverpool Marshall Feds | 2-1 | 30 |
| 4 | Peterborough Northern Star | v | Radcliffe Olympic | 1-1aet | 30 |
| | (Radcliffe Olympic won 4-2 on kicks from the penalty mark) | | | | |
| 5 | Long Eaton United | v | Wolverhampton Wanderers | 3-2 | |
| 6 | Leicester City Women | v | Stone Dominoes | 8-0 | 89 |
| 7 | Milton Keynes Dons | v | Crystal Palace | 0-4 | 83 |
| 8 | London Corinthians | v | Gillingham | 3-4aet | |
| 9 | Bedford | v | Luton Town | 2-3 | |
| 10 | Fulham Foundation | v | Enfield Town | 3-3aet | 75 |
| | (Fulham Foundation won 3-1 on kicks from the penalty mark) | | | | |
| 11 | Chichester City | v | Keynsham Town (13/12) | 6-0 | |
| 12 | Old Actonians | v | Swindon Town | 0-1 | 13 |

## SECOND ROUND

| | | | | | |
|---|---|---|---|---|---|
| 1 | Whitley Bay Women | v | Stoke City (24/1) | 0-2 | |
| 2 | Bradford City Women's | v | Huddersfield Town (24/1) | 3-0 | |
| 3 | Preston North End | v | Derby County | 2-1 | 42 |
| 4 | Nuneaton Town | v | Blackburn Rovers (31/1) | 0-3 | |
| | (tie reversed – at JMO Sports Park 3G, Skelmersdale) | | | | |
| 5 | Sporting Club Albion | v | Long Eaton United (17/1) | 3-0 | |
| 6 | Loughborough Foxes | v | Guiseley AFC Vixens (24/1) | 4-1 | |
| 7 | Leicester City Women | v | Radcliffe Olympic | 2-1 | 105 |
| 8 | Newcastle United | v | Mossley Hill | 4-1 | |
| 9 | Nottingham Forest | v | Morecambe (2.00) | 3-0 | |
| 10 | Chichester City | v | Queens Park Rangers (24/1) | 3-4 | |
| 11 | Crystal Palace | v | West Ham United (24/1) | 1-2 | 104 |
| 12 | Fulham Foundation | v | Lewes | 0-10 | 74 |
| 13 | Charlton Athletic | v | Plymouth Argyle | 9-0 | 92 |
| 14 | Swindon Town | v | Tottenham Hotspur (24/1) | 1-4 | |
| 15 | Forest Green Rovers | v | Gillingham (17/1) | 1-1aet | |
| | (Gillingham won 3-1 on kicks from the penalty mark) | | | | |
| 16 | Brighton & Hove Albion | v | Luton Town (2.00) | 7-0 | 143 |
| 17 | Portsmouth FC Ladies | v | Cardiff City | 2-0 | 50 |
| 18 | C&K Basildon | v | Coventry United (17/1) | 0-2 | |

## THIRD ROUND

| | | | | | |
|---|---|---|---|---|---|
| 1 | Aston Villa | v | Portsmouth FC Ladies | 1-0 | 183 |
| 2 | Charlton Athletic | v | Newcastle United | 10-0 | 325 |
| 3 | Sheffield | v | Leicester City Women (1.30) | 5-1 | |
| | (tie reversed – at Riverside Pavilion, Leicester) | | | | |
| 4 | London Bees | v | Durham Women (12.00) | 0-9 | |
| 5 | Brighton & Hove Albion | v | Oxford United | 10-0 | 402 |
| 6 | West Ham United | v | Blackburn Rovers | 0-7 | 39 |
| 7 | Gillingham | v | Tottenham Hotspur | 0-1 | |
| 8 | Sporting Club Albion | v | Coventry United | 1-0 | |
| 9 | Everton | v | Stoke City | 7-0 | 484 |
| 10 | Loughborough Foxes | v | Lewes (14/2) | 1-1aet | 45 |
| | (Loughborough Foxes won 6-5 on kicks from the penalty mark) | | | | |
| 11 | Yeovil Town | v | Bradford City Women's (14/2) | 2-0 | 175 |
| 12 | Nottingham Forest | v | Preston North End (14/2) | 2-0 | |
| | (at Basford United FC) | | | | |
| 13 | Watford | v | Millwall Lionesses | 1-3 | |
| | (at Berkhamsted FC) | | | | |
| 14 | Bristol City | v | Queens Park Rangers (14/2) | 7-1 | 376 |
| | (at Stoke Gifford Stadium) | | | | |

## FOURTH ROUND

| | | | | | |
|---|---|---|---|---|---|
| 1 | Bristol City | v | Yeovil Town | 0-0aet | 436 |
| | (Yeovil Town won 3-2 on kicks from the penalty mark – at Stoke Gifford Stadium) | | | | |
| 2 | Sheffield FC | v | Sporting Club Albion | 1-3 | |
| | (at Sheffield FC) | | | | |
| 3 | Loughborough Foxes | v | Millwall Lionesses | 1-2aet | 80 |
| | (at Loughborough University Stadium) | | | | |
| 4 | Brighton & Hove Albion | v | Blackburn Rovers (13/3) | 5-2 | 135 |
| | (at Bognor Regis Town FC - 28/2, tie ordered to be replayed) | | | | |
| 5 | Everton | v | Nottingham Forest | 5-0 | 304 |
| | (at Select Security Stadium, Widnes) | | | | |
| 6 | Durham | v | Charlton Athletic | 3-1 | |
| | (at New Ferens Park, Durham) | | | | |
| 7 | Tottenham Hotspur | v | Aston Villa | 2-3aet | |
| | (at Cheshunt FC) | | | | |

## FIFTH ROUND

| | | | | | |
|---|---|---|---|---|---|
| 1 | Birmingham City | v | Arsenal | 1-1aet | |
| | (Arsenal won 5-3 on kicks from the penalty mark) | | | | |
| 2 | Doncaster Rovers Belles | v | Chelsea | 1-4 | 525 |
| 3 | Brighton & Hove Albion | v | Sporting Club Albion | 3-4 | |
| 4 | Reading | v | Millwall Lionesses | 2-0 | |
| 5 | Yeovil Town | v | Sunderland | 0-2 | 517 |
| 6 | Liverpool | v | Manchester City (19/3) | 0-2 | 743 |
| 7 | Notts County | v | Durham | 3-1 | |
| 8 | Aston Villa | v | Everton | 1-0 | |

## SIXTH ROUND

| | | | | | |
|---|---|---|---|---|---|
| 1 | Manchester City | v | Sporting Club Albion | 2-0 | |
| 2 | Sunderland | v | Reading | 3-0 | |
| 3 | Chelsea | v | Aston Villa | 6-0 | 1147 |
| 4 | Arsenal | v | Notts County | 2-2aet | |
| | (Arsenal won 5-4 on kicks from the penalty mark) | | | | |

## SEMI FINALS

| | | | | | |
|---|---|---|---|---|---|
| 1 | Arsenal | v | Sunderland | 7-0 | 902 |
| | (at Boreham Wood FC) | | | | |
| 2 | Chelsea | v | Manchester City | 2-1aet | 2278 |
| | (at Staines Town FC) | | | | |

## THE FINAL

Saturday 14 May - @ Wembley Stadium

| | | | | |
|---|---|---|---|---|
| Arsenal | v | Chelsea | 1-0 | 32,912 |

Record crowd for Women's FA Cup

# THE FA INTER-LEAGUE CUP

## FIRST ROUND

| | | | | |
|---|---|---|---|---|
| 1 | Chester & Wirral | v | Isle of Man (26/9) | 1-7 |
| 2 | Cheshire | v | West Riding County Amateur (5/9) | 4-2 |
| 3 | Lincolnshire | v | Staffordshire County (19/9) | 1-4 |
| 4 | Yorkshire Amateur | v | West Yorkshire (26/9) | 1-4 |
| 5 | Cumberland County | v | Teesside (12/9) | 1-3 |
| 6 | Humber Premier | v | Lancashire Amateur (12/9) | 2-4 |
| 7 | Liverpool County Premier | v | West Cheshire (26/9) | 1-3 |
| 8 | Southern Amateur | v | Hampshire Premier (19/9) | 3-2 |
| 9 | Cambridgeshire County | v | Essex Olympian | |
| | (walkover for Cambridgeshire County – Essex Olympian removed) | | | |
| 10 | Guernsey County Senior | v | Gloucestershire County | |
| | (walkover for Guernsey County Senior – Gloucestershire County withdrawn) | | | |
| 11 | Herts Senior County | v | Somerset County (19/9) | 4-1 |
| 12 | Amateur Football Combination | v | Jersey Football Combination (26/9) | 1-2 |
| 13 | Spartan South Midlands (Div 2) | v | Bedfordshire County (16/9) | 4-0 |
| 14 | Anglian Combination | v | Thames Valley Premier (12/9) | 3-2aet |
| 15 | Peterborough & District | v | Dorset Premier (19/9) | 3-4 |
| 16 | Brighton Worthing & District | v | Essex & Suffolk Border (26/9) | 1-3 |

## SECOND ROUND

| | | | | |
|---|---|---|---|---|
| 1 | Staffordshire County | v | Teesside (5/12) | 1-3 |
| | (at Newcastle Town FC) | | | |
| 2 | West Cheshire | v | West Yorkshire (21/11) | 1-2 |
| | (at Cammell Laird 1907 FC) | | | |
| 3 | Cheshire | v | Isle of Man (7/11) | 0-9 |
| | (at Knutsford FC) | | | |
| 4 | Lancashire Amateur | v | Cambridgeshire County (21/11) | 0-2aet |
| | (at Daisy Hill FC) | | | |
| 5 | Jersey | v | Essex & Suffolk Border (28/11) | 0-1aet |
| | (at Springfield Stadium, St Helier) | | | |
| 6 | Herts Senior County | v | Dorset Premier (28/11) | 3-0 |
| | (at Colney Heath FC) | | | |
| 7 | Guernsey Senior County | v | Southern Amateur (28/11) | 0-1aet |
| | (at The Track, Guernsey) | | | |
| 8 | Anglian Combination | v | Spartan South Midlands (Div 2) (28/11) | 1-4aet |
| | (at Wroxham FC) | | | |

## THIRD ROUND

| | | | | |
|---|---|---|---|---|
| 1 | Isle of Man | v | Teesside (6/2) | 1-3 |
| | (at Peel AFC) | | | |
| 2 | West Yorkshire | v | Cambridgeshire County (23/1) | 1-0 |
| | (at Nostell MW FC) | | | |
| 3 | Essex & Suffolk Border | v | Spartan South Midlands (30/1) | 1-5 |
| | (at Harwich & Parkeston FC) | | | |
| 4 | Herts Senior County League | v | Southern Amateur League (23/1) | 0-4 |
| | (at Colney Heath FC) | | | |

## SEMI FINALS

| | | | | |
|---|---|---|---|---|
| 1 | Southern Amateur League | v | Teesside League (5/3) | 0-1 |
| 2 | Spartan South Midlands (Div 2) | v | West Yorkshire League (27/2) | 3-2 |
| | (Spartan South Midlands League removed for playing an ineligible player) | | | |

## FINAL

| | | | | |
|---|---|---|---|---|
| Teeside League | v | West Yorkshire League | 2-3 | 312 |

The West Yorkshire League will now progress into the UEFA Regions Cup qualifying competition, where they will face tough opposition from Romania, Russia and Serbia in a week long mini tournament in Romania from 18 to 25 September, with the winners progressing to the Finals in June 2017.

## UEFA REGIONS CUP 2015
## INTERMEDIARY ROUND

| GROUP 2 | P | W | D | L | F | A | GD | Pts |
|---|---|---|---|---|---|---|---|---|
| 1 Württemberg (Germany) | 3 | 3 | 0 | 0 | 10 | 1 | 9 | 9 |
| 2 Eastern Slovakia | 3 | 2 | 0 | 1 | 4 | 2 | 2 | 6 |
| **3 ISLE OF MAN** | **3** | **1** | **0** | **2** | **2** | **8** | **-6** | **3** |
| 4 EWC Scotland | 3 | 0 | 0 | 3 | 0 | 5 | -5 | 0 |

| | | | |
|---|---|---|---|
| Württemberg | v | Eastern Slovakia | 2-1 |
| **ISLE OF MAN** | v | EWC Scotland | 2-0 |
| Württemberg | v | **ISLE OF MAN** | 7-0 |
| EWC Scotland | v | Eastern Slovakia | 0-2 |
| EWC Scotland | v | Württemberg | 0-1 |
| Eastern Slovakia | v | **ISLE OF MAN** | 1-0 |

## FINAL TOURNAMENT

| GROUP A | P | W | D | L | F | A | GD | Pts |
|---|---|---|---|---|---|---|---|---|
| 1 Eastern Region (IRE) | 3 | 3 | 0 | 0 | 6 | 1 | 5 | 9 |
| 2 Ankara (Turkey) | 3 | 2 | 0 | 1 | 6 | 5 | 1 | 6 |
| 3 South Moravia (Czech Rep) | 3 | 1 | 0 | 2 | 3 | 6 | -3 | 3 |
| 4 Tuzla (Bosnia & Herzegovina) | 3 | 0 | 0 | 3 | 2 | 5 | -3 | 0 |

| GROUP B | P | W | D | L | F | A | GD | Pts |
|---|---|---|---|---|---|---|---|---|
| 1 Zagreb (Croatia) | 3 | 3 | 0 | 0 | 9 | 2 | 7 | 9 |
| 2 Württemberg (Germany) | 3 | 1 | 1 | 1 | 4 | 4 | 0 | 4 |
| 3 Eastern Region (NI) | 3 | 1 | 1 | 1 | 5 | 6 | -1 | 4 |
| 4 Dolnóslaski (Poland) | 3 | 0 | 0 | 3 | 1 | 7 | -6 | 0 |

## FINAL

| | | | |
|---|---|---|---|
| Eastern Region (IRE) | v | Zagreb | 1-0 |

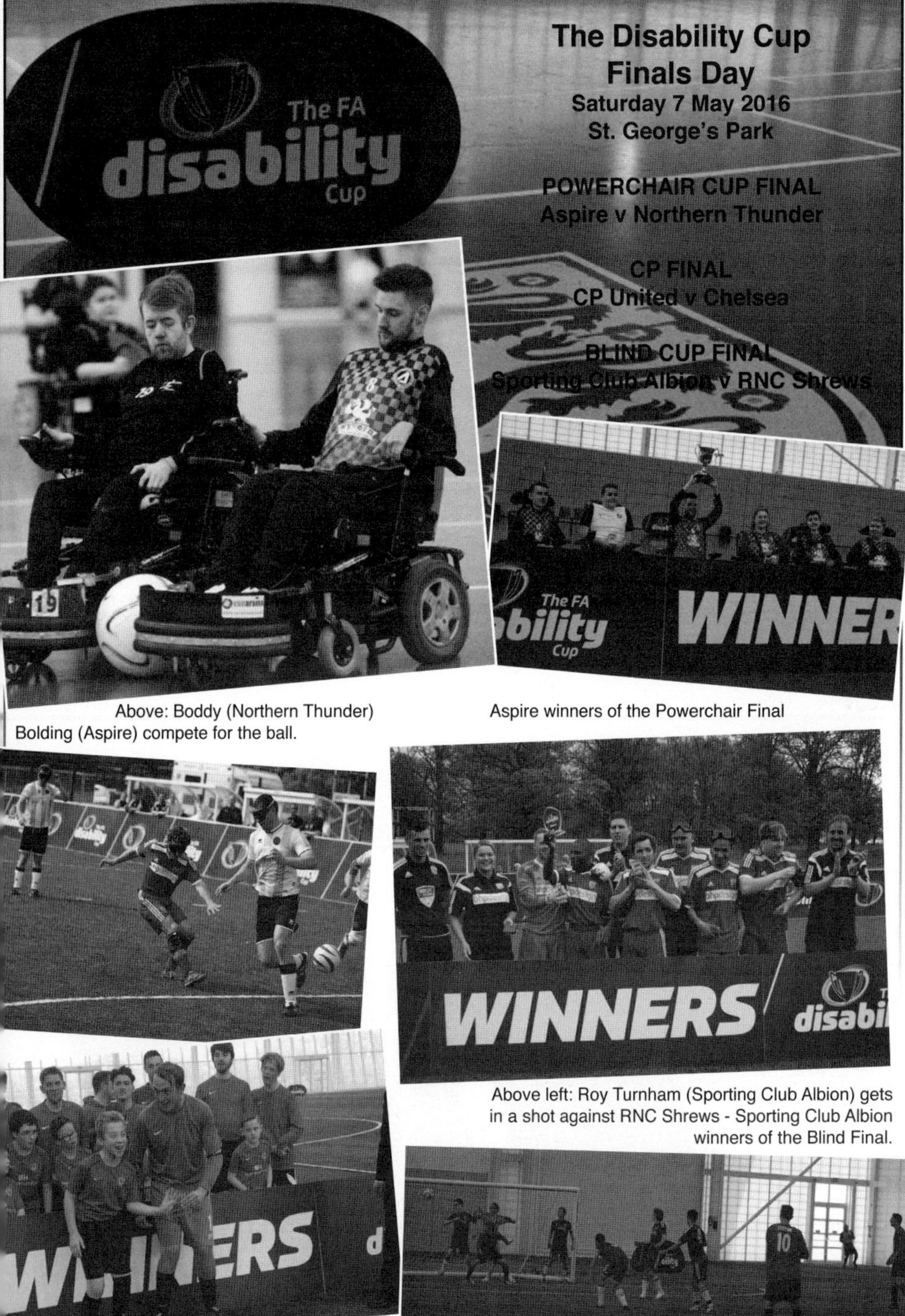


## The Disability Cup Finals Day

**Saturday 7 May 2016**
**St. George's Park**

**POWERCHAIR CUP FINAL**
**Aspire v Northern Thunder**

**CP FINAL**
**CP United v Chelsea**

**BLIND CUP FINAL**
**Sporting Club Albion v RNC Shrews**

Above: Boddy (Northern Thunder) Bolding (Aspire) compete for the ball.

Aspire winners of the Powerchair Final

Above left: Roy Turnham (Sporting Club Albion) gets in a shot against RNC Shrews - Sporting Club Albion winners of the Blind Final.

Jordan Raynes receives the cup for CP United in the Cerebral Palsy Final, whilst the action above sees John Foster (CP United) fires home the first of eight goals to win the cup. Photos: Keith Clayton

## A lot has changed in 40 years!

*Believe it or not next year's edition (2018) will be the 40th.*

*We'd liked to hear from you, in your view how has non-League football changed, for the better or worse.*

*Share with us some of your high points, and memories the game has brought you.*

*And anything you'd like to change about the Directory itself, please get in touch by emailing to* ***tw.publications@btinternet.com***

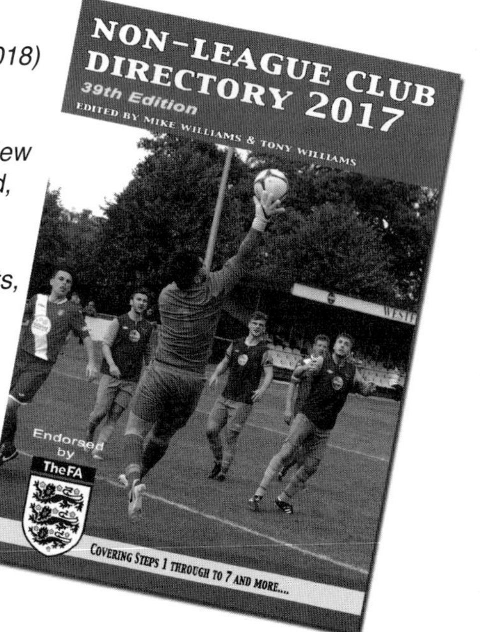

# COUNTY FOOTBALL ASSOCIATION CONTACTS

**AMATEUR FOOTBALL ALLIANCE**
CEO: Mike Brown
Address: Unit 3, 7 Wenlock Road, London, N1 7SL
Tel: 020 8733 2613
Fax: 020 7250 1338
Website: www.amateur-fa.com
Email: info@amateur-fa.com
Chairman: David Dunn

**ARMY FA**
Secretary: Major Billy Thomson
Address: Army Football Association, Fox Lines, Queens Avenue, Aldershot, Hampshire GU11 2LB
Tel: 01252 787 067
Fax: 01252 787 072
Website: www.armyfa.com
Email: info@armyfa.com
Chairman: Brigadier G I Mitchell MBE

**BEDFORDSHIRE FA**
CEO: Dan Robathan
Address: Century House, Skimpot Road, Dunstable, Bedfordshire, LU5 4JU
Tel: 01582 565 111
Fax: 01582 565 222/b
Website: www.bedfordshirefa.com
Email: info@bedfordshirefa.com
Chairman: Richard Robinson

**BERKS & BUCKS FA**
CEO: Liz Verrall
Address: 15a London Street, Faringdon, Oxon, SN7 7HD
Tel: 01367 242 099
Fax: 01367 242 158
Website: www.berks-bucksfa.com
Email: info@berks-bucksfa.com
Chairman: Jim Atkins

**BIRMINGHAM FA**
CEO: Chad Elhertson
Address: Ray Hall Lane, Great Barr, Birmingham, B43 6JF
Tel: 0121 357 4278
Fax: 0121 358 1661
Website: www.birminghamfa.com
Email: info@birminghamfa.com
Chairman: Mike Penn

**CAMBRIDGESHIRE FA**
Chief Executive: Chris Pringle
Address: Bridge Road, Impington, Cambridgeshire, CB24 9PH
Tel: 01223 209 025
Fax: 01223 209 030
Website: www.cambridgeshirefa.com
Email: info@cambridgeshirefa.com
Chairman: Bill Coad

**CHESHIRE FA**
CEO: Simon Gerrard
Address: Hartford House, Hartford Moss Recreation Centre, Northwich, Cheshire, CW8 4BG
Tel: 01606 871 166
Fax: 01606 871 292
Website: www.cheshirefa.com
Email: info@cheshirefa.com
Chairman: David Edmunds

**CORNWALL FA**
CEO: Dawn Aberdeen
Address: Kernow House, 15 Callywith Gate, Launceston Road, Bodmin, Cornwall, PL31 2RQ
Tel: 01208 269010
Fax: 01208 892665
Website: www.cornwallfa.com
Email: secretary@cornwallfa.com
Chairman: Geoff Lee

**CUMBERLAND FA**
CEO: Ben Snowden
Address: 17 Oxford Street, Workington, Cumbria, CA14 2AL
Tel: 01900 872 310
Fax: 01900 616 470
Website: www.cumberlandfa.com
Email: secretary@cumberlandfa.com
Chairman: Fred Conway

**DERBYSHIRE FA**
CEO: Dawn Heron
Address: Units 8-9 Stadium Business Ct, Millenium Way, Pride Park, Derby, DE24 8HZ
Tel: 01332 361 422
Fax: 01332 360 130
Website: www.derbyshirefa.com
Email: info@derbyshirefa.com
Chairman: Dave Heron

**DEVON FA**
CEO: Paul Morrison
Address: Coach Road, Newton Abbot, Devon, TQ12 1EJ
Tel: 01626 332 077
Fax: 01626 336 814/b
Website: www.devonfa.com
Email: info@devonfa.com
Chairman: Dennis Smith

**DORSET FA**
CEO: Sue Hough
Address: County Ground, Blanford Close, Hamworthy, Poole, BH15 4BF
Tel: 01202 682 375
Fax: 01202 666 577
Website: www.dorsetfa.com
Email: footballoperations@dorsetfa.com
Chairman: Stephen Whittle

**DURHAM FA**
CEO: John Topping
Address: Chester le Street Riverside South, Chester le Street, Co. Durham, DH3 3SJ
Tel: 01913 872 929
Website: www.durhamfa.com
Email: info@durhamfa.com
Chairman: Frank Pattison

**EAST RIDING FA**
CEO: Adam Lowthorpe
Address: Roy West Centre, 220 Inglemire Lane, Hull, HU6 7TS
Tel: 01482 221 158
Fax: 01482 221 169
Website: www.eastridingfa.com
Email: info@eastridingfa.com
Chairman: John Suddards

**ENGLISH SCHOOLS FA**
Secretary: John Read
Address: 4 Parker Court, Staffordshire Technology Park, Stafford, ST18 0WP
Tel: 01785 785 970
Fax: 01785 785 971
Website: www.esfa.co.uk
Email: info@schoolsfa.com
Chairman: Phil Harding

**ESSEX FA**
CEO: Phil Sammons
Address: The County Office, Springfield Lyons Approach, Springfield, Chelmsford, Essex, CM2 5EY
Tel: 01245 465 271
Fax: 01245 393 089
Website: www.essexfa.com
Email: info@essexfa.com
Chairman: Eddie Rhymes

**GLOUCESTERSHIRE FA**
CEO: David Neale
Address: Oaklands Park, Almondsbury, Bristol, BS32 4AG
Tel: 01454 615 888
Fax: 01454 618 088
Website: www.gloucestershirefa.com
Email: info@gloucestershirefa.com
Chairman: Roger Burden

**GUERNSEY FA**
County Secretary: Gary Roberts
Address: GFA Headquarters, Corbet Field, Grand Fort Road, St Sampsons, Guernsey, GY2 4FG
Tel: 01481 200 443
Fax: 01481 200 451
Website: www.guernseyfa.com
Email: info@guernseyfa.com

**HAMPSHIRE FA**
CEO: Neil Cassar
Address: Winklebury Football Complex, Winklebury Way, Basingstoke, RG23 8BF
Tel: 01256 853 000
Fax: 01256 357 973
Website: www.hampshirefa.com
Email: info@hampshirefa.com
Chairman: Robert Osborne

**HEREFORDSHIRE FA**
CEO: Jim Lambert
Address: County Ground Offices, Widemarsh Common, Hereford, HR4 9NA
Tel: 01432 342 179
Fax: 01432 279 265
Website: www.herefordshirefa.com
Email: val.lambert@herefordshirefa.com
Chairman: Bill Shorten

**HERTFORDSHIRE FA**
CEO: Vicki Askew
Address: The County Ground, Baldock Road, LETCHWORTH. Hertfordshire, SG6 2EN
Tel: 01462 677622
Fax: 01462 677624
Website: www.hertfordshirefa.com
Email: contactus@hertfordshirefa.com
Chairman: Paul Mallett

**HUNTINGDONSHIRE FA**
Secretary: Mark Frost
Address: Hunts FA Ltd, Ambury House, Sovereign Court, Lancaster Way, Ermine Business Park, Huntingdon, PE29 6XU
Website: www.huntsfa.com
Email: info@huntsfa.com
Chairman: Maurice Armstrong

**ISLE OF MAN FA**
CEO: Frank Stennett
Address: PO Box 53, The Bowl, Douglas, Isle of Man, IM2 1AD
Tel: 01624 615 576
Fax: 01624 615 578
Website: www.isleofmanfa.com
Email: ann.garrett@isleofmanfa.com
Chairman: Tony Jones

**JERSEY FA**
CEO: Neville Davidson
Address: Springfield Stadium, St Helier, Jersey, JE2 4LF
Tel: 01534 730 433
Fax: 01534 500 029
Website: www.jerseyfa.com
Email: paul.creeden@jerseyfa.com
Chairman: Ricky Weir

**KENT FA**
CEO: Paul Dolan
Address: Invicta House, Cobdown Park, London Road, Ditton, Nr Aylesford, Kent, ME20 6DQ.
Tel: Governance 01622 791850, Development 01622 792140
Fax: 01622 790658
Website: www.kentfa.com
Email: info@kentfa.com
Chairman: Barry Bright

**LANCASHIRE FA**
CEO: Roger De Nobrega
Address: The County Ground, Thurston Road, Leyland, Preston, PR25 2LF
Tel: 01772 624 000
Fax: 01772 624 700
Website: www.lancashirefa.com
Email: secretary@lancashirefa.com
Chairman: Brett Warburton

**LEICESTERSHIRE & RUTLAND FA**
CEO: Keith Murdoch
Address: Holmes Park, Dog & Gun Lane, Whetstone, Leicestershire, LE8 6FA
Tel: 01162 867 828
Website: www.leicestershirefa.com
Email: info@leicestershirefa.com
Chairman: David Jamieson

LINCOLNSHIRE FA
CEO: Phil Hough
Secretary: John Griffin
Address: Deepdale Enterprise Park, Deepdale Lane, Nettleham, Lincoln, LN2 2LL
Tel: 01522 524 917
Fax: 01522 528 859
Website: www.lincolnshirefa.com
Email: secretary@lincolnshirefa.com
Chairman: Grahame Lyner

**LIVERPOOL FA**
CEO: David Pugh
Address: Liverpool Soccer Centre, Walton Hall Park, Walton Hall Avenue, Liverpool, L4 9XP
Tel: 01515 234 488
Fax: 01515 234 477
Website: www.liverpoolfa.com
Email: info@liverpoolfa.com
Chairman: C Welsh

**LONDON FA**
CEO: David Fowkes
Address: 11 Hurlington Business Park, Sulivan Road, Fulham, London, SW6 3DU
Tel: 020 7610 8360
Fax: 020 7610 8370
Website: www.londonfa.com
Email: info@londonfa.com
Chairman: Tony Sharples

**MANCHESTER FA**
CEO: Colin Bridgford
Address: Manchester BT Academy, Silchester Drive, Manchester, M40 8NT
Tel: 01616 047 620
Fax: 01616 047 622
Website: www.manchesterfa.com
Email: info@manchesterfa.com
Chairman: Frank Hannah

**MIDDLESEX FA**
CEO: Peter Clayton
Address: 39 Roxborough Road, Harrow, Middlesex, HA1 1NS
Tel: 020 8515 1919
Fax: 020 8515 1910
Website: www.middlesexfa.com
Email: info@middlesexfa.com
Chairman: Jim Taylor

**NORFOLK FA**
CEO: Shaun Turner
Address: 11 Meridian Way, Thorpe St Andrew, Norwich, NR7 0TA
Tel: 01603 704 050
Fax: 01603 704 059
Website: www.norfolkfa.com
Email: info@norfolkfa.com
Chairman: Michael Banham

**NORTHAMPTONSHIRE FA**
CEO: Kevin Shoemake
Address: 9 Duncan Close, Red House Square, Moulton Park, Northampton, NN3 6WL
Tel: 01604 670 741
Fax: 01604 670 742
Website: www.northamptonshirefa.com
Email: N/A
Chairman: Bob Cotter

**NORTH RIDING FA**
CEO: Tom Radigan
Address: Broughton Road, Stokesley, Middlesborough, TS9 5NY
Tel: 01642 717 770
Fax: 01642 717 776
Website: www.northridingfa.com
Email: info@northridingfa.com
Chairman: Len Scott

**NORTHUMBERLAND FA**
CEO: John Ackerley
Address: Whitley Park, Whitley Road, Newcastle upon Tyne, NE12 9FA
Tel: 01912 700 700
Fax: 01912 700 700
Website: www.northumberlandfa.com
Email: rowland.maughan@northumberlandfa.com
Chairman: Alan Wright

**NOTTINGHAMSHIRE FA**
CEO: Elaine Oram
Address: Unit 6b, Chetwynd Business Park, Chilwell, Nottinghamshire, NG9 6RZ
Tel: 0115 983 7400
Fax: 0115 946 1977
Website: www.nottinghamshirefa.com
Email: info@nottinghamshirefa.com
Chairman: Malcolm Fox

**OXFORDSHIRE FA**
CEO: Ian Mason
Address: Unit 3, Witan Park, Avenue 2, Station Lane, Witney, Oxfordshire, OX28 4FH
Tel: 01993 894400
Fax: 01993 772 191
Website: www.oxfordshirefa.com
Email: Ian.Mason@oxfordshirefa.com
Chairman: Terry Williams

**RAF FA**
Secretary: Vince Williams
Address: RAF FA, RAF Brize Norton, Carterton, Oxfordshire, OX18 3LX
Tel: 01993 895 704
Fax: 01993 895 545
Website: www.royalairforcefa.com
Email: info@royalairforcefa.com
Chairman: Group Captain Rich Patley

**ROYAL NAVY FA**
CEO: Steve Johnson
Address: HMS Temeraire, Burnaby Road, Portsmouth, Hampshire, PO1 2HB
Tel: 02392 722 671
Fax: 02932 724 923
Website: www.royalnavyfa.com
Email: secretary@navyfa.com
Chairman: Capt Rupert Wallace

**SHEFFIELD & HALLAMSHIRE FA**
CEO: Roger Reade
Address: Clegg House, 204 Meadowhall Road, Sheffield, S9 1BN
Tel: 0114 261 5500
Website: www.sheffieldfa.com
Email: info@sheffieldfa.com
Chairman: Brian Jones

**SHROPSHIRE FA**
CEO: Roy Waterfield
Address: The New Stadium, Oteley Road, Shrewsbury, Shropshire, SY2 6ST
Tel: 01743 362 769
Fax: 01743 270 494
Website: www.shropshirefa.com
Email: secretary@shropshirefa.com
Chairman: Tom Farmer

**SOMERSET FA**
CEO: Jon Pike
Address: Charles Lewin House, Unit 10 Landmark House, Wirral Business Park, Glastonbury, BA6 9FR
Tel: 01458 832359
Fax: 01458 835588
Website: www.somersetfa.com
Email: info@somersetfa.com
Chairman: Alan Hobbs

**STAFFORDSHIRE FA**
CEO: Brian Adshead
Address: Dyson Court, Staffordshire Technology Park, Beaconside, Stafford, ST18 0LQ
Tel: 01785 256 994
Fax: 01785 279 837
Website: www.staffordshirefa.com
Email: secretary@staffordshirefa.com
Chairman: David Ramsbottom

**SUFFOLK FA**
CEO: Laura Smith
Address: The Buntings, Cedars Park, Stowmarket, Suffolk, IP14 5GZ
Tel: 01449 616 606
Fax: 01449 616 607
Website: www.suffolkfa.com
Email: info@suffolkfa.com
Chairman: Mick Pearce

**SURREY FA**
CEO: Caroline McRoyall
Address: Connaught House, 36 Bridge Street, Leatherhead, Surrey, KT22 8BZ
Tel: 01372 373 543
Fax: 01372 361 310
Website: www.surreyfa.com
Email: info@surreyfa.com
Chairman: Les Pharo

**SUSSEX FA**
CEO: Ken Benham
Address: SCFA Headquarters, Culver Road, Lancing, West Sussex, BN15 9AX
Tel: 01903 753 547
Fax: 01903 761 608
Website: www.sussexfa.com
Email: info@sussexfa.com
Chairman: Matthew Major

**WESTMORLAND FA**
CEO: Peter Ducksbury
Address: 35/37 Appleby Road, Kendal, LA9 6ET
Tel: 01539 730 946
Fax: 01539 740 567
Website: www.westmorlandfa.com
Email: info@westmorlandfa.com
Chairman: Gary Aplin

**WEST RIDING FA**
CEO: Hannah Simpson
Address: Fleet Lane, Woodlesford, Leeds, LS26 8NX
Tel: 01132 821 222
Fax: 01132 821 525
Website: www.wrcfa.com
Email: info@wrcfa.com
Chairman: Peter Marsden

**WILTSHIRE FA**
CEO: Kirsty Frior
Address: Units 2/3 Dorcan Business Village, Murdock Road, Dorcan, Swindon, SN3 5HY
Tel: 01793 486 047
Fax: 01793 692 699
Website: www.wiltshirefa.com
Email: Kirsty.Frior@wiltshirefa.com
Chairman: Sean Brosnan

**WORCESTERSHIRE FA**
CEO: Nichola Trigg
Address: Craftsman House, De Salis Drive, Hampton Lovett Industrial Estate, Droitwich, Worcestershire, WR9 0QE
Tel: 01905 827 137
Fax: 01905 798 963
Website: www.worcestershirefa.com
Email: info@worcestershirefa.com
Chairman: Roy Northall

# COUNTY & MISCELLANEOUS CUPS

## A.F.A. Senior Cup

Quarter finals

| | | | |
|---|---|---|---|
| West Wickham | v | Old Hamptonians | 1-0 |
| NUFC Oilers | v | Old Garchonians | 1-3 |
| Old Parkonians | v | Honourable Artillery Company | 2-1 |
| Old Owens | v | Old Manorians | 3-1 |

Semi-finals

| | | | |
|---|---|---|---|
| West Wickham | v | Old Parkonians | 2-0 |
| Old Garchonians | v | Old Owens | 3-2 |

Final

| | | | |
|---|---|---|---|
| West Wickham | v | Old Garchonians | 2-0 |

## A.F.A. Middlesex/Essex Senior Cup

Quarter finals

| | | | |
|---|---|---|---|
| Old Aloysians | v | Actonians Association | 2-3 |
| Old Parkonians | v | Queen Mary College Old Boys | 2-1 |
| Old Manorians | v | Polytechnic | 2-3 |
| NUFC Oilers | v | Broomfield | 1-2 |

Semi-finals

| | | | |
|---|---|---|---|
| Polytechnic | v | Broomfield | 6-0 |
| Actonians Association | v | Old Parkonians | 1-2 |

Final

| | | | |
|---|---|---|---|
| Polytechnic | v | Old Parkonians | 4-1 |

## A.F.A. Surrey/Kent Senior Cup

Quarter finals

| | | | |
|---|---|---|---|
| West Wickham | v | Kings Old Boys | 4-0 |
| Reigatians | v | Nottsborough | 2-6 |
| Old Wokingians | v | Honourable Artillery Company | 2-2, 5-4p |
| Economicals | v | Lloyds Warren | 3-1 |

Semi-finals

| | | | |
|---|---|---|---|
| Nottsborough | v | West Wickham | 4-2 |
| Economicals | v | Old Wokingians | 1-2 aet |

Final

| | | | |
|---|---|---|---|
| Nottsborough | v | Old Wokingians | 3-1 aet |

## Arthur Dunn Cup

Quarter Finals

| | | | |
|---|---|---|---|
| Old Haileyburians | v | Old Reptonians | 0-1 |
| Old Harrovians | v | Old Salopians | 1-2 |
| Old Alleynians AFC | v | Lancing Old Boys | 3-2 |
| Old Radleians | v | Old Tonbridgians | 1-4 |

Semi-Finals

| | | | |
|---|---|---|---|
| Old Alleynians AFC | v | Old Salopians | 0-2 |
| Old Reptonians | v | Old Tonbridgians | 0-1 |

Final

| | | | |
|---|---|---|---|
| Old Salopians | v | Old Tonbridgians | 0-1 |

## Bedfordshire Senior Challenge Cup

Quarter Finals

| | | | |
|---|---|---|---|
| Arlesey Town | v | Stotfold | 4-2 |
| Biggleswade Town | v | Bedford | Void |

(Both teams removed from the Competition for fielding Ineligible Players)

| | | | |
|---|---|---|---|
| Barton Rovers | v | Bedford Town | 2-0 |
| Dunstable Town | v | AFC Dunstable | 0-1 |

Semi Finals

| | | | |
|---|---|---|---|
| Arlesey Town | v | Barton Rovers | 1-1, 5-6p |
| AFC Dunstable | - | BYE | |

Final

| | | | |
|---|---|---|---|
| AFC Dunstable | v | Barton Rovers | 1-2 |

## Bedfordshire Senior Trophy

Quarter Finals

| | | | |
|---|---|---|---|
| Ickwell & Old Warden | v | Kent Athletic | 1-6 |
| AFC Kempston T. & Bedford Col. | v | Arlesey Town Reserves | 5-2 |
| Langford | v | Potton United | 0-2 |
| Ampthill Town | v | Flitwick Town | 2-1 |

Semi Finals

| | | | |
|---|---|---|---|
| AFC Kempston T. & Bedford Col. | v | Potton United | 2-1 |
| Kent Athletic | v | Ampthill Town | 1-2 |

Final

| | | | |
|---|---|---|---|
| AFC Kempston T. & Bedford Col. | v | Ampthill Town | 1-4 |

## Bedfordshire Intermediate Cup

Final

| | | | |
|---|---|---|---|
| Crawley Green Reserves | v | Sundon Park Rangers | 2-2, 5-6p |

## Bedfordshire Junior Cup

Final

| | | | |
|---|---|---|---|
| Cople & Bedford S.A. | v | Kempston Hammers Sports | 3-1 aet |

## Berks & Bucks Senior Cup

Quarter Finals

| | | | |
|---|---|---|---|
| Maidenhead United | v | Milton Keynes Dons | 1-4 |
| Burnham | v | Chesham United | 1-3 |
| Wantage Town | v | Aylesbury | 1-3 |
| Beaconsfield SYCOB | v | Aylesbury United | 2-1 |

Semi Finals

| | | | |
|---|---|---|---|
| Beaconsfield SYCOB | v | Aylesbury | 2-3 |
| Chesham United | v | Milton Keynes Dons | 4-4, 4-3p |

Final

| | | | |
|---|---|---|---|
| Aylesbury | v | Chesham United | 1-0 |

## Berks & Bucks Senior Trophy

Quarter Finals

| | | | |
|---|---|---|---|
| Holmer Green | v | Milton United | 5-3 |
| Ascot United | v | Binfield | 1-3 |
| Flackwell Heath | v | Thatcham Town | 3-2 |
| Windsor | v | Newport Pagnell Town | 1-3 |

Semi Finals

| | | | |
|---|---|---|---|
| Flackwell Heath | v | Binfield | 2-0 |
| Newport Pagnell Town | v | Holmer Green | 1-0 |

Final

| | | | |
|---|---|---|---|
| Flackwell Heath | v | Newport Pagnell Town | 2-0 |

## Berks & Bucks Intermediate Cup

Final

| | | | |
|---|---|---|---|
| Olney Town | v | Risborough Rangers | 1-2 aet |

## Berks & Bucks Junior Cup

Final

| | | | |
|---|---|---|---|
| kintbury Rangers Reserves | v | MK Gallacticos | 3-1 |

## Birmingham Senior Cup

Quarter Finals

| | | | |
|---|---|---|---|
| Nuneaton Town | v | Burton Albion | 4-3 |
| Lye Town | v | Birmingham City | 0-0, 2-4p |
| Stratford Town | v | Rushall Olympic | 2-1 |
| Solihull Moors | v | Wolverhampton Wanderers | 1-1, 5-4p |

Semi Finals

| | | | |
|---|---|---|---|
| Stratford Town | v | Solihull Moors | 0-2 |
| Nuneaton Town | v | Birmingham City | 0-1 |

Final

| | | | |
|---|---|---|---|
| Solihull Moors | v | Birmingham City | 2-1 |

## Birmingham Vase

Final

| | | | |
|---|---|---|---|
| A E I Rugby | v | Jet Blades | 2-2, 11-10p |

## Birmingham Amateur Cup

Final

| | | | |
|---|---|---|---|
| Cadbury Athletic Reserves | v | Peugeot Millpool | 1-1, 4-3p |

## Cambridgeshire Professional Cup

Final

| | | | |
|---|---|---|---|
| Cambridge City | v | Histon | 0-3 |

## Cambridgeshire Invitation Cup

Quarter Finals

| | | | |
|---|---|---|---|
| Cambridge City | v | Ely City | 4-2 aet |
| March Town United | v | Fulbourn Institute | 1-5 |
| Wisbech Town | v | Soham Town Rangers | 3-1 |
| Histon | v | Hardwick | 0-1 |

Semi-Finals

| | | | |
|---|---|---|---|
| Cambridge City | v | Fulbourn Institute | 3-0 |
| Wisbech Town | v | Hardwick | 3-0 |

Final

| | | | |
|---|---|---|---|
| Cambridge City | v | Wisbech Town | |

## Cambridgeshire Challenge Cup

Final

| | | | |
|---|---|---|---|
| Sawston United Reserves | v | Whittlesford United | 0-4 |

## Cambridgeshire Intermediate Cup

Final

| | | | |
|---|---|---|---|
| Chatteris Town | v | Outwell Swifts | 1-0 |

## Cambridgeshire Junior Challenge Cup

Final

| | | | |
|---|---|---|---|
| Fordham | v | Littleport Town | 0-0, 3-1p |

## Channel Islands - Muratti Vase (100th Final)

Final

| | | | |
|---|---|---|---|
| Guernsey | v | Jersey | 0-1 |

**Break down of Muratti Vase Wins**

Jersey 53 Guernsey 45 Shared 1 Alderney 1

## Cheshire Senior Cup

| | | | |
|---|---|---|---|
| Cammell Laird 1907 | v | Tranmere Rovers | 0-5 |
| Chester | v | Warrington Town | 4-0 |
| Stockport County | v | Crewe Alexandra | 4-1 |
| Alsager Town | v | Northwich Victoria | 0-3 |

Semi Finals

| | | | |
|---|---|---|---|
| Stockport County | v | Northwich Victoria | 3-0 |
| Tranmere Rovers | v | Chester | 1-0 |

Final

| | | | |
|---|---|---|---|
| Stockport County | v | Tranmere Rovers | 2-1 aet |

## Cornwall Senior Cup

Quarter Finals

| | | | |
|---|---|---|---|
| Bude Town | v | Helston Athletic | 1-2 |
| Godolphin Atlantic | v | Saltash United | 2-0 |
| AFC St Austell | v | Penryn Athletic | 3-1 |
| Newquay | v | Bodmin Town | 3-4 aet |

Semi Finals

| | | | |
|---|---|---|---|
| Godolphin Atlantic | v | AFC St Austell | 2-1 |
| Helston Athletic | v | Bodmin Town | 2-5 |

Final

| | | | |
|---|---|---|---|
| Bodmin Town | v | Godolphin Atlantic | 7-0 |

## Cornwall Junior Cup

Final

| | | | |
|---|---|---|---|
| St Stephen | v | Callington Town 3rds | 1-2 |

## Cumberland Senior Cup

Final

| | | | |
|---|---|---|---|
| Workington | v | Aspatria | 4-1 |

## Derbyshire Senior Challenge Cup

Quarter Finals

| | | | |
|---|---|---|---|
| Heanor Town | v | Stapenhill | 2-1 |
| Glossop North End | v | Belper Town | 1-2 |
| Gresley | v | Pinxton | 4-1 |
| Alfreton Town | v | Long Eaton United | 6-0 |

Semi-Finals

| | | | |
|---|---|---|---|
| Heanor Town | v | Belper Town | 1-2 |
| Gresley Town | v | Alfreton Town | 1-2 |

Final

| | | | |
|---|---|---|---|
| Alfreton Town | v | Belper Town | 0-0, 4-3p |

**AMPTHILL TOWN**
Bedfordshire Senior Trophy
Winners

**RISBOROUGH RANGERS**
Berks & Bucks Intermediate Cup
Winners

**HOUGHTON & WYTON**
Huntingdonshire Junior Cup
Winners

**PETERBOROUGH SPORTS**
Northants Junior Cup
Winners

Photos: Gordon Whittington

## Devon St Lukes Cup

Quarter Finals

| | | | |
|---|---|---|---|
| Exeter City | v | Cullompton Rangers | 1-0 |
| Witheridge | v | Willand Rovers | 3-1 |
| Plymouth Argyle | v | Tiverton Town | 2-1 |
| Buckland Athletic | v | Stoke Gabriel | 2-2, 4-3p |

Semi Finals

| | | | |
|---|---|---|---|
| Exeter City | v | Plymouth Argyle | 0-1 |
| Buckland Athletic | v | Witheridge | 1-1, 4-5p |

Final

| | | | |
|---|---|---|---|
| Witheridge | v | Plymouth Argyle | 0-0, 3-5p |

## Devon Premier Cup

Quarter Finals

| | | | |
|---|---|---|---|
| Elmore | v | Buckland Athletic Reserves | 2-2, 4-2p |
| Newton Abbot Spurs | v | Plymouth Marjon | 4-0 |
| Teignmouth | v | Braunton | 1-1, 5-4p |
| Appledore | v | Roborough | 1-0 aet |

Semi Finals

| | | | |
|---|---|---|---|
| Newton Abbot Spurs | v | Teignmouth | 1-0 |
| Appledore | v | Elmore | 2-1 |

Final

| | | | |
|---|---|---|---|
| Newton Abbot Spurs | v | Appledore | 0-1 |

## Devon Senior Cup

Quarter Finals

| | | | |
|---|---|---|---|
| Ashburton Association | v | University of Exeter Reserves | 1-2 |
| Chulmleigh | v | Millbridge | 4-6 |
| Lapford | v | Hartland | 3-2 |
| Exmouth Amateurs | v | Roselands | 3-1 |

Semi Finals

| | | | |
|---|---|---|---|
| Lapford | v | Millbridge | 3-0 |
| University of Exeter Reserves | v | Exmouth Amateurs | 1-1, 4-2p |

Final

| | | | |
|---|---|---|---|
| Lapford | v | University of Exeter Reserves | 2-4 |

## Devon Intermediate Cup

Final

| | | | |
|---|---|---|---|
| Whipton & Pinhoe | v | Sporting Barum | 3-5 |

## Dorset Senior Cup

Quarter Finals

| | | | |
|---|---|---|---|
| Portland United | v | Dorchester Town | 0-1 |
| Gillingham Town | v | Hamworthy United | 3-2 |
| Verwood Town | v | Weymouth | 0-2 |
| Poole Town | v | Sherborne Town | 1-2 aet |

Semi Finals

| | | | |
|---|---|---|---|
| Weymouth | v | Dorchester Town | 5-1 |
| Gillingham Town | v | Sherborne Town | 5-3 |

Final

| | | | |
|---|---|---|---|
| Gillingham Town | v | Weymouth | 1-2 |

## Dorset Senior Trophy

Quarter Finals

| | | | |
|---|---|---|---|
| Sherborne Town Reserves | v | Holt United | 3-2 |
| Sturminster Newton United | v | Parley Sports | 1-2 |
| Merley Cobham Sports | v | Balti Sports | 8-2 |
| Bridport Reserves | v | Dorchester Sports | 3-3, 4-2p |

Semi Finals

| | | | |
|---|---|---|---|
| Bridport Reserves | v | Parley Sports | 3-1 |
| Sherborne Town Reserves | v | Merley Cobham Sports | 2-3 |

Final

| | | | |
|---|---|---|---|
| Merley Cobham Sports | v | Bridport Reserves | 4-3 |

## Dorset Intermediate Cup

Final

| | | | |
|---|---|---|---|
| Chickerell United Reserves | v | Wool and Winfrith | 4-0 |

## Dorset Junior Cup

Final

| | | | |
|---|---|---|---|
| Drimpton | v | Portland United Youth | 1-3 |

## Durham Senior Challenge Cup

Final

| | | | |
|---|---|---|---|
| West Auckland Town | v | Newton Aycliffe | 1-3 aet |

## East Riding Senior Cup

Quarter Finals

| | | | |
|---|---|---|---|
| Riccall United | v | East Yorkshire Carnegie | 1-0 aet |
| Hull United | v | North Ferriby United | 1-2 |
| Hall Road Rangers | v | Hull City | 2-1 |
| Westella VIP | v | Bridlington Town | 2-3 |

Semi Finals

| | | | |
|---|---|---|---|
| Bridlington Town | v | Riccall United | 8-1 |
| Hall Road Rangers | v | North Ferriby United | 1-1, 2-4p |

Final

| | | | |
|---|---|---|---|
| North Ferriby United | v | Bridlington Town | 0-1 |

## Essex Senior Cup

Quarter Finals

| | | | |
|---|---|---|---|
| Colchester United | v | Bowers & Pitsea | 3-1 |
| Concord Rangers | v | Chelmsford City | 2-0 |
| Heybridge Swifts | v | Aveley | 3-2 |
| Redbridge | v | Tilbury | 1-1, 4-1p |

Semi Finals

| | | | |
|---|---|---|---|
| Colchester United | v | Concord Rangers | 1-3 |
| Heybridge Swifts | v | Redbridge | 2-0 |

Final

| | | | |
|---|---|---|---|
| Concord Rangers | v | Heybridge Swifts | 1-0 |

## Essex Premier Cup

Quarter Finals

| | | | |
|---|---|---|---|
| Frenford Senior | v | West Essex | 1-0 |
| Harold Wood Athletic | v | Weeley Athletic | 2-3 aet |
| Little Oakley | v | White Ensign | 3-1 |
| Springfield | v | Great Baddow | 1-0 |

Semi Finals

| | | | |
|---|---|---|---|
| Frenford Senior | v | Weeley Athletic | 4-1 |
| Little Oakley | v | Springfield | 1-0 |

Final

| | | | |
|---|---|---|---|
| Frenford Senior | v | Little Oakley | 4-1 |

## Essex Junior Cup

Final

| | | | |
|---|---|---|---|
| Chingford Athletic | v | Iona | 2-0 |

## Gloucestershire Senior Challenge Cup

Quarter Finals

| | | | |
|---|---|---|---|
| Mangotsfield United | v | Bristol Rovers U21/Reserves | 1-4 |
| Slimbridge AFC | v | Cheltenham Town Reserves | 2-0 |
| Forest Green Rovers | v | Shortwood United | 1-1, 4-3p |
| Bishops Cleeve | v | Yate Town | 3-2 |

Semi Finals

| | | | |
|---|---|---|---|
| Bishops Cleeve | v | Slimbridge | 3-0 |
| Bristol Rovers U21/Reserves | v | Forest Green Rovers | 3-4 |

Final

| | | | |
|---|---|---|---|
| Forest Green Rovers | v | Bishops Cleeve | 1-0 |

## Gloucestershire Challenge Trophy

Quarter Finals

| | | | |
|---|---|---|---|
| Lydney Town | v | Cribbs | 1-0 |
| Bitton | v | Bristol Manor Farm | 0-5 |
| Frampton United | v | Cheltenham Saracens | 1-1, 2-4p |
| Cirencester Town | - | BYE | |

Semi Finals

| | | | |
|---|---|---|---|
| Cirencester Town | v | Bristol Manor Farm | 2-5 |
| Cheltenham Saracens | v | Lydney Town | 3-3, 4-5p |

Final

| | | | |
|---|---|---|---|
| Lydney Town | v | Bristol Manor Farm | 2-9 |

## Hampshire Senior Cup

Quarter Finals

| | | | |
|---|---|---|---|
| Fleet Town | v | Lymington Town | 1-1, 3-2p |
| Winchester City | v | Sholing | 2-0 |
| Basingstoke Town | v | Horndean | 5-1 |
| Havant & Waterlooville | v | AFC Portchester | 2-2, 4-2p |

Semi Finals

| | | | |
|---|---|---|---|
| Fleet Town | v | Winchester City | 0-3 |
| Havant & Waterlooville | v | Basingstoke Town | 2-0 |

Final

| | | | |
|---|---|---|---|
| Winchester City | v | Havant & Waterlooville | 1-1, 3-5p |

## Herefordshire Challenge Cup

Quarter Finals

| | | | |
|---|---|---|---|
| Hereford | v | Bromyard Town | 6-0 |
| Kington Town | v | Pegasus Juniors | 4-2 |
| Leominster Town | v | Lads Club | 1-6 |
| Westfields | v | Wellington | 2-0 |

Semi Finals

| | | | |
|---|---|---|---|
| Hereford | v | Kington Town | 4-0 |
| Lads Club | v | Westfields | 0-3 |

Final

| | | | |
|---|---|---|---|
| Hereford | v | Westfields | 5-1 |

## Herts Senior Challenge Cup

Quarter Finals

| | | | |
|---|---|---|---|
| Bishop's Stortford | v | Ware | 1-0 |
| Hitchin Town | v | Cheshunt | 1-0 |
| Boreham Wood | v | Watford | 1-0 |
| St Albans City | v | Hadley | 2-1 |

Semi Finals

| | | | |
|---|---|---|---|
| Bishop's Stortford | v | Boreham Wood | 2-2, 5-6p |
| Hitchin Town | v | St Albans City | 2-0 |

Final

| | | | |
|---|---|---|---|
| Hitchin Town | v | Boreham Wood | 3-1 |

## Hertfordshire Senior Centenary Trophy

Quarter Finals

| | | | |
|---|---|---|---|
| Baldock Town | v | London Lions | 2-1 |
| Ware Sports | v | Bishop's Stortford Swifts | 2-6 |
| Chipperfield Corinthians | v | Letchworth Garden City Eagles | 2-5 |
| Harpenden Town | v | Old Parmiterians | 3-0 |

Semi Finals

| | | | |
|---|---|---|---|
| Baldock Town | v | Letchworth Garden City Eagles | 1-2 |
| Bishop's Stortford Swifts | v | Harpenden Town | 4-2 |

Final

| | | | |
|---|---|---|---|
| Bishop's Stortford Swifts | v | Letchworth Garden City Eagles | 5-0 |

## Huntingdonshire Senior Cup

Round One

| | | | |
|---|---|---|---|
| Eynesbury Rovers | v | Huntingdon Town | 7-3 |
| Godmanchester Rovers | v | St Neots Town Saints | 5-0 |
| Yaxley | v | St Neots Town | 1-6 |

Semi Finals

| | | | |
|---|---|---|---|
| St Neots Town | v | St Ives Town | 1-2 |
| Godmanchester Rovers | v | Eynesbury Rovers | 0-4 |

Final

| | | | |
|---|---|---|---|
| St Ives Town | v | Eynesbury Rovers | 2-0 |

## Huntingdonshire Intermediate Cup

Final

| | | | |
|---|---|---|---|
| Warboys Town | v | Brampton | 1-2 |

## Huntingdonshire Junior Cup

Final

| | | | |
|---|---|---|---|
| Houghton & Wyton | v | Alconbury | 2-2, 5-3p |

## Isle of Man FA Cup

Quarter Finals

| | | | |
|---|---|---|---|
| Union Mills | v | RYCOB | 4-2 |
| Peel | v | Ayre United | 4-0 |
| Douglas Royal | v | St Georges | 0-13 |
| Laxey | v | Malew | 3-2 |

SEMI-FINALS

| | | | |
|---|---|---|---|
| Union Mills | v | Peel | 0-7 |
| St Georges | v | Laxey | 3-0 |

FINAL

| | | | |
|---|---|---|---|
| Peel | v | St Georges | 3-2 aet |

## Kent Senior Cup

Quarter Finals

| | | | |
|---|---|---|---|
| Bromley | v | Charlton Athletic | 0-2 |
| Herne Bay | v | Dartford | 0-3 |
| Ebbsfleet United | v | Phoenix Sports | 1-0 |
| Greenwich Borough | v | Tonbridge Angels | 2-2, 3-2p |

Semi Finals

| | | | |
|---|---|---|---|
| Ebbsfleet United | v | Charlton Athletic | 1-2 |
| Greenwich Borough | v | Dartford | 1-2 |

Final

| | | | |
|---|---|---|---|
| Dartford | v | Charlton Athletic | 3-1 |

## Kent Senior Trophy
Quarter Finals

| | | | |
|---|---|---|---|
| Canterbury City | v | Ashford United | 2-3 |
| Holmesdale | v | Erith & Belvedere | 1-6 |
| Sheppey United | v | Glebe | 2-2, 5-3p |
| Erith Town | v | Corinthain | 1-4 |

Semi Finals

| | | | |
|---|---|---|---|
| Ashford United | v | Corinthain | 1-1, 4-2p |
| Erith & Belvedere | v | Sheppey United | 0-1 |

Final

| | | | |
|---|---|---|---|
| shford United | v | Sheppey United | 0-0, 6-7p |

## Kent Intermediate Cup
Final

| | | | |
|---|---|---|---|
| aversham Town | v | Greenwich Borough Reserves | 1-2 |

## .ancashire Challenge Trophy
uarter Finals

| | | | |
|---|---|---|---|
| horley | v | Clitheroe | 2-1 |
| therton Collieries | v | Padham | 2-4 |
| amber Bridge | v | Colne | 0-1 |
| ancaster City | v | Ashton Athletic | 2-0 |

emi Finals

| | | | |
|---|---|---|---|
| ancaster City | v | Padiham | 3-3, 2-0p |
| olne | v | Chorley | 0-3 |

inal

| | | | |
|---|---|---|---|
| horley (Retained) | v | Lancaster City | 2-2, 3-1 |

## eicestershire Challenge Cup
uarter Finals

| | | | |
|---|---|---|---|
| listown & Ibstock United | v | St Andrews | 0-4 |
| oalville Town | v | Shepshed Dynamo | 4-3 aet |
| icester Nirvana | v | Ashby Ivanhoe | 2-1 |
| oorn | v | Barwell | 0-3 |

emi Finals

| | | | |
|---|---|---|---|
| oalville Town | v | Barwell | 0-3 |
| Andrews | v | Leicester Nirvana | 2-4 |

nal

| | | | |
|---|---|---|---|
| rwell | v | Leicester Nirvana | 0-3 |

## eicestershire Senior Cup
uarter Finals

| | | | |
|---|---|---|---|
| stall United Social | v | Blaby & Whetstone Ath. Res. | 0-0, 4-2p |
| lestone Park Youth | v | Heather St Johns | 1-1, 7-6p |
| nckley AFC | v | Leicester Road | 4-3 |
| ttesmore Amateurs | v | Oakham United | 0-2 |

mi Finals

| | | | |
|---|---|---|---|
| kham United | v | Aylestone Park Youth | 3-1 |
| stall United Social | v | Hinckley AFC | 0-4 |

al

| | | | |
|---|---|---|---|
| kham United | v | Hinckley AFC | 1-5 |

## Lincolnshire Senior Trophy
Quarter Finals

| | | | |
|---|---|---|---|
| Deeping Rangers | v | Boston Town | 1-2 |
| Bourne Town | v | Blackstones | 1-2 |
| Lincoln Moorlands Railway | v | Winterton Rangers | 1-3 |
| Cleethorpes Town | v | Barton Town Old Boys | 2-2, 3-4p |

Semi Finals

| | | | |
|---|---|---|---|
| Blackstones | v | Boston Town | 2-1 |
| Winterton Rangers | v | Barton Town Old Boys | 1-0 |

Final

| | | | |
|---|---|---|---|
| Blackstones | v | Winterton Rangers | 2-2, 6-7 |

## Liverpool Senior Cup
Quarter Finals

| | | | |
|---|---|---|---|
| Prescot Cables | v | Tranmere Rovers | 2-1 |
| Widnes | v | Everton | 0-8 |
| Bootle | v | Skelmersdale United | 1-1, 4-5p |
| Ltherland Remyca | v | Southport | 1-0 |

Semi Finals

| | | | |
|---|---|---|---|
| Litherland Remyca | v | Prescot Cables | TBC |
| Skelmersdale United | v | Everton | TBC |

Final - TBC

| | | | |
|---|---|---|---|
| | v | | |

## Liverpool Challenge Cup
Quarter Finals

| | | | |
|---|---|---|---|
| Redgate Rovers | v | Eagle Sports | 0-3 |
| Kirkby Town Railway | v | Alumni | 2-4 |
| Hale | v | Richmond Raith Rovers | 1-4 |
| South Liverpool | v | Warbreck | 2-1 |

Semi Finals

| | | | |
|---|---|---|---|
| Alumni | v | Richmond Raith Rovers | 1-4 aet |
| South Liverpool | v | Eagle Sports | 4-1 |

Final

| | | | |
|---|---|---|---|
| South Liverpool | v | Richmond Raith Rovers | 4-2 aet |

## London Senior Cup
Quarter Finals

| | | | |
|---|---|---|---|
| Dulwich Hamlet | v | London Bari | 1-0 |
| Tooting & Mitcham United | v | Harrow Borough | 1-0 |
| Hendon | v | Croydon | 2-1 |
| Wingate & Finchley | v | Redbridge | 2-3 |

Semi Finals

| | | | |
|---|---|---|---|
| Redbridge | v | Hendon | 0-1 |
| Tooting & Mitcham United | v | Dulwich Hamlet | 3-0 |

Final

| | | | |
|---|---|---|---|
| Tooting & Mitcham United | v | Hendon | 2-0 |

## London Senior Trophy
Quarter Finals

| | | | |
|---|---|---|---|
| Kilburn | v | Forest Hill Park | 1-1, 4-3p |
| Tooting Bec | v | South Kilburn | 6-0 |
| Corinthian Casuals Reserves | v | Club Langley | 1-0 |
| Bridon Ropes | v | Glebe | 1-1, 0-3p |

Semi Finals

| | | | |
|---|---|---|---|
| Tooting Bec | v | Kilburn | 3-2 |
| Glebe | v | Corinthian Casuals Reserves | 4-0 |

Final

| | | | |
|---|---|---|---|
| Glebe | v | Tooting Bec | 4-1 |

## Manchester Premier Cup

Final

| | | | |
|---|---|---|---|
| Mossley (Retained) | v | Stalybridge Celtic | 3-1 |

## Middlesex Senior Challenge Cup

Quarter Finals

| | | | |
|---|---|---|---|
| Staines Town | v | Uxbridge | 3-0 |
| Hampton & Richmond Borough | v | Enfield Town | 2-3 |
| Ashford Town (Mddx) | v | Harrow Borough | 3-0 |
| Northwood | v | Spelthorne Sports Club | 2-1 |

Semi Finals

| | | | |
|---|---|---|---|
| Enfield Town | v | Ashford Town (Mddx) | 6-4 aet |
| Northwood | v | Staines Town | 2-0 |

Final

| | | | |
|---|---|---|---|
| Northwood | v | Enfield Town | 2-0 |

## Middlesex Premier Cup

Quarter Finals

| | | | |
|---|---|---|---|
| Enfield Town U21 | v | Woodford Town | 4-7 aet |
| Edgware Town | v | Hillingdon Borough | 0-1 |
| Staines Lammas | v | Northwood Reserves | 8-0 |
| Southall | v | Bedfont & Feltham | 2-6 aet |

Semi Finals

| | | | |
|---|---|---|---|
| Hillingdon Borough | v | Staines Lammas | 3-1 |
| Woodford Town | v | Bedfont & Feltham | 5-1 |

Final

| | | | |
|---|---|---|---|
| Hillingdon Borough | v | Woodford Town | 3-4 |

## Norfolk Senior Cup

Quarter Finals

| | | | |
|---|---|---|---|
| Spixworth | v | Dereham Town | 0-2 |
| Gorleston | v | Thetford Town | 2-1 |
| Norwich United | v | Acle United | 7-1 |
| Wroxham | v | King's Lynn Town Reserves | 1-2 aet |

Semi Finals

| | | | |
|---|---|---|---|
| King's Lynn Town Reserves | v | Dereham Town | 1-3 |
| Norwich United | v | Gorleston | 3-0 |

Final

| | | | |
|---|---|---|---|
| Dereham Town | v | Norwich United | 2-0 |

## Northamptonshire Senior Cup

Quarter Finals

| | | | |
|---|---|---|---|
| AFC Rushden & Diamonds | v | Desborough Town | 2-2, 6-5p |
| Brackley Town Saints | v | Kettering Town | 1-2 |
| Brackley Town | v | Daventry Town | 4-0 |
| Rothwell Corinthians | v | Northampton Sileby Rangers | 2-1 |

Semi-Finals

| | | | |
|---|---|---|---|
| Rothwell Corinthians | v | Kettering Town | 0-2 |
| AFC Rushden & Diamonds | v | Brackley Town | 2-1 |

Final

| | | | |
|---|---|---|---|
| AFC Rushden & Diamonds | v | Kettering Town | 2-1 |

## Northamptonshire Senior Cup

Final

| | | | |
|---|---|---|---|
| Netherton United | v | Peterborough Sports | 0-5 |

## North Riding Senior Cup

Quarter Finals

| | | | |
|---|---|---|---|
| Guisborough Town | v | York City | 0-0, 4-3p |
| Scarborough Athletic | v | Marske United | 1-2 |
| Northallerton Town | v | Middlesbrough U21/Reserves | 1-2 |
| Thornaby | v | Redcar Athletic | 1-1, 4-1p |

Semi-Finals

| | | | |
|---|---|---|---|
| Middlesbrough U21/Reserves | v | Thornaby | 5-1 |
| Guisborough Town | v | Marske United | 2-1 |

Final

| | | | |
|---|---|---|---|
| Guisborough Town | v | Middlesbrough U21/Res (Retained) | 1-3 |

## Northumberland Senior Cup

Quarter Finals

| | | | |
|---|---|---|---|
| Whitley Bay | v | Morpeth Town | 0-1 |
| North Shields | v | Ashington | 2-1 |
| Blyth Spartans | v | Newcastle United U21 | 2-0 |
| Bedlington Terriers | v | Heaton Stannington | 0-3 |

Semi Finals

| | | | |
|---|---|---|---|
| Heaton Stannington | v | Blyth Spartans | 0-6 |
| North Shields | v | Morpeth Town | 2-1 |

Final

| | | | |
|---|---|---|---|
| Blyth Spartans | v | North Shields | 3-4 |

## Nottinghamshire Senior Cup

Quarter Finals

| | | | |
|---|---|---|---|
| Carlton Town | v | Basford United | 0-3 |
| Clipstone | v | Kimberley Miners Welfare | 5-2 |
| Rainworth MW | v | Sherwood Colliery | 6-0 |
| Retford United | v | Radford | 2-3 aet |

Semi Finals

| | | | |
|---|---|---|---|
| Basford United | v | Rainworth MW | 2-0 |
| Radford | v | Clipstone | 1-2 |

Final

| | | | |
|---|---|---|---|
| Clipstone | v | Basford United (Retained) | 2-3 aet |

## Oxfordshire Senior Cup

Quarter Finals

| | | | |
|---|---|---|---|
| Thame United | v | Kidlington | 0-1 |
| Oxford City | v | Banbury United | 1-0 |
| Oxford University Press | v | North Leigh | 0-1 |
| Oxford United | v | Ardley United | 3-0 |

Semi Finals

| | | | |
|---|---|---|---|
| Oxford United | v | North Leigh | 1-0 |
| Oxford City | v | Kidlington | 2-1 |

Final

| | | | |
|---|---|---|---|
| Oxford United | v | Oxford City | 6-1 |

## Sheffield & Hallamshire Senior Challenge Cup

Quarter Finals

| | | | |
|---|---|---|---|
| Handsworth Parramore | v | Worksop Town | 4-2 |
| Houghton Main | v | Hallam | 1-2 |
| North Gawber Colliery | v | Shaw Lane Association | 1-2 |
| Frickley Athletic | v | AFC Emley | 4-1 |

Semi Finals

| | | | |
|---|---|---|---|
| Hallam | v | Frickley Athletic | 1-5 |
| Shaw Lane Association | v | Handsworth Parramore | 2-1 |

Final

| | | | |
|---|---|---|---|
| Frickley Athletic (Retained) | v | Shaw Lane Association | HW |

## Shropshire Challenge Cup

Semi-finals

| | | | |
|---|---|---|---|
| Shifnal Town | v | AFC Telford United | 0-4 |
| Market Drayton Town | v | Shrewsbury Town | 0-6 |

Final

| | | | |
|---|---|---|---|
| Shrewsbury Town | v | AFC Telford United | 1-1, 3-2p |

## Somerset Premier Cup

Quarter Finals

| | | | |
|---|---|---|---|
| Bridgwater Town | v | Larkhall Athletic | 0-2 |
| Weston-S-Mare | v | Odd Down | 2-0 |
| Frome Town | v | Wells City | 1-2 |
| Keynsham Town | v | Street | 0-1 |

Semi Finals

| | | | |
|---|---|---|---|
| Weston-S-Mare | v | Wells City | 1-2 |
| Street | v | Larkhall Athletic | 1-3 |

Final

| | | | |
|---|---|---|---|
| Larkhall Athletic | v | Wells City | 1-2 |

## Somerset Senior Cup

Quarter Finals

| | | | |
|---|---|---|---|
| Nailsea & Tickenham | v | Worle | 4-0 |
| ighridge United | v | Frome Town Sports | 2-0 |
| ridgwater Town Reserves | v | Street Reserves | HW |
| Vrington Redhill | v | Fry Club | 0-3 |

Semi Finals

| | | | |
|---|---|---|---|
| Nailsea & Tickenham | v | Fry Club | 3-1 |
| ighridge United | v | Bridgwater Town Reserves | 2-1 |

Final

| | | | |
|---|---|---|---|
| ighridge United | v | Nailsea & Tickenham | 0-2 |

## Staffordshire Senior Cup

Quarter Finals

| | | | |
|---|---|---|---|
| ushall Olympic | v | Stoke City | 2-0 |
| eek Town | v | Port Vale | 4-1 aet |
| tafford Rangers | v | Hednesford Town | 1-4 |
| ocester | v | Kidsgrove Athletic | 0-5 |

Semi Finals

| | | | |
|---|---|---|---|
| ushall Olympic | v | Leek Town | 2-0 |
| idsgrove Athletic | v | Hednesford Town | 2-2, 5-4p |

Final

| | | | |
|---|---|---|---|
| idsgrove Athletic | v | Rushall Olympic | 1-4 |

## (Staffordshire) Walsall Senior Cup

Quarter Finals

| | | | |
|---|---|---|---|
| omulus | v | Rushall Olympic | 0-1 |
| chfield City | v | Walsall | 3-2 |
| porting Khalsa | v | Pelsall Villa | 3-0 |
| olverhampton Casuals | v | Walsall Wood | 2-4 |

Semi Finals

| | | | |
|---|---|---|---|
| ushall Olympic | v | Sporting Khalsa | 1-0 |
| chfield City | v | Walsall Wood | 2-1 |

Final

| | | | |
|---|---|---|---|
| chfield City | v | Rushall Olympic | AW |

## Suffolk Premier Cup

Quarter Finals

| | | | |
|---|---|---|---|
| Walsham Le Willows | v | Needham Market | 0-2 |
| Leiston | v | Ipswich Wanderers | 5-1 |
| Haverhill Rovers | v | Lowestoft Town | 2-4 |
| Felixstowe & Walton United | v | Bury Town | 3-3, 5-6p |

Semi-Finals

| | | | |
|---|---|---|---|
| Leiston | v | Needham Market | 1-0 |
| Bury Town | v | Lowestoft Town | 2-3 aet |

Final

| | | | |
|---|---|---|---|
| Leiston | v | Lowestoft Town (Retained) | 1-3 |

## Suffolk Senior Cup

Quarter Finals

| | | | |
|---|---|---|---|
| Ipswich Athletic | v | Haverhill Borough | 0-3 |
| Haughley United | v | Crane Sports | 0-0, 3-2p |
| Grundisburgh | v | Waveney | 0-3 |
| AFC Sudbury Reserves | v | Cornard United | 1-2 |

Semi Finals

| | | | |
|---|---|---|---|
| Cornard United | v | Haughley United | 1-2 |
| Haverhill Borough | v | Waveney | 2-2, 4-5p |

Final

| | | | |
|---|---|---|---|
| Haughley United | v | Waveney | 2-3 |

## Surrey Senior Cup

Quarter Finals

| | | | |
|---|---|---|---|
| Leatherhead | v | Merstham | 0-4 |
| Whyteleafe | v | Godalming Town | 0-3 |
| Sutton United | v | Knaphill | 1-0 |
| Molesey | v | Woking | 1-3 |

Semi-Finals

| | | | |
|---|---|---|---|
| Woking | v | Merstham | 1-3 |
| Sutton United | v | Godalming Town | 1-3 |

Final

| | | | |
|---|---|---|---|
| Godalming Town | v | Merstham | 1-4 |

## Surrey Premier Cup

Quarter Finals

| | | | |
|---|---|---|---|
| Farleigh Rovers | v | Frimley Green | 2-3 |
| Dorking Wanderers Reserves | v | Banstead Athletic | 0-5 |
| Abbey Rangers | v | Worcester Park | 1-2 |
| Metropolitan Police Reserves | v | Nottsborough | 0-1 |

Semi-Finals

| | | | |
|---|---|---|---|
| Nottsborough | v | Worcester Park | 2-1 |
| Frimley Green | v | Dorking Wanderers Reserves | 1-0 |

Final

| | | | |
|---|---|---|---|
| Nottsborough | v | Frimley Green | 2-0 |

## Surrey Intermediate Cup

Final

| | | | |
|---|---|---|---|
| Horsley (Retained) | v | Project Clapham | 0-0, 5-3p |

## Surrey Junior Cup

Final

| | | | |
|---|---|---|---|
| Lyne | v | Holland Sports | 3-0 |

## Sussex Senior Challenge Cup

Quarter Finals

| | | | |
|---|---|---|---|
| Littlehampton Town | v | Eastbourne Borough | 1-3 |
| Worthing | v | Little Common | 6-1 |
| Whitehawk | v | Steyning Town Community | 4-0 |
| Bognor Regis Town | v | Burgess Hill Town | 2-1 |

Semi Finals

| | | | |
|---|---|---|---|
| Worthing | v | Whitehawk | 2-2, 5-4p |
| Bognor Regis Town | v | Eastbourne Borough | 2-3 aet |

Final

| | | | |
|---|---|---|---|
| Eastbourne Borough | v | Worthing | 1-0 |

## Sussex Intermediate Cup

Final

| | | | |
|---|---|---|---|
| Lewes U21 | v | Worthing U21 | 2-1 |

## Sussex Junior Cup

Final

| | | | |
|---|---|---|---|
| Sidley United | v | Wadhurst United | 6-4 aet |

## West Riding County Cup

Quarter Finals

| | | | |
|---|---|---|---|
| Thackley | v | Silsden | 2-3 |
| Harrogate Town | v | Barnoldswick Town | 6-1 |
| Ossett Albion | v | Garforth Town | 2-0 |
| FC Halifax Town | v | Bradford Park Avenue | 3-3, 4-5p |

Semi-Finals

| | | | |
|---|---|---|---|
| Harrogate Town | v | Silsden | 7-1 |
| Bradford Park Avenue | v | Ossett Albion | 6-2 |

Final

| | | | |
|---|---|---|---|
| Bradford Park Avenue (Retained) | v | Harrogate Town | 3-2 |

## Westmorland Senior Challenge Cup

Quarter Finals

| | | | |
|---|---|---|---|
| Coniston | v | Burneside | 1-2 |
| Wetheriggs United | v | Corinthians | 0-1 |
| Appleby | v | Keswick | 0-1 |
| Cartmel & District | v | Unisun Athletic | 9-0 |

Semi-Finals

| | | | |
|---|---|---|---|
| Cartmel & District | v | Keswick | 3-3, 3-0p |
| Burneside | v | Corinthians | 1-2 |

Final

| | | | |
|---|---|---|---|
| Cartmel & District | v | Corinthians | 2-3 |

## Wiltshire Senior Cup

Quarter Finals

| | | | |
|---|---|---|---|
| Highworth Town | v | Corsham Town | 1-2 |
| Royal Wootton Bassett Town | v | Melksham Town | 0-1 |
| Trowbridge Town | v | Bemerton Heath Harlequins | 1-2 |
| Salisbury | v | Laverstock & Ford | 6-1 |

Semi Finals

| | | | |
|---|---|---|---|
| Bemerton Heath Harlequins | v | Melksham Town | 1-5 |
| Salisbury | v | Corsham Town | 6-2 |

Final

| | | | |
|---|---|---|---|
| Salisbury | v | Melksham Town | 0-2 |

## Wiltshire Junior Cup

Final

| | | | |
|---|---|---|---|
| Stockton & Codford | v | Freshford United | 4-2 aet |

## Worcestershire Senior Invitation Urn

Quarter Finals

| | | | |
|---|---|---|---|
| Bromsgrove Sporting | v | Malvern Town | 4-1 |
| Littleton | v | Pershore Town 88 | 5-0 |
| Highgate United | v | Stourport Swifts | 2-2, 5-4p |
| Studley | v | Alvechurch | 2-2, 3-5p |

Semi Finals

| | | | |
|---|---|---|---|
| Littleton | v | Bromsgrove Sporting | 5-6 |
| Alvechurch | v | Highgate United | 1-1, 9-8p |

Final

| | | | |
|---|---|---|---|
| Alvechurch | v | Bromsgrove Sporting | 3-0 |

## Worcestershire Junior Cup

Final

| | | | |
|---|---|---|---|
| Droitwich Spa | v | Worcester Raiders | 3-2 |

# ENGLISH SCHOOLS' FOOTBALL ASSOCIATION

4, Parker Court, Staffordshire Technology Park, Beaconside, Stafford ST 18 0WP

Tel: 01785 785970; website: www.esfa.co.uk

Chief Executive : Andrea Chilton (andrea.chilton@esfa.com)

Competitions Manager: Darren Alcock (Darren.alcock@schoolsfa.com)

Non-League Directory Contributor: Mike Simmonds (m.simmonds31@btinternet.com)

(0115 9313299)

## The Inspiresport Centenary Shield 2016

England Schools' Under 18 international squad won the Inspiresport Centenary Shied for the Home Nations and the Republic of Ireland for the second time in three seasons to finish their season with an unbeaten record. Their final match in the tournament was against the Republic, last season's winners who were their closest rivals for the Shield. England's chances seem to have disappeared when the visitors to New Saints F.C., Oswestry took the lead after only 3 minutes thanks to a Jamie Aherne goal and made the score 2-0 just before the interval through Dylan Grimes.

The Republic lost their composure after the break and Aaron Smith reduced the arrears with a superb shot from outside the penalty area but the visitors recovered from this blow as they kept Wycherley busy in England's goal but he was up to the task. Sam Grouse became England hero, though, as he was brought on with just over two minutes left and with almost his first touch, scrambled in England's equaliser which ensured the point which brought England the Centenary Shield.

Late comebacks and successful substitutions were the stories of England's season. Their opening goal after 69 minites against Northern Ireland came when Joe Thomas made an immediate impact with a close range header. Ireland equalised in the 80th minute but after 88 minutes , a rash tackle resulted in a penalty from which Zak Lilly found the bottom corner to give Enaldn a 2-1 victory. In the game against Wales which was also an away, Wales took the lead but this time, it was a late first half goal from George Lamb which put England level. Despite heavy second half pressure, it was again close to full time when a low corner skidded off a Welsh defender to Aaron Smith who stabbed in the winner.

England's penultimate game was against Scotland at Fleetwood Town. After both sides had gone close in the first ten minutes, the lashing rain made conditions difficult and chances were few. After the break, Smith broke the deadlock when Smith netted from Shonibare's croos but a scrappy goal brought Scotland level. With both teams needing victory if they were to win the Shield, there were close shaves at both ends before Smith with a clever lob from the edge of the penalty area took England to 9 points which meant that that England had only had to draw against the Republic had to take the Shield which they achieved with that late goal from Grouse.

### RESULTS

| | | | | |
|---|---|---|---|---|
| 6/02/2016 | Scotland | 1 – 1 | Northern Ireland | Lesser Hampden |
| 4/03/2016 | Northern Ireland | 1 – 2 | England | Comber Rec FC |
| 7/03/2016 | Republic of Ireland | 0 – 0 | N Ireland | Arklow Town FC |
| 8/03/2016 | Wales | 1 – 2 | England | Bangor City FC |
| 4/03/2016 | Scotland | 0 – 1 | Wales | Inverurie Loco FC |
| 1/04/2016 | England | 2 – 1 | Scotland | Fleetwood Town FC |
| 8/04/2016 | England | 2 – 2 | Republic of Ireland | The New Saints FC |
| 4/04/2016 | Northern Ireland | 2 – 0 | Wales | Comber Rec FC |
| 4/04/2016 | Republic of Ireland | 3 – 1 | Scotland | Kilarney Celtic FC |
| 8/04/2016 | Wales | 0 – 3 | Republic of Ireland | Maesdu Park |

## UNDER 18 INTERNATIONAL SHIELD 2015

| | P | W | D | L | F | A | Pts |
|---|---|---|---|---|---|---|---|
| England | 4 | 3 | 1 | 0 | 8 | 5 | 10 |
| Republic of Ireland | 4 | 2 | 2 | 0 | 8 | 3 | 8 |
| Northern Ireland | 4 | 1 | 2 | 1 | 4 | 3 | 5 |
| Wales | 4 | 1 | 0 | 3 | 2 | 7 | 3 |
| Scotland | 4 | 0 | 1 | 3 | 4 | 5 | 1 |

## SAFIB UNDER 15 BOB DOCHERTY SCHOOLGIRLS' CUP 2016

### RESULTS

| | | | | |
|---|---|---|---|---|
| England | 2-0 | Wales | Dragon Park, Newport | 01.04.2016 |
| England | 2-0 | Scotland | Dragon Park, Newport | 03.04.2016 |
| England | 1-0 | Republic of Ireland | Dragon Park, Newport | 04.04.2016 |

| GROUP A | P | W | PW | PL | L | Pts |
|---|---|---|---|---|---|---|
| Republic of Ireland | 2 | 2 | 0 | 0 | 0 | 6 |
| Wales 2001 | 2 | 1 | 0 | 0 | 1 | 3 |
| Northern Ireland | 2 | 0 | 0 | 0 | 2 | 0 |

| GROUP B | P | W | PW | PL | L | Pts |
|---|---|---|---|---|---|---|
| England | 2 | 2 | 0 | 0 | 0 | 6 |
| Scotland | 2 | 1 | 0 | 0 | 1 | 3 |
| Wales 2002 | 2 | 0 | 0 | 0 | 2 | 0 |

### FINAL POSITIONS IN BOB DOCHERTY CUP (AFTER PLAY-OFFS)

1. England
2. Republic of Irealnd
3. Scotland
4. Wales 2001 (selected from players in Uefa age groupp 2001 birthdays)
5. Northern Ireland
6. Wales 2002 (selected from players in UEFA age group 2002 birthdays)

## SAFIB UNDER 15 JOHN READ TROPHY

### RESULTS

| | | | | |
|---|---|---|---|---|
| England | 1-0 | Republic of Ireland | Egerton Football Club | 06.03.2016 |

# INDIVIDUAL SCHOOLS', DISTRICT AND COUNTY NATIONAL COMPETITIONS

## The National Finals

The significant change in emphasis in the English Schools' F.A. in the last ten years is illustrated by the growth of competitions for individual schools and by the decline in the number of entries and in many cases the quality of the events for representative sides. Last season, the excellent Competitions Department of the Association organised 32 competitions for individual schools plus seven for representative sides and another three in association with the National Deaf Children's Sports Association.
While the inter-school competitions provide great opportunities for the 'ordinary' school footballers, both boys and girls, there is a worrying tendency for the later stages to be dominated by large schools and Academies which have large numbers of pupils from whom to choose or by those who employ specialist sports coaches or are linked with professional club Academies. While Thomas Telford School from Shropshire are to be congratulated on their magnificent achievement of reaching 12 E.S.F.A. Finals in 2015-2016, winning six and being runners-up in the others, one wonders whether the dominance of a few schools may discourage others not as well resourced from taking part. The Association does try to deal with this problem by providing competitions for which players from professional Academies are not eligible and others for 'B. teams and for schools with limited numbers of pupils.
All this activity would not be possible without the hard work of the members of the Competitions Department and the support of a number of generous sponsors as the list below indicates. Special mention must be made of PlayStation who supported the Individual Schools' events almost across the board while other long term sponsors are the F.A. Premier League and Danone UK. The Football Association's financial help for the Competitions Department is also vital.
Apart from the performances of Thomas Telford School, the other highlight was the success of the Liverpool representative sides who won both the Under 13 and Under 15 Inter-Association Finals. The latter, of course, was the competition which was linked with the formation of the English Schools' F.A. in the 1904-05 season. By their 1-0 win over Bristol and South Gloucestershirei n the final at Nottingham Forest's City Ground, Liverpool increased their lead at the top of the Under 15 Honours List with their 19th success, well ahead of Sheffield in second place.

**U11 Schools' Cup for School Teams Final**
Sponsored By Danone UK
Sunday 22 May 2016
King Power Stadium, Leicester City FC

| | | | |
|---|---|---|---|
| St Teresa's Catholic Primary School | 0 (AET) 2 (PENS) | St Clement's Primary School | 0 (AET) 4 (PENS) |
| (Staffordshire CSFA) | | (Channel Islands CSFA) | |

**U11 Small Schools' Cup Final**
Sponsored By Danone UK
Sunday 22 May 2016
King Power Stadium, Leicester City FC

| | | | |
|---|---|---|---|
| Kilham CE VC Primary School | 0 (AET) | Barkston Ash Primary School 2 (PENS) | 0 (AET) 3 (PENS) |
| (Humberside CSFA) | | (North Yorkshire CSFA) | |

**U11 Inter Association Trophy Final**
Sponsored By Danone UK
Sunday 22 May 2016
King Power Stadium, Leicester City FC

| | | | |
|---|---|---|---|
| Brighton, Hove & Portslade PSFA | 0 | Lewisham PSFA | 2 |

**U11 Schools' Cup for Girls**
Sponsored By Danone UK
Sunday 22 May 2016
King Power Stadium, Leicester City FC

| | | | |
|---|---|---|---|
| St Edward's RC Primary School | 0 (AET) | Blue Coat CE Primary School 4 (PENS) | 0 (AET) 3 (PENS) |
| (Cleveland CSFA) | | (Gloucestershire CSFA) | |

**U12 Boys Indoor 5-A-Side Cup Final**
Sponsored By Impact Trophies
Monday 7 March 2016
Powerleague, Derby

| | | | |
|---|---|---|---|
| Sandwell Academy | 2 | St Aloysius College | 4 |
| (Sandwell SFA) | | (Islington & Camden SFA) | |

**U12 Girls Indoor 5-A-Side Cup Final**
Sponsored By Impact Trophies
Monday 7 March 2016
Powerleague, Derby

| | | | |
|---|---|---|---|
| Alder Community High School | 2 | Gordano School | 1 |
| (Tameside SFA) | | (North Somerset SFA) | |

**U12 Boys Schools Cup Final**
Sponsored By PlayStation
Monday 16 May 2016
The Madejski Stadium, Reading FC

| | | | |
|---|---|---|---|
| Whitgift School<br>(Croydon SFA) | 3 | Moorland School<br>(Hyndburn & Ribble Valley SFA) | 1 |

**U12 Boys Schools Cup for B Teams Final**
Sponsored By PlayStation
Monday 16 May 2016
The Madejski Stadium, Reading FC

| | | | |
|---|---|---|---|
| Glyn School<br>(Sutton SFA) | 2 | Thomas Telford School<br>(Telford & Wrekin SFA) | 3 |

**U12 9 a side Schools Cup for Girls**
Tuesday 28 June 2016
Lilleshall National Sports Centre

| | | | |
|---|---|---|---|
| St Ivo School<br>(HuntingdonSFA) | 3 | Gordano School<br>(North Somerset SFA) | 2 |

**U12 9 a side Small Schools Cup**
Tuesday 28 June 2016
Lilleshall National Sports Centre

| | | | |
|---|---|---|---|
| Shenfield High School<br>(Chelmsford & Mid Essex SFA) | 0 | Priory School<br>(Kings Norton & South Birmingham SFA) | 4 |

**U13 Boys Schools Cup Final**
Sponsored By PlayStation
Tuesday 17 May 2016
The Madejski Stadium, Reading FC

| | | | |
|---|---|---|---|
| Whitgift School<br>(Croydon SFA) | 0 | Thomas Telford School<br>(Telford & Wrekin SFA) | 7 |

**U13 Boys Schools Cup for B Teams Final**
Sponsored By PlayStation
Tuesday 17 May 2016
The Madejski Stadium, Reading FC

| | | | |
|---|---|---|---|
| Hurstmere School<br>(North Kent SFA) | 1 | Stanley High School<br>(Sefton SFA) | 3 |

**U13 Girls Schools Cup Final**
Sponsored By PlayStation
Tuesday 17 May 2016
The Madejski Stadium, Reading FC

| | | | |
|---|---|---|---|
| St Ivo School<br>(Huntingdon SFA) | 3 | Thomas Telford School<br>(Telford & Wrekin SFA) | 0 |

**U13 Boys Small Schools Cup Final**
Sponsored By PlayStation
Tuesday 17 May 2016
The Madejski Stadium, Reading FC

| | | | |
|---|---|---|---|
| The Causeway School<br>(South East Sussex SFA) | 3 | Clitheroe Royal Grammar School<br>(Hyndburn & Ribble Valley SFA) | 2 |

The girls of Lancashire Schools' F.A. celebrate their victory over Essex in the final of the PlayStation Under 14 Inter-County Final at Birmingham City

**U13 Inter Association Trophy Final**
Sponsored By PlayStation
Wednesday 11 May 2016
St Andrew's Stadium, Birmingham City FC

| | | | |
|---|---|---|---|
| Chelmsford & Mid Essex SFA | 1 (AET) | Liverpool SFA | 1 (AET) |
| | | 3 (PENS) | 4 (PENS) |

**U14 Boys Inter County Trophy Final**
Sponsored By PlayStation
Tuesday 10 May 2016
St Andrew's Stadium, Birmingham City FC

| | | | |
|---|---|---|---|
| Surrey CSFA | 6 | Bedfordshire CSFA | 1 |

**U14 Girls Inter County Trophy Final**
Sponsored By PlayStation
Tuesday 10 May 2016
St Andrew's Stadium, Birmingham City FC

| | | | |
|---|---|---|---|
| Lancashire CSFA *(pictured above)* | 3 (AET) | Essex CSFA | 2 (AET) |

**U14 Boys Schools Cup Final**
Sponsored By PlayStation
Wednesday 18 May 2016
The Madejski Stadium, Reading FC

| | | | |
|---|---|---|---|
| Westfield School (Sheffield SFA) | 0 | St Aloysius College (Islington & Camden SFA) | 1 |

**U14 Boys Schools Cup for B Teams Final**
Sponsored By PlayStation
Wednesday 18 May 2016
The Madejski Stadium, Reading FC

| | | | |
|---|---|---|---|
| Ivybridge Community College (Plymouth SFA) | 0 | Cardinal Heenan Catholic Sports Coll (Liverpool SFA) | 2 |

**U14 Boys Small Schools Cup Final**
Sponsored By PlayStation
Tuesday 17 May 2016
The Madejski Stadium, Reading FC

| | | | |
|---|---|---|---|
| Shenfield High School | 0 (AET)<br>5 (PENS) | Stretford Grammar School<br>4 (PENS) | 0 (AET) |
| (Chelmsford & Mid Essex SFA) | | (Trafford SFA) | |

**U14 Boys Open Schools Cup Final**
Sponsored By PlayStation
Wednesday 18 May 2016
The Madejski Stadium, Reading FC

| | | | |
|---|---|---|---|
| Hove Park School | 0 | Thomas Telford School | 4 |
| (Brighton & Hove SFA) | | (Telford & Wrekin SFA) | |

**U14 Girls Schools Cup Final**
Sponsored By PlayStation
Wednesday 18 May 2016
The Madejski Stadium, Reading FC

| | | | |
|---|---|---|---|
| St Ivo School | 2 (AET) | Thomas Telford School<br>4 (PENS) | 2 (AET)<br>5 (PENS) |
| (Huntingdon SFA) | | (Telford & Wrekin SFA) | |

**U15 Inter Association Trophy Final**
Sponsored By PlayStation
Tuesday 3 May 2016
The City Ground, Nottingham Forest FC

| | | | |
|---|---|---|---|
| Bristol & South Gloucestershire SFA | 0 | Liverpool SFA | 1 |

**U15 Boys Schools Cup Final**
Sponsored By PlayStation
Wednesday 18 May 2016
The Madejski Stadium, Reading FC

| | | | |
|---|---|---|---|
| Bishop's Strortford High School | 5 | Thomas Telford School | 4 |
| (Lea Valley SFA) | | (Telford & Wrekin SFA) | |

Cardinal Heenan Catholci School (Liverpool) celebrate following their 2-1 win in the ESFA PlayStationUnder 15 Boys Cup for 'B' teams over Weydon School (Aldershot and Farnborough).

**U15 Boys Small Schools Cup Final**
Sponsored By PlayStation
Monday 16 May 2016
The Madejski Stadium, Reading FC

| | | | |
|---|---|---|---|
| Gosford Hill School<br>(Banbury SFA) | 6 | Howden School<br>(East Riding SFA) | 3 |

**U15 Boys Open Schools Cup Final**
Sponsored By PlayStation
Monday 16 May 2016
The Madejski Stadium, Reading FC

| | | | |
|---|---|---|---|
| Northampton School for Boys<br>(Northampton SFA) | 2 | Thomas Telford School<br>(Telford & Wrekin SFA) | 1 |

**U15 Boys Schools Cup for B Teams Final**
Sponsored By PlayStation
Monday 9 May 2016
St Andrew's Stadium, Birmingham City FC

| | | | |
|---|---|---|---|
| Weydon School<br>(Aldershot & Farnborough SFA) | 1 | Cardinal Heenan Catholic Sports Coll<br>(Liverpool SFA) - *pictured opposite* | 2 |

**U15 Girls Schools Cup Final**
Sponsored By PlayStation
Monday 16 May 2016
The Madejski Stadium, Reading FC

| | | | |
|---|---|---|---|
| Shenfield High School<br>(Chelmsford & Mid Essex SFA) | 1 | Thomas Telford School<br>(Telford & Wrekin SFA) | 2 |

**U16 Inter County Boys Trophy Final**
Saturday 7 May 2016
The City Ground, Nottingham Forest FC

| | | | |
|---|---|---|---|
| North Yorkshire CSFA | 1 | Sussex CSFA | 2 |

**U16 Inter County Girls Trophy Final**
Wednesday 11 May 2016
St Andrew's Stadium, Birmingham City FC

| | | | |
|---|---|---|---|
| Somerset CSFA | 1 | Staffordshire CSFA | 2 |

**U16 Boys Schools Cup Final**
Sponsored By The Premier League
Wednesday 4 May 2016
Etihad Academy Stadium, Manchester City FC

| | | | |
|---|---|---|---|
| Thomas Telford School<br>(Telford & Wrekin SFA) | 4 | Samuel Whitbread Academy<br>(Bedford & District SFA) | 2 |

**U16 Boys Small Schools Cup Final**
Sponsored By The Premier League
Wednesday 4 May 2016
Etihad Academy Stadium, Manchester City FC

| | | | |
|---|---|---|---|
| King Edward's School Witley<br><br>(Guildford & District SFA) | 2 (AET)<br>9 (PENS) | Blacon High School<br>8 (PENS)<br>(Chester SFA) | 2 (AET) |

**U16 Boys Open Schools Cup Final**
Sponsored By The Premier League
Friday 6 May 2016
Etihad Academy Stadium, Manchester City FC

| | | | |
|---|---|---|---|
| Dorothy Stringer School<br>(Brighton & Hove SFA) | 0 | Thomas Telford School<br>(Telford & Wrekin SFA) | 3 |

**U16 Girls Schools Cup Final**
Sponsored By The Premier League
Friday 6 May 2016
Etihad Academy Stadium, Manchester City FC

| | | | |
|---|---|---|---|
| St Bede's RC High School (Blackburn & Darwen SFA) | 4 (AET) 5 (PENS) | Kings' School (Eastleigh & Winchester SFA) | 4 (AET) 3 (PENS) |

**U17 Boys Schools Trophy Final**
Wednesday 27 April 2016
The Keepmoat Stadium, Doncaster Rovers FC

| | | | |
|---|---|---|---|
| Harris Academy Chafford Hundred (Thurrock SFA) | 3 (AET) 1 (PENS) | Benton Park School (Leeds SFA) | 3 (AET) 4 (PENS) |

**U18 Boys Inter County Trophy Final**
Monday 9 May 2016
St Andrew's Stadium, Birmingham City FC

| | | | |
|---|---|---|---|
| Sussex CSFA | 2 | Northumberland CSFA | 0 |

**U18 Girls Schools Trophy Final**
Wednesday 16 March 2016
The Pirelli Stadium, Burton Albion FC

| | | | |
|---|---|---|---|
| Thomas Telford School (Telford & Wrekin SFA) | 0 | John Madejski Academy (Reading SFA) | 10 |

**U18 Boys Schools Trophy Final**
Wednesday 20 April 2016
The Abbey Stadium, Cambridge United FC

| | | | |
|---|---|---|---|
| Shenfield High School (Chelmsford & Mid Essex SFA) | 0 | Thomas Telford School (Telford & Wrekin SFA) | 1 |

**U18 Boys Colleges Trophy Final**
Wednesday 27 April 2016
The Keepmoat Stadium, Doncaster Rovers FC

| | | | |
|---|---|---|---|
| Hartpury College (West Gloucestershire SFA) | 3 | Gateshead College (Gateshead SFA) | 2 |

**U18 Girls Colleges Trophy Final**
Wednesday 16 March 2016
The Pirelli Stadium, Burton Albion FC

| | | | |
|---|---|---|---|
| Accrington & Rossendale College (Hyndburn & Ribble Valley SFA) | 1 | Solihull College (Solihull SFA) | 0 |

**ESFA / NDCSA Senior Boys 5-a-side Cup**
Tuesday 2 February 2016
Powerleague, Derby

| | | | |
|---|---|---|---|
| Braidwood School | 1 (AET) 4 (PENS) | Allerton Grange School | 1 (AET) 3 (PENS) |

**ESFA / NDCSA Junior Boys 5-a-side Cup**
Tuesday 2 February 2016
Powerleague, Derby

| | | | |
|---|---|---|---|
| Royal School for the Deaf, Derby | 1 | Braidwood School | 3 |

**ESFA / NDCSA Girls 5-a-side Cup**
Tuesday 2 February 2016
Powerleague, Derby

| | | | |
|---|---|---|---|
| Royal School for the Deaf, Derby | 0 | Heathlands School | 1 |

***NUMBERS WITH (L) RELATE TO THE PAGE NUMBER OF THE LEAGUE THE CLUB ARE FEATURED IN.***

NON-LEAGUE CLUB DIRECTORY 2017
39th Edition
EDITED BY MIKE WILLIAMS & TONY WILLIAMS
Endorsed by The FA
COVERING STEPS 1 THROUGH TO 7 AND MORE...
The F.A. NON-LEAGUE FOOTBALL ANNUAL 1978-79